The Elements

Element	Symbol	Atomic Number	Atomic Mass*	Element	Symbol	Atomic Number	Atomic Mass*
Actinium	Ac	89	(227)	Mercury	Hg	80	200.6
Aluminum	Al	13	26.98	Molybdenum	Mo	42	95.94
Americium	Am	95	(243)	Neodymium	Nd	60	144.2
Antimony	Sb	51	121.8	Neon	Ne	10	20.18
Argon	Ar	18	39.95	Neptunium	Np	93	(244)
Arsenic	As	33	74.92	Nickel	Ni	28	58.70
Astatine	At	85	(210)	Niobium	Nb	41	92.91
Barium	Ba	56	137.3	Nitrogen	N	7	14.01
Berkelium	Bk	97	(247)	Nobelium	No	102	(253)
Beryllium	Be	4	9.012	Osmium	Os	76	190.2
Bismuth	Bi	83	209.0	Oxygen	O	8	16.00
Bohrium	Bh	107	(262)	Palladium	Pd	46	106.4
Boron	B	5	10.81	Phosphorus	P	15	30.97
Bromine	Br	35	79.90	Platinum	Pt	78	195.1
Cadmium	Cd	48	112.4	Plutonium	Pu	94	(242)
Calcium	Ca	20	40.08	Polonium	Po	84	(209)
Californium	Cf	98	(249)	Potassium	K	19	39.10
Carbon	C	6	12.01	Praseodymium	Pr	59	140.9
Cerium	Ce	58	140.1	Promethium	Pm	61	(145)
Cesium	Cs	55	132.9	Protactinium	Pa	91	(231)
Chlorine	Cl	17	35.45	Radium	Ra	88	(226)
Chromium	Cr	24	52.00	Radon	Rn	86	(222)
Cobalt	Co	27	58.93	Rhenium	Re	75	186.2
Copper	Cu	29	63.55	Rhodium	Rh	45	102.9
Curium	Cm	96	(247)	Rubidium	Rb	37	85.47
Dubnium	Db	105	(262)	Ruthenium	Ru	44	101.1
Dysprosium	Dy	66	162.5	Rutherfordium	Rf	104	(261)
Einsteinium	Es	99	(254)	Samarium	Sm	62	150.4
Erbium	Er	68	167.3	Scandium	Sc	21	44.96
Europium	Eu	63	152.0	Seaborgium	Sg	106	(266)
Fermium	Fm	100	(253)	Selenium	Se	34	78.96
Fluorine	F	9	19.00	Silicon	Si	14	28.09
Francium	Fr	87	(223)	Silver	Ag	47	107.9
Gadolinium	Gd	64	157.3	Sodium	Na	11	22.99
Gallium	Ga	31	69.72	Strontium	Sr	38	87.62
Germanium	Ge	32	72.61	Sulfur	S	16	32.07
Gold	Au	79	197.0	Tantalum	Ta	73	180.9
Hafnium	Hf	72	178.5	Technetium	Tc	43	(98)
Hassium	Hs	108	(265)	Tellurium	Te	52	127.6
Helium	He	2	4.003	Terbium	Tb	65	158.9
Holmium	Ho	67	164.9	Thallium	Tl	81	204.4
Hydrogen	H	1	1.008	Thorium	Th	90	232.0
Indium	In	49	114.8	Thulium	Tm	69	168.9
Iodine	I	53	126.9	Tin	Sn	50	118.7
Iridium	Ir	77	192.2	Titanium	Ti	22	47.88
Iron	Fe	26	55.85	Tungsten	W	74	183.9
Krypton	Kr	36	83.80	Uranium	U	92	238.0
Lanthanum	La	57	138.9	Vanadium	V	23	50.94
Lawrencium	Lr	103	(257)	Xenon	Xe	54	131.3
Lead	Pb	82	207.2	Ytterbium	Yb	70	173.0
Lithium	Li	3	6.941	Yttrium	Y	39	88.91
Lutetium	Lu	71	175.0	Zinc	Zn	30	65.39
Magnesium	Mg	12	24.31	Zirconium	Zr	40	91.22
Manganese	Mn	25	54.94			110**	(269)
Meitnerium	Mt	109	(266)			111	(272)
Mendelevium	Md	101	(256)			112	(277)

*All atomic masses are given to four significant figures. Values in parentheses represent the mass number of the most stable isotope.
**The names and symbols for elements 110 through 112 have not yet been chosen.

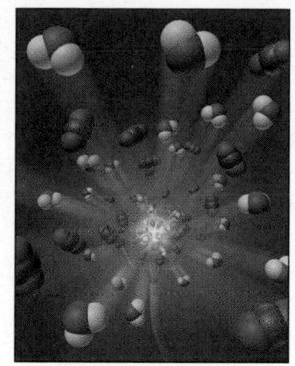

CHEMISTRY

The Molecular Nature of Matter and Change

Second Edition

Martin S. Silberberg

Consultants

Randy Duran
University of Florida, Gainesville

L. Peter Gold
Pennsylvania State University

Charles G. Haas (emeritus)
Pennsylvania State University

Robert L. Loeschen
California State University, Long Beach

Arlan D. Norman
University of Colorado, Boulder

Boston   Burr Ridge, IL   Dubuque, IA   Madison, WI   New York   San Fransisco   St. Louis
Bangkok   Bogotá   Caracas   Lisbon   London   Madrid
Mexico City   Milan   New Delhi   Seoul   Singapore   Sydney   Taipei   Toronto

McGraw-Hill Higher Education

A Division of The **McGraw-Hill** *Companies*

CHEMISTRY: THE MOLECULAR NATURE OF MATTER AND CHANGE, SECOND EDITION

This book is printed on acid-free paper.

5 6 7 8 9 0 VNH/VNH 0 9 8 7 6 5 4 3 2 1

ISBN 0–697–39597–9

Vice president and editorial director: *Kevin T. Kane*
Publisher: *James M. Smith*
Sponsoring editor: *Kent A. Peterson*
Developmental editor: *Margaret B. Horn*
Marketing manager: *Martin J. Lange*
Senior project manager: *Jayne Klein*
Senior production supervisor: *Sandra Hahn*
Design manager: *Stuart D. Paterson*
Senior photo research coordinator: *Lori Hancock*
Supplement coordinator: *Stacy A. Patch*
Composition and additional project management: *GTS Graphics, Inc.*
Typeface: *10/12 Meridien*
Printer: *Von Hoffmann Press, Inc.*

Cover design: *Stuart D. Paterson*
Cover image: *Federico/Goodman Studios*
Page layout/special features designer: *Ruth Melnick*
Illustrations: *ArtScribe, Inc.* and *Federico/Goodman Studios*
Photo research: *Feldman and Associates*

COVER IMAGE: On the molecular level, molecules of methane and oxygen react near the tip of a laboratory burner to form molecules of carbon dioxide and water. As in all chemical change, the number of each type of atom is the same before and after the change: one carbon dioxide and two waters form for every one methane and two oxygens that react.

The credits section for this book begins on page C-1 and is considered an extension of the copyright page.

Library of Congress Cataloging-in-Publication Data

Silberberg, Martin S.
    Chemistry : the molecular nature of matter and change / Martin S.
  Silberberg. — 2nd ed.
        p.   cm.
    Includes index.
    ISBN 0–697–39597–9
    1. Chemistry.   I. Title.
  QD33.S576   2000
  540—dc21   98–4528
                                                    CIP

INTERNATIONAL EDITION   ISBN 0–07–116832–X
Copyright © 2000. Exclusive rights by The McGraw-Hill Companies, Inc. for manufacture and export. This book cannot be re-exported from the country to which it is consigned by McGraw-Hill.
The International Edition is not available in North America.

www.mhhe.com

With love and gratitude

To Ruth,
whose insight and experience
made this project possible

and

To Daniel,
whose optimism and creativity
make everything seem possible

Brief Contents

Detailed Contents

4 The Major Classes of Chemical Reactions   133

5 Gases and the Kinetic-Molecular Theory   176

13 The Properties of Mixtures: Solutions and Colloids   480

Inter-chapter A Perspective on the Properties of the Elements   529

14 Periodic Patterns in the Main-Group Elements: Bonding, Structure, and Reactivity   540

15 Organic Compounds and the Atomic Properties of Carbon   604

19 Ionic Equilibria in Aqueous Systems   805

20 Thermodynamics: Entropy, Free Energy, and the Direction of Chemical Reactions   856

21 Electrochemistry: Chemical Change and Electrical Work   894

22 The Elements in Nature and Industry   952

Preface

As we move through the turn of the millennium, everything seems to be changing. New medical imaging devices that peer into body parts to observe function join a family of new microscopes that peer at material surfaces to observe their atomic landscapes. Computer-aided design of new drugs is becoming routine, creating "cocktails" that arrest the progress of new diseases. And these will soon be surpassed by medicines borne from our complete analysis of the human genome. New electronic technologies are already redefining global communications, and we will soon be driving cars powered by new, cleaner energy sources. Alas, even our climate may be changing, as evidenced by the 1990s being proclaimed the hottest decade in recorded history.

Yet, in the face of all this change, certain things stay the same: the value of a good science course to teach logical thinking, the role of a good professor to inspire students and explain concepts—*and* the central importance of a good textbook that allows student and professor to realize their goals for the course.

To address current directions in the curriculum, *Chemistry: The Molecular Nature of Matter and Change* and its supplements have changed in some major ways, but the philosophy of the text, its student-oriented presentation, and its overall topic sequence have not. As in the first edition, my goal for the second edition was to write a teaching text, one with clear, lively explanations allied to realistic, pedagogic illustrations that help students learn chemistry with confidence—and maybe even a sense of awe!

Revising a textbook, especially one so well received in its first edition, is a challenge based on a simple mandate—listen to your readers to enhance the many aspects of the text that work well and strengthen the inevitable weak spots. This *Preface* and the illustrated *Guided Tour* that follows it highlight features introduced in the *First Edition* and some of the many specific ways that the *Second Edition* has changed to become an even more effective teaching tool.

Approach to Teaching Chemistry

The most important aspect of the text that has not changed (and never will!) is its three-pronged approach to teaching chemistry—visualizing chemical models, thinking through a quantitative problem, and demonstrating the tremendous relevance of chemistry to society.

Visualizing Chemical Models

Chemistry deals with changes that we observe in the world around us and with the atomic-scale events that cause them. Throughout the text, discussions team up with illustrations to bring home this central theme. Models are explained at the observable level and then from a close-up, molecular point of view. To bridge the mind-boggling size gap between these two levels of reality, the first edition broke new ground in chemical illustration with an art program that juxtaposed the macroscopic and atomic views, and, wherever meaningful, the symbolic view in the form of the balanced equation. The response from teachers and students was extremely positive, and it has been gratifying to see this approach attempted in the generation of texts that followed the first edition. Today's more visually oriented students will surely benefit from this trend. The second edition expands this approach considerably and introduces further innovations.

New for the second edition are the following enhancements:

- To optimize comprehension of text and related art, every two-page spread has been designed to place a figure or table as near to its related text as possible, with many figures wrapped by the text so the student reads an explanation and sees it depicted simultaneously.
- To enrich the visualization of chemical events, many macro-to-molecular-to-equation figures have been added.
- To help students mentally translate line structures into molecular shapes, many molecular models have been added.
- To simultaneously depict both shape *and* polarity, a new type of model has been introduced that adapts the most advanced chemical modeling software.

In the *Guided Tour*, pages xx and xxi display the outstanding pedagogy of the new art program.

Thinking Logically to Solve Problems

Another innovation of the first edition that is enhanced in the second is the powerful problem-solving pedagogy, which is based on widely accepted modern principles of education. This approach encourages students to first plan a logical method for attacking a problem, and only then proceed to solve it quantitatively. For the more visually-oriented student, a block diagram *specific* for the problem appears alongside the plan whenever appropriate *throughout* the text. A step unique to this text fosters the habit of checking the reasonableness and magnitude of the answer, a habit universally recommended by professors. The check is followed immediately by practice with a similar type of problem.

New for the second edition are the following improvements:

- To help students develop a sound problem-solving strategy, every Sample Problem has been inspected for clarity and the adjacent block-diagram "roadmap" made more informative.
- To provide adequate practice for new ideas and skills, every set of chapter problems has been expanded, many with molecular art incorporated, and the problems have been classified by type.

In the *Guided Tour*, page xxii explains the approach in detail, and page xxiv shows the unique way that end-of-chapter problems are classified and sequenced.

Applying Ideas and Skills to the Real World

The influence of modern chemistry in everyday life is spreading enormously, informing global concerns about the environment, disease, energy resources, and countless other issues. In the process, many new hybrid fields are being spawned—biomaterials science, nanotechnology, enzyme engineering, planetary geochemistry, and the like. Today's students will enter some of these fields and generate still newer ones in which the principles of chemistry have an ever greater impact.

As in the first edition, the relevance of chemistry is always presented to highlight or expand upon a principle being discussed. In addition to countless places in the main text, four key displayed features—Chemical Connections essays, Tools of the Chemistry Laboratory essays, Galleries, and Margin Notes—provide practical handles to what may seem abstract ideas.

New for the second edition are the following improvements:

- To maintain currency, text discussions and boxed essays have been updated with the latest government and industry data.

- To demonstrate the relevance of chemistry in everyday life, many new photos, Margin Notes, and Galleries have been added.
  In the *Guided Tour*, page xxiii demonstrates the relevance of these features.

Helping Students Learn Chemistry

My guiding principle throughout the conception, writing, and illustrating of both editions has been to create a "teaching" text, one that provides a clear path through the material with thorough explanations that foresee potential student confusion before it arises. To that end, each chapter has been designed with as many helpful learning aids as possible. Many first-edition users praised the usefulness of the Concepts and Skills to Review, Section Summaries, Chapter Perspectives, and the abundance of chapter endmatter for review.

New for the second edition are the following improvements and additions:
- To improve readability, every paragraph was examined line by line and revised, whenever necessary, for clarity and directness.
- To help orient the student to the upcoming flow of ideas, every chapter now opens with a *detailed* Chapter Outline of the content.
- To make the coverage as flexible as possible, every chapter now includes many more heads that subdivide the material.
- To better highlight concepts, every chapter now includes many more summarized lists of central points and italicized key ideas.
- To focus the student on major topics, every chapter now ends with a numbered list of learning objectives indicating section and/or sample problem.
- To provide an alternative means of review, certain figures/tables are highlighted and listed with other review material at the end of each chapter.
  In the *Guided Tour*, pages xix and xxiv show examples of these features.

Innovative Treatments of Chapter Sequence and Content

The second edition of *Chemistry: The Molecular Nature of Matter and Change* retains the modern topic order suited to the great majority of today's general chemistry courses. At the same time, it provides the flexible chapter sequence that many professors desire for their own approach to the subject. Innovative treatments of the material appear in each chapter, including many topics geared toward students planning medical, scientific, and engineering careers, with some especially novel approaches to the chemistry of the elements, organic chemistry, and biochemistry.

Flexible Chapter Sequence

As the Detailed Contents shows, the main chapter order begins with coverage of basic concepts of matter and energy, including units and measurement, elements and compounds, stoichiometry, reaction classes, gas behavior, and thermochemistry (Chapters 1–6). It then moves on to a sequence of topics that build upon each other, from atomic structure and electron configuration to bonding and shape to the properties of liquids, solids, and solutions (Chapters 7–13). A unique treatment of the chemistry of the elements and organic and biochemistry (Interchapter and Chapters 14 and 15) is placed centrally but can be covered at many other places in the course. The central topics of physical chemistry are presented next, including one chapter on kinetics, three chapters on equilibrium, and two chapters on thermodynamics and its application to electrochemistry (Chapters 16–21). The text ends with selected topics in environmental and industrial chemistry, transition metal chemistry, and nuclear reactions (Chapters 22–24).

New for the second edition are the following key organizational changes:

- To clarify the distinctions among bonding models and facilitate molecular visualization, the discussion of Lewis structures was moved from the end of Chapter 9 to the beginning of Chapter 10. Thus, Chapter 9 now directly compares the three types of bonding (ionic, covalent, and metallic) on the atomic and macroscopic scales, and Chapter 10 focuses on depicting molecules, from Lewis structures to VSEPR shapes.

- To allow selected coverage of the more abstract aspects of covalent bonding, the discussions of valence-bond and molecular-orbital theories have been moved from the end of Chapter 10 to their own new Chapter 11.

- To apply the topics of physical chemistry immediately after they are discussed, the chapter on the elements in nature and industry has been moved from the end of the text to follow the chapter on electrochemistry, and the chapter on nuclear reactions now ends the text.

Integrated Chapter Content

What may not be immediately apparent from the Detailed Contents are the novel ways that many topics are presented. Of special note are the treatments of descriptive chemistry and organic chemistry. Rather than leaving these important topics for the end of the course, professors can elect to cover them immediately after Chapters 7–13. The Interchapter and Chapter 14 apply the principles from these chapters to *all* the main-group elements, emphasizing the *gradation* in element properties throughout the periodic table, rather than fostering misleading divisions between metals and nonmetals. Chapter 15 is a natural extension of descriptive chemistry, showing how the chemistry of organic and biological compounds arises from the atomic properties of carbon and its few bonding partners. Chapter 22 follows the example of Chapter 14 by applying the principles of kinetics, equilibrium, thermodynamics, and electrochemistry from Chapters 16–21 to the geochemistry, environmental chemistry, and industrial chemistry of the elements.

The text's devotion to biochemistry is unique. There is more coverage of this exciting field than in any other mainstream text, but it is integrated into discussions, margin notes, and boxed essays. Biopolymer structure and function forms a major portion of Chapter 15, while other discussions explore molecular shape in physiology, solubility factors in the structures of cell membranes and the action of antibiotics, principles of catalysis that apply to enzyme specificity and activity, principles of equilibrium that relate to metabolic control, electrochemical processes that produce and utilize ATP, and many more topics.

New for the second edition are countless small improvements to art and text in every chapter, including the following significant changes:

- Chapter 2 now includes a focus on organic structures and introduces Coulomb's law in an early discussion of ionic and covalent bonding that proves highly useful in Chapters 8 and 9.

- Chapter 4 is now completely revised to highlight precipitation, acid-base, and redox reactions. It also includes an introduction to the Brønsted-Lowry proton-transfer concept and a new section on the activity series of metals.

- Chapter 12 now includes a major new section highlighting the production and function of advanced materials—liquid crystals, electronic semiconductors, modern ceramics, and nanotechnological devices.

- Chapter 13 now introduces the concept of entropy for application to solution behavior and colligative properties.

- Chapters 15 and 23 now include an up-to-date and more visualizable treatment of isomers.

GUIDED TOUR

The pages in this Guided Tour to Chemistry: The Molecular Nature of Matter and Change, Second Edition, *have been selected to walk you through the features of a chapter. As you examine them, note that a chapter begins by orienting you to the topic flow; the illustrations are placed very close to the related text; the art depicts a chemical reaction on several levels of reality simultaneously; the multipart sample problems help you plan, execute, and check the solution; the relevance of chemistry is clearly demonstrated; and the material at the end of the chapter provides many ways to review and practice the concepts and skills covered.*

Displayed Topic Flow

Orienting your focus on the content of the upcoming chapter—

Chapter Opener

The opener provides a thought-provoking figure and legend that relate to a main topic of the chapter.

Concepts and Skills to Review

This feature helps you prepare for the current chapter by listing important material from previous chapters that you should understand *before* you start reading.

A living cell is a remarkable chemical system. Through elegantly controlled mechanisms, it oxidizes food for energy, maintains the concentrations of thousands of aqueous components, interacts continuously with its environment, synthesizes both simple and complex molecules for its survival and growth, and even reproduces itself. With all our technological prowess, no human-made system even approaches the cell for sheer artistry of function. This amazing chemical machine consumes, creates, and consists largely of *organic compounds*. Except for a few inorganic salts and ever-present water, everything you put into or on your body—food, medicine, cosmetics, and clothing—consists of organic compounds. Organic fuels warm our homes, cook our meals, and power our society. Major industries are devoted to producing organic compounds, such as polymers, pharmaceuticals, and insecticides.

What *is* an organic compound? Dictionaries define it as "a compound of carbon," but that definition would include carbonates, cyanides, carbides, cyanates, and other carbon-containing ionic compounds most chemists would classify as inorganic. Here is a practical, working definition: all **organic compounds** contain carbon, nearly always bonded to itself and to hydrogen, and often to other elements as well.

The word *organic* has a biological connotation arising from a major misconception that stifled research into the chemistry of living systems for many decades. In the early 19th century, many prominent thinkers believed that an unobservable spiritual energy, a "vital force," existed *within the* compounds of living things, making them impossible to synthesize and fundamentally different from compounds of the mineral world. This idea of *vitalism* was challenged in 1828, when the young German chemist Friedrich Wöhler heated ammonium cyanate, a "mineral-world" compound, and produced urea, a "living-world" compound:

$$NH_4OCN \xrightarrow{\Delta} H_2N-\overset{\overset{O}{\|}}{C}-NH_2$$

Although Wöhler did not appreciate the significance of this reaction—he was more interested by the fact that two compounds had the same molecular formula—his experiment is considered a key event in the origin of organic chemistry. Chemists soon synthesized methane, acetic acid, acetylene, and many other organic compounds from inorganic sources. ◆ Today we know that *the same chemical principles govern organic and inorganic systems* because the behavior of a compound arises from the properties of its elements, no matter how marvelous that behavior may be.

In this brief introduction to an enormous and ever-growing field, we continue the text's central theme—how the structure and reactivity of organic molecules emerge naturally from the properties of the component atoms, in this case carbon and its handful of bonding partners. First, we review the rather special atomic properties of carbon and see how they relate to organic molecules. We focus on hydrocarbons initially to give you a feel for writing and naming organic compounds. Then we classify the main types of organic reactions and, in the central portion of the chapter, apply them to the major families of organic compounds. Finally, we extend these ideas to the giant molecules of commerce and life—synthetic and natural polymers.

15.1 The Special Nature of Carbon and the Characteristics of Organic Molecules

Although there is nothing mystical about organic molecules, their indispensable role in biology and industry leads us to ask if carbon has some extraordinary attributes that give it a special chemical "personality." Of course,

Chapter Outline

The outline details the topic flow of the chapter by listing the major topics and the subtopics within them.

Introduction

The introduction points out the relevance of the topic, and the last paragraph corresponds to the sequence of topics in the Chapter Outline.

Integrated Text and Art

Using text *and* art to help you visualize chemical events and facilitate your study of the material—

Page Layout

Author and pager worked side by side to create a book of two-page spreads that place figures as close as possible to their related text. In some cases, art is even wrapped by text, so you can read concepts and see them depicted simultaneously.

Explanatory Legends

These rephrase the main text concept, so you can review much of the chapter content just by studying figures and legends. Especially significant pieces are highlighted with a red number on a yellow panel and are listed at the end of the chapter.

The Formation of Ionic Compounds

Ionic compounds are composed of **ions,** charged particles that form when an atom (or small group of atoms) gains or loses one or more electrons. The simplest type of ionic compound is a **binary ionic compound,** one composed of just two elements. It typically forms *when a metal reacts with a nonmetal.* Each metal atom loses a certain number of its electrons and becomes a **cation,** a positively charged ion. At the same time, the nonmetal atoms gain the electrons lost by the metal atoms and become **anions,** negatively charged ions. The resulting cations and anions attract each other through electrostatic forces and form the ionic compound. A cation or anion derived from a single atom is called a **monatomic ion;** we'll discuss polyatomic ions, those derived from a small group of atoms, later.

The formation of the binary ionic compound sodium chloride, common table salt, is depicted in Figure 2.18, from the elements through the atomic-scale electron transfer to the compound. In the electron transfer, a sodium atom, which is neutral because it has the same number of protons as electrons, *loses* 1 electron and forms a sodium cation, Na^+. (The charge on the ion is written as a *right superscript.*) A chlorine atom *gains* the electron and becomes a chloride anion, Cl^-. (The name change from the nonmetal atom to the ion is discussed in the next section.) Even the tiniest visible grain of

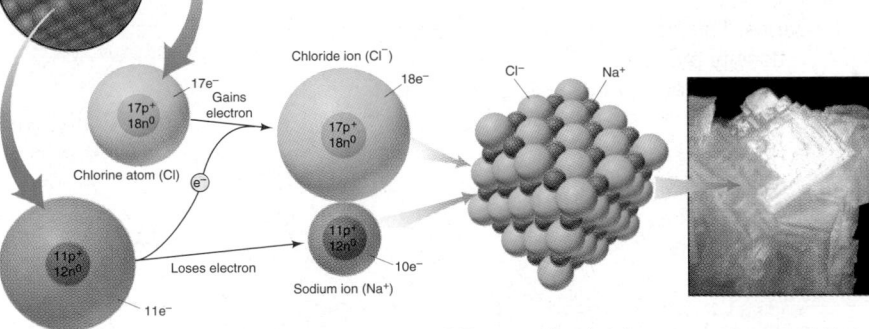

Figure 2.18 The formation of an ionic compound. A, The two elements as seen in the laboratory. **B,** The elements as they might appear on the atomic scale. **C,** The neutral sodium atom loses 1 electron to become a sodium cation (Na^+), and the chlorine atom gains 1 electron to become a chloride anion (Cl^-). (Note that when atoms lose electrons, they become smaller, and when they gain

electrons, they become larger.) **D,** Na^+ and Cl^- ions attract each other and lie in a three-dimensional crystalline array. **E,** This cubic array is reflected in the structure of crystalline NaCl, which occurs naturally as the mineral halite, hence the name *halogens* for the Group 7A(17) elements.

Figure 4.15 Three views of a combination reaction between elements. When the metal potassium and the nonmetal chlorine react, they form the solid ionic compound potassium chloride. The photos *(top)* present the view the chemist sees in the laboratory. The blow-up arrows lead to an atomic-scale view *(middle)*; the stoichiometry is indicated by the more darkly colored spheres. The balanced redox equation is shown with oxidation numbers *(bottom)*.

Three-Level Art

Innovated in the first edition, these provide macroscopic and molecular views of a process, so you learn to connect these two levels of reality with each other and with the chemical equation that describes the process in symbols.

cis   *trans*

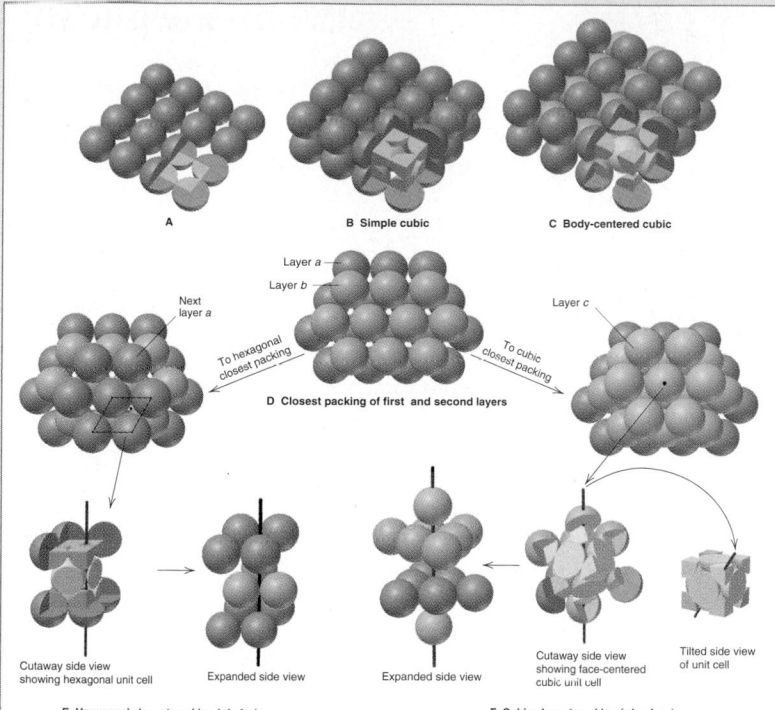

E **Hexagonal closest packing** (*abab...*)

Cutaway side view
showing hexagonal unit cell

Expanded side view

Expanded side view

Cutaway side view
showing face-centered
cubic unit cell

Tilted side view
of unit cell

F **Cubic closest packing** (*abcabc...*)

A

B **Simple cubic**

C **Body-centered cubic**

Layer *a*
Layer *b*

Next
layer *a*

Layer *c*

To hexagonal
closest packing

To cubic
closest packing

D **Closest packing of first and second layers**

Figure 12.29 Packing of spheres. A, In the first layer, each sphere lies next to another horizontally and vertically; note the large diamond-shaped spaces *(cutaway)*. **B,** If the next layers lie *directly* over the first, the packing is based on the *simple cubic* unit cell *(pale orange cube, lower right corner)*. **C,** If the next layers lie in the diamond-shaped spaces of each preceding layer, the packing is based on the *body-centered cubic* unit cell *(lower right corner)*. **D,** The closest possible packing of the first layer *(a; orange)* is obtained by shifting every other row in **A,** thus reducing the diamond-shaped spaces to smaller triangular spaces. The spheres of the second layer *(b; green)* are placed above these spaces; note the orange and white spaces that result. **E,** Follow the left arrow from **D** to obtain hexagonal closest packing. When the third layer *(a; orange)* is placed directly over the first, that is, over the orange spaces, we obtain an *abab . . .* pattern. Rotating the layers up produces the side view, with the hexagonal unit cell shown as a cutaway segment, and the expanded side view. **F,** Follow the right arrow from **D** to obtain cubic closest packing. When the third layer *(c; blue)* covers the white spaces, it lies in a different position from the first *and* second layers to give an *abcabc . . .* pattern. Rotating the layers up shows the side view, with the face-centered cubic unit cell as a cutaway, and a further tilt shows the unit cell clearly; finally, we see the expanded view.

Cutting-Edge Molecular Models

Author and artist worked side by side and employed the most advanced computer-graphic software to provide accurate molecular models and vivid molecular-level scenes. This edition introduces electron density models, which depict shape, structure, and variations in electron charge within the same image.

MATTER
Anything that has mass and volume
Exists in three physical states: solid, liquid, gas

MIXTURES
Two or more elements or compounds in variable proportions
Components retain their properties

Heterogeneous Mixtures
• Visible parts
• Differing regional composition

Homogeneous Mixtures (Solutions)
• No visible parts
• Same composition throughout

**PHYSICAL
CHANGES**
Filtration
Extraction
Distillation
Crystallization
Chromatography

PURE SUBSTANCES
Fixed composition throughout

Elements
• Composed of one type of atom
• Classified as metal, nonmetal, or metalloid
• Simplest type of matter that retains characteristic properties
• May occur as individual atoms or as molecules
• Atomic mass is average of isotopic masses weighted by abundance

Compounds
• Two or more elements combined in fixed fraction by mass
• Properties differ from those of component elements
• Molecular mass is sum of atomic masses

CHEMICAL CHANGES

Atoms
• Protons (p^+) and neutrons (n^0) in tiny, massive, positive nucleus; number of p^+ = atomic number (Z)
• Electrons (e^-) occupy surrounding volume, number of p^+ = number of e^-

Ionic Compounds
• Solids composed of cations and anions
• Ions arise through e^- transfer from metal to nonmetal

Covalent Compounds
• Often consist of separate molecules
• Atoms (usually nonmetals) bonded by shared e^- pairs

Figure 2.26 The classification of matter from a chemical point of view. Mixtures are separated by physical changes into elements and compounds. Chemical changes are required to convert elements into compounds, and vice versa.

Summary Diagrams

These illustrations show interconnections among many ideas to make your review more efficient.

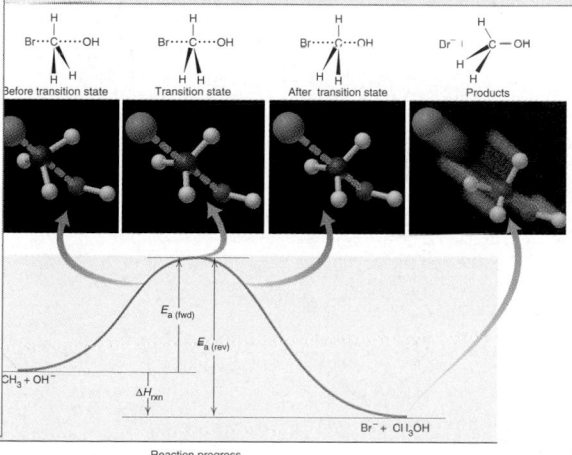

Before transition state

Transition state

After transition state

Products

$E_{a \text{ (fwd)}}$

$E_{a \text{ (rev)}}$

ΔH_{rxn}

$CH_3 + OH^-$

$Br^- + CH_3OH$

Reaction progress

Problem-Solving Method

Approaching chemistry problem solving with novel four-part Sample Problems that help you plan a strategy, solve the calculation, check the answer, and practice the new skill—

Sample Problem

A multipart worked-out problem appears when an important new concept or skill is introduced.

Plan

analyzes the steps needed to take what is known and find what is unknown. This approach helps you think through the solution *before* performing calculations.

Solution

shows the calculation steps in the same order as detailed in the Plan and Roadmap.

Check

fosters the habit of quickly going over your work to make sure the answer is chemically and mathematically reasonable—a great way to avoid careless errors on exams.

Follow-Up Problem

gives you immediate practice with the new skill by presenting a similar problem.

Sample Problem 5.2   Applying the Volume-Pressure Relationship

PROBLEM An apprentice of Boyle finds that the air trapped in a J tube occupies 24.8 cm³ at 1.12 atm. By adding mercury to the tube, he increases the pressure on the trapped air to 2.64 atm. Assuming constant temperature, what is the new volume of air (in L)?

PLAN We must find the final volume (V_2) in liters, given the initial volume (V_1), initial pressure (P_1), and final pressure (P_2). The temperature and amount of gas are fixed. We convert the units of V_1 from cm³ to mL and then to L, rearrange the ideal gas law to the appropriate form, and solve for V_2. We can predict the direction of the change: since P increases, V will decrease; thus, $V_2 < V_1$. (Note the two-part roadmap.)

SOLUTION Summarizing the gas variables:

$P_1 = 1.12$ atm $P_2 = 2.64$ atm
$V_1 = 24.8$ cm³ (convert to L) $V_2 =$ unknown T and n remain constant

Converting V_1 from cm³ to L:

$$V_1 = 24.8 \text{ cm}^3 \times \frac{1 \text{ mL}}{1 \text{ cm}^3} \times \frac{1 \text{ L}}{1000 \text{ mL}} = 0.0248 \text{ L}$$

Arranging the ideal gas law and solving for V_2: At fixed n and T, we have

$$\frac{P_1 V_1}{n_T T_T} = \frac{P_2 V_2}{n_2 T_2} \qquad \text{or} \qquad P_1 V_1 = P_2 V_2$$

$$V_2 = V_1 \times \frac{P_1}{P_2} = 0.0248 \text{ L} \times \frac{1.12 \text{ atm}}{2.64 \text{ atm}} = 0.0105 \text{ L}$$

CHECK As we predicted, $V_2 < V_1$. The pressure more than doubled, so V_2 should be less than $\frac{1}{2}V_1$ ($0.0105/0.0248 < \frac{1}{2}$).

COMMENT Predicting the direction of the change provides another check on the problem setup: To make $V_2 < V_1$, we must multiply V_1 by a number *less than* 1. This means the ratio of pressures must be *less than* 1, so the larger pressure (P_2) must be in the denominator, P_1/P_2.

Follow-up Problem 5.2   A sample of argon gas occupies 105 mL at 0.871 atm. If the temperature remains constant, what is the volume (in L) at 26.3 kPa?

Roadmap
is included in many Plans. It is a block diagram, *specific* to the problem, that visually leads you through the steps.

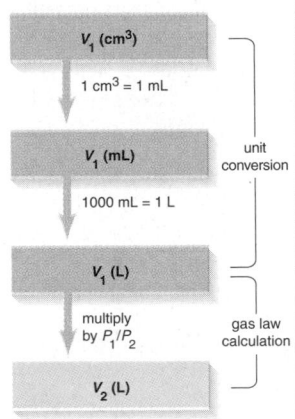

Comment
may be added to point out a common pitfall, alternative approach, modern application, or summarizing insight.

Answers to Follow-up Problems

These provide *brief solutions* at the end of the chapter, not just a numerical answer at the back of the book. This fuller treatment effectively doubles the number of worked-out problems and is an excellent way for you to reinforce skills.

Answers to Follow-up Problems

5.1 P_{CO_2} (torr) = (753.6 mmHg − 174.0 mmHg)

$\times \dfrac{1 \text{ torr}}{1 \text{ mmHg}} = 579.6$ torr

P_{CO_2} (Pa) = 579.6 torr $\times \dfrac{1 \text{ atm}}{760 \text{ torr}} \times \dfrac{1.01325 \times 10^5 \text{ Pa}}{1 \text{ atm}}$

$= 7.727 \times 10^4$ Pa

P_{CO_2} (lb/in²) = 579.6 torr $\times \dfrac{1 \text{ atm}}{760 \text{ torr}} \times \dfrac{14.7 \text{ lb/in}^2}{1 \text{ atm}}$

$= 11.2$ lb/in²

5.2 P_2 (atm) = 26.3 kPa $\times \dfrac{1 \text{ atm}}{101.325 \text{ kPa}} = 0.260$ atm

V_2 (L) = 105 mL $\times \dfrac{1 \text{ L}}{1000 \text{ mL}} \times \dfrac{0.871 \text{ atm}}{0.260 \text{ atm}} = 0.352$ L

Real-World Applications

Seeing the relevance of text discussions with *concept-based* applications and four features that demonstrate how a principle affects your daily life and perhaps your future career—

Tools of the Chemistry Laboratory

These essays describe the key instruments and techniques that chemists use in modern practice to obtain the facts that underlie their theories.

Chemical Connections

These essays show the interdisciplinary nature of chemistry by applying chemical principles to related scientific fields, including physiology, geology, biochemistry, engineering, and environmental science.

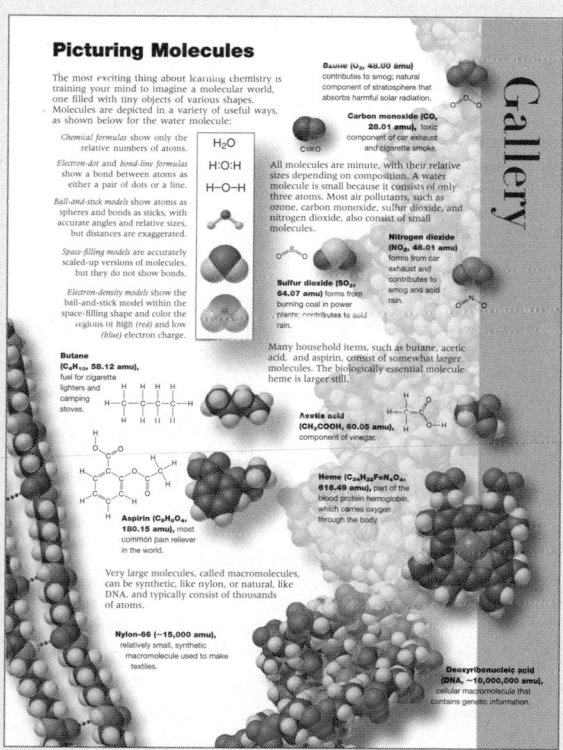

Galleries

These illustrated summaries of applications show how common and unusual substances and products relate to chemical principles. You'll learn how a ball-point pen works, why bubbles in a drink are round, why contact-lens rinse must have a certain concentration, how disposable and rechargeable batteries differ, and many other intriguing applications.

Margin Notes

Over 145 short, lively explanations apply ideas in the related text. You'll explore how your body and the Earth control their temperatures, how crime labs track illegal drugs, how your lungs work, how fat-free chips and decaf coffee are made, the principle of a winning poker hand, the risks of nuclear radiation, handy tips for memorizing relationships, and much more.

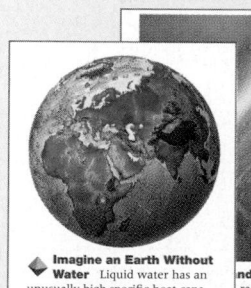

Review and Reinforcement

Reviewing key ideas and skills both during and after reading the main content—

Section Summary

These concise paragraphs conclude each section, immediately restating the major ideas just covered.

Section Summary

An atom's electronegativity is related to its ability to pull bonded electrons toward it, which generates partial charges at the ends of the bond. Electronegativity increases across a period and decreases down a group, the reverse of the trend in size. The greater the ΔEN of the atoms in a bond, the more polar the bond is and the greater its ionic character. There is a gradation of bond type, from ionic to polar covalent to nonpolar covalent, which can be seen by combining a halogen with the other elements in its period.

Chapter Perspective and Learning Objectives

A brief overview at the end places the chapter in the context of previous and upcoming topics. Next, a numbered list, providing section and/or sample problem numbers, helps you focus on key concepts and skills.

Chapter Perspective

With this introduction to chemical kinetics, we have begun to explore the dynamic inner workings of chemical change. Variations in reaction rate are observed through concentration and temperature changes, which operate on the molecular level through the frequency and energetics of particle collisions and the details of reactant structure. Kinetics allows us to speculate about the molecular pathway of a reaction. Modern industry and biochemistry depend on its principles. However, speed and yield are very different aspects of a reaction. In Chapter 17, you'll see how opposing reaction rates give rise to the equilibrium state and examine how much product has formed once the net reaction has stopped.

The following learning objectives, with section and/or sample problem (SP) numbers in parentheses, can help focus your study:

Understand These Concepts

1. How reaction rate depends on concentration, particle size, and temperature (Section 16.1)
2. The meaning of reaction rate in terms of changing concentrations over time (Section 16.2)
3. How the rate can be expressed in terms of reactant or product concentrations (Section 16.2)
4. The distinction between average and instantaneous rate and why the instantaneous rate changes during the reaction (Section 16.2)
5. The interpretation of reaction rate in terms of reactant and product concentrations (Section 16.2)
6. The experimental basis of the rate law and the

17. How a reaction mechanism consists of several elementary steps, with the slowest step determining the overall rate (Section 16.7)
18. The criteria for a valid mechanism (Section 16.7)
19. How a catalyst speeds a reaction by lowering the activation energy (Section 16.8)
20. The distinction between homogeneous and heterogeneous catalysis (Section 16.8)

Master These Skills

1. Calculating instantaneous rate from the slope of a tangent to a concentration vs. time plot (Section 16.2)
2. Expressing rate in terms of changes in concentra-

Key Terms, Equations, and Figures

Key Terms

are boldfaced within the chapter. They are arranged here by section and defined again in the Glossary (with specific page reference).

Key Equations and Relationships

are numbered within the chapter and listed here with page number.

Highlighted Figures and Tables

are listed by page number, so you can find them easily and review their essential content.

For Review and Reference

Key Terms

	Section 3.3	**Section 3.4**	**Section 3.5**
stoichiometry	chemical equation	overall (net) equation	solute
Section 3.1	reactant	limiting reactant	solvent
mole (mol)	product	theoretical yield	concentration
Avogadro's number	balancing (stoichiometric)	side reaction	molarity (M)
molar mass (M)	coefficient	actual yield	
Section 3.2		percent yield (% yield)	
combustion analysis			

Key Equations and Relationships

3.1 Number of entities in one mole (p. 89):
1 mole contains 6.022×10^{23} entities (to 4 significant figures)

3.2 Converting amount (mol) to mass using M (p. 93):
$$\text{Mass (g)} = \text{no. of moles} \times \frac{\text{no. of grams}}{1 \text{ mol}}$$

3.3 Converting mass to amount (mol) using $\frac{1}{M}$ (p. 93):
$$\text{No. of moles} = \text{mass (g)} \times \frac{1 \text{ mol}}{\text{no. of grams}}$$

3.4 Converting amount (mol) to number of entities (p. 93):
$$\text{No. of entities} = \text{no. of moles} \times \frac{6.022 \times 10^{23} \text{ entities}}{1 \text{ mol}}$$

3.5 Converting number of entities to amount (mol) (p. 93):
$$\text{No. of moles} = \text{no. of entities} \times \frac{1 \text{ mol}}{6.022 \times 10^{23} \text{ entities}}$$

3.6 Calculating mass % (p. 96):
Mass % of element X
$$= \frac{\text{moles of X in formula} \times \text{molar mass of X (g/mol)}}{\text{mass of 1 mol of compound (g)}} \times 100$$

3.7 Calculating percent yield (p. 114):
$$\% \text{ yield} = \frac{\text{actual yield}}{\text{theoretical yield}} \times 100$$

3.8 Defining molarity (p. 116):
$$\text{Molarity} = \frac{\text{moles of solute}}{\text{liters of solution}} \quad \text{or} \quad M = \frac{\text{mol solute}}{\text{L soln}}$$

3.9 Diluting a concentrated solution (p. 119):
$$M_{\text{dil}} \times V_{\text{dil}} = \text{number of moles} = M_{\text{conc}} \times V_{\text{conc}}$$

Highlighted Figures and Tables

These figures (F) and tables (T) provide a quick review of key ideas.
T3.1 Summary of mass terminology (p. 91)
T3.2 Information contained in a formula (p. 93)
F3.3 Summary of mass-mole-number relationships for elements and compounds (p. 94)

T3.5 Information contained in a balanced equation (p. 107)
F3.8 Summary of mass-mole-number relationships in a chemical reaction (p. 109)
F3.11 Summary of mass-mole-number-volume relationships in solution (p. 117)
F3.14 Overview of mole-mass-number relationships (p. 122)

End-of-Chapter Problems

An exceptionally large number of homework problems lets you practice the ideas and skills from the chapter. Three types of problems are keyed by chapter section.

Concept Review Questions

test your qualitative understanding of key ideas.

Skill-Building Exercises

are written in pairs, with one of each pair answered in the back of the book. A series of similar problems begins with a simple pair and increases in difficulty to build your confidence through a unique "weaning" process, which gradually eliminates multistep directions.

Problems in Context

apply the learned skills to interesting scenarios, with many examples from industry, medicine, and the environment.

Comprehensive Problems

follow the section-based problems. These more challenging problems rely on material from any section or earlier chapter.

Figure P2.110   Figure P2.111

Mixtures: Classification and Separation

■ **Concept Review Questions**

2.112 In what main way is separating the components of a mixture different from separating the components of a compound?

2.113 What is the difference between a homogeneous and a heterogeneous mixture?

2.114 Is a solution a homogeneous or a heterogeneous mixture? Give an example of an aqueous solution.

■ **Skill-Building Exercises (paired)**

2.115 Classify each of the following as a compound, a homogeneous mixture, or a heterogeneous mixture: (a) distilled water; (b) gasoline; (c) beach sand; (d) wine; (e) air.

2.116 Classify each of the following as a compound, a homogeneous mixture, or a heterogeneous mixture: (a) orange juice; (b) vegetable soup; (c) cement; (d) calcium sulfate; (e) tea.

2.117 Name the technique(s) and briefly describe the procedure you would use to separate each of the following mixtures into two components: (a) table salt and pepper; (b) table sugar and sand; (c) drinking water contaminated with fuel oil; (d) vegetable oil and vinegar.

2.118 Name the technique(s) and briefly describe the procedure you would use to separate each of the following mixtures into two components: (a) crushed ice and crushed glass; (b) table sugar dissolved in ethanol; (c) iron and sulfur; (d) two pigments (chlorophyll *a* and chlorophyll *b*) from spinach leaves.

■ **Problems in Context**

2.119 Which separation method is operating in each of the following procedures?
(a) Pouring a mixture of cooked pasta and boiling water into a colander
(b) Removing colored impurities from raw sugar to make refined sugar
(c) Preparing coffee by pouring hot water through ground coffee beans

2.120 Illicit "street" drugs are often mixed with an inactive substance, such as ascorbic acid (vitamin C). After obtaining a sample of cocaine, government chemists separate the mixture into its component substances. By calculating the mass of vitamin C per gram of drug sample, they can track the drug's distribution. For example, if different samples of cocaine obtained on the streets of New York, Los Angeles, and Paris all contain 0.6384 g vitamin C per gram of sample, they very likely come from a common source. Is this street sam-

Comprehensive Problems

Problems with an asterisk (*) are more challenging.

2.121 Helium is the lightest noble gas and the second most abundant element (after hydrogen) in the universe.
(a) The radius of a helium atom is 3.1×10^{-11} m, and the radius of its nucleus is 2.5×10^{-15} m. What fraction of the spherical atomic volume is occupied by the nucleus (V of a sphere $= \frac{4}{3}\pi r^3$)?
(b) The mass of a helium-4 atom is 6.64648×10^{-24} g, and each of its two electrons has a mass of 9.10939×10^{-28} g. What fraction of this atom's mass is contributed by its nucleus?

2.122 Before neutrons were discovered, Rutherford suggested that electrons resided both within the nucleus *and* around it. How could such a model give an atom with mass and charge similar to that of our current model?

2.123 Why is the atomic mass unit very close to the mass of a proton or a neutron?

2.124 The scenes lettered A-I depict various types of matter on the atomic scale. Choose the correct scene(s) for each of the following:
(a) A mixture that fills its container
(b) A substance that cannot be broken down into any simpler substances
(c) An element with a very high resistance to flow
(d) A homogeneous mixture
(e) An element that fills its container but displays a surface
(f) A gas consisting of diatomic particles
(g) A gas that can be broken down into simpler substances
(h) A substance with a 2:1 number ratio of its component atoms
(i) Matter that can be separated into its component substances by physical means

Learning the Chemistry of the Elements

The periodic table, the central organizing icon for the chemistry of the elements, is introduced in Chapter 2 and applied throughout the book. Helping you understand this rich, diverse material with two unique features—

Interchapter

This multipage, illustrated *Perspective on the Properties of the Elements* reviews the major points in Chapters 7–13 that deal with atomic properties and their resulting effects on element behavior.

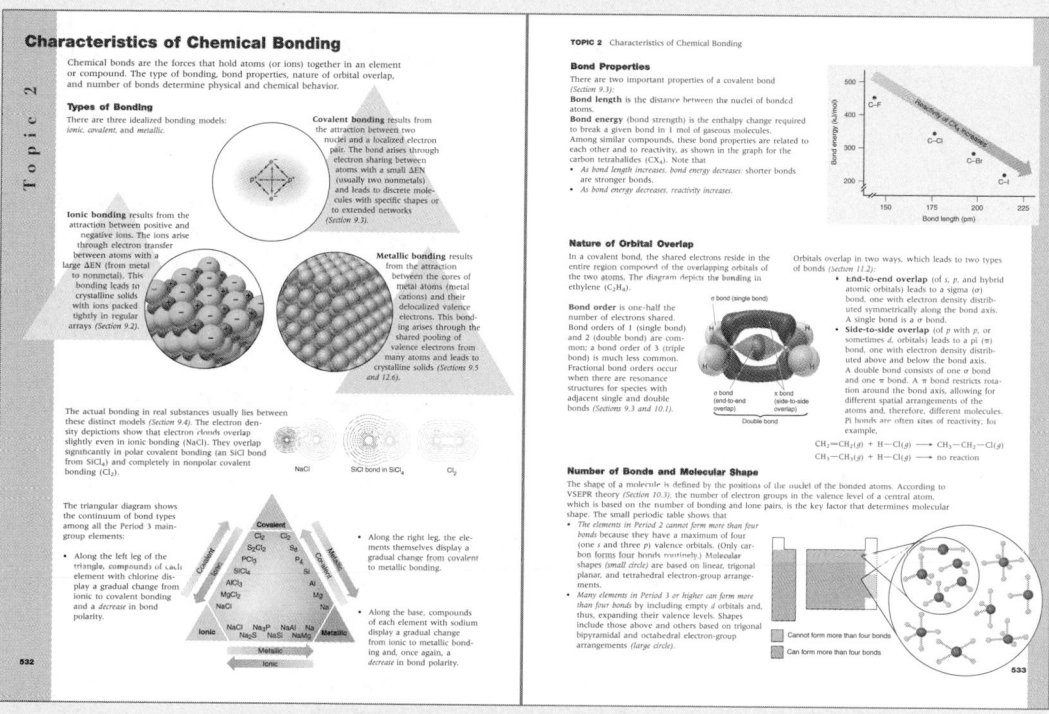

Family Portraits

These two-page illustrated summaries appear in Chapter 14 and detail the atomic, physical, and chemical properties of each main group.

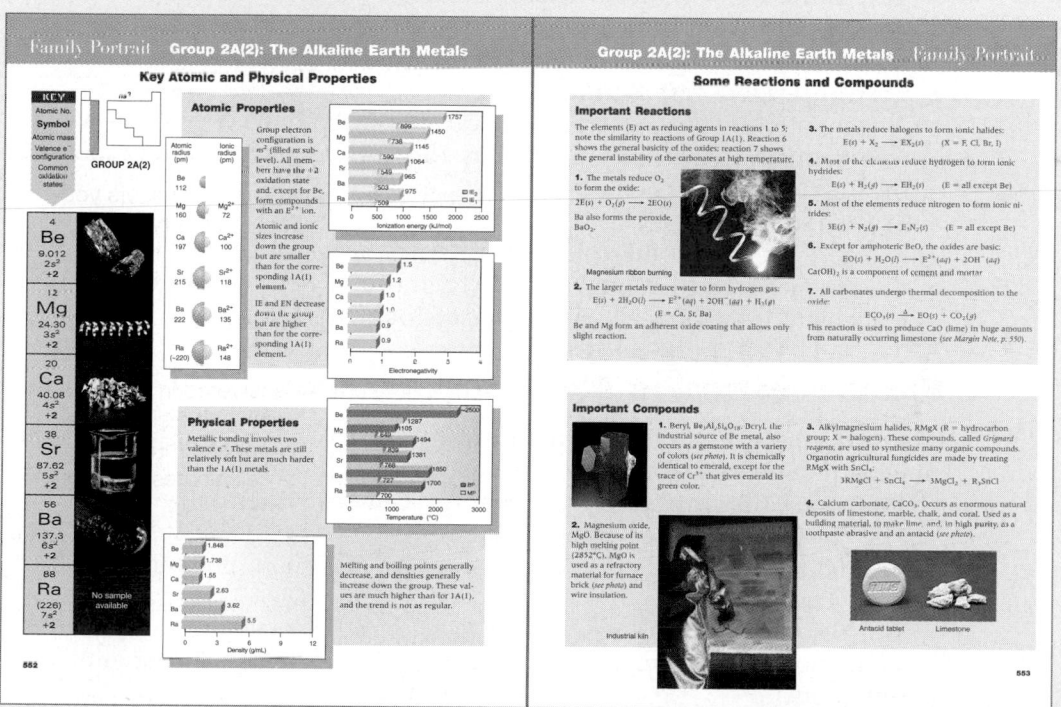

A Complete Package of Supplements for Instructor and Student

Even though the written text remains at the core of the great majority of general chemistry courses, the modern presentation of concepts and the practice of skills now uses many other resources. Several excellent print and multimedia supplements have been prepared to accompany the text and make learning chemistry as meaningful and up-to-date as possible:

For the Instructor: *Print Supplements*

- **Instructor's Resource Manual** by Martin Silberberg
  This manual, which is also available via the Silberberg On-Line Learning Center *(www.mhhe.com/silberberg)*, contains discussions of chapter purpose and approach, alternative topic sequences, chapter outlines, strategies for incorporating descriptive chemistry, and recommended lab separates.
- **Instructor's Solutions Manual** by Alan Pribula, Frank Milio, and Thomas Berg, Towson University
  This manual contains complete, worked-out solutions for all end-of-chapter problems in the text.
- **Test Bank** by S. Walter Orchard, University of Puget Sound
  This valuable resource contains over 1,800 questions organized by chapter. Question types include multiple choice, true/false, and short answer.
- **Computerized Test Bank**
  A computerized test generator is available in both Windows and Macintosh formats and enables instructors to generate tests from questions in the Test Bank.
- **Transparencies**
  A boxed set of 300 full-color transparency acetates features images from the text selected by Martin Silberberg and modified to ensure maximum readability in both small and large classroom settings.

For the Instructor: *Media Supplements*

The Silberberg Visual Resource Library CD-ROM is an outstanding multimedia product that combines three exceptional resources:
- **McGraw-Hill Animation Library for General Chemistry**
  This resource features over 50 high-quality animations of topics from throughout the course that can be used for classroom presentation.
- **Text Image Library**
  This resource contains over 500 images from the text that can be used for stand-alone classroom presentation or inclusion into a PowerPoint presentation.
- **PowerPoint Lecture Presentation** by William Zoller, University of Washington
  This fully editable presentation includes slides outlining the content from each chapter of the text. Where appropriate, illustrations from the Text Image Library have been included.

For the Student: *Print Supplements*

- **Student Study Guide** by Elizabeth Weberg
  This excellent resource covers the most important points in every chapter of the text. Clearly formatted and illustrated, it develops concepts and skills in a friendly, relaxed style that forestalls student confusion. The guide contains numerous worked-out examples, key points to keep in mind, and a large number of additional problems (with answers) for self-test purposes.
- **Student Solutions Manual** by Deborah Wiegand, University of Washington, and Tris Samberg, Cascadia Community College
  This manual contains complete worked-out solutions to all follow-up problems and the end-of-chapter problems designated with colored numbers. It presents solutions using the same problem-solving approach that is presented in the text.
- **Schaum's Outline of College Chemistry** by Jerome Rosenberg, Michigan State University, and Lawrence Epstein, University of Pittsburgh
  This helpful study aid provides students with hundreds of solved and supplementary problems for the general chemistry course.

For the Student: *Media Supplements*

- **Silberberg 2/e On-Line Learning Center** *www.mhhe.com/silberberg*
  Free to students and instructors using the text, the Silberberg On-Line Learning Center offers a variety of supplementary material to enhance the study of chemistry. A key feature of the Center is the over 1,800 interactive quiz questions (75 per chapter) that allow students to quiz themselves on the concepts presented in the text. The Center also offers additional activities for each chapter in the text, including Super Challenge exercises, ChemQuest web exercises, and molecular modeling exercises.
- **Chemistry Study Partner** by Martin Silberberg
  Through the use of interactive problem solving and state-of-the-art animations that incorporate student-controlled simulations, this unique CD-ROM tutors students in many of the central ideas and skills from the course. Moreover, the CD-ROM links to the Silberberg On-Line Learning Center, so students can quiz themselves on concepts as they are presented.
- **Cyberchem**
  This innovative CD-ROM provides a highly interactive study and tutorial package for the one-year general chemistry course. It contains 60 animations of concepts, 25 interactive lab simulations, and 25 movies focusing on real-world applications, along with interactive problem-solving and quizzing modules.
- **Molecules 3D: Molecular Modeling Software** by Molecular Arts Corporation
  This powerful and innovative, yet inexpensive, software for Windows and Macintosh incorporates an expandable library of more than 100 structures to allow construction of virtually any molecule for 3D examination. It also allows conversion of Lewis structures to VSEPR-based molecular shapes at the click of a button.
- **Chem Skill Builder** by Electronic Homework Systems
  This extremely useful CD-ROM generates questions for students for every topic in the general chemistry course. The questions are presented in a randomized fashion with a constant mix of variables so that no two students will receive the same questions. The application provides feedback for students when incorrect answers are entered, and the answers can be submitted to an instructor for grading.

About the Author and Consultants

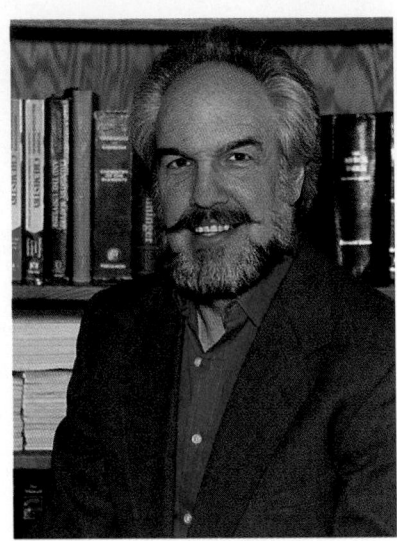

Martin Silberberg received his B.S. in chemistry from the City University of New York in 1966 and his Ph.D. in chemistry from the University of Oklahoma in 1971. He then accepted a research position at the Albert Einstein College of Medicine, where he studied the chemical nature of neurotransmission and Parkinson's disease. In 1977, Dr. Silberberg joined the faculty of Simon's Rock College of Bard (Massachusetts), a liberal arts college known for its excellence in teaching small classes of highly motivated students. As Head of the Natural Sciences Major and Director of Premedical Studies, he taught courses in general chemistry, organic chemistry, biochemistry, and nonmajors chemistry. The close student contact afforded him insights into how students learn chemistry, where they have difficulties, and what strategies can help them succeed. In 1983, Dr. Silberberg decided to apply these insights in a broader context and established a text writing and editing company. Before writing his own text, he worked on chemistry, biochemistry, and physics texts for several major college publishers. He resides with his wife and child in the Berkshire Mountains of western Massachusetts, where he enjoys the rich cultural life of the area, dabbles in the alchemy of European breadmaking, and haltingly practices the German classical song literature.

Randy Duran is an Associate Professor in Chemistry within the Butler Polymer Laboratories and Adjunct Professor in Materials Science at the University of Florida. He obtained a B.S. degree in polymer engineering from Case Western Reserve University and a Ph.D. in polymer physical chemistry from the University Louis Pasteur, Strasbourg, France. In addition to teaching general chemistry and advanced courses in physical and polymer chemistry, Dr. Duran maintains an active research program in the area of polymer surfaces and interfaces. Dr. Duran is Florida's Executive Committee Member, coordinating activities at the Material Research Collaborative Access Team Beamline at the Advanced Photon Source Synchrotron at Argonne National Laboratories. He also directs the National Science Foundation Research Experiences for Undergraduates site in chemistry at the University of Florida.

L. Peter Gold grew up in Massachusetts and obtained his undergraduate and graduate education at Harvard University. He is Professor of Chemistry at The Pennsylvania State University, where he has been since 1965. During that time he has taught general chemistry (to over 10,000 students) as well as physical chemistry and physical chemistry lab. His hobbies include music, both as a performer and a listener, computers, and omnivorous reading.

Charles Haas, emeritus Professor of Chemistry at The Pennsylvania State University, earned his Ph.D. at the University of Chicago under the supervision of Norman Nachtrieb. During his 38-year career at Penn State, he taught general chemistry, undergraduate and graduate inorganic chemistry, and courses in chemical education for public school teachers at all levels. He was honored with both the College of Science Noll Award and the University Amoco Award for teaching. His research focus is on transition metals chemistry and coordination compounds. Since his retirement, he has spent much of his time reading, traveling worldwide, and enjoying collegiate athletics.

Robert Loeschen earned a B.S. in Chemistry from the University of Illinois and a Ph.D. from the University of Chicago. He joined the faculty at California State University–Long Beach in 1969. Trained as an organic chemist, he teaches a wide variety of courses, including general chemistry for science majors, chemistry for nursing majors (he coauthored a text for this subject), organic chemistry for nonmajors, organic chemistry for majors, and occasionally a graduate course in his research specialty, organic photochemistry. At present, he spends half his time in the chemistry department and half his time as Associate Dean for the College of Natural Sciences and Mathematics. When he is not teaching or deaning, he plays golf or putters in his woodworking shop.

Arlan Norman conducted undergraduate studies at the University of North Dakota, graduate work at Indiana University, and postdoctoral research at the University of California–Berkeley; he is a Distinguished Alumnus of the University of North Dakota. Dr. Norman is Professor of Chemistry and Biochemistry at the University of Colorado at Boulder, where he has taught general and inorganic chemistry for the past 32 years, concentrating on the teaching of molecular graphics, modeling, and visualization techniques. He is a main-group element synthetic chemist, with research interests in structure/reactivity relationships and new materials applications of phosphorus compounds, for which he has been awarded Alfred P. Sloan and University of Colorado Council of Research and Creative Work fellowships. Professor Norman is a Nordic skier and an avid cyclist: he has cycled extensively in Italy, New Zealand, and Ireland.

Acknowledgments

The great success of the first edition made work on the second a daunting prospect, but I am especially fortunate to have a very supportive publisher and an exceptional group of colleagues to help me create this revision.

As in the first edition, I feel privileged to share center stage with my consultants. Through extensive input based on nearly a century-and-a-half of combined teaching experience, they focused my efforts and provided detailed suggestions on every chapter. For the second edition, I am very pleased that the original consultant team of Peter Gold, Chuck Haas, Bob Loeschen, and Arlan Norman has been joined by Randy Duran. Randy's knowledge of materials and polymer science, as well as multimedia education, has enriched the project in many ways.

Professors willing to share their knowledge and experience to make better textbooks for their students are invaluable to any project of this type. Special thanks go to Professors Neil Weinstein of Santa Fe Community College and Nordulf Debye of Towson University, who provided in-depth, post-publication reviews of the first edition, which I then used extensively in preparing this revision. McGraw-Hill chose an outstanding group of professors to review second-edition manuscript. All have my sincerest gratitude and assurance that their comments received the most serious consideration:

Hugh Akers *Lamar University–Beaumont*
Robert Allendoerfer *SUNY–Buffalo*
Margaret Asirvatham *University of Colorado–Boulder*
David Ballantine *Northern Illinois University*
Michael Batley *Macquarie University*
G. Ronald Brown *University of Northern British Columbia*
Elaine Carter *Los Angeles City College*
Dominick Casadonte *Texas Tech University*
Thomas Chasteen *Sam Houston State University*
Nadia Cordero de Figuero *University of Puerto Rico*
Richard Daake *Bartlesville Wesleyan College*
George Fleck *Smith College*
Dennis Flentge *Cedarville College*
Ron Garber *California State University–Long Beach*
John Garland *Washington State University*
Marcia Gillette *Indiana University–Kokomo*

David Grainger *Colorado State University*
Arthur Grosser *McGill University*
Tandy Grubbs *Stetson University*
Alton Hassell *Baylor University*
Ronald Johnson *Emory University*
Michael W. Jones *New Mexico Military Institute*
Silvia Kölchens *Pima Community College*
Robert Kren *University of Michigan–Flint*
Julie Kuehn *William Rainey Harper College*
Dorothy Kurland *West Virginia University Institute of Technology*
Richard H. Langley *Stephen F. Austin State University*
Joseph D. Laposa *McMaster University*
Thornton Lipscomb *University of Louisville*
Ian McNaught *University of Sydney*
Richard S. Mitchell *Arkansas State University*
Pamela New *University of Central Oklahoma*

S. Walter Orchard *University of Puget Sound*
Larry Pedersen *College of Misericordia*
Joann Pfeiffer *University of Wyoming*
James Purcell *Manor Junior College*
James Reilly *Indiana University*
Melvin Roberts *Columbia University*
Theodore Sakano *Rockland City Community College*
Karl Seff *University of Hawaii–Honolulu*
Mary Jane Shultz *Tufts University*
Scott Sinex *Prince Georges Community College*
Barbara Spohr *Dodge City Community College*
Peter John Stiles *Macquarie University*
Bruce Storhoff *Ball State University*
Sharon Vincent *Shelton State Community College*
Howard Wiley, Jr. *Middlesex Community Technical College*
Thao Yang *University of Wisconsin–Eau Claire*

The following professors provided invaluable assistance by reviewing McGraw-Hill's multimedia supplements for general chemistry or by authoring content for the Silberberg On-Line Learning Center (*www.mhhe.com/silberberg*):

Hugh Akers *Lamar University*
Dominick Casadonte *Texas Tech University*
Randy Duran *University of Florida*
David Erwin *Rose-Hulman Institute of Technology*
Peter Gold *Pennsylvania State University*

Paul Kelter *University of Nebraska*
Christa Koval *University of Colorado*
Robert Kren *University of Michigan-Flint*
Patricia Lang *Ball State University*
David Nachman *Phoenix College*
Mark Noble *University of Louisville*

Arlan Norman *University of Colorado*
Scott Perry *University of Houston*
Keith Peterman *York College of Pennsylvania*
James Reilly *Indiana University*
Scot Wherland *Washington State University*

The following professors provided reviews, problems, or other invaluable advice for preparation of the first edition:

David L. Adams *Babson College*
Robert Allendoerfer *State University of New York–Buffalo*
Elizabeth J. Armstrong *Cañada College*
Charles Baker *Chemical Engineer*
Claire Baker *Butler University*
Irwin Becker *Villanova University*
Mark Bishop *Monterey Peninsula College*
Robert Bohn *University of Connecticut*
Kenneth L. Busch *Georgia Institute of Technology*
Ian Butler *McGill University*
Harvey Carroll *Kingsborough Community College*
John Clevenger *Truckee Meadows Community College*
Derck A. Davenport *Purdue University*
William Durfee *Buffalo State College*
William Durham *University of Arkansas*
Helmut Eckert *University of Munster*
Karen Eichstadt *Ohio University, Athens*
John H. Fortman *Wright State University*
DonnaJean Fredeen *Southern Connecticut State University*
Dennis Fujita *Santa Rosa Junior College*
Dorothy Gabel *Indiana University–Bloomington*
Donald F. Gaines *University of Wisconsin–Madison*
Ronald Garber *California State University–Long Beach*
Patrick M. Garvey *Des Moines Area Community College*
Edward Genser *California State University–Hayward*

Charles Greenlief *Emporia State University*
Kenneth Hardcastle *California State University–Northridge*
Stephen Hawkes *Oregon State University*
Dorothea H. Hedges *Texas A & M University*
John Hutchinson *Rice University*
Earl Huyser *University of Kansas*
Richard F. Jones *Sinclair Community College*
Edward L. King *University of Colorado–Boulder*
Leo Kling III *Faulkner State Junior College*
James Krueger *Oregon State University*
Larry Little *Georgia Perimeter College*
John R. Luoma *Cleveland State University*
Leslie J. Lyons *Grinnell College*
Jack McKenna *St. Cloud State University*
Jerry L. Mills *Texas Technical University*
Steven Murov *Modesto Junior College*
John H. Nelson *University of Nevada–Reno*
Alan J. Pribula *Towson University*
John L. Ragle *University of Massachusetts–Amherst*
Ronald Ragsdale *University of Utah*
Robert R. Reeves *Rensselaer Polytechnic Institute*
T. W. Richardson *North Georgia State University*
B. Ken Robertson *University of Missouri–Rolla*

Steve Ruis *American River College*
Barbara Sawrey *University of California–San Diego*
Henry Shanfield *University of Houston, Central Campus*
C. Frank Shaw *University of Wisconsin–Milwaukee*
Donald Showalter *University of Wisconsin–Stevens Point*
Mary Jane Shultz *Tufts University*
Dennis Staley *Southern Illinois University–Edwardsville*
Lee Summerlin *University of Alabama–Birmingham*
Tamar Y. Susskind *Oakland Community College*
Yi-Noo Tang *Texas A & M University*
Martin L. Thompson *Lake Forest College*
Robert West *University of Wisconsin–Madison*
Robert Widing *University of Illinois–Chicago*
David Williamson *California Polytechnic State University*
John R. Wilson *Shippensburg University*
Steven Woeste *Scholl College*
George Woodbury *University of Montana*
Linda Zarzana *American River College*
Arden Zipp *State University of New York–Cortland*
William Zoller *University of Washington–Seattle*

I am particularly grateful to Professors S. Walter Orchard of the University of Puget Sound and Stephen Hawkes of Oregon State University for their excellent chapter problems, which greatly enhance the range and relevance of the problem sets.

Once again, I was very fortunate to have had Professor Dorothy B. Kurland of the West Virginia Institute of Technology participate in the project. In addition to reviewing the second half of the manuscript, she performed her usual outstanding role as accuracy checker of the entire book in galleys. Dr. John S. Murdzek of Millennium Business Services helped clarify the art *and* checked the galleys. His remarkably thorough and meticulous review improved the book in many ways. Katie Aiken did a superb job copyediting the manuscript, and Jane Hoover performed an equally superb job proofreading the pages. Sincere thanks also go to Jill Birschbach of Feldman & Associates for tracking down the excellent new photos. The first-edition team of artists—Michael Goodman of Federico/Goodman Studios and Carolyn Duffy and Greg Duffy of ArtScribe, Inc.—returned for this edition and, as anyone can see, the results are magnificent. The striking cover is a perfect example of Michael's magical ability, as we sat together before his computer screen, to turn my concept into a dramatic molecular scene.

Within McGraw-Hill, I found editorial, production, and marketing teams dedicated to making a text of the highest possible quality. My publisher Jim Smith led the editorial team with his good-natured blend of integrity, insight, and experience. I cannot imagine a more steadfast advocate for the new edition than Kent Peterson, my sponsoring editor. With clear thinking, openness, and never-failing good humor, he always placed the book's quality at the top of his bottomless list. In addition to the numberless duties of project developmental editor and coordinator of the print supplements, Margaret Horn always stopped to calm a sometimes frazzled author with patience and cheerfulness. My sincerest thanks goes to the production team, headed by Kim David and led for my project by Janice Roerig-Blong and Jayne Klein, for being so understanding and flexible around the endless input from an often obsessive author. Especially appreciated is their fostering of the unprecedented cooperation of author, artists, pager, and compositor. Lori Johnson of GTS Graphics coordinated the production of the text with expertise, personal warmth, and calm efficiency in the face of innumerable details. Presenting the text with a masterful flair to the world of professors and students has been the province of the excellent marketing team, headed by Marty Lange. My warmest thanks go as well to all the superb assistants of these principals, without whose tireless, unsung efforts no project of this scope could possibly ever fly.

But, truth be told, the project would never have left the ground, let alone soared, without the loving support of my family—my son Daniel, who helped select many of the new photos and whose unwavering belief in me brightened each day; and Ruth, my "in-house" project manager—and sweetheart. In the second edition, as in the first, Ruth's skill and experience have been paramount. Her input on the editing, art, and production was invaluable, and she performed the enormous job of laying out the pages. Yet, with all her responsibilites, she somehow managed to smooth my path with an encouraging smile and a soft, loving touch.

Martin Silberberg

Keys to the Study of Chemistry

1

Figure: A different view of everyday life. With molecular sight, a typical beach scene of air, sea, and sand becomes a panorama of spherical objects joined in myriad patterns—the separated particles of atmospheric gases, the crowded jumble of water and salts in the liquid ocean, the lockstep order of the solid silicates underfoot. The study of chemistry explains that the world we observe is the direct consequence of a hidden, molecular reality—one we can measure and change—and this chapter opens the door to it.

Specialized steels in bicycles; synthetic polymers in clothing and helmets.

Advanced composites in sports equipment.

Liquid crystals in computer screens.

High-tension polymers in synthetic hip joints.

With the world striding into the 21st century, it is an especially exciting time to be studying chemistry. Wherever you look—from gene technology to electric cars and even to the question of life on other worlds—challenges and opportunities appear as never before, and all of them depend on an understanding of the concepts you will learn in this course.

The principles of the dynamic, modern science of chemistry did not appear fully formed but changed through time and are still evolving today. Look back and imagine how differently humans learned about the material world tens of thousands of years ago. At the dawn of human experience, our ancestors survived through knowledge acquired by the *trial and error* of everyday observation: which types of stone were hard enough to shape others, which types of wood were rigid and which flexible, which hides could be treated to make clothing, which plants were edible and which poisonous. Today, the science of chemistry, with its powerful *quantitative theories,* helps us understand the nature of materials, so that we can make better use of them and create new ones: specialized steels, advanced composites, synthetic polymers, and countless other new materials (see photos).

You know that chemistry has an impact on your daily life, but the extent of that impact can be mind-boggling. Consider just the beginning of a typical day from a chemical point of view. Molecules align in the liquid crystal display of your clock, electrons flow through its circuitry to create a rousing sound, and you throw off a thermal insulator of manufactured polymer. You jump in the shower to emulsify fatty substances on your skin and hair with chemically treated water and formulated detergents. You adorn yourself in an array of processed chemicals—pleasant-smelling pigmented materials suspended in cosmetic gels, dyed polymeric fibers, synthetic footwear, and metal-alloyed jewelry. Today, breakfast is a bowl of nutrient-enriched, spoilage-retarded cereal and milk, a piece of fertilizer-grown, pesticide-treated fruit, and a cup of a hot aqueous solution of neurally stimulating alkaloid. Ready to leave, you collect some books—processed cellulose and plastic, electronically printed with light- and oxygen-resistant inks—hop in your hydrocarbon-fueled, metal-vinyl-ceramic vehicle, electrically ignite a synchronized series of controlled gaseous explosions, and you're off to class!

The influence of chemistry extends to the natural environment as well. The air, water, land, and organisms that thrive there form a remarkably complex system of chemical interactions. There is no question that modern chemical products have enhanced the quality of our lives, but their manufacture and use also pose increasing dangers, such as toxic waste, acid rain, global warming, and ozone depletion. If our heedless application of chemical principles has led to some of these problems, our thoughtful application of the same principles will play a major role in solving them.

Perhaps the significance of chemistry is most amazing when you ponder the underlying chemical nature of biology. Molecular events taking place within you right now allow your eyes to scan this page and your brain cells to translate fluxes of electric charge into thoughts. The most vital biological questions—How did life arise and evolve? How does an organism reproduce, grow, and age? What is the essence of health and disease?—ultimately have chemical answers.

This course comes with a bonus, the development of a mental skill you can apply to any science-related field. As you comprehend the ideas of chemistry, a hidden level of the universe will unfold before your mind's eye, one filled with incredibly minute particles hurtling at fantastic speeds and colliding billions of times a second. It is the interactions of these particles that result in everything within and around you.

The first chapter holds the keys to help you enter this new world. It begins with some fundamental definitions and concepts and then examines the historical origins of the science of chemistry and the approach that chemists take to understand nature. We discuss modern systems of measurement and calculation and consider an all-important topic that may be concerning you: how to solve chemistry problems. Finally, we look at one of many examples of chemistry and other sciences working together for society's benefit. If you are still wondering whether chemistry is important to you, rest assured that soon you will be wondering how any educated person can function today without a knowledge of chemistry!

1.1 Some Fundamental Definitions

The science of chemistry deals with the makeup of the entire physical universe. Perhaps a good place to begin is with the definition of a few central ideas, some of which are probably familiar to you. **Chemistry** is *the study of matter and its properties, the changes that matter undergoes, and the energy associated with those changes.*

The Properties of Matter

Matter is the "stuff" of the universe: air, glass, planets, students—*anything that has mass and volume.* (In Section 1.5, we discuss the meanings of mass and volume in terms of how they are measured.) Chemists are particularly interested in the **composition** of matter, *the types and amounts of simpler substances that make up a sample.* A *substance* is a type of matter that has a defined, fixed composition throughout. (We discuss this idea from an atomic point of view in Chapter 2.)

We learn about matter by observing its **properties,** *the characteristics that give each substance its unique identity.* In people, we observe such properties as height, weight, hair and eye color, fingerprints, blood type, and so on, until we arrive at a unique identification. To identify a substance, chemists observe two distinct types of properties, physical and chemical, which are closely related to two types of change that matter undergoes. **Physical properties** are those that a substance shows *by itself, without changing into or interacting with another substance.* Some physical properties are color, melting point, electrical conductivity, and density. A **physical change** occurs when a substance *alters its physical form, **not** its composition.* A physical change results in different physical properties. For example, Figure 1.1A shows the physical change that occurs when ice melts. Liquid water looks different from ice because several *physical* properties have changed, such as hardness, density, and ability to flow. But the sample has *not* changed its composition because it is still water. *Physical change (same substance before and after the change):*

Ice (solid form) $\longrightarrow$ water (liquid form)

On the other hand, **chemical properties** are those that a substance shows *as it changes into or interacts with another substance (or substances).* Examples of chemical properties include flammability, corrosiveness, and reactivity with acids. A **chemical change,** also called a **chemical reaction,** occurs when *a substance (or substances) is converted into a different substance (or substances).* Because the new substance (or substances) has a different composition, it also has different chemical and physical properties. Figure 1.1B shows that a chemical change (reaction) occurs when you pass an electric current through water: the water decomposes (breaks down) into two substances, hydrogen gas and oxygen gas, each with physical and chemical properties different from each other *and* from the water. The sample *has* changed its composition because it is no longer water.

Chemical change (different substances before and after):

Water $\xrightarrow{\text{electric current}}$ hydrogen gas + oxygen gas

A

Hydrogen gas

Oxygen gas

B

Figure 1.1 **The distinction between physical and chemical change. A,** The solid form of water undergoes a physical change to become the liquid form, but its composition remains the same. **B,** A chemical change occurs when an electric current passes through water and the water decomposes into hydrogen gas and oxygen gas.

Table 1.1 Some Characteristic Properties of Copper

Physical Properties	Chemical Properties
Reddish brown, metallic luster	

	Slowly forms a green carbonate in moist air
Easily shaped into sheets (malleable) and wires (ductile)	

Good conductor of heat and electricity

Reacts with nitric acid (photo) and sulfuric acid

Can be melted and mixed with zinc to form brass

Slowly forms deep-blue solution in aqueous ammonia

Density = 8.95 g/cm³
Melting point = 1083°C
Boiling point = 2570°C

A substance is defined by its own unique set of physical and chemical properties. Some properties of copper appear in Table 1.1. When we observe a substance with this set of properties, we identify it as copper.

Figure 1.2 **The physical states of matter.** A solid *(left)* has its own shape regardless of the container's shape. A liquid *(center)* conforms to the container's shape but has a surface. A gas *(right)* fills the container completely. The magnified ("blow-up") views of the states show the atomic-scale arrangement of the particles—close together and highly organized in the solid, close together but disorganized in the liquid, and far apart and disorganized in the gas.

The Three States of Matter

Matter occurs commonly in three physical forms called **states**: solid, liquid, and gas. As shown in Figure 1.2 for a general substance, each state is defined by the way it fills a container. A **solid** *has a fixed shape that does not conform to the container shape.* Solids are *not* defined by rigidity or hardness: solid iron is rigid, but solid lead is flexible and solid wax is soft. A **liquid** *conforms to the container shape but fills the container only to the extent of the liquid's own volume;* thus, a liquid forms a *surface.* A **gas** *conforms to the container shape also, but it fills the entire container;* thus, a gas does *not* form a surface. Now, in your imagination, move in close enough to see the particles that make up these states, and look at the views within the "blow-up" circles of Figure 1.2. The particles in the solid lie relatively fixed in a regular, three-dimensional array with a definite shape. Particles in the liquid move randomly around and near one another, colliding continually. Particles in the gas move randomly throughout the container, usually with relatively great distances between them, but sometimes crashing into one another.

Depending on the temperature and pressure of the surroundings, many substances can exist in each of the three physical states and undergo changes in state as well. As the temperature increases, solid water melts to liquid water, and liquid water boils to gaseous water (also called *water vapor*). Similarly, with decreasing temperature, water vapor condenses to liquid water, and with further cooling, the liquid freezes to ice. Many other substances behave in the same way: solid iron melts to liquid (molten) iron and then boils to iron gas at a higher temperature. Cooling the iron gas changes it to liquid and then to solid iron. ◆

You can see that changes in state are physical, not chemical, changes. Moreover, a physical change caused by heating can generally be reversed by cooling, and vice versa. This is *not* generally true for a chemical change. For example, heating iron in moist air causes a chemical reaction that yields a brown, crumbly substance known as rust. Cooling does not reverse this change; rather, another chemical change (or series of them) is required.

To summarize the key distinctions:

- A physical change leads to a different form of the same substance (same composition), whereas a chemical change leads to a different substance (different composition).
- A physical change caused by a temperature change can generally be reversed by the opposite temperature change, whereas this is not generally true of a chemical change.

The following sample problem provides more examples that distinguish between these types of change.

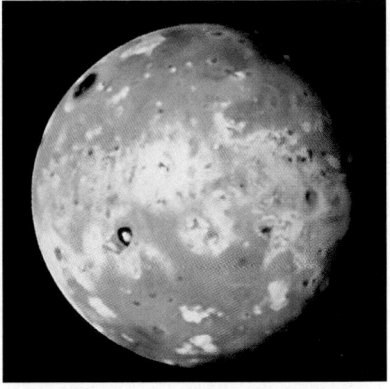

◆ **The Incredible Range of Physical Change** Scientists often study physical change in remarkable settings, using instruments that allow observation far beyond the confines of the laboratory. Instruments aboard the *Voyager* and *Galileo* spacecrafts and the Hubble Space Telescope measure temperatures on Jupiter's moon Io (shown here) that are hot enough to maintain lakes of molten sulfur, and that are cold enough to create vast snowfields of sulfur dioxide and polar caps swathed in hydrogen sulfide frost. (On Earth, sulfur dioxide is one of the gases released from volcanoes and coal-fired power plants, and hydrogen sulfide occurs in swamp gas.)

Sample Problem 1.1   Distinguishing Between Physical and Chemical Change

PROBLEM Decide whether each of the following processes is primarily a physical or a chemical change, and explain briefly:

(a) Frost forms as the temperature drops on a humid winter night (see photo).
(b) A cornstalk grows from a seed that is watered and fertilized.
(c) Dynamite explodes to form a mixture of gases.
(d) Perspiration evaporates when you relax after jogging.
(e) A silver fork tarnishes in air.

PLAN The basic question we ask to decide whether a change is chemical or physical is, "Does the substance change composition or just change form?"

SOLUTION (a) Frost forming is a physical change: the temperature changes water vapor (gaseous water) in humid air to ice crystals (solid water).
(b) A seed growing is a chemical change: the seed, air, fertilizer, soil, and water use energy from sunlight to undergo complex changes in composition.
(c) Dynamite exploding is a chemical change: the dynamite is converted into other substances.
(d) Perspiration evaporating is a physical change: the water in sweat changes its form, from liquid to gas, but not its composition.
(e) Tarnishing is a chemical change: silver changes to silver sulfide by reacting with sulfur-containing substances in the air.

Follow-up Problem 1.1   Decide whether each of the following processes is primarily a physical or a chemical change, and explain briefly:
(a) Purple iodine vapor appears when solid iodine is warmed.
(b) Gasoline fumes are ignited by a spark in an automobile engine cylinder.
(c) A scab forms over an open cut.

Frost forming.

Understanding the properties of a substance and the changes it undergoes leads to the central theme in chemistry: *macroscopic* properties and behavior, such as the ones just discussed, are the results of *submicroscopic* properties and behavior. The defining properties of the three states of matter, for example, are macroscopic ones. They arise from the submicroscopic behavior depicted in the magnified views in Figure 1.2. Throughout this text we return to this basic idea: we study *observable* changes in matter to understand their *unobservable* causes. What is really happening when water boils? Why do iron and copper melt at different temperatures? What events occur in the invisible world of minute particles that cause dynamite to explode, a neon light to glow, or a nail to rust?

The Importance of Energy in the Study of Matter

In general, physical and chemical changes are accompanied by energy changes. **Energy** is often defined as *the ability to do work;* let's see what this definition means. Essentially, all work involves moving something. Work is done when your arm lifts a book, when an engine moves a car's wheels, or when a falling rock moves the ground as it lands. The object doing the work (arm, engine, rock) transfers some of the energy it possesses to the object on which the work is done (book, wheels, ground).

The total energy an object possesses is the sum of its potential energy and its kinetic energy. **Potential energy** is the *energy due to the **position** of the object.* **Kinetic energy** is the *energy due to the **motion** of the object.* Let's examine four systems that illustrate the relationship between these two forms of energy: (1) a weight above the Earth, (2) two balls attached by a spring, (3) two electrically charged particles, and (4) a fuel and its waste products. A key concept illustrated by all four cases is that *energy is conserved: it may be converted from one form to the other, but it is not destroyed.*

Look at Figure 1.3A and consider a weight you lift above the ground. The energy you use to move the weight against the gravitational attraction of the Earth increases the weight's potential energy (energy due to its position). When the weight is dropped, this change in potential energy is converted to kinetic energy (energy due to motion). Some of this kinetic energy is transferred to the ground as the weight does work, such as driving a stake or simply moving dirt and pebbles. As you can see, the change in potential energy is not destroyed: it is converted to kinetic energy.

In nature, situations of lower energy are typically favored over those of higher energy: because the weight has less potential energy (and thus less total energy) at rest on the ground than held in the air, it will fall when released. We can think of the situation with the weight elevated and higher in potential energy as being *less stable,* and the situation after the weight has fallen and lower in potential energy as being *more stable.*

To bring the concept somewhat closer to chemistry, consider the two balls attached by a relaxed spring in Figure 1.3B. When you pull the balls apart, the energy you exert to stretch the spring increases its potential energy. This change in potential energy is converted to kinetic energy when you release the balls and they move closer together. In the stretched position, the system of balls and spring is less stable (has more potential energy) than when the spring is relaxed. You can also increase the spring's potential energy by pushing the balls together and compressing the spring. The balls move apart when released, once again converting the change in potential energy into kinetic energy. Similarly, when you wind a clock, the potential energy in the mainspring increases as the spring is compressed. As the spring relaxes, its potential energy is slowly converted into the kinetic energy of the moving gears and hands.

There are no springs in a chemical substance, of course, but the situation is similar in terms of energy. Much of the matter in the universe is composed of positively and negatively charged particles. A well-known behavior of charged particles (similar to the behavior of the poles of magnets) results from interactions known as *electrostatic forces: opposite charges attract each other and like*

A **A gravitational system.** The E_p gained when a weight is lifted is converted to E_k as the weight falls.

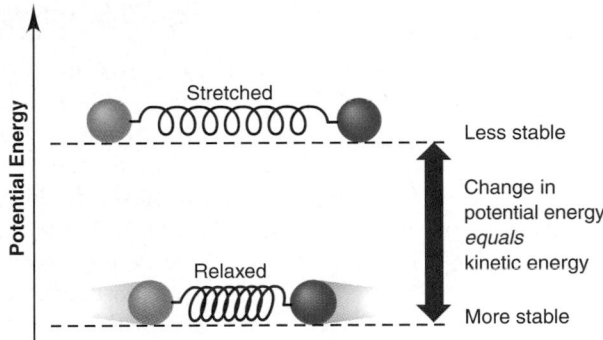

B **A system of two balls attached by a spring.** The E_p gained when the spring is stretched is converted to E_k of the moving balls when it is released.

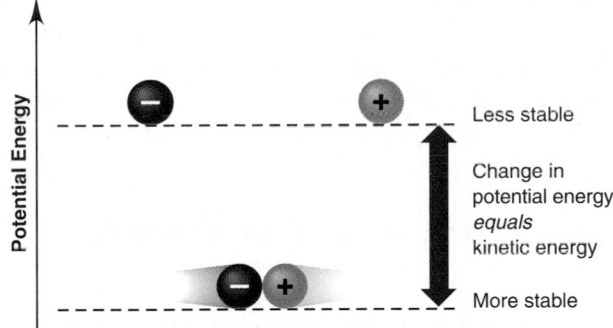

C **A system of oppositely charged particles.** The E_p gained when the charges are separated is converted to E_k as the attraction pulls them together.

D **A system of fuel and exhaust.** A fuel is higher in chemical E_p than the exhaust. As the fuel burns, some of its E_p is converted to E_k of the moving car.

Figure 1.3 **Potential energy (E_p) is converted to kinetic energy (E_k), shown in four systems.** In all figure parts, the dashed horizontal lines indicate the potential energy of the system in each situation.

charges repel each other. When work is done to separate a positive particle from a negative one (like stretching a spring), the potential energy of the particles increases. As Figure 1.3C shows, that change in potential energy is converted to kinetic energy when the particles move together again. Also, when two positive (or two negative) particles are pushed toward each other (like compressing a spring), their potential energy increases, and when they are allowed to move apart, that increase in potential energy is changed into kinetic energy. As with the weight above the ground and the balls connected by a spring, charged particles move naturally toward a position of lower energy, one that is more stable.

The chemical potential energy of a substance results from the relative positions and the attractions and repulsions among all its particles, and some substances are richer in this energy than others. Fuels and foods, for example, contain more potential energy than the waste products they form. Figure 1.3D shows that when gasoline burns in a car engine, substances with higher chemical potential energy (gasoline and air) form substances with lower potential energy (exhaust gases). This change in potential energy is converted into the kinetic energy that moves the car, heats the passenger compartment, makes the lights shine, and so forth. Similarly, the difference in potential energy between the food and air we take in and the waste products we excrete is used to move, grow, keep warm, study chemistry, and so on. Note again the essential point: energy is neither created nor destroyed—it is always conserved as it is converted from one form to the other.

Section Summary

Chemists study the composition and properties of matter and how they change. Each substance has a unique set of physical properties (attributes of the substance itself) and chemical properties (attributes of the substance as it interacts with or changes to other substances). Changes in matter can be physical (different form of the same substance) or chemical (different substance). Matter exists in three physical states—solid, liquid, and gas. The observable features that distinguish these states reflect the arrangement of their particles. A change in physical state brought about by heating may be reversed by cooling. A chemical change can be reversed only by other chemical changes. Macroscopic changes result from submicroscopic changes.

Changes in matter are accompanied by changes in energy. An object's potential energy is due to its position; an object's kinetic energy is due to its motion. Energy used to lift a weight, stretch a spring, or separate opposite charges increases the system's potential energy. Chemical potential energy arises from the positions and interactions of the particles in a substance. Higher energy substances are less stable than lower energy ones. Through physical or chemical changes, a less stable substance changes to a more stable form or a more stable substance as some of its potential energy is converted into kinetic energy, which can do work.

1.2   Chemical Arts and the Origins of Modern Chemistry

Chemistry has a rich, colorful history. Even some concepts and discoveries that led temporarily along a confusing path have contributed to the heritage of chemistry. This brief overview of early breakthroughs and false directions provides some insight into how modern chemistry arose and how science progresses.

Prechemical Traditions

Chemistry has its origin in a prescientific past that incorporated three overlapping traditions: alchemy, medicine, and technology.

The Alchemical Tradition   The occult study of nature practiced in the 1st century AD by Greeks living in northern Egypt later became known by the Arabic name **alchemy.** Its practice spread through the Near East and into Europe, where it dominated Western thinking about matter well into the 16th century. Alchemists were influenced by the Greek idea that matter naturally strives toward perfection, and they searched for ways to change less valued substances into precious ones. What started as a mystical search for spiritual properties in matter evolved over a thousand years into an obsession with potions to bestow eternal youth and elixirs to transmute "baser" metals, such as lead, into "purer" ones, such as gold. Greed tempted some later European alchemists into painting lead objects with a thin coating of gold to fool wealthy patrons.

Alchemy's legacy to chemistry is mixed at best. The confusion arising from alchemists' use of alternative names for the same substance and from their belief that matter could be altered magically was very difficult to eliminate. Nevertheless, through centuries of laboratory inquiry, alchemists invented the chemical methods of distillation, percolation, and extraction, and they devised apparatus that chemists still use routinely today (Figure 1.4). Most important, alchemists encouraged the widespread acceptance of observation and experimentation, which replaced the Greek approach of studying nature solely through reason.

Figure 1.4 An alchemist at work. The alchemical tradition influenced ideas about matter and its changes for 1500 years. This is a portion of a painting by the Englishman Joseph Wright entitled "The Alchymist, in search of the Philosopher's Stone, Discovers Phosphorus, and prays for the successful Conclusion of his Operation as was the custom of the Ancient Chymical Astrologers." Some suggest it portrays the German alchemist Hennig Brand in his laboratory lit by the glow of phosphorus, which he discovered in 1669. A great legacy of the alchemists was their invention of several major laboratory processes. The apparatus shown here is used for distillation, a process still commonly used to separate substances.

The Medical Tradition Alchemists greatly influenced medical practice in medieval Europe. Since the 13th century, distillates of roots, herbs, and other plant matter have been used as sources of medicines. Paracelsus (1493–1541) was an active alchemist and important physician of the time. His writings are difficult to comprehend, but he seems to have considered the body to be a chemical system whose balance of substances could be restored by medical treatment. His followers introduced mineral drugs into 17th-century pharmacy. Although many of these drugs were useless and some harmful, later practitioners employed other mineral prescriptions with increasing success. Thus began an alliance between medicine and chemistry that thrives today.

The Technological Tradition For thousands of years, people have developed technological skills to carry out changes in matter. Pottery making, dyeing, and especially metallurgy (begun about 7000 years ago) contributed greatly to human understanding of the properties of materials. During the Middle Ages and the Renaissance, such technology flourished and several important treatises on metallurgy and geology were written. Books describing how to purify, assay, and coin silver and gold and how to use balances (Figure 1.5), furnaces, and crucibles were published and regularly updated. Other writings discussed making glass, pottery, dyes, and gunpowder. Some of these treatises introduced quantitative measurement, which had been lacking in the alchemical literature.

Many creations of these early artisans are unsurpassed even today. Yet, while their working knowledge of substances was expert, their approach to understanding matter was different from ours: as in earliest times, techniques

Figure 1.5 An antique balance used to assay gold and other metals.

were discovered and developed by trial and error. The surviving writings indicate little interest in exploring *why* a substance changes or *how to predict* the behavior of matter.

The Phlogiston Fiasco and the Impact of Lavoisier

Chemical investigation in the modern sense—inquiry into the *causes* of changes in matter—began in the late 17th century, most notably with the work of the English scientists Robert Hooke and Robert Boyle, who were friends and collaborated on some important experiments. Alchemical influences persisted, however, and understanding was hampered by an incorrect theory of **combustion,** the process of burning. Although fire had been used since prehistoric times, no one could explain satisfactorily why some things burn and others do not, or what actually happens when a substance burns.

Hooke suggested that burning substances combine with air, but unfortunately most scientists rejected this idea to embrace the **phlogiston theory,** which held sway for the next hundred years. According to this theory, combustible materials contain phlogiston, an undetectable substance that is released when the material burns. A highly combustible material such as charcoal contains large amounts of phlogiston, which is released when the charcoal burns and forms charcoal ash (charcoal without phlogiston):

$$\text{Charcoal} \longrightarrow \text{charcoal ash} + \text{phlogiston (large amount)}$$

Slightly combustible materials such as metals contain small amounts of phlogiston. When a metal burns in air, it forms its *calx* (as metal oxides were then called), which is the metal without phlogiston:

$$\text{Metal} \longrightarrow \text{metal calx} + \text{phlogiston (small amount)}$$

Consider how the theory's proponents might have explained *smelting,* an industrial process that converts a metal calx to the metal by heating the calx with charcoal: when phlogiston-rich charcoal burns, it transfers phlogiston to phlogiston-poor calx, and this transfer converts charcoal to charcoal ash and the calx to the pure metal:

$$\text{Metal calx} + \text{charcoal} \longrightarrow \text{metal} + \text{charcoal ash}$$

These schemes may have seemed logical, but they ignored certain key observations. Why, the theory's critics asked, is air needed for combustion, and why does charcoal burn only for a short time in a closed vessel? Phlogistonists responded that air is needed to "attract" the phlogiston out of the charcoal, and that burning in a vessel stops when the air is "saturated" with phlogiston. Knowing that a calx weighs more than the metal from which it is formed, critics asked how the *loss* of phlogiston when a metal burns could cause a *gain* in mass. Phlogistonists either dismissed the importance of weighing or proposed that phlogiston had negative mass! Some of these responses seem ridiculous to us now, but they point out that the pursuit of science, like any other human endeavor, is subject to human failings; even today it is easier to dismiss conflicting evidence than to give up an established idea.

Into this chaos of "explanations" entered the young French chemist Antoine Lavoisier (1743–1794), who demonstrated the true nature of combustion through a series of careful measurements that emphasized the importance of mass. ◆ Lavoisier heated mercury calx (mercuric oxide), decomposing it into mercury and a gas, whose combined masses equaled the starting mass of calx. The reverse experiment—heating mercury with the gas—reformed the mercury calx, and again, *the total mass remained constant.* Lavoisier proposed that when a metal forms its calx, it does not lose phlogiston but rather combines with this gas, which must be a component of air.

◆ **Scientific Thinker Extraordinaire** Lavoisier's fame would be widespread, even if he had never performed a chemical experiment. A short list of his other contributions: He improved the production of French gunpowder, which became a key factor in the success of the American Revolution. He established on his farm a scientific balance between cattle, pasture, and cultivated acreage to optimize crop yield. He developed public assistance programs for widows and orphans. He quantified the relation of fiscal policy to agricultural production. He proposed a system of free public education and of societies to foster science, politics, and the arts. He sat on the committee that unified weights and measures in the new metric system. His research into combustion clarified the essence of respiration and metabolism. To support these pursuits, he joined a firm that collected taxes for the King, and only this role was remembered during the French Revolution. Despite his devotion to French society, the father of modern chemistry was guillotined at the age of 50.

① The total volume of air is determined at the start

② Liquid mercury is heated

③ Mercury calx accumulates during heating

④ Four-fifths of the original air volume remains at the end

Water

Furnace

A   B

Figure 1.6 Lavoisier's experiment to test his proposal that a component of air is required for combustion.

In a test of his proposal, shown in Figure 1.6, Lavoisier heated mercury in a measured volume of air until no further change occurred; mercury calx formed, and four-fifths of the air volume remained. This result confirmed that the gas was a component of air. A burning candle placed in the remaining volume of air was quickly extinguished, showing that the gas that had combined with the mercury was necessary for combustion. Lavoisier named the gas *oxygen* and called metal calxes *metal oxides*.

The new theory of combustion made sense of the earlier confusion. A combustible substance such as charcoal stops burning in a closed vessel once it has combined with all the available oxygen. A metal oxide weighs more than the metal because it contains the added mass of oxygen. The true nature of smelting is that when charcoal and a metal oxide are heated together, the carbon in charcoal combines with the oxygen in the metal oxide to produce the metal, charcoal ash, and carbon dioxide gas:

$$\text{Metal calx (metal oxide)} + \overbrace{\text{charcoal (carbon)}}^{\text{oxygen}} \longrightarrow$$
$$\text{metal} + \text{charcoal ash} + \text{carbon dioxide}$$

Lavoisier's theory of combustion triumphed because it explained observations more clearly and consistently than any other theory. ◆ Most important, the new theory relied on *quantitative, reproducible measurements*, not on strange properties of undetectable substances. Because this approach is at the heart of science, many propose that the *science* of chemistry began with Lavoisier.

Section Summary

Alchemy, medicine, and technology established processes that have been important to chemists since the 17th century. These prescientific traditions placed little emphasis on objective experimentation, focusing instead on practical experience or mystical explanations. The phlogiston theory dominated thinking about combustion for almost 100 years, leading chemistry down a faulty theoretical path. In the mid-1770s, Lavoisier showed that oxygen, a component of air, is required for combustion and combines with a substance as it burns.

1.3 The Scientific Approach: Developing a Model

If we could break down a "typical" modern scientist's thought processes, we could organize them into an approach called the **scientific method.** This approach is not a stepwise checklist, but rather *a flexible process of creative thinking and testing aimed at objective, verifiable discoveries of how nature works.* It is very important to realize that there is no typical scientist and no single method, and that over the years even luck has played a role in scientific

A Great Chemist and Strict Phlogistonist
Despite the phlogiston theory, chemists made key discoveries during the years it held sway. Many were made by the English clergyman Joseph Priestley (1733–1804), who systematically studied the physical and chemical properties of many gases (inventing "soda water," carbon dioxide dissolved in water, along the way). The gas obtained by heating mercury calx was of special interest to him. In 1775, he wrote to his friend Benjamin Franklin: "Hitherto only two mice and myself have had the privilege of breathing it." Priestley also demonstrated that the gas supports combustion, but he drew the wrong conclusion about it. He called the gas "dephlogisticated air," air devoid of phlogiston, and thus ready to attract it from a burning substance. Priestley's contributions make him one of the great chemists of all time. Priestley was a liberal thinker, favoring freedom of conscience and supporting both the French and American Revolutions, positions that caused severe personal problems throughout his later life. But, scientifically, he remained a conservative, believing strictly in phlogiston and refusing to accept the new theory of combustion.

Figure 1.7 **The scientific approach to understanding nature.** Note that hypotheses and models are mental pictures that are changed to match observations and experimental results, *not* the other way around.

discovery. In general terms, the scientific approach often includes the following parts, which are related to one another as shown in Figure 1.7:

- **Observations.** These are the *facts* that our ideas must explain. Observation is basic to scientific thinking. The most useful observations are quantitative because they can be compared and allow consistent changes to be seen. Pieces of *quantitative* information are **data.** When the same observation is made by many investigators in many situations with no clear exceptions, it is summarized, often in mathematical terms, in the form of a **natural law.** The observation that mass remains constant during chemical change—made by Lavoisier and numerous experimenters since—has been summarized as the law of mass conservation, which we discuss in Chapter 2.

- **Hypothesis.** Whether derived from actual observation or from a "spark of intuition," a hypothesis is a proposal made to explain an observation. A valid hypothesis need not be correct, but it must be *testable.* Thus, a hypothesis is often the reason for performing an experiment. If the hypothesis turns out to be inconsistent with the experimental results, it must be either revised or discarded.

- **Experiment.** An experiment is a clear set of procedural steps that tests a hypothesis. Experimentation is the connection between our ideas, or hypotheses, about nature and nature itself. Often, hypothesis leads to experiment, which leads to revised hypothesis, and so forth. Hypotheses can be altered, but the results of an experiment cannot.

  An experiment typically contains at least two **variables,** quantities that can have more than a single value; it is designed to show how a change in one variable affects another. A well-designed experiment is **controlled** in that it measures the effect of each variable separately by keeping the others constant. For experimental results to be accepted, they must be *reproducible,* not only by the person who designed the experiment, but also by others. Both skill and creativity play a part in great experimental design.

- **Model.** Formulating conceptual models, or **theories,** *based on experiments* is what distinguishes scientific thinking from speculation. As hypotheses are altered according to experimental results, a model gradually emerges that describes how the observed phenomenon occurs. A model is not an exact representation of nature, but rather a simplified version of nature that can be used to make *predictions* about related phenomena. Further investigation refines a model by testing its predictions and altering it to account for new facts.

Lavoisier's overthrow of the phlogiston theory demonstrates the scientific approach. Observations of burning and smelting led some to hypothesize that combustion involved the loss of phlogiston. Experiments by others showing that air is required for burning and that a metal gains mass during combustion led Lavoisier to propose a new hypothesis, which he tested repeatedly with quantitative experiments. Accumulating evidence lent support to his developing model (theory) that combustion involves combination with a component of air (oxygen). Innumerable predictions based on this theory have supported its validity. A sound theory remains useful even when minor exceptions appear. An unsound one, such as the phlogiston theory, eventually crumbles under the weight of contrary evidence and absurd refinements.

Section Summary

The scientific method is not a rigid sequence of steps, but rather a dynamic process designed to explain and predict real phenomena. ◆ Observations (sometimes expressed as natural laws) lead to hypotheses about how or why something occurs. Hypotheses are tested in controlled experiments and adjusted if necessary. If all the data collected support a hypothesis, a model (theory) can be developed to explain the observations. A good model is useful in predicting related phenomena but must be refined if conflicting data appear.

1.4 Chemical Problem Solving

In many ways, learning chemistry is learning how to solve chemistry problems, not only those on an exam or a homework assignment, but also more complex ones in society and in many professions. (The Chemical Connections essay at the end of this chapter provides an example.) This text has been designed to help you strengthen your problem-solving skills. Almost every chapter contains sample problems that are worked out in detail and apply an important idea or skill that was just introduced. In this section, we discuss the approach used in the text for solving them. Because many include calculations, let's first go over some important (and familiar) ideas about measured quantities.

Units and Conversion Factors in Calculations

All measured quantities consist of a number *and* a unit; a person's height is "6 feet," not "6." Ratios of quantities have ratios of units, such as miles/hour. (We discuss the most important units in chemistry in the next section.) To minimize errors, try to make a habit of including units in all calculations.

The arithmetic operations used with measured quantities are the same as those used with pure numbers; in other words, units can be multiplied, divided, and canceled:

- A carpet measuring 3 feet (ft) by 4 ft has an area of

$$\text{Area} = 3 \text{ ft} \times 4 \text{ ft} = (3 \times 4) \ (\text{ft} \times \text{ft}) = 12 \text{ ft}^2$$

- A car traveling 350 miles (mi) in 7 hours (h) has a speed of

$$\text{Speed} = \frac{350 \text{ mi}}{7 \text{ h}} = \frac{50 \text{ mi}}{1 \text{ h}} \ (\text{often written } 50 \text{ mi} \cdot \text{h}^{-1})$$

- In 3 hours, the car travels a distance of

$$\text{Distance} = 3 \text{ h} \times \frac{50 \text{ mi}}{1 \text{ h}} = 150 \text{ mi}$$

◢ **Everyday Scientific Thinking** In an informal way, we often employ a scientific approach to decide on a course of action. Consider this familiar scenario. While listening to an FM broadcast on your stereo system, you notice the sound is garbled (observation) and assume it is caused by poor reception (hypothesis). To isolate this variable, you play a CD (experiment): the sound is still garbled. If the problem is not poor reception, perhaps the speakers are at fault (new hypothesis). To isolate this variable, you play the CD and listen with headphones (experiment): the sound is clear. You conclude that the speakers need to be repaired (model). The repair shop says the speakers check out fine (new observation), but the power amplifier may be at fault (new hypothesis). Replacing a transistor in the amplifier corrects the garbled sound (new experiment), so the power amplifier was the problem (revised model). Approaching a problem scientifically is a common practice, even if you're not aware of it.

Conversion factors are ratios used to express a measured quantity in different units. Suppose we want to know the distance of that 150-mile car trip in feet. To convert the distance between miles and feet, we use equivalent quantities to construct the desired conversion factor. The equivalent quantities in this case are "1 mile" and "the number of feet in 1 mile":

$$1 \text{ mi} = 5280 \text{ ft}$$

We can construct two conversion factors from this equivalency. Dividing both sides by 5280 ft gives one conversion factor (blue):

$$\frac{1 \text{ mi}}{5280 \text{ ft}} = \frac{5280 \text{ ft}}{5280 \text{ ft}} = 1$$

And, dividing both sides by 1 mi gives the other conversion factor (blue):

$$\frac{1 \text{ mi}}{1 \text{ mi}} = \frac{5280 \text{ ft}}{1 \text{ mi}} = 1$$

It's very important to see that, since the numerator and denominator of a conversion factor are equal, multiplying by a conversion factor is the same as multiplying by one. Therefore, *even though the number and unit of the quantity change, the size of the quantity does **not**.*

In our example, we want to convert the distance in miles to the equivalent distance in feet. Therefore, we choose the conversion factor with units of feet in the numerator because it cancels units of miles and gives units of feet:

$$\text{Distance (ft)} = 150 \text{ mi} \times \frac{5280 \text{ ft}}{1 \text{ mi}} = 792{,}000 \text{ ft}$$
$$\text{mi} \implies \text{ft}$$

Choosing the correct conversion factor is not a matter of chance or memorization. The primary consideration is that *the chosen conversion factor cancels all units except those required for the answer.* Set up the calculation so that the unit you are converting *from* (beginning unit) is on the *opposite part of the conversion factor* (numerator or denominator) from the unit you are converting *to* (final unit):

$$\text{beginning unit} \times \frac{\text{final unit}}{\text{beginning unit}} = \text{final unit} \qquad \text{as in} \qquad \text{mi} \times \frac{\text{ft}}{\text{mi}} = \text{ft}$$

Or, in cases that involve a ratio of units,

$$\frac{\text{beginning unit}}{\text{final unit}_1} \times \frac{\text{final unit}_2}{\text{beginning unit}} = \frac{\text{final unit}_2}{\text{final unit}_1} \qquad \text{as in} \qquad \frac{\text{mi}}{\text{h}} \times \frac{\text{ft}}{\text{mi}} = \frac{\text{ft}}{\text{h}}$$

It is also important that you think through the calculation to decide whether the answer expressed in the new units should have a larger or smaller number and whether the conversion factor you choose will accomplish this change. In the earlier case, since a foot is *smaller* than a mile, the distance in feet should have a *larger* number (792,000) than the distance in miles (150). Note that the conversion factor we chose has the larger number in the numerator, so it gave a larger number in the answer.

We use the same procedure to convert between systems of units, for example, between the English (or American) unit system and the International System (a revised metric system discussed fully in the next section). Suppose we know that Angel Falls in Venezuela (Figure 1.8), the world's tallest waterfall, is 3212 ft high and we have found its height in miles as

$$\text{Height (mi)} = 3212 \text{ ft} \times \frac{1 \text{ mi}}{5280 \text{ ft}} = 0.6083 \text{ mi}$$
$$\text{ft} \implies \text{mi}$$

Now, we want its height in kilometers (km). The equivalent quantities are

$$1.609 \text{ km} = 1 \text{ mi}$$

Figure 1.8   Angel Falls.

Since we are converting from miles to kilometers, we use the conversion factor with kilometers in the numerator in order to cancel miles:

$$\text{Height (km)} = 0.6083 \text{ mi} \times \frac{1.609 \text{ km}}{1 \text{ mi}} = 0.9788 \text{ km}$$

$$\text{mi} \implies \text{km}$$

Notice that, since kilometers are *smaller* than miles, this conversion factor gave us a *larger* number (0.9788 is larger than 0.6083).

If we want the height of Angel Falls in meters (m), we use the equivalent quantities 1 km = 1000 m to construct the conversion factor:

$$\text{Height (m)} = 0.9788 \text{ km} \times \frac{1000 \text{ m}}{1 \text{ km}} = 978.8 \text{ m}$$

$$\text{km} \implies \text{m}$$

In longer calculations, we often string together several conversion steps:

$$\text{Height (m)} = 3212 \text{ ft} \times \frac{1 \text{ mi}}{5280 \text{ ft}} \times \frac{1.609 \text{ km}}{1 \text{ mi}} \times \frac{1000 \text{ m}}{1 \text{ km}} = 978.8 \text{ m}$$

$$\text{ft} \implies \text{mi} \implies \text{km} \implies \text{m}$$

The use of conversion factors in calculations is known by various names, such as the factor-label method or **dimensional analysis** (because units represent physical dimensions). We'll use this method in quantitative problems throughout this text.

A Systematic Approach to Solving Chemistry Problems

The approach used throughout this text provides a systematic way to work through a problem and emphasizes reasoning, not memorizing. It is based on a very simple idea: plan how to solve the problem *before* you go on to solve it, and then check your answer. Try to develop a similar approach on homework and exams. In general, the sample problems within a chapter consist of several parts:

1. **PROBLEM.** This part states all the information you need to solve the problem (usually framed in some interesting context).
2. **PLAN.** The overall solution is broken up into two parts, *plan* and *solution*, to make a point: *think* about how to solve the problem *before* juggling numbers. If a plan is clear in your mind, the actual calculations will make sense. Of course, there is often more than one way to solve a problem, so the plan shown in a given problem is one possibility. The plan will
   - Clarify the known and unknown. (What information do you have, and what are you trying to find?)
   - Suggest the steps needed to find the solution. (What ideas, conversions, or equations link the known to the unknown?)
   - Present a "roadmap" of the solution for many quantitative problems in early chapters (and some in later ones). The roadmap is a visual summary of the planned steps that shows the "stops" on the way from the known to the unknown. Each step is shown by an arrow labeled with information about the conversion factor or operation needed.
3. **SOLUTION.** In this part, the steps appear in the same general order as they were planned.
4. **CHECK.** In most cases, a quick check is provided to see if the results make sense: Is the answer chemically reasonable? Are the units correct? Does the answer seem to be the right size? Did the change occur in the expected direction? We sometimes do an approximate calculation to see if the answer is "in the right ballpark." It's *always* a good idea to check your answers, especially in a multipart problem, where an error in an early step can affect all later steps.

5. **COMMENT.** This part is included occasionally to provide additional information, such as an application, an alternative approach, a common mistake to avoid, or an overview.

6. **FOLLOW-UP PROBLEM.** This part, which consists of a problem statement only, provides practice by applying the same ideas that were used in the sample problem. Try to solve it *before* you look at the brief worked-out solution at the end of the chapter.

Of course, you cannot learn to solve problems by reading a problem-solving approach, any more than you can learn to swim by reading about it. As in swimming, practice is the key to mastery. Here are a few suggestions that can help:

- Follow along in the sample problem with pencil, paper, and calculator.
- Do the follow-up problem as soon as you finish studying the sample problem. Check your answer against the solution at the end of the chapter.
- Read the sample problem and relevant text explanations again if you have trouble.
- Work on as many of the problems at the end of the chapter as you can. They review and extend the concepts and skills presented in the text and sample problems. Answers are given in the back of the book for problems with a colored number, but try to solve the problem yourself first.

Length (cm) of wire

2.54 cm = 1 in

Length (in) of wire

12 in = 1 ft

Length (ft) of wire

1 ft = $0.15

Price ($) of wire

Sample Problem 1.2 Using the Sample Problem Approach to Convert Units of Length

PROBLEM What is the price of a piece of copper wire 325 centimeters (cm) long that sells for $0.15/ft?

PLAN We know the length of wire in centimeters and the cost in dollars per foot ($/ft). We can find the unknown price of the piece of wire by converting the length from centimeters to inches (in) and from inches to feet. Then the cost (1 ft = $0.15) gives us the equivalent quantities to construct the factor that converts feet of wire to dollars. The roadmap starts with the known and moves through the calculation steps to the unknown.

SOLUTION Converting the known length from centimeters to inches: The equivalent quantities alongside the roadmap arrow are the ones needed to construct the conversion factor. We choose 1 in/2.54 cm, rather than the inverse, because it gives an answer in inches:

$$\text{Length (in)} = \text{length (cm)} \times \text{conversion factor} = 325 \text{ cm} \times \frac{1 \text{ in}}{2.54 \text{ cm}} = 128 \text{ in}$$

Converting the length from inches to feet:

$$\text{Length (ft)} = \text{length (in)} \times \text{conversion factor} = 128 \text{ in} \times \frac{1 \text{ ft}}{12 \text{ in}} = 10.7 \text{ ft}$$

Converting the length from feet to dollars:

$$\text{Price (\$)} = \text{length (ft)} \times \text{conversion factor} = 10.7 \text{ ft} \times \frac{\$0.15}{1 \text{ ft}} = \boxed{\$1.60}$$

CHECK The units are correct for each step. The conversion factors make sense in terms of the relative unit sizes: the number of inches is *smaller* than the number of centimeters (an inch is *larger* than a centimeter), and the number of feet is *smaller* than the number of inches. The total price seems reasonable: a little more than 10 ft of wire at $0.15/ft should cost a little more than $1.50.

COMMENT 1. We could also have strung the three steps together:

$$\text{Price (\$)} = 325 \text{ cm} \times \frac{1 \text{ in}}{2.54 \text{ cm}} \times \frac{1 \text{ ft}}{12 \text{ in}} \times \frac{\$0.15}{1 \text{ ft}} = \$1.60$$

2. There are usually alternative sequences in unit conversion problems. Here, for example, we would get the same answer if we first converted the cost of wire from $/ft to $/cm and kept the wire length in cm. Try it yourself.

Follow-up Problem 1.2 A furniture factory needs 31.5 ft² of fabric to upholster one chair. Its Dutch supplier sends the fabric in bolts of exactly 200 m². What is the maximum number of chairs that can be upholstered by 3 bolts of fabric (1 m = 3.281 ft)?

Section Summary

A measured quantity consists of a number and a unit. Conversion factors are used to express a quantity in different units and are constructed as a ratio of equivalent quantities. The problem-solving approach used in this text usually has four parts: (1) devise a plan for the solution, (2) put the plan into effect in the calculations, (3) check to see if the answer makes sense, and (4) practice with similar problems.

1.5 Measurement in Scientific Study

Almost everything we own—clothes, house, food, vehicle—is manufactured with measured parts, sold in measured amounts, and paid for with measured currency. Measurement is so commonplace that it's easy to take for granted, but it has a long and fascinating history characterized by the search for *exact, invariable standards.* ◆

Our current system of measurement began in 1790, when the newly formed National Assembly of France, of which Lavoisier was a member, set up a committee to establish consistent unit standards. This effort led to the development of the *metric system.* In 1960, another international committee met in France to establish the International System of Units, a revised metric system now accepted by scientists throughout the world. The units of this system are called **SI units,** from the French **S**ystème **I**nternational d'Unités.

General Features of SI Units

As Table 1.2 shows, the SI system is based on a set of seven **fundamental units,** or **base units,** each of which is identified with a physical quantity. All other units, called **derived units,** are combinations of these seven base units. For example, the derived unit for speed, meters per second (m/s), is the base unit for length (m) divided by the base unit for time (s). (Derived units can be used as conversion factors because they contain two or more base units.)

How Many Barleycorns from His Majesty's Nose to His Thumb? Systems of measurement began thousands of years ago as trade, building, and land surveying spread through the civilized world. For most of that time, however, measurement was based on inexact physical standards. For example, an inch was the length of three barleycorns (seeds) placed end to end; a yard was the distance from the tip of King Edgar's nose to the tip of his thumb with his arm outstretched; and an acre was the area tilled by one man working with a pair of oxen in a day.

Table 1.2 SI Base Units

Physical Quantity (Dimension)	Unit Name	Unit Abbreviation
Mass	kilogram	kg
Length	meter	m
Time	second	s
Temperature	kelvin	K
Electric current	ampere	A
Amount of substance	mole	mol
Luminous intensity	candela	cd

For quantities that are much smaller or much larger than the base unit, we use decimal prefixes and exponential (scientific) notation. Because these prefixes are based on powers of 10, SI units are easier to use in calculations than English units such as pounds and inches. Table 1.3 shows the most

Table 1.3 Common Decimal Prefixes Used with SI Units

Prefix*	Prefix Symbol	Meaning — Number	Meaning — Word	Exponential Notation
tera	T	1,000,000,000,000	trillion	10^{12}
giga	G	1,000,000,000	billion	10^{9}
mega	M	1,000,000	million	10^{6}
kilo	k	1,000	thousand	10^{3}
hecto	h	100	hundred	10^{2}
deka	da	10	ten	10^{1}
—	—	1	one	10^{0}
deci	d	0.1	tenth	10^{-1}
centi	c	0.01	hundredth	10^{-2}
milli	m	0.001	thousandth	10^{-3}
micro	μ	0.000001	millionth	10^{-6}
nano	n	0.000000001	billionth	10^{-9}
pico	p	0.000000000001	trillionth	10^{-12}
femto	f	0.000000000000001	quadrillionth	10^{-15}

*The prefixes most frequently used by chemists appear in bold type.

important prefixes. Many of the calculations you'll perform involve numbers written in exponential notation:

$$A \times 10^{n}$$

where A is greater than or equal to 1 and less than 10 ($1 \leq A < 10$) and n is an integer. If you are not familiar with this method of expressing numbers or just need a review, be sure to read Appendix A.

Some Important SI Units in Chemistry

Let's discuss some of the SI units for quantities that we use early in the text: length, volume, mass, density, temperature, and time. Units for other quantities are presented later. Table 1.4 shows some useful SI-English equivalent quantities for length, volume, and mass.

Table 1.4 Common SI-English Equivalent Quantities

Quantity	SI	SI Equivalents	English Equivalents	English to SI Equivalent
Length	1 kilometer (km)	1000 (10^{3}) meters	0.6214 mile (mi)	1 mile = 1.609 km
	1 meter (m)	100 (10^{2}) centimeters	1.094 yards (yd)	1 yard = 0.9144 m
		1000 millimeters (mm)	39.37 inches (in)	1 foot (ft) = 0.3048 m
	1 centimeter (cm)	0.01 (10^{-2}) meter	0.3937 inch	1 inch = 2.54 cm (exactly)
Volume	1 cubic meter (m^{3})	1,000,000 (10^{6}) cubic centimeters	35.31 cubic feet (ft^{3})	1 cubic foot = 0.02832 m^{3}
	1 cubic decimeter (dm^{3})	1000 cubic centimeters	0.2642 gallon (gal)	1 gallon = 3.785 dm^{3}
			1.057 quarts (qt)	1 quart = 0.9464 dm^{3}
	1 cubic centimeter (cm^{3})	0.001 dm^{3}	0.03381 fluid ounce	1 quart = 946.4 cm^{3}
				1 fluid ounce = 29.57 cm^{3}
Mass	1 kilogram (kg)	1000 grams	2.205 pounds (lb)	1 pound = 0.4536 kg
	1 gram (g)	1000 milligrams (mg)	0.03527 ounce (oz)	1 ounce = 28.35 g

Lynnwood CHC Pharmacy

4111 194th St SW #204 Lynnwood, WA (425) 835-5202

Local

Rx **L688748**   No Refills

For: **Yeshareg Tefera**   *Filled:* 10/25/2010

Medication: RA TABLET CUTTER   Qty: 1

Directions for Use:

Use as directed to cut pills

(**New**)

25
26
20

Thursd.

26th Thursday.

Lynnwood CHC Pharmacy

4111 194th St SW #204 Lynnwood, WA (425) 835-5202

Yeshareg Tefera   **DOB: 9/27/1947**

15324 45th Pl W

Lynnwood, WA 98087

(425) 741-8335

Rx **L688748**   10/25/2010   Dr. Jennifer Lonac PAC

RA TABLET CUTTER   RITE AID CORP.   # 1

NDC   11822377360   Days Supply   1.00   *YOU*

CHPW Healthy Options   Rph jw   **0.00**   *PAY*

CHPW Healthy Options   DAW *No*

AUTH # 94765595

H

O

H₂O

L₂O

SALT

NaCl

Length The SI base unit of length is the **meter (m).** The standard meter is now based on two quantities, the speed of light in a vacuum and the second. ◆ A meter is a little longer than a yard (1 m = 1.094 yd); a centimeter (10^{-2} m) is about two-fifths of an inch (1 cm = 0.3937 in; 1 in = 2.54 cm). Biological cells are often measured in micrometers (1 μm = 10^{-6} m). On the atomic-size scale, nanometers and picometers are used (1 nm = 10^{-9} m; 1 pm = 10^{-12} m). An older unit still in common use is the angstrom (1 Å = 10^{-10} m = 0.1 nm = 100 pm).

Volume Any sample of matter has a certain **volume (V),** the amount of space it occupies. The SI unit of volume is the **cubic meter (m^3).** In chemistry, the most important volume units are non-SI units, the **liter (L)** and the **milliliter (mL).** (Note the uppercase L in the abbreviation.) Physicians and other medical practitioners measure body fluids in cubic decimeters (dm^3), which is equivalent to liters:

$$1 \text{ L} = 1 \text{ dm}^3 = 10^{-3} \text{ m}^3$$

As the prefix *milli-* indicates, 1 mL is $\frac{1}{1000}$ of a liter, and it is equal to exactly 1 cubic centimeter (cm^3):

$$1 \text{ mL} = 1 \text{ cm}^3 = 10^{-3} \text{ dm}^3 = 10^{-3} \text{ L} = 10^{-6} \text{ m}^3$$

A liter is slightly larger than a quart (qt) (1 L = 1.057 qt; 1 qt = 946.4 mL); 1 fluid ounce ($\frac{1}{32}$ of a quart) equals 29.57 mL (29.57 cm^3). Figure 1.9 shows the successive 1000-fold decreases in volume from the cubic meter to the cubic millimeter.

How Long Is a Meter?
The history of the meter points up the ongoing drive to define units based on unchanging standards. The French scientists who set up the metric system defined the meter as 1/10,000,000, the distance from the equator (through Paris!) to the North Pole. The meter was later redefined as the distance between two fine lines engraved on a corrosion-resistant metal bar kept at the International Bureau of Weights and Measures in France. Fear that the bar would be damaged by war led to an exact, unchanging, universally available atomic standard: 1,650,763.73 wavelengths of orange-red light from electrically excited krypton atoms. The current standard is even more reliable: 1 meter is the distance light travels in a vacuum in 1/299,792,458 second.

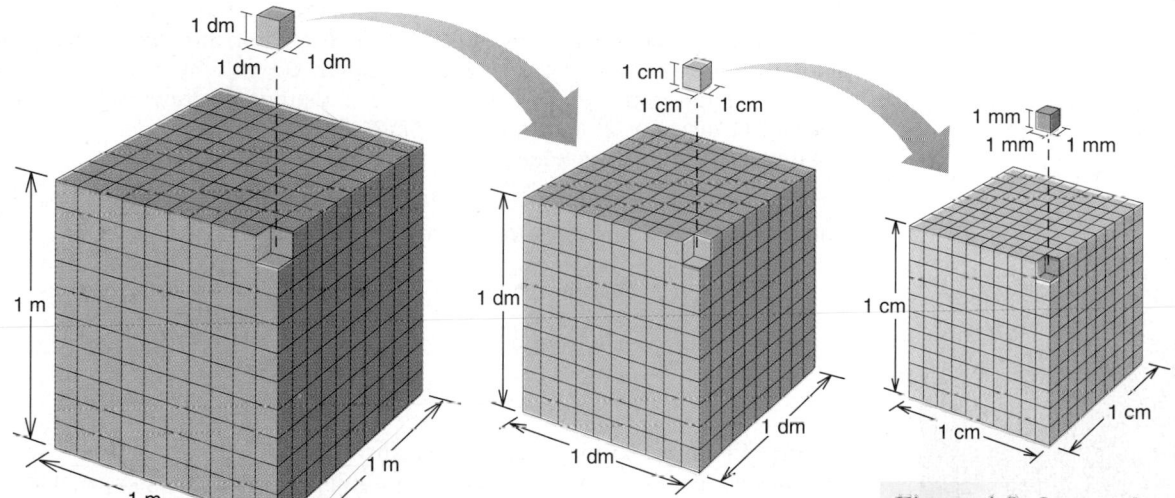

Figure 1.9 Some volume relationships in SI. The three cubes (not drawn to scale) demonstrate the decimal usefulness of SI units. The left cube is 1 m^3; each side is 1 m long and is divided into 10 dm. There are 1000 dm^3 in 1 m^3. The center cube is 1 dm^3; each side is 1 dm long and is divided into 10 cm; 1000 cm^3 = 1 dm^3 = 1 L. The right cube is 1 cm^3; each side is 1 cm long and is divided into 10 mm; 1 cm^3 = 1 mL. There are 1000 mL (1000 cm^3) in 1 L.

Figure 1.10 on the next page shows some of the types of laboratory glassware designed to contain liquids or measure their volume. Many come in sizes from a few milliliters to a few liters. Erlenmeyer flasks and beakers are used to contain liquids. Graduated cylinders, pipets, and burets are used to measure and transfer liquids. Volumetric flasks and many pipets have a fixed volume indicated by a mark on the neck. In quantitative work, liquid solutions are prepared in volumetric flasks, measured in cylinders, pipets, and burets, and then transferred to beakers or flasks for further chemical operations. Automatic pipets transfer a given volume of liquid accurately and quickly.

Figure 1.10 **Common laboratory volumetric glassware. A,** From left to right are two graduated cylinders, a pipet emptying into a beaker, a buret delivering liquid to an Erlenmeyer flask, and two volumetric flasks. **Inset,** In contact with glass, this liquid forms a concave meniscus (curved surface). **B,** Automatic pipets are used to deliver a given volume of liquid repeatedly.

Volume (mL) before and after addition

↓ subtract

Volume (mL) of galena

↓ 1 mL = 1 cm³   ↓ 1 mL = 10⁻³ L

Volume (cm³) of galena   Volume (L) of galena

◆ **Don't Drop That Kilogram!**
The U.S. copy of the master kilogram is kept in a vault at the National Institute of Standards and Technology near Washington, D.C. Since 1889, it has been taken to France only twice for comparison with the master kilogram, which is removed from its vault only once a year for such purposes. Two people are always present when it is moved: one to carry it with forceps, the other to catch it if the first person stumbles.

Sample Problem 1.3   Determining the Volume of a Solid by Displacement of Water

PROBLEM The volume of an irregularly shaped solid can be determined from the volume of water it displaces. A graduated cylinder contains 19.9 mL water. When a small piece of galena, an ore of lead, is added, it sinks and the volume increases to 24.5 mL. What is the volume of the piece of galena in cm^3 and in L?

PLAN Since the change in volume of the cylinder contents equals the volume of the added galena, we find the volume of galena in mL from the difference in the known volumes before and after the addition. Since mL and cm^3 represent identical volumes, the volume of the galena in mL equals the volume in cm^3. We convert the volume from mL to L by constructing the appropriate conversion factor. The calculation steps are shown in the roadmap.

SOLUTION Finding the volume of galena:

Volume (mL) = volume after − volume before = 24.5 mL − 19.9 mL = 4.6 mL

Converting the volume from mL to cm^3:

$$\text{Volume (cm}^3) = 4.6 \ \cancel{\text{mL}} \times \frac{1 \ cm^3}{1 \ \cancel{\text{mL}}} = \boxed{4.6 \ cm^3}$$

Converting the volume from mL to L:

$$\text{Volume (L)} = 4.6 \ \cancel{\text{mL}} \times \frac{10^{-3} \ L}{1 \ \cancel{\text{mL}}} = \boxed{4.6 \times 10^{-3} \ L}$$

CHECK The units and magnitude of the answers seem correct. It makes sense that the volume expressed in mL would have a number 1000 times larger than the volume expressed in L, because a milliliter is $\frac{1}{1000}$ of a liter.

Follow-up Problem 1.3   If you submerge a steel cube 15.0 mm on each side in 31.8 mL of water in a graduated cylinder, what is the total final volume (in L) of the cylinder contents?

Mass   The **mass** of an object refers to the quantity of matter it contains. The SI unit of mass is the **kilogram (kg),** the only base unit whose standard is a physical object—a platinum-iridium cylinder kept in France.* ◆

The terms *mass* and *weight* have distinct meanings. Since a given object's quantity of matter cannot change, its *mass is constant.* Its **weight,** on the other

---

*The kilogram is unusual in another way. It is the only base unit whose name has a prefix. Unlike the practice with other base units, however, we attach prefixes to the word "gram," as in "microgram," rather than to the word "kilogram"; thus, we never say "microkilogram."

hand, depends on its mass *and* the strength of the local gravitational field pulling on it. Because this field varies with height above the Earth's surface, the object's weight varies also. For instance, you actually weigh slightly less on a high mountaintop than at sea level.

Does this mean that if you weighed an object on a laboratory balance in Miami (sea level) and in Denver (about 1.7 km above sea level), you would obtain different results? Fortunately not. Such balances are designed to measure mass rather than weight, so this chaotic situation does not occur. (We are actually "massing" an object when we weigh it on a balance, but we rarely use that term.) Mechanical balances compare the object's unknown mass with known masses built into the balance, so the local gravitational field pulls equally on them. Electronic (analytical) balances determine mass by generating an electric field that counteracts the local gravitational field. The magnitude of the current needed to restore the pan to its zero position is then displayed as the object's mass. Therefore, an electronic balance must be readjusted with standard masses when it is moved to a different location. Figure 1.11 is an interesting look at the ranges of some common lengths, volumes, and masses.

Figure 1.11 **Some interesting quantities of length (A), volume (B), and mass (C).** Note that the scales are exponential.

Optical fibers in cable.

Sample Problem 1.4   Converting Units of Mass

PROBLEM International computer communications may soon be carried by optical fibers in cables laid along the ocean floor. If one strand of optical fiber weighs 1.19×10^{-3} lb/m, what is the mass (in kg) of a cable made of six strands of optical fiber, each long enough to link New York and Paris (8.84×10^{3} km)?

PLAN We have to find the mass of cable (in kg) from the given mass/length of fiber, number of fibers/cable, and the length (distance from New York to Paris). One way to do this (as shown in the roadmap) is to first find the mass of one fiber and then find the mass of cable. We convert the length of one fiber from km to m and then find its mass (in lb) by using the lb/m factor. The cable mass is six times the fiber mass, and finally we convert lb to kg.

SOLUTION Converting the fiber length from km to m:

$$\text{Length (m) of fiber} = 8.84\times10^{3}\ \cancel{km} \times \frac{10^{3}\ m}{1\ \cancel{km}} = 8.84\times10^{6}\ m$$

Converting the length of one fiber to mass (lb):

$$\text{Mass (lb) of fiber} = 8.84\times10^{6}\ \cancel{m} \times \frac{1.19\times10^{-3}\ lb}{1\ \cancel{m}} = 1.05\times10^{4}\ lb$$

Finding the mass of the cable (lb):

$$\text{Mass (lb) of cable} = \frac{1.05\times10^{4}\ lb}{1\ \cancel{fiber}} \times \frac{6\ \cancel{fibers}}{1\ cable} = 6.30\times10^{4}\ lb/cable$$

Converting the mass of cable from lb to kg:

$$\text{Mass (kg) of cable} = \frac{6.30\times10^{4}\ \cancel{lb}}{1\ cable} \times \frac{1\ kg}{2.205\ \cancel{lb}} = \boxed{2.86\times10^{4}\ kg/cable}$$

CHECK The units are correct, and the relative size of the number in each step seems reasonable. The number of m should be 10^{3} larger than the number of km. If 1 m of fiber weighs about 10^{-3} lb, about 10^{7} m should weigh about 10^{4} lb. The cable mass is six times as much, or about 6×10^{4} lb. Since 1 lb is about $\frac{1}{2}$ kg, the number of kg should be about half the number of lb.

COMMENT Actually, the pound (lb) is the English unit of *weight*, not *mass*. The English unit of mass, called the *slug*, is rarely used.

Follow-up Problem 1.4   If a raindrop weighs 65 mg on average and 5.1×10^{5} raindrops fall on a lawn every minute, what mass (in kg) of rain falls in 1.5 h?

Density   The **density (d)** of an object is its mass divided by its volume:

$$\text{Density} = \frac{\text{mass}}{\text{volume}} \tag{1.1}$$

Whenever needed, you can isolate mathematically each of the component variables by treating density as a conversion factor:

$$\text{Mass} = \text{volume} \times \text{density} = \cancel{\text{volume}} \times \frac{\text{mass}}{\cancel{\text{volume}}}$$

Or, $$\text{Volume} = \text{mass} \times \frac{1}{\text{density}} = \cancel{\text{mass}} \times \frac{\text{volume}}{\cancel{\text{mass}}}$$

Under given conditions of temperature and pressure, *density is a characteristic physical property of a substance,* even though the mass and volume of the substance vary widely. Mass and volume are examples of **extensive properties,** those dependent on the amount of substance present. Density, on the other hand, is an **intensive property,** one that is independent of the amount of substance present. For example, the mass of a gallon of water is four times the mass of a quart of water, but its volume is also four times greater; therefore, the density of the water, the *ratio* of its mass to its volume, is constant at a particular temperature and pressure, regardless of the sample size.

Table 1.5 Densities of Some Common Substances*

Substance	Physical State	Density (g/cm³)
Hydrogen	gas	0.0000899
Oxygen	gas	0.00133
Grain alcohol	liquid	0.789
Water	liquid	0.998
Table salt	solid	2.16
Aluminum	solid	2.70
Lead	solid	11.3
Gold	solid	19.3

*At room temperature (20°C) and normal atmospheric pressure (1 atm).

The SI unit of density is the kilogram per cubic meter (kg/m^3), but in chemistry density is typically given in units of g/L (g/dm^3) or g/mL (g/cm^3). For example, the density of liquid water at ordinary pressure and room temperature (20°C) is 1.0 g/mL. The densities of some common substances are given in Table 1.5. As you might expect from the magnified views of the physical states (see Figure 1.2), the densities of gases are much lower than those of liquids or solids.

Sample Problem 1.5 Calculating Density from Mass and Length

PROBLEM Lithium is a soft, gray solid that has the lowest density of any metal. It is an essential component of some advanced batteries. If a small rectangular slab of lithium weighs 1.49×10^3 mg and has sides that measure 20.9 mm by 11.1 mm by 11.9 mm, what is the density of lithium in g/cm^3?

PLAN To find the density in g/cm^3, we need the mass of lithium in g and the volume in cm^3. The mass is given in mg, so we convert mg to g. Volume data are not given, but we can convert the given side lengths from mm to cm, and then multiply them to find the volume in cm^3. Finally, we divide mass by volume to get density. The steps are shown in the roadmap.

SOLUTION Converting the mass from mg to g:

$$\text{Mass (g) of lithium} = 1.49 \times 10^3 \text{ mg} \left(\frac{10^{-3} \text{ g}}{1 \text{ mg}} \right) = 1.49 \text{ g}$$

Converting side lengths from mm to cm:

$$\text{Length (cm) of one side} = 20.9 \text{ mm} \times \frac{1 \text{ cm}}{10 \text{ mm}} = 2.09 \text{ cm}$$

Similarly, the other side lengths are 1.11 cm and 1.19 cm.
Finding the volume:

$$\text{Volume (cm}^3) = 2.09 \text{ cm} \times 1.11 \text{ cm} \times 1.19 \text{ cm} = 2.76 \text{ cm}^3$$

Calculating the density:

$$\text{Density of lithium} = \frac{1.49 \text{ g}}{2.76 \text{ cm}^3} = \boxed{0.540 \text{ g/cm}^3}$$

CHECK Since 1 cm = 10 mm, the number of cm in each length should be $\frac{1}{10}$ the number of mm. The units for density are correct, and the size of the answer (~0.5 g/cm^3) seems correct since the number of g is about half the number of cm^3. Given the photo (see margin) of lithium floating in oil that is floating on water ($d = 1.0$ g/cm^3), this answer makes sense.

Follow-up Problem 1.5 The piece of galena in Sample Problem 1.3 has a volume of 4.6 cm^3. If the density of galena is 7.5 g/cm^3, what is the mass (in kg) of that piece of galena?

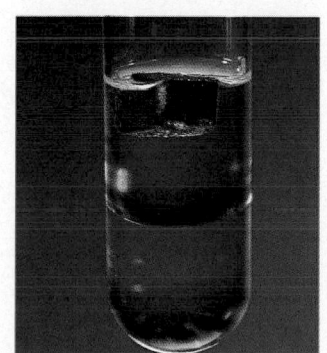

Lithium floating in oil floating on water.

Figure 1.12 **Some interesting temperatures.**

Temperature   There is a common misunderstanding about heat and temperature. **Temperature (_T_)** is a measure of how hot or cold a substance is *relative to another substance.* **Heat** is the energy that flows between objects that are at different temperatures. Temperature is related to the *direction* of that energy flow: when two objects at different temperatures touch, energy flows from the one with the higher temperature to the one with the lower temperature until their temperatures are equal. When you hold an ice cube, its "cold" seems to flow *into* your hand; actually, heat flows *from* your hand into the ice. (In Chapter 6, we will see how heat is measured and how it is related to chemical and physical change.) Energy is an *extensive* property (as is volume), but temperature is an *intensive* property (as is density): a vat of boiling water has more energy than a cup of boiling water, but the temperatures of the two water samples are the same.

In the laboratory, the most common means for measuring temperature is the **thermometer,** a device that contains a fluid that expands when it is heated. When the thermometer's fluid-filled bulb is immersed in a substance hotter than itself, heat flows from the substance through the glass and into the fluid, which expands and rises within the thermometer tube. If a substance is colder than the thermometer, heat flows outward from the fluid, which contracts and falls within the tube.

The three temperature scales most important for us to consider are the Celsius, formerly called centigrade (°C), Kelvin (K), and Fahrenheit (°F) scales. The SI base unit of temperature is the **kelvin (K);** note that the kelvin has no degree sign (°). The **Kelvin scale,** also known as the **absolute scale,** is preferred in all scientific work, although the Celsius scale is used frequently also. In the United States, the Fahrenheit scale is still used for weather reporting, body temperature, and other everyday purposes. *The three scales differ in the size of the unit and/or the temperature of the zero point.* Figure 1.12 shows some interesting temperatures. Figure 1.13 shows the freezing and boiling points of water in the three scales.

The **Celsius scale,** devised in the 18th century by the Swedish astronomer Anders Celsius, is based on changes in the physical state of water: 0°C is set at water's freezing point and 100°C at its boiling point (at normal atmospheric pressure). The Kelvin (absolute) scale was devised by the English physicist William Thomson, known as Lord Kelvin, in 1854 during his experiments on the expansion and contraction of gases. *The Kelvin scale uses the same size degree unit as the Celsius scale,* that is, $\frac{1}{100}$ of the difference between the freezing and boiling points of water, but it differs in zero point. The zero point in the Kelvin scale, 0 K, is called *absolute zero* and equals -273.15°C. Therefore, water freezes at $+273.15$ K (0°C) and boils at $+373.15$ K (100°C). In the Kelvin scale, *all temperatures have positive values.* We can convert any temperature between the Celsius and Kelvin scales by remembering the difference in zero points: since 0°C = 273.15 K,

$$T \text{ (in K)} = T \text{ (in °C)} + 273.15 \tag{1.2}$$

$$T \text{ (in °C)} = T \text{ (in K)} - 273.15 \tag{1.3}$$

The Fahrenheit scale differs from the other scales in its zero point *and* in the size of its unit. Water freezes at 32°F and boils at 212°F. Therefore, 180 Fahrenheit degrees (212°F − 32°F) represents the same temperature change as 100 Celsius degrees (or 100 kelvins). Since 100 Celsius degrees equal 180 Fahrenheit degrees,

$$1 \text{ Celsius degree} = \tfrac{180}{100} \text{ Fahrenheit degrees} = \tfrac{9}{5} \text{ Fahrenheit degrees}$$

To convert a temperature in °C to °F, first change the degree size and then adjust the zero point:

$$T \text{ (in °F)} = \tfrac{9}{5}T \text{ (in °C)} + 32 \tag{1.4}$$

Figure 1.13 **The freezing point and boiling point of water in Celsius, Kelvin (absolute), and Fahrenheit temperature scales.** A portion of each of the three thermometer scales is expanded to show the sizes of the units: a Celsius degree (°C) and a kelvin (K) are the same size, and each is $\frac{9}{5}$ the size of a Fahrenheit degree (°F).

To convert a temperature in °F to °C, do the two steps in the opposite order; that is, first adjust the zero point and then change the degree size:

$$T \text{ (in °C)} = [T \text{ (in °F)} - 32]\tfrac{5}{9} \qquad (1.5)$$

(The only temperature with the same numerical value in the Celsius and Fahrenheit scales is −40°; that is, −40°F = −40°C.)

Sample Problem 1.6   Converting Units of Temperature

PROBLEM A child has a body temperature of 38.7°C.
(a) If normal body temperature is 98.6°F, does the child have a fever?
(b) What is the child's temperature in kelvins?
PLAN (a) To find out if the child has a fever, we use Equation 1.4 to determine whether 38.7°C is higher than 98.6°F.
(b) We use Equation 1.2 to convert the temperature in °C to K.
SOLUTION (a) Converting the temperature from °C to °F:

$$T \text{ (in °F)} = \tfrac{9}{5}T \text{ (in °C)} + 32 = \tfrac{9}{5}(38.7°C) + 32$$

$$= \boxed{101.7°F; \text{ yes, the child has a fever.}}$$

(b) Converting the temperature from °C to K:

$$T \text{ (in K)} = T \text{ (in °C)} + 273.15 = 38.7°C + 273.15 = \boxed{311.8 \text{ K}}$$

CHECK (a) From everyday experience, you know that 101.7°F is a reasonable temperature for someone with a fever.
(b) Since a Celsius degree and a kelvin are the same size, we can estimate our answer by approximating the Celsius value to 40°C and adding 273: 40 + 273 = 313, so the answer is reasonable.

Follow-up Problem 1.6   Mercury melts at 234 K, lower than any other pure metal. What is its melting point in °C and °F?

Figure 1.14 The cesium atomic clock. The accuracy of the best pendulum clock is to within 3 seconds per year and that of the best quartz clock is 1000 times greater. The latest version of the atomic clock, NIST-7, is over 2000 times more accurate still, to within 1 second in 6 million years. Rather than using the oscillations of a pendulum, the atomic clock measures the natural oscillation frequency of cesium atoms absorbing microwave radiation: 1 second is defined as 9,192,631,770 of these oscillations. Current plans to place an advanced laser-cooled cesium atomic clock on the International Space Station will allow longer observation times of the atoms, for at least a 10-fold increase in accuracy.

◆ The Central Importance of Measurement in Science

It's important to keep in mind *why* scientists measure things: "When you can measure what you are speaking about, and express it in numbers, you know something about it; but when you cannot measure it, . . . your knowledge is of a meager and unsatisfactory kind; it may be the beginning of knowledge, but you have scarcely, in your thoughts, advanced to the stage of science" (William Thomson, Lord Kelvin, 1824–1907).

Time   The SI base unit of time is the **second (s).** Although time was once measured by the day and year, it is now based on an atomic standard: microwave radiation from excited cesium atoms (Figure 1.14). In the laboratory, we study the speed of a reaction by measuring the time it takes a fixed amount of substance to undergo a chemical change. The range of reaction speeds is enormous: a fast chemical change is over in a few nanoseconds (10^{-9} s), whereas slow ones, such as rusting or biological aging, take years. Chemists now use lasers to study changes that occur in a few picoseconds (10^{-12} s) or even femtoseconds (10^{-15} s).

Section Summary

SI units consist of seven base units and numerous derived units. Exponential notation and prefixes based on powers of 10 are used to express very small and very large numbers. The SI base unit of length is the meter (m). Length units on the atomic scale are the nanometer (nm) and picometer (pm). Volume units are derived from length units; the most important volume units in chemistry are the cubic meter (m^3) and the liter (L). The mass of an object, a measure of the quantity of matter present in it, is constant. The SI unit of mass is the kilogram (kg). The weight of an object varies with the gravitational field influencing it. Density *(d)* is the ratio of mass to volume of a substance and is one of its characteristic physical properties. Temperature *(T)* is a measure of the relative hotness of an object. Heat is energy that flows from an object at higher temperature to one at lower temperature. Temperature scales differ in the size of the degree unit and/or zero point. In chemistry, temperature is measured in kelvins (K) or degrees Celsius (°C). Extensive properties, such as mass, volume, and energy, depend on an object's size (extent). Intensive properties, such as density and temperature, are independent of size. ◆

1.6 Uncertainty in Measurement: Significant Figures

Because measuring devices are manufactured to limited specifications, and because we use our imperfect senses and skills to read them, we can never measure something exactly or know a quantity with absolute certainty. In other words, every measurement we make includes some **uncertainty.**

The particular measuring device we choose in a given situation depends on how much uncertainty in a measurement we are willing to accept. When you buy potatoes, a supermarket scale that measures in 0.1-kg increments is perfectly acceptable; it tells you that the mass is, for example, 2.0 ± 0.1 kg. The term "± 0.1 kg" expresses the uncertainty in the measurement: the potatoes weigh between 1.9 and 2.1 kg. For a large-scale reaction, a chemist might need a balance that measures in 0.001-kg increments in order to obtain 2.036 ± 0.001 kg of a chemical, that is, between 2.035 and 2.037 kg. The greater number of digits in the mass of the chemical indicates that we know its mass with *more certainty* than the mass of potatoes. Even though there is more certainty in the measurement of the chemical, the rightmost digit is still uncertain. In fact, we *always estimate the rightmost digit* when reading a measuring device. The uncertainty can be expressed with the ± sign, but generally we drop the sign and *assume an uncertainty of one unit in the rightmost digit.* The digits we record in a measurement, both the certain and the uncertain ones, are called **significant figures.** There are four significant figures in 2.036 kg and two in 2.0 kg. *The greater the number of significant figures in a measurement, the greater is the certainty.* Figure 1.15 shows this point in the case of two thermometers.

Figure 1.15 **The number of significant figures in a measurement depends on the measuring device. A,** Two thermometers measuring the same temperature are shown with expanded views. The thermometer on the left is graduated in 0.1°C and reads 32.33°C; the one on the right is graduated in 1°C and reads 32.3°C. Therefore, a reading with more significant figures (more certainty) can be made with the thermometer on the left. **B,** This modern electronic thermometer measures the resistance through a fine platinum wire in the probe to determine temperatures to the nearest microkelvin (10^{-6} K).

Determining Which Digits Are Significant

When you take measurements or use them in calculations, you must know the number of digits that are significant. In general, *all digits are significant, except zeros that are not measured but are used only to position the decimal point.* Here is a simple procedure that applies this generalization:

1. Make sure that the measured quantity has a decimal point.
2. Start at the left of the number and move right until you reach the first nonzero digit.
3. Count that digit and every digit to its right as significant.

   Sometimes, there may be a slight complication with zeros that *end* a number. Zeros that end a number and lie either after or before the decimal point *are* significant; thus, 1.030 mL has four significant figures, and 5300. L has four significant figures also. The problem arises if there is no decimal point, as in 5300 L. In such cases, it would be assumed that the zeros are *not* significant, so exponential notation is needed to show which of the zeros, if any, were measured and therefore are significant. Thus, 5.300×10^3 L has four significant figures, 5.30×10^3 L has three, and 5.3×10^3 L has only two. In this and other modern texts (and research articles), a terminal decimal point is used when necessary to clarify the situation; thus, 500 mL has one significant figure, but 5.00×10^2 mL, 500. mL, and 0.500 L have three.

Sample Problem 1.7   Determining the Number of Significant Figures

PROBLEM For each of the following quantities, underline the zeros that are significant figures (sf), and determine the number of significant figures in each quantity. For **(d)** to **(f),** express each in exponential notation first.

(a) 0.0030 L   (b) 0.1044 g   (c) 53,069 mL
(d) 0.00004715 m   (e) 57,600. s   (f) 0.0000007160 cm^3

PLAN We determine the number of significant figures by counting digits, as just presented, paying particular attention to the position of zeros in relation to the decimal point.

SOLUTION (a) 0.003<u>0</u> L has two sf.

(b) 0.1<u>0</u>44 g has four sf.

(c) 53,<u>0</u>69 mL has five sf.

(d) 0.00004715 m, or 4.715×10^{-5} m, has four sf.

(e) 57,6<u>00</u>. s, or $5.76\underline{00} \times 10^4$ s, has five sf.

(f) 0.000000716<u>0</u> cm^3, or $7.16\underline{0} \times 10^{-7}$ cm^3, has four sf.

CHECK Be sure that every zero counted as significant comes after nonzero digit(s) in the number.

Follow-up Problem 1.7 For each of the following quantities, underline the zeros that are significant figures and determine the number of significant figures (sf) in each quantity. For (d) to (f), express each in exponential notation first.

(a) 31.070 mg (b) 0.06060 g (c) 850.°C

(d) 200.0 mL (e) 0.0000039 m (f) 0.000401 L

Working with Significant Figures in Calculations

Measurements taken during experiments may contain differing numbers of significant figures. In a calculation, we keep track of the number of significant figures in each quantity so that we do not claim more significant figures (more certainty) in the answer than the original data justify. If we have too many figures, we **round off** the answer to obtain the proper number of significant figures.

Suppose you want to find the density of a new ceramic material. You measure the mass of a piece on an analytical balance and obtain 3.8056 g; you measure its volume as 2.5 mL by displacement of water in a graduated cylinder. The mass measurement has five significant figures, but the volume measurement has only two. Should you report the density as 3.8056 g/2.5 mL = 1.5222 g/mL or as 1.5 g/mL? The answer with five significant figures implies much more certainty in all the measurements than the answer with two. But if you did not measure the volume to five significant figures, you cannot possibly know the density with that much certainty. Therefore, you report the answer as 1.5 g/mL. In other words, *the least certain measurement sets the limit on certainty for the entire calculation and determines the number of significant figures in the final answer.*

Rules for Significant Figures in Answers The following two rules tell how many significant figures to show in the final answer of a calculation:

1. *For multiplication and division.* The answer contains the same number of *significant figures* as there are in the measurement with the fewest significant figures. Suppose you are determining the volume of a sheet of a new graphite composite. The length (9.2 cm) and width (6.8 cm) are obtained with a meter stick and the thickness (0.3744 cm) with a set of fine calipers. The volume calculation would be

$$\text{Volume (cm}^3) = 9.2 \text{ cm} \times 6.8 \text{ cm} \times 0.3744 \text{ cm} = 23 \text{ cm}^3$$

The calculator may show 23.4225 cm^3, but the answer should be reported as 23 cm^3, with two significant figures, because the length and width measurements contain only two significant figures.

2. *For addition and subtraction.* The answer has the same number of *decimal places* as there are in the measurement with the fewest decimal places. Suppose you measure 83.5 mL water in a graduated cylinder and add 23.28 mL protein solution from a buret. The total volume is

$$\text{Volume (mL)} = 83.5 \text{ mL} + 23.28 \text{ mL} = 106.8 \text{ mL}$$

Here the calculator shows 106.78 mL, but you report the volume as 106.8 mL, with one decimal place, because this is the number in the measurement with the fewest decimal places (83.5 mL).

Rules for Rounding Off In most calculations, you need to round off the answer to obtain the proper number of significant figures or decimal places. Notice that in calculating the volume of the graphite composite above, we removed the extra digits, but in calculating the total solution volume, we removed the extra digit and increased the last digit by one. The following is a set of rules for rounding off:

1. If the digit removed is *more than 5,* the preceding number is increased by 1: 5.379 rounds to 5.38 if three significant figures are retained and to 5.4 if two significant figures are retained.

2. If the digit removed is *less than 5,* the preceding number is unchanged: 0.2413 rounds to 0.241 if three significant figures are retained and to 0.24 if two significant figures are retained.

3. If the digit removed *is 5,* the preceding number is increased by 1 if it is odd and remains unchanged if it is even: 17.75 rounds to 17.8, but 17.65 rounds to 17.6. If the 5 is followed only by zeros, rule 3 is followed; if the 5 is followed by nonzeros, rule 1 is followed: 17.6500 rounds to 17.6, but 17.6513 rounds to 17.7.

4. *Always carry one or two additional significant figures through a multistep calculation and round off the final answer* **only.**

Don't be concerned if you string together a calculation to check a sample or follow-up problem and find your answer differs in the last decimal place from that in the book. In text calculations, we round off intermediate steps to show the correct number of significant figures, and this process may sometimes change the last digit.

Significant Figures and Electronic Calculators A calculator usually gives answers with too many significant figures. For example, if your calculator displays ten digits and you divide 15.6 by 9.1, it will show 1.714285714. Obviously, most of these digits are not significant; the answer should be rounded off to 1.7 so that it has the same number of significant figures as in 9.1. A good way to prove to yourself that the additional digits are not significant is to perform two calculations, indicated by the uncertainty in each of the last digits, to obtain the highest and lowest possible answers. For $(15.6 \pm 0.1)/(9.1 \pm 0.1)$,

$$\text{the highest answer is } \frac{15.7}{9.0} = 1.744444\ldots$$

$$\text{the lowest answer is } \frac{15.5}{9.2} = 1.684782\ldots$$

No matter how many digits the calculator displays, the values differ in the first decimal place, so the answer has two significant figures and should be reported as 1.7. Many calculators have a FIX button that allows you to set the number of digits displayed.

Significant Figures and Choice of Measuring Device As mentioned earlier, the measuring device you choose determines the number of significant figures you can obtain. Suppose you are doing an experiment that requires mixing a liquid with a solid. You weigh the solid on the analytical balance and obtain a value with five significant figures. It would make sense to measure the liquid with a buret or pipet, which measures volumes to more significant figures than a graduated cylinder. If you chose the cylinder, you would have to round off more digits in the calculations, so the certainty in the mass value would be wasted (Figure 1.16). As you gain experience in the laboratory, you will learn to choose a measuring device based on the number of significant figures you need in the final answer.

Figure 1.16 Significant figures and measuring devices. Mass measured with an analytical balance *(left)* has more significant figures than volume measured with a graduated cylinder *(right)*.

Exact Numbers Some numbers are called **exact numbers** because they have no uncertainty associated with them. Some exact numbers are part of a unit definition: there are 60 minutes in 1 hour, 1000 micrograms in 1 milligram, and 2.54 centimeters in 1 inch. Other exact numbers result from actually counting individual items: there are exactly 3 quarters in my hand, 26 letters in the English alphabet, and so forth. Since they have no uncertainty, *exact numbers do not limit the number of significant figures in the answer.* Put another way, exact numbers have as many significant figures as a calculation requires.

Sample Problem 1.8 Working with Significant Figures and Rounding

PROBLEM Perform each of the following calculations and round the answer to the correct number of significant figures:

(a) $\dfrac{16.3521 \text{ cm}^2 - 1.448 \text{ cm}^2}{7.085 \text{ cm}}$

(b) $\dfrac{(4.80 \times 10^4 \text{ mg})\left(\dfrac{1 \text{ g}}{1000 \text{ mg}}\right)}{11.55 \text{ cm}^3}$

PLAN We use the rules just presented in the text. In **(a)**, we subtract before we divide. In **(b)**, we note that the unit conversion involves an exact number.

SOLUTION **(a)** $\dfrac{16.3521 \text{ cm}^2 - 1.448 \text{ cm}^2}{7.085 \text{ cm}} = \dfrac{14.904 \text{ cm}^2}{7.085 \text{ cm}} = 2.104 \text{ cm}$

(b) $\dfrac{(4.80 \times 10^4 \text{ mg})\left(\dfrac{1 \text{ g}}{1000 \text{ mg}}\right)}{11.55 \text{ cm}^3} = \dfrac{48.0 \text{ g}}{11.55 \text{ cm}^3} = 4.16 \text{ g/cm}^3$

CHECK Note that in (a) we lose a decimal place in the numerator, and in (b) we retain 3 sf in the answer because there are 3 sf in "4.80." Rounding to the nearest whole number is a useful way to check: **(a)** $(16 - 1)/7 \approx 2$ **(b)** $(5 \times 10^4 / 1 \times 10^3)/12 \approx 4$

Follow-up Problem 1.8 Perform the following calculation and round the answer to the correct number of significant figures:

$$\dfrac{25.65 \text{ mL} + 37.4 \text{ mL}}{73.55 \text{ s}\left(\dfrac{1 \text{ min}}{60 \text{ s}}\right)}$$

Precision, Accuracy, and Instrument Calibration

Precision and accuracy are two aspects of certainty. In everyday speech, we often use these terms interchangeably, but in scientific measurements they have distinct meanings. **Precision,** or *reproducibility,* refers to how close the measurements in a series are to each other. **Accuracy** refers to how close a measurement is to the real value.

The concepts of precision and accuracy are linked with two common types of error:

1. **Systematic error** produces values that are *either* all higher or all lower than the actual value. Such error is part of the experimental system, perhaps caused by a faulty measuring device or by a consistent mistake in taking a reading.

2. **Random error,** in the absence of systematic error, produces some values that are higher *and* some that are lower than the actual value. Random error always occurs, but its size depends on the measurer's skill and the instrument's precision.

Precise measurements have low random error, that is, small deviations from the average. *Accurate measurements have low systematic error and, generally, low random error as well.* In some cases, when many measurements are taken that have a high random error, the *average* may still be accurate.

Suppose each of four students measures 25.0 mL water in a graduated cylinder and then weighs the water in the cylinder on a balance. If the den-

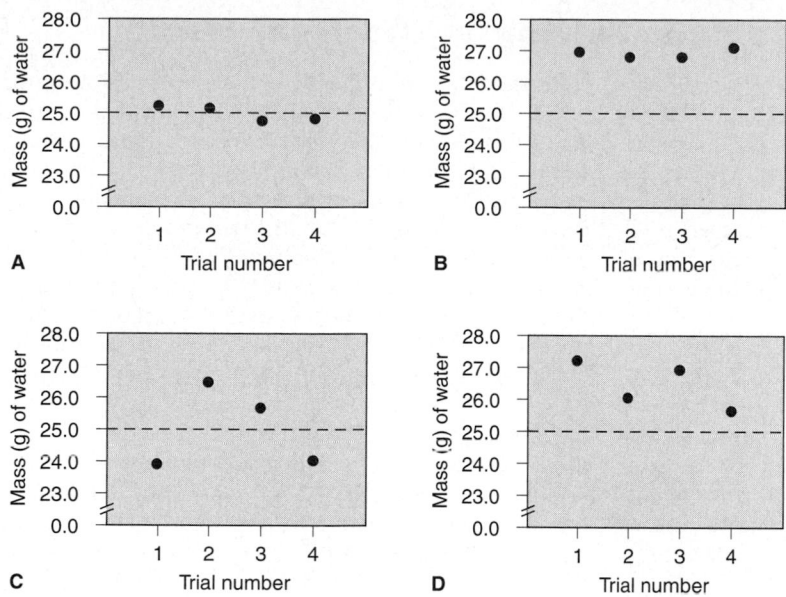

sity of water is 1.00 g/mL at the temperature of the experiment, the actual mass of 25.0 mL water is 25.0 g. Each student performs the operation four times, subtracts the mass of the empty cylinder, and obtains one of the four graphs in Figure 1.17. In graphs A and B, the random error is small; that is, the precision is high (the weighings are reproducible). In A, however, the accuracy is high as well (all the values are close to 25.0 g), whereas in B the accuracy is low (there is a systematic error). In graphs C and D, there is a large random error; that is, the precision is low. Large random error is often called large *scatter*. Note, however, that in D there is also a systematic error (all the values are high), whereas in C the average of the values is close to the actual value.

Systematic error can be avoided, or at least taken into account, through **calibration** of the measuring device, that is, by comparing it with a known standard. The systematic error in graph B, for example, might be caused by a poorly manufactured cylinder that reads "25.0" when it actually contains about 27 mL. If you suspect such an error based on a calibration procedure, you could adjust all volumes measured with that cylinder. Instrument calibration is an essential part of careful measurement.

Section Summary

Because the final digit of a measurement is estimated, all measurements contain some uncertainty, which is expressed by the number of significant figures. The certainty of a calculated result depends on the certainty of the data, so the answer has as many significant figures as in the least certain measurement. Excess digits are rounded off in the final answer. The choice of laboratory device depends on the certainty needed. Exact numbers have as many significant figures as the calculation requires.

Precision (how close values are to each other) and accuracy (how close values are to the actual value) are two aspects of certainty. Systematic errors result in values that are either all higher or all lower than the actual value. Random errors result in some higher and some lower values than the actual value. Precise measurements have low random error; accurate measurements have low systematic and often low random error. The size of random errors depends on skill and instrument precision. A systematic error is often caused by faulty equipment and can be compensated for by calibration.

Chemical Connections

Chemistry Problem Solving in the Real World

Working through the problems in this text will greatly improve your chances of doing well in the course, but that is not really the final goal. Even though you may not choose to become a chemist, learning chemistry is essential to many fields, including medicine, engineering, and environmental science. It is also essential to an understanding of complex science-related issues, such as the recycling of plastics, the reduction of urban smog, and the potential of genetic cloning—to mention just three of many.

A major scientific discipline such as chemistry consists of several subdisciplines that form connections with other sciences to spawn new fields. Traditionally, chemistry has five main branches—organic, inorganic, analytical, physical, and biological chemistry—but these have long ago formed interconnections, such as physical organic and bioinorganic chemistry. The problems of today and tomorrow require further connections to solve them, such as ecological chemistry, materials science, planetary chemistry, and molecular biology. The more complex the system under study, the greater is the need for interdisciplinary thinking.

Environmental issues are especially complex, and one of the most intractable is the acid rain problem. Let's see how it is being approached by chemists interacting with scientists in related fields. Acid rain results in large part from burning high-sulfur coal, a major fuel used throughout much of North America and Europe. As the coal burns, the gaseous products, including those of its sulfur impurities, are carried away by prevailing winds. In contact with oxygen and rain, these sulfur oxides undergo chemical changes, yielding acid rain. (We discuss the chemical details in later chapters.) In the northeastern United States and adjacent parts of Canada, acid rain has killed fish, decimated forests, injured crops, and released harmful substances into the soil. Acid rain has severely damaged many forests and lakes in Germany, Sweden, Norway, and several countries in central and eastern Europe. Acidic precipitation has now even been observed on both Poles!

Chemists and other scientists are currently working together to solve this problem (Figures 1.A and 1.B). As geochemists search for low-sulfur coal deposits, their engineering colleagues design better ways of removing sulfur oxides from smokestack gases. Atmospheric chemists and meteorologists track changes through the affected regions, develop computer models to predict the changes, and coordinate their findings

A

Figure 1.A **The central role of chemistry in solving real-world problems.** Researchers in many chemical specialties join with those in other sciences to investigate complex modern issues such as acid rain. **A,** The sulfur oxides in power plant emissions will be reduced by devices that remove them from flue gases. **B,** Atmospheric chemists study the location and concentration of air pollutants with balloons that carry monitoring equipment aloft.

B

with environmental chemists at ground stations. Agricultural chemists and agronomists study ways to protect crop yields. Ecological chemists and aquatic biologists monitor the effects of acid rain on insects, birds, and fish. Biochemists and genetic engineers develop new, more acid-resistant crop species. Soil chemists measure changes in mineral content, sharing their data with forestry scientists to save valuable timber and recreational woodlands. Organic chemists and chemical engineers convert coal to cleaner fuels. Superimposed on this intense experimental activity are scientifically trained economic and policy experts who provide business and government leaders with the information to make their decisions. With all this input, interdisciplinary understanding of the acid

rain problem has increased enormously and will continue to do so.

These professions are just a few of those involved in studying a single chemistry-related issue. Chemical principles apply to many other specialties, from medicine and pharmacology to art restoration and criminology, from genetics and space research to archaeology and oceanography. Chemistry problem solving has far-reaching relevance to many aspects of your daily life and your future career as well.

 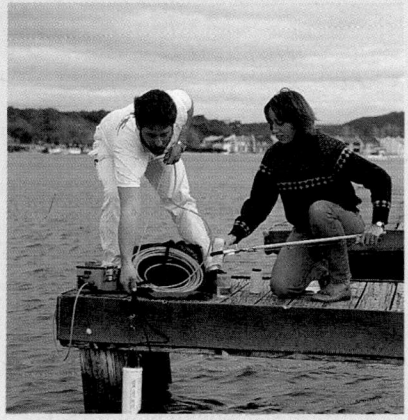

Figure 1.B **Field scientists studying the effects of acid rain. A,** Agronomists and other soil scientists use miniaturized equipment to measure acidity in plant and soil samples. **B,** Ecologists sample lake, pond, and river water and wildlife to learn the effects of acidic precipitation on aquatic environments.

A

B

Chapter Perspective

This chapter has provided several keys for you to use repeatedly in your study of chemistry: descriptions of some essential concepts; insight into how scientists think; the units of modern measurement and the mathematical skills to apply them; and a systematic approach to solving problems. You can begin using these keys in the next chapter, where we discuss the components of matter and their classification and see the winding path of scientific discovery that led to our current model of atomic structure.

The following learning objectives, with section and/or sample problem (SP) numbers in parentheses, can help focus your study:

Understand These Concepts

1. The distinction between physical and chemical properties and changes (1.1; SP 1.1)
2. The defining features of the states of matter (1.1)
3. The nature of potential and kinetic energy and their interconversion (1.1)
4. The process of approaching a phenomenon scientifically, and the distinctions between observation, hypothesis, experiment, and model (1.3)
5. The common units of length, volume, mass, and temperature and their numerical prefixes (1.5)
6. The distinction between mass and weight, between heat and temperature, and between intensive and extensive properties (1.5)

7. The meaning of uncertainty in measurements and the use of significant figures (1.6)
8. The distinction between accuracy and precision and the types of errors (1.6)

Master These Skills

1. Using conversion factors in calculations (1.4; SPs 1.2–1.4)
2. Finding density from mass and volume (SP 1.5)
3. Converting among the Kelvin, Celsius, and Fahrenheit scales (SP 1.6)
4. Determining the number of significant figures (SP 1.7) and rounding to the correct number of digits (SP 1.8)

For Review and Reference

Key Terms

Section 1.1
chemistry
matter
composition
property
physical property
physical change
chemical property
chemical change (chemical reaction)
state of matter
solid
liquid
gas
energy
potential energy
kinetic energy

Section 1.2
alchemy
combustion
phlogiston theory
Section 1.3
scientific method
observation
data
natural law
hypothesis
experiment
variable
controlled experiment
model (theory)
Section 1.4
conversion factor
dimensional analysis

Section 1.5
SI unit
base (fundamental) unit
derived unit
meter (m)
volume (V)
cubic meter (m³)
liter (L)
milliliter (mL)
mass
kilogram (kg)
weight
density (d)
extensive property
intensive property
temperature (T)
heat

thermometer
Kelvin (K)
Kelvin (absolute) scale
Celsius scale
second (s)
Section 1.6
uncertainty
significant figures
rounding off
exact number
precision
accuracy
systematic error
random error
calibration

Key Equations and Relationships

1.1 Calculating density from mass and volume (p. 22):

$$\text{Density} = \frac{\text{mass}}{\text{volume}}$$

1.2 Converting temperature from °C to K (p. 24):

$$T \text{ (in K)} = T \text{ (in °C)} + 273.15$$

1.3 Converting temperature from K to °C (p. 24):

$$T \text{ (in °C)} = T \text{ (in K)} - 273.15$$

1.4 Converting temperature from °C to °F (p. 24):

$$T \text{ (in °F)} = \tfrac{9}{5}T \text{ (in °C)} + 32$$

1.5 Converting temperature from °F to °C (p. 25):

$$T \text{ (in °C)} = [T \text{ (in °F)} - 32]\tfrac{5}{9}$$

Highlighted Figures and Tables

These figures (F) and tables (T) provide a quick review of key ideas. Entries in color contain frequently used data.
F1.2 The physical states of matter (p. 4)
F1.3 Potential energy and kinetic energy (p. 7)
F1.7 The scientific approach (p. 12)

T1.2 SI base units (p. 17)
T1.3 Decimal prefixes used with SI units (p. 18)
T1.4 SI-English equivalent quantities (p. 18)
F1.9 Some volume relationships in SI (p. 19)

Answers to Follow-up Problems

1.1 (a) Physical. Solid iodine changes to gaseous iodine.
(b) Chemical. Gasoline burns in air to form different substances.
(c) Chemical. In contact with air, torn skin and blood react to form different substances.

1.2 No. of chairs = $3 \text{ bolts} \times \dfrac{200 \text{ m}^2}{1 \text{ bolt}} \times \dfrac{3.281 \text{ ft}}{1 \text{ m}}$

$\times \dfrac{3.281 \text{ ft}}{1 \text{ m}} \times \dfrac{1 \text{ chair}}{31.5 \text{ ft}^2} = 205 \text{ chairs}$

1.3 Volume (mL) = $15.0^3 \text{ mm}^3 \times \dfrac{1^3 \text{ cm}^3}{10^3 \text{ mm}^3} \times \dfrac{1 \text{ mL}}{1 \text{ cm}^3}$

$= 3.38 \text{ mL}$

Total volume (L) = $(31.8 \text{ mL} + 3.38 \text{ mL}) \times \dfrac{10^{-3} \text{ L}}{1 \text{ mL}}$

$= 3.52 \times 10^{-2} \text{ L}$

1.4 Mass (kg) of rain

$$= 1.5 \, \text{h} \times \frac{60 \, \text{min}}{1 \, \text{h}} \times \frac{5.1 \times 10^5 \, \text{drops}}{1 \, \text{min}}$$

$$\times \frac{65 \, \text{mg}}{1 \, \text{drop}} \times \frac{1 \, \text{g}}{10^3 \, \text{mg}} \times \frac{1 \, \text{kg}}{10^3 \, \text{g}}$$

$$= 3.0 \times 10^3 \, \text{kg}$$

1.5 Mass (kg) of sample $= 4.6 \, \text{cm}^3 \times \frac{7.5 \, \text{g}}{1 \, \text{cm}^3} \times \frac{1 \, \text{kg}}{10^3 \, \text{g}}$

$$= 0.034 \, \text{kg}$$

1.6 T (in °C) $= 234 \, \text{K} - 273.15 = -39°\text{C}$;
T (in °F) $= \frac{9}{5}(-39°\text{C}) + 32 = -38°\text{F}$; answer contains two significant figures (see Section 1.6)
1.7 (a) 31.0$\underline{7}$0 mg, 5 sf; (b) 0.060$\underline{6}$0 g, 4 sf;
(c) 85$\underline{0}$.°C, 3 sf; (d) 2.$\underline{000}$×10^2 mL, 4 sf;
(e) 3.9×10^{-6} m, 2 sf; (f) 4.$\underline{0}$1×10^{-4} L, 3 sf
1.8 $\dfrac{25.65 \, \text{mL} + 37.4 \, \text{mL}}{73.55 \, \text{s} \left(\dfrac{1 \, \text{min}}{60 \, \text{s}}\right)} = 51.4 \, \text{mL/min}$

Problems

Problems with a colored number are answered at the back of the text. Problem sections match the text and provide the number(s) of relevant sample problems. Most offer concept review questions, skill-building exercises (written in similar pairs), and problems in a relevant context. Following these are comprehensive problems based on material from any section.

Some Fundamental Definitions

(Sample Problem 1.1)

■ Concept Review Questions

1.1 Define the following terms and give an example of each in the act of frying an egg for breakfast: (a) matter; (b) energy; (c) chemical change; (d) physical change.

■ Skill-Building Exercises *(paired)*

1.2 Describe solids, liquids, and gases in terms of how they fill a container. Use your descriptions to identify the physical state (at room temperature) of each of the following: (a) helium in a toy balloon; (b) mercury in a thermometer; (c) soup in a bowl.

1.3 Use your descriptions in the previous problem to identify the physical state (at room temperature) of each of the following: (a) air in your room; (b) vitamin tablets in a bottle; (c) sugar in a packet.

1.4 Define *physical property* and *chemical property*. Identify each type of property in the following statements:
(a) Yellow-green chlorine gas attacks silvery sodium metal to form white crystals of sodium chloride (table salt).
(b) A magnet separates a mixture of black iron shavings and white sand.

1.5 Identify physical and chemical properties in the following statements:
(a) Heating orange mercuric oxide powder produces silvery liquid mercury and colorless gaseous oxygen.
(b) The iron in discarded automobiles slowly forms reddish brown, crumbly rust.

1.6 Which of the following is a chemical change? Explain your reasoning: (a) boiling canned soup; (b) toasting a slice of bread; (c) chopping a log; (d) burning a log.

1.7 Which of the following changes can be reversed by changing the temperature (that is, which are physical changes)? (a) dew condensing on a leaf; (b) an egg turning

hard when it is boiled; (c) ice cream melting; (d) a spoonful of batter cooking on a hot griddle.

1.8 For each of the following pairs of objects or substances, which has higher potential energy?
(a) The fuel in your car or the products in its exhaust
(b) Wood in a fireplace or the ashes in the fireplace after the wood burns

1.9 For each of the following pairs of objects or substances, which has higher kinetic energy?
(a) A sled resting at the top of a hill or the sled sliding down the hill
(b) Water above a dam or water falling over the dam

Chemical Arts and the Origins of Modern Chemistry

■ Concept Review Questions

1.10 The alchemical, medical, and technological traditions were precursors to chemistry. State a contribution that each made to the development of the science of chemistry.

1.11 How did the phlogiston theory explain combustion?

1.12 One important observation that supporters of the phlogiston theory had trouble explaining was that the calx of a metal weighs more than the metal itself. Why was that observation important? How did the phlogistonists respond?

1.13 Lavoisier developed a new theory of combustion that overturned the phlogiston theory. What measurements were central to his theory, and what key discovery did he make?

The Scientific Approach: Developing a Model

■ Concept Review Questions

1.14 How are the key elements of scientific thinking used in the following scenario? While making your breakfast toast, you notice it fails to pop out of the toaster. T~~~king the spring mechanism is stuck, you notice that ~ changed. Assuming you forgot to plug in th~ check and find it is plugged in. When you ~ into the dining room and plug it into a diff~ find the toaster works. Returning to the kitchen, you~ on the switch for the overhead light and nothing happens.

1.15 Why is a quantitative observation more useful than a nonquantitative one? Which of the following observations are quantitative?

(a) The sun rises in the east.
(b) An astronaut weighs one-sixth as much on the Moon as on Earth.
(c) Ice floats on water.
(d) An old-fashioned hand pump cannot draw water from a well more than 34 ft deep.

1.16 Describe the essential features of a well-designed experiment.

1.17 Describe the essential features of a scientific model.

Chemical Problem Solving
(Sample Problem 1.2)

■ Concept Review Questions

1.18 When you convert feet to inches, how do you decide which portion of the conversion factor should be in the numerator and which in the denominator?

■ Skill-Building Exercises (paired)

1.19 Write the conversion factor(s) for each of the following: (a) in^2 to cm^2; (b) km^2 to m^2; (c) mi/h to cm/s.

1.20 Write the conversion factor(s) for each of the following: (a) cm/min to in/min; (b) m^3 to in^3; (c) m/s^2 to km/h^2.

Measurement in Scientific Study
(Sample Problems 1.3 to 1.6)

■ Concept Review Questions

1.21 Describe the difference between intensive and extensive properties. Which of the following properties are intensive: (a) mass; (b) density; (c) volume; (d) melting point?

1.22 Explain the difference between mass and weight. Why is your weight on the Moon one-sixth that on Earth?

1.23 For each of the following cases, state whether the density of the object increases, decreases, or remains the same:
(a) A sample of chlorine gas is compressed.
(b) A lead weight is carried from sea level to the top of a high mountain.
(c) A sample of water is frozen.
(d) An iron bar is cooled.
(e) A diamond is submerged in water.

1.24 Explain the difference between heat and temperature. Does 1 L water at 65°F have more, less, or the same quantity of energy as 1 L water at 65°C?

1.25 Why can't a temperature in the Celsius scale be converted into the Fahrenheit scale with a simple one-step conversion factor?

■ Skill-Building Exercises (paired)

1.26 The radius of a copper atom is 128 pm. What is its radius in nanometers (nm)?

1.27 The radius of a barium atom is 2.22×10^{-10} m. What is its radius in angstroms (Å)?

1.28 A soccer field is 100. m long. What is its length in feet (ft)?

1.29 The center on your basketball team is 7 ft 1 in tall. How tall is the player in centimeters (cm)?

1.30 A small hole in the wing of a space shuttle requires a 32.7-cm² patch. (a) What is the patch's area in square kilometers (km²)? (b) If the patching material costs NASA $2.75/in², what is the cost of the patch?

1.31 The area of a telescope lens is 5786 mm². (a) What is its area in square feet (ft²)? (b) If it takes a technician 45 s to polish 150. mm², how long does it take to polish the lens?

1.32 Express your body weight in kilograms (kg).

1.33 There are 2.60×10^{15} short tons of oxygen in the atmosphere (1 short ton = 2000 lb). How many metric tons of oxygen are present (1 metric ton = 1000 kg)?

1.34 The average density of the Earth is 5.52 g/cm³. What is its density in (a) kg/m³? (b) lb/ft³?

1.35 The speed of light in a vacuum is 2.998×10^8 m/s. What is its speed in (a) km/h? (b) mi/min?

1.36 The volume of a certain bacterial cell is 1.35 μm³. (a) What is its volume in cubic millimeters (mm³)? (b) What is the volume of 10^5 cells in liters (L)?

1.37 (a) How many cubic meters of milk are in 1 qt (946.4 mL)? (b) How many liters of milk are in 425 gallons (gal) (1 gal = 4 qt)?

1.38 An empty vial weighs 42.45 g. (a) If the vial weighs 185.56 g when filled with liquid mercury ($d = 13.53$ g/cm³), what is its volume? (b) How much would the vial weigh if it were filled with water ($d = 0.997$ g/cm³ at 25°C)?

1.39 An Erlenmeyer flask weighs 141.3 g when empty. When filled with water ($d = 1.00$ g/cm³), the flask and its contents weigh 283.2 g. (a) What is the flask's volume? (b) How much does the flask weigh when filled with chloroform ($d = 1.48$ g/cm³)?

1.40 A small cube of aluminum measures 15.6 mm on a side and weighs 10.25 g. What is the density of aluminum in g/cm³?

1.41 A steel ball-bearing with a circumference of 32.5 mm weighs 4.20 g. What is the density of the steel in g/cm³ (V of a sphere = $\frac{4}{3}\pi r^3$; circumference of a circle = $2\pi r$)?

1.42 Perform the following conversions:
(a) 72°F (a pleasant spring day) to °C and K
(b) −164°C (the boiling point of methane, the main component of natural gas) to K and °F
(c) 0 K (absolute zero, theoretically the coldest possible temperature) to °C and °F

1.43 Perform the following conversions:
(a) 106°F (the body temperature of many birds) to K and °C
(b) 3410°C (the melting point of tungsten, the highest for any element) to K and °F
(c) 6.1×10^3 K (the surface temperature of the sun) to °F and °C

■ Problems in Context

1.44 Anton van Leeuwenhoek, a 17th-century pioneer in the use of the microscope, described the microorganisms he saw as "animalcules" whose length was "25 thousandths of an inch." How long were the animalcules in meters?

1.45 The distance between two adjacent peaks on a wave is called the *wavelength*. The wavelength of visible light determines its color.
(a) The wavelength of a beam of green light is 513 nanometers (nm). What is its wavelength in meters?
(b) The wavelength of a beam of red light is 710 nm. What is its wavelength in angstroms (Å)?

1.46 To the alchemists, gold was the material representation of purity. It is a very soft metal that can be hammered into extremely thin sheets. If a 1.10-g piece of gold ($d = 19.32$ g/cm^3) is hammered into a sheet whose area is 40.0 ft^2, what is the average thickness of the sheet in centimeters?

1.47 A cylindrical tube 13.0 cm high and 1.5 cm in diameter is used to collect blood samples. How many cubic decimeters (dm^3) of blood can it hold (V of a cylinder $= \pi r^2 h$)?

1.48 English and non-English units appear on grocery items. (a) If the label on a bottle of cooking oil shows "48 fl oz (1.41 L)," how many fluid ounces are in 1.00 L? (b) If the serving size of oil is exactly 1 tablespoon, which has a mass of 14 g, and there are 96 servings in the container, what is the density of the oil in grams per milliliter (g/mL)?

Uncertainty in Measurement: Significant Figures

■ Concept Review Questions

1.49 What is an exact number? How are exact numbers treated differently from other numbers in a calculation?

1.50 All digits other than zero are significant. State a rule that tells which zeros are significant.

1.51 A newspaper reported that the attendance at Slippery Rock's home football game was 5209. (a) How many significant figures does this number contain? (b) Was the actual number of people counted? (c) After Slippery Rock's next home game, the newspaper reported an attendance of 5000. If you assume that this number contains two significant figures, how many people could actually have been at the game?

■ Skill-Building Exercises (paired)

1.52 Underline the significant zeros in the following numbers: (a) 0.39; (b) 0.039; (c) 0.0390; (d) 3.0900×10^4.

1.53 Underline the significant zeros in the following numbers: (a) 5.08; (b) 508; (c) 5.080×10^3; (d) 0.05080.

1.54 Round off the following numbers to the indicated number of significant figures (sf): (a) 0.0003554 (to 2 sf); (b) 35.8348 (to 4 sf); (c) 22.4555 (to 3 sf).

1.55 Round off the following numbers to the indicated number of significant figures (sf): (a) 231.554 (to 4 sf); (b) 0.00845 (to 2 sf); (c) 144,000 (to 1 sf).

1.56 Round off each number in the following calculation to one fewer significant figure, and find the answer:

$$\frac{12 \times 155 \times 7.6}{2.3 \times 2.9 \times 4.1}$$

1.57 Round off each number in the following calculation to one fewer significant figure, and find the answer:

$$\frac{13.8 \times 6.18 \times 2.54}{24.3 \times 2.7 \times 18.5}$$

1.58 Carry out the following calculations, making sure that your answer has the correct number of significant figures:

(a) $\dfrac{2.795 \text{ m} \times 3.10 \text{ m}}{6.48 \text{ m}}$

(b) $V = \frac{4}{3}\pi r^3$, where $r = 7.14$ cm

(c) 1.110 cm + 17.3 cm + 108.2 cm + 316 cm

1.59 Carry out the following calculations, making sure that your answer has the correct number of significant figures:

(a) $\dfrac{2.420 \text{ g} + 15.6 \text{ g}}{5.31 \text{ g}}$ (b) $\dfrac{7.87 \text{ mL}}{16.1 \text{ mL} - 8.44 \text{ mL}}$

(c) $V = \pi r^2 h$, where $r = 6.23$ cm and $h = 4.630$ cm

1.60 Write the following numbers in scientific notation: (a) 131,000.0 (b) 0.00047 (c) 210,006 (d) 2160.5

1.61 Write the following numbers in scientific notation: (a) 281.0 (b) 0.00380 (c) 4270.8 (d) 58,200.9

1.62 Write the following numbers in standard notation. Use a terminal decimal point when needed: (a) 5.55×10^3 (b) 1.0070×10^4 (c) 8.85×10^{-7} (d) 3.004×10^{-3}

1.63 Write the following numbers in standard notation. Use a terminal decimal point when needed: (a) 6.500×10^3 (b) 3.46×10^{-5} (c) 7.5×10^2 (d) 1.8856×10^2

1.64 Convert the following numbers into correct scientific notation: (a) 802.5×10^2 (b) 1009.8×10^{-6} (c) 0.077×10^{-9}

1.65 Convert the following numbers into correct scientific notation: (a) 14.3×10^1 (b) 851×10^{-2} (c) 7500×10^{-3}

1.66 Carry out each of the following calculations, paying special attention to significant figures, rounding, and units (J = joule, the SI unit of energy; mol = mole, the SI unit for amount of substance):

(a) $\dfrac{(6.626 \times 10^{-34} \text{ J} \cdot \text{s})(2.9979 \times 10^8 \text{ m/s})}{576 \times 10^{-9} \text{ m}}$

(b) $\dfrac{(6.022 \times 10^{23} \text{ molecules/mol})(7.04 \times 10^2 \text{ g})}{46.07 \text{ g/mol}}$

(c) $(6.022 \times 10^{23} \text{ atoms/mol})(2.18 \times 10^{-18} \text{ J/atom})\left(\dfrac{1}{2^2} - \dfrac{1}{3^2}\right)$,

where the numbers 2 and 3 in the last term are exact.

1.67 Carry out each of the following calculations, paying special attention to significant figures, rounding, and units:

(a) $\dfrac{4.816 \times 10^7 \text{ g}}{\frac{4}{3}(3.1416)(1.95 \times 10^2 \text{ cm})^3}$ (The term $\frac{4}{3}$ is exact.)

(b) $\dfrac{(2.45 \times 10^2 \text{ g})(44.7 \text{ m/s})^2}{2}$ (The term 2 is exact.)

(c) $\dfrac{(1.07 \times 10^{-4} \text{ mol/L})^2(2.6 \times 10^{-3} \text{ mol/L})}{(8.35 \times 10^{-5} \text{ mol/L})(1.48 \times 10^{-2} \text{ mol/L})^3}$

1.68 Which statements include exact numbers?
(a) Jane Smith is 63 in tall.
(b) There are nine known planets in the solar system.
(c) There are 453.59 g in 1 lb.
(d) There are 1000 mm in 1 m.

1.69 Which of the following include exact numbers?
(a) The speed of light in a vacuum is a physical constant; to six significant figures, it is 2.99792×10^8 m/s.
(b) The density of mercury at 25°C is 13.53 g/mL.
(c) There are 3600 s in 1 h.
(d) In 1986, there were 7.5 million residents of New York City.

1.70 How long is the metal strip in the figure shown below? Be sure to report your answer with the correct number of significant figures.

1.71 What volume of liquid is in the beaker shown in the figure? Be sure to report your answer with the correct number of significant figures.

■ Problems in Context

1.72 A gathering of 300 families attends a Founder's Day picnic in a small town, and the local Chamber of Commerce provides 3 bagels, 2 donuts, and 4 cans of iced tea to each family. After the picnic, 18 kg of garbage is collected. Which of the numbers—300, 3, 2, 3, 18—are exact numbers? Explain.

1.73 The following dart boards illustrate the types of errors often seen in measurements. The bull's-eye represents the actual value, and the darts represent the data.

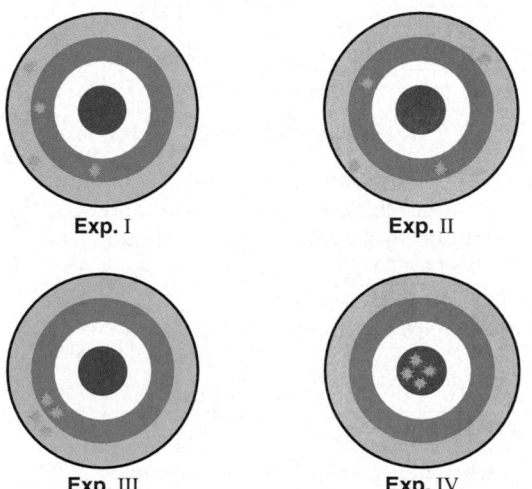

Exp. I   Exp. II

Exp. III   Exp. IV

(a) Which experiments yield the same average result?
(b) Which experiment(s) display(s) high precision?
(c) Which experiment(s) display(s) high accuracy?
(d) Which experiment(s) show(s) a systematic error?

1.74 A laboratory instructor gives a sample of powdered metal to each of four students, I, II, III, and IV, and they weigh the samples. The results of their multiple trials follow. The true value is 8.72 g.

I: 8.72 g, 8.74 g, 8.70 g   II: 8.56 g, 8.77 g, 8.83 g
III: 8.50 g, 8.48 g, 8.51 g   IV: 8.41 g, 8.72 g, 8.55 g

(a) Calculate the average mass from each set of data, and tell which set is the most accurate.
(b) Precision is a measure of the average of the deviations of each piece of data from the average value. Which set of data is the most precise? Is this set also the most accurate?
(c) Which set of data has the best combination of accuracy and precision?
(d) Which set of data has the worst combination of accuracy and precision?

Comprehensive Problems

Problems marked with an asterisk (*) are more challenging.

1.75 Your sports car gets 25.4 mi/gal and holds 70.1 L gasoline. (a) How far can you drive on a tankful? (b) If gas costs $0.51/L, how much does the trip cost? (c) If your average speed is 86.6 km/h, how much time does the trip take?

1.76 Two blank potential energy diagrams, similar to those in Figure 1.3, appear below. Beneath each diagram are objects to be placed in the diagram. Draw the objects on the dashed lines to indicate higher or lower potential energy and label each case as more or less stable:

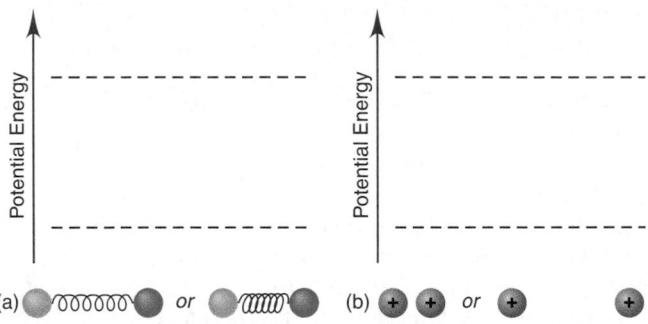

(a) Two balls attached to a relaxed spring *or* to a compressed spring.
(b) Two positive charges near each other *or* apart from each other.

1.77 Until the 20th century, in the final steps of the extraction of copper from its ores, the copper metal was melted, together with some oxide impurities, and the molten mixture stirred with a wooden stick. (a) Use the phlogiston theory to explain how this treatment converted the impurities to copper. (b) Use Lavoisier's model to explain the conversion.

1.78 It is possible to estimate the mass of an object from its volume and density. Most common liquids have a density close to that of water (1.0 g/cm^3); many common metals, including iron, copper, and silver, have densities around 9.5 g/cm^3. (a) What is the mass of the liquid in a standard 12-oz bottle of spring water? (b) What is the mass of a dime? (*Hint:* A stack of five dimes has a volume of about 1 cm^3.)

1.79 Suppose your dorm room is 11 ft wide by 12 ft long by 8.5 ft high and has an air conditioner that exchanges 1200 L air/min. How long would it take the air conditioner to exchange the air in your room once?

1.80 The specifications for a one-hundred milliliter volumetric flask state that it is guaranteed to contain the specified volume to within 0.1 mL. How many significant figures should you use to record the volume contained in the flask? Explain.

1.81 An Olympic-size pool is 50.0 m long and 25.0 m wide. (a) How many gallons of water ($d = 1.0$ g/mL) are needed to fill the pool to an average depth of 5.5 ft? (b) What is the mass (in kg) of water in the pool?

*1.82 A medical researcher uses a rectangular piece of silicone-based polymer for an artificial skin graft and reports the following calculation in her notebook:

Area of polymer = 0.98 cm × 1.06 cm = 1.04 cm^2

Why does the answer have three significant figures?

1.83 Which of the following points relate to physical properties and which to chemical properties? Magnesium, the eighth most abundant element on Earth, is found in minerals, sea water, and all organisms. (a) Magnesium is an essential component of chlorophyll, the photosynthetic pigment of green plants. (b) Freshly cut solid magnesium metal has a silvery white luster that dulls somewhat in air as the metal reacts with oxygen. (c) Magnesium has a density of 1.738 g/cm^3. (d) Magnesium melts at 649°C and boils at 1105°C, a relatively low boiling temperature for a metal. (e) Care must be taken in handling magnesium, particularly in powdered form, because when heated in air, it burns rapidly with a dazzlingly bright flame. (f) Magnesium fires cannot be extinguished with water because the hot metal reacts with water to produce flammable hydrogen gas. (g) Commercial applications of magnesium include its use in lightweight alloys for aircraft and missile bodies and in incendiary flares and fireworks.

*1.84 The average atmospheric pressure in Utah is 655 torr. Use the pressure units on the rear endpaper of this text to express this pressure in units of kg/m · s^2.

1.85 According to the lore of ancient Greece, Archimedes discovered the displacement method of density determination while bathing and used it to find the composition of the king's crown. If a crown weighing 4 lb 13 oz displaces 186 mL water when placed in a bathtub, is the crown made of pure gold ($d = 19.3$ g/cm^3)?

1.86 Calculate the density of the following substances in lb/ft^3: (a) graphite, $d = 2.27$ g/cm^3; (b) tin, $d = 7.26$ g/cm^3; (c) carbon monoxide, $d = 1.25$ g/L. (*Hint:* The density of water is 62.4 lb/ft^3.)

1.87 A graduated cylinder weighs 45.80 g when empty and contains 42.0 mL water ($d = 1.00$ g/cm^3). A piece of lead submerged in the water brings the total volume to 67.4 mL and the mass of cylinder and contents to 396.5 g. What is the density of lead?

1.88 Liquid nitrogen is obtained from liquefied air and is used in the food industry to prepare frozen foods. It boils at 77.36 K. (a) What is this temperature in °C? (b) What is this temperature in °F? (c) At the boiling point, the density of the liquid is 809 g/L and that of the gas is 4.566 g/L. How many liters of liquid nitrogen are produced when 500.0 L of nitrogen gas is liquefied at this temperature?

1.89 The speed of sound varies according to the material through which it travels. Sound travels at 5.4×10^3 cm/s through rubber and at 1.97×10^4 ft/s through granite. Calculate each of these speeds in m/s.

1.90 A jogger runs at an average speed of 6.5 mi/h. (a) How fast is she running in m/s? (b) How many kilometers does she run in 115 min? (c) If she starts a run at 11:15 AM, what time is it after she covers 4.75×10^4 ft?

*1.91 The Environmental Protection Agency (EPA) has proposed a new standard for microparticulates in air: For particles up to 2.5 μm in diameter, the maximum allowable amount is 50. μg/m^3. If your 10.0 ft × 8.25 ft × 12.5 ft dorm room just meets the new EPA standard, how many of these particles are in your room? How many of these particles are in each 0.500-L breath you take? (Assume the particles are spheres of 2.5 μm diameter and made primarily of soot, a form of carbon with a density of 2.5 g/cm^3.)

*1.92 In the figure below, the cylinder contains liquid that will be added to the liquid in the flask. What volume of liquid is in the cylinder? What volume of liquid is in the flask? What will be the total volume of liquid when the cylinder is emptied into the flask?

*1.93 In the buoyancy method of density determination, an object's weight in air is compared with its weight in liquid. The weight is less in the liquid because the weight of the displaced liquid acts as a force that pushes the object upward.

(a) A brass cylinder weighs 75.14 g in air and 66.21 g in water ($d = 0.998$ g/mL). What is the density of the brass?

(b) Geologists in the field use mineral oil ($d = 1.75$ g/cm^3) to determine the density of mineral samples. A sample of galena (an ore of lead) weighs 24.61 g in air and 18.83 g in mineral oil. What is the density of galena?

1.94 Nutritional tables give the potassium content of a standard apple (about 3 apples/lb) as 159 mg. How many grams of potassium are in 3.75 kg of apples?

*1.95 "Copper" pennies actually contain very little copper. If a new penny is 97.3% zinc and 2.7% copper by mass, what is its density (d of copper = 8.95 g/cm^3; d of zinc = 7.14 g/cm^3)?

*1.96 The three states of matter differ greatly in their viscosity, a measure of their resistance to flow. Rank the three states from highest to lowest viscosity. Explain your ranking in submicroscopic terms.

*1.97 Temperature scales can be based on many pure liquids. If a temperature scale were based on the freezing point (5.5°C) and boiling point (80.1°C) of benzene and the temperature difference between these points was divided into 50 units (called °X), what would be the freezing and boiling points of water in °X? (See Figure 1.13 in text.)

2

The Components of Matter

Figure: Depicting the ultimate components of matter. Chemical science was reborn with John Dalton's early 19th-century revival of atomism, and progress toward the true nature of matter has occurred at a breathtaking pace ever since. Lying over Dalton's images of molecules are our modern ones (top row, left to right: sulfur dioxide, methane, phosphine; bottom row: ammonia, carbon dioxide, dinitrogen monoxide). This chapter highlights our current understanding of atoms as the fundamental component of matter.

ook closely at an unusual stone, a butterfly's wing, or even a compact disk, and one of the first questions that comes to mind is "What is it made of?" Wondering about the ultimate makeup of things is an age-old practice. The natural philosophers of ancient Greece believed that everything was made of one or, at most, a few elemental substances. Seeing that the rivers and oceans extend everywhere, some believed that elemental substance to be water. Others thought it was air, which could be "thinned" into fire and "thickened" into clouds, rain, and rock. Still others believed that there were four elemental substances—fire, air, water, and earth—and that their properties accounted for hotness, wetness, and many other characteristics of things (Figure 2.1).

Democritus (c. 460–370 BC) took a very different approach. Rather than considering a specific substance, he focused on the ultimate components of *all* substances. His reasoning went something like this: if you cut a piece of, say, copper smaller and smaller, you must eventually reach a particle of copper so small that it can no longer be cut. Therefore, matter must ultimately be composed of indivisible particles, with nothing between them but empty space. He called the particles *atoms* (from the Greek *atomos*, "uncuttable") and proclaimed: "According to convention, there is a sweet and a bitter, a hot and a cold, and according to convention, there is order. In truth, there are atoms and a void." However, Aristotle (384–322 BC), who elaborated the idea of four elemental substances, held that it was impossible for "nothing" to exist. Because of the powerful influence that Aristotle exerted on Western thinking, the concept of atoms was suppressed for 2000 years.

Finally, in 17th-century England, Robert Boyle argued that an element is composed of "simple Bodies, not made of any other Bodies, of which all mixed Bodies are compounded, and into which they are ultimately resolved," a description that is remarkably similar to the idea of an element we hold today, in which the "simple Bodies" are atoms. This began the wonderful process of discovery, debate, and rediscovery that marks scientific inquiry, as exemplified by Lavoisier's work. Further studies in the 18th century gave rise to laws concerning the relative masses of substances that react with each other. At the beginning of the 19th century, John Dalton proposed an atomic model that explained these laws and led to rapid progress in chemistry. By the century's close, however, further observation exposed the need for a revised model. Then, a burst of creativity in the early 20th century led to a picture of the atom with a complex internal structure, which led shortly thereafter to our current model.

In this chapter, we examine the properties and composition of the three types of matter—elements, compounds, and mixtures—on the macroscopic and atomic scales. We discuss the mass laws and the theory Dalton proposed to explain them. To gain insight into how science works, we look at some key experiments that gave rise to our current model of the atom. With a sound atomic model in hand, the main portion of the chapter considers how the elements are classified, how they combine to form compounds, how we derive compound names and formulas, and how mixtures are classified and separated.

Concepts and Skills to Review

before you study this chapter

- physical and chemical change (Section 1.1)
- states of matter (Section 1.1)
- attraction and repulsion between charged particles (Section 1.1)
- meaning of a scientific model (Section 1.3)
- SI units and conversion factors (Section 1.5)
- significant figures in calculations (Section 1.6)

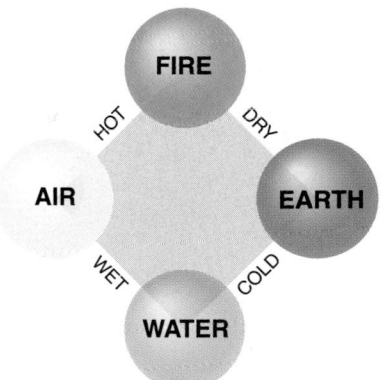

Figure 2.1 Elementary substances of the ancient Greeks. Each of the four supposed elementary substances—fire, air, water, and earth—was associated with two properties. Water was cold and wet, fire was hot and dry, and so forth. It was believed that various combinations of these properties could change one elementary substance into another: wetness could change fire into air, coldness could change air into water, and so forth.

2.1 Elements, Compounds, and Mixtures: An Atomic Overview

Matter can be broadly classified into three types—elements, compounds, and mixtures. An **element** is the simplest type of matter with unique physical and chemical properties. *An element consists of only one kind of atom.* Therefore, it cannot be broken down into a simpler type of matter by any physical or chemical methods. An element is considered a **pure substance** (or just a **substance**), a type of matter whose composition is fixed. Each element has a name, such as silicon, oxygen, or copper. A sample of silicon contains only silicon atoms. A key point to remember is that the *macroscopic* properties of a piece of silicon, such as color, density, and combustibility, are different from those of a piece of copper because silicon atoms are different from copper atoms; in other words, *each element is unique because its atomic properties are unique.*

Most elements exist in nature as populations of individual atoms, as shown in Figure 2.2A. However, several elements occur naturally in molecular form: a **molecule** is an independent structural unit consisting of two or more atoms that are chemically bound together. Figure 2.2B depicts an element that occurs in molecular form. Oxygen gas, for example, occurs in air as *diatomic* (two-atom) molecules.

A **compound** is a type of matter composed of *two or more different elements that are chemically bound together.* Be sure you understand that the elements in a compound are not just mixed together; rather, as Figure 2.2C shows, their atoms have joined chemically. Ammonia, water, and carbon dioxide are some common compounds. One defining feature of a compound is that *the elements are present in fixed parts by mass* (fixed mass ratio). A molecule of the compound maintains this fixed mass ratio because it consists of a *fixed number ratio* of atoms of the component elements. Because of this fixed composition, *a compound is also considered a substance.* For example, any sample of ammonia is fixed at 14 parts nitrogen by mass plus 3 parts hydrogen by mass. Since 1 nitrogen atom has 14 times the mass of 1 hydrogen atom, 1 molecule of ammonia consists of 1 nitrogen atom and 3 hydrogen atoms.

Another defining feature of a compound is that *its properties are different from those of its component elements.* Table 2.1 shows a striking example of this fact. Silvery sodium metal, which reacts violently with water, and yellow-green, poisonous chlorine gas have very different properties from the compound they form—white, crystalline sodium chloride, common table salt! Unlike an element, a compound *can* be broken down into simpler substances—its component elements. For example, an electric current can break down molten sodium chloride into metallic sodium and chlorine gas. By definition, this breakdown is a *chemical change,* not a physical one.

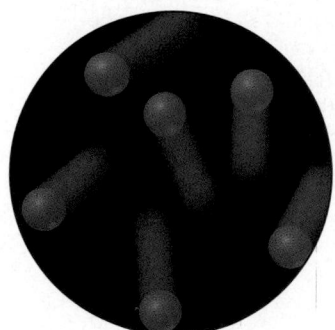

A Atoms of an element

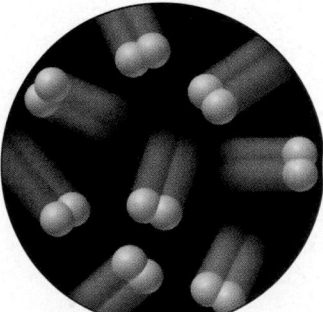

B Molecules of an element

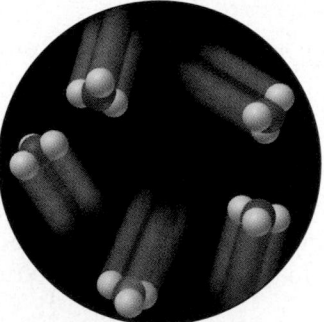

C Molecules of a compound

D Mixture of two elements and a compound

Figure 2.2 Elements, compounds, and mixtures on the atomic scale. A, Most elements consist of a large collection of identical atoms. **B,** Some elements occur as molecules. **C,** A molecule of a compound consists of characteristic numbers of atoms of two or more elements chemically bound together.

D, A mixture contains the individual units of two or more elements and/or compounds that are physically intermingled. The samples shown here are gases, but elements, compounds, and mixtures occur as liquids and solids also.

Table 2.1 Some Properties of Sodium, Chlorine, and Sodium Chloride

Property	Sodium	+	Chlorine	$\longrightarrow$ Sodium Chloride
Melting point	97.8°C		−101°C	801°C
Boiling point	881.4°C		−34°C	1413°C
Color	Silvery		Yellow-green	Colorless (white)
Density	0.97 g/cm^3		0.0032 g/cm^3	2.16 g/cm^3
Behavior in water	Reacts		Dissolves slightly	Dissolves freely

Figure 2.2D depicts a **mixture,** a group of two or more substances (elements and/or compounds) that are physically intermingled. In contrast to a compound, *the components of a mixture can vary in their mass ratio.* Since its composition is not fixed, a mixture is *not* a substance. A mixture of the two compounds sodium chloride and water, for example, can have many different mass ratios of salt to water. Since the components are physically mixed, not chemically combined, at the atomic scale a mixture is merely a group of the individual units that make up its component elements and compounds. Therefore, *a mixture retains many of the properties of its components.* Salt water, for instance, is colorless like water and tastes salty like sodium chloride. Unlike compounds, mixtures can be separated into their components by *physical changes;* chemical changes are not needed. In this case, the water in salt water can be boiled off, a physical process that leaves behind the sodium chloride, as shown in Figure 2.3.

Figure 2.3 Separating a mixture. Only physical processes are needed to separate a mixture. Boiling salt water removes the water, which can be condensed and collected if desired, and leaves the salt behind.

Section Summary

All matter exists as either elements, compounds, or mixtures. Elements are the simplest type of matter because they consist of only one type of atom. A compound contains two or more elements in chemical combination; it exhibits different properties from its component elements. The elements of a compound occur in a fixed mass ratio because their atoms are present in a fixed number ratio. Elements and compounds are referred to as substances because their compositions are fixed. A mixture results when two or more substances are mixed together; no chemical reaction need occur. The components can be present in any proportion, and they retain their individual properties.

2.2 The Observations That Led to an Atomic View of Matter

Any model of the composition of matter had to explain two extremely important chemical observations that were well established by the end of the 18th century: the *law of mass conservation* and the *law of definite (or constant) composition.* As you'll see, John Dalton's atomic theory explained these laws and another observation now known as the *law of multiple proportions.*

◆ **Immeasurable Changes in Mass** From the work of Albert Einstein (1879–1955), we now know that mass and energy are alternate aspects of a single entity called mass-energy. We also know that some mass *does* change into energy during any chemical reaction, but the amount is far below the limit of detection of the best modern balance. For example, when 100 g carbon burns in oxygen, only 0.000000036 g (3.6×10^{-8} g) of mass is converted to energy and, thus, not accounted for in the product, carbon dioxide. The energy yields of ordinary chemical reactions are relatively small, so that, for all practical purposes, mass *is* conserved. (As you'll see later, however, energy changes in nuclear reactions are so large that mass changes are measured easily.)

Figure 2.4 **The law of mass conservation: mass remains constant during a chemical reaction. A,** Before the reaction, a flask with lead nitrate solution and a cylinder with sodium chromate solution are placed on a balance and weighed. **B,** When the solutions are mixed, a chemical reaction occurs that forms lead chromate (yellow solid) and a sodium nitrate solution. Note that no change in mass has occurred.

Mass Conservation

The most fundamental chemical observation of the 18th century was the **law of mass conservation:** *the total mass of substances does not change during a chemical reaction.* The *number* of substances may change, and by definition their properties must, but the *total amount* of matter remains constant. Lavoisier had first stated this law on the basis of his combustion experiments, in which he found the mass of oxygen plus the mass of mercury equal to the mass of mercuric oxide they formed. Figure 2.4 illustrates mass conservation in a reaction that occurs in water. Even in a complex biochemical change within an organism involving many reactions, such as the metabolism of the sugar glucose, mass is conserved:

$$180 \text{ g glucose} + 192 \text{ g oxygen gas} \longrightarrow 264 \text{ g carbon dioxide} + 108 \text{ g water}$$

$$372 \text{ g material before change} \longrightarrow 372 \text{ g material after change}$$

Mass conservation means that, based on all chemical experience, *matter cannot be created or destroyed.* ◆

Definite Composition

Another fundamental chemical observation is summarized as the **law of definite (or constant) composition:** *no matter what its source, a particular chemical compound is composed of the same elements in the same parts (fractions) by mass.* The **fraction by mass (mass fraction)** is that part of the compound's mass contributed by the element. It is obtained by dividing the mass of each element by the total mass of compound. The **percent by mass (mass percent, mass %)** is the fraction by mass expressed as a percentage. Figure 2.5 depicts the meanings of these ideas in terms of a box of marbles.

Consider the compound calcium carbonate, the major substance in a piece of chalk. The following results are obtained for the elemental mass composition of 20.0 g calcium carbonate (for example, 8.0 g calcium/20.0 g = 0.40 parts calcium):

Figure 2.5 **The meaning of mass fraction and mass percent.** The box contains three types of marbles: yellow marbles weigh 1.0 g each, purple marbles 2.0 g each, and red marbles 3.0 g each. Each type makes up a fraction of the total mass of marbles, 16.0 g. The *mass fraction* of the yellow marbles is their number times their mass divided by the total mass, or (3 × 1.0 g)/16.0 g = 0.19. The *mass percent* (parts per 100 parts) of the yellow marbles is 0.19 × 100 = 19% by mass. The purple marbles have a mass fraction of 0.25 and are 25% by mass, and the red marbles have a mass fraction of 0.56 and are 56% by mass. Similarly, in a compound, each element has a *fixed* mass fraction (and mass %).

ANALYSIS BY MASS (grams/20.0g)	MASS FRACTION (parts/1.00 part)	PERCENT BY MASS (parts/100 parts)
8.0 g calcium	0.40 calcium	40% calcium
2.4 g carbon	0.12 carbon	12% carbon
9.6 g oxygen	0.48 oxygen	48% oxygen
20.0 g	1.00 part by mass	100% by mass

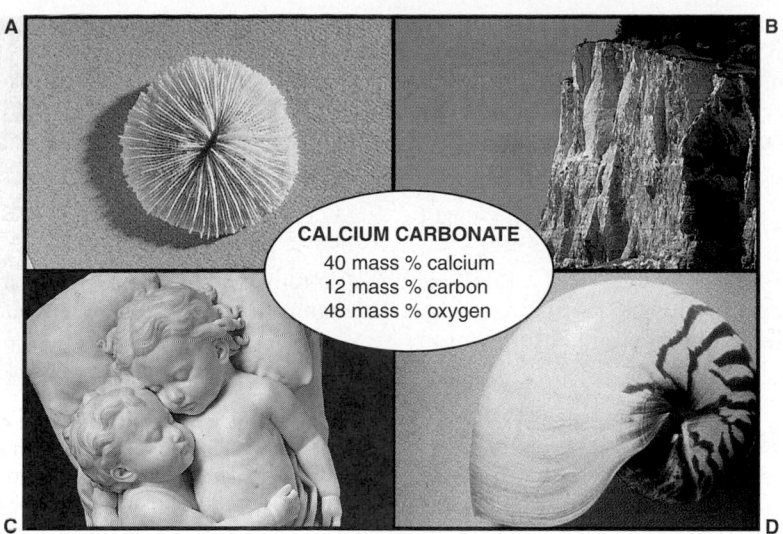

Figure 2.6 **The law of definite composition.** Calcium carbonate is found naturally in many forms, including **A,** coral; **B,** the white cliffs of Dover, England; **C,** marble; and **D,** seashells. The mass percents of its component elements do not change regardless of the compound's source.

CALCIUM CARBONATE
40 mass % calcium
12 mass % carbon
48 mass % oxygen

As you can see, the sum of the mass fractions (or mass percents) equals 1.00 part (or 100%) by mass. The law of definite composition tells us, and Figure 2.6 shows, that pure samples of calcium carbonate always contain the same elements in the same percent by mass.

Because a given element always constitutes the same mass fraction of a given compound, we can use the mass fraction to find the actual mass of the element in any mass of the compound:

$$\text{Mass of element} = \text{mass of compound} \times \frac{\text{part by mass of element}}{\text{one part by mass of compound}} \quad \textbf{(2.1)}$$

In a calculation, we can express the mass fraction in whatever mass units are needed.

Sample Problem 2.1 Calculating the Mass of an Element in a Compound

PROBLEM Pitchblende is the most commercially important compound of uranium. Analysis shows that 84.2 g pitchblende contains 71.4 g uranium, with oxygen as the only other element. How many grams of uranium can be obtained from 102 kg pitchblende?

PLAN We have to find the mass of uranium in a known mass of pitchblende, given the mass of uranium in a different mass of pitchblende, so we need the mass fraction. The mass fraction applies to any sample of a given compound, so we find the mass fraction by dividing the given mass of uranium by the given mass of the smaller sample of pitchblende. Then we multiply it by the mass of the larger sample to get the mass (in kg) of uranium. Then we just convert kg to g.

SOLUTION Finding the mass fraction of uranium:

$$\text{Mass fraction of uranium} = \frac{\text{mass of uranium}}{\text{mass of pitchblende}} = \frac{71.4 \text{ g uranium}}{84.2 \text{ g pitchblende}}$$

$$= \frac{0.848 \text{ part by mass uranium}}{1.00 \text{ part by mass pitchblende}}$$

Finding the mass of uranium in 102 kg pitchblende:

$$\text{Mass (kg) of uranium} = \text{mass (kg) of pitchblende} \times \text{mass fraction of uranium}$$

$$= 102 \text{ kg pitchblende} \times \frac{0.848 \text{ kg uranium}}{1.00 \text{ kg pitchblende}}$$

$$= 86.5 \text{ kg uranium}$$

Converting the mass from kg to g:

$$\text{Mass (g) of uranium} = 86.5 \text{ kg uranium} \times \frac{1000 \text{ g}}{1 \text{ kg}} = \boxed{8.65 \times 10^4 \text{ g uranium}}$$

Mass (g) of uranium
from analysis

divide by mass (g)
of pitchblende

Mass fraction of uranium
in pitchblende

multiply by mass (kg)
of pitchblende

Mass (kg) of uranium in
sample of pitchblende

1 kg = 1000 g

Mass (g) of uranium in
sample of pitchblende

CHECK The analysis showed that most of the mass of pitchblende is due to uranium, so the large mass fraction seems correct. Rounding off to check the mass of uranium in pitchblende shows the answer is correct: ~100 kg pitchblende × ~0.85 mass fraction uranium = 85 kg uranium.

COMMENT Mass analysis provides parts by mass, so you can use it directly *with **any** mass unit* (kg are shown) and eliminate the step to find the mass fraction:

$$\text{Mass (kg) of uranium} = 102 \text{ } \cancel{\text{kg pitchblende}} \times \frac{71.4 \text{ kg uranium}}{84.2 \text{ } \cancel{\text{kg pitchblende}}} = 86.5 \text{ kg uranium}$$

Follow-up Problem 2.1 How many metric tons (t) of oxygen are combined in a sample of pitchblende that contains 2.3 t uranium? (*Hint:* Remember that oxygen is the only other element present.)

Multiple Proportions

Dalton described a phenomenon that occurs when two elements form more than one compound. His observation is now called the **law of multiple proportions:** *if elements A and B react to form two compounds, the different masses of B that combine with a fixed mass of A can be expressed as a ratio of small whole numbers.* Consider, for example, two compounds that form from carbon and oxygen; for now, let's call them carbon oxides I and II. They have very different properties. For example, measured at the same temperature and pressure, the density of carbon oxide I is 1.25 g/L, whereas that of II is 1.98 g/L. Moreover, I is poisonous and flammable, but II is not. Analysis shows that their compositions by mass are

> Carbon oxide I: 57.1 mass % oxygen and 42.9 mass % carbon
>
> Carbon oxide II: 72.7 mass % oxygen and 27.3 mass % carbon

To see the phenomenon of multiple proportions, we use the mass percents of oxygen and of carbon in each compound to find the masses of these elements in a given mass, for example 100 g, of each compound. Then we divide the mass of oxygen by the mass of carbon in each compound to obtain the mass of oxygen that combines with a fixed mass of carbon:

	CARBON OXIDE I	CARBON OXIDE II
g oxygen/100 g compound	57.1	72.7
g carbon/100 g compound	42.9	27.3
g oxygen/g carbon	$\dfrac{57.1}{42.9} = 1.33$	$\dfrac{72.7}{27.3} = 2.66$

If we then divide the grams of oxygen per gram of carbon in II by that in I, we obtain a ratio of small whole numbers:

$$\frac{2.66 \text{ g oxygen/g carbon in II}}{1.33 \text{ g oxygen/g carbon in I}} = \frac{2}{1}$$

The law of multiple proportions tells us that in two compounds of the same elements, the mass fraction of one element relative to the other element changes in *increments based on ratios of small whole numbers.* In this case, the ratio is 2:1—for a given mass of carbon, II contains *2 times* as much oxygen as I, not 1.583 times, 1.716 times, or any other intermediate amount. As you'll see next, Dalton's theory allows us to explain the composition of carbon oxides I and II on the atomic scale.

Section Summary

Three widespread observations known as mass laws state that (1) the total mass remains constant during a chemical reaction; (2) any sample of a given compound has the same elements present in the same mass fractions; and

(3) in different compounds of the same elements, the masses of one element that combine with a fixed mass of the other can be expressed as a ratio of small whole numbers.

2.3 Dalton's Atomic Theory

With almost 200 years of hindsight, it may be easy to see how the mass laws could be explained by an atomic model—matter existing in indestructible units, each with a particular mass—but it was a major breakthrough in 1808 when John Dalton (1766–1844) presented his atomic theory of matter in *A New System of Chemical Philosophy.* ◆

Postulates of the Atomic Theory

Dalton expressed his theory in a series of postulates. Like most great thinkers, Dalton incorporated the ideas of others into his own to create the new theory. As we go through the postulates, which are presented here in modern terminology, let's see which were original and which came from others. (Later, we can examine the key differences between Dalton's postulates and our present understanding.)

1. All matter consists of **atoms,** tiny indivisible particles of an element that cannot be created or destroyed. (Derives from the "eternal, indestructible atoms" of Democritus more than 2000 years earlier and conforms to mass conservation as stated by Lavoisier.)
2. Atoms of one element *cannot* be converted into atoms of another element. In chemical reactions, the original substances separate into atoms, which recombine to form different substances. (Rejects the alchemical belief in the magical transmutation of elements.)
3. Atoms of an element are identical in mass and other properties and are different from atoms of any other element. (Contains Dalton's major new ideas: unique mass and properties for all the atoms of a given element.)
4. Compounds result from the chemical combination of a specific ratio of atoms of different elements. (Follows directly from the fact of definite composition.)

How the Theory Explains the Mass Laws

Let's see how Dalton's postulates explain the mass laws:

- *Mass conservation.* Atoms cannot be created or destroyed (postulate 1) or converted into other types of atoms (postulate 2). Since each type of atom has a fixed mass (postulate 3), a chemical reaction, in which atoms are just combined differently with each other, cannot possibly result in a mass change.
- *Definite composition.* A compound is a combination of a *specific* ratio of different atoms (postulate 4), each of which has a particular mass (postulate 3). Therefore, each element in a compound always constitutes a fixed fraction of the total mass.
- *Multiple proportions.* Atoms of an element have the same mass (postulate 3) and are indivisible (postulate 1). Because different numbers of B atoms combine with each A atom in different compounds, the masses of element B that combine with a fixed mass of element A will give a small, whole-number ratio.

The *simplest* arrangement consistent with the mass data for carbon oxides I and II in our earlier example is that one atom of oxygen combines with one atom of carbon in compound I (carbon monoxide) and that two atoms of oxygen combine with one atom of carbon in compound II (carbon dioxide). Figure 2.7 shows molecular models of these two compounds.

◆ **Dalton's Revival of Atomism** Although John Dalton, the son of a poor weaver, had no formal education, he established one of the most powerful concepts in science. Dalton began teaching science at 12 years of age, and later studied color blindness, a personal affliction still known as *daltonism.* In 1787, he began his life's work in meteorology, recording daily weather data until his death 57 years later. His studies on humidity and dew point led to a key discovery in the behavior of gases (Section 5.4) and eventually to his atomic theory. In 1803, he stated, "I am nearly persuaded that [the mixing of gases and their solubility in water] depends upon the mass and number of the ultimate particles . . . . An enquiry into the relative masses of [these] particles of bodies is a subject . . . I have lately been prosecuting . . . with remarkable success." The atomic theory was published 5 years later.

Carbon oxide I (carbon monoxide)   Carbon oxide II (carbon dioxide)

Figure 2.7 The atomic basis of the law of multiple proportions. Carbon and oxygen combine to form carbon oxide I (carbon monoxide) and carbon oxide II (carbon dioxide). The masses of oxygen in the two compounds relative to a fixed mass of carbon are in a ratio of small whole numbers.

The Theory's First Challenge: The Relative Masses of Atoms

After publication of the atomic theory, investigators tried to determine the masses of atoms from the mass ratios of elements in compounds. Because an individual atom is so small, we can only determine the mass of all the atoms of one element in a compound *relative* to the mass of all the atoms of another element. As a basis for these relative masses, Dalton assigned a mass of 1 to the hydrogen atom, the lightest known substance. Then, based on the work of Lavoisier, who had shown earlier that water contains 8 g oxygen for every 1 g hydrogen, Dalton assigned a relative mass of 8 to the oxygen atom. However, this relative mass for oxygen would be correct *only* if there were the same number of oxygen atoms in 8 g oxygen as there are hydrogen atoms in 1 g hydrogen, which in turn would be true *only* if a water molecule consisted of one oxygen atom for every hydrogen atom (symbolized HO).

At about the same time, the French chemist Joseph Gay-Lussac (1778–1850) also began to study the atom ratio of water. Rather than measuring *masses*, however, he measured the *volumes* of hydrogen gas and oxygen gas that react to form water vapor. Gay-Lussac found that 2 L hydrogen gas combine with 1 L oxygen gas. This result implied that each water molecule consists of two hydrogen atoms and one oxygen atom (symbolized H_2O). However, another of Gay-Lussac's results was confusing: 2 L water vapor were produced for every 2 L hydrogen gas that reacted. Here are the expected and actual results:

If water is HO: 1 L hydrogen gas + 1 L oxygen gas $\longrightarrow$ 1 L water vapor

If water is H_2O: 2 L hydrogen gas + 1 L oxygen gas $\longrightarrow$ 1 L water vapor

Actual result: 2 L hydrogen gas + 1 L oxygen gas $\longrightarrow$ 2 L water vapor

At this time, it was assumed that elements, including hydrogen and oxygen, existed as individual atoms. But, then, how could 2 L of individual H atoms combine with 1 L of individual O atoms to yield more than 1 L of water molecules? One suggestion was that each O atom splits in half as two molecules of water form! If that were the case, it meant that atoms were divisible and that the atomic theory was wrong. Dalton vigorously attacked Gay-Lussac's technique and results. In 1811, the Italian physicist Amedeo Avogadro (1776–1856) made two proposals that explained these confusing results:

- Each hydrogen gas particle and each oxygen gas particle is actually a molecule composed of two atoms. The molecules, not the atoms, split apart, and the separate atoms recombine to form molecules of water vapor.
- Equal volumes of a gas contain equal numbers of gas particles (under identical conditions). Therefore, 2 L hydrogen gas contain twice the number of gas particles as 1 L oxygen gas and the same number as 2 L water vapor. Figure 2.8 shows how Avogadro's hypotheses accounted for Gay-Lussac's results.

Even though Avogadro's explanation is correct, it was ignored because it was presented with difficult terminology and complex mathematics. Almost 50 years later, his ideas were revived and led to the determination of the correct relative mass of the oxygen atom as 16. Since the mass ratio of water is 8 g oxygen to 1 g hydrogen, the ratio of combining volumes means that 1 oxygen atom weighs 16 times as much as 1 hydrogen atom:

$$\text{(Volume ratio)} \ \frac{1 \text{ oxygen (16)}}{2 \text{ hydrogen (1 each)}} \Longrightarrow \frac{16}{2} = \frac{8}{1} \ \text{(mass ratio)}$$

Dalton's model of the atom had survived its first test. Because his model explained the masses of reacting elements in terms of atoms, it encouraged the establishment of atomic masses and eventually of chemical formulas, such as NH_3 for ammonia and H_2O for water. However, the model soon proved to be too limited. It could not explain *why* elements combine as they do: why,

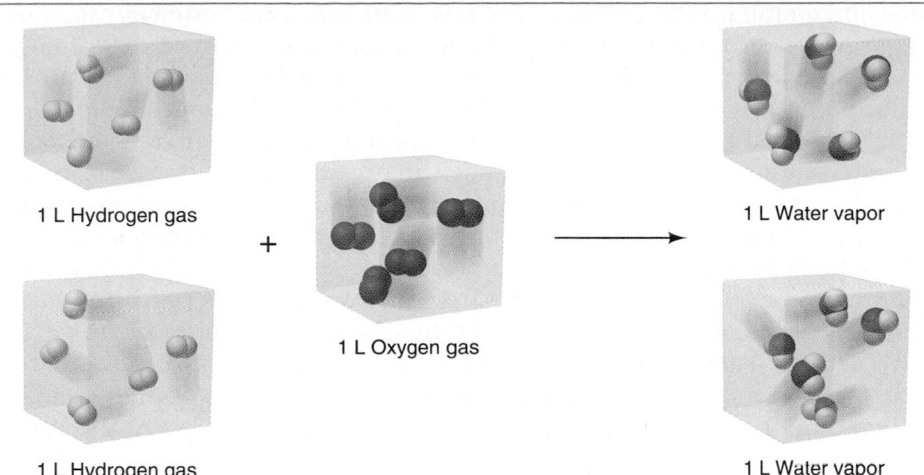

Figure 2.8 **The combining volumes of hydrogen and oxygen in the formation of water vapor.** To explain Gay-Lussac's results, Avogadro hypothesized that gas volume is proportional to the number of gas particles present. Thus, two volumes of hydrogen gas (or water vapor) contain twice as many particles as one volume of oxygen gas. If hydrogen gas and oxygen gas occur as diatomic molecules, two hydrogen "particles" (two molecules of two atoms each) combine with one oxygen "particle" (one molecule of two atoms) to form two water "particles" (two molecules each consisting of two H atoms and one O atom).

1 L Hydrogen gas

+

1 L Oxygen gas

1 L Hydrogen gas

1 L Water vapor

1 L Water vapor

for example, are two, and not three, H atoms combined with one O atom in a water molecule? Also, Dalton's "billiard ball" view of the atom could not account for the electrically charged particles that would soon be seen in many experiments. A more complex model of the atom would be needed to understand those observations. ◆

Section Summary

Dalton's atomic theory explained the mass laws by proposing that all matter consists of indivisible, unchangeable atoms of fixed, unique mass. Mass is constant during a reaction because atoms form new combinations; each compound has a fixed mass fraction of its elements because it is composed of a fixed number of each type of atom; and different compounds of the same elements exhibit multiple proportions because they each consist of whole atoms. Studies of the masses and volumes of elements that combine eventually led to consistent values for relative masses of atoms.

2.4 The Observations That Led to the Nuclear Atom Model

The path of discovery is often winding and unpredictable. Basic research into the nature of electricity eventually led to the discovery of *electrons,* negatively charged particles that are part of all atoms. Soon thereafter, other experiments revealed that the atom has a *nucleus*—a tiny, central core of mass and positive charge. In this section, we examine some key experiments that led to our current model of the nuclear atom.

Discovery of the Electron and Its Properties

Nineteenth-century investigators of electricity knew that matter and electric charge were somehow related. When amber is rubbed with fur, or glass with silk, positive and negative charges form—the same charges that make your hair crackle and cling to your comb on a dry day. They also knew that an electric current could decompose certain compounds into their elements.

What they did not know, however, was how electricity could be studied in the *absence* of matter. A powerful vacuum pump had been invented recently, so some investigators tried passing an electric current through nearly evacuated glass tubes. The tubes, fitted with metal electrodes that were sealed in place, were connected to an external source of electricity. When the power was turned on, a "ray" could be seen striking the phosphor-coated end of the

Atoms? Humbug! Rarely does a major new concept receive unanimous acceptance. Despite the atomic theory's impact, for another century several major scientists denied the existence of atoms. In 1877, Adolf Kolbe, an eminent organic chemist, said, "[Dalton's atoms are] . . . no more than stupid hallucinations . . . mere table-tapping and supernatural explanations." The influential physicist Ernst Mach believed that scientists should look at facts, not hypothetical entities such as atoms. It was not until 1908 that the famous chemist and outspoken opponent of atomism Wilhelm Ostwald wrote, "I am now convinced [by recent] experimental evidence of the discrete or grained nature of matter, which the atomic hypothesis sought in vain for hundreds and thousands of years." He was referring to the discovery of the electron.

The Familiar Glow of Colliding Particles The electric and magnetic properties of charged particles that collide with gas particles or hit phosphor-coated screens have familiar applications. "Neon" signs glow because electrons collide with the gas particles in the tube, causing them to give off light. An aurora display occurs when the Earth's magnetic field bends streams of charged particles coming from the Sun, which then collide with gases in the atmosphere. In a television tube or computer monitor, the cathode ray passes back and forth over the coated screen, creating a pattern that the eye sees as a picture.

tube and emitting a flash of light. The rays were called **cathode rays** because they originated at the negative electrode (cathode) and moved to the positive electrode (anode). They were shown to travel in straight lines, to be deflected by magnetic or electric fields, and to be identical, no matter what metal was used as the cathode. Figure 2.9 summarizes the investigations of cathode ray properties. It was concluded that cathode rays consist of negatively charged particles that are found in all matter and that the rays appear when these particles collide with the few remaining gas molecules in the evacuated tubes. ◆ Cathode ray particles were later named *electrons*.

Just over a century ago, in 1897, J. J. Thomson (1856–1940) used magnetic and electric fields to measure the ratio of the cathode ray particle's mass to its charge (Figure 2.10). By comparing this value with the mass/charge ratio for the lightest charged particle in solution, Thomson estimated that the cathode ray particle weighed less than $\frac{1}{1000}$ as much as hydrogen, the lightest atom! He was shocked because this implied that, contrary to Dalton's atomic theory, *atoms are divisible into even smaller particles*. Thomson concluded, "We have in the cathode rays matter in a new state, . . . in which the subdivision of matter is carried much further . . . ; this matter being the substance from which the chemical elements are built up." Fellow scientists reacted at first with disbelief, and some even thought Thomson was joking.

In 1909, the American physicist Robert Millikan (1868–1953) measured the *charge* of the electron. He did so by observing the movement of tiny droplets of the "highest grade clock oil" in an apparatus that contained electrically charged plates and an x-ray source, as depicted in Figure 2.11. Here is a description of the basis of the experiment: X-rays knocked electrons from gas molecules in the air, and as an oil droplet fell through a hole in the pos-

Figure 2.9 **Experiments to determine the properties of cathode rays.** A cathode ray forms when high voltage is applied across the electrodes in a partially evacuated tube. A hole in the anode allows the ray to pass through and hit the coated end of the tube. **A,** In the absence of an external field, the ray travels in a straight path. **B,** The ray bends in an external magnetic field, so it must consist of charged particles. **C,** In an external electric field, the ray bends toward the positive plate, so the particles' charge must be negative. **D,** Any electrode material produces an identical ray, so the particles must be part of all matter—a universal negatively charged particle.

itive (upper) plate, the electrons stuck to the drop, giving it a negative charge. With the electric field off, Millikan measured the mass of the droplet from its rate of fall. By turning on the field and varying its strength, he could make the drop fall more slowly, rise, or pause suspended. From these data, Millikan calculated the total charge of the droplet.

After studying many droplets, Millikan confirmed his expectation that their various charges were always some *whole-number multiple of a minimum charge.* He reasoned that different oil droplets picked up different numbers of electrons, so this minimum charge must be that of the electron itself. The value, which he calculated 90 years ago, is within 1% of the modern value of the electron's charge, -1.602×10^{-19} C (C stands for *coulomb,* the SI unit of charge). Armed with values for the electron's mass/charge ratio from the work of Thomson and others and this value for the electron's charge, let's calculate the electron's *extremely* small mass the way Millikan did:

$$\text{Mass of electron} = \frac{\text{mass}}{\text{charge}} \times \text{charge} = \left(-5.686 \times 10^{-12} \frac{\text{kg}}{\cancel{\text{C}}}\right)\left(-1.602 \times 10^{-19} \cancel{\text{C}}\right)$$
$$= 9.109 \times 10^{-31} \text{ kg} = 9.109 \times 10^{-28} \text{ g}$$

Figure 2.10 Joseph John Thomson. J. J. Thomson is shown at work on his experiments to determine the mass-to-charge ratio of cathode ray particles. He received the Nobel Prize in physics in 1906 for this work.

Discovery of the Atomic Nucleus

Clearly, the properties of the electron posed problems about the inner structure of atoms. Since matter is electrically neutral, atoms must be neutral also. But if atoms contain negatively charged electrons, what positive charges balance them? And if an electron has such an incredibly tiny mass, what accounts for an atom's much higher mass? To address these issues, Thomson proposed a model of a spherical atom composed of diffuse, positively charged matter, in which electrons were embedded like "raisins in a plum pudding."

Near the turn of the 20th century, French scientists discovered radioactivity, the emission of particles and/or radiation from atoms of certain elements. A few years later, in 1910, the New Zealand-born physicist Ernest Rutherford (1871–1937) used one type of these emitted particles in a series of exper-

Figure 2.11 Millikan's oil-drop experiment for measuring an electron's charge. The motion of a given oil droplet depends on the variation in electric field and the total charge on the droplet, which depends in turn on the number of attached electrons. Millikan reasoned that the total charge must be some whole-number multiple of the charge of the electron.

A Hypothesis: Expected result based on "plum pudding" model

Incoming α particles

Almost no deflection

Cross section of gold foil composed of "plum pudding" atoms

B Experiment

① *Radioactive sample emits beam of α particles*

② *Beam of α particles strikes gold foil*

Lead block

Gold foil

⑤ *Major deflections of α particles are seen very rarely*

④ *Minor deflections of α particles are seen occasionally*

③ *Flashes of light produced when α particles strike zinc-sulfide screen show that most α particles are transmitted with little or no deflection*

C Actual Result

Incoming α particles

Major deflection

Minor deflection

Cross section of gold foil composed of atoms with a tiny, massive, positive nucleus

Figure 2.12 Rutherford's α-scattering experiment and discovery of the atomic nucleus.
A, The hypothesis stated that atoms consist of electrons embedded in diffuse, positively charged matter, so the speeding α particles should pass through the gold foil with, at most, minor deflections. **B,** In the experiment, α particles aimed at gold foil emit a flash of light when they pass through the gold atoms and hit a phosphor-coated screen. **C,** The actual results show occasional minor deflections and very infrequent major deflections. This could happen only if very high mass and positive charge are concentrated in a small region within the atom, the nucleus.

iments that solved this dilemma of atomic structure. Figure 2.12 is a three-part representation of Rutherford's experiment in which tiny, dense, positively charged alpha (α) particles emitted from radium were aimed, like minute projectiles, at thin metal foils. The figure depicts (A) the hypothesis, (B) the apparatus that his researchers used to measure the deflection (scattering) of the α particles by observing the light flashes created when the particles struck a circular, coated screen, and (C) the actual result that Rutherford obtained.

With Thomson's plum-pudding model in mind, Rutherford expected only minor, if any, deflections of the α particles because they should act as tiny, dense, positively charged "bullets" and go right through the gold atoms. According to the model, the embedded electrons could not deflect the α particles any more than a Ping-Pong ball could deflect a speeding baseball. Initial results confirmed this, but soon the unexpected happened. As Rutherford recalled: "Then I remember two or three days later Geiger [one of his co-workers] coming to me in great excitement and saying, 'We have been able to get some of the α particles coming backwards. . . . ' It was quite the most incredible event that has ever happened to me in my life. It was almost as incredible as if you fired a 15-inch shell at a piece of tissue paper and it came back and hit you."

The data showed that very few α particles were deflected at all, and that only 1 in 20,000 were deflected by more than 90° ("coming backwards"). It seemed that these few α particles were being repelled by something small, dense, and positive within the gold atoms. From the mass, charge, and velocity of the α particles, the frequency of these large-angle deflections, and the properties of electrons, Rutherford calculated that an atom is mostly space occupied by electrons, but centrally located within that space lies a tiny region, which he called the **nucleus,** that contains *all the positive charge and essentially all the mass of the atom.* He proposed that positive particles lay within the nucleus and called them *protons,* and then calculated the magnitude of the nuclear charge with remarkable accuracy. Rutherford's model explained the charged nature of matter, but it could not account for all the atom's mass.

It took more than 20 years for this issue to be fully resolved when, in 1932, James Chadwick discovered the *neutron,* an uncharged dense particle that also resides in the nucleus. ◆

Section Summary

Several major discoveries at the turn of the 20th century led to our current model of atomic structure. Cathode rays were shown to consist of negative particles (electrons) that exist in all matter. J. J. Thomson measured their mass/charge ratio and concluded that they are much smaller and lighter than atoms. Robert Millikan determined the charge of the electron, which he could combine with other data to calculate its mass. Ernest Rutherford proposed that atoms consist of a tiny, massive, positive nucleus surrounded by electrons.

2.5 The Atomic Theory Today

For nearly 200 years, we have known that all matter consists of atoms, and we have learned astonishing things about them. Dalton's hard, impenetrable spheres have given way to atoms with "fuzzy," indistinct boundaries and an elaborate internal architecture of subatomic particles. In this section, we examine our current model and begin to see how the properties of these particles affect the properties of atoms. Then we can reassess the atomic theory in the light of our present knowledge.

Structure of the Atom

An *atom* is an electrically neutral, spherical entity composed of a positively charged central nucleus surrounded by one or more negatively charged electrons, as shown in Figure 2.13. The electrons move rapidly through the available atomic volume, held there by the attraction of the nucleus. The nucleus is incredibly dense: it contributes 99.97% of the atom's mass but occupies only about 1 ten-trillionth of its volume. A nucleus the size of a period on this page would weigh about 100 tons, as much as 50 cars! An atom's diameter ($\sim 10^{-10}$ m) is about 10,000 times the diameter of its nucleus ($\sim 10^{-14}$ m).

An *atomic nucleus consists of protons and neutrons,* except for the simplest hydrogen nucleus, which is a single proton. The **proton (p^+)** has a positive charge, and the **neutron (n^0)** has no charge; thus, the positive charge of the nucleus results from the combined charges of its protons. The *magnitude* of charge possessed by a proton is equal to that of an **electron (e^-),** but the *signs* of the charges are opposite. *The number of protons in the nucleus of the atom equals the number of electrons surrounding the nucleus.* Some properties of these three subatomic particles are listed in Table 2.2.

The "Big Three" Subatomic Particles Of all the subatomic particles discovered (at latest count, well over 40), the electron, proton, and neutron are the most important in chemistry because they are so long-lived. Theory postulates that, while bound in the nucleus, the neutron and proton are stable for at least 10^{30} years. The electron is considered eternal.

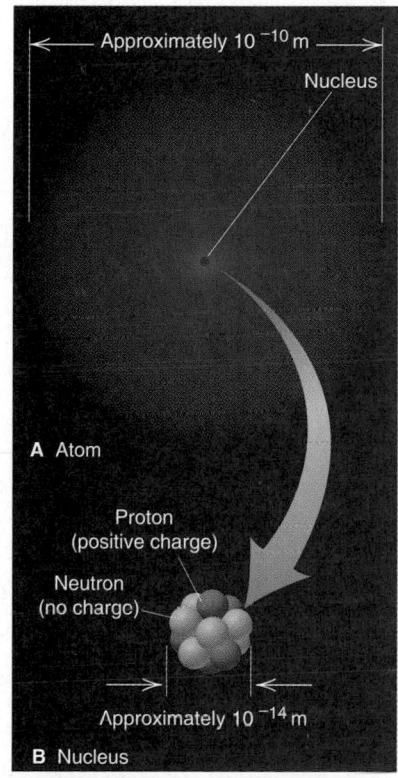

Figure 2.13 General features of the atom. A, A "cloud" of rapidly moving, negatively charged electrons occupies virtually all the atomic volume and surrounds the tiny, central nucleus. **B,** The nucleus contains virtually all the mass of the atom and consists of positively charged protons and uncharged neutrons. If the nucleus were actually the size in the figure ($\sim$1 cm across), the atom would be about 100 m across—slightly longer than a football field!

Table 2.2 Properties of the Three Key Subatomic Particles

Name (Symbol)	Charge		Mass		Location in Atom
	Relative	**Absolute (C)***	**Relative (amu)†**	**Absolute (g)**	
Proton (p^+)	1+	$+1.60218 \times 10^{-19}$	1.00727	1.67262×10^{-24}	Nucleus
Neutron (n^0)	0	0	1.00866	1.67493×10^{-24}	Nucleus
Electron (e^-)	1−	-1.60218×10^{-19}	0.00054858	9.10939×10^{-28}	Outside nucleus

*The coulomb (C) is the SI unit of charge.
†The atomic mass unit (amu) equals 1.66054×10^{-24} g; discussed later in this section.

◆ **Naming an Element**
Element names have a variety of origins. Carbon comes from coal (Latin *carbo,* "ember"). Mercury (Hg) is named for the planet, but its symbol reveals its earlier name *hydragyrum* (Latin "liquid silver"). Some names are based on a chemical action, such as hydrogen (Greek *hydros,* "water," and *genes,* "producer"), or an obvious property, such as chlorine (Greek *chloros,* "yellow-green"). Sometimes, countries are used in the name, as in germanium for Germany and americium for America. Ytterbium, yttrium, erbium, and terbium are all named for Ytterby, the Swedish town where these elements were discovered. Paying homage to great scientists was the impetus for the names of some of the synthetic elements, such as einsteinium for Albert Einstein and curium for Marie and Pierre Curie.

Atomic Number, Mass Number, and Atomic Symbols

The **atomic number (Z)** of an element equals the number of protons in the nucleus of each of its atoms. *All atoms of a particular element have the same atomic number, and each element has a different atomic number from that of any other element.* All carbon atoms ($Z = 6$) have 6 protons, all oxygen atoms ($Z = 8$) have 8 protons, and all uranium atoms ($Z = 92$) have 92 protons. There are currently 112 known elements, of which 90 occur in nature; the remaining 22 have been synthesized by nuclear processes.

The total number of protons and neutrons in the nucleus of an atom is its **mass number (A);** each proton and each neutron contributes one unit to the mass number. Thus, a carbon atom with 6 protons and 6 neutrons in its nucleus has a mass number of 12, and a uranium atom with 92 protons and 146 neutrons in its nucleus has a mass number of 238.

Information about the nuclear mass and charge is often included with the **atomic symbol** (or element symbol). Every element has a symbol based on its English or its Latin or Greek name, such as C for carbon, O for oxygen, S for sulfur, and Na for sodium (Latin *natrium*). ◆ The atomic number (Z) is written as a left subscript and the mass number (A) as a left superscript, so element X would be symbolized $^A_Z X$. Since the mass number is the sum of protons and neutrons, the number of neutrons (N) equals the mass number minus the atomic number:

Number of neutrons = mass number − atomic number,   or $N = A - Z$ **(2.2)**

Thus, a chlorine atom that is symbolized $^{35}_{17}Cl$ has $A = 35$, $Z = 17$, and $N = 35 - 17 = 18$. Since a given element has its own specific atomic number, we know the atomic number from the symbol. For example, every carbon atom has 6 protons, so we can write ^{12}C (spoken "carbon twelve"), with $Z = 6$ understood, for carbon with mass number 12. Another way to write this atom is carbon-12. Figure 2.14 depicts this information for three atoms.

Isotopes and Atomic Masses of the Elements

All atoms of an element are identical in atomic number but not in mass number. All carbon atoms have six protons in the nucleus ($Z = 6$), but only 98.89% of naturally occurring carbon atoms have 6 neutrons in the nucleus ($A = 12$). A small percentage (1.11%) have 7 neutrons in the nucleus ($A = 13$), and even fewer (less than 0.01%) have 8 ($A = 14$). **Isotopes** of an element are atoms that have *different numbers of neutrons* and therefore different mass numbers. Carbon has three naturally occurring isotopes, ^{12}C, ^{13}C, and ^{14}C. Five other isotopes of carbon, ^{9}C, ^{10}C, ^{11}C, ^{15}C, and ^{16}C, have been observed in the laboratory. All of these carbon isotopes have 6 protons and 6 electrons. A key point that we will note many times is that the chemical properties of an element are primarily determined by the number of electrons, so *all isotopes of an element have nearly identical chemical behavior,* even though they have different masses.

Sample Problem 2.2   Determining the Number of Subatomic Particles in the Isotopes of an Element

PROBLEM Silicon (Si) is essential to the computer industry as a major component of semiconductor chips. It has three naturally occurring isotopes: ^{28}Si, ^{29}Si, and ^{30}Si. Determine the number of protons, neutrons, and electrons in each silicon isotope.
PLAN The mass numbers of the three isotopes are given, so we know the sum of protons and neutrons. From the elements list on the text's inside front cover, we find the atomic number (number of protons), which equals the number of electrons. We obtain the number of neutrons from Equation 2.2.

SOLUTION From the elements list, the atomic number of silicon is 14. Therefore,

$$^{28}\text{Si has } 14p^+, 14e^-, \text{ and } 14n^0 \ (28 - 14)$$

$$^{29}\text{Si has } 14p^+, 14e^-, \text{ and } 15n^0 \ (29 - 14)$$

$$^{30}\text{Si has } 14p^+, 14e^-, \text{ and } 16n^0 \ (30 - 14)$$

Follow-up Problem 2.2 How many protons, neutrons, and electrons are in each of the following?
(a) $^{11}_{5}\text{Q}$ **(b)** $^{41}_{20}\text{X}$ **(c)** $^{131}_{53}\text{Y}$
What element symbols do Q, X, and Y represent?

The mass of an atom is measured most easily *relative* to the mass of a chosen atomic standard. The modern atomic mass standard is the carbon-12 atom. Its mass is defined as *exactly* 12 atomic mass units. Thus, the **atomic mass unit (amu)** is $\frac{1}{12}$ the mass of a carbon-12 atom. Based on this standard, the ^1H atom has a mass of 1.008 amu; in other words, a ^{12}C atom has almost 12 times the mass of an ^1H atom. We will continue to use the term *atomic mass unit* in the text, even though the name has recently been changed to the **dalton (D)**; thus, one ^{12}C atom has a mass of 12 daltons (12 D, or 12 amu). The atomic mass unit, which is a unit of relative mass, equals 1.66054×10^{-24} g.

The isotopic makeup of an element is determined by **mass spectrometry,** a method for measuring the relative masses and abundances of particles very precisely (described in the next Tools of the Chemistry Laboratory). For example, using a mass spectrometer, we measure the mass ratio of ^{28}Si to ^{12}C as

$$\frac{\text{Mass of } ^{28}\text{Si atom}}{\text{Mass of } ^{12}\text{C standard}} = 2.331411$$

From this mass ratio, we find the **isotopic mass** of the ^{28}Si atom, the mass of the isotope relative to the mass of the standard carbon-12 isotope:

$$\text{Isotopic mass of } ^{28}\text{Si} = \text{measured mass ratio} \times \text{mass of } ^{12}\text{C}$$

$$= 2.331411 \times 12 \text{ amu}$$

$$= 27.97693 \text{ amu}$$

Along with the isotopic mass, the mass spectrometer gives the relative abundance (fraction) of each isotope in a sample of the element. For example, the percent abundance of ^{28}Si is 92.23%. Such measurements provide data for obtaining the **atomic mass** (also called *atomic weight*) of an element, the *average* of the masses of its naturally occurring isotopes weighted according to their abundances.

Each naturally occurring isotope of an element contributes a certain portion to the atomic mass. For instance, we know that 92.23% of Si is ^{28}Si. Using this percent abundance as a fraction and multiplying by its isotopic mass gives the portion contributed by ^{28}Si:

Portion of Si atomic mass from $^{28}\text{Si} = 27.97693 \text{ amu} \times 0.9223 = 25.8031 \text{ amu}$
(retaining two additional significant figures)

Similar calculations give the portions contributed by ^{29}Si (28.976495 $\times$ 0.0467 = 1.3532 amu) and by ^{30}Si (29.973770 $\times$ 0.0310 = 0.9292 amu), and adding the three portions together (rounding to two decimal places at the end) gives the atomic mass of silicon:

$$\text{Atomic mass of Si} = 25.8031 \text{ amu} + 1.3532 \text{ amu} + 0.9292 \text{ amu}$$

$$= 28.0855 \text{ amu} = 28.09 \text{ amu}$$

The next sample problem reviews the method.

Figure 2.14 Depicting the atom.
Atoms of carbon-12, oxygen-16, and uranium-238 are shown (nuclei not drawn to scale) with their symbolic representations. The sum of the number of protons (Z) and the number of neutrons (N) equals the mass number (A). An atom is neutral, so the number of protons in the nucleus equals the number of electrons around the nucleus.

Tools of the Chemistry Laboratory

Mass Spectrometry

Mass spectrometry, the most powerful technique for measuring the mass and abundance of charged particles, is an outgrowth of electric and magnetic deflection studies on particles formed in cathode ray experiments. When a high-energy electron collides with an atom of neon-20, for example, one of the atom's electrons is knocked away and the resulting particle has one positive charge, Ne^+ (Figure 2.A). Therefore, its mass/charge ratio (m/e) equals the mass divided by 1+. These m/e values are measured to identify the masses of different isotopes of an element.

Figure 2.B depicts the core of one type of mass spectrometer and the data it provides. The sample is introduced and vaporized (if liquid or solid), then bombarded by high-energy electrons to form positively charged particles. These are attracted toward a series of negatively charged plates with slits in them, and some particles pass through into an evacuated tube exposed to a magnetic field. As the particles zoom through this region, they are deflected according to their m/e: the lightest particles are deflected most and the heaviest particles least. At the end of the magnetic region, the particles strike a detector, which records their relative position and abundance. For extremely precise work, such as determining isotopic masses and abundances, the instrument is calibrated with a substance of known amount and mass.

Figure 2.A **Formation of a positively charged neon (Ne) particle.**

Figure 2.B **The mass spectrometer and its data. A,** The instrument separates charged particles on the basis of their mass/charge ratios (m/e). Atmospheric neon is the sample. In very exact work, the spectrometer can be tuned to measure m/e values to six decimal places. **B,** Mass spectral data from the sample show the abundance of each particle present. The three peaks correspond to three neon isotopes. **C,** The data are recalculated to show the percent abundance of each particle. **D,** The mass spectrum of a protein molecule.

Figure 2.C A modern mass spectrometer.
Some modern instruments have extremely powerful magnets that allow measurement of the masses of large molecules in the 10^5 amu range to an accuracy of better than 1 amu. Even the masses of single molecules in the 10^8 amu range have been measured. The instrument shown is a Fourier Transform Ion Cyclotron Resonance Mass Spectrometer located at the NSF-sponsored National High Magnetic Field Laboratory.

Mass spectrometry is also used in structural chemistry and separations science to measure the mass of virtually any atom, molecule, or fragment of a molecule (Figure 2.C). Among its many applications, mass spectrometry is employed by bio-chemists determining protein structures, materials scientists examining catalyst surfaces, forensic chemists analyzing criminal evidence, organic chemists designing new drugs, and industrial chemists investigating petroleum components.

Sample Problem 2.3   Calculating the Atomic Mass of an Element

PROBLEM Silver (Ag; $Z = 47$) has 46 known isotopes, but only two occur naturally, ^{107}Ag and ^{109}Ag. Given the following mass spectrometric data, calculate the atomic mass of silver:

ISOTOPE	MASS (amu)	ABUNDANCE (%)
^{107}Ag	106.90509	51.84
^{109}Ag	108.90476	48.16

PLAN From the mass and abundance of the two Ag isotopes, we have to find the atomic mass of Ag (weighted average of the isotopic masses). We multiply each isotopic mass by its fractional abundance to find the portion of the atomic mass contributed by each isotope. The sum of the isotopic portions is the atomic mass.

SOLUTION Finding the portion of the atomic mass from each isotope:

Portion of atomic mass from ^{107}Ag: = isotopic mass × fractional abundance

$$= 106.90509 \text{ amu} \times 0.5184 = 55.42 \text{ amu}$$

Portion of atomic mass from ^{109}Ag: $= 108.90476 \text{ amu} \times 0.4816 = 52.45 \text{ amu}$

Finding the atomic mass of silver:

$$\text{Atomic mass of Ag} = 55.42 \text{ amu} + 52.45 \text{ amu} = \boxed{107.87 \text{ amu}}$$

CHECK The individual portions seem right: ~100 amu × 0.50 = 50 amu. The portions are almost the same because the two isotopic abundances are almost the same. We rounded each portion to four significant figures because that is the number of significant figures in the abundance values. This is the correct atomic mass (to two decimal places), as shown in the list of elements.

COMMENT Averages must be interpreted carefully. The number of children in an average American family in 1985 was 2.4. Just as you know that no family actually has 2.4 children, you should also know that no individual silver atom has a mass of 107.87 amu. But for most laboratory purposes, we consider the sample to consist of atoms with this average mass.

Follow-up Problem 2.3   Boron (B; $Z = 5$) has two naturally occurring isotopes. Calculate the percent abundances of ^{10}B and ^{11}B from the following: atomic mass of B = 10.81 amu; isotopic mass of ^{10}B = 10.0129 amu; isotopic mass of ^{11}B = 11.0093 amu. (*Hint:* The sum of the fractional abundances is 1. If x = abundance of ^{10}B, then $1 - x$ = abundance of ^{11}B.)

Mass (g) of each isotope

↓ multiply by fractional abundance of each isotope

Portion of atomic mass from each isotope

↓ add isotopic portions

Atomic mass

◆ **The Heresy of Radioactive "Transmutation"** In 1902, Rutherford performed a series of experiments with radioactive elements that shocked the scientific world. When a radioactive atom of thorium ($Z = 90$) emits an α particle ($Z = 2$), it becomes an atom of radium ($Z = 88$), which then emits another α particle and becomes an atom of radon ($Z = 86$). Rutherford proposed that when an atom emits an α particle, it turns into a different atom—one element changes into another! Many viewed this conclusion as a return to alchemy, and, as with Thomson's discovery that atoms contain smaller particles, Rutherford's findings fell on disbelieving ears.

A Modern Reassessment of the Atomic Theory

We began discussing the atomic basis of matter with Dalton's model, which proved inaccurate in several respects. What happens to a model whose postulates are found by later experiment to be incorrect? No model can predict every possible future observation, but a powerful model evolves to retain its usefulness. After all, continual testing and revising of models are the essence of science. Let's reconstruct the postulates of the atomic theory in light of what we know now:

1. *All matter is composed of atoms.* We now know that atoms *are* divisible and composed of smaller, subatomic particles (electrons, protons, and neutrons), but the atom is still the smallest body that *retains the unique identity* of an element.

2. *Atoms of one element cannot be converted into atoms of another element in a chemical reaction.* We now know that, in nuclear reactions, atoms of one element often change into atoms of another, but this *never* happens in a chemical change. ◆

3. *All atoms of an element have the same number of protons and electrons, which determines the chemical behavior of the element.* We now know that isotopes of an element differ in the number of neutrons, and thus in mass number, but a sample of the element is treated as though its atoms have an *average* mass.

4. *Compounds are formed by the chemical combination of two or more elements in specific ratios.* We now know that a few compounds can have slight variations in their atom ratios, but this postulate remains essentially unchanged.

   Even today, our picture of the atom is being revised. Although we are confident about the distribution of electrons within the atom (Chapters 7 and 8), the interactions among protons and neutrons within the nucleus are still on the frontier of discovery (Chapter 24).

Section Summary

An atom has a central nucleus, which contains positively charged protons and uncharged neutrons and is surrounded by negatively charged electrons. An atom is neutral because the number of electrons equals the number of protons. An atom is represented by the notation $^A_Z X$, in which Z is the atomic number (number of protons), A the mass number (sum of protons and neutrons), and X the atomic symbol. An element occurs naturally as a mixture of isotopes, atoms with the same number of protons but different numbers of neutrons. Each isotope has a mass relative to the ^{12}C mass standard. The atomic mass of an element is the average of its isotopic masses weighted according to their natural abundances and is determined by modern instruments, such as the mass spectrometer.

2.6 Elements: A First Look at the Periodic Table

At the end of the 18th century, Lavoisier compiled a list of the 23 elements known at that time; by 1870, 65 were known; by 1925, 88; today, there are 112 and still counting! These elements combine to form millions of compounds, so we clearly need some way to organize what we know about their behavior. By the mid-19th century, enormous amounts of information concerning reactions, properties, and atomic masses of the elements had been accumulated. Several researchers noted recurring, or *periodic*, patterns of behavior and proposed schemes to organize the elements according to some fundamental property.

   In 1871, the Russian chemist Dmitri Mendeleev (Figure 2.15) published the most successful of these organizing schemes, a table that listed the elements by increasing atomic mass, arranged so that elements with similar chemical properties fell in the same column. The modern **periodic table of the elements,** based on Mendeleev's earlier version, is one of the great classifying schemes in science and has become an indispensable tool to chemists. Throughout your study of chemistry, the periodic table will guide you through an otherwise dizzying amount of chemical and physical behavior.

A modern version of the periodic table appears in Figure 2.16 on the next page and inside the front cover of this text. The table is formatted as follows:

1. Each element has a box that contains its atomic number, atomic symbol, and atomic mass. The boxes lie in order of *increasing atomic number* as you move from left to right.
2. The boxes are arranged into a grid of **periods** (horizontal rows) and **groups** (vertical columns). Each period has a number from 1 to 7. Each group has a number from 1 to 8 *and* either the letter A or B. A new system, with group numbers from 1 to 18 but no letters, appears in parentheses under the number-letter designation. (Most chemists still use the number-letter system, so the text retains it, but shows the new numbering system in parentheses.)
3. The eight A-groups (two on the left and six on the right) contain the *maingroup,* or *representative, elements.* The ten B-groups, located between Groups 2A(2) and 3A(13), contain the *transition elements.* Two horizontal series of *inner transition elements,* the lanthanides and the actinides, fit *between* the elements in Group 3B(3) and Group 4B(4) and are usually placed below the main body of the table.

At this introductory stage, the clearest distinction among the elements is their classification as metals, nonmetals, or metalloids. The "staircase" line that runs from the top of Group 3A(13) to the bottom of Group 6A(16) is a dividing line for this classification. The **metals** (three shades of blue) appear in the large left and lower portion of the table. About three-quarters of the elements are metals, including many main-group elements and all the transition and inner transition elements. They are generally shiny solids at room temperature (mercury is the only liquid), conduct heat and electricity well, and can be tooled into sheets (malleable) and wires (ductile). The **nonmetals** (yellow) appear in the small upper right portion of the table. They are generally gases or dull, brittle solids at room temperature (bromine is the only liquid) and conduct heat and electricity poorly. Along the staircase line lie the **metalloids** (green; also called **semimetals**), elements that have properties between those of metals and nonmetals. Several metalloids play major roles in modern electronics. Figure 2.17 shows examples of these three classes of elements.

Two major branches of chemistry can almost be defined by the elements that each studies. *Organic chemistry* studies the compounds of carbon, especially those that contain hydrogen and often oxygen, nitrogen, and a few other elements as well. This branch is concerned with fuels, drugs, dyes, polymers, and the like. *Inorganic chemistry,* on the other hand, focuses mainly on the compounds of all the other elements. It is concerned with catalysts, electronic materials, metal alloys, mineral salts, and the like. With the explosive growth in biomedical and advanced materials research, the distinction between these traditional branches is fading.

It is important to learn some of the group (family) names. Group 1A(1), except for hydrogen, consists of the *alkali metals,* and Group 2A(2) consists of the *alkaline earth metals.* Both groups of metals are highly reactive elements. The *halogens,* Group 7A(17), are highly reactive nonmetals, whereas the *noble gases,* Group 8A(18), are relatively unreactive nonmetals. Other main groups [3A(13) to 6A(16)] are often named by the first element in the group; for example, Group 6A is the oxygen family.

Figure 2.15 Dmitri Ivanovich Mendeleev. Born in a small Siberian town, Mendeleev was the youngest of 17 children of the local schoolteacher. He showed early talent for mathematics and science, so his mother took him to St. Petersburg, where he remained to study and work for much of his life. Early research interests centered on the physical properties of gases and liquids, and later he was consulted frequently on the industrial processing of petroleum. In developing his periodic table, he prepared a note card of the properties of each element and arranged and rearranged them until he realized that properties repeated when the elements were placed in order of increasing atomic mass.

Figure 2.16 **The modern periodic table.** The table consists of element boxes arranged by *increasing* atomic number into groups (vertical columns) and periods (horizontal rows). Each box contains the atomic number, atomic symbol, and atomic mass. (A mass in parentheses is the mass number of the most stable isotope of that element.) The periods are numbered 1 to 7. The groups (sometimes called *families*) have a number-letter designation and a new group number in parentheses. The A groups are the main-group elements; the B groups are the transition elements. Two series of inner transition elements are placed below the main body of the table but fit between the elements indicated. The great majority of elements are metals, which lie below and to the left of the thick "staircase" line [top of 3A(13) to bottom of 6A(16)] and include main-group metals *(purple-blue),* transition elements *(blue),* and inner transition elements *(gray-blue).* Nonmetals *(yellow)* lie to the right of the line. Metalloids *(green)* lie along the line. Hydrogen is placed at the top of Group 1A(1) because it has similarities with other elements in that group, but it can also be placed at the top of Group 7A(17). New names have been proposed and, after considerable debate and compromise, finally accepted for elements 104 to 109 (see inside front cover). As of late 1998, elements 110 to 112 have not yet been named.

Metals

Metalloids

Nonmetals

Figure 2.17 Metals, metalloids, and nonmetals. Metals *(blue)*, from left to right: chromium, copper, cadmium, lead, and bismuth. Metalloids *(green)*, from left to right: boron, silicon, arsenic, antimony, and tellurium. Nonmetals *(yellow)*, from left to right: carbon (graphite), sulfur, chlorine, bromine, and iodine.

A key point that we return to many times is that *elements in a group have **similar** chemical properties and elements in a period have **different** chemical properties.* We begin applying the organizing power of the periodic table in the next section, where we discuss how elements combine to form compounds.

Section Summary

In the periodic table, the elements are arranged by atomic number into horizontal periods and vertical groups. Because of the periodic recurrence of certain key properties, elements within a group have similar behavior, whereas elements in a period have dissimilar behavior. Nonmetals appear in the upper right portion of the table, metalloids lie along a staircase line, and metals fill the rest of the table.

2.7 Compounds: Introduction to Bonding

The overwhelming majority of elements occur in chemical combination with other elements. In fact, only a few elements occur free in nature. The noble gases—helium (He), neon (Ne), argon (Ar), krypton (Kr), xenon (Xe), and radon (Rn)—occur as separate atoms. In addition to occurring in compounds, oxygen (O), nitrogen (N), and sulfur (S) also occur commonly as uncombined molecules, such as O_2, N_2, and S_8, and carbon (C) occurs in vast, nearly pure deposits of coal. Some of the metals, such as copper (Cu), silver (Ag), gold (Au), and platinum (Pt), may also occur uncombined with other elements. But these relatively few exceptions reinforce the general rule that elements occur as constituents of compounds.

The *electrons* of the atoms of interacting elements are involved in compound formation. Elements combine in two general ways:

1. *Transferring electrons* from the atoms of one element to those of another to form **ionic compounds**
2. *Sharing electrons* between atoms of different elements to form **covalent compounds**

These processes generate **chemical bonds,** the forces that hold the atoms of elements together in a compound.

The Formation of Ionic Compounds

Ionic compounds are composed of **ions,** charged particles that form when an atom (or small group of atoms) gains or loses one or more electrons. The simplest type of ionic compound is a **binary ionic compound,** one composed of just two elements. It typically forms *when a metal reacts with a nonmetal.* Each metal atom loses a certain number of its electrons and becomes a **cation,** a positively charged ion. At the same time, the nonmetal atoms gain the electrons lost by the metal atoms and become **anions,** negatively charged ions. The resulting cations and anions attract each other through electrostatic forces and form the ionic compound. A cation or anion derived from a single atom is called a **monatomic ion;** we'll discuss polyatomic ions, those derived from a small group of atoms, later.

The formation of the binary ionic compound sodium chloride, common table salt, is depicted in Figure 2.18, from the elements through the atomic-scale electron transfer to the compound. In the electron transfer, a sodium atom, which is neutral because it has the same number of protons as electrons, *loses* 1 electron and forms a sodium cation, Na^+. (The charge on the ion is written as a *right superscript.*) A chlorine atom *gains* the electron and becomes a chloride anion, Cl^-. (The name change from the nonmetal atom to the ion is discussed in the next section.) Even the tiniest visible grain of

A The elements (lab view)

Chlorine gas

Sodium metal

B The elements (atomic view)

Chloride ion (Cl^-)

$17e^-$ Gains electron

$17p^+$ $18n^0$

Chlorine atom (Cl)

e^-

$18e^-$

$17p^+$ $18n^0$

Cl^- Na^+

$11p^+$ $12n^0$

Loses electron

$11p^+$ $12n^0$

$10e^-$

Sodium ion (Na^+)

$11e^-$

Sodium atom (Na)

C Electron transfer

D The compound (atomic view): Na^+ and Cl^- in the crystal

E The compound (lab view): sodium chloride crystal

Figure 2.18 The formation of an ionic compound. A, The two elements as seen in the laboratory. **B,** The elements as they might appear on the atomic scale. **C,** The neutral sodium atom loses 1 electron to become a sodium cation (Na^+), and the chlorine atom gains 1 electron to become a chloride anion (Cl^-). (Note that when atoms lose electrons, they become smaller, and when they gain electrons, they become larger.) **D,** Na^+ and Cl^- ions attract each other and lie in a three-dimensional crystalline array. **E,** This cubic array is reflected in the structure of crystalline NaCl, which occurs naturally as the mineral halite, hence the name *halogens* for the Group 7A(17) elements.

table salt contains an *enormous* number of sodium and chloride ions. The oppositely charged ions (Na^+ and Cl^-) attract each other, and the similarly charged ions (Na^+ and Na^+, or Cl^- and Cl^-) repel each other. The resulting aggregation is a regular array of alternating Na^+ and Cl^- ions that extends in all three dimensions.

The strength of the ionic bonding depends to a great extent on the net strength of these attractions and repulsions and is described by *Coulomb's law,* which can be expressed as follows: *the energy of attraction (or repulsion) between two particles is directly proportional to the product of the charges and inversely proportional to the distance between them.*

$$\text{Energy} \propto \frac{\text{charge 1} \times \text{charge 2}}{\text{distance}}$$

In other words, ions with higher charges attract (or repel) each other more strongly than ions with lower charges. Likewise, smaller ions attract (or repel) each other more strongly than larger ions, because their charges are closer together. These effects are summarized in Figure 2.19.

Ionic compounds are neutral; that is, they possess no net charge. For this to occur, they must contain equal numbers of positive and negative *charges*. This does *not* mean, however, that they must contain equal numbers of positive and negative *ions*. Because Na^+ and Cl^- each bear a unit charge ($1+$ or $1-$), equal numbers of the ions are present in sodium chloride. However, in sodium oxide, for example, twice as many Na^+ ions balance the charge of the oxide ions, O^{2-}.

Can we predict the number of electrons a given atom will lose or gain when it forms an ion? In the formation of sodium chloride, for example, why does each sodium atom give up only 1 of its 11 electrons? Why doesn't each chlorine atom gain two electrons, instead of just one? For A-group elements, the periodic table provides some insight. In ionic compound formation, we generally find that metals lose electrons and nonmetals gain electrons to *form ions with the same number of electrons as in the nearest noble gas* [Group 8A(18)]. Noble gases have a stability (low reactivity) that is associated with their particular number (and arrangement) of electrons. A sodium atom ($11e^-$) can attain the stability of neon ($10e^-$), the nearest noble gas, by losing one electron; similarly, by gaining one electron, a chlorine atom ($17e^-$) attains the stability of argon ($18e^-$), its nearest noble gas. Thus, when an element located near a noble gas forms a monatomic ion, it gains or loses enough electrons to attain the number in that noble gas. Specifically, the elements in Group 1A(1) lose one electron, those in Group 2A(2) lose two, and aluminum in Group 3A(13) loses three; the elements in Group 7A(17) gain one electron, oxygen and sulfur in Group 6A(16) gain two, and nitrogen in Group 5A(15) gains three.

With the periodic table printed on a two-dimensional surface, as in Figure 2.16, it is easy to get the false impression that the elements in Group 7A(17) are "closer" to the noble gases than the elements in Group 1A(1). Actually, both groups are only one electron away from having the same number of electrons as the noble gases. To make this point, Figure 2.20 shows a modified periodic table that is cut and rejoined, with the noble gases in the center. Now you can see that fluorine (F; $Z=9$) has one electron less and sodium (Na; $Z=11$) has one electron more than the noble gas neon (Ne; $Z=10$); thus they form the F^- and Na^+ ions. Similarly, oxygen (O; $Z=8$) gains two electrons and magnesium (Mg; $Z=12$) loses two to form the O^{2-} and Mg^{2+} ions and attain the same number of electrons as neon.

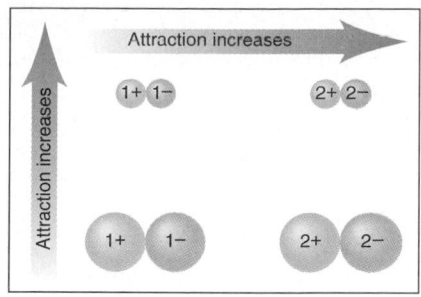

Figure 2.19 Factors that influence the strength of ionic bonding. For ions of a given size, strength of attraction *(arrows)* increases with higher ionic charge *(left to right)*. For ions of a given charge, strength of attraction increases with smaller ionic size *(bottom to top)*.

Figure 2.20 The relationship between ions formed and the nearest noble gas. This periodic table was redrawn to show (1) the positions of nonmetals *(yellow)* and metals *(blue)* relative to the noble gases and (2) the ions these elements form. The ionic charges arise from the number of electrons lost or gained to attain the same number of electrons as the nearest noble gas. Species in the same row have the same number of electrons. For example, H^-, He, and Li^+ all have two electrons. [Note that H is shown here in Group 7A(17).]

A No interaction

B Attraction begins

C Covalent bond

D Combination of forces

Figure 2.21 Formation of a covalent bond between two H atoms. A, The distance is too great for the atoms to affect each other. **B,** As the distance decreases, the nucleus of each atom begins to attract the electron of the other. **C,** The covalent bond forms when the two nuclei mutually attract the pair of electrons at some optimum distance. **D,** The H_2 molecule is more stable than the separate atoms because the attractive forces (*black arrows*) between each nucleus and the 2 electrons are greater than the repulsive forces (*red arrows*) between electrons and between nuclei.

Sample Problem 2.4   Predicting the Ion an Element Forms

PROBLEM What monatomic ions do the following elements form?
(a) Iodine ($Z = 53$)   **(b)** Calcium ($Z = 20$)   **(c)** Aluminum ($Z = 13$)
PLAN We use the given Z value to find the element in the periodic table and where it lies relative to the *nearest* noble gas. Elements that lie *after* the noble gas *lose* electrons to attain the same number as the noble gas and become positive ions; those that lie *before* the noble gas *gain* electrons and become negative ions.
SOLUTION (a) I^- Iodine [$_{53}$I; Group 7A(17)] is a nonmetal, one of the halogens, that gains 1 electron to have the same number as $_{54}$Xe.
(b) Ca^{2+} Calcium [$_{20}$Ca; Group 2A(2)] is one of the alkaline earth metals and loses 2 electrons to attain the same number as $_{18}$Ar.
(c) Al^{3+} Aluminum [$_{13}$Al; Group 3A(13)] is a metal in the boron family and loses 3 electrons to attain the same number as $_{10}$Ne.

Follow-up Problem 2.4 What monatomic ion does each of the following elements form?
(a) $_{16}$S   **(b)** $_{37}$Rb   **(c)** $_{56}$Ba

The Formation of Covalent Compounds

Covalent compounds form when elements share electrons, which usually occurs between nonmetals. Even though relatively few nonmetals exist, they interact in many combinations to form a very large number of covalent compounds.

The simplest case of electron sharing occurs not in a compound but between two hydrogen atoms (H; $Z = 1$). Imagine two separated H atoms approaching each other, as in Figure 2.21. As they get closer, the nucleus of each atom attracts the electron of the other atom more and more strongly, and the separated atoms begin to interpenetrate each other. At some optimum distance between the nuclei, the two atoms form a **covalent bond,** a pair of electrons mutually attracted by the two nuclei. The result is a hydrogen molecule, in which each electron no longer "belongs" to a particular H atom: the two electrons are *shared* by the two nuclei. Repulsions between the nuclei and between the electrons also occur, but the net attraction is greater than the net repulsion. (We discuss the properties of covalent bonds in great detail in Chapter 9.)

A sample of hydrogen gas consists of these diatomic molecules (H_2)—pairs of atoms that are chemically bound and behave as an independent unit—*not* separate H atoms. Other nonmetals that exist as diatomic molecules are nitrogen (N_2), oxygen (O_2), and the halogens [fluorine (F_2), chlorine (Cl_2), bromine (Br_2), and iodine(I_2)].

In a similar way, atoms of *different* elements share electrons to form the molecules of a covalent compound. A sample of hydrogen chloride, for example, consists of molecules in which one H atom forms a covalent bond with one Cl atom; ammonia consists of molecules in which one N atom forms covalent bonds with three H atoms. (As you'll see in Chapter 9, covalent bonding provides another way for atoms to attain the same number of electrons as the nearest noble gas.)

Distinguishing the Entities Involved in Covalent and Ionic Bonding A key distinction exists between the chemical entities in covalent and ionic substances. *Most covalent substances consist of molecules.* A cup of water, for example, contains a collection of individual water molecules, each surrounded by other water molecules. Each water molecule consists of an O atom connected by covalent bonds to two H atoms. In contrast, under ordinary conditions, *no molecules exist in a sample of an ionic compound.* A piece of sodium chloride, for example, is a continuous array of oppositely charged sodium and chloride ions, *not* a collection of individual "sodium chloride molecules."

Another key distinction exists between the entities involved in the attractions themselves. Covalent bonding is based on the mutual attraction between two (positively charged) nuclei and the two (negatively charged) electrons that reside between them. Ionic bonding is based on the mutual attraction between positive and negative ions.

Polyatomic Ions: Covalent Bonds Within Ions

Many ionic compounds contain **polyatomic ions,** which consist of two or more atoms bonded *covalently* and have a net positive or negative charge. A polyatomic ion has its own identity and stays together as a unit during interactions with other ions. For example, the ionic compound calcium carbonate is an array of polyatomic carbonate anions and monatomic calcium cations attracted to each other. The carbonate ion consists of a carbon atom covalently bonded to three oxygen atoms, and two additional electrons give the ion its 2− charge (Figure 2.22).

Section Summary

Although a few elements occur uncombined in nature, the great majority exist in compounds. Ionic compounds form when a metal *transfers electrons* to a nonmetal, and the resulting positive and negative ions attract each other to form a three-dimensional array. In many cases, metal atoms lose and nonmetal atoms gain enough electrons to attain the same number of electrons as in atoms of the nearest noble gas. Covalent compounds form when elements, usually nonmetals, *share electrons*. Each covalent bond is an electron pair mutually attracted by two atomic nuclei. Monatomic ions are derived from one atom. Polyatomic ions consist of two or more covalently bonded atoms that have a net positive or negative charge due to a deficit or excess of electrons.

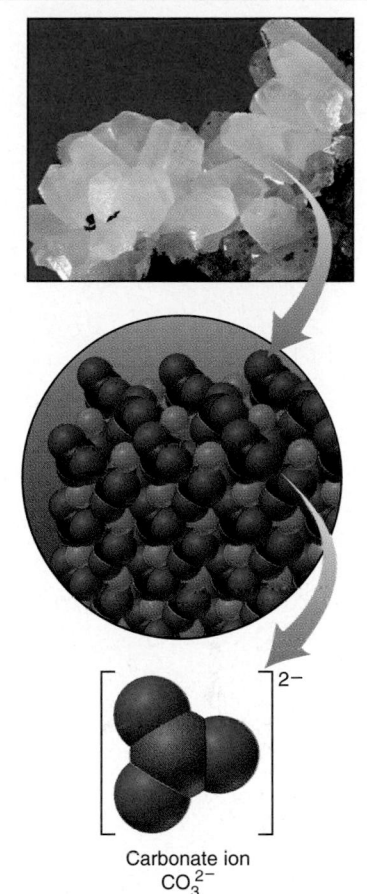

Figure 2.22 A polyatomic ion. Calcium carbonate is a three-dimensional array of monatomic calcium cations (*purple spheres*) and polyatomic carbonate anions. As the bottom structure shows, each carbonate ion consists of four covalently bonded atoms.

Carbonate ion
CO_3^{2-}

2.8 Compounds: Formulas, Names, and Masses

In a **chemical formula,** element symbols and numerical subscripts show the type and number of each atom present in a unit of the substance. There are several types of chemical formulas for a compound:

1. The **empirical formula** shows the *relative* number of atoms of each element in the compound. It is the simplest type of formula and is derived from the masses of the component elements. For example, the empirical formula of hydrogen peroxide is HO; there is one H atom for every O atom.

2. The **molecular formula** shows the *actual* number of atoms of each element in a molecule of the compound. The molecular formula of hydrogen peroxide is H_2O_2; there are *actually* two H atoms and two O atoms in each molecule.

3. A **structural formula** shows the number of atoms and *the bonds between them;* that is, the relative placement and connections of atoms in the molecule. The structural formula of hydrogen peroxide is H—O—O—H; each H is bonded to an O, and the O's are bonded to each other.

Names and formulas of compounds form the vocabulary of the chemical language; now it's time for you to begin speaking and writing this language. In this discussion, you'll learn the names and formulas of ionic and simple covalent compounds and how to calculate the mass of a unit of a compound from its formula.

Some Advice about Learning Names and Formulas

In the future, systematic naming of compounds may be applied universally. For now, however, many reference books, chemical supply catalogs, and practicing chemists still use many common (trivial) names, so you should learn them as well. Of course, the best way to learn names is to use them!

Here are some points to note about ion formulas:

- Members of a periodic table group have the same ionic charge; for example, Li, Na, and K are all in Group 1A and all have a 1+ charge.
- For A-group cations, the ion charge = group number: for example, Na^+ is in Group 1A, Ba^{2+} in Group 2A. (Exceptions in Figure 2.23 are Sn^{2+} and Pb^{2+}.)
- For anions, the ion charge = group number minus 8: for example, S is in Group 6A (6 − 8 = −2), so the ion is S^{2-}.

Here are some suggestions about how to approach the task:

1. Memorize the A-group monatomic ions of Table 2.3 (all except Ag^+, Zn^{2+}, and Cd^{2+}) according to their position in the periodic table of Figure 2.23. These ions have the same number of electrons as an atom of the nearest noble gas.
2. Consult Table 2.4 (page 69) and Figure 2.23 for some metals that form two different monatomic ions.
3. Divide the tables of names and charges into smaller batches, and learn a batch each day. Try note cards, with the name on one side and the ion formula on the other. The most common ions are shown in **boldface** in Tables 2.3, 2.4, and 2.5, so you can focus on learning them first.

Figure 2.23 Some common monatomic ions of the elements. Main-group elements usually form a single monatomic ion. Note that members of a group have ions with the same charge. [Hydrogen is shown as both the cation H^+ in Group 1A(1) and the anion H^- in Group 7A(17).] Many transition elements form two different monatomic ions. (Although Hg_2^{2+} is a diatomic ion, it is included for comparison with Hg^{2+}.)

Table 2.3 Common Monatomic Ions*

Cations			Anions		
Charge	Formula	Name	Charge	Formula	Name
1+	H^+	hydrogen	1−	H^-	hydride
	Li^+	**lithium**		F^-	**fluoride**
	Na^+	**sodium**		Cl^-	**chloride**
	K^+	**potassium**		Br^-	**bromide**
	Cs^+	cesium		I^-	**iodide**
	Ag^+	**silver**			
2+	Mg^{2+}	**magnesium**	2−	O^{2-}	**oxide**
	Ca^{2+}	**calcium**		S^{2-}	**sulfide**
	Sr^{2+}	strontium			
	Ba^{2+}	**barium**			
	Zn^{2+}	**zinc**			
	Cd^{2+}	cadmium			
3+	Al^{3+}	**aluminum**	3−	N^{3-}	nitride

*Listed by charge; those in **boldface** are most common.

Names and Formulas of Ionic Compounds

All ionic compound names give the positive ion (cation) first and the negative ion (anion) second.

Compounds Formed from Monatomic Ions Let's first consider binary ionic compounds, those composed of ions from two elements.

- *The name of the cation is the same as the name of the metal.* Many metal names end in -ium.
- *The name of the anion takes the root of the nonmetal name and adds the suffix "-ide."*

For example, the anion formed from brom*ine* is named brom*ide* (brom+ide). Therefore, the compound formed from the metal calcium and the nonmetal bromine is "calcium bromide."

Sample Problem 2.5 Naming Binary Ionic Compounds

PROBLEM Name the ionic compound formed from the following pairs of elements:
(a) Magnesium and nitrogen   **(b)** Iodine and cadmium
(c) Strontium and fluorine   **(d)** Sulfur and cesium

PLAN The key to naming a binary ionic compound is to recognize which element is the metal and which is the nonmetal. When in doubt, check the periodic table. We place the cation name first, add the suffix *-ide* to the nonmetal root, and place the anion name last.

SOLUTION **(a)** Magnesium is the metal; "nitr-" is the nonmetal root: magnesium nitride

(b) Cadmium is the metal; "iod-" is the nonmetal root: cadmium iodide

(c) Strontium is the metal; "fluor-" is the nonmetal root: strontium fluoride
(Note the spelling is fl*uo*ride, not fl*ou*ride.)

(d) Cesium is the metal; "sulf-" is the nonmetal root: cesium sulfide

Follow-up Problem 2.5 For the following ionic compounds, give the name and periodic table group number of each of the elements present: **(a)** zinc oxide; **(b)** silver bromide; **(c)** lithium chloride; **(d)** aluminum sulfide.

Since ionic compounds are arrays of oppositely charged ions rather than separate molecular units, we write a formula for the **formula unit,** the *relative* numbers of cations and anions in the compound. In other words, ionic compounds generally have only empirical formulas.* Since the compound has zero net charge, the positive charges of the cations must balance the negative charges of the anions. For example, calcium bromide is composed of Ca^{2+} ions and Br^- ions; therefore, two Br^- balance each Ca^{2+}. The formula is $CaBr_2$, not Ca_2Br. In this and all other formulas,

- The subscript refers to the element *preceding* it.
- The *subscript 1 is understood* from the presence of the element symbol alone (that is, we do not write Ca_1Br_2).
- The charge (without the sign) of one ion becomes the subscript of the other:

$$Ca^{2+} \quad Br^{1-} \qquad \text{gives} \qquad Ca_1Br_2 \quad \text{or} \quad CaBr_2$$

(Reduce the subscripts to the smallest whole numbers that retain the ratio of ions. Thus, for example, from the ions Ca^{2+} and O^{2-} we have Ca_2O_2, which we reduce to the formula CaO.)

Sample Problem 2.6   Determining the Formulas of Binary Ionic Compounds

PROBLEM Write the empirical formulas for the compounds named in Sample Problem 2.5.

PLAN We write the empirical formula by finding the smallest number of each ion that gives the neutral compound. These numbers appear as *right subscripts* to the element symbol.

SOLUTION (a) Mg^{2+} and N^{3-}; three Mg^{2+} ions (6+) balance two N^{3-} ions (6−): Mg_3N_2

(b) Cd^{2+} and I^-; one Cd^{2+} ion (2+) balances two I^- ions (2−): CdI_2

(c) Sr^{2+} and F^-; one Sr^{2+} ion (2+) balances two F^- ions (2−): SrF_2

(d) Cs^+ and S^{2-}; two Cs^+ ions (2+) balance one S^{2-} ion (2−): Cs_2S

COMMENT Note that ion charges do *not* appear in the compound formula. That is, for cadmium iodide, we do *not* write $Cd^{2+}I^-_2$.

Follow-up Problem 2.6   Write the formulas of the compounds named in Follow-up Problem 2.5.

Compounds with Metals That Can Form More Than One Ion   Many metals, particularly the transition elements (B groups), can form more than one ion, each with a particular charge. Table 2.4 shows some examples. Names of compounds containing these elements include a *Roman numeral within parentheses* immediately after the metal ion's name to indicate its ionic charge. For example, iron can form Fe^{2+} and Fe^{3+} ions. The two compounds that iron forms with chlorine are $FeCl_2$, named iron(II) chloride (spoken "iron two chloride"), and $FeCl_3$, named iron(III) chloride.

In common names, the Latin root of the metal is followed by either of two suffixes:

- The suffix *-ous* for the ion with the lower charge
- The suffix *-ic* for the ion with the higher charge

Thus, iron(II) chloride is also called fer*rous* chloride and iron(III) chloride is fer*ric* chloride. (You can easily remember this naming relationship because there is an *o* in *ous* and *lower,* and an *i* in *ic* and *higher.*)

---

*Compounds of the mercury(I) ion, such as Hg_2Cl_2, and peroxides of the alkali metals, such as Na_2O_2, are the only two common exceptions. The empirical formulas are $HgCl$ and NaO, respectively.

Table 2.4 Some Metals That Form More Than One Monatomic Ion*

Element	Ion Formula	Systematic Name	Common (Trivial) Name
Chromium	Cr^{2+}	chromium(II)	chromous
	Cr^{3+}	**chromium(III)**	chromic
Cobalt	Co^{2+}	cobalt(II)	
	Co^{3+}	cobalt(III)	
Copper	**Cu^+**	**copper(I)**	cuprous
	Cu^{2+}	**copper(II)**	cupric
Iron	**Fe^{2+}**	**iron(II)**	ferrous
	Fe^{3+}	**iron(III)**	ferric
Lead	**Pb^{2+}**	**lead(II)**	
	Pb^{4+}	lead(IV)	
Manganese	**Mn^{2+}**	**manganese(II)**	
	Mn^{3+}	manganese(III)	
Mercury	Hg_2^{2+}	mercury(I)	mercurous
	Hg^{2+}	**mercury(II)**	mercuric
Tin	**Sn^{2+}**	**tin(II)**	stannous
	Sn^{4+}	tin(IV)	stannic

*Listed alphabetically by metal name; those in **boldface** are most common.

Table 2.5 Common Polyatomic Ions*

Formula	Name
Cations	
NH_4^+	**ammonium**
H_3O^+	**hydronium**
Anions	
CH_3COO^- (or **$C_2H_3O_2^-$**)	**acetate**
CN^-	cyanide
OH^-	**hydroxide**
ClO^-	hypochlorite
ClO_2^-	chlorite
ClO_3^-	**chlorate**
ClO_4^-	**perchlorate**
NO_2^-	nitrite
NO_3^-	**nitrate**
MnO_4^-	**permanganate**
CO_3^{2-}	**carbonate**
HCO_3^-	**hydrogen carbonate** (or **bicarbonate**)
CrO_4^{2-}	chromate
$Cr_2O_7^{2-}$	**dichromate**
O_2^{2-}	peroxide
PO_4^{3-}	**phosphate**
HPO_4^{2-}	hydrogen phosphate
$H_2PO_4^-$	dihydrogen phosphate
SO_3^{2-}	sulfite
SO_4^{2-}	**sulfate**
HSO_4^-	hydrogen sulfate (or bisulfate)

*Boldface ions are most common.

Sample Problem 2.7   Determining Names and Formulas of Ionic Compounds of Elements That Form More Than One Ion

PROBLEM Give the systematic names for the formulas or the formulas for the names of the following compounds:
(a) Tin(II) fluoride   **(b)** CrI_3 **(c)** Ferric oxide   **(d)** MnS

SOLUTION (a) Tin(II) is Sn^{2+}; fluoride is F^-. Two F^- ions balance one Sn^{2+} ion: tin(II) fluoride is SnF_2. (The common name is stannous fluoride.)

(b) The anion is I^-, iodide, and the formula shows three I^-. Therefore, the cation must be Cr^{3+}, chromium(III): CrI_3 is chromium(III) iodide. (The common name is chromic iodide.)

(c) Ferric is the common name for iron(III), Fe^{3+}; oxide ion is O^{2-}. To balance the ionic charges, the formula of ferric oxide is Fe_2O_3. (The systematic name is iron(III) oxide.)

(d) The anion is sulfide, S^{2-}, which requires that the cation be Mn^{2+}. The name is manganese(II) sulfide.

Follow-up Problem 2.7   Give the systematic names for the formulas or the formulas for the names of the following compounds: **(a)** lead(IV) oxide; **(b)** Cu_2S; **(c)** $FeBr_2$; **(d)** mercuric chloride.

Compounds Formed from Polyatomic Ions Ionic compounds in which one or both of the ions are polyatomic are very common. Table 2.5 gives the formulas and the names of some common polyatomic ions. Remember that *the polyatomic ion stays together as a charged unit.* The formula for potassium nitrate is KNO_3: each K^+ balances one NO_3^-. The formula for sodium carbonate is Na_2CO_3: two Na^+ balance one CO_3^{2-}. *When two or more of the same polyatomic ion are present in the formula, that ion appears in parentheses with the subscript written outside.* For example, calcium nitrate, which contains one Ca^{2+} and two NO_3^- ions, has the formula $Ca(NO_3)_2$. Parentheses and a subscript are *not* used unless *more than one* of the polyatomic ions is present; thus, sodium nitrate is $NaNO_3$, *not* $Na(NO_3)$.

Families of Oxoanions As Table 2.5 shows, most polyatomic ions are **oxoanions,** those in which an element, usually a nonmetal, is bonded to one or more oxygen atoms. In several cases, there exist families of two or four oxoanions that differ only in the number of oxygen atoms. A simple naming convention is used with these ions.

With two oxoanions in the family:
- The ion with *more* O atoms takes the nonmetal root and the suffix *-ate*.
- The ion with *fewer* O atoms takes the nonmetal root and the suffix *-ite*.

For example, SO_4^{2-} is the sulf*ate* ion; SO_3^{2-} is the sulf*ite* ion; similarly, NO_3^- is nitr*ate*, and NO_2^- is nitr*ite*.

With four oxoanions in the family (usually a halogen bonded to O), as Figure 2.24 shows:
- The ion with *most* O atoms has the prefix *per-,* the nonmetal root, and the suffix *-ate*.
- The ion with *one fewer* O atom has just the root and the suffix *-ate*.
- The ion with *two fewer* O atoms has just the root and the suffix *-ite*.
- The ion with *least (three fewer)* O atoms has the prefix *hypo-,* the root, and the suffix *-ite*.

per	*root*	ate
	root	ate
	root	ite
hypo	*root*	ite

No. of O atoms ↑

Figure 2.24 Naming oxoanions. Prefixes and suffixes indicate the number of O atoms in the anion.

For example, for the four chlorine oxoanions,

ClO_4^- is *per*chlor*ate*, ClO_3^- is chlor*ate*, ClO_2^- is chlor*ite*, ClO^- is *hypo*chlor*ite*

Hydrated Ionic Compounds Ionic compounds called **hydrates** have a specific number of water molecules associated with each formula unit. In their formulas, this number is shown after a centered dot. It is indicated in the systematic name by a Greek numerical prefix before the word *hydrate*. Table 2.6 shows these prefixes. For example, Epsom salt has the formula $MgSO_4 \cdot 7H_2O$ and the name magnesium sulfate *hepta*hydrate. Similarly, the mineral gypsum has the formula $CaSO_4 \cdot 2H_2O$ and the name calcium sulfate *di*hydrate. These so-called "waters of hydration" are part of the hydrate's structure. Heating can remove some or all of them, leading to a different substance. For example, the photos below show blue copper(II) sulfate pentahydrate ($CuSO_4 \cdot 5H_2O$) *(left)* being converted to white copper(II) sulfate ($CuSO_4$) *(right)*.

Table 2.6 Numerical Prefixes for Hydrates and Binary Covalent Compounds

Number	Prefix
1	mono-
2	di-
3	tri-
4	tetra-
5	penta-
6	hexa-
7	hepta-
8	octa-
9	nona-
10	deca-

Sample Problem 2.8 Determining Names and Formulas of Ionic Compounds Containing Polyatomic Ions

PROBLEM Give the systematic names for the formulas or the formulas for the names of the following compounds:

(a) $Fe(ClO_3)_2$ (b) Sodium sulfite   (c) $Ba(OH)_2 \cdot 8H_2O$

SOLUTION (a) ClO_3^- is chlorate; since it has a 1− charge, the cation must be Fe^{2+}. The name is iron(II) chlorate. (The common name is ferrous chlorate.)

(b) Sodium is Na^+; sulfite is SO_3^{2-}. Therefore, two Na^+ ions balance one SO_3^{2-} ion. The formula is Na_2SO_3.

(c) Ba^{2+} is barium; OH^- is hydroxide. There are eight (octa-) water molecules in each formula unit. The name is barium hydroxide octahydrate.

Follow-up Problem 2.8 Give the systematic names for the formulas or the formulas for the names of the following compounds: **(a)** cupric sulfate pentahydrate; **(b)** zinc hydroxide; **(c)** LiCN.

Sample Problem 2.9 Recognizing Incorrect Names and Formulas of Ionic Compounds

PROBLEM Something is wrong with the second part of each statement. Provide the correct name or formula.
(a) $Ba(C_2H_3O_2)_2$ is called barium diacetate.
(b) Sodium sulfide has the formula $(Na)_2SO_3$.
(c) Iron(II) sulfate has the formula $Fe_2(SO_4)_3$.
(d) Cesium carbonate has the formula $Cs_2(CO_3)$.
SOLUTION (a) The charge of the Ba^{2+} ion *must* be balanced by *two* $C_2H_3O_2^-$ ions, so the prefix *di-* is unnecessary. For ionic compounds, we do not indicate the number of ions with numerical prefixes. The correct name is barium acetate.
(b) Two mistakes occur here. The sodium ion is monatomic, so it does *not* require parentheses. The sulfide ion is S^{2-}, *not* SO_3^{2-} (called "sulfite"). The correct formula is Na_2S.
(c) The Roman numeral refers to the charge of the ion, *not* the number of ions in the formula. Fe^{2+} is the cation, so it requires one SO_4^{2-} to balance its charge. The correct formula is $FeSO_4$.
(d) Parentheses are *not* required when only one polyatomic ion of a kind is present. The correct formula is Cs_2CO_3.

Follow-up Problem 2.9 State why the second part of each statement is incorrect, and correct it:
(a) Ammonium phosphate is $(NH_3)_4PO_4$.
(b) Aluminum hydroxide is $AlOH_3$.
(c) $Mg(HCO_3)_2$ is manganese(II) carbonate.
(d) $Cr(NO_3)_3$ is chromic(III) nitride.
(e) $Ca(NO_2)_2$ is cadmium nitrate.

Naming Acids Acids are an important group of hydrogen-containing compounds that have been used in chemical reactions since before alchemical times. In the laboratory, acids are typically used in water solution. When naming them and writing their formulas, we can consider them as anions connected to the number of hydrogen ions (H^+) needed for charge neutrality. The two common types of acids are binary acids and oxoacids:

1. *Binary acid* solutions form when certain gaseous compounds dissolve in water. For example, when gaseous hydrogen chloride (HCl) dissolves in water, it forms a solution called hydrochloric acid. The name consists of the following parts:

   Prefix *hydro-* + nonmetal *root* + suffix *-ic* + separate word *acid*

   hydro + chlor + ic + acid

   or hydrochloric acid. This naming pattern holds for many compounds in which hydrogen combines with an anion that has an *-ide* suffix.

2. *Oxoacid* names are similar to those of the oxoanions, except for two suffix changes:
   - *-ate* in the anion becomes *-ic* in the acid
   - *-ite* in the anion becomes *-ous* in the acid

   The oxoanion prefixes *hypo-* and *per-* are kept. Thus,

   BrO_4^- is *per*brom*ate*, and $HBrO_4$ is *per*brom*ic* acid

   IO_2^- is iod*ite*, and HIO_2 is iod*ous* acid

Sample Problem 2.10 Determining Names and Formulas of Anions and Acids

PROBLEM Name the following anions and give the names and formulas of the acids derived from them:
(a) Br^- **(b)** IO_3^- **(c)** CN^- **(d)** SO_4^{2-} **(e)** NO_2^-

SOLUTION (a) The anion is bromide; the acid is hydrobromic acid, HBr.

(b) The anion is iodate; the acid is iodic acid, HIO_3.

(c) The anion is cyanide; the acid is hydrocyanic acid, HCN.

(d) The anion is sulfate; the acid is sulfuric acid, H_2SO_4. (In this case, the suffix is added to the element name *sulfur*, not to the root, *sulf-*.)

(e) The anion is nitrite; the acid is nitrous acid, HNO_2.

Follow-up Problem 2.10 Write formulas for the names or names for the formulas of the following acids: **(a)** chloric acid; **(b)** HF; **(c)** acetic acid; **(d)** sulfurous acid; **(e)** HBrO.

Names and Formulas of Binary Covalent Compounds

Binary covalent compounds are formed by the combination of two elements, usually nonmetals. Several are so familiar, such as ammonia (NH_3), methane (CH_4), and water (H_2O), that we use their common names, but most are named in a systematic way:

1. The element with the lower group number in the periodic table is the first word in the name; the element with the higher group number is the second word. [*Important exception:* When the compound contains oxygen and a halogen, Group 7A(17), the halogen is named first.]
2. If both elements are in the same group, the one with the higher period number is named first.
3. The second element is named with its root and the suffix *-ide*.
4. Covalent compounds have Greek numerical prefixes (see Table 2.6) to indicate the number of atoms of each element in the compound. The first word has a prefix *only* when more than one atom of the element is present; the second word *usually* has a numerical prefix.

Sample Problem 2.11 Determining Names and Formulas of Binary Covalent Compounds

PROBLEM (a) What is the formula of carbon disulfide?
(b) What is the name of PCl_5?
(c) Give the name and formula of the compound whose molecules each consist of two N atoms and four O atoms.

SOLUTION (a) The prefix *di-* means "two." The formula is CS_2.

(b) P is the symbol for phosphorus; there are five chlorine atoms, which requires the prefix *penta-*. The name is phosphorus pentachloride.

(c) Nitrogen (N) comes first in the name (lower group number). The compound is dinitrogen tetraoxide, N_2O_4.

Follow-up Problem 2.11 Give the name or formula for **(a)** SO_3; **(b)** SiO_2; **(c)** dinitrogen monoxide; **(d)** selenium hexafluoride.

Sample Problem 2.12 Recognizing Incorrect Names and Formulas of Binary Covalent Compounds

PROBLEM Explain what is wrong with the name or formula in the second part of each statement and correct it:
(a) SF_4 is monosulfur pentafluoride.
(b) Dichlorine heptaoxide is Cl_2O_6.
(c) N_2O_3 is dinitrotrioxide.
SOLUTION **(a)** There are two mistakes. *Mono-* is not needed if there is only one atom of the first element, and the prefix for four is *tetra-*, not *penta-*. The correct name is   sulfur tetrafluoride.

(b) The prefix *hepta-* indicates seven, not six. The correct formula is Cl_2O_7.

(c) The full name of the first element is needed, and a space separates the two element names. The correct name is   dinitrogen trioxide.

Follow-up Problem 2.12 Explain what is wrong with the second part of each statement and correct it:
(a) S_2Cl_2 is disulfurous dichloride.
(b) Nitrogen monoxide is N_2O.
(c) $BrCl_3$ is trichlorine bromide.

Naming Alkanes Many organic compounds have complex structural formulas that consist of chains and/or rings of carbon atoms with branches of carbon and other atoms. Hydrocarbons, the simplest type of organic compound, contain *only* carbon and hydrogen. *Alkanes* are the simplest type of hydrocarbon, and the simplest type of alkanes are called straight-chain alkanes because they consist of chains of carbon atoms with no branches. In all alkanes, each carbon atom forms four covalent bonds. Alkanes are highly combustible and several are important fuels, such as methane, propane, butane, and the mixture of alkanes in gasoline.

Hydrocarbons are binary covalent compounds, but they are not named in the typical way. Alkanes are named with a prefix plus the suffix *-ane*. Table 2.7 gives the names and formulas of the first 10 straight-chain alkanes. Note that only the prefixes for the four smallest are new; larger alkane prefixes are the same as the Greek prefixes in Table 2.6. You'll see organic compounds throughout the book and we'll discuss the naming of more structurally complex organic compounds in Chapter 15.

Table 2.7 The First 10 Straight-Chain Alkanes

Name	Formula
Methane	CH_4
Ethane	C_2H_6
Propane	C_3H_8
Butane	C_4H_{10}
Pentane	C_5H_{12}
Hexane	C_6H_{14}
Heptane	C_7H_{16}
Octane	C_8H_{18}
Nonane	C_9H_{20}
Decane	$C_{10}H_{22}$

Molecular Masses from Chemical Formulas

In Section 2.4, we defined atomic mass as the weighted average of an element's isotopic masses in accordance with their fractional natural abundance. Using the formula of a compound and the periodic table, we calculate the **molecular mass** (also called *molecular weight*) of a formula unit of the compound as the sum of the atomic masses:

$$\text{Molecular mass} = \text{sum of atomic masses} \qquad (2.3)$$

The molecular mass of a water molecule (using atomic masses to four significant figures) is

$$\text{Molecular mass of } H_2O = (2 \times \text{atomic mass of H}) + (1 \times \text{atomic mass of O})$$
$$= (2 \times 1.008 \text{ amu}) + 16.00 \text{ amu}$$
$$= 18.02 \text{ amu}$$

Because molecules do not exist in ionic compounds, we use the term *formula mass* for the mass of a formula unit of an ionic compound. Consider barium nitrate, $Ba(NO_3)_2$. To calculate its formula mass, *the number of atoms of each element inside the parentheses is multiplied by the subscript outside the parentheses*:

Formula mass of $Ba(NO_3)_2$

     $= (1 \times \text{atomic mass of Ba}) + (2 \times \text{atomic mass of N}) + (6 \times \text{atomic mass of O})$

     $= 137.3 \text{ amu} + (2 \times 14.01 \text{ amu}) + (6 \times 16.00 \text{ amu}) = 261.3 \text{ amu}$

Note that atomic, not ionic, masses are used. Although masses of ions differ from those of their atoms by the masses of the electrons, electron loss equals electron gain in the compound, so electron mass is balanced.

Sample Problem 2.13   Calculating the Molecular Mass of a Compound

PROBLEM Using the data in the periodic table, calculate the molecular (or formula) mass of the following compounds:
(a) Tetraphosphorus trisulfide **(b)** Ammonium nitrate
PLAN We first write the formula, then multiply the number of atoms (or ions) of each element by its atomic mass, and find the sum.
SOLUTION **(a)** The formula is P_4S_3.

     Molecular mass $= (4 \times \text{atomic mass of P}) + (3 \times \text{atomic mass of S})$

                 $= (4 \times 30.97 \text{ amu}) + (3 \times 32.07 \text{ amu})$

                  $= \boxed{220.09 \text{ amu}}$

(b) The formula is NH_4NO_3. We count the total number of N atoms even though they belong to different ions:

Formula mass

     $= (2 \times \text{atomic mass of N}) + (4 \times \text{atomic mass of H}) + (3 \times \text{atomic mass of O})$

     $= (2 \times 14.01 \text{ amu}) + (4 \times 1.008 \text{ amu}) + (3 \times 16.00 \text{ amu})$

     $= \boxed{80.05 \text{ amu}}$

CHECK You can often find large errors by rounding atomic masses to the nearest 5 and adding: **(a)** $7 \times 30 = 210 \approx 220.09$. The sum has two decimal places because the atomic masses have two. **(b)** $(2 \times 15) + 5 + (3 \times 15) = 80 \approx 80.05$.

Follow-up Problem 2.13   What is the formula and molecular (or formula) mass of each of the following compounds: **(a)** hydrogen peroxide; **(b)** cesium chloride; **(c)** sulfuric acid; **(d)** potassium sulfate?

The upcoming Gallery shows some of the ways that chemists picture molecules and the enormous range of molecular size.

Section Summary

Chemical formulas describe the simplest atom ratio (empirical formula), actual atom number (molecular formula), and atom arrangement (structural formula) of one unit of a compound. An ionic compound is named with cation first and anion last. For metals that can form more than one ion, the charge is shown with a Roman numeral. Oxoanions have suffixes, and sometimes prefixes, attached to the element root name to indicate the number of oxygen atoms. Names of hydrates give the number of water molecules with numerical prefixes. Acid names are based on anion names. Names of covalent compounds have the element that is leftmost or lower down in the periodic table first, and prefixes show the number of each atom. The molecular (or formula) mass of a compound is the sum of the atomic masses in the formula. Molecules are three-dimensional objects that range in size from H_2 to biological and synthetic macromolecules.

Picturing Molecules

The most exciting thing about learning chemistry is training your mind to imagine a molecular world, one filled with tiny objects of various shapes. Molecules are depicted in a variety of useful ways, as shown below for the water molecule:

Chemical formulas show only the relative numbers of atoms.

Electron-dot and *bond-line formulas* show a bond between atoms as either a pair of dots or a line.

Ball-and-stick models show atoms as spheres and bonds as sticks, with accurate angles and relative sizes, but distances are exaggerated.

Space-filling models are accurately scaled-up versions of molecules, but they do not show bonds.

Electron-density models show the ball-and-stick model within the space-filling shape and color the regions of high (*red*) and low (*blue*) electron charge.

H_2O

$H:O:H$

$H-O-H$

Ozone (O_3, 48.00 amu) contributes to smog; natural component of stratosphere that absorbs harmful solar radiation.

Carbon monoxide (CO, 28.01 amu), toxic component of car exhaust and cigarette smoke.

$C≡O$

All molecules are minute, with their relative sizes depending on composition. A water molecule is small because it consists of only three atoms. Most air pollutants, such as ozone, carbon monoxide, sulfur dioxide, and nitrogen dioxide, also consist of small molecules.

Nitrogen dioxide (NO_2, 46.01 amu) forms from car exhaust and contributes to smog and acid rain.

Sulfur dioxide (SO_2, 64.07 amu) forms from burning coal in power plants; contributes to acid rain.

Many household items, such as butane, acetic acid, and aspirin, consist of somewhat larger molecules. The biologically essential molecule heme is larger still.

Butane (C_4H_{10}, 58.12 amu), fuel for cigarette lighters and camping stoves.

Acetic acid (CH_3COOH, 60.05 amu), component of vinegar.

Aspirin ($C_9H_8O_4$, 180.15 amu), most common pain reliever in the world.

Heme ($C_{34}H_{32}FeN_4O_4$, 616.49 amu), part of the blood protein hemoglobin, which carries oxygen through the body.

Very large molecules, called macromolecules, can be synthetic, like nylon, or natural, like DNA, and typically consist of thousands of atoms.

Nylon-66 (~15,000 amu), relatively small, synthetic macromolecule used to make textiles.

Deoxyribonucleic acid (DNA, ~10,000,000 amu), cellular macromolecule that contains genetic information.

2.9 Mixtures: Classification and Separation

Although we pay a great deal of attention to pure substances, they almost never occur around us. In the natural world, *matter usually occurs as mixtures*. A sample of clean air, for example, consists of many elements and compounds physically mixed together, including oxygen (O_2), nitrogen (N_2), carbon dioxide (CO_2), the six noble gases [Group 8A(18)], and water vapor (H_2O). The oceans are complex mixtures of dissolved ions and covalent substances, including Na^+, Mg^{2+}, Cl^-, SO_4^{2-}, O_2, CO_2, and of course H_2O. Rocks and soils are mixtures of numerous compounds—calcium carbonate ($CaCO_3$), silicon dioxide (SiO_2), aluminum oxide (Al_2O_3), iron(III) oxide (Fe_2O_3)—perhaps a few elements (gold, silver, and carbon in the form of diamond), and petroleum and coal, which are complex mixtures themselves. Living things contain thousands of substances: carbohydrates, lipids, proteins, nucleic acids, and many simpler ionic and covalent compounds.

There are two broad classes of mixtures. A **heterogeneous mixture** has one or more observable boundaries between the components. Thus, its composition is *not* uniform. Many rocks are heterogeneous, showing individual grains and flecks of different minerals. In some cases, as in milk and blood, the boundaries can be seen only with a microscope. A **homogeneous mixture** has no observable boundaries because the components are mixed as individual atoms, ions, and molecules. Thus, its composition *is* uniform. A mixture of sugar dissolved in water is homogeneous, for example, because the sugar molecules and water molecules are uniformly intermingled on the molecular level. We have no way to tell visually whether an object is a substance (element or compound) or a homogeneous mixture.

A homogeneous mixture is also called a **solution.** Although we usually think of solutions as liquid, they can exist in all three physical states. For example, air is a gaseous solution of mostly oxygen and nitrogen molecules, and wax is a solid solution of several fatty substances. Solutions in water, called **aqueous solutions,** are especially important in chemistry and comprise a major portion of the environment and of all organisms.

Recall that mixtures differ fundamentally from compounds in three ways: (1) the proportions of the components can vary; (2) the individual properties of the components are observable; and (3) the components can be separated by physical means. In some cases, if we apply enough energy to the components of the mixture, they react with each other chemically and form a compound, after which their individual properties are no longer observable. Figure 2.25 shows such a case with a mixture of iron and sulfur.

In order to investigate the properties of substances, chemists have devised many procedures for separating a mixture into its component elements and compounds. Indeed, the laws and models of chemistry could never have been formulated without this ability. In fact, many of Dalton's critics, who thought they had found compounds with varying composition, were unknowingly studying mixtures! The upcoming Tools of the Chemistry Laboratory essay describes some of the more common laboratory separation methods.

Figure 2.25 The distinction between mixtures and compounds. A, A *mixture* of iron and sulfur can be separated with a magnet. The blow-up shows the separate components. **B,** After strong heating, the *compound* iron(II) sulfide forms, which is no longer magnetic. The blow-up shows the absence of separable components.

Section Summary

Heterogeneous mixtures have visible boundaries between the components. Homogeneous mixtures have no visible boundaries because mixing occurs at the molecular level. A solution is a homogeneous mixture and can occur in any physical state. Mixtures (not compounds) can have variable proportions, can be separated physically, and retain their components' properties. Common physical separation processes include filtration, crystallization, extraction, chromatography, and distillation.

Tools of the Chemistry Laboratory

Basic Separation Techniques

Some of the most challenging and time-consuming laboratory procedures involve separating mixtures and purifying the components. Several common separation techniques are described here. Note that all these methods depend on the *physical properties* of the substances in the mixture; no chemical changes occur.

Filtration separates the components of a mixture on the basis of *differences in particle size*. It is used most often to separate a liquid (smaller particles) from a solid (larger particles). Figure 2.D shows simple filtration of a solid reaction product. In vacuum filtration, reduced pressure within the flask speeds the flow of the liquid through the filter. Filtration is a key step in the purification of the tap water you drink.

Figure 2.D Filtration.

Crystallization is based on *differences in solubility.* The *solubility* of a substance is the amount that dissolves in a fixed volume of solvent at a given temperature. The procedure shown in Figure 2.E applies the fact that many substances are more soluble in hot solvent than in cold. Purified compound is shown crystallizing out of the solution as it is cooled. Essential substances in computer chips and other modern electronic devices are purified by a type of crystallization.

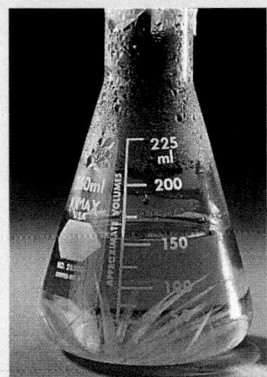

Figure 2.E
Crystallization.

Distillation separates components through *differences in volatility,* the tendency of a substance to become a gas. Ether, for example, is more volatile than water, which is much more volatile than sodium chloride. As the mixture boils, the vapor is richer in the more volatile component, which can be condensed and collected separately. The simple distillation apparatus shown in Figure 2.F is used to separate components with *large* differences in volatility, such as water from dissolved ionic compounds. Separating components with small volatility differences requires many vaporization-condensation steps (as discussed in Chapter 13).

Extraction is also based on *differences in solubility*. In a typical procedure, a natural (often plant or animal) material is ground in a blender with a solvent that extracts (dissolves) soluble compound(s) embedded in insoluble material. This extract is separated further by the addition of a second solvent

① Mixture is heated and volatile component vaporizes

Thermometer

② Vapors in contact with cool glass condense to form pure liquid distillate

Distilling flask

Water-cooled condenser

Water out to sink

Water in

③ Distillate collected in separate flask

Figure 2.F Distillation.

that does not dissolve in the first. After shaking in a separatory funnel, some components are extracted into the new solvent. Figure 2.G shows the extraction of plant pigments from water into hexane, an organic solvent.

① Hexane shakon with water solution of plant material extracts some dissolved substances.

Hexane layer

Water layer

② Upon standing, solutions separate into layers.

③ Stopcock is opened to drain bottom layer, and top layer is collected.

Figure 2.G Extraction.

Tools of the Chemistry Laboratory *(continued)*

Chromatography is a third technique based on *differences in solubility.* The mixture is dissolved in a gas or liquid called the *mobile phase,* and the components are separated as this phase moves over a solid (or viscous liquid) surface called the *stationary phase.* A component with low solubility in the stationary phase spends less time there, thus moving faster, than a component that is highly soluble in it. Figure 2.H depicts the separation of a mixture of pigments in ink. Many types of chromatography are used to separate a wide variety of substances, from simple gases to biological macromolecules. In *gas-liquid chromatography (GLC),* the mobile phase is an inert gas, such as helium, that carries the previously vaporized components into a long tube that contains the stationary phase (Figure 2.I, part A). The components emerge separately and reach a detector to create a chromatogram. A typical chromatogram has numerous peaks of specific position and height, each of which represents the amount of a given component (Figure 2.I, part B). The principle of *high-performance (high-pressure) liquid chromatography (HPLC)* is very similar, but the mixture is not vaporized, so a more diverse group of mixtures, which may include nonvolatile compounds, can be separated (Figure 2.J).

Figure 2.H **Procedure for column chromatography.**

Figure 2.I Principle of gas-liquid chromatography (GLC). A, The moblile phase *(purple arrow)* carries the sample mixture into a tube packed with the stationary phase *(gray outine on yellow spheres),* and each component dissolves in the stationary phase to a different extent. A component *(red)* that dissolves less readily than another *(blue)* emerges from the tube sooner. **B,** A typical gas-liquid chromatogram displays each component as a peak.

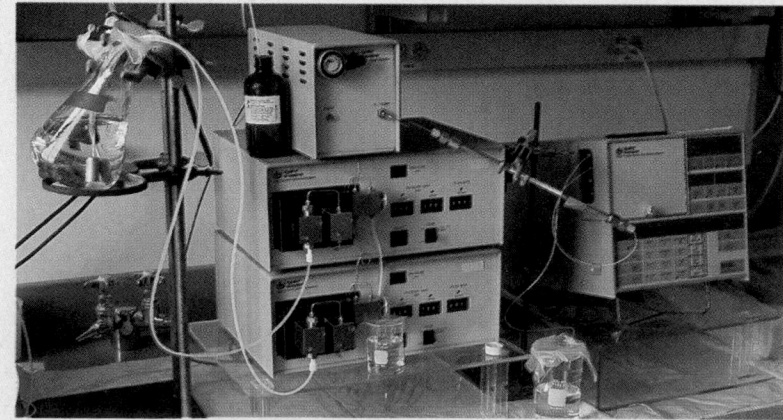

Figure 2.J **A high-performance liquid chromatograph.**

Chapter Perspective

An understanding of matter at the observable and atomic levels is the essence of chemistry. In this chapter, you have learned how matter is classified in terms of its composition and how it is named in words and formulas, which are major steps toward that understanding. Figure 2.26 provides a visual re- *view of many key terms and ideas in this chapter. In Chapter 3, we explore one of the central quantitative ideas in chemistry: how the observable amount of a substance relates to the number of atoms, molecules, or ions that make it up.*

MATTER
Anything that has mass and volume
Exists in three physical states: solid, liquid, gas

MIXTURES
Two or more elements or compounds in variable proportions
Components retain their properties

Heterogeneous Mixtures
- Visible parts
- Differing regional composition

Homogeneous Mixtures (Solutions)
- No visible parts
- Same composition throughout

PHYSICAL CHANGES
Filtration
Extraction
Distillation
Crystallization
Chromatography

PURE SUBSTANCES
Fixed composition throughout

Elements
- Composed of one type of atom
- Classified as metal, nonmetal, or metalloid
- Simplest type of matter that retains characteristic properties
- May occur as individual atoms or as molecules
- Atomic mass is average of isotopic masses weighted by abundance

Compounds
- Two or more elements combined in fixed fraction by mass
- Properties differ from those of component elements
- Molecular mass is sum of atomic masses

CHEMICAL CHANGES

Atoms
- Protons (p^+) and neutrons (n^0) in tiny, massive, positive nucleus; number of p^+ = atomic number (Z)
- Electrons (e^-) occupy surrounding volume; number of p^+ = number of e^-

Ionic Compounds
- Solids composed of cations and anions
- Ions arise through e^- transfer from metal to nonmetal

Covalent Compounds
- Often consist of separate molecules
- Atoms (usually nonmetals) bonded by shared e^- pairs

Figure 2.26 The classification of matter from a chemical point of view. Mixtures are separated by physical changes into elements and compounds. Chemical changes are required to convert elements into compounds, and vice versa.

The following learning objectives, with section and/or sample problem (SP) numbers in parentheses, can help focus your study:

Understand These Concepts

1. The defining characteristics of the three forms of matter—element, compound, and mixture—on the macroscopic and molecular levels (2.1)
2. The significance of the three mass laws—mass conservation, definite composition, and multiple proportions (2.2)
3. The postulates of Dalton's atomic theory and how it explains the mass laws (2.3)
4. The major contribution of experiments by Thomson, Millikan, and Rutherford concerning atomic structure (2.4)
5. The structure of the atom, the main features of the subatomic particles, and the importance of isotopes (2.5)
6. The format of the periodic table and general location and characteristics of metals, metalloids, and nonmetals (2.6)

7. The essential features of ionic and covalent bonding and the distinction between them (2.7)
8. The types of mixtures and their properties (2.9)

Master These Skills

1. Using the mass fraction to find the mass of an element in a compound (SP 2.1)
2. Using atomic notation to express the subatomic makeup of an isotope (SP 2.2)
3. Calculating an atomic mass from isotopic composition (SP 2.3)
4. Predicting the monatomic ion formed from a main-group element (SP 2.4)
5. Naming and writing the formula of an ionic compound formed from the ions in Tables 2.3 to 2.5 (SP 2.5 to 2.10)
6. Naming and writing the formula of an inorganic binary covalent compound (SP 2.11 and 2.12)
7. Calculating the molecular mass of a compound (SP 2.13)

For Review and Reference

Key Terms

Section 2.1
element
pure substance
molecule
compound
mixture
Section 2.2
law of mass conservation
law of definite (or constant) composition
fraction by mass (mass fraction)
percent by mass (mass percent, mass %)
law of multiple proportions
Section 2.3
atom
Section 2.4
cathode ray
nucleus

Section 2.5
proton (p^+)
neutron (n^0)
electron (e^-)
atomic number (Z)
mass number (A)
atomic symbol
isotope
atomic mass unit (amu)
dalton (D)
mass spectrometry
isotopic mass
atomic mass
Section 2.6
periodic table of the elements
period
group
metal

nonmetal
metalloid (semimetal)
Section 2.7
ionic compound
covalent compound
chemical bond
ion
binary ionic compound
cation
anion
monatomic ion
covalent bond
polyatomic ion
Section 2.8
chemical formula
empirical formula
molecular formula
structural formula

formula unit
hydrate
oxoanion
binary covalent compound
molecular mass
Section 2.9
heterogeneous mixture
homogeneous mixture
solution
aqueous solution
filtration
crystallization
distillation
volatility
extraction
chromatography

Key Equations and Relationships

2.1 Finding the mass of an element in a given mass of compound (p. 45):

Mass of element =

$$\text{mass of compound} \times \frac{\text{part by mass of element}}{\text{one part by mass of compound}}$$

2.2 Calculating the number of neutrons in an atom (p. 54):

Number of neutrons = mass number − atomic number

or $\qquad N = A - Z$

2.3 Determining the molecular mass of a formula unit of a compound (p. 73):

Molecular mass = sum of atomic masses

Highlighted Figures and Tables

These figures (F) and tables (T) provide a quick review of key ideas. Entries in **color** contain frequently used data.
F2.2 Elements, compounds, and mixtures on the atomic scale (p. 42)
F2.13 General features of the atom (p. 53)
T2.2 Properties of the subatomic particles (p. 53)
F2.16 The modern periodic table (p. 60)
F2.19 Factors that influence the strength of ionic bonding (p. 63)
F2.20 The relationship between ions formed and the nearest noble gas (p. 63)

F2.21 Formation of a covalent bond between two H atoms (p. 64)
F2.23 Some common monatomic ions of the elements (p. 66)
T2.3 **Common monatomic ions (p. 67)**
T2.4 **Metals that form more than one monatomic ion (p. 69)**
T2.5 **Common polyatomic ions (p. 69)**
T2.6 Greek numerical prefixes (p. 70)
F2.26 The classification of matter from a chemical point of view (p. 79)

Answers to Follow-up Problems

2.1 Mass (t) of pitchblende

$$= 2.3 \text{ t uranium} \times \frac{1.00 \text{ t pitchblende}}{0.848 \text{ t uranium}}$$

$$= 2.7 \text{ t pitchblende}$$

Mass (t) of oxygen

$$= 2.7 \text{ t pitchblende} \times \frac{0.152 \text{ t oxygen}}{1.00 \text{ t pitchblende}}$$

$$= 0.41 \text{ t oxygen}$$

2.2 (a) Q = B; $5p^+$, $6n^0$, $5e^-$
(b) X = Ca; $20p^+$, $21n^0$, $20e^-$
(c) Y = I; $53p^+$, $78n^0$, $53e^-$
2.3 $10.0129x + [11.0093(1 - x)] = 10.81$; $0.9964x = 0.1993$; $x = 0.2000$ and $1 - x = 0.8000$; % abundance of $^{10}B = 20.00\%$; % abundance of $^{11}B = 80.00\%$
2.4 (a) S^{2-}; (b) Rb^+; (c) Ba^{2+}
2.5 (a) Zinc [Group 2B(12)] and oxygen [Group 6A(16)]
(b) Silver [Group 1B(11)] and bromine [Group 7A(17)]
(c) Lithium [Group 1A(1)] and chlorine [Group 7A(17)]
(d) Aluminum [Group 3A(13)] and sulfur [Group 6A(16)]
2.6 (a) ZnO; (b) AgBr; (c) LiCl; (d) Al_2S_3

2.7 (a) PbO_2; (b) copper(I) sulfide (cuprous sulfide); (c) iron(II) bromide (ferrous bromide); (d) $HgCl_2$
2.8 (a) $CuSO_4 \cdot 5H_2O$; (b) $Zn(OH)_2$; (c) lithium cyanide
2.9 (a) $(NH_4)_3PO_4$; ammonium is NH_4^+ and phosphate is PO_4^{3-}.
(b) $Al(OH)_3$; parentheses are needed around the polyatomic ion OH^-.
(c) Magnesium hydrogen carbonate; Mg^{2+} is magnesium and can have only a 2+ charge, so it does not need (II); HCO_3^- is hydrogen carbonate (or bicarbonate).
(d) Chromium(III) nitrate; the *-ic* ending is not used with Roman numerals; NO_3^- is nit*rate*.
(e) Calcium nitrite; Ca^{2+} is calcium and NO_2^- is nit*rite*.
2.10 (a) $HClO_3$; (b) hydrofluoric acid; (c) CH_3COOH (or $HC_2H_3O_2$); (d) H_2SO_3; (e) hypobromous acid
2.11 (a) Sulfur trioxide; (b) silicon dioxide; (c) N_2O; (d) SeF_6
2.12 (a) Disulfur dichloride; the *-ous* suffix is not used.
(b) NO; the name indicates one nitrogen.
(c) Bromine trichloride; Br is in a higher period in Group 7A(17), so it is named first.
2.13 (a) H_2O_2, 34.02 amu; (b) CsCl, 168.4 amu; (c) H_2SO_4, 98.09 amu; (d) K_2SO_4, 174.27 amu

Problems

Problems with a **colored** number are answered at the back of the text. Problem sections match the text and provide the number(s) of relevant sample problems. Most offer concept review questions, skill-building exercises (written in similar pairs), and problems in a relevant context. Following these are comprehensive problems based on material from any section and/or previous chapter.

Elements, Compounds, and Mixtures: An Atomic Overview

■ Concept Review Questions

2.1 What is the key difference between an element and a compound?
2.2 What are two differences between a compound and a mixture?
2.3 Which of the following are pure substances? Explain your choices.

(a) Calcium chloride, used to melt ice on roads, consists of two elements, calcium and chlorine, in fixed mass ratios.
(b) Sulfur, which was known to the ancients, consists entirely of sulfur atoms chemically combined into molecules.
(c) Baking powder, a leavening agent, contains 26% to 30% sodium hydrogen carbonate and 30% to 35% calcium dihydrogen phosphate by mass.
(d) Sand.
2.4 Classify each substance in Problem 2.3 as an element, compound, or mixture, and explain your answers.
2.5 Explain the following statement: The smallest particles unique to an element may be atoms or molecules.
2.6 Explain the following statement: The smallest particles unique to a compound cannot be atoms.
2.7 Can the relative amounts of the components of a mixture vary? Can the relative amounts of the components of a compound vary? Explain.

■ **Problems in Context**

2.8 The tap water found in many areas of the United States leaves white deposits when it evaporates. Is this tap water a mixture or a compound? Explain.

2.9 To determine whether a mineral sample is a substance or a mixture, a student grinds a portion of it to a powder, adds 150 mL of pure water, and finds that much of the powder does not dissolve. She carefully removes some of the liquid, allows the water in it to evaporate, and a white, powdery deposit remains. She weighs the deposit and dissolves it completely in a small volume of water. An identical mass of the original, powdered mineral sample does not dissolve in the same volume of water. Was the original sample a substance or a mixture? Explain.

The Observations That Led to an Atomic View of Matter
(Sample Problem 2.1)

■ **Concept Review Questions**

2.10 Why was it necessary for separation techniques and methods of chemical analysis to be developed before the laws of definite composition or multiple proportions could be formulated?

2.11 To what classes of matter—element, compound, and/or mixture—do the following laws apply: (a) law of mass conservation; (b) law of definite composition; (c) law of multiple proportions?

2.12 In view of our modern understanding of matter and energy, is the law of mass conservation still relevant to chemical reactions? Explain.

2.13 Identify the mass law that each of the following observations demonstrates, and explain your reasoning:
(a) A sample of potassium chloride from Chile contains the same percent by mass of potassium as one from Poland.
(b) A flashbulb contains magnesium and oxygen before being used and magnesium oxide afterward, but its mass does not change.
(c) Arsenic and oxygen form one compound that is 65.2 mass % arsenic and another that is 75.8 mass % arsenic.

2.14 (a) Does the percent by mass of each element in a compound depend on the amount of compound? Explain.
(b) Does the mass of each element in a compound depend on the amount of compound? Explain.

2.15 Does the percent by mass of the elements in a compound depend on the amounts of the elements used to make the compound? Explain.

■ **Skill-Building Exercises** *(paired)*

2.16 State the mass law(s) demonstrated by the following experimental results, and explain your reasoning:
Experiment 1:   A student heats 1.00 g of a blue compound and obtains 0.64 g of a white compound and 0.36 g of a colorless gas.
Experiment 2:   A second student heats 2.50 g of the same blue compound and obtains 1.60 g of a white compound and 0.90 g of a colorless gas.

2.17 State the mass law(s) demonstrated by the following experimental results, and explain your reasoning:
Experiment 1:   A student heats 1.27 g copper in 3.50 g iodine to produce 3.81 g of a white compound, and 0.96 g iodine remains.

Experiment 2:   A second student heats 2.55 g copper in 3.50 g iodine to form 5.25 g of a white compound, and 0.80 g copper remains.

2.18 Fluorite, a mineral of calcium, is a compound of the metal with fluorine. Analysis shows that a 2.76-g sample of fluorite contains 1.42 g calcium. Calculate the (a) Mass of fluorine in the sample; (b) mass fraction of calcium and fluorine in fluorite; (c) mass percent of calcium and fluorine in fluorite.

2.19 Galena, a mineral of lead, is a compound of the metal with sulfur. Analysis shows that a 1.27-g sample of galena contains 1.10 g lead. Calculate the (a) mass of sulfur in the sample; (b) mass fraction of lead and sulfur in galena; (c) mass percent of lead and sulfur in galena.

2.20 Magnesium oxide is 60.3% magnesium by mass.
(a) What is the mass fraction of magnesium in magnesium oxide? (b) How many grams of magnesium can be obtained from 332 g magnesium oxide?

2.21 Zinc sulfide is 67.1% zinc by mass. (a) What is the mass fraction of zinc in zinc sulfide? (b) How many grams of zinc can be obtained from 1.18 kg zinc sulfide?

2.22 A compound of copper and sulfur is 65.43% copper by mass. How many grams of copper can be obtained from 631 g of this compound? How many grams of sulfur remain?

2.23 A compound of cesium and iodine is 51.16% cesium by mass. How many grams of cesium can be obtained from 85.5 g of this compound? How many grams of iodine remain?

2.24 Show, with calculations, how the following data illustrate the law of multiple proportions:
    Compound 1:   47.5 mass % sulfur and 52.5 mass % chlorine
    Compound 2:   31.1 mass % sulfur and 68.9 mass % chlorine

2.25 Show, with calculations, how the following data illustrate the law of multiple proportions:
    Compound 1:   77.6 mass % xenon and 22.4 mass % fluorine
    Compound 2:   63.3 mass % xenon and 36.7 mass % fluorine

■ **Problems in Context**

2.26 Dolomite is a carbonate of magnesium and calcium. Analysis shows that 5.42 g dolomite contains 1.18 g calcium. Calculate the mass percent of calcium in dolomite. On the basis of the mass percent of calcium, and neglecting all other factors, which is the richer source of calcium, dolomite or fluorite (see Problem 2.18)?

2.27 The mass percent of sulfur in a sample of coal is a key factor in the environmental impact of the coal because the sulfur combines with oxygen when the coal is burned and the oxide can then be incorporated into acid rain. Which of the following coals would have the smallest environmental impact?

	MASS (g) OF SAMPLE	MASS (g) OF SULFUR IN SAMPLE
Coal A	378	11.3
Coal B	286	11.0
Coal C	675	20.6

Dalton's Atomic Theory

■ Concept Review Questions

2.28 Which of Dalton's postulates about atoms are inconsistent with later observations? Do these inconsistencies mean that Dalton was wrong? Is Dalton's model still useful? Explain.

2.29 At a given set of conditions, 1 L hydrogen gas combines with 1 L chlorine gas to form 2 L hydrogen chloride gas.
(a) Does chlorine gas exist as single atoms or as diatomic molecules? Explain.
(b) How many chlorine atoms are present for every hydrogen atom in a hydrogen chloride molecule?
(c) Mass analysis of hydrogen chloride shows 0.0284 g hydrogen for every gram of chlorine. Suggest a relative atomic mass for chlorine.

The Observations That Led to the Nuclear Atom Model

■ Concept Review Questions

2.30 Thomson was able to determine the mass/charge ratio of the electron but not its mass. How did Millikan's experiment allow determination of the electron's mass?

2.31 The following charges on individual oil droplets were obtained during an experiment similar to Millikan's. Determine a charge for the electron (in C, coulomb), and explain your answer: -3.204×10^{-19} C; -4.806×10^{-19} C; -8.010×10^{-19} C; -1.442×10^{-18} C.

2.32 Describe Thomson's model of the atom. How might it account for the production of cathode rays?

2.33 When Rutherford's co-workers bombarded gold foil with α particles, they obtained results that overturned the existing (Thomson) model of the atom. Explain.

The Atomic Theory Today

(Sample Problems 2.2 and 2.3)

■ Concept Review Questions

2.34 Define atomic number and mass number. Which can vary without changing the identity of the element?

2.35 Choose the correct answer. The difference between the mass number of an isotope and its atomic number is (a) directly related to the identity of the element; (b) the number of electrons; (c) the number of neutrons; (d) the number of isotopes.

2.36 Even though several elements have only one naturally occurring isotope and all atomic nuclei have whole numbers of protons and neutrons, no atomic mass is a whole number. Use the data from Table 2.2 to explain this fact.

■ Skill-Building Exercises (paired)

2.37 Argon has three naturally occurring isotopes, ^{36}Ar, ^{38}Ar, and ^{40}Ar. What is the mass number of each? How many protons, neutrons, and electrons are present in each?

2.38 Chlorine has two naturally occurring isotopes, ^{35}Cl and ^{37}Cl. What is the mass number of each isotope? How many protons, neutrons, and electrons are present in each?

2.39 Do both members of the following pairs have the same number of protons? Neutrons? Electrons?
(a) $^{16}_{8}$O and $^{17}_{8}$O (b) $^{40}_{18}$Ar and $^{41}_{19}$K (c) $^{60}_{27}$Co and $^{60}_{28}$Ni
Which pair(s) consist(s) of atoms with the same Z value? N value? A value?

2.40 Do both members of the following pairs have the same number of protons? Neutrons? Electrons?
(a) $^{3}_{1}$H and $^{3}_{2}$He (b) $^{14}_{6}$C and $^{15}_{7}$N (c) $^{19}_{9}$F and $^{18}_{9}$F
Which pair(s) consist(s) of atoms with the same Z value? N value? A value?

2.41 Draw atomic depictions similar to those in Figure 2.14 for (a) $^{48}_{22}$Ti; (b) $^{79}_{34}$Se; (c) $^{11}_{5}$B.

2.42 Draw atomic depictions similar to those in Figure 2.14 for (a) $^{207}_{82}$Pb; (b) $^{9}_{4}$Be; (c) $^{75}_{33}$As.

2.43 Write the $^{A}_{Z}$X notation for each atomic depiction:

2.44 Write the $^{A}_{Z}$X notation for each atomic depiction:

2.45 Gallium has two naturally occurring isotopes, ^{69}Ga (isotopic mass 68.9256 amu, abundance 60.11%) and ^{71}Ga (isotopic mass 70.9247 amu, abundance 39.89%). Calculate the atomic mass of gallium.

2.46 Magnesium has three naturally occurring isotopes, ^{24}Mg (isotopic mass 23.9850 amu, abundance 78.99%), ^{25}Mg (isotopic mass 24.9858 amu, abundance 10.00%), and ^{26}Mg (isotopic mass 25.9826 amu, abundance 11.01%). Calculate the atomic mass of magnesium.

2.47 Chlorine has two naturally occurring isotopes, ^{35}Cl (isotopic mass 34.9689 amu) and ^{37}Cl (isotopic mass 36.9659 amu). If chlorine has an atomic mass of 35.4527 amu, what is the percent abundance of each isotope?

2.48 Copper has two naturally occurring isotopes, ^{63}Cu (isotopic mass 62.9396 amu) and ^{65}Cu (isotopic mass 64.9278 amu). If copper has an atomic mass of 63.546 amu, what is the percent abundance of each copper isotope?

Elements: A First Look at the Periodic Table

■ Concept Review Questions

2.49 Why is it useful to organize the elements in the form of the periodic table?

2.50 Correct each of the following statements:
(a) In the modern periodic table, the elements are arranged in order of increasing atomic mass.
(b) Elements in a period have similar chemical properties.
(c) Elements can be classified as either metalloids or nonmetals.

2.51 What class of elements lies along the "staircase" line in the periodic table? How do their properties compare with those of metals and nonmetals?

2.52 What are some characteristic properties of elements to the left of the elements along the "staircase"? To the right?

2.53 The elements in Groups 1A(1) and 7A(17) are all quite reactive. What is a major difference between them?

■ **Skill-Building Exercises (paired)**

2.54 Give the name, atomic symbol, and group number of the element with the following Z value, and classify it as a metal, metalloid, or nonmetal: (a) $Z = 32$; (b) $Z = 16$; (c) $Z = 2$; (d) $Z = 3$; (e) $Z = 42$.

2.55 Give the name, atomic symbol, and group number of the element with the following Z value, and classify it as a metal, metalloid, or nonmetal: (a) $Z = 33$; (b) $Z = 20$; (c) $Z = 35$; (d) $Z = 19$; (e) $Z = 12$.

2.56 Fill in the blanks:
(a) The symbol and atomic number of the heaviest alkaline earth metal are _____ and _____.
(b) The symbol and atomic number of the lightest metalloid in Group 5A(15) are _____ and _____.
(c) Group 1B(11) consists of the *coinage metals*. The symbol and atomic mass of the coinage metal whose atoms have the fewest electrons are _____ and _____.
(d) The symbol and atomic mass of the halogen in Period 4 are _____ and _____.

2.57 Fill in the blanks:
(a) The symbol and atomic number of the heaviest noble gas are _____ and _____.
(b) The symbol and group number of the Period 5 transition element whose atoms have the fewest protons are _____ and _____.
(c) The elements in Group 6A(16) are sometimes called the *chalcogens*. The symbol and atomic number of the only metallic chalcogen are _____ and _____.
(d) The symbol and number of protons of the Period 4 alkali metal atom are _____ and _____.

Compounds: Introduction to Bonding
(Sample Problem 2.4)

■ **Concept Review Questions**

2.58 Describe the type and nature of the bonding that occurs between active metals and nonmetals.

2.59 Describe the type and nature of the bonding that often occurs between two nonmetals.

2.60 How can ionic compounds be neutral if they consist of positive and negative ions?

2.61 Given that the ions in LiF or MgO are of similar size, which compound has stronger ionic bonding? Use Coulomb's law in your explanation.

2.62 Are molecules present in a sample of potassium bromide (KBr)? Explain.

2.63 Are ions present in a sample of ammonia (NH_3)? Explain.

2.64 The monatomic ions of Group 1A(1) and Group 7A(17) atoms are all singly charged. In what major way do they differ? Why?

2.65 Describe the formation of solid magnesium chloride ($MgCl_2$) from large numbers of magnesium and chlorine atoms.

2.66 Describe the formation of solid potassium sulfide (K_2S) from large numbers of potassium and sulfur atoms.

2.67 Does magnesium carbonate ($MgCO_3$) incorporate ionic bonding, covalent bonding, or both? Explain.

■ **Skill-Building Exercises (paired)**

2.68 What monatomic ions do cesium ($Z = 55$) and bromine ($Z = 35$) form?

2.69 What monatomic ions do strontium ($Z = 38$) and selenium ($Z = 34$) form?

2.70 For each ionic depiction, give the name of the parent atom, its mass number, and its group and period numbers:

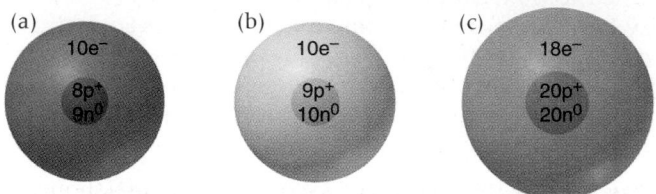

2.71 For each ionic depiction, give the name of the parent atom, its mass number, and its group and period numbers:

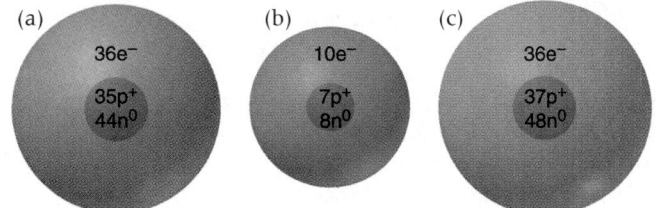

2.72 An ionic compound forms when lithium ($Z = 3$) reacts with oxygen ($Z = 8$). If a sample of the compound contains 2.8×10^{20} lithium ions, how many oxide ions does it contain?

2.73 An ionic compound forms when calcium ($Z = 20$) reacts with iodine ($Z = 53$). If a sample of the compound contains 1.2×10^{19} calcium ions, how many iodide ions does it contain?

2.74 The radii of the sodium and potassium ions are 102 pm and 138 pm, respectively. Which compound has stronger ionic attractions, sodium chloride or potassium chloride?

2.75 The radii of the lithium and magnesium ions are 76 pm and 72 pm, respectively. Which compound has stronger ionic attractions, lithium oxide or magnesium oxide?

Compounds: Formulas, Names, and Masses
(Sample Problems 2.5 to 2.13)

■ **Concept Review Questions**

2.76 What is the difference between an empirical formula and a molecular formula? Can they ever be the same?

2.77 How is a structural formula similar to a molecular formula? How is it different?

2.78 Consider a mixture of 10 billion O_2 molecules and 10 billion H_2 molecules. In what way is this mixture similar to a sample containing 10 billion hydrogen peroxide (H_2O_2) molecules? In what way is it different?

2.79 For what type(s) of compound do we use Roman numerals in the name?

2.80 For what type(s) of compound do we use Greek numerical prefixes in the name?

2.81 For what type of compound are we unable to write a molecular formula?

■ **Skill-Building Exercises** *(paired)*

2.82 Write an empirical formula for each of the following:
(a) Hydrazine, a rocket fuel, molecular formula N_2H_4
(b) Glucose, a sugar, molecular formula $C_6H_{12}O_6$
2.83 Write an empirical formula for each of the following:
(a) Ethylene glycol, a radiator antifreeze, molecular formula $C_2H_6O_2$
(b) Peroxodisulfuric acid, a compound used to make bleaching agents, molecular formula $H_2S_2O_8$

2.84 Give the name and formula of the compound formed from the following elements: (a) lithium and nitrogen; (b) oxygen and strontium; (c) aluminum and chlorine.
2.85 Give the name and formula of the compound formed from the following elements: (a) rubidium and bromine; (b) sulfur and barium; (c) calcium and fluorine.

2.86 Give the name and formula of the compound formed from the following elements: (a) $_{12}L$ and $_9M$; (b) $_{11}L$ and $_{16}M$; (c) $_{17}L$ and $_{38}M$.
2.87 Give the name and formula of the compound formed from the following elements: (a) $_3Q$ and $_{35}R$; (b) $_8Q$ and $_{13}R$; (c) $_{19}Q$ and $_{53}R$.

2.88 Give the systematic names for the formulas, or the formulas for the names: (a) tin(IV) chloride; (b) $FeBr_3$; (c) cuprous bromide; (d) Mn_2O_3.
2.89 Give the systematic names for the formulas, or the formulas for the names: (a) Na_2HPO_4; (b) potassium carbonate dihydrate; (c) $NaNO_2$; (d) ammonium perchlorate.

2.90 Give the systematic names for the formulas, or the formulas for the names: (a) CoO; (b) mercury(I) chloride; (c) $Pb(C_2H_3O_2)_2 \cdot 3H_2O$; (d) chromic oxide.
2.91 Give the systematic names for the formulas, or the formulas for the names: (a) $Sn(SO_3)_2$; (b) potassium dichromate; (c) $FeCO_3$; (d) copper(II) nitrate.

2.92 Correct each of the following formulas:
(a) Barium oxide is BaO_2.
(b) Iron(II) nitrate is $Fe(NO_3)_3$.
(c) Magnesium sulfide is $MnSO_3$.
2.93 Correct each of the following names:
(a) CuI is cobalt(II) iodide.
(b) $Fe(HSO_4)_3$ is iron(II) sulfate.
(c) $MgCr_2O_7$ is magnesium dichromium heptaoxide.

2.94 Give the name and formula for the acid derived from each of the following anions: (a) hydrogen sulfate; (b) IO_3^-; (c) cyanide; (d) HS^-.
2.95 Give the name and formula for the acid derived from each of the following anions: (a) perchlorate; (b) NO_3^-; (c) bromite; (d) F^-.

2.96 Write names for the formulas, or formulas for the names, of the following compounds: (a) N_2O_5; (b) chlorine trifluoride; (c) SiS_2.
2.97 Write names for the formulas, or formulas for the names, of the following compounds: (a) N_2O_3; (b) sulfur hexafluoride; (c) ICl_3.
2.98 Give the name and formula of the compound whose molecules consist of two sulfur atoms and four fluorine atoms.

2.99 Give the name and formula of the compound whose molecules consist of two iodine atoms and seven oxygen atoms.

2.100 Correct the names of the following compounds:
(a) CO is carbon oxide.
(b) SO_2 is sodium dioxide.
(c) Cl_2O is chlorine dioxide.
2.101 Correct the formulas of the following compounds:
(a) Chlorine monoxide is ClO_1.
(b) Disulfur decafluoride is SF_{10}.
(c) Phosphorus pentafluoride is KF_5.

2.102 Give the number of atoms of the specified element in a formula unit of each of the following compounds, and calculate the molecular (formula) mass:
(a) Oxygen in aluminum sulfate, $Al_2(SO_4)_3$
(b) Hydrogen in ammonium hydrogen phosphate, $(NH_4)_2HPO_4$
(c) Oxygen in the mineral azurite, $Cu_3(OH)_2(CO_3)_2$
2.103 Give the number of atoms of the specified element in a formula unit of each of the following compounds, and calculate the molecular (formula) mass:
(a) Hydrogen in ammonium benzoate, $C_6H_5COONH_4$
(b) Nitrogen in hydrazinium sulfate, $N_2H_6SO_4$
(c) Oxygen atoms in the mineral leadhillite, $Pb_4SO_4(CO_3)_2(OH)_2$

2.104 Write the formula of each compound, and determine its molecular (formula) mass:
(a) ammonium sulfate; (b) sodium dihydrogen phosphate; (c) potassium bicarbonate.
2.105 Write the formula of each compound, and determine its molecular (formula) mass: (a) sodium dichromate; (b) ammonium perchlorate; (c) magnesium nitrite trihydrate.

2.106 Calculate the molecular (formula) mass of each compound: (a) dinitrogen pentaoxide; (b) lead(II) nitrate; (c) calcium peroxide.
2.107 Calculate the molecular (formula) mass of each compound: (a) iron(II) acetate tetrahydrate; (b) sulfur tetrachloride; (c) potassium permanganate.

2.108 Give the formula, name, and molecular mass of the following molecules:

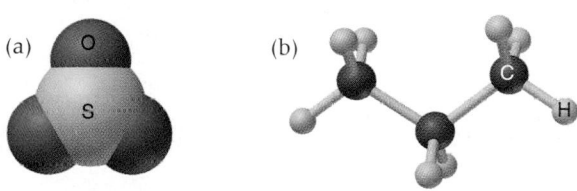

(a)   (b)

2.109 Give the formula, name, and molecular mass of the following molecules:

(a)   (b)

2.110 Give the name, empirical formula, and molecular mass of the molecule depicted in Figure P2.110.

2.111 Give the name, empirical formula, and molecular mass of the molecule depicted in Figure P2.111

Figure P2.110　　　　　Figure P2.111

Mixtures: Classification and Separation

■ Concept Review Questions

2.112 In what main way is separating the components of a mixture different from separating the components of a compound?

2.113 What is the difference between a homogeneous and a heterogeneous mixture?

2.114 Is a solution a homogeneous or a heterogeneous mixture? Give an example of an aqueous solution.

■ Skill-Building Exercises (paired)

2.115 Classify each of the following as a compound, a homogeneous mixture, or a heterogeneous mixture: (a) distilled water; (b) gasoline; (c) beach sand; (d) wine; (e) air.

2.116 Classify each of the following as a compound, a homogeneous mixture, or a heterogeneous mixture: (a) orange juice; (b) vegetable soup; (c) cement; (d) calcium sulfate; (e) tea.

2.117 Name the technique(s) and briefly describe the procedure you would use to separate each of the following mixtures into two components: (a) table salt and pepper; (b) table sugar and sand; (c) drinking water contaminated with fuel oil; (d) vegetable oil and vinegar.

2.118 Name the technique(s) and briefly describe the procedure you would use to separate each of the following mixtures into two components: (a) crushed ice and crushed glass; (b) table sugar dissolved in ethanol; (c) iron and sulfur; (d) two pigments (chlorophyll *a* and chlorophyll *b*) from spinach leaves.

■ Problems in Context

2.119 Which separation method is operating in each of the following procedures?
(a) Pouring a mixture of cooked pasta and boiling water into a colander
(b) Removing colored impurities from raw sugar to make refined sugar
(c) Preparing coffee by pouring hot water through ground coffee beans

2.120 Illicit "street" drugs are often mixed with an inactive substance, such as ascorbic acid (vitamin C). After obtaining a sample of cocaine, government chemists separate the mixture into its component substances. By calculating the mass of vitamin C per gram of drug sample, they can track the drug's distribution. For example, if different samples of cocaine obtained on the streets of New York, Los Angeles, and Paris all contain 0.6384 g vitamin C per gram of sample, they very likely come from a common source. Is this street sam-

ple a compound, element, or mixture? In this case, does the constant mass ratio of the components exemplify the law of definite composition? Explain.

Comprehensive Problems

Problems with an asterisk (*) are more challenging.

2.121 Helium is the lightest noble gas and the second most abundant element (after hydrogen) in the universe.
(a) The radius of a helium atom is 3.1×10^{-11} m, and the radius of its nucleus is 2.5×10^{-15} m. What fraction of the spherical atomic volume is occupied by the nucleus (V of a sphere $= \frac{4}{3}\pi r^3$)?
(b) The mass of a helium-4 atom is 6.64648×10^{-24} g, and each of its two electrons has a mass of 9.10939×10^{-28} g. What fraction of this atom's mass is contributed by its nucleus?

2.122 Before neutrons were discovered, Rutherford suggested that electrons resided both within the nucleus *and* around it. How could such a model give an atom with mass and charge similar to that of our current model?

2.123 Why is the atomic mass unit very close to the mass of a proton or of a neutron?

2.124 Hematite and magnetite are two minerals of iron from which the metal can be extracted profitably for use in making steel. If 1.64 g hematite yields 1.15 g iron, and 2.25 g magnetite yields 1.63 g iron, which mineral is a richer source of iron?

2.125 Use the results of Lavoisier's experiment on the combustion of mercury (see Section 1.2) to decide whether air is an element, compound, or mixture.

2.126 Many 19th-century chemists applied Dalton's atomic theory in calculating the results of experiments, even though they did not believe that atoms existed. How does this behavior fit with the "scientific method"?

2.127 How can iodine ($Z = 53$) have a higher atomic number yet lower atomic mass than tellurium ($Z = 52$)?

2.128 The number of atoms in 1 dm^3 of aluminum is nearly the same as the number of atoms in 1 dm^3 of lead, but the densities of these metals are very different (see Table 1.5). Explain.

2.129 You are working in the laboratory preparing sodium chloride. Consider the following results for three preparations of the compound:

Case 1:　39.34 g Na + 60.66 g Cl_2 ⟶ 100.00 g NaCl
Case 2:　39.34 g Na + 70.00 g Cl_2 ⟶
　　　　　　　　　　　　　　　　100.00 g NaCl + 9.34 g Cl_2
Case 3:　50.00 g Na + 50.00 g Cl_2 ⟶
　　　　　　　　　　　　　　　　82.43 g NaCl + 17.57 g Na

Explain these results in terms of the laws of conservation of mass and definite composition.

2.130 Cotunnite is a mineral form of lead chloride. Analysis shows that 2.00 g cotunnite contains 1.49 g lead. On the basis of the mass percent of lead, and neglecting all other factors, which is the better source of lead, cotunnite or galena (see Problem 2.19)?

2.131 The seven most abundant ions in sea water make up more than 99% by mass of the dissolved compounds. They are listed below in units of mg ion/kg sea water: chloride 18,980; sodium 10,560; sulfate 2,650; magnesium 1,270; calcium 400; potassium 380; hydrogen carbonate 140.

(a) What is the mass % of each ion in sea water?

(b) What percent of the total mass of ions does sodium ion represent?

(c) How does the total mass % of alkaline earth metal ions compare with the total mass % of alkali metal ions?

(d) Which makes up the larger mass fraction of dissolved components, anions or cations?

2.132 Succinic acid *(right)* is an important metabolite in biological energy production. Give the molecular formula, empirical formula, and molecular mass of succinic acid.

2.133 Fluoride ion is poisonous in relatively low amounts: 0.2 g F^- per 70 kg body weight can cause death. Nevertheless, in order to prevent tooth decay, F^- ions are added to drinking water at a concentration of 1 mg F^- ion per L water. How many liters of fluoridated drinking water would a 70-kg person have to consume in one day to reach this toxic level? How many kilograms of sodium fluoride would be needed to treat a 7.00×10^7 gal reservoir?

2.134 Chromium is a component of many useful alloys, including stainless steel used in knives and kitchenware. Given the following data, calculate chromium's atomic mass to the appropriate number of significant figures:

ISOTOPE	NATURAL ABUNDANCE (%)	ISOTOPIC MASS (amu)
^{50}Cr	4.35	49.946046
^{52}Cr	83.79	51.940509
^{53}Cr	9.50	52.940651
^{54}Cr	2.36	53.938882

2.135 Antimony (Latin *stibium*) was one of the elements known to the alchemists. Two antimony isotopes occur naturally: ^{121}Sb (isotopic mass 120.904 amu) and ^{123}Sb (isotopic mass 122.904 amu). If the atomic mass of antimony is 121.76 amu, what is the natural abundance of each isotope?

2.136 The two isotopes of potassium with significant abundance in nature are ^{39}K (isotopic mass 38.9637 amu, 93.258%) and ^{41}K (isotopic mass 40.9618 amu, 6.730%). Fluorine has only one naturally occurring isotope, ^{19}F (isotopic mass 18.9984 amu). Use this information to calculate the formula mass of potassium fluoride.

2.137 What is the empirical formula of each of the following compounds: (a) $C_6H_{12}O_6$; (b) CH_2O; (c) $C_2H_4O_2$; (d) $C_4H_8O_4$? Explain how different compounds can have the same empirical formula.

2.138 Give an example of the following:

(a) An element undergoing a physical change

(b) A compound undergoing a chemical change

(c) A solution that is hard and shiny

(d) A homogeneous mixture of elements that completely fills its container

(e) An element found both free and combined in nature

2.139 The scenes lettered A-I depict various types of matter on the atomic scale. Choose the correct scene(s) for each of the following:

(a) A mixture that fills its container

(b) A substance that cannot be broken down into any simpler substances

(c) An element with a very high resistance to flow

(d) A homogeneous mixture

(e) An element that fills its container but displays a surface

(f) A gas consisting of diatomic particles

(g) A gas that can be broken down into simpler substances

(h) A substance with a 2:1 number ratio of its component atoms

(i) Matter that can be separated into its component substances by physical means

(j) A heterogeneous mixture

(k) Matter that obeys the law of definite composition

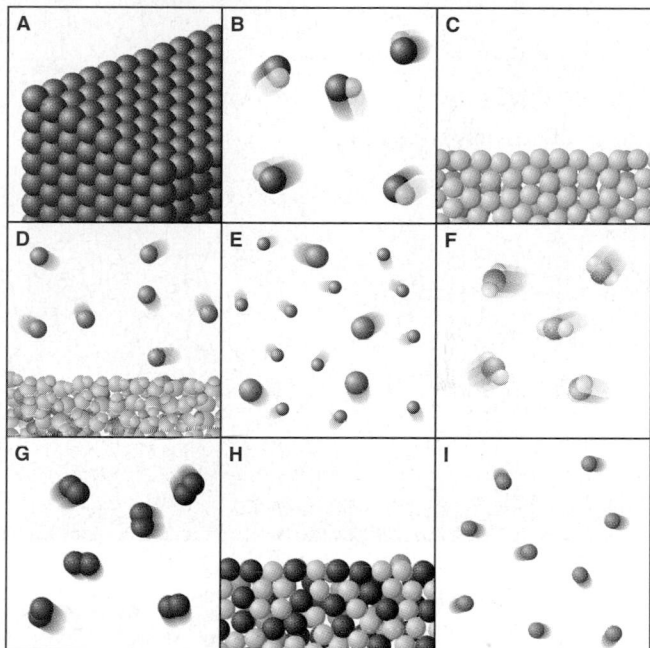

*2.140 The 17th-century scientist Robert Boyle reasoned in his treatise *The Skyptical Chymist* that it would be impossible to know for certain whether a substance is an element even if it had not been decomposed into simpler substances, because that did not *prove* it could not be. He argued further that it could never be known that matter consisted of atoms because they could not be detected individually. Write a short paragraph discussing how Dalton's atomic theory, Mendeleev's periodic table, and our modern understanding of atomic structure have changed the impact of Boyle's reasoning.

*2.141 Knowing the atomic mass and the number of atoms of an element in one molecule in a compound, you can find the mass percent of that element in the compound. A member of the family of dioxin compounds, abbreviated TCDD, is one of the most toxic compounds known. It is formed as an unwanted by-product in the manufacture of herbicides. The molecular formula of TCDD is $C_{12}H_4Cl_4O_2$. Calculate the mass % of Cl in TCDD.

*2.142 TNT (trinitrotoluene; *right*) is used as a high explosive in construction. Calculate the mass % of each element in TNT (see Problem 2.141).

3

Stoichiometry
Mole-Mass-Number Relationships in Chemical Systems

Figure: Balancing changes in matter. The quantitative basis of chemical change is the balance between the amounts of substances reacting and produced. This reaction between calcium and oxygen (*left, before reaction*) to produce calcium oxide (*right, after reaction*) depicts such a balance. Knowing how to find these amounts on the observable and molecular levels is the essence of this chapter.

Chemistry is a practical science, and nowhere is this fact more obvious than in the determination of a formula or the prediction of the amounts of substances consumed and produced in a reaction. Just imagine for a moment how important this information can be. Suppose you are a polymer chemist preparing a new plastic: how much of this new material will a given polymerization reaction yield? Or suppose you are a chemical engineer studying rocket engine thrust: what amount of exhaust gases will a test of this fuel mixture produce? Perhaps you are on a team of environmental chemists examining coal samples: what quantity of air pollutants will this sample release when burned? Or, maybe you are a biomedical researcher who has extracted a new cancer-preventing substance from a tropical plant: what is its formula, and what quantity of metabolic products will establish a safe dosage level? You can answer such questions by knowing the formulas and amounts of substances involved in the reactions.

Stoichiometry (pronounced "stoy-key-AHM-uh-tree"; Greek *stoicheion*, "element or part," + *metron*, "measure") is the study of the quantitative aspects of chemical formulas and reactions: if you know *what* is in a formula or reaction, stoichiometry tells you *how much*. In this chapter, you'll develop some essential skills of the chemist's trade: relating the mass of a substance to the number of chemical entities (atoms, molecules, or formula units); converting the results of composition analysis into a chemical formula; reading, writing, and thinking in the language of chemical equations; and applying the quantitative information held within them. All these abilities depend on an understanding of the *mole* concept, a central idea in all of chemistry, so that is where this chapter begins.

3.1 The Mole

In daily life, objects are typically measured out either by counting or by weighing, with the choice based on convenience. For instance, it is more convenient to weigh beans or rice than to count individual pieces, and it is more convenient to count eggs or pencils than to weigh them. To measure out such things, we use mass units (a kilogram of rice) or counting units (a dozen pencils). Similarly, part of daily life in the laboratory involves measuring out chemical substances to prepare a solution or "run" a reaction. However, an obvious problem arises when you need to do this. Since the atoms, molecules, or formula units of a substance are the entities that react with one another, we would like to know the numbers of them that are mixed together. But, how can we possibly count entities that are so small? To do this, chemists have devised a unit called the mole to *count these chemical entities by weighing them.*

Defining the Mole

The **mole** (abbreviated **mol**) is the SI unit for amount of substance. It is defined as *the amount of a substance that contains the same number of entities as there are atoms in exactly 12 g of carbon-12.* This number is called **Avogadro's number,** in honor of the 19th-century Italian physicist Amedeo Avogadro, and as you can tell from the definition it is enormous: ◆

One mole (1 mol) contains 6.022×10^{23} entities (to four significant figures)   **(3.1)**

Thus,

1 mol carbon-12	contains	6.022×10^{23} atoms
1 mol H_2O	contains	6.022×10^{23} molecules
1 mol NaCl	contains	6.022×10^{23} formula units

Concepts and Skills to Review

before you study this chapter

- isotopes and atomic mass (Section 2.4)
- names and formulas of compounds (Section 2.8)
- molecular mass of a compound (Section 2.8)
- empirical and molecular formulas (Section 2.8)
- mass laws in chemical reactions (Section 2.2)

◆ Imagine a Mole of . . .

A mole of any ordinary object is a staggering amount: a mole of periods (.) lined up side by side would equal the radius of our galaxy; a mole of marbles stacked tightly together would cover the United States 70 miles deep. (The figure is obviously not drawn to scale.) However, atoms and molecules are not ordinary objects: a mole of water molecules (about 18 mL) can be swallowed in one gulp!

Figure 3.1 Counting objects of fixed relative mass. A, If marbles had a fixed mass, we could count them by weighing them. Each red marble weighs 7 g, and each yellow marble weighs 4 g, so 84 g of red marbles and 48 g of yellow marbles each contains 12 marbles. Equal numbers of the two types of marbles always have a 7:4 mass ratio of red:yellow marbles. **B,** Since atoms of a substance have a fixed mass, we can weigh the substance to count the atoms. For example, 55.85 g Fe (left pan) and 32.07 g S (right pan) each contains 6.022×10^{23} atoms (1 mol of atoms). Any two samples of iron and sulfur that contain equal numbers of atoms have a 55.85:32.07 mass ratio of iron:sulfur.

A   **B**

However, the mole is not just a counting unit, like the dozen, which specifies only the *number* of objects. The definition of the mole specifies the number of objects in a fixed *mass* of substance. Therefore, *1 mole of a substance represents a fixed number of chemical entities **and** has a fixed mass.* To see why this is important, consider the marbles with fixed masses in Figure 3.1A, which we'll use as an analogy for atoms. Suppose you have large groups of red marbles and yellow marbles; each red marble weighs 7 g and each yellow marble weighs 4 g. Right away you know that there are 12 marbles in 84 g of red marbles or in 48 g of yellow marbles. Moreover, because one red marble weighs $\frac{7}{4}$ as much as one yellow marble, any given *number* of red and of yellow marbles always has this 7:4 *mass* ratio. By the same token, any given *mass* of red and of yellow marbles always has the same 4:7 *number* ratio. For example, 280 g of red marbles contains 40 marbles, and 280 g of yellow marbles contains 70 marbles. As you can see, the fixed masses of the marbles allow you to count marbles by weighing them.

Atoms have fixed masses also, and the mole gives us a practical way to determine the number of atoms, molecules, or formula units in a sample by weighing it. Let's focus on elements first and recall a key point from Chapter 2: the atomic mass of an element (which appears on the periodic table) is the weighted average of the masses of its naturally occurring isotopes. For purposes of weighing, all atoms of an element are considered to have this atomic mass. That is, all iron (Fe) atoms are considered to have an atomic mass of 55.85 amu, all sulfur (S) atoms are considered to have an atomic mass of 32.07 amu, and so forth.

The central relationship between the mass of one atom and the mass of 1 mole of those atoms is that *the atomic mass of an element expressed in **amu** is numerically the same as the mass of 1 mole of atoms of the element expressed in **grams**.* You can see this from the definition of the mole, which referred to the number of atoms in "**12** g of carbon-**12.**" In the same way,

1 Fe atom has a mass of 55.85 amu	and	1 mol Fe atoms has a mass of 55.85 g
1 S atom has a mass of 32.07 amu	and	1 mol S atoms has a mass of 32.07 g
1 O atom has a mass of 16.00 amu	and	1 mol O atoms has a mass of 16.00 g
1 O_2 molecule has a mass of 32.00 amu	and	1 mol O_2 molecules has a mass of 32.00 g

Moreover, because of their fixed atomic masses, we know that 55.85 g Fe atoms and 32.07 g S atoms each contains 6.022×10^{23} atoms. As with marbles of fixed mass, one Fe atom weighs $\frac{55.85}{32.07}$ as much as one S atom, and

1 mol Fe atoms weighs $\frac{55.85}{32.07}$ as much as 1 mol S atoms, as shown in Figure 3.1B.

A similar relationship holds for compounds: *the molecular mass (or formula mass) of a compound expressed in* **amu** *is numerically the same as the mass of 1 mole of the compound expressed in* **grams.** Thus, for example,

1 molecule of H_2O has a   and   1 mol H_2O (6.022×10^{23} molecules) has a
molecular mass of 18.02 amu   mass of 18.02 g

1 formula unit of NaCl has a   and   1 mol NaCl (6.022×10^{23} formula units) has a
formula mass of 58.44 amu   mass of 58.44 g

To summarize the two key points:

- The mole maintains the *same mass relationship* between macroscopic samples as exists between individual chemical entities.
- The mole is so useful because it relates the *number* of chemical entities to the *mass* of a sample of those entities.

A grocer cannot obtain 1 dozen eggs by weighing them, and a printer cannot obtain 1 ream (500 sheets) of paper by weighing it, because eggs and sheets of paper vary in mass. But a chemist *can* obtain 1 mol copper atoms (6.022×10^{23} atoms) simply by weighing out 63.55 g copper. Figure 3.2 shows 1 mole of some familiar elements and compounds.

The mole concept allows us to find the mass in grams of an atomic mass unit. You know from the mole definition that 1 mol carbon-12 atoms, each with a mass of exactly 12 amu, has a mass of exactly 12 g. It follows that $\frac{1}{12}$ mol ^{12}C atoms has a mass of 1 g. Put another way, *1 mole (6.022×10^{23}) of atomic mass units is equal to 1 gram:*

$$6.022\times10^{23} \text{ amu} = 1.000 \text{ g}$$

Dividing both sides by 6.022×10^{23}, we can find the number of grams in 1 amu:

$$\frac{6.022\times10^{23} \text{ amu}}{6.022\times10^{23}} = \frac{1.000 \text{ g}}{6.022\times10^{23}}$$

Therefore,

$$1 \text{ amu} = 1.661\times10^{-24} \text{ g}$$

Molar Mass

The **molar mass ($\mathcal{M}$)** of a substance is the mass per mole of its entities (atoms, molecules, or formula units). Thus, molar mass has units of grams per mole (g/mol). Table 3.1 summarizes the meanings of this and other mass units in the text.

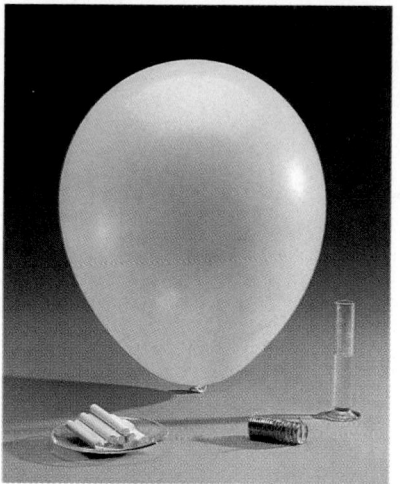

Figure 3.2 One mole of some familiar substances. One mole of a substance is the amount that contains 6.022×10^{23} atoms, molecules, or formula units. From left to right: 1 mol (100.09 g) calcium carbonate, 1 mol (32.00 g) gaseous O_2, 1 mol (63.55 g) copper, and 1 mol (18.02 g) liquid H_2O. (The balloon material restricts the O_2 gas from expanding to its actual volume of 24 L at 1 atm and 20°C.)

Table 3.1 Summary of Mass Terminology*

Term	Definition	Unit
Isotopic mass	Mass of an isotope of an element	amu
Atomic mass (also called atomic weight)	Average of the masses of the naturally occurring isotopes of an element weighted according to their abundance	amu
Molecular (or formula) mass (also called molecular weight)	Sum of the atomic masses of the atoms (or ions) in a molecule (or formula unit)	amu
Molar mass ($\mathcal{M}$) (also called gram-molecular weight)	Mass of 1 mole of chemical entities (atoms, ions, molecules, formula units)	g/mol

*All terms based on the ^{12}C standard: 1 atomic mass unit = $\frac{1}{12}$ mass of one ^{12}C atom.

The periodic table is indispensable for calculating the molar mass of a substance. Here's how the calculations are done:

1. **Elements.** You find the molar mass of an element simply by looking up its atomic mass in the periodic table. Some elements occur naturally as atoms, whereas others occur as molecules, so whenever necessary be sure to specify the entity you are considering.

- *Monatomic elements.* For elements that occur as collections of individual atoms, the molar mass is the numerical value from the periodic table expressed in units of grams/mole.* Thus, the molar mass of neon is 20.18 g/mol, the molar mass of iron is 55.85 g/mol, and the molar mass of gold is 197.0 g/mol.

- *Molecular elements.* For elements that occur naturally as molecules, you must know the molecular formula to determine the molar mass. For example, oxygen exists normally in air as diatomic molecules, O_2 (called *dioxygen*), so the molar mass of O_2 molecules is twice that of O atoms:

    Molar mass ($\mathcal{M}$) of O_2 = 2 × $\mathcal{M}$ of O = 2 × 16.00 g/mol = 32.00 g/mol

    Similarly, the most common form of sulfur consists of octatomic molecules, S_8:

    $\mathcal{M}$ of S_8 = 8 × $\mathcal{M}$ of S = 8 × 32.07 g/mol = 256.6 g/mol

2. **Compounds.** *The molar mass of a compound is the sum of the molar masses of the elements in the formula.* For example, the formula of sulfur dioxide (SO_2) tells us that 1 mol SO_2 molecules contains 1 mol S atoms and 2 mol O atoms:

$$\mathcal{M} \text{ of } SO_2 = \mathcal{M} \text{ of S} + (2 \times \mathcal{M} \text{ of O})$$
$$= 32.07 \text{ g/mol} + (2 \times 16.00 \text{ g/mol})$$
$$= 64.07 \text{ g/mol}$$

Similarly, for ionic compounds, such as potassium sulfide (K_2S), we have

$$\mathcal{M} \text{ of } K_2S = (2 \times \mathcal{M} \text{ of K}) + \mathcal{M} \text{ of S}$$
$$= (2 \times 39.10 \text{ g/mol}) + 32.07 \text{ g/mol}$$
$$= 110.27 \text{ g/mol}$$

A key point to note is that *the subscripts in a formula refer to individual atoms (or ions), as well as to moles of atoms (or ions).* Table 3.2 presents this idea for glucose ($C_6H_{12}O_6$).

Interconverting Moles, Mass, and Number of Chemical Entities

One of the reasons the mole is such a convenient unit for laboratory work is that it allows you to calculate the mass (or the number of chemical entities) of a substance in a sample if you know the amount (number of moles) of the substance. Conversely, if you know the mass (or number of entities) of a substance, you can calculate the number of moles.

The molar mass, which expresses the equivalent relationship between 1 mole of a substance and its mass in grams, can be used as a conversion

---

*The mass value in the periodic table is unitless because it is a *relative* atomic mass, given by the atomic mass (in amu) divided by 1 amu ($\frac{1}{12}$ mass of one ^{12}C atom in amu):

$$\text{Relative atomic mass} = \frac{\text{atomic mass (amu)}}{\frac{1}{12} \text{ mass of } ^{12}C \text{ (amu)}}$$

Therefore, you use the same number for the atomic mass (weighted average mass of one atom in amu) and the molar mass (mass of 1 mole of atoms in grams).

Table 3.2 Information Contained in the Chemical Formula of Glucose, $C_6H_{12}O_6$ ($\mathcal{M} = 180.16$ g/mol)

	Carbon (C)	Hydrogen (H)	Oxygen (O)
Atoms/molecule of compound	6 atoms	12 atoms	6 atoms
Moles of atoms/ mole of compound	6 mol of atoms	12 mol of atoms	6 mol of atoms
Atoms/mole of compound	$6(6.022\times10^{23})$ atoms	$12(6.022\times10^{23})$ atoms	$6(6.022\times10^{23})$ atoms
Mass/molecule of compound	6(12.01 amu) = 72.06 amu	12(1.008 amu) = 12.10 amu	6(16.00 amu) = 96.00 amu
Mass/mole of compound	72.06 g	12.10 g	96.00 g

factor. We multiply by the molar mass of an element or compound ($\mathcal{M}$, in g/mol) to convert a given amount (in moles) to mass (in grams):

$$\text{Mass (g)} = \text{no. of moles} \times \frac{\text{no. of grams}}{1 \text{ mol}} \qquad \textbf{(3.2)}$$

Or, we divide by the molar mass (multiply by $1/\mathcal{M}$) to convert a given mass (in grams) to amount (in moles):

$$\text{No. of moles} = \text{mass (g)} \times \frac{1 \text{ mol}}{\text{no. of grams}} \qquad \textbf{(3.3)}$$

In a similar way, we use Avogadro's number, which expresses the equivalent relationship between 1 mole of a substance and the number of entities it contains, as a conversion factor. We multiply by Avogadro's number to convert amount of substance (in moles) to the number of entities (atoms, molecules, or formula units):

$$\text{No. of entities} = \text{no. of moles} \times \frac{6.022\times10^{23} \text{ entities}}{1 \text{ mol}} \qquad \textbf{(3.4)}$$

Or, we divide by Avogadro's number to do the reverse:

$$\text{No. of moles} = \text{no. of entities} \times \frac{1 \text{ mol}}{6.022\times10^{23} \text{ entities}} \qquad \textbf{(3.5)}$$

Converting Moles of Elements For problems involving mass-mole-number relationships of elements, keep these points in mind:
- To convert between amount (mol) and mass (g), use the molar mass ($\mathcal{M}$ in g/mol).
- To convert between amount (mol) and number of entities, use Avogadro's number (6.022×10^{23} entities/mol). For elements that occur as molecules, use the formula to find atoms/mol.
- Mass and number of entities relate directly to number of moles, *not* to each other. Therefore, to convert between number of entities and mass, *first convert to number of moles.*

These relationships are summarized in Figure 3.3A and demonstrated in Sample Problem 3.1 on the next page.

Figure 3.3 Summary of the mass-mole-number relationships for elements and compounds. A, The amount (in mol) of an element is related to its mass (in g) through the molar mass ($\mathcal{M}$ in g/mol) and to the number of atoms through Avogadro's number (6.022×10^{23} atoms/mol). For elements that occur as molecules, Avogadro's number gives the number of *molecules* per mole. **B,** Similarly, moles of a compound are related to grams of the compound through the molar mass ($\mathcal{M}$ in g/mol) and to the number of molecules (or formula units) through Avogadro's number (6.022×10^{23} molecules/mol). To find the number of atoms (molecules or formula units) in a given mass, or vice versa, convert the information to moles first. With the chemical formula, you can calculate mass-mole-number information about each component element.

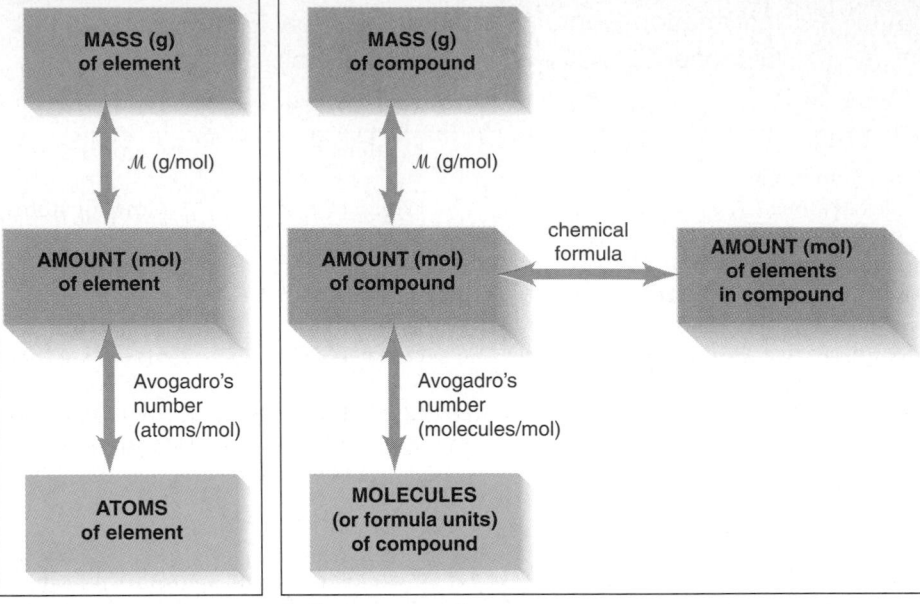

A For an element   **B For a compound**

Sample Problem 3.1 Calculating the Mass and Number of Atoms in a Given Number of Moles of an Element

PROBLEM (a) Silver (Ag) is used in jewelry and tableware but no longer in U.S. coins. How many grams of Ag are in 0.0342 mol Ag?
(b) Iron (Fe), the main component of steel, is the most important metal in industrial society. How many Fe atoms are in 95.8 g Fe?
PLAN (a) We know the number of moles of Ag and have to find the mass (in g). To convert *moles* of Ag to *grams* of Ag, we multiply by the *molar mass* of Ag from the periodic table (*top roadmap*). **(b)** We know the grams of Fe and need the number of Fe atoms. We cannot convert directly from grams to number of entities, so we convert to moles by dividing the grams of Fe by its molar mass, then multiply by Avogadro's number to convert moles to number of atoms (*bottom roadmap*).
SOLUTION (a) Converting from moles of Ag to grams:

$$\text{Mass (g) of Ag} = 0.0342 \text{ mol Ag} \times \frac{107.9 \text{ g Ag}}{1 \text{ mol Ag}} = \boxed{3.69 \text{ g Ag}}$$

(b) Converting from grams of Fe to moles:

$$\text{Moles of Fe} = 95.8 \text{ g Fe} \times \frac{1 \text{ mol Fe}}{55.85 \text{ g Fe}} = 1.72 \text{ mol Fe}$$

Converting from moles of Fe to number of atoms:

$$\text{No. of Fe atoms} = 1.72 \text{ mol Fe} \times \frac{6.022\times10^{23} \text{ atoms Fe}}{1 \text{ mol Fe}}$$
$$= 10.4\times10^{23} \text{ atoms Fe} = \boxed{1.04\times10^{24} \text{ atoms Fe}}$$

CHECK (a) We rounded the mass to three significant figures because the number of moles has three. The units are correct. About 0.03 mol × 100 g/mol gives 3 g; the small mass makes sense because 0.0342 is a small fraction of a mole. **(b)** Approximating the mass and molar mass of Fe, we have about 2 mol Fe: ~100 g/~50 g/mol = 2 mol. Therefore, the number of atoms should be about twice Avogadro's number: $2(6\times10^{23}) = 1.2\times10^{24}$.

Follow-up Problem 3.1 **(a)** Graphite is the crystalline form of carbon used in "lead" pencils. How many moles of carbon are in 315 mg graphite?
(b) Manganese (Mn) is a transition element essential for the growth of bones. What is the mass in grams of 3.22×10^{20} Mn atoms, the number found in 1 kg of bone?

Converting Moles of Compounds Solving mass-mole-number problems involving compounds requires a very similar approach to the one for elements. We need the chemical formula to find the molar mass and to determine the moles of a given element in the compound. These relationships are shown in Figure 3.3B, and worked through in Sample Problem 3.2.

Sample Problem 3.2   Calculating the Moles and Number of Formula Units in a Given Mass of a Compound

PROBLEM Ammonium carbonate is a white crystalline powder that decomposes with warming. Among its many uses, it is a component of baking powder, fire extinguishers, and smelling salts. How many moles and formula units are in 41.6 g ammonium carbonate?

PLAN We know the mass (g) of compound and need to find the amount (mol) and number of formula units. We cannot convert directly from grams to number of entities, so we divide the grams by the molar mass ($\mathcal{M}$) to find moles. To find $\mathcal{M}$, we determine the formula (see Table 2.5) and take the sum of the element molar masses. Once we have the number of moles, we multiply by Avogadro's number to find the number of formula units.

SOLUTION The formula is $(NH_4)_2CO_3$. Calculating molar mass:

$$\mathcal{M} = (2 \times \mathcal{M} \text{ of N}) + (8 \times \mathcal{M} \text{ of H}) + (1 \times \mathcal{M} \text{ of C}) + (3 \times \mathcal{M} \text{ of O})$$
$$= (2 \times 14.01 \text{ g/mol}) + (8 \times 1.008 \text{ g/mol}) + 12.01 \text{ g/mol} + (3 \times 16.00 \text{ g/mol})$$
$$= 96.09 \text{ g/mol}$$

Converting from grams to moles:

$$\text{Moles of } (NH_4)_2CO_3 = 41.6 \text{ g } (NH_4)_2CO_3 \times \frac{1 \text{ mol } (NH_4)_2CO_3}{96.09 \text{ g } (NH_4)_2CO_3}$$
$$= \boxed{0.433 \text{ mol } (NH_4)_2CO_3}$$

Converting from moles to formula units:

$$\text{Formula units of } (NH_4)_2CO_3 = 0.433 \text{ mol } (NH_4)_2CO_3$$
$$\times \frac{6.022 \times 10^{23} \text{ formula units } (NH_4)_2CO_3}{1 \text{ mol } (NH_4)_2CO_3}$$
$$= \boxed{2.61 \times 10^{23} \text{ formula units } (NH_4)_2CO_3}$$

CHECK The units are correct in both cases. Since the mass is less than half the molar mass ($\sim 42/96 < 0.5$), the number of formula units should be less than half Avogadro's number ($\sim 2.6 \times 10^{23}/6.0 \times 10^{23} < 0.5$). A *common mistake* is to forget the subscript 2 outside the parentheses in $(NH_4)_2CO_3$, which would give a much lower molar mass.

COMMENT From here on, you should be able to determine the molar mass of a compound, so that calculation will no longer be shown.

Follow-up Problem 3.2 Tetraphosphorus decaoxide reacts with water to form phosphoric acid, a major industrial acid. In the laboratory, the oxide is used as a drying agent.
(a) What is the mass (in g) of 4.65×10^{22} molecules of tetraphosphorus decaoxide?
(b) How many P atoms are present in this sample?

Mass Percent from the Chemical Formula

Each element in a compound constitutes its own particular portion of the compound's mass. For an individual molecule (or formula unit), we use the molecular (or formula) mass and chemical formula to find the mass percent of any element X in the compound:

$$\text{Mass \% of element X} = \frac{\text{atoms of X in formula} \times \text{atomic mass of X (amu)}}{\text{molecular (or formula) mass of compound (amu)}} \times 100$$

Since the formula also tells the number of *moles* of each element in the compound, we use the molar mass to find the mass percent of each element on a mole basis:

$$\text{Mass \% of element X} = \frac{\text{moles of X in formula} \times \text{molar mass of X (g/mol)}}{\text{mass of 1 mole of compound (g)}} \times 100 \quad \textbf{(3.6)}$$

As always, the individual mass percents of the elements in the compound must add up to 100% (within rounding). As Sample Problem 3.3 demonstrates, an important practical use of mass percent is to determine the amount of an element in any size sample of a compound.

Sample Problem 3.3   Calculating Mass Percents and Masses of Elements in a Sample of Compound

PROBLEM Glucose ($C_6H_{12}O_6$) is the most important nutrient in the living cell for generating chemical potential energy.
(a) What is the mass percent of each element in glucose?
(b) How many grams of carbon are in 16.55 g glucose?

(a) Determining the mass percent of each element

PLAN We know the relative number of moles of each element (C, H, and O) in glucose from the formula. We multiply the number of moles of each element by its molar mass to find grams. Dividing each element mass by the mass of 1 mol glucose gives the element mass fraction, and multiplying this fraction by 100 gives the mass percent. The calculation steps for any element X are shown in the roadmap.
SOLUTION The mass of 1 mol $C_6H_{12}O_6$ is 180.16 g. Converting moles of C to grams: There are 6 mol C/1 mol glucose, so

$$\text{Mass (g) of C} = 6 \text{ mol C} \times \frac{12.01 \text{ g C}}{1 \text{ mol C}} = 72.06 \text{ g C}$$

Finding the mass fraction of C in glucose:

$$\text{Mass fraction of C} = \frac{\text{total mass C}}{\text{mass of 1 mol glucose}} = \frac{72.06 \text{ g}}{180.16 \text{ g}} = 0.4000 \text{ g C/g glucose}$$

Finding the mass percent of C:

$$\text{Mass \% of C} = \text{mass fraction of C} \times 100 = 0.4000 \times 100 = \boxed{40.00 \text{ mass \% C}}$$

Combining the steps for each of the other two elements:

$$\text{Mass \% of H} = \frac{\text{mol H} \times \mathcal{M} \text{ of H}}{\text{mass of 1 mol glucose}} \times 100 = \frac{12 \text{ mol H} \times \dfrac{1.008 \text{ g H}}{1 \text{ mol H}}}{180.16 \text{ g}} \times 100$$

$$= \boxed{6.714 \text{ mass \% H}}$$

$$\text{Mass \% of O} = \frac{\text{mol O} \times \mathcal{M} \text{ of O}}{\text{mass of 1 mol glucose}} \times 100 = \frac{6 \text{ mol O} \times \dfrac{16.00 \text{ g O}}{1 \text{ mol O}}}{180.16 \text{ g}} \times 100$$

$$= \boxed{53.29 \text{ mass \% O}}$$

(b) Determining the mass (g) of carbon

PLAN To find the mass of C in the glucose sample, we multiply the mass of the sample by the mass fraction of C from part (a).
SOLUTION Finding the mass of C in a given mass of glucose (showing units for mass fraction):

$$\text{Mass (g) of C} = \text{mass of glucose} \times \text{mass fraction of C}$$

$$= 16.55 \text{ g glucose} \times \frac{0.4000 \text{ g C}}{1 \text{ g glucose}} = \boxed{6.620 \text{ g C}}$$

CHECK (a) The answers make sense: the mass % of O is greater than the mass % of C because, even though there are equal numbers of moles of each in the compound, the molar mass of O is greater than the molar mass of C. The mass % of H is small because the molar mass of H is small. The total is 100.00%. **(b)** The answer makes sense: 16 g times less than 0.5 parts by mass should be less than 8 g.

Amount (mol) of element X in 1 mol of compound

multiply by
$\mathcal{M}$ (g/mol) of X

Mass (g) of X in 1 mol of compound

divide by mass (g) of 1 mol of compound

Mass fraction of X

multiply by 100

Mass % of X

COMMENT A *more direct approach* to finding the mass of element eliminates the need to calculate the mass fraction. Just multiply the given mass of compound by the ratio of total mass of element to mass of 1 mol of compound. For carbon, we get

$$\text{Mass (g) of C} = 16.55 \text{ g glucose} \times \frac{72.06 \text{ g C}}{180.16 \text{ g glucose}} = 6.620 \text{ g C}$$

Follow-up Problem 3.3 Ammonium nitrate is used as a fertilizer and to manufacture explosives. Agronomists base the effectiveness of fertilizers on their nitrogen content.
(a) Calculate the mass percent of N in ammonium nitrate.
(b) How many grams of N are in 35.8 kg ammonium nitrate?

Section Summary

A mole of substance is the *amount* that contains Avogadro's number (6.022×10^{23}) of atoms, molecules, or formula units. The mass (in grams) of a mole has the same numerical value as the mass (in amu) of the entity. Thus, the mole allows us to count entities by weighing them. Using the molar mass ($\mathcal{M}$, g/mol) of an element (or compound) and Avogadro's number as conversion factors, we can convert among amount (mol), mass (g), and number of entities. The mass fraction of element X in a compound is used to calculate the mass of X in any amount of the compound.

3.2 Determining the Formula of an Unknown Compound

In Sample Problem 3.3, we knew the chemical formula and used it to find the mass percent (or mass fraction) of an element in a compound *and* the mass of the element in a given mass of compound. In this section, we do the reverse: use the masses of elements in a compound to find its formula.

Empirical Formulas

An analytical chemist investigating a compound decomposes it into simpler substances, finds the mass of each component element, converts these masses to numbers of moles, and then mathematically converts the moles to whole-number subscripts. ◆ This procedure yields the empirical formula, the *simplest whole-number ratio* of moles of each element in the compound (see Section 2.8, p. 65). Here's an example to show how the subscripts are obtained from the moles of each element.

Analysis of an unknown compound shows that the sample contains 0.21 mol zinc, 0.14 mol phosphorus, and 0.56 mol oxygen. Since the subscripts in a formula represent individual atoms or moles of atoms, we write a preliminary formula that contains fractional subscripts: $Zn_{0.21}P_{0.14}O_{0.56}$. Next, we convert these fractional subscripts to whole numbers using one or two simple arithmetic steps (rounding when needed):
1. Divide each subscript by the smallest subscript:

$$Zn_{\frac{0.21}{0.14}}P_{\frac{0.14}{0.14}}O_{\frac{0.56}{0.14}} \longrightarrow Zn_{1.5}P_{1.0}O_{4.0}$$

This step alone often gives integer subscripts.
2. If any of the subscripts are still not integers, multiply through by the *smallest integer* that will turn all the subscripts into integers. In this case, we multiply by 2, the smallest integer that will make 1.5 (the subscript for Zn) into an integer:

$$Zn_{(1.5 \times 2)}P_{(1.0 \times 2)}O_{(4.0 \times 2)} \longrightarrow Zn_{3.0}P_{2.0}O_{8.0}, \quad \text{or} \quad Zn_3P_2O_8$$

Notice that since we multiplied *all* the subscripts by 2, the *relative* number of moles has not changed. Always check that the subscripts are the smallest set

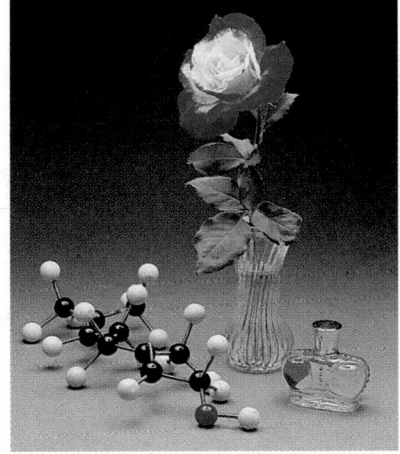

◆ **A Rose by Any Other Name . . .** Chemists studying natural substances from animals and plants isolate compounds and determine their formulas. Geraniol ($C_{10}H_{18}O$) is the main compound that gives a rose its odor. It is used in many perfumes and cosmetics. Geraniol is also found in citronella and lemongrass oils and as part of a larger compound in geranium leaves, from which its name is derived.

of integers with the same ratio as the original numbers of moles; that is, 3:2:8 are *in the same ratio* as 0.21:0.14:0.56. A more conventional way to write this formula is $Zn_3(PO_4)_2$; the compound is zinc phosphate, a dental cement.

The following three sample problems show other common approaches to determining chemical formulas. In the first, the empirical formula is found from analytical data given as grams of each element rather than as moles.

Sample Problem 3.4   Determining an Empirical Formula from Masses of Elements

PROBLEM Elemental analysis of a sample of ionic compound gave the following results: 2.82 g Na, 4.35 g Cl, and 7.83 g O. What is the empirical formula and name of the compound?

PLAN This problem is similar to the one just discussed, except that we are given element *masses*, so we first divide each mass by its molar mass to find *number of moles*. Then we construct a preliminary formula and convert to integer subscripts.

SOLUTION Finding moles of elements:

$$\text{Moles of Na} = 2.82 \; \cancel{\text{g Na}} \times \frac{1 \text{ mol Na}}{22.99 \; \cancel{\text{g Na}}} = 0.123 \text{ mol Na}$$

$$\text{Moles of Cl} = 4.35 \; \cancel{\text{g Cl}} \times \frac{1 \text{ mol Cl}}{35.45 \; \cancel{\text{g Cl}}} = 0.123 \text{ mol Cl}$$

$$\text{Moles of O} = 7.83 \; \cancel{\text{g O}} \times \frac{1 \text{ mol O}}{16.00 \; \cancel{\text{g O}}} = 0.489 \text{ mol O}$$

Constructing a preliminary formula:

$$Na_{0.123}Cl_{0.123}O_{0.489}$$

Converting to integer subscripts (dividing all by smallest subscript):

$$Na_{\frac{0.123}{0.123}}Cl_{\frac{0.123}{0.123}}O_{\frac{0.489}{0.123}} \longrightarrow Na_{1.00}Cl_{1.00}O_{3.98} \approx Na_1Cl_1O_4, \quad \text{or} \quad NaClO_4$$

We rounded the subscript of O from 3.98 to 4. The empirical formula is $NaClO_4$; the name is sodium perchlorate.

CHECK The masses of Na and Cl are slightly more than 0.1 of their molar masses. The mass of O is greatest and its molar mass is smallest, so it should have the greatest number of moles. The ratio 1:1:4 is the same as 0.123:0.123:0.489 (within rounding).

Follow-up Problem 3.4
An unknown metal M reacts with sulfur to form a compound with formula M_2S_3. If 3.12 g M reacts with exactly 2.88 g S, what are the names of M and M_2S_3? (*Hint:* Determine number of moles of S and use the formula to find number of moles of M.)

Side flowchart:

Mass (g) of each element

divide by
$\mathcal{M}$ (g/mol)

Amount (mol) of each element

use nos. of moles as subscripts

Preliminary formula

change to integer subscripts

Empirical formula

Molecular Formulas

If we know the molar mass of a compound, we can use the empirical formula to obtain the molecular formula, the *actual* number of moles of each element in 1 mole of compound. In some cases, such as water (H_2O), ammonia (NH_3), and methane (CH_4), the empirical and molecular formulas are identical, but in many others the molecular formula is a *whole-number multiple* of the empirical formula. Hydrogen peroxide, for example, has the empirical formula HO and the molecular formula H_2O_2. Dividing the molar mass of H_2O_2 (34.02 g/mol) by the empirical formula mass (17.01 g/mol) gives the whole-number multiple:

$$\text{Whole-number multiple} = \frac{\text{molar mass (g/mol)}}{\text{empirical formula mass (g/mol)}}$$

$$= \frac{34.02 \; \cancel{\text{g/mol}}}{17.01 \; \cancel{\text{g/mol}}} = 2.000 = 2$$

Commercial analytical laboratories often provide composition data as mass percent of each element. From this, we can determine the empirical formula by (1) assuming 100.0 g of compound, which allows us to express mass percent directly as mass, (2) converting the mass to number of moles, and (3) constructing the empirical formula. With the molar mass available to find the whole-number multiple, we can then determine the molecular formula.

Sample Problem 3.5   Determining a Molecular Formula from Elemental Analysis and Molar Mass

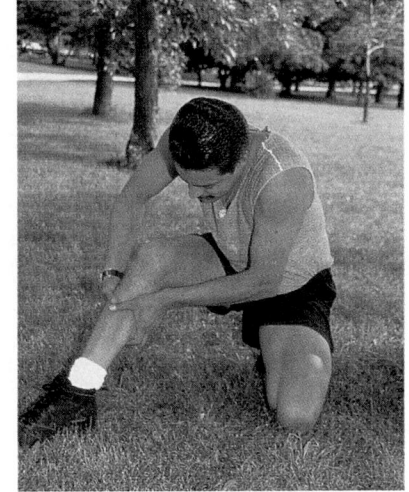

PROBLEM During physical activity, lactic acid ($\mathcal{M}$ = 90.08 g/mol) forms in muscle tissue and is responsible for muscle soreness. Elemental analysis shows that it contains 40.0 mass % C, 6.71 mass % H, and 53.3 mass % O.
(a) Determine the empirical formula of lactic acid.
(b) Determine the molecular formula.

(a) Determining the empirical formula
PLAN The masses of elements are given as mass %, but no mass of compound is given. Since mass % is the same for any mass of compound, we can assume exactly 100.0 g lactic acid and thus express each mass % directly as grams. Then, we convert grams to moles and construct the empirical formula as we did in Sample Problem 3.4.
SOLUTION Expressing mass % as grams, assuming 100.0 g lactic acid:

$$\text{Mass (g) of C} = \frac{40.0 \text{ parts C by mass}}{100 \text{ parts by mass}} \times 100.0 \text{ g} = 40.0 \text{ g C}$$

Similarly, we have 6.71 g H and 53.3 g O.
Converting from grams of elements to moles:

$$\text{Moles of C} = \text{mass of C} \times \frac{1}{\mathcal{M} \text{ of C}} = 40.0 \text{ g C} \times \frac{1 \text{ mol C}}{12.01 \text{ g C}} = 3.33 \text{ mol C}$$

Similarly, we have 6.66 mol H and 3.33 mol O.
Constructing the preliminary formula: $C_{3.33}H_{6.66}O_{3.33}$
Converting to integer subscripts:

$$C_{\frac{3.33}{3.33}H_{\frac{6.66}{3.33}}O_{\frac{3.33}{3.33}}} \longrightarrow C_{1.00}H_{2.00}O_{1.00} \approx C_1H_2O_1; \text{ the empirical formula is } \boxed{CH_2O}$$

(b) Determining the molecular formula
PLAN The molecular formula subscripts are whole-number multiples of the empirical formula subscripts. To find this whole number, we divide the given molar mass by the empirical formula mass. Then we multiply the whole number by each empirical formula subscript.
SOLUTION From the sum of the element molar masses in the empirical formula, the empirical-formula molar mass is 30.03 g/mol. Finding the whole-number multiple:

$$\text{Whole-number multiple} = \frac{\mathcal{M} \text{ of lactic acid}}{\mathcal{M} \text{ of empirical formula}} = \frac{90.08 \text{ g/mol}}{30.03 \text{ g/mol}} = 3.000 = 3$$

Determining the molecular formula:

$$C_{(1\times 3)}H_{(2\times 3)}O_{(1\times 3)} = \boxed{C_3H_6O_3}$$

CHECK **(a)** See Check in Sample Problem 3.4. **(b)** The calculated molecular formula has the same ratio of moles of elements (3:6:3) as the empirical formula (1:2:1) and corresponds to the given molar mass:

$$\mathcal{M} \text{ of lactic acid} = (3 \times \mathcal{M} \text{ of C}) + (6 \times \mathcal{M} \text{ of H}) + (3 \times \mathcal{M} \text{ of O})$$
$$= (3 \times 12.01) + (6 \times 1.008) + (3 \times 16.00) = 90.08 \text{ g/mol}$$

Follow-up Problem 3.5
One of the most widespread environmental carcinogens (cancer-causing agents) is benzo[a]pyrene ($\mathcal{M}$ = 252.30 g/mol). It is found in coal dust, cigarette smoke, and even charcoal-grilled meat. Analysis of this hydrocarbon shows 95.21 mass % C and 4.79 mass % H. What is the molecular formula of benzo[a]pyrene?

Figure 3.4 **Combustion apparatus for determining formulas of organic compounds.** A sample of compound that contains C and H (and perhaps other elements) is burned in a stream of O_2 gas. The CO_2 and H_2O formed from the C and H in the sample are absorbed separately, while any other element oxides are carried through by the O_2 gas stream. H_2O is absorbed by $Mg(ClO_4)_2$; CO_2 is absorbed by NaOH on asbestos. The changes in mass of the CO_2 and H_2O absorbers before and after the combustion are used to calculate the amounts (mol) of C and H present in the sample.

Combustion Analysis

A third approach to determining a chemical formula is **combustion analysis,** a method used to measure the amounts of carbon and hydrogen in a combustible organic compound. The unknown is placed in an apparatus with several chambers and burned in pure O_2 (Figure 3.4). All the H in the compound is converted to H_2O, which is absorbed in the first chamber, and all the C is converted to CO_2, which is absorbed in the second. By weighing the contents of the chambers before and after combustion, we find the masses of CO_2 and H_2O and use them to calculate the masses of C and H in the compound, from which the empirical formula is found. Many organic compounds also contain oxygen, nitrogen, or halogen. As long as this third element does not interfere with the absorption of CO_2 and H_2O in the apparatus, we can calculate its mass by subtracting the masses of C and H from the compound's original mass.

Sample Problem 3.6   Determining a Chemical Formula from Combustion Analysis

PROBLEM Vitamin C ($\mathcal{M}$ = 176.12 g/mol) is a compound of C, H, and O found in many natural sources, especially citrus fruits. When a 1.000-g sample of vitamin C is placed in a combustion chamber and burned, the following data are obtained:

Mass of CO_2 absorber after combustion = 85.35 g

Mass of CO_2 absorber before combustion = 83.85 g

Mass of H_2O absorber after combustion = 37.96 g

Mass of H_2O absorber before combustion = 37.55 g

What is the molecular formula of vitamin C?

PLAN We find the masses of CO_2 and H_2O by subtracting the masses of the absorbers before the reaction from the masses after. From the mass of CO_2, we use the mass fraction of C in CO_2 to find the mass of C (see Comment in Sample Problem 3.3). Similarly, we find the mass of H from the mass of H_2O. The mass of vitamin C minus the sum of the C and H masses gives the mass of O, the third element present. Then, we proceed as in Sample Problem 3.5: calculate numbers of moles using the element molar masses, construct the empirical formula, determine the whole-number multiple from the given molar mass, and construct the molecular formula.

SOLUTION Finding the masses of combustion products:

$$\text{Mass (g) of } CO_2 = \text{mass of } CO_2 \text{ absorber after} - \text{mass before}$$
$$= 85.35 \text{ g} - 83.85 \text{ g}$$
$$= 1.50 \text{ g } CO_2$$

$$\text{Mass (g) of } H_2O = \text{mass of } H_2O \text{ absorber after} - \text{mass before}$$
$$= 37.96 \text{ g} - 37.55 \text{ g}$$
$$= 0.41 \text{ g } H_2O$$

Calculating masses of C and H using their mass fractions:

$$\text{Mass of element} = \text{mass of compound} \times \frac{\text{mass of element in compound}}{\text{mass of 1 mol of compound}}$$

$$\text{Mass (g) of C} = \text{mass of } CO_2 \times \frac{1 \text{ mol C} \times \mathcal{M} \text{ of C}}{\text{mass of 1 mol } CO_2}$$

$$= 1.50 \text{ g } CO_2 \times \frac{12.01 \text{ g C}}{44.01 \text{ g } CO_2} = 0.409 \text{ g C}$$

$$\text{Mass (g) of H} = \text{mass of } H_2O \times \frac{2 \text{ mol H} \times \mathcal{M} \text{ of H}}{\text{mass of 1 mol } H_2O}$$

$$= 0.41 \text{ g } H_2O \times \frac{2.016 \text{ g H}}{18.02 \text{ g } H_2O} = 0.046 \text{ g H}$$

Calculating the mass of O:

$$\text{Mass (g) of O} = \text{mass of vitamin C sample} - (\text{mass of C} + \text{mass of H})$$
$$= 1.000 \text{ g} - (0.409 \text{ g} + 0.046 \text{ g}) = 0.545 \text{ g O}$$

Finding the amount (mol) of elements: Dividing the grams of each element by its molar mass gives 0.0341 mol C, 0.046 mol H, and 0.0341 mol O.

Constructing the preliminary formula: $C_{0.0341}H_{0.046}O_{0.0341}$

Determining the empirical formula: Dividing through by the smallest subscript gives

$$C_{\frac{0.0341}{0.0341}}H_{\frac{0.046}{0.0341}}O_{\frac{0.0341}{0.0341}} = C_{1.00}H_{1.3}O_{1.00}$$

By trial and error, we find that 3 is the smallest integer that will make all subscripts approximately into integers:

$$C_{(1.00 \times 3)}H_{(1.3 \times 3)}O_{(1.00 \times 3)} = C_{3.00}H_{3.9}O_{3.00} \approx C_3H_4O_3$$

Determining the molecular formula:

$$\text{Whole-number multiple} = \frac{\mathcal{M} \text{ of vitamin C}}{\mathcal{M} \text{ of empirical formula}} = \frac{176.12 \text{ g/mol}}{88.06 \text{ g/mol}} = 2.000 = 2$$

$$C_{(3 \times 2)}H_{(4 \times 2)}O_{(3 \times 2)} = \boxed{C_6H_8O_6}$$

CHECK The element masses seem correct: C makes up slightly more than 0.25 of the mass of CO_2 (12 g/44 g > 0.25), as do the masses in the problem (0.409 g/1.50 g > 0.25). H makes up slightly more than 0.10 of the mass of H_2O (2 g/18 g > 0.10), as do the masses in the problem (0.046 g/0.41 g > 0.10). The molecular formula has the same ratio of subscripts (6:8:6) as the empirical formula (3:4:3) and adds up to the given molar mass:

$$(6 \times \mathcal{M} \text{ of C}) + (8 \times \mathcal{M} \text{ of H}) + (6 \times \mathcal{M} \text{ of O}) = \mathcal{M} \text{ of vitamin C}$$

$$(6 \times 12.01) + (8 \times 1.008) + (6 \times 16.00) = 176.12 \text{ g/mol}$$

COMMENT In determining the empirical formula, note that if we round the calculation for H at the end, we obtain a subscript of 4.0, rather than 3.9:

$$\text{Subscript of H} = 0.41 \text{ g } H_2O \times \frac{2.016 \text{ g H}}{18.02 \text{ g } H_2O} \times \frac{1 \text{ mol H}}{1.008 \text{ g H}} \times \frac{1}{0.0341 \text{ mol}} \times 3 = 4.0$$

Follow-up Problem 3.6 A dry-cleaning solvent ($\mathcal{M}$ = 146.99 g/mol) that contains C, H, and Cl is suspected as a cancer-causing agent. When a 0.250-g sample was studied by combustion analysis, 0.451 g CO_2 and 0.0617 g H_2O formed. Calculate the molecular formula.

Chemical Formulas and the Structures of Molecules

Let's take a short break from calculations to recall a key point: a formula represents a real three-dimensional object. How much information about the structure of the object is contained in its formula? The empirical formula tells only the *relative* numbers of each type of atom. However, as you can see in Table 3.3 (next page), *different compounds can have the same **empirical** formula.*

Table 3.3 Some Compounds with Empirical Formula CH_2O
(Composition by Mass 40.0% C, 6.71% H, 53.3% O)

Name	Molecular Formula	Whole-Number Multiple	$\mathcal{M}$ (g/mol)	Use or Function
Formaldehyde	CH_2O	1	30.03	Disinfectant; biological preservative
Acetic acid	$C_2H_4O_2$	2	60.05	Acetate polymers; vinegar (5% solution)
Lactic acid	$C_3H_6O_3$	3	90.08	Causes milk to sour; forms in muscle during exercise
Erythrose	$C_4H_8O_4$	4	120.10	Forms during sugar metabolism
Ribose	$C_5H_{10}O_5$	5	150.13	Component of many nucleic acids and vitamin B_2
Glucose	$C_6H_{12}O_6$	6	180.16	Major nutrient for energy in cells

A molecular formula, which tells the *actual* number of each type of atom, provides as much information as it is possible to obtain from mass analysis. Yet *different compounds can also have the same* **molecular** *formula* because the same types and numbers of atoms can bond to each other in more than one arrangement; that is, in more than one *structural formula*. (Such compounds are called *structural isomers* of each other, and we'll discuss them fully later in the text.) Only by knowing a molecule's structure—the relative placement of atoms and the distances and angles separating them—can we begin to predict its behavior. For example, as Table 3.4 shows, two *very* different compounds have the molecular formula C_2H_6O. Their distinct physical and chemical behaviors result from their different molecular structures.

As molecular complexity (the number and types of atoms) increases, the number of structural formulas that can be written for a given molecular formula also increases: C_2H_6O has two possible structural formulas, C_3H_8O three, and $C_4H_{10}O$, seven. Imagine how many there are for $C_{16}H_{19}N_3O_4S$! Of all the possible structural formulas for this molecular formula, only one is the antibiotic ampicillin (Figure 3.5). Whenever you write or think about a formula, try to remember that it represents a real object.

Table 3.4 Two Compounds with Molecular Formula C_2H_6O

Property	Ethanol	Dimethyl Ether
$\mathcal{M}$ (g/mol)	46.07	46.07
Color	Colorless	Colorless
Melting point	−117°C	−138.5°C
Boiling point	78.5°C	−25°C
Density (at 20°C)	0.789 g/mL (liquid)	0.00195 g/mL (gas)
Use	Intoxicant in alcoholic beverages	In refrigeration
Structural formula and space-filling model		

Section Summary

From the masses of elements in an unknown compound, the relative amounts (in moles) can be found and the empirical formula determined. If the molar mass is known, the molecular formula can also be determined. Methods such as combustion analysis provide data on the masses of elements in a compound, which can be used to obtain the formula. Because atoms can bond in different arrangements, a single molecular formula may correspond to more than one compound.

3.3 Writing and Balancing Chemical Equations

Perhaps the most important reason for thinking in terms of moles is that doing so greatly clarifies the amounts of substances taking part in a reaction. Comparing masses does not tell the ratio of substances reacting but comparing numbers of moles does. It allows us to view substances as large populations of interacting particles rather than as grams of material. To clarify this idea, consider the formation of hydrogen fluoride gas from H_2 and F_2, a reaction that occurs explosively at room temperature. If we weigh the gases, we find that

2.016 g H_2 and 38.00 g F_2 react to form 40.02 g HF

This information tells us little except that mass is conserved. However, if we convert these masses (in grams) to amounts (in moles), we find that

1 mol H_2 and 1 mol F_2 react to form 2 mol HF

This information reveals that equal-size populations of H_2 and F_2 molecules combine to form a population of HF molecules twice as large as either one. Dividing through by Avogadro's number shows us the chemical event as it occurs between individual molecules:

1 H_2 molecule and 1 F_2 molecule react to form 2 HF molecules

Figure 3.6 shows that when we express the reaction in terms of moles, *the macroscopic (molar) change corresponds to the submicroscopic (molecular) change.* As you'll see, a balanced chemical equation shows both changes.

A **chemical equation** is a statement in formulas that expresses the identities and quantities of the substances involved in a chemical or physical change. Equations are the "sentences" of chemistry, just as chemical formulas are the "words" and atomic symbols are the "letters." The left side of an equation shows the amount of each substance present before the change, and

Figure 3.5 Ampicillin. Only this particular arrangement of the atoms in the formula $C_{16}H_{19}N_3O_4S$ is the widely used antibiotic.

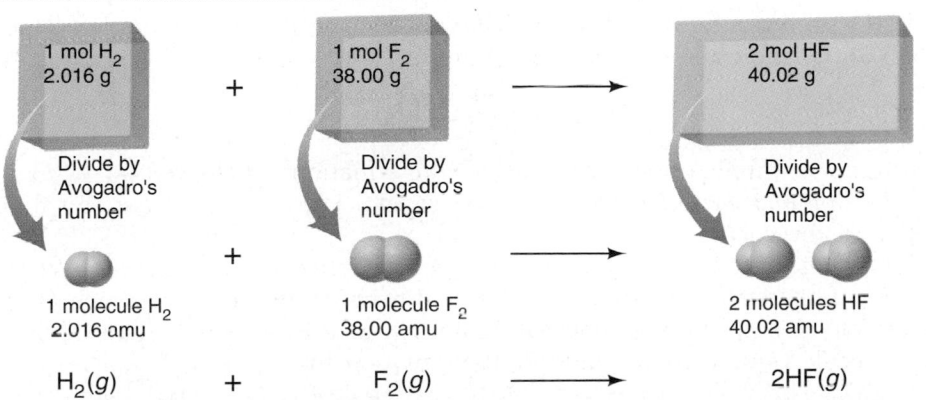

Figure 3.6 The formation of HF gas on the macroscopic and molecular levels. When 1 mol H_2 (2.016 g) and 1 mol F_2 (38.00 g) react, 2 mol HF (40.02 g) form. Dividing by Avogadro's number shows the change at the molecular level.

the right side shows the amounts present afterward. *For an equation to depict these amounts accurately, it must be balanced; that is, the same number of each type of atom must appear on both sides of the equation.* This requirement follows directly from the mass laws and the atomic theory:

- In a chemical process, atoms cannot be created, destroyed, or changed, only rearranged into different combinations.
- Compound formulas represent fixed ratios of component elements, so a different ratio represents a different compound.

Consider the chemical change that occurs inside a photographic flashbulb: magnesium wire and oxygen gas yield powdery magnesium oxide. (Light and heat are produced as well, but here we're concerned only with the substances involved.) Let's convert this chemical statement into a balanced equation through the following steps:

1. *Translating the statement.* We first translate the chemical statement into a "skeleton" equation: correct chemical formulas arranged in an equation format. All the substances that react in the change, called **reactants,** are placed to the left of a "yield" arrow, which points to all the substances produced, called **products:**

$$\underset{\text{reactants}}{\underline{}Mg \quad + \quad \underline{}O_2} \quad \xrightarrow{\text{yield}} \quad \underset{\text{product}}{\underline{}MgO}$$

Magnesium and oxygen gas yield magnesium oxide

At the beginning of the balancing process, we put a blank in front of each substance to remind us that we must account for its atoms.

2. *Balancing the atoms.* The next step involves shifting your attention back and forth from right to left in order to *match the number of each type of atom on each side.* At the end of this step, each blank will contain a **balancing (stoichiometric) coefficient,** a numerical multiplier of *all the atoms* in the formula that follows it. In general,

- Start with the most complex substance, the one with the largest number of atoms or different types of atoms.
- End with the least complex substance, such as an element by itself.

In this case, MgO is the most complex, so we place a coefficient 1 *in front of* the compound:

$$\underline{}Mg + \underline{}O_2 \longrightarrow \underline{1}\,MgO$$

To balance the Mg in MgO on the right, we place a 1 in front of Mg on the left:

$$\underline{1}\,Mg + \underline{}O_2 \longrightarrow \underline{1}\,MgO$$

The O atom on the right must be balanced by one O atom on the left. One-half an O_2 molecule provides one O atom:

$$\underline{1}\,Mg + \underline{\tfrac{1}{2}}\,O_2 \longrightarrow \underline{1}\,MgO$$

In terms of number and type of atom, the equation is balanced.

3. *Adjusting the coefficients.* There are several conventions about the final form of the coefficients:

- In most cases, *the smallest whole-number coefficients are preferred.* Whole numbers allow us to show the actual reacting entities intact, such as O_2 molecules. Although one-half mole O_2 can exist, one-half of an O_2 molecule cannot, so we multiply the equation by 2:

$$2Mg + 1O_2 \longrightarrow 2MgO$$

- We used the coefficient 1 to remind us to balance each substance. In the final form, a coefficient of 1 is implied by the formula of the substance, so we don't need to write it:

$$2Mg + O_2 \longrightarrow 2MgO$$

(This convention is similar to the practice of not writing a subscript 1 in a formula.)

4. *Checking.* After balancing and adjusting the coefficients, always check that the equation is balanced:

$$\text{Reactants (2 Mg, 2 O)} \longrightarrow \text{products (2 Mg, 2 O)}$$

5. *Specifying the states of matter.* The final equation also indicates the physical state of each substance or whether it is dissolved in water. The abbreviations used for these states are solid (*s*), liquid (*l*), gas (*g*), and aqueous solution (*aq*). From the original statement, Mg "wire" is solid, O_2 is a gas, and "powdery" MgO is also solid. The balanced equation is

$$2Mg(s) + O_2(g) \longrightarrow 2MgO(s)$$

Figure 3.7 shows this reaction from three points of view—as you see it on the macroscopic level, as chemists (and you!) can imagine it on the atomic level (darker colored atoms represent the stoichiometry), and on the symbolic level of the chemical equation.

Figure 3.7 A three-level view of the chemical reaction in a flashbulb. The photos present the macroscopic view that the chemist sees in the laboratory. Before the reaction occurs, a fine magnesium filament is surrounded by oxygen (*left*). After the reaction, white, powdery magnesium oxide coats the bulb's inner surface (*right*). The blow-up arrows lead to an atomic-scale view, a representation of the chemist's mental picture of the reaction. The darker colored spheres show the stoichiometry. By knowing the substances present before and after a reaction, we can write a balanced equation (*bottom*), the chemist's symbolic shorthand for the change.

Keep in mind these other key points about the balancing process:

- A coefficient operates on *all the atoms in the formula* that follows it: 2MgO means 2 × (MgO), or 2 Mg atoms and 2 O atoms; 2Ca(NO$_3$)$_2$ means 2 × [Ca(NO$_3$)$_2$], or 2 Ca atoms, 4 N atoms, and 12 O atoms.
- In balancing an equation, *chemical formulas cannot be altered*. In step 2 of our flashbulb example, we *cannot* balance the O atoms by changing MgO to MgO$_2$ because MgO$_2$ has a different elemental composition and is thus a different compound.
- We *cannot add other reactants or products* to balance the equation because this represents a different chemical reaction. For example, we *cannot* balance the O atoms by changing O$_2$ to O or by adding one O atom to the products, because the chemical statement does not say that the reaction involves O atoms.
- A balanced equation remains balanced even if you multiply all the coefficients by the same number. For example,

$$4Mg(s) + 2O_2(g) \longrightarrow 4MgO(s)$$

is also balanced: it is just the original balanced equation multiplied by 2. But, we balance an equation with the *smallest* whole-number coefficients.

Sample Problem 3.7   Balancing Chemical Equations

PROBLEM Within the cylinders of a car's engine, the hydrocarbon octane (C$_8$H$_{18}$), one of many components of gasoline, mixes with oxygen from the air and burns to form carbon dioxide and water vapor. Write a balanced equation for this reaction.

SOLUTION

1. *Translate* the statement into a skeleton equation (with coefficient blanks). Octane and oxygen are reactants; "oxygen from the air" implies molecular oxygen, O$_2$. Carbon dioxide and water vapor are products:

$$\_C_8H_{18} + \_O_2 \longrightarrow \_CO_2 + \_H_2O$$

2. *Balance the atoms.* We start with the most complex substance, C$_8$H$_{18}$, and balance O$_2$ last:

$$\underline{1}C_8H_{18} + \_O_2 \longrightarrow \_CO_2 + \_H_2O$$

The C atoms in C$_8$H$_{18}$ end up in CO$_2$. Each CO$_2$ contains one C atom, so 8 molecules of CO$_2$ are needed to balance the 8 C atoms in each C$_8$H$_{18}$:

$$\underline{1}C_8H_{18} + \_O_2 \longrightarrow \underline{8}CO_2 + \_H_2O$$

The H atoms in C$_8$H$_{18}$ end up in H$_2$O. The 18 H atoms in C$_8$H$_{18}$ require a coefficient 9 in front of H$_2$O:

$$\underline{1}C_8H_{18} + \_O_2 \longrightarrow \underline{8}CO_2 + \underline{9}H_2O$$

There are 25 atoms of O on the right (16 in 8CO$_2$ plus 9 in 9H$_2$O), so we place the coefficient $\frac{25}{2}$ in front of O$_2$:

$$\underline{1}C_8H_{18} + \frac{25}{2}O_2 \longrightarrow \underline{8}CO_2 + \underline{9}H_2O$$

3. *Adjust the coefficients.* Multiply through by 2 to obtain whole numbers:

$$2C_8H_{18} + 25O_2 \longrightarrow 16CO_2 + 18H_2O$$

4. *Check* that the equation is balanced:

$$\text{Reactants (16 C, 36 H, 50 O)} \longrightarrow \text{products (16 C, 36 H, 50 O)}$$

5. *Specify* states of matter. C$_8$H$_{18}$ is liquid; O$_2$, CO$_2$, and H$_2$O vapor are gases:

$$2C_8H_{18}(l) + 25O_2(g) \longrightarrow 16CO_2(g) + 18H_2O(g)$$

COMMENT This is an example of a combustion reaction. *Any* C,H-containing compound that burns in an excess of air produces CO_2 and H_2O.

Follow-up Problem 3.7 Write balanced equations for each of the following chemical statements:
(a) A characteristic reaction of Group 1A(1) elements: chunks of sodium react violently with water to form hydrogen gas and sodium hydroxide solution.
(b) The destruction of marble statuary by acid rain: aqueous nitric acid reacts with calcium carbonate to form carbon dioxide, water, and aqueous calcium nitrate.
(c) Halogen compounds exchanging bonding partners: phosphorus trifluoride is prepared by the reaction of phosphorus trichloride and hydrogen fluoride; hydrogen chloride is the other product. The reaction involves gases only.
(d) Explosive decomposition of dynamite: liquid nitroglycerine ($C_3H_5N_3O_9$) explodes to produce a mixture of gases—carbon dioxide, water vapor, nitrogen, and oxygen.

Section Summary

To conserve mass and maintain the fixed composition of compounds, a chemical equation must be balanced in terms of number and type of each atom. A balanced equation consists of reactant formulas on the left of a yield arrow and product formulas on the right. The coefficients used to balance the atoms are integer multipliers that apply to *all* the atoms in a formula.

3.4 Calculating Amounts of Reactant and Product

A balanced equation contains a wealth of quantitative information relating individual chemical entities, amounts of chemical entities, and masses of substances. Table 3.5 presents this information for the combustion of propane, a hydrocarbon fuel used in cooking and water heating. A balanced equation is essential for all calculations involving amounts of reactants and products: *if you know the number of moles of one substance, the balanced equation tells you the number of moles of all the others in the reaction.*

Table 3.5 Information Contained in a Balanced Equation

Viewed in Terms of	Reactants $C_3H_8(g) + 5O_2(g)$	$\longrightarrow$	Products $3CO_2(g) + 4H_2O(g)$
Molecules	1 molecule C_3H_8 + 5 molecules O_2	$\longrightarrow$	3 molecules CO_2 + 4 molecules H_2O
Amount (mol)	1 mol C_3H_8 + 5 mol O_2	$\longrightarrow$	3 mol CO_2 + 4 mol H_2O
Mass (amu)	44.09 amu C_3H_8 + 160.00 amu O_2	$\longrightarrow$	132.03 amu CO_2 + 72.06 amu H_2O
Mass (g)	44.09 g C_3H_8 + 160.00 g O_2	$\longrightarrow$	132.03 g CO_2 + 72.06 g H_2O
Total mass (g)	204.09 g	$\longrightarrow$	204.09 g

Stoichiometrically Equivalent Molar Ratios from the Balanced Equation

In a balanced equation, *the number of moles of one substance is stoichiometrically equivalent to the number of moles of any other substance.* The term *stoichiometrically equivalent* means that a definite amount of one substance is formed from, produces, or reacts with a definite amount of another. These quantitative relationships are expressed as *stoichiometrically equivalent molar ratios* that we use as conversion factors to calculate these amounts. The propane combustion reaction (Table 3.5) serves as our example:

$$C_3H_8(g) + 5O_2(g) \longrightarrow 3CO_2(g) + 4H_2O(g)$$

If we view the reaction quantitatively in terms of C_3H_8, we see that

1 mol C_3H_8 reacts with 5 mol O_2

1 mol C_3H_8 produces 3 mol CO_2

1 mol C_3H_8 produces 4 mol H_2O

Therefore, in this reaction,

1 mol C_3H_8 is stoichiometrically equivalent to 5 mol O_2

1 mol C_3H_8 is stoichiometrically equivalent to 3 mol CO_2

1 mol C_3H_8 is stoichiometrically equivalent to 4 mol H_2O

We chose to look at C_3H_8, but any two of the substances are stoichiometrically equivalent to each other. Thus,

3 mol CO_2 is stoichiometrically equivalent to 4 mol H_2O

5 mol O_2 is stoichiometrically equivalent to 3 mol CO_2

and so on.

Here's a typical problem that shows how stoichiometric equivalence is used to create conversion factors: In the combustion of propane, how many moles of O_2 are consumed when 10.0 mol H_2O are produced? To solve this problem, we have to find the molar ratio between O_2 and H_2O. From the balanced equation, we see that for every 5 mol O_2 consumed, 4 mol H_2O are formed:

5 mol O_2 is stoichiometrically equivalent to 4 mol H_2O

We can construct two conversion factors from this equivalence depending on the quantity we are trying to find:

$$\frac{5 \text{ mol } O_2}{4 \text{ mol } H_2O} \quad \text{or} \quad \frac{4 \text{ mol } H_2O}{5 \text{ mol } O_2}$$

Since we want to find moles of O_2 and we know moles of H_2O, we choose "5 mol O_2/4 mol H_2O" to cancel "mol H_2O":

$$\text{Moles of } O_2 \text{ consumed} = 10.0 \text{ mol } H_2O \times \frac{5 \text{ mol } O_2}{4 \text{ mol } H_2O} = 12.5 \text{ mol } O_2$$

$$\text{mol } H_2O \underset{\substack{\text{molar ratio as} \\ \text{conversion factor}}}{\Longrightarrow} \text{mol } O_2$$

Obviously, we could not have solved this problem without the balanced equation. Here is a general approach for solving *any* stoichiometry problem that involves a chemical reaction:

1. Write a balanced equation for the reaction.
2. Convert the given mass (or number of entities) of the first substance to amount (mol).
3. Use the appropriate molar ratio from the balanced equation to calculate the amount (mol) of the second substance.
4. Convert the amount of the second substance to the desired mass (or number of entities).

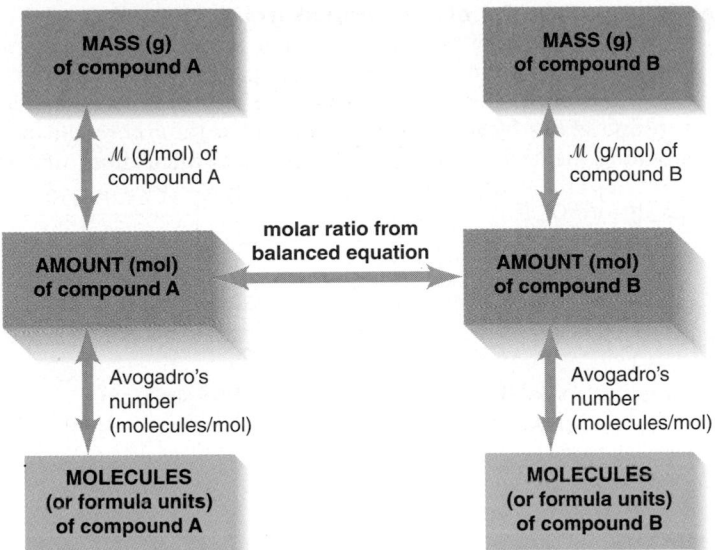

Figure 3.8 **Summary of the mass-mole-number relationships in a chemical reaction.** The amount of one substance in a reaction is related to that of any other. Quantities are expressed in terms of grams, moles, or number of entities (atoms, molecules, or formula units). Start at any box in the diagram (known) and move to any other box (unknown) by using the information on the arrows as conversion factors. As an example, if you know the mass (in g) of A and want to know the number of molecules of B, the path involves three calculation steps:
1. Grams of A to moles of A, using the molar mass ($\mathcal{M}$) of A
2. Moles of A to moles of B, using the molar ratio from the balanced equation
3. Moles of B to molecules of B, using Avogadro's number
Steps 1 and 3 refer to calculations discussed in Section 3.1 (see Figure 3.3).

This approach is depicted in Figure 3.8 and demonstrated in the following sample problems.

Sample Problem 3.8 Calculating Amounts of Reactants and Products

PROBLEM In a lifetime, the average American uses 1750 lb (794 kg) of copper in coins, plumbing, and wiring. Copper is obtained from sulfide ores, such as chalcocite, or copper(I) sulfide, by a multistage process. After an initial grinding step, the first stage is to "roast" the ore (heat it strongly with oxygen gas) to form powdered copper(I) oxide and gaseous sulfur dioxide.
(a) How many moles of oxygen are required to roast 10.0 mol copper(I) sulfide?
(b) How many grams of sulfur dioxide are formed when 10.0 mol copper(I) sulfide is roasted?
(c) How many kilograms of oxygen are required to form 2.86 kg copper(I) oxide?

(a) Determining the moles of O_2 needed to react with 10.0 mol Cu_2S
PLAN We *always* write the balanced equation first. The reactants are Cu_2S and O_2, and the products are Cu_2O and SO_2:

$$2Cu_2S(s) + 3O_2(g) \longrightarrow 2Cu_2O(s) + 2SO_2(g)$$

We are given the *moles* of Cu_2S and need to find the *moles* of O_2. The balanced equation shows that 3 mol O_2 is needed for every 2 mol Cu_2S consumed, so the conversion factor is "3 mol O_2/2 mol Cu_2S." This calculation step appears in the roadmap.
SOLUTION Calculating number of moles of O_2:

$$\text{Moles of } O_2 = 10.0 \text{ mol } Cu_2S \times \frac{3 \text{ mol } O_2}{2 \text{ mol } Cu_2S} = \boxed{15.0 \text{ mol } O_2}$$

CHECK The answer is reasonable, since this O_2/Cu_2S molar ratio (15:10) is the same as the ratio in the balanced equation (3:2).
COMMENT A *common mistake* is to use the incorrect conversion factor; the calculation would then be

$$\text{Moles of } O_2 = 10.0 \text{ mol } Cu_2S \times \frac{2 \text{ mol } Cu_2S}{3 \text{ mol } O_2} = \frac{6.67 \text{ mol}^2 \ Cu_2S}{1 \text{ mol } O_2}$$

These strange units should signal that you made an error in setting up the conversion factor. In addition, the size of the answer, 6.67, is *less* than 10.0, whereas the balanced equation shows that *more* moles of O_2 than of Cu_2S are needed. Be sure to *think through the calculation when setting up the conversion factor and keep track of units*.

Amount (mol) of Cu_2S

molar ratio

Amount (mol) of O_2

(b) Determining the mass (g) of SO_2 formed from 10.0 mol Cu_2S

PLAN Here we need the *grams* of product (SO_2) that forms from the given *moles* of reactant (Cu_2S). We first find the moles of SO_2 using the molar ratio from the balanced equation (2 mol SO_2/2 mol Cu_2S) and then multiply by its molar mass (64.07 g/mol) to find grams of SO_2. The steps appear in the top roadmap.

SOLUTION Combining the two conversion steps into one calculation, we have

$$\text{Mass (g) of } SO_2 = 10.0 \text{ mol } Cu_2S \times \frac{2 \text{ mol } SO_2}{2 \text{ mol } Cu_2S} \times \frac{64.07 \text{ g } SO_2}{1 \text{ mol } SO_2}$$

$$= \boxed{641 \text{ g } SO_2}$$

CHECK The answer makes sense, since the molar ratio shows that 10.0 mol SO_2 are formed and each weighs about 64 g. We rounded to three significant figures.

(c) Determining the mass (kg) of O_2 that yields 2.86 kg Cu_2O

PLAN Here the mass of product (Cu_2O) is known, and we need the mass of reactant (O_2) that reacts to form it. We first convert the quantity of Cu_2O from *kilograms* to *moles* (in two steps, as shown on the bottom roadmap). Then, we use the molar ratio (3 mol O_2/2 mol Cu_2O) to find the *moles* of O_2 required. Finally, we convert *moles* of O_2 to *kilograms* (in two steps).

SOLUTION Converting from kilograms of Cu_2O to moles of Cu_2O: Combining the mass unit conversion with the mass-to-mole conversion gives

$$\text{Moles of } Cu_2O = 2.86 \text{ kg } Cu_2O \times \frac{10^3 \text{ g}}{1 \text{ kg}} \times \frac{1 \text{ mol } Cu_2O}{143.10 \text{ g } Cu_2O} = 20.0 \text{ mol } Cu_2O$$

Converting from moles of Cu_2O to moles of O_2:

$$\text{Moles of } O_2 = 20.0 \text{ mol } Cu_2O \times \frac{3 \text{ mol } O_2}{2 \text{ mol } Cu_2O} = 30.0 \text{ mol } O_2$$

Converting from moles of O_2 to kilograms of O_2: Combining the mole-to-mass conversion with the mass unit conversion gives

$$\text{Mass (kg) of } O_2 = 30.0 \text{ mol } O_2 \times \frac{32.00 \text{ g } O_2}{1 \text{ mol } O_2} \times \frac{1 \text{ kg}}{10^3 \text{ g}}$$

$$= \boxed{0.960 \text{ kg } O_2}$$

CHECK The units are correct. Round off to check the math: for example, in the final step, ~30 mol × 30 g/mol × 1 kg/10^3 g = 0.90 kg. The answer seems reasonable: even though the amount (mol) of O_2 is greater than the amount (mol) of Cu_2O, the mass of O_2 is less than the mass of Cu_2O because M of O_2 is less than M of Cu_2O.

COMMENT This problem highlights a key point for solving stoichiometry problems: *convert the information given into moles.* Then, use the appropriate molar ratio and any other conversion factors to complete the problem.

Follow-up Problem 3.8 Thermite is a mixture of iron(III) oxide and aluminum powders that was once used to weld railroad tracks. It undergoes a spectacular reaction to yield solid aluminum oxide and molten iron.
(a) How many grams of iron form when 135 g aluminum react?
(b) How many atoms of aluminum react for every 1.00 g aluminum oxide that forms?

Chemical Reactions That Occur in a Sequence

In many situations, a product of one reaction becomes a reactant of the next in a sequence of reactions. For stoichiometric purposes, when a given substance forms in one reaction and is used up in the next, we eliminate this common substance in an **overall (net) equation:**

1. Write the sequence of balanced equations.
2. Adjust the equations arithmetically to cancel out the common substance.
3. Add the adjusted equations together to obtain the overall balanced equation.

Sample Problem 3.9 shows the approach by continuing the copper recovery process that was begun in Sample Problem 3.8.

Sample Problem 3.9 Calculating Amounts of Reactants and Products in a Reaction Sequence

Chalcocite, a sulfide ore of copper.

PROBLEM Roasting is the first step in extracting copper from chalcocite, the ore used in the previous problem (*see photo*). In the next step, copper(I) oxide reacts with powdered carbon to yield copper metal and carbon monoxide gas. Write a balanced overall equation for the two-step sequence.

PLAN To obtain the overall equation, we write the individual equations in sequence, adjust coefficients to cancel the common substance (or substances), and add the equations together. In this case, only Cu_2O appears as a product in one equation and as a reactant in the other, so it is the common substance.

SOLUTION Writing the individual balanced equations:

$$2Cu_2S(s) + 3O_2(g) \longrightarrow 2Cu_2O(s) + 2SO_2(g) \text{ [equation 1; see Sample Problem 3.8(a)]}$$

$$Cu_2O(s) + C(s) \longrightarrow 2Cu(s) + CO(g) \text{ [equation 2]}$$

Adjusting the coefficients: Since 2 mol Cu_2O are produced in equation 1 but only 1 mol Cu_2O reacts in equation 2, we double *all* the coefficients in equation 2. Thus, the Cu_2O from equation 1 is used up in equation 2:

$$2Cu_2S(s) + 3O_2(g) \longrightarrow 2Cu_2O(s) + 2SO_2(g) \quad \text{[equation 1]}$$

$$2Cu_2O(s) + 2C(s) \longrightarrow 4Cu(s) + 2CO(g) \quad \text{[equation 2, doubled]}$$

Adding the two equations and canceling the common substance: We keep the reactants of both equations on the left and the products of both equations on the right:

$$2Cu_2S(s) + 3O_2(g) + \cancel{2Cu_2O(s)} + 2C(s) \longrightarrow \cancel{2Cu_2O(s)} + 2SO_2(g) + 4Cu(s) + 2CO(g)$$

Or,

$$2Cu_2S(s) + 3O_2(g) + 2C(s) \longrightarrow 2SO_2(g) + 4Cu(s) + 2CO(g)$$

CHECK Reactants (4 Cu, 2 S, 6 O, 2 C) $\longrightarrow$ products (4 Cu, 2 S, 6 O, 2 C)

COMMENT 1. Even though Cu_2O *does* participate in the chemical change, it is not involved in the reaction stoichiometry. An overall equation *may not* show which substances actually react; for example, C(s) and $Cu_2S(s)$ do not interact directly here, even though both are shown as reactants.
2. The SO_2 formed in metal extraction contributes to acid rain. To help control the problem, chemists have devised microbial and electrochemical extraction methods that avoid the roasting of sulfide ores to obtain copper and other metals.
3. These reactions were shown to explain how to obtain an overall equation. The actual extraction of copper is somewhat more complex and will be discussed later in the text (Chapter 22).

Follow-up Problem 3.9 The SO_2 produced in copper recovery reacts in air with oxygen and forms sulfur trioxide. This gas, in turn, reacts with water to form a sulfuric acid solution that falls as rain or snow. Write a balanced overall equation for this process.

Multistep reaction sequences called *metabolic pathways* are common in biological systems. In most cells, the chemical energy in glucose is released through a sequence of about 30 individual reactions. The product of each reaction is the reactant of the next, so that all the common substances cancel. The overall equation is

$$C_6H_{12}O_6(aq) + 6O_2(g) \longrightarrow 6CO_2(g) + 6H_2O(l)$$

We eat food that contains glucose, inhale O_2, and excrete CO_2 and H_2O. In our cells, these reactants and products are many steps apart: O_2 never reacts *directly* with glucose. However, the molar ratios are the same as if the glucose burned in a combustion apparatus filled with pure O_2 and formed CO_2 and H_2O directly.

Chemical Reactions That Involve a Limiting Reactant

In problems up to now, the amount of *one* reactant was given, and we assumed there was enough of any other reactant for the first reactant to be completely used up. For example, to find the amount of SO_2 that forms when 100 g Cu_2S reacts, we convert the grams of Cu_2S to moles and assume it reacts with as much O_2 as needed. Since all the Cu_2S is used up, its initial amount determines, or limits, how much SO_2 can form. We call Cu_2S the **limiting reactant** (or *limiting reagent*) because the reaction stops once the Cu_2S is gone, no matter how much O_2 is present. Suppose, however, that the amounts of both Cu_2S *and* O_2 are given and we want to know how much SO_2 forms. We first have to determine whether Cu_2S *or* O_2 is the limiting reactant because *its* amount limits how much SO_2 can form. The other reactant is present *in excess,* and however much of it is not used is left over.

To clarify the idea of limiting reactant, let's consider a much more appetizing situation. Suppose you have a job making sundaes in an ice cream parlor. Each sundae requires two scoops (12 oz) of ice cream, one cherry, and 50 mL chocolate syrup:

$$\text{2 scoops (12 oz)} + \text{1 cherry} + \text{50 mL syrup} \longrightarrow \text{1 sundae}$$

A mob of 25 ravenous school kids enters, and every one wants a vanilla sundae. Can you feed them all? You have 300 oz of vanilla ice cream, 30 cherries, and 1 L of syrup, so a quick calculation shows the number of sundaes you can make from each ingredient:

Ice cream: No. of sundaes $= 300 \; \text{oz} \times \dfrac{2 \; \text{scoops}}{12 \; \text{oz}} \times \dfrac{1 \; \text{sundae}}{2 \; \text{scoops}} = 25 \; \text{sundaes}$

Cherries: No. of sundaes $= 30 \; \text{cherries} \times \dfrac{1 \; \text{sundae}}{1 \; \text{cherry}} = 30 \; \text{sundaes}$

Syrup: No. of sundaes $= 1000 \; \text{mL syrup} \times \dfrac{1 \; \text{sundae}}{50 \; \text{mL syrup}} = 20 \; \text{sundaes}$

The syrup is the limiting "reactant" here because it limits the total amount of "product" that can "form": of the three ingredients, the syrup allowed the *fewest* sundaes to be made (Figure 3.9).

Figure 3.9 An ice cream sundae analogy for limiting reactants. A, The "components" combine in specific amounts to form a sundae. **B,** In this example, the number of sundaes possible is limited by the amount of syrup, the limiting "reactant." Here, only two sundaes can be made. Four scoops of ice cream and four cherries remain "in excess." See text for another example.

Some ice cream and cherries are left "unreacted" when all the syrup is gone, so they are present in excess:

300 oz (50 scoops) + 30 cherries + 1 L syrup $\longrightarrow$

20 sundaes + 60 oz (10 scoops) + 10 cherries

In limiting-reactant problems, the amounts of two (or more) reactants are given, and we must first determine which is limiting. To do so, *we choose the reactant that yields the **lower** amount of product.* One approach, illustrated in Sample Problem 3.10, is to perform two calculations, each of which assumes an excess of one or the other reactant. ◆

Sample Problem 3.10 Calculating Amounts of Reactant and Product in Reactions Involving a Limiting Reactant

PROBLEM A fuel mixture used in the early days of rocketry is composed of two liquids, hydrazine (N_2H_4) and dinitrogen tetraoxide (N_2O_4), which ignite on contact to form nitrogen gas and water vapor. How many grams of nitrogen gas form when 1.00×10^2 g N_2H_4 and 2.00×10^2 g N_2O_4 are mixed?

PLAN As always, we first write the balanced equation. *The fact that the amounts of two reactants are given tells us that this is a limiting-reactant problem.* To determine which reactant is limiting, we calculate the mass of N_2 formed from each reactant *assuming an excess of the other.* We convert the mass of each reactant to number of moles and use the appropriate molar ratio to find the number of moles of N_2 each forms. Whichever yields *less* N_2 is the limiting reactant. Then, we convert this lower number of moles of N_2 to mass. The roadmap shows the steps.

SOLUTION Writing the balanced equation:

$$2N_2H_4(l) + N_2O_4(l) \longrightarrow 3N_2(g) + 4H_2O(g)$$

Finding the moles of N_2 from the moles of N_2H_4 (if N_2H_4 is limiting):

$$\text{Moles of } N_2H_4 = 1.00 \times 10^2 \text{ g } N_2H_4 \times \frac{1 \text{ mol } N_2H_4}{32.05 \text{ g } N_2H_4} = 3.12 \text{ mol } N_2H_4$$

$$\text{Moles of } N_2 = 3.12 \text{ mol } N_2H_4 \times \frac{3 \text{ mol } N_2}{2 \text{ mol } N_2H_4} = \textbf{4.68 mol } N_2$$

Finding the moles of N_2 from the moles of N_2O_4 (if N_2O_4 is limiting):

$$\text{Moles of } N_2O_4 = 2.00 \times 10^2 \text{ g } N_2O_4 \times \frac{1 \text{ mol } N_2O_4}{92.02 \text{ g } N_2O_4} = 2.17 \text{ mol } N_2O_4$$

$$\text{Moles of } N_2 = 2.17 \text{ mol } N_2O_4 \times \frac{3 \text{ mol } N_2}{1 \text{ mol } N_2O_4} = \textbf{6.51 mol } N_2$$

Thus, N_2H_4 is the limiting reactant because it yields fewer moles of N_2. Converting from moles of N_2 to grams:

$$\text{Mass (g) of } N_2 = 4.68 \text{ mol } N_2 \times \frac{28.02 \text{ g } N_2}{1 \text{ mol } N_2} = \boxed{131 \text{ g } N_2}$$

CHECK Even though the mass of N_2O_4 is greater than that of N_2H_4, there are fewer moles because $\mathcal{M}$ of N_2O_4 is much higher. Round off to check the math; for example, for N_2H_4, 100 g $N_2H_4 \times 1 \text{ mol}/32 \text{ g} \approx 3 \text{ mol}$; $\sim3 \text{ mol} \times \frac{3}{2} \approx 4.5 \text{ mol } N_2$; $\sim4.5 \text{ mol} \times 30 \text{ g/mol} \approx 135 \text{ g } N_2$

COMMENT 1. Two *common mistakes* that arise in limiting-reactant problems are
- To choose the *reactant* present in fewer moles (2.17 mol N_2O_4 vs. 3.12 mol N_2H_4) as the limiting reactant. Rather, it is the reactant that forms fewer moles of *product.*
- To choose the *reactant* with lower mass as the limiting reactant. Rather, it is the reactant that forms the lower mass of *product.*

2. Here is an *alternative approach* to determining which reactant is limiting. Find the moles of each reactant that would be required to react with the other. Then see which of the amounts actually given in the problem is sufficient. That substance is in excess and the other is limiting. For example, the balanced equation shows that

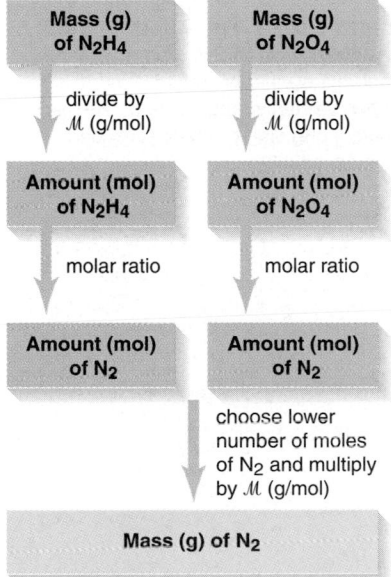

2 mol N_2H_4 react with 1 mol N_2O_4. The moles of N_2O_4 needed to react with the given N_2H_4 are

$$\text{Moles of } N_2O_4 \text{ needed} = 3.12 \cancel{\text{ mol } N_2H_4} \times \frac{1 \text{ mol } N_2O_4}{2 \cancel{\text{ mol } N_2H_4}} = 1.56 \text{ mol } N_2O_4$$

The moles of N_2H_4 needed to react with the given N_2O_4 are

$$\text{Moles of } N_2H_4 \text{ needed} = 2.17 \cancel{\text{ mol } N_2O_4} \times \frac{2 \text{ mol } N_2H_4}{1 \cancel{\text{ mol } N_2O_4}} = 4.34 \text{ mol } N_2H_4$$

We are given 2.17 mol N_2O_4, *more* than the amount of N_2O_4 needed (1.56 mol) to react with the given amount of N_2H_4, and we are given 3.12 mol N_2H_4, *less* than the amount of N_2H_4 needed (4.34 mol) to react with the given amount of N_2O_4. Therefore, N_2H_4 is limiting, and N_2O_4 is in excess. Then, we continue with the final calculation to find the amount of N_2.

Follow-up Problem 3.10 How many grams of solid aluminum sulfide can be prepared by the reaction of 10.0 g aluminum and 15.0 g sulfur? How much of the nonlimiting reactant is in excess?

Chemical Reactions in Practice: Theoretical, Actual, and Percent Yields

Up until now, we've been optimistic about the amount of product obtained from a reaction. We have assumed that 100% of the limiting reactant becomes product, that ideal separation and purification methods exist for isolating the product, and that we use perfect laboratory technique to collect all the product formed. In other words, we have assumed that we obtain the **theoretical yield,** the amount indicated by the stoichiometrically equivalent molar ratio in the balanced equation.

It's time to face reality. The theoretical yield is *never* obtained, for reasons that are largely uncontrollable. For one thing, although the major reaction predominates, many reactant mixtures also proceed through one or more **side reactions** that form smaller amounts of different products, as shown in Figure 3.10. In the previous rocket fuel reaction, for example, the reactants might form some NO in the following side reaction:

$$2N_2O_4(l) + N_2H_4(l) \longrightarrow 6NO(g) + 2H_2O(g)$$

This reaction decreases the amounts of reactants available for N_2 production (see Problem 3.116 at the end of the chapter). Even more important, as we'll discuss in Chapter 4, many reactions seem to stop before they are complete, leaving some limiting reactant unreacted. But, even when a reaction does go completely to product, losses occur in virtually every step of a separation procedure (see Tools of the Chemistry Laboratory, Section 2.9): a tiny amount of product clings to filter paper, some distillate evaporates, a small amount of extract remains in the separatory funnel, and so forth. With careful technique, you can minimize these losses but never eliminate them. The amount of product that you actually obtain is the **actual yield.** The **percent yield (% yield)** is the actual yield expressed as a percent of the theoretical yield:

$$\% \text{ yield} = \frac{\text{actual yield}}{\text{theoretical yield}} \times 100 \tag{3.7}$$

Since the actual yield must be less than the theoretical yield, the percent yield is always less than 100%. Theoretical and actual yields are expressed in units of amount (moles) or mass (grams).

A + B
(reactants)

C
(main product)

D
(side product)

Figure 3.10 The effect of side reactions on yield. One reason the theoretical yield is never obtained is that other reactions lead some of the reactants along side paths to form undesired product.

Sample Problem 3.11 Calculating Percent Yield

PROBLEM Silicon carbide (SiC) is an important ceramic material that is made by allowing sand (silicon dioxide, SiO_2) to react with powdered carbon at high temperature. Carbon monoxide is also formed. When 100.0 kg of sand are processed, 51.4 kg SiC are recovered. What is the percent yield of SiC in this process?

PLAN We are given the actual yield of SiC, so we need the theoretical yield to calculate the percent yield. After writing the balanced equation, we convert the given mass (kg) of SiO_2 to amount (mol), find the amount of SiC formed from the molar ratio, and convert amount of SiC to mass (kg) to obtain the theoretical yield [see roadmap for Sample Problem 3.8(c)]. Then, we apply Equation 3.7 to find the percent yield.

SOLUTION Writing the balanced equation:

$$SiO_2(s) + 3C(s) \longrightarrow SiC(s) + 2CO(g)$$

Converting from kilograms of SiO_2 to moles:

$$\text{Moles of } SiO_2 = 100.0 \ \text{kg SiO}_2 \times \frac{1000 \ \text{g}}{1 \ \text{kg}} \times \frac{1 \ \text{mol } SiO_2}{60.09 \ \text{g SiO}_2} = 1664 \ \text{mol } SiO_2$$

Converting from moles of SiO_2 to moles of SiC: The molar ratio is 1 mol SiC/1 mol SiO_2, so

$$\text{Moles of } SiO_2 = \text{moles of SiC} = 1664 \ \text{mol SiC}$$

Converting from moles of SiC to kilograms:

$$\text{Mass (kg) of SiC} = 1664 \ \text{mol SiC} \times \frac{40.10 \ \text{g SiC}}{1 \ \text{mol SiC}} \times \frac{1 \ \text{kg}}{1000 \ \text{g}} = 66.73 \ \text{kg SiC}$$

Calculating the percent yield:

$$\% \text{ yield of SiC} = \frac{\text{actual yield}}{\text{theoretical yield}} \times 100 = \frac{51.4 \ \text{kg}}{66.73 \ \text{kg}} \times 100 = \boxed{77.0\%}$$

CHECK The mass of SiC seems correct: ~1500 mol × 40 g/mol × 1 kg/1000 g = 60 kg. The molar ratio of SiC/SiO_2 is 1/1, and the $\mathcal{M}$ of SiC is about two-thirds ($\frac{40}{60}$) the $\mathcal{M}$ of SiO_2, so 100 kg SiO_2 should form about 66 kg SiC.

Follow-up Problem 3.11   Marble (calcium carbonate) reacts with hydrochloric acid solution to form calcium chloride solution, water, and carbon dioxide. What is the percent yield of carbon dioxide if 3.65 g of the gas is collected when 10.0 g of marble reacts?

In multistep reaction sequences, the percent yields of the steps are expressed as fractions and multiplied together to find the overall percent yield. Even when the yield of each step is high, the final result can be surprisingly low. For example, suppose a six-step reaction sequence has a 90.0% yield for each step; that is, you are able to recover 90.0% of the theoretical yield of product in each step. The overall recovery is only slightly more than 50%:

$$\text{Overall } \% \text{ yield} = (0.900 \times 0.900 \times 0.900 \times 0.900 \times 0.900 \times 0.900) \times 100$$
$$= 53.1\%$$

Such multistep sequences are common in the synthesis of medicines, dyes, pesticides, and many other organic compounds. In a typical synthesis, large amounts of inexpensive, simple reactants are converted to small amounts of expensive, complex product, so overall percent yield greatly influences the commercial potential of a product.

Section Summary

The substances in a balanced equation are related to each other by stoichiometrically equivalent molar ratios, which can be used as conversion factors to find the moles of one substance given the moles of another. In limiting-reactant problems, the amounts of two (or more) reactants are given, and one of them limits the amount of product that forms. The limiting reactant is not necessarily the reactant present in lower amount but the one that forms the lower amount of product. In practice, side reactions, incomplete reactions, and physical losses result in an actual yield of product that is less than the theoretical yield, the amount based solely on the molar ratio.

3.5   Fundamentals of Solution Stoichiometry

In the popular media, you may have seen a chemist portrayed as a person in a white lab coat, surrounded by odd-shaped glassware, pouring one colored solution into another, which forms a rage of bubbles and billowing fumes. Although most reactions in solution are not this dramatic and good technique offers safer mixing procedures, the image is true to the extent that aqueous solution chemistry is a central part of laboratory activity. Liquid solutions are more convenient to store and mix than solids or gases, and the amounts of substances in solution can be measured very precisely. Since many environmental reactions and almost all biochemical reactions occur in solution, an understanding of reactions in solution is extremely important in chemistry and related sciences.

Only one aspect of the stoichiometry of dissolved substances is different from what we've seen so far. We know the amounts of pure substances by converting their masses directly into moles. For dissolved substances, we must know the *concentration*—the number of moles present in a certain volume of solution—to find the volume that contains a given number of moles. Of the many ways to express concentration, the most important is *molarity*, so we discuss it here (and wait until Chapter 13 to discuss the other ways). Then, we see how to prepare a solution of a specific molarity and how to use solutions in stoichiometric calculations.

Expressing Concentration in Terms of Molarity

A typical solution consists of a smaller amount of one substance, the **solute,** dissolved in a larger amount of another substance, the **solvent.** When a solution forms, the solute's individual chemical entities become *evenly dispersed* throughout the available volume and surrounded by solvent molecules. The **concentration** of a solution is usually expressed as *the amount of solute dissolved in a given amount of solution.* Concentration is an *intensive* quantity (like density or temperature) and thus independent of the volume of solution: a 50-L tank of a solution has the *same concentration* (solute amount/solution amount) as a 50-mL beaker of the solution. **Molarity *(M)*** expresses the concentration in terms of *moles of solute per liter of solution:*

$$\text{Molarity} = \frac{\text{moles of solute}}{\text{liters of solution}} \qquad \text{or} \qquad M = \frac{\text{mol solute}}{\text{L soln}} \qquad \textbf{(3.8)}$$

Sample Problem 3.12   Calculating the Molarity of a Solution

Amount (mol) of HBr

divide by volume (mL)

Concentration (mol/mL) of HBr

10^3 mL = 1 L

Molarity (mol/L) of HBr

PROBLEM Hydrobromic acid (HBr) is a solution of hydrogen bromide gas in water. Calculate the molarity of hydrobromic acid solution if 455 mL contains 1.80 mol hydrogen bromide.

PLAN The molarity is the number of moles of solute in each liter of solution. We are given the number of moles and the volume (in mL), so we divide moles by volume and convert the volume to liters to find the molarity.

SOLUTION

$$\text{Molarity} = \frac{1.80 \text{ mol HBr}}{455 \text{ mL soln}} \times \frac{1000 \text{ mL}}{1 \text{ L}}$$

$$= \boxed{3.96 \ M \text{ HBr}}$$

CHECK There are almost 2 mol HBr and about 0.5 L of solution, so the concentration should be about 4 mol/L, or 4 *M*.

Follow-up Problem 3.12   How many moles of KI are in 84 mL of 0.50 *M* KI?

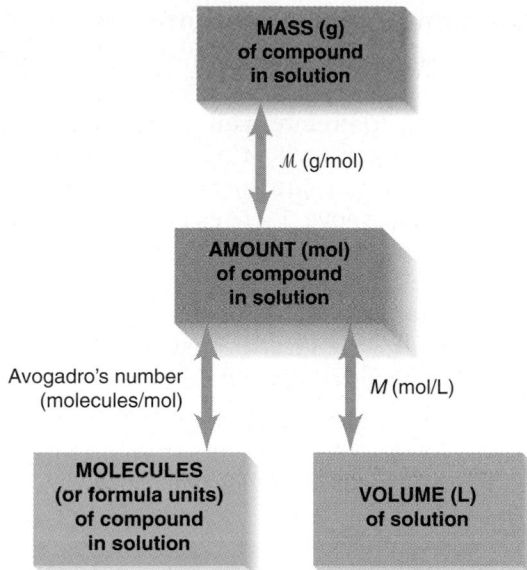

Figure 3.11 **Summary of mass-mole-number-volume relationships in solution.**
The amount (in moles) of a compound in solution is related to the volume of solution in liters through the molarity (M) in moles per liter. The other relationships shown are identical to those in Figure 3.3, except that here they refer to the quantities *in solution*. As in previous cases, to find the quantity of substance expressed in one form or another, convert the given information to moles first.

Mole-Mass-Number Conversions Involving Solutions

Molarity can be thought of as a conversion factor used to convert between volume of solution and amount (mol) of solute, from which we find the mass or number of entities of solute. Figure 3.11 shows this new stoichiometric relationship and Sample Problem 3.13 applies it.

Sample Problem 3.13   Calculating Mass of Solute in a Given Volume of Solution

PROBLEM How many grams of solute are in 1.75 L of 0.460 M sodium monohydrogen phosphate?

PLAN We know the solution volume and molarity, so we can find the amount (mol) of solute. Then, we convert moles to grams with the solute molar mass.

SOLUTION Calculating moles of solute in solution:

$$\text{Moles of Na}_2\text{HPO}_4 = 1.75 \; \cancel{\text{L soln}} \times \frac{0.460 \; \text{mol Na}_2\text{HPO}_4}{1 \; \cancel{\text{L soln}}}$$

$$= 0.805 \; \text{mol Na}_2\text{HPO}_4$$

Converting from moles of solute to grams:

$$\text{Mass (g) Na}_2\text{HPO}_4 = 0.805 \; \cancel{\text{mol Na}_2\text{HPO}_4} \times \frac{141.96 \; \text{g Na}_2\text{HPO}_4}{1 \; \cancel{\text{mol Na}_2\text{HPO}_4}}$$

$$= \boxed{114 \; \text{g Na}_2\text{HPO}_4}$$

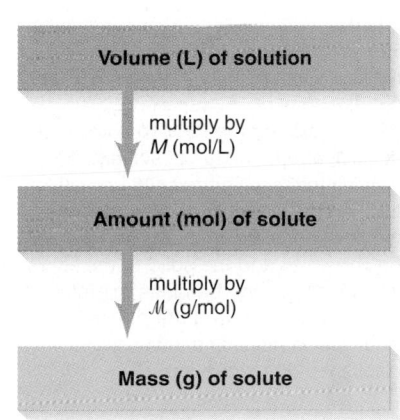

CHECK The answer seems correct: 1.5 L of 0.5 mol/L contains 0.75 mol, and 150 g/mol × 0.75 mol = 112 g, which is very close to 114 g of solute.

Follow-up Problem 3.13 Solutions of sucrose (table sugar; $C_{12}H_{22}O_{11}$) are used in high-speed centrifuges to separate the parts of a biological cell. How many liters of 3.30 M sucrose contain 135 g of solute?

Laboratory Preparation of Molar Solutions

Whenever you prepare a solution of specific molarity, remember that the volume term in the denominator of the molarity expression is the *solution* volume, ***not*** the *solvent* volume. Therefore, you cannot simply dissolve 1 mol of solute in 1 L of solvent and expect a 1 *M* solution. Because the solution volume includes contributions from solute *and* solvent, the added solute would increase the solution volume above 1 L, resulting in a lower concentration than expected. The correct preparation of a solution containing a solid solute consists of four steps. Let's go through them to prepare 0.500 L of 0.350 *M* nickel(II) nitrate hexahydrate [$Ni(NO_3)_2 \cdot 6H_2O$]:

1. *Weigh the solid needed.* First, calculate the mass of solid needed by converting from liters to moles and from moles to grams:

$$\text{Mass (g) of solute} = 0.500 \; \cancel{\text{L soln}} \times \frac{0.350 \; \cancel{\text{mol } Ni(NO_3)_2 \cdot 6H_2O}}{1 \; \cancel{\text{L soln}}}$$

$$\times \frac{290.82 \text{ g } Ni(NO_3)_2 \cdot 6H_2O}{1 \; \cancel{\text{mol } Ni(NO_3)_2 \cdot 6H_2O}}$$

$$= 50.9 \text{ g } Ni(NO_3)_2 \cdot 6H_2O$$

2. *Carefully transfer the solid to a volumetric flask that contains about half the final volume of solvent.* Since we need 0.500 L solution, we choose a 500-mL volumetric flask. Add about 250 mL distilled water and then transfer the solid. Wash down any solid clinging to the neck with a small amount of solvent.

3. *Dissolve the solid thoroughly by swirling.* If some solute remains undissolved, the solution will be less concentrated than expected, so be sure the solute is dissolved. If necessary, wait for the solution to reach room temperature. (As we'll discuss in Chapter 13, the solution process is often accompanied by heating or cooling.)

4. *Add solvent until the solution reaches its final volume.* Add distilled water to bring the volume exactly to the line on the flask neck, then cover and mix thoroughly again. Figure 3.12 shows the last three steps.

Figure 3.12 Laboratory preparation of molar solutions. After the desired mass of solid has been weighed out, the solution is prepared by **A,** carefully adding the solid to a volumetric flask about half full of solvent; **B,** swirling to dissolve the solid completely; and **C,** adding solvent to the mark on the flask neck shown in **D.** It would *not* be correct to add the solid to the entire volume of solvent, because the total volume would exceed the desired volume and result in a lower-than-calculated concentration.

As Figure 3.13 shows, *only solvent is added when a solution is diluted,* so the solute is dispersed in a larger final volume. Thus, a given volume of the final solution contains fewer solute particles and has a lower concentration. If lower concentrations of a solution are used frequently, it is common practice to prepare a more concentrated *stock* solution, which is stored and diluted as needed.

Sample Problem 3.14   Preparing a Dilute Solution from a Concentrated Solution

PROBLEM "Isotonic saline" is a 0.15 *M* aqueous solution of NaCl that simulates the total concentration of ions found in many cellular fluids. Its uses range from a cleansing rinse for contact lenses to a washing medium for red blood cells. How would you prepare 0.80 L isotonic saline from a 6.0 *M* stock solution?

PLAN To dilute a concentrated solution, we add only solvent, so the *moles of solute are the same in both solutions.* We know the volume and molarity of dilute (dil) NaCl, so we find the moles of NaCl it contains and then calculate the volume of concentrated (conc) NaCl that contains the same number of moles. Then we dilute this volume with pure solvent *up to* the final volume.

Figure 3.13 Converting a concentrated solution to a dilute solution. When a solution is diluted, only solvent is added. The solution volume increases while the total number of moles of solute remains the same. Therefore, as shown in the expanded views, a unit volume of concentrated solution contains more solute particles than the same unit volume of dilute solution.

Add solvent

Concentrated solution: More solute particles per unit volume

Dilute solution: Fewer solute particles per unit volume

SOLUTION Finding moles of solute in dilute solution:

$$\text{Moles of NaCl in dil soln} = 0.80 \; \text{L soln} \times \frac{0.15 \; \text{mol NaCl}}{1 \; \text{L soln}} = 0.12 \; \text{mol NaCl}$$

Finding moles of solute in concentrated solution: Since we add only solvent to dilute the solution,

$$\text{Moles of NaCl in dil soln} = \text{moles of NaCl in conc soln} = 0.12 \; \text{mol NaCl}$$

Finding the volume of concentrated solution that contains 0.12 mol NaCl:

$$\text{Volume (L) of conc NaCl soln} = 0.12 \; \text{mol NaCl} \times \frac{1 \; \text{L soln}}{6.0 \; \text{mol NaCl}} = 0.020 \; \text{L soln}$$

To prepare 0.80 L dilute solution, place 0.020 L of 6.0 M NaCl in a 1.0-L cylinder, add distilled water (~780 mL) to the 0.80-L mark, and stir thoroughly.

CHECK The answer seems reasonable because a small volume of concentrated solution is used to prepare a large volume of dilute solution. Also, the ratio of volumes (0.020 L:0.80 L) is the same as the ratio of concentrations (0.15 M:6.0 M).

COMMENT An *alternative approach* to solving dilution problems makes use of the formula

$$M_{\text{dil}} \times V_{\text{dil}} = \text{number of moles} = M_{\text{conc}} \times V_{\text{conc}} \tag{3.9}$$

where the *M* and *V* terms are the molarity and volume of the *dil*ute and *conc*entrated solutions. We need the volume of concentrated solution to use, so we solve for V_{conc}:

$$V_{\text{conc}} = \frac{M_{\text{dil}} \times V_{\text{dil}}}{M_{\text{conc}}} = \frac{0.15 \; M \times 0.80 \; \text{L}}{6.0 \; M} = 0.020 \; \text{L}$$

The method worked out in the Solution section earlier is actually the *same calculation broken into two parts* to emphasize the thinking process:

$$V_{\text{conc}} = 0.80 \; \text{L} \times \frac{0.15 \; \text{mol NaCl}}{1 \; \text{L}} \times \frac{1 \; \text{L}}{6.0 \; \text{mol NaCl}} = 0.020 \; \text{L}$$

Follow-up Problem 3.14 If 25.0 mL of 7.50 *M* sulfuric acid is diluted to exactly 500. mL, what is the mass of sulfuric acid per milliliter?

Volume (L) of dilute solution

multiply by *M* (mol/L) of dilute solution

Amount (mol) of NaCl in dilute solution = Amount (mol) of NaCl in concentrated solution

divide by *M* (mol/L) of concentrated solution

Volume (L) of concentrated solution

Stoichiometry of Chemical Reactions in Solution

Solving stoichiometry problems for reactions in solution requires the same approach as before, with the additional step of converting the volume of reactant or product to moles: (1) balance the equation, (2) find the number of moles of one substance, (3) relate it to the stoichiometrically equivalent number of moles of another substance, and (4) convert to the desired units. In limiting-reactant problems for reactions in solution, we first determine which reactant is limiting and then determine the yield.

Sample Problem 3.15   Calculating Amounts of Reactants and Products for a Reaction in Solution

PROBLEM Specialized cells in the stomach release HCl to aid digestion. If they release too much, the excess can be neutralized with antacids. A common antacid contains magnesium hydroxide, which reacts with the acid to form water and magnesium chloride solution. As a government chemist testing commercial antacids, you use 0.10 M HCl to simulate the acid concentration in the stomach. How many liters of "stomach acid" react with a tablet containing 0.10 g magnesium hydroxide?

PLAN We know the mass of $Mg(OH)_2$ that reacts and the acid concentration, and we must find the acid volume. After writing the balanced equation, we convert the grams of $Mg(OH)_2$ to moles, use the molar ratio to find the moles of HCl that react with these moles of $Mg(OH)_2$, and then use the molarity of HCl to find the volume that contains this number of moles. The steps appear in the roadmap.

SOLUTION Writing the balanced equation:

$$Mg(OH)_2(s) + 2HCl(aq) \longrightarrow MgCl_2(aq) + 2H_2O(l)$$

Converting from grams of $Mg(OH)_2$ to moles:

$$\text{Moles of } Mg(OH)_2 = 0.10 \text{ g } Mg(OH)_2 \times \frac{1 \text{ mol } Mg(OH)_2}{58.33 \text{ g } Mg(OH)_2}$$

$$= 1.7 \times 10^{-3} \text{ mol } Mg(OH)_2$$

Converting from moles of $Mg(OH)_2$ to moles of HCl:

$$\text{Moles of HCl} = 1.7 \times 10^{-3} \text{ mol } Mg(OH)_2 \times \frac{2 \text{ mol HCl}}{1 \text{ mol } Mg(OH)_2} = 3.4 \times 10^{-3} \text{ mol HCl}$$

Converting from moles of HCl to liters:

$$\text{Volume (L) of HCl} = 3.4 \times 10^{-3} \text{ mol HCl} \times \frac{1 \text{ L}}{0.10 \text{ mol HCl}} = \boxed{3.4 \times 10^{-2} \text{ L}}$$

CHECK The size of the answer seems reasonable: a small volume of dilute acid (0.034 L of 0.10 M) reacts with a small amount of antacid (0.0017 mol).

COMMENT As stated in the advertisements, antacids "neutralize" stomach acid. Neutralization reactions occur between an acid (in this case HCl) and a base [in this case $Mg(OH)_2$] to produce water and a solution of a salt (in this case $MgCl_2$). We introduce this class of reactions in Chapter 4 and discuss it in detail in Chapter 18.

Follow-up Problem 3.15   Another active ingredient found in some antacids is aluminum hydroxide. Which is more effective at neutralizing stomach acid, magnesium hydroxide or aluminum hydroxide? [*Hint:* Effectiveness refers to the amount of acid that reacts with a given mass of antacid. You already know the effectiveness of 0.10 g $Mg(OH)_2$.]

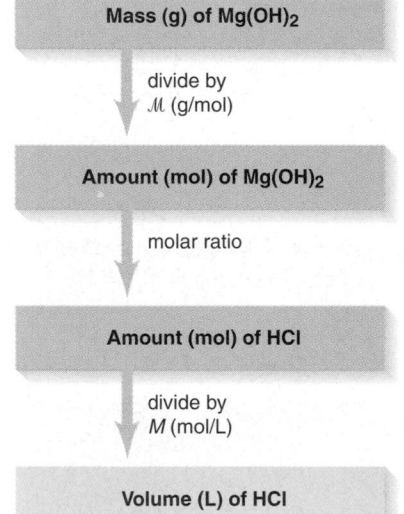

Mass (g) of $Mg(OH)_2$

divide by
$\mathcal{M}$ (g/mol)

Amount (mol) of $Mg(OH)_2$

molar ratio

Amount (mol) of HCl

divide by
M (mol/L)

Volume (L) of HCl

Sample Problem 3.16   Solving Limiting-Reactant Problems for Reactions in Solution

PROBLEM Mercury and its compounds have many uses, from filling teeth (as an alloy with silver, copper, and tin) to the industrial production of chlorine. Because of their toxicity, however, soluble mercury compounds, such as mercury(II) nitrate, must be removed from industrial wastewater. One removal method reacts the wastewater with sodium sulfide solution to produce solid mercury(II) sulfide and sodium nitrate solution. In a laboratory simulation, 0.050 L of 0.010 M mercury(II) nitrate reacts with 0.020 L of 0.10 M sodium sulfide. How many grams of mercury(II) sulfide form?

PLAN This is a limiting-reactant problem because *the amounts of two reactants are given.* After balancing the equation, we determine the limiting reactant. We first calculate the moles of each reactant from its volume and molarity. Then, we use the molar ratio to find the moles of HgS formed from each reactant, *assuming the other is present in excess.* The limiting reactant forms fewer moles of HgS, which we convert to mass using the molar mass of HgS. The roadmap shows the process.

SOLUTION Writing the balanced equation:

$$Hg(NO_3)_2(aq) + Na_2S(aq) \longrightarrow HgS(s) + 2NaNO_3(aq)$$

Finding moles of HgS assuming $Hg(NO_3)_2$ is limiting: Combining the steps gives

$$\text{Moles of HgS} = 0.050 \text{ L soln} \times \frac{0.010 \text{ mol Hg(NO}_3)_2}{1 \text{ L soln}} \times \frac{1 \text{ mol HgS}}{1 \text{ mol Hg(NO}_3)_2}$$

$$= \mathbf{5.0 \times 10^{-4} \text{ mol HgS}}$$

Finding moles of HgS assuming Na_2S is limiting: Combining the steps gives

$$\text{Moles of HgS} = 0.020 \text{ L soln} \times \frac{0.10 \text{ mol Na}_2S}{1 \text{ L soln}} \times \frac{1 \text{ mol HgS}}{1 \text{ mol Na}_2S}$$

$$= \mathbf{2.0 \times 10^{-3} \text{ mol HgS}}$$

Therefore, $Hg(NO_3)_2$ is the limiting reactant.

Converting the moles of HgS formed from $Hg(NO_3)_2$ to grams:

$$\text{Mass (g) of HgS} = 5.0 \times 10^{-4} \text{ mol HgS} \times \frac{232.7 \text{ g HgS}}{1 \text{ mol HgS}}$$

$$= \boxed{0.12 \text{ g HgS}}$$

CHECK Let's use the alternative method for finding the limiting reactant as a check (see Comment in Sample Problem 3.14, p. 113). Finding moles of reactants available:

$$\text{Moles of Hg(NO}_3)_2 = 0.050 \text{ L soln} \times \frac{0.010 \text{ mol Hg(NO}_3)_2}{1 \text{ L soln}}$$

$$= 5.0 \times 10^{-4} \text{ mol Hg(NO}_3)_2$$

$$\text{Moles of Na}_2S = 0.020 \text{ L soln} \times \frac{0.10 \text{ mol Na}_2S}{1 \text{ L soln}}$$

$$= 2.0 \times 10^{-3} \text{ mol Na}_2S$$

Since the molar ratios are both 1:1, $Hg(NO_3)_2$ is limiting because there are fewer moles present than are needed to react with the moles of Na_2S present.

Finding grams of product from moles of limiting reactant and the molar ratio:

$$\text{Mass (g) of HgS} = 5.0 \times 10^{-4} \text{ mol Hg(NO}_3)_2 \times \frac{1 \text{ mol HgS}}{1 \text{ mol Hg(NO}_3)_2} \times \frac{232.7 \text{ g HgS}}{1 \text{ mol HgS}}$$

$$= 0.12 \text{ g HgS}$$

Follow-up Problem 3.16 Despite their toxicity, many compounds of lead are used as pigments.
(a) What volume of 1.50 M lead(II) acetate contains 0.400 mol Pb^{2+} ions?
(b) When this volume reacts with 125 mL of 3.40 M sodium chloride, how many grams of solid lead(II) chloride can form? (Sodium acetate solution also forms.)

Section Summary

When reactions occur in solution, reactant and product amounts are given in terms of their concentration and volume. Molarity is the number of moles of solute dissolved in one liter of solution. Using molarity as a conversion factor, we apply the principles of stoichiometry to all aspects of reactions in solution.

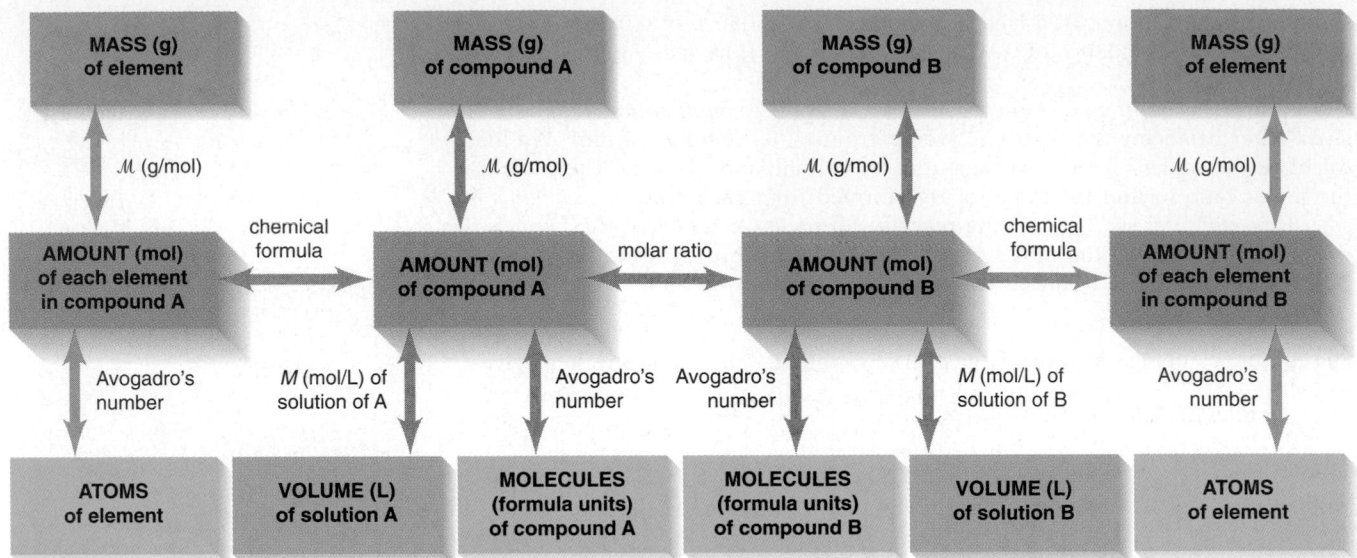

Figure 3.14 **An overview of the key mole-mass-number stoichiometric relationships.**

Chapter Perspective

Few quantitative ideas are more central to your understanding of chemistry than the mole and its relation to the amounts of substances on the macroscopic and molecular levels. You apply the mole concept every time you measure a substance or think about how much of it will react. For a general summary, Figure 3.14 combines the individual stoichiometry summary diagrams into one overall review diagram. Use it for homework, when you study for examinations, or just to obtain an

overview of the various ways that the amounts involved in a reaction are interrelated.

We apply stoichiometry next to some of the most important types of chemical reactions (Chapter 4), to systems of reacting gases (Chapter 5), and to the heat involved in a reaction (Chapter 6). Stoichiometry appears at many places later in the text as well.

The following learning objectives, with section and/or sample problem (SP) numbers in parentheses, can help focus your study:

Understand These Concepts

1. The meaning and usefulness of the mole (3.1)
2. The relation between molecular (or formula) mass and molar mass (3.1)
3. The relations among amount of substance (in moles), mass (in grams), and number of chemical entities (3.1)
4. The information in a chemical formula (3.1)
5. The procedure for finding the empirical and molecular formulas of a compound (3.2)
6. The importance of balancing equations for the quantitative study of chemical reactions (3.3)
7. The mole-mass-number information contained in a balanced equation (3.4)
8. The relation between amounts of reactants and products (3.4)
9. Why one reactant limits the yield of product (3.4)
10. The causes of lower-than-expected yields and the distinction between theoretical and actual yields (3.4)
11. The meanings of concentration and molarity (3.5)
12. The effect of dilution on the concentration of solute (3.5)

13. How reactions in solution differ from those of pure reactants (3.5)

Master These Skills

1. Calculating the molar mass of any substance (3.1)
2. Converting between amount of substance (in moles), mass (in grams), and number of chemical entities (SPs 3.1 and 3.2)
3. Using mass percent to find the mass of element in a given mass of compound (SP 3.3)
4. Determining the empirical and molecular formulas of a compound from mass % and molar mass of elements (SPs 3.4 and 3.5)
5. Determining a molecular formula from combustion analysis (SP 3.6)
6. Converting a chemical statement into a balanced equation (SP 3.7)
7. Using stoichiometrically equivalent molar ratios to calculate amounts of reactants and products in reactions of pure and dissolved substances (SPs 3.8 and 3.15)
8. Writing an overall equation from a series of equations (SP 3.9)

9. Recognizing limiting-reactant problems and choosing the limiting reactant in reactions of pure and dissolved substances (SPs 3.10 and 3.16)
10. Calculating % yield (SP 3.11)
11. Calculating molarity and the mass of substance in solution (SPs 3.12 and 3.13)
12. Preparing a dilute solution from a concentrated one (SP 3.14)

For Review and Reference

Key Terms

stoichiometry

Section 3.1
mole (mol)
Avogadro's number
molar mass ($\mathcal{M}$)
Section 3.2
combustion analysis

Section 3.3
chemical equation
reactant
product
balancing (stoichiometric) coefficient

Section 3.4
overall (net) equation
limiting reactant
theoretical yield
side reaction
actual yield
percent yield (% yield)

Section 3.5
solute
solvent
concentration
molarity (M)

Key Equations and Relationships

3.1 Number of entities in one mole (p. 89):

1 mole contains 6.022×10^{23} entities (to 4 significant figures)

3.2 Converting amount (mol) to mass using $\mathcal{M}$ (p. 93):

$$\text{Mass (g)} = \text{no. of moles} \times \frac{\text{no. of grams}}{1 \text{ mol}}$$

3.3 Converting mass to amount (mol) using $\frac{1}{\mathcal{M}}$ (p. 93):

$$\text{No. of moles} = \text{mass (g)} \times \frac{1 \text{ mol}}{\text{no. of grams}}$$

3.4 Converting amount (mol) to number of entities (p. 93):

$$\text{No. of entities} = \text{no. of moles} \times \frac{6.022 \times 10^{23} \text{ entities}}{1 \text{ mol}}$$

3.5 Converting number of entities to amount (mol) (p. 93):

$$\text{No. of moles} = \text{no. of entities} \times \frac{1 \text{ mol}}{6.022 \times 10^{23} \text{ entities}}$$

3.6 Calculating mass % (p. 96):

Mass % of element X

$$= \frac{\text{moles of X in formula} \times \text{molar mass of X (g/mol)}}{\text{mass of 1 mol of compound (g)}} \times 100$$

3.7 Calculating percent yield (p. 114):

$$\% \text{ yield} = \frac{\text{actual yield}}{\text{theoretical yield}} \times 100$$

3.8 Defining molarity (p. 116):

$$\text{Molarity} = \frac{\text{moles of solute}}{\text{liters of solution}} \quad \text{or} \quad M = \frac{\text{mol solute}}{\text{L soln}}$$

3.9 Diluting a concentrated solution (p. 119):

$$M_{\text{dil}} \times V_{\text{dil}} = \text{number of moles} = M_{\text{conc}} \times V_{\text{conc}}$$

Highlighted Figures and Tables

These figures (F) and tables (T) provide a quick review of key ideas.
T3.1 Summary of mass terminology (p. 91)
T3.2 Information contained in a formula (p. 93)
F3.3 Summary of mass-mole-number relationships for elements and compounds (p. 94)

T3.5 Information contained in a balanced equation (p. 107)
F3.8 Summary of mass-mole-number relationships in a chemical reaction (p. 109)
F3.11 Summary of mass-mole-number-volume relationships in solution (p. 117)
F3.14 Overview of mole-mass-number relationships (p. 122)

Answers to Follow-up Problems

3.1 (a) Moles of C = $315 \text{ mg C} \times \dfrac{1 \text{ g}}{10^3 \text{ mg}} \times \dfrac{1 \text{ mol C}}{12.01 \text{ g C}}$

$$= 0.0262 \text{ mol C}$$

(b) Mass (g) of Mn = $3.22 \times 10^{20} \text{ Mn atoms}$

$$\times \frac{1 \text{ mol Mn}}{6.022 \times 10^{23} \text{ Mn atoms}} \times \frac{54.94 \text{ g Mn}}{1 \text{ mol Mn}}$$

$$= 2.94 \times 10^{-2} \text{ g Mn}$$

3.2 (a) Mass (g) of $P_4O_{10} = 4.65 \times 10^{22}$ molecules P_4O_{10}

$$\times \frac{1 \text{ mol } P_4O_{10}}{6.022 \times 10^{23} \text{ molecules } P_4O_{10}} \times \frac{283.88 \text{ g } P_4O_{10}}{1 \text{ mol } P_4O_{10}}$$

$$= 21.9 \text{ g } P_4O_{10}$$

(b) No. of P atoms = 4.65×10^{22} molecules P_4O_{10}

$$\times \frac{4 \text{ atoms P}}{1 \text{ molecule } P_4O_{10}} = 1.86 \times 10^{23} \text{ P atoms}$$

Answers to Follow-up Problems (continued)

3.3 (a) Mass % of N = $\dfrac{2\ \text{mol N} \times \dfrac{14.01\ \text{g N}}{1\ \text{mol N}}}{80.05\ \text{g NH}_4\text{NO}_3} \times 100$

$= 35.00$ mass % N

(b) Mass (g) of N = $35.8\ \text{kg NH}_4\text{NO}_3 \times \dfrac{10^3\ \text{g}}{1\ \text{kg}} \times \dfrac{0.3500\ \text{g N}}{1\ \text{g NH}_4\text{NO}_3}$

$= 1.25 \times 10^4$ g N

3.4 Moles of S = $2.88\ \text{g S} \times \dfrac{1\ \text{mol S}}{32.07\ \text{g S}} = 0.0898$ mol S

Moles of M = $0.0898\ \text{mol S} \times \dfrac{2\ \text{mol M}}{3\ \text{mol S}} = 0.0599$ mol M

Molar mass of M = $\dfrac{3.12\ \text{g M}}{0.0599\ \text{mol M}} = 52.1$ g/mol

M is chromium, and M_2S_3 is chromium(III) sulfide.

3.5 Assuming 100.00 g of compound, we have 95.21 g C and 4.79 g H:

Moles of C = $95.21\ \text{g C} \times \dfrac{1\ \text{mol C}}{12.01\ \text{g C}}$

$= 7.928$ mol C; also, 4.75 mol H

Preliminary formula = $C_{7.928}H_{4.75} \approx C_{1.67}H_{1.00}$

Empirical formula = C_5H_3

Whole-number multiple = $\dfrac{252.30\ \text{g/mol}}{63.07\ \text{g/mol}} = 4$

Molecular formula = $C_{20}H_{12}$

3.6 Mass (g) of C = $0.451\ \text{g CO}_2 \times \dfrac{12.01\ \text{g C}}{44.01\ \text{g CO}_2}$

$= 0.123$ g C; also, 0.00690 g H

Mass (g) of Cl = 0.250 g − (0.123 g + 0.00690 g)

$= 0.120$ g Cl

Moles of elements

$= 0.0102$ mol C; 0.00685 mol H; 0.00339 mol Cl

Empirical formula = C_3H_2Cl; multiple = 2

Molecular formula = $C_6H_4Cl_2$

3.7 (a) $2Na(s) + 2H_2O(l) \longrightarrow H_2(g) + 2NaOH(aq)$

(b) $2HNO_3(aq) + CaCO_3(s) \longrightarrow$

$\qquad\qquad Ca(NO_3)_2(aq) + H_2O(l) + CO_2(g)$

(c) $PCl_3(g) + 3HF(g) \longrightarrow PF_3(g) + 3HCl(g)$

(d) $4C_3H_5N_3O_9(l) \longrightarrow$

$\qquad 12CO_2(g) + 10H_2O(g) + 6N_2(g) + O_2(g)$

3.8 $Fe_2O_3(s) + 2Al(s) \longrightarrow Al_2O_3(s) + 2Fe(l)$

(a) Mass (g) of Fe = $135\ \text{g Al} \times \dfrac{1\ \text{mol Al}}{26.98\ \text{g Al}} \times \dfrac{2\ \text{mol Fe}}{2\ \text{mol Al}}$

$\times \dfrac{55.85\ \text{g Fe}}{1\ \text{mol Fe}} = 279$ g Fe

(b) No. of Al atoms

$= 1.00\ \text{g Al}_2\text{O}_3 \times \dfrac{1\ \text{mol Al}_2\text{O}_3}{101.96\ \text{g Al}_2\text{O}_3} \times \dfrac{2\ \text{mol Al}}{1\ \text{mol Al}_2\text{O}_3}$

$\times \dfrac{6.022 \times 10^{23}\ \text{Al atoms}}{1\ \text{mol Al}} = 1.18 \times 10^{22}$ Al atoms

3.9
$$2SO_2(g) + O_2(g) \longrightarrow 2SO_3(g)$$
$$2SO_3(g) + 2H_2O(l) \longrightarrow 2H_2SO_4(aq)$$
$$\overline{2SO_2(g) + O_2(g) + 2H_2O(l) \longrightarrow 2H_2SO_4(aq)}$$

3.10 $2Al(s) + 3S(s) \longrightarrow Al_2S_3(s)$

Mass (g) of Al_2S_3 formed from Al

$= 10.0\ \text{g Al} \times \dfrac{1\ \text{mol Al}}{26.98\ \text{g Al}} \times \dfrac{1\ \text{mol Al}_2\text{S}_3}{2\ \text{mol Al}} \times \dfrac{150.17\ \text{g Al}_2\text{S}_3}{1\ \text{mol Al}_2\text{S}_3}$

$= 27.8$ g Al_2S_3

Similarly, mass (g) of Al_2S_3 formed from S = 23.4 g Al_2S_3. Therefore, S is limiting reactant and 23.4 g Al_2S_3 can form.

Mass (g) of Al in excess

= total mass of Al − mass of Al used

$= 10.0\ \text{g Al} - \left(15.0\ \text{g S} \times \dfrac{1\ \text{mol S}}{32.07\ \text{g S}} \times \dfrac{2\ \text{mol Al}}{3\ \text{mol S}} \times \dfrac{26.98\ \text{Al}}{1\ \text{mol Al}}\right)$

$= 1.6$ g Al

(We would obtain the same answer if sulfur were shown more correctly as S_8.)

3.11 $2HCl(aq) + CaCO_3(s) \longrightarrow$

$\qquad\qquad CaCl_2(aq) + H_2O(l) + CO_2(g)$

Theoretical yield (g) of CO_2

$= 10.0\ \text{g CaCO}_3 \times \dfrac{1\ \text{mol CaCO}_3}{100.09\ \text{g CaCO}_3} \times \dfrac{1\ \text{mol CO}_2}{1\ \text{mol CaCO}_3}$

$\times \dfrac{44.01\ \text{g CO}_2}{1\ \text{mol CO}_2} = 4.40$ g CO_2

% yield = $\dfrac{3.65\ \text{g CO}_2}{4.40\ \text{g CO}_2} \times 100 = 83.0\%$

3.12 Moles of KI = $84\ \text{mL soln} \times \dfrac{1\ \text{L}}{10^3\ \text{mL}} \times \dfrac{0.50\ \text{mol KI}}{1\ \text{L soln}}$

$= 0.042$ mol KI

3.13 Volume (L) of soln = $135\ \text{g sucrose} \times \dfrac{1\ \text{mol sucrose}}{342.30\ \text{g sucrose}}$

$\times \dfrac{1\ \text{L soln}}{3.30\ \text{mol sucrose}} = 0.120$ L soln

3.14 M_{dil} of H_2SO_4 = $\dfrac{7.50\ M \times 25.0\ \text{mL}}{500.\ \text{mL}} = 0.375\ M\ H_2SO_4$

Mass (g) of H_2SO_4/mL soln

$= \dfrac{0.375\ \text{mol H}_2\text{SO}_4}{1\ \text{L soln}} \times \dfrac{1\ \text{L}}{10^3\ \text{mL}} \times \dfrac{98.09\ \text{g H}_2\text{SO}_4}{1\ \text{mol H}_2\text{SO}_4}$

$= 3.68 \times 10^{-2}$ g/mL soln

3.15 $Al(OH)_3(s) + 3HCl(aq) \longrightarrow AlCl_3(aq) + 3H_2O(l)$

Volume (L) of HCl consumed

$= 0.10\ \text{g Al(OH)}_3 \times \dfrac{1\ \text{mol Al(OH)}_3}{78.00\ \text{g Al(OH)}_3} \times \dfrac{3\ \text{mol HCl}}{1\ \text{mol Al(OH)}_3}$

$\times \dfrac{1\ \text{L soln}}{0.10\ \text{mol HCl}} = 3.8 \times 10^{-2}$ L soln

Therefore, $Al(OH)_3$ is more effective than $Mg(OH)_2$.

3.16 (a) Volume (L) of soln

$= 0.400\ \text{mol Pb}^{2+} \times \dfrac{1\ \text{mol Pb(C}_2\text{H}_3\text{O}_2)_2}{1\ \text{mol Pb}^{2+}}$

$\times \dfrac{1\ \text{L soln}}{1.50\ \text{mol Pb(C}_2\text{H}_3\text{O}_2)_2} = 0.267$ L soln

(b) $Pb(C_2H_3O_2)_2(aq) + 2NaCl(aq) \longrightarrow$

$\qquad\qquad PbCl_2(s) + 2NaC_2H_3O_2(aq)$

Mass (g) of $PbCl_2$ from $Pb(C_2H_3O_2)_2$ soln = 111 g $PbCl_2$

Mass (g) of $PbCl_2$ from NaCl soln = 59.1 g $PbCl_2$

Thus, NaCl is the limiting reactant and 59.1 g $PbCl_2$ can form.

Problems

Problems with a **colored** number are answered at the back of the text. Problem sections match the text and provide the number(s) of relevant sample problems. Most offer concept review questions, skill-building exercises (written in similar pairs), and problems in a relevant context. Following these are comprehensive problems based on material from any section and/or previous chapter.

The Mole
(Sample Problems 3.1 to 3.3)

■ Concept Review Questions

3.1 The atomic mass of Cl is 35.45 amu and that of Al is 26.98 amu. What are the masses in grams of 2 mol Al atoms and of 3 mol Cl atoms?

3.2 (a) How many moles of C atoms are in 1 mol sucrose ($C_{12}H_{22}O_{11}$)? (b) How many C atoms are in 1 mol sucrose?

3.3 Why might the expression "1 mol of nitrogen" be confusing? What change would remove any uncertainty? For what other elements might a similar confusion exist? Why?

3.4 (a) How many grams (g) are equal to 1 atomic mass unit (amu)? (b) What is the ratio of the gram to the atomic mass unit?

3.5 Why is a counting unit (the mole) used so often in chemistry instead of a mass unit?

3.6 Each of the following balances weighs the indicated numbers of atoms of two elements:

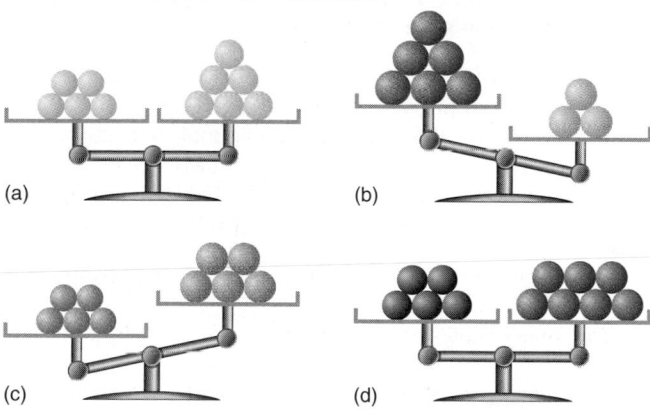

(a)   (b)

(c)   (d)

(a) Which element—left, right, or neither—has the higher molar mass?
(b) Which element—left, right, or neither—has more atoms per gram?
(c) Which element—left, right, or neither—has fewer atoms per gram?
(d) Which element—left, right, or neither—has more atoms per mole?

3.7 You need to calculate the number of P_4 molecules that can be formed from 2.5 g $Ca_3(PO_4)_2$. Explain how you would proceed (that is, write a solution "plan" without doing any calculations).

■ Skill-Building Exercises (paired)

3.8 Calculate the molar mass of each of the following:
(a) $Sr(OH)_2$ (b) N_2O (c) $KClO_3$ (d) CrO_3

3.9 Calculate the molar mass of each of the following:
(a) $(NH_4)_3PO_4$ (b) CH_3Cl (c) $CuSO_4 \cdot 5H_2O$ (d) BrF_3

3.10 Calculate the molar mass of each of the following:
(a) PbO_2 (b) CaF_2 (c) $Al_2(SO_4)_3$ (d) $MnCl_2$

3.11 Calculate the molar mass of each of the following:
(a) N_2O_4 (b) C_7H_8 (c) $MgSO_4 \cdot 7H_2O$ (d) $Ba(C_2H_3O_2)_2$

3.12 Calculate each of the following quantities:
(a) Mass in grams of 0.74 mol $NaMnO_4$
(b) Moles of O atoms in 9.22 g $Mn(NO_3)_2$
(c) Number of O atoms in 0.037 g $CuSO_4 \cdot 5H_2O$

3.13 Calculate each of the following quantities:
(a) Mass in kilograms of 2.6×10^{20} molecules of NO_2
(b) Moles of Cl atoms in 0.622 g $C_2H_4Cl_2$
(c) Number of H^- ions in 1.88 g CaH_2

3.14 Calculate each of the following quantities:
(a) Mass in grams of 0.55 mol $CaSO_4$
(b) Moles of compound in 313 g $Fe(ClO_4)_3$
(c) Number of N atoms in 0.76 g NH_4NO_3

3.15 Calculate each of the following quantities:
(a) Total number of ions in 14.3 g $CaBr_2$
(b) Mass in milligrams of 0.45 mol $CuCl_2 \cdot 2H_2O$
(c) Mass in kilograms of 8.75×10^{25} formula units of $Bi(NO_3)_3 \cdot 5H_2O$

3.16 Calculate each of the following quantities:
(a) Mass in grams of 5.36 mol copper(I) carbonate
(b) Mass in grams of 3.78×10^{21} molecules of dinitrogen pentaoxide
(c) Number of moles and formula units in 57.9 g sodium perchlorate
(d) Number of sodium ions, perchlorate ions, Cl atoms, and O atoms in the mass in part (c)

3.17 Calculate each of the following quantities:
(a) Mass in grams of 2.60 mol chromium(III) sulfate decahydrate
(b) Mass in grams of 8.55×10^{22} molecules of disulfur tetrafluoride
(c) Number of moles and formula units in 56.2 g lithium sulfate
(d) Number of lithium ions, sulfate ions, S atoms, and O atoms in the mass in part (c)

3.18 Calculate each of the following:
(a) Mass % of H in ammonium bicarbonate
(b) Mass % of O in sodium dihydrogen phosphate heptahydrate

3.19 Calculate each of the following:
(a) Mass % of I in strontium iodate
(b) Mass % of Mn in potassium permanganate

3.20 Calculate each of the following:
(a) Mass fraction of C in cesium acetate
(b) Mass fraction of O in uranyl sulfate trihydrate (the uranyl ion is UO_2^{2+})

3.21 Calculate each of the following:
(a) Mass fraction of Cl in calcium perchlorate
(b) Mass fraction of P in tetraphosphorus hexaoxide

■ Problems in Context

3.22 Oxygen is required for metabolic combustion of foods. Calculate the number of atoms in 38.0 g oxygen gas, the amount absorbed from the lungs at rest in about 15 minutes.

3.23 Cisplatin (*right*) is a powerful drug used in the treatment of certain cancers. Calculate (a) the moles of compound in 146.5 g cisplatin; (b) the number of hydrogen atoms in 1.25 mol cisplatin.

3.24 Allyl sulfide gives garlic its characteristic odor.

Calculate (a) the mass in grams of 0.82 mol allyl sulfide; (b) the number of carbon atoms in 0.30 g allyl sulfide.

3.25 Iron reacts slowly with oxygen and water to form a compound commonly called rust ($Fe_2O_3 \cdot 4H_2O$). For 15.0 kg rust, calculate (a) the moles of compound; (b) the moles of Fe_2O_3; (c) the grams of iron.

3.26 Propane is widely used in liquid form as a fuel for barbecue grills and camp stoves. For 38.0 g propane, calculate (a) the moles of compound; (b) the grams of carbon.

3.27 The effectiveness of a nitrogen fertilizer is determined mainly by its mass % N. Rank the following fertilizers in terms of their effectiveness: potassium nitrate; ammonium nitrate; ammonium sulfate; urea, $CO(NH_2)_2$.

3.28 One useful method for recycling scrap aluminum converts some of it to common alum [potassium aluminum sulfate dodecahydrate, $KAl(SO_4)_2 \cdot 12H_2O$], an important dye fixative and food preservative.
(a) How many moles of potassium ions are in 288 g alum?
(b) What is the mass % S in alum?
(c) What is the maximum amount of alum (in metric tons) that can be prepared from 15.0 metric tons of scrap aluminum (1 metric ton = 1000 kg)?

3.29 Hemoglobin, a protein found in red blood cells, carries O_2 from the lungs to the body's cells. Iron (as ferrous ion, Fe^{2+}) makes up 0.33 mass % of hemoglobin. If the molar mass of hemoglobin is 6.8×10^4 g/mol, how many Fe^{2+} ions are present in one molecule?

Determining the Formula of an Unknown Compound
(Sample Problems 3.4 to 3.6)

■ Concept Review Questions

3.30 List three ways compositional data may be given in a problem that involves finding an empirical formula.

3.31 Which of the following sets of information allows you to obtain the molecular formula of a covalent compound? In each case that allows it, explain how you would proceed (write a solution "plan").
(a) Number of moles of each type of atom in a given sample of the compound
(b) Mass % of each element and the total number of atoms in a molecule of the compound
(c) Mass % of each element and the number of atoms of one element in a molecule of the compound
(d) Empirical formula and the mass % of each element in the compound
(e) Structural formula of the compound

3.32 Is $MgCl_2$ an empirical or a molecular formula for magnesium chloride? Explain.

■ Skill-Building Exercises (paired)

3.33 What is the empirical formula and empirical formula mass for each of the following compounds?
(a) C_2H_4 (b) $C_2H_6O_2$ (c) N_2O_5 (d) $Ba_3(PO_4)_2$ (e) Te_4I_{16}

3.34 What is the empirical formula and empirical formula mass for each of the following compounds?
(a) C_4H_8 (b) $C_3H_6O_3$ (c) P_4O_{10} (d) $Ga_2(SO_4)_3$ (e) Al_2Br_6

3.35 What is the molecular formula of each compound?
(a) Empirical formula CH_2 ($\mathscr{M} = 42.08$ g/mol)
(b) Empirical formula NH_2 ($\mathscr{M} = 32.05$ g/mol)
(c) Empirical formula NO_2 ($\mathscr{M} = 92.02$ g/mol)
(d) Empirical formula CHN ($\mathscr{M} = 135.14$ g/mol)

3.36 What is the molecular formula of each compound?
(a) Empirical formula CH ($\mathscr{M} = 78.11$ g/mol)
(b) Empirical formula $C_3H_6O_2$ ($\mathscr{M} = 74.08$ g/mol)
(c) Empirical formula $HgCl$ ($\mathscr{M} = 472.1$ g/mol)
(d) Empirical formula $C_7H_4O_2$ ($\mathscr{M} = 240.20$ g/mol)

3.37 Determine the empirical formula of each of the following compounds:
(a) 0.063 mol chlorine atoms combined with 0.22 mol oxygen atoms
(b) 2.45 g silicon combined with 12.4 g chlorine
(c) 27.3 mass % carbon and 72.7 mass % oxygen

3.38 Determine the empirical formula of each of the following compounds:
(a) 0.039 mol iron atoms combined with 0.052 mol oxygen atoms
(b) 0.903 g phosphorus combined with 6.99 g bromine
(c) A hydrocarbon with 79.9 mass % carbon

3.39 An oxide of nitrogen contains 30.45 mass % N.
(a) What is the empirical formula of the oxide? (b) If the molar mass is 90 ± 5 g/mol, what is the molecular formula?

3.40 A chloride of silicon contains 79.1 mass % Cl.
(a) What is the empirical formula of the chloride? (b) If the molar mass is 269 g/mol, what is the molecular formula?

3.41 A sample of 0.600 mol of a metal M reacts completely with excess fluorine to form 46.8 g MF_2.
(a) How many moles of F are in the sample of MF_2 that forms?
(b) How many grams of M are in this sample of MF_2?
(c) What element is represented by the symbol M?

3.42 A sample of 0.370 mol of a metal oxide (M_2O_3) weighs 55.4 g.
(a) How many moles of O are in the sample?
(b) How many grams of M are in the sample?
(c) What element is represented by the symbol M?

■ Problems in Context

3.43 Nicotine is a poisonous, addictive compound found in tobacco. A sample of nicotine contains 6.16 mmol C, 8.56 mmol H, and 1.23 mmol N [1 mmol (one millimole) = 10^{-3} mol]. What is the empirical formula?

3.44 Cortisol ($\mathscr{M} = 362.47$ g/mol), one of the major steroid hormones, is a key factor in the synthesis of protein. Its profound effect on the reduction of inflammation explains its use in the treatment of rheumatoid arthritis. Cortisol is 69.6% C, 8.34% H, and 22.1% O by mass. What is its molecular formula?

3.45 Acetaminophen *(right)* is one of the most popular nonaspirin, "over-the-counter" pain relievers. What is the mass % of each element in acetaminophen?

3.46 Menthol ($\mathcal{M}$ = 156.3 g/mol), a strong-smelling substance used in cough drops, is a compound of carbon, hydrogen, and oxygen. When 0.1595 g menthol was subjected to combustion analysis, it produced 0.449 g CO_2 and 0.184 g H_2O. What is its molecular formula?

Writing and Balancing Chemical Equations
(Sample Problem 3.7)

■ **Concept Review Questions**

3.47 What three types of information does a balanced chemical equation provide? How?

3.48 How does a balanced chemical equation apply the law of conservation of mass?

3.49 In the process of balancing the equation

$$Al + Cl_2 \longrightarrow AlCl_3$$

Student I writes: $Al + Cl_2 \longrightarrow AlCl_2$
Student II writes: $Al + Cl_2 + Cl \longrightarrow AlCl_3$
Student III writes: $2Al + 3Cl_2 \longrightarrow 2AlCl_3$
Is the approach of Student I valid? of Student II? of Student III? Explain.

3.50 The following boxes represent a chemical reaction between elements A (red) and B (green):

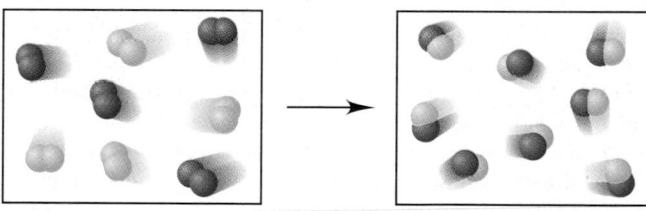

Which of the following best represents the balanced equation for the reaction?
(a) $2A + 2B \longrightarrow A_2 + B_2$ (b) $A_2 + B_2 \longrightarrow 2AB$
(c) $B_2 + 2AB \longrightarrow 2B_2 + A_2$ (d) $4A_2 + 4B_2 \longrightarrow 8AB$

■ **Skill-Building Exercises (paired)**

3.51 Write balanced equations for each of the following by inserting the correct coefficients in the blanks:
(a) __$Cu(s)$ + __$S_8(s)$ $\longrightarrow$ __$Cu_2S(s)$
(b) __$P_4O_{10}(s)$ + __$H_2O(l)$ $\longrightarrow$ __$H_3PO_4(l)$
(c) __$B_2O_3(s)$ + __$NaOH(aq)$ $\longrightarrow$ __$Na_3BO_3(aq)$ + __$H_2O(l)$
(d) __$CH_3NH_2(g)$ + __$O_2(g)$ $\longrightarrow$
$$\text{__}CO_2(g) + \text{__}H_2O(g) + \text{__}N_2(g)$$

3.52 Write balanced equations for each of the following by inserting the correct coefficients in the blanks:
(a) __$Cu(NO_3)_2(aq)$ + __$KOH(aq)$ $\longrightarrow$
$$\text{__}Cu(OH)_2(s) + \text{__}KNO_3(aq)$$
(b) __$BCl_3(g)$ + __$H_2O(l)$ $\longrightarrow$ __$H_3BO_3(s)$ + __$HCl(g)$
(c) __$CaSiO_3(s)$ + __$HF(g)$ $\longrightarrow$
$$\text{__}SiF_4(g) + \text{__}CaF_2(s) + \text{__}H_2O(l)$$
(d) __$(CN)_2(g)$ + __$H_2O(l)$ $\longrightarrow$ __$H_2C_2O_4(aq)$ + __$NH_3(g)$

3.53 Write balanced equations for each of the following by inserting the correct coefficients in the blanks:
(a) __$SO_2(g)$ + __$O_2(g)$ $\longrightarrow$ __$SO_3(g)$
(b) __$Sc_2O_3(s)$ + __$H_2O(l)$ $\longrightarrow$ __$Sc(OH)_3(s)$
(c) __$H_3PO_4(aq)$ + __$NaOH(aq)$ $\longrightarrow$
$$\text{__}Na_2HPO_4(aq) + \text{__}H_2O(l)$$
(d) __$C_6H_{10}O_5(s)$ + __$O_2(g)$ $\longrightarrow$ __$CO_2(g)$ + __$H_2O(g)$

3.54 Write balanced equations for each of the following by inserting the correct coefficients in the blanks:
(a) __$As_4S_6(s)$ + __$O_2(g)$ $\longrightarrow$ __$As_4O_6(s)$ + __$SO_2(g)$
(b) __$Ca_3(PO_4)_2(s)$ + __$SiO_2(s)$ + __$C(s)$ $\longrightarrow$
$$\text{__}P_4(g) + \text{__}CaSiO_3(l) + \text{__}CO(g)$$
(c) __$Fe(s)$ + __$H_2O(g)$ $\longrightarrow$ __$Fe_3O_4(s)$ + __$H_2(g)$
(d) __$S_2Cl_2(l)$ + __$NH_3(g)$ $\longrightarrow$
$$\text{__}S_4N_4(s) + S_8(s) + \text{__}NH_4Cl(s)$$

3.55 Convert the following into balanced equations:
(a) When gallium metal is heated in oxygen gas, it melts and forms solid gallium(III) oxide.
(b) Liquid hexane burns in oxygen gas to form carbon dioxide gas and water vapor.
(c) When solutions of calcium chloride and sodium phosphate are mixed, solid calcium phosphate forms and sodium chloride remains in solution.

3.56 Convert the following into balanced equations:
(a) When lead(II) nitrate solution is added to potassium iodide solution, solid lead(II) iodide forms and potassium nitrate solution remains.
(b) Liquid disilicon hexachloride reacts with water to form solid silicon dioxide, hydrogen chloride gas, and hydrogen gas.
(c) When nitrogen dioxide is bubbled into water, a solution of nitric acid forms and gaseous nitrogen monoxide is released.

Calculating Amounts of Reactant and Product
(Sample Problems 3.8 to 3.11)

■ **Concept Review Questions**

3.57 What does the term *stoichiometrically equivalent molar ratio* mean, and how is it applied in solving problems?

3.58 Reactants A and B form product C. Write a detailed "plan" to find the mass of C that forms when 5 g of A reacts with excess B.

3.59 Reactants D and E form product F. Write a detailed "plan" to find the mass of F that forms when 5 g of D reacts with 8 g of E.

3.60 Percent yields are generally calculated from mass quantities. Would the result be the same if mole quantities were used instead? Why?

■ **Skill-Building Exercises (paired)**

3.61 Chlorine gas can be made in the laboratory by the reaction of hydrochloric acid and manganese(IV) oxide:

$$4HCl(aq) + MnO_2(s) \longrightarrow MnCl_2(aq) + 2H_2O(g) + Cl_2(g)$$

When 0.475 mol HCl reacts with excess MnO_2, (a) how many moles of Cl_2 form? (b) how many grams of Cl_2 form?

3.62 Bismuth oxide reacts with carbon to form bismuth metal: $Bi_2O_3(s) + 3C(s) \longrightarrow 2Bi(s) + 3CO(g)$. When 60.7 g Bi_2O_3 reacts with excess carbon, (a) how many moles of Bi_2O_3 react? (b) How many moles of Bi form?

3.63 Potassium nitrate decomposes on heating, producing potassium oxide and gaseous nitrogen and oxygen:

$$4KNO_3(s) \longrightarrow 2K_2O(s) + 2N_2(g) + 5O_2(g)$$

To produce 1.35 kg oxygen, how many (a) moles of KNO_3 must be heated? (b) Grams of KNO_3 must be heated?

3.64 Chromium(III) oxide reacts with hydrogen sulfide (H_2S) gas to form chromium(III) sulfide and water:

$$Cr_2O_3(s) + 3H_2S(g) \longrightarrow Cr_2S_3(s) + 3H_2O(l)$$

To produce 83.4 g Cr_2S_3, (a) how many moles of Cr_2O_3 are required? (b) How many grams of Cr_2O_3 are required?

3.65 Calculate the mass of each product formed when 6.082 g diborane (B_2H_6) reacts with excess water:

$$B_2H_6(g) + H_2O(l) \longrightarrow H_3BO_3(s) + H_2(g) \quad \text{[unbalanced]}$$

3.66 Calculate the mass of each product formed when 86.3 g silver sulfide reacts with excess hydrochloric acid:

$$Ag_2S(s) + HCl(aq) \longrightarrow AgCl(s) + H_2S(g) \quad \text{[unbalanced]}$$

3.67 Elemental phosphorus occurs as tetratomic molecules, P_4. What mass of chlorine gas is needed for complete reaction with 251 g phosphorus to form phosphorus pentachloride?

3.68 Elemental sulfur occurs as octatomic molecules, S_8. What mass of fluorine gas is needed for complete reaction with 385 g sulfur to form sulfur hexafluoride?

3.69 Solid iodine trichloride is prepared by reaction between solid iodine and gaseous chlorine to form iodine monochloride crystals, followed by treatment with additional chlorine.
(a) Write a balanced equation for each step.
(b) Write an overall balanced equation for the formation of iodine trichloride.
(c) How many grams of iodine are needed to prepare 25.8 kg of final product?

3.70 Lead can be prepared from galena [lead(II) sulfide] by first roasting in oxygen gas to form lead(II) oxide and sulfur dioxide. Heating the metal oxide with more galena forms the molten metal and more sulfur dioxide.
(a) Write a balanced equation for each step.
(b) Write an overall balanced equation for the process.
(c) How many metric tons of sulfur dioxide form for every metric ton of lead obtained?

3.71 Many metals react with oxygen gas to form the metal oxide. For example, calcium reacts as follows:

$$2Ca(s) + O_2(g) \longrightarrow 2CaO(s)$$

You wish to calculate the mass of calcium oxide that can be prepared from 4.20 g Ca and 1.60 g O_2.
(a) How many moles of CaO can be produced from the given mass of Ca?
(b) How many moles of CaO can be produced from the given mass of O_2?
(c) Which is the limiting reactant?
(d) How many grams of CaO can be produced?

3.72 Metal hydrides react with water to form hydrogen gas and the metal hydroxide. For example,

$$SrH_2(s) + 2H_2O(l) \longrightarrow Sr(OH)_2(s) + 2H_2(g)$$

You wish to calculate the mass of hydrogen gas that can be prepared from 5.00 g SrH_2 and 4.80 g H_2O.
(a) How many moles of H_2 can be produced from the given mass of SrH_2?

(b) How many moles of H_2 can be produced from the given mass of H_2O?
(c) Which is the limiting reactant?
(d) How many grams of H_2 can be produced?

3.73 Calculate the maximum number of moles and mass of iodic acid (HIO_3) that can form when 735 g iodine trichloride reacts with 107.7 g water:

$$ICl_3 + H_2O \longrightarrow ICl + HIO_3 + HCl \quad \text{[unbalanced]}$$

What mass of the excess reactant remains?

3.74 Calculate the maximum number of moles and grams of H_2S that can form when 165 g aluminum sulfide reacts with 125 g water:

$$Al_2S_3 + H_2O \longrightarrow Al(OH)_3 + H_2S \quad \text{[unbalanced]}$$

What mass of the excess reactant remains?

3.75 When 0.100 mol carbon is burned in a closed vessel with 8.00 g oxygen, how many grams of carbon dioxide can form? Which reactant is in excess, and how many grams of it remain after the reaction?

3.76 A mixture of 0.0359 g hydrogen and 0.0175 mol oxygen in a closed container is sparked to initiate a reaction. How many grams of water can form? Which reactant is in excess, and how many grams of it remain after the reaction?

3.77 Aluminum nitrite and ammonium chloride react to form aluminum chloride, nitrogen, and water. What mass of each substance is present after 53.0 g aluminum nitrite and 48.9 g ammonium chloride react completely?

3.78 Calcium nitrate and ammonium fluoride react to form calcium fluoride, dinitrogen monoxide, and water vapor. What mass of each substance is present after 15.0 g calcium nitrate and 17.50 g ammonium fluoride react completely?

3.79 Two successive reactions, A $\longrightarrow$ B and B $\longrightarrow$ C, have yields of 75% and 65%, respectively. What is the overall percent yield for conversion of A to C?

3.80 Two successive reactions, D $\longrightarrow$ E and E $\longrightarrow$ F, have yields of 48% and 86%, respectively. What is the overall percent yield for conversion of D to F?

3.81 What is the percent yield of a reaction in which 41.5 g tungsten(VI) oxide (WO_3) reacts with excess hydrogen gas to produce metallic tungsten and 9.50 mL water ($d = 1.00$ g/mL)?

3.82 What is the percent yield of a reaction in which 200. g phosphorus trichloride reacts with excess water to form 128 g HCl and aqueous phosphorous acid (H_3PO_3)?

3.83 When 153 g methane and 43.0 g chlorine gas undergo a reaction that has an 80.0% yield, what mass of chloromethane (CH_3Cl) forms? Hydrogen chloride also forms.

3.84 When 56.6 g calcium and 30.5 g nitrogen gas undergo a reaction that has a 90.0% yield, what mass of calcium nitride forms?

■ Problems in Context

3.85 Cyanogen, $(CN)_2$, has been observed in the atmosphere of Titan, Saturn's largest moon, and in the gases of interstellar nebulas. On Earth, it is used as a welding gas and a fumigant. In its reaction with fluorine gas, carbon tetrafluoride and nitrogen trifluoride gases are produced. What mass of carbon tetrafluoride forms when 80.0 g of each reactant are mixed?

3.86 An intermediate step in the industrial production of nitric acid involves the reaction of ammonia with oxygen gas to form nitrogen monoxide and water. How many grams of nitrogen monoxide can form by the reaction of 466 g ammonia with 812 g oxygen?

3.87 Gaseous butane is compressed and used as a liquid fuel in disposable cigarette lighters and lightweight camping stoves. Suppose a lighter contains 5.00 mL butane ($d = 0.579$ g/mL).
(a) How many grams of oxygen are needed to burn the butane completely?
(b) How many moles of CO_2 form when all the butane burns?
(c) How many total molecules of gas form when the butane burns completely?

3.88 Diborane (B_2H_6), a useful reactant in organic synthesis, may be prepared by the following reaction, which occurs in a nonaqueous solvent:

$$NaBH_4(s) + BF_3(g) \longrightarrow B_2H_6(g) + NaBF_4(s) \quad \text{[unbalanced]}$$

If the reaction has a 75.0% yield of diborane, how many grams of $NaBH_4$ are needed to make 20.0 g B_2H_6?

Fundamentals of Solution Stoichiometry
(Sample Problems 3.12 to 3.16)

■ Concept Review Questions

3.89 Box A represents a unit volume of a solution. Choose from boxes B or C the one representing the same unit volume of solution that has (a) more solute added; (b) more solvent added; (c) higher molarity; (d) lower concentration.

A   B   C

3.90 Given the volume and molarity of a $CaCl_2$ solution, how would you determine the number of moles and the mass of solute?

3.91 Are the following instructions for diluting a 10.0 M solution to a 1.00 M solution correct: "Take 100.0 mL of the 10.0 M solution and add 900.0 mL water"? Explain.

■ Skill-Building Exercises (paired)

3.92 Calculate each of the following quantities:
(a) Grams of solute in 175.8 mL of 0.0565 M calcium acetate
(b) Molarity of a 500.-mL solution containing 3.83 g potassium iodide
(c) Moles of solute in 3.011 L of 0.850 M sodium cyanide

3.93 Calculate each of the following quantities:
(a) Volume in liters of 2.26 M potassium hydroxide that contains 8.42 g of solute
(b) Number of Cu^{2+} ions in 52 L of 2.3 M copper(II) chloride
(c) Molarity of a 275-mL solution containing 135 mmol glucose

3.94 Calculate each of the following quantities:
(a) Grams of solute needed to make 475 mL of 5.62×10^{-2} M potassium sulfate
(b) Molarity of a solution that contains 6.55 mg calcium chloride in each milliliter
(c) Number of Mg^{2+} ions in each milliliter of 0.184 M magnesium bromide

3.95 Calculate each of the following quantities:
(a) Molarity of the solution that results when 46.0 g silver nitrate is dissolved in enough water to give a final volume of 335 mL.
(b) Volume in liters of 0.385 M manganese(II) sulfate that contains 57.0 g of solute
(c) Volume in milliliters of 6.44×10^{-2} M adenosine triphosphate (ATP) that contains 1.68 mmol ATP

3.96 Calculate each of the following quantities:
(a) Molarity of a solution prepared by diluting 37.00 mL of 0.250 M potassium chloride to 150.00 mL
(b) Molarity of a solution prepared by diluting 25.71 mL of 0.0706 M ammonium sulfate to 500.00 mL
(c) Molarity of sodium ion in a solution made by mixing 3.58 mL of 0.288 M sodium chloride with 500. mL of 6.51×10^{-3} M sodium sulfate (assume volumes are additive)

3.97 Calculate each of the following quantities:
(a) Volume of 2.050 M copper(II) nitrate that must be diluted with water to prepare 750.0 mL of a 0.8543 M solution
(b) Volume of 1.03 M calcium chloride that must be diluted with water to prepare 350. mL of a 2.66×10^{-2} M chloride ion solution
(c) Final volume of a 0.0700 M solution prepared by diluting 18.0 mL of 0.155 M lithium carbonate with water

3.98 A sample of concentrated nitric acid has a density of 1.41 g/mL and contains 70.0% HNO_3 by mass.
(a) What mass of HNO_3 is present per liter of solution?
(b) What is the molarity of the solution?

3.99 Concentrated sulfuric acid (18.3 M) has a density of 1.84 g/mL.
(a) How many moles of sulfuric acid are present per milliliter of solution?
(b) What is the mass % of H_2SO_4 in the solution?

3.100 How many milliliters of 0.55 M HCl are needed to react with 5.7 g $CaCO_3$?

$$2HCl(aq) + CaCO_3(s) \longrightarrow CaCl_2(aq) + CO_2(g) + H_2O(l)$$

3.101 How many grams of NaH_2PO_4 are needed to react with 38.74 mL of 0.275 M NaOH?

$$NaH_2PO_4(s) + 2NaOH(aq) \longrightarrow Na_3PO_4(aq) + 2H_2O(l)$$

3.102 How many grams of solid barium sulfate form when 25.0 mL of 0.160 M barium chloride reacts with 68.0 mL of 0.055 M sodium sulfate? Aqueous sodium chloride is the other product.

3.103 How many moles of which reactant are in excess when 350.0 mL of 0.210 M sulfuric acid reacts with 0.500 L of 0.196 M sodium hydroxide to form water and aqueous sodium sulfate?

■ Problems in Context

3.104 Ordinary household bleach is an aqueous solution of sodium hypochlorite. What is the molarity of a bleach solution that contains 20.5 g sodium hypochlorite in a total volume of 375 mL?

3.105 Muriatic acid, an industrial grade of concentrated HCl, is used to clean masonry and etch cement for painting. Its concentration is 11.7 M.
(a) Write instructions for diluting the concentrated acid to make 5.0 gallons of 3.5 M acid for routine use (1 gal = 4 qt; 1 qt = 0.946 L).

(b) How many milliliters of the muriatic acid solution contain 9.55 g HCl?

3.106 A sample of impure magnesium was analyzed by allowing it to react with excess HCl solution:

$$Mg(s) + 2HCl(aq) \longrightarrow MgCl_2(aq) + H_2(g)$$

After 1.32 g of the impure metal was treated with 0.100 L of 0.750 M HCl, 0.0125 mol HCl remained. Assuming the impurities do not react with the acid, what is the mass % Mg in the sample?

Comprehensive Problems

Problems with an asterisk (*) are more challenging.

3.107 The study of sulfur-nitrogen compounds is an active area of chemical research, made more so by the discovery in the early 1980s of one such compound that conducts electricity like a metal. The first sulfur-nitrogen compound was prepared in 1835 and serves today as a reactant for preparing many of the others. Mass spectrometry of the compound shows a molar mass of 184.27 g/mol, and analysis shows it to contain 2.288 g S for every 1.000 g N. What is its molecular formula?

3.108 Hydrogen-containing fuels have a "fuel value" based on their mass % H. Rank the following compounds from highest mass % H to lowest: ethane, propane, benzene, ethanol, cetyl palmitate (whale oil, $C_{32}H_{64}O_2$).

ethane   propane   benzene

ethanol

3.109 Plaster of Paris [$(CaSO_4)_2 \cdot H_2O$] is often used in making surgical casts.
(a) How many moles of calcium ions are in 58.5 kg plaster of Paris?
(b) What is the mass % O in plaster of Paris?
(c) The industrial source of calcium compounds is limestone (calcium carbonate). How many metric tons of plaster of Paris can be made from 50.0 metric tons of limestone (1 metric ton = 1000 kg)?

3.110 Narceine is a narcotic in opium. It crystallizes from water solution as a hydrate that contains 10.8 mass % water. If the molar mass of narceine hydrate is 499.52 g/mol, determine x in narceine·xH_2O.

3.111 Serotonin ($\mathcal{M} = 176$ g/mol) is a compound that conducts nerve impulses in brain and muscle. It contains 68.2 mass % C, 6.86 mass % H, 15.9 mass % N, and 9.08 mass % O. What is its molecular formula?

3.112 Convert the following descriptions of reactions into balanced equations:
(a) In a gaseous reaction, hydrogen sulfide burns in oxygen to form sulfur dioxide and water vapor.
(b) When crystalline potassium chlorate is heated to just above its melting point, it reacts to form two different crystalline compounds, potassium chloride and potassium perchlorate.

(c) When hydrogen gas is passed over powdered iron(III) oxide, iron metal and water vapor form.
(d) The combustion of gaseous ethane in air forms carbon dioxide and water vapor.
(e) Iron(II) chloride can be converted to iron(III) flouride by treatment with chlorine trifluoride gas. Chlorine gas is also formed.

3.113 The smelting of ferric oxide to form elemental iron occurs at high temperatures in a blast furnace through a reaction sequence with carbon monoxide. In the first step, ferric oxide reacts with carbon monoxide to form Fe_3O_4. This substance reacts with more carbon monoxide to form iron(II) oxide, which reacts with still more carbon monoxide to form molten iron. Carbon dioxide is also produced in each step. (a) Write an overall balanced equation for the iron-smelting process. (b) How many grams of carbon monoxide are required to form 40.0 metric tons of iron from ferric oxide?

3.114 Isobutylene is a hydrocarbon used in the manufacture of synthetic rubber. When 0.847 g isobutylene was analyzed by combustion (using an apparatus similar to that of Figure 3.4), the gain in mass of the CO_2 absorber was 2.657 g and that of the H_2O absorber was 1.089 g. What is the empirical formula of isobutylene?

3.115 One of the compounds used to increase the octane rating of gasoline is toluene *(right)*. Suppose 15.0 mL toluene ($d = 0.867$ g/mL) is consumed when a sample of gasoline burns in air.
(a) How many grams of oxygen are needed for complete combustion of the toluene?
(b) How many total moles of gaseous products form?
(c) How many molecules of water vapor form?

3.116 During studies of the reaction in Sample Problem 3.10,

$$N_2O_4(l) + 2N_2H_4(l) \longrightarrow 3N_2(g) + 4H_2O(g)$$

a chemical engineer measured a less-than-expected yield of N_2 and discovered that the following side reaction occurs:

$$2N_2O_4(l) + N_2H_4(l) \longrightarrow 6NO(g) + 2H_2O(g)$$

In one experiment 10.0 g NO formed when 100.0 g of each reactant were mixed. What is the highest percent yield of N_2 that can be expected?

3.117 A mathematical equation useful for dilution calculations is $M_{dil} \times V_{dil} = M_{conc} \times V_{conc}$. What does each symbol mean, and why does the equation work?

3.118 The following boxes represent a chemical reaction between AB_2 and B_2:

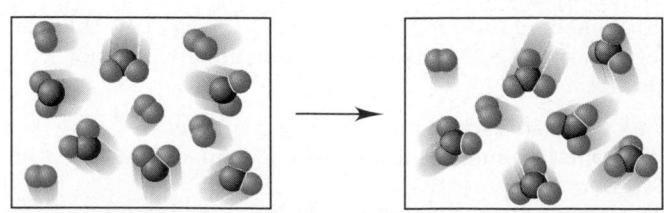

(a) Write a balanced equation for the reaction.
(b) What is the limiting reactant in this reaction?

(c) How many moles of product can be made from 3.0 mol B_2 and 5.0 mol AB_2?

(d) How many moles of excess reactant remain after the reaction in part (c)?

3.119 Calculate each of the following quantities:

(a) Volume of 18.0 M sulfuric acid that must be added to water to prepare 2.00 L of a 0.309 M solution

(b) Molarity of the solution obtained by diluting 80.6 mL of 0.225 M ammonium chloride to 0.250 L

(c) Volume of water added to 0.150 L of 0.0262 M sodium hydroxide to obtain a 0.0100 M solution (assume the volumes are additive at these low concentrations)

(d) Mass of calcium nitrate in each milliliter of a solution prepared by diluting 64.0 mL of 0.745 M calcium nitrate to a final volume of 0.100 L

3.120 Potassium permanganate solutions are extremely useful in laboratory analysis. Their concentrations are determined by a reaction with ferrous ammonium sulfate hexahydrate $Fe(NH_4)_2(SO_4)_2 \cdot 6H_2O$, which behaves in solution as though it were simply iron(II) sulfate:

$$2KMnO_4(aq) + 10FeSO_4(aq) + 8H_2SO_4(aq) \longrightarrow$$
$$5Fe_2(SO_4)_3(aq) + 2MnSO_4(aq) + K_2SO_4(aq) + 8H_2O(l)$$

In an experiment, 2.50 g $Fe(NH_4)_2(SO_4)_2 \cdot 6H_2O$ reacted completely with 37.0 mL of a $KMnO_4$ solution. What is the molarity of the $KMnO_4$ solution?

3.121 Agricultural biochemists use 6-benzylaminopurine $(C_{12}H_{11}N_5)$ in trace amounts as a plant growth regulator. In a typical application, 150. mL of a solution contains 0.030 mg of the compound. What is the molarity of the solution?

3.122 One of Germany's largest chemical manufacturers is building a new plant to produce 3.74×10^8 lb vinyl acetate per year. This compound *(right)* is used to make some of the polymers in adhesives, paints, fabric coatings, floppy disks, plastic films, and so on. Assuming production goals are met, how many moles of vinyl acetate will the plant produce each month?

*3.123 Government and industry analysts routinely measure the quantity of ascorbic acid (vitamin C; $C_6H_8O_6$) in commercial products such as fruit juices and vitamin tablets. The ascorbic acid reacts with excess iodine, and the I_2 remaining is determined with sodium thiosulfate $(Na_2S_2O_3)$. In one analysis, a vitamin tablet is mixed in water and treated with 53.20 mL of 0.1030 M I_2 according to the equation

$$C_6H_8O_6(s) + I_2(aq) \longrightarrow C_6H_6O_6(aq) + 2HI(aq)$$

After all the ascorbic acid reacts, the excess I_2 reacts with 27.54 mL of 0.1153 M $Na_2S_2O_3$ according to the equation

$$I_2(aq) + 2Na_2S_2O_3(aq) \longrightarrow 2NaI(aq) + Na_2S_4O_6(aq)$$

How many grams of ascorbic acid are in the vitamin tablet?

3.124 Is each of the following statements true or false? Correct any that are false:

(a) A mole of one substance has the same number of atoms as a mole of any other substance.

(b) The theoretical yield for a reaction is based on the balanced chemical equation.

(c) A limiting-reactant problem is presented when the quantity of available material is given in moles for one of the reactants.

(d) To prepare 1.00 L of 3.00 M NaCl, weigh 175.5 g of NaCl and dissolve it in 1.00 L distilled water.

(e) The concentration of a solution is an intensive property, whereas the amount of solute in a solution is an extensive property.

3.125 Box A represents one unit volume of solution A. Which box—B, C, or D—represents one unit volume after adding enough solvent to solution A to (a) triple its volume; (b) double its volume; (c) quadruple its volume?

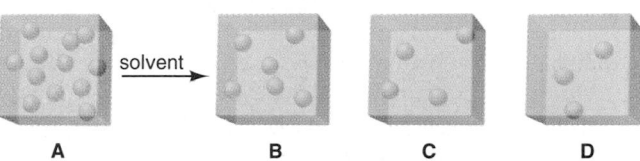

3.126 In each pair, choose the larger of the indicated quantity, or state if the samples are equal:

(a) Entities: 0.4 mol O_3 molecules or 0.4 mol O atoms

(b) Grams: 0.4 mol O_3 molecules or 0.4 mol O atoms

(c) Moles: 4.0 g N_2O_4 or 3.3 g SO_2

(d) Grams: 0.6 mol C_2H_4 or 0.6 mol F_2

(e) Total ions: 2.3 mol sodium chlorate or 2.2 mol magnesium chloride

(f) Molecules: 1.0 g H_2O or 1.0 g H_2O_2

(g) Na^+ ions: 0.500 L of 0.500 M NaBr or 0.0146 kg NaCl

(h) Grams: 6.022×10^{23} atoms of ^{235}U or 6.022×10^{23} atoms of ^{238}U

3.127 The number of objects in a mole is so fantastically large as to be incomprehensible from everyday experience. If a mole of ice cubes (each 1 in^3) were stacked neatly edge to edge over the entire continental United States (area = 3.0×10^6 mi^2), how high would the stack be? (Assume the land area is flat.)

3.128 Oleic acid, a component of olive oil, is 76.54% C, 12.13% H, and 11.33% O by mass. An approximate determination of its molar mass gave a value of 274 ± 20 g/mol. What is the molecular formula of oleic acid?

3.129 A balanced equation may be interpreted in several ways (see Table 3.5). Write a balanced equation for the reaction between solid tetraphosphorus trisulfide and oxygen to form solid tetraphosphorus decaoxide and gaseous sulfur trioxide. Tabulate the equation in terms of (a) molecules, (b) moles, and (c) grams.

3.130 Hydrogen gas has been suggested as a clean fuel because it produces only water vapor when it burns. If the reaction has a 98.8% yield, what mass of hydrogen forms 85.0 kg water?

3.131 Assuming that the volumes are additive, what is the concentration of KBr in a solution prepared by mixing 0.200 L of 0.053 M KBr with 0.550 L of 0.078 M KBr?

3.132 Many reactive boron compounds are analyzed by reaction with water, which converts the boron to boric acid (H_3BO_3). The boric acid content is then determined with NaOH, which reacts with boric acid on a 1:1 mole basis. If 0.1352 g of a boron compound reacts with water, and the resulting boric acid requires 23.47 mL of 0.205 M NaOH for reaction, what was the mass % of boron in the compound?

3.133 The explosive pentaerythritol tetranitrate (PETN; *right*) is a white powder that can be set off by friction. It is more stable when mixed with latex to make plastic explosives, which are used in welding, demolition, and even for creating sculptures. (a) What is the mass % of each element in PETN? (b) How many moles are in 26.5 μg of PETN?

3.134 Calculate each of the following quantities:
(a) Moles of compound in 0.588 g ammonium bromide
(b) Number of potassium ions in 68.5 g potassium nitrate
(c) Mass in grams of 5.85 mol glycerol ($C_3H_8O_3$)
(d) Volume of 2.55 mol chloroform ($CHCl_3$; d = 1.48 g/mL)
(e) Number of sodium ions in 2.11 mol sodium carbonate
(f) Number of atoms in 10.0 μg of cadmium
(g) Number of atoms in 0.0015 mol fluorine gas

3.135 Elements X (green) and Y (purple) react according to the following equation: $X_2 + 3Y_2 \longrightarrow 2XY_3$. Which molecular scene represents the product of the reaction?

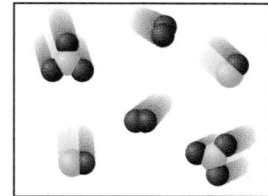

A   B   C   D

3.136 Hydrocarbon mixtures are used as fuels. How many grams of $CO_2(g)$ are produced by the combustion of 200. g of a mixture that is 25.0% CH_4 and 75.0% C_3H_8 by mass?

3.137 To 1.20 L of 0.325 *M* HCl, you add 3.37 L of a second HCl solution of unknown concentration. The resulting solution is 0.893 *M* HCl. Assuming the volumes are additive, calculate the molarity of the second HCl solution.

*3.138 Nitrogen (N), phosphorus (P), and potassium (K) are the main nutrients in plant fertilizers. According to an industry convention, the numbers on the label refer to the mass % of N, P_2O_5, and K_2O, in that order. Calculate the N:P:K ratio of a 30:10:10 fertilizer in terms of moles of each element, and express it as *x*:*y*:1.0.

3.139 A 0.652-g sample of a pure strontium halide reacts with excess sulfuric acid, and the solid strontium sulfate formed is separated, dried, and found to weigh 0.755 g. What is the formula of the original halide?

3.140 Methane and ethane are the two simplest hydrocarbons. What is the mass % C in a mixture that is 40.0% methane and 60.0% ethane by mass?

*3.141 When carbon-containing compounds are burned in a limited amount of air, some $CO(g)$ as well as $CO_2(g)$ is pro-

duced. A gaseous product mixture is 35.0 mass % CO and 65.0 mass % CO_2. What is the mass % C in the mixture?

3.142 When ferrocene was synthesized in 1951, it was shown to be the first organic iron compound with direct Fe—C bonds. An understanding of ferrocene's structure gave rise to new ideas about chemical bonding and led to the preparation of many useful compounds. In the combustion analysis of ferrocene, which contains only Fe, C, and H, a 0.9437-g sample produced 2.233 g CO_2 and 0.457 g H_2O. What is the empirical formula of ferrocene?

*3.143 Citric acid *(right)* is concentrated in citrus fruits and plays a central metabolic role in nearly every animal and plant cell. (a) What are the molar mass and formula of citric acid? (b) How many moles of citric acid are in 1.50 qt of lemon juice (d = 1.09 g/mL) that is 6.82% citric acid by mass?

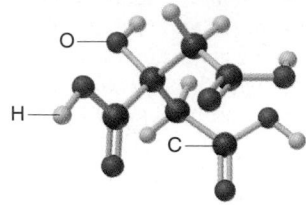

*3.144 Various nitrogen oxides, as well as oxides of sulfur, contribute to acidic rainfall through complex reaction sequences. Atmospheric nitrogen and oxygen combine to form nitrogen monoxide gas, which reacts with more oxygen to form nitrogen dioxide gas. In contact with water vapor, nitrogen dioxide forms aqueous nitric acid and more nitrogen monoxide. (a) Write balanced equations for these reactions. (b) Use the three equations to write one overall balanced equation that does *not* include nitrogen monoxide and nitrogen dioxide. (c) How many metric tons (t) of nitric acid form when 1.25×10^3 t of atmospheric nitrogen is consumed (1 t = 1000 kg)?

*3.145 In the chemical analysis of an unknown, chemists often add an excess of a reactant, determine the amount of that reactant remaining after the reaction with the unknown, and use those amounts to calculate the amount of the unknown. For the analysis of an unknown NaOH solution, you add 50.0 mL of the solution to 0.150 L of an acid solution prepared by dissolving 0.588 g solid oxalic acid dihydrate ($H_2C_2O_4 \cdot 2H_2O$) in water:

$$2NaOH(aq) + H_2C_2O_4(aq) \longrightarrow 2H_2O(l) + Na_2C_2O_4(aq)$$

The unreacted NaOH then reacts completely with 9.65 mL of 0.116 *M* HCl:

$$NaOH(aq) + HCl(aq) \longrightarrow H_2O(l) + NaCl(aq)$$

What is the molarity of the original NaOH solution?

*3.146 When 1.5173 g of an organic iron compound containing Fe, C, H, and O was burned in oxygen, 2.838 g CO_2 and 0.8122 g H_2O were produced. In a separate experiment to determine the mass % of iron, 0.3355 g of the compound yielded 0.0758 g Fe_2O_3. What is the empirical formula of the compound?

*3.147 Fluorides of the relatively unreactive noble gas xenon can be formed by direct reaction of the elements at high pressure and temperature. Depending on the temperature and the reactant amounts, the product mixture may include XeF_2, XeF_4, and XeF_6. Under conditions that produce only XeF_4 and XeF_6, 1.85×10^{-4} mol Xe reacted with 5.00×10^{-4} mol F_2, and 9.00×10^{-6} mol Xe was found to be in excess. What are the mass percents of XeF_4 and XeF_6 in the product?

The Major Classes of Chemical Reactions

4

Figure: The universality of chemical change. Sparks fly as iron reacts with oxygen, one example from one class of the myriad reactions that chemists examine. Within each of the surrounding red blood cells, an example of a very different class of reactions, still between iron and oxygen, takes place. We lay the groundwork for reaction classes in this chapter and revisit their endless variety throughout the text.

The amazing variety that we see in nature is largely a consequence of the amazing variety of chemical reactions. Rapid chemical changes occur among gas molecules as sunlight bathes the atmosphere or lightning rips through a stormy sky (see margin). Oceans are gigantic containers in which aqueous reaction chemistry goes on unceasingly. In every cell of your body, thousands of reactions are taking place right now.

Of the millions of chemical reactions occurring in and around you, we have examined only a tiny fraction so far, and it would be impossible to examine them all. Fortunately, it isn't necessary to catalog every reaction, because when we survey even a small percentage of them, a few major patterns of chemical change emerge.

In this chapter, we examine the underlying nature of the three most common *reaction processes*. Since one of our main themes is aqueous reaction chemistry, we first investigate the crucial role water plays as a solvent for many reactions. Using those ideas, we then focus on two of these major processes—precipitation and acid-base—examining why they occur and describing the use of ionic equations to depict them. Next, we discuss the nature of the third process—oxidation-reduction—perhaps the most important of all. Then, we classify reactions by their *change in numbers* of reactants and products and see how these classes overlap with the three reaction processes. The chapter ends with an introductory look at the reversible nature of all chemical reactions.

4.1 The Role of Water as a Solvent

Many reactions take place in an aqueous environment, and our first step toward comprehending them is to understand how water acts as a solvent. The role a solvent plays in a reaction depends on its chemical nature. Some solvents play a passive role. They disperse the substances into individual molecules but do not interact with them in other ways. Water plays a much more active role. It interacts strongly with the reactants and, in some cases, even affects their bonds. Water is crucial to many chemical and physical processes, and we will discuss its properties frequently in the text.

The Solubility of Ionic Compounds

When water dissolves an ionic solid, such as potassium bromide (KBr), an important change occurs. Figure 4.1 shows this change with a simple apparatus that measures *electrical conductivity,* the flow of electric current. When the electrodes are immersed in pure water or pushed into solid KBr, no current flows. In the aqueous KBr solution, however, a significant current flows, as shown by the brightly lit bulb. The current flow in the solution implies the *movement of charged particles:* when KBr dissolves in water, the K^+ and Br^- ions in the solid separate from each other (dissociate) and move toward the electrode whose charge is opposite the ion's charge. A substance that conducts a current when dissolved in water is an **electrolyte.** Soluble ionic compounds dissociate completely and create a large current, so they are called *strong* electrolytes.

As the KBr dissolves, each ion becomes **solvated,** surrounded by solvent molecules. We express this dissociation into solvated ions as follows:

$$KBr(s) \xrightarrow{\text{H}_2\text{O}} K^+(aq) + Br^-(aq)$$

The "H_2O" above the arrow indicates that water is required but is not a reactant in the usual sense. When any water-soluble ionic compound dissolves, *the oppositely charged ions separate from each other, become surrounded by water*

A Distilled water does not conduct a current

B Positive and negative ions fixed in a solid do not conduct a current

To (+) electrode   To (−) electrode

C In solution, positive and negative ions move and conduct a current

Figure 4.1 The electrical conductivity of ionic solutions.
A, When electrodes connected to a power source are placed in distilled water, no current flows and the bulb is unlit. **B,** A solid ionic compound, such as KBr, conducts no current because the ions are bound tightly together. **C,** When KBr dissolves in H_2O, the ions separate and move through the solution, thereby conducting a current.

molecules, and move throughout the solution. The formula of the compound tells us the number of moles of different ions that result when the compound dissolves. Thus, 1 mol KBr dissociates into 2 mol of ions, 1 mol K^+ and 1 mol Br^-.

Sample Problem 4.1   Determining Moles of Ions in Aqueous Ionic Solutions

PROBLEM How many moles of each ion are in the following solutions?
(a) 5.0 mol ammonium sulfate dissolved in water
(b) 78.5 g cesium bromide dissolved in water
(c) 7.42×10^{22} formula units copper(II) nitrate dissolved in water
(d) 35 mL of 0.84 M zinc chloride

PLAN We write an equation that shows the numbers of moles of ions released when *1 mol* of compound dissolves. In **(a)**, we multiply the moles of ions released by 5.0. In **(b)**, we first convert grams to moles. In **(c)**, we first convert formula units to moles. In **(d)**, we first convert molarity and volume to moles.

SOLUTION (a) $(NH_4)_2SO_4(s) \xrightarrow{H_2O} 2NH_4^+(aq) + SO_4^{2-}(aq)$

Remember that *polyatomic ions remain as intact units in solution.*
Calculating moles of NH_4^+ ions:

$$\text{Moles of } NH_4^+ = 5.0 \text{ mol } (NH_4)_2SO_4 \times \frac{2 \text{ mol } NH_4^+}{1 \text{ mol } (NH_4)_2SO_4} = 10. \text{ mol } NH_4^+$$

5.0 mol SO_4^{2-} is also present.

(b) $CsBr(s) \xrightarrow{H_2O} Cs^+(aq) + Br^-(aq)$

Converting from grams to moles:

$$\text{Moles of CsBr} = 78.5 \ \cancel{\text{g CsBr}} \times \frac{1 \text{ mol CsBr}}{212.8 \ \cancel{\text{g CsBr}}} = 0.369 \text{ mol CsBr}$$

Thus, $\boxed{0.369 \text{ mol } Cs^+ \text{ and } 0.369 \text{ mol } Br^-}$ are present.

(c) $Cu(NO_3)_2(s) \xrightarrow{H_2O} Cu^{2+}(aq) + 2NO_3^-(aq)$

Converting from formula units to moles:

$$\text{Moles of Cu(NO}_3)_2 = 7.42 \times 10^{22} \ \cancel{\text{formula units Cu(NO}_3)_2}$$

$$\times \frac{1 \text{ mol Cu(NO}_3)_2}{6.022 \times 10^{23} \ \cancel{\text{formula units Cu(NO}_3)_2}}$$

$$= 0.123 \text{ mol Cu(NO}_3)_2$$

$$\text{Moles of NO}_3^- = 0.123 \ \cancel{\text{mol Cu(NO}_3)_2} \times \frac{2 \text{ mol NO}_3^-}{1 \ \cancel{\text{mol Cu(NO}_3)_2}}$$

$$= \boxed{0.246 \text{ mol NO}_3^-}$$

$\boxed{0.123 \text{ mol } Cu^{2+}}$ is also present.

(d) $ZnCl_2(aq) \longrightarrow Zn^{2+}(aq) + 2Cl^-(aq)$

Converting from liters to moles:

$$\text{Moles of ZnCl}_2 = 35 \ \cancel{\text{mL}} \times \frac{1 \ \cancel{\text{L}}}{10^3 \ \cancel{\text{mL}}} \times \frac{0.84 \text{ mol ZnCl}_2}{1 \ \cancel{\text{L}}} = 2.9 \times 10^{-2} \text{ mol ZnCl}_2$$

$$\text{Moles of Cl}^- = 2.9 \times 10^{-2} \ \cancel{\text{mol ZnCl}_2} \times \frac{2 \text{ mol Cl}^-}{1 \ \cancel{\text{mol ZnCl}_2}} = \boxed{5.8 \times 10^{-2} \text{ mol Cl}^-}$$

$\boxed{2.9 \times 10^{-2} \text{ mol } Zn^{2+}}$ is also present.

CHECK After you round off to check the math, see if the relative moles of ions are consistent with the formula. For instance, in (a), 10 mol NH_4^+/5.0 mol SO_4^{2-} = 2 NH_4^+/1 SO_4^{2-}, or $(NH_4)_2SO_4$. In (d), 0.029 mol Zn^{2+}/0.058 mol Cl^- = 1 Zn^{2+}/2 Cl^-, or $ZnCl_2$.

Follow-up Problem 4.1   How many moles of each ion are in each of the following solutions?
(a) 2 mol potassium perchlorate dissolved in water
(b) 354 g magnesium acetate dissolved in water
(c) 1.88×10^{24} formula units of ammonium chromate dissolved in water
(d) 1.32 L of 0.55 M sodium bisulfate

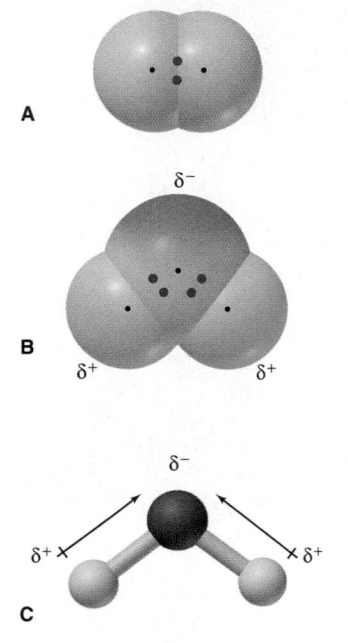

Figure 4.2 Electron distribution in molecules of H₂ and H₂O.
A, In H₂, the nuclei are identical, so they attract the electrons equally. Note that the pair of red dots lies equidistant between the nuclei, so electron density is balanced *(light gray)*. **B,** In H₂O, the O nucleus attracts the shared electrons more strongly than the H nucleus, creating an uneven charge distribution in each bond *(shading)*. The partially negative O end is designated δ⁻ and the partially positive H end is designated δ⁺. Note the regions of greater *(red)* and lesser *(blue)* electron density. **C,** In this ball-and-stick model of H₂O, a polar arrow points to the negative end of each O—H bond. **D,** The two polar O—H bonds and the bent molecular shape give rise to the polar H₂O molecule, with the partially positive end located *between* the two H atoms.

The Polar Nature of Water

Water separates ions in a process that greatly reduces the *electrostatic force* of attraction between them. To see how it does this, let's examine the water molecule closely. Water's power as an ionizing solvent results from two features of the water molecule: *the distribution of its bonding electrons* and *its overall shape.*

Recall from Section 2.7 that the electrons in a covalent bond are shared between the bonded atoms. In a covalent bond that exists between identical atoms (as in H₂, Cl₂, and O₂), the sharing is equal. As Figure 4.2A shows, the shared electrons in H₂ are distributed equally, so no imbalance of charge appears. On the other hand, in covalent bonds between nonidentical atoms, the sharing is unequal: one atom attracts the electron pair more strongly than the other. For reasons that we'll discuss in Chapter 9, the O atom attracts electrons more strongly than the H atom. Therefore, in each of the O—H bonds of water, the electrons spend more time closer to the O, as shown in Figure 4.2B. This unequal distribution of the electron pair's negative charge creates partially charged "poles" at the ends of each O—H bond. The O end acts as a slightly negative pole (represented by the red shading and the δ⁻), and the H end acts as a slightly positive pole (represented by the blue shading and the δ^+). In Figure 4.2C, the bond's polarity is indicated by a *polar arrow* (the arrowhead points to the negative pole and the tail is crossed to make a "plus"). The partial charges on the O and H atoms in water are *much less* than full ionic charges. In KBr, for instance, the electron has been *transferred* from the K atom to the Br atom and two ions form. In the polar O—H bond, no ions exist; the electrons have just *shifted* their average position nearer to the O atom.

The water molecule also has a bent shape: the H—O—H atoms form an angle, not a straight line. The combined effects of its bent shape and its polar bonds make water a **polar molecule.** As you can see in Figure 4.2D, the O portion of the molecule is the partially negative pole, and the region midway between the H atoms is the partially positive pole.

Ionic Compounds in Water With these bent, polar water molecules in mind, imagine a granule of an ionic compound in water. Figure 4.3 shows water molecules congregating over the orderly array of ions at the granule's surface; the negative ends of some are attracted to the cations, and the positive ends of others are attracted to the anions. An electrostatic "tug of war" occurs as the ions become partially solvated. The attraction between each ion and water molecules gradually replaces the attraction of the oppositely charged ions for each other. As a result, the ions become completely solvated, separate from one another, and move randomly throughout the solution. A similar scene occurs whenever an ionic compound dissolves in water. ◆

Although many ionic compounds dissolve in water, many others do not. In such cases, the electrostatic attraction among ions in the compound is greater that the attraction between ions and water molecules, so the substance remains intact. Actually, these so-called insoluble substances *do* dissolve to a very small extent, usually several orders of magnitude less than so-called soluble substances. Compare, for example, the solubilities of NaCl (a "soluble" compound) and AgCl (an "insoluble" compound):

$$\text{Solubility of NaCl in } H_2O \text{ at } 20°C = 365 \text{ g/L}$$

$$\text{Solubility of AgCl in } H_2O \text{ at } 20°C = 0.009 \text{ g/L}$$

In Chapter 13, we examine the factors that influence solubility quantitatively, but the simple distinction between "soluble" and "insoluble" is useful for our purposes in this chapter.

◆ Solid Solvents for Ions
Because of its partial charges, water is an excellent liquid solvent for ionic species, but some solids behave in a similar way. For example, poly(ethylene oxide) is a polymer with a repeating structure written as

where the *n* indicates many identical groups linked covalently together. The partial negative charges on the oxygen atoms can surround metal cations, such as Li^+, and solvate them while remaining in the solid state. Poly(ethylene oxide) and related polymers are essential parts of the lithium-ion batteries used in laptop computers and other portable electronic devices.

Figure 4.3 The dissolution of an ionic compound. When an ionic compound dissolves in water, H_2O molecules separate, surround, and disperse the ions into the liquid. Note that the negative ends of the H_2O molecules face the positive ions and the positive ends face the negative ions.

Covalent Compounds in Water   Water dissolves many covalent substances also. Table sugar (sucrose, $C_{12}H_{22}O_{11}$), beverage (grain) alcohol (ethanol, C_2H_6O), and automobile antifreeze (ethylene glycol, $C_2H_6O_2$) are some familiar examples. All contain their own polar O—H bonds, which interact with those of water. However, even though these substances dissolve, they do *not* dissociate into ions *but remain as intact molecules.* Since their aqueous solutions do not conduct an electric current, these substances are called **nonelectrolytes.** Many other covalent substances, such as benzene (C_6H_6) and octane (C_8H_{18}), do not contain polar bonds, and these substances do not dissolve appreciably in water.

A small, but very important, group of H-containing covalent molecules interacts so strongly with water that their molecules *do* dissociate into ions. In aqueous solution, they are all *acids,* as you'll see shortly. The molecules contain polar bonds to hydrogen, such that the atom bonded to H pulls more strongly on the shared electron pair. A good example is hydrogen chloride gas. The Cl end of the HCl molecule is partially negative, and the H end is partially positive. When HCl dissolves in water, the partially charged poles of H_2O molecules are attracted to the oppositely charged poles of HCl. The H—Cl bond breaks, with the H becoming the solvated cation $H^+(aq)$ and the Cl becoming the solvated anion $Cl^-(aq)$. Hydrogen bromide behaves similarly when it dissolves in water:

$$HBr(g) \xrightarrow{H_2O} H^+(aq) + Br^-(aq)$$

Sample Problem 4.2   Determining the Molarity of H^+ Ions in Aqueous Solutions of Acids

PROBLEM Nitric acid is a major chemical in the fertilizer and explosives industries. In aqueous solution, each molecule dissociates and the H becomes a solvated H^+ ion. What is the molarity of $H^+(aq)$ in 1.4 M nitric acid?
PLAN The molarity of acid is given, so we determine the formula to find the number of moles of $H^+(aq)$ present in 1 L solution.
SOLUTION Nitrate ion is NO_3^-, so nitric acid is HNO_3. Thus, 1 mol $H^+(aq)$ is released per mole of acid:

$$HNO_3(l) \xrightarrow{H_2O} H^+(aq) + NO_3^-(aq)$$

Therefore, 1.4 M HNO_3 contains 1.4 mol $H^+(aq)$/L, or   1.4 M $H^+(aq)$.

Follow-up Problem 4.2   How many moles of $H^+(aq)$ are present in 451 mL of 3.20 M hydrobromic acid?

Figure 4.4 The hydrated proton. The charge of the H^+ ion is highly concentrated because the ion is so small. In aqueous solution, it forms a covalent bond to a water molecule and exists as an H_3O^+ ion associated tightly with other H_2O molecules. Here, the $H_7O_3^+$ ion is shown.

The solvated hydrogen cation, $H^+(aq)$, is an unusual species. The H atom is a proton surrounded by an electron, so the H^+ ion is just a proton. Because its positive charge is concentrated in such a tiny volume, H^+ attracts the negative pole of surrounding water molecules very strongly and actually forms a covalent bond to one of the molecules. This fact is indicated by writing the aqueous H^+ ion as H_3O^+ (hydronium ion), but to make a point here, we write it as $(H_2O)H^+$. The hydronium ion associates tightly with other water molecules in a mixture that includes $H_5O_2^+$ [or $(H_2O)_2H^+$], $H_7O_3^+$ [or $(H_2O)_3H^+$], $H_9O_4^+$ [or $(H_2O)_4H^+$], and still larger aggregates; $H_7O_3^+$ is shown in Figure 4.4. These various forms exist together, but $H^+(aq)$ is often used as a general, simplified notation. Later, to emphasize the role of water, we show the solvated proton as $H_3O^+(aq)$.

When an ionic compound dissolves in water, the ions dissociate and are solvated by water molecules. Because the ions are free to move, their solutions conduct electricity. Water plays an active role in dissolving ionic compounds because it consists of polar molecules that are attracted to the ions. Water also dissolves many covalent substances, and it interacts with some H-containing molecules so strongly that it breaks covalent bonds and dissociates them into $H^+(aq)$ ions and anions.

4.2 Precipitation Reactions and Acid-Base Reactions

Of the many thousands of reactions that occur in the environment and in organisms, the overwhelming majority take place in aqueous solution. In this section, we focus on two of the three most important reaction processes—precipitation and acid-base. We begin by asking *why* these reactions occur and *how* to write equations that depict the essential chemical change.

The Driving Force for Many Aqueous Ionic Reactions

Because aqueous ionic reactions are so common, you may think that a reaction occurs whenever solutions of two ionic compounds are mixed, but that is not the case. What "drives" an aqueous ionic reaction to occur? In many cases, particularly for precipitation and acid-base processes, *a reaction occurs because certain ions attract each other so strongly that they are removed from solution in formation of the product.* Consider this example. Prepare separate solutions of sodium iodide and potassium nitrate, and their ions disperse throughout the solutions:

$$NaI(s) \xrightarrow{\text{H}_2\text{O}} Na^+(aq) + I^-(aq)$$

$$KNO_3(s) \xrightarrow{\text{H}_2\text{O}} K^+(aq) + NO_3^-(aq)$$

If you mix these solutions, does a reaction occur? In order to decide, *you must examine the ion combinations to see if any of the possible products are insoluble, that is, do **not** dissociate into ions.* In other words, you must see if ions are removed from solution. The reactant ions are

$$Na^+(aq) + I^-(aq) + K^+(aq) + NO_3^-(aq) \longrightarrow ?$$

In addition to the two original reactants, NaI and KNO_3, which you know are soluble, the possible cation-anion combinations are $NaNO_3$ and KI. In this case, a reaction does *not* occur because these two are also soluble ionic compounds. Therefore, the ions just remain in solution. (You'll see shortly how to determine if a product is soluble.)

Next, you substitute a solution of $Pb(NO_3)_2$ for the KNO_3, and a yellow solid forms, as shown in Figure 4.5. In addition to the two soluble reactants, the possible ion combinations are $NaNO_3$ and PbI_2, so the solid must be lead(II) iodide. In this case, a reaction *does* occur because ions are removed from the solution to form PbI_2:

$$2Na^+(aq) + 2I^-(aq) + Pb^{2+}(aq) + 2NO_3^-(aq) \longrightarrow 2Na^+(aq) + 2NO_3^-(aq) + PbI_2(s)$$

Writing Ionic Equations for Aqueous Ionic Reactions

Chemists write three types of equations to represent aqueous ionic reactions: molecular, total ionic, and net ionic equations. In ionic equations, atoms *and* charges must balance; as you'll see, by balancing the atoms, we balance the charges also. Let's examine a reaction to see what each of these equations shows. When solutions of silver nitrate and sodium chromate are mixed, the

Figure 4.5 The reaction of $Pb(NO_3)_2$ and NaI. When aqueous solutions of these ionic compounds are mixed, the yellow solid PbI_2 forms.

Figure 4.6 A precipitation reaction and its equations. When silver nitrate and sodium chromate solutions are mixed, a reaction occurs that forms solid silver chromate and a solution of sodium nitrate. The photos *(top)* present the macroscopic view of the reaction, the view the chemist sees in the lab. The blow-up arrows lead to an atomic-scale view *(middle)*, a representation of the chemist's mental picture of the reactants and products. (The pale ions are spectator ions, present for electrical neutrality, but not involved in the reaction.) Three equations represent the reaction in symbols. The molecular equation shows all substances intact. The total ionic equation shows all *soluble* substances as separate, solvated ions. The net ionic equation eliminates the spectator ions to show only the reacting species.

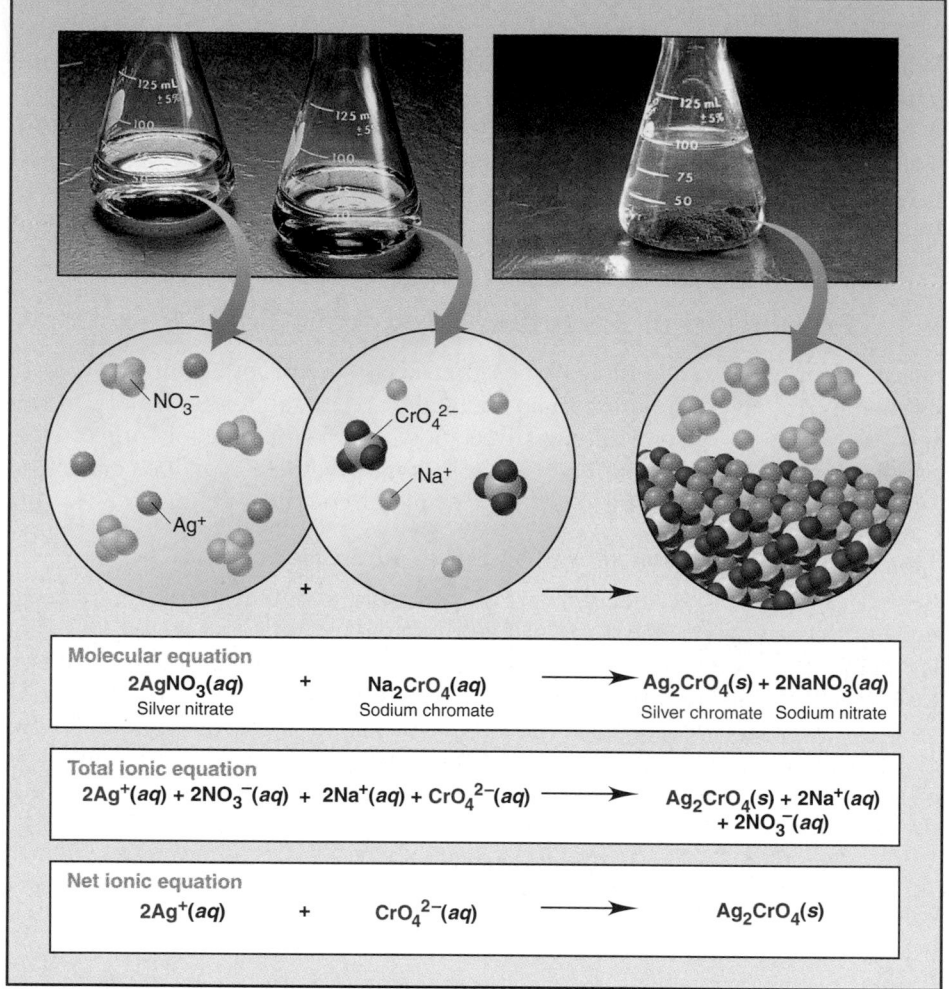

Molecular equation

$$2AgNO_3(aq) \quad + \quad Na_2CrO_4(aq) \quad \longrightarrow \quad Ag_2CrO_4(s) + 2NaNO_3(aq)$$

Silver nitrate   Sodium chromate   Silver chromate   Sodium nitrate

Total ionic equation

$$2Ag^+(aq) + 2NO_3^-(aq) + 2Na^+(aq) + CrO_4^{2-}(aq) \longrightarrow Ag_2CrO_4(s) + 2Na^+(aq) + 2NO_3^-(aq)$$

Net ionic equation

$$2Ag^+(aq) \quad + \quad CrO_4^{2-}(aq) \quad \longrightarrow \quad Ag_2CrO_4(s)$$

brick-red solid silver chromate (Ag_2CrO_4) forms. Figure 4.6 depicts the change you would see if you mixed these solutions in the lab, how you might imagine the change at the atomic level among the ions, and how you can symbolize the change with the three types of ionic equations.

The **molecular equation** *(top)* reveals the least about the actual change because *the reactants and products are written as if they were intact, undissociated compounds*:

$$2AgNO_3(aq) + Na_2CrO_4(aq) \longrightarrow Ag_2CrO_4(s) + 2NaNO_3(aq)$$

The **total ionic equation** *(middle)* shows the reaction more realistically because *all the soluble ionic substances are dissociated into ions*. Now the $Ag_2CrO_4(s)$ stands out as the only undissociated substance:

$$2Ag^+(aq) + 2NO_3^-(aq) + 2Na^+(aq) + CrO_4^{2-}(aq) \longrightarrow$$
$$Ag_2CrO_4(s) + 2Na^+(aq) + 2NO_3^-(aq)$$

Notice that the $Na^+(aq)$ and $NO_3^-(aq)$ ions are *unchanged* in the equation. They are called **spectator ions** because they are not involved in the actual chemical change. These ions are present as part of the reactants. In other words, we could not have added Ag^+ ions without also adding an anion, in this case NO_3^- ion.

The **net ionic equation** *(bottom)* eliminates the spectator ions to show the *actual chemical change taking place*:

$$2Ag^+(aq) + CrO_4^{2-}(aq) \longrightarrow Ag_2CrO_4(s)$$

Table 4.1 Solubility Rules for Ionic Compounds in Water

Soluble Ionic Compounds	**Insoluble Ionic Compounds**
1. All common compounds of Group 1A(1) ions (Li^+, Na^+, K^+, etc.) and ammonium ion (NH_4^+) are soluble.	1. All common metal hydroxides are insoluble, *except* those of Group 1A(1) and the larger members of Group 2A(2) (beginning with Ca^{2+}).
2. All common nitrates (NO_3^-), acetates (CH_3COO^-), and most perchlorates (ClO_4^-) are soluble.	2. All common carbonates (CO_3^{2-}) and phosphates (PO_4^{3-}) are insoluble, *except* those of Group 1A(1) and NH_4^+.
3. All common chlorides (Cl^-), bromides (Br^-), and iodides (I^-) are soluble, *except* those of Ag^+, Pb^{2+}, Cu^+, and Hg_2^{2+}.	3. All common sulfides are insoluble *except* those of Group 1A(1), Group 2A(2), and NH_4^+.
4. All common sulfates (SO_4^{2-}) are soluble, *except* those of Ca^{2+}, Sr^{2+}, Ba^{2+}, and Pb^{2+}.	

The formation of solid silver chromate from silver ions and chromate ions *is* the only change. In fact, if we had originally mixed solutions of potassium chromate, $K_2CrO_4(aq)$, and silver acetate, $AgC_2H_3O_2(aq)$, the same change would have occurred. Only the spectator ions would differ—$K^+(aq)$ and $C_2H_3O_2^-(aq)$ instead of $Na^+(aq)$ and $NO_3^-(aq)$. Thus, writing the net ionic equation is an excellent way to isolate the key chemical event.

Precipitation Reactions

In **precipitation** reactions, two soluble ionic compounds react to form an insoluble product, a **precipitate.** The two reactions that you just saw between lead(II) nitrate and sodium iodide and between silver nitrate and sodium chromate are examples. Precipitates form for the same reason that some ionic compounds do not dissolve: the electrostatic attraction between the ions of the precipitate outweighs the tendency of the ions to become solvated and move randomly throughout the solution. When solutions of such ions are mixed, the ions collide and stay together, and the resulting substance "comes out of solution" as a solid. As you've seen, if all the ions remain in solution, no reaction occurs, but if ions precipitate, a reaction *does* occur. Thus, the event that drives a precipitation reaction to occur is *the mutual attraction between ions and their removal from solution in the form of an insoluble ionic compound.*

How can we predict whether a precipitate will form when we mix aqueous solutions of two ionic compounds? As you saw above, three steps are involved:

1. Note the ions present in the reactants.
2. Consider the possible cation-anion combinations.
3. Predict whether any of the combinations is insoluble.

A difficulty arises immediately with the last step because there is no simple way to predict solubility. Instead, you must memorize the short list of solubility rules shown in Table 4.1. These rules don't cover every possible ionic compound, but learning them allows you to predict the outcome of a great number of precipitation reactions.

Sample Problem 4.3 Predicting Whether a Precipitation Reaction Occurs; Writing Ionic Equations

PROBLEM Predict whether a reaction occurs when each of the following pairs of solutions are mixed. If a reaction does occur, write balanced molecular, total ionic, and net ionic equations, and identify the spectator ions.
(a) Sodium sulfate(*aq*) + strontium nitrate(*aq*) $\longrightarrow$
(b) Ammonium perchlorate(*aq*) + sodium bromide(*aq*) $\longrightarrow$

PLAN For each pair of solutions, we note the ions present in the reactants, write the cation-anion combinations, and refer to Table 4.1 to see if any are insoluble. For the molecular equation, we predict the products. For the total ionic equation, we write the soluble compounds as separate ions. For the net ionic equation, we eliminate the spectator ions.

SOLUTION **(a)** In addition to the reactants, the two other ion combinations are strontium sulfate and sodium nitrate. Table 4.1 shows that strontium sulfate is insoluble, so a reaction *does* occur. Writing the molecular equation:

$$Na_2SO_4(aq) + Sr(NO_3)_2(aq) \longrightarrow SrSO_4(s) + 2NaNO_3(aq)$$

Writing the total ionic equation:

$$2Na^+(aq) + SO_4^{2-}(aq) + Sr^{2+}(aq) + 2NO_3^-(aq) \longrightarrow$$
$$SrSO_4(s) + 2Na^+(aq) + 2NO_3^-(aq)$$

Writing the net ionic equation:

$$Sr^{2+}(aq) + SO_4^{2-}(aq) \longrightarrow SrSO_4(s)$$

The spectator ions are Na^+ and NO_3^-.

(b) The other ion combinations are ammonium bromide and sodium perchlorate. Table 4.1 shows that all ammonium, sodium, and most perchlorate compounds are soluble, and all bromides are soluble except those of Ag^+, Pb^{2+}, Cu^+, and Hg_2^{2+}. Therefore, *no* reaction occurs. The compounds remain dissociated in solution as solvated ions.

Follow-up Problem 4.3   Predict whether a reaction occurs, and write balanced total and net ionic equations:
(a) Iron(III) chloride(*aq*) + cesium phosphate(*aq*) $\longrightarrow$
(b) Sodium hydroxide(*aq*) + cadmium nitrate(*aq*) $\longrightarrow$
(c) Magnesium bromide(*aq*) + potassium acetate(*aq*) $\longrightarrow$
(d) Silver sulfate(*aq*) + barium chloride(*aq*) $\longrightarrow$

Acid-Base Reactions

Aqueous acid-base reactions involve water not only as solvent but also in the more active roles of reactant and product. These reactions are the essential chemical events in processes as diverse as the biochemical synthesis of proteins, the industrial production of several fertilizers, and some of the proposed methods for revitalizing lakes damaged by acid rain.

Obviously, an **acid-base reaction** (also called a **neutralization reaction**) occurs when an acid reacts with a base, but the definitions of these terms and the scope of this reaction process have changed considerably over the years. For our purposes at this point, we'll use definitions proposed by the great Swedish chemist Svante Arrhenius,

- An ***acid*** is a substance that produces H^+ ions when dissolved in water.
- A ***base*** is a substance that produces OH^- ions when dissolved in water.

(Other definitions of acid and base are presented later in this section and again in Chapter 18, along with a fuller meaning of neutralization.) Acids and bases are the active ingredients in many everyday products: most drain, window, and oven cleaners contain bases; vinegar and lemon juice contain acids.

Acids and bases are electrolytes and are often categorized in terms of "strength," which refers to their degree of dissociation into ions in aqueous solution. *Strong acids and strong bases dissociate completely into ions when they dissolve in water.* Therefore, like soluble ionic compounds, they are *strong* electrolytes. In contrast, *weak acids and weak bases dissociate so little that most of their molecules remain intact.* As a result, they conduct a small current, as shown in Figure 4.7, and are *weak* electrolytes. Table 4.2 lists some laboratory acids and bases in terms of their strength.

Figure 4.7 The behavior of strong and weak electrolytes. **A,** Strong electrolytes include soluble ionic compounds, strong acids, and strong bases. They dissociate completely into ions, so they conduct a large current. **B,** Weak electrolytes include weak acids and weak bases. They dissociate only partially into ions, so they conduct a small current.

A Strong electrolyte

B Weak electrolyte

Both strong and weak acids have one or more H atoms as part of their structure. Strong bases have either the OH^- or the O^{2-} ion as part of their structure. Soluble ionic oxides, such as K_2O, act as strong bases because the oxide ion reacts with water to form hydroxide ion:

$$O^{2-}(aq) + H_2O(l) \longrightarrow 2OH^-(aq)$$

Weak bases, such as ammonia, do not contain OH^- ions, but they produce them in a reaction with water that occurs to a small extent:

$$NH_3(g) + H_2O(l) \rightleftharpoons NH_4^+(aq) + OH^-(aq)$$

(Note the reaction arrow in the preceding equation. This type of arrow indicates that the reaction proceeds in both directions; we'll discuss this important idea further in Section 4.5.)

The Net Change: Formation of H₂O from H⁺ and OH⁻. Let's use ionic equations to examine acid-base reactions. We begin with the molecular equation for the reaction between the strong acid HCl and the strong base $Ba(OH)_2$:

$$2HCl(aq) + Ba(OH)_2(aq) \longrightarrow BaCl_2(aq) + 2H_2O(l)$$

Since HCl and $Ba(OH)_2$ dissociate completely and H_2O remains undissociated, the total ionic equation is

$$2H^+(aq) + 2Cl^-(aq) + Ba^{2+}(aq) + 2OH^-(aq) \longrightarrow Ba^{2+}(aq) + 2Cl^-(aq) + 2H_2O(l)$$

Note the *removal of ions* to form H_2O. In the net ionic equation, we eliminate the spectator ions $Ba^{2+}(aq)$ and $Cl^-(aq)$ and see the actual reaction:

$$2H^+(aq) + 2OH^-(aq) \longrightarrow 2H_2O(l) \quad \text{or} \quad H^+(aq) + OH^-(aq) \longrightarrow H_2O(l)$$

Thus, *the essential chemical change in all aqueous reactions between strong acids and strong bases is that an H⁺ ion from the acid and an OH⁻ ion from the base form a water molecule;* only the spectator ions differ from one reaction to another.

A key point to note is that, like precipitation reactions, acid-base reactions are driven by *the electrostatic attraction of ions and their removal from solution* in the formation of the product. In this case, the ions are H^+ and OH^- and the product is H_2O, which consists almost entirely of undissociated molecules. (Actually, water molecules dissociate *very* slightly, as you'll see in later chapters, but the formation of water in a neutralization reaction represents an enormous net removal of H^+ and OH^- ions.)

If we evaporate the water from the above reaction mixture, the ionic solid barium chloride remains. An ionic compound that results from the reaction of an acid and a base is called a **salt.** Thus, in a typical aqueous neutralization reaction, *the reactants are an acid and a base, and the products are a salt and water:*

$$\underset{\text{acid}}{HX(aq)} + \underset{\text{base}}{MOH(aq)} \longrightarrow \underset{\text{salt}}{MX(aq)} + \underset{\text{water}}{H_2O(l)}$$

Note that *the cation of the salt comes from the base and the anion comes from the acid.*

Table 4.2 Selected Acids and Bases

Acids

Strong
Hydrochloric acid, HCl
Hydrobromic acid, HBr
Hydriodic acid, HI
Nitric acid, HNO_3
Sulfuric acid, H_2SO_4
Perchloric acid, $HClO_4$

Weak
Hydrofluoric acid, HF
Phosphoric acid, H_3PO_4
Acetic acid, CH_3COOH
  (or $HC_2H_3O_2$)

Bases

Strong
Sodium hydroxide, NaOH
Potassium hydroxide, KOH
Calcium hydroxide, $Ca(OH)_2$
Strontium hydroxide, $Sr(OH)_2$
Barium hydroxide, $Ba(OH)_2$

Weak
Ammonia, NH_3

Sample Problem 4.4 Writing Ionic Equations for Acid-Base Reactions

PROBLEM Write balanced molecular, total ionic, and net ionic equations for each of the following acid-base reactions and identify the spectator ions:
(a) Strontium hydroxide(*aq*) + perchloric acid(*aq*) $\longrightarrow$
(b) Barium hydroxide(*aq*) + sulfuric acid(*aq*) $\longrightarrow$
PLAN All are strong acids and bases (see Table 4.2), so the essential reaction is between H^+ and OH^-. The products are H_2O and a salt made from the spectator ions. Note that in **(b),** the salt ($BaSO_4$) is insoluble (see Table 4.1), so virtually all ions are removed from solution.

SOLUTION (a) Writing the molecular equation:
$$Sr(OH)_2(aq) + 2HClO_4(aq) \longrightarrow Sr(ClO_4)_2(aq) + 2H_2O(l)$$
Writing the total ionic equation:
$$Sr^{2+}(aq) + 2OH^-(aq) + 2H^+(aq) + 2ClO_4^-(aq) \longrightarrow$$
$$Sr^{2+}(aq) + 2ClO_4^-(aq) + 2H_2O(l)$$
Writing the net ionic equation:
$$2OH^-(aq) + 2H^+(aq) \longrightarrow 2H_2O(l) \quad \text{or} \quad OH^-(aq) + H^+(aq) \longrightarrow H_2O(l)$$
$Sr^{2+}(aq)$ and $ClO_4^-(aq)$ are the spectator ions.
(b) Writing the molecular equation:
$$Ba(OH)_2(aq) + H_2SO_4(aq) \longrightarrow BaSO_4(s) + 2H_2O(l)$$
Writing the total ionic equation:
$$Ba^{2+}(aq) + 2OH^-(aq) + 2H^+(aq) + SO_4^{2-}(aq) \longrightarrow BaSO_4(s) + 2H_2O(l)$$
The net ionic equation is the same as the total ionic equation. This is a precipitation *and* a neutralization reaction. There are no spectator ions because all the ions are used to form the two products.

Follow-up Problem 4.4   Write balanced molecular, total ionic, and net ionic equations for the reaction between aqueous solutions of calcium hydroxide and nitric acid.

Acid-Base Titrations   Chemists apply stoichiometry to study acid-base reactions quantitatively through a titration. In any **titration,** *one solution of known concentration is used to determine the concentration of another solution through a monitored reaction.* In a typical acid-base titration, a *standardized* solution of base, one whose concentration is *known,* is added slowly to an acid solution of *unknown* concentration.

The laboratory procedure is straightforward but requires careful technique, as shown in Figure 4.8. A known volume of the acid solution is placed in a flask, and a few drops of indicator solution are added. An **acid-base indi-**

Figure 4.8 An acid-base titration. A, In this procedure, a measured volume of the unknown acid solution is placed in a flask beneath a buret containing the known (standardized) base solution. A few drops of indicator are added to the flask; the indicator used here is phenolphthalein, which is colorless in acid and pink in base. After an initial buret reading, base (OH^- ions) is added slowly to the acid (H^+ ions). **B,** Near the end of the titration, the indicator momentarily changes to its base color but reverts to its acid color with swirling. **C,** When the end point is reached, a tiny excess of OH^- is present, shown by the permanent change in color of the indicator. The difference between the final buret reading and the initial buret reading gives the volume of base used.

A   B   C

$$H^+(aq) + X^-(aq) + M^+(aq) + OH^-(aq) \longrightarrow H_2O(l) + M^+(aq) + X^-(aq)$$

cator is a substance whose color is different in acid than in base. (In Chapter 18 we examine indicators more fully.) The standardized solution of base is added slowly from a buret clamped above the flask. As the titration nears its end, indicator molecules change color near a drop of added base due to the temporary excess of OH^- ions there. As soon as the solution is swirled, however, the indicator's acidic color returns. The **equivalence point** in the titration occurs when *all the moles of H^+ ions present in the original volume of acid solution have reacted with an equivalent number of moles of OH^- ions added from the buret:*

Moles of H^+ (originally in flask) = moles of OH^- (added from buret)

The **end point** of the titration occurs when a tiny excess of OH^- ions changes the indicator permanently to its color in base. In calculations, we assume this tiny excess is insignificant, and therefore *the amount of base needed to reach the end point is the same as the amount needed to reach the equivalence point.*

Sample Problem 4.5   Finding the Concentration of Acid from an Acid-Base Titration

PROBLEM You perform an acid-base titration to standardize an HCl solution by placing 50.00 mL HCl in a flask with a few drops of indicator solution. You put 0.1524 *M* NaOH into the buret and the initial reading is 0.55 mL. At the end point, the buret reading is 33.87 mL. What is the concentration of the HCl solution?

PLAN We must find the molarity of acid from the volume of acid, the initial and final volumes of base, and the molarity of base. First, we balance the equation. We find the volume of base added from the difference in buret readings and use its molarity to calculate the amount (mol) of base added. Then, we use the molar ratio from the balanced equation to find the amount (mol) of acid originally present and divide by its original volume to find the molarity.

SOLUTION Writing the balanced equation:

$$NaOH(aq) + HCl(aq) \longrightarrow NaCl(aq) + H_2O(l)$$

Finding volume (L) of NaOH solution added:

$$\text{Volume (L) of solution} = (33.87 \text{ mL soln} - 0.55 \text{ mL soln}) \times \frac{1 \text{ L}}{1000 \text{ mL}}$$

$$= 0.03332 \text{ L soln}$$

Finding amount (mol) of NaOH added:

$$\text{Moles of NaOH} = 0.03332 \text{ L soln} \times \frac{0.1524 \text{ mol NaOH}}{1 \text{ L soln}}$$

$$= 5.078 \times 10^{-3} \text{ mol NaOH}$$

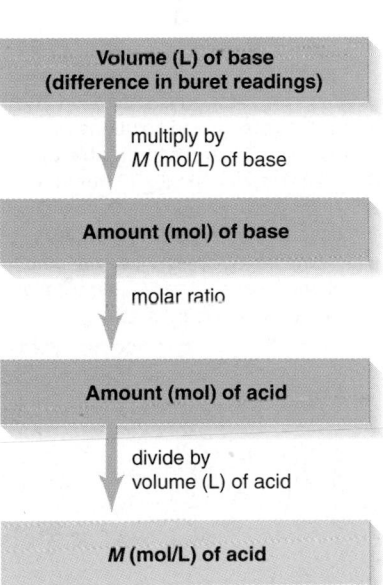

Volume (L) of base
(difference in buret readings)

multiply by
M (mol/L) of base

Amount (mol) of base

molar ratio

Amount (mol) of acid

divide by
volume (L) of acid

M (mol/L) of acid

Finding amount (mol) of HCl originally present: Since the molar ratio is 1:1,

$$\text{Moles of HCl} = 5.078 \times 10^{-3} \text{ mol NaOH} \times \frac{1 \text{ mol HCl}}{1 \text{ mol NaOH}} = 5.078 \times 10^{-3} \text{ mol HCl}$$

Calculating molarity of HCl:

$$\text{Molarity of HCl} = \frac{5.078 \times 10^{-3} \text{ mol HCl}}{50.00 \text{ mL}} \times \frac{1000 \text{ mL}}{1 \text{ L}} = \boxed{0.1016 \ M \text{ HCl}}$$

CHECK The answer seems reasonable because a larger volume of less concentrated acid neutralized a smaller volume of more concentrated base. Also check that the moles of H^+ and OH^- are about equal: 50 mL $\times$ 0.1 *M* H^+ = 0.005 mol = 33 mL $\times$ 0.15 *M* OH^-.

Follow-up Problem 4.5   What volume of 0.1292 *M* $Ba(OH)_2$ would neutralize 50.00 mL of the HCl solution standardized in the sample problem above?

A Closer Look at Acid-Base Reactions　We gain deeper insight into acid-base reactions if we look more closely at the actual species present in solution. Let's see what takes place when a substance like HCl gas dissolves in water. As we discussed earlier, the polar water molecules pull apart the HCl molecule and the H^+ ion bonds to a water molecule. In essence, we can say that HCl *transfers its proton* to H_2O:

$$\overset{\overset{\displaystyle H^+ \text{ transfer}}{\frown}}{HCl(g) \;+\; H_2O(l)} \longrightarrow H_3O^+(aq) + Cl^-(aq)$$

Thus, a solution of hydrochloric acid actually consists of solvated H_3O^+ and solvated Cl^- ions.

When sodium hydroxide solution is added, the H_3O^+ ion transfers a proton to the OH^- ion of the base (with the product water shown here as HOH):

$$\overset{\overset{\displaystyle H^+ \text{ transfer}}{\frown}}{[H_3O^+(aq) + Cl^-(aq)] + [Na^+(aq) + OH^-(aq)]} \longrightarrow$$
$$H_2O(l) + Na^+(aq) + Cl^-(aq) + HOH(l)$$

Without the spectator ions, the transfer of a proton from H_3O^+ to OH^- is obvious:

$$\overset{\overset{\displaystyle H^+ \text{ transfer}}{\frown}}{H_3O^+(aq) \;+\; OH^-(aq)} \longrightarrow H_2O(l) + HOH(l) \quad [\text{or } 2H_2O(l)]$$

Compare this net ionic reaction with the one we saw earlier,

$$H^+(aq) + OH^-(aq) \longrightarrow H_2O(l)$$

Figure 4.9 An aqueous strong acid–strong base reaction on the atomic scale. When solutions of a strong acid (HX) and a strong base (MOH) are mixed, the H_3O^+ from the acid transfers a proton to the OH^- from the base to form an H_2O molecule. Evaporation of the water leaves the spectator ions, X^- and M^+, as a solid ionic compound called a *salt*.

and you'll see they are identical (with the additional H_2O molecule coming from the H_3O^+). Clearly, *an acid-base reaction is a proton-transfer process*. The Na^+ and Cl^- ions remain in solution, and if the water is evaporated, they crystallize as the salt NaCl. Figure 4.9 shows this process on the atomic level.

In the early 20th century, the chemists Johannes Brønsted and Thomas Lowry realized the proton-transfer nature of acid-base reactions. They defined *an acid as a molecule (or ion) that donates a proton, and a base as a molecule (or ion) that accepts a proton.* Therefore, in the aqueous reaction between strong acid and strong base, *H_3O^+ ion acts as the acid and OH^- ion acts as the base.* Because they ionize completely, a given amount of strong acid (or strong base) creates an equivalent amount of H_3O^+ (or OH^-) when it dissolves in water. (We discuss the Brønsted-Lowry concept thoroughly in Chapter 18.)

Acid-Base Reactions That Form a Gaseous Product   Thinking of acid-base reactions as proton-transfer processes helps us understand another common type of aqueous ionic reaction, those that form a gaseous product. For example, when an ionic carbonate, such as K_2CO_3, is treated with an acid, such as HCl, one of the products is carbon dioxide. *The driving force for this and similar reactions is formation of a gas **and** water because both products remove reactant ions from solution:*

$$2HCl(aq) + K_2CO_3(aq) \longrightarrow 2KCl(aq) + [H_2CO_3(aq)]$$

The product H_2CO_3 is often shown in brackets to indicate that it is very unstable. It decomposes immediately into water and carbon dioxide:

$$[H_2CO_3(aq)] \longrightarrow H_2O(l) + CO_2(g)$$

Combining these gives the overall equation:

$$2HCl(aq) + K_2CO_3(aq) \longrightarrow 2KCl(aq) + H_2O(l) + CO_2(g)$$

When we show H_3O^+ ions from the HCl as the actual species in solution and write the net ionic equation, Cl^- and K^+ ions are eliminated. Note that each of the two H_3O^+ ions transfers a proton to the carbonate ion:

$$2H_3O^+(aq) + \overset{\frown \text{2H}^+ \text{ transfer} \searrow}{CO_3{}^{2-}(aq)} \longrightarrow 2H_2O(l) + [H_2CO_3(aq)] \longrightarrow 3H_2O(l) + CO_2(g)$$

In essence, then, this is an acid-base reaction, with carbonate ion accepting the protons and, therefore, acting as the base.

Several other polyatomic ions act similarly in reaction with acid, as in the formation of SO_2 from ionic sulfites. For a reaction of an ionic sulfite with strong acid, the net ionic equation is

$$\overset{\frown \text{2H}^+ \text{ transfer} \frown}{SO_3{}^{2-}(aq) + 2H_3O^+(aq)} \longrightarrow SO_2(g) + 3H_2O(l)$$

Ionic equations are written differently for the reactions of weak acids. Figure 4.10 shows a household example of the gas-forming reaction between vinegar (an aqueous 5% solution of acetic acid) and baking soda (sodium hydrogen carbonate) solution. Look closely at the equations. Since acetic acid is a weak acid (see Table 4.2), it dissociates very little. To show this, *weak acids appear undissociated in the net ionic equation;* note that H_3O^+ does not appear. Therefore, only $Na^+(aq)$ is a spectator ion; $CH_3COO^-(aq)$ is not.

Figure 4.10 An acid-base reaction that forms a gaseous product. Carbonates and hydrogen carbonates react with acids to form gaseous CO_2 and H_2O. Here, dilute acetic acid solution (vinegar) is added to sodium hydrogen carbonate (baking soda) solution and bubbles of CO_2 gas form. (Note that the net ionic equation includes acetic acid because it is a weak acid and does *not* dissociate into ions to an appreciable extent.)

Molecular equation
$$NaHCO_3(aq) + CH_3COOH(aq) \longrightarrow CH_3COONa(aq) + CO_2(g) + H_2O(l)$$

Total ionic equation
$$Na^+(aq) + HCO_3^-(aq) + CH_3COOH(aq) \longrightarrow CH_3COO^-(aq) + Na^+(aq) + CO_2(g) + H_2O(l)$$

Net ionic equation
$$HCO_3^-(aq) + CH_3COOH(aq) \longrightarrow CH_3COO^-(aq) + CO_2(g) + H_2O(l)$$

Section Summary

When solutions of ionic compounds are mixed, a reaction occurs only if a product forms that removes ions from the solution. A molecular equation shows reactants and products as undissociated compounds. A total ionic equation shows soluble ionic compounds (and other strong electrolytes) as solvated ions. A net ionic equation shows only those species that change during the reaction; those that do not change are spectator ions. Precipitation reactions occur when ions are removed from solution to form an insoluble ionic compound. Acid-base (neutralization) reactions occur when ions are removed as an acid (an H^+-yielding substance) and a base (an OH^--yielding substance) form a water molecule. Strong acids and bases dissociate completely; weak acids and bases dissociate slightly. In titrations, a known concentration of one reactant is used to determine the concentration of the other. Acid-base reactions can also be viewed as the transfer of a proton from an acid to a base. An ionic gas-forming reaction is an acid-base reaction in which an acid transfers a proton to a polyatomic ion (carbonate or sulfite), and a gas forms that leaves the reaction mixture.

4.3 Oxidation-Reduction (Redox) Reactions

Redox reactions are the third and, perhaps, most important of all chemical processes. They include the formation of a compound from its elements (and vice versa), all combustion reactions, the reactions that generate electricity in batteries, and the production of cellular energy. In this section, we examine the redox process in detail and learn some essential terminology. We see one way to balance redox equations and how to apply them quantitatively.

Redox Processes in the Formation of Ionic and Covalent Compounds

In **oxidation-reduction** (or **redox**) **reactions,** the key chemical event is the *net movement of electrons* from one reactant to the other. Such movement of electron charge occurs in the formation of both ionic and covalent compounds. As an example, let's reconsider the flashbulb reaction (see Figure 3.7, p. 105), in which an ionic compound, MgO, forms from its elements:

$$2Mg(s) + O_2(g) \longrightarrow 2MgO(s)$$

Figure 4.11A shows that during the reaction, each Mg atom loses two electrons and each O atom gains them; that is, two electrons move from each Mg atom to each O atom. This change represents a *transfer* of electron charge away from each Mg atom and toward each O atom, resulting in the formation of Mg^{2+} and O^{2-} ions. Attractions among the ions form the solid.

During the formation of a covalent compound from its elements, there is a net movement of electrons also, but it is more of a "shift" in electron charge than a transfer, and thus, *not* enough to form ions. Consider the formation of HCl gas:

$$H_2(g) + Cl_2(g) \longrightarrow 2HCl(g)$$

To see the electron movement here, we compare the electron charge distributions in the reactant bonds and in the product bonds. As Figure 4.11B shows, H_2 and Cl_2 molecules are each held together by pure covalent bonds; that is, the electrons are shared equally between the bonded atoms. In the HCl molecule, the electrons are shared unequally because the Cl atom attracts them more strongly than the H atom does. Thus, in HCl, the H has less electron charge *(blue shading)* than it had in H_2, whereas the Cl has more charge *(red shading)* than it had in Cl_2. In other words, in HCl there has been a *shift of electron charge* away from the H atom and toward the Cl atom. Be sure you

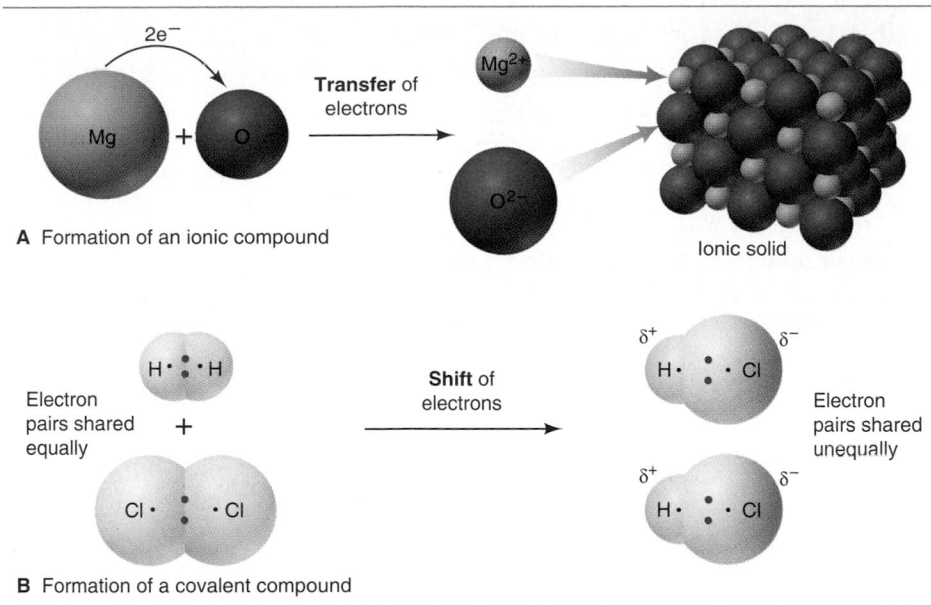

A Formation of an ionic compound

B Formation of a covalent compound

Figure 4.11 **The redox process in compound formation. A,** In forming the ionic compound MgO, each Mg atom transfers two electrons to each O atom. (Note that atoms become smaller when they lose electrons and larger when they gain them.) The resulting Mg^{2+} and O^{2-} ions aggregate with many others to form an ionic solid. **B,** In the reactants H_2 and Cl_2, the electron pairs are shown centrally located to indicate that they are shared equally. In the covalent compound HCl, the Cl attracts the shared electron pair more strongly than the H does. In effect, H shifts its electron toward Cl. Note the polar nature of the HCl molecule, as shown by higher electron density *(red)* near the Cl end and lower electron density *(blue)* near the H end.

realize that this electron *shift* is not nearly as extreme as the electron *transfer* during MgO formation. In fact, in some cases, the net movement of electrons is slight but still constitutes a redox reaction.

Some Essential Redox Terminology

Chemists use some important terminology to describe the movement of electrons that occurs in oxidation-reduction reactions. **Oxidation** is the *loss* of electrons, and **reduction** is the *gain* of electrons. (The original meaning of *reduction* comes from the process of reducing large amounts of metal ore to smaller amounts of metal, but you'll see shortly why we use the term for the act of gaining.) Thus, during the formation of magnesium oxide, Mg undergoes oxidation (electron loss) and O_2 undergoes reduction (electron gain). The loss and gain are simultaneous, but we can imagine them occurring in separate steps:

Oxidation (electron loss by Mg): $\qquad Mg \longrightarrow Mg^{2+} + 2e^-$

Reduction (electron gain by O_2): $\quad \frac{1}{2}O_2 + 2e^- \longrightarrow O^{2-}$

Since O_2 gained the electrons that Mg lost when it was oxidized, we say that *O_2 oxidized Mg.* Thus, O_2 is the **oxidizing agent,** the species doing the oxidizing. Similarly, since Mg gave up the electrons that O_2 gained when it was reduced, we say that *Mg reduced O_2.* Thus, Mg is the **reducing agent,** the species doing the reducing.

Once this relationship is clear, you will realize that *the oxidizing agent becomes reduced* because it removes the electrons (and thus gains them), whereas *the reducing agent becomes oxidized* because it gives up the electrons (and thus loses them). In the formation of HCl, Cl_2 oxidizes H_2 (H loses some electron charge and Cl gains it), which is the same as saying that H_2 reduces Cl_2. The reducing agent, H_2, is oxidized and the oxidizing agent, Cl_2, is reduced.

Using Oxidation Numbers to Monitor the Movement of Electron Charge

Chemists have devised a useful "bookkeeping" system to monitor which atom loses electron charge and which atom gains it. Each atom in a molecule (or ionic compound) is assigned an **oxidation number (O.N.),** or *oxidation state,*

Table 4.3 Rules for Assigning an Oxidation Number (O.N.)

General rules
1. For an atom in its elemental form (Na, O_2, Cl_2, etc.):   O.N. = 0
2. For a monatomic ion: O.N. = ion charge
3. The sum of O.N. values for the atoms in a compound equals zero. The sum of O.N. values for the atoms in a polyatomic ion equals the ion charge.

Rules for specific atoms or periodic table groups
1. For Group 1A(1):   O.N. = +1 in all compounds
2. For Group 2A(2):   O.N. = +2 in all compounds
3. For hydrogen: O.N. = +1 in combination with nonmetals
    O.N. = −1 in combination with metals and boron
4. For fluorine: O.N. = −1 in all compounds
5. For oxygen: O.N. = −1 in peroxides
    O.N. = −2 in all other compounds (except with F)
6. For Group 7A(17):   O.N. = −1 in combination with metals, nonmetals (except O), and other halogens lower in the group

the charge the atom would have *if* electrons were not shared but were transferred completely. Oxidation numbers are determined by the set of rules in Table 4.3. [Note that an oxidation number has the sign *before* the number (+2), whereas an ionic charge has the sign *after* the number (2+).]

Sample Problem 4.6   Determining the Oxidation Number of an Element

PROBLEM Determine the oxidation number (O.N.) of each element in the following compounds:
(a) Zinc chloride   **(b)** Sulfur trioxide   **(c)** Nitric acid
PLAN We apply Table 4.3, especially noting the general rules that the O.N. values in a compound add up to zero, and the O.N. values in a polyatomic ion add up to the ion's charge.
SOLUTION (a) $ZnCl_2$. The sum of O.N.s for the monatomic ions in the compound must equal zero. The O.N. of the Zn^{2+} ion is +2. The O.N. of each Cl^- ion is −1, for a total of −2.
(b) SO_3. The O.N. of each oxygen is −2, for a total of −6. Since the O.N.s must add up to zero, the O.N. of S is +6.
(c) HNO_3. The O.N. of H is +1, so the O.N.s of the NO_3 group must add up to −1 to give zero for the compound. The O.N. of each O is −2 for a total of −6. Therefore, the O.N. of N is +5.

Follow-up Problem 4.6   Determine the O.N. of each element in the following: **(a)** scandium oxide (Sc_2O_3); **(b)** gallium chloride ($GaCl_3$); **(c)** hydrogen phosphate ion; **(d)** iodine trifluoride.

Figure 4.12 Highest and lowest oxidation numbers of reactive main-group elements. The A-group number shows the highest possible oxidation number (O.N.) for a main-group element. (Two important exceptions are O, which never has an O.N. of +6, and F, which never has an O.N. of +7.) For nonmetals *(yellow)* and metalloids *(green)*, the A-group number minus 8 gives the lowest possible oxidation number.

The periodic table is a great help in learning the highest and lowest oxidation numbers of most main-group elements, as Figure 4.12 shows:
- For most main-group elements, the A-group number (1A, 2A, and so on) is the *highest* oxidation number (always positive) of any element in the group. The exceptions are O and F (see Table 4.3).
- For the main-group nonmetals and some metalloids, the A-group number minus 8 gives the *lowest* oxidation number (always negative) of any element in the group.

For example, the highest oxidation number of S (Group 6A) is +6, as in SF_6, and the lowest is (6 − 8), or −2, as in FeS and other metal sulfides.

As you can see, the oxidation number for an element in a binary *ionic* compound has a realistic value, because it usually equals the ionic charge. On the other hand, the oxidation number has a very unrealistic value for an element in a *covalent* compound (or polyatomic ion) because whole charges don't exist on the atoms in those species.

Another way to define a redox reaction is one in which *the oxidation numbers of the species change,* and the most important use of oxidation numbers is to monitor these changes:

- If a given atom has a higher (more positive or less negative) oxidation number in the product than it had in the reactant, the reactant molecule or ion that contained the atom was oxidized (lost electrons). Thus, *oxidation is represented by an increase in oxidation number.*

- If an atom has a lower (more negative or less positive) oxidation number in the product than it had in the reactant, the reactant molecule or ion that contained the atom was reduced (gained electrons). Thus, *the gain of electrons is represented by a decrease (a "reduction") in oxidation number.* (The term *reduction,* as mentioned earlier, refers to an ore being "reduced" to the metal. In modern terms, the reducing agents used, such as charcoal and hydrogen, provide electrons that convert the metal ion to its elemental form.)

Figure 4.13 gives a compact summary of redox terminology. Since oxidation numbers are assigned according to the atom that pulls more strongly on the electrons, they are ultimately based on atomic properties, as you'll see in Chapters 8 and 9.

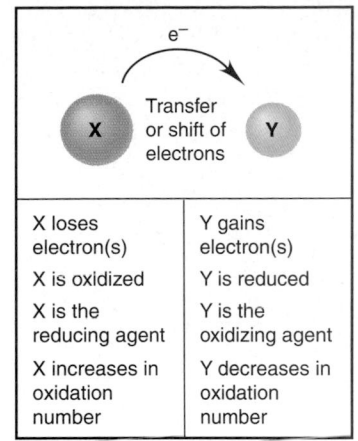

X loses electron(s)	Y gains electron(s)
X is oxidized	Y is reduced
X is the reducing agent	Y is the oxidizing agent
X increases in oxidation number	Y decreases in oxidation number

Figure 4.13 **A summary of terminology for oxidation-reduction (redox) reactions.**

Sample Problem 4.7   Recognizing Oxidizing and Reducing Agents

PROBLEM Identify the oxidizing agent and reducing agent in each of the following:
(a) $2Al(s) + 3H_2SO_4(aq) \longrightarrow Al_2(SO_4)_3(aq) + 3H_2(g)$
(b) $PbO(s) + CO(g) \longrightarrow Pb(s) + CO_2(g)$
(c) $2H_2(g) + O_2(g) \longrightarrow 2H_2O(g)$

PLAN We first assign an oxidation number (O.N.) to each atom (or ion) based on the rules in Table 4.3. The reactant is the reducing agent if it contains an atom that is oxidized (O.N. increased in the reaction). The reactant is the oxidizing agent if it contains an atom that is reduced (O.N. decreased).

SOLUTION **(a)** Assigning oxidation numbers:

$$\overset{0}{2Al}(s) + \overset{+1}{3H_2}\overset{+6}{S}\overset{-2}{O_4}(aq) \longrightarrow \overset{+3}{Al_2}(\overset{+6}{S}\overset{-2}{O_4})_3(aq) + \overset{0}{3H_2}(g)$$

The O.N. of Al increased from 0 to +3 (Al lost electrons), so Al was oxidized; Al is the reducing agent.

The O.N. of H decreased from +1 to 0 (H gained electrons), so H^+ was reduced; H_2SO_4 is the oxidizing agent.

(b) Assigning oxidation numbers:

$$\overset{+2}{Pb}\overset{-2}{O}(s) + \overset{+2}{C}\overset{-2}{O}(g) \longrightarrow \overset{0}{Pb}(s) + \overset{+4}{C}\overset{-2}{O_2}(g)$$

Pb decreased its O.N. from +2 to 0, so PbO was reduced; PbO is the oxidizing agent.

C increased its O.N. from +2 to +4, so CO was oxidized; CO is the reducing agent. In general, when a substance (such as CO) bonds to more O atoms (as in CO_2), it is oxidized, and when a substance (such as PbO) bonds to fewer O atoms (as in Pb), it is reduced.

(c) Assigning oxidation numbers:

$$\overset{0}{\underset{|}{2H_2}}(g) + \overset{0}{\underset{|}{O_2}}(g) \longrightarrow \overset{+1 \ -2}{\underset{|\ \ |}{2H_2O}}(g)$$

O_2 was reduced (O.N. of O decreased from 0 to -2); O_2 is the oxidizing agent.
H_2 was oxidized (O.N. of H increased from 0 to $+1$); H_2 is the reducing agent.
Oxygen is always the oxidizing agent in a combustion reaction.

COMMENT 1. Compare the O.N. values in (c) with those in another common reaction that forms water—the net ionic equation for an acid-base reaction:

$$\overset{+1}{\underset{|}{H^+}}(aq) + \overset{-2 \quad \overset{+1}{|}}{\underset{|\ |}{OH^-}}(aq) \longrightarrow \overset{+1 \ -2}{\underset{|\ |}{H_2O}}(l)$$

Note that O.N. values remain the same on both sides of the acid-base equation. Therefore, *an acid-base reaction is not a redox reaction.*

2. If an elemental substance occurs as reactant or product, it could not possibly be in its elemental form on the other side of the equation, so the reaction must be a redox process. Notice that elements appear in all three cases above.

Follow-up Problem 4.7 Identify the oxidizing agent and reducing agent in the following:
(a) $2Fe(s) + 3Cl_2(g) \longrightarrow 2FeCl_3(s)$
(b) $2C_2H_6(g) + 7O_2(g) \longrightarrow 4CO_2(g) + 6H_2O(g)$
(c) $5CO(g) + I_2O_5(s) \longrightarrow I_2(s) + 5CO_2(g)$

Balancing Redox Equations

It is extremely important to realize that *the reducing agent loses electrons and the oxidizing agent gains them* **simultaneously.** A chemical change cannot be an "oxidation reaction" *or* a "reduction reaction"; only an "oxidation-reduction reaction" can occur. The transferred electrons are never free, which means that we can balance a redox reaction by making sure that *the number of electrons lost by the reducing agent equals the number of electrons gained by the oxidizing agent.*

Two methods used to balance redox equations are the *oxidation number* method and the *half-reaction* method. This section describes the oxidation number method in detail; the half-reaction method is covered in Chapter 21.*

The **oxidation number method** for balancing redox equations consists of five steps that use the changes in oxidation numbers to generate balancing coefficients. The first two steps are identical to those in Sample Problem 4.7:

Step 1. Assign oxidation numbers to all elements in the reaction.
Step 2. From the changes in oxidation numbers, identify the oxidized and reduced species.
Step 3. Compute the number of electrons lost in the oxidation and gained in the reduction from the oxidation number changes. (Draw tie-lines between these atoms to show the changes.)
Step 4. Multiply one or both of these numbers by appropriate factors to make the electrons lost equal the electrons gained, and use the factors as balancing coefficients.
Step 5. Complete the balancing by inspection, adding states of matter.

---

*A thorough discussion of the half-reaction method appears in Section 21.1 for use in electrochemistry. However, if your professor chooses to cover that section here, it is completely transferrable with no loss in continuity.

Sample Problem 4.8 — Balancing Redox Equations by the Oxidation Number Method

PROBLEM Use the oxidation number method to balance the following equations:
(a) $Cu(s) + HNO_3(aq) \longrightarrow Cu(NO_3)_2(aq) + NO_2(g) + H_2O(l)$
(b) $PbS(s) + O_2(g) \longrightarrow PbO(s) + SO_2(g)$

SOLUTION (a) *Step 1.* Assign oxidation numbers to all elements:

$$\overset{0}{Cu} + \overset{+1}{H}\overset{+5}{N}\overset{-2}{O_3} \longrightarrow \overset{+2}{Cu}(\overset{+5}{N}\overset{-2}{O_3})_2 + \overset{+4}{N}\overset{-2}{O_2} + \overset{+1}{H_2}\overset{-2}{O}$$

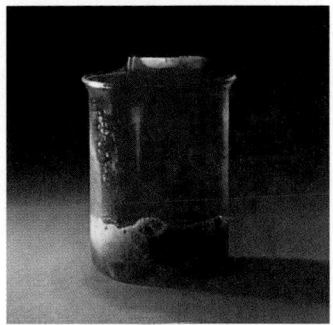

Copper in nitric acid.

Step 2. Identify oxidized and reduced species. The O.N. of Cu increased from 0 (in Cu metal) to +2 (in Cu^{2+}); Cu was oxidized. The O.N. of N decreased from +5 (in HNO_3) to +4 (in NO_2); HNO_3 was reduced. Note that some NO_3^- also acts as a spectator ion, appearing unchanged in the $Cu(NO_3)_2$; this is quite common in redox reactions. We focus now on HNO_3, the species in which N *did* change its O.N.

Step 3. Compute e^- lost and e^- gained and draw tie-lines between the atoms. In the oxidation, $2e^-$ were lost from each Cu. In the reduction, $1e^-$ was gained by each N:

$$\overset{\overbrace{\qquad\qquad}^{-2e^-}}{Cu + HNO_3} \longrightarrow \underset{\underbrace{\qquad\qquad}_{+1e^-}}{Cu(NO_3)_2 + NO_2} + H_2O$$

Step 4. Multiply by factors to make e^- lost equal e^- gained, and use the factors as coefficients. Cu lost $2e^-$, so the $1e^-$ gained by N should be multiplied by 2. Using 2 as a coefficient for NO_2 and HNO_3 gives

$$Cu + 2HNO_3 \longrightarrow Cu(NO_3)_2 + 2NO_2 + H_2O$$

Step 5. Complete the balancing by inspection. Balancing N atoms requires a 4 in front of HNO_3 because of the additional two NO_3^- ions in $Cu(NO_3)_2$:

$$Cu + 4HNO_3 \longrightarrow Cu(NO_3)_2 + 2NO_2 + H_2O$$

Balancing H atoms requires a 2 in front of H_2O, and we add states of matter:

$$Cu(s) + 4HNO_3(aq) \longrightarrow Cu(NO_3)_2(aq) + 2NO_2(g) + 2H_2O(l)$$

CHECK Reactants (1 Cu, 4 H, 4 N, 12 O) $\longrightarrow$ products [1 Cu, 4 H, (2 + 2) N, (6 + 4 + 2) O]

(b) *Step 1.* Assign oxidation numbers:

$$\overset{+2}{Pb}\overset{-2}{S} + \overset{0}{O_2} \longrightarrow \overset{+2}{Pb}\overset{-2}{O} + \overset{+4}{S}\overset{-2}{O_2}$$

Step 2. Identify species that are oxidized and reduced. PbS was oxidized. The O.N. of S increased from −2 in PbS to +4 in SO_2. O_2 was reduced. The O.N. of O decreased from 0 in O_2 to −2 in PbO and in SO_2.

Step 3. Compute e^- lost and e^- gained and draw tie-lines. The S lost $6e^-$ and each O gained $2e^-$:

$$\overset{\overbrace{\qquad\qquad}^{-6e^-}}{PbS + O_2} \longrightarrow \underset{\underbrace{\qquad\qquad}_{+4e\quad (2e^-\ per\ O)}}{PbO + SO_2}$$

Step 4. Multiply by factors to make e^- lost equal e^- gained. The single S atom loses $6e^-$. Each O in O_2 gains $2e^-$, for a total of $4e^-$ gained. Thus, using $\frac{3}{2}$ as a coefficient of O_2 gives 3 O atoms that each gain $2e^-$, for a total of $6e^-$ gained:

$$PbS + \tfrac{3}{2}O_2 \longrightarrow PbO + SO_2$$

Step 5. Complete the balancing by inspection. The atoms are balanced, but all coefficients must be multiplied by 2 to obtain integers, and we add states of matter:

$$2PbS(s) + 3O_2(g) \longrightarrow 2PbO(s) + 2SO_2(g)$$

CHECK Reactants (2 Pb, 2 S, 6 O) $\longrightarrow$ products [2 Pb, 2 S, (2 + 4) O]

Follow-up Problem 4.8 Use the oxidation number method to balance the following: $K_2Cr_2O_7(aq) + HI(aq) \longrightarrow KI(aq) + CrI_3(aq) + I_2(s) + H_2O(l)$

Redox Titrations

Just as a base is used to find the concentration of an acid (or vice versa) in an acid-base titration, a known concentration of an oxidizing agent can be used to find the unknown concentration of a reducing agent (or vice versa) in a redox titration. This application of stoichiometry is used in a wide range of situations, including measuring the iron content in drinking water and the vitamin C content in fruits and vegetables.

The permanganate ion, MnO_4^-, is a common oxidizing agent in these titrations because it is strongly colored and, thus, also serves as an indicator. In the following example, MnO_4^- oxidizes the oxalate ion, $C_2O_4^{2-}$ to determine its concentration. As long as any $C_2O_4^{2-}$ is present, it reduces the deep purple MnO_4^- to the very faint pink (nearly colorless) Mn^{2+} ion (Figure 4.14, *left*). As soon as all the available $C_2O_4^{2-}$ has been oxidized, the next drop of MnO_4^- turns the solution light purple (Figure 4.14, *right*). This color change indicates the end point, the point at which the electrons lost by the oxidized species ($C_2O_4^{2-}$) equal the electrons gained by the reduced species (MnO_4^-). We then calculate the concentration of the $C_2O_4^{2-}$ solution from its known volume, the known volume and concentration of the MnO_4^- solution, and the balanced equation.

Preparing a sample for a redox titration sometimes requires several laboratory steps. In Sample Problem 4.9, for instance, the Ca^{2+} ion concentration of blood is determined. The Ca^{2+} is first precipitated as calcium oxalate (CaC_2O_4). Dilute H_2SO_4 dissolves the precipitate and releases the $C_2O_4^{2-}$ ion, which is then titrated with standardized MnO_4^- ion. After the $C_2O_4^{2-}$ concentration has been determined, it is used to find the original blood Ca^{2+} concentration.

Net ionic equation:

$$\overset{+7}{2MnO_4^-}(aq) + \overset{+3}{5C_2O_4^{2-}}(aq) + 16H^+(aq) \longrightarrow \overset{+2}{2Mn^{2+}}(aq) + \overset{+4}{10CO_2}(g) + 8H_2O(l)$$

Figure 4.14 A redox titration. The oxidizing agent in the buret, $KMnO_4$, is strongly colored, so it also serves as the indicator. When it reacts with the reducing agent $C_2O_4^{2-}$ in the flask, its color changes from deep purple to almost colorless *(left)*. When all the $C_2O_4^{2-}$ is oxidized, the next drop of $KMnO_4$ remains unreacted and turns the solution light purple *(right)*, signaling the end point of the titration.

Sample Problem 4.9 Finding an Unknown Concentration by a Redox Titration

PROBLEM Calcium ion (Ca^{2+}) is required for blood to clot and for many other biological processes. An abnormal Ca^{2+} concentration is indicative of several diseases. To measure the Ca^{2+} concentration, 1.00 mL of human blood was treated with $Na_2C_2O_4$ solution. The resulting CaC_2O_4 precipitate was dissolved in dilute H_2SO_4. This solution required 2.05 mL of 4.88×10^{-4} M $KMnO_4$ to reach the titration end point.
(a) Calculate the amount (mol) of Ca^{2+}.
(b) Calculate the Ca^{2+} ion concentration expressed in units of mg Ca^{2+}/100 mL blood.

(a) Calculating the moles of Ca^{2+}

PLAN As always, we first write the balanced equation. All the Ca^{2+} ion in the blood sample is precipitated and then dissolved in the H_2SO_4. We find the number of moles of $KMnO_4$ needed to reach the end point and use the molar ratio to calculate the number of moles of CaC_2O_4 dissolved in the H_2SO_4. Then, from the chemical formula, we find moles of Ca^{2+} ions.

SOLUTION Writing the balanced equation:

$$2KMnO_4(aq) + 5CaC_2O_4(aq) + 8H_2SO_4(aq) \longrightarrow$$
$$2MnSO_4(aq) + K_2SO_4(aq) + 5CaSO_4(aq) + 10CO_2(g) + 8H_2O(l)$$

Converting from volume (mL) to moles of $KMnO_4$ used to reach the end point:

$$\text{Moles of } KMnO_4 = 2.05 \text{ mL soln} \times \frac{1 \text{ L}}{1000 \text{ mL}} \times \frac{4.88\times10^{-4} \text{ mol } KMnO_4}{1 \text{ L soln}}$$

$$= 1.00\times10^{-6} \text{ mol } KMnO_4$$

Converting from moles of $KMnO_4$ to moles of CaC_2O_4 titrated:

$$\text{Moles of } CaC_2O_4 = 1.00\times10^{-6} \text{ mol } KMnO_4 \times \frac{5 \text{ mol } CaC_2O_4}{2 \text{ mol } KMnO_4}$$

$$= 2.50\times10^{-6} \text{ mol } CaC_2O_4$$

Finding moles of Ca^{2+} present:

$$\text{Moles of } Ca^{2+} = 2.50\times10^{-6} \text{ mol } CaC_2O_4 \times \frac{1 \text{ mol } Ca^{2+}}{1 \text{ mol } CaC_2O_4}$$

$$= 2.50\times10^{-6} \text{ mol } Ca^{2+}$$

CHECK A very small volume of dilute $KMnO_4$ is needed, so 10^{-6} mol of $KMnO_4$ seems reasonable. The molar ratio of $5CaC_2O_4/2KMnO_4$ gives 2.5×10^{-6} mol of CaC_2O_4 and thus 2.5×10^{-6} mol of Ca^{2+}.

Volume (L) of KMnO₄ solution

multiply by
M (mol/L)

Amount (mol) of KMnO₄

molar ratio

Amount (mol) of CaC₂O₄

ratio of elements in chemical formula

Amount (mol) of Ca²⁺

(b) Expressing the Ca^{2+} concentration as mg/100 mL blood

PLAN The amount in part **(a)** is the moles of Ca^{2+} ion present in 1.00 mL blood. We multiply by 100 to obtain the moles of Ca^{2+} ion in 100 mL blood, and then convert to milligrams of Ca^{2+}/100 mL blood.
SOLUTION Finding moles of Ca^{2+}/100 mL blood:

$$\text{Moles of } Ca^{2+}/100 \text{ mL blood} = \frac{2.50\times10^{-6} \text{ mol } Ca^{2+}}{1.00 \text{ mL blood}} \times 100$$

$$= 2.50\times10^{-4} \text{ mol } Ca^{2+}/100 \text{ mL blood}$$

Converting from moles of Ca^{2+} to milligrams:

$$\text{Mass (mg) } Ca^{2+}/100 \text{ mL blood} = \frac{2.50\times10^{-4} \text{ mol } Ca^{2+}}{100 \text{ mL blood}} \times \frac{40.08 \text{ g } Ca^{2+}}{1 \text{ mol } Ca^{2+}} \times \frac{1000 \text{ mg}}{1 \text{ g}}$$

$$= \boxed{10.0 \text{ mg } Ca^{2+}/100 \text{ mL blood}}$$

CHECK The relative amounts of Ca^{2+} make sense. If there is 2.5×10^{-6} mol/mL blood, there is 2.5×10^{-4} mol/100 mL blood. A molar mass of about 40 g/mol for Ca^{2+} gives 100×10^{-4} g, or 10×10^{-3} g/100 mL blood. It is easy to make an order-of-magnitude (power of 10) error in this type of calculation, so be sure to include all units.

Amount (mol) of Ca²⁺/1 mL blood

multiply by 100

Amount (mol) of Ca²⁺/100 mL blood

multiply by
M (g/mol)

Mass (g) of Ca²⁺/100 mL blood

1 g = 1000 mg

Mass (mg) of Ca²⁺/100 mL blood

COMMENT 1. The normal range of Ca^{2+} concentration in a human adult is 9.0 to 11.5 mg Ca^{2+}/100 mL blood, so our value seems reasonable.
2. When blood is donated, the receiving bag contains $Na_2C_2O_4$ solution, which precipitates the Ca^{2+} ion and, thus, prevents clotting.
3. A redox titration is analogous to an acid-base titration: in redox processes, electrons are lost and gained, whereas in acid-base processes, H^+ ions are lost and gained.

Follow-up Problem 4.9   A 2.50-mL sample of low-fat milk was treated with sodium oxalate, and the precipitate was dissolved in H_2SO_4. This solution required 6.53 mL of 4.56×10^{-3} M $KMnO_4$ to reach the end point.
(a) Calculate the molarity of Ca^{2+} in the milk.
(b) What is the concentration of Ca^{2+} in g/L? Is this value consistent with the typical value in milk of about 1.2 g Ca^{2+}/L?

Section Summary

When there is a net movement of electron charge from one reactant to another, a redox process takes place. Electron gain (reduction) and electron loss (oxidation) occur simultaneously. The redox process is tracked by assigning oxidation numbers to each atom in a reaction. The species that is oxidized (contains an atom that increases in oxidation number) is the reducing agent; the species that is reduced (contains an atom that decreases in oxidation number) is the oxidizing agent. Redox reactions can be balanced by keeping track of the changes in oxidation number. A redox titration is used to determine the concentration of either the oxidizing or the reducing agent from the known concentration of the other.

4.4   Counting Reactants and Products in Precipitation, Acid-Base, and Redox Processes

In previous sections, we classified chemical change according to one of the three major reaction processes—precipitation, acid-base, or oxidation-reduction. In this section, we overlap that classification scheme with a more historical one that relies on counting the numbers of reactants and products. One key point is that *whenever an element is involved as either reactant or product, the change is a redox reaction.* In fact, as you'll see, redox reactions dominate the reaction classes shown.

By definition, the essence of any reaction is that atoms or ions change their chemical attachments. Elements combine into compounds, or compounds decompose into elements. Large molecules break apart, or small molecules join together. In some cases, the atoms (or ions) in two compounds switch bonding partners to form a new pair of compounds. When we compare the number of reactant and product substances, three broad types of reactions arise—combination, decomposition, and displacement. We also consider a fourth type, combustion reactions, which have been used for millennia and understood ever since Lavoisier's experiments over two centuries ago.

Combination Reactions

In **combination reactions,** *two or more reactants combine to form one product*: X + Y $\longrightarrow$ Z. The following discussion organizes combination reactions by kinds of reactants.

Figure 4.15 Three views of a combination reaction between elements. When the metal potassium and the nonmetal chlorine react, they form the solid ionic compound potassium chloride. The photos *(top)* present the view the chemist sees in the laboratory. The blow-up arrows lead to an atomic-scale view *(middle)*; the stoichiometry is indicated by the more darkly colored spheres. The balanced redox equation is shown with oxidation numbers *(bottom)*.

Combination Reactions That *Are* Redox Reactions Note that in all the examples shown, an *element appears as a reactant.*

1. *Combination of two elements.* Two elements react to form binary ionic or covalent compounds. In every case, there is a net change in the distribution of electron charge, which means the elements change their oxidation numbers. Here are some important examples:

- *A metal and a nonmetal form an ionic compound.* Figure 4.15 shows the reaction between an alkali metal and a halogen on three levels—observable, atomic, and symbolic. Note the change in oxidation numbers. Thus, K is the reducing agent and Cl_2 is the oxidizing agent. Metals react with O_2 to form ionic oxides:

$$\overset{0}{2Al(s)} + \overset{0}{3O_2(g)} \longrightarrow \overset{+3\ -2}{Al_2O_3(s)}$$

- *Two nonmetals form a covalent compound.* In one of thousands of examples, ammonia forms from nitrogen and hydrogen in a reaction that occurs in industry on an enormous scale:

$$\overset{0}{N_2}(g) + 3\overset{0}{H_2}(g) \longrightarrow 2\overset{-3}{N}\overset{+1}{H_3}(g)$$

Halogens form many compounds with other nonmetals, as in the formation of phosphorus trichloride, a major reactant in the production of pesticides and other organic compounds:

$$\overset{0}{P_4}(s) + 6\overset{0}{Cl_2}(g) \longrightarrow 4\overset{+3}{P}\overset{-1}{Cl_3}(l)$$

Nearly every nonmetal reacts with O_2 to form a covalent oxide, as when nitrogen monoxide forms at the very high temperatures created in air by lightning:

$$\overset{0}{N_2}(g) + \overset{0}{O_2}(g) \longrightarrow 2\overset{+2}{N}\overset{-2}{O}(g)$$

2. *Combination of a compound and an element.* Many binary covalent compounds react with nonmetals to form larger compounds. Many nonmetal oxides react with additional O_2 to form "higher" oxides (those with more O atoms in each molecule). For example, a key step in the generation of urban smog is

$$2\overset{+2}{N}\overset{-2}{O}(g) + \overset{0}{O_2}(g) \longrightarrow 2\overset{+4}{N}\overset{-2}{O_2}(g)$$

Similarly, many nonmetal halides combine with additional halogen:

$$\overset{+3}{P}\overset{-1}{Cl_3}(l) + \overset{0}{Cl_2}(g) \longrightarrow \overset{+5}{P}\overset{-1}{Cl_5}(s)$$

Combination Reactions That Are *Not* Redox Reactions   Most combination reactions that involve *only compounds as reactants* are **not** *oxidation-reduction reactions.* (A few *are* redox reactions, however, so always check oxidation numbers to be sure.)

1. *A metal oxide and a nonmetal oxide form an ionic compound with a polyatomic anion.* One example is the formation of a metal carbonate, such as the drug lithium carbonate, from the metal oxide and carbon dioxide; note that the oxidation numbers do *not* change:

$$\overset{+1}{Li_2}\overset{-2}{O}(s) + \overset{+4}{C}\overset{-2}{O_2}(g) \longrightarrow \overset{+1}{Li_2}\overset{+4}{C}\overset{-2}{O_3}(s)$$

The pattern in this and other such reactions is that the O^{2-} ion in the metal oxide combines with the nonmetal oxide to form the polyatomic oxoanion.

2. *Metal oxides and water form bases.* Lime (calcium oxide) added to soil can provide a proper acid-base balance by forming "slaked" lime (calcium hydroxide):

$$CaO(s) + H_2O(l) \longrightarrow Ca(OH)_2(aq)$$

3. *Nonmetal oxides and water form acids.* Sulfur trioxide and water form sulfuric acid, the most abundantly produced chemical in the world:

$$SO_3(g) + H_2O(l) \longrightarrow H_2SO_4(aq)$$

Decomposition Reactions

Decomposition reactions are the reverse of combination reactions: one reactant breaks down into two or more products, Z ⟶ X + Y. They occur when the reactant absorbs enough energy for one or more of its bonds to break. Like a combination reaction, *a decomposition reaction is a redox process if an element is involved in the change.* In the combination the element is a reactant; in the decomposition it is a product.

Thermal Decomposition When the energy absorbed is heat, the reaction is a *thermal* decomposition. A *delta,* Δ, above a yield arrow indicates that heat is required for the reaction.

1. *Many ionic compounds with oxoanions form a metal oxide and a gaseous non-metal oxide.* Carbonates yield CO_2 when heated (and sulfites yield SO_2). More than 200 million tons of lime are produced annually for cement, glass, and steel manufacture by heating limestone (calcium carbonate):

$$CaCO_3(s) \xrightarrow{\Delta} CaO(s) + CO_2(g)$$

2. *Many metal oxides, chlorates, and perchlorates release oxygen.* Since an element is formed, these are redox reactions. The decomposition of mercury(II) oxide, used by Lavoisier and Priestley in their classic experiments, is an example. Figure 4.16 shows three representations of the reaction.

Figure 4.16 Three views of a decomposition reaction that forms elements. Heating solid mercury(II) oxide decomposes it to its elements, liquid mercury and gaseous oxygen: the macroscopic (laboratory) view *(top);* the atomic-scale view, with the more darkly colored spheres showing the stoichiometry *(middle);* and the balanced redox equation *(bottom).*

Heating potassium chlorate is a modern method for forming small amounts of oxygen in the laboratory:

$$2KClO_3(s) \xrightarrow{\Delta} 2KCl(s) + 3O_2(g)$$

Notice that, in these cases, the lone reactant is the oxidizing *and* the reducing agent. For example, in HgO, O^{2-} reduces Hg^{2+} (and Hg^{2+} oxidizes O^{2-}).

Electrolytic Decomposition Many compounds that absorb electrical energy decompose into their elements by the process of *electrolysis*. Such processes are redox reactions.

1. *Decomposition of water.* This reaction (see Figure 1.1B) was a key observation in the establishment of atomic masses:

$$2H_2O(l) \xrightarrow{\text{electricity}} 2H_2(g) + O_2(g)$$

2. *Decomposition of molten ionic compounds.* Sodium, magnesium, calcium, and several other metals are produced industrially by electrolysis of their molten halides:

$$MgCl_2(l) \xrightarrow{\text{electricity}} Mg(l) + Cl_2(g)$$

Displacement Reactions

Displacement (or *replacement*) **reactions** have the same number of reactants as products. They occur when an atom (or ion) in a compound is displaced by a different atom (or ion). Displacement reactions are either single-displacement or double-displacement (**metathesis;** pronounced *meh-TATH-uh-sis*) reactions:

$$X + YZ \longrightarrow XZ + Y \quad \text{[single]}$$
$$WX + YZ \longrightarrow WZ + YX \quad \text{[double; metathesis]}$$

Even though both types involve displacement, they differ fundamentally in the chemical nature of the underlying process:

- Single-displacement reactions are oxidation-reduction reactions.
- Metathesis reactions include precipitation and acid-base reactions. ◆

Single-Displacement Reactions; The Activity Series of the Metals Metals vary in their reactivity. They can be ranked according to their ability to displace H_2 from various sources or to displace one another from solution. Some nonmetals, especially the halogens, vary in their reactivity as well, and the differences can be seen in their ability to displace one another from solution.

1. *A metal displaces H_2 from water or acid.* The most reactive metals, such as those from Group 1A(1) and Ca, Sr, and Ba from Group 2A(2), displace H_2 from water, and they do so vigorously. Figure 4.17 shows the laboratory view, the atomic view, and the balanced equation of this reaction for lithium. Heat is needed to speed the reaction of less reactive metals, such as aluminum and zinc, so these displace H_2 from steam:

$$2Al(s) + 6H_2O(g) \longrightarrow 2Al(OH)_3(s) + 3H_2(g)$$

◆ Metathesis and Plastic Bags Although metathesis (double-displacement) reactions in aqueous solution are our focus in this discussion, these reactions can occur in organic solvents as well. This reaction type is currently being applied by polymer chemists as a new way to prepare polyethylene, the material used in plastic shopping bags. At the same time, metathesis reactions are being studied as a means of controlled disassembling of long polymer chains for plastic recycling.

Figure 4.17 Three views of a single-displacement reaction. Lithium displaces hydrogen from water in a vigorous reaction that yields an aqueous solution of lithium hydroxide and hydrogen gas, as shown on the macroscopic scale *(top)*, atomic scale *(mid-dle)*, and as a balanced equation *(bottom)*. (For clarity, the atomic view of water has been greatly simplified, and only water molecules involved in the reaction are colored red and blue.)

The balanced equation in the figure:

$$\underset{\text{Lithium}}{\overset{0}{2\text{Li}(s)}} + \underset{\text{Water}}{\overset{+1\ -2}{2\text{H}_2\text{O}(l)}} \longrightarrow \underset{\text{Lithium hydroxide}}{\overset{+1\ -2\ +1}{2\text{LiOH}(aq)}} + \underset{\text{Hydrogen}}{\overset{0}{\text{H}_2(g)}}$$

Still less reactive metals, such as nickel and tin, do not react with water but *do* react with acids, from which H_2 is displaced more easily (Figure 4.18). Here is the net ionic equation:

$$\overset{0}{\text{Ni}(s)} + \overset{+1}{2\text{H}^+}(aq) \longrightarrow \overset{+2}{\text{Ni}^{2+}}(aq) + \overset{0}{\text{H}_2(g)}$$

Notice that in all such reactions, the metal is the reducing agent (O.N. of metal increases) and water or acid is the oxidizing agent (O.N. of H decreases). The least reactive metals, such as silver and gold, cannot displace H_2 from any source.

2. *A metal displaces another metal ion from solution.* Direct comparisons of metal reactivity are clearest in these reactions. For example, zinc metal displaces copper(II) ion from solution, as the net ionic equation shows:

$$\overset{+2}{\text{Cu}^{2+}}(aq) + \overset{0}{\text{Zn}(s)} \longrightarrow \overset{0}{\text{Cu}(s)} + \overset{+2}{\text{Zn}^{2+}}(aq)$$

Figure 4.18 The displacement of H_2 from acid by nickel.

Figure 4.19 Three views of copper displacing silver ions from solution. More reactive metals can displace less reactive ones from solution. In this single-displacement reaction, Cu atoms become Cu^{2+} ions and leave the wire, as they transfer electrons to two Ag^+ ions that become Ag atoms and coat the wire: the laboratory view *(top)*, the atomic view *(middle)*, and the balanced redox equation *(bottom)*.

$$\underset{+1\ +5\ -2}{2AgNO_3(aq)} + \underset{0}{Cu(s)} \longrightarrow \underset{+2\ +5\ -2}{Cu(NO_3)_2(aq)} + \underset{0}{2Ag(s)}$$

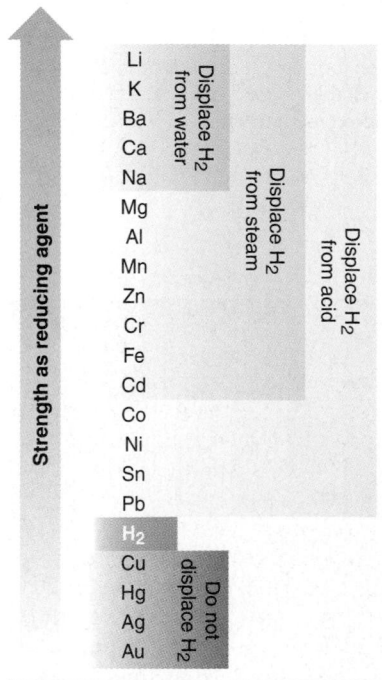

Figure 4.20 The activity series of the metals. This list of metals (and H_2) is arranged with the most active metal (strongest reducing agent) at the top and the least active (weakest reducing agent) at the bottom. The four metals below H_2 cannot displace it from any source. (The ranking refers to behavior in aqueous solution.)

Figure 4.19 shows in atomic detail that Cu metal can, in turn, displace Ag^+ ion from solution. Thus, Zn is more reactive than Cu, which is more reactive than Ag.

The results of many such single-displacement reactions between metals and water, aqueous acids, and metal-ion solutions form the basis of the **activity series of the metals.** It is shown in Figure 4.20 as a list arranged in *order of decreasing strength of the metal as a reducing agent.* Thus, elements higher on the list are stronger reducing agents than elements lower down. In other words, for those elements stable in water, elements higher on the list can displace from aqueous solution the ions of elements lower down. The list also shows whether the metal can displace H_2 and, if so, from which source. Using just the examples we've already discussed, you can see that Li, Al, and Ni lie above H_2, whereas Ag lies below it, and that Zn lies above Cu, which lies above Ag.

3. *A halogen displaces a halide ion from solution.* Reactivity decreases down Group 7A(17). Therefore, a halogen higher in the group can displace one lower down from aqueous solution. In this reaction, chlorine displaces bromine:

$$\underset{-1}{2Br^-(aq)} + \underset{0}{Cl_2(aq)} \longrightarrow \underset{0}{Br_2(aq)} + \underset{-1}{2Cl^-(aq)}$$

Double-Displacement Reactions Precipitation and acid-base reactions are the most important examples of metathesis reactions (see Section 4.2). Because none of the atoms changes its oxidation number, these are *not* redox processes. The following reactions are written as molecular equations with colored atoms to emphasize their double-displacement aspect.

1. *In precipitation reactions, an insoluble ionic compound forms.* Silver bromide, which is used to manufacture black-and-white film, forms in a double-displacement reaction:

$$AgNO_3(aq) + KBr(aq) \longrightarrow AgBr(s) + KNO_3(aq)$$

2. *In acid-base reactions, an acid and a base form a salt and water.* Aluminum hydroxide, the active ingredient in some antacid tablets, acts by a double-displacement reaction:

$$3HCl(aq) + Al(OH)_3(s) \longrightarrow AlCl_3(aq) + 3H_2O(l)$$

Displacement reactions occur frequently in the synthesis and breakdown of biological macromolecules. ◆

Combustion Reactions

Combustion is the process of combining with oxygen, usually with the release of large amounts of heat and light, often as a flame. ◆ Burning in air is a common example. Since O_2 is a reactant, *all combustion reactions are redox processes.*

These very common and essential reactions do not always fall neatly into classes based on the number of reactants and products, but the combustion of an element, such as the burning of sulfur, is always a *combination* reaction because two substances form one:

$$S_8(s) + 8O_2(g) \longrightarrow 8SO_2(g)$$

The combustion reactions we use to produce energy involve organic mixtures such as coal, gasoline, or natural gas as reactants. These mixtures consist of substances with many carbon-carbon and carbon-hydrogen bonds. During the reaction, these bonds break, and each C and H atom combines with oxygen. Therefore, the products typically consist of CO_2 and H_2O. The combustion of the hydrocarbon butane, which is used in cigarette lighters, is typical:

$$2C_4H_{10}(g) + 13O_2(g) \longrightarrow 8CO_2(g) + 10H_2O(g)$$

Cellular *respiration* can be thought of as a combustion process that occurs within our bodies' cells—fortunately without flame—when we "burn" organic foodstuffs, such as glucose, for energy:

$$C_6H_{12}O_6(s) + 6O_2(g) \longrightarrow 6CO_2(g) + 6H_2O(g) + energy$$

Amino acid units

Protein molecule

H_2O　　　H_2O

Synthesis of organism's proteins

Breakdown of food proteins

Amino acid molecules

◆ **Displacement Reactions Inside You** The digestion of food proteins is joined to the formation of a cell's own proteins in continuous cycles of displacement reactions. A protein consists of hundreds or thousands of smaller molecules, called *amino acids,* linked in a long chain. When you eat proteins, your digestive processes use H_2O to displace one amino acid at a time. These are transported by the blood to your cells, where other metabolic processes link them together, displacing H_2O, to make your own proteins.

Sample Problem 4.10　Identifying the Type of Chemical Reaction

PROBLEM Classify the following as combination, decomposition, or displacement reactions, identify the underlying chemical process as precipitation, acid-base, or redox, and write a balanced molecular equation for each. For any that are redox, identify the oxidizing and reducing agents:
(a) Lead(II) acetate(*aq*) + sodium sulfate(*aq*) $\longrightarrow$

　　　　　　　　　　　　　　lead(II) sulfate(*s*) + sodium acetate(*aq*)
(b) Magnesium(*s*) + nitrogen(*g*) $\longrightarrow$ magnesium nitride(*s*)
(c) $CH_2(COOH)_2(s)$ + sodium hydroxide(*aq*) $\longrightarrow$ $CH_2(COONa)_2(aq)$ + water
(d) Hydrogen peroxide(*l*) $\longrightarrow$ water + oxygen gas
(e) Aluminum(*s*) + lead(II) nitrate(*aq*) $\longrightarrow$ aluminum nitrate(*aq*) + lead(*s*)
PLAN To decide on reaction type, we recall that combination reactions produce fewer substances, decomposition reactions more substances, and displacement reactions the same number of substances. For precipitation processes, a solid forms; for acid-base, water and a salt form; and for redox, oxidation numbers change. The O.N. becomes more positive for the reducing agent and less positive for the oxidizing agent.
SOLUTION (a) Displacement (metathesis): two substances form two. This precipitation reaction forms a common white pigment:

$$Pb(C_2H_3O_2)_2(aq) + Na_2SO_4(aq) \longrightarrow PbSO_4(s) + 2NaC_2H_3O_2(aq)$$

◆ **Space-Age Combustion Without a Flame**
Combustion reactions are used to generate large amounts of energy. In most common applications, the fuel is burned and the energy is released as heat (in a furnace) or as a combination of work and heat (in a combustion engine). Aboard the Space Shuttle, devices called *fuel cells* generate electrical energy from the flameless combustion of hydrogen gas. The H_2 is the reducing agent, and O_2 is the oxidizing agent in a complex, controlled reaction process that yields water—which the astronauts use for drinking. On Earth, fuel cells based on the reaction of methanol (CH_3OH) and O_2 are being investigated for use in automobile engines.

(b) Combination: two substances form one. This redox reaction occurs, along with formation of the metal oxide, when magnesium burns in air:

$$\overset{0}{3Mg(s)} + \overset{0}{N_2(g)} \longrightarrow \overset{+2 \ -3}{Mg_3N_2(s)}$$

Mg is the reducing agent; N_2 is the oxidizing agent.

(c) Displacement (metathesis): two substances form two. The biomolecule malonic acid reacts with sodium hydroxide in this acid-base reaction. The two H^+ ions from the acid (—COOH) groups are transferred to the hydroxide ions to form water:

$$CH_2(COOH)_2(s) + 2NaOH(aq) \longrightarrow CH_2(COONa)_2(aq) + 2H_2O(l)$$

(d) Decomposition: one substance forms two. This redox reaction occurs within every bottle of this common household antiseptic. Hydrogen peroxide is very unstable and breaks down easily by heat, light, or just shaking:

$$\overset{+1 \ -1}{2H_2O_2(l)} \longrightarrow \overset{+1 \ -2}{2H_2O(l)} + \overset{0}{O_2(g)}$$

H_2O_2 is both oxidizing *and* reducing agent. (Note that the O.N. of O in peroxides is −1.)

(e) Displacement (single): two substances form two. This redox reaction occurs when the more reactive Al displaces the less reactive Pb (see Figure 4.20):

$$\overset{0}{2Al(s)} + \overset{+2 \ +5 \ -2}{3Pb(NO_3)_2(aq)} \longrightarrow \overset{+3 \ +5 \ -2}{2Al(NO_3)_3(aq)} + \overset{0}{3Pb(s)}$$

Al is the reducing agent; $Pb(NO_3)_2$ is the oxidizing agent.

Follow-up Problem 4.10   Classify each of the following reactions by number of reactants and products *and* by underlying chemical process, and write a balanced equation. Identify the oxidizing and reducing agents in any redox reactions:
(a) $S_8(s) + F_2(g) \longrightarrow SF_4(g)$
(b) $Na_2SO_3(aq) + HCl(aq) \longrightarrow NaCl(aq) + SO_2(g) + H_2O(l)$
(c) $Ni(NO_3)_2(aq) + Cr(s) \longrightarrow Cr(NO_3)_3(aq) + Ni(s)$

Section Summary

Any reaction with a substance in its elemental form as reactant or product is a redox reaction. Another way to classify reactions is by counting numbers of reactants and products. Combination reactions occur when two or more substances form one. All reactions between elements are of this type. In decomposition reactions, one substance forms two or more, usually by absorbing heat or electrical energy. In displacement reactions, the numbers of reactants and products are equal. Single-displacement reactions can rank metal (or halogen) reactivity by the ability to displace H_2 from water or acid or one another from solution. Precipitation and acid-base processes are common types of double-displacement (metathesis) reactions. Combustion reactions release energy through combination of a substance with O_2.

4.5 Reversible Reactions: An Introduction to Chemical Equilibrium

So far, we have viewed reactions as occurring from "left to right," from reactants to products and continuing until they are complete, that is, until the limiting reactant is used up. However, many reactions seem to stop before this happens. The reason is that another reaction, the reverse of the first one, is also taking place. The forward (left-to-right) reaction has not stopped, but the reverse (right-to-left) reaction is taking place at the same rate. Therefore, *no further changes occur in the amounts of reactants or products.* At this point, the reaction mixture has reached **dynamic equilibrium.** On the macroscopic scale, the reaction is *static,* but it is *dynamic* on the molecular scale. In principle, all reactions are reversible and will eventually reach dynamic equilibrium as long as all products remain available for the reverse reaction.

Let's examine equilibrium with a particular set of substances. Calcium carbonate can decompose to calcium oxide and carbon dioxide:

$$CaCO_3(s) \longrightarrow CaO(s) + CO_2(g) \quad [\text{decomposition}]$$

It can also form when calcium oxide and carbon dioxide combine:

$$CaO(s) + CO_2(g) \longrightarrow CaCO_3(s) \quad [\text{combination}]$$

The combination is just the reverse of the decomposition. Suppose we place 10 g $CaCO_3$ in an *open* steel reaction flask and heat it to around 900°C, as shown in Figure 4.21A. The $CaCO_3$ starts decomposing to CaO and CO_2, and the CO_2 escapes from the open flask. The decomposition goes to completion because the reverse reaction (combination) can occur only if CO_2 is present.

In Figure 4.21B, we perform the same experiment in a *closed* steel flask, so that the CO_2 remains in contact with the CaO. The decomposition (forward reaction) begins, but at first, when very little $CaCO_3$ has decomposed, very little CO_2 and CaO are available to combine, so the combination (reverse reaction) just barely begins. As the $CaCO_3$ continues to decompose, the concentrations of CO_2 and CaO in the flask increase. The CO_2 and CaO react with each other more frequently, and the combination occurs a bit faster. As the CaO and CO_2 concentrations increase, the combination reaction gradually speeds up. Eventually, the reverse reaction (combination) happens just as fast as the forward reaction (decomposition), and the amounts of $CaCO_3$, CaO, and CO_2 no longer change: the system has reached equilibrium. We indicate a reaction at equilibrium with a pair of arrows pointing in opposite directions:

$$CaCO_3(s) \rightleftharpoons CaO(s) + CO_2(g)$$

A Nonequilibrium system

CaCO₃(s) → CaO(s) + CO₂(g)

B Equilibrium system

CaCO₃(s) ⇌ CaO(s) + CO₂(g)

Figure 4.21 The equilibrium state. A, In an *open* steel reaction chamber, strong heating of $CaCO_3$ decomposes it completely because the product CO_2 escapes and is not present to react with the other product, CaO. **B,** When $CaCO_3$ decomposes in a *closed* chamber, the CO_2 *is* present to combine with CaO and re-form $CaCO_3$ in a reaction that is the reverse of the decomposition. At a given temperature, no further change in the amounts of products and reactants means that the reaction has reached equilibrium.

Bear in mind that equilibrium can be established only when *all the substances involved are kept in contact with each other.* The decomposition of $CaCO_3$ goes to completion in the open flask because the CO_2 escapes.

Aqueous acid-base reactions that form a gaseous product go to completion in an open flask for the same reason: the gas escapes, so the reverse reaction cannot take place. Precipitation and other acid-base reactions also go to completion, even though all the products remain in the reaction vessel. In those cases, the *ions* are unavailable for the reverse process to occur, because they are tied up either as an insoluble solid (precipitation) or as water molecules (acid-base).

The concept of reaction reversibility also explains why some acids and bases are weak electrolytes, that is, why they dissociate into ions only to a small extent. The dissociation quickly becomes balanced by a reassociation, such that equilibrium is reached with very few ions present. For example, when acetic acid dissolves in water, some of the CH_3COOH molecules transfer a proton to H_2O and form H_3O^+ and CH_3COO^- ions. As more ions form, they react with each other more often to re-form acetic acid and water:

$$CH_3COOH(aq) + H_2O(l) \rightleftharpoons H_3O^+(aq) + CH_3COO^-(aq)$$

In fact, in 0.1 M CH_3COOH at 25°C, only about 1.3% of the acid molecules are dissociated at any given moment. Similarly, the weak base ammonia reacts with water to form ions. As the product ions interact, the rate of the reverse reaction soon balances the forward one:

$$NH_3(aq) + H_2O(l) \rightleftharpoons NH_4^+(aq) + OH^-(aq)$$

Dynamic equilibrium is fundamental to the functioning of many natural systems, from the cycling of water in the environment to the population balance of lion and antelope on the plains of Africa to the nuclear processes occurring in stars. We return to the applications of equilibrium in chemical and physical systems in Chapters 12, 13, and 17 through 21.

Section Summary

Every reaction is reversible if all the substances are kept in contact with one another. As the amounts of products increase, the reactants begin to re-form. When the reverse reaction happens as rapidly as the forward reaction, the amounts of the substances no longer change, and the reaction mixture has reached dynamic equilibrium. A reaction goes to completion if products are removed from the system (as a gas) or exist in a form that prevents them from reacting (precipitate or undissociated molecule). Weak acids and bases reach equilibrium in water with a very small proportion of their molecules dissociated.

Chapter Perspective

Classifying facts is the first step toward understanding them, and this chapter has classified many of the most important facts of reaction chemistry into three major processes—precipitation, acid-base, and oxidation-reduction. We also examined the great influence that water has on reaction chemistry and introduced the dynamic equilibrium state, which is related to the central question of why physical and chemical changes occur. All these topics appear again at many places in the text.

In the next chapter, our focus changes to the physical behavior of gases. You'll find that your growing appreciation of events on the molecular level has become indispensable for understanding the nature of the three physical states.

The following learning objectives, with section and/or sample problem (SP) numbers in parentheses, can help focus your study:

Understand These Concepts

1. How water dissolves ionic compounds and dissociates them into ions (4.1)
2. Distinguish between the species present when ionic and covalent compounds dissolve in water; distinguish between strong and weak electrolytes (4.1)
3. The driving force for aqueous ionic reactions (4.2)
4. The use of ionic equations to specify the essential nature of an aqueous reaction (4.2)
5. How to decide whether a precipitation reaction occurs (4.2)
6. The main distinction between strong and weak aqueous acids and bases (4.2)
7. The essential character of aqueous acid-base reactions as proton-transfer processes (4.2)
8. The importance of net movement of electrons in the redox process (4.3)
9. The relation between change in oxidation number and identity of oxidizing and reducing agents (4.3)
10. The important types of redox reactions: combinations involving elements, decomposition, single displacement (4.4)
11. The balance between forward and reverse rates of a chemical reaction that leads to the equilibrium state; why some acids and bases are weak (4.5)

Master These Skills

1. Using the formula of a compound to find the number of moles of ions in solution (SP 4.1)
2. Determining the concentration of H^+ ion in an aqueous acid solution (SP 4.2)
3. Predicting the formula of a precipitate (SP 4.3)
4. Writing ionic equations to describe precipitation and acid-base reactions (SPs 4.3 and 4.4)
5. Calculating an unknown concentration from an acid-base or redox titration (SPs 4.5 and 4.9)

6. Determining the oxidation number of any atom in a compound (SP 4.6)
7. Selecting the oxidizing and reducing agents in a redox reaction (SP 4.7)
8. Balancing redox equations (SP 4.8)
9. Determining the chemical nature of combination, decomposition, and displacement reactions (SP 4.10); predicting the products of a single displacement reaction

For Review and Reference

Key Terms

Section 4.1
electrolyte
solvated
polar molecule
nonelectrolyte
Section 4.2
molecular equation
total ionic equation
spectator ion

net ionic equation
precipitation
precipitate
acid-base reaction
neutralization reaction
acid
base
salt
titration
acid-base indicator
equivalence point

end point
Section 4.3
oxidation-reduction
(redox) reaction
oxidation
reduction
oxidizing agent
reducing agent
oxidation number (O.N.)
(or oxidation state)
oxidation number method

Section 4.4
combination reaction
decomposition reaction
displacement reaction
metathesis reaction
activity series of the metals
Section 4.5
dynamic equilibrium

Highlighted Figures and Tables

These figures (F) and tables (T) provide a quick review of key ideas. Entries in color contain frequently used data.
F4.2 Electron distribution in H_2 and H_2O (p. 136)
F4.3 Dissolution of an ionic compound (p. 137)
F4.6 Depicting a precipitation reaction with ionic equations (p. 140)
T4.1 Solubility rules for ionic compounds (p. 141)
T4.2 Common acids and bases (p. 143)

F4.9 An aqueous strong acid–strong base reaction on the atomic scale (p. 146)
F4.11 The redox process in compound formation (p. 149)
T4.3 Rules for assigning an oxidation number (p. 150)
F4.12 Highest and lowest oxidation numbers of reactive main-group elements (p. 150)
F4.13 A summary of terminology for redox reactions (p. 151)
F4.20 The activity series of the metals (p. 162)

Answers to Follow-up Problems

4.1 (a) $KClO_4(s) \xrightarrow{H_2O} K^+(aq) + ClO_4^-(aq)$;
2 mol K^+ and 2 mol ClO_4^-

(b) $Mg(C_2H_3O_2)_2(s) \xrightarrow{H_2O} Mg^{2+}(aq) + 2C_2H_3O_2^-(aq)$;
2.49 mol Mg^{2+} and 4.97 mol $C_2H_3O_2^-$

(c) $(NH_4)_2CrO_4(s) \xrightarrow{H_2O} 2NH_4^+(aq) + CrO_4^{2-}(aq)$;
6.24 mol NH_4^+ and 3.12 mol CrO_4^{2-}

(d) $NaHSO_4(s) \xrightarrow{H_2O} Na^+(aq) + HSO_4^-(aq)$;
0.73 mol Na^+ and 0.73 mol HSO_4^-

4.2 Moles of H^+ = 451 mL $\times \dfrac{1 \text{ L}}{10^3 \text{ mL}} \times \dfrac{3.20 \text{ mol HBr}}{1 \text{ L soln}}$

$\times \dfrac{1 \text{ mol } H^+}{1 \text{ mol HBr}} = 1.44 \text{ mol } H^+$

4.3 (a) $Fe^{3+}(aq) + 3Cl^-(aq) + 3Cs^+(aq) + PO_4^{3-}(aq) \longrightarrow$
$FePO_4(s) + 3Cl^-(aq) + 3Cs^+(aq)$
$Fe^{3+}(aq) + PO_4^{3-}(aq) \longrightarrow FePO_4(s)$
(b) $2Na^+(aq) + 2OH^-(aq) + Cd^{2+}(aq) + 2NO_3^-(aq) \longrightarrow$
$2Na^+(aq) + 2NO_3^-(aq) + Cd(OH)_2(s)$
$2OH^-(aq) + Cd^{2+}(aq) \longrightarrow Cd(OH)_2(s)$
(c) No reaction occurs
(d) $2Ag^+(aq) + SO_4^{2-}(aq) + Ba^{2+}(aq) + 2Cl^-(aq) \longrightarrow$
$2AgCl(s) + BaSO_4(s)$

Total and net ionic equations are identical.
4.4 $2HNO_3(aq) + Ca(OH)_2(aq) \longrightarrow Ca(NO_3)_2(aq) + 2H_2O(l)$
$2H^+(aq) + 2NO_3^-(aq) + Ca^{2+}(aq) + 2OH^-(aq) \longrightarrow$
$Ca^{2+}(aq) + 2NO_3^-(aq) + 2H_2O(l)$
$H^+(aq) + OH^-(aq) \longrightarrow H_2O(l)$

Answers to Follow-up Problems (continued)

4.5 $2HCl(aq) + Ba(OH)_2(aq) \longrightarrow BaCl_2(aq) + 2H_2O(l)$
Volume (L) of soln

$$= 50.00 \text{ mL HCl soln} \times \frac{1 \text{ L}}{10^3 \text{ mL}} \times \frac{0.1016 \text{ mol HCl}}{1 \text{ L soln}}$$

$$\times \frac{1 \text{ mol Ba(OH)}_2}{2 \text{ mol HCl}} \times \frac{1 \text{ L soln}}{0.1292 \text{ mol Ba(OH)}_2}$$

$$= 0.01966 \text{ L}$$

4.6 (a) O.N. of Sc = +3; O.N. of O = -2
(b) O.N. of Ga = +3; O.N. of Cl = -1
(c) O.N. of H = +1; O.N. of P = +5; O.N. of O = -2
(d) O.N. of I = +3; O.N. of F = -1
4.7 (a) Fe is reducing agent; Cl_2 is oxidizing agent.
(b) C_2H_6 is reducing agent; O_2 is oxidizing agent.
(c) CO is reducing agent; I_2O_5 is oxidizing agent.
4.8 $K_2Cr_2O_7(aq) + 14HI(aq) \longrightarrow$
$$2KI(aq) + 2CrI_3(aq) + 3I_2(s) + 7H_2O(l)$$
4.9 (a) Moles of Ca^{2+}

$$= 6.53 \text{ mL soln} \times \frac{1 \text{ L}}{10^3 \text{ mL}} \times \frac{4.56 \times 10^{-3} \text{ mol KMnO}_4}{1 \text{ L soln}}$$

$$\times \frac{5 \text{ mol CaC}_2O_4}{2 \text{ mol KMnO}_4} \times \frac{1 \text{ mol Ca}^{2+}}{1 \text{ mol CaC}_2O_4}$$

$$= 7.44 \times 10^{-5} \text{ mol Ca}^{2+}$$

Molarity of $Ca^{2+} = \dfrac{7.44 \times 10^{-2} \text{ mol Ca}^{2+}}{2.50 \text{ mL milk}} \times \dfrac{10^3 \text{ mL}}{1 \text{ L}}$

$$= 2.98 \times 10^{-2} \text{ } M \text{ Ca}^{2+}$$

(b) Conc. of Ca^{2+} (g/L) $= \dfrac{2.98 \times 10^{-2} \text{ mol Ca}^{2+}}{1 \text{ L}}$

$$\times \frac{40.08 \text{ g Ca}^{2+}}{1 \text{ mol Ca}^{2+}}$$

$$= \frac{1.19 \text{ g Ca}^{2+}}{1 \text{ L}}$$

4.10 (a) Combination; redox:
$S_8(s) + 16F_2(g) \longrightarrow 8SF_4(g)$
S_8 is the reducing agent; F_2 is the oxidizing agent.
(b) Double displacement; acid-base with gaseous product:
$Na_2SO_3(aq) + 2HCl(aq) \longrightarrow 2NaCl(aq) + SO_2(g) + H_2O(l)$
(c) Single displacement; redox:
$3Ni(NO_3)_2(aq) + 2Cr(s) \longrightarrow 3Ni(s) + 2Cr(NO_3)_3(aq)$
Cr is the reducing agent; $Ni(NO_3)_2$ is the oxidizing agent.

Problems

Problems with a **colored** number are answered at the back of the text. Problem sections match the text and provide the number(s) of relevant sample problems. Most offer concept review questions, skill-building exercises (written in similar pairs), and problems in a relevant context. Following these are comprehensive problems based on material from any section and/or previous chapter.

The Role of Water as a Solvent
(Sample Problems 4.1 and 4.2)

■ Concept Review Questions
4.1 What two factors cause water to be polar?
4.2 What types of substances are most likely to be soluble in water?
4.3 What must be present in an aqueous solution for it to conduct an electric current? What general classes of compounds form solutions that conduct?
4.4 What occurs on the molecular level when an ionic compound dissolves in water?
4.5 Examine each of the following aqueous solutions and determine which represents: (a) $CaCl_2$ (b) Li_2SO_4 (c) NH_4Br

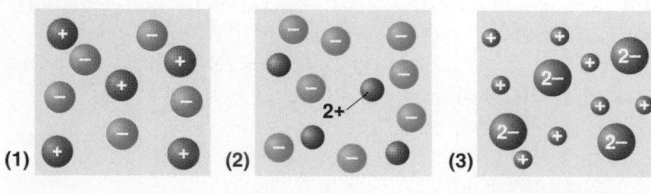

(1)   (2)   (3)

4.6 Which of the following best represents a volume from a solution of magnesium nitrate?

● = magnesium ion   ● = nitrate ion

(1)   (2)   (3)

4.7 Why do some ionic compounds dissolve in water and others do not?
4.8 Why are some covalent compounds soluble in water and others are not?
4.9 Some covalent compounds dissociate into ions when they dissolve in water. What atom do these compounds have in their structures? What type of aqueous solution do they form? Name three of these aqueous solutions.

■ Skill-Building Exercises (paired)
4.10 State whether each of the following substances is likely to be very soluble in water. Explain.
(a) Benzene, C_6H_6 (b) Sodium hydroxide
(c) Ethanol, CH_3CH_2OH (d) Potassium acetate
4.11 State whether each of the following substances is likely to be very soluble in water. Explain.
(a) Lithium nitrate   (b) Glycine, H_2NCH_2COOH
(c) Hexane   (d) Ethylene glycol, $HOCH_2CH_2OH$

4.12 State whether an aqueous solution of each of the following substances conducts an electric current. Explain your reasoning. (a) Sodium iodide (b) Hydrogen bromide

4.13 State whether an aqueous solution of each of the following substances conducts an electric current. Explain your reasoning. (a) Potassium hydroxide (b) Glucose, $C_6H_{12}O_6$

4.14 How many total moles of ions are released when each of the following samples dissolves completely in water?
(a) 0.25 mol NH_4Cl (b) 26.4 g $Ba(OH)_2 \cdot 8H_2O$
(c) 1.78×10^{20} formula units of $LiCl$

4.15 How many total moles of ions are released when each of the following samples dissolves completely in water?
(a) 0.805 mol Cs_2SO_4 (b) 1.55×10^{-3} g $Ca(NO_3)_2$
(c) 3.85×10^{27} formula units of $Sr(HCO_3)_2$

4.16 How many total moles of ions are released when each of the following samples dissolves completely in water?
(a) 0.15 mol Na_3PO_4 (b) 47.9 g $NiBr_2 \cdot 3H_2O$
(c) 4.23×10^{22} formula units of $FeCl_3$

4.17 How many total moles of ions are released when each of the following samples dissolves completely in water?
(a) 0.382 mol K_2HPO_4 (b) 6.80 g $MgSO_4 \cdot 7H_2O$
(c) 6.188×10^{21} formula units of $NiCl_2$

4.18 How many ions of each type are present in the following aqueous solutions?
(a) 95.5 mL of 2.45 M aluminum chloride
(b) 2.50 L of a solution containing 4.59 g/L sodium sulfate
(c) 80.5 mL of a solution containing 2.68×10^{22} formula units of magnesium bromide per liter

4.19 How many ions of each type are present in the following aqueous solutions?
(a) 3.8 mL of 1.88 M magnesium chloride
(b) 345 mL of a solution containing 4.22 g/L aluminum sulfate
(c) 2.66 L of a solution containing 6.63×10^{21} formula units of lithium nitrate per liter

4.20 How many moles of H^+ ions are present in the following aqueous solutions?
(a) 0.140 L of 2.5 M perchloric acid
(b) 6.8 mL of 0.52 M nitric acid
(c) 2.5 L of 0.056 M hydrochloric acid

4.21 How many moles of H^+ ions are present in the following aqueous solutions?
(a) 1.4 L of 0.48 M hydrobromic acid
(b) 47 mL of 1.8 M hydriodic acid
(c) 425 mL of 0.27 M nitric acid

■ **Problems in Context**
4.22 In laboratory studies of ocean-dwelling organisms, marine biologists use salt mixtures that simulate the ion concentrations in seawater. A 1.00-kg sample of simulated seawater is prepared by mixing 26.5 g $NaCl$, 2.40 g $MgCl_2$, 3.35 g $MgSO_4$, 1.20 g $CaCl_2$, 1.05 g KCl, 0.315 g $NaHCO_3$, and 0.098 g $NaBr$ in distilled water.
(a) If the density of this solution is 1.04 g/cm³, what is the molarity of each ion?
(b) What is the total molarity of alkali metal ions?
(c) What is the total molarity of alkaline earth metal ions?
(d) What is the total molarity of anions?
4.23 Water "softeners" remove metal ions such as Fe^{2+}, Fe^{3+}, Ca^{2+}, and Mg^{2+} (which make water "hard") by replac-

ing them with enough Na^+ ions to maintain the same number of positive charges in the solution. If 1.0×10^3 L hard water is 0.015 M Ca^{2+} and 0.0010 M Fe^{3+}, how many moles of Na^+ are needed to replace these ions?

Precipitation Reactions and Acid-Base Reactions
(Sample Problems 4.3 to 4.5)

■ **Concept Review Questions**
4.24 When two solutions of ionic compounds are mixed, a reaction occurs only if ions are removed from solution to form product. What are three ways in which this removal can occur? What type of reaction is involved in each case?
4.25 Why do some pairs of ions form precipitates and others do not?
4.26 Which ions do not appear in a net ionic equation? Why?
4.27 Use Table 4.1 to determine which of the following combinations leads to a reaction. How can you identify the spectator ions in the reaction?
(a) Calcium nitrate(aq) + potassium chloride(aq) ⟶
(b) Sodium chloride(aq) + lead(II) nitrate(aq) ⟶
4.28 Is the total ionic equation the same as the net ionic equation for the reaction between $Sr(OH)_2(aq)$ and $H_2SO_4(aq)$? Explain.
4.29 State a general equation for a neutralization reaction.
4.30 (a) Name three common strong acids.
(b) Name three common strong bases.
(c) What is a characteristic behavior of a strong acid or a strong base?
4.31 (a) Name three common weak acids.
(b) Name one common weak base.
(c) What is the major difference between a weak acid and a strong acid or between a weak base and a strong base, and what experiment would you perform to test it?
4.32 Do either of the following reactions go to completion? If so, what factor(s) drives each to completion?
(a) $MgSO_3(s) + 2HCl(aq) \longrightarrow MgCl_2(aq) + SO_2(g) + H_2O(l)$
(b) $3Ba(OH)_2(aq) + 2H_3PO_4(aq) \longrightarrow Ba_3(PO_4)_2(s) + 6H_2O(l)$
4.33 The net ionic equation for the aqueous neutralization reaction between acetic acid and sodium hydroxide is different from the equation for hydrochloric acid and sodium hydroxide. Explain by writing balanced net ionic equations.

■ **Skill-Building Exercises (paired)**
4.34 When each of the following pairs of aqueous solutions is mixed, does a precipitation reaction occur? If so, write the formula and name of the precipitate:
(a) Sodium nitrate + copper(II) sulfate
(b) Ammonium iodide + silver nitrate
4.35 When each of the following pairs of aqueous solutions is mixed, does a precipitation reaction occur? If so, write the formula and name of the precipitate:
(a) Potassium carbonate + barium hydroxide
(b) Aluminum nitrate + sodium phosphate

4.36 When each of the following pairs of aqueous solutions is mixed, does a precipitation reaction occur? If so, write the formula and name of the precipitate:
(a) Potassium chloride + iron(II) nitrate
(b) Ammonium sulfate + barium chloride

4.37 When each of the following pairs of aqueous solutions is mixed, does a precipitation reaction occur? If so, write the formula and name of the precipitate:
(a) Sodium sulfide + nickel(II) sulfate
(b) Lead(II) nitrate + potassium bromide

4.38 Complete the following precipitation reactions with balanced molecular, total ionic, and net ionic equations, and identify the spectator ions:
(a) $Hg_2(NO_3)_2(aq) + KI(aq) \longrightarrow$
(b) $FeSO_4(aq) + Ba(OH)_2(aq) \longrightarrow$

4.39 Complete the following precipitation reactions with balanced molecular, total ionic, and net ionic equations, and identify the spectator ions:
(a) $CaCl_2(aq) + Cs_3PO_4(aq) \longrightarrow$
(b) $Na_2S(aq) + ZnSO_4(aq) \longrightarrow$

4.40 Complete the following acid-base reactions with balanced molecular, total ionic, and net ionic equations, and identify the spectator ions:
(a) Potassium hydroxide(aq) + hydriodic acid(aq) $\longrightarrow$
(b) Ammonia(aq) + hydrochloric acid(aq) $\longrightarrow$

4.41 Complete the following acid-base reactions with balanced molecular, total ionic, and net ionic equations, and identify the spectator ions:
(a) Cesium hydroxide(aq) + nitric acid(aq) $\longrightarrow$
(b) Calcium hydroxide(aq) + acetic acid(aq) $\longrightarrow$

4.42 Limestone (calcium carbonate) is insoluble in water but dissolves when a hydrochloric acid solution is added. Why? Write balanced total ionic and net ionic equations, showing hydrochloric acid as it actually exists in water and the reaction as a proton-transfer process.

4.43 Zinc hydroxide is insoluble in water but dissolves when a nitric acid solution is added. Why? Write balanced total ionic and net ionic equations, showing nitric acid as it actually exists in water and the reaction as a proton-transfer process.

4.44 If 35.0 mL lead(II) nitrate solution reacts completely with excess sodium iodide solution to yield 0.628 g precipitate, what is the molarity of lead(II) ion in the original solution?

4.45 If 25.0 mL silver nitrate solution reacts with excess potassium chloride solution to yield 0.842 g precipitate, what is the molarity of silver ion in the original solution?

4.46 If 15.98 mL of a standard 0.1080 M KOH solution reacts with 52.00 mL of CH_3COOH solution, what is the molarity of the acid solution?

4.47 If 26.35 mL of a standard 0.1650 M NaOH solution is required to neutralize 35.00 mL H_2SO_4, what is the molarity of the acid solution?

■ **Problems in Context**

4.48 An auto mechanic spills 85 mL of 2.6 M H_2SO_4 solution from a rebuilt auto battery. How many milliliters of 2.5 M $NaHCO_3$ must be poured on the spill to react completely with the sulfuric acid?

4.49 Sodium hydroxide is used extensively in acid-base titrations because it is a strong, inexpensive base. A sodium hydroxide solution was standardized by titrating 25.00 mL of 0.1528 M standard hydrochloric acid. The initial buret reading of the sodium hydroxide was 2.24 mL and the final

reading was 39.21 mL. What was the molarity of the base solution?

4.50 The mass percent of Cl^- in a seawater sample is determined by titrating 25.00 mL seawater with $AgNO_3$ solution, causing a precipitation reaction. An indicator is used to detect the end point, which occurs when free Ag^+ ion is present in solution after all the Cl^- is consumed. If 43.63 mL of 0.3020 M $AgNO_3$ is required to reach the end point, what is the mass percent of Cl^- in the seawater? (d of seawater = 1.04 g/mL.)

4.51 Aluminum sulfate, known as cake alum, has a remarkably wide range of uses, from dyeing leather and cloth to purifying sewage. In aqueous solution, it reacts with base to form a white precipitate. (a) Write balanced total and net ionic equations for its reaction with aqueous NaOH. (b) What mass of precipitate forms when 135.5 mL of 0.633 M NaOH is added to 517 mL of a solution that contains 12.8 g aluminum sulfate per liter?

Oxidation-Reduction (Redox) Reactions
(Sample Problems 4.6 to 4.9)

■ **Concept Review Questions**

4.52 Describe how to determine the oxidation number of sulfur in (a) H_2S and (b) SO_3.

4.53 Is the following a redox reaction? Explain.
$$NH_3(aq) + HCl(aq) \longrightarrow NH_4Cl(aq)$$

4.54 Explain why an oxidizing agent undergoes reduction.

4.55 Why must every redox reaction involve an oxidizing agent and a reducing agent?

4.56 In which of the following equations does sulfuric acid act as an oxidizing agent? In which does it act as an acid? Explain.
(a) $4H^+(aq) + SO_4^{2-}(aq) + 2NaI(s) \longrightarrow$
$$2Na^+(aq) + I_2(s) + SO_2(g) + 2H_2O(l)$$
(b) $BaF_2(s) + 2H^+(aq) + SO_4^{2-}(aq) \longrightarrow$
$$2HF(aq) + BaSO_4(s)$$

4.57 Identify the oxidizing agent and the reducing agent in the following reaction, and explain your answer:
$$8NH_3(g) + 6NO_2(g) \longrightarrow 7N_2(g) + 12H_2O(l)$$

■ **Skill-Building Exercises (paired)**

4.58 Give the oxidation number of carbon in each of the following: (a) CF_2Cl_2 (b) $Na_2C_2O_4$ (c) HCO_3^- (d) C_2H_6

4.59 Give the oxidation number of bromine in each of the following: (a) KBr (b) BrF_3 (c) $HBrO_3$ (d) CBr_4

4.60 Give the oxidation number of nitrogen in each of the following: (a) NH_2OH (b) N_2H_4 (c) NH_4^+ (d) HNO_2

4.61 Give the oxidation number of sulfur in each of the following: (a) $SOCl_2$ (b) H_2S_2 (c) H_2SO_3 (d) Na_2S

4.62 Give the oxidation number of arsenic in each of the following: (a) AsH_3 (b) H_3AsO_4 (c) $AsCl_3$

4.63 Give the oxidation number of phosphorus in each of the following: (a) $H_2P_2O_7^{2-}$ (b) PH_4^+ (c) PCl_5

4.64 Give the oxidation number of manganese in each of the following: (a) MnO_4^{2-} (b) Mn_2O_3 (c) $KMnO_4$

4.65 Give the oxidation number of chromium in each of the following: (a) CrO_3 (b) $Cr_2O_7^{2-}$ (c) $Cr_2(SO_4)_3$

4.66 Identify the oxidizing agent and the reducing agent in each of the following:

(a) $5H_2C_2O_4(aq) + 2MnO_4^-(aq) + 6H^+(aq) \longrightarrow$
$$2Mn^{2+}(aq) + 10CO_2(g) + 8H_2O(l)$$
(b) $3Cu(s) + 8H^+(aq) + 2NO_3^-(aq) \longrightarrow$
$$3Cu^{2+}(aq) + 2NO(g) + 4H_2O(l)$$

4.67 Identify the oxidizing agent and the reducing agent in each of the following:
(a) $Sn(s) + 2H^+(aq) \longrightarrow Sn^{2+}(aq) + H_2(g)$
(b) $2H^+(aq) + H_2O_2(aq) + 2Fe^{2+}(aq) \longrightarrow$
$$2Fe^{3+}(aq) + 2H_2O(l)$$

4.68 Identify the oxidizing agent and the reducing agent in each of the following:
(a) $8H^+(aq) + 6Cl^-(aq) + Sn(s) + 4NO_3^-(aq) \longrightarrow$
$$SnCl_6^{2-}(aq) + 4NO_2(g) + 4H_2O(l)$$
(b) $2MnO_4^-(aq) + 10Cl^-(aq) + 16H^+(aq) \longrightarrow$
$$5Cl_2(g) + 2Mn^{2+}(aq) + 8H_2O(l)$$

4.69 Identify the oxidizing agent and the reducing agent in each of the following:
(a) $8H^+(aq) + Cr_2O_7^{2-}(aq) + 3SO_3^{2-}(aq) \longrightarrow$
$$2Cr^{3+}(aq) + 3SO_4^{2-}(aq) + 4H_2O(l)$$
(b) $NO_3^-(aq) + 4Zn(s) + 7OH^-(aq) + 6H_2O(l) \longrightarrow$
$$4Zn(OH)_4^{2-}(aq) + NH_3(aq)$$

4.70 Discuss each conclusion from a study of redox reactions:
(a) The sulfide ion functions only as a reducing agent.
(b) The sulfate ion functions only as an oxidizing agent.
(c) Sulfur dioxide functions as either an oxidizing or a reducing agent.

4.71 Discuss each conclusion from a study of redox reactions:
(a) The nitride ion functions only as a reducing agent.
(b) The nitrate ion functions only as an oxidizing agent.
(c) The nitrite ion functions as either an oxidizing or a reducing agent.

4.72 Use the oxidation number method to balance the following equations by placing coefficients in the blanks. Identify the reducing and oxidizing agents:
(a) $\_HNO_3(aq) + \_K_2CrO_4(aq) + \_Fe(NO_3)_2(aq) \longrightarrow$
$\_KNO_3(aq) + \_Fe(NO_3)_3(aq) + \_Cr(NO_3)_3(aq) + \_H_2O(l)$
(b) $\_HNO_3(aq) + \_C_2H_6O(l) + \_K_2Cr_2O_7(aq) \longrightarrow$
$\_KNO_3(aq) + \_C_2H_4O(l) + \_H_2O(l) + \_Cr(NO_3)_3(aq)$
(c) $\_HCl(aq) + \_NH_4Cl(aq) + \_K_2Cr_2O_7(aq) \longrightarrow$
$\_KCl(aq) + \_CrCl_3(aq) + \_N_2(g) + \_H_2O(l)$
(d) $\_KClO_3(aq) + \_HBr(aq) \longrightarrow$
$\_Br_2(l) + \_H_2O(l) + \_KCl(aq)$

4.73 Use the oxidation number method to balance the following equations by placing coefficients in the blanks. Identify the reducing and oxidizing agents:
(a) $\_HCl(aq) + \_FeCl_2(aq) + \_H_2O_2(aq) \longrightarrow$
$\_FeCl_3(aq) + \_H_2O(l)$
(b) $\_I_2(s) + \_Na_2S_2O_3(aq) \longrightarrow \_Na_2S_4O_6(aq) + \_NaI(aq)$
(c) $\_HNO_3(aq) + \_KI(aq) \longrightarrow$
$\_NO(g) + \_I_2(s) + \_H_2O(l) + \_KNO_3(aq)$
(d) $\_PbO(s) + \_NH_3(aq) \longrightarrow \_N_2(g) + \_H_2O(l) + \_Pb(s)$

Problems in Context

4.74 The active agent in many hair bleaches is hydrogen peroxide. The amount of hydrogen peroxide in 13.8 g hair bleach was determined by titration with a standard potassium permanganate solution:
$2MnO_4^-(aq) + 5H_2O_2(aq) + 6H^+(aq) \longrightarrow$
$$5O_2(g) + 2Mn^{2+}(aq) + 8H_2O(l)$$

(a) How many moles of MnO_4^- were required for the titration if 43.2 mL of 0.105 M $KMnO_4$ was needed to reach the end point?
(b) How many moles of H_2O_2 were present in the 13.8-g sample of bleach?
(c) How many grams of H_2O_2 were in the sample?
(d) What is the mass percent H_2O_2 in the sample?
(e) What is the reducing agent in the redox reaction?

4.75 The beakers represent the aqueous reaction of $AgNO_3$ and $NaCl$. If silver ions are gray, what colors are used to represent NO_3^-, Na^+, and Cl^-? Write molecular, total ionic, and net ionic equations for the reaction.

4.76 A person's blood alcohol (C_2H_5OH) level can be determined by titrating a sample of blood plasma with a potassium dichromate solution. The balanced equation is
$16H^+(aq) + 2Cr_2O_7^{2-}(aq) + C_2H_5OH(aq) \longrightarrow$
$$4Cr^{3+}(aq) + 2CO_2(g) + 11H_2O(l)$$

If 35.46 mL of 0.05961 M $Cr_2O_7^{2-}$ is required to titrate 28.00 g plasma, what is the mass percent of alcohol in the blood?

Counting Reactants and Products in Precipitation, Acid-Base, and Redox Processes

(Sample Problem 4.10)

▇ Concept Review Questions

4.77 What is the name of the type of reaction that leads to the following?
(a) An increase in the number of substances
(b) A decrease in the number of substances
(c) No change in the number of substances

4.78 Why do decomposition reactions typically have compounds as reactants, whereas combination and displacement reactions have either elements or compounds?

4.79 Which of the three types of reactions discussed in this section commonly produce one or more compounds?

4.80 Give an example of a combination reaction that is a redox reaction. Give an example of a combination reaction that is not a redox reaction.

4.81 Are all combustion reactions redox reactions? Explain.

▇ Skill-Building Exercises (paired)

4.82 Balance each of the following, classify it as a combination, decomposition, or displacement reaction, and state whether it is a redox process:
(a) $Ca(s) + H_2O(l) \longrightarrow Ca(OH)_2(aq) + H_2(g)$
(b) $NaNO_3(s) \longrightarrow NaNO_2(s) + O_2(g)$
(c) $C_2H_2(g) + H_2(g) \longrightarrow C_2H_6(g)$

4.83 Balance each of the following, classify it as a combination, decomposition, or displacement reaction, and state whether it is a redox process:
(a) $HI(g) \longrightarrow H_2(g) + I_2(g)$
(b) $Zn(s) + AgNO_3(aq) \longrightarrow Zn(NO_3)_2(aq) + Ag(s)$
(c) $NO(g) + O_2(g) \longrightarrow N_2O_4(l)$

4.84 Balance each of the following, classify it as a combination, decomposition, or displacement reaction, and state whether it is a redox process:
(a) $Sb(s) + Cl_2(g) \longrightarrow SbCl_3(s)$
(b) $AsH_3(g) \longrightarrow As(s) + H_2(g)$
(c) $C_2H_5OH(l) \overset{\Delta}{\longrightarrow} C_2H_4(g) + H_2O(g)$

4.85 Balance each of the following, classify it as a combination, decomposition, or displacement reaction, and state whether it is a redox process:
(a) $Mg(s) + H_2O(g) \longrightarrow Mg(OH)_2(s) + H_2(g)$
(b) $Cr(NO_3)_3(aq) + Al(s) \longrightarrow Al(NO_3)_3(aq) + Cr(s)$
(c) $PF_3(g) + F_2(g) \longrightarrow PF_5(g)$

4.86 Complete the following general reactions, and write a specific balanced equation to exemplify each:
(a) Metal + oxygen $\longrightarrow$
(b) Nonmetal halide + halogen $\longrightarrow$
(c) Nonmetal oxide + water $\longrightarrow$
(d) Metal hydroxide $\overset{\Delta}{\longrightarrow}$

4.87 Complete the following general reactions, and write a specific balanced equation to exemplify each:
(a) Nonmetal + nonmetal $\longrightarrow$
(b) Metal oxide + nonmetal oxide $\longrightarrow$
(c) Metal carbonate $\overset{\Delta}{\longrightarrow}$
(d) Acid + base $\longrightarrow$

4.88 Predict the product(s), write a balanced equation, and state whether each of the following is a redox reaction:
(a) $Ca(s) + Br_2(l) \longrightarrow$
(b) $Ag_2O(s) \overset{\Delta}{\longrightarrow}$
(c) $Mn(s) + Cu(NO_3)_2(aq) \longrightarrow$

4.89 Predict the product(s), write a balanced equation, and state whether each of the following is a redox reaction:
(a) $Ca(OH)_2(aq) + HCl(aq) \longrightarrow$
(b) $LiCl(l) \overset{electricity}{\longrightarrow}$
(c) $SnCl_2(aq) + Co(s) \longrightarrow$

4.90 Predict the product(s), write a balanced equation, and state whether each of the following is a redox reaction:
(a) $N_2(g) + H_2(g) \longrightarrow$
(b) $NaClO_3(s) \overset{\Delta}{\longrightarrow}$
(c) $Ba(s) + H_2O(l) \longrightarrow$

4.91 Predict the product(s), write a balanced equation, and state whether each of the following is a redox reaction:
(a) $KOH(aq) + HClO_4(aq) \longrightarrow$
(b) $S_8(s) + O_2(g) \longrightarrow$
(c) $BaCl_2(aq) + Na_2SO_4(aq) \longrightarrow$

4.92 Predict the product(s), write a balanced equation, and state whether each of the following is a redox reaction:
(a) Cesium + iodine $\longrightarrow$
(b) Aluminum + aqueous manganese(II) sulfate $\longrightarrow$
(c) Sulfur dioxide + oxygen $\longrightarrow$
(d) Carbon dioxide + barium oxide $\longrightarrow$
(e) Write a balanced net ionic equation for (b).

4.93 Predict the product(s), write a balanced equation, and state whether each of the following is a redox reaction:
(a) Calcium oxide + water $\longrightarrow$
(b) Phosphorus trichloride + chlorine $\longrightarrow$
(c) Zinc + hydrobromic acid $\longrightarrow$
(d) Aqueous potassium iodide + bromine $\longrightarrow$
(e) Write a balanced net ionic equation for (d).

4.94 How many grams of O_2 can be prepared from the complete decomposition of 4.27 kg HgO? Name and calculate the mass (in kg) of the other product.

4.95 How many grams of lime (CaO) can be produced from the complete decomposition of 114.52 g limestone ($CaCO_3$)? Name and calculate the mass (in grams) of the other product.

4.96 In a combination reaction, 1.62 g lithium is mixed with 6.00 g oxygen.
(a) Which reactant is present in excess?
(b) How many moles of product are formed?
(c) After reaction, how many grams of each reactant and product are present?

4.97 In a combination reaction, 2.22 g magnesium is heated with 3.75 g nitrogen.
(a) Which reactant is present in excess?
(b) How many moles of product are formed?
(c) After reaction, how many grams of each reactant and product are present?

4.98 A mixture of $KClO_3$ and KCl with a mass of 0.900 g was heated to produce O_2. After heating, the mass of residue was 0.700 g. Assuming all the $KClO_3$ decomposed to KCl and O_2, calculate the mass percent of $KClO_3$ in the original mixture.

4.99 A mixture of $CaCO_3$ and CaO weighing 0.693 g was heated to produce CO_2. After heating, the remaining solid weighed 0.508 g. Assuming all the $CaCO_3$ decomposed to CaO and CO_2, calculate the mass percent of $CaCO_3$ in the original mixture.

■ **Problems in Context**

4.100 Before arc welding was developed, a displacement reaction involving aluminum and iron(III) oxide was commonly used to produce molten iron (the thermite process; see photo). This reaction was used, for example, to connect sections of iron railroad track. Calculate the mass of molten iron produced when 1.00 kg aluminum reacts with 2.00 mol iron(III) oxide.

4.101 One of the first steps in the enrichment of uranium for use in nuclear power plants involves a displacement reaction between UO_2 and aqueous HF:

$$UO_2(s) + 4HF(aq) \longrightarrow UF_4(s) + 2H_2O(l)$$

How many liters of 6.50 *M* HF are needed to react with 3.25 kg UO_2?

4.102 The field of sports medicine has become an important specialty, with physicians routinely treating athletes and dancers. Ethyl chloride, a local anesthetic commonly used for simple injuries, is the product of the combination of ethylene with hydrogen chloride:

$$C_2H_4(g) + HCl(g) \longrightarrow C_2H_5Cl(g)$$

If 0.100 kg C_2H_4 and 0.100 kg HCl react,

(a) How many molecules of gas (reactants plus products) are present when the reaction is complete?

(b) How many moles of gas are present when half the product forms?

4.103 Iron reacts rapidly with chlorine gas to form Compound A, a reddish-brown ionic compound, which contains iron in the higher of its two common oxidation states *(see photo)*. Strong heating decomposes Compound A to Compound B, another ionic compound, which contains iron in the lower of its two oxidation states. When Compound A is formed by the reaction of 50.6 g Fe and 83.8 g Cl_2 and then heated, how much Compound B forms?

Reversible Reactions: An Introduction to Chemical Equilibrium

■ Concept Review Questions

4.104 Why is the equilibrium state called "dynamic"?

4.105 In a decomposition reaction involving a gaseous product, what must be done for the reaction to reach equilibrium?

4.106 Describe what happens on the molecular level when acetic acid dissolves in water.

4.107 When either a mixture of NO and Br_2 or pure nitrosyl bromide (NOBr) is placed in a reaction vessel, the product mixture contains NO, Br_2, and NOBr. Explain.

■ Problems in Context

4.108 Ammonia is produced by the millions of tons annually for use as a fertilizer. It is commonly made from N_2 and H_2 by the Haber process. Because the reaction reaches equilibrium before going completely to product, the stoichiometric amount of ammonia is not obtained. At a particular temperature and pressure, 10.0 g H_2 reacts with 20.0 g N_2 to form ammonia. When equilibrium is reached, 15.0 g NH_3 has formed.

(a) Calculate the percent yield.

(b) How many moles of N_2 and H_2 are present at equilibrium?

Comprehensive Problems

Problems with an asterisk (*) are more challenging.

4.109 Nutritional biochemists have known for decades that acidic foods cooked in cast-iron cookware can supply significant amounts of dietary (ferrous) iron.

(a) Write a balanced net ionic equation, with oxidation numbers, that supports this fact.

(b) Measurements show an increase from 3.3 mg iron to 49 mg iron per $\frac{1}{2}$-cup (125 g) serving during the slow preparation of tomato sauce in a cast-iron pot. How many ferrous ions are present in a 26-oz (737 g) jar of tomato sauce?

4.110 Limestone ($CaCO_3$) is used to remove acidic pollutants from smokestack flue gases in a sequence of decomposition-combination reactions. The limestone is heated to form lime (CaO), which reacts with sulfur dioxide to form calcium sulfite. Assuming a 70.% yield in the overall reaction, what mass of limestone is required to remove all the sulfur dioxide formed by the combustion of 8.5×10^4 kg coal that is 0.33 mass % sulfur?

4.111 The brewing industry uses yeast microorganisms to convert glucose to ethanol for wine and beer. The baking industry uses the carbon dioxide these single-celled fungi produce to make bread rise:

$$C_6H_{12}O_6(s) \xrightarrow{\text{yeast}} 2C_2H_5OH(l) + 2CO_2(g)$$

How many grams of ethanol can be produced from the decomposition of 10.0 g glucose? What volume of CO_2 is produced? (Assume 1 mol of gas occupies 22.4 L under the conditions used.)

4.112 A chemical engineer determines the mass percent of iron in an ore sample by converting the Fe to Fe^{2+} in acid and then titrating the Fe^{2+} with MnO_4^-. A 1.1081-g sample was dissolved in acid and then titrated with 39.32 mL of 0.03190 M $KMnO_4$. The balanced equation is

$$8H^+(aq) + 5Fe^{2+}(aq) + MnO_4^-(aq) \longrightarrow$$
$$5Fe^{3+}(aq) + Mn^{2+}(aq) + 4H_2O(l)$$

Calculate the mass percent of iron in the ore.

4.113 Mixtures of $CaCl_2$ and NaCl are used for salting roads to prevent ice formation. A dissolved 1.9348-g sample of such a mixture was analyzed by using excess $Na_2C_2O_4$ to completely precipitate the Ca^{2+} as CaC_2O_4. The CaC_2O_4 was separated from the solution and then dissolved with sulfuric acid. The resulting $H_2C_2O_4$ was titrated with 37.68 mL of 0.1019 M $KMnO_4$ solution.

(a) Write the balanced net ionic equation for the precipitation reaction.

(b) Write the balanced net ionic equation for the titration reaction. (See Sample Problem 4.9.)

(c) What is the oxidizing agent?

(d) What is the reducing agent?

(e) Calculate the mass percent of $CaCl_2$ in the original sample.

4.114 Nickel chloride solution is used industrially for plating zinc and other metals. The solution is shipped in tin-lined iron drums. Explain with balanced equations why the drums must be lined. What would happen to solution stored in an unlined drum?

4.115 Precipitation reactions are often used to prepare useful ionic compounds. For example, thousands of tons of silver bromide are prepared annually for use in making black-and-white photographic film. (a) What mass (in kilograms) of silver bromide forms when 5.85 m^3 of 1.68 M potassium bromide reacts with 3.51 m^3 of 2.04 M silver nitrate? (b) After the solid silver bromide is removed, what ions are present in the remaining solution? Determine the molarity of each ion. (Assume the total volume is the sum of the reactant volumes.)

4.116 The flask *(right)* depicts the products of the titration of 25 mL sulfuric acid with 25 mL sodium hydroxide.
(a) Write balanced molecular, total ionic, and net ionic equations for the reaction.
(b) If each orange sphere represents 0.010 mol sulfate ion, how many moles of acid and of base reacted?
(c) What are the molarities of the acid and the base?

4.117 To find the mass percent of dolomite [$CaMg(CO_3)_2$] in a soil sample, a geochemist titrates 12.86 g of the soil with 33.56 mL of 0.2516 M HCl. What is the mass percent of dolomite in the soil?

4.118 The calcium carbonate impurity in a sample of phosphate rock is removed by treatment with hydrochloric acid; the products are carbon dioxide, water, and aqueous calcium chloride. When 15.5 g of the rock is treated with excess hydrochloric acid, 1.81 g carbon dioxide is formed. Calculate the mass percent of calcium carbonate in the rock.

*4.119 When zinc metal is treated with dilute nitric acid, the reaction produces nitrogen gas, water, and aqueous zinc nitrate. Write a balanced equation for the reaction.

4.120 Complete each of the following reactions and write net ionic equations for them:
1. NaOH(aq) + HCl(aq) $\longrightarrow$
2. KOH(aq) + HNO$_3$(aq) $\longrightarrow$
3. Ba(OH)$_2$(aq) + 2HBr(aq) $\longrightarrow$
(a) What do you conclude from these equations about the nature of the reactants?
(b) What are the spectator ions in each reaction?

4.121 Use the oxidation number method to balance the following equations by placing coefficients in the blanks. Identify the reducing and oxidizing agents:
(a) __KOH(aq) + __H$_2$O$_2$(aq) + __Cr(OH)$_3$(s) $\longrightarrow$
   __K$_2$CrO$_4$(aq) + __H$_2$O(l)
(b) __MnO$_4^-$(aq) + __ClO$_2^-$(aq) + __H$_2$O(l) $\longrightarrow$
   __MnO$_2$(s) + __ClO$_4^-$(aq) + __OH$^-$(aq)
(c) __KMnO$_4$(aq) + __Na$_2$SO$_3$(aq) + __H$_2$O(l) $\longrightarrow$
   __MnO$_2$(s) + __Na$_2$SO$_4$(aq) + __KOH(aq)

4.122 In a key reaction during the industrial production of pig iron, a molten silicate "slag" forms in the blast furnace when sand (silicon dioxide) and lime (calcium oxide) react (see photo). (a) Write a balanced equation for this reaction. (b) Is this a redox reaction? Show with oxidation numbers.

4.123 Use the oxidation number method to balance the following reactions by placing coefficients in the blanks. Identify the reducing and oxidizing agents:
(a) __CrO$_4^{2-}$(aq) + __HSnO$_2^-$(aq) + __H$_2$O(l) $\longrightarrow$
   __CrO$_2^-$(aq) + __HSnO$_3^-$(aq) + __OH$^-$(aq)
(b) __KMnO$_4$(aq) + __NaNO$_2$(aq) + __H$_2$O(l) $\longrightarrow$
   __MnO$_2$(s) + __NaNO$_3$(aq) + __KOH(aq)
(c) __I$^-$(aq) + __O$_2$(g) + __H$_2$O(l) $\longrightarrow$ __I$_2$(s) + __OH$^-$(aq)

4.124 Sodium peroxide (Na$_2$O$_2$) is often used in self-contained breathing devices, such as those used in fire emergencies, because it reacts with exhaled CO$_2$ to form Na$_2$CO$_3$ and O$_2$. How many liters of respired air can react with 80.0 g Na$_2$O$_2$ if each liter of respired air contains 0.0720 g CO$_2$?

4.125 Magnesium is used in many lightweight alloys, including those in airplane bodies. The metal is obtained from seawater in an industrial process that includes precipitation, neutralization, evaporation, and electrolysis. How many kilograms of magnesium can be obtained from 1.00 km^3 seawater if the initial Mg^{2+} concentration is 0.13% by mass? (*d* of seawater = 1.04 g/mL.)

*4.126 A typical formulation for window glass is 75% SiO$_2$, 15% Na$_2$O, and 10.% CaO by mass. What masses of sand (SiO$_2$), sodium carbonate, and calcium carbonate must be combined to produce 1.00 kg glass after carbon dioxide is driven off by thermal decomposition of the carbonates?

4.127 The *salinity* of a solution is defined as the grams of total salts per kilogram of solution. An agricultural chemist uses a solution whose salinity is 35.0 g/kg to test the effect of irrigating farmland with high-salinity river water. The two solutes are NaCl and MgSO$_4$, and there are twice as many moles of NaCl as MgSO$_4$. What masses of NaCl and MgSO$_4$ are contained in 1.00 kg of the solution?

*4.128 Thyroxine (C$_{15}$H$_{11}$I$_4$NO$_4$) is a hormone synthesized by the thyroid gland and used to control many metabolic functions in the body. A physiologist determines the mass % of thyroxine in a thyroid extract by igniting 0.4332 g of extract with sodium carbonate, which converts the iodine to iodide. The iodide is dissolved in water, and bromine and hydrochloric acid are added, which convert the iodide to iodate.
(a) How many moles of iodate are produced per mole of thyroxine?
(b) Excess bromine is boiled off and more iodide is added, which reacts as follows:

IO$_3^-$(aq) + H$^+$(aq) + I$^-$(aq) $\longrightarrow$
   I$_2$(aq) + H$_2$O(l) [unbalanced]

How many moles of iodine are produced per mole of thyroxine? (*Hint:* Be sure to balance the charges as well as the atoms.) What are the oxidizing and reducing agents in the reaction?
(c) The iodine reacts completely with 17.23 mL of 0.1000 M thiosulfate as follows:

I$_2$(aq) + S$_2$O$_3^{2-}$(aq) $\longrightarrow$ I$^-$(aq) + S$_4$O$_6^{2-}$(aq) [unbalanced]

What is the mass % of thyroxine in the thyroid extract?

4.129 Carbon dioxide is removed from the atmosphere of space capsules by reaction with a solid metal hydroxide. The products are water and the metal carbonate.
(a) Calculate the mass of CO$_2$ that can be removed by reaction with 3.50 kg lithium hydroxide.

(b) How many grams of CO_2 can be removed by 1.00 g of each of the following: lithium hydroxide, magnesium hydroxide, and aluminum hydroxide?

*4.130 Calcium dihydrogen phosphate, $Ca(H_2PO_4)_2$, and sodium hydrogen carbonate, $NaHCO_3$, are ingredients of baking powder that react with each other to produce CO_2, which causes dough or batter to rise:

$$Ca(H_2PO_4)_2(s) + NaHCO_3(s) \longrightarrow$$
$$CO_2(g) + H_2O(g) + CaHPO_4(s) + Na_2HPO_4(s)$$
$$[unbalanced]$$

If the baking powder contains 31% $NaHCO_3$ and 35% $Ca(H_2PO_4)_2$ by mass,

(a) How many moles of CO_2 are produced from 1.00 g baking powder?

(b) If 1 mol CO_2 occupies 37.0 L at 350°F (a typical baking temperature), what volume of CO_2 is produced from 1.00 g baking powder?

4.131 During the process of developing black-and-white film, unexposed silver bromide is removed in a displacement reaction with sodium thiosulfate solution:

$$AgBr(s) + 2Na_2S_2O_3(aq) \longrightarrow Na_3Ag(S_2O_3)_2(aq) + NaBr(aq)$$

What volume of 0.105 M $Na_2S_2O_3$ solution is needed to remove 2.66 g AgBr from a roll of film?

4.132 Ionic hydrates lose their "waters of hydration" when thermally decomposed. When 25.36 g of hydrated copper(II) sulfate is heated, it forms 16.21 g of anhydrous copper(II) sulfate (see photo). What is the formula of the hydrate?

*4.133 In 1997, at the United Nations Conference on Climate Change, the major industrial nations agreed to expand their research efforts to develop renewable sources of carbon-based fuels. For more than a decade, Brazil has been engaged in a program to replace gasoline with ethanol derived from the root crop manioc (cassava).

(a) Write separate balanced equations for the complete combustion of ethanol (C_2H_5OH) and of gasoline (represented by the formula C_8H_{18}).

(b) What mass of oxygen is required to burn completely 1.00 L of a mixture that is 90.0% gasoline ($d = 0.742$ g/mL) and 10.0% ethanol ($d = 0.789$ g/mL) by volume?

(c) If 1.00 mol O_2 occupies 22.4 L, what volume of O_2 is needed to burn 1.00 L of the mixture?

(d) Air is 20.9% O_2 by volume. What volume of air is needed to burn 1.00 L of the mixture?

*4.134 When NaCl(s) dissolves in water, the ions separate; when the water evaporates, NaCl(s) re-forms. When HCl(g) dissolves in water, a covalent bond breaks; when the water evaporates, HCl(g) re-forms. Are either or both of these chemical changes? Discuss.

4.135 One of the molecules responsible for atmospheric ozone depletion is the refrigerant and aerosol propellant Freon-12 (CF_2Cl_2). It can be prepared commercially in a sequence of two reactions:

1. A combination reaction between hydrogen and fluorine gases

2. A displacement reaction between the product of the first reaction and liquid carbon tetrachloride. Hydrogen chloride gas also forms.

(a) Write balanced equations for the two reactions.

(b) What is the maximum mass (in kg) of Freon-12 that can be produced from 0.760 kg fluorine?

5

Gases and the Kinetic-Molecular Theory

Figure: Rising aloft on a gas law. The operation of this balloon is based fundamentally on a behavior of heated gases learned and applied over 200 years ago. In this chapter, you'll learn this and a great deal more about gas behavior and its countless applications in industry, everyday life, and beyond.

Chapter Outline

Take a deep breath. You have just inhaled a small portion of the colorless, odorless mixture of nearly 20 gases that surrounds our planet, and you changed the proportion of some of them to make the mixture you exhaled. The Earth's atmosphere extends from the planet's surface upward more than 500 km until it merges with outer space. Some of its components—O_2, N_2, H_2O vapor, and CO_2—are essential for life because they take part in complex cycles of redox reactions throughout the environment. ◆ Gases also have essential roles in industry, and some important gases, produced in multimillion-ton amounts annually, are listed in Table 5.1 on the next page.

People have been observing the behavior of gases and the other states of matter throughout history—three of the four "elements" of the ancients were air (gas), water (liquid), and earth (solid)—but many questions remain. In this chapter and its companion, Chapter 12, we examine these states and their interrelations. Here, we highlight the gaseous state, the one we understand best.

Although the *chemical* behavior of a gas depends on its composition, the *physical* behavior of all gases is remarkably similar. For instance, although the gases present differ, the same physical behavior is at work in the operation of a car and in the baking of bread, in the thrust of a rocket engine and in the explosion of a kernel of popcorn. The process of breathing arises from the same physical behavior as the creation of thunder.

The physical behaviors that gases have in common are the primary focus of this chapter. First we contrast gases with liquids and solids and then discuss gas pressure. Next, we consider several laws that describe gas behavior and then examine the ideal gas law, which encompasses the others, and apply it to reaction stoichiometry. We explain the observable behavior of gases with a molecular-level model, but find next that studies of real gas behavior under extreme conditions require a refinement of the ideal gas law. Finally, we apply these principles to the properties of planetary atmospheres.

5.1 An Overview of the Physical States of Matter

Under appropriate conditions of pressure and temperature, most substances can exist as a solid, a liquid, or a gas. In Chapters 1 and 2, we described these physical states in terms of how each fills a container and began to develop molecular pictures that explain this macroscopic behavior: a solid has a fixed shape regardless of the container shape because its particles are held rigidly in place; a liquid conforms to the container shape but has a definite volume and a surface because its particles are close together but free to move around each other; and a gas expands to fill the container because its particles are far apart and moving randomly. Several other aspects of their behavior distinguish gases from liquids and solids, and you'll learn molecular reasons for them as well:

1. *Gas volume changes greatly with pressure.* When a sample of gas is confined to a container of variable volume, such as the piston-cylinder assembly of a car engine, an external force can compress the gas. Removing the external force allows the gas volume to increase again. In contrast, a liquid or solid resists significant changes in volume.

2. *Gas volume changes greatly with temperature.* When a gas sample at constant pressure is heated, its volume increases; when it is cooled, its volume decreases. This volume change is 50 to 100 times greater for gases than for liquids or solids.

3. *Gases have relatively low viscosity.* Gases flow much more freely than liquids and solids. Low viscosity allows gases to flow through pipes over long distances and to leak rapidly out of small holes.

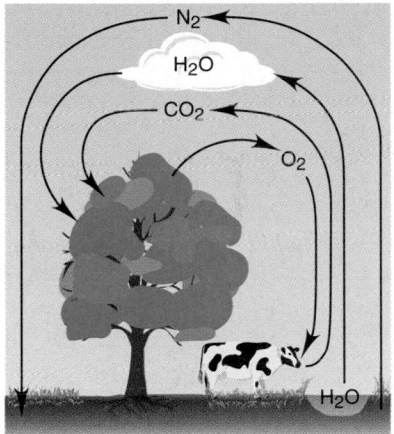

◆ **Atmosphere-Biosphere Redox Interconnections**
The great diversity of organisms that make up the biosphere interact intimately with the gases of the atmosphere. Powered by solar energy, green plants reduce atmospheric CO_2 and incorporate the C atoms into their own substance. In the process, O atoms in H_2O are oxidized and released to the air as O_2. Certain microbes that live on plant roots reduce N_2 to NH_3 and form compounds that the plant uses to make its proteins. Other microbes that feed on dead plants (and animals) oxidize the proteins and release N_2 again. Animals eat plants and other animals, use O_2 to oxidize their food, and return CO_2 and H_2O to the air.

Table 5.1 Some Important Industrial Gases

Name (Formula)	Origin and Use
Methane (CH_4)	Natural deposits; domestic fuel
Ammonia (NH_3)	From $N_2 + H_2$; fertilizers, explosives
Chlorine (Cl_2)	Electrolysis of seawater; bleaching and disinfecting
Oxygen (O_2)	Liquefied air; steelmaking
Ethylene (C_2H_4)	High-temperature decomposition of natural gas; plastics

◆ POW! P-s-s-s-t! POP!

A jackhammer uses the force of rapidly expanding compressed air to break through rock and cement. When the nozzle on a can of spray paint is pressed, the pressurized propellant gases expand into the lower pressure of the surroundings and expel droplets of paint. The rapid expansion of heated gases results in such phenomena as the destruction caused by a bomb, the liftoff of a rocket, and the formation of popped corn.

4. *Most gases have relatively low densities* under normal conditions. Gas density is usually tabulated in units of grams per *liter*, whereas liquid and solid densities are in grams per *milliliter*, about 1000 times as dense (see Table 1.5). For example, at 20°C and normal atmospheric pressure, the density of $O_2(g)$ is 1.3 g/**L**, whereas the density of $H_2O(l)$ is 1.0 g/**mL** and that of $NaCl(s)$ is 2.2 g/**mL**. When a gas is cooled, its density increases because its volume decreases: at 0°C, the density of $O_2(g)$ increases to 1.4 g/L.

5. *Gases are miscible. Miscible* substances mix with one another in any proportion to form a solution. Clean dry air, for example, is a solution of about 18 different gases. Two liquids, on the other hand, may or may not be miscible: water and ethanol are, but water and gasoline are not. Solids generally do not form solutions with each other unless they are mixed as molten liquids and then allowed to solidify.

Each of these observable gas properties offers a clue to the molecular properties of gases. For example, consider these density data. At 20°C and normal atmospheric pressure, gaseous N_2 has a density of 1.25 g/L. If cooled below −196°C, it condenses to liquid N_2 and its density becomes 0.808 g/mL. (Note the change in units.) The same amount of nitrogen occupies less than $\frac{1}{600}$ as much space! Further cooling to below −210°C yields solid N_2 ($d = 1.03$ g/mL), which is only somewhat more dense than the liquid. These values show again that *the molecules are much farther apart in the gas than in either the liquid or the solid.* Moreover, a large amount of space between molecules is consistent with gas compressibility, ◆ miscibility, and low viscosity. Figure 5.1 compares macroscopic and molecular views of the physical states of a real substance.

A Gas: Molecules are far apart and fill the available space

B Liquid: Molecules are close together but move relative to each other

C Solid: Molecules are close together, packed in a regular array, and move very little relative to each other

Figure 5.1 The three states of matter. Many pure substances, such as bromine (Br_2), can exist under appropriate conditions of pressure and temperature as **A**, a gas; **B**, a liquid; or **C**, a solid. In **A**, the liquid form of bromine has been vaporized, whereas in **C** it has been frozen. The molecular views show that molecules are much farther apart in a gas than in a liquid or solid.

Section Summary

The volume of a gas can be altered significantly by changing the applied external force or the temperature. The corresponding volume changes for liquids and solids are much smaller. Gases flow more freely and have lower densities than liquids and solids, and they mix in any proportion to form solutions. The major reason for these differences in properties is the greater distance between particles in a sample of gas than in liquids and solids.

5.2 Gas Pressure and Its Measurement

When you blow up a balloon or inflate a flat tire, you have clear evidence that a gas exerts pressure on the walls of its container. **Pressure (P)** is defined as the force exerted per unit of surface area:

$$\text{Pressure} = \frac{\text{force}}{\text{area}}$$

The Earth's gravitational attraction pulls the atmospheric gases toward its surface, where they exert a force on all objects. The force, or weight, of these gases creates a pressure of about 14.7 pounds per square inch (lb/in^2; psi) of surface. ◆

As we'll discuss later, the molecules in a gas are moving in every direction, so the pressure of the atmosphere is exerted uniformly on the floor, walls, ceiling, and every object in a room. The pressure on the outside of your body is equalized by the pressure on the inside, so there is no net pressure on your body's outer surface. What would happen if this were not the case? As an analogy, consider the empty metal can attached to a vacuum pump in Figure 5.2. With the pump off, the can maintains its shape because the pressure on the outside is equal to the pressure on the inside. With the pump on, the internal pressure decreases greatly, and the ever-present external pressure easily crushes the can. The vacuum-filtration flasks (and their tubing) that you may have used in the lab have thick walls that can withstand the external pressure when the flask is evacuated.

Laboratory Devices for Measuring Gas Pressure

A **barometer** is a device used to measure atmospheric pressure. Invented in 1643 by Evangelista Torricelli, the barometer is still basically just a tube about

◆ **Snowshoes and the Meaning of Pressure**
Snowshoes allow you to walk on powdery snow without sinking because they distribute your weight over a much larger area than a boot does, thereby greatly decreasing your weight per square inch. The area of a snowshoe is typically about 10 times as large as that of a boot sole, so the snowshoe exerts only about one-tenth as much pressure as the boot. The wide, padded paws of snow leopards accomplish this, too. For the same reason, high-heeled shoes exert much more pressure than flat shoes.

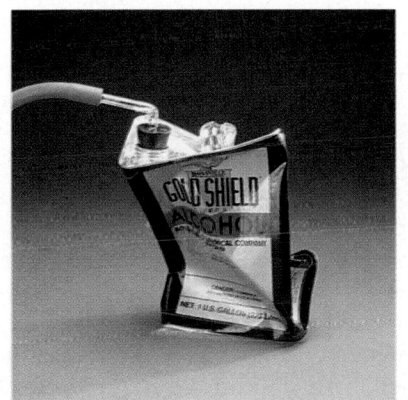

A   B

Figure 5.2 Effect of atmospheric pressure on objects at the Earth's surface.
A, A metal can filled with air has equal pressure on the inside and outside. **B,** When the air inside the can is removed, the atmospheric pressure crushes the can.

Vacuum

Δh = 760 mmHg

Pressure due to mercury column

Atmospheric pressure

P_{atm}

Dish filled with mercury

Figure 5.3 A mercury barometer.

Piston
Low P

Ground level

34 ft

P_{atm}

Underground water level

◆ **The Mystery of the Suction Pump** When you drink through a straw, you create lower pressure above the liquid, and the atmosphere pushes the liquid up. Similarly, a "suction" pump is a tube dipping into a water source, with a piston and handle that lower the air pressure above the water level. The pump can raise water from a well no deeper than 34 ft. This 34-ft limit was a mystery until the great 17th-century Italian scientist Galileo showed that the atmosphere pushes the water up into the tube and that its pressure can support only a 34-ft column of water. Modern pumps that draw water from deeper sources use compressed air to increase the pressure exerted on the water.

1 m long, closed at one end, filled with mercury, and inverted into a dish containing more mercury (Figure 5.3). When the tube is inverted, some mercury flows out, forming a vacuum above the mercury remaining in the tube. At sea level under ordinary atmospheric conditions, the outward flow of mercury stops when the surface of the mercury in the tube is about 760 mm above the surface of the mercury in the dish. It stops at 760 mm because at that point the column of mercury in the tube exerts the same pressure (weight/area) on the mercury surface in the dish as does the column of air that extends from the dish to the outer reaches of the atmosphere. The air pushing down keeps the mercury in the tube from flowing out any further. Likewise, if you place an evacuated tube into a dish filled with mercury, the mercury rises about 760 mm into the tube because the atmosphere pushes the mercury up to that height.

Several centuries ago, people ascribed mysterious "suction" forces to a vacuum. We know now that a vacuum does not suck up mercury into the barometer tube any more than it "sucks" in the walls of the crushed can in Figure 5.2. Only matter—in this case the atmospheric gases—can exert a force.

Notice that we did not specify the diameter of the barometer tube. If the mercury in a 1-cm diameter tube rises to a height of 760 mm, the mercury in a 2-cm diameter tube will rise to that height also. The *weight* of mercury is greater in the wider tube, but the area is larger also, so the *pressure*, the *ratio* of weight to area, is the same.

Since the pressure of the mercury column is directly proportional to its height, a unit commonly used for pressure is the height of the mercury (atomic symbol Hg) column in millimeters (mmHg). We discuss this and other units of pressure shortly. At sea level and 0°C, normal atmospheric pressure is 760 mmHg, but at the top of Mt. Everest (29,028 ft, or 8848 m), the atmospheric pressure is only about 270 mmHg. Thus, *pressure decreases with altitude:* the column of air above sea level is taller and weighs more than the column of air above Mt. Everest.

Laboratory barometers contain mercury rather than some other liquid because its high density allows the barometer to be a convenient size. For example, the pressure of the atmosphere would equal the pressure of a column of water about 10,300 mm, almost 34 ft, high. ◆ Note that, for a given pressure, the ratio of heights (h) of the liquid columns is inversely related to the ratio of the densities (d) of the liquids:

$$\frac{h_{H_2O}}{h_{Hg}} = \frac{d_{Hg}}{d_{H_2O}}$$

Manometers are devices used to measure the pressure of a gas in an experiment. Figure 5.4 shows two types of manometer. Part A shows a *closed-end manometer*, a mercury-filled, curved tube, *closed* at one end and attached to a flask at the other. When the flask is evacuated, the mercury levels in the two arms of the tube are the same because no gas exerts pressure on either mercury surface. When a gas is in the flask (part B), it pushes down the mercury level in the near arm, so the level rises in the far arm. The *difference* in column heights (Δh) equals the gas pressure. Note that if the flask is open to the atmosphere, Δh equals atmospheric pressure, and the closed-end manometer becomes a barometer.

The *open-end manometer*, shown in parts C–E, also consists of a curved tube filled with mercury, but one end of the tube is *open* to the atmosphere and the other is connected to the gas sample. The atmosphere pushes on one mercury level and the gas pushes on the other. Since Δh equals the difference between two pressures, we must measure the atmospheric pressure separately with a barometer to calculate the gas pressure.

A

B

C $P_{gas} = P_{atm}$

D $P_{gas} < P_{atm}$
   $P_{gas} = P_{atm} - \Delta h$

E $P_{gas} > P_{atm}$
   $P_{gas} = P_{atm} + \Delta h$

Figure 5.4 Two types of manometers. A, A closed-end manometer with an evacuated flask attached shows the mercury levels are equal. **B,** A gas exerts pressure on the mercury in the arm attached to the flask. The difference in heights (Δh) equals the gas pressure. **C–E,** An open-end manometer is shown with gas pressure equal to atmospheric pressure, **(C),** gas pressure lower than atmospheric pressure **(D),** and gas pressure higher than atmospheric pressure **(E).**

Units of Pressure

Pressure results from a force exerted on an area. The SI unit of force is the newton (N): $1\ N = 1\ kg \cdot m/s^2$. The SI unit of pressure is the **pascal (Pa),** which equals a force of one newton exerted on an area of one square meter:

$$1\ Pa = 1\ N/m^2$$

A much larger unit is the **standard atmosphere (atm),** the average atmospheric pressure measured at sea level and 0°C. It is defined in terms of the pascal:

$$1\ atm = 1.01325 \times 10^5\ Pa = 101.325\ kilopascals\ (kPa)$$

Another common pressure unit is the **millimeter of mercury (mmHg),** which is based on measurement with a barometer or manometer. In honor of Torricelli, this unit has been named the **torr:** $1\ mmHg = 1\ torr$. The torr is now defined in terms of the pascal:

$$1\ torr = \frac{1}{760}\ atm = \frac{101.325}{760}\ kPa$$

The *bar* is coming into more common use in chemistry:

$$1\ bar = 1 \times 10^2\ kPa = 1 \times 10^5\ Pa$$

Despite a gradual change to SI units, many chemists still express pressure in torr and atmospheres, so they are used in this text, with frequent reference to pascals. Table 5.2 lists the most important pressure units used in various scientific fields.

Table 5.2 Common Units of Pressure

Unit	Atmospheric Pressure	Scientific Field
pascal (Pa); kilopascal (kPa)	1.01325×10^5 Pa; 101.325 kPa	SI unit; physics, chemistry
atmosphere (atm)	1 atm[A]	Chemistry
millimeters of mercury (mmHg)	760 mmHg*	Chemistry, medicine, biology
torr	760 torr*	Chemistry
pounds per square inch (psi or lb/in²)	14.7 lb/in²	Engineering
bar	1.01325 bar	Meteorology, chemistry, physics

*This is an exact quantity; in calculations, we use as many significant figures as necessary.

Sample Problem 5.1 Converting Units of Pressure

PROBLEM A geochemist heats a limestone sample and collects the CO_2 released in an evacuated flask attached to a closed-end manometer (see Figure 5.4B). After the system comes to room temperature, $\Delta h = 291.4$ mmHg. Calculate the CO_2 pressure in torr, atmospheres, and kilopascals.

PLAN The CO_2 pressure is given in units of mmHg, so we construct conversion factors from Table 5.2 to find the pressure in the other units.

SOLUTION Converting from mmHg to torr:

$$P_{CO_2} \text{(torr)} = 291.4 \text{ mmHg} \times \frac{1 \text{ torr}}{1 \text{ mmHg}} = \boxed{291.4 \text{ torr}}$$

Converting from torr to atm:

$$P_{CO_2} \text{(atm)} = 291.4 \text{ torr} \times \frac{1 \text{ atm}}{760 \text{ torr}} = \boxed{0.3834 \text{ atm}}$$

Converting from atm to kPa:

$$P_{CO_2} \text{(kPa)} = 0.3834 \text{ atm} \times \frac{101.325 \text{ kPa}}{1 \text{ atm}} = \boxed{38.85 \text{ kPa}}$$

CHECK There are 760 torr in 1 atm, so 300 torr should be <0.5 atm. There are ~100 kPa in 1 atm, so <0.5 atm should be <50 kPa.

COMMENT 1. In the conversion from torr to atm, we retained four significant figures because this unit definition is an *exact* number; that is, 760 torr has as many significant figures as the calculation requires.
2. From here on, except in particularly complex situations, *the canceling of units in calculations is no longer shown.*

Follow-up Problem 5.1 The CO_2 released from another mineral sample was collected in an evacuated flask connected to an open-end manometer (see Figure 5.4D). If the barometer reading is 753.6 mmHg and Δh is 174.0 mmHg, calculate P_{CO_2} in torr, pascals, and lb/in^2.

Section Summary

Gases exert pressure (force/area) on all surfaces with which they make contact. A barometer measures atmospheric pressure by the height of the mercury column that the atmosphere can support (760 mmHg at sea level and 0°C). Both closed-end and open-end manometers are used to measure the pressure of a gas sample. Chemists measure pressure in units of atmospheres (atm), torr (equivalent to mmHg), or pascals (Pa, the SI unit).

5.3 The Gas Laws and Their Experimental Foundations

The physical behavior of a sample of gas can be described completely by four variables: pressure (P), volume (V), temperature (T), and amount (number of moles) of gas (n). The variables are interdependent: *any one of them can be determined by measuring the other three.* The gaseous state is unique among the states of matter in that the chemical nature of the gas does not significantly affect its physical behavior. We know now that this quantitatively predictable behavior is a direct outcome of the structure of gases on the molecular level. Yet, this predictable behavior was discovered by laboratory observations that were made, for the most part, even before Dalton's atomic theory was published!

Three key relationships exist among the four gas variables—Boyle's, Charles's, and Avogadro's laws. Each of these gas laws expresses the effect of one variable on another, with the remaining two variables held constant. Since the volume of a gas is so easy to measure, the laws are traditionally expressed as the effect on gas volume of changing the pressure, temperature, or amount of gas.

These three laws are special cases of an all-encompassing relationship among the variables called the *ideal gas law*. This unifying observation quantitatively describes the state of a so-called **ideal gas,** one that exhibits simple linear relationships among volume, pressure, temperature, and amount. Although no ideal gas actually exists, most simple gases, such as N_2, O_2, H_2, and the noble gases, show nearly ideal behavior at ordinary temperatures and pressures. We discuss the ideal gas law after the three special cases.

The Relationship Between Volume and Pressure: Boyle's Law

Following Torricelli's invention of the barometer, the great English chemist Robert Boyle performed a series of experiments that led him to conclude that at a given temperature, *the volume of a gas is inversely related to its pressure.* Figure 5.5 shows Boyle's experiment and some typical data he might have collected. Boyle fashioned a J-shaped glass tube, sealed the shorter end, and poured mercury into the longer end, thereby trapping some air. From the height of the trapped air column and the diameter of the tubing, he calculated the air volume. The total pressure applied to the trapped air was the pressure of the atmosphere (measured with a barometer) plus that of the mercury column (part A). By adding mercury, Boyle increased the total pressure exerted on the air, and the air volume decreased (part B). Since the temperature and amount of air were constant, Boyle could directly measure the relationship between the applied pressure and the volume of air.

Note the following results (Figure 5.5):
- The product of corresponding P and V values is a constant (part C, rightmost column)
- V is *inversely* proportional to P (part D)
- V is *directly* proportional to $1/P$ (part E) and generates a linear plot of V against $1/P$. This *linear relationship between two gas variables* is a hallmark of ideal gas behavior.

V (mL)	P (torr)			$\frac{1}{P_{total}}$	PV (torr • mL)
	Δh	+ P_{atm}	= P_{total}		
20.0	20.0	760	780	0.00128	1.56×10^4
15.0	278	760	1038	0.000963	1.56×10^4
10.0	800	760	1560	0.000641	1.56×10^4
5.0	2352	760	3112	0.000321	1.56×10^4

Figure 5.5 The relationship between the volume and pressure of a gas. A, A small amount of air is trapped in the short arm of a J tube; n and T are fixed. The total pressure on the gas (P_{total}) is the sum of the pressure due to the difference in heights of the mercury columns (Δh) and the pressure of the atmosphere (P_{atm}). If $P_{atm} = 760$ torr, $P_{total} = 780$ torr. **B,** As mercury is added, the total pressure on the gas (trapped air) increases and its volume (V) decreases. Note that if P_{total} is doubled (1560 torr), V is halved. (The mercury heights are not drawn to scale.) **C,** Some typical pressure-volume data from the experiment. **D,** A plot of V vs. P_{total} shows that V is inversely proportional to P. **E,** A plot of V vs. $1/P_{total}$ is a straight line whose slope is a constant characteristic of *any* gas that behaves ideally.

The generalization of Boyle's observations is known as **Boyle's law:** *at constant temperature, the volume of a fixed amount of gas is inversely proportional to the applied (external) pressure,* or

$$V \propto \frac{1}{P} \qquad [T \text{ and } n \text{ fixed}] \qquad \qquad \textbf{(5.1)}$$

This relationship can also be expressed as

$$PV = \text{constant} \qquad \text{or} \qquad V = \frac{\text{constant}}{P} \qquad [T \text{ and } n \text{ fixed}]$$

The constant is the same for the great majority of gases. Thus, tripling the external pressure reduces the volume to one-third its initial value; decreasing the external pressure by half doubles the volume; and so forth.

The wording of Boyle's law focuses on *external* pressure. In his experiment, however, adding more mercury causes the mercury level to rise until the pressure of the trapped air stops the rise at some new level. At that point the pressure exerted *on* the gas equals the pressure exerted *by* the gas. In other words, by measuring the applied pressure, Boyle was also measuring the gas pressure. Thus, when gas volume doubles, gas pressure is halved. In general, if V_{gas} increases, P_{gas} decreases, and vice versa.

The Relationship Between Volume and Temperature: Charles's Law

One question raised by Boyle's work was why the pressure-volume relationship holds only at constant temperature. Experience had shown that gas volume depends on temperature, but it was not until the early 19th century, through the separate work of the French scientists J. A. C. Charles and J. L. Gay-Lussac, that the relationship was clearly understood.

Let's examine this relationship by measuring the volume of a fixed amount of a gas under constant pressure but at different temperatures, as shown in Figure 5.6. A straight tube, closed at one end, traps a fixed amount of air under a small mercury plug. The tube is immersed in a water bath that can be warmed with a heater or cooled with ice. After each change of water temperature, we measure the length of the air column, which is proportional to its volume. The pressure exerted on the gas is constant because the mercury plug and the atmospheric pressure do not change.

Some typical data are shown in Figure 5.6C. Again, note the linear relationship, but this time the variables are *directly* proportional: for a given amount of gas at a given pressure, *volume increases as temperature increases.* The linear relationship means that the volume of a gas changes by a fixed increment for a given temperature change. For example, the line shows that the volume of 0.04 mol of gas at 1 atm pressure increases by 3.28 mL for each 1°C rise. Extrapolating the line to lower temperatures (dashed portion) shows that the volume shrinks until the gas occupies a theoretical zero volume at −273°C (the intercept of the temperature axis). Similar plots for different amounts of gas and different gas pressures show lines with different slopes, but they all converge at this temperature.

One-half century after Charles's and Gay-Lussac's work, William Thomson (Lord Kelvin) used this linear relation between gas volume and temperature to devise the absolute temperature scale (Section 1.5). In this scale, absolute zero (0 K or −273.15°C) is the temperature at which an ideal gas would have zero volume. (Absolute zero has never been reached, but physicists have attained temperatures as low as a small fraction of a kelvin.) Of course, no real sample of matter can have zero volume, and every real gas condenses to a liquid at some temperature higher than 0 K. Nevertheless, *this linear dependence of volume on absolute temperature holds for most common gases over a wide temperature range.*

A Ice water bath: 0°C (273 K)

B Boiling water bath: 100°C (373 K)

C

Figure 5.6 The relationship between the volume and temperature of a gas. A fixed amount of gas (air) is trapped under a small plug of mercury at a fixed pressure. The sample is in an ice water bath **(A)** and a boiling water bath **(B).** As the temperature increases, the volume of the gas increases, as shown in the linear plot **(C).** Note that a temperature increase of about one-third above its original value (from 273 to 373 K) causes an increase in the volume of the gas of about one-third. At constant P, the volume of a given amount of gas is *directly* proportional to the absolute temperature. The dashed line extrapolates the data to lower temperatures. For any amount of an ideal gas at any pressure, the volume is theoretically zero at $-273.15°C$ (0 K).

The modern statement of the volume-temperature relationship is known as **Charles's law:** *at constant pressure, the volume of a fixed amount of gas is directly proportional to its absolute temperature,* or

$$V \propto T \qquad [P \text{ and } n \text{ fixed}] \tag{5.2}$$

This relationship can also be expressed as

$$\frac{V}{T} = \text{constant} \qquad \text{or} \qquad V = \text{constant} \times T \qquad [P \text{ and } n \text{ fixed}]$$

If T increases, V increases, and vice versa. For any given P and n, the constant is the same regardless of the gas.

The dependence of gas volume on *absolute* temperature means that you must *use the Kelvin scale in gas law calculations.* For instance, if the temperature changes from 200 K to 400 K, the volume of 1 mol of gas doubles. But, if the temperature changes from 200°C to 400°C, the volume increases by a factor of 1.42; that is, $\left(\dfrac{400°C + 273.15}{200°C + 273.15}\right) = \dfrac{673}{473} = 1.42.$

Two other important relationships emerge from an understanding of Boyle's and Charles's laws:

1. *The pressure-temperature relationship.* Charles's law is expressed as the effect of a change on gas *volume.* However, volume and pressure are interdependent, so the effect of temperature on volume is closely related to its effect on pressure (sometimes referred to as *Amontons's law*). Measure the pressure in your automobile tires before and after a long drive, and you will find that it has risen. Frictional heating between the tire and the road increases the air temperature inside the tire; since the tire volume doesn't change appreciably, the air exerts more pressure. Thus, *at constant volume, the*

Cylinder A   Cylinder B

Figure 5.7 **An experiment to study the relationship between the volume and amount of a gas.** At a given external P and T, twice the mass of $CO_2(s)$ is put in tube B as in tube A. After the solid has changed to gas, the volume of cylinder B is twice that of cylinder A. Thus, at fixed P and T, the volume (V) of a gas is directly proportional to the amount of gas (n).

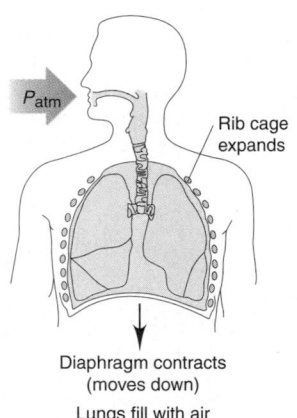

P_{atm}

Rib cage expands

Diaphragm contracts
(moves down)
Lungs fill with air

Breathing and the Gas Laws Taking a deep breath is a combined application of the gas laws. When you inhale, muscles are coordinated such that your diaphragm moves down and your rib cage moves out. This movement increases the volume of the lungs, which decreases the pressure of the air inside them relative to outside, so air rushes in (Boyle's). The greater amount of air stretches the elastic tissue of the lungs and expands the volume further (Avogadro's). The air also expands slightly as it warms to body temperature (Charles's). When you exhale, the diaphragm relaxes and moves up, the rib cage moves in, and the lung volume decreases. The inside air pressure becomes greater than the outside pressure, and air rushes out.

pressure exerted by a fixed amount of gas is directly proportional to the absolute temperature:

$$P \propto T \qquad [V \text{ and } n \text{ fixed}] \qquad \textbf{(5.3)}$$

or

$$\frac{P}{T} = \text{constant} \qquad \text{or} \qquad P = \text{constant} \times T$$

2. *The combined gas law.* A simple combination of Boyle's and Charles's laws gives the *combined gas law,* which applies to situations when two of the three variables (V, P, T) change and you must find the effect on the third:

$$V \propto \frac{T}{P} \qquad \text{or} \qquad V = \text{constant} \times \frac{T}{P} \qquad \text{or} \qquad \frac{PV}{T} = \text{constant}$$

The Relationship Between Volume and Amount: Avogadro's Law

Boyle's and Charles's laws both specify a fixed amount of gas. Let's see why. Figure 5.7 shows an experiment involving two small test tubes each fitted with a piston-cylinder assembly. We add 0.10 mol (4.4 g) of dry ice (frozen CO_2) to tube A and 0.20 mol (8.8 g) to tube B. As the solid warms, it changes directly to gaseous CO_2, which expands into the cylinder and pushes up the piston. When all the solid has changed to gas and the temperature is constant, we find that cylinder B has twice the volume of cylinder A. (We can neglect the volume of the tube because it is so much smaller than the volume of the cylinder.)

This result shows that twice the amount (mol) of gas occupies twice the volume. Note that for both cylinders, T of the gas equals room temperature and P of the gas equals atmospheric pressure. Thus, *at fixed temperature and pressure, the volume of gas is directly proportional to the amount (mol) of gas:*

$$V \propto n \qquad [P \text{ and } T \text{ fixed}] \qquad \textbf{(5.4)}$$

As n increases, V increases, and vice versa. This relationship can also be expressed as

$$\frac{V}{n} = \text{constant} \qquad \text{or} \qquad V = \text{constant} \times n$$

The constant is the same for all gases at a given temperature and pressure. This relationship is another way of expressing **Avogadro's law,** which states that *at fixed temperature and pressure, equal volumes of **any** ideal gas contain equal numbers of particles (or moles).* (Recall from Chapter 2 that Avogadro proposed this idea to explain Gay-Lussac's data for the combining volumes of gases.)

Many familiar phenomena are based on the relationships between volume, temperature, and amount of gas. For example, in a car engine, a reaction occurs in which fewer moles of gasoline and O_2 form more moles of CO_2 and H_2O vapor, which expand due to the released heat and push back the piston. Dynamite explodes because a solid decomposes rapidly to form hot gases. Dough rises in a warm room because yeast forms CO_2 bubbles in the dough, which expand during baking to give the bread a still larger volume. ◆

Gas Behavior at Standard Conditions

To better understand the factors that influence gas behavior, chemists have chosen a set of *standard conditions* called **standard temperature and pressure (STP):**

$$\text{STP:} \qquad 0°C \ (273.15 \text{ K}) \text{ and } 1 \text{ atm } (760 \text{ torr}) \qquad \textbf{(5.5)}$$

Under these conditions, the volume of 1 mol of an ideal gas is called the **standard molar volume:**

Standard molar volume = 22.414 L,   or 22.4 L (to 3 significant figures) **(5.6)**

$n = 1$ mol	$n = 1$ mol	$n = 1$ mol
$P = 1$ atm (760 torr)	$P = 1$ atm (760 torr)	$P = 1$ atm (760 torr)
$T = 0°C$ (273 K)	$T = 0°C$ (273 K)	$T = 0°C$ (273 K)
$V = 22.4$ L	$V = 22.4$ L	$V = 22.4$ L
Number of gas particles $= 6.022 \times 10^{23}$	Number of gas particles $= 6.022 \times 10^{23}$	Number of gas particles $= 6.022 \times 10^{23}$
Mass = 4.003 g	Mass = 28.02 g	Mass = 32.00 g
$d = 0.179$ g/L	$d = 1.25$ g/L	$d = 1.43$ g/L

Figure 5.8 Standard molar volume. One mole of an ideal gas occupies 22.4 L at standard temperature and pressure (STP; 0°C and 1 atm). Under these conditions, helium, nitrogen, oxygen, and most other simple gases behave ideally. Note that the *mass* of the gas sample, and thus its density (*d*), depend on the molar mass of the substance.

Figure 5.8 compares the properties of three simple gases at STP. Figure 5.9 compares the volumes of some familiar objects with the standard molar volume of an ideal gas.

The Ideal Gas Law

Each of the gas laws focuses on the effect of changes in one variable on gas volume:

- Boyle's law focuses on pressure ($V \propto 1/P$).
- Charles's law focuses on temperature ($V \propto T$).
- Avogadro's law focuses on amount (mol) of gas ($V \propto n$).

We can combine these individual effects into one relationship, called the **ideal gas law** (or *ideal gas equation*):

$$V \propto \frac{nT}{P} \qquad \text{or} \qquad PV \propto nT \qquad \text{or} \qquad \frac{PV}{nT} = R$$

where R is a proportionality constant known as the **universal gas constant.** Rearranging this mathematical statement gives the most common form of the ideal gas law:

$$PV = nRT \qquad (5.7)$$

We can obtain a value of R by measuring the volume, temperature, and pressure of a given amount of gas and substituting the values into the ideal gas law. For example, using standard conditions for the gas variables, we have

$$R = \frac{PV}{nT} = \frac{1 \text{ atm} \times 22.4 \text{ L}}{1 \text{ mol} \times 273.15 \text{ K}} = 0.0821 \frac{\text{atm} \cdot \text{L}}{\text{mol} \cdot \text{K}} \qquad \text{[3 significant figures]}$$

This numerical value of R corresponds to the gas variables P, V, and T expressed *in these units*. As Table 5.3 on the next page shows, R has a different numerical value when different units are used.

Figure 5.9 The volume of 1 mol of an ideal gas compared with some familiar objects. A basketball (7.5 L), 5-gal fish tank (18.9 L), 13-in television (21.6 L), and 1 mol He gas (22.4 L) in a balloon.

Figure 5.10 Relationship between the ideal gas law and the individual gas laws. Boyle's, Charles's, and Avogadro's laws are contained within the ideal gas law.

Figure 5.10 makes a central point: the ideal gas law *becomes* one of the individual gas laws when two of the four variables are kept constant. For situations when initial conditions, denoted by subscript $_1$, change to final conditions, denoted by subscript $_2$, we have

$$P_1V_1 = n_1RT_1 \quad \text{and} \quad P_2V_2 = n_2RT_2$$

Thus, $\quad \dfrac{P_1V_1}{n_1T_1} = R \quad \text{and} \quad \dfrac{P_2V_2}{n_2T_2} = R, \quad \text{so} \quad \dfrac{P_1V_1}{n_1T_1} = \dfrac{P_2V_2}{n_2T_2}$

Notice that if two of the variables remain constant, say P and T, then $P_1 = P_2$ and $T_1 = T_2$, and we obtain an expression for Avogadro's law:

$$\dfrac{\cancel{P_1}V_1}{n_1\cancel{T_1}} = \dfrac{\cancel{P_2}V_2}{n_2\cancel{T_2}} \qquad \text{or} \qquad \dfrac{V_1}{n_1} = \dfrac{V_2}{n_2}$$

We use rearrangements of the ideal gas law such as this one to solve gas law problems, as you'll see next. The point to remember is there is no need to memorize the individual gas laws.

Solving Gas Law Problems

Gas law problems are phrased in many ways, but they can usually be grouped into two main types:

1. *A change in one of the four variables causes a change in another, while the two remaining variables are held constant.* In this type, the ideal gas law reduces to one of the individual gas laws, and you solve for the new value of the variable. Units must be consistent, T must always be in kelvins, but R is not involved. Sample Problems 5.2 to 5.4 are of this type. [A variation on this type involves the combined gas law (p. 186) for simultaneous changes in two of the variables that cause a change in a third.]

2. *One variable is unknown, the other three are known, but no change occurs.* In this type, which is exemplified by Sample Problem 5.5, the ideal gas law is applied directly to find the unknown, and the units must conform to those in R.

These problems are far easier to solve if you follow a systematic approach:
- Summarize the information: identify the changing gas variables—knowns and unknown—and those held constant.
- Predict the direction of the change, and later check your answer against the prediction.
- Perform any necessary unit conversions.
- Rearrange the ideal gas law to obtain the appropriate relationship of gas variables and solve for the unknown variable.

The following series of sample problems applies each of the gas behaviors discussed above.

Table 5.3 Values of R (Universal Gas Constant) in Different Units

$R^* = 0.08206 \ \dfrac{\text{atm} \cdot \text{L}}{\text{mol} \cdot \text{K}}$

$R = 62.36 \ \dfrac{\text{torr} \cdot \text{L}}{\text{mol} \cdot \text{K}}$

$R = 8.314 \ \dfrac{\text{kPa} \cdot \text{dm}^3}{\text{mol} \cdot \text{K}}$

$R = 8.314 \ \dfrac{\text{J}^\dagger}{\text{mol} \cdot \text{K}}$

*Most calculations in this text use values of R to 3 significant figures.
†J is the abbreviation for joule, the SI unit of energy. The joule is a derived unit composed of the base units $\text{kg} \cdot \text{m}^2/\text{s}^2$.

Sample Problem 5.2 Applying the Volume-Pressure Relationship

PROBLEM An apprentice of Boyle finds that the air trapped in a J tube occupies 24.8 cm³ at 1.12 atm. By adding mercury to the tube, he increases the pressure on the trapped air to 2.64 atm. Assuming constant temperature, what is the new volume of air (in L)?

PLAN We must find the final volume (V_2) in liters, given the initial volume (V_1), initial pressure (P_1), and final pressure (P_2). The temperature and amount of gas are fixed. We convert the units of V_1 from cm³ to mL and then to L, rearrange the ideal gas law to the appropriate form, and solve for V_2. We can predict the direction of the change: since P increases, V will decrease; thus, $V_2 < V_1$. (Note the two-part roadmap.)

SOLUTION Summarizing the gas variables:

$P_1 = 1.12$ atm $\qquad\qquad P_2 = 2.64$ atm
$V_1 = 24.8$ cm³ (convert to L) $\qquad V_2 = $ unknown $\qquad$ *T* and *n* remain constant

Converting V_1 from cm³ to L:

$$V_1 = 24.8 \text{ cm}^3 \times \frac{1 \text{ mL}}{1 \text{ cm}^3} \times \frac{1 \text{ L}}{1000 \text{ mL}} = 0.0248 \text{ L}$$

Arranging the ideal gas law and solving for V_2: At fixed *n* and *T*, we have

$$\frac{P_1 V_1}{n_1 T_1} = \frac{P_2 V_2}{n_2 T_2} \qquad \text{or} \qquad P_1 V_1 = P_2 V_2$$

$$V_2 = V_1 \times \frac{P_1}{P_2} = 0.0248 \text{ L} \times \frac{1.12 \text{ atm}}{2.64 \text{ atm}} = \boxed{0.0105 \text{ L}}$$

CHECK As we predicted, $V_2 < V_1$. The pressure more than doubled, so V_2 should be less than $\frac{1}{2} V_1$ ($0.0105/0.0248 < \frac{1}{2}$).

COMMENT Predicting the direction of the change provides another check on the problem setup: To make $V_2 < V_1$, we must multiply V_1 by a number *less than* 1. This means the ratio of pressures must be *less than* 1, so the larger pressure (P_2) must be in the denominator, P_1/P_2.

Follow-up Problem 5.2 A sample of argon gas occupies 105 mL at 0.871 atm. If the temperature remains constant, what is the volume (in L) at 26.3 kPa?

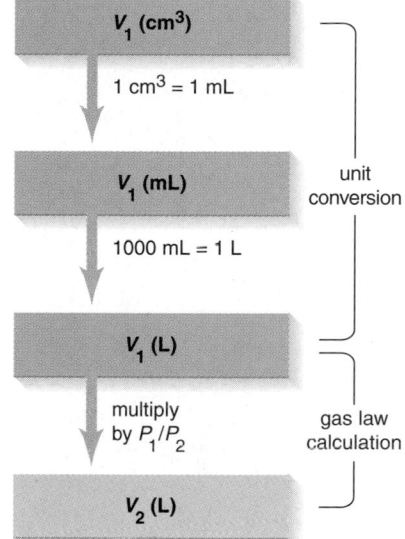

Sample Problem 5.3 Applying the Pressure-Temperature Relationship

PROBLEM A 1-L steel tank is fitted with a safety valve that opens if the internal pressure exceeds 1.00×10^3 torr. It is filled with helium at 23°C and 0.991 atm and placed in boiling water at exactly 100°C. Will the safety valve open?

PLAN The question "Will the safety valve open?" translates to "Is P_2 greater than 1.00×10^3 torr at T_2?" Thus, P_2 is the unknown and T_1, T_2, and P_1 are given, with *V* (steel container) and *n* fixed. Both *T* values must be converted to kelvins and P_1 must be converted to torr to compare it with the safety-limit pressure. We rearrange the ideal gas law to the appropriate form and solve for P_2. Since $T_2 > T_1$, we predict that $P_2 > P_1$.

SOLUTION Summary of gas variables:

$P_1 = 0.991$ atm (convert to torr) $\qquad P_2 = $ unknown
$T_1 = 23°C$ (convert to K) $\qquad\qquad T_2 = 100°C$ (convert to K)
V and *n* remain constant

Converting *T* from °C to K:

$$T_1 \text{ (K)} = 23°C + 273.15 = 296 \text{ K}$$

$$T_2 \text{ (K)} = 100°C + 273.15 = 373 \text{ K}$$

Converting *P* from atm to torr:

$$P_1 \text{ (torr)} = 0.991 \text{ atm} \times \frac{760 \text{ torr}}{1 \text{ atm}} = 753 \text{ torr}$$

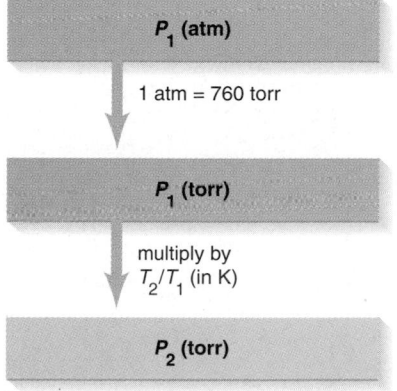

Arranging the ideal gas law and solving for P_2: At fixed n and V, we have

$$\frac{P_1 V_{\mathrm{T}}}{n_{\mathrm{T}} T_1} = \frac{P_2 V_2}{n_2 T_2} \qquad \text{or} \qquad \frac{P_1}{T_1} = \frac{P_2}{T_2}$$

$$P_2 = P_1 \times \frac{T_2}{T_1} = 753 \text{ torr} \times \frac{373 \text{ K}}{296 \text{ K}} = 949 \text{ torr}$$

P_2 is less than 1.00×10^3 torr, so the valve will *not* open.

CHECK Our prediction is correct: since $T_2 > T_1$, then $P_2 > P_1$. Thus, the temperature ratio should be >1 (T_2 in the numerator). The T ratio is about 1.25 (373/296), so the P ratio should also be about 1.25 (950/750 ≈ 1.25).

Follow-up Problem 5.3 An engineer pumps air at 0°C into a newly designed piston-cylinder assembly. The volume measures 6.83 cm³. At what temperature (in K) would the volume be 9.75 cm³?

Sample Problem 5.4 Applying the Volume-Amount Relationship

PROBLEM Blimps are being considered for use as freight carriers. A scale model rises when filled with helium to a volume of 55.0 dm³. When 1.10 mol He is added to the blimp, the volume is 26.2 dm³. How many more grams of He must be added to make it rise? Assume constant T and P.

PLAN We are given the initial amount of helium (n_1), the initial volume of the blimp (V_1), and the volume needed for it to rise (V_2), so we first need to find n_2. We rearrange the ideal gas law to the appropriate form, solve for n_2, subtract n_1 to find the additional amount ($n_{\mathrm{add'l}}$), and convert moles to grams. We predict that $n_2 > n_1$ because $V_2 > V_1$.

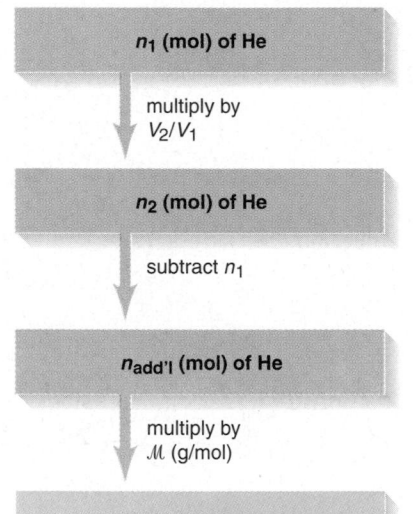

SOLUTION Summary of gas variables:

$$n_1 = 1.10 \text{ mol} \qquad n_2 = \text{unknown (then subtract } n_1\text{)}$$

$$V_1 = 26.2 \text{ dm}^3 \qquad V_2 = 55.0 \text{ dm}^3 \qquad P \text{ and } T \text{ remain constant}$$

Arranging the ideal gas law and solving for n_2: At fixed P and T, we have

$$\frac{P_{\mathrm{T}} V_1}{n_1 T_{\mathrm{T}}} = \frac{P_2 V_2}{n_2 T_2} \qquad \text{or} \qquad \frac{V_1}{n_1} = \frac{V_2}{n_2}$$

$$n_2 = n_1 \times \frac{V_2}{V_1} = 1.10 \text{ mol He} \times \frac{55.0 \text{ dm}^3}{26.2 \text{ dm}^3} = 2.31 \text{ mol He}$$

Finding the additional amount of He:

$$n_{\mathrm{add'l}} = n_2 - n_1 = 2.31 \text{ mol He} - 1.10 \text{ mol He} = 1.21 \text{ mol He}$$

Converting moles of He to grams:

$$\text{Mass (g) of He} = 1.21 \text{ mol He} \times \frac{4.003 \text{ g He}}{1 \text{ mol He}}$$

$$= 4.84 \text{ g He}$$

CHECK Since V_2 is about twice V_1 (55/26 ≈ 2), n_2 should be about twice n_1 (2.3/1.1 ≈ 2). Since $n_2 > n_1$, it made sense to multiply n_1 by a number >1 (that is, V_2/V_1). About 1.2 mol × 4 g/mol ≈ 4.8 g.

COMMENT 1. A different sequence of steps that obtains the same answer is to first find the additional volume ($V_{\mathrm{add'l}} = V_2 - V_1$) and then solve directly for $n_{\mathrm{add'l}}$. Try it for yourself.
2. You saw that Charles's law ($V \propto T$ at fixed P and n) translates into a similar relationship between P and T at fixed V and n. The follow-up problem shows that Avogadro's law ($V \propto n$ at fixed P and T) translates into an analogous relationship at fixed V and T.

Follow-up Problem 5.4 A rigid plastic container holds 35.0 g ethylene gas (C_2H_4) at a pressure of 793 torr. What is the pressure if 5.0 g ethylene is removed at constant temperature?

Sample Problem 5.5 Solving for an Unknown Gas Variable at Fixed Conditions

PROBLEM A steel tank has a volume of 438 L and is filled with 0.885 kg of O_2. Calculate the pressure of O_2 at 21°C.

PLAN We are given data for V, T, and n, and conditions are not changing, so we convert T to kelvins and mass of O_2 to moles, and apply the ideal gas law directly to solve for P.

SOLUTION Summary of gas variables:

$$V = 438 \text{ L} \qquad\qquad T = 21°C \text{ (convert to K)}$$
$$n = 0.885 \text{ kg } O_2 \text{ (convert to moles)} \qquad P = \text{unknown}$$

Converting T from °C to K:

$$T \text{ (K)} = 21°C + 273.15 = 294 \text{ K}$$

Converting from mass of O_2 to moles:

$$n = \text{moles of } O_2 = 0.885 \text{ kg } O_2 \times \frac{1000 \text{ g}}{1 \text{ kg}} \times \frac{1 \text{ mol } O_2}{32.00 \text{ g } O_2} = 27.7 \text{ mol } O_2$$

Solving for P (note the unit canceling here):

$$P = \frac{nRT}{V} = \frac{27.7 \text{ mol} \times 0.0821 \dfrac{\text{atm} \cdot \text{L}}{\text{mol} \cdot \text{K}} \times 294 \text{ K}}{438 \text{ L}} = \boxed{1.53 \text{ atm}}$$

CHECK The amount of O_2 seems correct: $\sim$900 g/(30 g/mol) = 30 mol. To check the approximate size of the final calculation, round off the values:

$$P = \frac{30 \text{ mol } O_2 \times 0.1 \text{ (rounded value of } R) \times 300 \text{ K}}{450 \text{ L}} = 2 \text{ atm}$$

which is reasonably close to 1.53 atm.

Follow-up Problem 5.5 The tank in the sample problem develops a slow leak that is discovered and sealed. The new measured pressure is 1.37 atm. How many grams of O_2 remain?

Section Summary

Four variables define the physical behavior of an ideal gas: volume (V), pressure (P), temperature (T), and amount (number of moles, n). Most simple gases display nearly ideal behavior at ordinary temperature and pressure. Boyle's, Charles's, and Avogadro's laws relate volume to pressure, temperature, and amount of gas, respectively. At STP (0°C and 1 atm), 1 mol of an ideal gas occupies 22.4 L. The ideal gas law incorporates the individual gas laws into one equation: $PV = nRT$, where R is the universal gas constant.

5.4 Further Applications of the Ideal Gas Law

The ideal gas law can be recast in additional ways to determine other properties of gases. In this section, we use it to find gas density, molar mass, and the partial pressure of each gas in a mixture.

The Density of a Gas

Since one mole of any gas occupies nearly the same volume at a given temperature and pressure, differences in gas density ($d = m/V$) depend on differences in molar mass (see Figure 5.8). For example, at STP, 1 mol O_2 occupies the same volume as 1 mol N_2, but since each O_2 molecule has a greater mass than each N_2 molecule, O_2 is denser.

All gases are miscible when thoroughly mixed, but in the absence of mixing, a less dense gas will lie above a more dense one. ◆ There are many

◆ **Gas Density and Human Disasters** Many gases that are denser than air have been involved in intentional or accidental disasters. The dense gases in smog that blanket urban centers, such as Los Angeles (see photo), contribute greatly to respiratory illness. On a far more horrific scale, in World War I, phosgene ($COCl_2$) was used against ground troops as they lay in trenches. More recently, the unintentional release of methylisocyanate from a Union Carbide India Ltd. chemical plant in Bhopal, India, killed thousands of people as vapors spread from the outskirts into the city. In 1986 in Cameroon, CO_2 released naturally from Lake Nyos suffocated thousands as it flowed down valleys into villages.

◆ **Up, Up, and Away!** When the gas in a hot-air balloon is heated, its volume increases and the balloon inflates. Further heating causes some of the gas to escape. By these means, the gas density decreases and the balloon rises. Two pioneering hot-air balloonists used their knowledge of gas behavior to pursue their hobby. Jacques Charles (of Charles's law) made one of the first balloon flights in 1783. Twenty years later, Joseph Gay-Lussac (who studied the pressure-temperature relationship) set a solo altitude record that lasted for 50 years.

familiar examples of this phenomenon. Some types of fire extinguishers release CO_2 because it is denser than air and sinks onto the fire, preventing more O_2 from reaching the burning material. Enormous air masses of different densities and temperatures moving past each other around the globe give rise to much of our weather.

We can rearrange the ideal gas law to calculate the density of a gas from its molar mass. Recall that the number of moles (n) is the mass (m) divided by the molar mass ($\mathcal{M}$), $n = m/\mathcal{M}$. Substituting for n in the ideal gas law gives

$$PV = \frac{m}{\mathcal{M}}RT$$

Rearranging to isolate m/V gives

$$\frac{m}{V} = d = \frac{\mathcal{M} \times P}{RT} \tag{5.8}$$

Two important ideas are expressed by Equation 5.8:
- *The density of a gas is directly proportional to its molar mass* because a given amount of a heavier gas occupies the same volume as that amount of a lighter gas (Avogadro's law).
- *The density of a gas is inversely proportional to the temperature.* As the volume of a gas increases with temperature (Charles's law), the same mass occupies more space, so the density is lower. ◆

Architectural designers and heating engineers apply the second idea when they place heating ducts near the floor of a room: the less dense warm air from the ducts rises and heats the room air. Safety experts recommend staying near the floor when escaping from a fire to avoid the hot, and therefore less dense, noxious gases. We use Equation 5.8 to find the density of a gas at any temperature and pressure near standard conditions.

Sample Problem 5.6   Calculating Gas Density

PROBLEM Calculate the density (in g/L) of carbon dioxide and the number of molecules per liter **(a)** at STP (0°C and 1 atm) and **(b)** at ordinary room conditions (20.°C and 1.00 atm).

PLAN We must find the density (d) and number of molecules at two sets of P and T. We convert T to kelvins, find $\mathcal{M}$ from the formula, and calculate d with Equation 5.8. Then we convert the mass per liter to molecules per liter with Avogadro's number.

SOLUTION **(a)** Density and molecules per liter of CO_2 at STP. Summary of gas properties:

$$T = 0°C + 273.15 = 273 \text{ K} \qquad P = 1 \text{ atm} \qquad \mathcal{M} \text{ of } CO_2 = 44.01 \text{ g/mol}$$

Calculating density (note the unit canceling here):

$$d = \frac{\mathcal{M} \times P}{RT} = \frac{44.01 \text{ g/mol} \times 1.00 \text{ atm}}{0.0821 \dfrac{\text{atm} \cdot \text{L}}{\text{mol} \cdot \text{K}} \times 273 \text{ K}} = \boxed{1.96 \text{ g/L}}$$

Converting from mass/L to molecules/L:

$$\text{Molecules } CO_2/\text{L} = \frac{1.96 \text{ g } CO_2}{1 \text{ L}} \times \frac{1 \text{ mol } CO_2}{44.01 \text{ g } CO_2} \times \frac{6.022 \times 10^{23} \text{ molecules } CO_2}{1 \text{ mol } CO_2}$$

$$= \boxed{2.68 \times 10^{22} \text{ molecules } CO_2/\text{L}}$$

(b) Density and molecules of CO_2 per liter at room conditions. Summary of gas properties:

$$T = 20.°C + 273.15 = 293 \text{ K} \qquad P = 1.00 \text{ atm} \qquad \mathcal{M} \text{ of } CO_2 = 44.01 \text{ g/mol}$$

Calculating density:

$$d = \frac{\mathcal{M} \times P}{RT} = \frac{44.01 \text{ g/mol} \times 1.00 \text{ atm}}{0.0821 \dfrac{\text{atm} \cdot \text{L}}{\text{mol} \cdot \text{K}} \times 293 \text{ K}} = \boxed{1.83 \text{ g/L}}$$

Converting from mass/L to molecules/L:

$$\text{Molecules CO}_2/\text{L} = \frac{1.83 \text{ g CO}_2}{1 \text{ L}} \times \frac{1 \text{ mol CO}_2}{44.01 \text{ g CO}_2} \times \frac{6.022 \times 10^{23} \text{ molecules CO}_2}{1 \text{ mol CO}_2}$$

$$= 2.50 \times 10^{22} \text{ molecules CO}_2/\text{L}$$

CHECK Round off to check the density values; for example, in **(a)**, at STP:

$$\frac{50 \text{ g/mol} \times 1 \text{ atm}}{0.1 \dfrac{\text{atm} \cdot \text{L}}{\text{mol} \cdot \text{K}} \times 250 \text{ K}} = 2 \text{ g/L} \approx 1.96 \text{ g/L}$$

At the higher temperature in **(b)**, the density should decrease, which can happen only if there are fewer molecules per liter, so the answer is reasonable.

COMMENT 1. An *alternative approach* for finding the density *at STP only* is to divide $\mathcal{M}$ by the standard molar volume, 22.4 L:

$$d = \frac{\mathcal{M}}{V} = \frac{44.01 \text{ g/mol}}{22.4 \text{ L/mol}} = 1.96 \text{ g/L}$$

Then, since you know the density at one temperature (0°C), you can find it at any other temperature from $d_1/d_2 = T_2/T_1$.

2. Note that we have different numbers of significant figures for the pressure values. In (a), "1 atm" is part of the definition of STP, so it is an exact number. In (b), we specified "1.00 atm" to allow 3 significant figures in the answer.

Follow-up Problem 5.6 Compare the density of CO_2 at 0°C and 380 torr with its density at STP.

The Molar Mass of a Gas

Through another simple rearrangement of the ideal gas law, we can determine the molar mass of an unknown gas or volatile liquid (one that is easily vaporized):

$$n = \frac{m}{\mathcal{M}} = \frac{PV}{RT} \qquad \text{so} \qquad \mathcal{M} = \frac{mRT}{PV} \qquad \text{or} \qquad \mathcal{M} = \frac{dRT}{P} \qquad \textbf{(5.9)}$$

This equation is just a rearrangement of Equation 5.8.

The French chemist J. B. A. Dumas (1800–1884) pioneered an ingenious method for finding the molar mass of a volatile liquid. Figure 5.11 shows the apparatus. Place a small volume of the liquid in a preweighed flask of known volume. Close the flask with a stopper that contains a narrow tube and immerse it in a water bath whose fixed temperature exceeds the liquid's boiling point. As the liquid vaporizes, the gas fills the flask and flows out the tube. When the liquid is gone, the pressure of the gas filling the flask equals the atmospheric pressure. Remove the flask from the water bath and cool it, and the gas condenses to a liquid. Reweigh the flask to obtain the mass of the liquid, *which equals the mass of gas* that remained in the flask.

Notice that by this procedure you have directly measured all the variables needed to calculate the molar mass of the gas: the mass of gas (m) occupies the flask volume (V) at a pressure (P) equal to the barometric pressure and at the temperature (T) of the water bath.

Figure 5.11 Determining the molar mass of an unknown volatile liquid. A small amount of unknown liquid is vaporized, and the gas fills the flask of known volume at the known temperature of the bath. Excess gas escapes through the capillary tube until $P_{gas} = P_{atm}$. When the flask is cooled, the gas condenses, the liquid is weighed, and the ideal gas law is used to calculate $\mathcal{M}$ (see text).

Sample Problem 5.7   Finding the Molar Mass of a Volatile Liquid

PROBLEM An organic chemist isolates a colorless liquid with the properties of cyclohexane (C_6H_{12}) from a petroleum sample. She uses the Dumas method and obtains the following data to determine its molar mass:

$$\text{Volume } (V) \text{ of flask} = 213 \text{ mL} \qquad T = 100.0°C \qquad P = 754 \text{ torr}$$
$$\text{Mass of flask} + \text{gas} = 78.416 \text{ g} \qquad \text{Mass of flask} = 77.834 \text{ g}$$

Is the molar mass consistent with the liquid being cyclohexane?

PLAN We convert V to liters, T to kelvins, and P to atmospheres, find the mass of gas by subtracting the mass of the empty flask, and use Equation 5.9 to solve for $\mathcal{M}$. Then we compare it with $\mathcal{M}$ obtained from the formula.

SOLUTION Summary of gas variables:

$$m = 78.416 \text{ g} - 77.834 \text{ g} = 0.582 \text{ g} \qquad P \text{ (atm)} = 754 \text{ torr} \times \frac{1 \text{ atm}}{760 \text{ torr}} = 0.992 \text{ atm}$$

$$V \text{ (L)} = 213 \text{ mL} \times \frac{1 \text{ L}}{1000 \text{ mL}} = 0.213 \text{ L} \qquad T \text{ (K)} = 100.0°C + 273.15 = 373.2 \text{ K}$$

Solving for $\mathcal{M}$:

$$\mathcal{M} = \frac{mRT}{PV} = \frac{0.582 \text{ g} \times 0.0821 \, \frac{\text{atm} \cdot \text{L}}{\text{mol} \cdot \text{K}} \times 373.2 \text{ K}}{0.992 \text{ atm} \times 0.213 \text{ L}} = 84.4 \text{ g/mol}$$

Finding $\mathcal{M}$ from the formula:

$$\mathcal{M} \text{ of } C_6H_{12} = (6 \times 12.01 \text{ g/mol}) + (12 \times 1.008 \text{ g/mol}) = 84.16 \text{ g/mol}$$

Within experimental error, the molar mass *is* consistent with the liquid being cyclohexane.

CHECK Rounding to check the arithmetic, we have

$$\frac{0.6 \text{ g} \times 0.08 \, \frac{\text{atm} \cdot \text{L}}{\text{mol} \cdot \text{K}} \times 375 \text{ K}}{1 \text{ atm} \times 0.2 \text{ L}} = 90 \text{ g/mol}$$

which is close to 84.4.

Follow-up Problem 5.7 At 10.0°C and 102.5 kPa, the density of dry air is 1.26 g/L. What is the average "molar mass" of dry air at these conditions?

The Partial Pressure of a Gas in a Mixture of Gases

Notice that all the behaviors we've discussed so far were observed from experiments with air, a complex mixture of gases. The ideal gas law holds for virtually any gas, pure or mixture, at ordinary conditions for two reasons:

- Gases mix homogeneously (form a solution) in any proportions.
- Each gas in a mixture behaves as if it were the only gas present (assuming no chemical interactions).

Dalton's Law of Partial Pressures The second point above was discovered by John Dalton in his studies of humidity. He observed that when water vapor is added to dry air, the total air pressure increases by an increment equal to the pressure of the water vapor:

$$P_{\text{humid air}} = P_{\text{dry air}} + P_{\text{added water vapor}}$$

In other words, each gas in the mixture exerts a **partial pressure,** a portion of the total pressure of the mixture, that is the same as the pressure it exerts *by itself*. This observation is formulated as **Dalton's law of partial pressures:** *in a mixture of unreacting gases, the total pressure is the sum of the partial pressures of the individual gases:*

$$P_{\text{total}} = P_1 + P_2 + P_3 + \cdots \tag{5.10}$$

As an example, suppose you have a tank of fixed volume that contains nitrogen gas at a certain pressure, and you introduce a sample of hydrogen gas into the tank. Since each gas behaves independently, we can write an ideal gas law expression for each:

$$P_{N_2} = \frac{n_{N_2}RT}{V} \qquad \text{and} \qquad P_{H_2} = \frac{n_{H_2}RT}{V}$$

Since each gas occupies the same total volume and has the same temperature, its pressure depends only on its amount, n. Therefore, the total pressure is

$$P_{total} = P_{N_2} + P_{H_2} = \frac{n_{N_2}RT}{V} + \frac{n_{H_2}RT}{V} = \frac{(n_{N_2} + n_{H_2})RT}{V} = \frac{n_{total}RT}{V}$$

where $n_{total} = n_{N_2} + n_{H_2}$.

Each component in a mixture contributes a fraction of the total number of moles in the mixture, which is the **mole fraction (X)** of that component. Keep in mind that the sum of the mole fractions of all components in any mixture must be 1. For N_2, the mole fraction is

$$X_{N_2} = \frac{n_{N_2}}{n_{total}} = \frac{n_{N_2}}{n_{N_2} + n_{H_2}}$$

Since the total pressure is due to the total number of moles, the partial pressure of gas A is the total pressure multiplied by the mole fraction of A, X_A:

$$P_A = X_A \times P_{total} \qquad \textbf{(5.11)}$$

Equation 5.11 is a very important result. To see that it is valid for the mixture of N_2 and H_2, we recall that $X_{N_2} + X_{H_2} = 1$ and obtain

$$P_{total} = \qquad P_{N_2} \qquad + \qquad P_{H_2}$$
$$= (X_{N_2} \times P_{total}) + (X_{H_2} \times P_{total}) = (X_{N_2} + X_{H_2})P_{total} = 1 \times P_{total}$$

Sample Problem 5.8   Applying Dalton's Law of Partial Pressures

PROBLEM In a study of O_2 uptake by muscle at high altitude, a physiologist prepares an atmosphere consisting of 79% N_2, 17% $^{16}O_2$, and 4.0% $^{18}O_2$ by volume. (The isotope ^{18}O will be measured to determine the O_2 uptake.) The pressure of the mixture is 0.75 atm to simulate high altitude. Calculate the mole fraction and partial pressure of $^{18}O_2$ in the mixture.

PLAN We must find $X_{^{18}O_2}$ and $P_{^{18}O_2}$ from P_{total} and the volume % of $^{18}O_2$. Since V is proportional to n (Avogadro's law), the volume % equals the mole %, so dividing the volume % by 100 gives the mole fraction, $X_{^{18}O_2}$. Then, using Equation 5.11, we multiply $X_{^{18}O_2}$ by P_{total} to find $P_{^{18}O_2}$.

SOLUTION Calculating the mole fraction of $^{18}O_2$: Since volume % equals mole %, 4.0 vol % $^{18}O_2$ = 4.0 mol % $^{18}O_2$. Thus,

$$X_{^{18}O_2} = \frac{4.0 \text{ mol \% } ^{18}O_2}{100} = \boxed{0.040}$$

Solving for the partial pressure of $^{18}O_2$:

$$P_{^{18}O_2} = X_{^{18}O_2} \times P_{total} = 0.040 \times 0.75 \text{ atm} = \boxed{0.030 \text{ atm}}$$

CHECK $X_{^{18}O_2}$ is small because the mole % is small, so $P_{^{18}O_2}$ should be small also.

COMMENT At high altitudes, specialized brain cells that are sensitive to blood O_2 and CO_2 levels trigger an increase in rate and depth of breathing for several days, until a person becomes acclimated.

Follow-up Problem 5.8   A mixture of noble gases consisting of 5.50 g He, 15.0 g Ne, and 35.0 g Kr is placed in a piston-cylinder assembly at STP. Calculate the partial pressure of each gas.

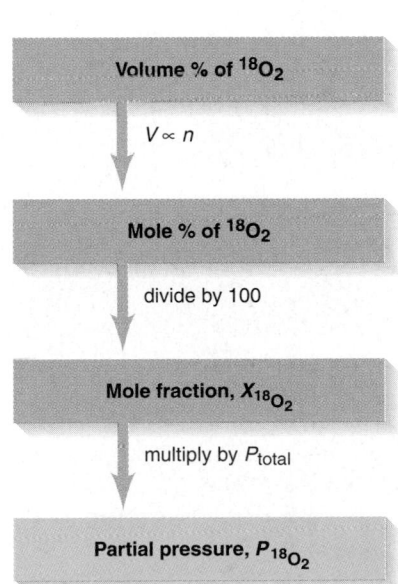

Volume % of $^{18}O_2$

$V \propto n$

Mole % of $^{18}O_2$

divide by 100

Mole fraction, $X_{^{18}O_2}$

multiply by P_{total}

Partial pressure, $P_{^{18}O_2}$

Table 5.4 Vapor Pressure of Water (P_{H_2O}) at Different Temperatures

T (°C)	P (torr)
0	4.6
5	6.5
10	9.2
11	9.8
12	10.5
13	11.2
14	12.0
15	12.8
16	13.6
18	15.5
20	17.5
22	19.8
24	22.4
26	25.2
28	28.3
30	31.8
35	42.2
40	55.3
45	71.9
50	92.5
55	118.0
60	149.4
65	187.5
70	233.7
75	289.1
80	355.1
85	433.6
90	525.8
95	633.9
100	760.0

① *Water-insoluble gaseous product bubbles through water into collection vessel*

② *P_{gas} adds to vapor pressure of water (P_{H_2O}) to give P_{total}. As shown $P_{total} < P_{atm}$.*

③ *P_{total} is made equal to P_{atm} by adjusting height of vessel until water level equals that in beaker*

④ *P_{total} equals P_{gas} plus P_{H_2O} at temperature of experiment. Therefore, $P_{gas} = P_{total} - P_{H_2O}$*

Figure 5.12 **Collecting a water-insoluble gaseous reaction product and determining its pressure.**

Collecting a Gas over Water The law of partial pressures is frequently used to determine the yield of a water-insoluble gas formed in a reaction. The gaseous product bubbles through water and is collected into an inverted container, as shown in Figure 5.12. The water vapor that mixes with the gas contributes a portion of the total pressure, called the *vapor pressure*, which depends only on the water temperature.

To determine the yield of gaseous product, we find the appropriate vapor pressure value from a list, such as the one in Table 5.4, and subtract it from the total gas pressure (adjusted to barometric pressure) to get the partial pressure of the gaseous product. With V and T known, we calculate the amount of product.

P_{total}

↓ subtract P_{H_2O}

$P_{C_2H_2}$

↓ $n = \dfrac{PV}{RT}$

$n_{C_2H_2}$

↓ multiply by $\mathcal{M}$ (g/mol)

Mass (g) of C_2H_2

Sample Problem 5.9   Calculating the Amount of Gas Collected over Water

PROBLEM Acetylene (C_2H_2), an important fuel in welding, is produced in the laboratory when calcium carbide (CaC_2) reacts with water:

$$CaC_2(s) + 2H_2O(l) \longrightarrow C_2H_2(g) + Ca(OH)_2(aq)$$

For a sample of C_2H_2 collected over water, the total gas pressure (adjusted to barometric pressure) is 738 torr and the volume is 523 mL. At the gas temperature (23°C), the vapor pressure of water is 21 torr. How many grams of acetylene were collected?

PLAN We need the mass of C_2H_2, so we first need to find $n_{C_2H_2}$, which we can get from the ideal gas law if we can calculate $P_{C_2H_2}$. The barometer reading gives us P_{total}, the sum of $P_{C_2H_2}$ and P_{H_2O}, and we are given P_{H_2O}, so we subtract to find $P_{C_2H_2}$. We are also given V and T, so we convert units, find $n_{C_2H_2}$ from the ideal gas law, and convert to grams with the formula.

SOLUTION Summary of gas variables:

$$P_{C_2H_2} \text{ (torr)} = P_{total} - P_{H_2O} = 738 \text{ torr} - 21 \text{ torr} = 717 \text{ torr}$$

$$P_{C_2H_2} \text{ (atm)} = 717 \text{ torr} \times \frac{1 \text{ atm}}{760 \text{ torr}} = 0.943 \text{ atm}$$

$$V \text{ (L)} = 523 \text{ mL} \times \frac{1 \text{ L}}{1000 \text{ mL}} = 0.523 \text{ L} \qquad T \text{ (K)} = 23°C + 273.15 = 296 \text{ K}$$

$$n_{C_2H_2} = \text{unknown}$$

Solving for $n_{C_2H_2}$:

$$n_{C_2H_2} = \frac{PV}{RT} = \frac{0.943 \text{ atm} \times 0.523 \text{ L}}{0.0821 \frac{\text{atm} \cdot \text{L}}{\text{mol} \cdot \text{K}} \times 296 \text{ K}} = 0.0203 \text{ mol}$$

Converting $n_{C_2H_2}$ to mass:

$$\text{Mass (g) of } C_2H_2 - 0.0203 \text{ mol } C_2H_2 \times \frac{26.04 \text{ g } C_2H_2}{1 \text{ mol } C_2H_2} = \boxed{0.529 \text{ g } C_2H_2}$$

CHECK We can do a quick arithmetic check for n:

$$n \approx \frac{1 \text{ atm} \times 0.5 \text{ L}}{0.1 \frac{\text{atm} \cdot \text{L}}{\text{mol} \cdot \text{K}} \times 300 \text{ K}} = 0.017 \text{ mol} \approx 0.0203 \text{ mol}$$

COMMENT The C_2^{2-} ion (called the *carbide* or *acetylide* ion) is an interesting anion. It is simply $^-C{\equiv}C^-$, which acts as a base in water, removing an H^+ ion from two H_2O molecules to form acetylene, $H{-}C{\equiv}C{-}H$.

Follow-up Problem 5.9 A small piece of zinc reacts with dilute HCl to form H_2, which is collected over water at 16°C into a large flask. The total pressure is adjusted to barometric pressure (752 torr), and the volume is 1495 mL. Use Table 5.4 to help calculate the partial pressure and mass of H_2.

As the Margin Note discusses, the method for collecting a gas over water was a major technical breakthrough that led to a burst of chemical discovery, as so often happens in science. ◆

Section Summary

The ideal gas law can be rearranged to calculate the density and molar mass of a gas. In a mixture of gases, each component contributes its own partial pressure to the total (Dalton's law of partial pressures). The mole fraction of each component is the ratio of its partial pressure to the total pressure. When a gas is in contact with water, the total pressure is the sum of the gas pressure and the vapor pressure of water at the prevailing temperature.

5.5 The Ideal Gas Law and Reaction Stoichiometry

In Chapters 3 and 4, we encountered many reactions that involved gases as reactants (e.g., combustion with O_2) or as products (e.g., acid treatment of a carbonate). From the balanced equation, we used stoichiometrically equivalent molar ratios to calculate the amounts (mol) of reactants and products and converted these quantities into mass, number of molecules, or solution volume (see Figures 3.11 and 3.14). Figure 5.13 shows how you can expand your problem-solving repertoire by using the ideal gas law to convert between gas variables (P, T, and V) and amount (mol) of gaseous reactants and products. In effect, you combine a gas law problem with a stoichiometry problem. Moreover, this approach presents more realistic situations because we usually measure gas volume, temperature, and pressure rather than mass.

S.G. *sculps*

▶ **Instrumentation and Discovery** In the early 18th century, the danger of explosion from collecting gases in closed containers was stifling research. Then, in 1727, the English biologist Stephen Hales invented the pneumatic trough (see figure; the delivery tube is a bent gun barrel), and used it to collect gases safely. The Scottish chemist Joseph Black applied the method to isolate "fixed air" (CO_2) by heating mineral carbonates. In doing so, Black established the idea that each "air" was a unique substance, not ordinary air with different impurities. In further studies with the device, Henry Cavendish, Joseph Priestley, and others isolated inflammable air (H_2), nitrous air (NO), marine acid air (HCl), dephlogisticated air (O_2), and a host of others: N_2, N_2O, SO_2, SiF_4, NH_3, H_2S, CO, CH_4, Cl_2, and PH_3. From these experiments and the contributions in theory made by Lavoisier, Charles, Gay-Lussac, Dalton, and others, chemistry emerged as a science.

Figure 5.13 Summary of the stoichiometric relationships among the amount (mol, *n*) of gaseous reactant or product and the gas variables pressure (*P*), volume (*V*), and temperature (*T*).

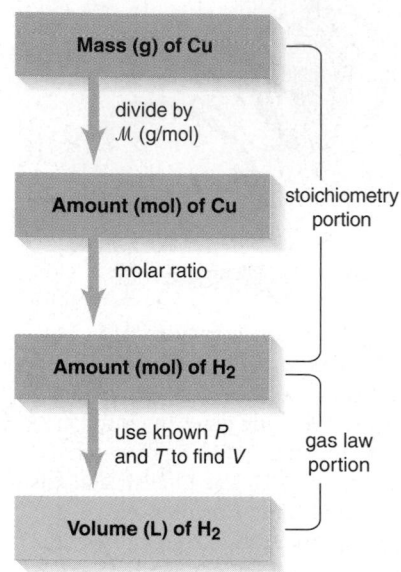

Mass (g) of Cu

divide by $\mathscr{M}$ (g/mol)

Amount (mol) of Cu

molar ratio

Amount (mol) of H$_2$

use known P and T to find V

Volume (L) of H$_2$

stoichiometry portion

gas law portion

Sample Problem 5.10   Using Gas Variables to Find Amounts of Reactants or Products

PROBLEM A laboratory-scale method for reducing a metal oxide is to heat it with H_2. The pure metal and H_2O are products. What volume of H_2 at 765 torr and 225°C is needed to form 35.5 g Cu from copper(II) oxide?

PLAN This is a stoichiometry *and* gas law problem. To find V_{H_2}, we first need n_{H_2}. We write and balance the equation. Then, we convert the given grams of Cu to moles and use the molar ratio to find moles of H_2 needed (stoichiometry portion). Then we use the ideal gas law to convert moles of H_2 to liters (gas law portion). A roadmap is shown, but you are familiar with all the steps.

SOLUTION Writing the balanced equation:

$$CuO(s) + H_2(g) \longrightarrow Cu(s) + H_2O(g)$$

Calculating n_{H_2}:

$$n_{H_2} = 35.5 \text{ g Cu} \times \frac{1 \text{ mol Cu}}{63.55 \text{ g Cu}} \times \frac{1 \text{ mol } H_2}{1 \text{ mol Cu}} = 0.559 \text{ mol } H_2$$

Summary of other gas variables:

$$V = \text{unknown} \qquad P \text{ (atm)} = 765 \text{ torr} \times \frac{1 \text{ atm}}{760 \text{ torr}} = 1.01 \text{ atm}$$

$$T \text{ (K)} = 225°C + 273.15 = 498 \text{ K}$$

Solving for V_{H_2}:

$$V = \frac{nRT}{P} = \frac{0.559 \text{ mol} \times 0.0821 \dfrac{\text{atm} \cdot \text{L}}{\text{mol} \cdot \text{K}} \times 498 \text{ K}}{1.01 \text{ atm}} = \boxed{22.6 \text{ L}}$$

CHECK Let's check the answer by comparing it with the molar volume of an ideal gas at STP (22.4 L at 273.15 K and 1 atm). Since 1 mol H_2 at STP occupies about 22 L, about half that amount would occupy about half that volume (11 L). Since T is about twice 273 K, V should be about twice 11 L. In this case, the decrease in amount and increase in T nearly cancel each other.

COMMENT The main point is that the stoichiometry provides the value of one gas variable (n), two more are given, and the ideal gas law is used to find the fourth.

Follow-up Problem 5.10 Sulfuric acid reacts with sodium chloride to form aqueous sodium sulfate and hydrogen chloride gas. How many milliliters of hydrogen chloride gas form at STP when 0.117 kg sodium chloride reacts with excess sulfuric acid?

Sample Problem 5.11   Using the Ideal Gas Law in a Limiting-Reactant Problem

PROBLEM The alkali metals [Group 1A(1)] react with the halogens [Group 7A(17)] to form ionic metal halides. What mass of potassium chloride forms when 5.25 L chlorine gas at 0.950 atm and 293 K reacts with 17.0 g potassium?

PLAN The only difference between this and previous limiting-reactant problems is that here we use the ideal gas law to find the amount (n) of gaseous reactant from the known V, P, and T. We first write the balanced equation and then use it to find the limiting reactant and the amount of product.

SOLUTION Writing the balanced equation:

$$2K(s) + Cl_2(g) \longrightarrow 2KCl(s)$$

Summary of gas variables:

$$P = 0.950 \text{ atm} \qquad V = 5.25 \text{ L} \qquad T = 293 \text{ K} \qquad n = \text{unknown}$$

Solving for n_{Cl_2}:

$$n_{Cl_2} = \frac{PV}{RT} = \frac{0.950 \text{ atm} \times 5.25 \text{ L}}{0.0821 \dfrac{\text{atm} \cdot \text{L}}{\text{mol} \cdot \text{K}} \times 293 \text{ K}} = 0.207 \text{ mol}$$

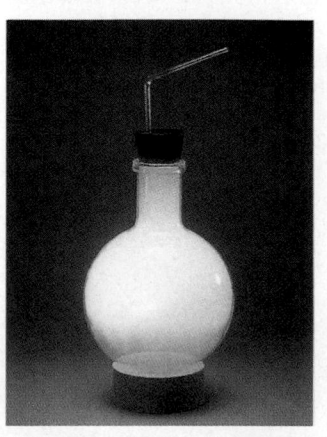

Chlorine gas reacting with potassium.

Converting from grams of potassium (K) to moles:

$$\text{Moles of K} = 17.0 \text{ g K} \times \frac{1 \text{ mol K}}{39.10 \text{ g K}} = 0.435 \text{ mol K}$$

Determining the limiting reactant: If Cl_2 is limiting,

$$\text{Moles of KCl} = 0.207 \text{ mol Cl}_2 \times \frac{2 \text{ mol KCl}}{1 \text{ mol Cl}_2} = 0.414 \text{ mol KCl}$$

If K is limiting,

$$\text{Moles of KCl} = 0.435 \text{ mol K} \times \frac{2 \text{ mol KCl}}{2 \text{ mol K}} = 0.435 \text{ mol KCl}$$

Therefore, since Cl_2 forms less KCl, it is the limiting reactant.
Converting from moles of KCl to grams:

$$\text{Mass (g) of KCl} = 0.414 \text{ mol KCl} \times \frac{74.55 \text{ g KCl}}{1 \text{ mol KCl}} = \boxed{30.9 \text{ g KCl}}$$

CHECK The gas law calculation seems correct. At STP, a 5-L volume would contain about 0.25 mol Cl_2. Since P (in numerator) is slightly lower and T (in denominator) slightly higher than STP, there should be slightly less than 0.25 mol. The mass of KCl seems reasonable: less than 0.5 mol KCl gives less than $0.5 \times \mathcal{M}$ (30.9 g $<$ 0.5×75 g).

Follow-up Problem 5.11 Ammonia and hydrogen chloride gases react to form solid ammonium chloride. A 10.0-L reaction flask contains ammonia at 0.452 atm and 22°C, and 155 mL hydrogen chloride gas at 7.50 atm and 271 K is introduced. After the reaction occurs and the temperature returns to 22°C, what is the pressure inside the flask? (Neglect the volume of the solid product.)

Section Summary

In any reaction that involves gases, we can express the amount of gaseous reactant or product in terms of the gas variables. In this way, the ideal gas law allows us to combine stoichiometry problems with those involving gas behavior.

5.6 The Kinetic-Molecular Theory: A Model for Gas Behavior

So far we have discussed observations of macroscopic samples of gas: decreasing cylinder volume, increasing tank pressure, and so forth. This section presents the central model that explains macroscopic gas behavior at the level of individual particles: the **kinetic-molecular theory.** The theory draws its conclusions through rigorous mathematical derivations, but our discussion will be largely qualitative.

How the Kinetic-Molecular Theory Explains the Gas Laws

Developed by some of the great scientists of the 19th century, most notably James Clerk Maxwell and Ludwig Boltzmann, the kinetic-molecular theory was able to explain the gas laws arrived at empirically by some of the great scientists of the century before.

Questions Concerning Gas Behavior To model gas behavior, we must rationalize certain questions at the molecular level:
1. *Origin of pressure.* Pressure is a measure of the force a gas exerts on a surface. How do individual gas particles create this force?
2. *Boyle's law.* A change in gas pressure in one direction causes a change in gas volume in the other. What happens to the particles when external pressure compresses the gas volume? And why aren't liquids and solids compressible?

3. *Dalton's law.* The pressure of a gas mixture is the sum of the pressures of the individual gases. Why does each gas contribute to the total pressure in proportion to its mole fraction?

4. *Charles's law.* A change in temperature is accompanied by a corresponding change in volume. What effect does higher temperature have on gas particles that increases the volume—or increases the pressure if volume is fixed? This question raises a more fundamental one: what does temperature measure on the molecular scale?

5. *Avogadro's law.* Gas volume (or pressure) depends on the number of moles present, not on the nature of the particular gas. But shouldn't 1 mole of larger molecules occupy more space than 1 mole of smaller ones? And why doesn't 1 mole of heavier molecules exert more pressure than 1 mole of lighter ones?

Postulates of the Kinetic-Molecular Theory   The theory is based on three postulates (assumptions). We paraphrase them here and state some of the conclusions they draw about particle behavior:

Postulate 1. *Particle volume.* A gas consists of a large collection of individual particles. The volume of an individual particle is *extremely* small compared with the volume of the container. In essence, the model pictures gas particles as having mass but no volume.

Postulate 2. *Particle motion.* Gas particles are in constant, random, straight-line motion, except when they collide with the container walls or with each other.

Postulate 3. *Particle collisions.* Collisions are *elastic,* which means that, somewhat like minute billiard balls, the colliding molecules exchange energy but do not lose any through friction. Thus, their total kinetic energy (E_k) is constant. Between collisions, the molecules do not influence each other at all.

A mental image of the scene envisioned by the postulates shows countless particles moving in every direction, smashing into the container walls and one another. If we assume, as did Maxwell and Boltzmann, that the particles obey the laws of motion, any given particle changes its speed with each collision, perhaps one instant standing nearly still from a head-on crash and the next instant zooming away from a smash on the side. Thus, taken together, the molecules have an average speed, with some moving faster than the average and others slower. Maxwell derived an equation showing that this *distribution* of particle speeds has characteristics that depend on temperature. Verification came much later through experiments in which particles in a beam of metal atoms (created by heating the metal in an oven) were separated according to their speeds.

Figure 5.14 depicts the distribution of molecular speeds (u) for N_2 gas at three temperatures. The curves flatten and spread at higher temperatures. Note especially that the *most probable speed* (the peak of each curve) *increases as the temperature increases*. This increase occurs because the average kinetic energy of the molecules ($\overline{E_k}$), which incorporates the most probable speed, is proportional to the absolute temperature: $\overline{E_k} \propto T$, or $\overline{E_k} = c \times T$, where c is a constant that is the same for any gas. (We'll return to this equation shortly.) Thus, a major conclusion based on the distribution of speeds, which arises directly from postulate 3, is that *at a given temperature, all gases have the same average kinetic energy.*

A Molecular View of the Gas Laws   Let's continue visualizing the particles to see how the theory explains the macroscopic behavior of gases and answers the questions posed above:

Figure 5.14 Distribution of molecular speeds at three temperatures. At a given temperature, a plot of the relative number of N_2 molecules vs. molecular speed (u) results in a skewed bell-shaped curve, with the most probable speed at the peak. Note that the curves spread at higher temperatures and the most probable speed is directly proportional to the temperature.

1. *Origin of pressure.* When a moving object collides with a surface, it exerts a force, as when a hailstone hits a window. We conclude from postulate 2, which describes particle motion, that when a particle collides with the container wall, it too exerts a force. Many such collisions result in the observed pressure. The greater the number of molecules in a given container or the more frequently they collide with the walls, the greater is the pressure.

2. *Boyle's law* ($V \propto 1/P$). Gas molecules are points of mass with empty space between them (postulate 1), so as the pressure exerted *on* the sample increases at constant temperature, the distance between molecules decreases, and the sample volume decreases. The pressure exerted *by* the gas increases simultaneously because a smaller volume has shorter distances between gas molecules and the walls and between the walls themselves, so collisions are more frequent (Figure 5.15). The fact that liquids and solids cannot be compressed very much means that there is very little free space between the molecules.

Figure 5.15 A molecular description of Boyle's law. At a given T, gas molecules collide with the walls across an average distance (d_1) and give rise to a pressure (P_{gas}) that equals the external pressure (P_{ext}). If P_{ext} increases, V decreases, so the average distance between a molecule and the walls is shorter ($d_2 < d_1$). Molecules strike the walls more often, and P_{gas} increases until it again equals P_{ext}. Thus, V decreases when P increases.

3. *Dalton's law of partial pressures* ($P_{total} = P_A + P_B$). Adding a specific amount of gas A to a specific amount of gas B causes an increase in total number of molecules in proportion to the amount of A that was added. This increase causes a corresponding increase in the number of collisions per second with the walls (postulate 2), which causes a corresponding increase in the pressure (Figure 5.16). Thus, each gas exerts a fraction of the total pressure based on the fraction of molecules (or moles) of that gas in the mixture (the mole fraction).

Figure 5.16 A molecular description of Dalton's law of partial pressures. A piston-cylinder assembly containing 0.30 mol of gas A at 0.50 atm is connected to a tank of fixed volume containing 0.60 mol of gas B at 1.0 atm. When the piston is depressed at fixed temperature, A is forced into the tank of B, the gases mix, and the new total pressure, 1.5 atm, now equals the sum of the partial pressures, which is related to the new total amount of gas, 0.90 mol. Thus, each gas undergoes a fraction of the total collisions related to its fraction of the total number of molecules (moles), which is equal to its mole fraction.

4. *Charles's law* ($V \propto T$). As the temperature increases, the most probable molecular speed and average kinetic energy increase (postulate 3). Thus, the molecules hit the walls more frequently *and* more energetically. A higher frequency of collisions causes higher internal pressure. As a result, the walls move outward, which increases the volume and restores the starting pressure (Figure 5.17).

Figure 5.17 **A molecular description of Charles's law.** At a given temperature (T_1), $P_{gas} = P_{atm}$. When the gas is heated to T_2, the molecules move faster and collide with the walls more often, which increases P_{gas}. This increases V, so the molecules collide less often until P_{gas} again equals P_{atm}. Thus, V increases when T increases.

$P_{gas} = P_{atm}$

T increases
fixed n

Higher T increases
collision frequency:
$P_{gas} > P_{atm}$

V increases

V increases until
$P_{gas} = P_{atm}$

5. *Avogadro's law* ($V \propto n$). Adding more molecules to a container increases the total number of collisions with the walls and, therefore, the internal pressure. As a result, the volume expands until the number of collisions per unit of wall area is the same as it was before the addition (Figure 5.18).

Figure 5.18 **A molecular description of Avogadro's law.** At a given T, a certain amount (n) of gas gives rise to a pressure (P_{gas}) equal to P_{atm}. When more gas is added, n increases, so collisions with the walls are more frequent and P_{gas} increases. This leads to an increase in V until $P_{gas} = P_{atm}$ again. Thus, V increases when n increases.

$P_{gas} = P_{atm}$

n increases
fixed T

More molecules
increase collisions:
$P_{gas} > P_{atm}$

V increases

V increases until
$P_{gas} = P_{atm}$

We still need to explain why equal numbers of molecules of two different gases, such as O_2 and He, occupy the same volume. To do so, we must first understand why the heavier O_2 particles *do not* hit the container walls with more energy than the lighter He particles. The reason involves the meaning of kinetic energy. Recall from Chapter 1 that the kinetic energy of an object is the energy associated with its motion. It is related to the mass *and* the speed of the object:

$$E_k = \tfrac{1}{2} \text{mass} \times (\text{speed})^2$$

This equation shows that if a heavy object and a light object have the same kinetic energy, *the heavy object must be moving more slowly.* For a large population of molecules, the average kinetic energy (designated by the overbar) is

$$\overline{E_k} = \tfrac{1}{2}m\overline{u^2}$$

where m is the molecular mass and $\overline{u^2}$ is the average of the squares of the molecular speeds. The square root of u^2 is called the root-mean-square speed, or **rms speed (u_{rms})**. *A molecule moving at this speed has the average kinetic energy.* The rms speed is somewhat higher than the most probable speed, but the speeds are proportional to each other and we will use them interchangeably. An expression for the rms speed has been derived and is shown by the following equation to be related to the temperature and the molar mass:

$$u_{rms} = \sqrt{\frac{3RT}{\mathcal{M}}} \qquad\qquad \textbf{(5.12)}$$

where R is the gas constant (8.31 J/mol · K), T is the temperature in kelvins, and $\mathcal{M}$ is the molar mass expressed, in this case, in units of *kg/mol.**

Postulate 3 leads to the conclusion that different gases at the same temperature have the same average kinetic energy. Therefore, Avogadro's law requires that, on average, *molecules with a higher mass have a lower speed.* In other words, at the same temperature, O_2 molecules move more slowly, on average, than He molecules. Figure 5.19 shows that, in general, at the same temperature, lighter gases have higher speeds. In other words, lighter molecules collide with the wall more often but each collision has less force, so both types of molecules hit the walls with the same average kinetic energy, which creates the same pressure.

Figure 5.19 Relationship between molar mass and molecular speed. At a given temperature, gases with lower molar masses (numbers in parentheses) have higher most probable speeds (peak of each curve).

The Meaning of Temperature Earlier we said that the average kinetic energy of a particle was equal to the absolute temperature times a constant, that is, $\overline{E_k}$ = constant × T. A derivation of the full relationship gives the following equation:

$$\overline{E_k} = \tfrac{3}{2}\left(\frac{R}{N_A}\right)T$$

where R is the gas constant and N_A is Avogadro's number. This equation expresses the important point that *temperature is a measure of the energy of molecular motion.* What occurs when, say, a beaker of water containing a

---

*To obtain a speed in m/s, we express the molar mass in kg/mol because R includes the joule, which has units of kg · m²/s².

thermometer is heated over a flame? The rapidly moving gas particles in the flame collide more energetically with the atoms of the beaker, transferring some of their kinetic energy. The atoms vibrate faster and transfer kinetic energy to the molecules of water, which move faster and transfer kinetic energy to the atoms in the thermometer bulb. These, in turn, transfer kinetic energy to the atoms of mercury. They collide with each other more frequently and more energetically, which causes the mercury volume to expand and the level to rise. In the macroscopic world, we see this as a temperature increase; in the molecular world, it is a sequence of kinetic energy transfers from higher energy particles to lower energy particles.

Effusion and Diffusion

The movement of gases, either through one another or into regions of very low pressure, has many important applications.

The Process of Effusion   One of the early triumphs of the kinetic-molecular theory was an explanation of **effusion,** the process by which a gas escapes from its container through a tiny hole into an evacuated space. In 1846, Thomas Graham studied this process and concluded that the effusion rate was inversely proportional to the square root of the gas density. The effusion rate is the number of moles (or molecules) of gas effusing per unit time. Since density is directly proportional to molar mass, we state **Graham's law of effusion** as follows: *the rate of effusion of a gas is inversely proportional to the square root of its molar mass,*

$$\text{Rate of effusion} \propto \frac{1}{\sqrt{\mathcal{M}}}$$

Argon (Ar) is lighter than krypton (Kr), so it effuses faster, assuming equal pressures of the two gases. Thus, the ratio of the rates is

$$\frac{\text{Rate}_{\text{Ar}}}{\text{Rate}_{\text{Kr}}} = \frac{\sqrt{\mathcal{M}_{\text{Kr}}}}{\sqrt{\mathcal{M}_{\text{Ar}}}} \qquad \text{or, in general,} \qquad \frac{\text{rate}_{\text{A}}}{\text{rate}_{\text{B}}} = \frac{\sqrt{\mathcal{M}_{\text{B}}}}{\sqrt{\mathcal{M}_{\text{A}}}} \qquad \textbf{(5.13)}$$

The kinetic-molecular theory explains that, at a given temperature and pressure, *the gas with the lower molar mass effuses faster because the most probable speed of its molecules is higher, therefore more molecules escape through the tiny hole per unit time.* ◆

Preparing Nuclear Fuel

The most important application of Graham's law is the enrichment of nuclear reactor fuel: separating nonfissionable, more abundant ^{238}U from fissionable ^{235}U to increase the proportion of ^{235}U in the mixture. Since the two isotopes have identical chemical properties, they are separated by differences in the effusion rates of their gaseous compounds. Uranium ore is converted to gaseous UF_6 (a mixture of $^{238}UF_6$ and $^{235}UF_6$), which is pumped through a series of chambers with porous barriers. Because they move very slightly faster , molecules of $^{235}UF_6$ ($\mathcal{M} = 349.03$) effuse through each barrier at a rate only 1.0043 times greater than that of molecules of $^{238}UF_6$ ($\mathcal{M} = 352.04$). Many passes are made, each increasing the fraction of $^{235}UF_6$ until a mixture is obtained that contains enough $^{235}UF_6$. This isotope-enrichment process was developed during the latter years of World War II and produced enough ^{235}U for two of the world's first three atomic bombs.

Sample Problem 5.12   Applying Graham's Law of Effusion

PROBLEM Calculate the ratio of the effusion rates of helium and methane (CH_4).
PLAN The effusion rate is inversely proportional to $\sqrt{\mathcal{M}}$, so we find the molar mass of each substance and take its square root. The inverse of the ratio of the square roots is the effusion rate ratio.
SOLUTION

$$\mathcal{M} \text{ of } CH_4 = 16.04 \text{ g/mol} \qquad \mathcal{M} \text{ of He} = 4.003 \text{ g/mol}$$

Calculating the effusion rate ratio:

$$\frac{\text{Rate}_{\text{He}}}{\text{Rate}_{CH_4}} = \sqrt{\frac{\mathcal{M}_{CH_4}}{\mathcal{M}_{\text{He}}}} = \sqrt{\frac{16.04 \text{ g/mol}}{4.003 \text{ g/mol}}} = \sqrt{4.007} = \boxed{2.002}$$

CHECK A rate ratio >1 makes sense because the lighter He should effuse faster than the heavier CH_4. Because the molar mass of He is about one-fourth that of CH_4, He should effuse about twice as fast.

Follow-up Problem 5.12   If it takes 1.25 minutes for 0.010 mol He to effuse, how long will it take for the same amount of ethane (C_2H_6) to effuse?

Graham's law is also used to determine the molar mass of an unknown gas, X, by comparing its effusion rate with that of a known gas, such as He:

$$\frac{\text{Rate}_X}{\text{Rate}_{He}} = \frac{\sqrt{\mathcal{M}_{He}}}{\sqrt{\mathcal{M}_X}}$$

Squaring both sides and solving for the molar mass of X gives

$$\mathcal{M}_X = \mathcal{M}_{He} \times \left(\frac{\text{rate}_{He}}{\text{rate}_X}\right)^2$$

The Process of Diffusion Closely related to effusion is the process of gaseous **diffusion**, the movement of one gas through another. Diffusion rates are also described generally by Graham's law:

$$\text{Rate of diffusion} \propto \frac{1}{\sqrt{\mathcal{M}}}$$

For two gases at equal pressures, such as NH_3 and HCl, moving through another gas or a mixture of gases, such as air, we find

$$\frac{\text{Rate}_{NH_3}}{\text{Rate}_{HCl}} = \sqrt{\frac{\mathcal{M}_{HCl}}{\mathcal{M}_{NH_3}}}$$

The reason for this dependence on molar mass is the same as for effusion rates: lighter molecules have higher molecular speeds than heavier molecules, so they move farther in a given amount of time.

If gas molecules move at hundreds of meters per second at ordinary temperatures (see Figure 5.14), why does it take a second or two after you open a bottle of perfume to smell the fragrance? Although convection plays an important role, a molecule moving by diffusion does not travel very far before it collides with a molecule in the air. As you can see from Figure 5.20, the path of each molecule is tortuous. Imagine walking through an empty room compared with walking through a room crowded with other moving people.

Diffusion also occurs in liquids (and even to a small extent in solids). However, because the distances between molecules are much shorter in a liquid than in a gas, collisions are much more frequent, so diffusion is *much* slower. Diffusion of a gas through a liquid is a vital process in biological systems. For example, it plays a key part in the movement of O_2 from lungs to blood. Many organisms have evolved elaborate ways to speed the diffusion of nutrients (for example, sugar and metal ions) through their cell membranes and to slow, or even stop, the diffusion of toxins.

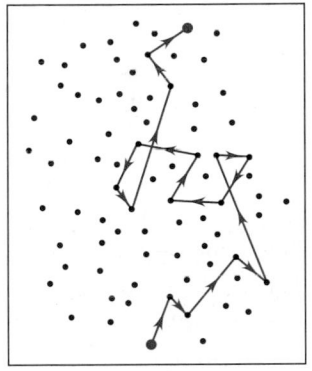

Figure 5.20 Diffusion of a gas particle through a space filled with other particles. In traversing a space, a gas molecule collides with many other molecules, which gives it a tortuous path. For clarity, the path of only one particle *(red dot)* is shown *(red lines)*.

The Chaotic World of Gases: Mean Free Path and Collision Frequency

Refinements of the basic kinetic-molecular theory provide a view into the amazing, chaotic world of gas molecules. Let's follow an "average" N_2 molecule in a room at 20°C and 1 atm pressure—perhaps the room you are in now.

Distribution of Molecular Speeds Our molecule is hurtling through the room at an average speed of 0.47 km/s, or nearly 1100 mi/h (rms speed = 0.51 km/s), and continually changing speed as it collides with other molecules. At any instant, it may be traveling at 2500 mi/h or standing still as it collides head on, but these extreme speeds are *much* less likely than the most probable one (see Figure 5.19).

Mean Free Path From a molecule's diameter, we can use the kinetic-molecular theory to obtain the **mean free path,** the average distance the molecule travels between collisions at a given temperature and pressure. Our average N_2 molecule (3.7×10^{-10} m in diameter) travels 6.6×10^{-8} m before smashing into a fellow traveler, which means it travels about 180 molecular diameters between collisions. (An analogy in the macroscopic world would be an N_2 molecule the size of a billiard ball traveling about 30 ft before colliding with another.) Therefore, even though gas molecules are *not* points of mass, a gas sample *is* mostly empty space. Mean free path is a key factor in the rate of diffusion and the rate of heat flow through a gas.

Collision Frequency Divide the most probable speed (distance per second) by the mean free path (distance per collision) and you obtain the **collision frequency,** the average number of collisions per second that each molecule undergoes: ◆

$$\text{Collision frequency} = \frac{4.7 \times 10^2 \text{ m/s}}{6.6 \times 10^{-8} \text{ m/collision}} = 7.1 \times 10^9 \text{ collisions/s}$$

Distribution of speed (and kinetic energy) and collision frequency are essential ideas for understanding the speed of a chemical reaction, as you'll see in Chapter 16. As the upcoming Chemical Connections essay shows, the kinetic-molecular theory applies directly to the behavior of our planet's atmosphere.

◆ **Danger on Molecular Highways** To give you some idea of how astounding events are in the molecular world, we can express the collision frequency of a molecule in terms of a common experience in the macroscopic world: driving your compact car on the highway. Since a car is much larger than an N_2 molecule, to match the collision frequency of the molecule you would have to travel 2.8 billion mi/s (an impossibility, given that it is much faster than the speed of light) and would smash into another car every 700 yd!

Section Summary

The kinetic-molecular theory postulates that gas molecules take up a negligible portion of the gas volume, move in straight-line paths between elastic collisions, and have average kinetic energies proportional to the absolute temperature. It explains the gas laws in terms of changes in distances between molecules and the container walls and changes in molecular speed. Temperature is a measure of the average kinetic energy of molecules. Effusion and diffusion rates are inversely proportional to the square root of the molar mass (Graham's law) because they are directly proportional to molecular speed. Molecular motion is characterized by a temperature-dependent most probable speed within a range of speeds, a mean free path, and a collision frequency. The atmosphere is a complex mixture of gases that exhibits variations in pressure, temperature, and composition with altitude.

5.7 Real Gases: Deviations from Ideal Behavior

A fundamental principle of science is that simpler models are more useful than complex ones—as long as they explain the data. You can certainly appreciate the usefulness of the kinetic-molecular theory. With simple postulates, it explains ideal gas behavior in terms of molecules acting like infinitesimal "billiard balls," moving at speeds governed by the absolute temperature, and experiencing only perfectly elastic collisions.

In reality, however, you know that *molecules have non-zero volumes* determined by the sizes of their atoms and the lengths of their bonds. You also know that these atoms contain charged particles, which can give rise to *interactions between molecules.* (In fact, such interactions cause gases to condense to liquids.) Therefore, we expect these real properties of molecules to cause deviations from ideal behavior under some conditions, and this is indeed the case. We must alter the simple model and the ideal gas law to predict gas behavior at low temperatures and very high pressures.

Structure and Composition of the Earth's Atmosphere

An **atmosphere** is the envelope of gases that extends continuously from a planet's surface outward, eventually thinning to a point at which it is indistinguishable from interplanetary space. On Earth, complex changes in pressure, temperature, and composition occur within this mixture of gases, and the present atmosphere is very different from the one that existed during our planet's early history.

Variation in Pressure

Since gases are compressible (Boyle's law), the pressure of the atmosphere *decreases* smoothly with distance from the surface, with a more rapid decrease at lower altitudes (Figure 5.A). Although no specific boundary delineates the outermost fringe of the atmosphere, the density and composition at around 10,000 km from the surface are identical with those of outer space. About 99% of the atmosphere's mass lies within 30 km of the surface, and 75% lies within the lowest 11 km.

Variation in Temperature

Unlike the change in pressure, temperature does *not* decrease smoothly with altitude, and the atmosphere is usually divided into regions based on the direction of temperature change (Figure 5.A). In the *troposphere*, which includes the region from the surface to around 11 km, temperatures *drop* 7°C per kilometer to −55°C (218 K). All our weather occurs in the troposphere, and all but a few aircraft fly there. Temperatures then *rise* through the *stratosphere* from −55°C to about 7°C (280 K) at 50 km; we'll discuss the reason shortly. In the *mesosphere*, temperatures *drop* smoothly again to −93°C (180 K) at around 80 km. Within the *thermosphere*, which extends to around 500 km, temperatures *rise* again, but vary between 700 and 2000 K, depending on the intensity of solar radiation and sunspot activity. The *exosphere*, the outermost region, maintains these temperatures and merges with outer space.

(continued)

Figure 5.A **Variations in pressure, temperature, and composition of the Earth's atmosphere.**

What does it actually mean to have a temperature of 2000 K at 500 km (300 mi) above the Earth's surface? Would a piece of iron (melting point $\approx$ 1700 K) glow red-hot and melt in the thermosphere? Our everyday use of the words "hot" and "cold" refers to measurements near the surface, where the density of the atmosphere is 10^6 times greater than in the thermosphere. At an altitude of 500 km, where collision frequency is extremely low, a thermometer, or any other object, experiences *very little transfer of kinetic energy.* Thus, the object does not become "hot" in the usual sense; in fact, it is very "cold." Recall that absolute temperature is a measure of average kinetic energy of the particles. The high-energy solar radiation reaching these outer regions is transferred to relatively few particles, so their average kinetic energy becomes extremely high, as indicated by the high temperature. For this reason, supersonic aircraft, such as the SST, do not reach maximum speed until they reach maximum altitude, where the air is less dense, so that collisions with gas molecules are less frequent and the aircraft material becomes less hot.

Variation in Composition

For a classification by chemical composition, the atmosphere is usually divided into two major regions, *homosphere* and *heterosphere.* Superimposing the regions defined by temperature on these shows that the homosphere includes the troposphere, stratosphere, and mesosphere, and the heterosphere includes the thermosphere and exosphere (Figure 5.A).

The Homosphere The homosphere has a relatively constant composition, containing, by volume, approximately 78% N_2, 21% O_2, and 1% a mixture of other gases (mostly argon). Under the conditions that occur in the homosphere, the atmospheric gases behave ideally, so volume percent is equal to mole percent (Avogadro's law), and the mole fraction of a component is directly related to its partial pressure (Dalton's law). Table 5.A shows the components of a sample of clean, dry air at sea level.

The composition of the homosphere is uniform because of *convective mixing.* Air directly in contact with land is warmer than the air above it. The warmer air expands (Charles's law), its density decreases, and it rises through the cooler, denser air, thereby mixing the components. The cooler air sinks, becomes warmer by contact with the land, and the convection continues. The warm air currents that rise from the ground, called *thermals,* are used by soaring birds and glider pilots to stay aloft.

An important effect of convection is that the air above industrialized areas becomes cleaner as the rising air near the surface carries up ground-level pollutants, which are dispersed by winds. However, under certain weather and geographical conditions, a warm air mass remains stationary over a cool one. The resulting *temperature inversion* blocks normal convection, and harmful pollutants build up, causing severe health problems.

The Heterosphere The heterosphere has variable composition, consisting of regions dominated by a few atomic or molecular species. Convective heating does not reach these heights, so the gas particles become layered according to molar mass: nitrogen and oxygen molecules in the lower levels,

Table 5.A Composition of Clean, Dry Air at Sea Level

Component	Mole Fraction
Nitrogen (N_2)	0.78084
Oxygen (O_2)	0.20946
Argon (Ar)	0.00934
Carbon dioxide (CO_2)	0.00033
Neon (Ne)	1.818×10^{-5}
Helium (He)	5.24×10^{-6}
Methane (CH_4)	2×10^{-6}
Krypton (Kr)	1.14×10^{-6}
Hydrogen (H_2)	5×10^{-7}
Dinitrogen monoxide (N_2O)	5×10^{-7}
Carbon monoxide (CO)	1×10^{-7}
Xenon (Xe)	8×10^{-8}
Ozone (O_3)	2×10^{-8}
Ammonia (NH_3)	6×10^{-9}
Nitrogen dioxide (NO_2)	6×10^{-9}
Nitrogen monoxide (NO)	6×10^{-10}
Sulfur dioxide (SO_2)	2×10^{-10}
Hydrogen sulfide (H_2S)	2×10^{-10}

oxygen atoms (O) in the next, then helium atoms (He), and free hydrogen atoms (H).

Embedded within the lower heterosphere is the ionosphere, containing ionic species such as O^+, NO^+, O_2^+, N_2^+, and free electrons (Figure 5.A). Ionospheric chemistry involves numerous light-induced bond breaking *(photodissociation)* and light-induced electron removal *(photoionization)* processes. One of the simpler ways that O atoms form, for instance, involves a four-step sequence that absorbs energy:

$$N_2 \longrightarrow N_2^+ + e^- \text{ [photoionization]}$$
$$N_2^+ + e^- \longrightarrow N + N$$
$$N + O_2 \longrightarrow NO + O$$
$$\underline{N + NO \longrightarrow N_2 + O}$$
$$O_2 \longrightarrow O + O \text{ [overall photodissociation]}$$

When the resulting high-energy O atoms collide with other neutral or ionic components, the average kinetic energy of thermospheric particles increases.

The Importance of Stratospheric Ozone Although most high-energy radiation is absorbed by the thermosphere, a small amount reaches the stratosphere and breaks O_2 into O atoms. The energetic O atoms collide with more O_2 to form ozone (O_3), another molecular form of oxygen:

$$O_2(g) \xrightarrow{\text{high-energy radiation}} 2O(g)$$
$$M + O(g) + O_2(g) \longrightarrow O_3(g) + M$$

where M is any particle that can carry away excess energy. This reaction releases heat, which is the reason stratospheric temperatures increase with altitude.

Stratospheric ozone is vital to life on the surface because it absorbs a great proportion of solar ultraviolet (UV) radiation, which results in decomposition of the ozone:

$$O_3(g) \xrightarrow{\text{UV light}} O_2(g) + O(g)$$

UV radiation is extremely harmful because it is strong enough to break chemical bonds and, thus, interrupt normal biological processes. Without the presence of stratospheric ozone, much more of this radiation would reach the surface, resulting in increased mutation and cancer rates. The depletion of the ozone layer as a result of industrial gases is discussed in Chapter 16.

Earth's Primitive Atmosphere

The composition of the present atmosphere bears little resemblance to that covering the young Earth, but scientists disagree about what that primitive composition actually was: Did the carbon and nitrogen have low oxidation numbers, as in CH_4 (O.N. of C = −4) and NH_3 (O.N. of N = −3)? Or did these atoms have higher oxidation numbers, as in CO_2 (O.N. of C = +4) and N_2 (O.N. of N = 0)? One point generally accepted is that the primitive mixture did not contain free O_2.

Origin-of-life models propose that about 1 billion years after the earliest organisms appeared, blue-green algae evolved. These one-celled plants used solar energy to produce glucose by photosynthesis:

$$6CO_2(g) + 6H_2O(l) \xrightarrow{\text{light}} C_6H_{12}O_6(\text{glucose}) + 6O_2(g)$$

As a result of this reaction, the O_2 content of the atmosphere increased and the CO_2 content decreased. This increase allowed more oxidation to occur, which changed the geological and biological makeup of the early Earth. Iron(II) minerals changed to iron(III) minerals, sulfites changed to sulfates, and eventually organisms evolved that could oxidize other organisms to obtain energy. For these organisms to have survived some of the more energetic forms of solar radiation, particularly UV light, enough O_2 must have formed to create a protective ozone layer. Estimates indicate that the level of O_2 may have increased to the current level of about 20 mol % approximately 1.5 billion years ago.

A Survey of Planetary Atmospheres

Earth's combination of pressure and temperature and its oxygen-rich atmosphere and watery surface are unique in the Solar System. (Indeed, if similar conditions and composition were discovered on a planet circling any other star, excitement about the possibility of life there would be enormous.) Atmospheres on the Sun's other planets are strikingly different from Earth's. Some, especially those on the outer planets, exist under conditions that cause extreme deviations from ideal gas behavior (Section 5.7). Based on current data from NASA spacecraft and Earth-based observations, Table 5.B lists conditions and composition of the atmospheres on the planets within the Solar System and on some of their moons.

Table 5.B Planetary Atmospheres

Planet (Satellite)	Pressure* (atm)	Temperature† (K)	Composition (mol %)
Mercury	$<10^{-12}$	~700 (day) ~100 (night)	He, H_2, O_2, Ar, Ne (Na and K from solar wind)
Venus	~90	~730	CO_2 (96), N_2 (3), He, SO_2, H_2O, Ar, Ne
Earth	1.0	avg. range 250–310	N_2 (78), O_2 (21), Ar (0.9), H_2O, CO_2, Ne, He, CH_4, Kr
(Moon)	$\sim2\times10^{-14}$	370 (day) 120 (night)	Ne, Ar, He
Mars	7×10^{-3}	300 (summer day) 140 (pole in winter) 218 average	CO_2 (95), N_2(3), Ar (1.6), O_2, H_2O, Ne, CO, Kr
Jupiter	($\sim4\times10^{6}$)	(~140)	H_2 (89), He (11), CH_4, NH_3, C_2H_6, C_2H_2, PH_3
(Io)	$\sim10^{-10}$	~110	SO_2, S vapor
Saturn	($\sim4\times10^{6}$)	(~130)	H_2 (93), He (7), CH_4, NH_3, H_2O, C_2H_6, PH_3
(Titan)	1.6	~94	N_2 (90), Ar (<6), CH_4 (3?), C_2H_6, C_2H_2, C_2H_4, HCN, H_2
Uranus	($>10^{6}$)	(~60)	H_2 (83), He (15), CH_4 (2)
Neptune	($>10^{6}$)	(~60)	H_2 (<90), He (~10), CH_4
Pluto	$\sim10^{-6}$	~50	N_2, CO, CH_4

*Values in parentheses refer to interior pressures.
†Values in parentheses refer to cloud-top temperatures.

Table 5.5 Molar Volume of Some Common Gases at STP (0°C and 1 atm)

Gas	Molar Volume (L/mol)	Condensation Point (°C)
He	22.435	−268.9
H_2	22.432	−252.8
Ne	22.422	−246.1
Ideal gas	**22.414**	**—**
Ar	22.397	−185.9
N_2	22.396	−195.8
O_2	22.390	−183.0
CO	22.388	−191.5
Cl_2	22.184	−34.0
NH_3	22.079	−33.4

Effects of Extreme Conditions on Gas Behavior

At ordinary conditions—relatively high temperatures and low pressures—most simple gases exhibit nearly ideal behavior. Even at STP (0°C and 1 atm however, gases deviate *slightly* from ideal behavior. Table 5.5 shows the sta dard molar volumes of several gases to five significant figures. Note that the do not quite equal the ideal value. The phenomena that cause these slig deviations under standard conditions exert more and more influence as th temperature decreases toward the condensation point of the gas, the ten perature at which it liquefies. As you can see, the largest deviations in th table are for Cl_2 and NH_3, which are already close to their condensatic points at 0°C.

At pressures greater than 10 atm, we begin to see significant deviation from ideal behavior in many gases. For 1 mol of *ideal* gas, the ratio *PV/RT* equal to 1 at any pressure. Figure 5.21 shows a plot of *PV/RT* versus P_{ext} f *1 mol* of several real gases compared with an ideal gas. The values on the axis are the external pressures at which the *PV/RT* ratios are calculated, ar they range from normal (*PV/RT* = 1 at 1 atm) to very high (*PV/RT* ≈ 1.6 2.3 at ~1000 atm).

The *PV/RT* curve for 1 mol methane (CH_4) is typical of most real gases: decreases below the ideal value at moderately high pressures and then ris above it as pressure increases further. The curve shape arises from two ove lapping effects of the two characteristics of real molecules just mentioned:
1. At moderately high pressure, values of *PV/RT* lower than ideal (less tha 1) are due predominantly to *intermolecular attractions.*
2. At very high pressure, values of *PV/RT* greater than ideal (more than are due predominantly to *molecular volume.*

Let's examine these effects on the molecular level:

1. *Intermolecular attractions.* Attractive forces between molecules are *mu* weaker than the covalent bonding forces that hold a molecule together. Mo intermolecular attractions are caused by slight imbalances in electron distr

Figure 5.21 **The behavior of several real gases with increasing external pressure.** The horizontal line shows the behavior of 1 mol of ideal gas: *PV/RT* = 1 at all P_{ext}. At very high pressures, all real gases deviate significantly from such ideal behavior. Even at ordinary pressures, these deviations begin to appear (expanded portion).

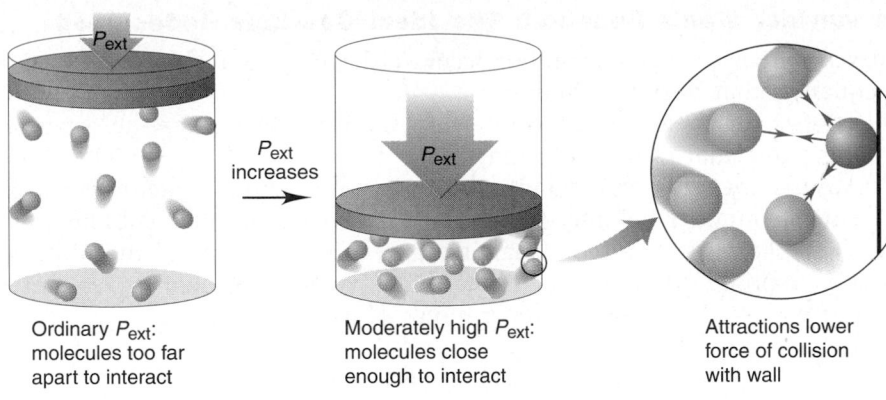

Ordinary P_{ext}: molecules too far apart to interact

P_{ext} increases

Moderately high P_{ext}: molecules close enough to interact

Attractions lower force of collision with wall

Figure 5.22 The effect of intermolecular attractions on measured gas pressure. At ordinary pressures, the volume is large and gas molecules are too far apart to experience significant attractions. At moderately high external pressures, the volume decreases enough for the molecules to influence each other. As the close-up shows, a gas molecule approaching the container wall experiences intermolecular attractions from neighboring molecules that reduce the force of its impact. As a result, gases exert *less* pressure than the ideal gas law predicts.

butions and are important only over relatively short distances. At normal pressures, the spaces between gas molecules are so large that attractions are negligible, and the gas behaves nearly ideally. As the pressure rises and the volume of the sample decreases, however, the average intermolecular distance becomes smaller and attractions have a greater effect.

Picture a molecule at these higher pressures, as in Figure 5.22. As it approaches the container wall, nearby molecules attract it, which lessens the force of its impact. *This effect repeated throughout the sample results in decreased gas pressure and thus a smaller numerator in PV/RT ratio.* Lowering the temperature significantly has the same effect because it slows the molecules, so attractive forces exert an influence for a longer time. At a low enough temperature, the attractions among molecules become overwhelming, and the gas condenses to a liquid.

2. *Molecular volume.* At normal pressures, the space between molecules (free volume) is enormous compared with the volume of the molecules *themselves* (molecular volume), so the free volume is essentially equal to the container volume. As the applied pressure increases, however, and the free volume decreases, the molecular volume makes up a greater proportion of the container volume, which you can see in Figure 5.23. Thus, at very high pressures, the free volume becomes significantly *less* than the container volume; we continue to use the container volume as the V in the PV/RT ratio, so the ratio is artificially high. The molecular volume effect becomes more important as the pressure increases, eventually outweighing the importance of the intermolecular attractions and causing PV/RT to rise above the ideal value.

In Figure 5.21 the H_2 and He curves do not show the typical dip at moderate pressures. These gases consist of particles with such weak intermolecular attractions that the molecular-volume effect predominates at all pressures.

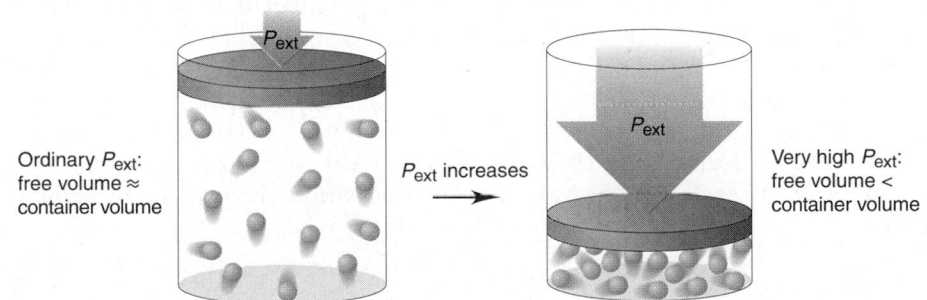

Ordinary P_{ext}: free volume ≈ container volume

P_{ext} increases

Very high P_{ext}: free volume < container volume

Figure 5.23 The effect of molecular volume on measured gas volume. At ordinary pressures, the volume *between* molecules (free volume) is essentially equal to the container volume because the molecules occupy only a tiny fraction of the available space. At very high external pressures, however, the free volume is significantly *less* than the container volume because of the volume of the molecules themselves.

Table 5.6 van der Waals
Constants for Some
Common Gases

Gas	$a \left(\dfrac{atm \cdot L^2}{mol^2} \right)$	$b \left(\dfrac{L}{mol} \right)$
He	0.034	0.0237
Ne	0.211	0.0171
Ar	1.35	0.0322
Kr	2.32	0.0398
Xe	4.19	0.0511
H_2	0.244	0.0266
N_2	1.39	0.0391
O_2	1.36	0.0318
Cl_2	6.49	0.0562
CO_2	3.59	0.0427
CH_4	2.25	0.0428
NH_3	4.17	0.0371
H_2O	5.46	0.0305

The van der Waals Equation: The Ideal Gas Law Redesigned

To describe real gas behavior more accurately, we need a "redesigned" ideal gas equation that does two things:

1. Adjusts the measured pressure *up* by adding a factor that accounts for intermolecular attractions, and
2. Adjusts the measured volume *down* by subtracting a factor from the entire container volume that accounts for the molecular volume.

In 1873, Johannes van der Waals realized the limitations of the ideal gas law and proposed an equation that accounts for the behavior of real gases. The **van der Waals equation** for n moles of a real gas is

$$\left(P + \frac{n^2 a}{V^2} \right) (V - nb) = nRT$$

$$\underset{\text{adjusts}\atop P\text{ up}}{} \quad \underset{\text{adjusts}\atop V\text{ down}}{}$$

where P is the measured pressure, V is the container volume, n and T have their usual meanings, and a and b are **van der Waals constants,** experimentally determined positive numbers specific for a given gas. Values for several gases are given in Table 5.6. The constant a relates to number of electrons, which correlates with the complexity of a molecule and the strength of its intermolecular attractions. The constant b relates to molecular volume.

Consider this typical application of the van der Waals equation to calculate a gas variable. A 1.98-L vessel contains 215 g (4.89 mol) of dry ice. After standing at 26°C (299 K), the $CO_2(s)$ changes to $CO_2(g)$. The pressure is measured (P_{real}) and calculated by the ideal gas law (P_{IGL}) and, using the appropriate values of a and b, by the van der Waals equation (P_{VDW}). The results are revealing:

$$P_{real} = 44.8 \text{ atm} \qquad P_{IGL} = 60.6 \text{ atm} \qquad P_{VDW} = 45.9 \text{ atm}$$

Comparing the real with each calculated value shows that P_{IGL} is 35.3% greater than P_{real}, but P_{VDW} is only 2.5% greater than P_{real}. Obviously, at these conditions, CO_2 deviates so much from ideal behavior that the ideal gas law is not very useful.

Here is one final point to realize. According to kinetic-molecular theory, the constants a and b are zero for an ideal gas because the particles do not attract each other and have no volume. Yet, even for a real gas at ordinary pressures, the molecules are very far apart. Thus,

- Attractive forces are miniscule, so $P + \dfrac{n^2 a}{V^2} \approx P$

- Molecular volume is a miniscule fraction of the container volume, so $V - nb \approx V$

Therefore, *at ordinary conditions, the van der Waals equation becomes the ideal gas law.*

Section Summary

At very high pressures or low temperatures, all gases deviate greatly from ideal behavior. As pressure increases, most real gases exhibit first a lower and then a higher PV/RT ratio than the value for 1 mol of an ideal gas. These deviations are due to attractions between molecules, which lower the pressure (and the ratio), and to the larger fraction of the container volume occupied by the molecules, which increases the ratio. By including parameters characteristic of each gas, the van der Waals equation corrects for these deviations.

Chapter Perspective

As with the atomic model (Chapter 2), we have seen in this chapter how a simple molecular-scale model can explain macroscopic observations and how it often must be revised to predict a wider range of chemical behavior. Gas behavior is relatively easy to understand because gas structure is so randomized—very different from the structures of liquids and *solids with their complex molecular interactions, as you'll see in Chapter 12. In Chapter 6, we return to chemical reactions, but from the standpoint of the heat involved in the change. The meaning of kinetic energy, which we discussed in this chapter, bears directly on this central topic.*

The following learning objectives, with section and/or sample problem (SP) numbers in parentheses, can help focus your study:

Understand These Concepts

1. How gases differ in their macroscopic properties from liquids and solids (5.1)
2. The meaning of pressure and the operation of a barometer and manometer (5.2)
3. The relations among gas variables expressed by Boyle's, Charles's, and Avogadro's laws (5.3)
4. How the individual gas laws are incorporated into the ideal gas law (5.3)
5. How the ideal gas law can be used to study gas density and molar mass (5.4)
6. The relation between gas density and temperature (5.4)
7. The meaning of Dalton's law and the relation between partial pressure and mole fraction of a gas; how Dalton's law applies to collecting a gas over water (5.4)
8. How the postulates of the kinetic-molecular theory can be used to explain the origin of pressure and the gas laws (5.6)
9. The relations among molecular speed, average kinetic energy, and temperature (5.6)
10. The meanings of effusion and diffusion and how their rates are related to molar mass (5.6)
11. The relations among mean free path, molecular speed, and collision frequency (5.6)
12. Why intermolecular attractions and molecular volume cause gases to deviate from ideal behavior at low temperature and high pressure (5.7)
13. How the van der Waals equation corrects the ideal gas law for extreme conditions (5.7)

Master These Skills

1. Interconverting among the units of pressure (atm, mmHg, torr, pascal, psi) (SP 5.1)
2. Reducing the ideal gas law to each of the individual gas laws (SPs 5.2–5.5)
3. Rearranging the ideal gas law to calculate gas density (SP 5.6) and molar mass of a volatile liquid (SP 5.7)
4. Calculating the mole fraction and partial pressure of a gas (SP 5.8)
5. Using the vapor pressure of water to find the amount of a gas collected over water (SP 5.9)
6. Applying stoichiometry and gas laws to calculate amounts of reactants and products (SPs 5.10 and 5.11)
7. Using Graham's law to solve problems of gaseous effusion (SP 5.12)

For Review and Reference

Key Terms

Section 5.2
pressure (P)
barometer
manometer
pascal (Pa)
standard atmosphere (atm)
millimeter of mercury (mmHg)
torr

Section 5.3
ideal gas
Boyle's law
Charles's law
Avogadro's law
standard temperature and pressure (STP)
standard molar volume
ideal gas law
universal gas constant (R)

Section 5.4
partial pressure
Dalton's law of partial pressures
mole fraction (X)

Section 5.6
kinetic-molecular theory
rms speed (u_{rms})
effusion

Graham's law of effusion
diffusion
mean free path
collision frequency
atmosphere

Section 5.7
van der Waals equation
van der Waals constant

Key Equations and Relationships

5.1 Expressing the volume-pressure relationship (Boyle's law) (p. 184):

$$V \propto \frac{1}{P} \quad \text{or} \quad PV = \text{constant} \quad [T \text{ and } n \text{ fixed}]$$

5.2 Expressing the volume-temperature relationship (Charles's law) (p. 185):

$$V \propto T \quad \text{or} \quad \frac{V}{T} = \text{constant} \quad [P \text{ and } n \text{ fixed}]$$

5.3 Expressing the pressure-temperature relationship (Amontons's law) (p. 186):

$$P \propto T \quad \text{or} \quad \frac{P}{T} = \text{constant} \quad [V \text{ and } n \text{ fixed}]$$

5.4 Expressing the volume-amount relationship (Avogadro's law) (p. 186):

$$V \propto n \quad \text{or} \quad \frac{V}{n} = \text{constant} \quad [P \text{ and } T \text{ fixed}]$$

5.5 Defining standard temperature and pressure (p. 186):

$$\text{STP: } 0°C \ (273.15 \text{ K}) \text{ and } 1 \text{ atm } (760 \text{ torr})$$

5.6 Defining the volume of 1 mol of a gas at STP (p. 186):

Standard molar volume = 22.4 L   [3 significant figures]

5.7 Relating volume to pressure, temperature, and amount (ideal gas law) (p. 187):

$$PV = nRT \quad \text{and} \quad \frac{P_1 V_1}{n_1 T_1} = \frac{P_2 V_2}{n_2 T_2}$$

5.8 Rearranging the ideal gas law to find gas density (p. 192):

$$PV = \frac{m}{\mathcal{M}} RT \quad \text{so} \quad \frac{m}{V} = d = \frac{\mathcal{M} \times P}{RT}$$

5.9 Rearranging the ideal gas law to find molar mass (p. 193):

$$n = \frac{m}{\mathcal{M}} = \frac{PV}{RT} \quad \text{so} \quad \mathcal{M} = \frac{mRT}{PV} \quad \text{or} \quad \mathcal{M} = \frac{dRT}{P}$$

5.10 Relating the total pressure of a gas mixture to the partial pressures of the components (Dalton's law of partial pressures) (p. 194):

$$P_{\text{total}} = P_1 + P_2 + P_3 + \cdots$$

5.11 Relating partial pressure to mole fraction (p. 195):

$$P_A = X_A \times P_{\text{total}}$$

5.12 Defining rms speed as a function of molar mass and temperature (p. 203):

$$u_{\text{rms}} = \sqrt{\frac{3RT}{\mathcal{M}}}$$

5.13 Applying Graham's law of effusion (p. 204):

$$\frac{\text{Rate}_A}{\text{Rate}_B} = \frac{\sqrt{\mathcal{M}_B}}{\sqrt{\mathcal{M}_A}}$$

Highlighted Figures and Tables

These figures (F) and tables (T) provide a quick review of key ideas. Entries in color contain frequently used data.

F5.1 A comparison of the three states of matter (p. 178)
T5.2 Common units of pressure (p. 181)
F5.5 The relationship between the volume and pressure of a gas (p. 183)
F5.6 The relationship between the volume and temperature of a gas (p. 185)
F5.8 Standard molar volume (p. 187)
F5.10 Relationship between the ideal gas law and the individual gas laws (p. 188)
T5.3. Values of R in different units (p. 188)
T5.4 Vapor pressure of water at different temperatures (p. 196)

F5.13 Stoichiometric relationships for gases (p. 197)
F5.14 Distribution of molecular speeds at three temperatures (p. 200)
F5.15 Molecular depiction of Boyle's law (p. 201)
F5.16 Molecular depiction of Dalton's law (p. 201)
F5.17 Molecular depiction of Charles's law (p. 202)
F5.18 Molecular depiction of Avogadro's law (p. 202)
F5.19 Relation between molar mass and molecular speed (p. 203)
F5.21 The behavior of several real gases with increasing external pressure (p. 210)
T5.6 Van der Waals constants for some gases (p. 212)

Answers to Follow-up Problems

5.1 P_{CO_2} (torr) = (753.6 mmHg − 174.0 mmHg)

$$\times \frac{1 \text{ torr}}{1 \text{ mmHg}} = 579.6 \text{ torr}$$

P_{CO_2} (Pa) = 579.6 torr $\times \dfrac{1 \text{ atm}}{760 \text{ torr}} \times \dfrac{1.01325 \times 10^5 \text{ Pa}}{1 \text{ atm}}$

$$= 7.727 \times 10^4 \text{ Pa}$$

P_{CO_2} (lb/in^2) = 579.6 torr $\times \dfrac{1 \text{ atm}}{760 \text{ torr}} \times \dfrac{14.7 \text{ lb/in}^2}{1 \text{ atm}}$

$$= 11.2 \text{ lb/in}^2$$

5.2 P_2 (atm) = 26.3 kPa $\times \dfrac{1 \text{ atm}}{101.325 \text{ kPa}} = 0.260 \text{ atm}$

V_2 (L) = 105 mL $\times \dfrac{1 \text{ L}}{1000 \text{ mL}} \times \dfrac{0.871 \text{ atm}}{0.260 \text{ atm}} = 0.352 \text{ L}$

5.3 T_2 (K) $= 273$ K $\times \dfrac{9.75 \text{ cm}^3}{6.83 \text{ cm}^3} = 390$ K

5.4 P_2 (torr) $= 793$ torr $\times \dfrac{35.0 \text{ g} - 5.0 \text{ g}}{35.0 \text{ g}} = 680$ torr

(There is no need to convert mass to moles because the ratio of masses equals the ratio of moles.)

5.5 $n = \dfrac{PV}{RT} = \dfrac{1.37 \text{ atm} \times 438 \text{ L}}{0.0821 \dfrac{\text{atm} \cdot \text{L}}{\text{mol} \cdot \text{K}} \times 294 \text{ K}} = 24.9$ mol O_2

Mass (g) of $O_2 = 24.9$ mol $O_2 \times \dfrac{32.00 \text{ g } O_2}{1 \text{ mol } O_2}$

$= 7.97 \times 10^2$ g O_2

5.6 $d = \dfrac{44.01 \text{ g/mol} \times \dfrac{380 \text{ torr}}{760 \text{ torr/atm}}}{0.0821 \dfrac{\text{atm} \cdot \text{L}}{\text{mol} \cdot \text{K}} \times 273 \text{ K}} = 0.982$ g/L

The density is lower at the smaller P because V is larger. In this case, d is lowered by one-half because P is one-half as much.

5.7 $\mathcal{M} = \dfrac{1.26 \text{ g} \times 0.0821 \dfrac{\text{atm} \cdot \text{L}}{\text{mol} \cdot \text{K}} \times 283.2 \text{ K}}{\dfrac{102.5 \text{ kPa}}{101.325 \text{ kPa/1 atm}} \times 1.00 \text{ L}} = 29.0$ g/mol

5.8 $n_{\text{total}} = \left(5.50 \text{ g He} \times \dfrac{1 \text{ mol He}}{4.003 \text{ g He}}\right)$

$+ \left(15.0 \text{ g Ne} \times \dfrac{1 \text{ mol Ne}}{20.18 \text{ g Ne}}\right)$

$+ \left(35.0 \text{ g Kr} \times \dfrac{1 \text{ mol Kr}}{83.80 \text{ g Kr}}\right)$

$= 2.53$ mol

5.9 $P_{H_2} = 752$ torr $- 13.6$ torr $= 738$ torr

$P_{\text{He}} = \left(\dfrac{5.50 \text{ g He} \times \dfrac{1 \text{ mol He}}{4.003 \text{ g He}}}{2.53 \text{ mol}}\right) \times 1 \text{ atm} = 0.543$ atm

$P_{\text{Ne}} = 0.294$ atm $P_{\text{Kr}} = 0.165$ atm

Mass (g) of $H_2 = \left(\dfrac{\dfrac{738 \text{ torr}}{760 \text{ torr/atm}} \times 1.495 \text{ L}}{0.0821 \dfrac{\text{atm} \cdot \text{L}}{\text{mol} \cdot \text{K}} \times 289 \text{ K}}\right) \times \dfrac{2.016 \text{ g } H_2}{1 \text{ mol } H_2}$

$= 0.123$ g H_2

5.10 $H_2SO_4(aq) + 2NaCl(s) \longrightarrow Na_2SO_4(aq) + 2HCl(g)$

$n_{\text{HCl}} = 0.117 \text{ kg NaCl} \times \dfrac{10^3 \text{ g}}{1 \text{ kg}} \times \dfrac{1 \text{ mol NaCl}}{58.44 \text{ g NaCl}} \times \dfrac{2 \text{ mol HCl}}{2 \text{ mol NaCl}}$

$= 2.00$ mol HCl

At STP, V(mL) $= 2.00$ mol $\times \dfrac{22.4 \text{ L}}{1 \text{ mol}} \times \dfrac{10^3 \text{ mL}}{1 \text{ L}}$

$= 4.48 \times 10^4$ mL

5.11 $NH_3(g) + HCl(g) \longrightarrow NH_4Cl(s)$

$n_{NH_3} = 0.187$ mol $n_{\text{HCl}} = 0.0522$ mol

n_{NH_3} after reaction

$= 0.187 \text{ mol } NH_3 - \left(0.0522 \text{ mol HCl} \times \dfrac{1 \text{ mol } NH_3}{1 \text{ mol HCl}}\right)$

$= 0.135$ mol NH_3

$P = \dfrac{0.135 \text{ mol} \times 0.0821 \dfrac{\text{atm} \cdot \text{L}}{\text{mol} \cdot \text{K}} \times 295 \text{ K}}{10.0 \text{ L}} = 0.327$ atm

5.12 $\dfrac{\text{Rate of He}}{\text{Rate of } C_2H_6} = \sqrt{\dfrac{30.07 \text{ g/mol}}{4.003 \text{ g/mol}}} = 2.741$

Time for C_2H_6 to effuse $= 1.25$ min $\times 2.741 = 3.43$ min

Problems

Problems with a **colored** number are answered at the back of the text. Problem sections match the text and provide the number(s) of relevant sample problems. Most offer concept review questions, skill-building exercises (written in similar pairs), and problems in a relevant context. Following these are comprehensive problems based on material from any section and/or previous chapter.

An Overview of the Physical States of Matter

■ Concept Review Questions

5.1 How does a sample of gas differ in its behavior from a sample of liquid in each of the following situations?
(a) The sample is transferred from one container to a larger one.
(b) The sample is heated in an expandable container, but no change of state occurs.
(c) The sample is placed in a cylinder with a piston, and an external force is applied.

5.2 Are particles in a gas farther apart or closer together than particles in a liquid? Use your answer to explain each of the following general observations:
(a) Gases are more compressible than liquids.
(b) Gases have lower viscosities than liquids.
(c) After thorough stirring, all gas mixtures are solutions.
(d) The density of a substance in the gas state is lower than in the liquid state.

Gas Pressure and Its Measurement

(Sample Problem 5.1)

■ Concept Review Questions

5.3 How does a barometer work? Is the column of mercury in a barometer shorter on a mountaintop or at sea level? Explain.

5.4 How can a length unit such as millimeter of mercury (mmHg) be used as a unit of pressure, which has the dimensions of force per unit area?

5.5 In a closed-end manometer, the mercury level in the arm attached to the flask can never be higher than that in the other arm, whereas in an open-end manometer, it *can* be higher. Explain.

■ **Skill-Building Exercises (paired)**

5.6 On a cool, rainy day, the barometric pressure is 725 mmHg. Calculate the barometric pressure in centimeters of water (cmH₂O). (*d* of Hg = 13.5 g/mL; *d* of H₂O = 1.00 g/mL.)

5.7 A long glass tube, sealed at one end, has an inner diameter of 10.0 mm. The tube is filled with water and inverted into a pail of water. If the atmospheric pressure is 755 mmHg, how high (in mmH₂O) is the column of water in the tube? (*d* of Hg = 13.5 g/mL; *d* of H₂O = 1.00 g/mL.)

5.8 Convert the following:
(a) 0.745 atm to mmHg   (b) 992 torr to atm
(c) 365 kPa to atm   (d) 804 mmHg to kPa

5.9 Convert the following:
(a) 74.8 cmHg to atm   (b) 27.0 atm to kPa
(c) 8.50 atm to torr   (d) 0.907 kPa to mmHg

5.10 If the barometer in Figure P5.10 reads 738.5 torr, what is the pressure of the gas in the flask in atmospheres?

5.11 If the barometer in Figure P5.11 reads 765.2 mmHg, what is the pressure of the gas in the flask in kilopascals?

Figure P5.10

Figure P5.11

5.12 If the sample flask in Figure P5.12 is open to the air, what is the atmospheric pressure in atmospheres?

5.13 What is the pressure in pascals of the gas in the flask in Figure P5.13?

Figure P5.12

Figure P5.13

■ **Problems in Context**

5.14 Convert the following pressures into atmospheres:
(a) At the peak of Mt. Everest, atmospheric pressure is only 2.75×10^2 mmHg.
(b) A cyclist fills her bike tires to 91 psi.
(c) The surface of Venus has an atmospheric pressure of 9.15×10^6 Pa.
(d) At 100 ft below sea level, a scuba diver experiences a pressure of 2.44×10^4 torr.

5.15 The gravitational force exerted by an object is given by $F = mg$, where F is the force in newtons, m is the mass in kilograms, and g is the acceleration due to gravity (9.81 m/s²).
(a) Use the definition of the pascal to calculate the mass (in kg) of the atmosphere on 1 m² of ocean.
(b) Osmium ($Z = 76$) has the highest density of any element (22.6 g/mL). If an osmium column is 1 m² in area, how high must it be for its pressure to equal atmospheric pressure? [Use the answer from part (a) in your calculation.]

The Gas Laws and Their Experimental Foundations

(Sample Problems 5.2 to 5.5)

■ **Concept Review Questions**

5.16 When asked to state Boyle's law, a student replies, "The volume of a gas is inversely proportional to its pressure." How is this statement incomplete? Give a correct statement of Boyle's law.

5.17 Which quantities are variables and which are fixed in each of the following: (a) Charles's law; (b) Avogadro's law; (c) Amontons's law?

5.18 Boyle's law relates gas volume to pressure, and Avogadro's law relates volume to number of moles. State a relationship between gas pressure and number of moles.

5.19 The volume of the cylinder in A can change to the volume in B in many ways. Describe three ways this can happen in which only one gas variable changes while the other two remain constant.

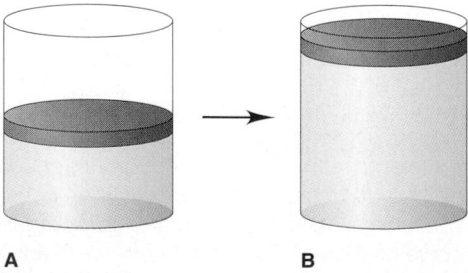

■ **Skill-Building Exercises (paired)**

5.20 What is the effect of the following on the volume of 1 mol of an ideal gas?
(a) The pressure is tripled (at constant T).
(b) The absolute temperature is increased by a factor of 2.5 (at constant P).
(c) Two more moles of the gas are added (at constant P and T).

5.21 What is the effect of the following on the volume of 1 mol of an ideal gas?

(a) The pressure is reduced by a factor of four (at constant T).
(b) The pressure changes from 760 torr to 202 kPa and the temperature changes from 37°C to 155 K.
(c) The temperature changes from 305 K to 32°C and the pressure changes from 2 atm to 101 kPa.

5.22 What is the effect of the following on the volume of 1 mol of an ideal gas?
(a) The temperature is decreased from 700 K to 350 K (at constant P).
(b) The temperature is increased from 350°C to 700°C (at constant P).
(c) The pressure is increased from 2 atm to 8 atm (at constant T).

5.23 What is the effect of the following on the volume of 1 mol of an ideal gas?
(a) Half the gas escapes through a stopcock (at constant P and T).
(b) The initial pressure is 722 torr, the final pressure is 0.950 atm, the initial temperature is 32°F, and the final temperature is 273 K.
(c) Both the pressure and temperature are reduced by one-fourth of their initial values.

5.24 A sample of sulfur hexafluoride gas occupies a volume of 5.10 L at 198°C. Assuming the pressure is constant, what temperature (in °C) is needed to reduce the volume to 2.50 L?

5.25 A 93-L sample of dry air is cooled from 145°C to −22°C while the pressure is maintained at 2.85 atm. What is the final volume?

5.26 A sample of Freon-12 (CF_2Cl_2) occupies 25.5 L at 298 K and 153.3 kPa. Find its volume at STP.

5.27 Calculate the volume of a sample of carbon monoxide at −14°C and 367 torr if it occupies 3.65 L at 298 K and 745 torr.

5.28 A sample of chlorine gas is confined in a 5.0-L container at 228 torr and 27°C. How many moles of gas are present in the sample?

5.29 If $1.47×10^{-3}$ mol argon occupies a 75.0-mL container at 26°C, what is the pressure (in torr)?

5.30 You have 207 mL chlorine trifluoride gas at 699 mmHg and 45°C. What is the mass (in g) of the sample?

5.31 A 75.0-g sample of dinitrogen monoxide is confined in a 3.1-L vessel. What is the pressure (in atm) at 115°C?

■ **Problems in Context**

5.32 In preparation for a demonstration, your professor brings a 1.5-L bottle of sulfur dioxide into the lecture hall before class to allow the gas to reach room temperature. If the pressure gauge reads 85 psi and the lecture hall is 23°C, how many moles of sulfur dioxide are in the bottle? (*Hint:* The gauge reads zero when 14.7 psi of gas remains.)

5.33 A gas-filled weather balloon with a volume of 55.0 L is released at sea-level conditions of 755 torr and 23°C. The balloon can expand to a maximum volume of 835 L. When the balloon rises to an altitude at which the temperature is −5°C and the pressure is 0.066 atm, will it reach its maximum volume?

Further Applications of the Ideal Gas Law
(Sample Problems 5.6 to 5.9)

■ **Concept Review Questions**

5.34 Why is moist air less dense than dry air?

5.35 To collect a beaker of H_2 gas by displacing the air already in the beaker, would you hold the beaker upright or inverted? Why? How would you hold the beaker to collect CO_2?

5.36 Why can we use a gas mixture, such as air, to study the general behavior of an ideal gas under ordinary conditions?

5.37 How does the partial pressure of gas A in a mixture compare to its mole fraction in the mixture? Explain.

■ **Skill-Building Exercises** *(paired)*

5.38 What is the density of Xe gas at STP?

5.39 What is the density of Freon-11 ($CFCl_3$) at 120°C and 1.5 atm?

5.40 How many moles of gaseous arsine (AsH_3) occupy 0.0400 L at STP? What is the density of gaseous arsine?

5.41 The density of a noble gas is 2.71 g/L at 3.00 atm and 0°C. Identify the gas.

5.42 Calculate the molar mass of a gas at 388 torr and 45°C if 206 ng occupies 0.206 μL.

5.43 When an evacuated 63.8-mL glass bulb is filled with a gas at 22°C and 747 mmHg, the bulb gains 0.103 g in mass. Is the gas N_2, Ne, or Ar?

5.44 When 0.600 L Ar at 1.20 atm and 227°C is mixed with 0.200 L O_2 at 501 torr and 127°C in a 400-mL flask at 27°C, what is the pressure in the flask?

5.45 A 355-mL container holds 0.146 g Ne and an unknown amount of Ar at 35°C and a total pressure of 626 mmHg. Calculate the moles of Ar present.

■ **Problems in Context**

5.46 The air in a hot-air balloon at 744 torr is heated from 17°C to 60.0°C. Assuming that the moles of air and the pressure remain constant, what is the density of the air at each temperature? (The average molar mass of air is 28.8 g/mol.)

5.47 On a certain winter day in Utah, the average atmospheric pressure is 650. torr. What is the molar density (in mol/L) of air when the temperature is −25°C?

5.48 A sample of a liquid hydrocarbon known to consist of molecules with five carbon atoms is vaporized in a 0.204-L flask by immersion in a water bath at 101°C. The barometric pressure is 767 torr, and the remaining gas condenses to 0.482 g of liquid. What is the molecular formula of the hydrocarbon?

5.49 A sample of air contains 78.08% nitrogen, 20.94% oxygen, 0.05% carbon dioxide, and 0.93% argon, by volume. How many molecules of each gas are present in 1.00 L of the sample at 25°C and 1.00 atm?

5.50 An environmental chemist sampling industrial exhaust gases from a coal-burning plant collects a CO_2-SO_2-H_2O mixture in a 21-L steel tank until the pressure reaches 850. torr at 45°C.
(a) How many moles of gas are collected?

(b) If the SO_2 concentration in the mixture is 7.95×10^3 parts per million by volume (ppmv), what is its partial pressure? [*Hint:* ppmv = (volume of component/volume of mixture) $\times$ 10^6.]

The Ideal Gas Law and Reaction Stoichiometry
(Sample Problems 5.10 and 5.11)

■ **Skill-Building Exercises (paired)**

5.51 How many grams of phosphorus react with 35.5 L O_2 at STP to form tetraphosphorus decaoxide?

$$P_4(s) + 5O_2(g) \longrightarrow P_4O_{10}(s)$$

5.52 How many grams of potassium chlorate decompose to form potassium chloride and 638 mL O_2 at 128°C and 752 torr?

$$2KClO_3(s) \longrightarrow 2KCl(s) + 3O_2(g)$$

5.53 How many grams of phosphine (PH_3) can form by the reaction of 37.5 g phosphorus and 83.0 L hydrogen gas at STP?

$$P_4(s) + H_2(g) \longrightarrow PH_3(g) \quad \text{[unbalanced]}$$

5.54 When 35.6 L ammonia and 40.5 L oxygen gas at STP burn, nitrogen monoxide and water are produced. After the products return to STP, how many grams of nitrogen monoxide are present?

$$NH_3(g) + O_2(g) \longrightarrow NO(g) + H_2O(l) \quad \text{[unbalanced]}$$

5.55 Aluminum reacts with excess hydrochloric acid to form aqueous aluminum chloride and 35.8 mL hydrogen gas over water at 27°C and 751 mmHg. How many grams of aluminum reacted?

5.56 How many liters of hydrogen gas are collected over water at 18°C and 725 mmHg when 0.84 g lithium reacts with water? Aqueous lithium hydroxide also forms.

■ **Problems in Context**

5.57 "Strike anywhere" matches contain the compound tetraphosphorus trisulfide, which burns to form tetraphosphorus decaoxide and sulfur dioxide gas. How many milliliters of sulfur dioxide, measured at 725 torr and 32°C, can be produced from the burning of 0.800 g tetraphosphorus trisulfide?

5.58 Freon-12 (CF_2Cl_2), a refrigerant and aerosol propellant, is a dangerous air pollutant. In the troposphere, it traps heat 25 times as effectively as CO_2 and in the stratosphere, it participates in the breakdown of ozone. It is prepared industrially by reaction of gaseous carbon tetrachloride with hydrogen fluoride. Hydrogen chloride gas also forms. How many grams of carbon tetrachloride are required for the production of 16.0 dm³ Freon-12 at 27°C and 1.20 atm?

5.59 Xenon hexafluoride was the first noble gas compound synthesized. The solid reacts rapidly with the silicon dioxide in glass or quartz containers to form liquid $XeOF_4$ and gaseous silicon tetrafluoride. What is the pressure in a 1.00-L container at 25°C after 2.00 g xenon hexafluoride reacts? (Assume that silicon tetrafluoride is the only gas present and that it occupies the entire volume.)

5.60 Roasting galena [lead(II) sulfide] is an early step in the industrial isolation of lead. How many liters of sulfur dioxide, measured at STP, are produced by the reaction of 3.75

kg galena with 228 L oxygen gas at 220°C and 2.0 atm. Lead(II) oxide also forms.

5.61 In one of his most critical studies into the nature of combustion, Lavoisier heated mercury(II) oxide and isolated elemental mercury and oxygen gas. If 40.0 g mercury(II) oxide are heated in a 502-mL vessel and 20.0% (by mass) decomposes, how many atmospheres of oxygen gas form at 25.0°C? (Assume the gas occupies the entire volume.)

The Kinetic-Molecular Theory: A Model for Gas Behavior
(Sample Problem 5.12)

■ **Concept Review Questions**

5.62 Use the kinetic-molecular theory to explain the change in gas pressure that results from warming a sample of gas.

5.63 How does the kinetic-molecular theory explain why 1 mol krypton and 1 mol helium have the same volume at STP?

5.64 Is the rate of effusion of a gas higher, lower, or equal to its rate of diffusion? Explain. For two gases with molecules of approximately the same size, is the ratio of their effusion rates higher, lower, or equal to the ratio of their diffusion rates? Explain.

5.65 Consider two 1-L samples of gas, one H_2 and one O_2, both at 1 atm and 25°C. How do the samples compare in terms of (a) mass, (b) density, (c) mean free path, (d) average molecular kinetic energy, (e) average molecular speed, and (f) time for a given fraction of molecules to effuse?

5.66 Three 5-L flasks, fixed with pressure gauges and small valves, each contain 4 g of gas at 273 K. Flask A contains H_2, flask B contains He, and flask C contains CH_4. Rank the flask contents in terms of (a) pressure, (b) average molecular kinetic energy, (c) diffusion rate after the valve is opened, (d) total kinetic energy of the molecules, (e) density, and (f) collision frequency.

■ **Skill-Building Exercises (paired)**

5.67 What is the ratio of effusion rates for the lightest gas, H_2, to the heaviest known gas, UF_6?

5.68 What is the ratio of effusion rates for O_2 to Kr?

5.69 At a particular pressure and temperature, it takes 4.55 min for a 1.5-L sample of He to effuse through a porous membrane. How long does it take for 1.5 L F_2 to effuse under the same conditions?

5.70 A sample of an unknown gas effuses in 11.1 min. An equal volume of H_2 in the same apparatus at the same temperature and pressure effuses in 2.42 min. What is the molar mass of the unknown gas?

5.71 The graph below shows the distribution of molecular speeds of argon and helium at the same temperature.

(a) Does curve 1 or 2 better represent the behavior of argon?
(b) Which curve represents the gas that effuses more slowly?
(c) Which curve more closely represents the behavior of fluorine gas? Explain.

5.72 The graph below shows the distribution of molecular speeds of a gas at two different temperatures.

(a) Does curve 1 or 2 better represent the behavior of the gas at the lower temperature?
(b) Which curve represents the sample with the higher $\bar{E}_k$?
(c) Which curve represents the sample that diffuses more quickly?

■ Problems in Context

5.73 Solid white phosphorus melts and then vaporizes at high temperature. Gaseous white phosphorus effuses at a rate that is 0.404 times that of neon in the same apparatus under the same conditions. How many atoms are in a molecule of gaseous white phosphorus?

5.74 Helium is the lightest noble gas component of air, and xenon is the heaviest.
(a) Calculate the rms speed of helium in winter (0.°C) and in summer (30.°C).
(b) Compare the rms speed of helium with that of xenon at 30.°C.
(c) Calculate the average kinetic energy per mole of helium and of xenon at 30.°C.
(d) Calculate the average kinetic energy per molecule of helium at 30.°C.

Real Gases: Deviations from Ideal Behavior

■ Skill-Building Exercises (paired)

5.75 Do intermolecular attractions cause negative or positive deviations from the PV/RT ratio of an ideal gas? Use data from Table 5.6 to rank Kr, CO_2, and N_2 in order of increasing magnitude of these deviations.

5.76 Does molecular size cause negative or positive deviations from the PV/RT ratio of an ideal gas? Use data from Table 5.6 to rank Cl_2, H_2, and O_2 in order of increasing magnitude of these deviations.

5.77 Does N_2 behave more ideally at 1 atm or at 500 atm? Explain.

5.78 Does SF_6 (boiling point 16°C at 1 atm) behave more ideally at 150°C or at 20°C? Explain.

Comprehensive Problems

Problems with an asterisk (*) are more challenging.

5.79 An "empty" gasoline can with dimensions 15.0 cm by 40.0 cm by 12.5 cm is attached to a vacuum pump and evacuated. If the atmospheric pressure is 14.7 lb/in^2, what is the total force (in pounds) on the outside of the can?

5.80 Hemoglobin is the protein that transports O_2 through the blood from the lungs to the rest of the body. In doing so, each molecule of hemoglobin combines with four molecules of O_2. If 1.00 g hemoglobin combines with 1.53 mL O_2 at 37°C and 743 torr, what is the molar mass of hemoglobin?

5.81 A baker uses sodium hydrogen carbonate (baking soda) as the leavening agent in a banana-nut quickbread. The baking soda decomposes according to two possible reactions:
Reaction 1: $2NaHCO_3(s) \longrightarrow Na_2CO_3(s) + H_2O(l) + CO_2(g)$
Reaction 2: $NaHCO_3(s) + H^+(aq) \longrightarrow$
$$H_2O(l) + CO_2(g) + Na^+(aq)$$
Calculate the mL of CO_2 that form at 200.°C and 0.975 atm per gram of $NaHCO_3$ by each of the reaction processes.

5.82 The vapors from gasoline (represented by C_8H_{18}) spilled at a service station can trigger a fire even if an open flame is several feet from the spill. How does an understanding of gas density help explain this behavior?

*5.83 Chlorine is produced from concentrated seawater by the electrochemical chlor-alkali process. During the process, the chlorine is collected in a container that is isolated from the other products to prevent unwanted (and explosive) reactions. If a 15.00-L container holds 0.5850 kg Cl_2 gas at 225°C, calculate
(a) P_{IGL}
(b) P_{VDW} $\left(\text{Use } R = 0.08206 \dfrac{atm \cdot L}{mol \cdot K}\right)$

*5.84 Hydrogen can also be produced industrially by the chlor-alkali process. When 1 mol $H_2(g)$ at 0°C is compressed until its volume is 0.4483 L, the pressure is observed to be 51.60 atm.
(a) If the hydrogen is behaving ideally, what is its calculated pressure?
(b) What is its real pressure?
(c) Compare the percentage errors in the pressures predicted by the two calculations.

5.85 Will the volume of a gas increase, decrease, or remain unchanged for each of the following sets of changes?
(a) The pressure is decreased from 2 atm to 1 atm, while the temperature is decreased from 200°C to 100°C.
(b) The pressure is increased from 1 atm to 3 atm, while the temperature is increased from 100°C to 300°C.
(c) The pressure is increased from 3 atm to 6 atm, while the temperature is increased from −73°C to 127°C.
(d) The pressure is increased from 0.2 atm to 0.4 atm, while the temperature is decreased from 300°C to 150°C.

5.86 When air is inhaled, it enters the alveoli of the lungs, and varying amounts of the component gases exchange with dissolved gases in the blood. As a result, the alveolar gas mixture is quite different from the atmospheric mixture. The following table presents selected data on the composition and partial pressure of four gases in the atmosphere and in the alveoli:

| GAS | ATMOSPHERE (sea level) | | ALVEOLI | |
	MOL %	PARTIAL PRESSURE (torr)	MOL %	PARTIAL PRESSURE (torr)
N_2	78.6	—	—	569
O_2	20.9	—	—	104
CO_2	0.04	—	—	40
H_2O	0.46	—	—	47

If the total pressure of each gas mixture is 1.00 atm, calculate

(a) the partial pressure (in torr) of each gas in the atmosphere

(b) the mol % of each gas in the alveoli

(c) the number of O_2 molecules in 0.50 L of alveolar air (volume of an average breath at rest) at 37°C.

5.87 Radon (Rn) is the heaviest, and only radioactive, member of Group 8A(18) (noble gases). It is a product of the disintegration of heavier radioactive nuclei found in minute concentrations in many common rocks used for building and construction. In recent years, health concerns about the cancers caused from inhaled residential radon have grown. If 1.0×10^{15} atoms of radium (Ra) produce an average of 1.373×10^4 atoms of Rn per second, how many liters of Rn, measured at STP, are produced per day by 1.0 g Ra?

5.88 In the collection of a gas by displacement of water (see Figure 5.12), a step in the procedure states: "Raise or lower the collection tube so that the water level inside the tube equals the water level outside." What does this step accomplish, why does it work, and how is it used to determine the pressure of the gas?

5.89 The mass of the Earth's atmosphere is estimated as 5.14×10^{15} t (1 t = 1000 kg).

(a) If the average molar mass of air is 28.8 g/mol, how many moles of gas are in the atmosphere?

(b) How many liters would the atmosphere occupy at 25°C and 1 atm?

(c) If the surface area of the Earth is 5.100×10^8 km^2, how high would this volume of air extend? Why does the atmosphere actually extend so much higher?

5.90 Nitrogen dioxide has opposing roles in our world. It is essential in the industrial production of nitric acid, but is also a contributor to acid rain and photochemical smog. Calculate the volume of nitrogen dioxide produced at 735 torr and 28.2°C by the reaction of 4.95 cm^3 copper ($d = 8.95$ g/cm^3) with 230.0 mL nitric acid ($d = 1.42$ g/cm^3, 68.0% HNO_3 by mass):

$$Cu(s) + 4HNO_3(aq) \longrightarrow Cu(NO_3)_2(aq) + 2NO_2(g) + 2H_2O(l)$$

5.91 In the average adult male, the residual volume (RV) of the lungs, the volume of air remaining after a forced exhalation, is 1200 mL.

(a) How many moles of air are present in the RV at 1.0 atm and 37°C?

(b) How many molecules of gas are present under these conditions?

5.92 In a bromine-producing plant, how many liters of gaseous elemental bromine at 300°C and 0.855 atm are formed by the reaction of 275 g sodium bromide and 175.6 g sodium bromate in aqueous acid solution? (Assume no Br_2 dissolves.)

$$5NaBr(aq) + NaBrO_3(aq) + 3H_2SO_4(aq) \longrightarrow$$
$$3Br_2(g) + 3Na_2SO_4(aq) + 3H_2O(g)$$

5.93 An anesthetic gas contains 64.81% carbon, 13.60% hydrogen, and 21.59% oxygen, by mass. If 2.00 L of the gas at 25°C and 0.420 atm weighs 2.57 g, what is the molecular formula of the anesthetic?

5.94 Aluminum chloride is easily vaporized at temperatures above 180°C. The gas escapes through a pinhole 0.122 times as fast as helium at the same conditions of temperature and pressure in the same apparatus. What is the molecular formula of gaseous aluminum chloride?

5.95 Automobile air bags respond to a collision of a preset strength by electrically triggering the explosive decomposition of sodium azide (NaN_3) to its elements. In an industrial lab simulation, 15.3 mL nitrogen gas was collected over water at 25°C and 755 torr. How many grams of azide decomposed?

*5.96 (a) What is the total volume of gaseous *products,* measured at 350°C and 735 torr, when an automobile engine burns 100. g C_8H_{18} (a typical component of gasoline)?

(b) For part (a), the source of O_2 is air, which is about 80% N_2 and 20% O_2 by volume. Assuming all the O_2 reacts, but none of the N_2 does, what is the total volume of gaseous *exhaust?*

*5.97 An atmospheric chemist studying the reactions of the pollutant SO_2 places a mixture of SO_2 and O_2 in a 2.00-L container at 900. K and an initial pressure of 1.95 atm. When the reaction occurs, gaseous SO_3 forms, and the pressure eventually falls to 1.65 atm. How many moles of SO_3 form?

5.98 A sample of liquid nitrogen trichloride was heated in a 2.50-L closed reaction vessel until it decomposed completely to gaseous elements. The resulting mixture exerted a pressure of 754 mmHg at 95°C.

(a) What was the partial pressure of each gas in the container?

(b) What was the mass of the original sample?

5.99 Ammonium nitrate, a common agricultural fertilizer, is used as an explosive in fireworks and, recently, by terrorists. It was the material used in the devastating and tragic explosion of an Oklahoma City federal building in 1995. How many liters of gas at 300°C and 1.00 atm are formed by the explosive decomposition of 12.0 kg ammonium nitrate to nitrogen, oxygen, and water vapor?

5.100 An environmental engineer brings a sample of air contaminated with sulfur dioxide to the lab for analysis. To a 500.-mL sample at 700. torr and 38°C, she adds 20.00 mL of 0.01017 M aqueous iodine, which reacts as follows:

$$SO_2(aq) + I_2(aq) + H_2O(l) \longrightarrow$$
$$HSO_3^-(aq) + I^-(aq) + H^+(aq) \quad \text{[unbalanced]}$$

The unreacted I_2 was titrated with 11.37 mL of 0.0105 M sodium thiosulfate:

$$I_2(aq) + S_2O_3^{2-}(aq) \longrightarrow I^-(aq) + S_4O_6^{2-}(aq) \quad \text{[unbalanced]}$$

What is the volume % of SO_2 in the air sample?

5.101 Canadian chemists have developed a modern variation of the 1899 Mond process for preparing extremely pure metallic nickel. A sample of impure nickel reacts with carbon monoxide at 50°C to form gaseous nickel carbonyl, $Ni(CO)_4$.
(a) How many grams of nickel can be converted to the carbonyl with 3.55 m^3 CO at 100.7 kPa?
(b) The carbonyl is then decomposed at 21 atm and 155°C to pure (>99.95%) nickel. How many grams of nickel are obtained per cubic meter of the carbonyl?
(c) The released carbon monoxide is cooled and collected for reuse by passing it through water at 35°C. If the barometric pressure is 769 torr, what volume (in m^3) of CO is formed per cubic meter of carbonyl?

5.102 Analysis of a newly discovered gaseous silicon-fluorine compound shows that it contains 33.01 mass % silicon. At 27°C, 2.60 g of the compound exerts a pressure of 1.50 atm in a 0.250-L vessel. What is the molecular formula of the compound?

5.103 A gaseous organic compound containing only carbon, hydrogen, and nitrogen is burned in oxygen gas, and the individual volume of each reactant and product is measured under the same conditions of temperature and pressure. Reaction of four volumes of the compound produces four volumes of CO_2, two volumes of N_2, and ten volumes of water vapor.
(a) What volume of oxygen gas was required?
(b) What is the empirical formula of the compound?

5.104 A piece of dry ice (solid CO_2, d = 0.900 g/mL) weighing 10.0 g is placed in a 0.800-L bottle filled with air at 0.980 atm and 550.0°C. The bottle is capped, and the dry ice changes to gas. What is the final pressure inside the bottle?

5.105 Containers A, B, and C are attached by closed stopcocks of negligible volume.

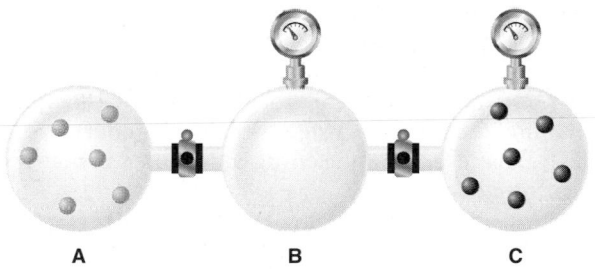

A   **B**   **C**

If each particle in the figure represents 10^6 particles,
(a) How many blue particles and black particles are in B after the stopcocks are opened and the system reaches equilibrium?
(b) How many blue particles and black particles are in A after the stopcocks are opened and the system reaches equilibrium?
(c) If the pressure in C, P_C, is 750 torr before the stopcocks are opened, what is P_C afterward?
(d) What is P_B afterward?

5.106 At the temperatures existing in the thermosphere (see Figure 5.A), instruments would break down and astronauts would be killed. Yet satellites function in orbit there for many years and astronauts routinely repair equipment on space walks. Explain.

*5.107 By what factor would a scuba diver's lungs expand if she ascended rapidly to the surface without inhaling or ex-

haling from a depth of 125 ft? If an expansion factor greater than 1.5 causes lung rupture, how far could the diver safely ascend from 125 ft without breathing? Assume constant temperature. (d of seawater = 1.04 g/mL; d of Hg = 13.5 g/mL.)

5.108 When 15.0 g of the mineral fluorite (CaF_2) reacts with excess sulfuric acid, hydrogen fluoride gas is collected at 744 torr and 25.5°C. Solid calcium sulfate is the other product. What gas temperature is required to store the gas in a 8.63-L container at 875 torr?

5.109 Dilute aqueous hydrogen peroxide is used as a bleaching agent and for disinfecting surfaces and small cuts. Its concentration is sometimes given as a certain number of "volumes hydrogen peroxide," which refers to the number of volumes of O_2 gas, measured at STP, that a given volume of hydrogen peroxide solution will release when it decomposes to O_2 and liquid H_2O. How many grams of hydrogen peroxide are in 0.100 L of "20 volumes hydrogen peroxide" solution?

5.110 At a height of 300 km above the Earth's surface, an astronaut finds that the atmospheric pressure is about 10^{-8} mmHg and the temperature is 500 K. How many molecules of gas are there per milliliter at this altitude?

5.111 (a) What is the rms speed of O_2 molecules at STP? (b) If the mean free path of O_2 molecules at STP is 6.33×10^{-8} m, what is their collision frequency?

5.112 A barometer tube is 1.00×10^2 cm long and has a cross-sectional area of 1.20 cm^2. The height of the mercury column is 74.0 cm, and the temperature is 24°C. A small amount of N_2 is introduced into the evacuated space above the mercury, which causes the mercury level to drop to a height of 66.0 cm. How many grams of N_2 were introduced?

5.113 What is the molar concentration of the cleaning solution formed when 10.0 L ammonia gas, measured at 31°C and 735 torr, dissolves in enough water to give a final volume of 0.750 L?

5.114 For each of the following, which shows the greater deviation from ideal behavior at the same set of conditions? Explain your choice.
(a) Argon or xenon
(b) Water vapor or neon
(c) Mercury vapor or radon
(d) Water vapor or methane

5.115 How many liters of gaseous hydrogen bromide at 27°C and 0.975 atm will a chemist need if she wishes to prepare 3.50 L of 1.20 M hydrobromic acid?

5.116 A mixture consisting of 7.0 g CO and 10.0 g SO_2, two atmospheric pollutants, has a pressure of 0.33 atm when placed in a sealed container. What is the partial pressure of the CO?

*5.117 A mixture of CO_2 and Kr weighs 35.0 g and exerts a pressure of 0.708 atm in its container. Since Kr is expensive, you wish to recover it from the mixture. After the CO_2 is completely removed by absorption with NaOH(s), the pressure in the container is 0.250 atm. How many grams of CO_2 were originally present? How many grams of Kr can you recover?

5.118 When 40.3 mL of 0.200 M calcium bicarbonate is treated with excess hydrochloric acid, how many milliliters of carbon dioxide will form at 30.°C and 506 torr?

*5.119 Aqueous sulfurous acid (H_2SO_3) was made by dissolving 0.200 L sulfur dioxide gas at 20.°C and 740. mmHg in water to yield 500.0 mL of solution. The acid solution required 10.0 mL sodium hydroxide solution to reach the titration end point. What was the molarity of the sodium hydroxide solution?

5.120 The lunar surface reaches 370 K at midday. The atmosphere consists of neon, argon, and traces of helium at a total pressure of only 2×10^{-14} atm. Calculate the rms speed of each component in the lunar atmosphere.

*5.121 A person inhales air richer in O_2 and exhales air richer in CO_2 and water vapor. During each hour of sleep, a person exhales a total of about 300 L of this CO_2-enriched and H_2O-enriched air.
(a) If the partial pressures of CO_2 and H_2O in exhaled air are each 30.0 torr at 37.0°C, calculate the mass of CO_2 and of H_2O exhaled in 1 hour of sleep.
(b) How many grams of body mass does the person lose in an 8-h sleep if all the CO_2 and H_2O exhaled come from the metabolism of glucose?

$$C_6H_{12}O_6(s) + 6O_2(g) \longrightarrow 6CO_2(g) + 6H_2O(g)$$

5.122 Prevailing theories of Solar System evolution state that swirling clouds consisting mostly of hydrogen, helium, and dust gradually accreted (were drawn together) into a central solar disk and protoplanets, and over time, the Sun and planets formed more spherical shapes. Given this origin, use the kinetic-molecular theory to explain why there is so little H_2 and He gas on Earth today.

*5.123 Given the following relationships for average kinetic energy,

$$\overline{E_k} = \tfrac{1}{2}m\overline{u^2} \qquad \text{and} \qquad \overline{E_k} = \tfrac{3}{2}\left(\frac{R}{N_A}\right)T$$

where m is molecular mass, u is rms speed, R is the gas constant (in J/mol · K), N_A is Avogadro's number, and T is absolute temperature:
(a) Derive Equation 5.12.
(b) Derive Equation 5.13.

5.124 What would you observe if you tilted the barometer shown in Figure 5.3 to 30° from the vertical? Explain.

5.125 The cylinder in A contains 0.1 mol of a gas that behaves ideally. Choose the cylinder (B, C, or D) that correctly represents the volume of the gas after each of the following changes. If none is correct, choose "none":
(a) P is doubled at fixed n and T.
(b) T is reduced from 400 K to 200 K at fixed n and P.

(c) T is increased from 100°C to 200°C at fixed n and P.
(d) 0.1 mol of gas is added at fixed P and T.
(e) 0.1 mol of gas is added and P is doubled at fixed T.

5.126 A 6.0-L flask contains a mixture of methane (CH_4), argon, and helium at 45°C and 1.75 atm. If the mole fractions of helium and argon are 0.25 and 0.35, respectively, how many molecules of methane are present?

*5.127 A large portion of metabolic energy arises from the biological combustion of glucose:

$$C_6H_{12}O_6(s) + 6O_2(g) \longrightarrow 6CO_2(g) + 6H_2O(g)$$

(a) If this reaction is carried out in an expandable container at 35°C and 780 torr, what volume of CO_2 is produced from 18.0 g glucose and excess O_2?
(b) If the reaction is carried out at the same conditions with the stoichiometric amount of O_2, what is the partial pressure of each gas when the reaction is 50% complete (9.0 g glucose has not yet reacted)?

5.128 What is the average kinetic energy and rms speed of N_2 molecules at STP? Compare these values with those of H_2 molecules under the same conditions.

*5.129 An equimolar mixture of Ne and Xe is accidentally placed in a container that has a tiny leak. After a short while, a very small proportion of the mixture has escaped. What is the mole fraction of Ne in the effusing gas?

*5.130 One way to utilize naturally occurring uranium (0.72% ^{235}U and 99.27% ^{238}U) as a nuclear fuel is to enrich it (increase its ^{235}U content) by allowing gaseous UF_6 to effuse through a porous membrane (see Margin Note, p. 204). From the relative rates of effusion of $^{235}UF_6$ and $^{238}UF_6$, find the number of steps needed to produce uranium that is 3.0 mole % ^{235}U, the enriched fuel used in many nuclear reactors.

*5.131 A slight deviation from ideal behavior exists even at normal conditions. If CO behaved ideally, 1 mol CO would occupy 22.414 L and exert 1 atm pressure at 273.15 K. Calculate P_{VDW} for 1.000 mol CO at 273.15 K.

$$\left(\text{Use } R = 0.08206 \; \frac{\text{atm} \cdot \text{L}}{\text{mol} \cdot \text{K}}\right)$$

Thermochemistry
Energy Flow and Chemical Change

6

Figure: The wonder of a burning match. When a match burns, the chemical reaction that occurs releases energy, as do many other processes. Still others absorb energy. Our ability to understand and measure changes in matter and energy is crucial to the ultimate fate of modern society, and in this chapter, we begin an exploration of the factors that govern them.

Concepts and
Skills to Review

before you study this chapter

- energy and its interconversion (Section 1.1)
- distinction between heat and temperature (Section 1.5)
- nature of chemical bonding (Section 2.7)
- calculations of reaction stoichiometry (Section 3.4)
- properties of the gaseous state (Section 5.1)
- relation between kinetic energy and temperature (Section 5.6)

All changes in matter, whether chemical or physical, are accompanied by changes in the *energy content* of the matter. In the inferno of a forest fire, as wood is converted to ash and gases, its energy content decreases, and that change in energy is *released* as heat and light. In contrast, some of the energy in a flash of lightning is *absorbed* when atmospheric N_2 and O_2 react to form NO. Energy is *absorbed* when snow melts and is *released* when water vapor condenses to rain.

The production and usage of energy in its many forms have an enormous impact on society. Some of the largest industries manufacture products that release, absorb, or limit the flow of energy. Common fuels—oil, wood, coal, and natural gas—release chemical energy for heating and to power combustion engines and steam turbines. Fertilizers help crops absorb solar energy and convert it to the chemical energy of food that our bodies convert into other forms. Many plastic, fiberglass, and ceramic materials serve as insulators that limit energy flow.

In this chapter, we investigate the heat associated with changes in matter. We first examine some basic ideas of **thermodynamics,** the study of heat and its transformations. Then, we discuss **thermochemistry,** the branch of thermodynamics that deals with the heat involved in chemical reactions. We explore changes at the molecular level to find out where the heat change of a reaction comes from. Then we learn how heat is measured, to focus on the key value: the quantity of heat released or absorbed in a reaction. The chapter ends with an overview of current and future energy sources and the conflicts between energy demand and environmental quality.

Thermodynamics is a fascinating field, a rigorously logical, highly mathematical branch of science that is as relevant in everyday life as it is in the laboratory or the environment. Our discussion of thermodynamics here, and later in Chapter 20, is confined mostly to chemical applications, but it shows how widely the ideas can be applied.

6.1 Forms of Energy and Their Interconversion

As we discussed in Chapter 1, all energy is either potential or kinetic, and these forms are convertible from one to the other. An object has potential energy by virtue of its position and kinetic energy by virtue of its motion. The potential energy of a weight raised above the ground is converted to kinetic energy as it falls (see Figure 1.3). When the weight hits the ground, it transfers some kinetic energy to the soil and pebbles, causing them to move, thereby doing *work*. In addition, some of the transferred kinetic energy appears as *heat*, as it slightly warms the soil and pebbles. Thus, the potential energy of the weight is converted to kinetic energy, which is transferred to the ground as work and as heat.

Modern atomic theory allows us to consider other forms of energy—electrical, solar, nuclear, and chemical—as examples of potential and kinetic energy on the atomic and molecular scales. No matter what the details of the situation, *when energy is transferred from one object to another, it appears as work and/or as heat.* In this section, we examine this idea in terms of the loss or gain of energy that takes place during a chemical or physical change.

The System and Its Surroundings

To have a meaningful discussion in daily life, we must first define the topic. In the same sense, to make a meaningful observation and measurement of a change in energy, we must first define the **system,** the part of the universe whose change we are going to observe. The moment we define the system, everything else relevant to the change is defined as the **surroundings.** ◆
Figure 6.1 shows a typical chemical system and its surroundings: the system

◆ **Wherever You Look There Is a System** In the earlier example of the weight hitting the ground, if we define the falling weight as the system, the soil and pebbles that are moved are the surroundings. An astronomer may define a galaxy as the system and nearby galaxies as the surroundings. An ecologist studying African wildlife can define a zebra herd as the system and other animals, plants, and water supplies as the surroundings. A biologist may define a particular cell as the system and the extracellular solution as the surroundings. Thus, in general, it is the experiment and the experimenter that define the system and the surroundings.

is the *contents* of the flask, and the flask itself, the other equipment, and perhaps the rest of the laboratory are the surroundings. In principle, the rest of the universe is the surroundings, but in practice, we need to consider only the portions of the universe relevant to the system. That is, it's not likely that a thunderstorm in central Asia or a methane blizzard on Neptune will affect the contents of the flask, but the temperature, pressure, and humidity of the lab might.

Energy Flow to and from a System

Each particle in a system has potential and kinetic energy, and the sum of these energies for all the particles in the system is the **internal energy, E** (some texts use the symbol U). When a chemical system, such as the contents of the flask in Figure 6.1, changes from reactants to products and the products return to the starting temperature, the internal energy has changed. To determine this change, ΔE, we measure the difference between the system's internal energy *after* the change (E_{final}) and *before* the change ($E_{initial}$):

$$\Delta E = E_{final} - E_{initial} = E_{products} - E_{reactants} \qquad \textbf{(6.1)}$$

where Δ (Greek *delta*) means "change (or difference) in." Note especially that Δ refers to the *final state of the system **minus** the initial state.*

*A change in the energy of the system is always accompanied by an **opposite** change in the energy of the surroundings.* We often represent this change with an *energy diagram* in which the final and initial states are horizontal lines on a vertical energy axis. The change in internal energy, ΔE, is the difference between the heights of the two lines. A reacting chemical system can change its internal energy in either of two ways:

1. By losing some energy *to* the surroundings, as shown in Figure 6.2A:

$$E_{final} < E_{initial} \qquad \Delta E < 0$$

2. By gaining some energy *from* the surroundings, as shown in Figure 6.2B:

$$E_{final} > E_{initial} \qquad \Delta E > 0$$

Note that the change is a *transfer* of energy from system to surroundings, and vice versa.

Figure 6.1 A chemical system and its surroundings. Once the contents of the flask (the orange solution) is defined as the system, the flask and the laboratory become defined as the surroundings.

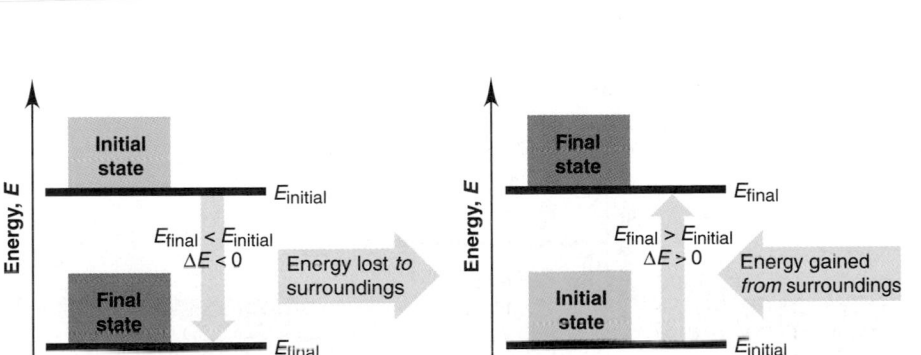

A

B

Figure 6.2 Energy diagrams for the transfer of internal energy (E) between a system and its surroundings. A, When the internal energy of a system *decreases*, the change in energy (ΔE) is lost *to* the surroundings; therefore, ΔE of the system ($E_{final} - E_{initial}$) is negative. **B,** When the system's internal energy *increases*, ΔE is gained *from* the surroundings and is positive. Note that the arrow signifying the direction of the change *always* has its tail at the initial state and its head at the final state.

Heat and Work: Two Forms of Energy Transfer

The energy transfer outward from the system or inward from the surroundings can appear in two forms, heat and work. **Heat** (or *thermal energy,* symbol q) is the energy transferred between a system and its surroundings as a result of a difference in their temperatures only. Energy in the form of heat is transferred from hot soup (system) to the bowl, air, and table (surroundings) because the surroundings have a lower temperature. All other forms of energy transfer (mechanical, electrical, and so on) involve some type of **work (w),** the energy transferred when an object is moved by a force. When you (system) kick a football (surroundings), energy is transferred as work to move the ball. If the football needs to be inflated, the inside air (system) exerts a force on the inner wall of the ball and nearby air (surroundings) and does work to move it outward.

Since energy can be transferred as heat and/or work, the total change in a system's internal energy is

$$\Delta E = q + w \qquad (6.2)$$

The numerical values of q and w can be either positive or negative, depending on the change the *system* undergoes. In other words, *we define the sign of the energy transfer from the system's perspective.* Energy *in to* the system is *positive.* Energy *out from* the system is *negative.* Of the innumerable changes possible in the system's internal energy, let's examine four simple cases—two that involve only heat and two that involve only work:

1. *Energy transfer as heat only.* For a system that does no work but transfers energy only as heat (q), we know that $w = 0$. Therefore, from Equation 6.2, we have $\Delta E = q$.

- *Heat **out from** a system.* Suppose a sample of hot water is the system; then, the beaker containing it and the rest of the lab are the surroundings. The water transfers energy as heat to the surroundings until the temperature of the water equals that of the surroundings. The system's energy decreases as heat flows *out from* the system, so the final energy of the system is less than its initial energy. Heat was lost by the system, so *q is negative,* and therefore ΔE *is negative.* Figure 6.3A shows this situation.

- *Heat **in to** a system.* On the other hand, if the system consists of ice water, it gains energy as heat from the surroundings until the temperature of the water equals that of the surroundings. In this case, energy is transferred *in to* the system, so the final energy of the system is higher than its initial energy. Heat was gained by the system, so *q is positive,* and therefore ΔE *is positive.* Figure 6.3B shows this situation. ◆

Thermodynamics in the Kitchen The air in a refrigerator (surroundings) has a lower temperature than a newly added piece of food (system), so the food loses energy as heat to the refrigerator air, $q < 0$. The air in a hot oven (surroundings) has a higher temperature than a newly added piece of food (system), so the food gains energy as heat from the oven air, $q > 0$.

Figure 6.3 A system transferring energy as heat only. A, The hot water transfers energy as heat (q) *to* the surroundings until $T_{sys} = T_{surr}$. Since $E_{initial} > E_{final}$ and $w = 0$, $\Delta E < 0$ and the sign of q is negative. **B,** The ice water gains energy as heat (q) *from* the surroundings until $T_{sys} = T_{surr}$. Since $E_{initial} < E_{final}$ and $w = 0$, $\Delta E > 0$ and the sign of q is positive.

Figure 6.4 **A system losing energy as work only.** The internal energy of the system decreases as the reactants form products because the $H_2(g)$ does work (w) *on* the surroundings by pushing back the piston. The reaction vessel is insulated, so $q = 0$. Since $E_{initial} > E_{final}$, $\Delta E < 0$ and the sign of w is negative.

2. *Energy transfer as work only.* For a system that transfers energy only as work (w) and not as heat, we know that $q = 0$; therefore, $\Delta E = w$.

- *Work done **by** a system.* Consider the reaction between zinc and hydrochloric acid that takes place in an insulated container attached to a piston-cylinder assembly. We define the system as the atoms that make up the substances. In the initial state, the system's internal energy is that of the atoms in the form of the reactants, metallic Zn and aqueous H^+ and Cl^- ions. In the final state, the system's internal energy is that of the same atoms in the form of the products, H_2 gas and aqueous Zn^{2+} and Cl^- ions:

$$Zn(s) + 2H^+(aq) + 2Cl^-(aq) \longrightarrow H_2(g) + Zn^{2+}(aq) + 2Cl^-(aq)$$

As the H_2 gas forms, some of the internal energy is used *by* the system to do work *on* the surroundings and push the piston outward. Energy is lost by the system as work, so *w is negative* and *ΔE is negative,* as you see in Figure 6.4. The H_2 gas is doing **pressure-volume work (PV work),** the type of work in which a volume changes against an external pressure. The work done here is not very useful because it simply pushes back the piston and air. But, if the system is a ton of burning coal and O_2, and the surroundings are a locomotive engine, much of the internal energy lost from the system does the work of moving a train.

- *Work done **on** a system.* If we increase the external pressure on the piston in Figure 6.4, the system gains energy because work is done *on* the system *by* the surroundings: *w is positive,* so *ΔE is positive.*

Table 6.1 summarizes the sign conventions of q and w and their effect on the sign of ΔE.

Table 6.1 The Sign Conventions* of q, w, and ΔE

q	$+$	w	$=$	ΔE
$+$		$+$		$+$
$+$		$-$		Depends on *sizes* of q and w
$-$		$+$		Depends on *sizes* of q and w
$-$		$-$		$-$

*For q: $+$ means system *gains* heat; $-$ means system *loses* heat.
For w: $+$ means work done *on* system; $-$ means work done *by* system.

The Law of Energy Conservation

As you've seen, when a system gains energy, the surroundings supply it, and when a system loses energy, the surroundings gain it. Energy can be converted from one form to another as these transfers take place, but it cannot simply appear or disappear—it cannot be created or destroyed. The **law of conservation of energy** restates this basic observation as follows: *the total energy of the universe is constant.* This law is also known as the **first law of thermodynamics** because it is so essential to that science. ◆

Conservation of energy appears everywhere. As gasoline burns in a car engine, the released energy appears as an equivalent amount of heat and work. The heat warms the car parts, passenger compartment, and surrounding air. The work appears as mechanical energy to turn the car's wheels and belts. That energy is converted further into the electrical energy of the clock and radio, the radiant energy of the headlights, the chemical energy of the battery, the heat due to friction, and so forth. If you took the sum of all these energy forms, you would find that it equals the change in energy between the reactants and products of the gasoline burned. Complex biological processes obey energy conservation also. Through photosynthesis, green plants convert radiant energy from the Sun into chemical energy, as low-energy CO_2 and H_2O are used to make high-energy carbohydrates (such as wood) and O_2. When the wood is burned in air, those low-energy compounds form again, and the energy difference is released to the surroundings.

Thus, energy transfers between system and surroundings can be in the forms of heat and various types of work—mechanical, electrical, radiant, chemical—but *the energy of the system plus the energy of the surroundings remains constant: energy is conserved.* A mathematical expression of the law of conservation of energy (first law) is

$$\Delta E_{universe} = \Delta E_{system} + \Delta E_{surroundings} = 0 \qquad \textbf{(6.3)}$$

This profound idea pertains to all systems, from a burning match to the movement of continents, from the inner workings of your heart to the formation of the Solar System.

Units of Energy

The SI unit of energy is the **joule (J),** a derived unit composed of three base units:

$$1 \text{ J} = \text{kg} \cdot \text{m}^2/\text{s}^2$$

Both heat and work are expressed in joules. Let's see how these units arise in the case of work. The work done on the mass (m) is the force (F) times the distance (d, in meters) that the mass moves. A *force* changes the velocity of (accelerates) a mass. Velocity has units of meters per second (m/s), so acceleration (a) has units of m/s^2. Force, therefore, has units of mass times acceleration:

$$F = m \times a \qquad \text{in units of} \qquad \text{kg} \cdot \text{m/s}^2$$

Therefore, $w = F \times d$ has units of $(\text{kg} \cdot \text{m/s}^2) \times \text{m} = \text{kg} \cdot \text{m}^2/\text{s}^2 = \text{J}$

Potential energy, kinetic energy, and PV work are combinations of the same physical quantities and are expressed in joules also.

The **calorie (cal)** is an older unit that was defined originally as the amount of energy needed to raise the temperature of 1 g of water by 1°C (from 14.5°C to 15.5°C). The calorie is now defined in terms of the joule:

$$1 \text{ cal} \equiv 4.184 \text{ J} \qquad \text{or} \qquad 1 \text{ J} = \frac{1}{4.184} \text{ cal} = 0.2390 \text{ cal}$$

Since the amounts of energy involved in chemical reactions are usually quite large, chemists use the kilojoule (kJ), or sometimes the kilocalorie (kcal):

$$1 \text{ kJ} = 1000 \text{ J} = 0.2390 \text{ kcal} = 239.0 \text{ cal}$$

The nutritional Calorie (note the capital C), the unit that diet tables use to show the energy available from food, is actually a kilocalorie. The *British thermal unit (Btu),* a unit in engineering that you may have seen used to indicate energy output of appliances, is the amount of energy required to raise the temperature of 1 lb of water by 1°F and is equivalent to 1055 J. In general, the SI unit (J or kJ) is used throughout this text. Some interesting quantities of energy appear in Figure 6.5.

Sample Problem 6.1   Determining the Change in Internal Energy of a System

PROBLEM When gasoline burns in a car engine, the heat released causes the products CO_2 and H_2O to expand, which pushes the pistons outward. Excess heat is removed by the car's cooling system. If the expanding gases do 451 J of work on the pistons and the system loses 325 J to the surroundings as heat, calculate the change in energy (ΔE) in J, kJ, and kcal.

PLAN The most important step is to define system and surroundings. We define the system as the reactants and products of the reaction. The surroundings are the pistons, the cooling system, and the rest of the car. Heat is released by the system, so q is negative. Work is done by the system to push the pistons outward, so w is also negative. ΔE is the sum of q and w. We obtain the answer in J and then convert it to kJ and kcal.

SOLUTION Calculating ΔE in J:

$$q = -325 \text{ J} \qquad w = -451 \text{ J}$$
$$\Delta E = q + w = -325 \text{ J} + (-451 \text{ J}) = \boxed{-776 \text{ J}}$$

Converting from J to kJ:

$$\Delta E = -776 \text{ J} \times \frac{1 \text{ kJ}}{1000 \text{ J}} = \boxed{-0.776 \text{ kJ}}$$

Converting kJ to kcal:

$$\Delta E = -0.776 \text{ kJ} \times \frac{1 \text{ kcal}}{4.184 \text{ kJ}} = \boxed{-0.185 \text{ kcal}}$$

CHECK The answer is reasonable: combustion releases energy from the system, so $E_{\text{final}} < E_{\text{initial}}$ and ΔE should be negative. Since 4 kJ ≈ 1 kcal, nearly 0.8 kJ should be nearly 0.2 kcal.

Follow-up Problem 6.1   In a reaction, gaseous reactants form a liquid product. The heat absorbed by the surroundings is 26.0 kcal, and the work done on the system is 15.0 Btu. Calculate ΔE (in kJ).

10^{24} J — Daily solar energy falling on Earth

10^{21} J — Energy of a strong earthquake

10^{18} J — Daily electrical output of Hoover Dam

10^{15} J — 1000 tons of coal burned

10^{12} J

10^{9} J — 1 ton of TNT exploded

10^{6} J — 1 kilowatt-hour of electrical energy / Heat released from combustion of 1 mol glucose

10^{3} J

10^{0} J — 1 calorie (4.184 J)

10^{-3} J

10^{-6} J

10^{-9} J — Heat absorbed during division of one bacterial cell

10^{-12} J — Energy from fission of one ^{235}U atom

10^{-15} J

10^{-18} J

10^{-21} J — Average kinetic energy of a molecule in air at 300 K

Figure 6.5 Some interesting quantities of energy. Note that the vertical scale is exponential.

State Functions and the Path Independence of the Energy Change

An important point to understand is that there is no particular sequence by which the internal energy (E) of a system must change. E is a **state function,** a property determined by the *current* state of the system (its composition, volume, pressure, and temperature) and is *not* dependent on the path the system took to reach that state. ◆ The pressure (P) of an ideal gas or the volume (V) of water in a beaker are other examples of state functions. This path independence means that *changes in state functions—ΔE, ΔP, and ΔV—depend only on their initial and final states.*

To put this idea another way, the energy change of a system can occur by many different combinations of heat (q) and work (w). No matter what the combination, however, the same overall energy change occurs, because ΔE *does **not** depend on how the change takes place.* As an example, let's define a system in its initial state as 1 mol octane (a component of gasoline) together with enough O_2 to burn it. In its final state, the system is the CO_2 and H_2O

◆ Your Personal Financial State Function The *balance* in your checkbook is a state function of your personal financial system. You can open a new account with a birthday gift of $50, or you can open a new account with a deposit of a $100 paycheck and then write two $25 checks. The two paths to the balance are different, but the balance (current state) is the same.

Figure 6.6 Two different paths for the energy change of a system. The change in internal energy when a given amount of octane burns in air is the same no matter how the energy is transferred. On the left, the fuel is burned in an open can, and the energy is lost almost entirely as heat. On the right, it is burned in a car engine, so a portion of the energy is lost as work to move the car, and thus less is lost as heat.

that form (a fractional coefficient is needed because we specified 1 mol octane):

$$C_8H_{18}(l) + \tfrac{25}{2}O_2(g) \longrightarrow 8CO_2(g) + 9H_2O(g)$$

initial state ($E_{initial}$)   final state (E_{final})

Energy is released to warm the surroundings and/or do work on them, so ΔE is negative. Two of the many possible ways the change can occur are shown in Figure 6.6. If we burn the octane in an open container, ΔE appears almost completely as heat (with a small amount of work done to push back the atmosphere). If we burn it in a car engine, a much larger portion (~30%) of ΔE appears as work that moves the car, with the rest used to heat the car, air, and exhaust gases. If we burn the octane in a lawnmower or a plane, ΔE appears as other combinations of work and heat.

Thus, the separate amounts of work and heat available from the change *do* depend on how the change occurs, but the *total* change in internal energy, the *sum* of the heat and work, *does not*. In other words, for a given change, ΔE *(sum of q and w) is constant, even though the specific values of q and w can vary.* Thus, heat and work are *not* state functions because their values *do* depend on the path the system takes in undergoing the energy change. (To remember this, note that symbols for state functions, such as *E*, *P*, and *V*, are capitalized.)

Section Summary

Energy is transferred as heat (*q*) when the system and surroundings are at different temperatures; energy is transferred as work (*w*) when an object is moved by a force. Heat or work gained by a system ($q > 0$; $w > 0$) increases its internal energy (*E*); heat or work lost by the system ($q < 0$; $w < 0$) decreases *E*. The total change in the system's internal energy is the sum of the heat and work: $\Delta E = q + w$. Heat and work are measured in joules (J). Energy is always conserved: it changes from one form into another, moving into or out of the system, but the total quantity of energy in the universe (system *plus* surroundings) is constant. Energy is a state function; therefore, the same ΔE can occur through any combination of *q* and *w*.

6.2 Enthalpy: Heats of Reaction and Chemical Change

Most physical and chemical changes occur at virtually constant atmospheric pressure—a reaction in an open flask, the freezing of a lake, a drug response in an organism. Defining a thermodynamic variable called *enthalpy*, which takes such constant pressure into account, makes it much easier to measure energy changes.

The Meaning of Enthalpy

To determine ΔE, we must measure both heat and work. The two most important types of chemical work are electrical work, the work done by moving charged particles (Chapter 21), and PV work, the work done by an expanding gas. We find the quantity of PV work done by multiplying the external pressure (P) by the change in volume of the gas (ΔV, or $V_{final} - V_{initial}$). In an open flask, a gas does work by pushing back the atmosphere. As Figure 6.7 shows, this work done *on* the surroundings is defined as negative because the system loses energy:

$$w = -P\Delta V \tag{6.4}$$

For reactions that occur at constant pressure, a thermodynamic variable called **enthalpy (H)** eliminates our need to consider PV work. The enthalpy of a system is defined as the internal energy *plus* the product of the pressure and volume:

$$H = E + PV$$

The **change in enthalpy (ΔH)** is the change in internal energy *plus* the product of the constant pressure and the change in volume:

$$\Delta H = \Delta E + P\Delta V \tag{6.5}$$

Combining Equations 6.2 ($\Delta E = q + w$) and 6.4 leads to a key point about ΔH:

$$\Delta E = q + w = q + (-P\Delta V) = q - P\Delta V$$

At constant pressure, we denote q as q_P and solve for it:

$$q_P = \Delta E + P\Delta V$$

Notice that the right side of this equation is identical to the right side of Equation 6.5; that is,

$$q_P = \Delta E + P\Delta V = \Delta H \tag{6.6}$$

Thus, *the change in enthalpy equals the heat gained or lost at constant pressure*. Since most changes occur at constant pressure, ΔH is more relevant than ΔE *and* easier to find: *To find ΔH, measure q_P.*

We discuss the laboratory method for measuring the heat involved in a chemical or physical change in Section 6.3.

Comparing ΔE and ΔH

Knowing the *enthalpy* change of a system tells us a lot about its *energy* change also. In fact, since many reactions involve little (if any) PV work, most (or all) of the energy change occurs as a transfer of heat. Here are three cases:

1. *Reactions that do not involve gases.* Gases do not appear in many reactions (precipitation, many acid-base, and many redox reactions). For example,

$$2KOH(aq) + H_2SO_4(aq) \longrightarrow K_2SO_4(aq) + 2H_2O(l)$$

Since liquids and solids undergo *very* small volume changes, $\Delta V \approx 0$, so $P\Delta V \approx 0$ and $\Delta H \approx \Delta E$.

2. *Reactions in which the amount (mol) of gas does **not** change.* When the total amount of gaseous reactants equals the total amount of gaseous products, $\Delta V = 0$, so $P\Delta V = 0$ and $\Delta H = \Delta E$. For example,

$$N_2(g) + O_2(g) \longrightarrow 2NO(g)$$

3. *Reactions in which the amount (mol) of gas **does** change.* In these cases, $P\Delta V \neq 0$. However, q_P is usually *much* larger than $P\Delta V$. For instance, in the combustion of H_2, 3 mol of gas yields 2:

$$2H_2(g) + O_2(g) \longrightarrow 2H_2O(g)$$

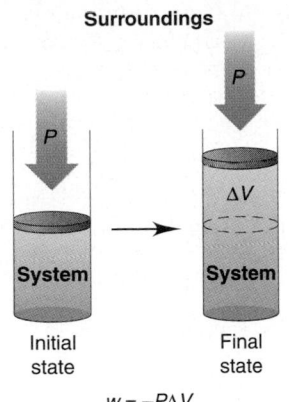

Surroundings

Figure 6.7 Pressure-volume work. When the volume (V) of a system increases by an amount ΔV against an external pressure (P), the system does PV work *on* the surroundings ($w = -P\Delta V$).

In this reaction, $\Delta H = -483.6$ kJ and $P\Delta V = -2.5$ kJ, so (from Equation 6.5), we get

$$\Delta E = \Delta H - P\Delta V = -483.6 \text{ kJ} + (-2.5 \text{ kJ}) = -481.1 \text{ kJ}$$

Obviously, most of ΔE occurs as heat transfer, so $\Delta H \approx \Delta E$.

The key point to realize from these three cases is that *for many reactions, ΔH equals, or is very close to, ΔE.*

Exothermic and Endothermic Processes

Since E, P, and V are state functions, H is also a state function, which means that ΔH depends only on the *difference* between H_{final} and H_{initial}. The enthalpy change of a reaction, also called the **heat of reaction, ΔH_{rxn},** *always refers to H_{final} **minus** H_{initial}:*

$$\Delta H = H_{\text{final}} - H_{\text{initial}} = H_{\text{products}} - H_{\text{reactants}}$$

Therefore, since H_{products} can be either more or less than $H_{\text{reactants}}$, the sign of ΔH indicates whether heat is absorbed or released in the change. We determine the sign of ΔH *by imagining the heat as a "reactant" or "product."* When methane burns in air, for example, we know that heat is produced, so we show it as a product (on the right):

$$CH_4(g) + 2O_2(g) \longrightarrow CO_2(g) + 2H_2O(g) + heat$$

Because heat is released to the surroundings, the products (1 mol CO_2 and 2 mol H_2O) must have less enthalpy than the reactants (1 mol CH_4 and 2 mol O_2). Therefore, ΔH ($H_{\text{final}} - H_{\text{initial}}$) is negative, as the **enthalpy diagram** in Figure 6.8A shows. An **exothermic** ("heat out") process *releases* heat and results in a *decrease* in the enthalpy of the system:

$$\text{Exothermic:} \quad H_{\text{final}} < H_{\text{initial}} \quad \Delta H < 0$$

An **endothermic** ("heat in") process *absorbs* heat and results in an *increase* in the enthalpy of the system. When ice melts, for instance, heat flows *into* the ice from the surroundings, so we show the heat as a reactant (on the left):

$$heat + H_2O(s) \longrightarrow H_2O(l)$$

Because heat is absorbed, the enthalpy of the liquid water is higher than that of the solid water, as Figure 6.8B shows. Therefore, ΔH ($H_{\text{water}} - H_{\text{ice}}$) is positive:

$$\text{Endothermic:} \quad H_{\text{final}} > H_{\text{initial}} \quad \Delta H > 0$$

Figure 6.8 Enthalpy diagrams for exothermic and endothermic processes. A, The combustion of methane occurs with a decrease in enthalpy because heat *leaves* the system. Therefore, $H_{\text{final}} < H_{\text{initial}}$, and the process is exothermic: $\Delta H < 0$. **B,** The melting of ice occurs with an increase in enthalpy because heat *enters* the system. Since $H_{\text{final}} > H_{\text{initial}}$, the process is endothermic: $\Delta H > 0$.

Sample Problem 6.2   Drawing Enthalpy Diagrams and Determining the Sign of ΔH

PROBLEM In each of the following cases, determine the sign of ΔH, state whether the reaction is exothermic or endothermic, and draw an enthalpy diagram:
(a) $H_2(g) + \frac{1}{2}O_2(g) \longrightarrow H_2O(l) + 285.8 \text{ kJ}$
(b) $40.7 \text{ kJ} + H_2O(l) \longrightarrow H_2O(g)$
PLAN We inspect each equation to see whether heat is a "product" (exothermic; $\Delta H < 0$) or a "reactant" (endothermic; $\Delta H > 0$). For exothermic reactions, reactants are above products on the enthalpy diagram; for endothermic reactions, reactants are below products. The ΔH arrow *always* points from reactants to products.
SOLUTION **(a)** Heat is a product (on the right), so $\boxed{\Delta H < 0}$ and the reaction is exothermic. The enthalpy diagram appears in the margin (*top*).

(b) Heat is a reactant (on the left), so $\boxed{\Delta H > 0}$ and the reaction is endothermic. The enthalpy diagram appears in the margin (*bottom*).
CHECK Substances on the same side of the equation as the heat have less enthalpy than substances on the other side, so make sure they are placed on the lower line of the diagram.
COMMENT ΔH values depend on conditions. In (b), for instance, $\Delta H = 40.7$ kJ at 1 atm and 100°C; at 1 atm and 25°C, $\Delta H = 44.0$ kJ.

Follow-up Problem 6.2   When 1 mol nitroglycerine decomposes, it causes a violent explosion and releases 5.72×10^3 kJ of heat:

$$C_3H_5(NO_3)_3(l) \longrightarrow 3CO_2(g) + \tfrac{5}{2}H_2O(g) + \tfrac{1}{4}O_2(g) + \tfrac{3}{2}N_2(g)$$

Is the reaction exothermic or endothermic? Draw an enthalpy diagram for it.

Some Important Types of Enthalpy Change

Certain enthalpy changes are very frequently studied and have special names:
- When 1 mole of a substance combines with O_2 in a combustion reaction as written, the heat of reaction is the **heat of combustion (ΔH_{comb}):**

$$C_4H_{10}(l) + \tfrac{13}{2}O_2(g) \longrightarrow 4CO_2(g) + 5H_2O(l) \qquad \Delta H = \Delta H_{comb}$$

- When 1 mole of a compound is produced from its elements, the heat of reaction is the **heat of formation (ΔH_f):**

$$K(s) + \tfrac{1}{2}Br_2(l) \longrightarrow KBr(s) \qquad \Delta H = \Delta H_f$$

- When 1 mole of a substance melts, the enthalpy change is the **heat of fusion (ΔH_{fus}):**

$$NaCl(s) \longrightarrow NaCl(l) \qquad \Delta H = \Delta H_{fus}$$

- When 1 mole of a substance vaporizes, the enthalpy change is the **heat of vaporization (ΔH_{vap}):**

$$C_6H_6(l) \longrightarrow C_6H_6(g) \qquad \Delta H = \Delta H_{vap}$$

We encounter heats of combustion and formation shortly; other special enthalpy changes are discussed in later chapters.

Changes in Bond Strengths, or Where Does the Heat of Reaction Come From?

Let's stop for a moment to consider a major question about the heat of reaction. When 2 g H_2 (1 mol) and 38 g F_2 (1 mol) react at 298 K (25°C), 40 g HF (2 mol) forms and 546 kJ of heat is released:

$$H_2(g) + F_2(g) \longrightarrow 2HF(g) + 546 \text{ kJ}$$

Where does this heat come from? The amount (mol) of gas does not change, so the change in enthalpy equals the change in internal energy. Let's break down the system's internal energy into its component kinetic energy (E_k) and potential energy (E_p) and examine the contributions to these components to see which one changes during the reaction.

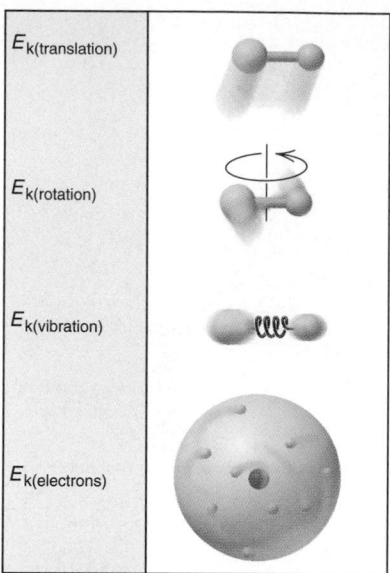

A Contributions to kinetic energy (E_k)

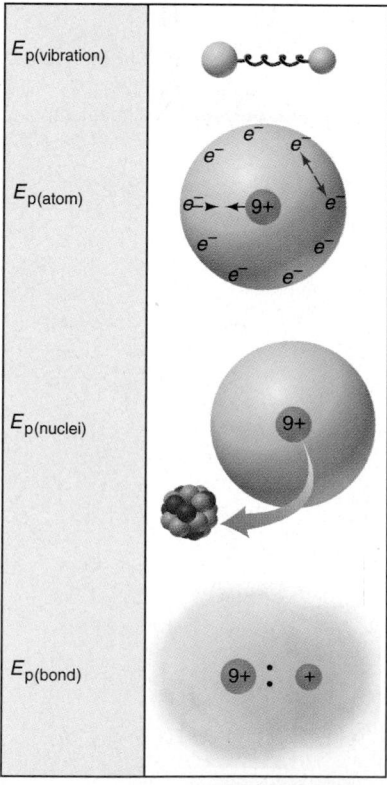

B Contributions to potential energy (E_p)

Figure 6.9 **Components of internal energy (E).** The total energy of a system is the sum of the E_k (**A**) and E_p (**B**) of its particles. The contributions to E_k and E_p are shown for a hydrogen fluoride molecule (or, where appropriate, just the fluorine atom). Only $E_{p(bond)}$ changes significantly during a chemical reaction.

There are several contributions to E_k and E_p, some major and some minor, but the most important are listed below and depicted schematically in Figure 6.9:

1. *Contributions to the kinetic energy:*
   - The molecule moving through space, $E_{k(translation)}$
   - The molecule rotating, $E_{k(rotation)}$
   - The bound atoms vibrating, $E_{k(vibration)}$
   - The electrons moving within each atom, $E_{k(electron)}$
2. *Contributions to the potential energy:*
   - Forces between the bound atoms vibrating, $E_{p(vibration)}$
   - Forces between nucleus and electrons and between electrons in each atom, $E_{p(atom)}$
   - Forces between the protons and neutrons in each nucleus, $E_{p(nuclei)}$
   - Forces between nuclei and shared electron pair in each bond, $E_{p(bond)}$

Now let's see which contributions we can eliminate because they don't change significantly during the reaction:

1. Among the *kinetic energy* contributions, the first three—$E_{k(translation)}$, $E_{k(rotation)}$, and $E_{k(vibration)}$—are proportional to the absolute temperature, which is constant at 298 K (25°C), so they don't change. Electron motion is not affected by the reaction, so $E_{k(electron)}$ doesn't change either. Therefore, the total E_k is virtually unchanged during the reaction.

2. Among the *potential energy* contributions, we can eliminate $E_{p(atom)}$ and $E_{p(nuclei)}$ because the atoms and nuclei don't change. The potential energy of vibration, $E_{p(vibration)}$, changes slightly because the bonded atoms change, but this change is small. The only energy contribution that changes significantly in a chemical reaction is $E_{p(bond)}$, the strength of attraction of the nuclei for the shared electron pair that constitutes the covalent bond. In other words, the answer to our opening question is that the heat doesn't really "come from" anywhere: *The energy released or absorbed during a chemical change is due to differences between the strengths of reactant bonds and product bonds.*

Breaking and Forming Bonds We can think of a reaction as a process in which *the bonds of the reactants absorb energy when they break, and the bonds of the products release energy when they form.* When 1 mol of H—H bonds and 1 mol of F—F bonds absorb energy and break, the atoms form 2 mol of H—F bonds, which releases energy. Since this reaction has a net release of energy (exothermic), more energy is released when the bonds in HF form than is absorbed when the bonds in H_2 and F_2 break. If, on the other hand, a reaction absorbs more energy to break reactant bonds than it releases to form product bonds, there is a net absorption of energy (endothermic). In either case, this difference in energy appears as the heat of reaction, ΔH_{rxn}.

Chemists speak in terms of the relative strengths of bonds. *Weaker bonds are easier to break than stronger bonds because they are higher in energy (less stable, more reactive).* As Figure 6.10 shows, heat is released when HF forms from its elements because the bonds in the reactants H_2 and F_2 are weaker (less sta-

Figure 6.10 **ΔH and the strengths of bonds.** An enthalpy diagram of the formation of HF shows that the reactants have more enthalpy than the product. When the weaker bonds in H_2 and F_2 break and the stronger bonds in HF form, the difference is released as ΔH_{rxn}.

Table 6.2 Heats of Combustion (ΔH_{comb}) of Some Carbon Compounds

Name (Formula)	Structural Formula	Sum of C—C and C—H Bonds	Sum of C—O and O—H Bonds	ΔH_{comb} (kJ/mol)	ΔH_{comb} (kJ/g)
Two-carbon compounds					
Ethane (C_2H_6)	H—C—C—H (with H's)	7	0	−1560	−51.88
Ethanol (C_2H_5OH)	H—C—C—O—H (with H's)	6	2	−1367	−29.67
One-carbon compounds					
Methane (CH_4)	H—C—H (with H's)	4	0	−890	−55.5
Methanol (CH_3OH)	H—C—O—H (with H's)	3	2	−727	−22.7

ble) than the bonds in the product HF (more stable). We'll discuss these ideas quantitatively in Chapter 9.

Bonds in Fuels and Foods The most common fuels for machines are hydrocarbons and coal, and the most common ones for organisms are fats and carbohydrates. Both types of fuel are composed of large organic molecules with mostly C—C and C—H bonds. When the fuel reacts with O_2, the bonds break, and the C, H, and O atoms form C—O and O—H bonds in the products CO_2 and H_2O. Since burning these fuels releases energy, we know that the total strength of the bonds in the products is greater than the total strength of the bonds in the fuel and O_2.

Fuels with more weak (less stable, higher energy) bonds yield more energy than fuels with fewer. Table 6.2 demonstrates this point for some small organic compounds. As the number of C—C and C—H bonds decreases and/or the number of C—O and O—H bonds increases, less energy is released from combustion; that is, ΔH_{comb} is less negative. In other words, the fewer bonds to O in a fuel, the more energy it releases when burned.

Both fats and carbohydrates are organic compounds that serve as high-energy food sources. Fats consist largely of chains of carbon atoms (C—C bonds) attached to hydrogen atoms (C—H bonds). Carbohydrates have these bonds and C—O and O—H bonds. Both foods are metabolized in the body to CO_2 and H_2O. Why, as any dieter knows, do fats "contain more Calories" per gram than carbohydrates? The reason is that fats have fewer bonds to O, so they release more energy than do carbohydrates, as Table 6.3 confirms.

Table 6.3 Heats of Combustion of Some Fats and Carbohydrates

Substance	ΔH_{comb} (kJ/g)
Fats	
Vegetable oil	37.0
Margarine	30.1
Butter	30.0
Carbohydrates	
Table sugar (sucrose)	16.2
Brown rice	14.9
Maple syrup	10.4

Section Summary

The change in enthalpy, ΔH, is the heat lost or gained at constant pressure, q_P. In most cases, ΔH is equal, or very close, to ΔE. A chemical (or physical) change that releases heat is exothermic ($\Delta H < 0$); one that absorbs heat is endothermic ($\Delta H > 0$). On the molecular level, the heat lost or gained represents a difference in the strengths of the bonds of the products and the reactants. A reaction involves breaking reactant bonds and forming product bonds. Bonds in fuels and foods are weaker (less stable, higher energy) than bonds in waste products.

6.3 Calorimetry: Laboratory Measurement of Heats of Reaction

Our previous discussion about the energy value of fuels and foods makes it clear that the heat of reaction is very useful to measure. For example, Table 6.3 shows that when 1 g of table sugar (sucrose, $C_{12}H_{22}O_{11}$) burns, 16.2 kJ of heat is released. But how do we make that measurement? It might seem that we can simply measure the enthalpies of the reactants and subtract them from the enthalpies of the products. The problem is that the enthalpy (H) of a system in a given state cannot be measured because we have no starting point with which to compare it, no zero enthalpy. However, we *can* measure the *change* in enthalpy (ΔH). Recall that ΔH is the heat released or absorbed by the system at constant pressure (q_P).

To measure q_P accurately, we construct "surroundings" that retain the heat and measure the temperature change on a thermometer immersed in the surroundings. Then, we have to relate the quantity of heat released (or absorbed) to the temperature change. This relation involves a physical property of a substance called the *specific heat capacity.*

Specific Heat Capacity

You know from everyday experience that the more heat an object absorbs, the hotter it gets; that is, the quantity of heat (q) absorbed by an object is proportional to its temperature change:

$$q \propto \Delta T \qquad \text{or} \qquad q = \text{constant} \times \Delta T \qquad \text{or} \qquad \frac{q}{\Delta T} = \text{constant}$$

Every object has its own particular capacity for absorbing heat, its own **heat capacity,** the quantity of heat required to change its temperature by 1 K. Heat capacity is the proportionality constant in the preceding equation:

$$\text{Heat capacity} = \frac{q}{\Delta T} \qquad \text{[in units of J/K]}$$

A related property is **specific heat capacity (c),** the quantity of heat required to change the temperature of 1 *gram* of a substance by 1 K:*

$$\text{Specific heat capacity } (c) = \frac{q}{\text{mass} \times \Delta T} \qquad \text{[in units of J/g} \cdot \text{K]}$$

If we know c of the substance being heated (or cooled), we can measure its mass and temperature change and calculate the heat absorbed or released:

$$q = c \times \text{mass} \times \Delta T \tag{6.7}$$

Notice that when an object gets hotter, ΔT (that is, $T_{\text{final}} - T_{\text{initial}}$) is positive. The object gains heat, so $q > 0$ as we expect. Similarly, when an object gets cooler, ΔT is negative, so $q < 0$ because heat is lost. Table 6.4 lists the specific heat capacities of several common substances. ◆

Closely related to the specific heat capacity is the **molar heat capacity (C;** note capital letter), the quantity of heat required to change the temperature of 1 *mole* of a substance by 1 K:

$$\text{Molar heat capacity } (C) = \frac{q}{\text{moles} \times \Delta T} \qquad \text{[in units of J/mol} \cdot \text{K]}$$

◆ Imagine an Earth Without Water Liquid water has an unusually high specific heat capacity of nearly 4.2 J/g · K, about six times that of rock (~0.7 J/g · K). If the Earth were devoid of oceans, the Sun's energy would heat a planet composed of rock. It would take only 0.7 J of energy to increase the temperature of each gram of rock by 1 K. Daytime temperatures would soar. The oceans also limit the temperature drop when the Sun sets, because the energy absorbed during the day is released at night. If the Earth had a rocky surface, temperatures would be frigid every night.

---

*Some texts use the term *specific heat* in place of *specific heat capacity.* This usage is very common but somewhat incorrect. *Specific heat* is the ratio of the heat capacity of 1 g of a substance to the heat capacity of 1 g H_2O and therefore has no units.

The specific heat capacity of liquid water is 4.184 J/g · K, so

$$C \text{ of } H_2O(l) = 4.184 \ \frac{J}{g \cdot K} \times \frac{18.02 \ g}{1 \ mol} = 75.40 \ \frac{J}{mol \cdot K}$$

Sample Problem 6.3 Calculating the Quantity of Heat from the Specific Heat Capacity

PROBLEM A welded layer of copper on the bottom of a skillet weighs 125 g. How much heat is needed to raise the temperature of the copper layer from 25°C to 300°C? The specific heat capacity (c) of Cu is 0.387 J/g · K.

PLAN We know the mass and c of Cu and can find ΔT in °C, which equals ΔT in K. We use this ΔT and Equation 6.7 to solve for the heat.

SOLUTION Calculating ΔT and q:

$$\Delta T = T_{final} - T_{initial} = 300°C - 25°C = 275°C = 275 \ K$$

$$q = c \times mass \ (g) \times \Delta T = 0.387 \ J/g \cdot K \times 125 \ g \times 275 \ K = \boxed{1.33 \times 10^4 \ J}$$

CHECK Heat is absorbed by the skillet, so q is positive. The arithmetic seems reasonable: $q \approx 0.4 \times 100 \times 300 = 1.2 \times 10^4$.

Follow-up Problem 6.3 Calculate the heat transferred when a 5.5-g iron nail is cooled from 37°C to 25°C. (See Table 6.4.)

The Practice of Calorimetry

The **calorimeter** is a device used to measure the heat released (or absorbed) by a physical or chemical process. We know that heat is transferred from system to surroundings (and vice versa). In essence, the calorimeter is the "surroundings" we construct to measure the temperature change that results from this transferred heat. Two common types are the constant-pressure and constant-volume calorimeters.

Constant-Pressure Calorimetry The "coffee-cup" calorimeter shown in Figure 6.11 is used to measure the heat (q_P) of many processes that are open to the laboratory atmosphere. A common use is to determine the specific heat capacity of a solid, one that does not react with or dissolve in water. The solid (system) is weighed, heated to some known temperature, and added to a sample of water (surroundings) of known temperature and mass in the calorimeter. Continual stirring distributes the released heat, and the final water temperature, which is also the final temperature of the solid, is measured.

The heat lost by the system ($-q$) is equal in magnitude but opposite in sign to the heat gained ($+q$) by the surroundings:

$$-q_{solid} = q_{H_2O}$$

Substituting Equation 6.7 gives

$$-(c_{solid} \times mass_{solid} \times \Delta T_{solid}) = c_{H_2O} \times mass_{H_2O} \times \Delta T_{H_2O}$$

All the quantities are known except c_{solid}:

$$c_{solid} = -\frac{c_{H_2O} \times mass_{H_2O} \times \Delta T_{H_2O}}{mass_{solid} \times \Delta T_{solid}}$$

Table 6.4 Specific Heat Capacities of Some Elements, Compounds, and Materials

Substance	Specific Heat Capacity (J/g · K)*
Elements	
Aluminum, Al	0.900
Graphite, C	0.711
Iron, Fe	0.450
Copper, Cu	0.387
Gold, Au	0.129
Compounds	
Ammonia, $NH_3(l)$	4.70
Water, $H_2O(l)$	4.184
Ethyl alcohol, $C_2H_5OH(l)$	2.46
Ethylene glycol, $(CH_2OH)_2(l)$	2.42
Carbon tetrachloride, $CCl_4(l)$	0.862
Solid materials	
Wood	1.76
Cement	0.88
Glass	0.84
Granite	0.79
Steel	0.45

*At 298 K (25°C).

Stirrer — Thermometer — Styrofoam cups (insulation) — Water (surroundings) — Sample (system)

Figure 6.11 A coffee-cup calorimeter. This simple apparatus is used to measure the heat at constant pressure (q_P). It consists of a known mass of water (or solution) in an insulated container equipped with a thermometer and stirrer. The initial temperature of the water is measured, the process takes place (addition of a heated object, a soluble salt, a solution, and so on), the contents are stirred, and the final temperature of the water is measured.

Sample Problem 6.4   Determining the Specific Heat Capacity of a Solid

PROBLEM A 25.64-g sample of a solid was heated in a test tube to 100.00°C in boiling water and carefully added to a coffee-cup calorimeter containing 50.00 g water. The water temperature increased from 25.10°C to 28.49°C. What is the specific heat capacity of the solid? (Assume all the heat is gained by the water.)

PLAN We know the masses of water and solid. We subtract to find ΔT of the water and the solid and change ΔT (°C) directly to ΔT (K). We know c_{H_2O}, so we can find c_{solid}.

SOLUTION It is helpful to summarize the information given:

	MASS (g)	c (J/g · K)	$T_{initial}$ (°C)	T_{final} (°C)	ΔT (K)
Solid	25.64	?	100.00	28.49	−71.51
H_2O	50.00	4.184	25.10	28.49	3.39

Calculating c_{solid}:

$$c_{solid} = -\frac{c_{H_2O} \times mass_{H_2O} \times \Delta T_{H_2O}}{mass_{solid} \times \Delta T_{solid}} = -\frac{4.184 \text{ J/g} \cdot \text{K} \times 50.00 \text{ g} \times 3.39 \text{ K}}{25.64 \text{ g} \times (-71.51 \text{ K})}$$

$$= 0.387 \text{ J/g} \cdot \text{K}$$

CHECK Since $-q_{solid} = q_{H_2O}$, we can check to see if the numerical values are equal:

$$q_{H_2O} = 4.184 \text{ J/g} \cdot \text{K} \times 50.00 \text{ g} \times 3.39 \text{ K} = 709 \text{ J}$$

$$q_{solid} = 0.387 \text{ J/g} \cdot \text{K} \times 25.64 \text{ g} \times (-71.51 \text{ K}) = -710 \text{ J}$$

The slight difference is caused by rounding.

COMMENT 1. A *common mistake* is to write the wrong sign for ΔT. To avoid this, remember that Δ means *final − initial*.

2. The problem statement said to assume that all heat is absorbed by the water, but that is not valid for precise work because some heat must be gained by the other parts of the calorimeter (stirrer, thermometer, stopper, coffee-cup walls) as well. For more accurate measurements, as discussed next, the *heat capacity of the entire calorimeter* must be known.

Follow-up Problem 6.4 As a purity check for industrial diamonds, a 10.25-carat diamond is heated to 74.21°C and immersed in 26.05 g water in a constant-pressure calorimeter (1 carat = 0.2000 g). The initial temperature of the water is 27.20°C. Calculate ΔT of the water and of the diamond. ($c_{diamond} = 0.519$ J/g · K.)

Constant-Volume Calorimetry A common type of constant-volume apparatus is the *bomb calorimeter*, designed to measure very precisely the heat released in a combustion reaction. As you'll see in Sample Problem 6.5, this need for greater precision requires that we know (or determine) the heat capacity of the calorimeter.

Figure 6.12 depicts the preweighed combustible sample in a metal-walled chamber (bomb), which is filled with oxygen gas and immersed in an insulated water bath fitted with motorized stirrer and thermometer. A heating coil connected to an electrical source ignites the sample, and the heat evolved raises the temperature of the bomb, water, and other calorimeter parts. Knowing the mass of the sample and the heat capacity of the calorimeter, we use the measured ΔT to calculate the heat released.

Sample Problem 6.5   Calculating the Heat of Combustion

PROBLEM A manufacturer claims that its new dietetic dessert has "fewer than 10 Calories per serving." To test the claim, a chemist at the Department of Consumer Affairs places one serving in a bomb calorimeter and burns it in O_2. The temperature increases 4.937°C. Is the manufacturer's claim correct? (Heat capacity of the calorimeter = 8.151 kJ/K.)

PLAN When the dessert burns, the heat released is gained by the calorimeter:

$$-q_{sample} = q_{calorimeter}$$

We find the heat by multiplying the heat capacity of the calorimeter by ΔT.
SOLUTION Calculating the heat gained by the calorimeter:

$$q_{calorimeter} = \text{heat capacity} \times \Delta T = 8.151 \text{ kJ/K} \times 4.937 \text{ K} = 40.24 \text{ kJ}$$

Recall that 1 Calorie = 1 kcal = 4.184 kJ. Therefore, 10 Calories = 41.84 kJ, so the claim is correct.

CHECK A quick check shows the answer is reasonable: 8 kJ/K $\times$ 5 K = 40 kJ.
COMMENT Since the volume of the steel bomb is fixed, ΔV and thus $P\Delta V = 0$. Therefore, the energy change measured is the *heat at constant volume* (q_V), which equals ΔE, not ΔH:

$$\Delta E = q + w = q_V + 0 = q_V$$

Recall from Section 6.2, however, that even though the number of moles of gas may change, ΔH is usually very close to ΔE. For example, ΔH is only 0.5% larger than ΔE for the combustion of H_2 and 0.2% smaller for the combustion of octane (see Problem 6.105 at the end of the chapter).

Follow-up Problem 6.5 A chemist burns 0.8650 g graphite (a form of carbon) in a new bomb calorimeter, and CO_2 forms. If 393.5 kJ is released per mole of graphite burned and the temperature increase is 2.613 K, what is the heat capacity of the new bomb calorimeter?

Section Summary

We calculate ΔH of a process by measuring the heat at constant pressure (q_P). To do this, we determine ΔT of the surroundings and relate it to q_P through the mass of the substance and its specific heat capacity (c), the amount of energy needed to raise the temperature of 1 g of the substance by 1 K. Calorimeters measure the heat released from a system either at constant pressure ($q_P = \Delta H$) or at constant volume ($q_V = \Delta E$).

Figure 6.12 A bomb calorimeter. This device (not drawn to scale) is used to measure heat of combustion at constant volume (q_V). With continual stirring, the initial temperature of the preweighed water bath is taken. The electrically heated coil ignites the system (combustible substance in O_2) within the steel bomb. Heat released from the combustion reaction is transferred to the rest of the calorimeter, and the maximum temperature is measured.

6.4   Stoichiometry of Thermochemical Equations

A good way to record the enthalpy change for a particular reaction is through a **thermochemical equation,** a balanced equation that also states the heat of reaction (ΔH_{rxn}). One thing to always keep in mind is that the ΔH_{rxn} value shown refers to the enthalpy change *for the amounts of substances in that specific reaction.* The enthalpy change of any process has two aspects:

1. *Sign.* The sign of ΔH depends on the direction of the change. The sign of a forward reaction is *opposite* that of the reverse reaction.

Decomposition of 2 mol water to its elements (endothermic):

$$2H_2O(l) \longrightarrow 2H_2(g) + O_2(g) \qquad \Delta H_{rxn} = 572 \text{ kJ}$$

Formation of 2 mol water from its elements (exothermic):

$$2H_2(g) + O_2(g) \longrightarrow 2H_2O(l) \qquad \Delta H_{rxn} = -572 \text{ kJ}$$

2. *Magnitude.* The magnitude of ΔH is *proportional to the amount of substance* in the reaction.

Formation of 1 mol water from its elements (half the amount in the previous equation):

$$H_2(g) + \tfrac{1}{2}O_2(g) \longrightarrow H_2O(l) \qquad \Delta H_{rxn} = -286 \text{ kJ}$$

Note that, in thermochemical equations, we use fractional coefficients when necessary to specify the magnitude of ΔH_{rxn} for a *particular amount of substance.* Moreover, we find that, *in a particular reaction,* a certain amount of substance is thermochemically equivalent to a certain quantity of energy. Thus, *in this reaction,*

286 kJ is thermochemically equivalent to 1 mol $H_2(g)$
286 kJ is thermochemically equivalent to $\tfrac{1}{2}$ mol $O_2(g)$
286 kJ is thermochemically equivalent to 1 mol $H_2O(l)$

Just as we use stoichiometrically equivalent molar ratios to find amounts of substances, we use thermochemically equivalent quantities to find the heat of reaction for a given amount of substance. Also, just as we use molar mass (in g/mol of substance) to convert moles of a substance to mass, we use the heat of reaction (in kJ/mol of substance in the reaction) to convert moles of a substance to heat. Figure 6.13 shows this new relationship and the next sample problem applies it.

Figure 6.13 Summary of the relationship between amount (mol) of substance and the heat (kJ) transferred during a reaction.

Sample Problem 6.6   Using the Heat of Reaction (ΔH_{rxn}) to Find Amounts

PROBLEM The major source of aluminum in the world is bauxite (mostly aluminum oxide). Its thermal decomposition can be represented by

$$Al_2O_3(s) \xrightarrow{\Delta} 2Al(s) + \tfrac{3}{2}O_2(g) \qquad \Delta H_{rxn} = 1676 \text{ kJ}$$

If aluminum is produced this way (see Comment), how many grams of aluminum can form when 1.000×10^3 kJ of heat is transferred?

PLAN From the balanced equation and enthalpy change, we see that 2 mol Al forms when 1676 kJ of heat is absorbed. With this equivalent quantity, we convert the given kJ transferred to moles formed and then convert moles to grams.

SOLUTION Combining steps to convert from heat to mass of Al:

$$\text{Mass (g) of Al} = (1.000 \times 10^3 \text{ kJ}) \times \frac{2 \text{ mol Al}}{1676 \text{ kJ}} \times \frac{26.98 \text{ g Al}}{1 \text{ mol Al}} = \boxed{32.20 \text{ g Al}}$$

CHECK The mass of Al seems correct: ~1700 kJ can form 2 mol Al (54 g), so 1000 kJ should form between 27 g and 54 g.

COMMENT In practice, aluminum is not obtained by heating. Rather, it is obtained industrially by supplying electrical energy. Because ΔH is a state function, however, the total energy required for this chemical change is the same no matter how it occurs. (We examine the industrial method in Chapter 22.)

Follow-up Problem 6.6 As Lavoisier, Priestley, and others knew, mercury(II) oxide decomposes readily with heat. If it takes 90.8 kJ to decompose 1 mol HgO, how much heat is required to produce 1 short ton (2000 lb; 907 kg) of Hg?

Section Summary

A thermochemical equation shows the balanced equation *and* its ΔH_{rxn}. The sign of ΔH for a forward reaction is opposite that for the reverse reaction. The magnitude of ΔH depends on the amount of substance reacting and the ΔH per mole of substance. We use the thermochemically equivalent amounts of substance and heat from the balanced equation as conversion factors to find the amount of heat when a given amount of substance reacts.

6.5 Hess's Law of Heat Summation

Many reactions are difficult, even impossible, to perform as an individual change. A reaction may be part of a complex biochemical process; or it may take place only under extreme environmental conditions; or it may even require a change in conditions while it is occurring. If we can't run a reaction in the lab, is it possible to find its enthalpy change? One of the most powerful applications of the state-function property of enthalpy (H) allows us to do just that, to find the ΔH of *any* reaction for which we can write an equation, even if it is impossible to carry out. This application is expressed as **Hess's law of heat summation:** *the enthalpy change of an overall process is the sum of the enthalpy changes of its individual steps.* Using Hess's law, we imagine an overall reaction as the sum of a series of reaction steps, each chosen because its ΔH is known, whether or not it really occurs that way. Because the overall ΔH depends only on the initial and final states, we simply add together the known ΔH values for the steps to get ΔH of the overall reaction.

Let's see how we apply Hess's law in the case of the oxidation of sulfur to sulfur trioxide, the central process in the industrial production of sulfuric acid and in the formation of acid rain. (To introduce the approach, we'll simplify the equations by using S as the formula for sulfur, rather than the more correct S_8.) When we burn S in an excess of O_2, sulfur dioxide (SO_2) forms, *not* sulfur trioxide (SO_3). Equation 1 shows this step and its ΔH. If we change conditions and then add more O_2, we can oxidize SO_2 to SO_3 (Equation 2). In other words, we cannot put S and O_2 in a calorimeter and find ΔH for the overall reaction of S to SO_3 (Equation 3). But, we can find it with Hess's law. The three equations are

Equation 1:	$S(s) + O_2(g) \longrightarrow SO_2(g)$	$\Delta H_1 = -296.8$ kJ
Equation 2:	$2SO_2(g) + O_2(g) \longrightarrow 2SO_3(g)$	$\Delta H_2 = -198.4$ kJ
Equation 3:	$S(s) + \frac{3}{2}O_2(g) \longrightarrow SO_3(g)$	$\Delta H_3 = ?$

Hess's law tells us that if we can manipulate Equations 1 and/or 2 so that they add up to Equation 3, then ΔH_3 will be the sum of the manipulated ΔH values of Equations 1 and 2.

First, we identify Equation 3 as our "target" equation, the reaction whose ΔH we want to find, and we carefully note the number of moles of reactants and products in it. We also note that ΔH_1 and ΔH_2 are the values for Equations 1 and 2 *as written*. Now we manipulate Equations 1 and/or 2 by the following steps so they add up to Equation 3:

- Equations 1 and 3 contain the same amount of S, so we leave Equation 1 unchanged.
- Equation 2 has twice as much SO_3 as Equation 3, so we multiply it by $\frac{1}{2}$, being sure to halve ΔH_2 as well.
- With the targeted amounts of reactants and products present, we add Equation 1 to the halved Equation 2 and cancel terms that appear on both sides:

Equation 1:	$S(s) + O_2(g) \longrightarrow SO_2(g)$	$\Delta H_1 = -296.8 \text{ kJ}$
$\frac{1}{2}$(Equation 2):	$SO_2(g) + \frac{1}{2}O_2(g) \longrightarrow SO_3(g)$	$\frac{1}{2}(\Delta H_2) = -99.2 \text{ kJ}$

Equation 3: $S(s) + O_2(g) + \cancel{SO_2(g)} + \frac{1}{2}O_2(g) \longrightarrow \cancel{SO_2(g)} + SO_3(g)$ $\Delta H_3 = ?$

or, $\qquad\qquad\qquad S(s) + \frac{3}{2}O_2(g) \longrightarrow SO_3(g)$

Since Equation 1 plus the halved Equation 2 equals Equation 3, we have

$$\Delta H_3 = \Delta H_1 + \tfrac{1}{2}(\Delta H_2) = -296.8 \text{ kJ} + (-99.2 \text{ kJ}) = -396.0 \text{ kJ}$$

Once again, the key point is that H is a state function, so the overall ΔH depends on the difference between the initial and final enthalpies only. Hess's law tells us that the difference between the enthalpies of the reactants (1 mol S and $\frac{3}{2}$ mol O_2) and the product (1 mol SO_3) has the same value, whether S is oxidized directly to SO_3 (impossible) or through the formation of SO_2 first (actual).

To summarize, calculating an unknown ΔH involves three steps:

1. Identify the target equation, the step whose ΔH is unknown, and note the number of moles of reactants and products.
2. Manipulate the equations of known ΔH so that the target numbers of moles of reactants and products are on the correct sides. Remember to:
   - Change the sign of ΔH when you reverse an equation.
   - Multiply number of moles and ΔH by the same factor.
3. Add the manipulated equations to obtain the target equation. (All substances except those in the target equation must cancel.) Add their ΔH values to obtain the unknown ΔH.

Sample Problem 6.7   Using Hess's Law to Calculate an Unknown ΔH

PROBLEM Two gaseous pollutants that form in auto exhaust are CO and NO. An environmental chemist is studying ways to convert them to less harmful gases through the following equation:

$$CO(g) + NO(g) \longrightarrow CO_2(g) + \tfrac{1}{2}N_2(g) \qquad \Delta H = ?$$

Given the following information, calculate the unknown ΔH:

Equation A:	$CO(g) + \frac{1}{2}O_2(g) \longrightarrow CO_2(g)$	$\Delta H_A = -283.0 \text{ kJ}$
Equation B:	$N_2(g) + O_2(g) \longrightarrow 2NO(g)$	$\Delta H_B = 180.6 \text{ kJ}$

PLAN We note the numbers of moles of substances in the target equation, manipulate Equations A and/or B *and* their ΔH values, and then add them together to obtain the target equation and the unknown ΔH.

SOLUTION Noting moles of substances in the target equation: There is 1 mol each of reactants CO and NO, 1 mol of product CO_2, and $\frac{1}{2}$ mol of product N_2. Manipulating the given equations: Equation A has the same number of moles of CO and CO_2 as the target, so we leave it as written. Equation B has twice the needed amounts of N_2 and NO, and they are on the opposite sides from the target; therefore, we reverse Equation B, change the sign of ΔH_B, and multiply both by $\frac{1}{2}$:

$$\frac{1}{2}[2NO(g) \longrightarrow N_2(g) + O_2(g)] \qquad \Delta H = -\frac{1}{2}(\Delta H_B) = -\frac{1}{2}(180.6 \text{ kJ})$$

$$NO(g) \longrightarrow \frac{1}{2}N_2(g) + \frac{1}{2}O_2(g) \qquad \Delta H = -90.3 \text{ kJ}$$

Adding the manipulated equations to obtain the target equation:

Equation A:	$CO(g) + \frac{1}{2}O_2(g) \longrightarrow CO_2(g)$	$\Delta H = -283.0$ kJ
$\frac{1}{2}$(Equation B reversed):	$NO(g) \longrightarrow \frac{1}{2}N_2(g) + \frac{1}{2}O_2(g)$	$\Delta H = -90.3$ kJ
Target:	$CO(g) + NO(g) \longrightarrow CO_2(g) + \frac{1}{2}N_2(g)$	$\Delta H = -373.3$ kJ

CHECK Obtaining the desired target equation is its own check. Be sure to remember to change the sign of any equation you reversed.

Follow-up Problem 6.7 Nitrogen oxides undergo many interesting reactions. Calculate ΔH for the overall equation $2NO_2(g) + \frac{1}{2}O_2(g) \longrightarrow N_2O_5(s)$ from the following information:

$$N_2O_5(s) \longrightarrow 2NO(g) + \frac{3}{2}O_2(g) \qquad \Delta H = 223.7 \text{ kJ}$$

$$NO(g) + \frac{1}{2}O_2(g) \longrightarrow NO_2(g) \qquad \Delta H = -57.1 \text{ kJ}$$

Section Summary

Since H is a state function, $\Delta H = H_{final} - H_{initial}$ and does not depend on how the reaction takes place. Using Hess's law ($\Delta H_{total} = \Delta H_1 + \Delta H_2 + \cdots + \Delta H_n$), we can determine ΔH of any overall equation by manipulating the coefficients of appropriate individual reactions and their known ΔH values.

6.6 Standard Heats of Reaction (ΔH_{rxn}^{0})

In this section, we see how to apply Hess's law to determine the enthalpy changes for an enormous number of reactions. However, thermodynamic variables, such as ΔH, vary somewhat with conditions. Therefore, to compare heats of reaction as well as other thermodynamic data, chemists have established **standard states,** a set of specified conditions and concentrations:

- For a *gas*, the standard state is 1 atm.*
- For a substance in *aqueous solution,* the standard state is 1 M concentration (1 mol/L solution).
- For a *pure substance* (element or compound), the standard state is usually the most stable form of the substance at 1 atm and the temperature of interest. In this text, the temperature of interest is usually 25°C (298.15 K).†

A right superscript zero indicates when the thermodynamic variable has been determined with all substances in their standard states. For example, when ΔH_{rxn} has been measured with all substances in their standard states, it is the **standard heat of reaction, ΔH_{rxn}^{0}.**

---

*The definition of the standard state for gases has been changed to 1 bar, a slightly lower pressure than the 1 atm standard on which the data in this book are based (1 atm = 101.3 kPa = 1.013 bar). In most cases this makes *very* little difference in the standard enthalpy values.

†In the case of phosphorus, the most *common* form, white phosphorus (P_4), is chosen as the standard state, even though red phosphorus is more stable at 1 atm and 298.15 K.

Table 6.5 Selected Standard Heats of Formation at 25°C (298 K)

Formula	ΔH_f^0 (kJ/mol)
Calcium	
Ca(s)	0
CaO(s)	−635.1
CaCO$_3$(s)	−1206.9
Carbon	
C(graphite)	0
C(diamond)	1.9
CO(g)	−110.5
CO$_2$(g)	−393.5
CH$_4$(g)	−74.9
CH$_3$OH(l)	−238.6
HCN(g)	135
CS$_2$(l)	87.9
Chlorine	
Cl(g)	121.0
Cl$_2$(g)	0
HCl(g)	−92.3
Hydrogen	
H(g)	218.0
H$_2$(g)	0
Nitrogen	
N$_2$(g)	0
NH$_3$(g)	−45.9
NO(g)	90.3
Oxygen	
O$_2$(g)	0
O$_3$(g)	143
H$_2$O(g)	−241.8
H$_2$O(l)	−285.8
Silver	
Ag(s)	0
AgCl(s)	−127.0
Sodium	
Na(s)	0
Na(g)	107.8
NaCl(s)	−411.1
Sulfur	
S$_8$(rhombic)	0
S$_8$(monoclinic)	2
SO$_2$(g)	−296.8
SO$_3$(g)	−396.0

Formation Equations and Their Standard Enthalpy Changes

In a **formation equation,** 1 mole of a compound forms from its elements. The **standard heat of formation (ΔH_f^0)** is the enthalpy change accompanying the formation equation when all the substances are in their standard states. For instance, the formation equation for methane (CH$_4$) is

$$\text{C(graphite)} + 2H_2(g) \longrightarrow CH_4(g) \qquad \Delta H_f^0 = -74.9 \text{ kJ}$$

Thus, the standard heat of formation of methane is −74.9 kJ/mol. Some other examples are

$$Na(s) + \tfrac{1}{2}Cl_2(g) \longrightarrow NaCl(s) \qquad \Delta H_f^0 = -411.1 \text{ kJ}$$
$$2C(\text{graphite}) + 3H_2(g) + \tfrac{1}{2}O_2(g) \longrightarrow C_2H_5OH(l) \qquad \Delta H_f^0 = -277.6 \text{ kJ}$$

Standard heats of formation have been tabulated for many compounds. Table 6.5 shows ΔH_f^0 values for several substances, and a much more extensive table appears in Appendix B.

The values in Table 6.5 were selected to make two points:

1. *An element in its standard state is assigned a ΔH_f^0 of zero.* For example, note that $\Delta H_f^0 = 0$ for Na(s), but $\Delta H_f^0 = 107.8$ kJ/mol for Na(g). This means that the gaseous state is not the most stable state of sodium at 1 atm and 298.15 K, and that heat is required to form Na(g). Note also that the standard state of chlorine is Cl$_2$ molecules, not Cl atoms. Several elements exist in different forms, only one of which is the standard state. Thus, the standard state of carbon is graphite, not diamond, so ΔH_f^0 of C(graphite) = 0. Similarly, the standard state of oxygen is dioxygen (O$_2$), not ozone (O$_3$), and the standard state of sulfur is S$_8$ arranged in its rhombic crystal form, rather than its monoclinic form.

2. *Most compounds have a negative ΔH_f^0.* That is, most compounds have exothermic formation reactions under standard conditions. This means that, in most cases, *the compound is more stable than its component elements.*

Sample Problem 6.8   Writing Formation Equations

PROBLEM Write balanced equations for the formation of 1 mole of the following compounds from their elements in their standard states and include ΔH_f^0.
(a) Silver chloride, AgCl, a solid at standard conditions
(b) Calcium carbonate, CaCO$_3$, a solid at standard conditions
(c) Hydrogen cyanide, HCN, a gas at standard conditions
PLAN We write the elements as the reactants and 1 mole of the compound as the product, being sure all substances are in their standard states. Then we balance the atoms and obtain the ΔH_f^0 values from Table 6.5.
SOLUTION (a) $Ag(s) + \tfrac{1}{2}Cl_2(g) \longrightarrow AgCl(s) \qquad \Delta H_f^0 = -127.0$ kJ
(b) $Ca(s) + C(\text{graphite}) + \tfrac{3}{2}O_2(g) \longrightarrow CaCO_3(s) \qquad \Delta H_f^0 = -1206.9$ kJ
(c) $\tfrac{1}{2}H_2(g) + C(\text{graphite}) + \tfrac{1}{2}N_2(g) \longrightarrow HCN(g) \qquad \Delta H_f^0 = 135$ kJ

Follow-up Problem 6.8   Write balanced equations for the formation of 1 mole of **(a)** CH$_3$OH(l), **(b)** CaO(s), and **(c)** CS$_2$(l) from their elements in their standard states. Include ΔH_f^0 for each reaction.

Determining ΔH_{rxn}^0 from ΔH_f^0 Values of Reactants and Products

By applying Hess's law, we can use ΔH_f^0 values to determine ΔH_{rxn}^0 for any reaction. All we have to do is view the reaction as an imaginary two-step process.

$$\Delta H^0_{rxn} = \Sigma m \Delta H^0_{f(products)} - \Sigma n \Delta H^0_{f(reactants)}$$

Figure 6.14 The general process for determining ΔH^0_{rxn} from ΔH^0_f values.
For any reaction, ΔH^0_{rxn} can be considered as the sum of the enthalpy changes for the decomposition of reactants to their elements $[-\Sigma n\Delta H^0_{f\,(reactants)}]$ and the formation of products from their elements $[+\Sigma m\Delta H^0_{f\,(products)}]$. [The factors m and n are the amounts (mol) of the products and reactants and are equal to the coefficients in the balanced equation.]

Step 1. Each reactant decomposes to its elements. This step is the *reverse* of the formation reaction for each reactant, so each standard enthalpy change is $-\Delta H^0_f$.

Step 2. Each product forms from its elements. This step *is* the formation reaction for each product, so each standard enthalpy change is $+\Delta H^0_f$.

According to Hess's law, we add the enthalpy changes for these steps to obtain the overall enthalpy change for the reaction (ΔH^0_{rxn}). Figure 6.14 depicts the conceptual process. Suppose we want ΔH^0_{rxn} for

$$TiCl_4(l) + 2H_2O(g) \longrightarrow TiO_2(s) + 4HCl(g)$$

We write this equation as though it were the sum of four individual equations, one for each compound. Two of these equations show the decomposition of the reactants to their elements (the *reverse* of their formation), and two show the formation of the products from their elements:

$$
\begin{array}{ll}
TiCl_4(l) \longrightarrow Ti(s) + 2Cl_2(g) & -\Delta H^0_f[TiCl_4(l)] \\
2H_2O(g) \longrightarrow 2H_2(g) + O_2(g) & -2\Delta H^0_f[H_2O(g)] \\
Ti(s) + O_2(g) \longrightarrow TiO_2(s) & \Delta H^0_f[TiO_2(s)] \\
2H_2(g) + 2Cl_2(g) \longrightarrow 4HCl(g) & 4\Delta H^0_f[HCl(g)]
\end{array}
$$

$TiCl_4(l) + 2H_2O(g) + \cancel{Ti(s)} + \cancel{O_2(g)} + \cancel{2H_2(g)} + \cancel{2Cl_2(g)} \longrightarrow$

$$\cancel{Ti(s)} + \cancel{2Cl_2(g)} + \cancel{2H_2(g)} + \cancel{O_2(g)} + TiO_2(s) + 4HCl(g)$$

Or, $TiCl_4(l) + 2H_2O(g) \longrightarrow TiO_2(s) + 4HCl(g)$

It's important to realize that when titanium(IV) chloride and water react, the reactants don't *actually* decompose to their elements, which then recombine to form the products. But that is the great usefulness of Hess's law and the state-function concept. Since ΔH^0_{rxn} is the difference between two state functions, $H^0_{products}$ minus $H^0_{reactants}$, it doesn't matter *how* the change actually occurs. We simply add the individual enthalpy changes to find ΔH^0_{rxn}:

$$\Delta H^0_{rxn} = \Delta H^0_f[TiO_2(s)] + 4\Delta H^0_f[HCl(g)] + \{-\Delta H^0_f[TiCl_4(l)]\} + \{-2\Delta H^0_f[H_2O(g)]\}$$

$$= \{\Delta H^0_f[TiO_2(s)] + 4\Delta H^0_f[HCl(g)]\} - \{\Delta H^0_f[TiCl_4(l)] + 2\Delta H^0_f[H_2O(g)]\}$$

$$\underbrace{}_{\text{Products}} \qquad\qquad \underbrace{}_{\text{Reactants}}$$

Notice the pattern here. By generalizing it, we state that *the standard heat of reaction is the sum of the standard heats of formation of the **products** minus the sum of the standard heats of formation of the **reactants*** (see Figure 6.14):

$$\Delta H^0_{rxn} = \Sigma m \Delta H^0_{f(products)} - \Sigma n \Delta H^0_{f(reactants)} \qquad \textbf{(6.8)}$$

where the symbol Σ means "sum of," and m and n are the amounts (mol) of the products and reactants indicated by the coefficients from the balanced equation.

Sample Problem 6.9   Calculating the Heat of Reaction from Heats of Formation

PROBLEM Nitric acid, with an annual production of about 8 billion kg, is used to make many products, including fertilizers, dyes, and explosives. The first step in its industrial production is the oxidation of ammonia:

$$4NH_3(g) + 5O_2(g) \longrightarrow 4NO(g) + 6H_2O(g)$$

Calculate ΔH^0_{rxn} from ΔH^0_f values.

PLAN We look up ΔH^0_f values from Table 6.5 and apply Equation 6.8 to find ΔH^0_{rxn}.

SOLUTION Calculating ΔH^0_{rxn}:

$$\Delta H^0_{rxn} = \Sigma m \Delta H^0_{f(products)} - \Sigma n \Delta H^0_{f(reactants)}$$

$$= 4\Delta H^0_f[NO(g)] + 6\Delta H^0_f[H_2O(g)] - \{4\Delta H^0_f[NH_3(g)] + 5\Delta H^0_f[O_2(g)]\}$$

$$= 4 \text{ mol } (90.3 \text{ kJ/mol}) + 6 \text{ mol } (-241.8 \text{ kJ/mol})$$

$$-[4 \text{ mol } (-45.9 \text{ kJ/mol}) + 5 \text{ mol } (0 \text{ kJ/mol})]$$

$$= 361 \text{ kJ} - 1451 \text{ kJ} + 184 \text{ kJ} - 0 \text{ kJ} = \boxed{-906 \text{ kJ}}$$

CHECK One way to check is to write formation equations for the amounts of individual compounds in the correct direction and take their sum:

$4NH_3(g) \longrightarrow 2N_2(g) + 6H_2(g)$	$-4(-45.9 \text{ kJ}) =$	184 kJ
$2N_2(g) + 2O_2(g) \longrightarrow 4NO(g)$	$4(90.3 \text{ kJ}) =$	361 kJ
$6H_2(g) + 3O_2(g) \longrightarrow 6H_2O(g)$	$6(-241.8 \text{ kJ}) =$	-1451 kJ
$4NH_3(g) + 5O_2(g) \longrightarrow 4NO(g) + 6H_2O(g)$		-906 kJ

COMMENT In this problem, we know the individual ΔH^0_f values and find the sum, ΔH^0_{rxn}. In the follow-up problem, we know the sum and want to find an individual value.

Follow-up Problem 6.9   Use the following information to find ΔH^0_f of methanol [$CH_3OH(l)$]:

$$CH_3OH(l) + \tfrac{3}{2}O_2(g) \longrightarrow CO_2(g) + 2H_2O(g) \quad \Delta H^0_{comb} = -638.5 \text{ kJ}$$

$$\Delta H^0_f \text{ of } CO_2(g) = -393.5 \text{ kJ/mol} \qquad \Delta H^0_f \text{ of } H_2O(g) = -241.8 \text{ kJ/mol}$$

In the following Chemical Connections essay, we apply key ideas from the chapter to new approaches for energy utilization.

Section Summary

Standard states are chosen conditions for substances. When 1 mol of a compound forms from its elements with all substances in their standard states, the enthalpy change is ΔH^0_f. Hess's law allows us to picture a reaction as the decomposition of reactants to their elements, followed by the formation of products from their elements. We use tabulated ΔH^0_f values to find ΔH^0_{rxn} or use known ΔH^0_{rxn} and ΔH^0_f values to find an unknown ΔH^0_f. Because of dwindling resources and major environmental concerns, chemists are actively developing new energy alternatives, including coal and biomass conversion, hydrogen fuels, and noncombustible sources.

The Future of Energy Use

Out of necessity, we are seeing a global focus on rethinking our use of energy. The dwindling supply of the world's fuel and the environmental impact of its combustion threaten our standard of living and have become questions of survival for hundreds of millions of people in less developed countries. Chemical aspects of energy production and utilization provide scientists and engineers with some of the greatest challenges of our time.

Energy consumption increased enormously during the Industrial Revolution and again after World War II, and it continues to increase today. A century-long changeover has led from the use of wood to coal and then to petroleum. The **fossil fuels**—coal, petroleum, and natural gas—remain our major sources of energy, but their polluting combustion products and eventual depletion are major drawbacks to their use.

Natural processes form fossil fuels *much* more slowly than we consume them, so they are *nonrenewable:* once we use them up, they are gone. Estimates indicate that known oil reserves could be 90% depleted by the year 2020. Coal reserves are much more plentiful, so chemical research seeks new uses for coal. The most important *renewable* combustible fuels are wood, other fuels derived from *biomass* (plant and animal matter), and hydrogen gas. The following discussion highlights some current approaches to developing more rational energy use: converting coal to cleaner fuels, producing fuels from biomass, developing a hydrogen-fueled economy, understanding the effect of carbon-based fuels on climate, utilizing energy sources that do not involve combustion, and, perhaps most important, conserving the fuels we have.

Chemical Approaches to Cleaner Fuels

Coal, biomass, and hydrogen are the most important fuels of the future.

Coal Current U.S. reserves of coal are enormous, but coal is a highly polluting fuel because it produces SO_2 when it burns. Two processes—desulfurization and gasification—are designed to reduce this noxious pollutant.

Flue-gas *desulfurization* devices called *scrubbers* heat powdered limestone ($CaCO_3$) or spray lime-water slurries [$Ca(OH)_2$] to remove SO_2 from the gaseous product mixture:

$$CaCO_3(s) + SO_2(g) \xrightarrow{\Delta} CaSO_3(s) + CO_2(g)$$

$$2Ca(OH)_2(aq) + 2SO_2(g) + O_2(g) \longrightarrow 2CaSO_4(s) + 2H_2O(l)$$

Currently, however, the cost of operation plus disposal of the solids (nearly 1 ton per power-plant customer each year) present serious problems for this approach.

Coal gasification processes break bonds in the large molecules in coal to form much smaller molecules in sulfur-free gaseous fuels. First, high temperatures (600°C to 800°C) release volatile compounds that decompose coal to methane and a char:

$$Coal(s) \xrightarrow{\Delta} \text{coal volatiles}(g) \xrightarrow{\Delta} CH_4(g) + char(s)$$

The char (mostly carbon) reacts with steam in the endothermic *water-gas reaction* (also known as the steam-carbon reaction) to form a fuel mixture of CO and H_2 called synthesis gas (syngas):

$$C(s) + H_2O(g) \longrightarrow CO(g) + H_2(g) \qquad \Delta H^0 = 131 \text{ kJ}$$

However, syngas has a much lower fuel value than methane. For example, a mixture containing 0.5 mol CO and 0.5 mol H_2 (that is, 1.0 mol syngas) releases about one-third as much energy as 1.0 mol methane ($\Delta H^0_{comb} = -802$ kJ/mol):

$$\tfrac{1}{2}H_2(g) + \tfrac{1}{4}O_2(g) \longrightarrow \tfrac{1}{2}H_2O(g) \qquad \Delta H^0 = -121 \text{ kJ}$$

$$\tfrac{1}{2}CO(g) + \tfrac{1}{4}O_2(g) \longrightarrow \tfrac{1}{2}CO_2(g) \qquad \Delta H^0 = -142 \text{ kJ}$$

$$\tfrac{1}{2}H_2(g) + \tfrac{1}{2}CO(g) + \tfrac{1}{2}O_2(g) \longrightarrow \tfrac{1}{2}H_2O(g) + \tfrac{1}{2}CO_2(g)$$
$$\Delta H^0 = -263 \text{ kJ}$$

To upgrade its fuel value, syngas can be converted to other fuels, such as methane. In the *CO-shift reaction* (also known as the water-gas shift reaction), some CO reacts with more steam to form CO_2 and additional H_2:

$$CO(g) + H_2O(g) \longrightarrow CO_2(g) + H_2(g) \qquad \Delta H^0 = -41 \text{ kJ}$$

The CO_2 is removed, and the H_2-enriched mixture reacts to form methane and water vapor:

$$CO(g) + 3H_2(g) \longrightarrow CH_4(g) + H_2O(g) \qquad \Delta H^0 = -206 \text{ kJ}$$

Drying the product mixture gives **synthetic natural gas (SNG).** Thus, through a process that involves removal of volatiles and three reaction steps, coal is converted to methane.

Wood and Other Types of Biomass Nearly half of the world's people rely on wood for their energy. In principle, wood and other forms of biomass are renewable, but worldwide deforestation for fuel, and for lumber and paper in richer countries, has resulted in wood being depleted much faster than it can grow back.

A better use of vegetable (sugarcane, corn, beets) and tree waste is **biomass conversion,** which combines chemical and microbial methods to convert sugar, cellulose, and other plant matter into combustible fuels. One such fuel is ethanol (C_2H_5OH), which is mixed with gasoline to form *gasohol.* Another is methane, which is produced in bio-gas generators through the microbial breakdown of plant and animal waste. China has active facilities applying these techniques. The U.S. Department of Energy and the Environmental Protection Agency are actively funding long-range programs that employ similar technologies to produce gaseous fuels from garbage and sewage.

Hydrogen Although H_2 ($\Delta H^0_{comb} = -242$ kJ/mol) produces only about one-third as much energy per mole as CH_4 ($\Delta H^0_{comb} = -802$ kJ/mol), hydrogen combustion yields non-polluting water vapor. Its formation from the decomposition of water, however, is endothermic (ΔH^0_{rxn} with liquid $H_2O = 286$ kJ/mol) and *direct* methods are still very costly. For example, at present, decomposing water with electricity is too expensive, but if future methods for generating electricity prove economical, the oceans provide an inexhaustible source of starting material.

Promising alternative methods for producing hydrogen apply Hess's law to decompose water *indirectly* to its compo-

(continued)

nents (ΔH^0_{rxn} with gaseous H_2O = 242 kJ/mol). Here is one example:

$$3FeCl_2(s) + 4H_2O(g) \xrightarrow{500°C} Fe_3O_4(s) + 6HCl(g) + H_2(g) \qquad \Delta H^0 = \quad 318 \text{ kJ}$$

$$Fe_3O_4(s) + \tfrac{3}{2}Cl_2(g) + 6HCl(g) \xrightarrow{100°C} 3FeCl_3(s) + 3H_2O(g) + \tfrac{1}{2}O_2(g) \qquad \Delta H^0 = -249 \text{ kJ}$$

$$3FeCl_3(s) \xrightarrow{300°C} 3FeCl_2(s) + \tfrac{3}{2}Cl_2(g) \qquad \Delta H^0 = \quad 173 \text{ kJ}$$

$$H_2O(g) \longrightarrow H_2(g) + \tfrac{1}{2}O_2(g) \qquad \Delta H^0 = \quad 242 \text{ kJ}$$

Transporting and storing the H_2 fuel could be accomplished with technologies used currently by utility companies. However, the actual form the H_2 would take to fuel, say, the family car, is an open question. Earlier research showed that many metals, such as palladium and niobium, absorb large amounts of H_2 into the spaces between their atoms, and it was hoped that they might be used as fuel cartridges. But more recent studies show that the metals release the H_2 too slowly to be practical, so utilization of H_2 fuel is still an active area of research.

Carbon-Based Fuels and the "Greenhouse" Effect

Many natural processes produce CO_2, which plays a key temperature-regulating role in the atmosphere. Much of the sunlight that shines on the Earth is absorbed by the land and oceans and converted to heat (Figure 6.A). Atmospheric CO_2 does not absorb visible light from the Sun, but it does absorb heat. Thus, some of the heat radiating from the surface is trapped by the CO_2 and transferred to the atmosphere.

Over several billion years, due largely to the spread of plant life that uses CO_2 in photosynthesis, the large amount

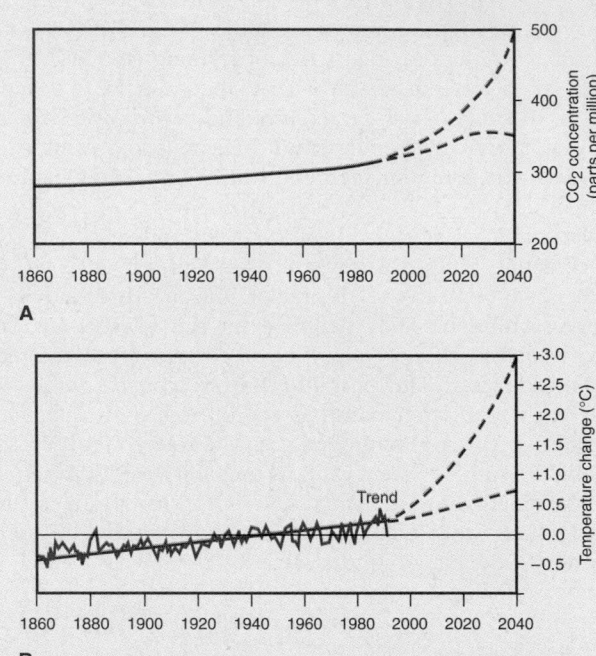

A

B

Figure 6.B Accumulating evidence for the greenhouse effect. A, As a result of increased fossil fuel use since the mid-1800s, atmospheric CO_2 concentrations have increased. **B,** Coincident with this CO_2 increase, the average global temperature has risen slightly more than 0.5°C. (Zero equals the average global temperature for the period 1957 to 1970.) The projections in both graphs *(dashed lines)* are based on current fossil fuel consumption and deforestation either continuing *(upper line)* or being curtailed *(lower line)*.

Figure 6.A The trapping of heat by the atmosphere. About 25% of sunlight is reflected by the atmosphere. The remainder enters the atmosphere, where much of it is converted into heat by the air and the Earth's surface. Some of the heat emanating from the surface is trapped by atmospheric gases, mostly CO_2, and some is lost to outer space.

of CO_2 originally present in the Earth's atmosphere decreased to a relatively constant 0.028% by volume. However, for about 150 years, this amount has been increasing as a result of human use of fossil fuels and has reached 0.036% today. Thus, although the same amount of solar energy passes through the atmosphere, more is being trapped as heat in a process called the "greenhouse" effect (Figure 6.B).

Based on current fossil fuel use, CO_2 concentrations are predicted to reach 0.070% to 0.075% by 2100, but how much will the temperature of the atmosphere rise? Many academic, government, and private laboratories are devising ever more sophisticated computer models to simulate the effects of increasing amounts of CO_2 and other greenhouse gases (most importantly, CH_4). However, the system is so complex that a definitive answer is difficult to obtain. Natural fluctuations in temperature must be taken into account, as well as cyclic changes in solar activity, which are expected to provide some additional warming for the next decade or so. Moreover, as the amount of CO_2 increases from fossil fuel burning, so does the amount of soot, which may block sunlight and have a cooling effect. Water vapor also traps heat, and as temperatures rise, more water vapor forms. But increased amounts of water vapor may thicken the cloud cover, which may also lead to cooling.

Despite these opposing factors, most atmospheric scientists predict a net warming of the atmosphere, and some are currently documenting climate disruptions that the models predict. When extra heat is trapped by elevated levels of greenhouse gases, 20% of the heat warms the air and 80% evaporates water. Globally, the 10 warmest years on record have occurred since 1980, with 1997 the second hottest. The decade from 1987 to 1997 included 10 times as many catastrophic floods from storms as did the previous decade, and this trend has continued in 1998. Moreover, observed shifts in rainfall over the last century—more in temperate regions, less in the tropics—are in keeping with expected circulation patterns.

Responsible conclusions indicate a range of possible temperature rises (from 1°C to 5°C is one common forecast), and several predictions of the effects have been made. An average increase of 1°C in the U.S. Midwest could lower the grain yield by 20%; an increase of 3°C could alter rainfall patterns and crop yields throughout the world; a 5°C increase could melt large parts of the polar ice caps, flooding coastal regions such as the Netherlands, half of Florida, and much of India, and even inundating low-lying island nations. To make matters worse, as we burn fossil fuels and wood, we simultaneously cut down the forests that naturally *absorb* CO_2. International conferences, such as the 1992 Earth Summit in Rio de Janeiro, Brazil, and the 1997 Conference on Climate Change in Kyoto, Japan, provide a forum for politicians, business interests, and scientists to grapple with these crucial issues.

Solar Energy and Other Noncombustible Energy Sources

The quantity of solar energy striking the United States annually is *600 times greater than all our energy needs*. Despite this astounding abundance, solar energy is difficult to collect, store, and convert to other forms of energy. The Sun's total output is enormous but not concentrated, so vast surface areas must be devoted to collecting it.

Storage of the solar energy is necessary because intense sunlight is available over most regions for only 6 to 8 hours a day, and it is greatly reduced in rainy or cloudy weather. One storage approach makes use of ionic hydrates, such as $Na_2SO_4\cdot10H_2O$. When warmed by sunlight to greater than 32°C, the 3 mol of ions dissolve in the 10 mol of water in an endothermic process:

$$Na_2SO_4\cdot10H_2O(s) \xrightarrow{>32°C} Na_2SO_4(aq) \qquad \Delta H^0 = 354 \text{ kJ}$$

When cooled to less than 32°C after sunset, the solution recrystallizes, releasing the absorbed energy for heating:

$$Na_2SO_4(aq) \xrightarrow{<32°C} Na_2SO_4\cdot10H_2O(s) \qquad \Delta H^0 = -354 \text{ kJ}$$

Photovoltaic cells convert light directly into electricity, but the electrical energy produced is only about 10% of the radiant energy supplied. However, novel combinations of elements from Groups 3A(13) and 5A(15), such as gallium arsenide (GaAs), result in higher yields and are approaching economic parity with certain types of fossil-fuel use.

Energy Conservation: More from Less

All systems in nature, whether living organisms or industrial power plants, waste some energy, which in effect is a waste of fuel. In terms of the energy used to produce it, for example, every discarded aluminum can is equivalent to 0.25 L of gasoline. Energy conservation lowers production costs, extends our supply of fossil fuels, and reduces pollution.

One example of an energy-conserving device is a high-efficiency gas-burning furnace for domestic heating. Its design channels hot waste gases through the furnace to transfer more heat to the room and to an attached domestic hot water system. Moreover, the channeling path cools the gases to <100°C, so the water vapor condenses, thus releasing about 10% more heat:

$$CH_4(g) + 2O_2(g) \longrightarrow CO_2(g) + 2H_2O(g) \qquad \Delta H^0 = -802 \text{ kJ}$$
$$\underline{2H_2O(g) \longrightarrow 2H_2O(l) \qquad\qquad\qquad \Delta H^0 = -88 \text{ kJ}}$$
$$CH_4(g) + 2O_2(g) \longrightarrow CO_2(g) + 2H_2O(l) \qquad \Delta H^0 = -890 \text{ kJ}$$

Although engineers and chemists will be in the forefront of these new energy directions, a more hopeful energy future ultimately depends on our wisdom in obtaining and conserving planetary resources.

Chapter Perspective

Our investigation of energy in this chapter helps explain many chemical and physical phenomena: how gases do work, how reactions release or absorb heat, how the chemical energy in fuels and foods changes to other forms, and how we can use energy more wisely. We reexamine several of these ideas later in the text to address the question of why physical and chemical changes occur. In Chapter 7, you'll see how the energy released or absorbed by the atom created a revolutionary view of matter and energy that led to our current model of atomic energy states.

The following learning objectives, with section and/or sample problem (SP) numbers in parentheses, can help focus your study:

Understand These Concepts

1. The distinction between a system and its surroundings (6.1)
2. How energy is transferred to or from a system as heat and/or work (6.1)
3. The relation between the internal energy change, heat, and work (6.1)
4. The meaning of energy conservation (6.1)
5. The meaning of a state function and why ΔE is constant even though q and w vary (6.1)
6. The meaning of enthalpy and the relation between ΔE and ΔH (6.2)
7. The meaning of ΔH and the distinction between exothermic and endothermic reactions (6.2)
8. How changes in bond strength account for the heat of reaction (6.2)
9. The relation between specific heat capacity and heat transferred (6.3)
10. How constant-pressure (coffee-cup) and constant-volume (bomb) calorimeters work (6.3)
11. The relation between ΔH^0_{rxn} and amount of substance (6.4)
12. The importance of Hess's law and the manipulation of ΔH values (6.5)
13. The meaning of a formation equation and the standard heat of formation (6.6)
14. How a reaction combines the decomposition of reactants and the formation of products (6.6)

Master These Skills

1. Interconverting energy units (J, cal, Btu) (SP 6.1)
2. Drawing enthalpy diagrams for chemical and physical changes (SP 6.2)
3. Solving problems involving specific heat capacity, change in temperature, and heat of reaction (SPs 6.3 to 6.5)
4. Relating the heat of reaction and the amount of substances changing (SP 6.6)
5. Using Hess's law to find an unknown ΔH (SP 6.7)
6. Writing formation equations and using ΔH^0_{f} values to find ΔH^0_{rxn} (SPs 6.8 and 6.9)

For Review and Reference

Key Terms

thermodynamics
thermochemistry
Section 6.1
system
surroundings
internal energy (E)
heat (q)
work (w)
pressure-volume work
   (PV work)
law of conservation of
   energy (first law of
   thermodynamics)

joule (J)
calorie (cal)
state function
Section 6.2
enthalphy (H)
change in enthalpy (ΔH)
heat of reaction (ΔH_{rxn})
enthalpy diagram
exothermic
endothermic
heat of combustion
   (ΔH_{comb})
heat of formation (ΔH_{f})

heat of fusion (ΔH_{fus})
heat of vaporization (ΔH_{vap})
Section 6.3
heat capacity
specific heat capacity (c)
molar heat capacity (C)
calorimeter
Section 6.4
thermochemical equation
Section 6.5
Hess's law of heat
   summation

Section 6.6
standard state
standard heat of reaction
   (ΔH^0_{rxn})
formation equation
standard heat of formation
   (ΔH^0_{f})
fossil fuel
coal gasification
syngas
synthetic natural gas (SNG)
biomass conversion
photovoltaic cell

Key Equations and Relationships

6.1 Defining the change in internal energy (p. 225):
$$\Delta E = E_{\text{final}} - E_{\text{initial}} = E_{\text{products}} - E_{\text{reactants}}$$

6.2 Expressing the change in internal energy in terms of heat and work (p. 226):
$$\Delta E = q + w$$

6.3 Stating the first law of thermodynamics (law of energy conservation) (p. 228):
$$\Delta E_{\text{universe}} = \Delta E_{\text{system}} + \Delta E_{\text{surroundings}} = 0$$

6.4 Determining the work due to a change in volume at constant pressure (PV work) (p. 231):
$$w = -P\Delta V$$

6.5 Relating the enthalpy change to the internal energy change (p. 231):
$$\Delta H = \Delta E + P\Delta V$$

6.6 Identifying the enthalpy change with the heat at constant pressure (p. 231):
$$q_P = \Delta E + P\Delta V = \Delta H$$

6.7 Calculating the heat when a substance undergoes a temperature change (p. 236):
$$q = c \times \text{mass} \times \Delta T$$

6.8 Calculating the standard heat of reaction (p. 246):
$$\Delta H^0_{\text{rxn}} = \Sigma m\Delta H^0_{\text{f (products)}} - \Sigma n\Delta H^0_{\text{f (reactants)}}$$

Highlighted Figures and Tables

These figures (F) and tables (T) provide a quick review of key ideas.

F6.2 Energy diagrams for the transfer of internal energy (E) between a system and its surroundings (p. 225)
T6.1 Sign conventions for q, w, and ΔE (p. 227)
F6.8 Enthalpy diagrams for exothermic and endothermic processes (p. 232)

T6.4 Specific heat capacities of some elements, compounds, and materials (p. 237)
F6.13 Summary of the relationship between amount (mol) of substance and the heat (kJ) transferred during a reaction (p. 240)
F6.14 The general process for determining ΔH^0_{rxn} from ΔH^0_f values (p. 246)

Answers to Follow-up Problems

6.1 $\Delta E = q + w = \left(-26.0 \text{ kcal} \times \dfrac{4.184 \text{ kJ}}{1 \text{ kcal}} \right)$

$\qquad + \left(+15.0 \text{ Btu} \times \dfrac{1.055 \text{ kJ}}{1 \text{ Btu}} \right)$

$\qquad = -93.0 \text{ kJ}$

6.2 The reaction is exothermic.

6.3 $\Delta T = 25°C - 37°C = -12°C = -12 \text{ K}$
$\qquad q = 0.450 \text{ J/g} \cdot \text{K} \times 5.5 \text{ g} \times (-12 \text{ K}) = -30 \text{ J}$

6.4 $-q_{solid} = q_{water}$
$- [(0.519 \text{ J/g} \cdot \text{K}) (2,050 \text{ g}) (x - 74.21)]$
$\qquad\qquad = [(4.184 \text{ J/g} \cdot \text{K}) (26.05 \text{ g}) (x - 27.20)]$
$\qquad\qquad x = 27.65 \text{ K}$
$\Delta T_{diamond} = -46.56 \text{ K} \quad \text{and} \quad \Delta T_{water} = 0.45 \text{K}$

6.5 $-q_{sample} = q_{calorimeter}$

$-(0.8650 \text{ g C})\left(\dfrac{1 \text{ mol C}}{12.01 \text{ g C}} \right)(-393.5 \text{ kJ/mol C}) = (2.613 \text{ K})x$

$\qquad\qquad x = 10.85 \text{ kJ/K}$

6.6 $HgO(s) \xrightarrow{\Delta} Hg(l) + \frac{1}{2}O_2(g) \qquad \Delta H = 90.8 \text{ kJ}$

Heat (kJ) $= 907 \text{ kg Hg} \times \dfrac{10^3 \text{ g}}{1 \text{ kg}} \times \dfrac{1 \text{ mol Hg}}{200.6 \text{ g Hg}} \times \dfrac{90.8 \text{ kJ}}{1 \text{ mol Hg}}$

$\qquad\qquad = 4.11 \times 10^5 \text{ kJ}$

6.7 $2NO(g) + \frac{3}{2}O_2(g) \longrightarrow N_2O_5(s) \qquad \Delta H = -223.7 \text{ kJ}$

$\underline{\quad 2NO_2(g) \longrightarrow 2NO(g) + O_2(g) \quad \Delta H = 114.2 \text{ kJ}}$

$\cancel{2NO(g)} + \frac{1}{2}\cancel{\frac{3}{2}}O_2(g) + 2NO_2(g) \longrightarrow$

$\qquad\qquad\qquad N_2O_5(s) + \cancel{2NO(g)} + \cancel{O_2(g)}$

$2NO_2(g) + \frac{1}{2}O_2(g) \longrightarrow N_2O_5(s) \qquad \Delta H = -109.5 \text{ kJ}$

6.8 (a) $C(graphite) + 2H_2(g) + \frac{1}{2}O_2(g) \longrightarrow CH_3OH(l)$
$\qquad\qquad\qquad\qquad\qquad\qquad \Delta H^0_f = -238.6 \text{ kJ}$

(b) $Ca(s) + \frac{1}{2}O_2(g) \longrightarrow CaO(s) \quad \Delta H^0_f = -635.1 \text{ kJ}$

(c) $C(graphite) + \frac{1}{4}S_8(rhombic) \longrightarrow CS_2(l) \quad \Delta H^0_f = 87.9 \text{ kJ}$

6.9 ΔH^0_f of $CH_3OH(l)$
$\qquad = -\Delta H^0_{comb} + 2\Delta H^0_f[H_2O(g)] + \Delta H^0_f[CO_2(g)]$
$\qquad = 638.5 \text{ kJ} + 2 \text{ mol}(-241.8 \text{ kJ/mol})$
$\qquad\quad + 1 \text{ mol }(-393.5 \text{ kJ/mol}) = -238.6 \text{ kJ}$

Problems

Problems with a colored number are answered at the back of the text. Problem sections match the text and provide the number(s) of relevant sample problems. Most offer concept review questions, skill-building exercises (written in similar pairs), and problems in a relevant context. Following these are comprehensive problems based on material from any section and/or previous chapter.

Forms of Energy and Their Interconversion
(Sample Problem 6.1)

■ **Concept Review Questions**

6.1 Why do heat (q) and work (w) have positive values when entering a system and negative values when leaving?
6.2 If you feel warm after exercising, have you increased the internal energy of your body? Explain.

6.3 An *adiabatic* process is one that involves no heat transfer. What is the relationship between work and the change in internal energy in an adiabatic process?
6.4 State two ways that you increase the internal energy of your body and two ways that you decrease it.
6.5 Name a common device in which each of the following energy changes occurs:
(a) Electrical energy to thermal energy
(b) Electrical energy to sound energy
(c) Electrical energy to light energy
(d) Mechanical energy to electrical energy
(e) Chemical energy to electrical energy
6.6 In winter, an electric space heater uses a certain amount of electrical energy to heat a room to 20°C. In summer, an air conditioner uses the same amount of electrical energy to

cool the room to 20°C. Is the change in internal energy of the heater larger, smaller, or the same as that of the air conditioner? Explain.

6.7 Consider lifting your textbook into the air and dropping it on your desk top. Describe all the energy transformations (from one form to another) that occur, moving backward in time from a moment after impact.

■ Skill-Building Exercises (*paired*)

6.8 A system receives 425 J of heat and delivers 425 J of work to its surroundings. What is the change in internal energy of the system (in J)?

6.9 A system conducts 255 cal of heat to the surroundings while delivering 428 cal of work. What is the change in internal energy of the system (in cal)?

6.10 What is the change in internal energy (in J) of a system that releases 675 J of thermal energy to its surroundings and has 525 cal of work done on it?

6.11 What is the change in internal energy (in J) of a system that absorbs 0.615 kJ of heat from its surroundings and has 0.247 kcal of work done on it?

6.12 Complete combustion of 1.0 metric ton of coal (assuming pure carbon) to gaseous carbon dioxide releases 3.3×10^{10} J of heat. Convert this energy to (a) kilojoules; (b) kilocalories; (c) British thermal units.

6.13 Thermal decomposition of 5.0 metric tons of limestone to lime and carbon dioxide requires 9.0×10^6 kJ of heat. Convert this energy to (a) joules; (b) calories; (c) British thermal units.

■ Problems in Context

6.14 The nutritional calorie (Calorie) is equivalent to 1 kcal. One pound of body fat is equivalent to about 4.1×10^3 Calories. Express this energy equivalence in joules and kilojoules.

6.15 If an athlete expends 1850 kJ/h playing tennis, how long does she have to play to work off 1.0 lb of body fat? (See Problem 6.14.)

Enthalpy: Heats of Reaction and Chemical Change
(Sample Problem 6.2)

■ Concept Review Questions

6.16 Why is a system that undergoes an expansion against a constant external pressure assigned a negative sign for the work done?

6.17 Why is it usually more convenient to measure ΔH than ΔE?

6.18 "Hot packs" used by skiers, climbers, and others for warmth are based on the crystallization of sodium acetate from a highly concentrated solution. What is the sign of ΔH for this crystallization reaction? Is the reaction exothermic or endothermic?

6.19 Classify the following processes as exothermic or endothermic: (a) freezing of water; (b) boiling of water; (c) digestion of food; (d) a person running; (e) a person growing; (f) wood being chopped; (g) heating with a furnace.

6.20 What are the two main components of the internal energy of a substance? On what are they based?

6.21 For each of the following processes, state whether ΔH is less than (more negative), equal to, or greater than ΔE of the system. Explain.

(a) An ideal gas is cooled at constant pressure.
(b) A mixture of gases undergoes an exothermic reaction in a container of fixed volume.
(c) A solid yields a mixture of gases in an exothermic reaction that takes place in a container of variable volume.

■ Skill-Building Exercises (*paired*)

6.22 Draw an enthalpy diagram for a general exothermic reaction; label axis, reactants, products, and ΔH with its sign.

6.23 Draw an enthalpy diagram for a general endothermic reaction; label axis, reactants, products, and ΔH with its sign.

6.24 Write a balanced equation and draw an approximate enthalpy diagram for each of the following changes: (a) the combustion of 1 mol methane in oxygen; (b) the freezing of liquid water.

6.25 Write a balanced equation and draw an approximate enthalpy diagram for each of the following changes: (a) the formation of 1 mol sodium chloride from its elements (heat is released); (b) the vaporization of liquid benzene.

6.26 Write a balanced equation and draw an approximate enthalpy diagram for each of the following changes: (a) the combustion of 1 mol liquid ethanol (C_2H_5OH); (b) the formation of 1 mol nitrogen dioxide from its elements (heat is absorbed).

6.27 Write a balanced equation and draw an approximate enthalpy diagram for each of the following changes: (a) the sublimation of dry ice [conversion of $CO_2(s)$ directly to $CO_2(g)$]; (b) the reaction of 1 mol sulfur dioxide with oxygen.

6.28 Which of the following gases would you expect to have the greater heat of combustion per mole? Why?

methane or formaldehyde

6.29 Which of the following two fuel candidates would you expect to have the greater heat of combustion per mole? Why?

ethanol or methanol

Calorimetry: Laboratory Measurement of Heats of Reaction
(Sample Problems 6.3 to 6.5)

■ Concept Review Questions

6.30 Why can we measure only *changes* in enthalpy, not absolute values?

6.31 What data do you need to determine the specific heat capacity of a substance?

6.32 Is the specific heat capacity of a substance an intensive or extensive property? Explain.

6.33 Distinguish between "specific heat capacity" and "heat capacity." Which parameter would you likely use if you were calculating heat changes in (a) a chrome-plated, brass bathroom fixture; (b) a sample of high-purity copper wire; (c) a sample of pure water? Explain.

6.34 Both a coffee-cup calorimeter and a bomb calorimeter can be used to measure the heat involved in a reaction. Which measures ΔE and which measures ΔH? Explain.

Skill-Building Exercises (paired)

6.35 Calculate q when 12.0 g water is heated from 20.°C to 100.°C.

6.36 Calculate q when 0.10 g ice is cooled from 10.°C to -75°C ($c_{ice} = 2.087$ J/g · K).

6.37 A 295-g aluminum engine part at an initial temperature of 3.00°C absorbs 85.0 kJ of heat. What is the final temperature of the part (c of Al = 0.900 J/g · K)?

6.38 A 27.7-g sample of ethylene glycol, a car radiator coolant, loses 688 J of heat. What was the initial temperature if the final temperature is 32.5°C (c of ethylene glycol = 2.42 J/g · K)?

6.39 Two iron bolts of equal mass—one at 100.°C, the other at 55°C—are placed in an insulated container. Assuming the heat capacity of the container is negligible, what is the final temperature inside the container (c of iron = 0.450 J/g · K)?

6.40 One piece of copper jewelry at 105°C has exactly twice the mass of another piece, which is at 45°C. Both pieces are placed inside a calorimeter whose heat capacity is negligible. What is the final temperature inside the calorimeter (c of copper = 0.387 J/g · K)?

6.41 When 165 mL water at 22°C is mixed with 85 mL water at 82°C, what is the final temperature? (Assume that no heat is lost to the surroundings and that the density of water is 1.00 g/mL.)

6.42 An unknown volume of water at 18.2°C is added to 24.4 mL water at 35.0°C. If the final temperature is 23.5°C, what was the unknown volume? (Assume that no heat is lost to the surroundings and that the density of water is 1.00 g/mL.)

6.43 A 505-g piece of copper tubing is heated to 99.9°C and placed in an insulated vessel containing 59.8 g water at 24.8°C. Assuming no loss of water and that the vessel has a heat capacity of 10.0 J/K, what is the final temperature of the system (c of copper = 0.387 J/g · K)?

6.44 A 30.5-g sample of an alloy at 93.0°C is placed into 50.0 g water at 22.0°C in an insulated coffee cup with a heat capacity of 9.2 J/K. If the final temperature of the system is 31.1°C, what is the specific heat capacity of the alloy?

Problems in Context

6.45 Two aircraft rivets, one of iron and the other of copper, are placed in a calorimeter that has an initial temperature of 20.°C. The data for the metals are as follows:

	IRON	COPPER
Mass (g)	30.0	20.0
Initial T (°C)	0.0	100.0
c (J/g · K)	0.450	0.387

(a) Will heat flow from Fe to Cu or from Cu to Fe?
(b) What other information is needed to correct any measurements that would be made in an actual experiment?
(c) What is the maximum attainable final temperature of the system (assuming the heat capacity of the calorimeter is negligible)?

6.46 A chemical engineer studying the properties of fuels placed 1.500 g of a hydrocarbon in the bomb of a calorimeter and filled it with O_2 gas (see Figure 6.12). The bomb was immersed in 2.500 L water and the reaction initiated. The water temperature rose from 20.00°C to 23.55°C. If the calorimeter (excluding the water) had a heat capacity of 403 J/K, what was the heat of combustion (q_v) per gram of the fuel?

Stoichiometry of Thermochemical Equations
(Sample Problem 6.6)

Concept Review Questions

6.47 Does a negative ΔH_{rxn} mean that the heat can be thought of as a reactant or as a product?

6.48 Would you expect $O_2(g) \longrightarrow 2O(g)$ to have a positive or a negative ΔH_{rxn}? Explain.

6.49 Is ΔH positive or negative when 1 mol water vapor condenses to liquid water? Why? How does this value compare with the value from the vaporization of 2 mol liquid water to water vapor?

Skill-Building Exercises (paired)

6.50 Consider the following balanced thermochemical equation, sometimes used for H_2S production:

$$\tfrac{1}{8}S_8(s) + H_2(g) \longrightarrow H_2S(g) \quad \Delta H_{rxn} = -20.2 \text{ kJ}$$

(a) Is this an exothermic or endothermic reaction?
(b) What is ΔH_{rxn} for the reverse reaction?
(c) What is ΔH when 3.2 mol S_8 reacts?
(d) What is ΔH when 20.0 g S_8 reacts?

6.51 Consider the following balanced thermochemical equation for the decomposition of the mineral magnesite:

$$MgCO_3(s) \longrightarrow MgO(s) + CO_2(g) \quad \Delta H_{rxn} = 117.3 \text{ kJ}$$

(a) Is heat absorbed or released in the reaction?
(b) What is ΔH_{rxn} for the reverse reaction?
(c) What is ΔH when 5.35 mol CO_2 reacts with excess MgO?
(d) What is ΔH when 35.5 g CO_2 reacts with excess MgO?

6.52 When 1 mol NO(g) forms from its elements, 90.29 kJ of heat is absorbed.
(a) Write a balanced thermochemical equation for this reaction.
(b) How much heat is involved when 1.50 g NO decomposes to its elements?

6.53 When 1 mol KBr(s) decomposes to its elements, 394 kJ of heat is absorbed.
(a) Write a balanced thermochemical equation for this reaction.
(b) How much heat is released when 10.0 kg KBr forms from its elements?

Problems in Context

6.54 Liquid hydrogen peroxide is an oxidizing agent in many rocket fuel mixtures because it releases oxygen gas on decomposition:

$$2H_2O_2(l) \longrightarrow 2H_2O(l) + O_2(g) \quad \Delta H_{rxn} = -196.1 \text{ kJ}$$

How much heat is released when 732 kg H_2O_2 decomposes?

6.55 Compounds of boron and hydrogen are remarkable, not only for their unusual bonding (described in Section 14.5), but also for their reactivity. With the more reactive halogens, for example, diborane (B_2H_6) forms trihalides even at low temperatures:

$$B_2H_6(g) + 6Cl_2(g) \longrightarrow 2BCl_3(g) + 6HCl(g)$$
$$\Delta H_{rxn} = -755.4 \text{ kJ}$$

How much heat is released per kilogram of diborane that reacts?

6.56 Deterioration of buildings, bridges, and other structures through the rusting of iron costs millions of dollars every day. Although the actual process also requires water, a simplified equation (with rust shown as Fe_2O_3) is

$$4Fe(s) + 3O_2(g) \longrightarrow 2Fe_2O_3(s) \quad \Delta H_{rxn} = -1.65 \times 10^3 \text{ kJ}$$

(a) How much heat is evolved when 0.100 kg iron rusts?
(b) How much rust forms when 4.93×10^3 kJ of heat is released?

6.57 A mercury mirror forms inside a test tube by the thermal decomposition of mercury(II) oxide:

$$2HgO(s) \longrightarrow 2Hg(l) + O_2(g) \quad \Delta H_{rxn} = 181.6 \text{ kJ}$$

(a) How much heat is needed to decompose 555 g of the oxide?
(b) If 275 kJ of heat is absorbed, how many grams of mercury form?

6.58 Ethylene (C_2H_4) is the starting material for the preparation of poly(ethylene). Although typically made during the processing of petroleum, ethylene occurs naturally as a fruit-ripening hormone and as a component of natural gas.
(a) If the heat of combustion of C_2H_4 is -1411 kJ/mol, write a balanced thermochemical equation for the combustion of C_2H_4.
(b) How many grams of C_2H_4 must be burned to give 70.0 kJ of heat?

6.59 Sucrose ($C_{12}H_{22}O_{11}$, table sugar) is oxidized in the body by O_2 via a complex set of reactions that ultimately produces $CO_2(g)$ and $H_2O(g)$ and releases 5.64×10^3 kJ/mol sucrose.
(a) Write a balanced thermochemical equation for this reaction.
(b) How much heat is released for every 1.00 g sucrose oxidized?

Hess's Law of Heat Summation
(Sample Problem 6.7)

■ Concept Review Questions

6.60 Express in your own words the main principle underlying Hess's law.

6.61 What is the main use of Hess's law?

6.62 It is very difficult to burn carbon in a deficiency of O_2 and produce only CO; some CO_2 forms as well. However, carbon burns in excess O_2 to form only CO_2, and CO burns in excess O_2 to form only CO_2. Use the heats of the latter two reactions (from Appendix B) to calculate the ΔH_{rxn} for the following reaction: $C(graphite) + \frac{1}{2}O_2(g) \longrightarrow CO(g)$

■ Skill-Building Exercises (paired)

6.63 Calculate ΔH_{rxn} for

$$Ca(s) + \tfrac{1}{2}O_2(g) + CO_2(g) \longrightarrow CaCO_3(s)$$

given the following set of reactions:

$$Ca(s) + \tfrac{1}{2}O_2(g) \longrightarrow CaO(s) \qquad \Delta H = -635.1 \text{ kJ}$$
$$CaCO_3(s) \longrightarrow CaO(s) + CO_2(g) \qquad \Delta H = 178.3 \text{ kJ}$$

6.64 Calculate ΔH_{rxn} for

$$2NOCl(g) \longrightarrow N_2(g) + O_2(g) + Cl_2(g)$$

given the following set of reactions:

$$\tfrac{1}{2}N_2(g) + \tfrac{1}{2}O_2(g) \longrightarrow NO(g) \qquad \Delta H = 90.3 \text{ kJ}$$
$$NO(g) + \tfrac{1}{2}Cl_2(g) \longrightarrow NOCl(g) \qquad \Delta H = -38.6 \text{ kJ}$$

6.65 At a specific set of conditions, 241.8 kJ is given off when 1 mol $H_2O(g)$ forms from its elements. Under the same conditions, 285.8 kJ is given off when 1 mol $H_2O(l)$ forms from its elements. Calculate the heat of vaporization of water at these conditions.

6.66 When 1 mol $CS_2(l)$ forms from its elements at 1 atm and 25°C, 89.7 kJ is absorbed, and it takes 27.7 kJ to vaporize 1 mol of the liquid. How much heat is absorbed when 1 mol $CS_2(g)$ forms from its elements at these conditions?

6.67 Write the balanced overall equation for the following process (equation 3), calculate $\Delta H_{overall}$, and match the number of the equation with the letter of the arrow in Figure P6.67:

1) $N_2(g) + O_2(g) \longrightarrow 2NO(g) \qquad \Delta H = 180.6 \text{ kJ}$
2) $2NO(g) + O_2(g) \longrightarrow 2NO_2(g) \qquad \Delta H = -114.2 \text{ kJ}$

---
3) $\Delta H_{overall} = ?$

6.68 Write the balanced overall equation for the following process (equation 3), calculate $\Delta H_{overall}$, and match the equation (number) with the arrow (letter) in Figure P6.68:

1) $P_4(s) + 6Cl_2(g) \longrightarrow 4PCl_3(g) \qquad \Delta H = -1148 \text{ kJ}$
2) $4PCl_3(g) + 4Cl_2(g) \longrightarrow 4PCl_5(g) \quad \Delta H = -460 \text{ kJ}$

---
3) $\Delta H_{overall} = ?$

Figure P6.67

Figure P6.68

■ Problems in Context

6.69 Diamond and graphite are two crystalline forms of carbon. At 1 atm and 25°C, diamond changes to graphite so slowly that the enthalpy change of the process must be obtained indirectly. Determine ΔH_{rxn} for

$$C(\text{diamond}) \longrightarrow C(\text{graphite})$$

with equations from the following list:

1) $C(\text{diamond}) + O_2(g) \longrightarrow CO_2(g) \qquad \Delta H = -395.4 \text{ kJ}$
2) $2CO_2(g) \longrightarrow 2CO(g) + O_2(g) \qquad \Delta H = 566.0 \text{ kJ}$
3) $C(\text{graphite}) + O_2(g) \longrightarrow CO_2(g) \qquad \Delta H = -393.5 \text{ kJ}$
4) $2CO(g) \longrightarrow C(\text{graphite}) + CO_2(g) \qquad \Delta H = -172.5 \text{ kJ}$

Standard Heats of Reaction (ΔH^0_{rxn})
(Sample Problems 6.8 and 6.9)

■ Concept Review Questions

6.70 What is the difference between the standard heat of formation and the standard heat of reaction?

6.71 How are ΔH^0_f values used to calculate ΔH^0_{rxn}?

6.72 Make any changes needed in each of the following equations to make the ΔH^0_{rxn} equal to ΔH^0_f for the compound present:

(a) $Cl(g) + Na(s) \longrightarrow NaCl(s)$

(b) $H_2O(g) \longrightarrow 2H(g) + \frac{1}{2}O_2(g)$

(c) $\frac{1}{2}N_2(g) + \frac{3}{2}H_2(g) \longrightarrow NH_3(g)$

■ Skill-Building Exercises (paired)

6.73 Use Table 6.5 or Appendix B to write balanced formation equations at standard conditions for each of the following compounds: (a) $CaCl_2$; (b) $NaHCO_3$; (c) CCl_4; (d) HNO_3.

6.74 Use Table 6.5 or Appendix B to write balanced formation equations at standard conditions for each of the following compounds: (a) HI; (b) SiF_4; (c) O_3; (d) $Ca_3(PO_4)_2$.

6.75 Calculate ΔH^0_{rxn} for each of the following:

(a) $2H_2S(g) + 3O_2(g) \longrightarrow 2SO_2(g) + 2H_2O(g)$

(b) $CH_4(g) + Cl_2(g) \longrightarrow CCl_4(l) + HCl(g)$ [unbalanced]

6.76 Calculate ΔH^0_{rxn} for each of the following:

(a) $SiO_2(s) + 4HF(g) \longrightarrow SiF_4(g) + 2H_2O(g)$

(b) $C_2H_6(g) + O_2(g) \longrightarrow CO_2(g) + H_2O(g)$ [unbalanced]

6.77 Copper(I) oxide is oxidized to copper(II) oxide according to the following equation:

$$Cu_2O(s) + \tfrac{1}{2}O_2(g) \longrightarrow 2CuO(s) \quad \Delta H^0_{rxn} = -146.0 \text{ kJ}$$

Given that ΔH^0_f of $Cu_2O(s) = -168.6$ kJ/mol, what is ΔH^0_f of $CuO(s)$?

6.78 Acetylene burns in air according to the following equation:

$$C_2H_2(g) + \tfrac{5}{2}O_2(g) \longrightarrow 2CO_2(g) + H_2O(g)$$
$$\Delta H^0_{rxn} = -1255.8 \text{ kJ}$$

Given that ΔH^0_f of $CO_2(g) = -393.5$ kJ/mol and ΔH^0_f of $H_2O(g) = -241.8$ kJ/mol, what is ΔH^0_f of $C_2H_2(g)$?

■ Problems in Context

6.79 Nitroglycerine, $C_3H_5(NO_3)_3(l)$, a powerful explosive used in mining, detonates to produce a hot gaseous mixture of nitrogen, water, carbon dioxide, and oxygen.

(a) Write a balanced equation for this reaction using the smallest whole-number coefficients.

(b) If $\Delta H^0_{rxn} = -2.29 \times 10^4$ kJ for the equation as written in part (a), calculate ΔH^0_f of nitroglycerine.

6.80 The common lead-acid car battery produces a large burst of current, even at low temperatures, and is rechargeable. The reaction that occurs while recharging a "dead" battery is

$$2PbSO_4(s) + 2H_2O(l) \longrightarrow Pb(s) + PbO_2(s) + 2H_2SO_4(l)$$

(a) Use ΔH^0_f values from Appendix B to calculate ΔH^0_{rxn}.

(b) Use the following equations to check your answer in part (a):

1) $Pb(s) + PbO_2(s) + 2SO_3(g) \longrightarrow 2PbSO_4(s)$
$$\Delta H^0 = -768 \text{ kJ}$$

2) $SO_3(g) + H_2O(l) \longrightarrow H_2SO_4(l)$
$$\Delta H^0 = -132 \text{ kJ}$$

Comprehensive Problems

Problems with an asterisk (*) are more challenging.

6.81 Stearic acid ($C_{18}H_{36}O_2$) is a typical fatty acid, a molecule with a long hydrocarbon chain and an organic acid group (COOH) at the end. It is used to make cosmetics, ointments, soaps, and candles and is found in animal tissue as part of many saturated fats. In fact, when you eat meat, chances are that you are ingesting some fats that contain stearic acid.

(a) Write a balanced equation for the complete combustion of stearic acid.

(b) Calculate its heat of combustion ($\Delta H^0_f = -948$ kJ/mol).

(c) Calculate the heat (q) in kJ and kcal when 1.00 g stearic acid is burned completely.

(d) The nutritional information on a popular candy bar states that 1 serving contains 11.0 g fat and 100. Cal derived from fat (1 Cal = 1 kcal). Is this information consistent with your answer in part (c)?

*6.82 Whenever you dilute sulfuric acid with water, you must exercise extreme caution because the dilution process is highly exothermic:

$$H_2SO_4(l) \xrightarrow{\text{H}_2\text{O}} H_2SO_4(aq) + heat$$

(a) Use Appendix B to calculate ΔH^0 for diluting 1.00 mol $H_2SO_4(l)$ to 1 L of 1.00 M $H_2SO_4(aq)$.

(b) Suppose you carry out the dilution in a calorimeter. The initial temperature is 25.0°C, the density of the final solution is 1.060 g/mL, and its specific heat capacity is 3.50 J/g · K. What is the final temperature?

(c) Use the idea of heat capacity to explain why you should carry out the dilution by adding acid to water rather than water to acid.

6.83 A would-be around-the-world balloonist is preparing to make the trip in a helium-filled balloon. The trip begins in early morning at a temperature of 15°C. By midafternoon, the temperature has increased to 30.°C. Assuming the pressure remains constant at 1.00 atm, for each mole of helium calculate:

(a) The initial and final volumes

(b) The change in internal energy, ΔE [Hint: Helium behaves like an ideal gas, so $E = \frac{3}{2}nRT$. Be sure the units of R are consistent with those of E.]

(c) The work (w) done by the helium (in J)

(d) The heat (q) transferred (in J)

(e) ΔH for the process (in J)

(f) Explain the relationship between the answers to parts (d) and (e).

6.84 In his studies of acid-base neutralization, Arrhenius discovered an important fact demonstrated by the following equations:

$$KOH(aq) + HNO_3(aq) \longrightarrow KNO_3(aq) + H_2O(l)$$
$$NaOH(aq) + HCl(aq) \longrightarrow NaCl(aq) + H_2O(l)$$

(a) Use the data for the individual ions in Appendix B to calculate ΔH^0 for these reactions.

(b) Explain your results and use them to predict ΔH^0 for

$$KOH(aq) + HCl(aq) \longrightarrow KCl(aq) + H_2O(l)$$

6.85 Iron metal is produced in a blast furnace through a complex series of reactions that involve reduction of iron(III) oxide with carbon monoxide.

(a) Write a balanced overall equation for the process, including the other product.

(b) Use the equations below to calculate ΔH^0_{rxn} for the overall equation:

1) $3Fe_2O_3(s) + CO(g) \longrightarrow 2Fe_3O_4(s) + CO_2(g)$
$$\Delta H^0 = -48.5 \text{ kJ}$$

2) $Fe(s) + CO_2(g) \longrightarrow FeO(s) + CO(g) \quad \Delta H^0 = -11.0 \text{ kJ}$

3) $Fe_3O_4(s) + CO(g) \longrightarrow 3FeO(s) + CO_2(g) \quad \Delta H^0 = 22 \text{ kJ}$

6.86 Pure liquid octane (C_8H_{18}; $d = 0.702$ g/mL) is used as the fuel in a test of a new automobile drive train.

(a) How much energy (in kJ) is released by complete combustion of all the octane in a 20.4-gal fuel tank ($\Delta H^0_{comb} = -5.45\times10^3$ kJ/mol)?

(b) The energy delivered to the drive wheels at 65 mph is 5.5×10^4 kJ/h. Assuming all the energy is transferred to the wheels, what is the cruising range (in km) of the car on a full tank?

(c) If the actual cruising range is 455 miles, explain your answer to part (b).

*6.87 Equation 6.8 relates the standard heat of reaction to the standard heats of formation of reactants and products. A similar equation relates the standard heat of reaction to the standard heats of combustion:

$$\Delta H^0_{rxn} = \Sigma m \Delta H^0_{comb(reactants)} - \Sigma n \Delta H^0_{comb(products)}$$

(a) Sketch an enthalpy diagram similar to Figure 6.14 that shows this relationship.

(b) Why are the reactant and product terms in a different order than in Equation 6.8?

6.88 Physicians and nutritional biochemists recommend eating foods that contain vegetable oils rather than animal fats to lower risks of heart disease, and olive oil is considered one of the "healthier" choices. The main fatty acid in olive oil is oleic acid ($C_{18}H_{34}O_2$), whose $\Delta H^0_{comb} = -1.11\times10^4$ kJ/mol. Calculate ΔH^0_f of oleic acid. [Assume $H_2O(g)$.]

6.89 Oxidation of ClF by F_2 yields ClF_3, an important fluorinating agent formerly used to produce the uranium compounds in nuclear fuels:

$$ClF(g) + F_2(g) \longrightarrow ClF_3(l)$$

Use the following thermochemical equations to calculate ΔH^0_{rxn} for the production of ClF_3:

1) $2ClF(g) + O_2(g) \longrightarrow Cl_2O(g) + OF_2(g) \quad \Delta H^0 = 167.5 \text{ kJ}$

2) $2F_2(g) + O_2(g) \longrightarrow 2OF_2(g) \quad \Delta H^0 = -43.5 \text{ kJ}$

3) $2ClF_3(l) + 2O_2(g) \longrightarrow Cl_2O(g) + 3OF_2(g) \quad \Delta H^0 = 394.1 \text{ kJ}$

6.90 Silver halides are essential components of black-and-white photography. Ordinary film is coated with the bromide, and extremely high-speed film, such as that used in sporting events, uses the iodide.

(a) When 50.0 mL of 5.0 g/L $AgNO_3$ is mixed with 50.0 mL of 5.0 g/L NaI at 25°C, what mass of AgI forms?

(b) Use Appendix B to find ΔH^0_{rxn}.

6.91 The calorie (4.184 J) was originally defined as the quantity of energy required to raise the temperature of 1.00 g liquid water 1.00°C. The British thermal unit (Btu) is defined as the quantity of energy required to raise the temperature of 1.00 lb liquid water 1.00°F.

(a) How many joules are in 1.00 British thermal unit (1 lb = 453.6 g; a change of 1.0°C = 1.8°F)?

(b) The "therm" is a unit of energy consumption used by natural gas companies in the United States and is defined as 100,000 Btu. How many joules are in 1.00 therm?

(c) How many moles of methane must be burned to give 1.00 therm of energy? (Assume water forms as a gas.)

(d) If natural gas costs $0.46 per therm, what is the cost per mole of methane (assume natural gas is pure methane)?

(e) How much would it cost to warm 308 gal water in a hot tub from 15.0°C to 40.0°C (1 gal = 3.78 L)?

6.92 A reaction is carried out in a steel reaction vessel within a chamber filled with argon gas. The figure depicts molecular views of the argon adjacent to the surface of the reaction vessel before and after the reaction. Was the reaction exothermic or endothermic? Explain.

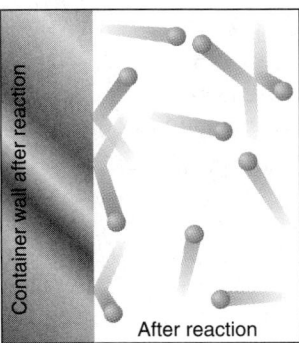

Before reaction · After reaction

6.93 The heat of atomization (ΔH^0_{atom}) is the heat needed to form separated gaseous atoms from a substance in its standard state. For example, the equation for the atomization of graphite is

$$C(graphite) \longrightarrow C(g)$$

Use Hess's law to calculate ΔH^0_{atom} of graphite from the following data:

1) ΔH^0_f of $CH_4 = -74.9$ kJ/mol

2) ΔH^0_{atom} of $CH_4 = 1660$ kJ/mol

3) ΔH^0_{atom} of $H_2 = 432$ kJ/mol

6.94 For each of the following events, the system is in *italics*. State whether heat, work, or both is (are) transferred and the direction of each transfer.

(a) You pump air into an automobile *tire*.

(b) A *tree* rots in a forest.

(c) You strike a *match*.

(d) You cool juice in an *ice chest*.

(e) You cook *food* on a kitchen range.

6.95 Triglycerides are the main storage form of fats in the body. During periods of starvation, a person's fat stores are used for energy. Tristearin ($C_{57}H_{110}O_6$) is a typical animal fat that is oxidized according to the following equation:

$$2C_{57}H_{110}O_6(s) + 163O_2(g) \longrightarrow 114CO_2(g) + 110H_2O(l)$$

If $\Delta H^0_{rxn} = -7.0\times10^4$ kJ, how much heat is released

(a) Per mole of O_2 consumed?

(b) Per mole of CO_2 formed?

(c) Per gram of tristearin oxidized?

(d) When 325 L O_2 at 37°C and 755 torr is used, how many grams of tristearin can be oxidized?

6.96 Show that the SI units for pressure times volume (PV) equal those for energy (E).

6.97 Kerosene, a common space-heater fuel, is a mixture of hydrocarbons whose "average" formula is $C_{12}H_{26}$.
(a) Write a balanced equation, using the simplest whole-number coefficients, for the complete combustion of kerosene to $CO_2(g)$ and $H_2O(g)$.
(b) If $\Delta H^0_{comb} = -1.50 \times 10^4$ kJ for the equation as written in part (a), determine ΔH^0_f of kerosene.
(c) Calculate the heat produced by combustion of 0.50 gal kerosene (d of kerosene = 0.749 g/mL).
(d) How many gallons of kerosene must be burned for a kerosene furnace to produce 1250. Btu (1 Btu = 1.055 kJ)?

6.98 Pioneers and cowboys sometimes heated their coffee by placing an iron poker from the fire directly into the coffee. If a cup held 0.50 L coffee at 18°C, what would be the final temperature of the coffee when a 502-g iron poker at 800.°C was placed in it? (Assume no heat is lost to the surroundings and no water vaporizes.)

6.99 Phosphorus pentachloride is used in the industrial preparation of organic phosphorus compounds. Equation 1 shows its preparation from PCl_3 and Cl_2:

1) $PCl_3(l) + Cl_2(g) \longrightarrow PCl_5(s)$

Use equations 2 and 3 to calculate ΔH_{rxn} of equation 1:

2) $P_4(s) + 6Cl_2(g) \longrightarrow 4PCl_3(l)$ $\qquad \Delta H = -1280$ kJ
3) $P_4(s) + 10Cl_2(g) \longrightarrow 4PCl_5(s)$ $\qquad \Delta H = -1774$ kJ

*6.100 Water has a particularly high specific heat capacity and heat of fusion. Explain the role of water in the following two common practices:
(a) During especially cold days, people place large tubs of water in the "root cellar" of their old country homes to prevent the stored garden vegetables from freezing.
(b) Citrus growers in Florida spray their orchards with water when a frost is predicted.

6.101 Consider the following hydrocarbon fuels: (I) $CH_4(g)$; (II) $C_2H_4(g)$; (III) $C_2H_6(g)$.
(a) Rank them in terms of heat released per mole. [Assume $H_2O(g)$ forms and combustion is complete.]
(b) Rank them in terms of heat released per gram.

6.102 A typical candy bar weighs about 2 oz (1.00 oz = 28.4 g).
(a) Assuming that a candy bar is 100% sugar and that 1.0 g sugar is equivalent to about 4.0 Calories of energy, calculate the energy (in kilojoules) contained in a typical candy bar.
(b) Assuming that your mass is 58 kg and you convert chemical potential energy to work with 100% efficiency, how high would you have to climb to work off the energy in a candy bar? (Potential energy = mass × g × height, where g = 9.8 m/s^2.)
(c) Why is your actual conversion of potential energy to work less than 100% efficient?

*6.103 You want to determine ΔH^0 for the reaction

$$Zn(s) + 2HCl(aq) \longrightarrow ZnCl_2(aq) + H_2(g)$$

(a) To do so, you first determine the heat capacity of a calorimeter using the following reaction, whose ΔH is known:

$$NaOH(aq) + HCl(aq) \longrightarrow NaCl(aq) + H_2O(l)$$
$$\Delta H^0 = -57.32 \text{ kJ}$$

Calculate the heat capacity of the calorimeter from the following:
> Amounts used: 50.0 mL of 2.00 M HCl and 50.0 mL of 2.00 M NaOH
> Initial T of both solutions: 16.9°C
> Maximum T recorded during reaction: 30.4°C
> Density of resulting NaCl solution: 1.04 g/mL
> c of 1.00 M NaCl(aq) = 3.93 J/g · K

(b) Use the result from part (a) and the following data to determine ΔH^0_{rxn} for the reaction between zinc and HCl(aq):
> Amounts used: 100.0 mL of 1.00 M HCl and 1.3078 g Zn
> Initial T of HCl solution and Zn: 16.8°C
> Maximum T recorded during reaction: 24.1°C
> Density of 1.0 M HCl solution = 1.015 g/mL
> c of resulting $ZnCl_2(aq)$ = 3.95 J/g · K

(c) Given the following values, what is the error in your experiment?

$$\Delta H^0_f \text{ of HCl}(aq) = -1.652 \times 10^2 \text{ kJ/mol}$$
$$\Delta H^0_f \text{ of ZnCl}_2(aq) = -4.822 \times 10^2 \text{ kJ/mol}$$

*6.104 One mole of nitrogen gas confined within a cylinder by a piston is heated from 0°C to 819°C at 1.00 atm.
(a) Calculate the work of expansion in joules (1 J = 9.87×10^{-3} atm · L). Assume all the energy is used to do work.
(b) What would be the temperature change if the gas had been heated with the same amount of energy in a container of fixed volume? (Assume the specific heat capacity of N_2 is 1.00 J/g · K.)

*6.105 The combustion of eight-carbon hydrocarbons (C_8H_{18}), such as those found in gasoline, is one of the most common redox reactions in modern society.
(a) Calculate ΔH^0_{comb} of 1 mol C_8H_{18} in excess O_2, assuming water forms as a gas.
(b) Calculate ΔE for this reaction (1 J = 9.87×10^{-3} atm · L). (Hint: Use $P\Delta V = \Delta n_{gas}RT$ to convert between ΔH and ΔE.)

6.106 High-purity benzoic acid (C_6H_5COOH; ΔH_{comb} = −3227 kJ/mol) is a combustion standard for calibrating bomb calorimeters. A 1.221-g sample burns in a calorimeter (heat capacity = 1365 J/°C) that contains exactly 1.200 kg water. What temperature change is observed?

*6.107 Liquid methanol (CH_3OH) is being used as an alternative fuel in cars and trucks, and some predict it will be the fuel of choice in the future. An industrial method for preparing methanol, sometimes called the *Fischer-Tropsch process*, occurs through the catalytic hydrogenation of carbon monoxide:

$$CO(g) + 2H_2(g) \xrightarrow{\text{catalyst}} CH_3OH(l)$$

How much heat (in kJ) is released when 15.0 L CO at 85°C and 112 kPa reacts with 18.5 L H_2 at 75°C and 744 torr?

*6.108 (a) How much heat is released when 25.0 g methane burns in excess O_2 to form gaseous products?
(b) Calculate the temperature of the product mixture if the methane and air are both at an initial temperature of 0.0°C. Assume a stoichiometric ratio of methane with oxygen from the air and that air is 21% O_2 by volume. (The c of CO_2 = 57.2 J/mol · K; the c of $H_2O(g)$ = 36.0 J/mol · K; and the c of N_2 = 30.5 J/mol · K.)

7

Quantum Theory and Atomic Structure

Figure: From experiment to model.
Through studies of light and its interactions with matter, the human mind overthrew the classical distinction between matter and energy to create a new model of atomic structure. In this chapter, we follow the interplay of experiment and theory that culminated in this remarkable understanding.

Revolutions in science are not the violent upheavals of political overthrow. Rather, flaws appear in an established model as conflicting evidence mounts, a startling discovery or two widens the flaws into cracks, and the conceptual structure crumbles gradually as a result of its inconsistencies. New insight, verified by experiment, then guides the building of a model more consistent with reality. So it was when Lavoisier's theory of combustion overthrew the phlogiston model, when Dalton's atomic theory established the idea of individual units of matter, and when Rutherford's nuclear model substituted an atom with rich internal structure for "billiard balls" or "plum puddings." In this chapter, you will see this process unfold again with the development of modern atomic theory. ◆

Almost as soon as Rutherford proposed his nuclear model, a major problem arose. A nucleus and an electron attract each other, so if they are to remain apart, the energy of the electron's motion (kinetic energy) must balance the energy of attraction (potential energy). However, the laws of classical physics had established that a negative particle moving in a curved path around a positive one *must* emit radiation and thus lose energy. If this requirement applied to atoms, why didn't the orbiting electron lose energy continuously and spiral into the nucleus? Clearly, if electrons behaved the way classical physics predicted, all atoms would have collapsed eons ago! The behavior of subatomic matter seemed to violate common experience and accepted principles.

The breakthroughs that soon followed forced a complete rethinking of the classical picture of matter and energy. In the macroscopic world, the two are distinct. Matter occurs in chunks you can hold and weigh, and you can change the amount of matter in a sample piece by piece. In contrast, energy is "massless," and its quantity changes in a continuous manner. Matter moves in specific paths, whereas light and other types of energy travel in diffuse waves. As soon as 20th-century scientists probed the subatomic world, however, these clear distinctions between particulate matter and wavelike energy began to fade.

In this chapter and the next, we discuss *quantum mechanics*, the theory that explains our current picture of atomic structure. After considering the wave properties of energy, we examine the theories and experiments that led to a *quantized*, or particulate, model of light. We see why the light emitted by an excited hydrogen (H) atom—its *atomic spectrum*—suggests an atom with distinct energy levels, and we look briefly at how atomic spectra are applied to chemical analysis today. Then we examine wave-particle duality, the central idea of quantum mechanics. The last section describes the current model of the H atom and presents the quantum numbers we use to identify the regions of space an electron occupies in an atom. In Chapter 8, we consider atoms with more than one electron and relate the number and distribution of their electrons to chemical behavior.

7.1 The Nature of Light

Visible light is one type of **electromagnetic (EM) radiation** (also called *electromagnetic energy* and *radiant energy*). Other familiar types include x-rays, microwaves, and radio waves. All electromagnetic radiation consists of energy propagated by means of electric and magnetic fields that alternately increase and decrease in intensity as they move through space. This classical wave model distinguishes clearly between waves and particles, and is essential for understanding why rainbows form, how magnifying glasses work, why objects look distorted under water, and many other everyday observations. But, it cannot explain observations on the atomic scale because, in those cases, energy behaves as though it consists of particles!

Concepts and Skills to Review

before you study this chapter:

- discovery of the electron and atomic nucleus (Section 2.4)
- major features of atomic structure (Section 2.5)
- changes in energy state of a system (Section 6.1)

◆ **Hurrah for the Human Mind** The first decades of the 20th century and the few years leading up to it were one of the most exciting periods in recent history for science and the arts. The invention of the car, radio, and airplane fostered a feeling of unlimited human ability. The discovery of x-rays, radioactivity, the electron, and the atomic nucleus led to the sense that the human mind would soon uncover all of nature's mysteries. Indeed, some people were convinced that few, if any, mysteries remained.

1895 Röntgen discovers x-rays.
1896 Becquerel discovers radioactivity.
1897 Thomson discovers the electron.
1898 Curie discovers radium.
1900 Freud proposes theory of the unconscious mind.
1900 Planck develops quantum theory.
1901 Marconi invents the radio.
1903 Wright brothers fly an airplane.
1905 Ford uses assembly line to build cars.
1905 Rutherford develops radioactivity theory.
1905 Einstein publishes relativity and photon theories.
1906 St. Denis develops modern dance.
1908 Matisse and Picasso develop modern art.
1909 Schönberg and Berg develop modern music.
1911 Rutherford presents nuclear model of the atom.
1913 Bohr proposes atomic model.
1914 to 1918 World War I is fought.
1923 Compton demonstrates photon momentum.
1924 De Broglie publishes wave theory of matter.
1926 Schrödinger develops wave equation.
1927 Heisenberg presents uncertainty principle.
1932 Chadwick discovers the neutron.

Figure 7.1 Frequency and wavelength. Three waves with different wavelengths (λ) and thus different frequencies (ν) are shown. Note that as the wavelength decreases, the frequency increases, and vice versa.

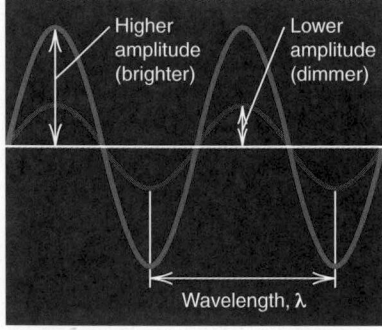

Figure 7.2 Amplitude (intensity) of a wave. Amplitude is represented by the height of the crest (or depth of the trough) of the wave. The two waves shown have the same wavelength (color) but different amplitudes and, therefore, different brightnesses (intensities).

The Wave Nature of Light

The wave properties of EM radiation are described by two interdependent variables, as Figure 7.1 shows:

- **Frequency** (ν, Greek *nu*) is the number of cycles the wave undergoes per second, and is expressed in units of 1/second [s^{-1}; also called *hertz* (Hz)].
- **Wavelength** (λ, Greek *lambda*) is the distance between any point on a wave and the corresponding point on the next wave; that is, the distance the wave travels during one cycle. Wavelength is expressed in meters and often, to express very short wavelengths, nanometers (nm, 10^{-9} m), picometers (pm, 10^{-12} m), or the non-SI unit angstroms (Å, 10^{-10} m).

The speed of the wave, the distance traveled per unit time (in units of meters per second), is the product of its frequency (cycles per second) and its wavelength (meters per cycle):

$$\text{Units for speed of wave:} \quad \frac{\text{cycles}}{\text{s}} \times \frac{\text{m}}{\text{cycle}} = \frac{\text{m}}{\text{s}}$$

In a vacuum, all electromagnetic radiation travels at 2.99792458×10^8 m/s (3.00×10^8 m/s to three significant figures), a constant called the **speed of light** (c):

$$c = \nu \times \lambda \tag{7.1}$$

Since, as Equation 7.1 shows, the product of ν and λ is a constant, the individual terms have a reciprocal relationship to each other: *radiation with a high frequency has a short wavelength, and vice versa.*

Another characteristic of a wave is its **amplitude.** As Figure 7.2 shows, amplitude is the height of the crest (or depth of the trough) of each wave. The amplitude of an electromagnetic wave is a measure of the strength of its electric and magnetic fields. Thus, amplitude is related to the *intensity* of the radiation, which we perceive as brightness in the case of visible light. Light of a particular color, fire-engine red for instance, has a specific frequency and wavelength, but it can be dimmer (lower amplitude) or brighter (higher amplitude).

The Electromagnetic Spectrum   Visible light represents a small portion of the continuum of radiant energy known as the **electromagnetic spectrum** (Figure 7.3). *The waves in the spectrum all travel at the same speed through a vacu-*

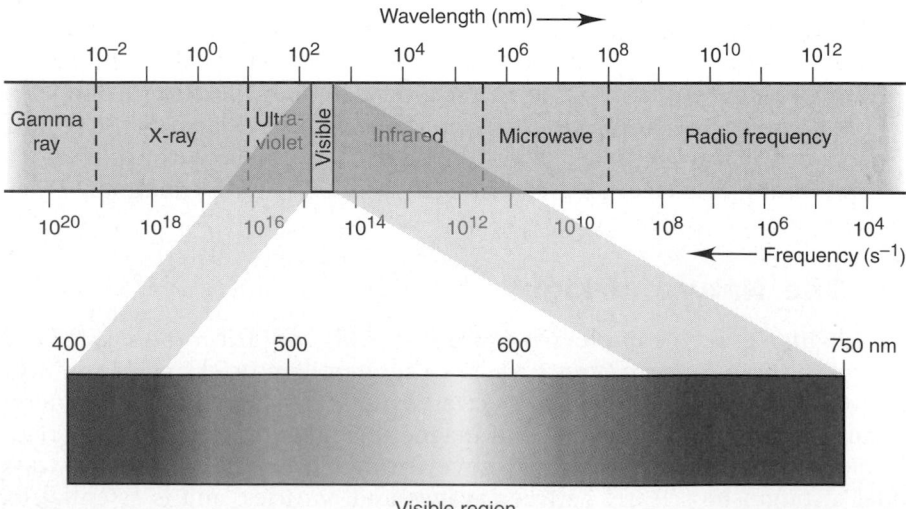

Figure 7.3 Regions of the electromagnetic spectrum. The electromagnetic spectrum extends from the very short wavelengths (very high frequencies) of gamma rays through the very long wavelengths (very low frequencies) of radio waves. The relatively narrow visible region is expanded (and the scale made linear) to show the component colors.

um but differ in frequency and, therefore, wavelength. Some regions of the spectrum are utilized by particular devices; for example, the long-wavelength, low-frequency portion makes up the microwave and radio regions. Note that each region overlaps the next. For instance, the **infrared (IR)** region overlaps the microwave region on one end and the visible region on the other.

We perceive different wavelengths (or frequencies) of *visible* light as different colors, from red ($\lambda \approx 750$ nm) to violet ($\lambda \approx 400$ nm). Light of a single wavelength is called *monochromatic* (Greek, "one color"), whereas light of many wavelengths is *polychromatic* (Greek, "many colors"). White light is polychromatic. The region adjacent to visible light on the short-wavelength end consists of **ultraviolet (UV)** radiation (also called *ultraviolet light*). Still shorter wavelengths (higher frequencies) make up the x-ray and gamma (γ) ray regions. Thus, a TV signal, the light from a traffic signal, and a γ ray emitted by a radioactive element differ in their frequency and wavelength. ◆

Sample Problem 7.1 Interconverting Wavelength and Frequency

PROBLEM A dental hygienist uses x-rays ($\lambda = 1.00$ Å) to take a series of dental radiographs while the patient listens to a radio station ($\lambda - 325$ cm) and looks out the window at the blue sky ($\lambda = 473$ nm). What is the frequency (in s^{-1}) of the electromagnetic radiation from each source? (Assume that the radiation travels at the speed of light, 3.00×10^8 m/s.)

PLAN We are given the wavelengths, so we use Equation 7.1 to find the frequencies. However, we must first convert the wavelengths to meters because c has units of m/s.

SOLUTION For x-rays. Converting from angstroms to meters:

$$\lambda = 1.00 \text{ Å} \times \frac{10^{-10} \text{ m}}{1 \text{ Å}} = 1.00\times10^{-10} \text{ m}$$

Calculating the frequency:

$$\nu = \frac{c}{\lambda} = \frac{3.00\times10^8 \text{ m/s}}{1.00\times10^{-10} \text{ m}} = 3.00\times10^{18} \text{ s}^{-1}$$

For the radio station: Combining steps to calculate the frequency,

$$\nu = \frac{c}{\lambda} = \frac{3.00\times10^8 \text{ m/s}}{325 \text{ cm} \times \dfrac{10^{-2} \text{ m}}{1 \text{ cm}}} = 9.23\times10^7 \text{ s}^{-1}$$

For the blue sky: Combining steps to calculate the frequency,

$$\nu = \frac{c}{\lambda} = \frac{3.00\times10^8 \text{ m/s}}{473 \text{ nm} \times \dfrac{10^{-9} \text{ m}}{1 \text{ nm}}} = 6.34\times10^{14} \text{ s}^{-1}$$

CHECK The orders of magnitude are correct for the regions of the electromagnetic spectrum (see Figure 7.3): x-rays (10^{19} to 10^{16} s^{-1}), radio waves (10^8 to 10^7 s^{-1}), and visible light (7.5×10^{14} to 4.0×10^{14} s^{-1}).

COMMENT The radio station in this problem is broadcasting at a frequency of 92.3×10^6 s^{-1}, or 92.3 million Hz (92.3 MHz), about midway in the FM range.

Follow-up Problem 7.1 Some diamonds appear yellow because they contain nitrogen compounds that absorb purple light of frequency 7.23×10^{14} Hz. Calculate the wavelength (in nm and Å) of the absorbed light.

◆ **Electromagnetic Emissions Everywhere**
We are bathed in electromagnetic radiation from the Sun. Man-made sources of radiation bombard us as well: radio and TV signals; microwave radiation from traffic radar systems and telephone relay stations; and radiation given off by light bulbs, medical x-ray equipment, car motors, and so forth. Natural sources on Earth bombard us also: lightning, radioactive decay, and even fireflies! Virtually all our knowledge of the distant universe comes from radiation entering our light, x-ray, and radio telescopes.

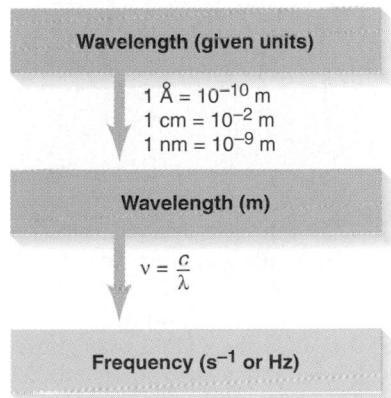

The Distinction Between Energy and Matter

In the everyday world around us, energy and matter behave very differently. Let's examine some important observations about light and see how they contrast with the behavior of particles. Light of a given wavelength travels at different speeds through different transparent media—vacuum, air, water, quartz, and so forth. Therefore,

◆ **Refraction in Chemical Analysis** The index of refraction of a material equals c/v, where v is the speed at which light travels through the material. Since c is always greater than v, the index of refraction is always greater than 1. In the analytical technique of *refractometry,* the index of refraction is determined with light of a known wavelength passing through a fixed thickness of the substance at a known temperature. Refractometry is often used to identify a pure substance. Using yellow light (λ = 589 nm), for example, the index of refraction of water (at 20°C) is 1.33, of NaCl is 1.53, and of diamond is 2.42. With known standards, refractometry is also used to determine the composition of solutions from antifreeze to maple syrup.

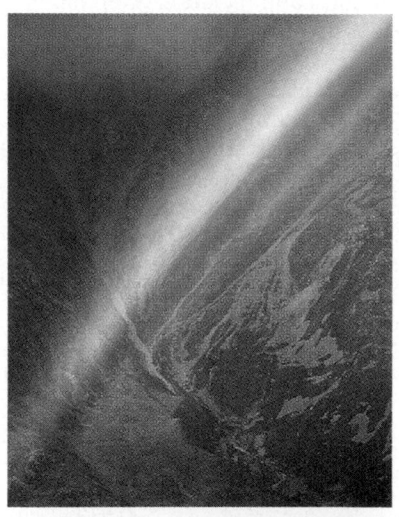

◆ **Rainbows and Diamonds** You can see a rainbow only when the Sun is at your back. Light entering the near surface of a water droplet is dispersed and reflected off the far surface. Since red light is bent least, it reaches your eye from droplets higher in the sky, whereas violet appears from droplets that are lower. The colors in a diamond's sparkle are due to its facets, which are cleaved at angles that disperse and reflect the incoming light, lengthening its path enough for the different wavelengths to separate.

when a light wave passes through the boundary from one medium into another, the speed of the wave changes. Figure 7.4A shows the phenomenon known as **refraction.** If the wave strikes the boundary, say between air and water, at an angle other than 90°, the change in speed causes a change in direction, and the wave continues at a different angle. The new angle (angle of refraction) depends on the materials on either side of the boundary and the wavelength of the light. ◆ In the process of *dispersion,* white light separates (disperses) into its component colors, as when it passes through a prism, because each incoming wavelength is refracted at a slightly different angle. ◆ In contrast, particles do not undergo refraction when passing from one medium to another. Figure 7.4B shows that when a pebble thrown through the air enters a lake, its speed changes abruptly and then it continues to slow down gradually in a curved path.

When a wave strikes the edge of an object, it bends around it in a phenomenon called **diffraction.** If the wave passes through a slit about as wide as its wavelength, it bends around both edges of the slit and forms a semicircular wave on the other side of the opening, as shown in Figure 7.4C. Once again, particles act very differently. Figure 7.4D shows that if a collection of particles is aimed at a small opening, some particles hit the edge, while others go through and continue linearly in a narrower group.

If waves of light pass through two adjacent slits, the emerging circular waves interact through the process of *interference* to create a diffraction pattern of brighter and darker regions (Figure 7.5). Streams of particles, however, moving through adjacent openings continue in straight paths, with some possibly colliding and moving at different angles. At the end of the 19th century, all experience seemed to confirm these classical distinctions between the wave nature of energy and the particle nature of matter.

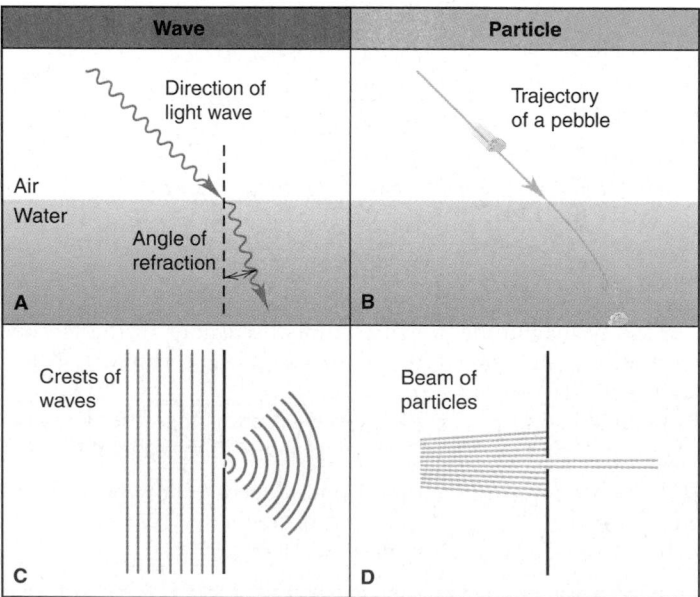

Figure 7.4 Different behaviors of waves and particles. A, A wave passing from air into water is *refracted* (bent at an angle). **B,** In contrast, a particle of matter (such as a pebble) entering a pond moves in a curved path, because gravity and the greater resistance (drag) of the water slow it down. **C,** A wave is *diffracted* through a small opening, which gives rise to a circular wave on the other side. (The lines represent the crests of water waves as seen from above.) **D,** In contrast, when the particles in a collection approach an opening, such as when a handful of sand is thrown at a hole in a fence, some move through and continue along individual paths.

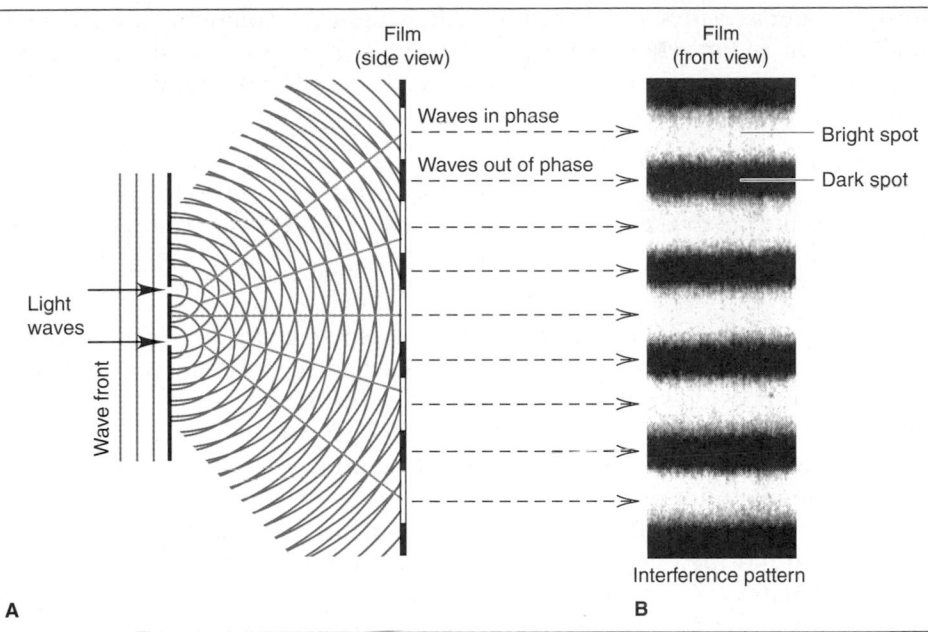

Film (side view)

Waves in phase

Waves out of phase

Light waves

Wave front

Film (front view)

Bright spot

Dark spot

Interference pattern

A

B

Figure 7.5 **The diffraction pattern caused by light passing through two adjacent slits. A,** After passing through two closely spaced slits, emerging circular waves interfere with each other. They create a diffraction (interference) pattern on a sheet of film. Bright regions appear where crests coincide and enhance each other (in phase), and dark regions appear where crests meet troughs and cancel each other (out of phase). **B,** The interference pattern obtained on the film.

The Particle Nature of Light

Three phenomena involving matter and light were especially confounding to physicists of the early 20th century: (1) blackbody radiation, (2) the photoelectric effect, and (3) atomic spectra. Explaining these phenomena required a radically new way to picture energy. We discuss the first two here and the third in the next section.

Blackbody Radiation and the Quantization of Energy   When a solid object is heated to about 1000 K, it begins to emit visible light, as you can see in the soft red glow of smoldering coal. At about 1500 K, the light is brighter and more orange, like the heating coil of a toaster. At temperatures greater than 2000 K, the light is still brighter and whiter, like the filament of a light bulb. These changes in intensity and wavelength of emitted light as an object is heated are characteristic of *blackbody radiation,* light given off by a hot *blackbody* (Figure 7.6A). All attempts to account for the observed changes by applying classical electromagnetic theory failed.

In 1900, the German physicist Max Planck (1858–1947) developed a formula that fit the data perfectly (Figure 7.6B). To find a physical explanation

Energy, *E*

Wavelength, λ

B

A

Figure 7.6 Fitting theory to data in the blackbody problem. A, The interior of a cold ceramic-firing kiln approximates a blackbody, an object that absorbs all radiation falling on it and appears black. A hot kiln emits light characteristic of blackbody radiation. **B,** Planck's formula generates a curve that fits perfectly the changes in energy and intensity of light emitted by a blackbody at different wavelengths for a given temperature. At higher temperatures, the peak of the curve is higher and shifts to shorter wavelengths.

for his formula, Planck was forced to make a radical assumption, which eventually led to an entirely new view of energy. He proposed that the hot, glowing object could emit (or absorb) only *certain quantities* of energy:

$$E = nh\nu$$

where E is the energy of the radiation, ν is its frequency, n is a positive integer (1, 2, 3, and so on) called a **quantum number,** and h is a proportionality constant now called **Planck's constant.** With energy in joules (J) and frequency in s^{-1}, h has units of J · s:

$$h = 6.626{\times}10^{-34} \text{ J · s}$$

Later interpretations of Planck's proposal stated that the hot object's radiation is emitted by the atoms contained within it. If an atom can *emit* only certain quantities of energy, it follows that *the atom itself can have only certain quantities of energy.* Thus, the energy of an atom is *quantized:* it exists only in certain fixed quantities, rather than being continuous. Each change in the atom's energy results from the gain or loss of one or more "packets" of energy. Each energy packet is called a **quantum** ("fixed quantity"; plural, *quanta*) and has the energy $h\nu$. To restate this idea, *an atom changes its energy state by emitting (or absorbing) one or more quanta of energy.* Thus, the energy of the emitted (or absorbed) radiation is equal to the *difference in the atom's energy states:*

$$\Delta E_{\text{atom}} = E_{\text{emitted (or absorbed) radiation}} = \Delta nh\nu$$

Since n is a positive integer, the atom can change its energy only by integer multiples of $h\nu$. Therefore, the smallest possible energy change for an atom in a given energy state occurs when it changes to an adjacent energy state, that is, when $\Delta n = 1$:

$$\Delta E = h\nu \qquad\qquad\qquad \textbf{(7.2)}$$

The Photoelectric Effect and the Photon Theory of Light   Despite the idea that energy is quantized, Planck and other physicists continued to picture the emitted energy as traveling in waves. However, the wave model could not explain the **photoelectric effect,** the flow of current when monochromatic light of sufficient energy shines on a metal plate (Figure 7.7). The existence of the current was not puzzling: it could be understood as arising when the light transfers energy to the electrons at the metal surface, which break free and are collected by the positive electrode. However, the photoelectric effect had certain features that were confusing, in particular the *presence of a threshold frequency* and the *absence of a time lag:*

1. *Presence of a threshold frequency.* Light shining on the metal must have a minimum *frequency* or no current flows. (Different metals have different minimum frequencies.) The wave theory, however, associates the energy of the light with the *amplitude* (intensity) of the wave, not with its frequency (color). Thus, the wave theory predicts that an electron would break free when it absorbs enough energy from light of *any* color.

2. *Absence of a time lag.* Current flows the moment light of this minimum frequency shines on the metal, regardless of the intensity of the light. The wave theory, however, predicts that in dim light there would be a time lag before the current flows, because the electrons have to absorb enough energy to break free.

Carrying Planck's idea of packeted energy further, Einstein proposed that light itself is particulate, occurring as quanta of electromagnetic energy, later

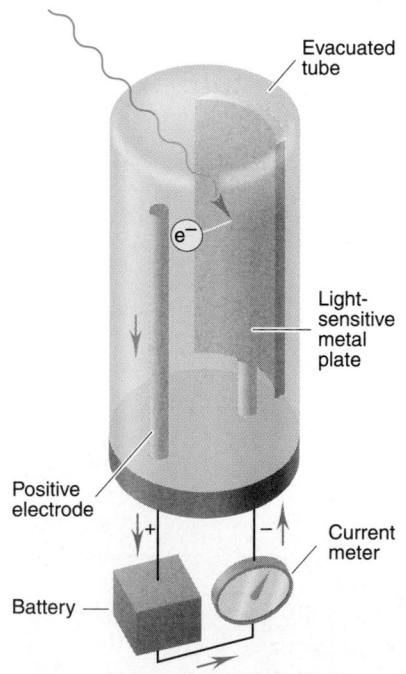

Figure 7.7 Demonstration of the photoelectric effect. When monochromatic light of high enough frequency strikes the metal plate, electrons are freed from the plate and travel to the positive electrode, which creates a current.

called **photons.** ◆ In terms of Planck's work, we can say that each atom changes its energy whenever it absorbs or emits one photon, one "particle" of light, whose energy is fixed by its *frequency:*

$$E_{photon} = h\nu = \Delta E_{atom}$$

Let's see how Einstein's photon theory explains the photoelectric effect:

1. *Presence of a threshold frequency.* According to the photon theory, a beam of light consists of an enormous number of photons. Light intensity (brightness) is related to the number of photons striking the surface per unit time, but *not* to their energy. Therefore, a photon of a certain minimum *energy* must be absorbed for an electron to be freed. Since energy depends on frequency ($h\nu$), the theory predicts a threshold frequency.

2. *Absence of a time lag.* An electron cannot gradually "save up" energy from several photons below the minimum energy until it has enough to break free. Rather, one electron breaks free the moment it absorbs one photon of *enough* energy. The current is weaker in dim light than in bright light because fewer photons of enough energy are present, so fewer electrons break free per unit time. But *some* current flows the moment photons reach the metal plate. ◆

◆ **Infinitesimal Quanta** Why don't we see separate packets of light coming from a light bulb? The answer is that Planck's constant ($h = 6.626 \times 10^{-34}$ J·s) is so small that a single photon has *very* little energy. The quantity of light needed to read a chemistry text, for instance, consists of an enormous number of photons. Similarly, the tiny size of an atom, the quantum of mass, keeps us unaware that we are breathing individual O_2 and N_2 molecules. In addition, the quantum of charge, the electron's charge, is too small for us to realize that electricity also occurs in "pieces": in a 100-watt bulb, 6×10^{18} quanta of charge enter and leave the filament every second!

Sample Problem 7.2 Calculating the Energy of Radiation from Its Frequency

PROBLEM A cook uses a microwave oven to heat a meal. The wavelength of the radiation is 12.0 cm. What is the energy of one photon of this microwave radiation?

PLAN We know λ in centimeters so we convert to meters, find the frequency from Equation 7.1, and then find the energy of one photon by using $E = h\nu$.

SOLUTION Combining steps to find the energy:

$$E = h\nu = \frac{hc}{\lambda} = \frac{(6.626 \times 10^{-34}\ \text{J·s})(3.00 \times 10^8\ \text{m/s})}{(12.0\ \text{cm})\left(\dfrac{10^{-2}\ \text{m}}{1\ \text{cm}}\right)}$$

$$= \boxed{1.66 \times 10^{-24}\ \text{J}}$$

CHECK Rounding to check the order of magnitude gives $\dfrac{10^{-33} \times 10^8}{10^{-1}} = 10^{-24}$.

Follow-up Problem 7.2 Calculate the energies of one photon of ultraviolet ($\lambda = 1 \times 10^{-8}$ m), visible ($\lambda = 5 \times 10^{-7}$ m), and infrared ($\lambda = 1 \times 10^{-4}$ m) light. What do the answers indicate about the relationship between the wavelength and the energy of light?

Planck's quantum theory and Einstein's photon theory assigned properties to energy that, until then, had always been reserved for matter: fixed quantity and discrete particles. These properties have since proved essential to explaining the interactions of matter and energy at the atomic level. But how can we match a particulate model of energy with the facts of diffraction and refraction, phenomena explained only in terms of waves? As you'll see shortly, the photon model does not *replace* the wave model. Rather, we have to accept *both* to understand reality. Before we discuss this astonishing notion, however, let's see how the new idea of quantized energy led to a key understanding about atomic behavior.

◆ **Ping-Pong Photons** Consider this analogy for the fact that light of insufficient energy cannot free an electron from the metal surface. If one Ping-Pong ball does not have enough energy to knock a book off a shelf, neither does a series of Ping-Pong balls, because the book cannot save up the energy from the individual impacts. But one baseball traveling at the same speed does have enough energy. Whereas the energy of a ball is related to its mass and velocity, the energy of a photon is related to its frequency.

Section Summary

Electromagnetic radiation travels in waves of specific wavelength (λ) and frequency (ν). All electromagnetic waves travel through a vacuum at the speed of light, c (3.00×10^8 m/s), which is equal to $\nu \times \lambda$. The intensity (brightness) of a light wave is related to its amplitude. The electromagnetic spectrum ranges from very long radio waves to very short γ rays and includes the visible region [750 nm (red) to 400 nm (violet)]. Refraction and diffraction indicate that electromagnetic radiation is wavelike, but blackbody radiation and the photoelectric effect indicate that it is particle-like. Light exists as photons (quanta) that have an energy proportional to the frequency. According to quantum theory, an atom can have only certain quantities of energy ($E = nh\nu$), which it can change only by absorbing or emitting a photon.

7.2 Atomic Spectra

The third key observation about matter and energy that late 19th century physicists could not explain involved the light emitted when an element is vaporized and then thermally or electrically excited, as you see in a neon sign. If the light passes through a narrow slit and is then refracted by a prism, it does not create a *continuous spectrum,* or rainbow, as sunlight does. Instead, it creates a **line spectrum,** a series of fine lines of individual colors separated by colorless (black) spaces.* As Figure 7.8 shows, the wavelengths of these spectral lines are characteristic of the element producing them.

---

*The appearance of the spectrum as a series of lines results from the construction of the apparatus. If the light passed through a small hole, rather than a narrow slit, the spectrum would appear as a circular field of dots rather than a horizontal series of lines. The key point is that *the spectrum is discrete, rather than continuous.*

Figure 7.8 **The line spectra of several elements. A,** A sample of gaseous H_2 is dissociated into atoms and excited by an electric discharge. The emitted light passes through a slit and a prism, which disperses the light into individual wavelengths. The line spectrum of atomic H is shown *(top).* **B,** The continuous spectrum of white light is compared with the line spectra of mercury and strontium. Note that each line spectrum is different from the others.

Figure 7.9 Three series of spectral lines of atomic hydrogen. These series appear in different regions of the electromagnetic spectrum. The hydrogen spectrum shown in Figure 7.8. A is the visible series.

Spectroscopists studying the spectrum of atomic hydrogen had identified several series of such lines in different regions of the electromagnetic spectrum. Figure 7.9 shows three of these series of lines. Equations of the following general form, called the *Rydberg equation*, were found to predict the position and wavelength of any line in a given series:

$$\frac{1}{\lambda} = R\left(\frac{1}{n_1^2} - \frac{1}{n_2^2}\right) \tag{7.3}$$

where λ is the wavelength of a spectral line, n_1 and n_2 are positive integers with $n_2 > n_1$, and R is the Rydberg constant (1.096776×10^7 m^{-1}). For the series of spectral lines in the visible range, $n_1 = 2$:

$$\frac{1}{\lambda} = R\left(\frac{1}{2^2} - \frac{1}{n_2^2}\right), \quad \text{with } n_2 = 3, 4, 5, \ldots$$

The Rydberg equation and the constant R are *empirical*, that is, based on data rather than theory. No one knew *why* the spectral lines of hydrogen appear in this pattern.

The presence of line spectra did not correlate with classical theory for one major reason. As was mentioned in the chapter introduction, as the electron spiraled into the nucleus, it should emit radiation. Moreover, the frequency of the radiation is related to the time of revolution. On the spiral path inward, the time should decrease smoothly, so the frequency of the radiation should change smoothly and create a continuous spectrum. Rutherford's nuclear model seemed totally at odds with atomic spectra.

The Bohr Model of the Hydrogen Atom

Soon after the nuclear model was proposed, Niels Bohr (1885–1962), a young Danish physicist working in Rutherford's laboratory, suggested a model for the H atom that predicted the existence of line spectra. In his model, Bohr used Planck's and Einstein's ideas about quantized energy and proposed three postulates:

1. *The H atom has only certain allowable energy levels*, which Bohr called **stationary states.** Each of these states is associated with a fixed circular orbit of the electron around the nucleus (Figure 7.10A, next page).
2. *The atom does **not** radiate energy while in one of its stationary states.* That is, even though it violates the ideas of classical physics, the atom does not change energy while the electron moves *within* an orbit.
3. The atom changes to another stationary state (the electron moves to another orbit) *only by absorbing or emitting a photon whose energy equals the difference in energy between the two states:*

$$E_{\text{photon}} = E_{\text{state A}} - E_{\text{state B}} = h\nu$$

where the energy of state A is higher than that of state B. A spectral line results when a photon of specific energy (and thus specific frequency) is *emitted* as the electron moves from a higher energy state to a lower one. Therefore, Bohr's model concludes that an atomic spectrum is not continuous because *the atom's energy has only certain discrete levels, or states.*

A

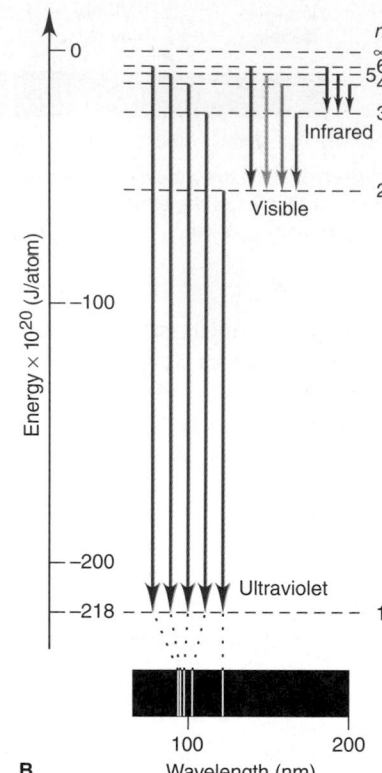

B

Figure 7.10 **The Bohr model explanation of the three series of spectral lines.** **A,** According to the Bohr model, when an electron drops from an outer orbit (one farther from the nucleus) to an inner orbit (one closer to the nucleus), it emits a photon of a specific energy. Note that each of the three series is characterized by a particular inner orbit (value of n_1 in the Rydberg equation). The orbit radius is proportional to n^2. Only the first five orbits are shown. **B,** An energy diagram shows how a series arises. When an electron drops from a specific outer to a specific inner orbit, the energy difference (depicted as a downward arrow) appears as a photon of specific wavelength and gives rise to one of the spectral lines in the series. (The origin of the ultraviolet series of lines is shown.) Within each series, the greater the *difference* in orbit radii, the greater the difference in energy levels, and the higher the energy of the photon emitted. For example, in the ultraviolet series, in which $n_1 = 1$, a drop from $n = 5$ to $n = 1$ emits a photon with more energy (shorter λ, higher ν) than a drop from $n = 2$ to $n = 1$. [The axis shows negative values because $n = \infty$ (the electron completely separated from the nucleus) is *defined* as zero energy.]

In Bohr's model, the quantum number n (1, 2, 3, . . .) is associated with the radius of an electron orbit, which is directly related to the electron's energy: *the lower the n value, the smaller the radius of the orbit, and the lower the energy level.* When the electron is in the first orbit ($n = 1$), the orbit closest to the nucleus, the H atom is in its lowest (first) energy level, called the **ground state.** If the H atom absorbs a photon whose energy equals the *difference* between the first and second energy levels, the electron moves to the second orbit ($n = 2$), the next orbit out from the nucleus. When the electron is in the second or any higher orbit, the atom is said to be in an **excited state.** If the H atom in the first excited state (the electron in the second orbit) emits a photon of that same energy, it returns to the ground state.

Figure 7.10B shows how Bohr's model accounts for the three line spectra. When a sample of gaseous H atoms is excited, different atoms absorb different quantities of energy. Even though each atom has only one electron, so many atoms are present that all the energy levels (orbits) are populated by electrons. When the electrons drop from outer orbits to the $n = 3$ orbit (second excited state), the emitted photons create the infrared series of spectral lines. The visible series arises when electrons drop to the $n = 2$ orbit (first excited state). The figure highlights the ultraviolet series, which arises when electrons drop to the $n = 1$ orbit (ground state).

Limitations of the Bohr Model

Despite its great success in accounting for the spectral lines of the H atom, the Bohr model failed to predict the spectrum of any other atom, even that of helium, the next simplest element. In essence, the Bohr model is a one-electron model. It works beautifully for the H atom and for other one-electron species, such as several created in the lab or seen in the spectra of stars: He^+ ($Z = 2$), Li^{2+} ($Z = 3$), Be^{3+} ($Z = 4$), B^{4+} ($Z = 5$), C^{5+} ($Z = 6$),

N^{6+} ($Z = 7$), and O^{7+} ($Z = 8$). But, it does not work for atoms with more than one electron because in these systems, additional nucleus-electron attractions and electron-electron repulsions are present. However, there is a more fundamental reason for the model's limitations: electrons do *not* travel in fixed orbits. As you'll see, electron movement is far less clearly defined. As a picture of the atom, the Bohr model is incorrect, but we still use the terms "ground state" and "excited state" and retain one of its central ideas in our current model: *the energy of an atom occurs in discrete levels.*

The Energy States of the Hydrogen Atom

A very useful result from Bohr's work is an equation for calculating the energy levels of an atom, which he derived from the classical principles of electrostatic attraction and circular motion:

$$E = -2.18 \times 10^{-18} \text{ J} \left(\frac{Z^2}{n^2} \right)$$

where Z is the charge of the nucleus. For the H atom, $Z = 1$, so we have

$$E = -2.18 \times 10^{-18} \text{ J} \left(\frac{1^2}{n^2} \right) = -2.18 \times 10^{-18} \text{ J} \left(\frac{1}{n^2} \right)$$

Therefore, the energy of the ground state ($n = 1$) is

$$E = -2.18 \times 10^{-18} \text{ J} \left(\frac{1}{1^2} \right) = -2.18 \times 10^{-18} \text{ J}$$

Don't be confused by the negative sign for the energy values (see the axis in Figure 7.10B). It appears because we *define* the zero point of the atom's energy when *the electron is completely removed from the nucleus.* Thus, $E = 0$ when $n = \infty$, so $E < 0$ for any smaller n. As an analogy, consider a book resting on the floor. You can define the zero point of the book's potential energy in many ways. If you define zero when the book is on the floor, the energy is positive when the book is on your desk. But, if you define zero when the book is on your desk, the energy is negative when the book lies on the floor; the latter case is analogous to the energy of the H atom (Figure 7.11).

Since n is in the denominator of the energy equation, as the electron moves closer to the nucleus (n decreases), the atom becomes more stable (less energetic) and its energy becomes a *larger negative number.* As the electron moves away from the nucleus (n increases), the atom's energy increases (becomes a smaller negative number).

This equation is easily adapted to find the energy difference between any two levels:

$$\Delta E = E_{\text{final}} - E_{\text{initial}} = -2.18 \times 10^{-18} \text{ J} \left(\frac{1}{n_{\text{final}}^2} - \frac{1}{n_{\text{initial}}^2} \right) \qquad \textbf{(7.4)}$$

With it, we can predict the wavelengths of the spectral lines of the H atom. (In fact, Bohr obtained a value for the Rydberg constant that differed from the spectroscopists' empirical value by only 0.05%!) Note that if we combine Equation 7.4 with Planck's expression for the change in an atom's energy (Equation 7.2), we obtain the Rydberg equation (Equation 7.3):

$$\Delta E = h\nu = \frac{hc}{\lambda} = -2.18 \times 10^{-18} \text{ J} \left(\frac{1}{n_{\text{final}}^2} - \frac{1}{n_{\text{initial}}^2} \right)$$

Therefore, $\dfrac{1}{\lambda} = -\dfrac{2.18 \times 10^{-18} \text{ J}}{hc} \left(\dfrac{1}{n_{\text{final}}^2} - \dfrac{1}{n_{\text{initial}}^2} \right)$

$$= -\frac{2.18 \times 10^{-18} \text{ J}}{(6.626 \times 10^{-34} \text{ J} \cdot \text{s})(3.00 \times 10^8 \text{ m/s})} \left(\frac{1}{n_{\text{final}}^2} - \frac{1}{n_{\text{initial}}^2} \right)$$

$$= 1.10 \times 10^7 \text{ m}^{-1} \left(\frac{1}{n_{\text{final}}^2} - \frac{1}{n_{\text{initial}}^2} \right)$$

Figure 7.11 A desktop analogy for the H atom's energy. If you define the potential energy of the system as zero when a book rests on a desk, the system has negative energy when the book lies on the floor. Similarly, the H atom is defined as having zero energy when its electron is completely separated from the nucleus, so its energy is negative when the electron is attracted by the nucleus.

where $n_{final} = n_2$, $n_{initial} = n_1$, and 1.10×10^7 m^{-1} is the Rydberg constant $(1.096776 \times 10^7$ m$^{-1})$ to three significant figures. Thus, from classical relationships of charge and of motion combined with the idea that the H atom can have only certain values of energy, we obtain an equation that leads directly to the empirical one!

We can use Equation 7.4 to find the quantity of energy needed to completely remove the electron from an H atom. In other words, what is ΔE for the following change?

$$H(g) \longrightarrow H^+(g) + e^-$$

We substitute $n_{final} = \infty$ and $n_{initial} = 1$ and obtain

$$\Delta E = E_{final} - E_{initial} = -2.18 \times 10^{-18} \text{ J}\left(\frac{1}{\infty^2} - \frac{1}{1^2}\right)$$

$$= -2.18 \times 10^{-18} \text{ J}(0 - 1) = 2.18 \times 10^{-18} \text{ J}$$

ΔE is positive because energy is *absorbed* to remove the electron from the vicinity of the nucleus. For 1 mol H atoms,

$$\Delta E = \left(2.18 \times 10^{-18} \frac{\text{J}}{\text{atom}}\right)\left(6.022 \times 10^{23} \frac{\text{atoms}}{\text{mol}}\right)\left(\frac{1 \text{ kJ}}{10^3 \text{ J}}\right) = 1.31 \times 10^3 \text{ kJ/mol}$$

This is the *ionization energy* of the H atom, the quantity of energy required to form 1 mol gaseous H$^+$ ions from 1 mol gaseous H atoms. We return to this idea in Chapter 8.

Spectroscopic analysis of the H atom led to the Bohr model, the first step toward our current model of the atom. From its use by 19th-century chemists as a means of identifying elements and compounds, spectrometry has become a major field and a central tool of modern chemistry (see Tools of the Chemistry Laboratory). ◆

Section Summary

To explain the line spectrum of atomic hydrogen, Bohr proposed that the atom's energy is quantized because the electron's motion is restricted to fixed orbits. The electron can move from one orbit to another only if the atom absorbs or emits a photon whose energy equals the difference in energy levels (orbits). Line spectra are produced because these energy changes correspond to photons of specific wavelength. Bohr's model predicted the H atom spectrum but could not predict that of any other atom because electrons do not have fixed orbits. Despite this, Bohr's idea that atoms have quantized energy levels is a cornerstone of our current model. Spectrophotometry is an instrumental technique in which emission and absorption spectra are used to identify and measure concentrations of substances.

7.3   The Wave-Particle Duality of Matter and Energy

The year 1905 was a busy one for Albert Einstein. In addition to presenting the photon theory of light and explaining the photoelectric effect, he found time to explain Brownian motion (Chapter 13), which helped establish the molecular view of matter, and to introduce a new branch of physics with his theory of relativity. One of its many startling revelations was that matter and energy are alternate forms of the same entity. This idea is embodied in his famous equation $E = mc^2$, which relates the quantity of energy equivalent to a given mass, and vice versa. Relativity theory does not depend on quantum theory, but together they have completely blurred the sharp divisions between matter (chunky and massive) and energy (diffuse and massless) that we see around us. ◆

Tools of the Chemistry Laboratory

Spectrophotometry in Chemical Analysis

The use of spectral data to identify and quantify substances is essential to modern chemical analysis. The terms *spectroscopy, spectrometry,* and **spectrophotometry** denote a large group of instrumental techniques that obtain spectra corresponding to a substance's atomic and molecular energy levels.

The two types of spectra most often obtained are emission and absorption spectra. An **emission spectrum,** such as the H atom line spectrum, is produced when atoms in an excited state *emit* photons characteristic of the element as they return to lower energy states. Some elements produce a very intense spectral line (or several closely spaced ones) that serves as a marker of the element's presence. Such an intense line is the basis of **flame tests,** rapid qualitative procedures performed by placing a granule of an ionic compound or a drop of its solution in a flame (Figure 7.A, part

A). Some of the colors of fireworks and flares are due to emissions from the same elements shown in the flame tests: crimson from strontium salts and blue-green from copper salts (Figure 7.A, part B). The characteristic colors of sodium-vapor and mercury-vapor streetlamps, seen in many towns and cities, are due to one or a few prominent lines in their emission spectra.

An **absorption spectrum** is produced when atoms *absorb* photons of certain wavelengths and become excited from lower to higher energy states. Therefore, the absorption spectrum of an element appears as dark lines against a bright background. When white light passes through sodium vapor, for example, it gives rise to a sodium absorption spectrum, and the dark lines appear at the same wavelengths where yellow-orange lines appear in the sodium emission spectrum (Figure 7.B). *(continued)*

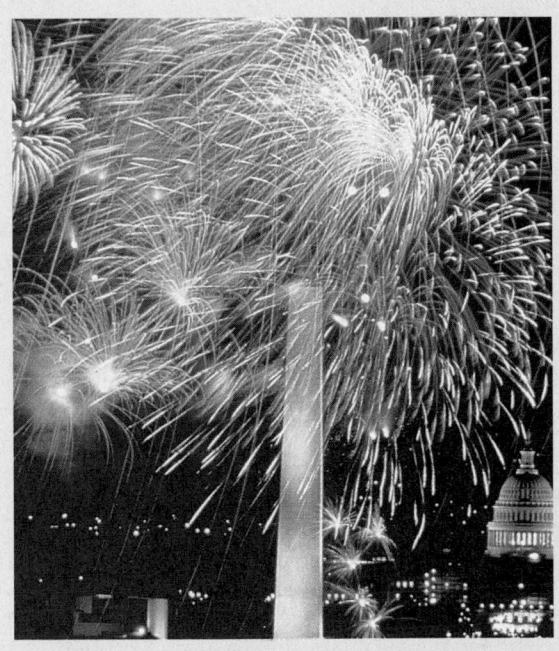

Figure 7.A Flame tests and fireworks. A, In general, the color of the flame is created by a strong emission in the line spectrum of the element and therefore is often taken as preliminary evidence of the presence of the element in a sample. Shown here are the crimson of strontium and the blue-green of copper. **B,** The same emissions from compounds that contain these elements often appear in the brilliant displays of fireworks.

Figure 7.B Emission and absorption spectra of sodium atoms. The wavelengths of the bright emission lines correspond to those of the dark absorption lines because both are created by the same energy change: $\Delta E_{\text{emission}} = -\Delta E_{\text{absorption}}$. (Only the two most intense lines in the sodium atomic spectra are shown here.)

Source *produces radiation in region of interest. Must be stable and reproducible. In most cases, the source emits many wavelengths.*

Lenses/slits/ collimators *narrow and align beam.*

Monochromator *(wavelength selector) disperses incoming radiation into continuum of component wavelengths that are scanned or individually selected.*

Sample *in compartment absorbs characteristic amount of each incoming wavelength.*

Detector *converts transmitted radiation into amplified electrical signal.*

Computer *converts signal into displayed data.*

Figure 7.C **The main components of a typical spectrometer.**

Instruments based on absorption spectra are much more common than those based on emission spectra, for several reasons. When a solid, liquid, or dense gas is excited, it *emits* so many lines that the spectrum is a continuum (recall the continuum of colors in sunlight). Absorption is also less destructive of fragile organic and biological molecules.

Despite differences that depend on the region of the electromagnetic spectrum used to irradiate the sample, all modern spectrometers have components that perform the same basic functions (Figure 7.C). (We discuss infrared spectroscopy and nuclear magnetic resonance spectroscopy in later chapters.)

Visible light is often used to study colored substances, which absorb only some of the wavelengths from white light. A leaf looks green, for example, because its chlorophyll absorbs red and blue wavelengths strongly and green weakly, so most of the green is reflected. The absorption spectrum of chlorophyll *a* in ether solution appears in Figure 7.D.

The overall shape of the curve and the wavelengths of the major peaks are characteristic of chlorophyll *a*, so its spectrum serves as a means of identifying it from an unknown source. The curve varies in height because chlorophyll absorbs incoming wavelengths to different extents. The

absorptions appear as broad bands, rather than as the distinct lines we saw earlier for individual gaseous atoms, because dissolved substances, as well as pure solids and liquids, absorb many more wavelengths due to the greater numbers and types of energy levels within a molecule, among molecules, and between molecules and solvent.

In addition to identifying a substance, a spectrometer can be used to measure its concentration because *the absorbance, the amount of light of a given wavelength absorbed by a substance, is proportional to the number of molecules.* Suppose you want to determine the concentration of chlorophyll in an ether solution of leaf extract. You select a strongly absorbed wavelength from the chlorophyll spectrum (such as 663 nm in Figure 7.D), measure the absorbance of the leaf-extract solution, and compare it with the absorbances of a series of ether solutions with known chlorophyll concentrations.

Figure 7.D **The absorption spectrum of chlorophyll *a*.**
Chlorophyll *a* is one of several leaf pigments. It absorbs red and blue wavelengths strongly but almost no green or yellow wavelengths. Thus, leaves containing large amounts of chlorophyll *a* appear green. The strong absorption at 663 nm can be used to quantify the amount of chlorophyll *a* present in a plant extract.

663 nm

Absorbance

400   500   600   700
Wavelength (nm)

The early proponents of quantum theory demonstrated that *energy is particle-like.* Physicists who developed the theory turned this proposition upside down and showed that *matter is wavelike.* Strange as this idea may seem, it is the key to our modern atomic model.

The Wave Nature of Electrons and the Particle Nature of Photons

Bohr's efforts were a perfect case of fitting theory to data: he *assumed* that an atom has only certain allowable energy levels in order to *explain* the observed line spectrum. However, his assumption had no basis in physical theory. Then, in the early 1920s, a young French physics student named Louis de Broglie proposed a startling reason for fixed energy levels: *if energy is particle-like, perhaps matter is wavelike.* De Broglie had been thinking of other systems that display only certain allowed motions, such as the wave of a plucked guitar string. Figure 7.12 shows that, because the ends of the string are fixed, only certain vibrational frequencies (and wavelengths) are possible. De Broglie reasoned that *if electrons have wavelike motion* and are restricted to orbits of fixed radii, that would explain why they have only certain possible frequencies and energies.

Combining the equation for mass-energy equivalence ($E = mc^2$) with that for the energy of a photon ($E = h\nu = hc/\lambda$), de Broglie derived an equation for the wavelength of any particle of mass m—whether planet, baseball, or electron—moving at speed u:

$$\lambda = \frac{h}{mu} \tag{7.5}$$

According to this equation for the **de Broglie wavelength,** *matter behaves as though it moves in a wave.* Note also that an object's wavelength is *inversely* proportional to its mass, so heavy objects such as planets and baseballs have wavelengths that are *many* orders of magnitude smaller than the object itself, as you can see in Table 7.1 on the next page.

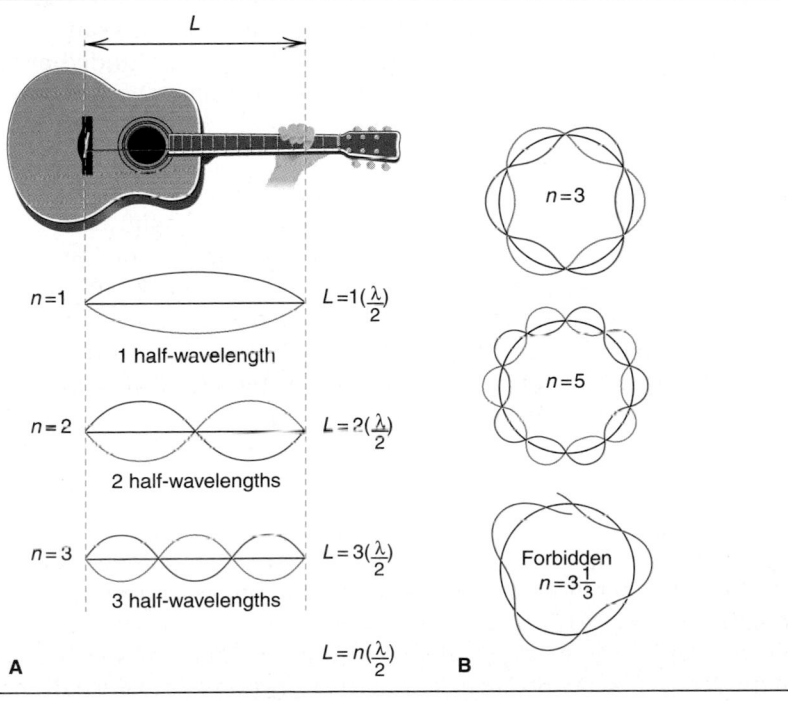

A

B

Figure 7.12 Wave motion in restricted systems. A, In a musical analogy to electron waves, one half-wavelength ($\lambda/2$) is the "quantum" of the guitar string's vibration. The string length L is fixed, so the only allowed vibrations occur when L is a whole-number multiple (n) of $\lambda/2$. **B,** If an electron occupies a circular orbit, only whole numbers of wavelengths are allowed ($n = 3$ and $n = 5$ are shown). A wave with a fractional number of wavelengths (such as $n = 3\frac{1}{3}$) is "forbidden" because it rapidly dies out through overlap of crests and troughs.

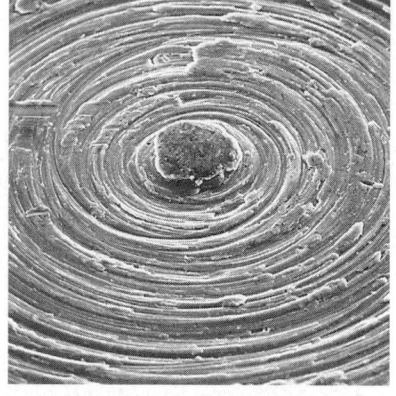

Table 7.1 The de Broglie Wavelengths of Several Objects

Substance	Mass (g)	Speed (m/s)	λ (m)
Slow electron	9×10^{-28}	1.0	7×10^{-4}
Fast electron	9×10^{-28}	5.9×10^{6}	1×10^{-10}
Alpha particle	6.6×10^{-24}	1.5×10^{7}	7×10^{-15}
One-gram mass	1.0	0.01	7×10^{-29}
Baseball	142	25.0	2×10^{-34}
Earth	6.0×10^{27}	3.0×10^{4}	4×10^{-63}

Sample Problem 7.3   Calculating the de Broglie Wavelength of an Electron

PROBLEM Calculate the de Broglie wavelength of an electron with a speed of 1.00×10^{6} m/s. (Electron mass = 9.11×10^{-31} kg; $h = 6.626\times10^{-34}$ kg · m²/s.)

PLAN We know the speed and mass of the electron, so we substitute these into Equation 7.5 to find λ.

SOLUTION

$$\lambda = \frac{h}{mu} = \frac{6.626\times10^{-34}\,\text{kg}\cdot\text{m}^2/\text{s}}{(9.11\times10^{-31}\,\text{kg})(1.00\times10^{6}\,\text{m/s})} = \boxed{7.27\times10^{-10}\,\text{m}}$$

CHECK The order of magnitude and units seem correct:

$$\lambda \approx \frac{10^{-33}\,\text{kg}\cdot\text{m}^2/\text{s}}{(10^{-30}\,\text{kg})(10^{6}\,\text{m/s})} = 10^{-9}\,\text{m}$$

COMMENT As you'll see in the upcoming discussion, such fast-moving electrons, with wavelengths in the range of atomic sizes, exhibit remarkable properties.

Follow-up Problem 7.3   What is the speed of an electron that has a de Broglie wavelength of 100. nm?

◆ The Electron Microscope
In a transmission electron microscope, a beam is focused by a lens and passes through a thin section of the specimen to a second lens. The resulting image is then magnified by a third lens to a final image. The differences between this and a light microscope are that the "beam" consists of high-speed electrons and the "lenses" are electromagnetic fields, which can be adjusted to give up to 200,000-fold magnification and 0.5 nm resolution. In a scanning electron microscope, the electron beam scans the specimen, knocking electrons from it, which creates a current that varies with surface irregularities. The current generates an image that looks like the object's surface [see photos: cancer cell attacked by T-lymphocytes, 1000× (top); tool marks on steel, 290× (bottom)]. The great advantage of electron microscopes is that high-speed electrons have wavelengths much smaller than those of visible light and, thus, allow much greater image resolution.

If particles travel in waves, electrons should exhibit diffraction and interference (see Section 7.1). ◆ Since a fast-moving electron has a wavelength of about 10^{-10} m, the spaces between atoms in a crystal serve as perfect "adjacent slits." In 1927, C. Davisson and L. Germer guided a beam of electrons at a nickel crystal and obtained a diffraction pattern. Figure 7.13 shows the diffraction patterns obtained when either x-rays or electrons impinge on aluminum foil. Apparently, electrons—particles with mass and charge—create diffraction patterns, just as electromagnetic waves do! Even though electrons do not have orbits of fixed radius, as de Broglie thought, the energy levels of the atom *are* related to the wave nature of the electron.

If electrons have properties of energy, do photons have properties of matter? The de Broglie equation suggests that we can calculate the momentum (p), the product of mass and speed, for a photon of a given wavelength. Solving Equation 7.5 for p, while substituting the speed of light (c) for speed u, gives

$$\lambda = \frac{h}{mc} = \frac{h}{p} \qquad \text{and} \qquad p = \frac{h}{\lambda}$$

Notice the inverse relationship between p and λ. This means that shorter wavelength (higher energy) photons have greater momentum. Thus, a decrease in a photon's momentum should appear as an increase in its wavelength. In 1923, Arthur Compton directed a beam of x-ray photons at a sample of graphite and observed that the wavelength of the reflected photons increased. This result means that the photons transferred some of their momentum to the electrons in the carbon atoms of the graphite, just as colliding billiard balls transfer momentum to one another. In this experiment, photons behave as particles with momentum!

To scientists of the time, these results were very unsettling. Classical experiments had shown matter to be particulate and energy to be wavelike, but these new studies showed just the opposite. The understanding of matter and energy had come full circle: every characteristic trait used to define the one now also defined the other. Figure 7.14 summarizes the conceptual and experimental breakthroughs that led to this juncture.

The truth is that *both* matter and energy show *both* behaviors: each possesses both "faces." In some experiments, we observe one face; in other experiments, we observe the other face. The distinction between a particle and a wave is meaningful only in the macroscopic world, *not* in the atomic world. The distinction between matter and energy is in our minds and our limiting definitions, not in nature. This dual character of matter and energy is known as the **wave-particle duality.**

The Heisenberg Uncertainty Principle

In the macroscopic world, a moving particle has a definite location at any instant, whereas a wave is spread out in space. If an electron has the properties of both a particle and a wave, what can we determine about its position

A

B

Figure 7.13 Diffraction patterns of x-rays and electrons. A, X-ray diffraction pattern of Al foil. **B,** Electron diffraction pattern of Al foil. This behavior implies that both x-rays, which are electromagnetic radiation, and electrons, which are particles, travel in waves.

CLASSICAL THEORY

| **Matter** | **Energy** |
| particulate, massive | continuous, wavelike |

*Since **matter** is discontinuous and particulate perhaps **energy** is discontinuous and particulate*

Observation	*Theory*
Blackbody radiation	Planck: Energy is quantized; only certain values allowed
Photoelectric effect	Einstein: Light has particulate behavior (photons)
Atomic line spectra	Bohr: Energy of atoms is quantized; photon emitted when electron changes orbit

*Since **energy** is wavelike perhaps **matter** is wavelike*

Observation	*Theory*
Davisson/Germer: electron diffraction by metal crystal	de Broglie: All matter travels in waves: energy of atom is quantized due to wave motion of electrons

*Since **matter** has mass perhaps **energy** has mass*

Observation	*Theory*
Compton: photon wavelength increases (momentum decreases) after colliding with electron	Einstein/de Broglie: Mass and energy are equivalent: particles have wavelength and photons have momentum

QUANTUM THEORY

Energy *same as* **Matter**
particulate, massive, wavelike

Figure 7.14 Summary of the major observations and theories leading from classical theory to quantum theory. As often happens in science, an observation (experiment) stimulates the need for an explanation (theory), and/or a theoretical insight provides the impetus for an experimental test.

Certain speed, uncertain position

Certain position, uncertain speed

If we know the speed of a particle with
certainty, its position is uncertain, and
vice versa.

in the atom? In 1927, the German physicist Werner Heisenberg postulated
the **uncertainty principle,** which states that it is impossible to know simultaneously the exact position *and* momentum of a particle. For a particle with
constant mass m, the principle is expressed mathematically as

$$\Delta x \cdot m\Delta u \geq \frac{h}{4\pi} \tag{7.6}$$

where Δx is the uncertainty in position and Δu is the uncertainty in speed.
The more accurately we know the position of the particle (smaller Δx), the
less accurately we know its speed (larger Δu), and vice versa (see margin).

By knowing the position and speed of a pitched baseball and using the
classical laws of motion, we can predict its trajectory and whether it will be
a strike or a ball. For a baseball, Δx and Δu are insignificant because its mass
is enormous compared with $h/4\pi$. Knowing the position and speed of an electron, and from them its trajectory, is another matter entirely, as Sample Problem 7.4 shows.

Sample Problem 7.4   Applying the Uncertainty Principle

PROBLEM An electron moving near an atomic nucleus has a speed of
$6\times10^6 \pm 1\%$ m/s. What is the uncertainty in its position?
PLAN The uncertainty in the speed (Δu) is given as 1%, so we calculate its value,
substitute it into Equation 7.6, and solve for the uncertainty in position (Δx).
SOLUTION Finding the uncertainty in speed, Δu:

$$\Delta u = (6\times10^6 \text{ m/s})(0.01) = 6\times10^4 \text{ m/s}$$

Calculating the uncertainty in position, Δx:

$$\Delta x \geq \frac{h}{4\pi m\Delta u} \geq \frac{6.626\times10^{-34} \text{ kg}\cdot\text{m}^2/\text{s}}{4\pi(9.11\times10^{-31} \text{ kg})(6\times10^4 \text{ m/s})} \geq \boxed{1\times10^{-9} \text{ m}}$$

CHECK Be sure to round off and check the order of magnitude of the answer:

$$\Delta x \geq \frac{10^{-33}}{(10^1)(10^{-30})(10^5)} = 10^{-9}$$

COMMENT The uncertainty in the electron's position is about 10 times greater than
the diameter of the entire atom (10^{-10} m), so we have no precise idea where in
the atom it is located! In the follow-up problem, see if an umpire has any better
idea where a baseball is located when calling balls and strikes.

Follow-up Problem 7.4 How accurately can an umpire know the position of
a baseball (mass = 0.142 kg) moving at $100.0 \pm 1.00\%$ mi/h ($44.7 \pm 1.00\%$ m/s)?

◆ **Uncertainty Is
Unacceptable?** Although
the uncertainty principle is universally accepted by today's physicists,
Einstein found some aspects of it
difficult to accept, as reflected in his
famous statement that "God does
not play dice with the universe."
Rutherford was also skeptical.
When Niels Bohr *(right)*, who had
become a champion of the new
physics, delivered a lecture in
Rutherford's laboratory on the
principle, Rutherford *(left)* said,
"You know, Bohr, your conclusions
seem to me as uncertain as the
premises on which they are built."
Acceptance of radical ideas does
not come easily, even to fellow
geniuses.

As the results of Sample Problem 7.4 show, the uncertainty principle has
profound implications for an atomic model. It means that *we cannot assign fixed
paths for electrons,* such as the circular orbits of Bohr's model. As you'll see in
the next section, the most we can ever hope to know is the *probability*—the
odds—of finding an electron in a given region of space. However, we are not
sure it is there any more than a gambler is sure of the next roll of the dice. ◆

Section Summary

As a result of quantum theory and relativity theory, we can no longer view
matter and energy as distinct entities. The de Broglie wavelength proposes
that electrons (and all matter) have wavelike motion. Allowed atomic energy
levels are related to allowed wavelengths of the electron's motion. Electrons
exhibit diffraction patterns, as do waves of energy, and photons exhibit transfer of momentum, as do particles of mass. The wave-particle duality of matter and energy is observable only on the atomic scale. According to the uncertainty principle, we cannot know simultaneously the exact position and speed
of an electron.

7.4 The Quantum-Mechanical Model of the Atom

Acceptance of the dual nature of matter and energy and of the uncertainty principle culminated in the field of **quantum mechanics,** which examines the wave motion of objects on the atomic scale. In 1926, Erwin Schrödinger derived an equation that is the basis for the quantum-mechanical model of the hydrogen atom. The model describes an atom that has certain allowed quantities of energy due to the allowed wavelike motion of an electron whose exact location is impossible to know.

The Atomic Orbital and the Probable Location of the Electron

The electron's matter-wave moves in three-dimensional space near the nucleus and experiences a continuous, but varying, influence from the nuclear charge. As a result, the **Schrödinger equation** is quite complex, but a simplified form of the equation is

$$\mathcal{H}\psi = E\psi$$

where E is the energy of the atom. The symbol ψ (Greek *psi,* pronounced "sigh") is called a **wave function,** a mathematical description of the motion of the electron's matter-wave as a function of time and position. The symbol $\mathcal{H}$, called the Hamiltonian operator, represents a set of mathematical operations that, when carried out on a particular ψ, yields an allowed energy state.*

Each solution to the equation (that is, each energy state of the atom) is associated with a given wave function, also called an **atomic orbital.** It's important to keep in mind that an "orbital" in the quantum-mechanical model *bears no resemblance* to an "orbit" in the Bohr model: the *orbit* was a path supposedly followed by the electron, whereas the *orbital* is a mathematical function with no physical meaning.

We cannot know precisely where the electron is at any moment, but we can describe where it *probably* is, that is, where it is most likely to be found, or where it spends most of its time. Although the wave function (atomic orbital) has no physical meaning, we do ascribe a physical meaning to the square of the wave function, ψ^2. The quantity ψ^2 expresses the *probability* that the electron is at a particular point (or, more precisely, in a particular very small volume) within the atom. (Whereas ψ can have positive or negative values, ψ^2 is always positive, which makes sense for a value that expresses a probability.) For a given energy level, we can depict this probability with an *electron probability density diagram,* or more simply, an **electron density diagram.** In Figure 7.15A (on the next page), the value of ψ^2 for a given volume is represented by a certain density of dots (the electron density): the greater the density of dots, the higher the probability of finding the electron within that volume.

Electron density diagrams are sometimes called **electron cloud** representations. If we *could* take a time-exposure snapshot of the electron whirling around the nucleus in wavelike motion, it would appear as a "cloud" of electron positions. The electron cloud is an *imaginary* picture of the electron changing its position rapidly over time; it does *not* mean that an electron is a diffuse cloud of charge. Note that *the electron density decreases with distance*

---

*The complete form of the Schrödinger equation in terms of the three linear axes is

$$\frac{d^2\psi}{dx^2} + \frac{d^2\psi}{dy^2} + \frac{d^2\psi}{dz^2} + \frac{8\pi^2 m_e}{h^2}[E - V(x,y,z)]\psi(x,y,z) = 0$$

where ψ is the wave function; the first three terms describe how ψ changes in space; m_e is the electron's mass; E is the total quantized energy of the atomic system; and V is the potential energy at point (x,y,z). Solving the equation for almost any practical application requires a significant amount of computer time.

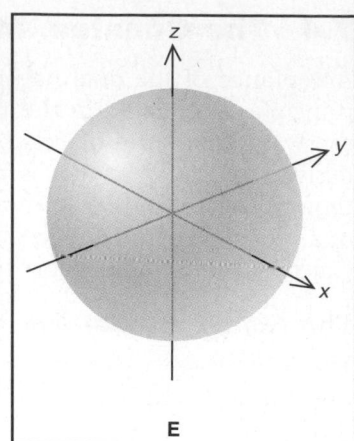

Figure 7.15 **Electron probability in the H atom ground state.**
A, An electron density diagram shows a cross section of the H atom, with dots representing the probability of the electron being at any point (actually, a tiny volume). The probability decreases along a line emanating outward from the nucleus. **B,** A plot of the information in **A** shows that the probability (ψ^2) at any point along the line decreases with distance from the nucleus but does not reach zero (although the thickness of the printed line makes it appear to do so). **C,** Dividing the atom's volume into thin, concentric, spherical layers (shown in cross section) and counting the dots within each layer gives the total probability of finding the electron within that layer. **D,** A radial probability distribution plot shows total electron density in each spherical layer vs. r. Since electron density decreases more slowly than the volume of each concentric spherical layer increases, the plot shows a peak. **E,** A 90% probability contour depicts the ground state of the H atom and represents the volume in which the electron spends 90% of its time.

from the nucleus along a line, r. The same concept is shown graphically in the plot of ψ^2 vs. r in Figure 7.15B. Although the thickness of the printed line shows the curve touching the axis, *the probability of the electron being far from the nucleus is very small, but not zero.*

The *total* probability of finding the electron at any distance r from the nucleus is also important. To find this, we mentally divide the volume around the nucleus into thin, concentric, spherical layers, like the layers of an onion (shown in cross section in Figure 7.15C), and ask in which *spherical layer* we are most likely to find the electron. This is the same as asking for the *sum of ψ^2 values* within each spherical layer. The steep falloff in electron density with distance (see Figure 7.15B) has an important effect. Near the nucleus, the volume of each layer increases faster than its electron density decreases. As a result, the *total* probability of finding the electron in the second layer is higher than in the first. Electron density drops off so quickly, however, that this effect soon diminishes with greater distance. Thus, even though the volume of each layer continues to increase, the total probability in a given layer eventually decreases. Because of these opposing effects of decreasing electron density and increasing layer volume, the total probability peaks in some layer near the nucleus but beyond the first one. We show this graphically in Figure 7.15D by means of a **radial probability distribution plot.** (See Margin Note ◆ on opposite page.)

The peak of the radial probability distribution for the ground-state H atom appears at the same distance from the nucleus (0.529Å, or 5.29×10^{-11} m) as the closest Bohr orbit. Thus, at least for the ground state, the Schrödinger model predicts that the electron spends *most* of its time at the same distance that the Bohr model predicted it spent *all* of its time. The difference between "most" and "all" reflects the uncertainty of the electron's location incorporated in the Schrödinger model.

How far away from the nucleus can we find the electron? This is the same as asking "How large is the atom?" Recall from Figure 7.15B that the probability of finding the electron far from the nucleus is not zero. Therefore, we *cannot* assign a definite volume to an atom. However, we often visualize atoms with a 90% **probability contour,** such as in Figure 7.15E, which shows the volume within which the electron spends 90% of its time.

Quantum Numbers of an Atomic Orbital

So far we have discussed the electron density for the *ground* state of the H atom. When the atom absorbs energy, it exists in an *excited* state and the wave motion of the electron is described by a different atomic orbital (wave function). As you'll see, each atomic orbital has a distinctive radial probability distribution and probability contour.

An atomic orbital is specified by three quantum numbers. One is related to the orbital's size, another to its shape, and the third to its orientation in space.* The quantum numbers have a hierarchical relationship: the size-related number limits the shape-related number, which limits the orientation-related number. Let's examine this hierarchy and then look at the shapes and orientations.

1. The **principal quantum number (n)** *is a positive integer* (1, 2, 3, and so forth). It indicates the relative *size* of the orbital and therefore the relative *distance from the nucleus* of the peak in the radial probability distribution plot. The principal quantum number specifies the *energy level* of the H atom: *the higher the n value, the higher the energy level.* When the electron occupies an orbital with $n = 1$, the H atom is in its ground state and has lower energy than when the electron occupies the $n = 2$ orbital (first excited state).

2. The **angular momentum quantum number (l)** *is an integer from 0 to $n - 1$.* It is related to the *shape* of the orbital and is sometimes called the *orbital-shape quantum number.* Note that the principal quantum number sets a limit on the values for the angular momentum quantum number; that is, n limits l. For an orbital with $n = 1$, l can have a value of only 0. For orbitals with $n = 2$, l can have a value of 0 or 1; for those with $n = 3$, l can be 0, 1, or 2; and so forth. Note that the number of possible l values equals the value of n.

3. The **magnetic quantum number (m_l)** *is an integer from $-l$ through 0 to $+l$.* It prescribes the *orientation* of the orbital in the space around the nucleus and is sometimes called the *orbital-orientation quantum number.* The possible values of an orbital's magnetic quantum number are set by its angular momentum quantum number (that is, l determines m_l). An orbital with $l = 0$ can have only $m_l = 0$. However, an orbital with $l = 1$ can have any one of three m_l values, -1, 0, or $+1$; thus, there are three possible orbitals with $l = 1$, each with its own orientation. Note that the number of possible m_l values *equals* the number of orbitals, which is $2l + 1$ for a given l value.

Table 7.2 summarizes the relationships among the three quantum numbers. The total number of orbitals for a given n value is n^2.

---

*For ease in discussion, we refer to the size, shape, and orientation of an "atomic orbital," although we really mean the size, shape, and orientation of an "atomic orbital's radial probability distribution." This usage is common in both introductory and advanced texts.

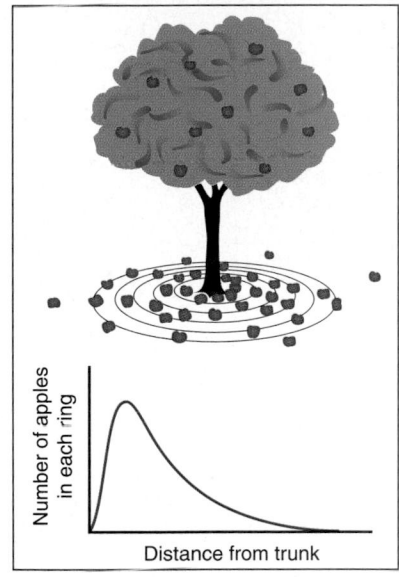

◆ A Radial Probability Distribution of Apples
An analogy might clarify why the curve in the radial probability distribution plot peaks and then falls off. Picture the fallen apples around the base of an apple tree: the density of apples is greatest near the trunk and decreases with distance. Divide the ground under the tree into foot-wide concentric rings and collect the apples within each ring. Apple density is greatest in the first ring, but the area of the second ring is larger, so it contains a greater *total* number of apples. Farther out near the edge of the tree, rings have more area but lower apple "density," so the total number of apples decreases. A plot of "number of apples within a ring" vs. "distance of ring from trunk" shows a peak at some close distance from the trunk, as in Figure 7.15D.

Table 7.2 The Hierarchy of Quantum Numbers for Atomic Orbitals

Name, Symbol (Property)	Allowed Values	Quantum Numbers							
Principal, n (size, energy)	Positive integer (1, 2, 3, . . .)	1		2			3		
Angular momentum, l (shape)	0 to $n - 1$	0	0	1		0	1	2	
Magnetic, m_l (orientation)	$-l$, . . ., 0, . . ., $+l$	0	0	-1 0 $+1$		0	-1 0 $+1$	-2 -1 0 $+1$ $+2$	

Sample Problem 7.5 Determining Quantum Numbers for an Energy Level

PROBLEM What values of the angular momentum (l) and magnetic (m_l) quantum numbers are allowed for a principal quantum number (n) of 3? How many orbitals are allowed for $n = 3$?

PLAN We determine the allowable quantum numbers with the rules outlined in the text: l values are integers from 0 to $n - 1$, and those for m_l are integers from $-l$ to 0 to $+l$. One m_l value is assigned to each orbital, so the number of m_l values gives the number of orbitals.

SOLUTION Determining l values:

$$\text{For } n = 3, \quad l = 0, 1, 2$$

Determining m_l for each l value:

$$\text{For } l = 0, \quad m_l = 0$$

$$\text{For } l = 1, \quad m_l = -1, 0, +1$$

$$\text{For } l = 2, \quad m_l = -2, -1, 0, +1, +2$$

There are nine m_l values, so there are nine orbitals with $n = 3$.

CHECK Table 7.2 shows that we are correct. The total number of orbitals with a given n is n^2, and for $n = 3$, $n^2 = 9$.

Follow-up Problem 7.5 Write l and m_l values for $n = 4$.

The energy states and orbitals of the atom are described with specific terms and associated with one or more quantum numbers:

- The atom's energy **levels,** or *shells,* are given by the n value: the smaller the n value, the lower the energy level and the greater the probability of the electron being closer to the nucleus.
- The atom's levels contain **sublevels,** or *subshells,* which designate the orbital shape. Each sublevel has a letter designation:
  $l = 0$ is an *s* sublevel.
  $l = 1$ is a *p* sublevel.
  $l = 2$ is a *d* sublevel.
  $l = 3$ is an *f* sublevel.
  (The letters derive from the names of spectroscopic lines: *s*harp, *p*rincipal, *d*iffuse, and *f*undamental.) Sublevels are named by joining the n value and the letter designation. For example, the sublevel (subshell) with $n = 2$ and $l = 0$ is called the 2*s* sublevel.
- Each allowed combination of n, l, and m_l values specifies one of the atom's *orbitals.* Thus, the three quantum numbers that describe an orbital express its size (energy), shape, and spatial orientation. You can easily give the quantum numbers of the orbitals in any sublevel by knowing the sublevel letter designation and the quantum-number hierarchy. For example, the hierarchy prescribes that the 2*s* sublevel has only one orbital, and its quantum numbers are $n = 2$, $l = 0$, and $m_l = 0$. The 3*p* sublevel has three orbitals: one with $n = 3$, $l = 1$, and $m_l = -1$; another with $n = 3$, $l = 1$, and $m_l = 0$; and a third with $n = 3$, $l = 1$, and $m_l = +1$.

Sample Problem 7.6 Determining Sublevel Names and Orbital Quantum Numbers

PROBLEM Give the name, magnetic quantum numbers, and number of orbitals for each sublevel with the following quantum numbers:
(a) $n = 3, l = 2$ **(b)** $n = 2, l = 0$
(c) $n = 5, l = 1$ **(d)** $n = 4, l = 3$

PLAN To name the sublevel (subshell), we combine the n value and l letter designation. Since we know l, we can find the possible m_l values, whose total number equals the number of orbitals.

SOLUTION

	n	l	SUBLEVEL NAME	POSSIBLE m_l VALUES	NO. OF ORBITALS
(a)	3	2	$3d$	$-2, -1, 0, +1, +2$	5
(b)	2	0	$2s$	0	1
(c)	5	1	$5p$	$-1, 0, +1$	3
(d)	4	3	$4f$	$-3, -2, -1, 0, +1, +2, +3$	7

CHECK Check the number of orbitals in each sublevel using

No. of orbitals = no. of m_l values = $2l + 1$

Follow-up Problem 7.6 What are the n, l, and possible m_l values for the $2p$ and $5f$ subshells?

Sample Problem 7.7 Identifying Incorrect Quantum Numbers

PROBLEM What is wrong with each of the following quantum number designations and/or sublevel names?

	n	l	m_l	NAME
(a)	1	1	0	$1p$
(b)	4	3	+1	$4d$
(c)	3	1	-2	$3p$

SOLUTION (a) A sublevel with $n = 1$ can have only $l = 0$, not $l = 1$. The only possible sublevel name is $1s$.
(b) A sublevel with $l = 3$ is an f sublevel, not a d sublevel. The sublevel name should be $4f$.
(c) A sublevel with $l = 1$ can have only m_l of $-1, 0, +1$, not -2.

CHECK Check that l is always less than n, and m_l is always $\geq -l$ and $\leq +l$.

Follow-up Problem 7.7
Supply the missing quantum number(s) or sublevel names.

	n	l	m_l	NAME
(a)	?	?	0	$4p$
(b)	2	1	0	?
(c)	3	2	-2	?
(d)	?	?	?	$2s$

Shapes of Atomic Orbitals

Each sublevel of the H atom corresponds to orbitals with characteristic shapes. As you'll see in Chapter 8, orbitals for the other atoms have similar shapes.

The s Orbital An orbital with $l = 0$ has a *spherical* shape with the nucleus at its center and is called an *s* orbital. The H atom's ground state, for example, has the electron in the $1s$ orbital. Figure 7.16A on the next page shows that the electron density is highest at the nucleus, whether depicted graphically *(top)* or as a section of a three-dimensional electron cloud *(middle)*. On the other hand, the radial probability distribution *(bottom)*, which represents the *total* probability of finding the electron (that is, where the electron spends most of its time), is highest slightly out from the nucleus. Both plots fall off smoothly with distance.

A 1s orbital

B 2s orbital

C 3s orbital

Figure 7.16 The 1s, 2s, and 3s orbitals. Information for each of the s orbitals is shown as a plot of electron density *(top)*, an electron cloud representation *(middle)*, in which shading coincides with peaks in the plot above, and a radial probability distribution *(bottom)* that shows where the electron spends its time. **A,** The 1s orbital. **B,** The 2s orbital. **C,** The 3s orbital. Note the nodes (regions of zero probability) in the 2s and 3s orbitals.

The 2s orbital, shown in Figure 7.16B, has two regions of higher electron density. The radial probability distribution *(total* probability; *bottom)* of the more distant region is *higher* than that of the closer one because the sum of its ψ^2 is taken over a much larger volume. Between the two regions is a spherical **node,** a shell-like region where the probability drops to zero ($\psi^2 = 0$ at the node, analogous to zero amplitude of a wave). Because the 2s orbital is larger than the 1s, an electron in this orbital spends more time *farther* from the nucleus than when it occupies the 1s.

The 3s orbital, shown in Figure 7.16C, has three regions of higher electron density and two nodes. Here again, the highest radial probability is at the greatest distance from the nucleus because the sum of all ψ^2 is taken over a larger volume. This pattern of more nodes and higher probability with distance continues for s orbitals of higher n value. Since an s orbital has a spherical shape, it can have only one orientation and, thus, only one value for the magnetic quantum number: For any s orbital, $m_l = 0$.

The p Orbital   An orbital with $l = 1$ has two regions (lobes) of high probability, one on *either side* of the nucleus and is called a *p* **orbital.** Thus, as you can see in Figure 7.17, the *nucleus lies at the nodal plane* of this "dumbbell-shaped" orbital. Since the maximum value of l is $n - 1$, only levels with

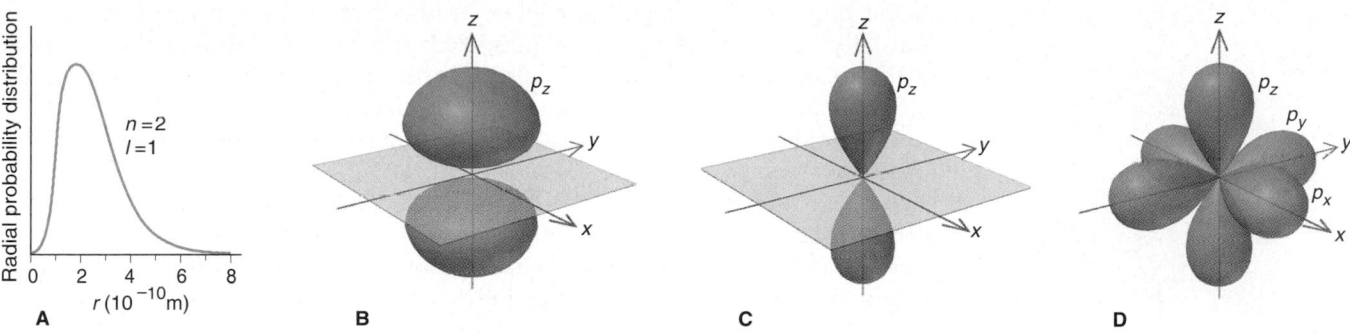

$n = 2$ or higher can have a p orbital. Therefore, the lowest energy p orbital (the one closest to the nucleus) is the $2p$. Keep in mind that *one p orbital consists of both lobes* and that the electron spends *equal* time in both. As we would expect from the pattern of s orbitals, a $3p$ orbital is larger than a $2p$ orbital, a $4p$ is larger than a $3p$, and so forth.

Unlike the s orbital, each p orbital has a specific orientation in space. The $l = 1$ value has three possible m_l values: -1, 0, and $+1$, which refer to three *mutually perpendicular p orbitals*. They are identical in size, shape, and energy, differing only in orientation. For convenience we associate p orbitals with the x, y, and z axes (but there is no necessary relation between a spatial axis and a given m_l value): the p_x orbital lies along the x axis, the p_y along the y axis, and the p_z along the z axis.

The *d* Orbital   An orbital with $l = 2$ is called a ***d* orbital**. There are five possible m_l values for the $l = 2$ value: -2, -1, 0, $+1$, and $+2$. Thus, a d orbital can have any one of five different orientations, as shown in Figure 7.18. Four

Figure 7.17 The 2*p* orbitals.
A, A radial probability distribution plot of the *2p* orbital shows a single peak. It lies at nearly the same distance from the nucleus as the larger peak in the 2s plot (see Figure 7.16B). **B,** An accurate representation of the probability contour of the 2*p*~z~ orbital. Note the nodal plane at the nucleus. An electron occupies both regions of the orbital equally and spends 90% of its time within this volume. The 2*p*~x~ and 2*p*~y~ orbitals have identical shapes but lie along the *x* and *y* axes, respectively. **C,** The stylized depiction of the 2*p* contour used throughout the text. **D,** In the atom, the three 2*p* orbitals occupy mutually perpendicular regions of space, giving the atom an overall spherical shape.

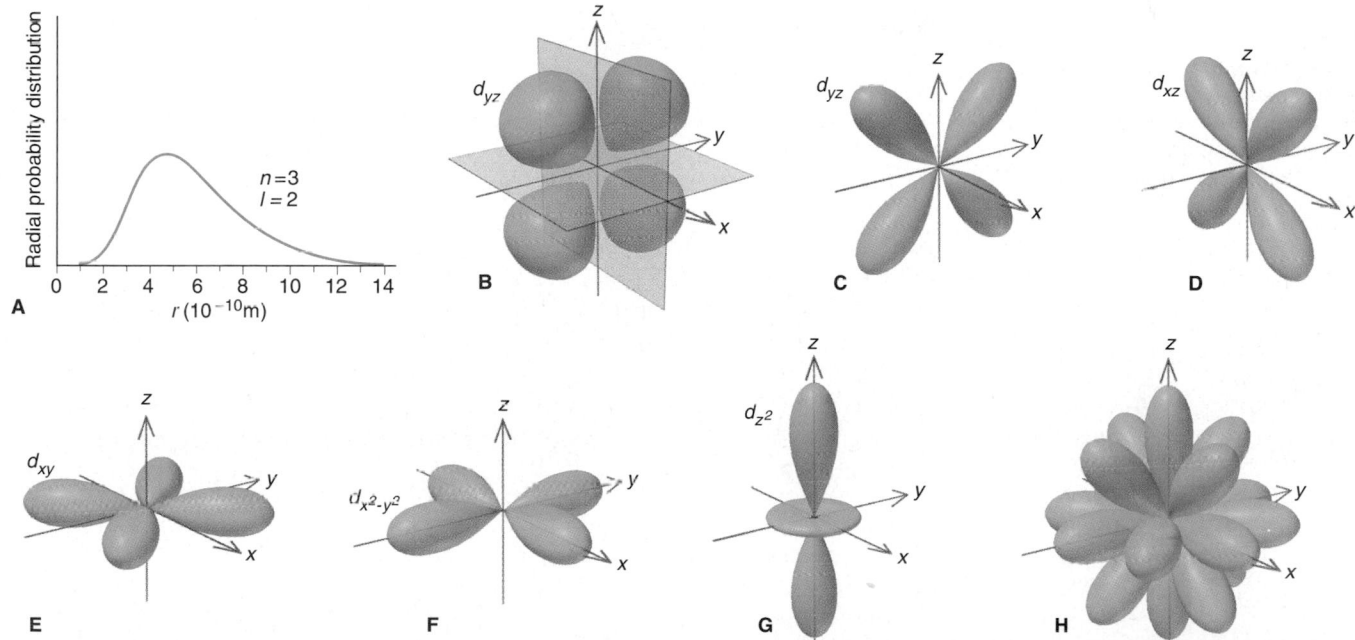

Figure 7.18 The 3*d* orbitals. A, A radial probability distribution plot. **B,** An accurate representation of the 3*d*~yz~ orbital probability contour. Note the mutually perpendicular nodal planes and the lobes lying *between* the axes. **C,** The stylized depiction of the 3*d*~yz~ orbital used throughout the text. **D,** The 3*d*~xz~ orbital. **E,** The 3*d*~xy~

orbital. **F,** The lobes of the 3*d*~x²−y²~ orbital lie *on* the *x* and *y* axes. **G,** The 3*d*~z²~ orbital has two lobes and a central, donut-shaped region. **H,** A composite of the five 3*d* orbitals, which again gives the atom an overall spherical shape.

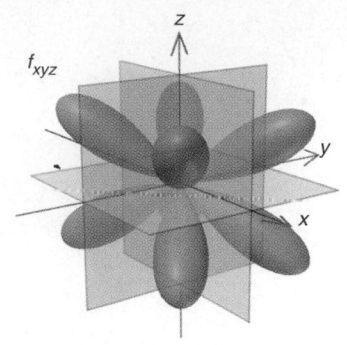

Figure 7.19 **One of the seven possible 4f orbitals.** The $4f_{xyz}$ orbital has eight lobes and three nodal planes. The other six 4f orbitals have multilobed contours also.

of the five *d* orbitals have four lobes ("cloverleaf shape") prescribed by two mutually perpendicular nodal planes, with the nucleus lying at the junction of the lobes. Three of these orbitals lie in the mutually perpendicular *xy*, *xz*, and *yz* planes, with their lobes *between* the axes, and are called the d_{xy}, d_{xz}, and d_{yz} orbitals. A fourth, the $d_{x^2-y^2}$ orbital, also lies in the *xy* plane, but its lobes are directed *along* the axes. The fifth *d* orbital, the d_{z^2}, has a different shape: two major lobes lie along the *z* axis, and a donut-shaped region of electron density girdles the center. An electron associated with a given *d* orbital has equal probability of being in any of the orbital's lobes. As we said for the *p* orbitals, the axis designations are *not* associated with a given m_l value. In keeping with the quantum number rules, a *d* orbital (*l* = 2) must have a principal quantum number of *n* = 3 or greater. The 4*d* orbitals extend farther from the nucleus than the 3*d* orbitals, and the 5*d* orbitals extend still farther.

Orbitals with Higher *l* Values   Orbitals with *l* = 3 are *f* orbitals and must have a principal quantum number of at least *n* = 4. There are seven *f* orbitals (2*l* + 1 = 7), each with a complex, multilobed shape (Figure 7.19). Orbitals with *l* = 4 are *g* orbitals, but we will not discuss them further because they play no known role in chemical bonding.

Energy Levels of the Hydrogen Atom

The energy state of the H atom depends on the principal quantum number *n* only. An electron in an orbital with a higher *n* value spends its time, on the average, farther from the nucleus, so it is higher in energy. As you'll see in Chapter 8, the energy state of an atom with more than one electron depends on both the *n and l* values of the occupied orbitals. Thus, in the case of the H atom *only*, all four *n* = 2 orbitals (one 2*s* and three 2*p*) have the same energy, and all nine *n* = 3 orbitals (one 3*s*, three 3*p*, and five 3*d*) have the same energy (Figure 7.20).

Figure 7.20 **The energy levels in the H atom.** In the H atom, the energy level depends only on the *n* value of the orbital. (As you'll see in the next chapter, atoms with more than one electron exhibit a more complex pattern of energy levels.)

Section Summary

The electron's wave function (ψ, atomic orbital) is a mathematical description of the electron's wavelike motion in an atom. Each wave function is associated with one of the atom's allowed energy states. The probability of finding the electron at a particular location is represented by ψ^2. An electron density diagram and a radial probability distribution plot show how the electron occupies the space near the nucleus for a particular energy level. Three features of the atomic orbital are described by quantum numbers: size (*n*), shape (*l*), and orientation (m_l). Orbitals with the same *n* and *l* values constitute a sublevel; sublevels with the same *n* value constitute an energy level. A sublevel with *l* = 0 has a spherical (*s*) orbital; a sublevel with *l* = 1 has three, two-lobed (*p*) orbitals; and a sublevel with *l* = 2 has five, four-lobed (*d*) orbitals. In the case of the H atom, the energy levels depend on the *n* value only.

Chapter Perspective

In this brief exploration of the origins of quantum physics, we see the everyday distinctions between matter and energy disappear and a new picture of the hydrogen atom gradually come into focus. By the atom's very nature, however, this focus cannot be perfectly sharp. The sequel to these remarkable discoveries unfolds in Chapter 8, where we begin our discussion of how the periodic behavior of the elements emerges from the properties of the atom, which in turn arise from the electron occupancy of its orbitals.

The following learning objectives, with section and/or sample problem (SP) numbers in parentheses, can help focus your study:

Understand These Concepts

1. The wave characteristics of light (the interrelations of frequency, wavelength, and speed; the meaning of amplitude) and a general overview of the electromagnetic spectrum (7.1)
2. How particles and waves differ in terms of the phenomena of refraction, diffraction, and interference (7.1)
3. The quantization of energy and the fact that an atom changes its energy by emitting or absorbing quanta of radiation (7.1)
4. How the photon theory explains the photoelectric effect and the relation between photon absorbed and electron released (7.1)
5. How the Bohr theory explained line spectra of the H atom; the importance of discrete atomic energy levels (7.2)
6. The wave-particle duality of matter and energy and the relevant theories and experiments that led to it (de Broglie wavelength, electron diffraction, photon momentum) (7.3)
7. The meaning of the uncertainty principle and how it limits our knowledge of electron properties (7.3)
8. The distinction between ψ (atomic orbital) and ψ^2 (probability of finding the electron at some distance from the nucleus) (7.4)
9. How electron density diagrams and radial distribution plots depict the probability of electron location within the atom (7.4)
10. The hierarchy of the quantum numbers that describe the size (n, energy), shape (l), and orientation (m_l) of an orbital (7.4)
11. The distinction between level (shell), sublevel (subshell), and orbital (7.4)
12. The shapes and nodes of s, p, and d orbitals (7.4)

Master These Skills

1. Interconverting frequency and wavelength (SP 7.1)
2. Interconverting the energy of a photon with its frequency and/or wavelength (SP 7.2)
3. Applying de Broglie's equation to find the wavelength of a particle (SP 7.3)
4. Applying the uncertainty principle to see that location and speed cannot be determined simultaneously for particles of extremely small mass (SP 7.4)
5. Determining quantum numbers and sublevel designations (SPs 7.5 to 7.7)

For Review and Reference

Key Terms

Section 7.1
electromagnetic (EM) radiation
frequency (ν)
wavelength (λ)
speed of light (c)
amplitude
electromagnetic spectrum
infrared (IR)
ultraviolet (UV)
refraction
diffraction
quantum number

Planck's constant (h)
quantum
photoelectric effect
photon

Section 7.2
line spectrum
stationary state
ground state
excited state
spectrophotometry
emission spectrum
flame test
absorption spectrum

Section 7.3
de Broglie wavelength
wave-particle duality
uncertainty principle

Section 7.4
quantum mechanics
Schrödinger equation
wave function (atomic orbital)
electron probability density diagram (electron density diagram)
electron cloud
radial probability distribution plot

probability contour
principal quantum number (n)
angular momentum quantum number (l)
magnetic quantum number (m_l)
level (shell)
sublevel (subshell)
s orbital
node
p orbital
d orbital

Key Equations and Relationships

7.1 Relating the speed of light to its frequency and wavelength (p. 260):

$$c = \nu\lambda$$

7.2 Determining the smallest change in an atom's energy (p. 264):

$$\Delta E = h\nu$$

7.3 Calculating the wavelength of any line in the H atom spectrum (Rydberg equation) (p. 267):

$$\frac{1}{\lambda} = R\left(\frac{1}{n_1{}^2} - \frac{1}{n_2{}^2}\right)$$

7.4 Finding the difference between two energy levels in the H atom (p. 269):

$$\Delta E = E_{final} - E_{initial} = -2.18\times10^{-18}\ \text{J}\left(\frac{1}{n_{final}^2} - \frac{1}{n_{initial}^2}\right)$$

7.5 Calculating the wavelength of any moving object (de Broglie wavelength) (p. 273):

$$\lambda = \frac{h}{mu}$$

7.6 Finding the uncertainty in position or speed of a particle (Heisenberg uncertainty principle) (p. 276):

$$\Delta x \cdot m\Delta u \geq \frac{h}{4\pi}$$

Highlighted Figures and Tables

These figures (F) and tables (T) provide a quick review of key ideas.
F7.3 The electromagnetic spectrum (p. 260)
F7.14 From classical to quantum theory (p. 275)
F7.15 Electron probability in the H atom (p. 278)

T7.2 The hierarchy of quantum numbers (p. 279)
F7.16 The $1s$, $2s$, and $3s$ orbitals (p. 282)
F7.17 The $2p$ orbitals (p. 283)
F7.18 The $3d$ orbitals (p. 283)

Answers to Follow-up Problems

7.1 $\lambda\ \text{(nm)} = \dfrac{3.00\times10^8\ \text{m/s}}{7.23\times10^{14}\ \text{s}^{-1}} \times \dfrac{10^9\ \text{nm}}{1\ \text{m}} = 415\ \text{nm}$

$\lambda\ \text{(Å)} = 415\ \text{nm} \times \dfrac{10\ \text{Å}}{1\ \text{nm}} = 4150\ \text{Å}$

7.2 UV: $E = hc/\lambda$

$= \dfrac{(6.626\times10^{-34}\ \text{J}\cdot\text{s})(3.00\times10^8\ \text{m/s})}{1\times10^{-8}\ \text{m}} = 2\times10^{-17}\ \text{J}$

Visible: $E = 4\times10^{-19}$ J; IR: $E = 2\times10^{-21}$ J
As λ increases, E decreases.

7.3 $u = h/m\lambda = \dfrac{6.626\times10^{-34}\ \text{kg}\cdot\text{m}^2/\text{s}}{(9.11\times10^{-31}\ \text{kg})\left(100\ \text{nm} \times \dfrac{1\ \text{m}}{10^9\ \text{nm}}\right)}$

$= 7.27\times10^3\ \text{m/s}$

7.4 $\Delta x \geq \dfrac{6.626\times10^{-34}\ \text{kg}\cdot\text{m}^2/\text{s}}{4\pi(0.142\ \text{kg})(0.447\ \text{m/s})} \geq 8.31\times10^{-34}\ \text{m}$

7.5 $n = 4$, so $l = 0, 1, 2, 3$. In addition to the m_l values in Sample Problem 7.5, we have those for $l = 3$:

$$m_l = -3, -2, -1, 0, +1, +2, +3$$

7.6 For $2p$: $n = 2$, $l = 1$, $m_l = -1, 0, +1$
For $5f$: $n = 5$, $l = 3$, $m_l = -3, -2, -1, 0, +1, +2, +3$

7.7 (a) $n = 4$, $l = 1$; (b) name is $2p$; (c) name is $3d$;
(d) $n = 2$, $l = 0$, $m_l = 0$

Problems

Problems with a colored number are answered at the back of the text. Problem sections match the text and provide the number(s) of relevant sample problems. Most offer concept review questions, skill-building exercises (written in similar pairs), and problems in a relevant context. Following these are comprehensive problems based on material from any section and/or previous chapter.

The Nature of Light

(Sample Problems 7.1 and 7.2)

■ Concept Review Questions

7.1 In what ways are microwave and ultraviolet radiation the same? In what ways are they different?

7.2 Consider the following types of electromagnetic radiation:

(1) microwave   (2) ultraviolet   (3) radio waves
(4) infrared   (5) x-ray   (6) visible
(a) Arrange them in order of increasing wavelength.
(b) Arrange them in order of increasing frequency.
(c) Arrange them in order of increasing energy.

7.3 Define each of the following wave phenomena, and give an example of where each occurs: (a) refraction; (b) diffraction; (c) dispersion; (d) interference.

7.4 In the mid-17th century, Isaac Newton proposed that light existed as a stream of particles, and the wave-particle debate continued for over 250 years until the revolutionary ideas of Planck and Einstein. Give two pieces of evidence for the wave model and two for the particle model.

7.5 What new idea about energy did Planck use to explain blackbody radiation?

7.6 What new idea about light did Einstein use to explain the photoelectric effect? Why does the photoelectric effect exhibit a threshold frequency? Why does it *not* exhibit a time lag?

■ Skill-Building Exercises (paired)

7.7 An AM station broadcasts rock music at "960 on your radio dial." Units for AM frequencies are given in kilohertz (kHz). Find the wavelength of these radio waves in meters (m), nanometers (nm), and angstroms (Å).

7.8 An FM station broadcasts classical music at 93.5 MHz (megahertz, or 10^6 Hz). Find the wavelength (in m, nm, and Å) of these radio waves.

7.9 A radio wave has a frequency of 3.6×10^{10} Hz. What is the energy (in J) of one photon of this radiation?

7.10 An x-ray has a wavelength of 1.3 Å. Calculate the energy (in J) of one photon of this radiation.

7.11 Rank the following photons in terms of increasing energy: (a) blue ($\lambda = 453$ nm); (b) red ($\lambda = 660$ nm); (c) yellow ($\lambda = 595$ nm).

7.12 Rank the following photons in terms of decreasing energy: (a) IR ($\nu = 6.5 \times 10^{13}$ s^{-1}); (b) microwave ($\nu = 9.8 \times 10^{11}$ s^{-1}); (c) UV ($\nu = 8.0 \times 10^{15}$ s^{-1}).

■ Problems in Context

7.13 In the United States, police often monitor traffic with "K-band" radar guns, which operate in the microwave region at 22.235 GHz (1 GHz = 10^9 Hz). Find the wavelength (in nm and Å) of this radiation.

7.14 Covalent bonds in a molecule absorb radiation in the IR range and vibrate at characteristic frequencies.
(a) The C—O bond in an organic compound absorbs radiation of wavelength 9.6 μm. What frequency (in s^{-1}) corresponds to that wavelength?
(b) The H—Cl bond has a frequency of vibration of 8.652×10^{13} Hz. What wavelength (in μm) corresponds to that frequency?

7.15 Cobalt-60 is a radioactive isotope used to treat cancers of the brain and other tissues. A gamma ray emitted by an atom of this isotope has an energy of 1.33 MeV (million electron volts; 1 eV = 1.602×10^{-19} J). What is the frequency (in Hz) and wavelength (in m) of this gamma ray?

7.16 (a) The first step in the formation of ozone in the upper atmosphere occurs when oxygen molecules absorb UV radiation of wavelengths ≤ 242 nm. Calculate the frequency and energy of the least energetic of these photons.
(b) Ozone absorbs light having wavelengths of 2200 to 2900 Å, thus protecting organisms on the Earth's surface from this high-energy UV radiation. What are the frequency and energy of the most energetic of these photons?

Atomic Spectra

■ Concept Review Questions

7.17 How is n_1 in the Rydberg equation (Equation 7.3) related to the quantum number n in the Bohr model?

7.18 How would a planetary (solar system) model of the atom differ from a key assumption in Bohr's model? What was the theoretical basis from which Bohr made this assumption?

7.19 Distinguish between an absorption spectrum and an emission spectrum. With which did Bohr work?

7.20 Which of these electron transitions correspond to absorption of energy and which to emission: (a) $n = 2$ to $n = 4$; (b) $n = 3$ to $n = 1$; (c) $n = 5$ to $n = 2$; (d) $n = 3$ to $n = 4$?

7.21 Why could the Bohr model not predict line spectra for atoms other than hydrogen?

7.22 The H atom and Be^{3+} ion each have one electron. Does the Bohr model predict their spectra accurately? Would you expect their line spectra to be identical? Explain.

■ Skill-Building Exercises (paired)

7.23 Use the Rydberg equation (Equation 7.3) to calculate the wavelength (in nm) of the photon emitted when a hydrogen atom undergoes a transition from $n = 5$ to $n = 2$.

7.24 Use the Rydberg equation to calculate the wavelength (in Å) of the photon absorbed when a hydrogen atom undergoes a transition from $n = 1$ to $n = 3$.

7.25 What is the wavelength (in nm) of the least energetic spectral line in the infrared series of the H atom?

7.26 What is the wavelength (in nm) of the least energetic spectral line in the visible series of the H atom?

7.27 Calculate the energy difference (ΔE) for the transition in Problem 7.23 for 1 mol H atoms.

7.28 Calculate the energy difference (ΔE) for the transition in Problem 7.24 for 1 mol H atoms.

7.29 Arrange the following H atom electron transitions in order of *increasing* frequency of the photon absorbed or emitted: (a) $n = 2$ to $n = 4$; (b) $n = 2$ to $n = 1$; (c) $n = 2$ to $n = 5$; (d) $n = 4$ to $n = 3$.

7.30 Arrange the following H atom electron transitions in order of *decreasing* wavelength of the photon absorbed or emitted: (a) $n = 2$ to $n = \infty$; (b) $n = 4$ to $n = 20$; (c) $n = 3$ to $n = 10$; (d) $n = 2$ to $n = 1$.

7.31 The electron in a ground-state H atom absorbs a photon of wavelength 97.20 nm. To what energy level does the electron move?

7.32 An electron in the $n = 5$ level of an H atom emits a photon of wavelength 1281 nm. To what energy level does the electron move?

■ Problems in Context

7.33 In addition to continuous radiation, fluorescent lamps emit sharp lines in the visible region from a mercury discharge within the tube. Much of this light has a wavelength of 436 nm. What is the energy (in J) of one photon of this light?

7.34 The oxidizing agents used in most fireworks consist of potassium salts, such as KClO$_4$ or KClO$_3$, rather than the corresponding sodium salts. One of the problems with using sodium salts is their extremely intense yellow-orange emission at 589 nm, which obscures other colors in the display. What is the energy (in J) of one photon of this light? What is the energy (in kJ) of 1 einstein of this light (1 einstein = 1 mol photons)?

The Wave-Particle Duality of Matter and Energy
(Sample Problems 7.3 and 7.4)

■ Concept Review Questions

7.35 In what sense is the wave motion of a guitar string analogous to the motion of an electron in an atom?

7.36 What experimental support did de Broglie's concept receive?

7.37 If particles have wavelike motion, why don't we observe that motion in the macroscopic world?

7.38 Why can't we overcome the uncertainty predicted by Heisenberg's principle by building more precise devices to reduce the error in measurements below the $h/4\pi$ limit?

■ Skill-Building Exercises *(paired)*

7.39 A 220-lb fullback runs the 40-yd dash at a speed of 19.6 ± 0.1 mi/h.
(a) What is his de Broglie wavelength (in meters)?
(b) What is the uncertainty in his position?

7.40 An alpha particle (mass $= 6.6\times10^{-24}$ g) emitted by radium travels at $3.4\times10^{7} \pm 0.1\times10^{7}$ mi/h.
(a) What is its de Broglie wavelength (in meters)?
(b) What is the uncertainty in its position?

7.41 How fast must a 56.5-g tennis ball travel to have a de Broglie wavelength equal to that of a photon of green light (5400 Å)?

7.42 How fast must a 142-g baseball travel to have a de Broglie wavelength equal to that of an x-ray photon with $\lambda = 100.$ pm?

7.43 The yellow color characteristic of a sodium flame test is due to emissions of photons of wavelength 589 nm. What is the mass equivalence of one photon of this wavelength $(1 \text{ J} = 1 \text{ kg} \cdot \text{m}^2/\text{s}^2)$?

7.44 The red color characteristic of a lithium flame test is due to emissions of photons of wavelength 671 nm. What is the mass equivalence of 1 mol photons of this wavelength $(1 \text{ J} = 1 \text{ kg} \cdot \text{m}^2/\text{s}^2)$?

The Quantum-Mechanical Model of the Atom
(Sample Problems 7.5 to 7.7)

■ Concept Review Questions

7.45 What physical meaning is attributed to the square of the wave function, ψ^2?

7.46 Explain in your own words what the "electron density" in a particular tiny volume of space means.

7.47 Explain in your own words what it means for the peak in the radial probability distribution of the $n = 1$ level of a hydrogen atom to be at 0.529 Å. Is the probability of finding an electron at 0.529 Å from the nucleus greater for the $1s$ or the $2s$ orbital?

7.48 What feature of an orbital is related to each of the following: (a) principal quantum number (n); (b) angular momentum quantum number (l); (c) magnetic quantum number (m_l)?

■ Skill-Building Exercises *(paired)*

7.49 How many orbitals in an atom can have each of the following designations: (a) $1s$; (b) $4d$; (c) $3p$; (d) $n = 3$?

7.50 How many orbitals in an atom can have each of the following designations: (a) $5f$; (b) $4p$; (c) $5d$; (d) $n = 2$?

7.51 Give all possible m_l values for orbitals that have each of the following: (a) $l = 2$; (b) $n = 1$; (c) $n = 4, l = 3$.

7.52 Give all possible m_l values for orbitals that have each of the following: (a) $l = 3$; (b) $n = 2$; (c) $n = 6, l = 1$.

7.53 Draw probability contours (with axes) for each of the following orbitals: (a) s; (b) p_x.

7.54 Draw probability contours (with axes) for each of the following orbitals: (a) p_z; (b) d_{xy}.

7.55 For each of the following, give the sublevel designation, the allowable m_l values, and the number of orbitals: (a) $n = 4, l = 2$; (b) $n = 5, l = 1$; (c) $n = 6, l = 3$.

7.56 For each of the following, give the sublevel designation, the allowable m_l values, and the number of orbitals: (a) $n = 2, l = 0$; (b) $n = 3, l = 2$; (c) $n = 5, l = 1$.

7.57 For each of the following sublevels, give the n and l values and the number of orbitals: (a) $5s$; (b) $3p$; (c) $4f$.

7.58 For each of the following sublevels, give the n and l values and the number of orbitals: (a) $6g$; (b) $4s$; (c) $3d$.

7.59 Are the following quantum number combinations allowed? If not, show two ways to correct them:
(a) $n = 2; l = 0; m_l = -1$ (b) $n = 4; l = 3; m_l = -1$
(c) $n = 3; l = 1; m_l = 0$ (d) $n = 5; l = 2; m_l = +3$

7.60 Are the following quantum number combinations allowed? If not, show two ways to correct them:
(a) $n = 1; l = 0; m_l = 0$ (b) $n = 2; l = 2; m_l = +1$
(c) $n = 7; l = 1; m_l = +2$ (d) $n = 3; l = 1; m_l = -2$

Comprehensive Problems
Problems with an asterisk (*) are more challenging.

7.61 The orange pigment in carrots and orange peel is mostly β-carotene, an organic compound that is insoluble in water but very soluble in benzene and chloroform. Describe an experimental method for determining the concentration of β-carotene in the oil expressed from orange peel.

7.62 The quantum-mechanical treatment of the hydrogen atom gives the energy, E, of the electron as a function of the principal quantum number, n:

$$E = -\frac{h^2}{8\pi^2 m_e a_0^2 n^2} \qquad (n = 1, 2, 3, \ldots)$$

where h is Planck's constant, m_e is the electron mass, and a_0 is 52.92×10^{-12} m.

(a) Write the expression in the form $E = -(\text{constant})\dfrac{1}{n^2}$, evaluate the constant (in J), and compare it with the corresponding expression from Bohr's theory.
(b) Use the expression to find the energy change between $n = 2$ and $n = 3$.
(c) Calculate the wavelength of the photon that corresponds to this energy change. Is this photon seen in the hydrogen spectrum obtained from experiment (see Figure 7.8)?

7.63 The following figure illustrates the photoelectric effect graphically. It is a plot of the kinetic energies of electrons ejected from the surface of potassium metal or silver metal at different frequencies of incident light.

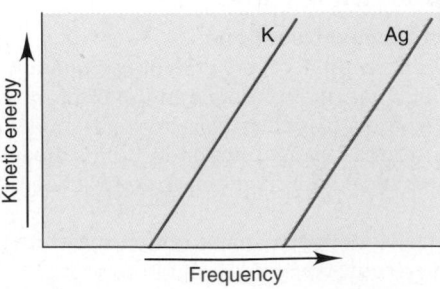

(a) Why don't the lines begin at the origin?

(b) Why don't the lines begin at the same point?

(c) Which metal requires light of shorter wavelength to eject an electron?

(d) Why are the slopes of the lines equal?

7.64 Secondary colors—orange, purple, green—are formed by mixing two primary colors—red, yellow, blue. Arrange the secondary colors in order of increasing wavelength, increasing frequency, and increasing energy.

7.65 One reason carbon monoxide (CO) is toxic is that it binds to the blood protein hemoglobin more strongly than oxygen does. The hemoglobin—CO bond absorbs radiation of 1953 cm^{-1}. (The units are the reciprocal of the wavelength in centimeters.) Calculate the wavelength (in nm and Å) and the frequency (in Hz) of the absorbed radiation.

7.66 A metal ion M^{n+} has a single electron. The highest energy line in its emission spectrum occurs at a frequency of 2.961×10^{16} Hz. Identify the ion.

7.67 TV and radio stations transmit in specific frequency bands of the radio region of the electromagnetic spectrum.

(a) TV channels 2 to 13 (VHF) broadcast signals between the frequencies 59.5 and 215.8 MHz, whereas FM radio broadcasts signals with wavelengths between 2.78 and 3.41 m. Do these bands of signals overlap?

(b) AM radio broadcasts signals with frequencies between 550 and 1600 kHz. Which has a broader transmission band, AM or FM?

7.68 Compare the wavelengths of an electron (mass = 9.11×10^{-31} kg) and a proton (mass = 1.67×10^{-27} kg) that each have (a) a speed of 3.0×10^6 m/s; (b) a kinetic energy of 2.5×10^{-15} J.

*7.69 Five lines in the H atom spectrum have the following wavelengths (in Å): (a) 1212.7; (b) 4340.5; (c) 4861.3; (d) 6562.8; (e) 10938. Three lines result from transitions to $n_{final} = 2$ (visible series). The other two result from transitions in different series, one with $n_{final} = 1$ and the other with $n_{final} = 3$. Identify $n_{initial}$ for each line.

7.70 In his explanation of the threshold frequency in the photoelectric effect, Einstein reasoned that the absorbed photon must have the minimum energy required to dislodge an electron from the metal surface. This energy is called the *work function* (ϕ) of that metal. What is the longest wavelength of radiation (in nm) that could cause the photoelectric effect in each of the following metals?

(a) Potassium, $\phi = 3.68 \times 10^{-19}$ J

(b) Silver, $\phi = 7.59 \times 10^{-19}$ J

(c) Sodium, $\phi = 4.41 \times 10^{-19}$ J

7.71 Which of the following elements can be used for a photocell that will operate with visible light? [The work function, ϕ, of each metal is given. (See explanation in Problem 7.70.)]

(a) Tantalum, $\phi = 6.41 \times 10^{-19}$ J

(b) Barium, $\phi = 4.3 \times 10^{-19}$ J

(c) Tungsten, $\phi = 7.16 \times 10^{-19}$ J

7.72 Refractometry is a method of chemical analysis based on the change in the speed of light as it travels through a substance compared with its speed in a vacuum (see the first Margin Note on p. 262).

(a) The refractive index of water is 1.33 (at 20°C). Calculate the speed of light in water.

(b) The refractive index of diamond is 2.42 (at 20°C). Calculate the speed of light in diamond.

7.73 The carbon-carbon bond forms the "backbone" of nearly every organic and biological molecule. The average bond energy of the C—C bond is 347 kJ/mol. Calculate the frequency and wavelength of the least energetic photon that can break this bond. In what region of the electromagnetic spectrum is this radiation?

7.74 Imagining a world in which some physical constants have radically different values can often be fascinating. For example, suppose Planck's constant were 1.13×10^{-9} J · s, and a single photon of light had enough energy to vaporize a cup of coffee (6.00×10^5 J). What is the maximum wavelength of this photon, and what color would it be?

7.75 The following quantum number combinations are not allowed. Assuming the n and m_l values are correct, change the l value to create an allowable combination:

(a) $n = 3$; $l = 0$; $m_l = -1$ (b) $n = 3$; $l = 3$; $m_l = +1$

(c) $n = 7$; $l = 2$; $m_l = +3$ (d) $n = 4$; $l = 1$; $m_l = -2$

*7.76 A ground-state H atom absorbs a photon of wavelength 94.91 nm and its electron attains a higher energy level. The atom then emits two photons: one of wavelength 1281 nm to reach an intermediate level and a second to return to the ground state.

(a) What higher level did the electron reach?

(b) What intermediate level did the electron reach?

(c) What was the wavelength of the second photon emitted?

*7.77 Consider these ground-state ionization energies of one-electron species:
$$H = 1.31 \times 10^3 \text{ kJ/mol}$$
$$He^+ = 5.24 \times 10^3 \text{ kJ/mol}$$
$$Li^{2+} = 1.18 \times 10^4 \text{ kJ/mol}$$

Write a general expression for the ionization energy of any one-electron species and use it to calculate the ionization energy of B^{4+}.

*7.78 Why do the spaces between spectral lines within a series decrease as the wavelength becomes shorter?

*7.79 In the course of developing his model, Bohr arrived at a formula for the radius of the electron's orbit: $r_n = n^2 h^2 \epsilon_0 / \pi m_e e^2$, where m_e is the electron mass, e is its charge, and ϵ_0 is a constant related to charge attraction in a vacuum. Given $m_e = 9.109 \times 10^{-31}$ kg, $e = 1.602 \times 10^{-19}$ C, and $\epsilon_0 = 8.854 \times 10^{-12}$ C^2/J · m, calculate the following:

(a) The radius of the 1st ($n = 1$) orbit in the H atom

(b) The radius of the 10th ($n = 10$) orbit in the H atom

*7.80 (a) Calculate the Bohr radius of an electron in the $n = 3$ orbit of a hydrogen atom. (See Problem 7.79.)

(b) What is the energy (in J) of the atom in part (a)?

(c) What is the energy of an Li^{2+} ion when its electron is in the $n = 3$ orbit?

(d) Why are the answers to parts (b) and (c) different?

7.81 Enormous numbers of microwave photons are needed to warm macroscopic samples of matter. A portion of soup containing 252 g water is heated in a microwave oven from 20°C to 98°C, with radiation of wavelength 1.55×10^{-2} m. How many photons are absorbed by the water in the soup?

*7.82 The quantum-mechanical treatment of the hydrogen atom gives an expression for the wave function, ψ, of the 1s orbital:

$$\psi = \frac{1}{\sqrt{\pi}}\left(\frac{1}{a_0}\right)^{\frac{3}{2}} e^{-r/a_0}$$

where r is the distance from the nucleus and a_0 is 52.92 pm. The electron density is the probability of finding the electron at a particular point (or tiny volume) at distance r from the nucleus and is proportional to ψ^2. The radial probability is the total probability of finding the electron at all points at distance r from the nucleus and is proportional to $4\pi r^2\psi^2$. Calculate the values (to three significant figures) of ψ, ψ^2, and $4\pi r^2\psi^2$ to fill in the following table, and sketch plots of these quantities versus r. Compare the latter two plots with those in Figure 7.16A:

r (pm)	ψ (pm$^{-\frac{3}{2}}$)	ψ^2 (pm^{-3})	$4\pi r^2\psi^2$ (pm^{-1})
0			
50			
100			
200			

*7.83 Lines in a given spectral series can overlap lines in another series.
(a) Use the Rydberg equation to show whether the range of wavelengths in the $n_1 = 1$ series overlaps with the range of the $n_1 = 2$ series.
(b) Use the Rydberg equation to show whether the range of wavelengths in the $n_1 = 3$ series overlaps with the range of the $n_1 = 4$ series.
(c) How many lines in the $n_1 = 4$ series lie in the range of the $n_1 = 5$ series?
(d) What does this overlap imply about the hydrogen spectrum at longer wavelengths?

*7.84 The following values are the only allowable energy levels of a hypothetical one-electron atom:

$$E_6 = -2\times10^{-19}\text{ J} \quad E_5 = -7\times10^{-19}\text{ J} \quad E_4 = -11\times10^{-19}\text{ J}$$
$$E_3 = -15\times10^{-19}\text{ J} \quad E_2 = -17\times10^{-19}\text{ J} \quad E_1 = -20\times10^{-19}\text{ J}$$

(a) If the electron were in the $n = 3$ level, what would be the highest frequency (and minimum wavelength) of radiation that could be emitted?
(b) What is the ionization energy (in kJ/mol) of the atom in its ground state?
(c) If the electron were in the $n = 4$ level, what would be the shortest wavelength (in nm) of radiation that could be absorbed without causing ionization?

7.85 In fireworks displays, light of a characteristic wavelength is related to the presence of a particular element. What are the frequency and color of the light associated with each of the following?
(a) Ba^{2+}, $\lambda = 551$ nm   (b) Li^+, $\lambda = 671$ nm
(c) Cs^+, $\lambda = 456$ nm   (d) Ca^{2+}, $\lambda = 649$ nm
(e) Na^+, $\lambda = 589$ nm   (f) Sr^{2+}, $\lambda = 661$ nm

7.86 Visible light provides green plants with the energy needed to drive photosynthesis. Horticulturists know that, for many plants, leaf color depends on how brightly lit the growing area is: dark green leaves are associated with low light levels and pale green with high levels. (a) Use the photon theory of light to explain why a plant adapts this way.
(b) What change in leaf composition might account for this behavior?

*7.87 In compliance with conservation of energy, Einstein explained that in the photoelectric effect, the energy of a photon ($h\nu$) absorbed by a metal is the sum of the work function (ϕ), the minimum energy needed to dislodge an electron from the metal's surface, and the kinetic energy (E_k) of the electron: $h\nu = \phi + E_k$. When light of wavelength 358.1 nm falls on the surface of potassium metal, the speed (u) of the dislodged electron is 6.40×10^5 m/s.
(a) What is $E_k(\frac{1}{2}mu^2)$ of the dislodged electron?
(b) What is ϕ (in J) of potassium?

*7.88 Atomic hydrogen produces well-known series of spectral lines in several regions of the electromagnetic spectrum. Each series fits the Rydberg equation with its own particular n_1 value. Calculate the value of n_1 (by trial and error if necessary) that would produce a series of lines in which:
(a) The *highest* energy line has a wavelength of 3282 nm.
(b) The *lowest* energy line has a wavelength of 7460 nm.

7.89 Fish-liver oil is an excellent animal source of vitamin A. Its concentration is measured spectrophotometrically at a wavelength of 329 nm.
(a) Suggest a reason for using this wavelength.
(b) In what region of the spectrum does this wavelength lie?
(c) When 0.1232 g fish-liver oil is dissolved in 500. mL of solvent, the absorbance is 0.724 units. When 1.67×10^{-3} g vitamin A is dissolved in 250. mL of solvent, the absorbance is 1.018 units. Calculate the vitamin A concentration in the fish-liver oil.

7.90 In the 1998 Winter Olympics, Claudia Pechstein of Germany won the 5000-m speed skating competition with a time of 6 minutes 59.61 seconds. (a) Assuming the rightmost digit in the distance and time values has an uncertainty of one unit, what is her speed in mi/h? (b) Assuming her racing weight is 134 lbs, what is her de Broglie wavelength? (c) What is the uncertainty in her position as she crossed the finish line?

7.91 Electric power is typically stated in units of watts (W; 1 W = 1 J/s). About 95% of the power output of an incandescent bulb is converted to heat and 5% to light. If 10% of that light shines on your chemistry text, how many photons per second shine on the book from a 75-W bulb? (Assume the photons have a wavelength of 550 nm.)

7.92 The use of phosphate compounds in detergents and their subsequent environmental discharge has led to serious imbalances in the natural life cycle of freshwater lakes. A chemist studying water pollution used a spectrophotometric method to measure total phosphate and obtained the following data for known standards:

ABSORBANCE (400 nm)	CONCENTRATION (mol/L)
0	0.0
0.10	2.5×10^{-5}
0.16	3.2×10^{-5}
0.20	4.4×10^{-5}
0.25	5.6×10^{-5}
0.38	8.4×10^{-5}
0.48	10.5×10^{-5}
0.62	13.8×10^{-5}
0.76	17.0×10^{-5}
0.88	19.4×10^{-5}

(a) Draw a standard curve of absorbance at 400 nm vs. phosphate concentration.
(b) If a lake water sample has an absorbance of 0.55, what is its phosphate concentration?

Electron Configuration and Chemical Periodicity

8

Figure: Periodicity in nature. Some natural occurrences, such as solar eclipses, recur with such periodic regularity that they can be predicted with remarkable accuracy. As you'll see in this chapter, the arrangement of electrons in atoms recurs periodically, which allows us to explain why many properties of the elements recur periodically and to predict physical and chemical behavior.

In Chapter 7, you saw how an outpouring of scientific creativity by early 20th-century physicists led to a new understanding of matter and energy, which in turn led to the quantum-mechanical model of the atom. But you can be sure that late 19th-century chemists were not sitting idly by, waiting for their colleagues in physics to develop that model. They were exploring the nature of electrolytes, establishing the kinetic-molecular theory, and developing chemical thermodynamics. The fields of organic chemistry and biochemistry were born, as were the fertilizer, explosive, glassmaking, soap-making, bleaching, and dyestuff industries. And, for the first time, chemistry became a major university subject in Europe and America. Superimposed on this activity was the accumulation of an enormous body of facts about the elements, which became organized into the periodic table.

The goal of this chapter is to show how the organization of the table, condensed from countless hours of laboratory work, was explained perfectly by the new quantum-mechanical atomic model—an explanation that is one of the most satisfying intellectual achievements in science. This model answers one of the central questions in chemistry: why do the elements behave as they do? Or, rephrasing the question to fit the main topic of this chapter: how does the **electron configuration** of an element—*the distribution of electrons within the orbitals of its atoms*—relate to its chemical and physical properties?

First we briefly discuss the historical development of the periodic table. Then we take up where Chapter 7 left off, extending the quantum-mechanical model to *many-electron atoms,* those with more than one electron, to show how it defines a unique set of quantum numbers for every electron in the atoms of every element. We consider the order of filling orbitals with electrons and see how it correlates with the order of placing elements in the periodic table. All this leads to understanding how electron configuration and nuclear charge give rise to trends in atomic properties and how these trends account for the periodic patterns of chemical reactivity. Finally we apply this understanding to a discussion of metals, nonmetals, and their ions.

8.1 Development of the Periodic Table

An essential requirement for the amazing growth in theoretical and practical chemistry in the second half of the 19th century was the ability to organize the facts known about element behavior. The earliest organizing attempt was made by Johann Döbereiner, who placed groups of three elements with similar properties, such as calcium, strontium, and barium, into "triads." Later, John Newlands noted similarities between every eighth element (arranged by atomic mass), like the similarity between every eighth note in the musical scale, and placed them in "octaves." As more elements were discovered, however, these early numerical attempts lost much of their validity.

In Chapter 2, you saw that the most successful organizing scheme was made by the Russian chemist Dmitri Mendeleev. In 1870, he arranged the 65 elements then known into a *periodic table* and summarized their behavior in the **periodic law:** when arranged by atomic mass, the elements exhibit a periodic recurrence of similar properties. It is a curious quirk of history that Mendeleev and the German chemist Julius Lothar Meyer arrived at virtually the same organization simultaneously, yet independently. Mendeleev focused on chemical properties and Meyer on physical properties. The greater credit has gone to Mendeleev because he was able to *predict* the properties of several as-yet-undiscovered elements, for which he had left blank spaces in his table. Table 8.1 compares Mendeleev's predictions for germanium, which he

Table 8.1 Mendeleev's Predicted Properties of Germanium ("eka Silicon") and Its Actual Properties

Property	Predicted Properties of eka Silicon (E)	Actual Properties of Germanium (Ge)
Atomic mass	72 amu	72.61 amu
Appearance	Gray metal	Gray metal
Density	5.5 g/cm^3	5.32 g/cm^3
Molar volume	13 cm^3/mol	13.65 cm^3/mol
Specific heat capacity	0.31 J/g · K	0.32 J/g · K
Oxide formula	EO$_2$	GeO$_2$
Oxide density	4.7 g/cm^3	4.23 g/cm^3
Sulfide formula and solubility	ES$_2$; insoluble in H$_2$O; soluble in aqueous (NH$_4$)$_2$S	GeS$_2$; insoluble in H$_2$O; soluble in aqueous (NH$_4$)$_2$S
Chloride formula (boiling point)	ECl$_4$ (<100°C)	GeCl$_4$ (84°C)
Chloride density	1.9 g/cm^3	1.844 g/cm^3
Element preparation	Reduction of K$_2$EF$_6$ with sodium	Reduction of K$_2$GeF$_6$ with sodium

$\sqrt{v}$ of largest x-ray peak

Atomic number, Z

◆ Moseley and Atomic Number When a metal is bombarded with high-energy electrons, an inner electron is knocked from the atom, an outer electron moves down to fill in the space, and x-rays are emitted. In his studies of atomic line spectra, Bohr proposed that the x-ray spectrum of an element had wavelengths proportional to the nuclear charge. In 1913, stimulated by this proposal, Moseley studied the x-ray spectra of a series of metals to determine their nuclear charges. He was able to correlate the x-ray spectrum of each metal with its order in the periodic table (its *atomic number*) and realized that the nuclear charge increased by one unit for each element. A plot of Moseley's data shows the smooth correlation (*graph above*). Among other results, the findings confirmed the placement of Co ($Z = 28$) *before* Ni ($Z = 29$), despite its higher atomic mass, and the gap between Cl ($Z = 17$) and K ($Z = 19$) as the place for Ar ($Z = 18$). Tragically, Moseley died the next year as a pilot in World War I.

gave the provisional name "eka silicon" ("first under silicon"), with its actual properties.

Today's periodic table, which appears on the inside front cover of this text, resembles Mendeleev's in most details, although it includes 47 elements that were unknown in 1870. The only substantive change is that the elements are now arranged in order of *atomic number* (number of protons) rather than atomic mass. This change was based on the work of the 26-year-old British physicist Henry G. J. Moseley, who found a direct dependence between an element's nuclear charge and its position in the periodic table. ◆

8.2 Characteristics of Many-Electron Atoms

Like the Bohr model, the Schrödinger equation does not give exact solutions for many-electron atoms. However, unlike the Bohr model, the Schrödinger equation gives very good approximate solutions using modern computers. These solutions show that the atomic orbitals of many-electron atoms are *hydrogen-like*, that is, they resemble those of the H atom. This conclusion is very important because it means we can use the same quantum numbers that we used for the H atom to describe the orbitals of other atoms.

Nevertheless, the existence of more than one electron in an atom requires us to consider three features that were not relevant in the case of hydrogen: (1) the need for a fourth quantum number, (2) a limit on the number of electrons allowed in a given orbital, and (3) a more complex set of orbital energy levels. Let's examine these new features and then go on to determine the electron configuration for each element.

The Electron-Spin Quantum Number

Recall from Chapter 7 that the three quantum numbers n, l, and m_l describe the size (energy), shape, and orientation, respectively, of an atomic orbital. However, an additional quantum number is needed to describe a property of the electron itself, called *spin*, which is not a property of the orbital.

Figure 8.1 Observing the effect of electron spin. A nonuniform magnetic field, created by magnet faces with different shapes, splits a beam of hydrogen atoms in two. The split beam results from the two possible directions of each electron's spin.

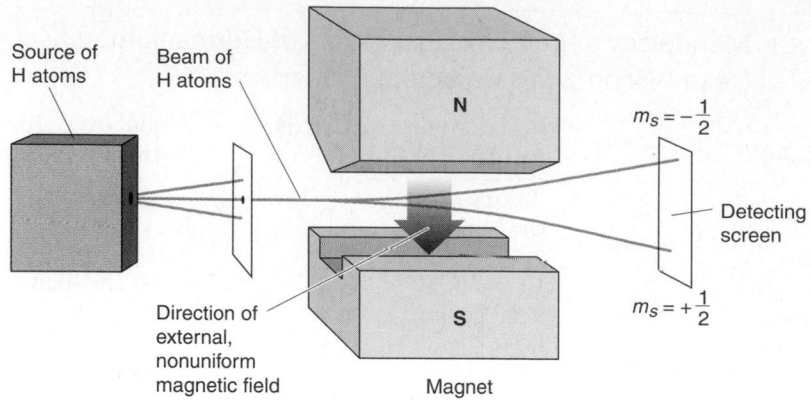

When a beam of H atoms passes through a nonuniform magnetic field, as shown in Figure 8.1, it splits into two beams that bend away from each other. The explanation of the split beam is that the electron generates a tiny magnetic field, as though it were a spinning charge. The single electron in each H atom can spin in one of two opposite directions, each of which generates a magnetic field. The opposing directions of these fields cause one half of the electrons to be attracted into the region of the large external magnetic field and the other half to be repelled; so the beam of H atoms splits.

The **spin quantum number (m_s)** indicates the direction of the electron spin about its own axis and can have one of two possible values, $+\frac{1}{2}$ or $-\frac{1}{2}$. As a result, each electron in an atom is described completely by a set of *four* quantum numbers: *the first three describe its orbital and the fourth describes its spin.* The quantum numbers are summarized in Table 8.2.

Now we can write a set of four quantum numbers for any electron in the ground state of any atom. For example, the set of quantum numbers for the lone electron in hydrogen (H; $Z = 1$) is $n = 1$, $l = 0$, $m_l = 0$, and $m_s = +\frac{1}{2}$. (The spin quantum number for this electron could just as well have been $-\frac{1}{2}$ but, by convention, we assign $+\frac{1}{2}$ for the first electron in an orbital.)

The Exclusion Principle

The element after hydrogen is helium (He; $Z = 2$), the first with atoms having more than one electron. The first electron in the He ground state has the same set of quantum numbers as the electron in the H atom, but the second He electron does not. Based on observations of the excited states of atoms, the Austrian physicist Wolfgang Pauli formulated the **exclusion principle:** *no two electrons in the same atom can have the same four quantum numbers.* That

Table 8.2 Summary of Quantum Numbers of Electrons in Atoms

Name	Symbol	Permitted Values	Property
Principal	n	Positive integers (1, 2, 3, etc.)	Orbital energy (size)
Angular momentum	l	Integers from 0 to $n - 1$	Orbital shape (The l values 0, 1, 2, and 3 correspond to s, p, d, and f orbitals, respectively.)
Magnetic	m_l	Integers from $-l$ to 0 to $+l$	Orbital orientation
Spin	m_s	$+\frac{1}{2}$ or $-\frac{1}{2}$	Direction of e$^-$ spin

is, each electron must have a unique "identity" as expressed by its set of quantum numbers. Therefore, the second He electron occupies the same orbital as the first but has an opposite spin: $n = 1$, $l = 0$, $m_l = 0$, and $m_s = -\frac{1}{2}$. ◆

Because the spin quantum number (m_s) can have only two values, the major consequence of the exclusion principle is that *an atomic orbital can hold a maximum of two electrons and they must have opposing spins.* We say that the 1s orbital in He is *filled* and that the electrons have *paired spins.* Thus, a beam of He atoms is not split in an experiment like that in Figure 8.1.

The first two electrons in the ground state of lithium (Li; $Z = 3$) have the same two sets of quantum numbers as those in He, so the 1s orbital of Li is filled. By definition, *the electrons of an atom in its ground state occupy the orbitals of lowest energy.* Therefore, with the lowest energy orbital filled, the third Li electron must go into the orbital of next-lowest energy, the 2s. The set of quantum numbers for this electron are $n = 2$, $l = 0$, $m_l = 0$, and $m_s = +\frac{1}{2}$. Recall that the $n = 2$ energy level consists of both 2s and 2p orbitals. To see why the 2s orbital is lower in energy than the 2p, we must look more closely at the energy states of many-electron atoms.

Electrostatic Effects and the Splitting of Energy Levels

In an atom with more than one electron, electrostatic effects play a major role in determining the energy states of the atom. Two effects are particularly important, and both are described by Coulomb's law (see Section 2.7):

1. When opposite charges are far apart, the energy of the system is higher (the system is less stable) than when they are close together, because the charges attract each other less strongly. (See Figure 1.3C; in this figure, as well as in the energy-level diagrams in Chapter 6, a system with higher energy is placed higher up in the diagram than one with lower energy.)

2. When a large positive charge attracts a 1− charge, the energy of the system is lower (the system is more stable) than when a small positive charge does so, because the charges attract each other more strongly.

These effects lead to a more complex set of energy states than exists in the H atom. At the end of Chapter 7, we noted that the energy state of the H atom is determined *only* by the n value of the occupied orbital: all sublevels of a given level (for example, the 2s and 2p) have the same energy. The reason is that in the H atom, the only type of electrostatic interaction is the attraction between nucleus and electron. The higher the n value, the farther from the nucleus the electron spends its time, so the higher the energy state.

On the other hand, the energy states of many-electron atoms arise from two types of interactions: nucleus-electron attractions *and* electron-electron repulsions. One major consequence is the *splitting* of energy levels into sublevels of differing energies: *the energy of an orbital in a many-electron atom depends primarily on its n value (size) and secondarily on its l value (shape).* Evidence for the splitting of energy levels is seen in the complex line spectra of many-electron atoms. Figure 8.2 shows that even though helium has only one more electron than hydrogen, it displays many more spectral lines, indicating more available orbital energies.

◆ **Baseball Quantum Numbers** The unique set of quantum numbers that describes an electron is analogous to the unique location of a box seat at a baseball game. The stadium (atom) is divided into section (n, level), box (l, sublevel), row (m_l, orbital), and seat (m_s, spin). Only one person (electron) can have this particular set of stadium "quantum numbers."

Figure 8.2 Spectral evidence of energy-level splitting in many-electron atoms. More spectral lines for He than for H indicate more available orbital energies. This evidence is consistent with energy levels splitting into sublevels in many-electron atoms.

| A Nuclear charge | B Shielding | C Inner electron shielding | D Penetration |

Figure 8.3 **Electrostatic effects and orbital energies.** In each of the energy diagrams shown, similar atomic systems are compared to see the effect of one variable on orbital energies and the resulting ease of electron removal. (The axes are not drawn to scale and cannot be compared with each other.) **A,** The stronger attraction (*thicker arrows*) of the higher nuclear charge makes an electron more difficult to remove. **B,** Because of repulsions, elec-trons shield each other from the nuclear charge, making an electron easier to remove. **C,** Inner electron shielding makes an outer elec-tron much easier to remove. **D,** Radial probability distributions show that a 2s electron spends most of its time slightly farther from the nucleus than a 2p electron but penetrates near the nucleus for a small fraction of the time. Thus, the 2s electron experiences a greater *overall* attraction and is slightly more difficult to remove.

To uncover the cause of energy-level splitting, chemists measure the energy required to remove an electron from a given orbital in an atom (expressed as the removal of 1 mol of electrons from 1 mol of atoms). Recall that, by definition, an atom's energy has a negative value. An electron in a more stable (lower energy) orbital is more difficult to remove than an elec-tron in a less stable (higher energy) orbital. The more stable an orbital, the lower its energy, which is expressed with a *larger negative number.*

Let's compare several atomic systems to see how the orbital energy is affected by the (1) nuclear charge, (2) electron repulsions, and (3) orbital shape:

1. *The effect of nuclear charge (Z) on orbital energy.* To see the effect of nuclear charge, we compare two atomic systems with the same number of electrons in the same orbital, but with different nuclei. The H atom ($Z = 1$) and the He^+ ion ($Z = 2$) each have one electron in their 1s orbital, but the He^+ ion has a 2+ nuclear charge (Figure 8.3A). The orbital energies are

$$E \text{ of } 1s \text{ in } He^+ = -5250 \text{ kJ/mol} \quad \text{and} \quad E \text{ of } 1s \text{ in } H = -1311 \text{ kJ/mol}$$

The He^+ electron is attracted more strongly, which makes it harder to remove and makes its orbital more stable (lower in energy, larger negative number). Thus, *higher nuclear charge (Z) lowers orbital energy by increasing nucleus-electron attractions.*

2. *The effect of electron repulsions on orbital energy: the shielding effect.* Let's con-sider separately the effect of additional electrons in the same orbital and in inner orbitals.

- *Additional electron in the same orbital.* To see the effect of an additional elec-tron in the same orbital, we compare two atomic systems with the same nuclear charge, one with two electrons in a given orbital and the other with one electron. The 1s orbital in the He atom has two electrons, whereas the $1s$ orbital in the He^+ ion has only one (Figure 8.3B). The orbital energies are

$$E \text{ of } 1s \text{ in } He^+ = -5250 \text{ kJ/mol} \quad \text{and} \quad E \text{ of } 1s \text{ in } He = -2372 \text{ kJ/mol}$$

The two electrons in He repel each other, which makes the He $1s$ orbital less stable (higher energy, smaller negative number). Therefore, *an additional electron raises the orbital energy because of electron-electron repulsions.* The repulsions have the effect of lowering the nuclear attractions such that each electron feels a weaker nuclear charge than it would if the other electron were not present. It is almost as if each electron "shields" or "screens" the other somewhat from the full nuclear charge, and chemists use these terms to explain the data. **Shielding** (or *screening*) reduces the nuclear charge to an **effective nuclear charge (Z_{eff}),** *the nuclear charge an electron actually experiences.* Thus, *shielding makes the electron easier to remove.*

- *Additional electrons in inner orbitals.* To see the effect of additional electrons in inner orbitals, we compare two atomic systems with the same nuclear charge and a single electron in an outer orbital, one with inner electrons and the other without. The ground-state Li atom ($Z = 3$) has two inner ($1s$) electrons and one outer ($2s$) electron, whereas the first excited state of the Li^{2+} ion has only one electron (Figure 8.3C). The $2s$ orbital energies in Li^{2+} and in Li are

$$E \text{ of } 2s \text{ in } Li^{2+} = -2954 \text{ kJ/mol} \quad \text{and} \quad E \text{ of } 2s \text{ in } Li = -520 \text{ kJ/mol}$$

Since the inner electrons spend most of their time *between* the outer electron and the nucleus, they prevent the $2s$ electron from feeling the full nuclear attraction, which makes the electron much easier to remove. *Inner electrons shield outer electrons more effectively than do electrons in the same sublevel.*

3. *The effect of orbital shape (l value) on orbital energy: the penetration effect.* To see the effect of orbital shape, we compare two atomic systems that are identical except that electrons occupy orbitals with different *l* values. In addition to the filled $1s$ orbital, the Li atom in its ground state has an electron in the $2s$ orbital. In the first excited state of Li, this electron occupies a $2p$ orbital. The orbital energies are

$$E \text{ of } 2s \text{ in } Li = -520 \text{ kJ/mol} \quad \text{and} \quad E \text{ of } 2p \text{ in } Li = -341 \text{ kJ/mol}$$

Let's see why the $2s$ orbital is more stable. As the graph in Figure 8.3D shows, a $2s$ electron is, on average, slightly farther from the nucleus than a $2p$ electron. Therefore, we might expect the $2s$ electron to be easier to remove. But note that a small portion of the $2s$ radial probability distribution appears very near the nucleus. Chemists say that the $2s$ electron spends part of its time "penetrating" very close to the nucleus. **Penetration** by the $2s$ electron increases its overall attraction to the nucleus and allows it to shield the $2p$ electron somewhat more effectively. As a result, the $2p$ electron is easier to remove than the $2s$.

In general, *differences in radial probability distribution (orbital shape) lead to differences in penetration, which affect shielding.* These factors cause an energy level to split into sublevels. Radial probability distribution plots show that the lower the *l* value of an orbital, the more its electrons penetrate, and so the greater their attraction to the nucleus. Therefore, *for a given n value, the lower the l value is, the lower (more negative) the sublevel energy:*

$$\text{Order of sublevel energies:} \quad s < p < d < f$$

Figure 8.4 shows the general energy order in which levels and sublevels are filled with electrons. Note how a given energy level (*n* value) is split into several sublevels (*l* values) of differing energy. Next, we use this order to fill orbitals with electrons and construct a periodic table of ground-state atoms.

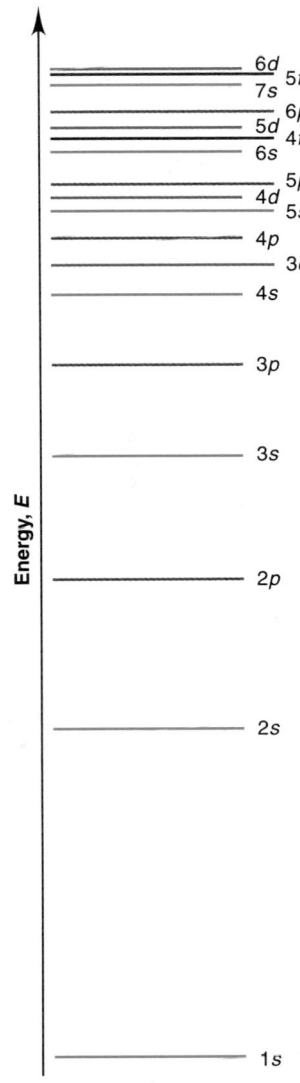

Figure 8.4 Order for filling energy sublevels with electrons. For filling many-electron atoms, the relative energies of sublevels increase with principal quantum number n ($1 < 2 < 3$, etc.) and angular momentum quantum number l ($s < p < d < f$). Note also that as n increases, the sublevel energies become closer together. The penetration effect, together with this narrowing of energy differences, results in the overlap of some sublevels; for example, the $4s$ sublevel is slightly lower in energy than the $3d$, so it is filled first. (The lines are color coded by sublevel type and have different lengths only for ease in labeling.)

Specifying electrons in many-electron atoms requires four quantum numbers: three (n, l, m_l) describe the orbitals, and a fourth (m_s) describes electron spin. The Pauli exclusion principle requires that each electron have a unique set of four quantum numbers; therefore, an orbital can hold no more than two electrons, and their spins must be paired (opposite). Electrostatic interactions determine orbital energies:

1. Greater nuclear charge lowers orbital energy and makes electrons harder to remove.
2. Electron-electron repulsions raise orbital energy and make electrons easier to remove. Repulsions have the effect of *shielding* electrons from the full nuclear charge, reducing it to an effective nuclear charge, Z_{eff}. Inner electrons shield outer electrons most effectively.
3. Greater radial probability distribution near the nucleus (greater penetration) makes the electron harder to remove because it is attracted more strongly and shielded less effectively. As a result, an energy level (shell) is split into sublevels (subshells) with the energy order $s < p < d < f$.

8.3 The Quantum-Mechanical Model and the Periodic Table

Quantum mechanics provides the theoretical foundation for the experimentally based periodic table. In this section, we fill the table with elements and determine their electron configurations—the distributions of electrons within their atoms' orbitals. Note especially the *recurring pattern in electron configurations, which is the basis for the recurring pattern in element behavior.*

Building Up Periods 1 and 2

A useful way to determine the electron configurations of the elements is to start at the beginning of the periodic table and add one electron per element to the *lowest energy orbital available*. (Of course, one proton and one or more neutrons are also added to the nucleus.) This approach is called the **aufbau principle** (German *aufbauen*, "to build up"), and it results in *ground-state* electron configurations. Let's use this method to assign sets of quantum numbers to the electrons in the ground state of the first 10 elements, those in the first two periods (horizontal rows).

For the electron in H, as you've seen, the set is

$$\text{H } (Z = 1): \quad n = 1, \, l = 0, \, m_l = 0, \, m_s = +\tfrac{1}{2}$$

You also saw that the first electron in He has the same set as the electron in H, but the second He electron has opposing spin (exclusion principle):

$$\text{He } (Z = 2): \quad n = 1, \, l = 0, \, m_l = 0, \, m_s = -\tfrac{1}{2}$$

When we present an element and its atomic number (Z) in this discussion, the quantum numbers that follow refer to the element's *last added* electron. [Of course, an atom is neutral, so the number of protons (Z) equals the *total* number of electrons.]

Before proceeding, let's look at two common ways to show the orbital occupancy:

- *The electron configuration.* This shorthand notation consists of the principal energy level (n value), the letter designation of the sublevel (l value), and the number of electrons (#) in the sublevel, written as a superscript: ***nl**$^\#$*. The electron configuration of H is $1s^1$ (spoken "one-ess-one"); that of He is $1s^2$ (spoken "one-ess-two," *not* "one-ess-squared"). This notation does *not* indicate electron spin but assumes you know that the two electrons in the $1s$ orbital have paired (opposite) spins.

- *The orbital diagram.* An **orbital diagram** consists of a box (or circle, or just a line) for each orbital available in a given energy level, grouped by sublevel, with an arrow indicating the electron's presence *and* its direction of spin. (Traditionally, ↑ is $+\frac{1}{2}$ and ↓ is $-\frac{1}{2}$, but these are arbitrary, so it is necessary only to be consistent. Throughout the text, orbital occupancy is also indicated by color intensity: an orbital with no color is empty, pale color is half-filled, and full color is filled.) The orbital diagrams for the first two elements are

H ↑   He ↑↓
1s   1s

The exclusion principle tells us that an orbital can hold only two electrons, so the 1s orbital in He is filled, and the $n = 1$ level is also filled. The $n = 2$ level is filled next, beginning with the 2s orbital, the next lowest in energy. As we said earlier, the first two electrons in Li fill the 1s orbital, and the last added Li electron is $n = 2$, $l = 0$, $m_l = 0$, $m_s = +\frac{1}{2}$. The electron configuration for Li is $1s^2 2s^1$. Note that the orbital diagram shows all the orbitals in $n = 2$, whether or not they are occupied:

Li ↑↓   ↑
1s   2s   2p

Figure 8.5 A vertical orbital diagram for the Li ground state. Sublevel energy increases from bottom to top.

Keep in mind that the energy of each sublevel (each group of boxes) increases from left to right. Figure 8.5 emphasizes this energy order by arranging the sublevels vertically.

Since the 2s orbital is only half-filled in Li, the fourth electron of beryllium fills it with its spin paired: $n = 2$, $l = 0$, $m_l = 0$, $m_s = -\frac{1}{2}$.

Be ($Z = 4$) $1s^2 2s^2$

↑↓   ↑↓
1s   2s   2p

The next lowest energy sublevel is the 2p. A p sublevel has $l = 1$, so the m_l (orientation) values can be -1, 0, or $+1$. The three orbitals in the 2p sublevel have *equal energy* (same n and l values), which means that the fifth electron of boron can go into *any one of the 2p orbitals.* For convenience, let's label the boxes from left to right, -1, 0, $+1$. By convention, we place the electron in the $m_l = -1$ orbital: $n = 2$, $l = 1$, $m_l = -1$, $m_s = +\frac{1}{2}$.

B ($Z = 5$) $1s^2 2s^2 2p^1$
              -1 0 $+1$

↑↓   ↑↓   ↑
1s   2s   2p

To minimize electron-electron repulsions, the last added (sixth) electron of carbon enters one of the *unoccupied* 2p orbitals; by convention, we place it in the $m_l = 0$ orbital. Experiment shows that the spin of this electron is *parallel to* (in the same direction as) the spin of the other 2p electron: $n = 2$, $l = 1$, $m_l = 0$, $m_s = +\frac{1}{2}$.

C ($Z = 6$) $1s^2 2s^2 2p^2$

↑↓   ↑↓   ↑ ↑
1s   2s   2p

The placement of electrons for carbon exemplifies **Hund's rule:** *when orbitals of equal energy are available, the electron configuration of lowest energy has the maximum number of unpaired electrons with parallel spins.* Based on Hund's rule, nitrogen's seventh electron enters the last empty $2p$ orbital, with its spin parallel to the two other $2p$ electrons: $n = 2$, $l = 1$, $m_l = +1$, $m_s = +\frac{1}{2}$.

N ($Z = 7$) $1s^2 2s^2 2p^3$

↑↓	↑↓	↑	↑	↑
$1s$	$2s$		$2p$	

The eighth electron in oxygen must enter one of these three half-filled $2p$ orbitals and "pair up" with (have opposing spin to) the electron already present. Since the $2p$ orbitals all have the same energy, we proceed as before and place the electron in the orbital previously designated $m_l = -1$. The quantum numbers are $n = 2$, $l = 1$, $m_l = -1$, $m_s = -\frac{1}{2}$.

O ($Z = 8$) $1s^2 2s^2 2p^4$

↑↓	↑↓	↑↓	↑	↑
$1s$	$2s$		$2p$	

Fluorine's ninth electron enters either of the two remaining half-filled $2p$ orbitals: $n = 2$, $l = 1$, $m_l = 0$, $m_s = -\frac{1}{2}$.

F ($Z = 9$) $1s^2 2s^2 2p^5$

↑↓	↑↓	↑↓	↑↓	↑
$1s$	$2s$		$2p$	

Only one unfilled orbital remains in the $2p$ sublevel, so the tenth electron of neon occupies it: $n = 2$, $l = 1$, $m_l = +1$, $m_s = -\frac{1}{2}$. With neon, the $n = 2$ level is filled.

Ne ($Z = 10$) $1s^2 2s^2 2p^6$

↑↓	↑↓	↑↓	↑↓	↑↓
$1s$	$2s$		$2p$	

Sample Problem 8.1   Determining Quantum Numbers from Orbital Diagrams

PROBLEM Write a set of quantum numbers for the third and eighth electrons added to F.

PLAN Based on the orbital diagram, we count to the electron of interest and note its level (n), sublevel (l), orbital (m_l), and direction of spin (m_s).

SOLUTION The third electron is in the $2s$ orbital. The upward arrow indicates a spin of $+\frac{1}{2}$:

$$n = 2, l = 0, m_l = 0, m_s = +\frac{1}{2}$$

The eighth electron is in the first $2p$ orbital, which is designated $m_l = -1$, and has a downward arrow:

$$n = 2, l = 1, m_l = -1, m_s = -\frac{1}{2}$$

Follow-up Problem 8.1   Use the periodic table to identify the element with the electron configuration $1s^2 2s^2 2p^4$. Write its orbital diagram and give the quantum numbers of its sixth electron.

With so much attention paid to these notations, it's easy to forget that atoms are real spherical objects and that the electrons occupy volumes with specific shapes and orientations. Figure 8.6 shows the first 10 elements arranged in the periodic table format, with orbital contours depicted. Even at this early stage of filling the table, we can see an important correlation between chemical behavior and electron configuration. Helium and neon are in the same group and have similar electron configurations in that both have filled outer shells: $n = 1$ for He and $n = 2$ for Ne. Interestingly, neither element forms compounds. Apparently, *filled shells make these elements unreactive.*

Figure 8.6 Orbital occupancy for the first 10 elements, H through Ne. The first 10 elements are arranged in periodic table format with each box showing atomic number, atomic symbol, ground-state electron configuration, and a depiction of the atom based on the probability contours of its orbitals. Orbital occupancy is shown with shading: lighter color indicates half-filled (one e^-) orbitals, and darker color means filled (two e^-) orbitals. For clarity, only the outer region of the 2s orbital is included.

1A(1)							8A(18)
1 **H** $1s^1$							2 **He** $1s^2$

	2A(2)	3A(13)	4A(14)	5A(15)	6A(16)	7A(17)	
3 **Li** $1s^22s^1$	4 **Be** $1s^22s^2$	5 **B** $1s^22s^22p^1$	6 **C** $1s^22s^22p^2$	7 **N** $1s^22s^22p^3$	8 **O** $1s^22s^22p^4$	9 **F** $1s^22s^22p^5$	10 **Ne** $1s^22s^22p^6$

Building Up Period 3

The Period 3 elements, sodium through argon, lie directly under the Period 2 elements, lithium through neon. As the orbitals become filled, note the *group similarities in outer electron configuration.* The sublevels of the $n = 3$ level are filled in the order 3s, 3p, 3d. Table 8.3 presents *partial* orbital diagrams (3s and 3p sublevels only) and electron configurations for the eight elements in Period 3 (with *filled inner levels* in brackets and the sublevel to which the last electron is added in colored type).

In sodium (the second alkali metal) and magnesium (the second alkaline earth metal), electrons are added to the 3s sublevel, which contains the 3s orbital only, just as they filled the 2s sublevel in lithium and beryllium above. Then, just as in boron, carbon, and nitrogen in Period 2, the last electron added to aluminum, silicon, and phosphorus in Period 3 just below half-fills each of the 3p orbitals with spins parallel (Hund's rule). The last electrons added to sulfur, chlorine, and argon enter each of the half-filled 3p orbitals, thereby filling the 3p sublevel. With argon, the next noble gas after helium and neon, we arrive at the end of Period 3. (As you'll see shortly, the 3d orbitals are filled in Period 4.)

The rightmost column of Table 8.3 shows the *condensed electron configuration.* In this simplified notation, the electron configuration of the previous noble gas is represented by its element symbol in brackets, and it is followed by the electron configuration of the energy level being filled. The condensed electron configuration of oxygen, for example, is [He] $2s^22p^4$, where [He] represents $1s^2$; for sodium, the condensed electron configuration is [Ne] $3s^1$, where [Ne] stands for $1s^22s^22p^6$ (as Table 8.3 shows); and so forth.

Table 8.3 Partial Orbital Diagrams and Electron Configurations* for the Elements in Period 3

Atomic Number/ Element	Partial Orbital Diagram (3s and 3p Sublevels Only)		Full Electron Configuration	Condensed Electron Configuration
	3s	3p		
11/Na	↑	☐ ☐ ☐	$[1s^22s^22p^6]\ 3s^1$	[Ne] $3s^1$
12/Mg	↑↓	☐ ☐ ☐	$[1s^22s^22p^6]\ 3s^2$	[Ne] $3s^2$
13/Al	↑↓	↑ ☐ ☐	$[1s^22s^22p^6]\ 3s^23p^1$	[Ne] $3s^23p^1$
14/Si	↑↓	↑ ↑ ☐	$[1s^22s^22p^6]\ 3s^23p^2$	[Ne] $3s^23p^2$
15/P	↑↓	↑ ↑ ↑	$[1s^22s^22p^6]\ 3s^23p^3$	[Ne] $3s^23p^3$
16/S	↑↓	↑↓ ↑ ↑	$[1s^22s^22p^6]\ 3s^23p^4$	[Ne] $3s^23p^4$
17/Cl	↑↓	↑↓ ↑↓ ↑	$[1s^22s^22p^6]\ 3s^23p^5$	[Ne] $3s^23p^5$
18/Ar	↑↓	↑↓ ↑↓ ↑↓	$[1s^22s^22p^6]\ 3s^23p^6$	[Ne] $3s^23p^6$

*Colored type indicates sublevel to which last electron is added.

Figure 8.7 Condensed ground-state electron configurations in the first three periods. The first 18 elements, H through Ar, are arranged in three periods containing two, eight, and eight elements. Each box shows the atomic number, atomic symbol, and condensed ground-state electron configuration. Note that elements in a group have similar outer electron configurations (color).

	1A (1)	2A (2)	3A (13)	4A (14)	5A (15)	6A (16)	7A (17)	8A (18)
1	1 **H** $1s^1$							2 **He** $1s^2$
2	3 **Li** [He] $2s^1$	4 **Be** [He] $2s^2$	5 **B** [He] $2s^22p^1$	6 **C** [He] $2s^22p^2$	7 **N** [He] $2s^22p^3$	8 **O** [He] $2s^22p^4$	9 **F** [He] $2s^22p^5$	10 **Ne** [He] $2s^22p^6$
3	11 **Na** [Ne] $3s^1$	12 **Mg** [Ne] $3s^2$	13 **Al** [Ne] $3s^23p^1$	14 **Si** [Ne] $3s^23p^2$	15 **P** [Ne] $3s^23p^3$	16 **S** [Ne] $3s^23p^4$	17 **Cl** [Ne] $3s^23p^5$	18 **Ar** [Ne] $3s^23p^6$

(Period)

Electron Configurations Within Groups

One of the central points in all chemistry is that *similar outer electron configurations correlate with similar chemical behavior*. Figure 8.7 shows the condensed electron configurations of the first 18 elements. Note the similarities within each group. Here are some examples from just two groups:

- In Group 1A(1), lithium and sodium have the condensed electron configuration [noble gas] ns^1 (where n is the quantum number of the outermost energy level), as do all the other alkali metals (K, Rb, Cs, Fr). All are highly reactive metals that form ionic compounds with nonmetals with formulas such as MCl, M_2O, and M_2S (where M represents the alkali metal), and all react vigorously with water to displace H_2 (Figure 8.8A).
- In Group 7A(17), fluorine and chlorine have the condensed electron configuration [noble gas] ns^2np^5, as do the other halogens (Br, I, At). Little is known about rare, radioactive astatine (At), but all the others are reactive nonmetals that occur as diatomic molecules, X_2 (where X represents the halogen). All form ionic compounds with metals (KX, MgX_2) (Figure 8.8B), covalent compounds with hydrogen (HX) that yield acidic solutions in water, and covalent compounds with carbon (CX_4).

Restating the general theme that appears throughout the periodic table: *within a group, similarities in chemical behavior reflect similarities in the distribution of electrons in the highest energy orbitals* (outer electron configuration). Indeed, similarities in chemical behavior guided Mendeleev to place elements in vertical columns. Thus, two major connections between quantum mechanics and chemical periodicity are

- The recurrence of similar electron configurations is a natural consequence of the fact that *orbital filling occurs in order of increasing energy.*
- *Properties recur periodically because electron configurations recur periodically.*

A

B

Figure 8.8 Similar reactivities within a group. A, Potassium metal reacting. All alkali metals [Group 1A(1)] react vigorously with water and displace H_2. **B,** Chlorine and potassium metal reacting. All halogens [Group 7A(17)] react with metals to form ionic halides.

The First *d*-Orbital Transition Series; Building Up Period 4

The 3*d* orbitals are filled in Period 4. Note, however, that *the 4s orbital is filled before the 3d.* This switch in filling order is due to the shielding and penetration effects that we discussed in Section 8.2. The radial probability distribution of the 3*d* orbital is greater outside the filled inner $n = 1$ and $n = 2$ levels, so an electron in it is very effectively shielded from the nuclear charge. On the other hand, penetration by the 4*s* orbital means that an electron in it spends a significant part of its time near the nucleus and feels a greater nuclear attraction. Thus, the 4*s* orbital is slightly *lower* in energy than the 3*d*; as a result, the 4*s* fills first. For similar reasons, the 5*s* orbital fills before the 4*d*, and the 6*s* fills before the 5*d*. In general, then, *the ns sublevel fills before the (n − 1)d sublevel.* As we proceed through the transition series, however, you will see several exceptions to this pattern because the energies of the *ns* and (n − 1)d sublevels become extremely close with higher values of *n*.

Table 8.4 shows the partial orbital diagrams and ground-state electron configurations for the 18 elements in Period 4 (again with filled inner levels in

Table 8.4 Partial Orbital Diagrams and Electron Configurations* for the Elements in Period 4

Atomic Number	Element	Partial Orbital Diagram (4s, 3d, and 4p Sublevels Only)	Full Electron Configuration	Condensed Electron Configuration
19	K	4s [↑] 3d [ ][ ][ ][ ][ ] 4p [ ][ ][ ]	$[1s^22s^22p^63s^23p^6]\,4s^1$	$[\text{Ar}]\,4s^1$
20	Ca	4s [↑↓] 3d [ ][ ][ ][ ][ ] 4p [ ][ ][ ]	$[1s^22s^22p^63s^23p^6]\,4s^2$	$[\text{Ar}]\,4s^2$
21	Sc	4s [↑↓] 3d [↑][ ][ ][ ][ ] 4p [ ][ ][ ]	$[1s^22s^22p^63s^23p^6]\,4s^23d^1$	$[\text{Ar}]\,4s^23d^1$
22	Ti	4s [↑↓] 3d [↑][↑][ ][ ][ ] 4p [ ][ ][ ]	$[1s^22s^22p^63s^23p^6]\,4s^23d^2$	$[\text{Ar}]\,4s^23d^2$
23	V	4s [↑↓] 3d [↑][↑][↑][ ][ ] 4p [ ][ ][ ]	$[1s^22s^22p^63s^23p^6]\,4s^23d^3$	$[\text{Ar}]\,4s^23d^3$
24	Cr	4s [↑] 3d [↑][↑][↑][↑][↑] 4p [ ][ ][ ]	$[1s^22s^22p^63s^23p^6]\,4s^13d^5$	$[\text{Ar}]\,4s^13d^5$
25	Mn	4s [↑↓] 3d [↑][↑][↑][↑][↑] 4p [ ][ ][ ]	$[1s^22s^22p^63s^23p^6]\,4s^23d^5$	$[\text{Ar}]\,4s^23d^5$
26	Fe	4s [↑↓] 3d [↑↓][↑][↑][↑][↑] 4p [ ][ ][ ]	$[1s^22s^22p^63s^23p^6]\,4s^23d^6$	$[\text{Ar}]\,4s^23d^6$
27	Co	4s [↑↓] 3d [↑↓][↑↓][↑][↑][↑] 4p [ ][ ][ ]	$[1s^22s^22p^63s^23p^6]\,4s^23d^7$	$[\text{Ar}]\,4s^23d^7$
28	Ni	4s [↑↓] 3d [↑↓][↑↓][↑↓][↑][↑] 4p [ ][ ][ ]	$[1s^22s^22p^63s^23p^6]\,4s^23d^8$	$[\text{Ar}]\,4s^23d^8$
29	Cu	4s [↑] 3d [↑↓][↑↓][↑↓][↑↓][↑↓] 4p [ ][ ][ ]	$[1s^22s^22p^63s^23p^6]\,4s^13d^{10}$	$[\text{Ar}]\,4s^13d^{10}$
30	Zn	4s [↑↓] 3d [↑↓][↑↓][↑↓][↑↓][↑↓] 4p [ ][ ][ ]	$[1s^22s^22p^63s^23p^6]\,4s^23d^{10}$	$[\text{Ar}]\,4s^23d^{10}$
31	Ga	4s [↑↓] 3d [↑↓][↑↓][↑↓][↑↓][↑↓] 4p [↑][ ][ ]	$[1s^22s^22p^63s^23p^6]\,4s^23d^{10}4p^1$	$[\text{Ar}]\,4s^23d^{10}4p^1$
32	Ge	4s [↑↓] 3d [↑↓][↑↓][↑↓][↑↓][↑↓] 4p [↑][↑][ ]	$[1s^22s^22p^63s^23p^6]\,4s^23d^{10}4p^2$	$[\text{Ar}]\,4s^23d^{10}4p^2$
33	As	4s [↑↓] 3d [↑↓][↑↓][↑↓][↑↓][↑↓] 4p [↑][↑][↑]	$[1s^22s^22p^63s^23p^6]\,4s^23d^{10}4p^3$	$[\text{Ar}]\,4s^23d^{10}4p^3$
34	Se	4s [↑↓] 3d [↑↓][↑↓][↑↓][↑↓][↑↓] 4p [↑↓][↑][↑]	$[1s^22s^22p^63s^23p^6]\,4s^23d^{10}4p^4$	$[\text{Ar}]\,4s^23d^{10}4p^4$
35	Br	4s [↑↓] 3d [↑↓][↑↓][↑↓][↑↓][↑↓] 4p [↑↓][↑↓][↑]	$[1s^22s^22p^63s^23p^6]\,4s^23d^{10}4p^5$	$[\text{Ar}]\,4s^23d^{10}4p^5$
36	Kr	4s [↑↓] 3d [↑↓][↑↓][↑↓][↑↓][↑↓] 4p [↑↓][↑↓][↑↓]	$[1s^22s^22p^63s^23p^6]\,4s^23d^{10}4p^6$	$[\text{Ar}]\,4s^23d^{10}4p^6$

*Colored type indicates sublevel(s) whose occupancy changes when last electron is added.

brackets and the sublevel involved with the last electron being added in colored type). The first two elements of the period, potassium and calcium, are the next alkali and alkaline earth metals, respectively, and their electrons fill the 4s sublevel. The third element, scandium ($Z = 21$), is the first of the **transition elements,** those in which d orbitals are being filled. The last electron in scandium occupies one of the five 3d orbitals, which are equal in energy. Scandium has the electron configuration $[\text{Ar}]\,4s^23d^1$.

The filling of the 3d orbitals proceeds one at a time, as you saw with the p orbitals, except in two cases: chromium ($Z = 24$) and copper ($Z = 29$). Note that vanadium ($Z = 23$), the element before chromium, has three half-filled d orbitals ($[\text{Ar}]\,4s^23d^3$). Rather than chromium's last electron just entering a fourth empty d orbital to give $[\text{Ar}]\,4s^23d^4$, the element has one electron in the 4s sublevel and five in the 3d sublevel. Thus, in chromium, both the 4s and the 3d sublevels are *half-filled* (see margin).

Cr ($Z = 24$) $[\text{Ar}]\,4s^13d^5$

4s [↑]   3d [↑][↑][↑][↑][↑]   4p [ ][ ][ ]

Cu (Z = 29) [Ar] $4s^1 3d^{10}$

↑		↑↓	↑↓	↑↓	↑↓	↑↓				

4s   3d   4p

The other unexpected filling pattern occurs with copper, but it conforms to the pattern in chromium. Following nickel ([Ar] $4s^2 3d^8$), we would expect copper to have the [Ar] $4s^2 3d^9$ configuration. Instead, the 4s orbital of copper is half-filled (1 electron), and the 3d orbitals are *filled* with 10 electrons (see margin).

The unusual filling patterns in Cr and Cu lead us to conclude that *half-filled and filled sublevels are unexpectedly stable*. These are the first two cases of a pattern seen with many other elements.

In zinc, both the 4s and 3d sublevels are completely filled, and the first transition series ends. As Table 8.4 shows, the 4p sublevel is then filled by the next six elements. Period 4 ends with krypton, the next noble gas.

General Principles of Electron Configurations

There are 76 known elements beyond the 36 we have considered. Let's examine the ground-state electron configurations to highlight some key ideas.

Similar Outer Electron Configurations Within a Group To repeat one of chemistry's central themes and the key to the usefulness of the periodic table, *elements in a group have similar chemical properties because they have similar outer electron configurations* (Figure 8.9). Among the main-group elements (A

Figure 8.9 A periodic table of partial ground-state electron configurations. These ground-state electron configurations show the electrons beyond the previous noble gas in the sublevel block being filled (excluding filled inner sublevels). For the main-group elements, the group heading identifies the general outer configuration. Unexpected electron configurations occur often among the d-block and f-block elements, the first two appearing for Cr (Z = 24) and Cu (Z = 29), as discussed in the text. Helium is colored as an s-block element but placed with the other members of Group 8A(18).

A

Figure 8.10 **Relation between orbital filling and the periodic table.** If we "read" the periods like the words on a page, the elements are arranged into sublevel blocks that occur in the sequence of increasing energy. **A,** A long form of the periodic table, with sublevel blocks shown. (The *f* blocks fit between the first and second elements of the *d* blocks in Periods 6 and 7.) **B,** A simple version of the sublevel order.

groups)—the *s*-block and *p*-block elements—outer electron configurations within a group are essentially identical, as shown by the group headings in Figure 8.9. Some variations in the transition elements (B groups, *d* block) and inner transition elements (*f* block) occur, as you'll see.

Orbital Filling Order When the elements are "built up" by filling their levels and sublevels in order of increasing energy, we obtain the actual sequence of elements in the periodic table. Thus, reading the table from left to right, as you do words on a page, gives the energy order of levels and sublevels, which is shown in Figure 8.10. The arrangement of the periodic table is certainly the best way to learn the orbital filling order of the elements. ◆

Categories of Electrons A survey of the periodic table distinguishes three categories of electrons:
1. **Inner (core) electrons** are those in the previous noble gas and any completed transition series. They fill all the *lower energy levels* of an atom.
2. **Outer electrons** are those in the *highest energy level* (highest *n* value). They spend most of their time farthest from the nucleus.
3. **Valence electrons** are those involved in forming compounds. *Among the main-group elements, the valence electrons **are** the outer electrons.* Among the transition elements, some inner *d* electrons are also often involved in bonding and are counted among the valence electrons.

Group and Period Numbers Several key pieces of information are embedded in the periodic table:
1. Among the main-group elements (A groups), *the group number equals the number of outer electrons* (those with highest *n*). For example, chlorine (Cl; Period 3, Group **7**A) has 7 outer electrons, tellurium (Te; Period 5, Group **6**A) has 6, and so forth.
2. *The period number is the n value of the highest energy level.* Thus, in Period 2, the $n = 2$ level has the highest energy; in Period 5, it is the $n = 5$ level.
3. The *n* value squared (n^2) gives the total number of *orbitals* in that energy level. Since an orbital can hold no more than two electrons (exclusion principle), $2n^2$ gives the maximum number of *electrons* (or elements) in the energy level. For example, for the $n = 3$ level, the number of orbitals is $n^2 = 9$: one 3*s*, three 3*p*, and five 3*d*. The number of electrons is $2n^2$, or 18: two 3*s* and six 3*p* electrons occur in the eight elements of Period 3, and ten 3*d* electrons are added in the ten transition elements of Period 4.

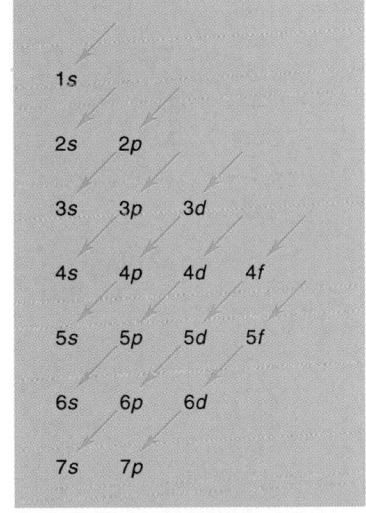

◆ **Periodic Memory Aids** If a periodic table is unavailable, this arrangement of sublevels can remind you of the filling order. List the sublevels as shown, and then read from 1*s*, following the direction of the arrows. Note that
- the values of *n* are constant horizontally
- the values of *l* are constant vertically
- the combined values of *n* + *l* are constant diagonally

Complex Patterns: The Transition and Inner Transition Elements

Periods 4, 5, 6, and 7 incorporate the *d*-orbital transition elements. The general pattern, as you've seen, is that the $(n - 1)d$ orbitals are filled between the *ns* and *np* orbitals. Thus, Period 5 follows the same general pattern as Period 4. In Period 6, the 6*s* sublevel is filled in cesium (Cs) and barium (Ba), and then lanthanum (La; $Z = 57$), the first member of the 5*d* transition series, occurs. At this point, the first series of **inner transition elements,** those in which *f* orbitals are being filled, intervenes (Figure 8.10). The *f* orbitals have $l = 3$, so the possible m_l values are −3, −2, −1, 0, +1, +2, and +3; that is, there are seven *f* orbitals, for a total of 14 elements in *each* of the two inner transition series.

The Period 6 inner transition series fills the 4*f* orbitals and consists of the **lanthanides** (or **rare earths**), so called because they occur after and are similar to lanthanum. The other inner transition series holds the **actinides,** which fill the 5*f* orbitals that appear in Period 7 after actinium (Ac; $Z = 89$). In both series, the $(n - 2)f$ orbitals are filled, after which the $(n - 1)d$ orbital filling proceeds. Period 6 ends by filling the 6*p* orbitals in the same way as other *p*-block elements. Period 7 is incomplete because no element with 7*p* electrons is known at this time.

Several irregularities in filling pattern occur in both the *d* and *f* series. Two already mentioned occur in chromium (Cr) and copper (Cu) in Period 4. Silver (Ag) and gold (Au), the two elements under Cu in Group 1B(11), follow copper's pattern. Molybdenum (Mo) follows the pattern of Cr in Group 6B(6), but tungsten (W) does not. Other unexpected configurations appear among the transition elements in Periods 5 and 6. Note, however, that even though minor variations from the expected configurations occur, the sum of *ns* electrons and $(n - 1)d$ electrons *always* equals the *new* group number. For instance, despite variations in the electron configurations in Group 6B(**6**)—Cr, Mo, W, and Sg—the sum of *ns* and $(n - 1)d$ electrons is 6; in Group 8B(**10**)—Ni, Pd, and Pt—the sum is 10.

Whenever our observations differ from our expectations, remember that the fact always takes precedence over the model; in other words, the electrons don't "care" what orbitals *we* think they should occupy. As the atomic orbitals are filled with more and more electrons in these larger atoms, sublevel energies differ very little, which results in these variations from the expected pattern.

Sample Problem 8.2 Determining Electron Configurations

PROBLEM Using the periodic table on the inside cover of the text (not Figure 8.9 or Table 8.4), give the (1) full and condensed electron configurations, (2) partial orbital diagrams for the valence electrons, and (3) number of inner electrons for the following elements:
(a) Potassium (K; $Z = 19$)
(b) Molybdenum (Mo; $Z = 42$)
(c) Lead (Pb; $Z = 82$)
PLAN We know the number of electrons in each element from its atomic number, and the periodic table shows the order for filling sublevels. In the partial orbital diagrams, we include all electrons after those of the previous noble gas *except* those in *filled* inner sublevels. The number of inner electrons is the sum of those in previous noble gas and in filled *d* and *f* sublevels.

SOLUTION (a) For K ($Z = 19$), the full electron configuration is $1s^2 2s^2 2p^6 3s^2 3p^6 4s^1$.
The condensed configuration is $[Ar] 4s^1$.
The partial orbital diagram for valence electrons is

K is a main-group element in Group 1A(1) of Period 4, so there are
18 inner electrons.
(b) For Mo ($Z = 42$), we would expect the full electron configuration to be
$1s^2 2s^2 2p^6 3s^2 3p^6 4s^2 3d^{10} 4p^6 5s^2 4d^4$. However, Mo lies under Cr in Group 6B(6) and
exhibits the same variation in filling pattern in the ns and $(n-1)d$ sublevels:
$1s^2 2s^2 2p^6 3s^2 3p^6 4s^2 3d^{10} 4p^6 5s^1 4d^5$.
The condensed electron configuration is $[Kr] 5s^1 4d^5$.
The partial orbital diagram for valence electrons is

Mo is a transition element in Group 6B(6) of Period 5, so there are
36 inner electrons.
(c) For Pb ($Z = 82$), the full electron configuration is
$1s^2 2s^2 2p^6 3s^2 3p^6 4s^2 3d^{10} 4p^6 5s^2 4d^{10} 5p^6 6s^2 4f^{14} 5d^{10} 6p^2$.
The condensed electron configuration is $[Xe] 6s^2 4f^{14} 5d^{10} 6p^2$.
The partial orbital diagram for valence electrons (no filled inner sublevels) is

Pb is a main-group element in Group 4A(14) of Period 6, so there are 54
(in Xe) + 14 (in $4f$ series) + 10 (in $5d$ series) = 78 inner electrons.
CHECK Be sure the sum of the superscripts (electrons) in the full electron configuration equals the atomic number, and that the number of *valence* electrons in the
condensed configuration equals the number of electrons in the partial orbital diagram.

Follow-up Problem 8.2 Without referring to Table 8.4 or Figure 8.9, give
full and condensed electron configurations, partial orbital diagrams for valence electrons, and the number of inner electrons for the following elements:
(a) Ni ($Z = 28$)   **(b)** Sr ($Z = 38$)   **(c)** Po ($Z = 84$)

Section Summary

In the aufbau method of filling energy levels, one electron is added to each
successive element in accord with the Pauli exclusion principle (no two electrons can have the same set of quantum numbers) and Hund's rule (orbitals
of equal energy become half filled, with electron spins parallel, before any
pairing occurs). The elements of a group have similar outer electron configurations and similar chemical behavior. For the main-group elements, valence
electrons (those involved in reactions) are in the outer (highest energy) level
only. For transition elements, inner d electrons are often involved in reactions also. In general, $(n-1)d$ orbitals fill after ns and before np orbitals. In
Periods 6 and 7, $(n-2)f$ orbitals fill after the first $(n-1)d$ orbital element.

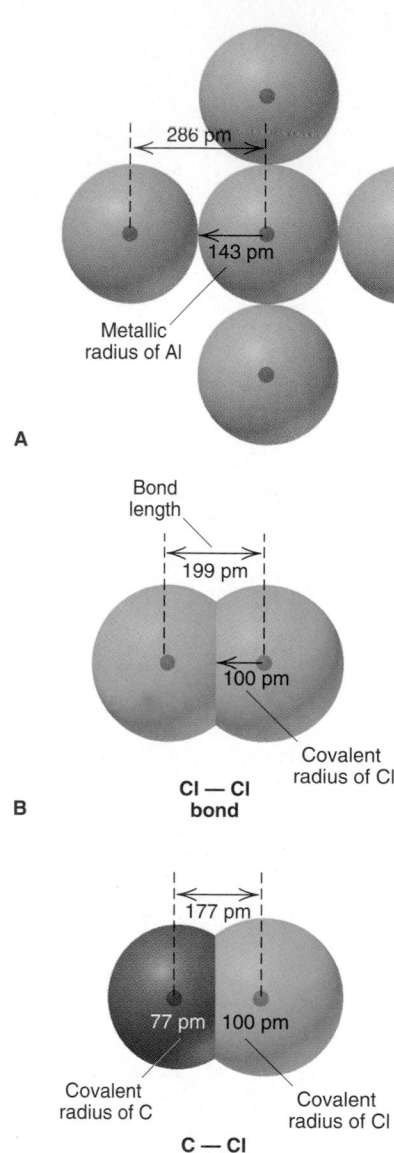

Figure 8.11 Defining metallic and covalent radii. A, The metallic radius is one-half the distance between nuclei of adjacent atoms in a crystal of the element, as shown here for aluminum. **B,** The covalent radius is one-half the distance between bonded nuclei in a diatomic molecule of the element, as shown here for chlorine. In effect, it is one-half the bond length. **C,** In a covalent compound, the bond length and known covalent radii are used to determine other radii. Here the C—Cl bond length (177 pm) and the covalent radius of Cl (100 pm) are used to find a value for the covalent radius of C (177 pm − 100 pm = 77 pm).

8.4 Trends in Some Key Periodic Atomic Properties

All physical and chemical behavior of the elements is based ultimately on the electron configurations of their atoms. In this section, we focus on three properties of atoms that are directly influenced by electron configuration: atomic size, ionization energy (the energy required to remove an electron from a gaseous atom), and electron affinity (the energy change involved in adding an electron to a gaseous atom). These properties are *periodic:* they generally increase and decrease in a recurring manner throughout the periodic table. As a result, their relative magnitudes can often be predicted, and they exhibit consistent changes, or *trends,* within a group or period that correlate with element behavior.

Trends in Atomic Size

In Chapter 7, we noted that an electron in an atom can lie relatively far from the nucleus, so we commonly represent atoms as spheres in which the electrons spend 90% of their time. However, atomic size is a measurable quantity that we *define in terms of how closely one atom lies next to another.* In practice, we measure the distance between identical, adjacent atomic nuclei in a sample of an element and divide that distance in half. (We discuss the experimental method in Chapter 12.) Of course, atoms do not have hard surfaces, so we might expect the size of an atom in a compound to depend somewhat on the atoms near it. In other words, *atomic size varies slightly from substance to substance.*

Two common definitions of atomic size are depicted in Figure 8.11. The **metallic radius** is one-half the distance between nuclei of adjacent atoms in a crystal of the element; we typically use this definition for metals. For elements that commonly occur as molecules, mostly nonmetals, we define atomic size by the **covalent radius,** one-half the distance between nuclei of identical covalently bonded atoms.

Atomic size greatly influences other atomic properties and is critical to understanding element behavior. Figure 8.12 shows the atomic radii of the main-group elements and most of the transition elements. Among the main-group elements, note that atomic size varies within both a group and a period. These variations in atomic size are the result of two opposing influences:

1. *Changes in n.* As the principal quantum number (*n*) increases, the outer electrons spend more time farther from the nucleus, so the atoms are larger.
2. *Changes in Z_{eff}.* As the effective nuclear charge (Z_{eff})—the positive charge "felt" by an electron—increases, outer electrons are pulled closer to the nucleus, so the atoms are smaller.

The net effect of these influences depends on inner electron shielding of the increasing nuclear charge:

1. *Down a group, n dominates.* As we move *down* a main group, each member has one more level of *inner* electrons, which shields the *outer* electrons very effectively. Calculations show Z_{eff} changes little, rising only slightly for each element, so the atomic radius increases as a result of increasing *n* value. *Atomic radius generally **increases** from top to bottom in a group.*
2. *Across a period, Z_{eff} dominates.* As we move *across* a period of main-group elements, electrons are added to the *same* outer level, so the shielding by inner electrons does not change. Since outer electrons shield each other ineffectively, Z_{eff} rises significantly, and so the outer electrons are pulled closer. *Atomic radius generally **decreases** from left to right in a period.*

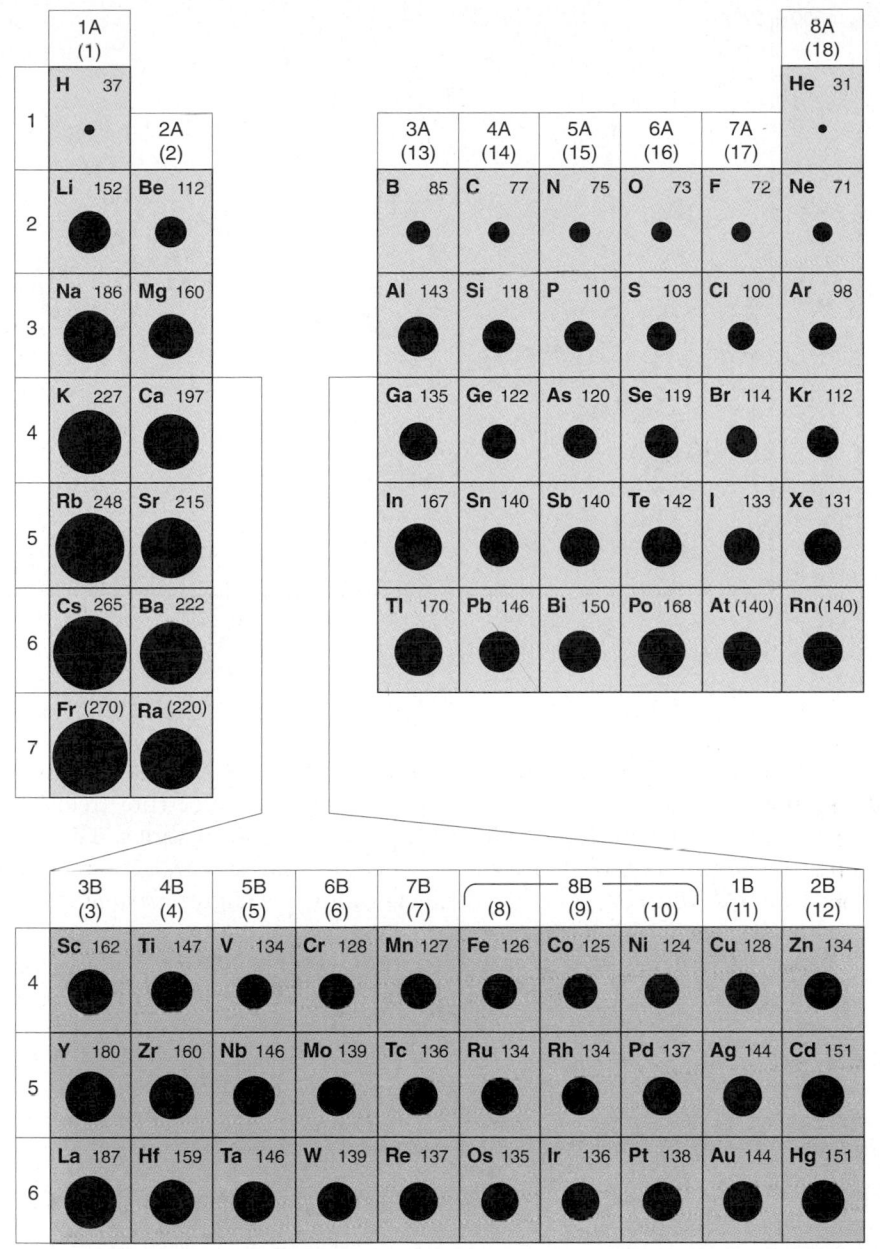

Figure 8.12 **Atomic radii of the main-group and transition elements.** The atomic radii (in picometers) are shown as circles of proportional size for the main-group elements (*tan*) and the transition elements (*blue*). Among the main-group elements, atomic radius generally increases from top to bottom and decreases from left to right. The transition elements do not exhibit this size trend. (Values in parentheses have only two significant figures.)

As you can see from Figure 8.12, these general trends hold quite well for the main-group elements but *not* for the transition elements. Remember that inner *d* orbitals are filled *within* a transition series. As we move from left to right, size shrinks through the first two or three elements because of the increasing nuclear charge. But, from then on, *the size remains relatively constant* because the shielding by these inner *d* electrons counteracts the usual increase in Z_{eff}. For instance, vanadium (V; $Z = 23$), the third Period 4 transition metal, has the same radius as zinc (Zn; $Z = 30$), the last. This pattern also appears in the Periods 5 and 6 *d*-transition series and in both inner transition series.

This intervening filling of *d* electrons causes a major size decrease from Group 2A(2) to 3A(13), the main groups that flank the transition series. The size decrease in Periods 4, 5, and 6 (*with* a transition series) is much greater

Figure 8.13 Periodicity of atomic radius. A plot of atomic radius vs. atomic number for the elements in Periods 1 through 6 shows a periodic change: the radius generally decreases through a period to the noble gas [Group 8A(18); *purple*] and then increases suddenly to the next alkali metal [Group 1A(1); *brown*].

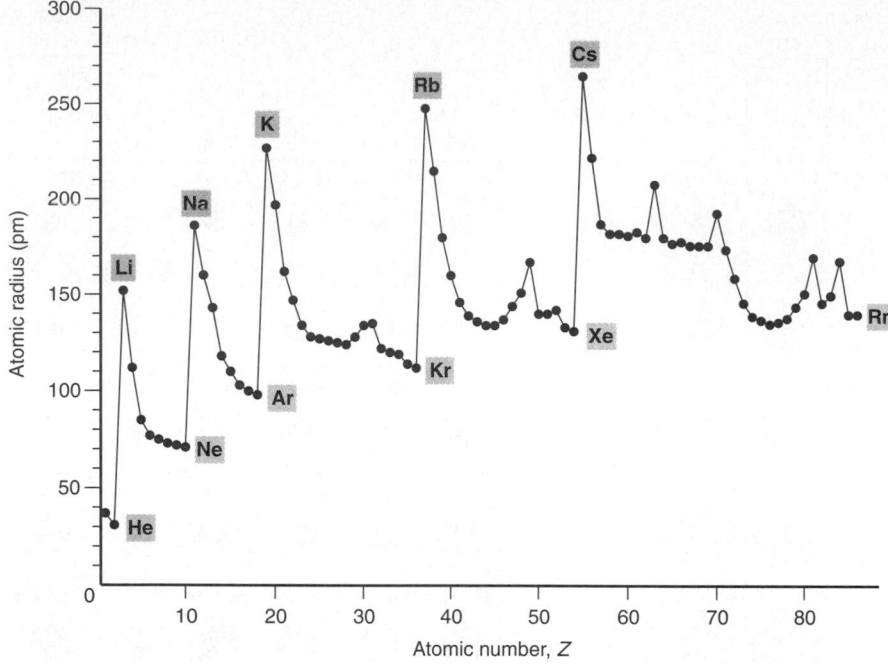

Packing 'Em In The increasing nuclear charge dramatically shrinks the space in which each electron can move. For example, in Group 1A(1), the atomic radius of cesium ($Z = 55$) is only 1.7 times that of lithium ($Z = 3$); so the volume of cesium is about five times as large, even though cesium has 18 times as many electrons. At the opposite ends of Period 2, neon ($Z = 10$) has only about $\frac{1}{8}$ the volume of lithium ($Z = 3$), but neon has three times as many electrons. Thus, whether the size increases down a group or decreases across a period, the attraction caused by the larger number of protons in the nucleus greatly crowds the electrons.

than in Period 3 (*without* a transition series). Because the *np* orbitals penetrate more than the $(n - 1)d$ orbitals, the first *np* electron "feels" a Z_{eff} increased by all the protons added during the transition series. The greatest change occurs in Period 4, in which calcium (Ca; $Z = 20$) is nearly 50% larger than gallium (Ga; $Z = 31$). In fact, gallium is slightly *smaller* than aluminum (Al; $Z = 13$), even though it is farther down the same group!

Figure 8.13 shows the overall variation in atomic size with increasing atomic number. Note the recurring up-and-down pattern as size drops across a period to the noble gas and then leaps up to the alkali metal that begins the next period. ◆

Sample Problem 8.3   Ranking Elements by Atomic Size

PROBLEM Using only the periodic table (not Figure 8.12), rank each set of main-group elements in order of *decreasing* atomic size:
(a) Ca, Mg, Sr   **(b)** K, Ga, Ca   **(c)** Br, Rb, Kr   **(d)** Sr, Ca, Rb
PLAN To rank the elements by atomic size, we find them in the periodic table and note that they are main-group elements, so size increases down a group and decreases across a period.
SOLUTION (a) Sr > Ca > Mg. These three elements are in Group 2A(2), so size decreases up the group.
(b) K > Ca > Ga. These three elements are in Period 4, so size decreases across a period.
(c) Rb > Br > Kr. Rb is largest because it has one more energy level and is farthest to the left. Kr is smaller than Br because Kr is farther to the right in Period 4.
(d) Rb > Sr > Ca. Ca is smallest because it has one fewer energy level. Sr is smaller than Rb because it is farther to the right.
CHECK From Figure 8.12, we see that the rankings are correct.

Follow-up Problem 8.3   Using only the periodic table, rank the elements in each set in order of *increasing* size: **(a)** Se, Br, Cl; **(b)** I, Xe, Ba.

Figure 8.14 Periodicity of first ionization energy (IE₁). A plot of IE₁ vs. atomic number for the elements in Periods 1 through 6 shows a periodic pattern: the lowest values occur for the alkali metals (*brown*) and the highest for the noble gases (*purple*). This is the *inverse* of the trend in atomic size (see Figure 8.13).

Trends in Ionization Energy

The **ionization energy (IE)** is the energy required for the *complete removal* of 1 mol of electrons from 1 mol of gaseous atoms or ions. Pulling an electron away from a nucleus *requires* energy to overcome the attraction. Since energy flows *into* the system, the ionization energy is always positive (like ΔH of an endothermic reaction).

In Chapter 7, you saw that the ionization energy of the H atom is the energy difference between $n = 1$ and $n = \infty$, the point at which the electron is completely removed. Many-electron atoms can lose more than one electron. The first ionization energy (IE_1) removes an outermost electron (highest energy sublevel) from the gaseous atom:

$$\text{Atom}(g) \longrightarrow \text{ion}^+(g) + e^- \qquad \Delta E = IE_1 > 0$$

The second ionization energy (IE_2) removes the second electron. Since this electron is pulled away from a positively charged ion, IE_2 is always larger than IE_1:

$$\text{Ion}^+(g) \longrightarrow \text{ion}^{2+}(g) + e^- \qquad \Delta E = IE_2 \text{ (always} > IE_1)$$

The first ionization energy, which we can measure directly, is a key factor in an element's chemical reactivity because, as you'll soon see, *atoms with a low IE_1 tend to form cations during reactions, whereas those with a high IE_1 (except the noble gases) often form anions.*

Variations in First Ionization Energy The elements exhibit a periodic pattern in first ionization energy, as shown in Figure 8.14. By comparing this figure with Figure 8.13, you can see a roughly *inverse* relationship between IE_1 and atomic size. The two trends, with exceptions, are:

1. *Down a group.* As we move *down* a main group, atomic size increases, so the distance from the nucleus to the outer electron does also. According to Coulomb's law, the attraction between them lessens, so the electron is easier to remove. Figure 8.15 on the next page shows that *ionization energy generally **decreases** down a group.*

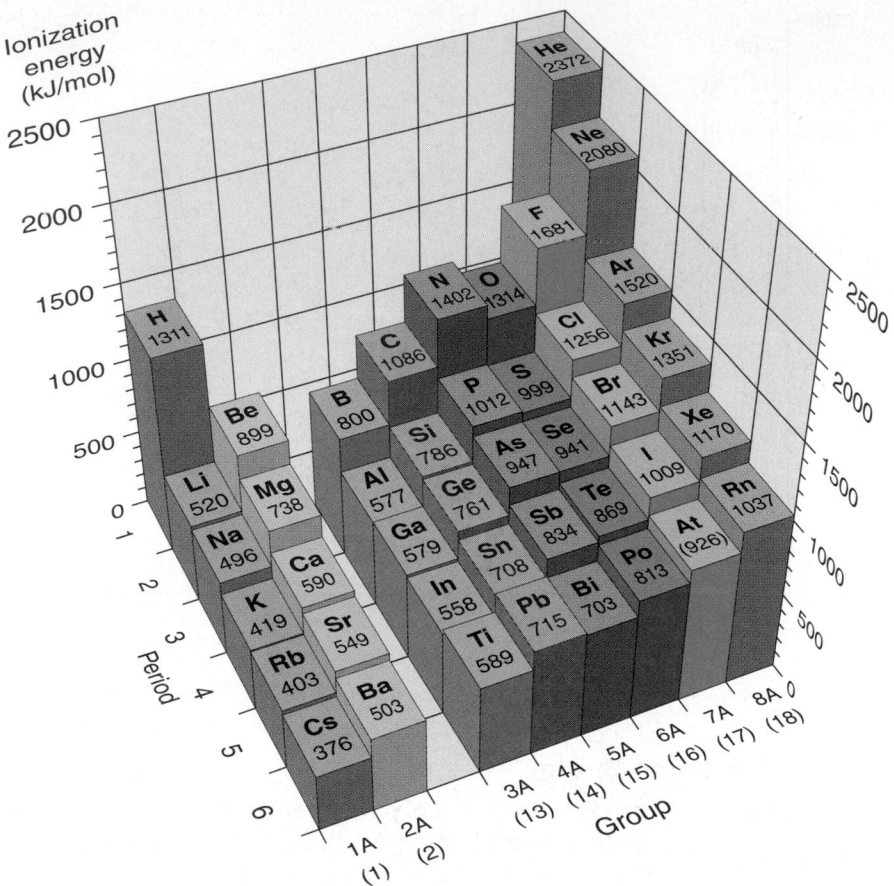

Figure 8.15 **First ionization energies of the main-group elements.** Values for IE_1 (in kJ/mol) of the main-group elements are shown as posts of varying height. Note the general increase within a period and decrease within a group. Thus, the lowest value is at the bottom of Group 1A(1), and the highest is at the top of Group 8A(18).

As we might have predicted from the effect of the transition series on atomic size, the only significant exception to this pattern occurs in Group 3A(13): IE_1 decreases from boron (B) to aluminum (Al), but not for the rest of the group. Filling the *d* sublevels in Periods 4, 5, and 6 causes a greater-than-expected Z_{eff}, which holds the outer electrons more tightly in the larger Group 3A members.

2. *Across a period.* As we move across a period, Z_{eff} increases, so atomic size decreases. As a result, the attraction between the nucleus and the outer electrons increases, so an electron is harder to remove. *Ionization energy generally* **increases** *across a period.* Clearly, it is easier to remove an electron from an alkali metal than from a noble gas.

There are several small "dips" in the otherwise smooth increase in ionization energy. They occur at Group 3A(13) for B and Al, and at Group 6A(16) for O and S. The dips at Group 3A occur because these electrons are the first in the *np* sublevel. This sublevel is higher in energy than the *ns*, so the electron is pulled off more easily, which leaves a stable, filled *ns* sublevel. The dips at Group 6A occur because the np^4 electron is the first to pair up with another *np* electron, and electron repulsions raise the orbital energy. Removing this electron relieves the repulsions and leaves a stable, half-filled *np* sublevel, so the fourth *p* electron comes off more easily than the third one.

Sample Problem 8.4   Ranking Elements by First Ionization Energy

PROBLEM Using the periodic table only, rank the elements in each of the following sets in order of *decreasing* IE_1:
(a) Kr, He, Ar   **(b)** Sb, Te, Sn   **(c)** K, Ca, Rb   **(d)** I, Xe, Cs

PLAN As in Sample Problem 8.3, we first find the elements in the periodic table and then apply the general trends of decreasing IE_1 down a group and increasing IE_1 across a period.

SOLUTION **(a)** He > Ar > Kr. These three are all in Group 8A(18), and IE_1 decreases down a group.

(b) Te > Sb > Sn. These three are all in Period 5, and IE_1 increases across a period.

(c) Ca > K > Rb. IE_1 of K is larger than IE_1 of Rb because K is higher in Group 1A(1). IE_1 of Ca is larger than IE_1 of K because Ca is farther to the right in Period 4.

(d) Xe > I > Cs. IE_1 of I is smaller than IE_1 of Xe because I is farther to the left. IE_1 of I is larger than IE_1 of Cs because I is farther to the right and in the previous period.

CHECK Since trends in IE_1 are generally opposite the trends in size, you can rank the elements by size and check that you obtain the reverse order.

Follow-up Problem 8.4   Rank the elements in each of the following sets in order of *increasing* IE_1: **(a)** Sb, Sn, I; **(b)** Sr, Ca, Ba.

Variations in Successive Ionization Energies   Successive ionization energies of a given element (IE_1, IE_2, and so on) increase because each electron is pulled away from an increasingly positive entity. Note from Figure 8.16, however, that this increase is not smooth, but includes an enormous jump. A more complete picture is presented in Table 8.5, which shows successive ionization energies for the elements in Period 2 and the first element in Period 3. Move horizontally through the values for a given element, and you reach a point that separates relatively low from relatively high IE values (shaded area to right of line). This jump appears *after* the outer (valence) electrons have been removed and, thus, represents the much greater energy needed to remove an inner (core) electron. As an example, for boron (B), IE_1 is lower than IE_2, which is lower than IE_3, which is *much* lower than IE_4. Thus, B has three electrons in the highest energy level ($1s^2 2s^2 2p^1$). Because of the great energy needed to remove core electrons, they are *not* involved in chemical reactions.

Ionization energy (MJ/mol)

IE_3 14.85

IE_2 1.76

IE_1 0.90

Figure 8.16 **The first three ionization energies of beryllium (in MJ/mol).** Successive ionization energies always increase, but an exceptionally large increase occurs when the first core electron is removed. For Be, this occurs with the third electron (IE_3). (Also see Table 8.5.)

Table 8.5 Successive Ionization Energies of the Elements Lithium Through Sodium

Z	Element	Number of Valence Electrons	Ionization Energy (MJ/mol)*									
			IE_1	IE_2	IE_3	IE_4	IE_5	IE_6	IE_7	IE_8	IE_9	IE_{10}
3	Li	1	0.52	7.30	11.81							
4	Be	2	0.90	1.76	14.85	21.01			Core electrons			
5	B	3	0.80	2.43	3.66	25.02	32.82					
6	C	4	1.09	2.35	4.62	6.22	37.83	47.28				
7	N	5	1.40	2.86	4.58	7.48	9.44	53.27	64.36			
8	O	6	1.31	3.39	5.30	7.47	10.98	13.33	71.33	84.08		
9	F	7	1.68	3.37	6.05	8.41	11.02	15.16	17.87	92.04	106.43	
10	Ne	8	2.08	3.95	6.12	9.37	12.18	15.24	20.00	23.07	115.38	131.43
11	Na	1	0.50	4.56	6.91	9.54	13.35	16.61	20.11	25.49	28.93	141.37

*MJ/mol, or megajoules per mole = 10^3 kJ/mol.

Sample Problem 8.5   Identifying an Element from Successive Ionization Energies

PROBLEM Name the Period 3 element with the following ionization energies (in kJ/mol) and write its electron configuration:

IE$_1$	IE$_2$	IE$_3$	IE$_4$	IE$_5$	IE$_6$
1012	1903	2910	4956	6278	22,230

PLAN We look for a large jump in the IE values, which occurs after all valence electrons have been removed. Then we refer to the periodic table to find the Period 3 element with this number of valence electrons and write its electron configuration.

SOLUTION The exceptionally large jump occurs after IE$_5$, so the element has five valence electrons and, thus, is in Group 5A(15). In Period 3, it is phosphorus (P; $Z = 15$). Its electron configuration is $1s^2 2s^2 2p^6 3s^2 3p^3$.

Follow-up Problem 8.5   Element Q is in Period 3 and has the following ionization energies (in kJ/mol):

IE$_1$	IE$_2$	IE$_3$	IE$_4$	IE$_5$	IE$_6$
577	1816	2744	11,576	14,829	18,375

Name element Q and write its electron configuration.

Trends in Electron Affinity

The **electron affinity (EA)** is the energy change accompanying the *addition* of 1 mol of electrons to 1 mol of gaseous atoms or ions. As with ionization energy, there is a first electron affinity, a second, and so forth. The *first electron affinity* (EA$_1$) accompanies the formation of 1 mol of monovalent (1−) gaseous anions:

$$\text{Atom}(g) + e^- \longrightarrow \text{ion}^-(g) \qquad \Delta E = EA_1$$

In most cases, *energy is released when the first electron is added* because it is attracted to the atom's nuclear charge. Thus, EA$_1$ is usually negative (just as ΔH for an exothermic reaction is negative).* The second electron affinity (EA$_2$), on the other hand, is always positive because energy must be *absorbed* in order to overcome electrostatic repulsions and add another electron to a negative ion.

Factors other than Z_{eff} and atomic size affect electron affinities, so trends are not as regular as those for the previous two properties. For instance, we might expect electron affinities to decrease smoothly down a group (smaller negative number) because the nucleus is farther away from an electron being added. But, as Figure 8.17 shows, only Group 1A(1) exhibits this behavior. We might also expect a regular increase in electron affinities across a period (larger negative number) because size decreases and the increasing Z_{eff} would attract the electron being added more strongly. The overall left-to-right increase in magnitude is there, but we certainly would not say that it is a regular increase. These exceptions arise from changes in sublevel energy and electron repulsion.

---

*Tables of first electron affinities often list them as positive values, showing the *quantity* of energy released, rather than the difference between the final and initial energy values. Keep this convention in mind when researching these values in reference texts. Electron affinities are more difficult to measure than ionization energies, so values are frequently being corrected with more accurate methods.

1A (1)	2A (2)		3A (13)	4A (14)	5A (15)	6A (16)	7A (17)	8A (18)
H −72.8								**He** (+21)
Li −59.6	**Be** (+241)		**B** −26.7	**C** −122	**N** 0	**O** −141	**F** −328	**Ne** (+29)
Na −52.9	**Mg** (+230)		**Al** −42.5	**Si** −134	**P** −72.0	**S** −200	**Cl** −349	**Ar** (+34)
K −48.4	**Ca** (+156)		**Ga** −28.9	**Ge** −119	**As** −78.2	**Se** −195	**Br** −325	**Kr** (+39)
Rb −46.9	**Sr** (+167)		**In** −28.9	**Sn** −107	**Sb** −103	**Te** −190	**I** −295	**Xe** (+40)
Cs −45.5	**Ba** (+52)		**Tl** −19.3	**Pb** −35.1	**Bi** −91.3	**Po** −183	**At** −270	**Rn** (+41)

Figure 8.17 Electron affinities of the main-group elements. The electron affinities (in kJ/mol) of the main-group elements are shown. Negative values indicate that energy is released when the anion forms. Positive values, which occur in Groups 2A(2) and 8A(18), indicate that energy is absorbed to form the anion; in fact, these anions are unstable and the values are estimated.

Despite irregularities, three key points emerge when we examine ionization energy and electron affinity values:

1. Elements in Groups 6A(16) and especially 7A(17) (halogens) have high ionization energies and highly negative (exothermic) electron affinities. These elements lose electrons with difficulty but attract them strongly. Therefore, *in their ionic compounds, they form negative ions.*

2. Elements in Groups 1A(1) and 2A(2) have low ionization energies and either slightly negative or positive (endothermic) electron affinities. These elements lose electrons readily but attract them weakly, if at all. Therefore, *in their ionic compounds, they form positive ions.*

3. The noble gases, Group 8A(18), have very high ionization energies and highly positive (endothermic) electron affinities. Therefore, *these elements do **not** tend to lose or gain electrons.* In fact, only the larger members of the group (Kr, Xe, Rn) form any compounds at all.

Section Summary

Trends in three atomic properties are summarized in Figure 8.18. Atomic size increases down a main group and decreases across a period. Across a transition series, size remains relatively constant. First ionization energy (the energy required to remove the outermost electron from a mole of gaseous atoms) is inversely related to atomic size: IE_1 decreases down a main group and increases across a period. Successive ionization energies show a large increase between outer and inner (core) electrons. Electron affinity (the energy involved in adding an electron to a mole of gaseous atoms) shows many variations from expected trends. Group 1A(1) and 2A(2) elements have low IEs and small EAs, whereas Group 6A(16) and 7A(17) elements have high IEs and large EAs.

A Atomic size

B Ionization energy

C Electron affinity

Figure 8.18 Trends in three atomic properties. Periodic trends are depicted as gradations in shading on miniature periodic tables, with arrows indicating the direction of general increase in a group or period. **A,** Atomic size. **B,** Ionization energy. **C,** Electron affinity [Group 8A(18) is not shown; the dashed arrows imply the numerous exceptions to expected trends].

8.5 The Connection Between Atomic Structure and Chemical Reactivity

Our main purpose for discussing atomic properties is, of course, to see how they affect element behavior. In this section, you'll see how the properties we just examined influence metallic behavior and determine the type of ion an element can form, as well as how electron configuration relates to magnetic properties.

Trends in Metallic Behavior

Metals are located in the left and lower three-quarters of the periodic table. They are typically shiny solids that have moderate to high melting points, are good thermal and electrical conductors, and tend to lose electrons in reactions with nonmetals. *Nonmetals* are located in the upper right quarter of the table. They are typically not shiny, have relatively low melting points, are poor thermal and electrical conductors, and tend to gain electrons in reactions with metals. *Metalloids* are located in the region between the other two classes and have properties between them as well. Thus, *metallic behavior decreases left to right and increases top to bottom* (Figure 8.19).

Figure 8.19 Trends in metallic behavior. The gradation in metallic behavior among the elements is depicted as a gradation in shading from bottom left to top right, with arrows showing the direction of increase. Elements that behave as metals appear in the left and lower three-quarters of the table. (Hydrogen, because it is a nonmetal, appears next to helium in this periodic table.)

It's important to keep in mind, however, that all the elements may not fall neatly into our classifications. For instance, carbon is a nonmetal, but in the form of graphite it is a good electrical conductor. Iodine, another nonmetal, is a shiny solid. Gallium and cesium are both metals, but they melt at temperatures below body temperature, and mercury is a liquid at room temperature. Although such exceptions exist, we can make several generalizations about metallic behavior.

Relative Tendency to Lose Electrons Metals tend to lose electrons during chemical reactions because they have low ionization energies relative to nonmetals. The increase in metallic behavior down a group is most obvious in the physical and chemical behavior of the elements in Groups 3A(13) through 6A(16), which contain more than one class of element. For example, consider the elements in Group 5A(15), which appear vertically in Figure 8.20. Here, the change is so great that, with regard to monatomic ions, *elements at the top tend to form anions and those at the bottom tend to form cations.* Nitrogen (N) is a gaseous nonmetal, and phosphorus (P) a solid nonmetal. Both occur occasionally as 3− anions in their compounds. Arsenic (As) and antimony (Sb) are metalloids, with Sb the more metallic of the two; neither forms ions readily. Bismuth (Bi), the largest member, is a typical metal, forming mostly ionic compounds in which it appears as a 3+ cation. Even in Group 2A(2), which consists entirely of metals, there is an increase from top to bottom in the tendency to form cations. Beryllium (Be), for example, forms covalent compounds with nonmetals, whereas the compounds of barium (Ba) are ionic.

As we move across a period, it becomes more difficult to lose an electron (IE increases) and easier to gain one (EA becomes more negative). Therefore, with regard to monatomic ions, *elements at the left tend to form cations and those at the right tend to form anions.* The typical decrease in metallic behavior across a period is clear among the elements in Period 3, which appear horizontally in Figure 8.20. Sodium and magnesium are metals. Sodium is shiny when freshly cut under mineral oil, but it loses an electron so readily to O_2 that, if cut in air, its surface is coated immediately with an oxide. These metals exist naturally as Na^+ and Mg^{2+} ions in oceans, minerals, and organisms. Aluminum is metallic in its physical properties and forms the Al^{3+} ion in some compounds, but it bonds covalently in most others. Silicon (Si) is a shiny metalloid that does not occur as a monatomic ion. The most common

Figure 8.20 The change in metallic behavior in Group 5A(15) and Period 3. Moving down from nitrogen to bismuth shows an *increase* in metallic behavior (and decrease in ionization energy). Moving left to right from sodium to chlorine shows a *decrease* in metallic behavior (and general increase in ionization energy). Each box shows the element and its atomic number, symbol, and first ionization energy (in kJ/mol).

Group 5A (15)

| 7 | N | 1402 |

Period 3

| 11 Na 496 | 12 Mg 738 | 13 Al 577 | 14 Si 786 | 15 P 1012 | 16 S 999 | 17 Cl 1256 |

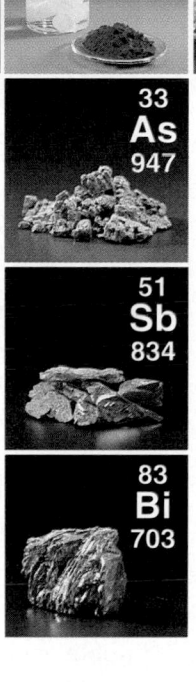

| 33 As 947 |
| 51 Sb 834 |
| 83 Bi 703 |

form of phosphorus is a white, waxy nonmetal that, as we said, forms the P^{3-} ion in a few compounds. Sulfur is a crumbly yellow nonmetal that forms the sulfide ion (S^{2-}) in many compounds. Diatomic chlorine (Cl_2) is a yellowish, gaseous nonmetal that attracts electrons avidly and exists in nature as the Cl^- ion.

Acid-Base Behavior of the Element Oxides Metals are also distinguished from nonmetals by the acid-base behavior of their oxides in water:

- Most main-group metals *transfer* electrons to oxygen, so their *metal oxides are ionic. In water, they act as bases,* producing OH^- ions and reacting with acids.
- Nonmetals *share* electrons with oxygen, so *nonmetal oxides are covalent. In water, they act as acids,* producing H^+ ions and reacting with bases.

Figure 8.21 shows an example of these two types of oxide. Some metals and many metalloids form oxides that are **amphoteric:** they can act as acids *and* as bases in water.

Figure 8.22 classifies the acid-base behavior of some common oxides, focusing once again on the elements in Group 5A(15) and Period 3. Note that *as the elements become more metallic down a group, their oxides become more basic.* In Group 5A, dinitrogen pentaoxide, N_2O_5, forms nitric acid:

$$N_2O_5(s) + H_2O(l) \longrightarrow 2HNO_3(aq)$$

Tetraphosphorus decaoxide, P_4O_{10}, forms the weaker acid H_3PO_4:

$$P_4O_{10}(s) + 6H_2O(l) \longrightarrow 4H_3PO_4(aq)$$

Figure 8.21 Acid-base behavior of a metal (ionic) oxide and a nonmetal (covalent) oxide. The acid-base indicator used here turns pink (base color) in an aqueous solution of CaO (*left*) because this ionic oxide is basic. The indicator turns yellow (acid color) in an aqueous solution of P_4O_{10} (*right*) because this covalent oxide is acidic.

					5A (15)			
					N_2O_5			
3	Na_2O	MgO	Al_2O_3	SiO_2	P_4O_{10}	SO_3	Cl_2O_7	Ar
					As_2O_5			
					Sb_2O_5			
					Bi_2O_3			

Figure 8.22 The trend in acid-base behavior of element oxides. The trend in acid-base behavior for common oxides in Group 5A(15) and Period 3 is shown as a gradation in color (*red* = acidic; *blue* = basic). Note that the metals form basic oxides and the nonmetals form acidic oxides. Aluminum forms an oxide (*purple*) that can act as an acid and as a base. Thus, as atomic size increases, oxide basicity increases.

The oxide of the metalloid arsenic is weakly acidic, whereas that of the metalloid antimony is weakly basic. Bismuth, the most metallic of the group, forms a basic oxide that is insoluble in water but forms a salt and water with acid:

$$Bi_2O_3(s) + 6HNO_3(aq) \longrightarrow 2Bi(NO_3)_3(aq) + 3H_2O(l)$$

Note that *as the elements become less metallic across a period, their oxides become more acidic.* In Period 3, sodium and magnesium form the strongly basic oxides Na_2O and MgO. Metallic aluminum forms amphoteric aluminum oxide (Al_2O_3), which reacts with acid and with base:

$$Al_2O_3(s) + 6HCl(aq) \longrightarrow 2AlCl_3(aq) + 3H_2O(l)$$
$$Al_2O_3(s) + 2NaOH(aq) + 3H_2O(l) \longrightarrow 2NaAl(OH)_4(aq)$$

Silicon dioxide is weakly acidic, forming a salt and water with base:

$$SiO_2(s) + 2NaOH(aq) \longrightarrow Na_2SiO_3(aq) + H_2O(l)$$

The common oxides of phosphorus, sulfur, and chlorine form acids of increasing strength: H_3PO_4, H_2SO_4, and $HClO_4$.

Properties of Monatomic Ions

So far we've focused on the reactants—the atoms—in the process of electron loss and gain. Now we focus on the products—the ions. In particular, we examine electron configurations, magnetic properties, and sizes of ions relative to those of their parent atoms.

Electron Configurations of Main-Group Ions In Chapter 2, you learned the symbols and charges of many monatomic ions. But *why* does the ion have that charge in its compounds? Why is a sodium ion Na^+ and not Na^{2+}, and why is a fluoride ion F^- and not F^{2-}? For elements at the left and right ends of the periodic table, the explanation concerns the very low reactivity of the noble gases. As we said earlier, because of their high IEs and positive (endothermic) EAs, the noble gases typically do not form ions and remain chemically stable with a *filled* outer energy level (ns^2np^6). *Elements in Groups 1A(1), 2A(2), 6A(16), and 7A(17) that readily form ions either lose or gain electrons to attain a filled outer level and thus a noble gas configuration.* Their ions are said to be **isoelectronic** (Greek *iso*, "same") with the nearest noble gas (Figure 8.23; also see Figure 2.20, p. 63).

When an alkali metal atom [Group 1A(1)] loses its single valence electron, it becomes isoelectronic with the *previous* noble gas. The Na^+ ion, for example, is isoelectronic with neon (Ne):

$$Na\ (1s^22s^22p^63s^1) \longrightarrow e^- + Na^+\ (1s^22s^22p^6)$$
isoelectronic with Ne ($1s^22s^22p^6$)

When a halogen atom [Group 7A(17)] adds a single electron to the seven in its valence shell, it becomes isoelectronic with the *next* noble gas. Bromide ion, for example, is isoelectronic with krypton (Kr):

$$Br\ ([Ar]\ 4s^23d^{10}4p^5) + e^- \longrightarrow Br^-\ ([Ar]\ 4s^23d^{10}4p^6)$$
isoelectronic with Kr ([Ar] $4s^23d^{10}4p^6$)

The energy needed to remove the electrons from metals to attain the previous noble gas configuration is supplied during their exothermic reactions with nonmetals. Removing more than one electron from Na or more than two from Mg means removing core electrons, which requires 5 to 10 times as much energy as is available in a reaction. This is the reason that Na^{2+} or Mg^{3+} ions do *not* form. Similarly, adding more than one electron to F to form F^{2-} or more than two to O to form O^{3-} means placing them in a higher outer energy level, which also requires much more energy than is available from a typical reaction.

Figure 8.23 Main-group ions and the noble gas electron configurations. Most of the elements that form monatomic ions isoelectronic with a noble gas lie in the four groups that flank Group 8A(18), two on either side.

How do the larger metals of Groups 3A(13), 4A(14), and 5A(15) form cations? After all, it would be energetically impossible to lose enough electrons to attain a noble gas configuration. For example, tin (Sn; $Z = 50$) would have to lose 14 electrons—two $5p$, ten $4d$, and two $5s$—to be isoelectronic with krypton (Kr; $Z = 36$), the previous noble gas. Instead, it loses far fewer electrons and attains two different stable configurations. In the tin(IV) ion (Sn^{4+}), the metal atom empties its outer energy level and attains the stability of empty $5s$ and $5p$ sublevels and a filled inner $4d$ sublevel. This $(n - 1)d^{10}$ configuration is called a **pseudo–noble gas configuration:**

$$Sn \ ([Kr] \ 5s^2 4d^{10} 5p^2) \longrightarrow Sn^{4+} \ ([Kr] \ 4d^{10}) + 4e^-$$

Alternatively, in the more common tin(II) ion (Sn^{2+}), the atom loses the two $5p$ electrons only and attains the stability of filled $5s$ and $4d$ sublevels:

$$Sn \ ([Kr] \ 5s^2 4d^{10} 5p^2) \longrightarrow Sn^{2+} \ ([Kr] \ 5s^2 4d^{10}) + 2e^-$$

The retained ns^2 electrons are sometimes called an *inert pair* because they seem difficult to remove. Thallium, lead, and bismuth, the largest, most metallic members of Groups 3A(13) to 5A(15), commonly form ions that retain the ns^2 pair of electrons: Tl^+, Pb^{2+}, and Bi^{3+}.

Excessively high energy cost is also the reason that some elements do not form monatomic ions at all in their reactions. For instance, carbon would have to lose four electrons to form C^{4+} and attain the He configuration, or gain four to form C^{4-} and attain the Ne configuration, but neither ion forms. (Such multivalent ions *are* observed in the spectra of stars, however, where temperatures exceed 10^6 K.) As you'll see in Chapter 9, carbon and other atoms that do not form ions attain a filled shell by *sharing* electrons through covalent bonding.

Sample Problem 8.6   Writing Electron Configurations of Main-Group Ions

PROBLEM Using condensed electron configurations, write reactions for the formation of the common ions of the following elements:
(a) Iodine ($Z = 53$)   **(b)** Potassium ($Z = 19$)   **(c)** Indium ($Z = 49$)

PLAN We identify the element's position in the periodic table and recall two general points:
• Ions of elements in Groups 1A(1), 2A(2), 6A(16), and 7A(17) are typically isoelectronic with the nearest noble gas.
• Metals in Groups 3A(13) to 5A(15) can lose the ns and np electrons or the np electrons only.

SOLUTION (a) Iodine is in Group 7A(17), so it gains one electron and is isoelectronic with xenon:

$$I \ ([Kr] \ 5s^2 4d^{10} 5p^5) + e^- \longrightarrow I^- \ ([Kr] \ 5s^2 4d^{10} 5p^6) \quad \text{(same as Xe)}$$

(b) Potassium is in Group 1A(1), so it loses one electron and is isoelectronic with argon:

$$K \ ([Ar] \ 4s^1) \longrightarrow K^+ \ ([Ar]) + e^-$$

(c) Indium is in Group 3A(13), so it either loses one electron to form In^+ (inert pair) or three to form In^{3+} (pseudo–noble gas):

$$In \ ([Kr] \ 5s^2 4d^{10} 5p^1) \longrightarrow In^+ \ ([Kr] \ 5s^2 4d^{10}) + e^-$$

$$In \ ([Kr] \ 5s^2 4d^{10} 5p^1) \longrightarrow In^{3+} \ ([Kr] \ 4d^{10}) + 3e^-$$

CHECK Be sure that the number of electrons in the ion electron configuration plus those gained or lost equals Z.

Follow-up Problem 8.6   Using condensed electron configurations, write reactions showing formation of the common ions of **(a)** Ba ($Z = 56$); **(b)** O ($Z = 8$); **(c)** Pb ($Z = 82$).

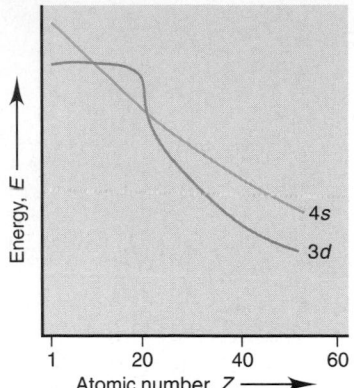

Figure 8.24 The Period 4 crossover in sublevel energies.
The 3d orbitals are empty at the beginning of Period 4. Because the 4s orbital penetrates, its energy is lower in K and Ca, so the 4s fills before the 3d. But as the 3d orbitals fill, beginning with $Z > 20$, these inner electrons are attracted by the increasing nuclear charge, and they also shield the 4s electrons. As a result, there is an energy crossover such that the 3d sublevel becomes lower in energy than the 4s. As a result, the 4s electrons are removed first when the transition-metal ion forms. In other words,

- For a main-group metal ion, the highest n level of electrons is "last-in, first-out"
- For a transition-metal ion, the highest n level of electrons is "first-in, first out."

Electron Configurations of Transition Metal Ions In contrast to most main-group ions, *transition metal ions rarely attain a noble gas configuration,* and the reason, once again, is that energy costs are too high. The exceptions in Period 4 are scandium, which forms Sc^{3+}, and occasionally titanium, which forms Ti^{4+} in some of its compounds. The typical behavior of a transition element is to *form more than one cation by losing all of its ns and some of its $(n - 1)d$ electrons.*

We focus here on the Period 4 transition series, but these points hold for the other series as well. In the aufbau process of building up the ground-state atoms, Period 3 ends with the noble gas argon. At the beginning of Period 4, the greater penetration of the 4s orbital makes it more stable than the empty 3d. Therefore, the first and second added electrons of the period enter the 4s in K and Ca. However, when we reach the transition elements and the 3d orbitals begin to fill, the increasing nuclear charge attracts their electrons more and more strongly. Moreover, since they fill inner orbitals, the added 3d electrons are not very well shielded from the increasing nuclear charge by the 4s electrons. As a result, the 3d orbital becomes *more stable* than the 4s. In effect, as Figure 8.24 shows, a *crossover in orbital energy* takes place as we proceed into the transition metals of Period 4. The effect on ion formation is critical: because the 3d orbitals are more stable, *the 4s electrons are lost first to form the Period 4 transition metal ions.*

Based on these points, it is clear that *electrons with the highest n value are removed first,* but here are a few simple rules for forming the ion of any main-group or transition element:

- For main-group, s-block metals, remove all electrons with the highest n value.
- For main-group, p-block metals, remove np electrons before ns electrons.
- For transition (d-block) metals, remove ns electrons before $(n - 1)d$ electrons.
- For nonmetals, add electrons to the p orbitals of highest n value.

Magnetic Properties of Transition Metal Ions Since we cannot *see* electrons in orbitals, how do we know that a particular electron configuration is correct? Although analysis of atomic spectra is the most important method for determining configuration, the magnetic properties of an element and its compounds can support or refute conclusions from spectra. Recall that an electron's spin generates a tiny magnetic field, and that a beam of H atoms splits in an external magnetic field (see Figure 8.1). Only chemical species (atoms, ions, or molecules) with one or more *unpaired* electrons are affected by the external field. The species used in the original 1921 split-beam experiment was silver atoms:

Ag ($Z = 47$)   [Kr] $5s^1 4d^{10}$

Note the unpaired 5s electron. A beam of cadmium atoms, the element after silver, is not split because its 5s electrons are *paired* (Cd: [Kr] $5s^2 4d^{10}$).

Paramagnetism is the tendency of a species with unpaired electrons to be attracted by an external magnetic field. A species with all electrons paired exhibits **diamagnetism:** it is not attracted (and in fact is slightly repelled) by a magnetic field, as you can see in Figure 8.25. Many transition metals and their compounds are paramagnetic because their atoms and ions have unpaired electrons.

Let's see how studies of paramagnetism might be used to provide additional evidence for a proposed configuration. Spectral analysis of the titanium atom yields the configuration [Ar] $4s^2 3d^2$. Experiment shows that Ti metal is paramagnetic, which is consistent with the presence of unpaired electrons in its atoms. Spectral analysis of the Ti^{2+} ion yields the configuration [Ar] $3d^2$, indicating loss of the two $4s$ electrons. Once again, experiment supports these findings by showing that Ti^{2+} compounds are paramagnetic. If Ti had lost its two $3d$ electrons during ion formation, its compounds would be diamagnetic because the $4s$ electrons are paired. Thus, the [Ar] $3d^2$ configuration supports the idea that electrons of highest n value are lost first:

$$Ti\ ([Ar]\ 4s^2 3d^2) \longrightarrow Ti^{2+}\ ([Ar]\ 3d^2) + 2e^-$$

The partial orbital diagrams are

An increase in paramagnetism occurs when iron metal (Fe) forms Fe^{3+} compounds. This fact is consistent with Fe losing its $4s$ electrons and one of its paired $3d$ electrons:

$$Fe\ ([Ar]\ 4s^2 3d^6) \longrightarrow Fe^{3+}\ ([Ar]\ 3d^5) + 3e^-$$

Copper (Cu) is paramagnetic but zinc (Zn) is diamagnetic, as are the Cu^+ and Zn^{2+} ions. These observations support the electron configurations proposed by spectral analysis. The ions happen to be isoelectronic with each other:

$$Cu\ ([Ar]\ 4s^1 3d^{10}) \longrightarrow Cu^+\ ([Ar]\ 3d^{10}) + e^-$$
$$Zn\ ([Ar]\ 4s^2 3d^{10}) \longrightarrow Zn^{2+}\ ([Ar]\ 3d^{10}) + 2e^-$$

A

B

Figure 8.25 Apparatus for measuring the magnetic behavior of a sample. The substance is weighed on a very sensitive balance in the absence of an external magnetic field. **A,** If a substance is diamagnetic (has no unpaired electrons), its apparent mass is unaffected (or slightly reduced) when the magnetic field is "on." **B,** If a substance is paramagnetic (has unpaired electrons), its apparent mass increases when the field is "on" because the balance arm feels an additional force. This method is used to estimate the number of unpaired electrons in transition-metal compounds.

Sample Problem 8.7   Writing Electron Configurations and Predicting Magnetic Behavior of Transition Metal Ions

PROBLEM Use condensed electron configurations to write reactions for the formation of the following transition metal ions, and predict whether the ion is paramagnetic: **(a)** Mn^{2+} ($Z = 25$); **(b)** Cr^{3+} ($Z = 24$); **(c)** Hg^{2+} ($Z = 80$).
PLAN We first write the condensed configuration of the atom, noting the irregularity in Cr in (b). Then we remove electrons, beginning with ns electrons, to attain the ion charge. If unpaired electrons are present, the ion is paramagnetic.
SOLUTION (a) $Mn\ ([Ar]\ 4s^2 3d^5) \longrightarrow Mn^{2+}\ ([Ar]\ 3d^5) + 2e^-$
There are five unpaired e^-, so Mn^{2+} is paramagnetic.
(b) $Cr\ ([Ar]\ 4s^1 3d^5) \longrightarrow Cr^{3+}\ ([Ar]\ 3d^3) + 3e^-$
There are three unpaired e^-, so Cr^{3+} is paramagnetic.
(c) $Hg\ ([Xe]\ 6s^2 4f^{14} 5d^{10}) \longrightarrow Hg^{2+}\ ([Xe]\ 4f^{14} 5d^{10}) + 2e^-$
There are no unpaired e^-, so Hg^{2+} is *not* paramagnetic (is diamagnetic).
CHECK We removed the ns electrons first, and the sum of the lost electrons and those in the electron configuration of the ion equals Z.

Follow-up Problem 8.7   Write the condensed electron configuration of the following transition metal ions and predict whether they are paramagnetic: (a) V^{3+} ($Z = 23$); (b) Ni^{2+} ($Z = 28$); (c) La^{3+} ($Z = 57$).

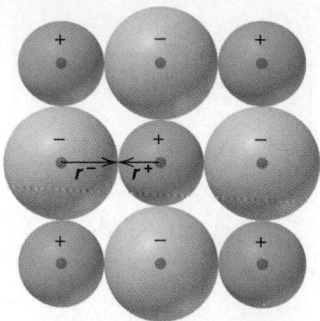

Figure 8.26 Depicting ionic radius. The cation radius (r^+) and the anion radius (r^-) each make up a portion of the total distance between the nuclei of adjacent ions in a crystalline ionic compound.

Ionic Size vs. Atomic Size The **ionic radius** is an estimate of the size of an ion in a crystalline ionic compound. You can picture it as the ion's portion of the distance between neighboring ions in the solid (Figure 8.26). From the relation between effective nuclear charge and atomic size, we can predict the size of an ion relative to its parent atom:

- *Cations are smaller than their parent atoms.* When a cation forms, electrons are *removed from* the outer level. The resulting decrease in electron repulsions allows the nuclear charge to pull the remaining electrons closer.
- *Anions are larger than their parent atoms.* When an anion forms, electrons are *added to* the outer level. The increase in repulsions causes the electrons to occupy more space.

Figure 8.27 shows the radii of some common main-group monatomic ions relative to their parent atoms. As you can see, *ionic size increases down a group* because the number of energy levels increases. Across a period, however, the pattern is more complex. Size decreases moderately among the cations, then increases tremendously when we reach the anions, and then decreases moderately again among the anions.

This pattern results from changes in effective nuclear charge and electron repulsions. In Period 3 (Na through Cl), for example, increasing Z_{eff} from left to right makes Na^+ larger than Mg^{2+}, which in turn is larger than Al^{3+}. The great jump in size from cations to anions occurs because we are *adding* electrons rather than removing them, so repulsions increase sharply. For instance, P^{3-} has eight more electrons than Al^{3+}. Then, the ongoing rise in Z_{eff} makes

Figure 8.27 Ionic vs. atomic radii. The atomic radii (*colored half-spheres*) and ionic radii (*grey half-spheres*) of some main-group elements are arranged in periodic table format (with all values in picometers). Note that metals (*blue*) form positive ions that are smaller than the atoms, whereas nonmetals (*tan*) form negative ions that are larger. The dashed outline includes ions of Period 2 nonmetals and Period 3 metals that are *isoelectronic* with each other. Note the size decrease from anion to cation.

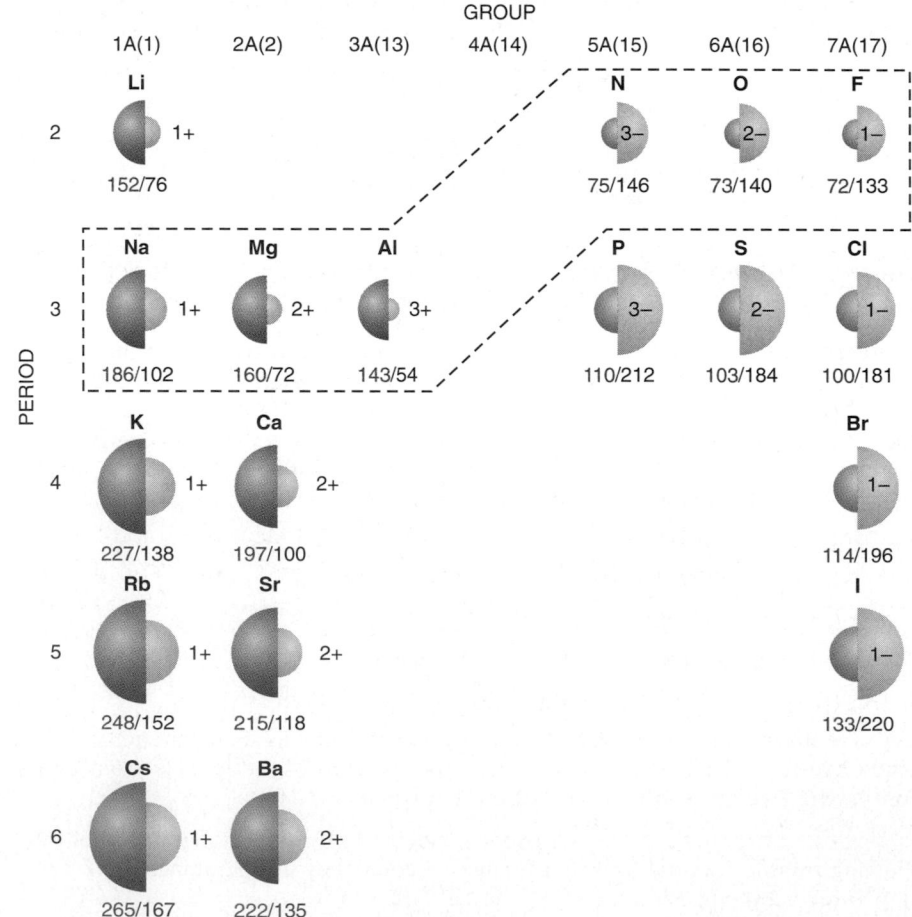

P^{3-} larger than S^{2-}, which is larger than Cl^-. These factors lead to some striking effects even among ions with the same number of electrons. Look at the ions within the dashed outline in Figure 8.27, which are all isoelectronic with neon. Even though the cations form from elements in the next period, the anions are still much larger. The pattern is

$$3- > 2- > 1- > 1+ > 2+ > 3+$$

When an element forms more than one cation, *the greater the ionic charge, the smaller the ionic radius.* Consider Fe^{2+} and Fe^{3+}. The number of protons is the same, but Fe^{3+} has one fewer electron, so electron repulsions are reduced somewhat. As a result, Z_{eff} increases, which pulls the electrons closer, so Fe^{3+} is smaller than Fe^{2+}.

To summarize the main points,

- Ionic size increases down a group.
- Ionic size decreases across a period but increases from cation to anion.
- Ionic size decreases with increasing positive (or decreasing negative) charge in an isoelectronic series.
- Ionic size decreases as charge increases for different cations of a given element.

Sample Problem 8.8   Ranking Ions by Size

PROBLEM Rank each set of ions in order of *decreasing* size, and explain your ranking:
(a) Ca^{2+}, Sr^{2+}, Mg^{2+}
(b) K^+, S^{2-}, Cl^-
(c) Au^+, Au^{3+}
PLAN We find the position of each element in the periodic table and apply the ideas presented in the text.
SOLUTION (a) Since Mg^{2+}, Ca^{2+}, and Sr^{2+} are all from Group 2A(2), they decrease in size up the group: $Sr^{2+} > Ca^{2+} > Mg^{2+}$.

(b) The ions K^+, S^{2-}, and Cl^- are isoelectronic. S^{2-} has a lower Z_{eff} than Cl^-, so it is larger. K^+ is a cation, and has the highest Z_{eff}, so it is smaller: $S^{2-} > Cl^- > K^+$.

(c) Au^+ has a lower charge than Au^{3+}, so it is larger: $Au^+ > Au^{3+}$.

Follow-up Problem 8.8   Rank the ions in each set in order of *increasing* size:
(a) Cl^-, Br^-, F^-
(b) Na^+, Mg^{2+}, F^-
(c) Cr^{2+}, Cr^{3+}

Section Summary

Highly metallic behavior correlates with large atomic size and low ionization energy. Thus, metallic behavior increases down a group and decreases across a period. Among the main groups, metal oxides are basic and nonmetal oxides acidic. Thus, oxides become more acidic across a period and more basic down a group. Many main-group elements form ions that are isoelectronic with the nearest noble gas. Removing (or adding) more electrons than needed to give the noble gas configuration involves a prohibitive amount of energy. Metals in Groups 3A(13) to 5A(15) lose either their np electrons or both their ns and np electrons. Transition metals lose ns electrons before $(n-1)d$ electrons and commonly form more than one ion. Many transition metals and their compounds are paramagnetic because their atoms (or ions) have unpaired electrons. Cations are smaller and anions larger than their parent atoms. Ionic radius increases down a group. Across a period, cationic and anionic radii decrease, but a large increase occurs from cation to anion.

Chapter Perspective

This chapter is our springboard to understanding the chemistry of the elements. We have begun to see that recurring electron configurations lead to trends in atomic properties, which in turn lead to trends in chemical behavior. With this insight, we can go on to investigate how atoms bond (Chapter 9), how molecular shapes arise (Chapter 10), the models we use to explain molecular shapes and other properties (Chapter 11), how the physical properties of liquids and solids emerge from

atomic properties (Chapter 12), and how those properties influence the solution process (Chapter 13). We will briefly review these ideas and gain a perspective on where they lead (Interchapter) before we can survey elemental behavior in greater detail (Chapter 14) and see how it applies to the remarkable diversity of organic compounds (Chapter 15). Within this group of chapters, you will see chemical models come alive in chemical facts.

The following learning objectives, with section and/or sample problem (SP) numbers in parentheses, can help focus your study:

Understand These Concepts

1. The meaning of the periodic law and the arrangement of elements by atomic number (8.1)
2. The reason for the spin quantum number and its two possible values (8.2)
3. How the exclusion principle applies to orbital filling (8.2)
4. The effects of nuclear charge, shielding, and penetration on the splitting of orbital energies; the meaning of effective nuclear charge (8.2)
5. How the order in the periodic table is based on the order of orbital energies (8.3)
6. How orbitals are filled in main-group and transition elements; the importance of Hund's rule (8.3)
7. How group outer electron configuration is related to chemical behavior (8.3)
8. The distinction among inner, outer, and valence electrons (8.3)
9. The meaning of atomic radius, ionization energy, and electron affinity (8.4)
10. How *n* value and effective nuclear charge give rise to the periodic trends of atomic size and ionization energy (8.4)
11. The effect of core electrons on the pattern of successive ionization energies (8.4)
12. How atomic properties are related to the tendency to form ions (8.4)
13. The general properties of metals and nonmetals (8.5)

14. How the vertical and horizontal trends in metallic behavior are related to ion formation and oxide acidity (8.5)
15. Why main-group monatomic ions are isoelectronic with either noble gas or pseudo–noble gas electron configurations (8.5)
16. The origin of paramagnetic and diamagnetic behavior (8.5)
17. The relation between ionic and atomic size and the trends in ionic size (8.5)

Master These Skills

1. Writing electron configurations and orbital diagrams and using them to learn the set of quantum numbers for any electron in an atom (SP 8.1)
2. Knowing the order of sublevel energies in the periodic table (8.3)
3. Writing full and condensed electron configurations of an element (SP 8.2)
4. Using periodic trends to rank elements by atomic size and ionization energy (SPs 8.3 and 8.4)
5. Identifying an element from its successive ionization energies (SP 8.5)
6. Writing electron configurations of main-group and transition element monatomic ions (SPs 8.6 and 8.7)
7. Using periodic trends to rank ions by relative size (SP 8.8)

For Review and Reference

Key Terms

electron configuration

Section 8.1
periodic law

Section 8.2
spin quantum number (m_s)
exclusion principle
shielding
effective nuclear charge (Z_{eff})
penetration

Section 8.3
aufbau principle
orbital diagram
Hund's rule
transition elements
inner (core) electrons
outer electrons
valence electrons

inner transition elements
lanthanides (rare earths)
actinides

Section 8.4
metallic radius
covalent radius
ionization energy (IE)
electron affinity (EA)

Section 8.5
amphoteric
isoelectronic
pseudo–noble gas configuration
paramagnetism
diamagnetism
ionic radius

Highlighted Figures and Tables

These figures (F) and tables (T) provide a quick review of key ideas. Entries in color contain frequently used data.

Answers to Follow-up Problems

8.1 The element has eight electrons, so $Z = 8$: oxygen.

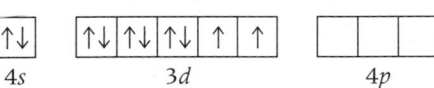

$$n = 2, \, l = 1, \, m_l = 0, \, m_s = +\tfrac{1}{2}$$

8.2 (a) For Ni, $1s^2 2s^2 2p^6 3s^2 3p^6 4s^2 3d^8$; [Ar] $4s^2 3d^8$

Ni has 18 inner electrons.
(b) For Sr, $1s^2 2s^2 2p^6 3s^2 3p^6 4s^2 3d^{10} 4p^6 5s^2$; [Kr] $5s^2$

Sr has 36 inner electrons.
(c) For Po,
$1s^2 2s^2 2p^6 3s^2 3p^6 4s^2 3d^{10} 4p^6 5s^2 4d^{10} 5p^6 6s^2 4f^{14} 5d^{10} 6p^4$

[Xe] $6s^2 4f^{14} 5d^{10} 6p^4$

Po has 78 inner electrons.
8.3 (a) Cl < Br < Se; (b) Xe < I < Ba
8.4 (a) Sn < Sb < I; (b) Ba < Sr < Ca
8.5 Q is aluminum: $1s^2 2s^2 2p^6 3s^2 3p^1$
8.6 (a) Ba ([Xe] $6s^2$) $\longrightarrow$ Ba^{2+} ([Xe]) + 2e$^-$
(b) O ([He] $2s^2 2p^4$) + 2e$^-$ $\longrightarrow$
$\qquad\qquad$ O^{2-} ([He] $2s^2 2p^6$) (same as Ne)
(c) Pb ([Xe] $6s^2 4f^{14} 5d^{10} 6p^2$) $\longrightarrow$
$\qquad\qquad$ Pb^{2+} ([Xe] $6s^2 4f^{14} 5d^{10}$) + 2e$^-$
Pb ([Xe] $6s^2 4f^{14} 5d^{10} 6p^2$) $\longrightarrow$ Pb^{4+} ([Xe] $4f^{14} 5d^{10}$) + 4e$^-$
8.7 (a) V^{3+}: [Ar] $3d^2$; paramagnetic
(b) Ni^{2+}: [Ar] $3d^8$; paramagnetic
(c) La^{3+}: [Xe]; not paramagnetic (diamagnetic)
8.8 (a) F$^-$ < Cl$^-$ < Br$^-$; (b) Mg^{2+} < Na$^+$ < F$^-$;
(c) Cr^{3+} < Cr^{2+}

Problems

Problems with a **colored** number are answered at the back of the text. Problem sections match the text and provide the number(s) of relevant sample problems. Most offer concept review questions, skill-building exercises (written in similar pairs), and problems in a relevant context. Following these are comprehensive problems based on material from any section and/or previous chapter.

Development of the Periodic Table

■ Concept Review Questions

8.1 What would be your reaction to a claim that a new element had been discovered that fit between tin (Sn) and antimony (Sb) in the periodic table?
8.2 In his study of atomic x-ray spectra, the English physicist Henry Moseley made a discovery that replaced atomic mass as the criterion for ordering the elements. By what criterion are the elements ordered in the periodic table now? Give an

example of a sequence of element order that was confirmed by Moseley's findings.

■ Skill-Building Exercises (paired)

8.3 Before Mendeleev published his periodic table, J. W. Döbereiner grouped similar elements into triads in which the unknown properties of one member could be predicted by averaging known values of the properties of the others. To test this idea, predict the values of the following quantities: (a) the atomic mass of K from the atomic masses of Na and Rb; (b) the melting point of Br$_2$ from the melting points of Cl$_2$ ($-101.0°$C) and I$_2$ ($113.6°$C) (actual value $= -7.2°$C).
8.4 To test Döbereiner's idea (see Problem 8.3), predict the values of the following quantities: (a) the boiling point of HBr from the boiling points of HCl ($-84.9°$C) and HI ($-35.4°$C) (actual value $= -67.0°$C); (b) the boiling point of AsH$_3$ from the boiling points of PH$_3$ ($-87.4°$C), and SbH$_3$ ($-17.1°$C) (actual value $= -55°$C).

Characteristics of Many-Electron Atoms

■ Concept Review Questions

8.5 Summarize the rules for the allowable values of the four quantum numbers of an electron in an atom.

8.6 Which of the quantum numbers relate(s) to the electron only? Which relate(s) to the orbital?

8.7 State the exclusion principle in your own words. What does it imply about the number and spin of electrons in an atomic orbital?

8.8 What is the key distinction between sublevel energies in one-electron species, such as the H atom, and in many-electron species, such as the C atom? What factors lead to this distinction? Would you expect the pattern of sublevel energies in Be^{3+} to be more like that in H or in C? Explain.

8.9 Define shielding and effective nuclear charge. What is the connection between the two?

8.10 What is the penetration effect? How is it related to shielding? Use the penetration effect to explain the difference in relative orbital energies of a $3p$ electron and a $3d$ electron in the same atom.

■ Skill-Building Exercises (paired)

8.11 How many electrons in an atom can have each of the following quantum number or sublevel designations?
(a) $n = 2, l = 1$ (b) $3d$ (c) $4s$

8.12 How many electrons in an atom can have each of the following quantum number or sublevel designations?
(a) $n = 2, l = 1, m_l = 0$ (b) $5p$ (c) $n = 4, l = 3$

8.13 How many electrons in an atom can have each of the following quantum number or sublevel designations?
(a) $4p$ (b) $n = 3, l = 1, m_l = +1$ (c) $n = 5, l = 3$

8.14 How many electrons in an atom can have each of the following quantum number or sublevel designations?
(a) $2s$ (b) $n = 3, l = 2$ (c) $6d$

The Quantum-Mechanical Model and the Periodic Table

(Sample Problems 8.1 and 8.2)

■ Concept Review Questions

8.15 State the periodic law in your own words, and explain its relation to electron configuration. (Use Na and K in your explanation.)

8.16 State Hund's rule in your own words, and show its application in the orbital box diagram of the nitrogen atom.

8.17 How does the aufbau principle, in connection with the periodic law, lead to the format of the periodic table?

8.18 For the main-group elements, are outer electron configurations similar or different within a group? Within a period? Explain.

8.19 For which blocks of elements are outer electrons the same as valence electrons? For which are d electrons often included among valence electrons?

8.20 What is the general rule for the total electron capacity of an energy level? Apply it to determine the capacity of the fourth level.

■ Skill-Building Exercises (paired)

8.21 Write a full set of quantum numbers for the following:
(a) The outermost electron in an Rb atom
(b) The electron gained when an S^- ion becomes an S^{2-} ion
(c) The electron lost when an Ag atom ionizes
(d) The electron gained when an F^- ion forms from an F atom

8.22 Write a full set of quantum numbers for the following:
(a) The outermost electron in an Li atom
(b) The electron gained when a Br atom becomes a Br^- ion
(c) The electron lost when a Cs atom ionizes
(d) The highest energy electron in the ground-state B atom

8.23 Write the full ground-state electron configuration for the following: (a) Rb; (b) Ge; (c) Ar.

8.24 Write the full ground-state electron configuration for the following: (a) Br; (b) Mg; (c) Se.

8.25 Write the full ground-state electron configuration for the following: (a) Cl; (b) Si; (c) Sr.

8.26 Write the full ground-state electron configuration for the following: (a) S; (b) Kr; (c) Cs.

8.27 Draw an orbital diagram showing valence electrons, and write the condensed ground-state electron configuration for each of the following: (a) Ti; (b) Cl; (c) V.

8.28 Draw an orbital diagram showing valence electrons, and write the condensed ground-state electron configuration for each of the following: (a) Ba; (b) Co; (c) Ag.

8.29 Draw an orbital diagram showing valence electrons, and write the condensed ground-state electron configuration for each of the following: (a) Mn; (b) P; (c) Fe.

8.30 Draw an orbital diagram showing valence electrons, and write the condensed ground-state electron configuration for each of the following: (a) Ga; (b) Zn; (c) Sc.

8.31 Draw the partial (valence-level) orbital diagram and write the symbol, group number, and period number of the element represented by each of the following:
(a) $[He] 2s^2 2p^4$ (b) $[Ne] 3s^2 3p^3$

8.32 Draw the partial (valence-level) orbital diagram and write the symbol, group number, and period number of the element represented by each of the following:
(a) $[Kr] 5s^2 4d^{10}$ (b) $[Ar] 4s^2 3d^8$

8.33 Draw the partial (valence-level) orbital diagram and write the symbol, group number, and period number of the element represented by each of the following:
(a) $[Ne] 3s^2 3p^5$ (b) $[Ar] 4s^2 3d^{10} 4p^3$

8.34 Draw the partial (valence-level) orbital diagram and write the symbol, group number, and period number of the element represented by each of the following:
(a) $[Ar] 4s^2 3d^5$ (b) $[Kr] 5s^2 4d^2$

8.35 From the following partial (valence-level) orbital diagram, write the ground-state electron configuration and the group number:

8.36 From the following partial (valence-level) orbital diagram, write the ground-state electron configuration and the group number:

8.37 How many inner, outer, and valence electrons are present in an atom of the following elements?
(a) O　　(b) Sn　　(c) Ca　　(d) Fe　　(e) Se

8.38 How many inner, outer, and valence electrons are present in an atom of the following elements?
(a) Br　　(b) Cs　　(c) Cr　　(d) Sr　　(e) F

8.39 Identify each element below, and give the symbols of the other elements in its group:
(a) [He] $2s^2 2p^1$　　(b) [Ne] $3s^2 3p^4$　　(c) [Xe] $6s^2 5d^1$

8.40 Identify each element below, and give the symbols of the other elements in its group:
(a) [Ar] $4s^2 3d^{10} 4p^4$　　(b) [Xe] $6s^2 4f^{14} 5d^2$　　(c) [Ar] $4s^2 3d^5$

8.41 Identify each element below, and give the symbols of the other elements in its group:
(a) [He] $2s^2 2p^2$　　(b) [Ar] $4s^2 3d^3$　　(c) [Ne] $3s^2 3p^3$

8.42 Identify each element below, and give the symbols of the other elements in its group:
(a) [Ar] $4s^2 3d^{10} 4p^2$　　(b) [Ar] $4s^2 3d^7$　　(c) [Kr] $5s^2 4d^5$

■ **Problems in Context**

8.43 After an atom in its ground state absorbs energy, it exists in an excited state. Spectral lines are produced when the atom returns to its ground state. The yellow-orange line in the sodium spectrum, for example, is produced by the emission of energy when excited sodium atoms return to their ground state. Write the electron configuration and the orbital diagram of the first excited state of sodium. (*Hint:* the outermost electron is excited.)

8.44 One reason spectroscopists study excited states is to gain information about the energies of orbitals that are unoccupied in an atom's ground state. Each of the following electron configurations represents an atom in an excited state. Identify the element, and write its condensed ground-state electron configuration:
(a) $1s^2 2s^2 2p^6 3s^1 3p^1$
(b) $1s^2 2s^2 2p^6 3s^2 3p^4 4s^1$
(c) $1s^2 2s^2 2p^6 3s^2 3p^6 4s^2 3d^4 4p^1$
(d) $1s^2 2s^2 2p^6 3s^2 3p^6 4s^2 3d^{10} 4p^6 5s^1 4d^2$
(e) $1s^2 2s^2 2p^5 3s^1$

Trends in Some Key Periodic Atomic Properties
(Sample Problems 8.3 to 8.5)

■ **Concept Review Questions**

8.45 Since the exact outer limit of an isolated atom cannot be measured, what criterion can we use to determine atomic radii? What is the difference between a covalent radius and a metallic radius?

8.46 Explain the relationship between the trends in atomic size and ionization energy (IE) within the main groups in the periodic table.

8.47 In what region of the periodic table will you find elements with relatively high IEs? With relatively low IEs?

8.48 Why do successive IEs of a given element always increase? When the difference between successive IEs of a given element is exceptionally large (for example, between IE_1 and IE_2 of K), what do we learn about its electron configuration?

8.49 In a plot of IE_1 for the Period 3 elements, why do the values for elements in Groups 3A(13) and 6A(16) drop slightly below the generally increasing trend?

8.50 Which group in the periodic table has elements with high (endothermic) IE_1 and very negative (exothermic) first electron affinities (EA_1)? What is the charge on the ions that these atoms form?

8.51 The EA_2 of an oxygen atom is positive, even though its EA_1 is negative. Why does this change of sign occur? Which other elements exhibit a positive EA_2? Explain.

8.52 How does *d*-electron shielding influence atomic size among the Period 4 transition elements?

■ **Skill-Building Exercises (paired)**

8.53 Arrange each set in order of *increasing* atomic size:
(a) Rb, K, Cs　　(b) C, O, Be　　(c) Cl, K, S　　(d) Mg, K, Ca

8.54 Arrange each set in order of *decreasing* atomic size:
(a) Ge, Pb, Sn　　(b) Sn, Te, Sr　　(c) F, Ne, Na　　(d) Be, Mg, Na

8.55 Arrange each set of atoms in order of *increasing* IE_1:
(a) Sr, Ca, Ba　　(b) N, B, Ne　　(c) Br, Rb, Se　　(d) As, Sb, Sn

8.56 Arrange each set of atoms in order of *decreasing* IE_1:
(a) Na, Li, K　　(b) Be, F, C　　(c) Cl, Ar, Na　　(d) Cl, Br, Se

8.57 Write the full electron configuration of the Period 2 element with the following successive IEs (in kJ/mol):
$IE_1 = 801$　　　　$IE_2 = 2427$　　　　$IE_3 = 3659$
$IE_4 = 25{,}022$　　$IE_5 = 32{,}822$

8.58 Write the full electron configuration of the Period 3 element with the following successive IEs (in kJ/mol):
$IE_1 = 738$　　　　$IE_2 = 1450$　　　　$IE_3 = 7732$
$IE_4 = 10{,}539$　　$IE_5 = 13{,}628$

8.59 Which element in each of the following sets would you expect to have the *highest* IE_2?
(a) Na, Mg, Al　　(b) Na, K, Fe　　(c) Sc, Be, Mg

8.60 Which element in each of the following sets would you expect to have the *lowest* IE_3?
(a) Na, Mg, Al　　(b) K, Ca, Sc　　(c) Li, Al, B

The Connection Between Atomic Structure and Chemical Reactivity
(Sample Problems 8.6 to 8.8)

■ **Concept Review Questions**

8.61 List three ways in which metals and nonmetals differ.

8.62 Summarize the trend in metallic character as a function of position in the periodic table. Is it the same as the trend in atomic size? Ionization energy?

8.63 Summarize the acid-base behavior of main-group metal and nonmetal oxides in water. How does oxide acidity in water change down a group and across a period?

8.64 What ions are possible for the two largest elements in Group 4A(14)? How does each arise?

8.65 What is a pseudo–noble gas configuration? Give an example of one from Group 3A(13).

8.66 How are measurements of paramagnetism used to support an electron configuration derived spectroscopically? Use Cu(I) and Cu(II) chlorides as examples.

8.67 The charges of a set of isoelectronic ions vary from 3+ to 3−. Place ions in order of increasing size.

■ **Skill-Building Exercises (paired)**

8.68 Which element would you expect to be *more* metallic:
(a) Ca or Rb; (b) Mg or Ra; (c) Br or I?

8.69 Which element would you expect to be *more* metallic:
(a) S or Cl; (b) In or Al; (c) As or Br?

8.70 Which element would you expect to be *less* metallic: (a) Sb or As; (b) Si or P; (c) Be or Na?

8.71 Which element would you expect to be *less* metallic: (a) Cs or Rn; (b) Sn or Te; (c) Se or Ge?

8.72 Does the reaction of a main-group nonmetal oxide in water produce an acidic or a basic solution? Write a balanced equation for the reaction of a Group 6A(16) nonmetal oxide with water.

8.73 Does the reaction of a main-group metal oxide in water produce an acidic or a basic solution? Write a balanced equation for the reaction of a Group 2A(2) oxide with water.

8.74 Write the charge and full ground-state electron configuration of the monatomic ion most likely to be formed by each of the following: (a) Cl; (b) Na; (c) Ca.

8.75 Write the charge and full ground-state electron configuration of the monatomic ion most likely to be formed by each of the following: (a) Rb; (b) N; (c) Br.

8.76 Write the charge and full ground-state electron configuration of the monatomic ion most likely to be formed by each of the following: (a) Al; (b) S; (c) Sr.

8.77 Write the charge and full ground-state electron configuration of the monatomic ion most likely to be formed by each of the following: (a) P; (b) Mg; (c) Se.

8.78 How many unpaired electrons are present in the ground state of an atom from each of the following groups: (a) 2A(2); (b) 5A(15); (c) 8A(18); (d) 3A(13)?

8.79 How many unpaired electrons are present in the ground state of an atom from each of the following groups: (a) 4A(14); (b) 7A(17); (c) 1A(1); (d) 6A(16)?

8.80 Which of the following elements are paramagnetic in their ground state: (a) Ga; (b) Si; (c) Be; (d) Te?

8.81 Are compounds of the following ground-state ions paramagnetic: (a) Ti^{2+}; (b) Zn^{2+}; (c) Ca^{2+}; (d) Sn^{2+}?

8.82 Write the condensed ground-state electron configurations of the following transition metal ions, and state which are paramagnetic: (a) V^{3+}; (b) Cd^{2+}; (c) Co^{3+}; (d) Ag^{+}.

8.83 Write the condensed ground-state electron configurations of the following transition metal ions, and state which are paramagnetic: (a) Mo^{3+}; (b) Au^{+}; (c) Mn^{2+}; (d) Hf^{2+}.

8.84 Palladium (Pd; $Z = 46$) is diamagnetic. Draw partial orbital diagrams to show which of the following electron configurations is consistent with this fact:
(a) [Kr] $5s^2 4d^8$; (b) [Kr] $4d^{10}$; (c) [Kr] $5s^1 4d^9$.

8.85 Niobium (Nb; $Z = 41$) has an unexpected ground-state electron configuration for a Group 5B(5) element: [Kr] $5s^1 4d^4$. What is the expected electron configuration for elements in this group? Draw partial orbital diagrams to show how paramagnetic measurements could be used to support niobium's actual configuration.

8.86 Rank the ions in each of the following sets in order of *increasing* size, and explain your ranking:
(a) Li^+, K^+, Na^+ (b) Se^{2-}, Rb^+, Br^- (c) O^{2-}, F^-, N^{3-}

8.87 Rank the ions in each of the following sets in order of *decreasing* size, and explain your ranking:
(a) Se^{2-}, S^{2-}, O^{2-} (b) Te^{2-}, Cs^+, I^- (c) Sr^{2+}, Ba^{2+}, Cs^+

Comprehensive Problems
Problems with an asterisk (*) are more challenging.

8.88 Some versions of the periodic table show hydrogen at the top of Group 1A(1) *and* at the top of Group 7A(17). What properties of hydrogen could justify each of these placements?

8.89 Test your familiarity with the layout of the periodic table. Which element is described by each of the following? Place the letter of the question (a, b, c, etc.) in the correct element box.
(a) Smallest atomic radius in Group 6A
(b) Largest atomic radius in Period 6
(c) Smallest atomic radius in Period 3
(d) Highest IE_1 in Group 14
(e) Lowest IE_1 in Period 5
(f) Most metallic in Group 15
(g) Group 3A element that forms most basic oxide
(h) Period 4 element with filled outer level
(i) Condensed ground-state electron configuration is [Ne] $3s^2 3p^2$
(j) Condensed ground-state electron configuration is [Kr] $5s^2 4d^6$
(k) Forms 2+ ion with electron configuration [Ar] $3d^3$
(l) Period 5 element that forms 3+ ion with pseudo–noble gas configuration
(m) Period 4 transition element that forms 3+ diamagnetic ion
(n) Period 4 transition element that forms 2+ ion with a half-filled d sublevel

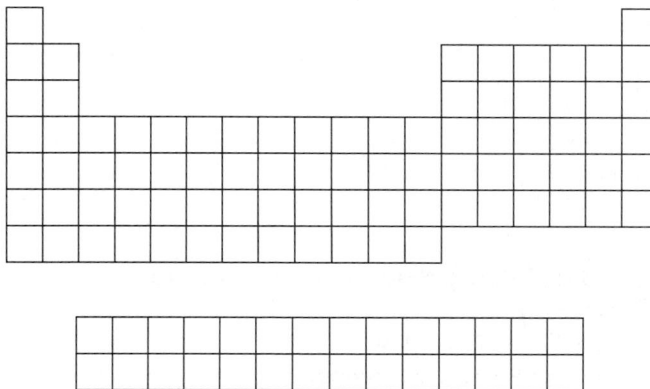

8.90 Based on the general vertical and horizontal trends in periodic properties, explain why it might be difficult to rank the following pairs:
(a) K and Sr in terms of atomic size
(b) Mn and Fe in terms of IE_1
(c) Na and Ca in terms of metallic character
(d) P and Se in terms of oxide acidity

8.91 Name each element and write its full ground-state electron configuration:
(a) The smallest metal in Period 3
(b) The heaviest lanthanide
(c) The lightest transition metal in Period 5
(d) The Period 3 member whose 2− ion is isoelectronic with Ar

(e) The alkaline earth metal whose cation is isoelectronic with Kr

(f) The Group 5A(15) metalloid with the most acidic oxide

*8.92 A fundamental relationship of electrostatics states that the energy required to separate opposite charges of magnitudes Q_1 and Q_2 that are distance d apart is proportional to $\dfrac{Q_1 \times Q_2}{d}$. Use this relationship and any other factors to explain the following observations: (a) the IE_2 of He ($Z = 2$) is *more* than twice the IE_1 of H ($Z = 1$); (b) the IE_1 of He is *less* than twice the IE_1 of H.

*8.93 You are trapped in an alternative universe in which the quantum number assignments are the same as in ours, except that the quantum number l is an integer from 0 to n. What are the atomic numbers for the two smallest noble gases in the alternative universe?

8.94 Write the formula and name of the compound formed from the following ionic interactions:

(a) The 2+ ion and the 1− ion are both isoelectronic with the atoms of a chemically unreactive Period 4 element.

(b) The 2+ ion and the 2− ion are both isoelectronic with the Period 3 noble gas.

(c) The 2+ ion is the smallest with a filled d subshell; the anion forms from the smallest halogen.

(d) The ions form from the largest and smallest ionizable elements in Period 2.

*8.95 For over a century, chemists have noted several "diagonal relationships" in the periodic table: exceptional similarities between an element in Period 2 and another in Period 3 in the next higher group. Suggest a reason based on atomic and ionic properties for each of the following: (a) the chemical behavior of Li is very similar to that of Mg; (b) the acidity of $Be(OH)_2$ is very similar to that of $Al(OH)_3$.

8.96 Predict the sign of ΔH for each of the following reactions and explain your prediction:

(a) $Li(g) + Na^-(g) \longrightarrow Li^-(g) + Na(g)$

(b) $Na^+(g) + K(g) \longrightarrow Na(g) + K^+(g)$

8.97 Calculate the longest wavelength of electromagnetic radiation that could ionize an atom of each of the following elements:

(a) Li; $IE_1 = 520.1$ kJ/mol   (b) Au; $IE_1 = 889.9$ kJ/mol
(c) Cl; $IE_1 = 1255.7$ kJ/mol

8.98 Gallium lies below aluminum in Group 3A(13), but it has a smaller radius. What causes this deviation from the general trend in atomic size? What other atomic property of Ga might also have a value outside the expected trend?

8.99 In Group 4A(14), carbon (a nonmetal) and silicon (a metalloid) have high melting points (4100°C and 1420°C,

respectively), whereas tin and lead are metals with low melting points (232°C and 327°C, respectively). Predict the full ground-state electron configuration and general physical properties of the as yet unknown Group 4A member with atomic number 114.

8.100 Scientists have speculated that as yet unknown superheavy elements might be moderately stable. In fact, in 1976, it was mistakenly believed that Element 126 had been discovered in a sample of mica. Predict the n and l quantum numbers for the outermost electron in an atom of this element. What is the sublevel designation of the outermost orbital? How many orbitals would be in this sublevel?

*8.101 A substance is colored because it absorbs only some of the wavelengths of incoming visible light. The absorbed light excites electrons into unfilled orbitals.

(a) Why are many salts of transition metals colored, whereas nearly all main-group salts are colorless?

(b) The energy difference between the $5d$ and $6s$ sublevels in gold accounts for its warm yellow color. Assuming this energy difference is about 2.7 eV (electron volt; 1 eV = 1.602×10^{-19} J), explain why gold has its characteristic color.

8.102 Draw the partial (valence-level) orbital diagram and electron configuration of the atom and monatomic ion of the element with the following ionization energies (kJ/mol):

IE_1	IE_2	IE_3	IE_4	IE_5	IE_6	IE_7	IE_8
999	2251	3361	4564	7013	8495	27,106	31,669

*8.103 Use electron configurations to account for the stability of the lanthanide ions Ce^{4+} and Eu^{2+}.

*8.104 On the planet Zog in the Andromeda galaxy, all of the stable elements have been studied. Data for some main-group elements are shown below (Zoggian units are unknown on Earth and, therefore, not shown). Limited communications with the Zoggians have indicated that balloonium is a monatomic gas with two positive charges in its nucleus. Use the data to deduce the names that Earthlings give to these elements:

NAME	ATOMIC RADIUS	IE_1	EA_1
Balloonium	10	339	+3.0
Inertium	24	297	+4.1
Allotropium	34	143	−28.6
Brinium	63	70.9	−7.6
Canium	47	101	−15.3
Fertilium	25	200	0
Liquidium	38	163	−46.4
Utilium	48	82.4	−6.1
Crimsonium	72	78.4	+23.9

9

Models of Chemical Bonding

Figure: Chemical bonds and macroscopic properties. The behavior of materials—hard or soft, conductor or insulator, brittle or malleable, high melting or low—emerges from the nature of their chemical bonds. Samples of fluorite, maple, and aluminum represent the three bonding models—ionic, covalent, and metallic—that we examine in this chapter, the three ways that combinations of attractive and repulsive forces join atoms together.

In Chapter 8, we examined the properties of individual atoms and ions. Yet, in nearly all natural substances these particles exist bound to one another. Indeed, much of the excitement of chemistry comes in discovering how atomic properties influence chemical bonding, which in turn is ultimately responsible for the behavior of the substances around us. Why, for instance, is table salt (or any other ionic compound) a hard, brittle, high-melting solid that conducts a current only when molten or dissolved in water? Why are wax and many other covalent substances low melting, nonbrittle, and nonconducting, whereas others, like diamond, are high melting and extremely hard? And why are metals shiny and bendable substances that conduct whether molten *or* solid? The answers lie in the *type of bonding* within the substance.

This chapter begins with an overview of how atomic properties give rise to the three major bonding models—ionic, covalent, and metallic. As each model is described, you'll see how it explains the properties of each type of substance. We discuss ionic bonding first and the energy involved in the formation of an ionic solid from its elements. Covalent bonding, which occurs in the vast majority of compounds, is treated in the next two sections. The first of these describes the formation and characteristics of a covalent bond. The second describes the range of bonding, from pure covalent to ionic, and shows that most bonds fall somewhere in between. The chapter ends with an introduction to metallic bonding.

9.1 Atomic Properties and Chemical Bonds

Before we examine the types of chemical bonding, we should ask *why* atoms bond at all. In general terms, they do so for one overriding reason: *bonding lowers the potential energy between positive and negative particles,* whether those particles are oppositely charged ions or atomic nuclei and the electrons between them. Just as the electron configuration and the strength of the nucleus-electron attraction determine the properties of an atom, the type and strength of chemical bonds determine the properties of a substance.

Types of Chemical Bonding

On the atomic level, we distinguish a metal from a nonmetal on the basis of several properties that correlate with position in the periodic table (Figure 9.1 and inside the front cover). Recall from Chapter 8 that metallic properties

Figure 9.1 A general comparison of metals and nonmetals. A, The relative magnitudes of some key atomic properties change within a period and correlate with an element being metallic or nonmetallic. **B,** Metals *(blue)* appear in the left and lower portions of the periodic table. Nonmetals *(yellow)* appear in the upper right portion and include hydrogen. Metalloids *(green)* are found along the stairlike line between metals and nonmetals.

PROPERTY	METAL ATOM	NONMETAL ATOM
Atomic size	Larger	Smaller
Z_{eff}	Lower	Higher
IE	Lower	Higher
EA	Lower	Higher

A Relative magnitudes of atomic properties within a period

B

Figure 9.2 **The three models of chemical bonding. A,** In ionic bonding, metal atoms transfer electron(s) to nonmetal atoms and form oppositely charged ions that attract each other to form a solid. **B,** In covalent bonding, two atoms share an electron pair localized between their nuclei (shown here as a bond line). Most covalent substances consist of individual molecules each consisting of two or more atoms. **C,** In metallic bonding, many metal atoms pool their valence electron(s) to form a delocalized "electron sea" that attracts the metal-ion cores together.

A Ionic bonding

B Covalent bonding

C Metallic bonding

generally decrease across a period and increase down a group. As a first step toward appreciating the importance of bonding, let's classify the types of bonding that result from the three combinations of the two types of atoms—metal with nonmetal, nonmetal with nonmetal, and metal with metal:

1. *Electron transfer and ionic bonding* (Figure 9.2A). We typically observe **ionic bonding** between atoms with large differences in their tendency to lose or gain electrons. Such differences occur between reactive metals [Groups 1A(1) and 2A(2)] and nonmetals [Groups 7A(17) and the top of 6A(16)]. The metal atom (low IE) loses its one or two valence electrons, whereas the nonmetal atom (highly negative EA) gains electrons. *Electron transfer* from metal to nonmetal occurs, and each atom forms an ion with a noble gas configuration. The electrostatic attraction between these positive and negative ions draws them into the three-dimensional array of an ionic solid, whose chemical formula represents the cation-to-anion ratio (empirical formula).

2. *Electron sharing and covalent bonding* (Figure 9.2B). When two atoms have a small difference in their tendency to lose or gain electrons, we observe *electron sharing* and **covalent bonding.** This type of bonding is most important between nonmetal atoms (although a pair of metal atoms can form a covalent bond also). Each nonmetal atom holds onto its own electrons tightly (high IE) and tends to attract other electrons as well. The attraction of each nucleus for the valence electrons of the other draws the atoms together. A shared electron pair is considered to be *localized* between the two atoms because it spends most of its time there, linking them in a covalent bond of a given length and strength. In most cases, separate molecules form when covalent bonding occurs, and the chemical formula reflects the actual numbers of atoms in the molecule (molecular formula).

3. *Electron pooling and metallic bonding* (Figure 9.2C). In general, metal atoms are relatively large, and their few outer electrons are well shielded by filled inner levels. Thus, they lose outer electrons comparatively easily (low IE) but do not gain them very readily (small or positive EA). These properties lead large numbers of metal atoms to share their valence electrons, but in a different way from covalent bonding. In the simplest model of **metallic bonding,** all the metal atoms in a sample *pool* their valence electrons into an evenly distributed "sea" of electrons that "flows" between and around the

metal-ion cores (nucleus plus inner electrons) and attracts them together. Unlike the localized electrons in covalent bonding, electrons in metallic bonding are *delocalized*, moving freely throughout the piece of metal.

It's important to remember that there are exceptions to these idealized bonding models in the world of real substances. You cannot always predict bond type solely from the elements' positions in the periodic table. For instance, all binary ionic compounds contain a metal and a nonmetal, but all metals do not form binary ionic compounds with all nonmetals. As just one example, when the metal beryllium [Group 2A(2)] combines with the non-metal chlorine [Group 7A(17)], the bonding fits the covalent model better than the ionic model. In other words, just as we see a gradation in metallic behavior within groups and periods, we also see a gradation in bonding from one type to another.

Lewis Electron-Dot Symbols: Depicting Atoms in Chemical Bonding

Before turning to the individual models, let's discuss a method for depicting the valence electrons of interacting atoms. In the **Lewis electron-dot symbol** (named for the American chemist G. N. Lewis), the element symbol represents the nucleus *and* inner electrons, and the surrounding dots represent the valence electrons, as shown in Figure 9.3. Note the recurring pattern of dots for elements within a group.

	1A(1)	2A(2)		3A(13)	4A(14)	5A(15)	6A(16)	7A(17)	8A(18)
	ns^1	ns^2		ns^2np^1	ns^2np^2	ns^2np^3	ns^2np^4	ns^2np^5	ns^2np^6
2	·Li	·Be·		·B·	·C·	·N·	:O·	:F:	:Ne:
3	·Na	·Mg·		·Al·	·Si·	·P·	:S·	:Cl:	:Ar:

Figure 9.3 Lewis electron-dot symbols for elements in Periods 2 and 3. The element symbol represents the nucleus and inner electrons, and the dots around it represent valence electrons. (The specific positions of the paired and unpaired dots are arbitrary.) The number of unpaired dots indicates the number of electrons a metal atom loses, the number a nonmetal gains, or the number of covalent bonds a non-metal atom usually forms.

It's easy to write the Lewis symbol for any main-group element:

1. Note its A-group number (1A to 8A), which gives the number of valence electrons.
2. Place one dot at a time on the four sides (top, right, bottom, left) of the symbol.
3. Pair up the dots until all are used.

The specific placement of dots is not important; that is, the Lewis symbol for nitrogen can *also* be written

$$·\overset{..}{N}: \quad \text{or} \quad ·\overset{.}{\underset{.}{N}}· \quad \text{or} \quad :\overset{.}{N}·$$

The number and pairing of dots provide information about an element's bonding behavior:

- For a metal, the *total* number of dots is the number of electrons it loses to form a cation.
- For a nonmetal, the number of *unpaired* dots is the number of electrons that become paired either through electron gain or electron sharing. Thus, the number of unpaired dots equals either the negative charge of the anion an atom forms or the number of covalent bonds it forms.

To illustrate the last point, look at the Lewis symbol for carbon. Rather than having one pair of dots and two unpaired dots, as its electron configuration ([He] $2s^22p^2$) would indicate, carbon has four unpaired dots because it forms four bonds. In the next chapter we use some other dot arrangements for the larger nonmetals.

The Remarkable Insights of G. N. Lewis Many of the ideas in this text emerged from the mind of Gilbert Newton Lewis (1875–1946). As early as 1902, nearly a decade *before* Rutherford even proposed the nuclear model of the atom, Lewis's notebooks show a scheme that involves the filling of outer electron "shells" to explain the way elements combine. His electron-dot symbols and associated structural formulas (discussed in Chapter 10) have become standards for representing bonding. Among his many other contributions are his insights into a general understanding of the behavior of acids and bases (which we discuss in Chapter 18).

Section Summary

Nearly all atoms occur bound to others. Chemical bonding allows atoms to lower their energy. Ionic bonding occurs when a metal atom transfers electrons to a nonmetal atom, and the resulting ions attract each other to form an ionic solid. Covalent bonding occurs most often between nonmetal atoms and commonly results in molecules. The bonded atoms share a pair of electrons, which remain localized between them. Metallic bonding occurs when many metal atoms pool their valence electrons in a delocalized electron sea that holds all the atoms together. The Lewis electron-dot symbol of an atom depicts the number of valence electrons for a main-group element.

9.2 The Ionic Bonding Model

The central theme of the ionic bonding model is the *transfer of electrons from metal to nonmetal to form ions that come together in a solid ionic compound.* In nearly every main-group element that forms a monatomic ion, the configuration has a filled outer level of electrons (either two or eight), the same number as in the nearest noble gas. Lewis incorporated this fact into the **octet rule:** *when atoms bond, they lose, gain, or share electrons to attain a filled outer shell of eight (or two) electrons.* The octet rule holds for all the compounds of Period 2 elements and a large number of others as well. ◆

Figure 9.4 shows three ways to depict the transfer of an electron from a lithium atom to a fluorine atom. In each, Li loses its single outer electron and is left with a filled $n = 1$ level, while F gains a single electron to fill its $n = 2$ level. In this case, each atom is one electron away from its nearest noble gas—He for Li and Ne for F, so the number of electrons lost by each Li equals the number gained by each F. Therefore, equal numbers of Li^+ and F^- ions form, as the formula LiF indicates. In all cases of ionic bonding, *the total number of electrons lost by the metal atoms equals the total number of electrons gained by the nonmetal atoms.*

Figure 9.4 Three ways to represent the formation of Li^+ and F^- through electron transfer. A, Electron configurations. **B,** Orbital diagrams. **C,** Lewis electron-dot symbols.

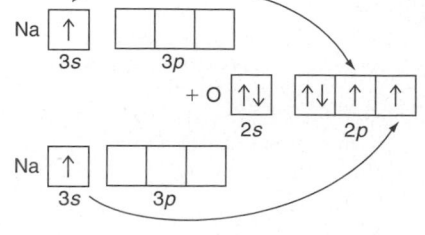

Sample Problem 9.1 Depicting Ion Formation

PROBLEM Use partial orbital diagrams and Lewis symbols to depict the formation of Na^+ and O^{2-} ions from the atoms, and determine the formula of the compound.

PLAN First we draw the orbital diagrams and Lewis symbols for the Na and O atoms. To attain filled outer levels, Na loses one electron and O gains two. Therefore, to make the number of electrons lost equal the number gained, two Na atoms are needed for each O atom.

SOLUTION

The formula is Na₂O.

Follow-up Problem 9.1 Use condensed electron configurations and Lewis electron-dot symbols to depict the formation of Mg^{2+} and Cl^- ions from the atoms, and write the formula of the compound.

Energy Considerations in Ionic Bonding: The Importance of Lattice Energy

You may be surprised to learn that the electron transfer process by itself actually *requires* energy! In fact, the reason ionic compounds form is because of the enormous *release* of energy that occurs when the ions come together and form the solid. Consider just the electron transfer process for lithium fluoride, which involves two steps—a gaseous Li atom losing an electron and a gaseous F atom gaining it:

- The first ionization energy (IE_1) of Li is the energy required for 1 mol gaseous Li atoms to lose 1 mol outer electrons:

$$Li(g) \longrightarrow Li^+(g) + e^- \qquad IE_1 = 520 \text{ kJ}$$

- The electron affinity (EA) of F is the energy change that occurs when 1 mol F atoms gains 1 mol electrons:

$$F(g) + e^- \longrightarrow F^-(g) \qquad EA = -328 \text{ kJ}$$

Adding these values, we find that the two-step electron transfer process *by itself* requires energy:

$$Li(g) + F(g) \longrightarrow Li^+(g) + F^-(g) \qquad IE_1 + EA = 192 \text{ kJ}$$

The total energy cost of ion formation is even greater than this because metallic lithium and diatomic fluorine must first be converted to the separate gaseous atoms, which also requires energy. Despite this, the standard heat of formation (ΔH_f^0) of solid LiF is -617 kJ/mol; that is, 617 kJ is *released* per mole of LiF(s) formed. The case of LiF is typical: despite an endothermic electron transfer, ionic solids form readily, often vigorously (Figure 9.5).

Clearly, if the overall reaction of Li(s) and $F_2(g)$ to form LiF(s) releases energy, there must be some other energy component(s) exothermic enough to overcome the endothermic steps. The exothermic component(s) result(s) from the strong *attraction between oppositely charged ions*. Even when 1 mol $Li^+(g)$ and 1 mol $F^-(g)$ form 1 mol gaseous LiF molecules, a large quantity of heat is released:

$$Li^+(g) + F^-(g) \longrightarrow LiF(g) \qquad \Delta H^0 = -755 \text{ kJ}$$

Of course, LiF does not consist of gaseous molecules under ordinary conditions because *much more energy is released when the gaseous ions coalesce into a crystalline solid*. When that occurs, each ion attracts several others of opposite charge. The **lattice energy** is the enthalpy change that accompanies gaseous ions coalescing into an ionic solid:

$$Li^+(g) + F^-(g) \longrightarrow LiF(s) \qquad \Delta H_{lattice}^0 \text{ of LiF = lattice energy} = -1050 \text{ kJ}$$

(You'll see how we calculate this value in a moment.) The magnitude of the lattice energy indicates the strength of ionic interactions and influences the melting point, hardness, and solubility of ionic compounds.

Lattice energy plays the critical role in ionic compound formation, but it cannot be measured directly. One way to determine lattice energy applies Hess's law (see Section 6.5), which states that the enthalpy change of an overall reaction is the sum of the enthalpy changes for the individual reactions that make it up: $\Delta H_{total} = \Delta H_1 + \Delta H_2 + \cdots$. Lattice energies are calculated through a **Born-Haber cycle,** a series of steps from elements to

A

B

Figure 9.5 **The reaction between sodium and bromine.** **A,** Despite the endothermic electron transfer process itself, all the Group 1A(1) metals react exothermically with all the Group 7A(17) nonmetals to form solid alkali-metal halides. The example shown is sodium (in beaker under mineral oil) and bromine (dark orange-brown liquid in flask). **B,** The reaction is usually rapid and vigorous.

Figure 9.6 The Born-Haber cycle for lithium fluoride. The formation of LiF(s) from its elements is shown happening either in one overall reaction *(black arrow)* or in five steps, each with its own enthalpy change *(orange arrows)*. The overall enthalpy change for the process (ΔH_f^0) is known, as are $\Delta H_{step\ 1}^0$ through $\Delta H_{step\ 4}^0$. Therefore, $\Delta H_{step\ 5}^0$, the lattice energy $(\Delta H_{lattice}^0$ of LiF), can be calculated. $(\Delta H_{atom}^0$ is the heat of atomization; BE is the bond energy.)

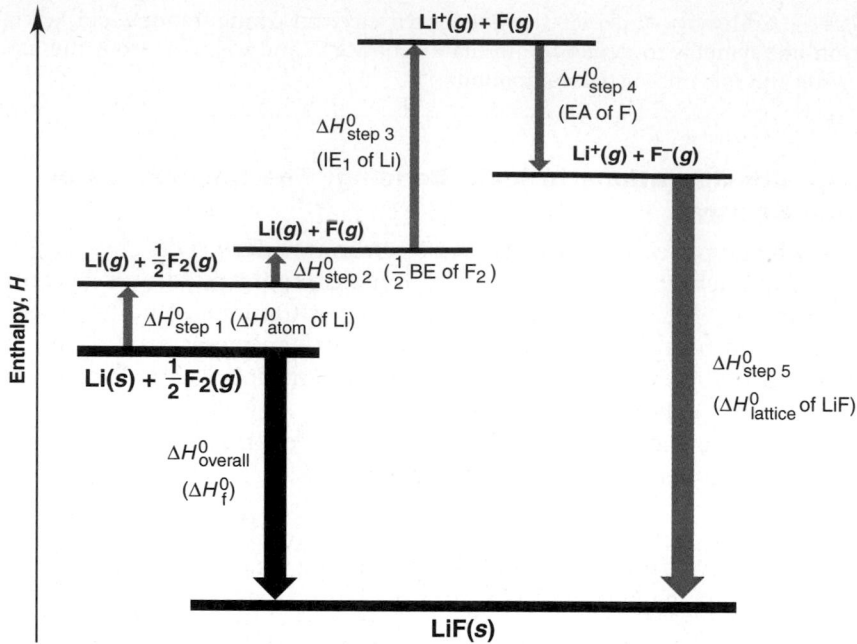

ionic compound for which all the enthalpies* are known except the lattice energy.

Let's go through the Born-Haber cycle for lithium fluoride. Figure 9.6 shows two possible paths, either the direct combination reaction (black arrow) or the multistep path (orange arrows), one step of which is the unknown lattice energy. Hess's law tells us that both paths involve the same overall enthalpy change:

$$\Delta H_f^0 \text{ of LiF}(s) = \text{sum of } \Delta H^0 \text{ for multistep path}$$

It's important to realize that we *choose steps that we can measure* to depict the energy components of LiF formation, even though these are *not* the actual steps that occur when lithium reacts with fluorine.

We begin with the elements in their standard states, metallic lithium and gaseous diatomic fluorine. In the multistep process, the elements are converted to individual gaseous atoms (steps 1 and 2), the electron transfer steps form gaseous ions (steps 3 and 4), and the ions form a solid (step 5). We identify each ΔH^0 by its step number:

Step 1. Converting 1 mol solid Li to separate gaseous Li atoms involves breaking metallic bonds, so it requires energy:

$$\text{Li}(s) \longrightarrow \text{Li}(g) \qquad \Delta H_{step\ 1}^0 = 161 \text{ kJ}$$

(This process is called *atomization*, and the enthalpy change is ΔH_{atom}^0.)

Step 2. Converting an F_2 molecule to F atoms involves breaking a covalent bond, so it requires energy. We need 1 mol F atoms for 1 mol LiF, so we start with $\frac{1}{2}$ mol F_2:

$$\tfrac{1}{2}F_2(g) \longrightarrow F(g) \qquad \Delta H_{step\ 2}^0 = \tfrac{1}{2} \text{ bond energy (BE) of } F_2$$
$$= \tfrac{1}{2}(159 \text{ kJ}) = 79.5 \text{ kJ}$$

Step 3. Removing the 2s electron from 1 mol Li to form 1 mol Li$^+$ requires energy:

$$\text{Li}(g) \longrightarrow \text{Li}^+(g) + e^- \qquad \Delta H_{step\ 3}^0 = \text{IE}_1 = 520 \text{ kJ}$$

---

*Strictly speaking, ionization energy (IE) and electron affinity (EA) are internal energy changes (ΔE), not enthalpy changes (ΔH), but in these cases, $\Delta H = \Delta E$ because $\Delta V = 0$ (see Section 6.2).

Step 4. Adding an electron to 1 mol F to form 1 mol F^- releases energy:

$$F(g) + e^- \longrightarrow F^-(g) \qquad \Delta H^0_{step\ 4} = EA = -328 \text{ kJ}$$

Step 5. Forming 1 mol of the crystalline ionic solid from the gaseous ions is the step whose enthalpy change (the lattice energy) is unknown:

$$Li^+(g) + F^-(g) \longrightarrow LiF(s) \qquad \Delta H^0_{step\ 5} = \Delta H^0_{lattice} \text{ of LiF} = ?$$

We know the enthalpy change of the formation reaction,

$$Li(s) + \tfrac{1}{2}F_2(g) \longrightarrow LiF(s) \qquad \Delta H^0_{overall} = \Delta H^0_f = -617 \text{ kJ}$$

Using Hess's law, we set the known ΔH^0_f equal to the sum of the steps and calculate the lattice energy:

$$\Delta H^0_f = \Delta H^0_{step\ 1} + \Delta H^0_{step\ 2} + \Delta H^0_{step\ 3} + \Delta H^0_{step\ 4} + \Delta H^0_{lattice} \text{ of LiF}$$

Solving for $\Delta H^0_{lattice}$ of LiF gives

$$\begin{aligned}
\Delta H^0_{lattice} \text{ of LiF} &= \Delta H^0_f - (\Delta H^0_{step\ 1} + \Delta H^0_{step\ 2} + \Delta H^0_{step\ 3} + \Delta H^0_{step\ 4}) \\
&= -617 \text{ kJ} - [161 \text{ kJ} + 79.5 \text{ kJ} + 520 \text{ kJ} + (-328 \text{ kJ})] \\
&= -1050 \text{ kJ}
\end{aligned}$$

Note that *the magnitude of the lattice energy dominates the multistep process.*

The Born-Haber cycle reveals a central point: *ionic solids exist **only** because the lattice energy drives the energetically unfavorable electron transfer.* In other words, the energy *required* for elements to lose or gain electrons is *supplied* by the electrostatic attraction between the ions they form: energy is expended to form the ions, but it is more than regained when they attract each other and form a solid.

Periodic Trends in Lattice Energy

Since the lattice energy is the result of electrostatic interactions among ions, we expect its magnitude to depend on several factors, including ionic size, ionic charge, and ionic arrangement in the solid. In Chapter 2, you were introduced to **Coulomb's law** as a fundamental aspect of ionic bonding, and we've applied it several times since to other situations in which charges attract each other. It states that the electrostatic *force* associated with two charges (A and B) is directly proportional to the product of their magnitudes and inversely proportional to the square of the distance between them:

$$\text{Electrostatic force} \propto \frac{\text{charge A} \times \text{charge B}}{\text{distance}^2}$$

Since energy = force × distance, the electrostatic *energy* is inversely proportional to the *first* power of the distance between the charges:

$$\text{Electrostatic energy} \propto \frac{\text{charge A} \times \text{charge B}}{\text{distance}} \qquad \textbf{(9.1)}$$

The situation in an ionic solid requires more than just a simple extension of Coulomb's law because there are charged particles at various distances, which complicates the calculation. Nevertheless, the lattice energy ($\Delta H^0_{lattice}$) is directly proportional to the electrostatic energy. Cations and anions lie as close to each other as possible, and the distance between them is the distance between their centers, which equals the sum of their radii (see Figure 8.26):

$$\text{Electrostatic energy} \propto \frac{\text{cation charge} \times \text{anion charge}}{\text{cation radius} + \text{anion radius}} \propto \Delta H^0_{lattice} \qquad \textbf{(9.2)}$$

This relationship helps us predict trends in lattice energy and explain the effects of ionic size and charge:

1. *Effect of ionic size.* As we move down a group of metals or nonmetals, ionic radii increase. Therefore, the energy of attraction between cations and anions should decrease because the interionic distance is greater; thus the lattice energy of their compounds should decrease as well. This prediction is

Figure 9.7 Trends in lattice energy. The lattice energies for many of the alkali halides are shown. Each series of four points represents a given 1A(1) cation *(left side)* combining with the various 7A(17) anions *(bottom)*. As ionic radii increase, the electrostatic attractions decrease, so the lattice energies of the compounds decrease as well. Thus, LiF (smallest ions) has the highest lattice energy and RbI (largest ions shown) has the lowest.

borne out in the lattice energies of the alkali halides shown in Figure 9.7. A smooth decrease occurs in lattice energy down a group whether we hold the cation constant (LiF to LiI) or the anion constant (LiF to RbF).

2. *Effect of ionic charge.* When we compare lithium fluoride with magnesium oxide, we find cations of about equal radii ($Li^+ = 76$ pm and $Mg^{2+} = 72$ pm), and anions of about equal radii ($F^- = 133$ pm and $O^{2-} = 140$ pm). Thus, the only significant difference is the ionic charge: LiF contains the univalent Li^+ and F^- ions, whereas MgO contains the divalent Mg^{2+} and O^{2-} ions. The difference in their lattice energies is striking:

$$\Delta H^0_{lattice} \text{ of LiF} = -1050 \text{ kJ/mol} \quad \text{and} \quad \Delta H^0_{lattice} \text{ of MgO} = -3923 \text{ kJ/mol}$$

This nearly fourfold increase in $\Delta H^0_{lattice}$ reflects the fourfold increase in the product of the charges (1×1 vs. 2×2) in the numerator of Equation 9.2.

The high lattice energy of MgO explains why ionic solids with 2+ ions even exist. After all, much more energy is needed to form 2+ ions than 1+ ions. Forming 1 mol Mg^{2+} involves loss of the first *and* second electrons (the sum of the first and second ionization energies):

$$Mg(g) \longrightarrow Mg^{2+}(g) + 2e^- \quad \Delta H^0 = IE_1 + IE_2 = 738 \text{ kJ} + 1450 \text{ kJ} = 2188 \text{ kJ}$$

Adding 1 mol electrons to 1 mol O atoms (first electron affinity, EA_1) is exothermic, but adding a second mole of electrons (second electron affinity, EA_2) is endothermic because an electron is being added to the negative O^- ion. The overall formation of 1 mol O^{2-} ions is endothermic:

$$
\begin{array}{ll}
O(g) + e^- \longrightarrow O^-(g) & \Delta H^0 = EA_1 = -141 \text{ kJ} \\
O^-(g) + e^- \longrightarrow O^{2-}(g) & \Delta H^0 = EA_2 = 878 \text{ kJ} \\
\hline
O(g) + 2e^- \longrightarrow O^{2-}(g) & \Delta H^0 = EA_1 + EA_2 = 737 \text{ kJ}
\end{array}
$$

In addition, there are the endothermic steps for converting 1 mol Mg(*s*) to Mg(*g*) (148 kJ) and breaking $\frac{1}{2}$ mol O_2 molecules into 1 mol O atoms (249 kJ). Nevertheless, as a result of the 2+ ion charges, solid MgO readily forms whenever Mg burns in air ($\Delta H^0_f = -601$ kJ/mol). Clearly, the enormous lattice energy ($\Delta H^0_{lattice}$ of MgO $= -3923$ kJ/mol) more than compensates for these endothermic steps.

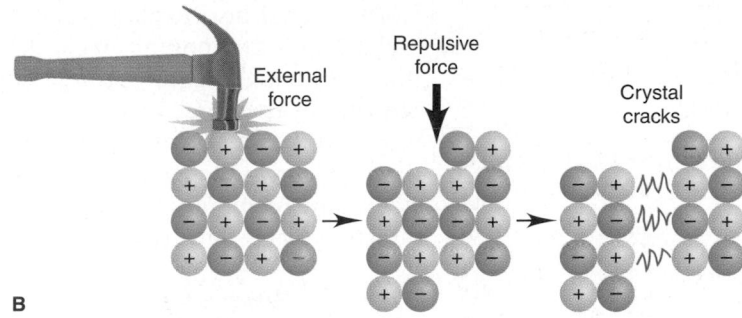

How the Model Explains the Properties of Ionic Compounds

The first and most important job of any model is to explain the facts. By magnifying our view, we can see how the ionic bonding model accounts for the properties of ionic solids. You may have seen a piece of rock salt (NaCl). It is *hard* (does not dent), *rigid* (does not bend), and *brittle* (cracks without deforming). These properties are due to the powerful attractive forces that hold the ions *in specific positions* throughout the crystal. Moving the ions out of position requires overcoming these forces, so the sample resists denting and bending. If *enough* pressure is applied, ions of like charge are brought next to each other, so their repulsions crack the sample suddenly (Figure 9.8).

Most ionic compounds *do not* conduct electricity in the solid state but *do* conduct when melted or when dissolved in water. (Notable exceptions include so-called superionic conductors, such as AgI, and the superconducting ceramics, which have remarkable conductivity in the solid state.) According to the ionic bonding model, the solid consists of immobilized ions. When it melts or dissolves, however, the ions are free to move and carry an electric current, as shown in Figure 9.9.

Figure 9.8 Electrostatic forces and the reason ionic compounds crack. A, Ionic compounds are hard and crack, rather than bend, when struck with enough force. **B,** The positive and negative ions in the crystal are arranged to maximize their attraction. When an external force is applied, similar charges move near each other, and the repulsions crack the piece apart.

A Solid ionic compound

B Molten ionic compound

C Ionic compound dissolved in water

Figure 9.9 Electrical conductance and ion mobility. A, No current flows in the solid because ions are immobile. **B,** In the molten compound, mobile ions flow toward the oppositely charged electrodes and carry a current. **C,** In an aqueous solution of the compound, mobile solvated ions carry a current.

Table 9.1 Melting and Boiling Points of Some Ionic Compounds

Compound	mp (°C)	bp (°C)
CsBr	636	1300
NaI	661	1304
$MgCl_2$	714	1412
KBr	734	1435
$CaCl_2$	782	>1600
NaCl	801	1413
LiF	845	1676
KF	858	1505
MgO	2852	3600

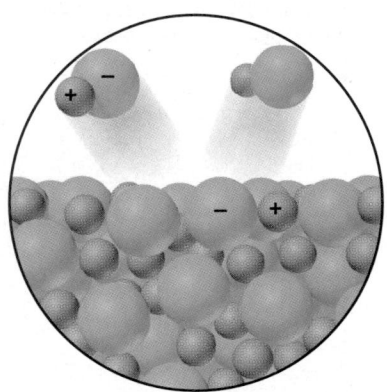

Figure 9.10 Vaporizing an ionic compound. Ionic compounds generally have very high boiling points because the ions must have high enough kinetic energies to break free from surrounding ions. In fact, ionic compounds usually vaporize as ion pairs.

The model also explains that high temperatures are needed to melt and boil an ionic compound (Table 9.1) because freeing the ions from their positions (melting) requires large amounts of energy, and vaporizing them requires even more. In fact, the ionic attraction is so strong that, as Figure 9.10 shows, the vapor consists of **ion pairs,** gaseous ionic molecules rather than individual ions. Keep in mind, however, that in their ordinary solid state, ionic compounds consist of rows of alternating ions that extend in all directions, and *no separate molecules exist.*

Section Summary

In ionic bonding, a metal transfers electrons to a nonmetal, and the resulting ions attract each other strongly to form a solid. Main-group elements often attain a filled outer level of electrons (either eight or two) by forming ions with the configuration of the nearest noble gas. Ion formation by itself *requires* energy. However, the lattice energy, the energy *released* when the gaseous ions form a solid, is large, and it is the major reason that ionic solids exist. The magnitude of the lattice energy, which depends on ionic size and charge, can be determined by applying Hess's law in a Born-Haber cycle.

The ionic bonding model pictures oppositely charged ions held rigidly in position by strong electrostatic attractions and explains why ionic solids crack rather than bend and why they conduct a current only when melted or dissolved. The ions occur as gaseous ion pairs when the compound vaporizes, which requires very high temperatures.

9.3 The Covalent Bonding Model

Look through any large reference source of chemical compounds, such as the *Handbook of Chemistry and Physics,* and you'll quickly find that the number of known covalent compounds dwarfs the number of known ionic compounds. Molecules held together by covalent bonds range from diatomic hydrogen to biological and synthetic macromolecules with molar masses of several million. We also find covalent bonds in the polyatomic ions of many ionic compounds. Without doubt, sharing electrons is the principal way that atoms interact chemically.

The Formation of a Covalent Bond

A sample of hydrogen gas consists of H_2 molecules. But why *do* the atoms exist bound together in pairs? Look at Figure 9.11 as you imagine what would happen to two isolated H atoms that approach each other from a distance. When the atoms are far apart, each behaves as though the other were not present (point 1). As the distance between the nuclei decreases, each nucleus starts to attract the other atom's electron, which lowers the potential energy of the system. The attractions continue to draw the atoms closer, and the system becomes progressively lower in energy (point 2). As attractions increase, however, so do repulsions between the nuclei and between the electron clouds. At some internuclear distance, the maximum attraction is achieved in the face of the increasing repulsion, and the system has its minimum energy (point 3). Any shorter distance would increase the repulsions and cause the potential energy to rise (point 4). The mutual attraction of nuclei and electron pair constitutes the **covalent bond** that holds the atoms together as an H_2 molecule.

Bonding Pairs and Lone Pairs In covalent bonding, as in ionic bonding, each atom achieves a full outer level of electrons, but by different means. *Each atom in a covalent bond "counts" the shared electrons as belonging entirely to*

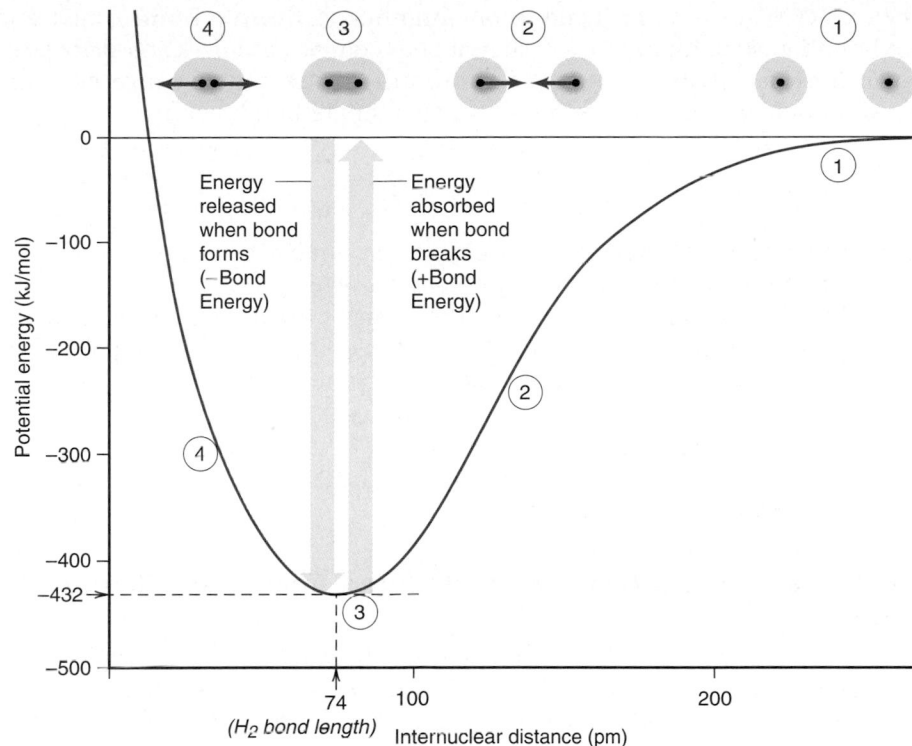

Figure 9.11 Covalent bond formation in H₂. The potential energy of a system of two H atoms plotted against the distance between the nuclei is shown, with a depiction of the atomic systems above. At 1, the atoms are too far apart to attract each other. At 2, each nucleus attracts the other atom's electron. At 3, the combination of nucleus-electron attractions and electron-electron and nucleus-nucleus repulsions gives the minimum energy of the system. The energy difference between points 1 and 3 is the H₂ bond energy (432 kJ/mol). It is released when the bond forms and absorbed when the bond breaks. The internuclear distance at point 3 is the H₂ bond length (74 pm). If the atoms move closer, as at point 4, repulsions increase the system's energy and force the atoms apart to point 3 again.

itself. Thus, one shared electron pair simultaneously fills the outer level of *both* H atoms. The **shared pair,** or **bonding pair,** is represented by either a pair of dots or a line, H:H or H—H.

An electron pair that is part of an atom's valence shell but *not* involved in bonding is called a **lone pair,** or **unshared pair.** The bonding pair in HF fills the outer shell of the H atom *and,* together with three lone pairs, fills the outer shell of the F atom as well:

Similarly, in F₂, the bonding pair and three lone pairs fill the outer shell of *each* F atom:

(This text generally shows bonding pairs as lines and lone pairs as dots.)

Types of Bonds and Bond Order The **bond order** is the number of electron pairs being shared between any two bonded atoms. The covalent bond in H₂, HF, and F₂ is a **single bond,** one that consists of a single bonding pair of electrons. A *single bond has a bond order of one.*

Single bonds are the most common type of bond, but many molecules (and ions) contain multiple bonds also. Multiple bonds occur most frequently

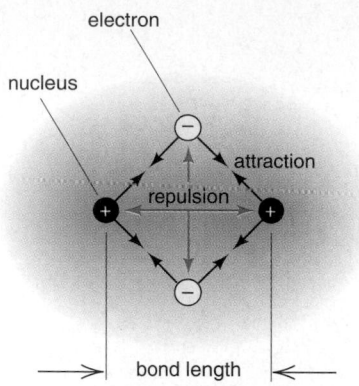

Figure 9.12 **The attractive and repulsive forces in covalent bonding.** Nucleus-electron attractions and nucleus-nucleus and electron-electron repulsions occur simultaneously. At some optimum distance (the bond length), the attractive forces are maximized in the presence of the repulsive forces. The net attraction determines the bond energy. (Although shown at specific locations in the figure, the electrons are actually distributed throughout the available volume.)

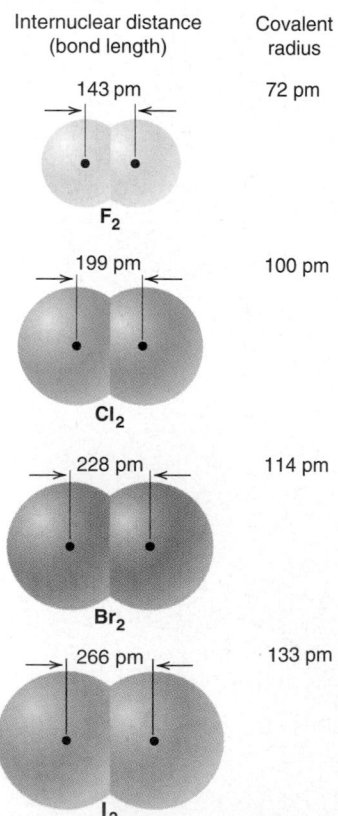

Figure 9.13 **Bond length and covalent radius.** Within a series of similar substances, such as the diatomic halogen molecules, bond length increases as covalent radius increases.

when C, O, N, or S atoms bond to one another. A **double bond** consists of two bonding pairs, four electrons shared between two atoms, so *the bond order is two.* Ethylene (C_2H_4) is a simple hydrocarbon that contains a carbon-carbon double bond and four carbon-hydrogen single bonds:

Each carbon "counts" the four electrons in the double bond and the four in its two single bonds to hydrogen to obtain an octet.

A **triple bond** consists of three bonding pairs, two atoms sharing six electrons, so *the bond order is three.* In the N_2 molecule, the atoms are held together by a triple bond, and each N atom also has a lone pair:

$$:N:::N: \quad \text{or} \quad :N\equiv N:$$

Six electrons from the triple bond and two from the lone pair give *each* N atom an octet.

The Properties of a Covalent Bond: Bond Energy and Bond Length

As we said earlier, and Figure 9.12 depicts, the covalent bond results from the balance between the nucleus-electron attractions and the electron-electron and nucleus-nucleus repulsions. The strength of the bond depends on the extent to which the attractions outweigh the repulsions. The **bond energy (BE)** (also called *bond enthalpy* or *bond strength*) is the energy required to overcome this net attraction. It is defined as the standard enthalpy change for breaking the bond in 1 mol of gaseous molecules. *Bond breakage is an endothermic process, so the bond energy is always positive:*

$$A-B(g) \longrightarrow A(g) + B(g) \qquad \Delta H^0_{\text{bond breaking}} = BE_{A-B} \text{ (always > 0)}$$

Put another way, the bond energy is the difference in energy between the separated atoms and the bonded atoms (the energy difference between points 1 and 3 of the potential energy "well" in Figure 9.11). The same amount of energy that is absorbed to break the bond is released when it forms. *Bond formation is an exothermic process, so the sign of the enthalpy change is negative:*

$$A(g) + B(g) \longrightarrow A-B(g) \qquad \Delta H^0_{\text{bond forming}} = -BE_{A-B} \text{ (always < 0)}$$

Since bond energies depend on the bonded atoms—their electron configurations, nuclear charges, and atomic radii—each type of bond has its own bond energy. Table 9.2 lists bond energies for some common bonds. Moreover, the energy of a given bond varies slightly from molecule to molecule, and even within the same molecule, so *the tabulated value is an average bond energy.*

A covalent bond has a **bond length,** the distance between the nuclei of two bonded atoms. In Figure 9.11, it is shown as the distance between the nuclei at the point of minimum energy. Table 9.3 shows the lengths of some covalent bonds. Here, too, the values represent *average* bond lengths for the given bond in different substances. Bond length is related to the radii of the bonded atoms. In fact, most atomic radii are obtained from bond lengths that were determined experimentally (see Figure 8.11C). Bond lengths within a series of similar bonds increase with atomic size, as shown in Figure 9.13 for the halogens.

A close relationship exists among bond order, bond length, and bond energy. Two nuclei are more strongly attracted to two shared electron pairs than to one: the atoms are drawn closer together *and* are more difficult to pull apart. Therefore, *for a given pair of atoms, a higher bond order results in a shorter bond length and a higher bond energy.* To put this important point more

Table 9.2 Average Bond Energies (kJ/mol)

Bond	Energy	Bond	Energy	Bond	Energy	Bond	Energy
Single Bonds							
H—H	432	N—H	391	Si—H	323	S—H	347
H—F	565	N—N	160	Si—Si	226	S—S	266
H—Cl	427	N—P	209	Si—O	368	S—F	327
H—Br	363	N—O	201	Si—S	226	S—Cl	271
H—I	295	N—F	272	Si—F	565	S—Br	218
		N—Cl	200	Si—Cl	381	S—I	~170
		N—Br	243	Si—Br	310		
C—H	413	N—I	159	Si—I	234	F—F	159
C—C	347					F—Cl	193
C—Si	301					F—Br	212
C—N	305	O—H	467	P—H	320	F—I	263
C—O	358	O—P	351	P—Si	213	Cl—Cl	243
C—P	264	O—O	204	P—P	200	Cl—Br	215
C—S	259	O—S	265	P—F	490	Cl—I	208
C—F	453	O—F	190	P—Cl	331	Br—Br	193
C—Cl	339	O—Cl	203	P—Br	272	Br—I	175
C—Br	276	O—Br	234	P—I	184	I—I	151
C—I	216	O—I	234				
Multiple Bonds							
C=C	614	N=N	418	C≡C	839	N≡N	945
C=N	615	N=O	607	C≡N	891		
C=O	745	O_2	498	C≡O	1070		
	(799 in CO_2)						

Table 9.3 Average Bond Lengths (pm)

Bond	Length	Bond	Length	Bond	Length	Bond	Length
Single Bonds							
H—H	74	N—H	101	Si—H	148	S—H	134
H—F	92	N—N	146	Si—Si	234	S—P	210
H—Cl	127	N—P	177	Si—O	161	S—S	204
H—Br	141	N—O	144	Si—S	210	S—F	158
H—I	161	N—S	168	Si—N	172	S—Cl	201
		N—F	139	Si—F	156	S—Br	225
		N—Cl	191	Si—Cl	204	S—I	234
C—H	109	N—Br	214	Si—Br	216		
C—C	154	N—I	222	Si—I	240	F—F	143
C—Si	186					F—Cl	166
C—N	147	O—H	96	P—H	142	F—Br	178
C—O	143	O—P	160	P—Si	227	F—I	187
C—P	187	O—O	148	P—P	221	Cl—Cl	199
C—S	181	O—S	151	P—F	156	Cl—Br	214
C—F	133	O—F	142	P—Cl	204	Cl—I	243
C—Cl	177	O—Cl	164	P—Br	222	Br—Br	228
C—Br	194	O—Br	172	P—I	243	Br—I	248
C—I	213	O—I	194			I—I	266
Multiple Bonds							
C=C	134	N=N	122	C≡C	121	N≡N	110
C=N	127	N=O	120	C≡N	115	N≡O	106
C=O	123	O_2	121	C≡O	113		

Table 9.4 The Relation of Bond Order, Bond Length, and Bond Energy

Bond	Bond Order	Average Bond Length (pm)	Average Bond Energy (kJ/mol)
C—O	1	143	358
C=O	2	123	745
C≡O	3	113	1070
C—C	1	154	347
C=C	2	134	614
C≡C	3	121	839
N—N	1	146	160
N=N	2	122	418
N≡N	3	110	945

simply, as Table 9.4 shows, for a given pair of atoms, *a shorter bond is a stronger bond.*

In some cases, we can extend this relationship among atomic size, bond length, and bond strength by holding one atom in the bond constant and varying the other atom within a group or period. For example, the trend in single bond lengths, C—I > C—Br > C—Cl, parallels the trend in atomic size, I > Br > Cl, and is opposite to the trend in bond energy, C—Cl > C—Br > C—I. Thus, for *single bonds,* longer bonds are usually weaker.

Sample Problem 9.2 Comparing Bond Length and Bond Strength

PROBLEM Using the periodic table, but not Tables 9.2 and 9.3, rank the bonds in each set in order of *decreasing* bond length and bond strength:
(a) S—F, S—Br, S—Cl   **(b)** C=O, C—O, C≡O
PLAN In part **(a),** S is singly bonded to a halogen atom, so all members of the set have a bond order of one. The bond length increases and bond strength decreases as halogen atomic radius increases, which we find from the periodic table. In part **(b),** the same two atoms are bonded, but the bond orders differ. In this case, bond strength increases and bond length decreases as bond order increases.
SOLUTION **(a)** Atomic size increases down a group, so F < Cl < Br.

Bond length: S—Br > S—Cl > S—F

Bond strength: S—F > S—Cl > S—Br

(b) By ranking the bond orders, C≡O > C=O > C—O, we obtain

Bond length: C—O > C=O > C≡O

Bond strength: C≡O > C=O > C—O

CHECK From Tables 9.2 and 9.3, we see that the ranking is correct.
COMMENT Remember that for different atoms, as in part **(a),** *the relationship between length and strength holds* only *for single bonds* and not in every case, so apply it carefully.

Follow-up Problem 9.2 Rank the bonds in each set in order of *increasing* bond length and bond strength: **(a)** Si—F, Si—C, Si—O; **(b)** N=N, N—N, N≡N.

How the Model Explains the Properties of Covalent Compounds

The covalent bonding model proposes that electron sharing between pairs of atoms leads to strong, localized bonds, usually within individual molecules. At first glance, however, it seems that the model is inconsistent with some of the familiar physical properties of covalent substances. After all, most are

Strong covalent bonding forces *within* molecules

Gaseous phase

Liquid phase

Weak intermolecular forces *between* molecules

Figure 9.14 Strong forces within molecules and weak forces between them. When pentane boils, weak forces *between* molecules (intermolecular forces) are overcome, but the strong covalent bonds holding the atoms together within each molecule remain unaffected. Thus, the pentane molecules leave the liquid phase as intact units.

gases (such as methane and ammonia), liquids (such as benzene and water), or low-melting solids (such as sulfur and paraffin wax). If covalent bonds are strong (~200 to 500 kJ/mol), why do covalent substances melt and boil at such low temperatures?

To answer this question, we must distinguish between two completely different sets of forces: (1) the *strong covalent bonding forces* holding the atoms together within the molecule (those we have been discussing) and (2) the *weak intermolecular forces* holding the molecules near each other in the macroscopic sample. It is these weak forces *between* the molecules, not the strong covalent bonds *within* each molecule, that are responsible for the physical properties of covalent substances. Consider, for example, what happens when pentane (C_5H_{12}) boils. As Figure 9.14 shows, the weak interactions *between* the pentane molecules are affected, not the strong C—C and C—H covalent bonds *within* each molecule.

Some covalent substances, called *network covalent solids,* do not consist of separate molecules. Rather, they are held together by covalent bonds that extend in three dimensions *throughout* the sample. If the model is correct, the properties of these substances *should* reflect the strength of their covalent bonds, and this is indeed the case. Two examples, quartz and diamond, are shown in Figure 9.15. Quartz (SiO_2) is very hard and melts at 1550°C. It is composed of silicon and oxygen atoms connected by covalent bonds that extend throughout the sample; no separate SiO_2 molecules exist. Diamond consists of covalent bonds connecting each carbon atom to four others throughout the sample. It is the hardest substance known and melts at around 3550°C. Clearly, covalent bonds *are* strong, but since most covalent substances consist of separate molecules with weak forces between them, their physical properties do not reflect this strength. (We discuss intermolecular forces in detail in Chapter 12.)

Unlike ionic compounds, most covalent substances are poor electrical conductors, even when melted or when dissolved in water. An electric current is carried by either mobile electrons or ions. In covalent substances, the electrons are localized as either shared or unshared pairs, so they are not free to move, and no ions are present. The Tools of the Chemistry Laboratory essay describes an important laboratory tool for studying covalent substances.

A Quartz   Silicon   Oxygen

B Diamond   Carbon

Figure 9.15 Covalent bonds of network covalent solids. A, In quartz (SiO_2), each Si atom is bonded covalently to four O atoms and each O atom bonds to two Si atoms in a pattern that extends throughout the sample. Because no separate SiO_2 molecules are present, the melting point and hardness are very high. **B,** In diamond, each C atom is covalently bonded to four others throughout the crystal. Diamond is the hardest natural substance known and is extremely high melting.

Tools of the Chemistry Laboratory

Infrared Spectroscopy

Infrared (IR) spectroscopy is an instrumental technique used primarily for measuring the absorption of IR radiation by covalently bonded molecules. It plays a major role in our understanding of molecular structure and bonding. IR spectrometers are found in most research laboratories, particularly where organic molecules are studied, and are essential aids in identifying unknown substances. Their key components are the same as those of any spectrometer (see Tools of the Chemistry Laboratory, Section 7.2). The source emits radiation of many wavelengths, and those in the IR region are selected and directed at the sample. Certain wavelengths are absorbed more than others, and the IR spectrum of the compound is generated.

What property of a molecule is displayed in its IR spectrum? All molecules, whether in a gas, liquid, or solid, undergo continual rotations and vibrations. Consider, for instance, a sample of ethane gas. The $H_3C—CH_3$ molecules zoom throughout the container, colliding with the walls and each other. If we could look closely at one molecule, however, and disregard its motion through space, we would see the molecule rotating and its two CH_3 groups rotating relative to each other about the C—C bond. The bonded atoms also vibrate, that is, move back and forth as though their bonds were flexible springs: stretching and compressing, twisting, bending, rocking, and wagging (Figure 9.A). (Thus, the length of a given bond even within a given substance is actually the *average* distance between nuclei, analogous to the average length of a spring when it is stretching and compressing.)

Each vibrational motion has its own natural frequency, which is based on the type of motion, the masses of the atoms, and the strengths of the bonds between them. These frequen-

Figure 9.A **Some vibrational motions in general diatomic and triatomic molecules.**

Section Summary

A shared pair of valence electrons attracts the nuclei of two atoms and holds them together in a covalent bond while making each atom's outer shell complete. The number of shared pairs between the two atoms is the bond order. For a given type of bond, the bond energy is the average energy required to completely separate the bonded atoms; the bond length is the average distance between their nuclei. For a given pair of bonded atoms, bond order is directly related to bond energy and inversely related to bond length. Substances that consist of separate molecules are generally soft and low melting because of the weak *noncovalent* forces between molecules. Those held together throughout by covalent bonds are extremely hard and high melting. Most covalent substances have low electrical conductivity because electrons are localized and ions are absent. The atoms in a covalent bond vibrate, and the energy of these vibrations can be studied with IR spectroscopy.

cies correspond to wavelengths between 2.5 and 25 μm, which make up a part of the IR region of the electromagnetic spectrum (see Figure 7.3). The energy of each of these vibrations is quantized. Just as an atom can absorb a photon whose energy corresponds to the difference between two quantized *electron* energy levels, a molecule can absorb an IR photon whose energy corresponds to the difference between two of its quantized *vibrational* energy levels.

The IR spectrum is important in compound identification because of two related factors. First, *each kind of bond has a characteristic range of IR wavelengths it can absorb.* For example, a C—C bond absorbs IR photons of different wavelength range from those absorbed by a C=C bond, a C—H bond, a C=O bond, and so forth. Second, the exact wavelength and quantity of IR radiation absorbed by a given bond depend on the *overall structure* of the molecule. This means that *each compound has a characteristic IR spectrum* that can be used to identify it, much as a fingerprint identifies a person. The spectrum appears as a series of downward pointing peaks, varying in depth and sharpness, that correspond to absorption frequencies across the IR region scanned. Figure 9.B shows the IR spectrum of acrylonitrile, a compound that is used to manufacture synthetic rubber and plastics; no other compound has exactly the same IR spectrum.

Figure 9.B The infrared (IR) spectrum of acrylonitrile.
The IR spectrum of acrylonitrile is typical of a molecule with several types of covalent bonds. There are many absorption bands (peaks) of differing depth and sharpness. Most peaks correspond to a particular type of vibration in a particular group of bonded atoms. Some broad peaks (for example, "combination band") represent a variety of vibrational types that are overlapping. The spectrum is reproducible and unique for acrylonitrile. (The top axis shows wavenumbers, the inverse of wavelength, so its units are those of length^{-1}. The scale expands to the right of 2000 cm^{-1}.)

9.4 Between the Extremes: Electronegativity and Bond Polarity

Scientific models are idealized descriptions of reality. As we've discussed them so far, the ionic and covalent bonding models portray compounds as being formed by *either* complete electron transfer *or* complete electron sharing. However, the great majority of compounds have bonds that are more accurately thought of as partially ionic and partially covalent. Now that you're familiar with the ideal models, we can explore the actual continuum in bonding that lies between these extremes.

Electronegativity

One of the most important concepts in chemical bonding is **electronegativity (EN),** the relative ability of a bonded atom to attract the shared

Figure 9.16 The Pauling electronegativity (EN) scale. The EN is shown by the height of the post (the value appears in the element box). Four shades of green indicate arbitrary EN cutoffs (*see key*). In the main groups, EN generally *increases* from left to right and bottom to top. The noble gases are not shown because, except in a few cases, they do not form bonds. The transition and, especially, inner transition elements show relatively little change in EN. Hydrogen is shown near elements of similar EN to point out that its value is much higher than those of the Group 1A(1) metals.

electrons.* More than 50 years ago, the American chemist Linus Pauling developed the most common scale of relative EN values for the elements. Here is an example to show the basis of Pauling's approach. We might expect the bond energy of the HF bond to be the average of the energies of an H—H bond (432 kJ/mol) and an F—F bond (159 kJ/mol), or 296 kJ/mol. However, the actual bond energy of H—F is 565 kJ/mol, or 269 kJ/mol *higher* than the average. Pauling reasoned that this difference is due to an *electrostatic (charge) contribution* to the H—F bond energy. If F attracts the shared electron pair more strongly than H, that is, if F is more electronegative than H, the electrons will spend more time closer to F. This unequal sharing of electrons makes the F end of the bond partially negative and the H end partially positive, and the attraction between these partial charges *increases* the energy required to break the bond.

From similar studies with the remaining hydrogen halides and many other compounds, Pauling arrived at the scale of *relative EN values* shown in Figure 9.16. The values themselves are not measured quantities but are based on Pauling's assignment of the highest EN value, 4.0, to fluorine.

Trends in Electronegativity In general, an atom's electronegativity is inversely related to its size, as you can see from Figure 9.17. Thus, *electronegativity generally increases up a group and across a period.* Because the

---

*Electronegativity is not the same as electron affinity (EA), although many elements with a high EN also have a highly negative EA. Electronegativity refers to a bonded atom attracting the shared electron pair; electron affinity refers to a separate atom in the gas phase gaining an electron to form a gaseous anion.

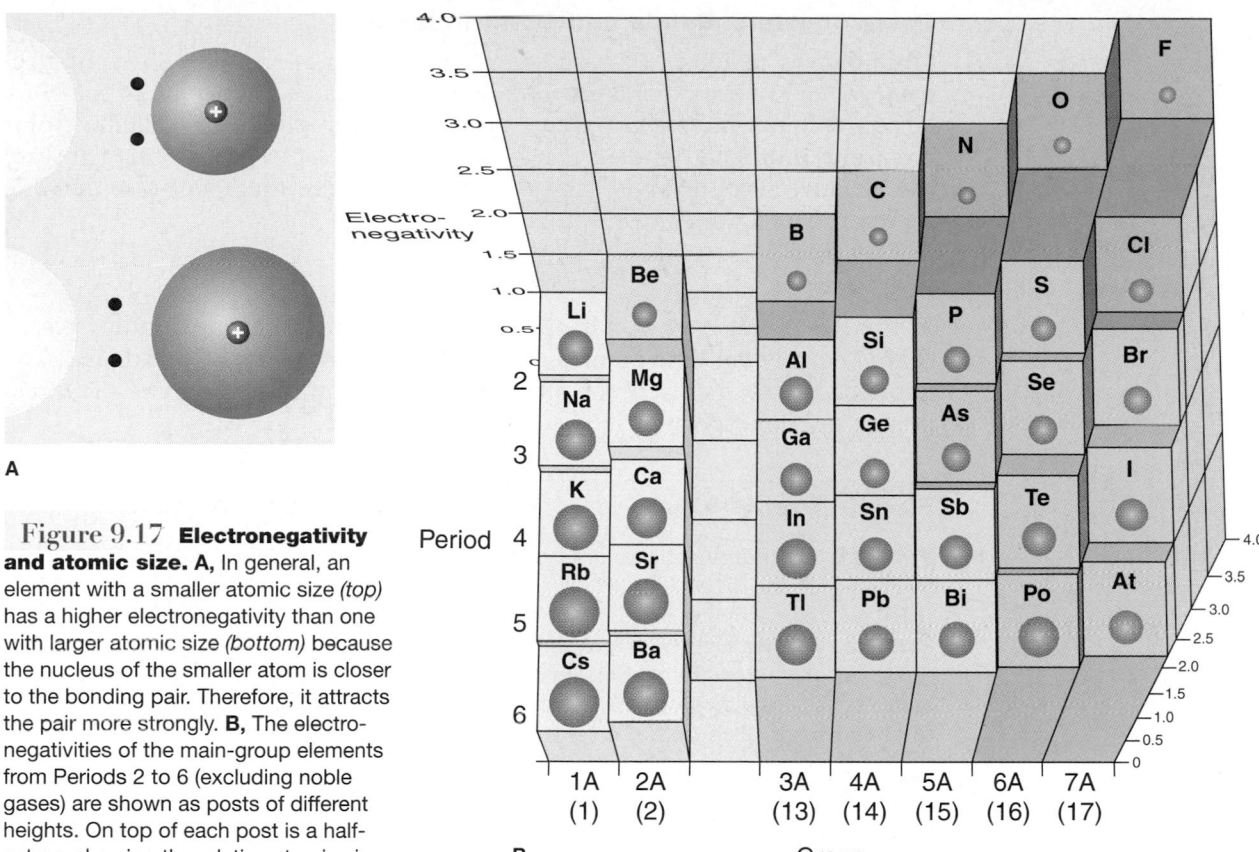

Figure 9.17 Electronegativity and atomic size. A, In general, an element with a smaller atomic size *(top)* has a higher electronegativity than one with larger atomic size *(bottom)* because the nucleus of the smaller atom is closer to the bonding pair. Therefore, it attracts the pair more strongly. **B,** The electro-negativities of the main-group elements from Periods 2 to 6 (excluding noble gases) are shown as posts of different heights. On top of each post is a half-sphere showing the relative atomic size.

nucleus of a smaller atom is closer to the shared pair than that of a larger atom, it attracts bonding electrons more strongly. In Pauling's electronega-tivity scale and in any of the several others available, *nonmetals are more elec-tronegative than metals.* The most electronegative element is fluorine, with oxy-gen a close second. Thus, except when it bonds with fluorine, oxygen always pulls bonding electrons toward itself. The least electronegative element (also referred to as the most *electropositive*) is francium, in the lower left corner of the periodic table, but it is radioactive and extremely rare, so for all practi-cal purposes, we consider cesium the most electropositive.*

Electronegativity and Oxidation Number One important use of electroneg-ativity is in determining an atom's oxidation number (O.N.; see Section 4.3):

1. The more electronegative atom in a bond is assigned *all* the *shared* elec-trons; the less electronegative atom is assigned *none*.
2. Each atom in a bond is assigned *all* of its *unshared* electrons.
3. The oxidation number is given by

$$\text{O.N.} = \text{no. of valence e}^- - (\text{no. of shared e}^- + \text{no. of unshared e}^-)$$

In HCl, for example, Cl is more electronegative than H. It has 7 valence elec-trons but is assigned 8 (2 shared + 6 unshared), so its oxidation number is $7 - 8 = -1$. The H atom has 1 valence electron and is assigned none, so its oxidation number is $1 - 0 = +1$.

---

*In 1934, the American physicist Robert S. Mulliken developed an approach to electronegativ-ity based solely on atomic properties: $\text{EN} = (\text{IE} - \text{EA})/2$. By this approach as well, fluorine, with a high ionization energy (IE) and a large negative electron affinity (EA), has a high EN; and cesium, with a low IE and small EA, has a low EN.

Polar Covalent Bonds and Bond Polarity

From our discussion of HF, you can see that when atoms with different electronegativities form a bond, the bonding pair is shared *un*equally, so the bond has partially negative and positive poles. This type of bond is called a **polar covalent bond** and is depicted by a polar arrow ($\longmapsto$) pointing toward the negative pole, or by $\delta+$ and $\delta-$ symbols, where the lower-case delta, δ, represents a partial charge:

$$\overset{\longmapsto}{\text{H—}\ddot{\text{F}}\text{:}} \qquad \text{or} \qquad \overset{\delta+\ \ \delta-}{\text{H—}\ddot{\text{F}}\text{:}}$$

In the H—H and F—F bonds, the atoms are identical, so the bonding pair is shared equally, and the bond is called a **nonpolar covalent bond.** Thus, by knowing the EN values of the atoms in a bond, you can determine the direction of the bond polarity.

Sample Problem 9.3   Determining Bond Polarity from EN Values

PROBLEM **(a)** Indicate the polarity of the following bonds with a polar arrow: N—H, F—N, I—Cl.
(b) Rank the following bonds in order of increasing polarity: H—N, H—O, H—C.
PLAN **(a)** We use Figure 9.16 to find the EN values of the bonded atoms and point the polar arrow toward the negative end. **(b)** Each choice has H bonded to an atom from Period 2. Since EN increases across a period, the polarity is greatest for the bond whose Period 2 atom is farthest to the right.

SOLUTION **(a)** The EN of N = 3.0 and the EN of H = 2.1, so N is more electronegative than H: $\overset{\longleftarrow}{\text{N—H}}$

The EN of F = 4.0 and the EN of N = 3.0, so F is more electronegative: $\overset{\longleftarrow}{\text{F—N}}$

The EN of I = 2.5 and the EN of Cl = 3.0, so I is less electronegative: $\overset{\longmapsto}{\text{I—Cl}}$
(b) The order of increasing EN is C < N < O, so the order of bond polarity is
H—C < H—N < H—O.
COMMENT In Chapter 10, you'll see that the polarity of the bonds in a molecule contributes to the overall polarity of the molecule, which is a major factor determining the magnitudes of physical properties.

Follow-up Problem 9.3   Arrange each set of bonds in order of increasing polarity, and designate the direction of bond polarity with $\delta+$ and $\delta-$ symbols: **(a)** Cl—F, Br—Cl, Cl—Cl; **(b)** Si—Cl, P—Cl, S—Cl, Si—Si.

The Partial Ionic Character of Polar Covalent Bonds

If you ask "Is an X—Y bond ionic or covalent?" the answer in almost every case is "Both, partially!" A better question is *"To what extent* is the bond ionic or covalent?" The existence of partial charges means that a polar covalent bond behaves as if it were partially ionic. The **partial ionic character** of a bond is related directly to the **electronegativity difference (ΔEN),** the difference between the EN values of the bonded atoms: *a greater ΔEN results in larger partial charges and a higher partial ionic character.* For example, ΔEN for LiF(g) is $4.0 - 1.0 = 3.0$; for HF(g), it is $4.0 - 2.1 = 1.9$; and for $F_2(g)$, it is $4.0 - 4.0 = 0$. Thus, the bond in LiF has more ionic character than the H—F bond, which has more than the F—F bond.

Various attempts have been made to classify the ionic character of bonds, but they all use arbitrary cutoff values, which is inconsistent with the gradation of ionic character observed experimentally. One approach uses ΔEN values to divide bonds into ionic, polar covalent, and nonpolar covalent. Based on a ΔEN range from 0 (completely nonpolar) to 3.3 (highly ionic), some approximate guidelines appear in Figure 9.18.

Another approach calculates the *percent ionic character* of a bond by comparing the actual behavior of a polar molecule in an electric field with the behavior it would have if the electron were transferred completely (pure ionic). A value of 50% ionic character is often chosen to divide substances we recognize as "ionic" from those we recognize as "covalent." Such methods show 43% ionic character for the H—F bond and expected decreases for the other hydrogen halides: H—Cl is 19% ionic, H—Br 11%, and H—I 4%. A plot of percent ionic character vs. ΔEN for a variety of gaseous binary (two-atom) molecules is shown in Figure 9.19. The specific values are not important, but note that *percent ionic character generally increases with ΔEN*. Another point to note is that whereas some molecules, such as $Cl_2(g)$, have 0% ionic character, none has 100% ionic character. Thus, *electron sharing occurs to some extent in every bond*, even one between an alkali metal and a halogen (Figure 9.20).

ΔEN	IONIC CHARACTER
>1.7	Mostly ionic
0.4-1.7	Polar covalent
<0.4	Mostly covalent
0	Nonpolar covalent

A

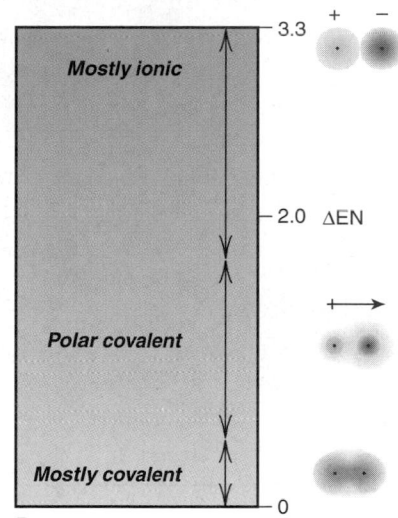

B

Figure 9.18 Boundary ranges for classifying ionic character of chemical bonds. A, The electronegativity difference (ΔEN) between bonded atoms shows cutoff values that act as a general guide to a bond's relative ionic character. **B,** The gradation in ionic character is shown with shading across the entire bonding range from ionic *(green)* to covalent *(yellow)*.

Figure 9.19 Percent ionic character as a function of electronegativity difference (ΔEN). The percent ionic character is plotted against ΔEN for some simple gaseous diatomic molecules. Note that, in general, ΔEN correlates with ionic character. (The arbitrary cutoff for an ionic compound is >50% ionic character.)

The Continuum of Bonding Across a Period

A metal and a nonmetal—elements from opposite sides of the periodic table—have a relatively large ΔEN and typically interact by electron transfer to form an ionic compound. Two nonmetals—elements from the same side of the table—have a small ΔEN and interact by electron sharing to form a covalent compound. If we combine a nonmetal such as Cl_2 with each of the other elements in Period 3, we expect to observe a steady decrease in ΔEN and a gradation in type of bonding from ionic to polar covalent to nonpolar covalent.

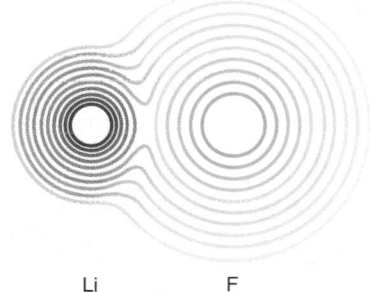

Figure 9.20 The charge density of LiF. A cross section of a diatomic LiF molecule showing contours of electron charge density *(color intensity)* that decrease from the nuclei outward. Note that even in this ionic interaction, there is significant overlap of electron density between the atoms, indicating some covalent character.

Figure 9.21 Properties of the Period 3 chlorides. Samples of the compound formed from each Period 3 element with chlorine are shown in periodic table sequence in the photo, with their structural formulas below. Note the trend in properties displayed in the bar graphs: as ΔEN decreases, both melting point and electrical conductivity (at the melting point) decrease as well. These trends are consistent with a change in bond type from ionic through polar covalent to nonpolar covalent.

Figure 9.21 shows samples of the most common Period 3 chlorides—NaCl, $MgCl_2$, $AlCl_3$, $SiCl_4$, PCl_3, S_2Cl_2, and Cl_2—along with structural formulas (discussed at the beginning of the next chapter) and some properties. The first compound is sodium chloride, a white (colorless) crystalline solid with typical ionic properties: high melting point and high conductivity when molten or dissolved. With these properties and a ΔEN of 2.1, it is ionic by any criterion. Magnesium chloride is still considered ionic, with a ΔEN of 1.8, but it has a lower melting point and lower conductivity.

Aluminum chloride is still less ionic. Its ΔEN value of 1.5 indicates a highly polar covalent Al—Cl bond. Rather than a lattice of Al^{3+} and Cl^- ions, it consists of extended layers of linked Al and Cl atoms. Strong polar interactions hold the particles together in the layer, but weak forces between layers result in a much lower melting point. The low electrical conductivity of molten $AlCl_3$ is consistent with a scarcity of ions.

Silicon tetrachloride's melting point is very low because of weak forces *between* separate molecules, and it has no measurable electrical conductivity. Each molecule consists of strong Si—Cl bonds with a ΔEN value of 1.2, near the middle of the polar covalent region. With a ΔEN value of 0.9, phosphorus trichloride continues the trend toward lower bond polarity, as evidenced by its very low melting point. The bonds in disulfur dichloride are even less polar (ΔEN = 0.5). The series ends with nonpolar, diatomic chlorine, the only one of these substances that is a gas at room temperature.

Thus, *as ΔEN becomes smaller, the bond becomes more covalent,* and the properties of the Period 3 chlorides change from those of a solid consisting of ions to those of a gas consisting of individual molecules.

Section Summary

An atom's electronegativity is related to its ability to pull bonded electrons toward it, which generates partial charges at the ends of the bond. Electronegativity increases across a period and decreases down a group, the reverse of the trend in size. The greater the ΔEN of the atoms in a bond, the more polar the bond is and the greater its ionic character. There is a gradation of bond type, from ionic to polar covalent to nonpolar covalent, which can be seen by combining a halogen with the other elements in its period.

9.5 An Introduction to Metallic Bonding

The third type of chemical bonding we consider is metallic bonding, which occurs among large numbers of metal atoms. In this section, you'll see a qualitative model; a more quantitative one is presented in Chapter 12.

The Electron-Sea Model

In reactions with nonmetals, reactive metals (such as Na) transfer their outer electrons and form ionic solids (such as NaCl). Two metal atoms can also share their valence electrons in a covalent bond and form gaseous, diatomic molecules (such as Na_2). But what holds the atoms together in a piece of sodium metal? The **electron-sea model** of metallic bonding proposes that all the metal atoms in the sample contribute their valence electrons to form an "electron sea" that is delocalized throughout the substance. The metal ions (the nuclei with their core electrons) are submerged within this electron sea in an orderly array (see Figure 9.2C).

In contrast to ionic bonding, the metal ions are not held in place as rigidly as in an ionic solid. In contrast to covalent bonding, no particular pair of metal atoms is bonded through any localized pair of electrons. Rather, *the valence electrons are shared among all the atoms in the substance,* which is held together by the mutual attraction of the metal cations for the mobile, highly delocalized electrons.

Although there are metallic compounds, it is more typical for metals to form **alloys,** solid mixtures with variable composition. Familiar metallic substances used for car parts, airplane bodies, building and bridge supports, coins, jewelry, and dental work are all alloys.

How the Model Explains the Properties of Metals

Although the physical properties of metals vary over a wide range, most are solids with moderate to high melting points and much higher boiling points (Table 9.5). Metals typically bend or dent rather than crack or shatter. Many can be flattened into sheets (malleable) and pulled into wires (ductile). Unlike typical ionic and covalent substances, metals conduct heat and electricity well in *both* the solid and liquid states.

Two features of the electron-sea model that account for these properties are the *regularity,* but not rigidity, of the metal-ion array and the *mobility* of the valence electrons. The melting and boiling points of metals are related to the energy of the metallic bonding. Melting points are only moderately high because the attractions between moveable cations and electrons need not be broken during melting. Boiling a metal requires each cation and its electron(s) to break away from the others, so the boiling points are quite high. As shown in Figure 9.22, gallium provides a striking example: it melts in your hand but doesn't boil until the temperature reaches over 2400°C.

Table 9.5 Melting and Boiling Points of Some Metals

Element	mp (°C)	bp (°C)
Lithium (Li)	180	1347
Tin (Sn)	232	2623
Aluminum (Al)	660	2467
Barium (Ba)	727	1850
Silver (Ag)	961	2155
Copper (Cu)	1083	2570
Uranium (U)	1130	3930

Figure 9.22 The unusually low melting point of gallium. Gallium has the widest liquid range of any element. Its melting point (29.8°C) is below body temperature, because metallic bonding forces need not be broken when the metal ions move from their lattice positions, but it boils at 2403°C because these forces are strong enough to resist separation of the atoms.

Melting point (°C)

Figure 9.23 **Melting points of the Group 1A(1) and Group 2A(2) elements.** The alkaline earth metals [Group 2A(2), *blue*] have higher melting points than the alkali metals [Group 1A(1), *brown*] because the ions have 2+ charges and the electron "sea" has twice as many valence electrons, which results in stronger attractions.

Periodic trends are also consistent with the model. As Figure 9.23 shows, the alkaline earth metals [Group 2A(2)] have higher melting points than the alkali metals [Group 1A(1)]. The 2A metal atoms have two valence electrons and form 2+ cations. Greater attraction between these cations and twice as many electrons means stronger metallic bonding than in Group 1A, so higher temperatures are needed to melt the 2A solids.

Mechanical and conducting properties are explained by the model as well. When a piece of metal is struck by a hammer, the metal ions slide past each other through the electron sea to new lattice positions. Thus, as Figure 9.24 shows, the metal-ion cores do not repel each other when the sample is deformed. Compare this behavior with the repulsions that occur when an ionic solid is struck (see Figure 9.8). ◆

Metals are good conductors of electricity because they have mobile electrons. When a piece of metal is attached to the two terminals of a battery, electrons flow from the battery into the metal and replace electrons flowing from the metal into the battery. Irregularities in the array of metal atoms reduce this conductivity. Ordinary copper wire used to carry an electric cur-

◆ The Amazing Malleability of Gold All the Group 1B(11) metals—copper, silver, and gold—are soft enough to be machined easily, but gold is in a class by itself. One gram of gold would form a cube 0.37 cm on a side or a sphere the size of a small ball-bearing. It is so ductile that it can be drawn into a wire 20 μm thick and 165 m long, and so malleable that it can be hammered into a 1.0-m² sheet that is only 230 atoms (about 70 nm) thick!

A

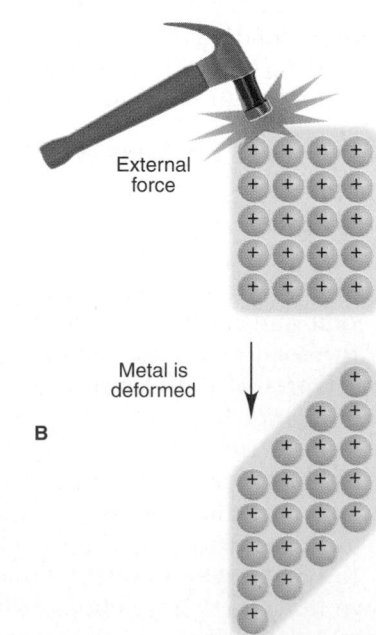

B

External force

Metal is deformed

Figure 9.24 **The reason metals deform. A,** An external force applied to a piece of metal deforms the piece without breaking it. **B,** At the atomic level, the force simply moves metal ions past each other through the surrounding electron sea.

rent, for example, is greater than 99.99% pure because traces of other atoms can drastically restrict the flow of electrons.

The mobile electrons also make metals good conductors of heat. If you place your hand on a piece of metal and a piece of wood that are both at room temperature, the metal feels colder because it conducts body heat away from your hand much faster than the wood. The delocalized electrons in the metal disperse the heat from your hand more quickly than the localized electron pairs in the covalent bonds of wood.

Section Summary

In the electron-sea model, the valence electrons of the metal atoms in a sample are highly delocalized and attract the metal cations together. Metals have only moderate melting points because the metal ions remain attracted to the electron sea even if their relative positions change. Yet they have high boiling points because boiling requires overcoming the bonding attractions. Metals can be deformed because the electron sea prevents repulsions among the cations. Metals conduct electricity and heat because their electrons are mobile.

Chapter Perspective

Our theme throughout this chapter has been that the particular type of chemical bonding—whether ionic, covalent, metallic, or some blend of these—is governed by the properties of the bonding atoms. This fundamental idea reappears many times as we investigate the forces that give rise to the properties of liquids, solids, and solutions (Chapters 12 and 13), the behavior of the main-group elements (Chapter 14), and the organic chemistry of carbon (Chapter 15). Before we can develop these topics, however, you'll see in Chapter 10 how the relative placement of atoms and the arrangement of bonding and lone pairs gives a molecule its characteristic shape and how that shape influences many of the compound's properties. Then, in Chapter 11, you'll see how covalent bonding theory explains the nature of the bond itself and the properties of compounds.

The following learning objectives, with section and/or sample problem (SP) numbers in parentheses, can help focus your study:

Understand These Concepts

1. How differences in atomic properties lead to differences in bond type and the basic distinctions among the three types of bonding (9.1)
2. The essential features of ionic bonding: electron transfer to form ions, and their electrostatic attraction to form a solid (9.2)
3. How lattice energy is ultimately responsible for formation of ionic compounds (9.2)
4. How ionic compound formation is analyzed conceptually into hypothetical steps (Born-Haber cycle) to calculate lattice energy (9.2)
5. How Coulomb's law explains the periodic trends in lattice energy (9.2)
6. Why ionic compounds are brittle, high melting, and conduct electricity only when molten or dissolved in water (9.2)
7. How nonmetal atoms overlap to form a covalent bond (9.3)
8. How bonding and lone pairs fill the valence shell of each atom in the molecule (9.3)
9. The interrelationships among bond order, bond length, and bond energy (9.3)
10. How the distinction between bonding and nonbonding forces explains the properties of covalent molecules and network compounds (9.3)
11. The periodic trends in electronegativity and their inverse relation to atomic size (9.4)
12. How bond polarity arises from differences in electronegativity of bonded atoms; the direction of polarity (9.4)
13. The change in partial ionic character with ΔEN and the change in bonding from ionic to polar covalent to nonpolar covalent across a period (9.4)
14. The distinction between localized and delocalized electrons in bonding (9.5)
15. How the electron-sea model explains why metals bend, have very high boiling points, and conduct electricity in solid or molten forms (9.5)

Master These Skills

1. Using Lewis electron-dot symbols to depict main-group atoms (9.1)
2. Depicting the formation of binary ionic compounds with electron configurations, orbital diagrams, and Lewis electron-dot symbols (SP 9.1)
3. Calculating lattice energy from the energy components of ionic compound formation (9.2)
4. Ranking lengths and strengths of similar covalent bonds (SP 9.2)
5. Ranking bond polarity and predicting its direction (SP 9.3)

For Review and Reference

Key Terms

Section 9.1
ionic bonding
covalent bonding
metallic bonding
Lewis electron-dot symbol
Section 9.2
octet rule
lattice energy

Born-Haber cycle
Coulomb's law
ion pair
Section 9.3
covalent bond
bonding (shared) pair
lone (unshared) pair
bond order

single bond
double bond
triple bond
bond energy (BE)
bond length
infrared (IR) spectroscopy
Section 9.4
electronegativity (EN)

polar covalent bond
nonpolar covalent bond
partial ionic character
electronegativity difference
  (ΔEN)
Section 9.5
electron-sea model
alloy

Key Equations and Relationships

9.1 Expressing the energy of attraction (or repulsion) between changes (p. 337):

$$\text{Electrostatic energy} \propto \frac{\text{charge A} \times \text{charge B}}{\text{distance}}$$

9.2 Relating the energy of attraction to the lattice energy (p. 337):

$$\text{Electrostatic energy} \propto \frac{\text{cation charge} \times \text{anion charge}}{\text{cation radius} + \text{anion radius}}$$
$$\propto \Delta H^0_{\text{lattice}}$$

Highlighted Figures and Tables

These figures (F) and tables (T) provide a quick review of key ideas. Entries in color contain frequently used data.
F9.1 A general comparison of metals and nonmetals (p. 331)
F9.2 The three models of chemical bonding (p. 332)
F9.3 Lewis electron-dot symbols for elements in Periods 2 and 3 (p. 333)
F9.6 The Born-Haber cycle for LiF (p. 336)

F9.7 Trends in lattice energy (p. 338)
F9.11 Covalent bond formation in H_2 (p. 341)
T9.2 Average bond energies (p. 343)
T9.3 Average bond lengths (p. 343)
F9.16 The Pauling electronegativity scale (p. 348)
F9.17 Electronegativity and atomic size (p. 349)
F9.21 Properties of the Period 3 chlorides (p. 352)

Answers to Follow-up Problems

9.1 Mg ([Ne] $3s^2$) + 2 Cl ([Ne] $3s^2 3p^5$) $\longrightarrow$
$\quad\quad\quad\quad\quad$ Mg^{2+} ([Ne]) + $2Cl^-$ ([Ne] $3s^2 3p^6$)

Formula is $MgCl_2$

9.2 (a) Bond length: Si—F < Si—O < Si—C
Bond strength: Si—C < Si—O < Si—F

(b) Bond length: N≡N < N=N < N—N
Bond strength: N—N < N=N < N≡N
9.3 (a) $\overset{\delta+}{\text{Cl}}-\overset{\delta-}{\text{Cl}}$ < $\overset{\delta+}{\text{Br}}-\overset{\delta-}{\text{Cl}}$ < $\overset{\delta+}{\text{Cl}}-\overset{\delta-}{\text{F}}$;
(b) $\overset{\delta+}{\text{Si}}-\overset{\delta-}{\text{Si}}$ < $\overset{\delta+}{\text{S}}-\overset{\delta-}{\text{Cl}}$ < $\overset{\delta+}{\text{P}}-\overset{\delta-}{\text{Cl}}$ < $\overset{\delta+}{\text{Si}}-\overset{\delta-}{\text{Cl}}$

Problems

Problems with a **colored** number are answered at the back of the text. Problem sections match the text and provide the number(s) of relevant sample problems. Most offer concept review questions, skill-building exercises (written in similar pairs), and problems in a relevant context. Following these are comprehensive problems based on material from any section and/or previous chapter.

Atomic Properties and Chemical Bonds

■ Concept Review Questions
9.1 In general terms, how does each of these atomic properties influence the metallic character of the main-group ele-

ments in a period: (a) ionization energy; (b) atomic radius; (c) number of outer electrons; (d) effective nuclear charge?
9.2 Both nitrogen and bismuth are members of Group 5A(15). Which is more metallic? Explain your answer in terms of atomic properties.
9.3 What is the relationship between the tendency of a main-group element to form a monatomic ion and its position in the periodic table? Where are the main-group elements located that typically form cations? Anions?

■ Skill-Building Exercises (paired)
9.4 Which member of each of the following pairs is *more* metallic: (a) Na or Cs; (b) Mg or Rb; (c) As or N?

9.5 Which member of each of the following pairs is *less* metallic: (a) I or O; (b) Be or Ba; (c) Se or Ge?

9.6 State the type of bonding—ionic, covalent, or metallic—you would expect in (a) CsF(s); (b) N$_2$(g); (c) Na(s).
9.7 State the type of bonding—ionic, covalent, or metallic—you would expect in (a) ICl$_3$(g); (b) N$_2$O(g); (c) LiCl(s).

9.8 State the type of bonding—ionic, covalent, or metallic—you would expect in (a) O$_3$(g); (b) MgCl$_2$(s); (c) BrO$_2$(g).
9.9 State the type of bonding—ionic, covalent, or metallic—you would expect in (a) Cr(s); (b) H$_2$S(s); (c) CaO(s).

9.10 Draw a Lewis electron-dot symbol for each of the following atoms: (a) Rb; (b) Si; (c) I.
9.11 Draw a Lewis electron-dot symbol for each of the following atoms: (a) Ba; (b) Kr; (c) Br.

9.12 Draw a Lewis electron-dot symbol for each of the following atoms: (a) Sr; (b) P; (c) S.
9.13 Draw a Lewis electron-dot symbol for each of the following atoms: (a) As; (b) Se; (c) Ga.

9.14 Give the group number and general electron configuration of an element with the following electron-dot symbol:
(a) $\cdot\ddot{\text{X}}\colon$ (b) $\dot{\text{X}}\cdot$
9.15 Give the group number and general electron configuration of an element with the following electron-dot symbol:
(a) $\cdot\ddot{\text{X}}\colon$ (b) $\cdot\dot{\text{X}}\cdot$

The Ionic Bonding Model
(Sample Problem 9.1)

■ Concept Review Questions
9.16 If energy is required to form monatomic ions from metals and nonmetals, why do ionic compounds exist?
9.17 In general, how does the lattice energy of an ionic compound depend on the charges and sizes of the ions?
9.18 When gaseous Na$^+$ and Cl$^-$ ions form gaseous NaCl ion pairs, 548 kJ/mol is released. Why, then, does NaCl occur as a solid under ordinary conditions?
9.19 To form S^{2-} ions from gaseous sulfur atoms requires 214 kJ/mol, but these ions exist in solids such as K$_2$S. Explain.

■ Skill-Building Exercises (paired)
9.20 Use condensed electron configurations and electron-dot symbols to depict the monatomic ions formed from each of the following, and predict the formula of the compound the ions produce: (a) Ba and Cl; (b) Sr and O; (c) Al and F; (d) Rb and O.
9.21 Use condensed electron configurations and electron-dot symbols to depict the monatomic ions formed from each of the following, and predict the formula of the compound the ions produce: (a) Cs and S; (b) O and Ga; (c) N and Mg; (d) Br and Li.

9.22 Identify the main group to which X belongs in each ionic compound formula: (a) XF$_2$; (b) MgX; (c) X$_2$SO$_4$.
9.23 Identify the main group to which X belongs in each ionic compound formula: (a) X$_3$PO$_4$; (b) X$_2$(SO$_4$)$_3$; (c) X(NO$_3$)$_2$.

9.24 Identify the main group to which X belongs in each ionic compound formula: (a) X$_2$O$_3$; (b) XCO$_3$; (c) Na$_2$X.

9.25 Identify the main group to which X belongs in each ionic compound formula: (a) CaX$_2$; (b) Al$_2$X$_3$; (c) XPO$_4$.

9.26 For each pair, choose the compound with the higher (more negative) lattice energy, and explain your choice: (a) BaS or CsCl; (b) LiCl or CsCl.
9.27 For each pair, choose the compound with the higher (more negative) lattice energy, and explain your choice: (a) CaO or CaS; (b) BaO or SrO.

9.28 For each pair, choose the compound with the lower (less negative) lattice energy, and explain your choice: (a) CaS or BaS; (b) NaF or MgO.
9.29 For each pair, choose the compound with the lower (less negative) lattice energy, and explain your choice: (a) NaF or NaCl; (b) K$_2$O or K$_2$S.

9.30 Use the following to calculate the $\Delta H^0_{\text{lattice}}$ of NaCl:

$$\text{Na}(s) \longrightarrow \text{Na}(g) \quad \Delta H^0 = 109 \text{ kJ}$$
$$\text{Cl}_2(g) \longrightarrow 2\text{Cl}(g) \quad \Delta H^0 = 243 \text{ kJ}$$
$$\text{Na}(g) \longrightarrow \text{Na}^+(g) + \text{e}^- \quad \Delta H^0 = 496 \text{ kJ}$$
$$\text{Cl}(g) + \text{e}^- \longrightarrow \text{Cl}^-(g) \quad \Delta H^0 = -349 \text{ kJ}$$
$$\text{Na}(s) + \tfrac{1}{2}\text{Cl}_2(g) \longrightarrow \text{NaCl}(s) \quad \Delta H^0_{\text{f}} = -411 \text{ kJ}$$

Compared with the lattice energy of LiF (-1050 kJ/mol), is the relative magnitude of the NaCl value expected? Explain.
9.31 Use the following to calculate the $\Delta H^0_{\text{lattice}}$ of MgF$_2$:

$$\text{Mg}(s) \longrightarrow \text{Mg}(g) \quad \Delta H^0 = 148 \text{ kJ}$$
$$\text{F}_2(g) \longrightarrow 2\text{F}(g) \quad \Delta H^0 = 159 \text{ kJ}$$
$$\text{Mg}(g) \longrightarrow \text{Mg}^+(g) + \text{e}^- \quad \Delta H^0 = 738 \text{ kJ}$$
$$\text{Mg}^+(g) \longrightarrow \text{Mg}^{2+}(g) + \text{e}^- \quad \Delta H^0 = 1450 \text{ kJ}$$
$$\text{F}(g) + \text{e}^- \longrightarrow \text{F}^-(g) \quad \Delta H^0 = -328 \text{ kJ}$$
$$\text{Mg}(s) + \text{F}_2(g) \longrightarrow \text{MgF}_2(s) \quad \Delta H^0_{\text{f}} = -1123 \text{ kJ}$$

Compared with the lattice energy of LiF (-1050 kJ/mol) or the lattice energy that you calculated for NaCl in Problem 9.30, does the relative magnitude of the value for MgF$_2$ surprise you? Explain.

■ Problems in Context
9.32 Aluminum oxide (Al$_2$O$_3$) is a widely used industrial abrasive (emery, corundum), with its specific application depending on the hardness of the crystal. What does this hardness imply about the magnitude of the lattice energy? Would you have predicted from the chemical formula that Al$_2$O$_3$ is hard? Explain.
9.33 Born-Haber cycles were used to obtain the first reliable values for electron affinity by considering the EA value as the unknown and using a theoretically calculated value for the lattice energy. Use a Born-Haber cycle for KF and the following values to calculate a value for the electron affinity of fluorine:

$$\text{K}(s) \longrightarrow \text{K}(g) \quad \Delta H^0 = 90 \text{ kJ}$$
$$\text{K}(g) \longrightarrow \text{K}^+(g) + \text{e}^- \quad \Delta H^0 = 419 \text{ kJ}$$
$$\text{F}_2(g) \longrightarrow 2\text{F}(g) \quad \Delta H^0 = 159 \text{ kJ}$$
$$\text{K}(s) + \tfrac{1}{2}\text{F}_2(g) \longrightarrow \text{KF}(s) \quad \Delta H^0_{\text{f}} = -569 \text{ kJ}$$
$$\text{K}^+(g) + \text{F}^-(g) \longrightarrow \text{KF}(s) \quad \Delta H^0_{\text{lattice}} = -821 \text{ kJ}$$

The Covalent Bonding Model
(Sample Problem 9.2)

■ Concept Review Questions

9.34 Describe the interactions that occur between individual chlorine atoms as they approach each other and form Cl_2. What combination of forces gives rise to the energy holding the atoms together and to the final internuclear distance?

9.35 Define bond energy using the H—Cl bond as an example. When this bond breaks, is energy absorbed or released? Is the accompanying ΔH value positive or negative? How do the magnitude and sign of this ΔH value relate to the value that accompanies H—Cl bond formation?

9.36 For single bonds between similar types of atoms, how does the strength of the bond relate to the sizes of the atoms? Explain.

9.37 How does the bond energy between a given pair of atoms relate to the bond order? Why?

9.38 When liquid benzene (C_6H_6) boils, does the gas consist of C_6H_6 molecules, molecule fragments, or separate C and H atoms? Explain.

■ Skill-Building Exercises (paired)

9.39 Using the periodic table only, arrange the members of each of the following sets in order of increasing bond *strength:* (a) Br—Br, Cl—Cl, I—I; (b) S—H, S—Br, S—Cl; (c) C=N, C—N, C≡N.

9.40 Using the periodic table only, arrange the members of each of the following sets in order of increasing bond *length:* (a) H—F, H—I, H—Cl; (b) C—S, C=O, C—O; (c) N—H, N—S, N—O.

■ Problems in Context

9.41 Formic acid (HCOOH) is secreted by certain species of ants when they bite. It has the structural formula:

$$\overset{\displaystyle :\!O:}{\underset{\displaystyle H-C-\overset{\displaystyle ..}{\underset{\displaystyle ..}{O}}-H}{\|}}$$

Rank the relative strengths of the C—O bond, C=O bond, and attractive force between two HCOOH molecules.

9.42 In Figure 9.B, the peak labeled "C=C stretch" occurs at a shorter wavelength than that labeled "C—C stretch," as it would in the infrared spectrum of any substance with those types of bonds. Explain the relative positions of these peaks. In what relative position along the wavelength scale of Figure 9.B would you expect to find a peak characteristic of a C≡C stretch? Explain.

Between the Extremes: Electronegativity and Bond Polarity
(Sample Problem 9.3)

■ Concept Review Questions

9.43 Describe the vertical and horizontal trends in electronegativity (EN) among the main-group elements. According to Pauling's scale, what are the two most electronegative elements? The two least electronegative elements?

9.44 What is the general relationship between IE_1 and EN for the elements? Why?

9.45 Is the H—O bond in water nonpolar covalent, polar covalent, or ionic? Define each term and explain your choice.

9.46 How does electronegativity differ from electron affinity?

9.47 How is the partial ionic character of a diatomic molecule related to the ΔEN of the bonded atoms? Why?

■ Skill-Building Exercises (paired)

9.48 Using the periodic table only, arrange the elements in each set in order of *increasing* EN: (a) S, O, Si; (b) Mg, P, As.

9.49 Using the periodic table only, arrange the elements in each set in order of *increasing* EN: (a) I, Br, N; (b) Ca, H, F.

9.50 Using the periodic table only, arrange the elements in each set in order of *decreasing* EN: (a) N, P, Si; (b) Ca, Ga, As.

9.51 Using the periodic table only, arrange the elements in each set in order of *decreasing* EN: (a) Br, Cl, P; (b) I, F, O.

9.52 Use Figure 9.16 and polar arrows to indicate the polarity of each bond with *polar arrows*: (a) N—B; (b) N—O; (c) C—S; (d) S—O; (e) N—H; (f) N—O.

9.53 Use Figure 9.16 and polar arrows to indicate the polarity of each bond with *polar arrows*: (a) Br—Cl; (b) F—Cl; (c) H—O; (d) Se—H; (e) As—H; (f) S—N.

9.54 Which is the more polar bond in each of the following pairs in Problem 9.52: (a) or (b); (c) or (d); (e) or (f).

9.55 Which is the more polar bond in each of the following pairs in Problem 9.53: (a) or (b); (c) or (d); (e) or (f).

9.56 Are the bonds in each of the following substances ionic, nonpolar covalent, or polar covalent? Arrange the substances with polar covalent bonds in order of increasing bond polarity: (a) S_8; (b) RbCl; (c) PF_3; (d) SCl_2; (e) F_2; (f) SF_2.

9.57 Are the bonds in each of the following substances ionic, nonpolar covalent, or polar covalent? Arrange the substances with polar covalent bonds in order of increasing bond polarity: (a) KCl; (b) P_4; (c) BF_3; (d) SO_2; (e) Br_2; (f) NO_2.

9.58 Rank the members of each set of compounds in order of *increasing* ionic character of their bonds. Use *polar arrows* to indicate the bond polarity of each: (a) HBr, HCl, HI; (b) H_2O, CH_4, HF; (c) SCl_2, PCl_3, $SiCl_4$.

9.59 Rank the members of each set of compounds in order of *decreasing* ionic character of their bonds. Use *partial charges* to indicate the bond polarity of each: (a) PCl_3, PBr_3, PF_3; (b) BF_3, NF_3, CF_4; (c) SeF_4, TeF_4, BrF_3.

■ Problems in Context

9.60 The bond energy of the C—C bond is 347 kJ/mol, and that of the Cl—Cl bond is 243 kJ/mol. Which of the following values might you expect for the C—Cl bond energy? Explain.
(a) 590 kJ/mol (sum of the values above)
(b) 104 kJ/mol (difference of the values above)
(c) 295 kJ/mol (average of the values above)
(d) 339 kJ/mol (value greater than the average of the values above)

An Introduction to Metallic Bonding

■ Concept Review Questions

9.61 (a) List four physical characteristics of a solid metal.
(b) List two chemical characteristics that lead to an element being classified as a metal.

9.62 Briefly account for the following relative values:
(a) The melting point of sodium is 89°C, whereas that of potassium is 63°C.
(b) The melting points of Li and Be are 180°C and 1287°C, respectively.
(c) Lithium boils more than 1100°C higher than it melts.

9.63 Magnesium metal is easily deformed by an applied force, whereas magnesium fluoride is shattered. Why do these two solids behave so differently?

Comprehensive Problems

Problems with an asterisk (*) are more challenging.

9.64 Geologists have a rule of thumb that, when molten rock cools and solidifies, crystals of compounds with the smallest (least negative) lattice energy appear at the bottom of the mass. Suggest a reason for this.

9.65 Use two compounds of sulfur to explain how the octet rule applies to the formation of many ionic and covalent compounds.

9.66 Use Lewis electron-dot symbols to represent the formation of (a) BrF_3 from bromine and fluorine atoms; (b) AlF_3 from aluminum and fluorine atoms.

*9.67 Even though so much energy is required to form a divalent metal cation, the alkaline earth metals form halides with general formula MX_2, rather than MX. Let's see why.
(a) Use the following data to calculate the ΔH_f^0 of MgCl:

$Mg(s) \longrightarrow Mg(g) \quad \Delta H^0 = 148 \text{ kJ}$

$Cl_2(g) \longrightarrow 2Cl(g) \quad \Delta H^0 = 243 \text{ kJ}$

$Mg(g) \longrightarrow Mg^+(g) + e^- \quad \Delta H^0 = 738 \text{ kJ}$

$Cl(g) + e^- \longrightarrow Cl^-(g) \quad \Delta H^0 = -349 \text{ kJ}$

$\Delta H_{lattice}^0$ of MgCl $= -783.5 \text{ kJ/mol}$

(b) Is MgCl stable relative to its elements? Explain.
(c) Use Hess's law to calculate ΔH^0 for the conversion of MgCl to $MgCl_2$ and Mg (ΔH_f^0 of $MgCl_2 = -641.6 \text{ kJ/mol}$).
(d) Is the formation of MgCl favored relative to the formation of $MgCl_2$? Explain.

9.68 Some gases react explosively with one another. If their reaction is sufficiently exothermic, the heat released as some product molecules form is transferred to other reactant molecules, which release more heat as they react, and so on. The rapid heat release causes a rapid expansion of the gases, and a thermal explosion results. Use bond energies to calculate ΔH^0 of the following reactions and predict which will react explosively:
(a) $H_2(g) + Cl_2(g) \longrightarrow 2HCl(g)$
(b) $H_2(g) + I_2(g) \longrightarrow 2HI(g)$
(c) $2H_2(g) + O_2(g) \longrightarrow 2H_2O(g)$

*9.69 By using photons of specific wavelengths, chemists can dissociate gaseous HI to produce H atoms with accurately known speeds. When HI dissociates, the H atoms move away rapidly, whereas the relatively heavy I atoms move little.
(a) What is the longest wavelength (in nm) that can dissociate a molecule of HI?
(b) If a photon of 254 nm is used, what is the excess energy (in J) over that needed for the dissociation?
(c) If all of this excess energy is carried away by the H atom as kinetic energy, what is its speed (in m/s)?

9.70 In developing the concept of electronegativity, Pauling used the term *excess bond energy* for the difference between the actual bond energy of X—Y and the average bond energies of X—X and Y—Y (see text discussion for the case of HF). Based on the values in Figure 9.16, which of the following substances contains bonds with *no* excess bond energy: (a) PH_3; (b) CS_2; (c) BrCl; (d) BH_3; (e) Se_8?

9.71 Use electron configurations to predict the relative hardnesses and melting points of rubidium ($Z = 37$), vanadium ($Z = 23$), and cadmium ($Z = 48$).

9.72 Chemists employ lasers to emit light of a given energy to initiate bond breakage. (a) What is the minimum energy and frequency of a photon that can cause the dissociation of a Cl_2 molecule? (b) The first key step in the destruction of stratospheric ozone by industrial chlorofluorocarbons is thought to be photodissociation of a C—Cl bond. What is the longest wavelength of a photon that can cause this dissociation?

*9.73 Bond energies can be combined with values for other atomic properties to obtain ΔH values that cannot be measured directly. Use bond energy, ionization energy, and electron affinity values to calculate the ΔH_{rxn}^0 for the ionic dissociation of Cl_2 gas:

$$Cl_2(g) \longrightarrow Cl^+(g) + Cl^-(g)$$

*9.74 The HF bond length is 92 pm, 16% shorter than the sum of the covalent radii of H (37 pm) and F (72 pm). Why is the bond length less than the sum of the covalent radii in HF? Similar calculations for the other hydrogen halides show that the difference between actual and calculated bond lengths becomes smaller down the group from HF to HI. Explain.

*9.75 Chemists distinguish between two modes of covalent bond breakage. Homolytic breakage occurs when each atom in the bond gets one of the shared electrons. Heterolytic breakage occurs when one atom gets both electrons and the other gets none. In some cases, the electronegativity of neighboring atoms affects the energy required for the breakage.
(a) Which type of bond breakage results in bond energies such as those in Table 9.2? Explain.
(b) Which type results in the formation of ions? Explain.
(c) Suggest a reason why the C—C bond energy in H_3C—CCl_3 (BE = 372 kJ/mol) deviates so far from the average C—C bond energy of 347 kJ/mol?
(d) Would you expect it to take more than 372 kJ/mol to break the C—C bond in H_3C—CH_3 heterolytically? Explain.

9.76 Lattice energies can also be calculated for covalent solids through a Born-Haber cycle, and the network solid silicon dioxide has one of the highest. Silicon dioxide is found in pure crystalline form as transparent rock quartz, the material of the fabled crystal ball. Much harder than glass, this material was once prized for making lenses for optical devices and expensive spectacles. Use Appendix B and the following data to calculate $\Delta H_{lattice}^0$ of SiO_2:

$Si(s) \longrightarrow Si(g) \qquad \Delta H^0 = 454 \text{ kJ}$

$Si(g) \longrightarrow Si^{4+}(g) + 4e^- \qquad \Delta H^0 = 9949 \text{ kJ}$

$O_2(g) \longrightarrow 2O(g) \qquad \Delta H^0 = 498 \text{ kJ}$

$O(g) + 2e^- \longrightarrow O^{2-}(g) \qquad \Delta H^0 = 737 \text{ kJ}$

10

The Shapes of Molecules

Figure: Interconnecting shapes.
In everyday life, the shapes of many objects fit together, like the gears of this machine, to perform a function—key and lock, mortise and tenon, hand and glove. Similarly, an organism's molecules have shapes that fit together to trigger the processes of life. In this chapter, we learn to depict molecules as two-dimensional drawings and, more importantly, to visualize them as three-dimensional objects.

Armed with your understanding of how atoms bond, you can now explore an idea essential to chemistry—*and* biology! The printed page, covered with atomic symbols, lines, and pairs of dots, makes it easy to forget the amazing, three-dimensional reality of molecular shape. Molecules are incredibly small conglomerations of mass and charge that twist and vibrate incessantly. Each atom, bonding pair, and lone pair has its own position in space relative to the others, determined by the attractive and repulsive forces that govern all matter. With definite angles and distances between the nuclei, a molecule is an independent, minute architecture, extending throughout its tiny volume of space. Whether we consider the details of simple reactions, the properties of synthetic materials, or the intricate life-sustaining processes of living cells, molecular shape is a crucial factor.

Although our focus in this chapter is the shapes of molecules, we begin by seeing how to convert the *molecular* formula of a compound into a flat *structural* formula, called a *Lewis structure*, which shows how the atoms are attached to each other within the molecule but does *not* reveal the overall shape. We use Lewis structures to calculate heats of reaction from bond energies. Then we examine VSEPR (valence-shell electron-pair repulsion) theory, with which we convert these two-dimensional structural formulas into three-dimensional shapes. We'll see the five basic shape classes that many simple molecules adopt and how they can combine to form the shapes of more complex molecules. You'll learn how shape and bond polarity create a polarity for the entire molecule and glimpse the influence of shape on biological function.

Concepts and Skills to Review

before you study this chapter

- electron configurations of main-group elements (Section 8.2)
- electron-dot symbols (Section 9.1)
- the octet rule (Section 9.2)
- bond order, bond length, and bond energy (Section 9.3)
- polar covalent bonds and bond polarity (Section 9.4)

10.1 Depicting Molecules and Ions with Lewis Structures

The first step toward visualizing what a molecule looks like is to convert its molecular formula to its **Lewis structure** (or **Lewis formula**). This two-dimensional structural formula consists of electron-dot symbols that depict each atom and its neighbors, the bonding pairs that hold them together, and the lone pairs that fill each atom's outer shell.* In many cases, the octet rule (Section 9.2) guides us in allotting electrons to the atoms in a Lewis structure; in many other cases, however, we set the rule aside.

Using the Octet Rule to Write Lewis Structures

To write a Lewis structure from the molecular formula, we decide on the relative placement of the atoms in the molecule (or ion)—that is, which atoms are adjacent and become bonded to each other—and distribute the total number of valence electrons as bonding and lone pairs. Let's begin by examining Lewis structures for species that "obey" the octet rule—those in which each atom fills its outer level with eight electrons (or two for hydrogen).

Lewis Structures for Molecules with Single Bonds   First, we discuss how to write Lewis structures for molecules that have only single bonds, using nitrogen trifluoride, NF_3, as an example.

Step 1. Place the atoms relative to each other. For compounds of molecular formula AB_n, place the atom with *lower group number* in the center because it needs more electrons to attain an octet. In NF_3, the N (Group 5A) has five

---

*A Lewis *structure* may be more correctly called a Lewis *formula* because it provides information about the relative placement of atoms in a molecule or ion and which atoms are bonded to each other, but *not* the three-dimensional shape. Nevertheless, use of the term Lewis "structure" is a convention that we follow.

electrons so it needs three, whereas F (Group 7A) has seven so it needs only one; thus, N goes in the center with the three F atoms around it:

$$\begin{array}{c} \text{F} \\[2pt] \text{N} \\[-4pt] \text{F} \qquad \text{F} \end{array}$$

If the atoms have the same group number, as for example in SO_3 or ClF_3, place the atom with the *higher period number* in the center. These placements usually result in the *least electronegative atom* in the center (EN of N = 3.0 and EN of F = 4.0). Since H can form only one bond, it is *never* a central atom.

   Step 2. Determine the total number of valence electrons available. For molecules, add up the valence electrons of all the atoms. (Recall that the number of valence electrons equals the A-group number.) In NF_3, N has five valence electrons, and each F has seven:

$$[1 \times N(5e^-)] + [3 \times F(7e^-)] = 5e^- + 21e^- = 26 \text{ valence } e^-$$

For polyatomic ions, *add* one e^- for each negative charge of the ion, or *subtract* one e^- for each positive charge.

   Step 3. Draw a single bond from each surrounding atom to the central atom, and subtract two valence electrons for each bond. There must be at least a single bond between bonded atoms:

$$\begin{array}{c} \text{F} \\ | \\ \text{F}-\text{N}-\text{F} \end{array}$$

Subtract $2e^-$ for each single bond from the total number of valence electrons available (from step 2) to find the number remaining:

$$3 \text{ N}-\text{F bonds} \times 2e^- = 6e^-, \text{ so } 26e^- - 6e^- = 20e^- \text{ remaining}$$

   Step 4. Distribute the remaining electrons in pairs so that each atom obtains eight electrons (or two for H). First place lone pairs on the *surrounding (more electronegative) atoms* to give each an octet. If any electrons remain, place them around the central atom. Then check that each atom has $8e^-$:

$$\begin{array}{c} :\ddot{\text{F}}: \\ | \\ :\ddot{\text{F}}-\text{N}-\ddot{\text{F}}: \end{array}$$

This is the Lewis structure for NF_3. It's always a good idea to check that the total number of electrons in the Lewis structure (bonds plus lone pairs) equals the sum of the valence electrons: $6e^-$ in three bonds plus $20e^-$ in ten lone pairs equals 26 valence electrons. This particular arrangement of F atoms around the N was chosen because it resembles the molecular shape of NF_3, as you'll see in Section 10.3. Lewis structures do not indicate shape, however, so an equally correct depiction of NF_3 would be

$$\begin{array}{c} :\ddot{\text{F}}: \\ | \\ :\ddot{\text{F}}-\ddot{\text{N}}-\ddot{\text{F}}: \end{array}$$

or any other that retains the *same connectivity* of atoms, that is, the same connections among the atoms—a central N atom connected by single bonds to three surrounding F atoms.

   Using these four steps (Figure 10.1), you can write a Lewis structure for any singly bonded molecule whose central atom is C, N, or O, as well as for some molecules with central atoms from higher periods.

Figure 10.1 The steps in converting a molecular formula into a Lewis structure.

| Molecular formula | Place atom with lowest EN in center | Atom placement | Add A-group numbers | Sum of valence e^- | Draw single bonds. Subtract $2e^-$ for each bond | Remaining valence e^- | Give each atom $8e^-$ ($2e^-$ for H) | Lewis structure |

Sample Problem 10.1 Writing Lewis Structures for Molecules with One Central Atom

PROBLEM Write a Lewis structure for CCl_2F_2, one of the compounds implicated in the depletion of stratospheric ozone.

SOLUTION *Step 1.* Place the atoms relative to each other. In CCl_2F_2, carbon has the lowest group number and EN, so it is the central atom. The other atoms surround it, but their specific positions are not important:

$$\begin{array}{c} Cl \\ F \quad C \quad F \\ Cl \end{array}$$

Step 2. Determine the total number of valence electrons:

$$[1 \times C(4e^-)] + [2 \times F(7e^-)] + [2 \times Cl(7e^-)] = 32 \text{ valence } e^-$$

Step 3. Draw single bonds to the central atom and subtract $2e^-$ for each bond:

$$\begin{array}{c} Cl \\ | \\ F—C—F \\ | \\ Cl \end{array}$$

Four single bonds use $8e^-$, so $32e^- - 8e^-$ leaves $24e^-$ remaining.

Step 4. Distribute the remaining electrons in pairs, beginning with the surrounding atoms, so that each atom has an octet:

$$\begin{array}{c} :\ddot{C}l: \\ | \\ :\ddot{F}—C—\ddot{F}: \\ | \\ :\ddot{C}l: \end{array}$$

CHECK Counting the electrons shows that each atom has an octet. Remember that bonding electrons are counted as belonging to each atom in the bond. The total number of electrons in bonds (8) and lone pairs (24) equals 32 valence electrons.

Follow-up Problem 10.1 Write Lewis structures for **(a)** H_2S; **(b)** OF_2; **(c)** $SOCl_2$.

More complex molecules have two or more central atoms bonded to each other, with the other atoms around them.

Sample Problem 10.2 Writing Lewis Structures for Molecules with More than One Central Atom

PROBLEM Write the Lewis structure for methanol (molecular formula CH_4O), an important industrial alcohol that is being used as a gasoline alternative in car engines.

SOLUTION *Step 1.* Place the atoms relative to each other. The H atoms can have only one bond, so C and O must be adjacent to each other. In nearly all their compounds, C has four bonds and O has two, so we arrange the H atoms to show this:

$$\begin{array}{c} H \\ H \quad C \quad O \quad H \\ H \end{array}$$

Step 2. Find sum of valence electrons:

$$[1 \times C(4e^-)] + [1 \times O(6e^-)] + [4 \times H(1e^-)] = 14e^-$$

Step 3. Add single bonds and subtract $2e^-$ for each bond:

$$\begin{array}{c} H \\ | \\ H—C—O—H \\ | \\ H \end{array}$$

Five bonds use $10e^-$, so $14e^- - 10e^-$ leaves $4e^-$ remaining.

Step 4. Add remaining electrons in pairs:

Carbon already has an octet, so the four remaining valence e^- form two lone pairs on O and give the Lewis structure for methanol.

CHECK Each H atom has $2e^-$, and the C and O each have $8e^-$. The total number of valence electrons is $14e^-$, which equals $10e^-$ in bonds plus $4e^-$ in lone pairs.

Follow-up Problem 10.2   Write Lewis structures for **(a)** hydroxylamine (NH_3O) and **(b)** dimethyl ether (C_2H_6O). (*Hint:* there are no O—H bonds in dimethyl ether.)

Lewis Structures for Molecules with Multiple Bonds   In writing some Lewis structures, you will find after Steps 1 to 4 that there are not enough electrons for the central atom (or one of the central atoms) to attain an octet. This usually means that a multiple bond is present, and the following additional step is needed:

Step 5. Cases involving multiple bonds. If, after Step 4, a central atom still does not have an octet, change a lone pair from one of the surrounding atoms into a bonding pair to the central atom to make a multiple bond.

Sample Problem 10.3   Writing Lewis Structures for Molecules with Multiple Bonds

PROBLEM Write Lewis structures for the following:
(a) Ethylene (C_2H_4), the most important reactant in polymer manufacture
(b) Nitrogen (N_2), the most abundant atmospheric gas
PLAN We begin the solution after Steps 1 to 4: placing the atoms, counting the total valence electrons, making single bonds, and distributing the remaining valence electrons in pairs to attain octets. Then we continue with Step 5, if needed.
SOLUTION **(a)** For C_2H_4. After Steps 1 to 4, we have

Step 5. Change a lone pair to a bonding pair. The C on the right has an octet, but the C on the left has only $6e^-$, so we convert the lone pair to another bonding pair between the two C atoms:

(b) For N_2. After Steps 1 to 4, we have :Ṅ—Ṅ:
Step 5. Neither N has an octet, so we change a lone pair to bonding pair:

$$:\ddot{N}=N:$$

In this case, moving one lone pair to make a double bond still does not give each N an octet, so we move another lone pair to make a triple bond:

$$:N\equiv N:$$

CHECK In part **(a),** since each C counts the $4e^-$ in the double bond as part of its own octet, each now has $8e^-$. The valence electron total is $12e^-$, all in six bonds. In part **(b),** since each N counts the $6e^-$ in the triple bond as part of its own octet, each now has $8e^-$. The valence electron total is $10e^-$, which equals the electrons in three bonds and two lone pairs.

Follow-up Problem 10.3   Write Lewis structures for **(a)** CO (the only common molecule in which C has only three bonds); **(b)** HCN; **(c)** CO_2.

Resonance: Delocalized Electron-Pair Bonding

It is often possible to write more than one Lewis structure, each with the *same* relative placement of atoms, for a molecule or ion with *double bonds next to single bonds.* Consider ozone (O_3), a serious air pollutant at ground level but a life-sustaining absorber of harmful ultraviolet (UV) radiation in the stratosphere. Two valid Lewis structures (with lettered O atoms for clarity) are

In structure I, oxygen B has a double bond to oxygen A and a single bond to oxygen C. In structure II, the single and double bonds are reversed. These are *not* two different types of O_3 molecules, just two different Lewis structures for the same molecule.

The fact is that *neither* Lewis structure depicts O_3 accurately. Bond length and bond energy measurements indicate that the two bonds in O_3 are *identical*, with properties that lie *between* those of an O—O bond and an O=O bond, something like a "one-and-a-half" bond. The molecule is shown more correctly with two Lewis structures, called **resonance structures** (or **resonance forms**), and a two-headed resonance arrow (⟷) between them. Resonance structures *have the same relative placement of atoms but different locations of bonding and lone electron pairs.* You can convert one resonance form to another by moving lone pairs to bonding positions, and vice versa:

Resonance structures are not real bonding depictions: O_3 does *not* change back and forth between structure I this instant and structure II the next. The actual molecule is a **resonance hybrid,** something like an average of the resonance forms. ◆

Our need for more than one Lewis structure to depict the ozone molecule is the result of **electron-pair delocalization.** In a single, double, or triple bond, each electron pair is attracted by the two bonded atoms, and the electron density is greatest in the region between the two nuclei: each electron pair is *localized.* In the resonance hybrid for O_3, however, two of the electron pairs (one bonding and one nonbonding) are *delocalized:* their density is "spread" over the entire molecule.* This results in two identical bonds, each consisting of a single bond (the localized electron pair) and a *partial bond* (the contribution from one of the delocalized electron pairs). We draw the resonance hybrid with a curved dashed line to show the delocalized pairs:

Electron delocalization diffuses electron density over a greater volume, which reduces electron-electron repulsions and thus stabilizes the molecule. Resonance is very common, and many molecules (and ions) with a double bond next to a single bond in their Lewis structures are resonance hybrids. Benzene (C_6H_6), for example, has two important resonance forms in which alternating single and double bonds have different positions. The actual molecule has six identical carbon-carbon bonds as a result of six C—C bonds and

Blue horse   Red donkey

◆ **A Purple Mule, Not a Blue Horse and a Red Donkey**
A mule is a genetic mix, a hybrid, of a horse and a donkey; it is not a horse one instant and a donkey the next. Similarly, the color purple is a mix of two other colors, red and blue, not red one instant and blue the next. In the same sense, a resonance hybrid is one molecular species, not this resonance form one instant and that resonance form the next. The problem lies in our inability to depict the hybrid accurately with a single Lewis structure.

---

*Keep in mind that electron delocalization in a metal (Section 9.5), which extends over the entire sample, is *much* greater than in a covalent resonance hybrid, where it extends over only a few atoms.

three electron pairs that are delocalized over all six C atoms, often shown as a dashed circle:

resonance forms   resonance hybrid

Partial bonding, such as occurs in resonance hybrids, often leads to fractional bond orders. The bond order in O_3 is

$$\frac{3 \text{ electron pairs}}{2 \text{ atom-to-atom linkages}} = 1\frac{1}{2}$$

The carbon-to-carbon bond order in benzene is 9 pairs/6 linkages, or $1\frac{1}{2}$ also. For the carbonate ion, CO_3^{2-}, three resonance structures can be drawn. Each has 4 electron pairs shared among 3 linkages, so the bond order is $1\frac{1}{3}$. One of the three resonance structures for CO_3^{2-} is

Note that *the Lewis structure of a polyatomic ion is shown in square brackets, with its charge as a right superscript outside the brackets.*

Sample Problem 10.4   Writing Resonance Structures

PROBLEM Write resonance structures for the nitrate ion, NO_3^-.

PLAN We write a Lewis structure using the steps outlined earlier, remembering to add 1e$^-$ to the total number of valence electrons because of the 1$-$ ionic charge. Then we move lone and bonding pairs to write other resonance forms and connect them with the resonance arrow.

SOLUTION After Steps 1 to 4, we have

Step 5. Since N has only 6e$^-$, we change one lone pair on an O atom to a bonding pair and form a double bond, which gives each atom an octet. All the O atoms are equivalent, however, so we can move a lone pair from any of the three O atoms and obtain three resonance structures:

CHECK Each structure has the same relative placement of atoms, an octet around each atom, and 24e$^-$ (the sum of the valence electron total and 1e$^-$ from the ionic charge distributed in four bonds and eight lone pairs).

COMMENT Remember that no double bond actually occurs in the NO_3^- ion. The ion is a resonance hybrid of these three structures with a bond order of $1\frac{1}{3}$.

Follow-up Problem 10.4   One of the three resonance structures for CO_3^{2-} was shown just before Sample Problem 10.4. Draw the other two.

Formal Charge: Selecting the Best Resonance Structure

In the previous examples, the resonance forms were *equally* mixed to form the resonance hybrid because the molecules (or ions) were symmetrical: the surrounding atoms were all the same. When this is not the case, one resonance form may look more like the hybrid than the others. In other words, since the resonance hybrid is an "average" of the resonance forms, one form may contribute more and "weight" the average in its favor. One way to select the most important resonance form is to determine each atom's **formal charge,** the charge it would have *if the bonding electrons were shared equally.* An atom's formal charge is its total number of atomic valence electrons *minus* the number of valence electrons it "owns" in the molecule: it owns *all* of its unshared valence electrons and *half* of its shared valence electrons. Thus,

Formal charge of atom =

$$\text{no. of valence e}^- - (\text{no. of unshared valence e}^- + \tfrac{1}{2}\text{ no. of shared valence e}^-)$$
(10.1)

For example, in the O_3 resonance forms, the formal charge of O_A in structure I is

$$6\text{ valence e}^- - (4\text{ unshared e}^- + \tfrac{1}{2}\text{ of 4 shared e}^-) = 6 - 4 - 2 = 0$$

The formal charges of all the atoms in the two O_3 resonance forms are

$$O_A[6 - 4 - \tfrac{1}{2}(4)] = 0 \qquad\qquad\qquad O_A[6 - 6 - \tfrac{1}{2}(2)] = -1$$

$$O_B[6 - 2 - \tfrac{1}{2}(6)] = +1 \qquad\qquad\qquad O_B[6 - 2 - \tfrac{1}{2}(6)] = +1$$

$$O_C[6 - 6 - \tfrac{1}{2}(2)] = -1 \qquad\qquad\qquad O_C[6 - 4 - \tfrac{1}{2}(4)] = 0$$

Forms I and II are symmetrical—each has the same formal charges but on different atoms—so they contribute equally to the resonance hybrid. Note that *the formal charges must sum to the actual charge on the species:* zero for a molecule and the ionic charge for an ion.

Three criteria help us choose the more important resonance structures:
* Smaller formal charges (whether positive or negative) are preferable to larger ones.
* Like charges on adjacent atoms are not desirable.
* A more negative formal charge should reside on a more electronegative atom.

Let's apply these criteria to the cyanate ion, NCO^-, which is not a symmetrical species. Three resonance forms with formal charges are

Formal charges: (−2) (0) (+1)   (−1) (0) (0)   (0) (0) (−1)

Resonance forms: $[:\ddot{N}-C\equiv O:]^-$ ⟷ $[\ddot{N}=C=\ddot{O}]^-$ ⟷ $[:N\equiv C-\ddot{O}:]^-$
                            A   B   C

We eliminate form A because it has larger formal charges than the others and a positive formal charge on the (more electronegative) O. Forms B and C have the same magnitude of formal charges, but form C has a −1 charge on O, which is more electronegative than N. Therefore, B and C are significant contributors to the resonance hybrid of the cyanate ion, with C the more important.

Formal charge (used to examine resonance structures) is *not* the same as oxidation number (used to monitor redox reactions):
* In determining formal charge, the bonding electrons are assigned *equally* to the bonded atoms (as if the bonding were *nonpolar covalent*), so each atom receives half of them:

$$\text{Formal charge} = \text{valence e}^- - (\text{lone pair e}^- + \tfrac{1}{2}\text{ bonding e}^-)$$

* In determining oxidation number, the bonding electrons are assigned *completely* to the more electronegative atom (as if the bonding were *ionic*):

$$\text{Oxidation number} = \text{valence e}^- - (\text{lone pair e}^- + \text{bonding e}^-)$$

Here are the formal charges and oxidation numbers of the three cyanate ion resonance structures:

Formal charges:

$$\underset{-3 \quad +4 \quad -2}{[:\!\overset{(-2)}{\ddot{N}}\!-\!\overset{(0)}{C}\!\equiv\!\overset{(+1)}{O}:]^-} \longleftrightarrow \underset{-3 \quad +4 \quad -2}{[:\!\overset{(-1)}{\ddot{N}}\!=\!\overset{(0)}{C}\!=\!\overset{(0)}{\ddot{O}}:]^-} \longleftrightarrow \underset{-3 \quad +4 \quad -2}{[:\!\overset{(0)}{N}\!\equiv\!\overset{(0)}{C}\!-\!\overset{(-1)}{\ddot{O}}:]^-}$$

Oxidation numbers:

Note that the oxidation numbers *do not* change from one resonance form to another (because the electronegativities do not change), but the formal charges *do* change (because the numbers of bonding and lone pairs change).

Lewis Structures for Exceptions to the Octet Rule

The octet rule is a useful guide for most simple molecules with Period 2 central atoms, but it does not hold for every one. Also, many molecules have central atoms from higher periods. As you'll see, some have fewer than eight electrons around the central atom, and others have more. The most significant octet rule exceptions are electron-deficient molecules, odd-electron molecules, and molecules with expanded valence shells.

Electron-Deficient Molecules   Gaseous compounds containing either beryllium or boron as the central atom are often **electron deficient;** that is, they have *fewer* than eight electrons around the Be or B atom. The Lewis structures of gaseous beryllium chloride* and boron trifluoride are

$$:\!\ddot{Cl}\!-\!Be\!-\!\ddot{Cl}\!: \qquad \overset{\displaystyle :\ddot{F}:}{\underset{:\ddot{F}\qquad\ddot{F}:}{B}}$$

Note that there are only four electrons around beryllium and six around boron. Why don't nonbonding pairs from the surrounding halogen atoms form multiple bonds to the central atoms, thereby satisfying the octet rule? Halogen atoms are much more electronegative than beryllium or boron, and formal charges show that the following are unlikely structures:

$$\underset{(+1) \quad (-2) \quad (+1)}{:\!\ddot{Cl}\!=\!Be\!=\!\ddot{Cl}:} \qquad \overset{\displaystyle :\ddot{F}:^{(0)}}{\underset{(0):\ddot{F}\qquad\ddot{F}:^{(+1)}}{\overset{(-1)}{B}}}$$

(Some data for BF$_3$ show a shorter than expected B—F bond. Since shorter bonds indicate double-bond character, the structure with the B=F bond may be a minor contributor to a resonance hybrid.) The main way that electron-deficient molecules attain an octet is by forming additional bonds in reactions. When BF$_3$ reacts with ammonia, for instance, a compound forms in which boron attains its octet:[†]

$$\underset{:\ddot{F}\quad\ddot{F}:}{\overset{:\ddot{F}:}{B}} + \underset{H\quad\quad H}{\overset{H}{\overset{|}{\ddot{N}}}} \longrightarrow \underset{:\ddot{F}:\quad H}{\overset{:\ddot{F}:\quad H}{\underset{|}{F}\!-\!\underset{|}{B}\!-\!\underset{|}{N}\!-\!H}}$$

Odd-Electron Molecules   A few molecules contain an odd number of valence electrons, so they cannot *possibly* have all their electrons in pairs. Such species, called **free radicals,** contain a lone (unpaired) electron, which makes them paramagnetic (Section 8.5) and extremely reactive. ◆ Most odd-

◆ **Deadly Free-Radical Activity**   Free radicals can be extremely dangerous to biological systems because they rupture bonds in a cell's biomolecules. If a free radical reacts with a biomolecule, it typically forms a covalent bond to one of the H atoms and removes it, and the biomolecule is left with an unpaired electron, thereby becoming a new free radical. That species repeats the process and creates other species with lone electrons that proliferate to rupture genes and cell membranes. We benefit from this ability when we apply the disinfectant hydrogen peroxide to a cut because it forms free radicals that destroy bacterial membranes. (The photo shows H$_2$O$_2$ reacting vigorously with a drop of blood.) On the other hand, recent studies have suggested that several disease states, including certain forms of cancer, may be attributed to free radicals, and a recently reported benefit of vitamin E is that it is thought to interrupt free-radical proliferation.

---

*Despite beryllium being a member of the alkaline earth metals [Group 2A(2)], most of its compounds have properties consistent with covalent, rather than ionic, bonding. For example, molten BeCl$_2$ does not conduct electricity, indicating the absence of ions (Chapter 14).

[†]Reactions of the sort shown here—in which one species "donates" an electron pair to another to form a covalent bond—are examples of Lewis acid-base reactions, an extremely important and widely encountered type of reaction that we discuss in Chapter 18.

electron molecules have a central atom from an odd-numbered group, such as N [Group 5A(15)] or Cl [Group 7A(17)]. An important example is NO_2:

Nitrogen dioxide is formed when the NO in auto exhaust reacts with O_2 in sunlight; it is a major contributor to urban smog. Free radicals can react with each other to pair up their lone electrons. When two NO_2 molecules collide, for example, they form dinitrogen tetraoxide, N_2O_4, and each N attains an octet:

Expanded Valence Shells Many molecules and ions have *more* than eight valence electrons around the central atom. *An atom expands its valence shell to form more bonds,* a process that releases energy. The only way to accommodate additional pairs is for the central atom to use its empty *outer d* orbitals in addition to its occupied *s* and *p* orbitals. Therefore, **expanded valence shells** occur around a *central nonmetal from Period 3 or higher,* those in which *d* orbitals are available.

One example is sulfur hexafluoride, SF_6, a remarkably dense and inert gas used as an insulator in electrical equipment. The central sulfur is surrounded by six covalent bonds, one to each fluorine, for a total of 12 electrons:

Another example is phosphorus pentachloride, PCl_5, a fuming yellow-white solid used in the manufacture of lacquers and films. PCl_5 is formed when phosphorus trichloride, PCl_3, reacts with chlorine gas. The P in PCl_3 has an octet, but it uses the lone pair to form two more bonds to chlorine and expands its valence shell in PCl_5 to a total of 10 electrons. Note that when PCl_5 forms, *one* Cl—Cl bond breaks (left side of the equation), and *two* P—Cl bonds form (right side), for a net increase of one bond:

In the previous cases, the central atom forms bonds to *more than four* atoms. But there are many cases of expanded valence shells in which the central atom bonds to *four or fewer* atoms. Consider sulfuric acid, the industrial chemical produced in the greatest quantity. Two of the Lewis structures for H_2SO_4, with formal charges, are

In structure B, sulfur has an expanded valence shell of 12 electrons. Structures A and B are both valid resonance forms of sulfuric acid, but B is a more significant contributor to the resonance hybrid because it has lower formal charges. Most importantly, structure B is consistent with observed bond lengths. In gaseous H_2SO_4, the two sulfur-oxygen bonds *with* H atoms attached to O are 157 pm long, whereas the two sulfur-oxygen bonds *without* H atoms attached to O are 142 pm long. This shorter bond indicates double-bond character, which is shown in structure B.

When sulfuric acid loses two H^+ ions, it forms the sulfate ion, SO_4^{2-}. All the sulfur-oxygen bonds in SO_4^{2-} are 149 pm long, which is intermediate in length between the two S=O bonds ($\sim$142 pm) and the two S—O bonds ($\sim$157 pm) in the parent acid. Two of the six resonance forms consistent with these data are

Thus, the SO_4^{2-} ion is a resonance hybrid with four S—O bonds and two more bonding pairs delocalized over the structure, so each sulfur-oxygen bond has a bond order of $1\frac{1}{2}$.

Measurements show that the sulfur-oxygen bonds in SO_2 and SO_3 are all approximately the S=O bond length (142 pm), so Lewis structures for these molecules, with formal charges, are

Sulfur and phosphorus can accommodate a maximum of 12 electrons, and iodine as many as 14. Keep in mind that these *atoms expand their valence shells to form more bonds and minimize formal charge.*

Sample Problem 10.5   Writing Lewis Structures for Octet Rule Exceptions

PROBLEM Write Lewis structures for **(a)** H_3PO_4 and **(b)** $BFCl_2$. In **(a)**, decide on the most likely structure.

PLAN We write each Lewis structure and examine it for exceptions to the octet rule. In **(a)** the central atom is P, which is in Period 3, so it can use *d* orbitals to have more than an octet. Therefore, we can write more than one Lewis structure. We use formal charge to decide if one resonance form is more important. In **(b)** the central atom is B, which can have fewer than an octet.

SOLUTION **(a)** For H_3PO_4, two possible Lewis structures, with formal charges, are

Structure **II** has lower formal charges, so it is a more important resonance form.
(b) For $BFCl_2$, the Lewis structure leaves B with only six electrons surrounding it:

COMMENT In (a), structure II is also consistent with bond length measurements, which show one shorter (152 pm) phosphorus-oxygen bond and three longer (157 pm) ones.

Follow-up Problem 10.5   Write the most likely Lewis structure for
(a) $POCl_3$; **(b)** ClO_2; **(c)** XeF_4.

A stepwise process converts a molecular formula into a Lewis structure, a *two-dimensional* representation of a molecule (or ion) that shows the relative placement of atoms and distribution of valence electrons among bonding and lone pairs. When two or more Lewis structures can be drawn for the same relative placement of atoms, the actual structure is a hybrid of those resonance forms. Formal charge can be used to determine the most important contributor to the hybrid. Electron-deficient molecules (central Be or B) and odd-electron species (free radicals) have fewer than an octet around the central atom but often attain an octet in reactions. A central nonmetal from Period 3 or higher in a molecule (or ion) can form more bonds by using *d* orbitals to expand its valence shell and hold more than eight electrons.

10.2 Using Lewis Structures and Bond Energies to Calculate Heats of Reaction

In addition to their use in predicting molecular shape (as you'll see in the next section), Lewis structures are indispensable for calculating heats of reaction based on bond breakage and formation. Covalent bond strength is an important factor in a molecule's chemical reactivity because, *for similar kinds of substances, a molecule with weaker bonds is usually more reactive than one with stronger bonds.* In Chapter 6, you saw that energy is released when a fuel's weaker (less stable, higher energy) bonds break apart and the waste product's stronger (more stable, lower energy) bonds form.

We can view a chemical reaction as a process in which certain bonds break in reacting species to give molecular fragments that recombine into product species by forming new bonds. We use Lewis structures and bond energies (bond enthalpies) to calculate the heat of reaction (ΔH^0_{rxn}) by noting which reactant bonds break and which product bonds form. In many cases, it is simpler to assume that all the reactant bonds break to give individual atoms, from which all the product bonds form (Figure 10.2). Even though the actual reaction may not occur this way, Hess's law allows us to sum the bond energies (with their appropriate signs) to arrive at the overall heat of reaction. (This method assumes that the heat of reaction is due entirely to changes in bond energy, which requires that all reactants and products be gases. When liquids or solids are present, the additional heat involved in changing physical state must be taken into account. We address this topic in Chapter 12.)

Figure 10.2 Using bond energies to calculate ΔH^0_{rxn}. Any chemical reaction can be divided conceptually into two hypothetical steps: (1) reactant bonds break to yield separate atoms in a step that absorbs heat (+ sum of BE), and (2) the atoms combine to form product bonds in a step that releases heat (− sum of BE). When the total bond energy of the products is greater than that of the reactants, more energy is released than is absorbed, so the reaction is exothermic (as shown); ΔH^0_{rxn} is negative. When the total bond energy of the products is less than that of the reactants, the reaction is endothermic; ΔH^0_{rxn} is positive.

Energy is absorbed to break bonds in the reactants (ΔH^0 is positive), and energy is released when bonds form and make products (ΔH^0 is negative). The sum of these enthalpy changes is the heat of reaction:

$$\Delta H^0_{rxn} = \Delta H^0_{\text{reactant bonds broken}} + \Delta H^0_{\text{product bonds formed}} \qquad \textbf{(10.2)}$$

As you can see from Equation 10.2,

- In an exothermic reaction, the total energy of product bonds formed is *higher* than that of reactant bonds broken, so the *larger* negative sum makes the net ΔH^0_{rxn} *negative.*
- In an endothermic reaction, the total energy of product bonds formed is *lower* than that of reactant bonds broken, so the *smaller* negative sum makes the net ΔH^0_{rxn} *positive.*

Let's apply this method to calculate ΔH^0_{rxn} for the combustion of methane and compare it with the value obtained from calorimetry, which is

$$CH_4(g) + 2O_2(g) \longrightarrow CO_2(g) + 2H_2O(g) \qquad \Delta H^0_{rxn} = -802 \text{ kJ}$$

What value do we obtain from bond energies? From the Lewis structures in Figure 10.3, we see that the reaction involves breaking all the bonds in CH_4 and O_2 and forming all the bonds in CO_2 and H_2O. We select appropriate bond energy values (see Table 9.2, p. 343) using a positive sign for bonds broken and a negative sign for bonds formed:

Bonds broken

$$
\begin{array}{r}
4 \times C{-}H = 4 \text{ mol } (413 \text{ kJ/mol}) = 1652 \text{ kJ} \\
\underline{2 \times O_2 = 2 \text{ mol } (498 \text{ kJ/mol}) =\ \ 996 \text{ kJ}} \\
\text{Total } \Delta H^0_{\text{reactant bonds broken}} = 2648 \text{ kJ}
\end{array}
$$

Bonds formed

$$
\begin{array}{r}
2 \times C{=}O = 2 \text{ mol } (-799 \text{ kJ/mol}) = -1598 \text{ kJ} \\
\underline{4 \times O{-}H = 4 \text{ mol } (-467 \text{ kJ/mol}) = -1868 \text{ kJ}} \\
\text{Total } \Delta H^0_{\text{product bonds formed}} = -3466 \text{ kJ}
\end{array}
$$

Adding these totals together gives

$$\Delta H^0_{rxn} = \Delta H^0_{\text{reactant bonds broken}} + \Delta H^0_{\text{product bonds formed}}$$
$$= 2648 \text{ kJ} + (-3466 \text{ kJ}) = -818 \text{ kJ}$$

Figure 10.3 Using bond energies to calculate ΔH^0_{rxn} of methane. By treating the combustion of methane as a hypothetical two-step process (see Figure 10.2), we find that the reaction is exothermic.

Why is there a discrepancy between the bond-energy value (−818 kJ) and the calorimetric value (−802 kJ)? Variations in experimental method always introduce small discrepancies, but a more basic reason exists. As noted earlier, bond energies are *average* values obtained from many different compounds in which the bond occurs. The energy of the bond *in a particular substance* is usually close, but not equal, to this average. For example, the tabulated C—H bond energy of 413 kJ/mol is the average value of C—H bonds in many different molecules. In fact, in methane, 1660 kJ is actually required to break 4 mol C—H bonds, or 415 kJ/mol C—H bonds, which gives a ΔH^0_{rxn} slightly closer to the calorimetric value. Thus, it isn't surprising to find discrepancies between the two ΔH^0_{rxn} values. What is surprising—and satisfying in its confirmation of bond theory—is that the values are so close.

Sample Problem 10.6   Calculating Enthalpy Changes from Bond Energies

PROBLEM Use Table 9.2 (p. 343) to calculate ΔH^0_{rxn} for the following reaction:

$$CH_4(g) + 3Cl_2(g) \longrightarrow CHCl_3(g) + 3HCl(g)$$

PLAN First we write the Lewis structures of all the substances. We assume that all reactant bonds break and all product bonds form, and we find their values in Table 9.2. Then we substitute the two sums with correct signs into Equation 10.2.

SOLUTION Writing the Lewis structures:

Calculating ΔH^0_{rxn}: For bonds broken, the values are

$$4 \times \text{C—H} = 4 \text{ mol } (413 \text{ kJ/mol}) = 1652 \text{ kJ}$$
$$3 \times \text{Cl—Cl} = 3 \text{ mol } (243 \text{ kJ/mol}) = 729 \text{ kJ}$$
$$\Delta H^0_{\text{bonds broken}} = 2381 \text{ kJ}$$

For bonds formed, the values are

$$3 \times \text{C—Cl} = 3 \text{ mol } (-339 \text{ kJ/mol}) = -1017 \text{ kJ}$$
$$1 \times \text{C—H} = 1 \text{ mol } (-413 \text{ kJ/mol}) = -413 \text{ kJ}$$
$$3 \times \text{H—Cl} = 3 \text{ mol } (-427 \text{ kJ/mol}) = -1281 \text{ kJ}$$
$$\Delta H^0_{\text{bonds formed}} = -2711 \text{ kJ}$$

$$\Delta H^0_{rxn} = \Delta H^0_{\text{bonds broken}} + \Delta H^0_{\text{bonds formed}} = 2381 \text{ kJ} + (-2711 \text{ kJ})$$

$$= \boxed{-330 \text{ kJ}}$$

CHECK The signs of the enthalpy changes are correct: $\Delta H^0_{\text{bonds broken}} > 0$ and $\Delta H^0_{\text{bonds formed}} < 0$. Since more energy is released than absorbed, ΔH^0_{rxn} is negative: $\sim 2400 + [\sim(-2700)] = -300$.

Follow-up Problem 10.6   Use bond energies to calculate the enthalpy changes for the following reactions:
(a) $N_2(g) + 3H_2(g) \longrightarrow 2NH_3(g)$
(b) $C_2H_4(g) + HBr(g) \longrightarrow C_2H_5Br(g)$

Section Summary

Lewis structures of reactants and products can be used to determine the bonds broken and the bonds formed during a reaction. By applying Hess's law, we use tabulated bond energies to calculate the heat of reaction.

10.3 Valence-Shell Electron-Pair Repulsion (VSEPR) Theory and Molecular Shape

Virtually every biochemical process hinges to a great extent on the shapes of interacting molecules. Every medicine you take, odor you smell, flavor you taste depends on part or all of one molecule fitting physically together with another. This universal importance of molecular shape in the functioning of each organism carries over to the surrounding ecosystem, where biologists have learned of complex systems regulating vital behaviors, such as mating, defense, navigation, and feeding, that depend on recognizing molecular shape. In this section, we discuss a model for understanding molecular shape.

The Lewis structure of a molecule is something like the blueprint of a building: a flat drawing showing the relative placement of parts (atom cores), the structural connections (groups of bonding valence electrons), and the various attachments (nonbonding lone pairs of valence electrons). To construct the molecular shape from the Lewis structure, chemists employ **valence-shell electron-pair repulsion (VSEPR) theory.** Its basic principle is that *each group of valence electrons around a central atom is located as far away from the others as possible in order to minimize repulsions.* We define a "group" of electrons as any number of electrons that occupy a localized region around an atom. Thus, an electron group may consist of a single bond, a double bond, a triple bond, a lone pair, or even a lone electron.* Each of these is a *separate* group of valence electrons that repels the other groups to maximize the angles between groups and occupy as much space as possible around the central atom. It is the three-dimensional arrangement of nuclei joined by these groups that gives rise to the molecular shape.

Electron-Group Arrangements and Molecular Shapes

When two, three, four, five, or six objects attached to a central point maximize the space each can occupy around that point, five three-dimensional patterns result. Figure 10.4 depicts these patterns with balloons. If the objects are the valence-electron groups of a central atom, their *repulsions* maximize the space each occupies and give rise to the five *electron-group arrangements* of minimum energy seen in the great majority of molecules and polyatomic ions.

The electron-group arrangement is defined by the *valence-electron groups,* both bonding and nonbonding, around the central atom. On the other hand, the **molecular shape** is defined by the relative positions of the *atomic nuclei.* Figure 10.5 shows the molecular shapes that occur when *all* the surrounding electron groups are *bonding* groups. When some are *nonbonding* groups, different molecular shapes occur. Thus, *the same electron-group arrangement can give rise to different molecular shapes:* some with all bonding groups (as in Figure 10.5) and others with bonding *and* nonbonding groups. To classify the various molecular shapes, we assign each a specific AX_mE_n designation, where m and n are integers, A is the central atom, X is a surrounding atom, and E is a nonbonding valence-electron group (usually a lone pair).

The **bond angle** is the angle formed by the nuclei of two surrounding atoms with the nucleus of the central atom at the vertex. The angles shown for the shapes in Figure 10.5 are *ideal* bond angles, those predicted by simple geometry alone. These are observed when all the bonding electron groups around a central atom are identical and are connected to atoms of the same element. When this is not the case, the bond angles deviate from the ideal angles. You'll see examples of these effects shortly.

---

*The two electron pairs in a double bond (or the three pairs in a triple bond) occupy separate orbitals, so they remain near each other and act as one electron group (see Chapter 11).

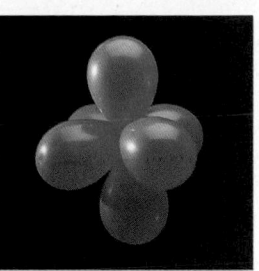

Figure 10.4 A balloon analogy for the mutual repulsion of electron groups. Attached balloons move apart so that each can occupy as much space as possible. Five geometric arrange- ments arise by attaching two, three, four, five, or six balloons. Electron groups repel each other and become arranged in a similar way around a central atom.

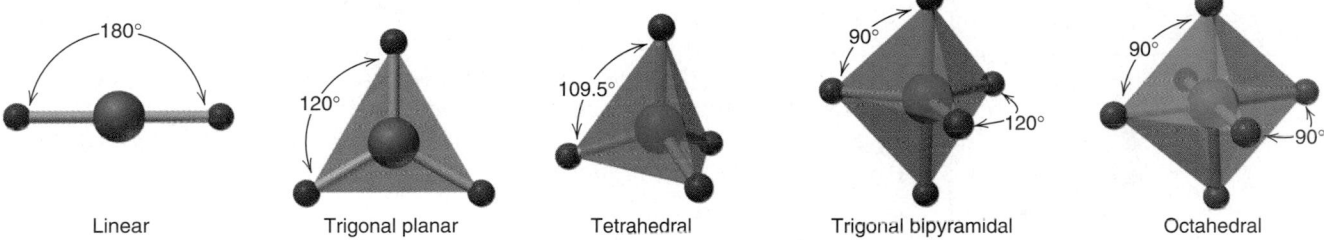

Linear   Trigonal planar   Tetrahedral   Trigonal bipyramidal   Octahedral

Figure 10.5 Electron-group repulsions and the five basic molecular shapes. When a given number of electron groups attached to a central atom (*red*) repel each other, they maxi- mize the angle between themselves and become oriented as far apart as possible in space. If each electron group is a bonding group to a surrounding atom (*black*), the molecular shapes and bond angles shown here are observed, and the name of the mole- cular shape is the same as that of the electron-group arrangement. When one or more of the electron groups is a lone pair, other mole- cular shapes are observed, as you'll see in upcoming figures.

It's important to realize that we use the VSEPR model to *account for* the molecular shapes we *observe* through various types of spectroscopy. In almost every case, *VSEPR predictions are in accord with our observations.* (We discuss some of these observational methods in Chapter 12.)

The Molecular Shape with Two Electron Groups (Linear Arrangement)

When two electron groups attached to a central atom are oriented as far apart as possible, they point in opposite directions. The **linear arrangement** of electron groups results in a linear molecular shape and a bond angle of 180°. Figure 10.6 shows the general arrangement (*top*), shape (*middle*) with VSEPR shape class (AX_2), and the formulas of some linear molecules.

Gaseous beryllium chloride ($BeCl_2$) is a linear molecule (AX_2). Gaseous Be compounds are electron deficient, with only two electron pairs around the central Be atom:

In carbon dioxide, the central C atom is surrounded by two double bonds:

Each double bond acts as a separate electron group and is oriented 180° away from the other, so CO_2 is linear. Notice that the lone pairs on the O atoms of CO_2 or on the Cl atoms of $BeCl_2$ are not involved in the molecular shape: only electron groups around the *central* atom influence shape.

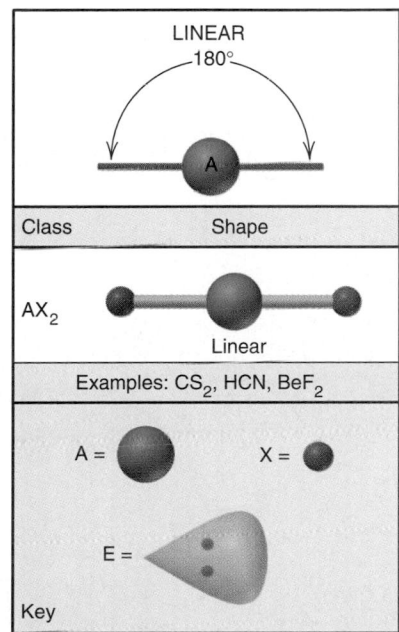

Figure 10.6 The single mole- cular shape of the linear electron- group arrangement. The key (*bottom*) for A, X, and E also refers to Figures 10.7, 10.8, 10.10, and 10.11.

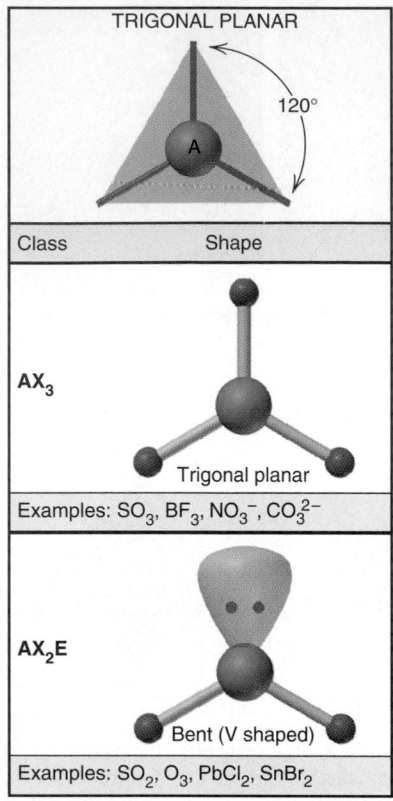

Figure 10.7 **The two molecular shapes of the trigonal planar electron-group arrangement.**

Molecular Shapes with Three Electron Groups (Trigonal Planar Arrangement)

Three electron groups around the central atom repel each other to the corners of an equilateral triangle, which gives the **trigonal planar arrangement,** shown in Figure 10.7, and an ideal bond angle of 120°. This arrangement has two possible molecular shapes, one with three surrounding atoms and the other with two atoms and one lone pair.

When the three electron groups are bonding groups, the molecular shape is also *trigonal planar* (AX_3). Boron trifluoride (BF_3), another electron-deficient molecule, is an example. It has six electrons around the central B atom in three single bonds to F atoms. The nuclei lie in a plane, and each F—B—F angle is 120°:

The nitrate ion (NO_3^-) is one of several polyatomic ions with the trigonal planar shape. One of three resonance forms of the nitrate ion is shown below (see Sample Problem 10.4). The resonance hybrid has three identical bonds of bond order $1\frac{1}{3}$, so the ideal bond angle is observed:

How do bond angles deviate from the ideal angles when the surrounding atoms and electron groups are not identical? Consider formaldehyde (CH_2O), a substance with many uses, including the manufacture of Formica countertops, the production of methanol, and the preservation of cadavers. Its trigonal planar shape is due to two types of surrounding atoms (O and H) and two types of electron groups (single and double bonds):

The actual bond angles deviate from the ideal because *the double bond, with its greater electron density, repels the two single bonds more strongly than they repel each other.*

Since the molecular shape is defined only by the positions of the nuclei, when one of the three electron groups is a lone pair (AX_2E), the shape is **bent** or **V shaped,** not trigonal planar. Gaseous tin(II) chloride is an example, with the three electron groups in a trigonal plane and the lone pair at one of the triangle's corners. *A lone pair can have a significant effect on the bond angle.* Since a lone pair is held by only one nucleus, it is less confined and exerts stronger repulsions than a bonding pair. Thus, *a lone pair repels bonding pairs more strongly than bonding pairs repel each other.* This stronger repulsion *decreases* the angle between bonding pairs. Note the large decrease from the ideal 120° angle in $SnCl_2$:

Molecular Shapes with Four Electron Groups (Tetrahedral Arrangement)

The shapes described so far have all been easy to depict in two dimensions, but four electron groups must use three dimensions to achieve maximal separation. This is a good time for you to recall that *Lewis structures do **not** depict shape*. Consider the shape of methane. The Lewis structure (shown below) indicates four bonds pointing to the corners of a square, which suggests a 90° bond angle. However, in three dimensions, the four electron groups can move farther apart than 90° and point to the vertices of a tetrahedron, a polyhedron with four faces made of identical equilateral triangles. Methane has a bond angle of 109.5°. Perspective drawings, such as these for methane, indicate depth by means of wedged (or sometimes dashed) lines:

The normal lines represent electron groups in the plane of the page, one wedge is the bond of a group lying toward you above the page, and the other wedge is the bond of a group lying away from you below the page. Another convention is to show the bond below the page as a dashed line. The ball-and-stick model shows the tetrahedral shape clearly.

*All molecules or ions with four electron groups around a central atom adopt the **tetrahedral arrangement*** (Figure 10.8). When all four electron groups are bonding groups, as in the case of methane, the molecular shape is also *tetrahedral* (AX_4), a very common geometry in organic molecules. In Sample Problem 10.1, we drew the Lewis structure for the tetrahedral molecule dichloro-difluoromethane (CCl_2F_2), without regard to how the halogen atoms surround the C atom. Because Lewis structures are flat, it seems we can write two different structures for CCl_2F_2, but they actually represent the same molecule, as Figure 10.9 makes clear.

When one of the four electron groups in the tetrahedral arrangement is a lone pair, the molecular shape is that of a **trigonal pyramid** (AX_3E), a tetrahedron with one vertex "missing." As we would expect from the stronger repulsions of a lone pair, the measured bond angle is slightly less than the ideal 109.5°. In ammonia (NH_3), for example, the lone pair forces the N—H bonding pairs closer, and the H—N—H bond angle is 107.3°.

Picturing molecular shapes is a great way to visualize what happens during a reaction. For instance, when ammonia reacts with the proton from an acid, the lone pair on the N atom of trigonal pyramidal NH_3 forms a covalent bond to the H^+ and yields the ammonium ion (NH_4^+), one of many

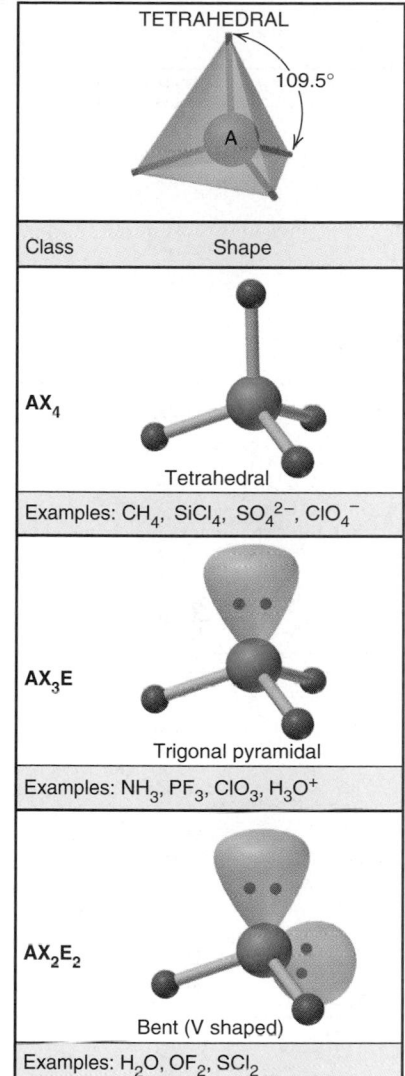

Class	Shape
AX_4	Tetrahedral Examples: CH_4, $SiCl_4$, SO_4^{2-}, ClO_4^-
AX_3E	Trigonal pyramidal Examples: NH_3, PF_3, ClO_3^-, H_3O^+
AX_2E_2	Bent (V shaped) Examples: H_2O, OF_2, SCl_2

Figure 10.8 **The three molecular shapes of the tetrahedral electron-group arrangement.**

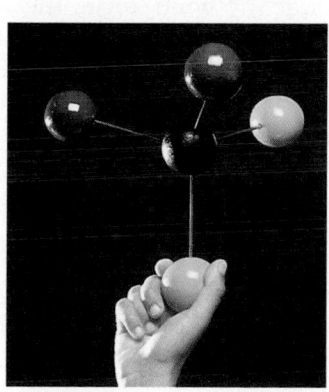

Figure 10.9 **Lewis structures and molecular shapes.** Lewis structures do not indicate geometry. For example, it may seem as if two different Lewis structures can be written for CCl_2F_2, but a twist of the ball-and-stick model shows that they represent the same molecule. (Cl, *green;* F, *yellow.*)

Figure 10.10 The four molecular shapes of the trigonal bipyramidal electron-group arrangement.

tetrahedral polyatomic ions. Note how the H—N—H bond angle expands from 107.3° in NH_3 to 109.5° in NH_4^+, as the lone pair becomes another bonding pair:

When the four electron groups around the central atom include two bonding and two nonbonding groups, the molecular shape is *bent or V shaped* (AX_2E_2). [In the trigonal planar arrangement, the shape with two bonding groups and one lone pair is also called bent (AX_2E), but its ideal bond angle is 120°, not 109.5°.] Water is the most important V-shaped molecule in the tetrahedral arrangement. We might expect the repulsions from its two lone pairs to have a *greater* effect on the bond angle than the repulsions from the single lone pair in NH_3. Indeed, the H—O—H bond angle is reduced to 104.5°:

Thus, for similar molecules with a given electron-group arrangement, electron-pair repulsions cause deviations from ideal bond angles in the following order:

Lone pair–lone pair > lone pair–bonding pair > bonding pair–bonding pair   **(10.3)**

Molecular Shapes with Five Electron Groups (Trigonal Bipyramidal Arrangement)

All molecules with five or six electron groups have a central atom from Period 3 or higher because only these atoms have the *d* orbitals available to expand the valence shell beyond eight electrons.

When five electron groups maximize their separation, they form the **trigonal bipyramidal arrangement.** In a trigonal bipyramid, two trigonal pyramids share a common base, as shown in Figure 10.10. Note that, in a molecule with this arrangement, *there are two types of positions for surrounding electron groups and two ideal bond angles.* Three **equatorial groups** lie in a trigonal plane that includes the central atom, and two **axial groups** lie above and below this plane. Therefore, a 120° bond angle separates equatorial groups, and a 90° angle separates axial from equatorial groups. In general, the greater the bond angle, the weaker the repulsions, so *equatorial-equatorial (120°) repulsions are weaker than axial-equatorial (90°) repulsions.* The tendency of the electron groups to occupy *equatorial* positions, and thus minimize these stronger 90° repulsions, governs the four shapes within the trigonal bipyramidal arrangement.

With all five positions occupied by bonded atoms, the molecule has the *trigonal bipyramidal* shape (AX_5), as in phosphorus pentachloride (PCl_5):

Three other shapes arise for molecules with lone pairs. Since lone pairs exert stronger repulsions than bonding pairs, we find that *lone pairs occupy equatorial positions.* With one lone pair present at an equatorial position, the molecule has a **seesaw shape** (AX_4E). Sulfur tetrafluoride (SF_4), a powerful fluorinating agent, has this shape, the "seesaw" shown here and in Figure 10.10 tipped up on an end. Note how the equatorial lone pair repels all four bonding pairs to reduce the bond angles:

The tendency of lone pairs to occupy equatorial positions causes molecules with three bonding groups and two lone pairs to have a **T shape** (AX_3E_2). Bromine trifluoride (BrF_3), one of many compounds with fluorine bound to a larger halogen, has this shape. Note the predicted decrease from the ideal 90° F—Br—F bond angle:

Molecules with three lone pairs in equatorial positions must have the two bonding groups in axial positions, which gives the molecule a *linear* shape (AX_2E_3) and a 180° axial-to-central-to-axial (X—A—X) bond angle. For example, the triiodide ion (I_3^-), which forms when I_2 dissolves in aqueous I^- solution, is linear:

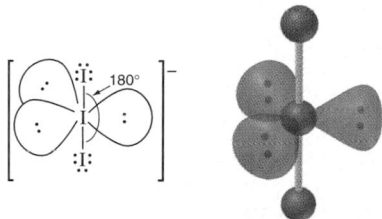

Molecular Shapes with Six Electron Groups (Octahedral Arrangement)

The last of the five major electron-group arrangements is the **octahedral arrangement.** An octahedron is a polyhedron with eight faces made of identical equilateral triangles and six identical vertices, as shown in Figure 10.11. In a molecule (or ion) with this arrangement, six electron groups surround the central atom and each points to one of the six vertices, which gives all the groups a 90° ideal bond angle. Three important molecular shapes occur within this arrangement.

With six bonding groups, the molecular shape is *octahedral* (AX_6). When seesaw-shaped SF_4 reacts with additional F_2, the central S atom expands its valence shell further to form octahedral sulfur hexafluoride (SF_6):

Figure 10.11 The three molecular shapes of the octahedral electron-group arrangement.

OCTAHEDRAL

90°

A

90°

Class	Shape

AX_6

Octahedral

Examples: SF_6, IOF_5

AX_5E

Square pyramidal

Examples: BrF_5, TeF_5^-, $XeOF_4$

AX_4E_2

Square planar

Examples: XeF_4, ICl_4^-

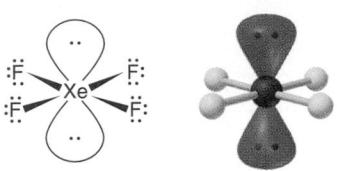

Square pyramidal shape, IF_5.

Square planar shape, XeF_4.

Because there is only one ideal bond angle, it makes no difference which position one lone pair occupies. Five bonded atoms and one lone pair define the **square pyramidal shape** (AX_5E), as shown in the margin for iodine pentafluoride (IF_5).

When a molecule has two lone pairs, however, they always lie at *opposite vertices* to avoid stronger lone pair–lone pair 90° repulsions. This positioning gives rise to the **square planar shape** (AX_4E_2). Experiment shows that xenon tetrafluoride (XeF_4), one of the first noble gas compounds to be prepared, has a square planar shape (see margin).

Using VSEPR Theory to Determine Molecular Shape

Let's apply a stepwise method for using the VSEPR theory to determine a molecular shape from a molecular formula:

1. *Write the Lewis structure* from the molecular formula to see the relative placement of atoms and the number of electron groups.
2. *Assign an electron-group arrangement* by counting *all* electron groups around the central atom, bonding *plus* nonbonding.
3. *Predict the ideal bond angle* from the electron-group arrangement and *the direction of any deviation* caused by lone pairs or double bonds.
4. *Draw and name the molecular shape* by counting bonding groups and non-bonding groups separately.

Figure 10.12 summarizes these steps, and the following two sample problems apply them.

Figure 10.12 The steps in determining a molecular shape. Four steps are needed to convert a molecular formula to a molecular shape. For the first step, writing the Lewis structure, see Figure 10.1.

Sample Problem 10.7   Predicting Molecular Shapes with Two, Three, or Four Electron Groups

PROBLEM Draw the molecular shape and predict the bond angles (relative to the ideal angles) of **(a)** PF_3 and **(b)** $COCl_2$.

SOLUTION **(a)** For PF_3.

1. Write the Lewis structure from the formula (see below left).
2. Assign the electron-group arrangement: Three bonding groups plus one lone pair give four electron groups around P and the *tetrahedral arrangement*.
3. Predict the bond angle: For the tetrahedral electron-group arrangement, the ideal angle is 109.5°. Since there is one lone pair, the actual bond angle should be less than 109.5°.
4. Draw and name the molecular shape: With four electron groups, one of them a lone pair, PF_3 has a trigonal pyramidal shape (AX_3E),

(b) For $COCl_2$.
1. Write the Lewis structure from the formula (see below left).
2. Assign the electron-group arrangement: Two single bonds plus one double bond give three electron groups around C and the *trigonal planar arrangement.*
3. Predict the bond angles: The ideal angle is 120°, but the double bond between C and O should compress the Cl—C—Cl angle to less than 120°.
4. Draw and name the molecular shape: With three electron groups and no lone pairs, $COCl_2$ has a trigonal planar shape (AX_3),

CHECK We compare the answers with the general information in Figures 10.7 and 10.8.

COMMENT Be sure the Lewis structure is correct because it determines the other steps.

Follow-up Problem 10.7 Draw the shape and predict the bond angles (relative to the ideal angles) of **(a)** CS_2; **(b)** $PbCl_2$; **(c)** CBr_4; **(d)** SF_2.

Sample Problem 10.8 Predicting Molecular Shapes with Five or Six Electron Groups

PROBLEM Determine the molecular shape and predict the bond angles (relative to the ideal angles) of **(a)** SbF_5 and **(b)** BrF_5.

PLAN We proceed as in Sample Problem 10.7, keeping in mind the need to minimize the number of 90° repulsions.

SOLUTION **(a)** For SbF_5.
1. Lewis structure (see below left)
2. Electron-group arrangement: With five electron groups, this is the *trigonal bipyramidal* arrangement.
3. Bond angles: Since all the groups and surrounding atoms are identical, the bond angles are ideal: 120° between equatorial groups and 90° between axial and equatorial groups.
4. Molecular shape: Five electrons groups and no lone pairs give the trigonal bipyramidal shape (AX_5),

(b) For BrF_5.
1. Lewis structure (see below left).
2. Electron-group arrangement: Six electron groups give the *octahedral* arrangement.
3. Bond angles: The lone pair should make all bond angles less than the ideal 90°.
4. Molecular shape: With six electron groups and one of them a lone pair, BrF_5 has the square pyramidal shape (AX_5E),

Figure 10.13 The tetrahedral centers of ethane and of ethanol.
When a molecule has more than one central atom, the shape is a composite of the shape around each center.
A, Ethane's shape can be viewed as two interlocking tetrahedra. **B,** Ethanol's shape can be viewed as three interlocking tetrahedral arrangements, with the shape around the O atom bent (V shaped) because of its two lone pairs.

CHECK We compare our answers with Figures 10.10 and 10.11.
COMMENT The linear, tetrahedral, square planar, and octahedral shapes also arise in an important group of substances called *coordination compounds* that we discuss in Chapter 23.

Follow-up Problem 10.8 Draw the molecular shapes and predict the bond angles (relative to the ideal angles) of **(a)** ICl_2^-; **(b)** ClF_3; **(c)** SOF_4.

Molecular Shapes with More Than One Central Atom

As you know, many molecules, especially those in living systems, have more than one central atom. The shapes of these molecules are combinations of the molecular shapes with a single central atom. Consider ethane (C_2H_6), a component of natural gas, shown in Figure 10.13A. With four bonding groups and no lone pairs around each of the two central carbons, ethane is shaped like two tetrahedra that combine to share a vertex.

Ethanol (CH_3CH_2OH; molecular formula C_2H_6O), the intoxicating substance in beer and wine, has three atom centers (Figure 10.13B). The CH_3— group is tetrahedrally shaped, and the —CH_2— group has four bonding groups around its central C atom, so it is tetrahedrally shaped also. The O atom has four electron groups and two lone pairs around it, which gives the V shape (AX_2E_2). For these more complex molecules, we find the molecular shape around one central atom at a time.

Sample Problem 10.9 Predicting Molecular Shapes with More Than One Central Atom

PROBLEM Determine the shape around each of the central atoms in acetone, $(CH_3)_2C=O$?
PLAN There are three central atoms, all C, two of which are in CH_3— groups. We determine the shape around one central atom at a time.
SOLUTION
1. Lewis structure (see below left).
2. Electron-group arrangement: Each CH_3— group has four electron groups around its central C, so its electron-group arrangement is *tetrahedral.* The third C atom has three electron groups around it, so it has the *trigonal planar* arrangement.
3. Bond angles: The H—C—H angle in the CH_3— groups should be near the tetrahedral ideal angle of 109.5°. The C=O double bond should compress the C—C—C angle to less than the ideal 120°.
4. Shapes around central atoms: With four electron groups and no lone pairs, the shapes around the two C atoms in the CH_3— groups are   tetrahedral   (AX_4). With three electron groups and no lone pairs, the shape around the middle C atom is   trigonal planar   (AX_3),

H :O: H	Trigonal planar (middle C)	C—C—O >120°
H—C—C—C—H	Tetrahedral (end C's)	C—C—C <120°
H H		H—C—H ~109.5°
		H—C—C ~109.5°

3 e⁻ groups (middle C) ⟹ 4 e⁻ groups (end C's) ⟹ 1 double bond (middle C) ⟹ all bonding groups ⟹

:O: 122° 116° ~109.5°

Follow-up Problem 10.9 Determine the shape around each central atom and predict any deviations from ideal bond angles in the following: **(a)** H_2SO_4; **(b)** C_3H_4 (there is one C≡C bond); **(c)** S_2F_2.

In recent years, chemists have synthesized some organic molecules with remarkable—some would say beautiful—shapes. Some of their uses may still be speculative, but there is no question about their geometric elegance. A few of these molecules appear in the upcoming Gallery.

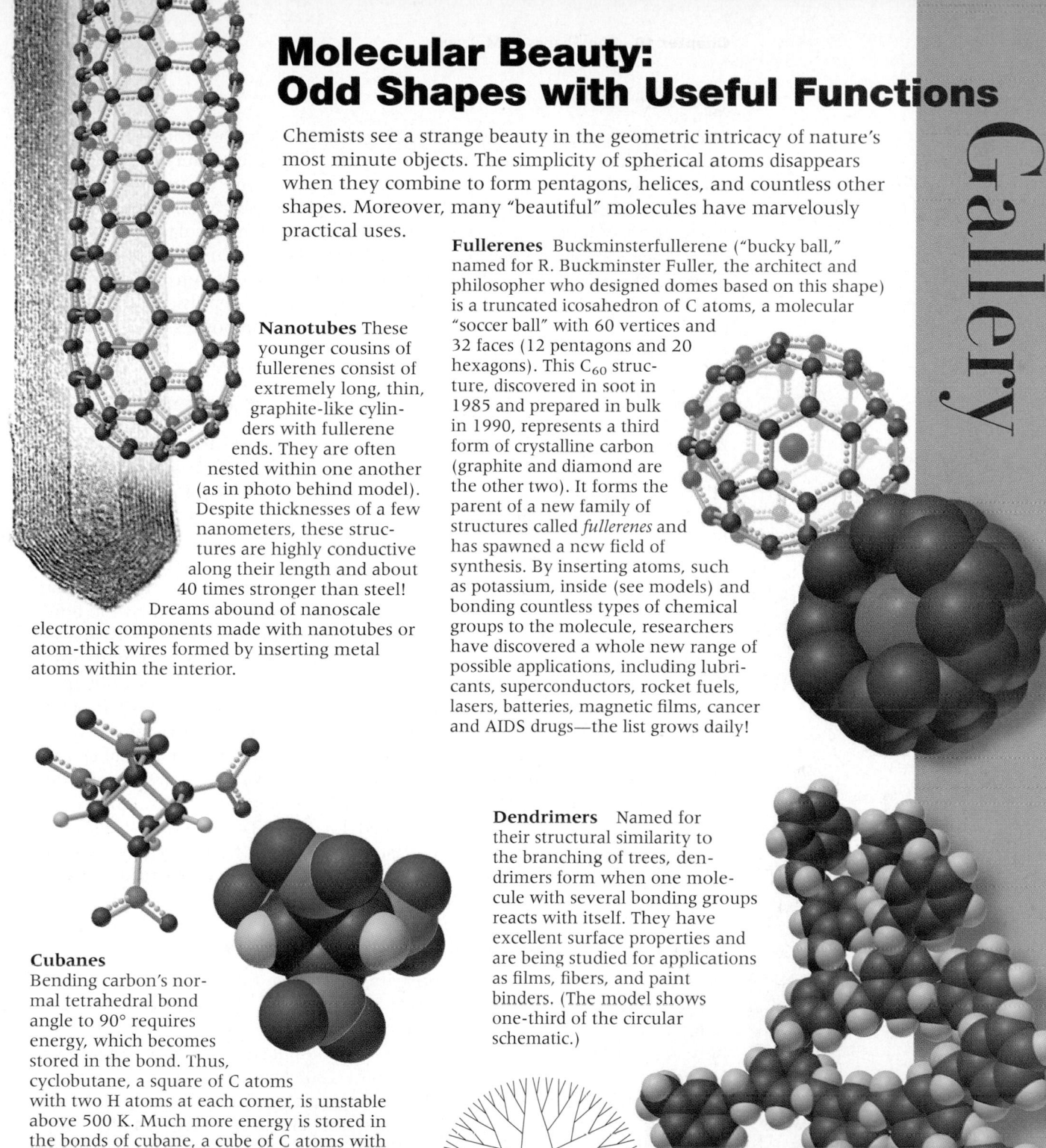

Molecular Beauty: Odd Shapes with Useful Functions

Chemists see a strange beauty in the geometric intricacy of nature's most minute objects. The simplicity of spherical atoms disappears when they combine to form pentagons, helices, and countless other shapes. Moreover, many "beautiful" molecules have marvelously practical uses.

Nanotubes These younger cousins of fullerenes consist of extremely long, thin, graphite-like cylinders with fullerene ends. They are often nested within one another (as in photo behind model). Despite thicknesses of a few nanometers, these structures are highly conductive along their length and about 40 times stronger than steel! Dreams abound of nanoscale electronic components made with nanotubes or atom-thick wires formed by inserting metal atoms within the interior.

Fullerenes Buckminsterfullerene ("bucky ball," named for R. Buckminster Fuller, the architect and philosopher who designed domes based on this shape) is a truncated icosahedron of C atoms, a molecular "soccer ball" with 60 vertices and 32 faces (12 pentagons and 20 hexagons). This C_{60} structure, discovered in soot in 1985 and prepared in bulk in 1990, represents a third form of crystalline carbon (graphite and diamond are the other two). It forms the parent of a new family of structures called *fullerenes* and has spawned a new field of synthesis. By inserting atoms, such as potassium, inside (see models) and bonding countless types of chemical groups to the molecule, researchers have discovered a whole new range of possible applications, including lubricants, superconductors, rocket fuels, lasers, batteries, magnetic films, cancer and AIDS drugs—the list grows daily!

Cubanes
Bending carbon's normal tetrahedral bond angle to 90° requires energy, which becomes stored in the bond. Thus, cyclobutane, a square of C atoms with two H atoms at each corner, is unstable above 500 K. Much more energy is stored in the bonds of cubane, a cube of C atoms with one H at each corner, synthesized in 1964. The "bond-strain" energy of cubane can yield enormous explosive power. Tetranitrocubane (shown here) is a very powerful explosive, and octanitrocubane, which has not yet been synthesized, is expected to be the most powerful non-nuclear explosive known. Other properties of cubanes, apparently unrelated to the bond energy, include attacking cancer cells and inactivating an enzyme involved in Parkinson's disease.

Dendrimers Named for their structural similarity to the branching of trees, dendrimers form when one molecule with several bonding groups reacts with itself. They have excellent surface properties and are being studied for applications as films, fibers, and paint binders. (The model shows one-third of the circular schematic.)

Section Summary

The VSEPR theory proposes that each group of electrons around the central atom (single bond, multiple bond, lone pair, or lone electron) remains as far away from the others as possible. Five electron-group arrangements result when two, three, four, five, and six electron groups surround a central atom. Each arrangement is associated with one or more molecular shapes. Ideal bond angles are prescribed by the regular geometric shapes; deviations from these angles occur when the surrounding atoms or electron groups are not identical. Lone pairs and double bonds exert more repulsions than single bonds. Larger molecules have shapes that are composites of the shapes around each central atom.

10.4 Molecular Shape and Molecular Polarity

Knowing the shape of a substance's molecules is a key to understanding its physical and chemical behavior. One of the most important and far-reaching effects of molecular shape is molecular polarity, which can influence melting and boiling points, solubility, chemical reactivity, and even biological function.

In Chapter 9, you learned that a covalent bond is *polar* when it joins atoms of different electronegativities because the atoms share the electrons unequally. In diatomic molecules, such as HF, where there is only one bond, the bond polarity causes the molecule itself to be polar. Molecules with a net imbalance of charge have a **molecular polarity.** In molecules with more than two atoms, *both shape and bond polarity determine molecular polarity.* In an electric field, polar molecules become oriented, on average, with their partial charges pointing toward the oppositely charged electric plates, as shown in Figure 10.14. The **dipole moment (μ)** is the product of these partial charges and the distance between them. It is typically measured in *debye* (D) units; using the SI units of charge (coulomb, C) and length (meter, m), $1\ D = 3.34 \times 10^{-30}\ C \cdot m$. [The unit is named for Peter Debye (1884–1966), the Dutch American chemist and physicist who won the Nobel Prize in 1936 for his major contributions to our understanding of molecular structure and solution behavior.]

Bond Polarity, Bond Angle, and Dipole Moment

When determining molecular polarity, we must take shape into account because the presence of polar bonds does not *always* lead to a polar molecule. In carbon dioxide, for example, the large electronegativity difference between C (EN = 2.5) and O (EN = 3.5) makes each C=O bond quite polar. However, CO_2 is linear, so its bonds point 180° from each other. As a result, these identical bond polarities are counterbalanced and give the molecule *no net dipole moment* ($\mu = 0$ D). Note that the electron density model shows regions of high negative charge (*red*) distributed equally on either side of the central region of high positive charge (*blue*):

Water also has identical atoms bonded to the central atom, but it *does* have a significant dipole moment ($\mu = 1.85$ D). In each O—H bond, electron density is pulled toward the more electronegative O atom. Here, the bond polarities are *not* counterbalanced because the water molecule is V shaped (also see Figure 4.2). Instead, the bond polarities are partially reinforced, and the

A

B Electric field off

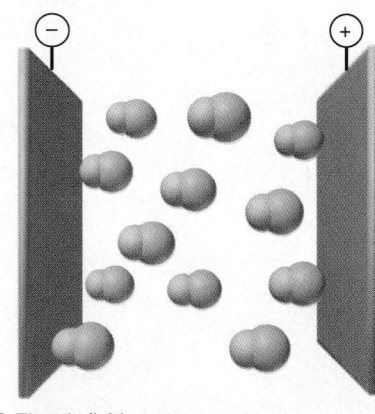

C Electric field on

Figure 10.14 The orientation of polar molecules in an electric field. A, A space-filling model of HF (*left*) shows the partial charges of this polar molecule. The electron density model (*right*) shows high electron density (*red*) associated with the F end and low electron density (*blue*) with the H end. **B,** In the absence of an external electric field, HF molecules are oriented randomly. **C,** In the presence of the field, the molecules, on average, become oriented with their partial charges pointing toward the oppositely charged plates.

O end of the molecule is more negative than the other end (the region between the H atoms), which the electron density model shows clearly:

(The molecular polarity of water has some amazing effects, from determining the composition of the oceans to supporting life itself, as you'll see in Chapter 12.)

In the two previous examples, molecular shape influences polarity. When different molecules have the same shape, the nature of the atoms surrounding the central atom can have a major effect on polarity. Consider carbon tetrachloride (CCl_4) and chloroform ($CHCl_3$), two tetrahedral molecules with very different polarities. In CCl_4, the surrounding atoms are all Cl atoms. Although each C—Cl bond is polar ($\Delta EN = 0.5$), the molecule is nonpolar ($\mu = 0$ D) because the individual bond polarities counterbalance each other. In $CHCl_3$, H substitutes for one Cl atom, disrupting the balance and giving chloroform a significant dipole moment ($\mu = 1.01$ D):

       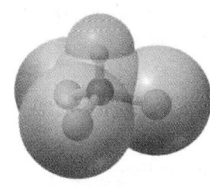

Sample Problem 10.10   Predicting the Polarity of Molecules

PROBLEM From electronegativity (EN) values and their periodic trends (see Figure 9.16), predict whether each of the following molecules is polar and show the direction of bond dipoles and the overall molecular dipole when applicable:
(a) Ammonia, NH_3 **(b)** Boron trifluoride, BF_3
(c) Carbonyl sulfide, COS (atom sequence SCO)
PLAN First, we draw and name the molecular shape. Then, using relative EN values, we decide on the direction of each bond dipole. Finally, we see if the bond dipoles balance or reinforce each other in the molecule as a whole.
SOLUTION **(a)** For NH_3. The molecular shape is trigonal pyramidal. From Figure 9.16, we see that N (EN = 3.0) is more electronegative than H (EN = 2.1), so the bond dipoles point toward N. Since the bond dipoles partially reinforce each other, the molecular dipole points toward N:

    molecular shape   bond dipoles   molecular dipole

Therefore, ammonia is polar.

(b) For BF_3. The molecular shape is trigonal planar. Since F (EN = 4.0) is farther to the right in Period 2 than B (EN = 2.0), it is more electronegative, so each bond dipole points toward F. However, the bond angle is 120°, so the three bond dipoles counterbalance each other, and BF_3 has no molecular dipole:

   molecular shape   bond dipoles   no molecular dipole

Therefore, boron trifluoride is nonpolar.

(c) For COS. The molecular shape is linear. Since C and S have the same EN, the C$=$S bond is nonpolar, but the C$=$O bond is quite polar (ΔEN = 1.0), so there is a net molecular dipole toward the O:

$\ddot{S}=C=\ddot{O}$	$\ddot{S}=C=\ddot{O}$	$\ddot{S}=C=\ddot{O}$
molecular shape	bond dipoles	molecular dipole

Therefore, carbonyl sulfide is polar.

Follow-up Problem 10.10 Show the bond dipoles and molecular dipole, if any, for **(a)** dichloromethane (CH_2Cl_2); **(b)** iodine oxide pentafluoride (IOF_5); **(c)** nitrogen tribromide (NBr_3).

The Effect of Molecular Polarity on Behavior

To get a sense of the influence of molecular polarity on physical behavior, consider what effect a molecular dipole might have when many polar molecules lie near each other, as they do in a liquid. How does a molecular property such as dipole moment affect a macroscopic property such as boiling point? A liquid boils when its molecules have enough energy to form bubbles of gas. To enter the bubble, the molecules in the liquid must overcome the weak attractive forces *between* them. A molecular dipole influences the strength of these attractions.

Consider the two dichloroethylenes shown below. These compounds have the *same* molecular formula ($C_2H_2Cl_2$) and therefore the *same* molar mass, but they have *different* physical and chemical properties. In particular, the *cis*-1,2-dichloroethylene boils 13°C higher than *trans*-1,2-dichloroethylene. VSEPR theory predicts, and spectroscopic analysis confirms, that all the nuclei lie in the same plane, with a trigonal planar shape around each C atom. The *trans* compound has no dipole moment (μ = 0 D) because the C—Cl bond polarities balance each other. In contrast, the *cis* compound *is* polar (μ = 1.90 D) because the bond dipoles partially reinforce each other, with the molecular dipole pointing between the Cl atoms. In the liquid state, the polar *cis* molecules attract each other more strongly than the nonpolar *trans* molecules, so more energy is needed to overcome these stronger forces. Therefore, the *cis* compound has a higher boiling point. We extend these ideas in Chapter 12. The Chemical Connections essay discusses some of the many essential effects of molecular shape and polarity on biological behavior.

cis	*trans*

Section Summary

Bond polarity and molecular shape determine molecular polarity, which is measured as a dipole moment. When bond polarities counterbalance each other, the molecule is nonpolar; when they reinforce each other, the molecule is polar. Molecular shape and polarity can affect physical properties, such as boiling point, and they play a central role in many aspects of biological function.

Chemical Connections   Chemistry in Physiology

Molecular Shape, Biological Receptors, and the Sense of Smell

In a very simple sense, a biological cell is a membrane-bound sack filled with molecular shapes interacting in an aqueous fluid. As a result of the magnificent internal organization of cells, many complex processes in an organism begin when a molecular "key" fits into a correspondingly shaped molecular "lock." The key can be a relatively small molecule circulating in a body fluid, whereas the lock is usually a large molecule, known as a biological receptor, that is often found embedded in a cell membrane. The receptor contains a precisely shaped cavity, or *receptor site,* that is exposed to the passing fluid. Thousands of molecules collide with this site, but when one with the correct shape (that is, the molecular key) lands on it, the receptor "grabs" it through intermolecular attractions, and the biological response begins.

Let's see how this fitting together of molecular shapes operates in the sense of smell (olfaction). A substance must have certain properties to have an odor. An odorous molecule travels through the air, so it must come from a gas or a volatile liquid or solid. To reach the receptor, it must be soluble, at least to a small extent, in the thin film of aqueous solution that lines the nasal passages. Most important, the odorous molecule, or a portion of it, must have a shape that fits into one of the olfactory receptor sites that cover the nerve endings deep within the nasal passage (Figure 10.A). When this happens, the resulting nerve impulses travel from these endings to the brain, which interprets the impulses as a specific odor.

In the 1950s, the stereochemical theory of odor (*stereo* means "three-dimensional") was introduced to explain the relationship between odor and molecular shape. Its basic premise is that a molecule's shape (and sometimes its polarity), but *not* its composition, is the primary determinant of its odor. According to this theory, there are seven primary odors, each corresponding to one of seven different types of olfactory receptor sites. The seven odors are camphor-like, musky, floral, minty, ethereal, pungent, and putrid. (The last two odors depend on molecular polarity more than shape, and their receptors have partial charges opposite to those of the molecules landing there.) Figure 10.B shows the proposed shapes of three of the seven receptor sites, each occupied by a molecule having the associated odor.

Several predictions of this original version of the theory have been verified by experiment. If two substances fit the same receptors, they should have the same odor, even if

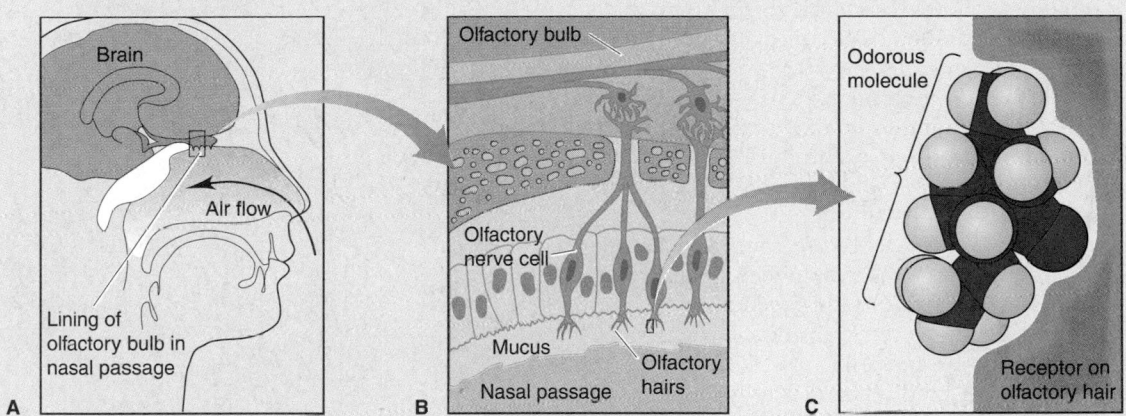

A

B

C

Figure 10.A The location of olfactory receptors within the nose. A, The olfactory area lies at the top of the nasal passage very close to the brain. Air containing the odorous molecules is sniffed in, warmed, moistened, and channeled toward this region. **B,** A blow-up of the region shows olfactory nerve cells and their hairlike endings protruding into the liquid-coated nasal passage. **C,** A further blow-up shows a receptor on one of the endings containing an odorous molecule that matches its shape. This particular molecule has a minty odor.

Floral

Camphor-like

Ethereal

Figure 10.B Shapes of some olfactory receptor sites. Three of the seven proposed olfactory receptors are shown with a molecule having that odor occupying the site.

Camphor

Hexachloroethane

Thiophosphoric acid
dichloride ethylamide

Cyclooctane

Figure 10.C Different molecules with the same odor. The theory stating that odor is based on shape, not composition, is supported by these four different substances: all have a camphor-like (moth repellent) odor.

their compositions vary. The four molecules in Figure 10.C all fit the "bowl-shaped" camphor-like receptor and all smell like moth repellent, despite their different formulas. If different portions of one molecule fit different receptors, the molecule should have a mixed odor. Portions of the benzaldehyde molecule fit the camphor-like, floral, and minty receptors, which gives it an almond odor; other molecules that smell like almonds also fit the same three receptors.

Despite these and other results consistent with the theory, recent evidence suggests that the original model is too simple. In many cases, a prediction of odor based on molecular shape turns out to be incorrect when the substance is actually smelled. One reason for this discrepancy is that a molecule in the gas phase may have a very different shape in solution at the receptor. By the early 1990s, evidence for the presence of some 1000 receptor sites had been obtained, and it is thought that various combinations of stimulation produce the more than 10,000 odors humans can distinguish. So, although a key premise of the theory is still accepted—odor depends on molecular shape—the nature of the dependence is complex and is an active area of research in the food, cosmetics, and insecticide industries. The sense of smell is so vital for survival that these topics are important areas of study for biologists as well.

Many other biochemical processes are controlled by one molecule fitting into a receptor site on another. Enzymes are proteins that bind cellular reactants and speed their reaction (Figure 10.D). Nerve impulses are transmitted when small molecules released from one nerve fit into receptors on the next. Mind-altering drugs act by chemically disrupting the molecular fit at such nerve receptors in the brain. One type of immune response is triggered when a molecule on a bacterial surface binds to the receptors on "killer" cells in the bloodstream. Hormones regulate energy production and growth by fitting into and activating key receptors. Genes function when certain nucleic acid molecules fit into specific regions of other nucleic acids. Indeed, *no molecular property is more crucial to living systems than shape.*

Figure 10.D Molecular shape and enzyme action. A small sugar molecule (*right*) is about to land on the receptor site of an enzyme molecule (*left*) and undergo reaction.

Chapter Perspective

In this chapter, you saw how chemists use the simple idea of electrostatic repulsion between shared and/or unshared electron groups to account for the shapes of molecules and, ultimately, their properties. In the next chapter, you'll learn how chemists explain molecular shape and behavior through the nature of the orbitals that electrons occupy. The landscape of a molecule—its geometric contours and regions of charge—

gives rise to all its other properties. In upcoming chapters, we'll explore the physical behavior of liquids and solids (Chapter 12), the properties of solutions (Chapter 13), and the behavior of the main-group elements (Chapter 14) and organic molecules (Chapter 15), all of which emerge from atomic properties and their resulting molecular properties.

The following learning objectives, with section and/or sample problem (SP) numbers in parentheses, can help focus your study:

Understand These Concepts

1. How Lewis structures depict the atoms and their bonding and nonbonding electron pairs in a molecule or ion (10.1)
2. How resonance and electron delocalization explain bond properties in many compounds with double bonds adjacent to single bonds (10.1)
3. The meaning of formal charge and how it is used to select the most important resonance structure; the difference between formal charge and oxidation number (10.1)
4. The octet rule and its three major exceptions—molecules with an electron deficiency, an odd number of electrons, or an expanded valence shell (10.1)
5. How a reaction can be divided conceptually into bond-breaking and bond-forming steps (10.2)
6. How electron-group repulsions give rise to molecular shapes (10.3)
7. The five electron-group arrangements and their associated molecular shapes (10.3)

8. Why double bonds and lone pairs cause deviations from ideal bond angles (10.3)
9. How bond polarities and molecular shape combine to give a molecular polarity (10.4)

Master These Skills

1. Using a stepwise method for writing a Lewis structure from a molecular formula (SPs 10.1 to 10.3 and 10.5)
2. Writing resonance structures for molecules and ions (SP 10.4)
3. Calculating the formal charge of any atom in a molecule or ion (10.1)
4. Using Lewis structures to calculate ΔH_{rxn}^0 from bond energies (SP 10.6)
5. Predicting molecular shapes from Lewis structures (SPs 10.7 to 10.9)
6. Using molecular shape and electronegativity values to predict the direction of a molecular dipole (SP 10.10)

For Review and Reference

Key Terms

Section 10.1
Lewis structure (Lewis formula)
resonance structure (resonance form)
resonance hybrid
electron-pair delocalization
formal charge
electron deficient

free radical
expanded valence shell
Section 10.3
valence-shell electron-pair repulsion (VSEPR) theory
molecular shape
bond angle
linear arrangement

trigonal planar arrangement
bent (V shaped)
tetrahedral arrangement
trigonal pyramidal shape
trigonal bipyramidal arrangement
equatorial group
axial group

seesaw shape
T shape
octahedral arrangement
square pyramidal shape
square planar shape
Section 10.4
molecular polarity
dipole moment (μ)

Key Equations and Relationships

10.1 Calculating the formal charge on an atom (p. 367):

Formal charge of atom = no. of valence e^-
  − (no. of unshared valence e^- + $\frac{1}{2}$ no. of shared valence e^-)

10.2 Calculating heat of reaction from bond energies (p. 372):

$$\Delta H_{rxn}^0 = \Delta H_{reactant\ bonds\ broken}^0 + \Delta H_{product\ bonds\ formed}^0$$

10.3 Ranking the effect of electron-pair repulsions on bond angle (p. 378):

Lone pair–lone pair > lone pair–bonding pair
                    > bonding pair–bonding pair

Highlighted Figures and Tables

These figures (F) and tables (T) provide a quick review of key ideas.
F10.1 The steps in writing a Lewis structure (p. 362)
F10.2 Using bond energies to calculate the enthalpy change of reaction (ΔH_{rxn}^0) (p. 371)
F10.5 Electron-group repulsions and the five basic molecular shapes (p. 375)
F10.6 The single molecular shape of the linear electron-group arrangement (p. 375)

F10.7 The two molecular shapes of the trigonal planar electron-group arrangement (p. 376)
F10.8 The three molecular shapes of the tetrahedral electron-group arrangement (p. 377)
F10.10 The four molecular shapes of the trigonal bipyramidal electron-group arrangement (p. 378)
F10.11 The three molecular shapes of the octahedral electron-group arrangement (p. 379)
F10.12 The steps in determining a molecular shape (p. 380)

Answers to Follow-up Problems

10.1 (a)   (b)   (c)

10.2 (a)   (b)

10.3 (a) :C≡O: (b) H—C≡N: (c) :O=C=O:

10.4

$$\left[\begin{array}{c}:O:\\ \| \\ C \\ :O: \quad :O:\end{array}\right]^{2-} \longleftrightarrow \left[\begin{array}{c}:O:\\ \| \\ C \\ :O: \quad :O:\end{array}\right]^{2-}$$

10.5 (a)   (b) :O=Cl—O: (c)

10.6 (a) :N≡N: + 3 H—H ⟶ 2 :N—H
$$\Delta H^{0}_{\text{bonds broken}} = 1\ \text{N} \equiv \text{N} + 3\ \text{H—H}$$
$$= 945\ \text{kJ} + 1296\ \text{kJ} = 2241\ \text{kJ}$$
$$\Delta H^{0}_{\text{bonds formed}} = 6\ \text{N—H} = -2346\ \text{kJ}$$
$$\Delta H^{0}_{\text{rxn}} = -105\ \text{kJ}$$

(b) C=C + H—Br: ⟶ H—C—C—Br:

$$\Delta H^{0}_{\text{bonds broken}} = 1\ \text{C} = \text{C} + 4\ \text{C—H} + 1\ \text{H—Br}$$
$$= 614\ \text{kJ} + 1652\ \text{kJ} + 363\ \text{kJ} = 2629\ \text{kJ}$$
$$\Delta H^{0}_{\text{bonds formed}} = 1\ \text{C—C} + 5\ \text{C—H} + 1\ \text{C—Br}$$
$$= -(347\ \text{kJ} + 2065\ \text{kJ} + 276\ \text{kJ}) = -2688\ \text{kJ}$$
$$\Delta H^{0}_{\text{rxn}} = -59\ \text{kJ}$$

10.7 (a) :S=C=S:
Linear, 180°

(b)
V shaped, <120°

(c)
Tetrahedral, 109.5°

(d)
V shaped, <109.5°

10.8 (a)
Linear, 180°

(b)
T shaped, <90°

(c)
Trigonal bipyramidal,
F_{eq}—S—F_{eq} angle <120° and
F_{ax}—S—F_{eq} angle <90°.

10.9 (a)
S is tetrahedral; double bonds compress O—S—O angle to <109.5°. Each central O is V shaped; lone pairs compress H—O—S angle to <109.5°.

(b)
Methyl C is tetrahedral ~109.5°; other C atoms are linear, 180°.

(c)
Each S is V shaped; F—S—S angle <109.5°.

10.10

(a)   (b)   (c)

Problems

Problems with a **colored** number are answered at the back of the text. Problem sections match the text and provide the number(s) of relevant sample problems. Most offer concept review questions, skill-building exercises (written in similar pairs), and problems in a relevant context. Following these are comprehensive problems based on material from any section and/or previous chapter.

Depicting Molecules and Ions with Lewis Structures
(Sample Problems 10.1 to 10.5)

■ **Concept Review Questions**

10.1 In which of the following patterns does X obey the octet rule?

(a)   (b)   (c)   (d)

(e)   (f)   (g)   (h)

10.2 Which of the following atoms *cannot* serve as a central atom in a Lewis structure: (a) O; (b) He; (c) F; (d) H; (e) P? Explain.

10.3 When is a resonance hybrid needed to adequately depict the bonding in a molecule? Using NO_2 as an example, explain how a resonance hybrid is consistent with the actual bond length, bond strength, and bond order.

10.4 What is required for an atom to expand its valence shell? Which of the following atoms can expand its valence shell: F, S, H, Al, Se, Cl?

■ **Skill-Building Exercises (paired)**

10.5 Draw a Lewis structure for (a) SiF_4; (b) $SeCl_2$; (c) COF_2 (C central).

10.6 Draw a Lewis structure for (a) PH_4^+; (b) C_2F_4; (c) SbH_3.

10.7 Draw a Lewis structure for (a) PF_3; (b) H_2CO_3 (both H attached to O atoms); (c) CS_2.

10.8 Draw a Lewis structure for (a) CH_4S; (b) S_2Cl_2; (c) $CHCl_3$.

10.9 Draw Lewis structures of all the important resonance forms of (a) NO_2; (b) NO_2F (N central).

10.10 Draw Lewis structures of all the important resonance forms of (a) HNO_3 ($HONO_2$); (b) $HAsO_4^{2-}$ ($HOAsO_3^{2-}$).

10.11 Draw Lewis structures of all the important resonance forms of (a) N_3^-; (b) NO_2^-.

10.12 Draw Lewis structures of all the important resonance forms of (a) HCO_2^- (H attached to C); (b) $HBrO_4$ ($HOBrO_3$).

10.13 Draw a Lewis structure and calculate the formal charge of each atom in (a) IF_5; (b) AlH_4^-.

10.14 Draw a Lewis structure and calculate the formal charge of each atom in (a) COS (C central); (b) NO.

10.15 Draw a Lewis structure and calculate the formal charge of each atom in (a) CN^-; (b) ClO^-.

10.16 Draw a Lewis structure and calculate the formal charge of each atom in (a) BF_4^-; (b) ClNO.

10.17 Draw a Lewis structure for the most important resonance form of each ion, showing formal charges and oxidation numbers of the atoms: (a) BrO_3^-; (b) SO_3^{2-}.

10.18 Draw a Lewis structure for the most important resonance form of each ion, showing formal charges and oxidation numbers of the atoms: (a) AsO_4^{3-}; (b) ClO_2^-.

10.19 The following species do not obey the octet rule. Draw a Lewis structure for each and state the octet rule exception: (a) BH_3; (b) AsF_4^-; (c) $SeCl_4$.

10.20 The following species do not obey the octet rule. Draw a Lewis structure for each and state the octet rule exception: (a) PF_6^-; (b) ClO_3; (c) H_3PO_3.

10.21 The following species do not obey the octet rule. Draw a Lewis structure for each and state the type of octet rule exception: (a) BrF_3; (b) ICl_2^-; (c) BeF_2.

10.22 The following species do not obey the octet rule. Draw a Lewis structure for each and state the type of octet rule exception: (a) O_3^-; (b) XeF_2; (c) SbF_4^-.

■ **Problems in Context**

10.23 Molten beryllium chloride reacts with chloride ion from molten NaCl to form the $BeCl_4^{2-}$ ion, in which the Be atom attains an octet. Use Lewis structures to depict the net ionic reaction.

10.24 Despite many attempts, the perbromate ion (BrO_4^-) was not prepared in the laboratory until about 1970. (Indeed, articles were published explaining theoretically why it could never be prepared!) Draw a Lewis structure for BrO_4^- that is consistent with minimal formal charges.

10.25 Phosgene is a colorless, highly toxic gas employed against troops in World War I and used today as a key reactant in organic synthesis. Use formal charges to select the most important of the following resonance structures:

A **B** **C**

10.26 Cryolite (Na_3AlF_6) is an indispensable component in the electrochemical manufacture of aluminum. Draw a Lewis structure for the AlF_6^{3-} ion.

Using Lewis Structures and Bond Energies to Calculate Heats of Reaction
(Sample Problem 10.6)

■ **Concept Review Questions**

10.27 Write a solution plan (without actual numbers, but including the bond energies you would use and how you would combine them algebraically) for calculating the enthalpy change of the following reaction:

$$H_2(g) + O_2(g) \longrightarrow H_2O_2(g)$$

10.28 The text points out that, for similar types of substances, one with weaker bonds is usually more reactive than one with stronger bonds. Why is this generally true?

10.29 Why is there often a small discrepancy between a heat of reaction obtained from ΔH_f^0 values and one obtained from bond energies?

■ **Skill-Building Exercises (paired)**

10.30 Use bond energies from Table 9.2 (p. 343) to calculate the heat of reaction:

10.31 Use bond energies from Table 9.2 (p. 343) to calculate the heat of reaction:

10.32 Use Lewis structures and bond energies to calculate the enthalpy change of the following reaction:

$$C_2H_4(g) + H_2O(g) \longrightarrow CH_3CH_2OH(g)$$

10.33 Use Lewis structures and bond energies to calculate the enthalpy change of the following reaction:

$$HCN(g) + 2H_2(g) \longrightarrow CH_3NH_2(g)$$

■ **Problems in Context**

10.34 An important industrial route to extremely pure acetic acid is the reaction of methanol with carbon monoxide. Calculate the heat of reaction for this process.

10.35 Acetylene gas (C_2H_2) burns with oxygen in an oxyacetylene torch to produce carbon dioxide, water vapor, and the great heat needed for welding metals. The heat of combustion of acetylene is 1259 kJ/mol. Estimate the bond energy of the $C\equiv C$ bond and compare your answer with the value in Table 9.2 (p. 343).

Valence-Shell Electron-Pair Repulsion (VSEPR) Theory and Molecular Shape

(Sample Problems 10.7 to 10.9)

■ Concept Review Questions

10.36 If you know the formula of a molecule or ion, what is the first step in predicting its shape?

10.37 In what situation is the name of the molecular shape the same as the name of the electron-group arrangement?

10.38 Which of the following numbers of electron groups can give rise to a bent (V-shaped) molecule: two, three, four, five, six? Draw an example with the shape classification (AX_mE_n) and ideal bond angle in each case.

10.39 Name all the molecular shapes that have a tetrahedral electron-group arrangement.

10.40 Why aren't lone pairs included with surrounding bonded groups when describing the molecular shape?

10.41 Use wedge-line perspective drawings (if necessary) to sketch the atom positions in a general molecule of formula (not shape class) AX_n that has the following shapes: (a) V shaped; (b) trigonal planar; (c) trigonal bipyramidal; (d) T shaped; (e) trigonal pyramidal; (f) square pyramidal.

10.42 What would you expect to be the electron-group arrangement around atom A in each of the following cases? For each arrangement, give the ideal bond angle and the direction of any expected deviation:

(a)
$$X-A: \quad \begin{matrix} X \\ | \\ | \\ X \end{matrix}$$

(b) $X-A\equiv X$

(c)
$$X=A-X \quad \begin{matrix} X \\ \| \\ \end{matrix}$$

(d) $X-\ddot{A}-X$

(e) $X=A=X$

(f)
$$:A\!\!\begin{matrix} X \\ \diagup \\ \diagdown \\ X \end{matrix}\!\!X$$

■ Skill-Building Exercises *(paired)*

10.43 Determine the electron-group arrangement, molecular shape, and ideal bond angle(s) for each of the following: (a) O_3; (b) H_3O^+; (c) NF_3.

10.44 Determine the electron-group arrangement, molecular shape, and ideal bond angle(s) for each of the following: (a) SO_4^{2-}; (b) NO_2^-; (c) PH_3.

10.45 Determine the electron-group arrangement, molecular shape, and ideal bond angle(s) for each of the following: (a) CO_3^{2-}; (b) SO_2; (c) CF_4.

10.46 Determine the electron-group arrangement, molecular shape, and ideal bond angle(s) for each of the following: (a) SO_3; (b) N_2O (N central); (c) CH_2Cl_2.

10.47 Name the shape and give the AX_mE_n classification and ideal bond angle(s) for each of the following general molecules:

(a)   (b)   (c)

10.48 Name the shape and give the AX_mE_n classification and ideal bond angle(s) for each of the following general molecules:

(a)   (b)   (c)

10.49 Determine the shape, ideal bond angle(s), and the direction of any deviation from these angles for each of the following: (a) ClO_2^-; (b) PF_5; (c) SeF_4; (d) KrF_2.

10.50 Determine the shape, ideal bond angle(s), and the direction of any deviation from these angles for each of the following: (a) ClO_3^-; (b) IF_4^-; (c) $SeOF_2$; (d) TeF_5^-.

10.51 Determine the shape around each central atom in each molecule, and explain any deviation from ideal bond angles: (a) CH_3OH; (b) N_2O_4 (O_2NNO_2).

10.52 Determine the shape around each central atom in each molecule, and explain any deviation from ideal bond angles: (a) H_3PO_4 (no H—P bond); (b) CH_3—O—CH_2CH_3.

10.53 Determine the shape around each central atom in each molecule, and explain any deviation from ideal bond angles: (a) CH_3COOH; (b) H_2O_2.

10.54 Determine the shape around each central atom in each molecule, and explain any deviation from ideal bond angles: (a) H_2SO_3 (no H—S bond); (b) N_2O_3 (ONNO$_2$).

10.55 Arrange the following AF_n species in order of *increasing* F—A—F bond angles: BF_3, BeF_2, CF_4, NF_3, OF_2.

10.56 Arrange the following ACl_n species in order of *decreasing* Cl—A—Cl bond angles: SCl_2, OCl_2, PCl_3, $SiCl_4$, $SiCl_6^{2-}$.

10.57 State ideal values for each of the bond angles in each molecule and where you expect deviations:

(a)
$$H-C=N-\ddot{O}-H$$
with an H on the C

(b)
$$H-C-\ddot{O}-C-H$$
with H above and below each C

(c)
$$H-\ddot{O}-B-\ddot{O}-H$$
with :O: above B and H above

10.58 State ideal values for each of the bond angles in each molecule and where you expect deviations:

(a)
$$\ddot{O}=N-\ddot{O}-H$$
with :O: below N

(b)
$$H-C-C=\ddot{O}$$
with H above and below

(c)
$$H-C-\ddot{O}-H$$
with :O: above C

■ Problems in Context

10.59 Because both tin and carbon are members of Group 4A(14), they form structurally similar compounds. However, tin exhibits a greater variety of structures because it forms several ionic species. Predict the shapes and ideal bond angles, including any deviations, for the following: (a) $Sn(CH_3)_2$; (b) $SnCl_3^-$; (c) $Sn(CH_3)_4$; (d) SnF_5^-; (e) SnF_6^{2-}.

10.60 In the gas phase, phosphorus pentachloride exists as separate molecules. In the solid phase, however, the compound is composed of alternating PCl_4^+ and PCl_6^- ions. What change(s) in molecular shape occur(s) as PCl_5 solidifies? How does the Cl—P—Cl angle change?

Molecular Shape and Molecular Polarity

(Sample Problem 10.10)

■ Concept Review Questions

10.61 For molecules of general formula AX_n (where $n > 2$), how do you determine if a molecule is polar?

10.62 How can a molecule with polar covalent bonds fail to be a polar molecule? Give an example.

10.63 Explain in general why the shape of a biomolecule is important to its function.

■ Skill-Building Exercises *(paired)*

10.64 Consider the molecules SCl_2, F_2, CS_2, CF_4, BrCl.
(a) Which has bonds that are most polar?
(b) Which have a molecular dipole moment?

10.65 Consider the molecules BF_3, PF_3, BrF_3, SF_4, SF_6.
(a) Which has bonds that are most polar?
(b) Which have a molecular dipole moment?

10.66 Which molecule in each pair has the greater dipole moment: (a) SO_2 or SO_3; (b) ICl or IF; (c) SiF_4 or SF_4; (d) H_2O or H_2S? Give the reason for your choice.

10.67 Which molecule in each pair has the greater dipole moment: (a) ClO_2 or SO_2; (b) HBr or HCl; (c) $BeCl_2$ or SCl_2; (d) AsF_3 or AsF_5? Give the reason for your choice.

■ Problems in Context

10.68 There are three different dichloroethylenes (molecular formula $C_2H_2Cl_2$), which we can designate X, Y, and Z. Compound X has no dipole moment, but compound Z does. Compounds X and Z each combine with hydrogen to give the same product:

$$C_2H_2Cl_2 \ (X \ or \ Z) + H_2 \longrightarrow ClCH_2{-}CH_2Cl$$

What are the structures of X, Y, and Z? Would you expect compound Y to have a dipole moment?

10.69 Dinitrogen difluoride, N_2F_2, is the only stable, simple inorganic molecule with an N=N bond. The compound occurs in *cis* and *trans* forms.
(a) Draw the molecular shapes of the two forms of N_2F_2.
(b) Predict the polarity, if any, of each form.

Comprehensive Problems

Problems with an asterisk (*) are more challenging.

10.70 Nitrogen forms the hydride hydrazine (N_2H_4), as well as two thermally unstable hydrides, diazene (N_2H_2) and tetrazene (N_4H_4).
(a) Use Lewis structures to compare the strength, length, and order of nitrogen-nitrogen bonds in diazene, hydrazine, and N_2.
(b) Tetrazene (atom sequence H_2NNNNH_2) decomposes above 0°C to hydrazine and nitrogen gas. Draw a Lewis structure for tetrazene and calculate the ΔH^0_{rxn} for this decomposition.

10.71 Draw a Lewis structure for each species: (a) PF_5; (b) CCl_4; (c) H_3O^+; (d) ICl_3; (e) BeH_2; (f) PH_2^-; (g) $GeBr_4$; (h) CH_3^-; (i) BCl_3; (j) BrF_4^+; (k) XeO_3; (l) TeF_4.

10.72 Determine the molecular shape of each of the species in Problem 10.71.

10.73 Among the more than 30 molecular species associated with the comet Hale-Bopp are CH_2O, C_2H_2, HCN, and CH_3CN. Many of the same molecules have also been proposed as occurring in the Earth's earliest atmosphere. State the molecular shape, show formal charges, and predict the deviation (if any) from ideal bond angles of these molecules.

10.74 Nitrosyl fluoride (NOF) has an atom sequence in which all atoms have formal charges of zero. Write the Lewis structure consistent with this fact.

10.75 The VSEPR model was developed in the 1950s, before any xenon compounds had been prepared. Thus, in the early 1960s, these compounds provided an excellent test of the model's predictive power. What would you have predicted for the shapes of XeF_2, XeF_4, and XeF_6?

10.76 Boron trifluoride is an important reactant in organic syntheses but is a very reactive gas at room temperature and thus difficult to handle. Boron's ability to accept another pair of electrons and attain an octet is used to prepare an easily stored liquid form: a compound of BF_3 and diethyl ether ($CH_3{-}CH_2{-}O{-}CH_2{-}CH_3$). Draw Lewis structures for BF_3, diethyl ether, and the product, and indicate how the molecular shapes around B and O change during the reaction.

10.77 The measured bond angle in NO_2 is 134.3°, and in NO_2^- it is 115.4°, even though the ideal bond angle is 120° in both. Explain.

10.78 "Inert" xenon actually forms several compounds, especially with the highly electronegative elements oxygen and fluorine. The simple fluorides XeF_2, XeF_4, and XeF_6 are all formed by direct reaction of the elements. As you might expect from the size of the xenon atom, the Xe—F bond is not a strong one. Calculate the Xe—F bond energy in XeF_6, given that the heat of formation is −402 kJ/mol.

10.79 Nitrobenzene (resonance hybrid shown at right) is used primarily to make aniline, one of the most important starting compounds in the industrial production of synthetic dyes, resins, varnishes, and perfumes. Draw the most important separate resonance forms that contribute to the resonance hybrid.

10.80 Chloral, $Cl_3C{-}CH{=}O$, the infamous "knock-out drops" of mystery stories and movies, reacts with water to form the sedative and hypnotic agent chloral hydrate, $Cl_3C{-}CH(OH)_2$. Draw Lewis structures for these substances and describe the change in molecular shape, if any, that occurs at each of the carbon atoms during the reaction.

10.81 The tricarboxylic acid (or citric acid) cycle is one of the central metabolic pathways in all animals. Through a complex series of steps that converts CH_3COO^- obtained from the degradation of foods into CO_2, it yields strong reducing agents, which go on to reduce O_2 to H_2O and generate the cell's energy. One of the key intermediates in this cycle is *cis*-aconitate *(right)*.
(a) What is the molecular shape around each carbon atom?
(b) Draw the resonance hybrid of *cis*-aconitate.

*10.82 Like several other bonds, carbon-oxygen bonds have lengths and strengths that depend on the bond order. Draw Lewis structures for the following species, and arrange them in order of increasing carbon-oxygen bond length, and increasing carbon-oxygen bond strength: (a) CO; (b) CO_3^{2-}; (c) H_2CO; (d) CH_4O; (e) HCO_3^- (H attached to O).

10.83 In the 1980s, countries signing international chemical weapons treaties agreed to destroy all stockpiles of mustard gas, $ClCH_2CH_2SCH_2CH_2Cl$. When this substance contacts the moisture in eyes, nasal passages, and skin, the OH groups in water replace the Cl atoms and create high local concentrations of hydrochloric acid, which cause severe blistering and tissue destruction. Write a balanced equation for this reaction and calculate ΔH^0_{rxn}.

10.84 Which of the following molecules have a dipole moment: (a) BI_3; (b) ClF_3; (c) XeO_3?

*10.85 Ethanol (CH_3CH_2OH) is being used as a gasoline additive in many parts of the United States and Canada and as a total gasoline alternative in Brazil.
(a) Use bond energies to calculate the heat of combustion of gaseous ethanol.
(b) In its standard state at 25°C, ethanol is a liquid. Its vaporization requires 40.5 kJ/mol. Correct the value from part (a) to find the heat of combustion of liquid ethanol.
(c) How does the value from part (b) compare with the value you calculate from standard heats of formation (Appendix B)?

*10.86 Organic compounds vary greatly in the way their C atoms bond to each other. In the following compounds, they form a single ring. Draw a Lewis structure for each, identify cases for which resonance exists, and determine the carbon-carbon bond order(s): (a) C_3H_4; (b) C_3H_6; (c) C_4H_6; (d) C_4H_4; (e) C_6H_6.

10.87 An oxide of nitrogen is 25.9% N by mass, has a molar mass of 108 g/mol, and contains no nitrogen-nitrogen or oxygen-oxygen bonds. Draw its Lewis structure and name it.

*10.88 An experiment requires 50.0 mL of 0.040 M NaOH for the titration of 1.00 mmol of acid. Analysis of the acid shows 2.24% hydrogen, 26.7% carbon, and 71.1% oxygen. Draw the Lewis structure of the acid.

*10.89 A gaseous compound has a composition by mass of 24.8% carbon, 2.08% hydrogen, and 73.1% chlorine. At STP, the gas has a density of 4.3 g/L. Draw a Lewis structure that satisfies these facts. Would a different structure satisfy them as well? Explain.

10.90 Perchlorates are powerful oxidizing agents used in fireworks, flares, and the booster rockets of the Space Shuttle. Lewis structures for the perchlorate ion (ClO_4^-) can be drawn with all single bonds or with one, two, or three double bonds. Draw each of these possible resonance forms, use formal charges to determine the most important form, and calculate its average bond order.

10.91 Use Lewis structures to determine which *two* of the following molecules are unstable: (a) SF_2; (b) SF_3; (c) SF_4; (d) SF_5; (e) SF_6.

*10.92 A major short-lived, neutral species in flames is OH.
(a) What is unusual about the electronic structure of OH?
(b) Use the standard heat of formation of OH(g) and bond energies to calculate the O—H bond energy in OH(g) (ΔH_f^0 of OH(g) = 39.0 kJ/mol).
(c) From the average value for the O—H bond energy in Table 9.2 and your value for the O—H bond energy in OH(g), calculate the energy needed to break the first O—H bond in water.

10.93 What is the distinction between oxidation number and formal charge? Which do you think is closer to the actual charges on the atoms in HF and in CO? Explain.

10.94 Except for nitrogen, the elements of Group 5A(15) all form pentafluorides and most form pentachlorides. The chlorine atoms of PCl_5 can be replaced with fluorine atoms one at a time to give, successively, PCl_4F, PCl_3F_2, ..., PF_5.
(a) Given the relative sizes of F and Cl, would you expect the first two F substitutions to be at axial or equatorial positions? Explain.
(b) Which of the five fluorine-containing molecules have no dipole moment?

10.95 Phosphoric acid (H_3PO_4) is a weak acid used in the manufacture of fertilizers and foodstuffs. In basic solution, it ionizes by sequentially forming $H_2PO_4^-$, HPO_4^{2-}, and PO_4^{3-}. Draw Lewis structures for phosphoric acid and its three ions, taking into account formal charge and resonance (all H's attached to O's). Comment on the relative lengths of their phosphorus-oxygen bonds.

10.96 Dinitrogen monoxide (N_2O), once widely used as the anesthetic "laughing gas" in dental surgery, supports combustion in a manner similar to oxygen, with the nitrogen atoms forming N_2. Draw three resonance structures for N_2O (one N is central) and use formal charges to decide the relative importance of each. What correlation can you suggest between the most important structure and the observation that N_2O supports combustion?

10.97 Oxalic acid ($H_2C_2O_4$) is found in toxic concentrations in rhubarb leaves. The connections among its atoms (showing single bonds only) are shown at right. The acid forms two ions, $HC_2O_4^-$ and $C_2O_4^{2-}$, by the sequential loss of H^+. Draw Lewis structures for the three species, and comment on the relative lengths and strengths of their carbon-oxygen bonds.

10.98 Hydrazine (N_2H_4) is used as a rocket fuel because it reacts very exothermically with oxygen to form nitrogen gas and water vapor. The heat released and the increase in number of moles of gas provide thrust. Calculate the heat of reaction.

10.99 A molecule of formula AY_3 is found experimentally to be polar. Which molecular shapes are possible and which impossible for AY_3?

*10.100 In contrast to the cyanate ion (NCO^-), which is stable and found in many compounds, the fulminate ion (CNO^-), with its different atom sequence, is unstable and forms compounds with heavy metal ions, such as Ag^+ and Hg^{2+}, that are explosive. Like the cyanate ion, the fulminate ion has three resonance structures. Which is the most important contributor to the resonance hybrid? Suggest a reason for the instability of fulminate.

10.101 The compounds 1,1-dichloroethane (Cl_2CHCH_3) and 1,2-dichloroethane ($ClCH_2CH_2Cl$) are used as wax solvents and as fumigants. Although both molecules contain the same types of bonds, one has a much higher dipole moment than the other. Draw structures to explain this fact.

10.102 Lewis structures of mescaline, a hallucinogenic compound in peyote cactus, and dopamine, a neurotransmitter in mammalian brain, appear below. Suggest a reason for mescaline's ability to disrupt nerve impulses.

mescaline   dopamine

Theories of Covalent Bonding

11

Figure: Bonding theory visualized. How do molecular shapes emerge from interacting atoms? One theory proposes that new types of orbitals arise during bonding, such as these of the central phosphorus in PCl_5. In this chapter, we explore two models that rationalize the rich properties of the covalent bond.

Concepts and Skills to Review

before you study this chapter

- atomic orbital shapes (Section 7.4)
- Pauli exclusion principle (Section 8.2)
- Hund's rule (Section 8.3)
- writing Lewis structures (Section 10.1)
- resonance in covalent bonding (Section 10.1)
- molecular shapes (Section 10.3)
- molecular polarity (Section 10.4)

A Hydrogen, H_2

B Hydrogen fluoride, HF

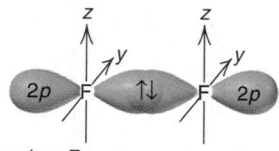

C Fluorine, F_2

Figure 11.1 Orbital overlap and spin pairing in three diatomic molecules. A, In the H_2 molecule the two overlapping $1s$ orbitals are occupied by the two $1s$ electrons with opposite spins. (The electrons, shown as arrows, spend most time between the nuclei but move throughout the overlapping orbitals.) **B,** To maximize overlap in HF, half-filled H $1s$ and F $2p$ orbitals overlap along the long axis of the $2p$ orbital involved in bonding. (The $2p_x$ orbital is shown bonding; the other two F $2p$ orbitals are not shown.) **C,** In F_2, the half-filled $2p_x$ orbital on one F points end to end toward the similar orbital on the other F to maximize overlap.

All scientific models have limitations because they are simplifications of reality. The VSEPR model accounts for molecular shapes by assuming that electron groups tend to minimize their repulsions, which results in their occupying as much space as possible around a central atom. But it does *not* tell us how those shapes, which we observe experimentally, can be explained from the interactions of atomic orbitals. After all, none of the orbitals we examined in Chapter 7 are oriented toward the vertices of a tetrahedron or a trigonal bipyramid, to mention just two of the common molecular shapes. Moreover, even though the shape of a molecule is crucial to many aspects of its behavior, the shape does not help us interpret its magnetic or spectral properties; only an understanding of its orbitals and their energy levels can do that.

To understand these factors, a quantum-mechanical model, which has been so successful in explaining atomic properties, is applied to the properties of molecules as well. In this chapter, we discuss two theories of covalent bonding that are based on quantum mechanics. Valence bond (VB) theory explains the interactions of atomic orbitals that create covalent bonds and shows how observed molecular shapes are rationalized by these interactions. We also apply VB theory to a description of the two types of covalent bonds. Molecular orbital (MO) theory explains molecular energy levels and associated properties by proposing the existence of orbitals that extend over the whole molecule. Each theory complements the other and is indispensable to a full understanding of covalent bonding.

Don't be discouraged by our need for more than a single model to explain the observations in a topic as universal as chemical bonding. What we find in every science is that one model accounts for a particular aspect of a topic better than another, and that several models are called into service to explain a broader range of phenomena.

11.1 Valence Bond (VB) Theory and Orbital Hybridization

What *is* a covalent bond, and what characteristic gives it strength? Most importantly, how can we explain the *molecular* shapes we see from the interactions of *atomic* orbitals? The most useful approach for answering these questions is **valence bond (VB) theory.**

The Central Themes of VB Theory

The basic principle of VB theory is that *a covalent bond forms when the orbitals of two atoms overlap and are occupied by a pair of electrons that have the highest probability of being located between the nuclei.* Three central themes of VB theory derive from this principle:

1. *Opposing spins of the electron pair.* As the exclusion principle (Section 8.2) prescribes, the space formed by the overlapping orbitals *has a maximum capacity of two electrons that must have opposite spins.* When a molecule of H_2 forms, for instance, the two $1s$ electrons of two H atoms occupy the overlapping $1s$ orbitals and have opposite spins (Figure 11.1A).

2. *Maximum overlap of bonding orbitals.* The bond strength depends on the attraction of the nuclei for the shared electrons, so *the greater the orbital overlap, the stronger (more stable) the bond.* The extent of overlap depends on the shape and direction of the orbitals involved. The *s* orbital is spherical, but *p* and *d* orbitals have more electron density in one direction than in another,

so a bond involving p or d orbitals tends to be oriented in the direction that maximizes overlap.

In the HF bond, for example, the $1s$ orbital of H overlaps the half-filled $2p$ orbital of F *along the long axis* of that orbital (Figure 11.1B). Any other direction would result in less overlap and, thus, a weaker bond. Similarly, in the F—F bond of F_2, the two $2p$ orbitals interact end to end, that is, *along the long axes* of the orbitals, to maximize overlap (Figure 11.1C).

3. *Hybridization of atomic orbitals.* To account for the bonding in simple diatomic molecules such as HF, we can picture the direct overlap of s and p orbitals of isolated atoms. But how can we account for the molecular shapes observed in so many polyatomic molecules and ions through the overlap of spherical s orbitals, dumbbell-shaped perpendicular p orbitals, and clover-leaved d orbitals?

Consider a methane molecule. It is composed of four H atoms bonded to a central C atom. An isolated ground-state C atom ([He] $2s^22p^2$) has four valence electrons, two in the $2s$ orbital and one each in two of the three $2p$ orbitals. We might easily see how the two half-filled p orbitals of C could overlap with the $1s$ orbitals of two H atoms to form *two* C—H bonds with a 90° H—C—H bond angle. But how can these orbitals overlap to form the *four* identical C—H bonds with the 109.5° bond angle that occurs in methane?

Linus Pauling answered such questions by proposing that *the valence atomic orbitals in the molecule are **different** from those in the isolated atoms.* Quantum-mechanical calculations show that mathematical mixing of certain combinations of orbitals in a given atom gives rise to *new atomic orbitals.* The spatial orientations of these new orbitals lead to more stable bonds and are consistent with the observed molecular shapes. The process of orbital mixing is called **hybridization,** and the new atomic orbitals are called **hybrid orbitals.** Two key points about the number and type of hybrid orbitals are that

- The *number* of hybrid orbitals obtained *equals* the number of atomic orbitals mixed.
- The *type* of hybrid orbitals obtained *varies* with the types of atomic orbitals mixed.

You can imagine hybridization as a process in which atomic orbitals mix, hybrid orbitals form, and electrons enter them with spins parallel (Hund's rule) to create stable bonds. In truth, though, hybridization is a mathematically derived result from quantum mechanics that accounts for the molecular shapes we observe.

Types of Hybrid Orbitals

Keep in mind that we postulate the presence of a certain type of hybrid orbital *after* we observe the molecular shape. As we discuss the five common types of hybridization, notice that the spatial orientation of each type of hybrid orbital corresponds with one of the five common electron-group arrangements predicted by VSEPR theory.

***sp* Hybridization** When two electron groups surround the central atom, we observe a linear shape, which means that the bonding orbitals must have a linear orientation. VB theory explains this by proposing that mixing two *non-equivalent* orbitals of a central atom, one s and one p, gives rise to two *equivalent* ***sp* hybrid orbitals** that lie 180° apart, as shown on the next page in

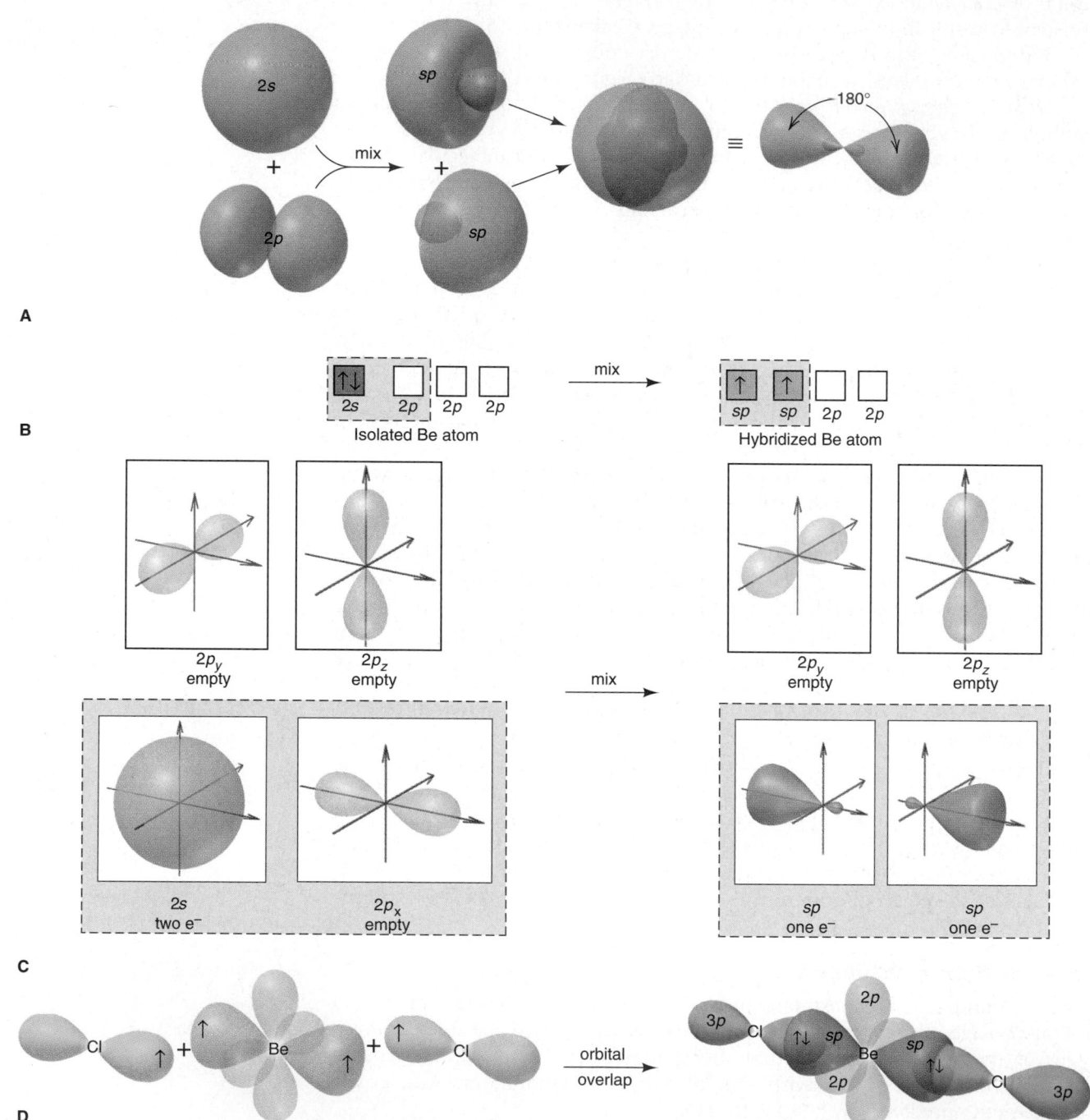

Figure 11.2 The *sp* hybrid orbitals in gaseous BeCl₂.
A, One 2*s* and one 2*p* atomic orbital mix to form two atomic *sp* hybrid orbitals (shown above and below one another and slightly to the side for ease in viewing). Note the large and small lobes of the hybrid orbitals. In the molecule, the two *sp* orbitals of Be lie in opposite directions. For clarity, the simplified hybrid orbitals shown at right will be used throughout the text, usually without the small lobe. **B,** The orbital box diagram for hybridization in Be shows that the 2*s* and one of the three 2*p* orbitals form two *sp* hybrid orbitals, and the two other 2*p* orbitals remain unhybridized. Electrons half-fill the *sp* hybrids. During bonding, each *sp* orbital fills by addition of an electron from Cl (not shown). **C,** The orbital box diagram is shown with orbital contours instead of electron arrows. **D,** BeCl₂ forms by overlap of the two *sp* hybrids with the 3*p* orbitals of two Cl atoms; the two unhybridized Be 2*p* orbitals lie perpendicular to the *sp* hybrids. (For clarity, only the 3*p* orbital of each Cl involved in bonding is shown.)

Figure 11.2A. Note the shape of the hybrid orbital: with one large and one small lobe, it differs markedly from the shapes of the atomic orbitals that were mixed. The orientations of hybrid orbitals extend electron density in the bonding direction and minimize repulsions between the electrons that occupy them. Thus, *both shape and orientation maximize overlap with the orbital of the other atom in the bond.*

In gaseous $BeCl_2$, for example, the Be atom is said to be *sp* hybridized. Figure 11.2B through D depicts the hybridization of Be in $BeCl_2$ in terms of a traditional orbital box diagram (B), a box diagram with orbital contours (C), and the bond formation with Cl (D). The 2s and one of the three 2p orbitals of Be mix and form two *sp* orbitals. These overlap 3p orbitals from two Cl atoms, and the four valence electrons—two from Be and one from each Cl—occupy the overlapped orbitals in pairs with opposite spins. The two unhybridized 2p orbitals of Be lie perpendicular to each other and to the bond axes. Thus, through hybridization, the paired 2s electrons in the isolated Be atom are distributed into two *sp* orbitals, which form two Be—Cl bonds.

sp^2 Hybridization In order to rationalize the trigonal planar electron-group arrangement and the shapes of molecules based on it, we introduce the mixing of one s and two p orbitals of the central atom to give three hybrid orbitals that point toward the vertices of an equilateral triangle, their axes 120° apart. These are called **sp^2 hybrid orbitals.** Note that, unlike electron configuration notation, here the superscript refers to the *number* of atomic orbitals of a given type that are mixed, *not* to the number of electrons in the orbital: one s and two p orbitals were mixed, so we have s^1p^2, or sp^2.

VB theory proposes that the central B atom in the BF_3 molecule is sp^2 hybridized. Figure 11.3 shows the three sp^2 orbitals in the trigonal plane, with the third 2p orbital unhybridized and perpendicular to this plane. Each sp^2 orbital overlaps the 2p orbital of an F atom, and the six valence electrons—three from B and one from each of the three F atoms—form three bonding pairs.

To account for other molecular shapes within a given electron-group arrangement, we postulate that one or more of the hybrid orbitals contains lone pairs. In ozone (O_3), for example, the central O is sp^2 hybridized and a lone pair fills one of its three sp^2 orbitals, so ozone has a bent molecular shape.

A   **B**

Figure 11.3 The sp^2 hybrid orbitals in BF$_3$. A, The orbital box diagram shows that the 2s and two of the three 2p orbitals of the B atom mix to make three sp^2 hybrid orbitals. Three electrons (shown as upward arrows) half-fill the sp^2 hybrids. The third 2p orbital remains empty and unhybridized. **B,** BF$_3$ forms through overlap of 2p orbitals on three F atoms with the sp^2 hybrids. During bonding, each sp^2 orbital fills by addition of an electron from F (shown as a downward arrow). The three sp^2 hybrids of B lie 120° apart, and its unhybridized 2p orbital is perpendicular to the trigonal bonding plane.

Figure 11.4 The sp³ hybrid orbitals in CH₄. A, The orbital box diagram shows that the 2s and all three 2p orbitals of C are mixed to form four sp³ hybrids. Carbon's four valence electrons half-fill the sp³ hybrids. **B,** In methane, the four sp³ orbitals of C point toward the corners of a tetrahedron and overlap the 1s orbitals of four H atoms. Each sp³ orbital fills by addition of an electron from H (shown as dots).

sp³ Hybridization Now let's return to the question posed earlier about the orbitals in methane, the same question that arises for any species with a tetrahedral electron-group arrangement. VB theory proposes that the one s and all three p orbitals of the central atom mix and form four **sp³ hybrid orbitals,** which point toward the vertices of a tetrahedron. As shown in Figure 11.4, the C atom in methane is sp³ hybridized. Its four valence electrons half-fill the four sp³ hybrids, which overlap the half-filled 1s orbitals of four H atoms and form four C—H bonds.

Figure 11.5 shows the bonding in molecules of the other shapes with the tetrahedral arrangement. The trigonal pyramidal shape of NH_3 arises when a lone pair fills one of the four sp³ orbitals of N, and the bent shape of H_2O arises when lone pairs fill two of the sp³ orbitals of O.

sp³d Hybridization The shapes of molecules with trigonal bipyramidal or octahedral electron-group arrangements are rationalized with VB theory through similar arguments. The only new point is that such molecules have central atoms from Period 3 or higher, so atomic d orbitals, as well as s and p orbitals, are mixed to form the hybrid orbitals.

Figure 11.5 The sp³ hybrid orbitals in NH₃ and H₂O.
A, The orbital box diagrams show sp³ hybridization, as in CH₄. In NH₃ *(top),* one of the sp³ orbitals is filled with a lone pair. In H₂O *(bottom),* two of the sp³ orbitals are filled with lone pairs. **B,** Contour diagrams show the tetrahedral orientation of the sp³ orbitals and the overlap of the bonded H atoms. Each half-filled sp³ orbital fills by addition of an electron from H. (Shared pairs and lone pairs are shown as dots.)

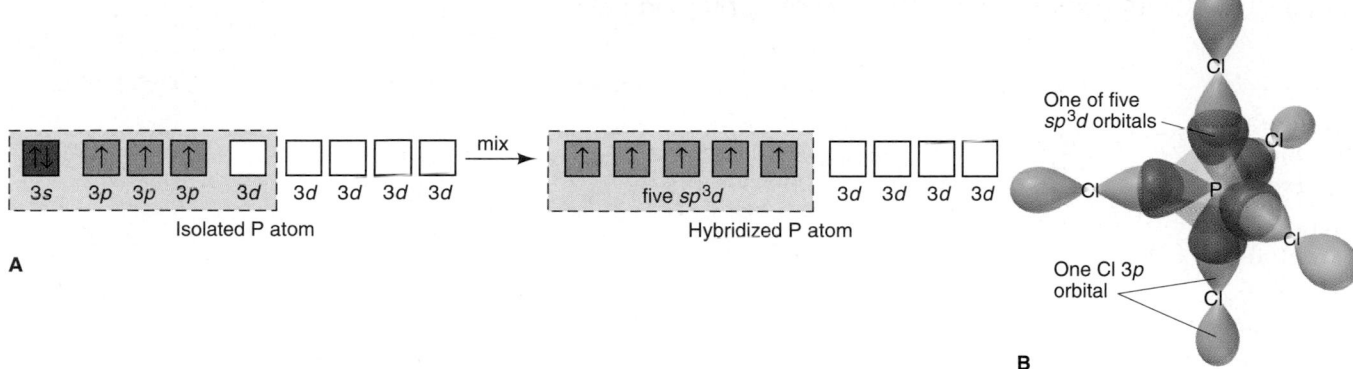

A

B

Figure 11.6 The *sp³d* hybrid orbitals in PCl₅. **A,** The orbital box diagram shows that one 3*s*, three 3*p*, and one of the five 3*d* orbitals of P mix to form five *sp³d* orbitals that are half-filled. Four 3*d* orbitals are unhybridized and empty. **B,** The trigonal bipyramidal PCl₅ molecule forms by the overlap of a 3*p* orbital from five Cl atoms with the *sp³d* hybrid orbitals of P (unhybridized, empty 3*d* orbitals not shown). During bonding, each *sp³d* orbital fills by addition of an electron from Cl. (The five bonding pairs are not shown.)

To rationalize the trigonal bipyramidal shape of the PCl₅ molecule, for example, the VB model proposes that the one 3*s*, the three 3*p*, and one of the five 3*d* orbitals of the central P atom mix and form five ***sp³d* hybrid orbitals,** which point to the vertices of a trigonal bipyramid. Each hybrid orbital overlaps a 3*p* orbital of a Cl atom, and the five valence electrons of P, together with one from each of the five Cl atoms, pair up to form five P—Cl bonds, as shown in Figure 11.6. Other shapes in this electron-group arrangement have lone pairs in one or more of the central atom's *sp³d* orbitals.

***sp³d²* Hybridization** To rationalize the shape of SF₆, the VB model proposes that the one 3*s*, the three 3*p*, and two of the five 3*d* orbitals of the central S atom mix and form six ***sp³d²* hybrid orbitals,** which point to the vertices of an octahedron. Each hybrid orbital overlaps a 2*p* orbital of an F atom, and the six valence electrons of S, together with one from each of the six F atoms, pair up to form six S—F bonds (Figure 11.7). Square pyramidal and square planar shapes have lone pairs in one or two of the central atom's *sp³d²* orbitals, respectively.

A

B

Figure 11.7 The *sp³d²* hybrid orbitals in SF₆. **A,** The orbital box diagram shows that one 3*s*, three 3*p*, and two 3*d* orbitals of S mix to form six *sp³d²* orbitals that are half-filled. Three 3*d* orbitals are unhybridized and empty. **B,** The octahedral SF₆ molecule forms from overlap of a 2*p* orbital from six F atoms with the *sp³d²* orbitals of S (unhybridized, empty 3*d* orbitals not shown). During bonding, each *sp³d²* orbital fills by addition of an electron from F. (The six bonding pairs are not shown.)

Table 11.1 Composition and Orientation of Hybrid Orbitals

	Linear	Trigonal Planar	Tetrahedral	Trigonal Bipyramidal	Octahedral
Atomic orbitals mixed	one s one p	one s two p	one s three p	one s three p one d	one s three p two d
Hybrid orbitals formed	two sp	three sp^2	four sp^3	five sp^3d	six sp^3d^2
Unhybridized orbitals remaining	two p	one p	none	four d	three d
Orientation	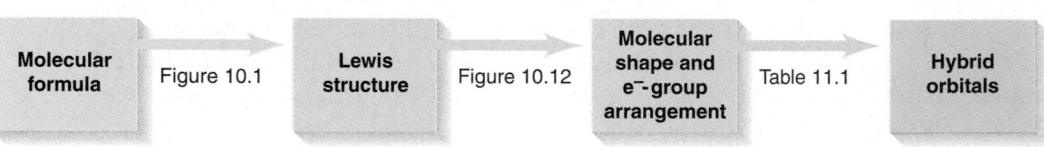				

Table 11.1 summarizes the number and types of atomic orbitals that are mixed to obtain the five types of hybrid atomic orbitals. Once again, note the similarities between the orientations of the hybrid orbitals proposed by VB theory and the shapes predicted by VSEPR theory (see Figure 10.5, p. 375). Figure 11.8 shows the conceptual stages from molecular formula to postulating the hybrid orbitals in the molecule, and the following sample problem details the end of that process.

Figure 11.8 The conceptual steps from molecular formula to the hybrid orbitals used in bonding. (See Figures 10.1, page 362, and 10.12, page 380.)

| Molecular formula | → Figure 10.1 → | Lewis structure | → Figure 10.12 → | Molecular shape and e⁻-group arrangement | → Table 11.1 → | Hybrid orbitals |

Sample Problem 11.1 Postulating the Hybrid Orbitals in a Molecule

PROBLEM Use partial orbital diagrams to describe how mixing of atomic orbitals on the central atoms leads to the hybrid orbitals in each of the following:
(a) Methanol, CH_3OH **(b)** Sulfur tetrafluoride, SF_4
PLAN We draw the molecular shape and find the number and arrangement of electron groups around the central atoms. From that, we postulate the type of hybrid orbitals involved. Then we write the partial orbital diagram for each central atom before and after the orbitals are hybridized.
SOLUTION (a) For CH_3OH. The electron-group arrangement is tetrahedral around the C and the O atoms. Therefore, each central atom is sp^3 hybridized. The C atom has four half-filled sp^3 orbitals:

The O atom has two half-filled sp^3 orbitals and two filled with lone pairs:

During bonding, each half-filled C or O orbital becomes filled, with the second electron in each case coming from H.

(b) For SF$_4$: The molecular shape is seesaw, which is based on the trigonal bipyramidal electron-group arrangement. Thus, the central S atom is surrounded by five electron groups, which implies sp^3d hybridization. One 3s, three 3p, and one 3d orbitals are mixed. One hybrid orbital is filled with a lone pair and four are half-filled. Four unhybridized 3d orbitals remain empty:

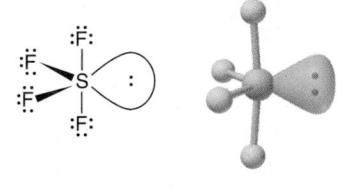

During bonding, each half-filled S orbital becomes filled, with the second electrons coming from F atoms.

Follow-up Problem 11.1 Use partial orbital diagrams to show how atomic orbitals on the central atoms lead to hybrid orbitals in **(a)** beryllium fluoride, BeF$_2$; **(b)** silicon tetrachloride, SiCl$_4$; **(c)** xenon tetrafluoride, XeF$_4$.

When the Concept of Hybridization May Not Apply We employ VSEPR theory and VB theory *whenever it is necessary* to rationalize an observed molecular shape in terms of atomic orbitals. In some cases, however, the theories may not be needed. Consider the Lewis structure and molecular shape of H$_2$S (see margin). Based on VSEPR theory, we would predict that, as in H$_2$O, the four electron groups around H$_2$S point to the vertices of a tetrahedron, and the two lone pairs compress the H—S—H bond angle somewhat below the ideal 109.5°. Based on VB theory, we would propose that the 3s and 3p orbitals of the central S atom mix and form four sp^3 hybrids, two of which are filled with lone pairs, while the other two overlap with 1s orbitals of two H atoms and are filled with bonding pairs.

The problem is that observation does *not* support these arguments. In fact, the H$_2$S molecule has a bond angle of 92°, close to the 90° angle expected between *unhybridized,* perpendicular, atomic p orbitals. Similar angles occur in the other Group 6A(16) hydrides and in the larger hydrides of Group 5A(15) also. It makes no sense to apply a theory when the facts don't warrant it. In the case of H$_2$S and these other nonmetal hydrides, neither VSEPR theory nor the concept of hybridization applies. It's important to remember that real factors, such as bond length, atomic size, and electron repulsions, influence molecular shape. Apparently, with these larger central atoms and their longer bonds to H, crowding and electron repulsions decrease, and the simple overlap of unhybridized atomic orbitals rationalizes the observed shapes perfectly well.

Section Summary

VB theory explains that a covalent bond forms when two atomic orbitals overlap. The bond holds two electrons with paired (opposite) spins. Orbital hybridization allows us to explain how orbitals on isolated atoms mix and change their characteristics during bonding. Based on the observed molecular shape (and the related electron-group arrangement), we postulate the type of hybrid orbital needed. In certain cases, we need not invoke hybridization at all.

Figure 11.9 **The σ bonds in ethane (C₂H₆). A,** Both C atoms in ethane are sp^3 hybridized. One sp^3 orbital of each C overlaps to form a C—C σ bond. The other sp^3 orbitals overlap the 1s orbitals of six H atoms to form six C—H σ bonds. **B,** Electron density is distributed relatively evenly among the σ bonds of the ethane molecule. **C,** Bond-line drawing.

11.2 The Mode of Orbital Overlap and the Types of Covalent Bonds

In this section, we use VB theory to focus on the *mode* by which orbitals overlap—end to end or side to side—to understand the types of covalent bonds and the detailed makeup of multiple bonds.

The VB Treatment of Single and Multiple Bonds

The VSEPR model predicts, and measurements verify, different shapes for the three two-carbon organic molecules ethane (C_2H_6), ethylene (C_2H_4), and acetylene (C_2H_2). Ethane is tetrahedrally shaped at both carbons, with bond angles of about 109.5°. Ethylene is trigonal planar at both carbons, with the double bond acting as one electron group and bond angles near the ideal 120°. Acetylene has a linear shape, with the triple bond acting as one electron group and bond angles of 180°:

ethane   ethylene   acetylene

A close look at the bonds shows two types of orbital overlap here:

1. *End-to-end overlap and sigma (σ) bonding.* Figure 11.9 shows that both C atoms of ethane are sp^3 hybridized. The C—C bond involves overlap of one sp^3 orbital from each C, and the six C—H bonds involve overlap of a C sp^3 orbital with an H 1s orbital. The bonds in ethane are like all the others described so far in this section. Look closely at the C—C bond, for example. It involves the overlap of the end of one orbital with the end of the other. The bond resulting from such *end-to-end* overlap is called a **sigma (σ) bond.** It has its *highest electron density along the bond axis* (an imaginary line joining the nuclei) and is shaped like an ellipse rotated about its long axis (somewhat like a football). All single bonds, formed by any combination of overlapping hybrid, s, or p orbitals, have their electron density concentrated along the bond axis and are therefore σ bonds.

2. *Side-to-side overlap and pi (π) bonding.* A close look at Figure 11.10 reveals the double nature of the carbon-carbon bond in ethylene. Here, each C atom is sp^2 hybridized. Each C atom's four valence electrons half-fill its three sp^2 orbitals and its unhybridized 2p orbital, which lies perpendicular to the sp^2 plane. Two sp^2 orbitals of each C form C—H σ bonds by overlapping the 1s orbitals of two H atoms. The third sp^2 orbital forms a C—C σ bond with an sp^2 orbital of the other C because their orientation allows end-to-end over-

Figure 11.10 **The σ and π bonds of ethylene (C₂H₄).**
A, The two C atoms are sp^2 hybridized and form one C—C σ bond and four C—H σ bonds. Their half-filled unhybridized 2p orbitals lie perpendicular to the σ-bond plane and are shown overlapping side to side. **B,** The two overlapping regions comprise *one* π bond,

which is occupied by two electrons. The σ bonds are shown as lines. The two lobes of one π bond lie above and below the C—C σ bond line. **C,** With four electrons—one σ bond and one π bond—beween the C atoms, the electron density *(red shading)* is greater. **D,** Bond-line drawing.

Figure 11.11 **The σ and π bonds of acetylene (C_2H_2).**
A, The σ bonds of acetylene consist of an *sp* orbital of each C overlapping to form a C—C σ bond, and the other *sp* orbital of each C overlapping an *s* orbital of an H atom, to form two C—H σ bonds. Two unhybridized $2p$ orbitals on each C remain and are shown overlapping. **B,** Two π bonds result from side-to-side overlap. In order to depict the π-bond formation, one π bond is shown with its lobes above and below the C—C σ bond, and the other is shown with its lobes in front of and behind it, with σ bonds shown as lines. In the actual molecule, however, the electron clouds of the two π bonds partially coincide, which gives the molecule cylindrical symmetry. **C,** The six electrons—one σ bond and two π bonds—create even greater electron density between the C atoms. **D,** Bond-line drawing.

lap. With the σ-bonded C atoms near each other, their half-filled unhybridized $2p$ orbitals are close enough to overlap *side to side*. Such overlap forms another type of covalent bond called a **pi (π) bond.** It has *two regions of electron density*, one above and one below the σ-bond axis. *One π bond holds two electrons that move through both regions of the bond. A double bond always consists of one σ bond and one π bond.* As Figure 11.10 shows, the double bond increases electron density between the C atoms.

Now we can answer a question left hanging in our discussion of VSEPR theory in Chapter 10: Why do the electron pairs in a double bond act as one electron group; that is, why don't the two electron pairs push each other apart? The answer is that each electron pair occupies a distinct orbital, a specific region of electron density, so repulsions are reduced.

A triple bond, such as the C≡C bond in acetylene, *consists of one σ and two π bonds* (Figure 11.11). To maximize overlap in a linear shape, one *s* and one *p* orbital in *each* C atom form two *sp* hybrids, and two $2p$ orbitals remain unhybridized. The four valence electrons half-fill all four orbitals. Each C uses one of its *sp* orbitals to form a σ bond with an H atom and uses the other to form the C—C σ bond. Side-to-side overlap of one pair of $2p$ orbitals gives one π bond, with electron density above and below the σ bond. Side-to-side overlap of the other pair of $2p$ orbitals gives the other π bond, 90° away from the first, with electron density in front of and behind the σ bond. The result is a *cylindrically symmetrical* H—C≡C—H molecule. Note the still greater electron density between the C atoms created by the six bonding electrons.

The extent of overlap influences bond strength. Since side-to-side overlap is not as extensive as end-to-end overlap, we expect a π bond to be weaker than a σ bond, and thus a double bond should be less than twice as strong as a single bond. Indeed, this expectation is borne out among carbon-carbon bonds (see Problem 11.42). However, many factors, such as lone-pair repulsions, bond polarities, and other electrostatic contributions, cloud this relationship in the bonds of other elements. Thus, as a rough approximation, it is safe to say that a double bond is about twice as strong as a single bond, and a triple bond is about three times as strong.

Sample Problem 11.2   Describing the Bonding in Molecules with Multiple Bonds

PROBLEM Describe the types of bonds and orbitals in acetone, $(CH_3)_2CO$.
PLAN Referring to Sample Problem 11.1, we note the shapes around each atom to postulate the hybrid orbitals used and pay special attention to the multiple bonding in the C=O bond.
SOLUTION In Sample Problem 10.9, we determined the shapes of the three central atoms of acetone to be tetrahedral around each C of the two CH_3 (methyl) groups and trigonal planar around the middle C atom. Thus, the middle C has three sp^2 orbitals and one unhybridized *p* orbital. Each of the two methyl C atoms has four sp^3 orbitals. Three of these sp^3 orbitals overlap the $1s$ orbitals of the H atoms to form σ bonds; the fourth overlaps an sp^2 orbital of the middle C atom. Thus, two of the three sp^2 orbitals of the middle C form σ bonds to the terminal C atoms.

The O atom is sp^2 hybridized also and has an unhybridized p orbital ready to form a π bond. Two of its sp^2 orbitals hold lone pairs, and the third forms a σ bond with the third sp^2 orbital of the middle C atom. The unhybridized, half-filled p orbitals on C and O form a π bond. The σ and π bonds constitute the C=O bond:

COMMENT Since the molecular shape is our guide to the orbitals used in bonding, we cannot know directly whether a terminal atom, such as the O atom in acetone, is hybridized. After all, it could use two perpendicular p orbitals for the σ and π bonds with C and leave the other p and the s orbitals to hold the two lone pairs. However, a lone pair in an s orbital would increase repulsions by having additional electrons located partly in the bonding region; having the lone pair in an sp^2 orbital away from the C=O bond avoids this. Furthermore, some compounds are known in which the O of a C=O group is bonded to another atom, and in those cases the bond angle does suggest that the O is sp^2 hybridized.

Follow-up Problem 11.2 Describe the types of bonds and the orbitals in (a) hydrogen cyanide, HCN, and (b) carbon dioxide, CO_2.

Orbital Overlap and Molecular Rotation

The type of bond influences the ability of one part of a molecule to rotate relative to another part. A *σ bond allows free rotation* of the atoms with respect to each other because the extent of overlap is not affected. If you could hold one CH_3 group of the ethane molecule, the other CH_3 group could spin like a pinwheel without affecting the C—C σ-bond overlap.

However, p orbitals must be parallel to engage in side-to-side overlap, so a *π bond restricts rotation* around it. Rotating one CH_2 group in ethylene with respect to the other must decrease the side-to-side overlap and break the π bond. Now you can see why separate *cis* and *trans* structures can exist in double-bonded molecules, such as 1,2-dichloroethylene (Section 10.4). As Figure 11.12 shows, the π bond allows two *different* arrangements of atoms around the two C atoms, which can have a major effect on molecular polarity (see p. 386). (Rotation around a triple bond is not meaningful: because each triple-bonded C atom is attached to only one other group, there can be no difference in their relative positions.)

Figure 11.12 **Restricted rotation of π-bonded molecules. A,** *Cis-* and **B,** *trans*-1,2-dichloroethylene occur as distinct molecules because the π bond between the C atoms restricts rotation and maintains two different positions of the H and Cl atoms.

End-to-end overlap of atomic orbitals forms a σ bond and allows free rotation of the atoms. Side-to-side overlap forms a π bond, which restricts rotation. A multiple bond consists of a σ bond and either one π bond (double bond) or two π bonds (triple bond). Multiple bonds have greater electron density than single bonds.

11.3 Molecular Orbital (MO) Theory and Electron Delocalization

Scientists choose the model that helps them answer a particular question best. If the question concerns shape, chemists choose the VSEPR model, followed by hybrid-orbital analysis with VB theory. But VB theory does not adequately explain the magnetic or spectral properties of molecules, and it understates the importance of electron delocalization. To deal with these phenomena, which involve a molecule's energy levels, chemists choose **molecular orbital (MO) theory.**

In VB theory, a molecule is pictured as a group of atoms bound together through *localized* overlap of valence-shell atomic orbitals. In MO theory, a molecule is pictured as a collection of nuclei with the electron orbitals *delocalized* over the entire molecule. The MO model is a quantum-mechanical treatment for molecules similar to the one for individual atoms that we discussed in Chapter 8. Just as atoms have atomic orbitals (AOs) of a given energy and shape that are occupied by the atom's electrons, molecules have **molecular orbitals (MOs)** of a given energy and shape that are occupied by the molecule's electrons. Despite the great usefulness of MO theory, it too has a drawback: molecular orbitals are more difficult to visualize than the easily depicted shapes of VSEPR theory or the hybrid orbitals of VB theory.

The Central Themes of MO Theory

Several key ideas of MO theory appear in its description of the hydrogen molecule and other simple species. These ideas include the formation of MOs, their energy and shape, and how they fill with electrons.

Formation of Molecular Orbitals Because electron motion is so complex, approximations are required to solve the Schrödinger equation for any atom with more than one electron. Similar complications arise even with H_2, the simplest molecule, so approximations are required to solve for the properties of MOs. The most common approximation mathematically *combines* (adds or subtracts) the atomic orbitals (atomic wave functions) of nearby atoms to form molecular orbitals (molecular wave functions).

When two H nuclei lie near each other, as in H_2, their AOs overlap. The two modes of combining the AOs are as follows:

- *Adding the wave functions together.* This combination forms a **bonding MO,** which has a *region of high electron density between the nuclei.* Additive overlap is analogous to the overlap of two light waves that reinforce each other and make the resulting wave brighter. For electron waves, the overlap *increases* the probability that the electrons are between the nuclei (Figure 11.13A).

- *Subtracting the wave functions from each other.* This combination forms an **antibonding MO,** which has a *node between the nuclei, a region of zero electron density* (Figure 11.13B). Subtractive overlap is analogous to two light waves that cancel each other, so the light disappears. With electron waves, it *decreases* to zero the probability that the electrons occupy the space between the nuclei.

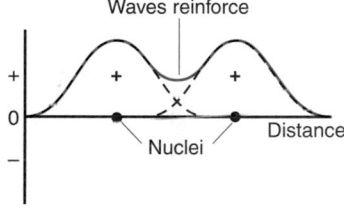

A Amplitudes of wave functions added

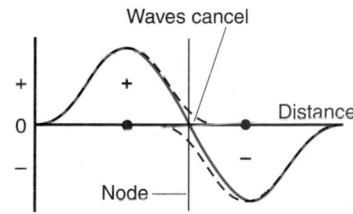

B Amplitudes of wave functions subtracted

Figure 11.13 An analogy between light waves and atomic wave functions. When light waves undergo interference, their amplitudes either add together or subtract. **A,** When the amplitudes of atomic wave functions *(dashed lines)* are added, a bonding molecular orbital (MO) results and electron density *(red line)* increases between the nuclei. **B,** Conversely, when the amplitudes of the wave functions are subtracted, an antibonding MO results, which has a node (region of zero electron density) between the nuclei.

The two possible combinations for hydrogen atoms H_A and H_B are

AO of H_A + AO of H_B = bonding MO of H_2 (more e$^-$ density between nuclei)

AO of H_A − AO of H_B = antibonding MO of H_2 (less e$^-$ density between nuclei)

Notice that *the number of AOs combined always equals the number of MOs formed:* two H atomic orbitals combine to form two H_2 molecular orbitals.

Energy and Shape of H_2 Molecular Orbitals *The bonding MO is lower in energy and the antibonding MO higher in energy than the AOs that combined to form them.* Let's examine Figure 11.14 to see why this is so.

Figure 11.14 Contours and energies of the bonding and antibonding molecular orbitals (MOs) in H_2. When two H 1*s* atomic orbitals (AOs) combine, they form two H_2 MOs. The bonding MO (σ_{1s}) forms from addition of the AOs and is lower in energy than the AOs because most of its electron density lies *between* the nuclei. The antibonding MO (σ_{1s}^*) forms from subtraction of the AOs and is higher in energy because there is a *node* between the nuclei and most of the electron density lies outside the internuclear region.

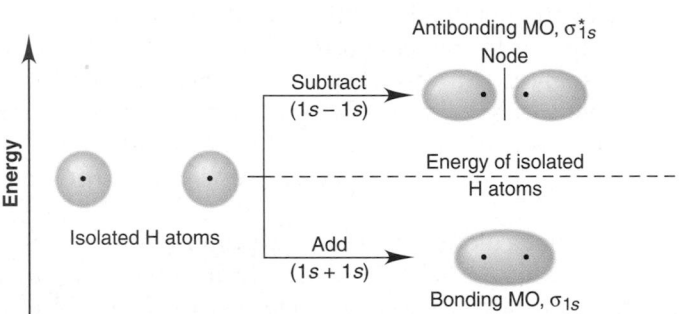

The bonding MO in H_2 is spread mostly *between* the nuclei, with the nuclei attracted to the intervening electrons. An electron in this MO can delocalize its charge over a much larger volume than is possible in its individual AO. Because the electron-electron repulsions are reduced, the bonding MO is *lower* in energy than the isolated AOs. Therefore, when electrons occupy this orbital, the molecule is *more stable* than the separate atoms. In contrast, the antibonding MO has a node between the nuclei and most of its electron density *outside* the internuclear region. The electrons do not shield one nucleus from the other, which increases nuclear repulsions and makes the antibonding MO *higher* in energy than the isolated AOs. Therefore, when the antibonding orbital is occupied, the molecule is *less stable* than when this orbital is empty.

Both the bonding and antibonding MOs of H_2 are **sigma (σ) MOs** because they are cylindrically symmetrical about an imaginary line that runs through the nuclei. The bonding MO is denoted by σ_{1s}, that is, a σ MO formed by combination of 1*s* AOs. Antibonding orbitals are denoted with a superscript star, so the one derived from the 1*s* AOs is σ_{1s}^* (spoken "sigma, one ess, star").

To interact effectively and form MOs, *atomic orbitals must have similar energy and orientation.* The 1*s* orbitals on two H atoms have identical energy and orientation, so they interact strongly. This point will be important when we consider molecules composed of atoms with many sublevels.

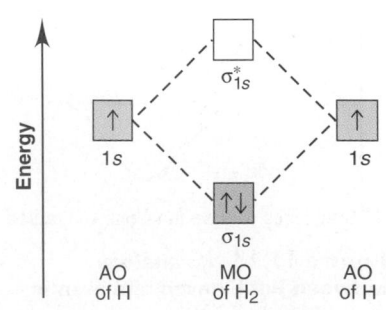

H_2 bond order = $\frac{1}{2}(2 - 0) = 1$

Figure 11.15 The MO diagram for H_2. The orbital boxes indicate the relative energies and electron occupancy of the MOs and the AOs from which they formed. Two electrons, one from each H atom, fill the lower energy σ_{1s} MO, while the higher energy σ_{1s}^* MO remains empty. (Orbital occupancy is also shown by full, half, or no color.)

Filling Molecular Orbitals with Electrons Electrons fill MOs just as they fill AOs:
- Orbitals are filled in order of increasing energy (aufbau principle).
- An orbital has a maximum capacity of two electrons with opposite spins (exclusion principle).
- Orbitals of equal energy are half filled, with spins parallel, before any is filled (Hund's rule).

Molecular orbital diagrams show the relative energy and number of electrons in each MO, as well as the AOs from which they formed. Figure 11.15 is the MO diagram for H_2.

MO theory redefines bond order. In a Lewis structure, bond order is the number of electron pairs per linkage. The **MO bond order** is the number of electrons in bonding MOs minus the number in antibonding MOs, divided by two:

Bond order = $\frac{1}{2}$[(no. of e⁻ in bonding MO) − (no. of e⁻ in antibonding MO)] **(11.1)**

Thus, for H_2, the bond order is $\frac{1}{2}(2 - 0) = 1$. A bond order greater than zero indicates that the molecular species is stable relative to the separate atoms, whereas a bond order of zero implies no net stability and, thus, no likelihood of forming. In general, *the higher the bond order, the stronger the bond.*

Another similarity between discussions of MOs and AOs is that we can write electron configurations for a molecule. The symbol of each occupied MO is shown in parentheses, and the number of electrons in it is written outside as a superscript. Thus, the electron configuration of H_2 is $(\sigma_{1s})^2$.

One of the early triumphs of MO theory was its ability to *predict* the existence of He_2^+, the dihelium molecule-ion, which is composed of two He nuclei and three electrons. Let's use MO theory to see why He_2^+ exists and, at the same time, why He_2 does not. In He_2^+, the $1s$ atomic orbitals form the molecular orbitals, so the MO diagram, shown in Figure 11.16A, is similar to that for H_2. The three electrons enter the MOs to give a pair in the σ_{1s} MO and a lone electron in the σ_{1s}^* MO. The bond order is $\frac{1}{2}(2 - 1) = \frac{1}{2}$. Thus, He_2^+ has a relatively weak bond, but it should exist. Indeed, this molecular ionic species has been observed frequently when He atoms collide with He^+ ions. Its electron configuration is $(\sigma_{1s})^2(\sigma_{1s}^*)^1$.

On the other hand, He_2 has four electrons to place in its σ_{1s} and σ_{1s}^* MOs. As Figure 11.16B shows, both the bonding and antibonding orbitals are filled. The stabilization gained by the electron pair in the bonding MO is canceled by the destabilization from the electron pair in the antibonding MO. From its zero bond order [$\frac{1}{2}(2 - 2) = 0$], we predict, and experiment has so far confirmed, that a covalent He_2 molecule does not exist.

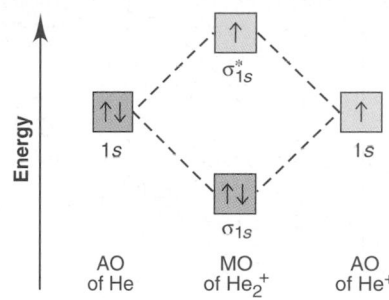

A He_2^+ bond order = $\frac{1}{2}$

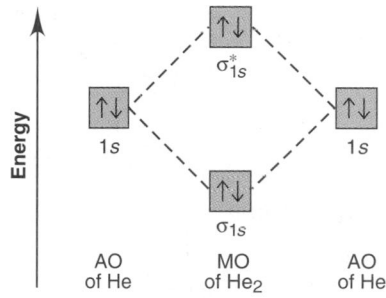

B He_2 bond order = 0

Figure 11.16 MO diagrams for He_2^+ and He_2. A, In He_2^+, three electrons are placed in MOs in order of increasing energy to give a filled σ_{1s} MO and a half-filled σ_{1s}^* MO. The bond order of $\frac{1}{2}$ implies that He_2^+ exists. **B,** In He_2, the four valence electrons fill both the σ_{1s} and the σ_{1s}^* MOs, so there is no net stabilization (bond order = 0).

Sample Problem 11.3 Predicting Species Stability Using MO Diagrams

PROBLEM Use MO diagrams to predict whether H_2^+ and H_2^- exist. Determine their bond orders and electron configurations.
PLAN In these species the $1s$ orbitals form MOs, so the MO diagrams are similar to that for H_2. We determine the number of electrons in each species and distribute them in pairs to the bonding and antibonding MOs in order of increasing energy. We obtain the bond order with Equation 11.1 and write the electron configuration as described in the text.
SOLUTION For H_2^+. Since H_2 has two e⁻, H_2^+ has only one, as shown in the margin *(top)*.
The bond order is $\frac{1}{2}(1 - 0) = \frac{1}{2}$, so we predict that H_2^+ does exist. The electron configuration is $(\sigma_{1s})^1$.
For H_2^-. Since H_2 has two e⁻, H_2^- has three, as shown in the margin *(bottom)*. The bond order is $\frac{1}{2}(2 - 1) = \frac{1}{2}$, so we predict that H_2^- does exist. The electron configuration is $(\sigma_{1s})^2(\sigma_{1s}^*)^1$.
CHECK The number of electrons in the MOs equals the number in the AOs, as it should.
COMMENT Both these species have been detected spectroscopically. H_2^+ occurs in the H-containing material around stars. H_2^- has been formed in the laboratory.

Follow-up Problem 11.3 Use an MO diagram to predict whether two hydride ions (H^-) would form H_2^{2-}. Calculate the bond order of H_2^{2-} and write its electron configuration.

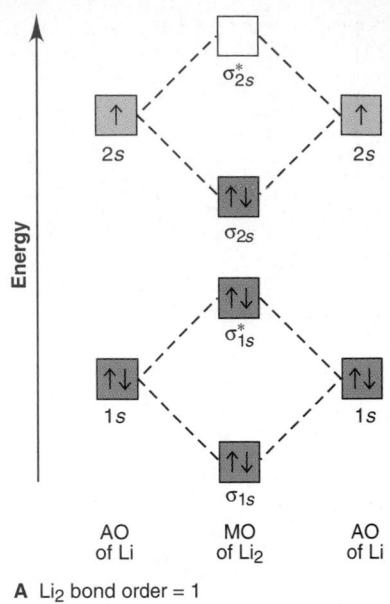

A Li$_2$ bond order = 1

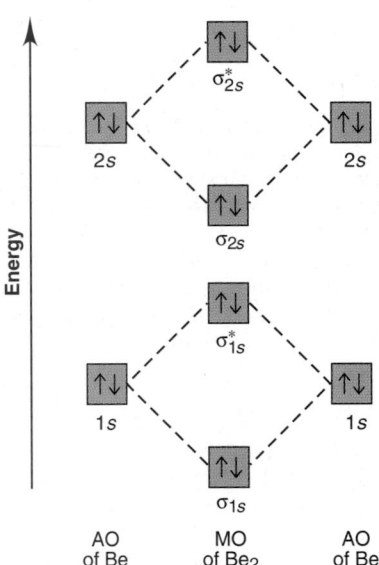

B Be$_2$ bond order = 0

Figure 11.17 Bonding in *s*-block homonuclear diatomic molecules. **A,** MO diagram for Li$_2$. MOs obtained from combinations of 1*s* orbitals are lower in energy than those obtained from 2*s* orbitals. The six electrons from two Li atoms fill the lowest three MOs, and the σ_{2s}^* remains empty. With a bond order of 1, Li$_2$ does form. **B,** MO diagram for Be$_2$. The eight electrons from two Be atoms fill all the available MOs to give no net stabilization. Ground-state Be$_2$ has a zero bond order and has never been observed.

Homonuclear Diatomic Molecules of the Period 2 Elements

Homonuclear diatomic molecules are those composed of two identical atoms. You're already familiar with several from Period 2—N$_2$, O$_2$, and F$_2$—as the elemental forms under standard conditions. Others in Period 2—Li$_2$, Be$_2$, B$_2$, C$_2$, and Ne$_2$—are observed, if at all, only in high-temperature gas-phase experiments. An MO description of these species provides some interesting tests of the model. Let's look at those from the *s* block, Groups 1A(1) and 2A(2), first and then at those from the *p* block, Groups 3A(13) through 8A(18).

Bonding in the *s*-Block Diatomic Molecules Both Li and Be occur as metals under normal conditions, but let's see what MO theory predicts for their stability as the diatomic gases dilithium (Li$_2$) and diberyllium (Be$_2$).

These atoms have both 1*s* and 2*s* electrons. Like the MOs formed from 1*s* orbitals, those formed from atomic 2*s* orbitals are σ orbitals, so they are cylindrically symmetrical around the internuclear axis. The relative energies of the MOs follow the order of the AOs that form them: a 2*s* AO is higher in energy than a 1*s*, so the σ_{2s} and σ_{2s}^* MOs are higher in energy than the σ_{1s} and σ_{1s}^* MOs. The six electrons from two Li atoms enter the MOs in order of increasing energy, two electrons per orbital with opposing spins, as in Figure 11.17A. Dilithium has four electrons in bonding MOs and two in the lower energy antibonding MO, so its bond order is $\frac{1}{2}(4 - 2) = 1$. Li$_2$ *has* been observed. Its complete electron configuration is $(\sigma_{1s})^2(\sigma_{1s}^*)^2(\sigma_{2s})^2$, but we usually show only the configuration formed from valence electrons, in this case, the 2*s*; thus, we have $(\sigma_{2s})^2$.

The MO diagram for Be$_2$, shown in Figure 11.17B, has filled σ_{2s} and σ_{2s}^* MOs. This situation is similar to that for He$_2$ discussed previously. The bond order is $\frac{1}{2}(4 - 4) = 0$; consistent with this, the ground state of the Be$_2$ molecule has never been observed.

Note that, in the MO diagrams for Li$_2$ and Be$_2$, the σ_{1s} and σ_{1s}^* MOs are filled. Since the stabilizing effect of the filled σ_{1s} MO cancels the destabilizing effect of the σ_{1s}^* MO, these MOs provide no *net* contribution to the bonding. From here on, the MO diagrams show only the MOs created by combinations of the *valence*-electron AOs.

Molecular Orbitals from Atomic *p*-Orbital Combinations As we move to the *p*-block, atomic 2*p* orbitals become involved, so let's first consider the shapes and energies of the MOs that result from their combinations. Recall that *p* orbitals can interact with each other from two different directions, as shown in Figure 11.18. End-to-end combination gives a pair of σ MOs, the σ_{2p} and σ_{2p}^*. Side-to-side combination gives a pair of **pi (π) MOs,** π_{2p} and π_{2p}^*. As with MOs from *s* orbitals, the bonding MOs from *p*-orbital combinations have their greatest electron density *between* the nuclei, whereas the antibonding MOs have a node between the nuclei and most of their electron density *outside* the internuclear region.

The order of MO energy levels, whether bonding or antibonding, is based on the order of AO energy levels *and* on the mode of the *p*-orbital combination:

• MOs formed from 2*s* orbitals are lower in energy than MOs formed from 2*p* orbitals because 2*s* AOs are lower in energy than 2*p* AOs.
• Bonding MOs are lower in energy than antibonding MOs, so σ_{2p} is lower in energy than σ_{2p}^* and π_{2p} is lower than π_{2p}^*.
• Atomic *p* orbitals can interact more extensively end to end than they can side to side. Therefore, the σ_{2p} MO is lower in energy than the π_{2p} MO. Similarly, the destabilizing effect of the σ_{2p}^* MO is greater than that of the π_{2p}^* MO.

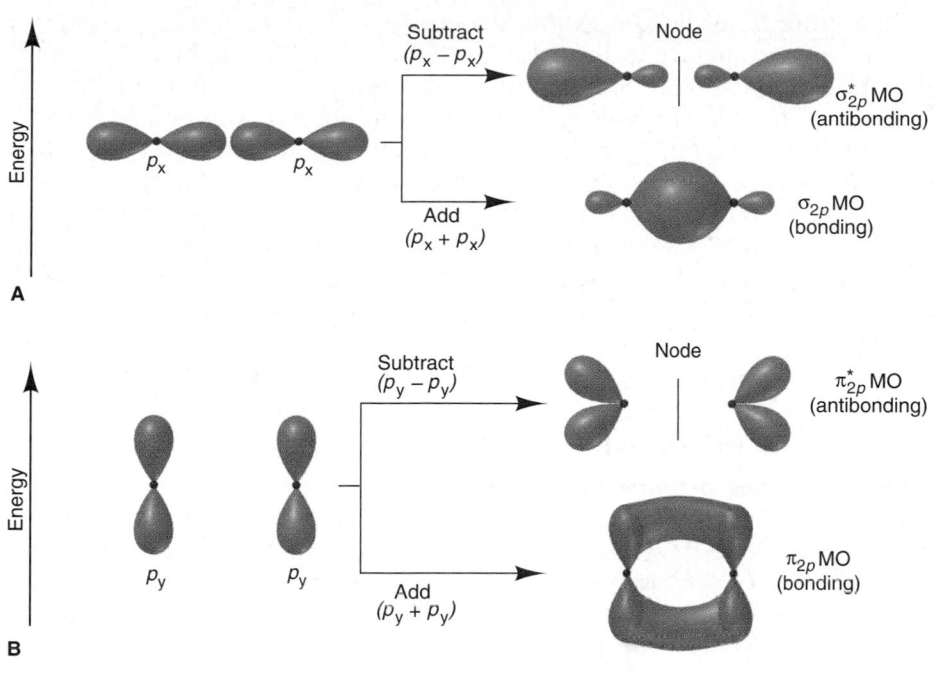

A

B

Figure 11.18 Contours and energies of σ and π MOs through combinations of atomic 2p orbitals. A, The p orbitals lying along the line between the atoms (usually designated p_x) undergo end-to-end overlap and form σ_{2p} and σ_{2p}^* MOs. Note the greater electron density between the nuclei for the bonding orbital and the node between the nuclei for the antibonding orbital. **B,** The p orbitals that lie perpendicular to the internuclear axis (p_y or p_z) undergo side-to-side overlap to form two π MOs. A π_{2p} is a bonding MO with its greatest density above and below the internuclear axis; a π_{2p}^* is an antibonding MO with a node between the nuclei and its electron density outside the internuclear region. (The p_z interactions are the same as those shown for the p_y.)

Thus, the energy order for MOs derived from 2p orbitals is

$$\sigma_{2p} < \pi_{2p} < \pi_{2p}^* < \sigma_{2p}^*$$

There are three perpendicular 2p orbitals on each atom, so when six p orbitals combine, the two facing each other end to end form a σ and a σ* MO, and the two pairs that interact side to side form two π MOs of the same energy and two π* MOs of the same energy. Combining these orientations with the energy order gives the *expected* MO diagram for the p-block Period 2 homonuclear diatomic molecules, which is shown in Figure 11.19A.

A MO energy levels for O_2, F_2, and Ne_2

B MO energy levels for B_2, C_2, and N_2

Figure 11.19 Relative MO energy levels for Period 2 homonuclear diatomic molecules. A, MO energy levels for O_2, F_2, and Ne_2. The six 2p orbitals of the two atoms form six MOs that are higher in energy than the two MOs formed from the two 2s AOs. The AOs forming π orbitals give rise to two bonding MOs (π_{2p}) of equal energy and two antibonding MOs (π_{2p}^*) of equal energy. This sequence of energy levels arises from minimal 2s-2p orbital mixing. **B,** MO energy levels for B_2, C_2, and N_2. Because of significant 2s-2p orbital mixing, the energies of σ MOs formed from 2p orbitals increase and those formed from 2s orbitals decrease. The major effect of this orbital mixing on the MO sequence is that the σ_{2p} is higher in energy than the π_{2p}. (For clarity, those MOs affected by mixing are shown in purple.)

One other factor influences the MO energy order. Recall that only AOs of similar energy interact to form MOs. The order in Figure 11.19A assumes that the s and p AOs are so different in energy that they do not interact with each other: in MO terminology, the orbitals do not *mix*. This is true for O, F, and Ne. In these atoms, repulsions occur as the $2p$ electrons pair up, which raise the energy of the $2p$ orbitals high enough above the energy of the $2s$ orbitals to minimize orbital mixing. However, when the $2p$ AOs are being half-filled, as in B, C, and N atoms, repulsions are small, so the $2p$ energies are much closer to the $2s$ energy. As a result, some mixing occurs between the $2s$ orbital of one atom and the end-on $2p$ orbital of the other. This orbital mixing *lowers* the energy of the σ_{2s} and σ_{2s}^* MOs and *raises* the energy of the σ_{2p} and σ_{2p}^* MOs; the π MOs are not affected. The MO diagram for B_2 through N_2 (Figure 11.19B, previous page) reflects this AO mixing. The only change that affects this discussion is the *reverse in order* of the σ_{2p} and π_{2p} MOs.

Bonding in the *p*-Block Diatomic Molecules Figure 11.20 shows the sequence of MOs, their electron occupancy, and some properties of B_2 through Ne_2. Note how *a higher bond order correlates with a greater bond energy and shorter bond length.* Also note how orbital occupancy correlates with magnetic behavior. Recall from Chapter 8 that the spins of unpaired electrons in an atom (or ion) cause the substance to be *paramagnetic,* attracted to an external magnetic field. If all the electron spins are paired, the substance is *diamagnetic,* unaffected (or weakly repelled) by the magnetic field. The same observations apply to molecules. These properties are not addressed directly in VSEPR or VB theory.

Figure 11.20 MO occupancy and molecular properties for B₂ through Ne₂. The sequence of MOs and their electron populations are shown for the homonuclear diatomic molecules in the *p* block of Period 2 [Groups 3A(13) to 8A(18)]. The bond order, bond length, bond energy, magnetic behavior, and valence electron configuration appear below. Note the correlation between bond order and bond energy, both of which are inversely related to bond length.

The B_2 molecule has six outer electrons to place in its MOs. Four of these fill the σ_{2s} and σ_{2s}^* MOs. The remaining two electrons enter the two π_{2p} MOs, one in each orbital, in keeping with Hund's rule. With four electrons in bonding MOs and two electrons in antibonding MOs, the bond order of B_2 is $\frac{1}{2}(4 - 2) = 1$. As expected from its MO diagram, B_2 is paramagnetic.

The two additional electrons present in C_2 fill the two π_{2p} MOs. Since C_2 has two more bonding electrons than B_2, it has a bond order of 2 and the expected stronger, shorter bond. All the electrons are paired and, as the model predicts, C_2 is diamagnetic.

In N_2, the two additional electrons enter and fill the σ_{2p} MO. The resulting bond order is 3, which is consistent with the triple bond in the Lewis structure. As the model predicts, the bond energy is higher and the bond length shorter, and N_2 is diamagnetic.

With O_2, we really see the power of MO theory over theories based on localized orbitals. For years, it seemed impossible to reconcile bonding theories with the bond strength and magnetic behavior of O_2. On the one hand, the data show a double-bonded molecule that is paramagnetic. On the other hand, we can write two possible Lewis structures for O_2, but neither gives such a molecule. One has a double bond and all electrons paired, the other a single bond and two electrons unpaired:

$$\ddot{O}{=}\ddot{O} \quad \text{or} \quad {:}\dot{O}{-}\dot{O}{:}$$

MO theory resolves this paradox beautifully. As Figure 11.20 shows, the bond order of O_2 is 2: eight electrons occupy bonding MOs and four occupy antibonding MOs [$\frac{1}{2}(8 - 4) = 2$]. Note the lower bond energy and greater bond length relative to N_2. The *two* electrons with highest energy occupy the *two* π_{2p}^* MOs with unpaired (parallel) spins, making the molecule paramagnetic. Figure 11.21 shows liquid O_2 suspended between the poles of a powerful magnet.

The two additional electrons in F_2 fill the π_{2p}^* orbitals, which decreases the bond order to 1, and the absence of unpaired electrons makes F_2 diamagnetic. As expected, the bond energy is lower and the bond distance longer than in O_2. Note that the bond energy of F_2 is only about half that of B_2, even though they have the same bond order. F is smaller than B, so we might expect a stronger bond. But the 18 electrons in the smaller volume of F_2 compared with the 10 electrons in B_2 cause greater repulsions and make the F_2 single bond easier to break.

The final member of the series, Ne_2, does not exist for the same reason that He_2 does not: all the MOs are filled, so the stabilization from bonding electrons cancels the destabilization from antibonding electrons, and the bond order is zero.

Figure 11.21 The paramagnetic properties of O_2. Liquid O_2 is attracted to the poles of a magnet because it is paramagnetic, as MO theory predicts. A diamagnetic substance would fall between the poles.

Sample Problem 11.4   Using MO Theory to Explain Bond Properties

PROBLEM As the following data show, removing an electron from N_2 forms an ion with a weaker, longer bond than the parent molecule, whereas the ion formed from O_2 has a stronger, shorter bond:

	N_2	N_2^+	O_2	O_2^+
Bond energy (kJ/mol)	945	841	498	623
Bond length (pm)	110	112	121	112

Explain these facts with diagrams that show the sequence and occupancy of MOs.
PLAN We first determine the number of valence electrons in each species. Then we draw the sequence of MO energy levels for the four species, recalling that they differ for N_2 and O_2 (see Figures 11.19 and 11.20), and fill them with electrons. Finally, we calculate bond orders and compare them with the data. Recall that bond order is related directly to bond energy and inversely to bond length.

SOLUTION Determining the valence electrons:

N has 5 valence e⁻, so N_2 has 10 and N_2^+ has 9

O has 6 valence e⁻, so O_2 has 12 and O_2^+ has 11

Drawing and filling the MO diagrams:

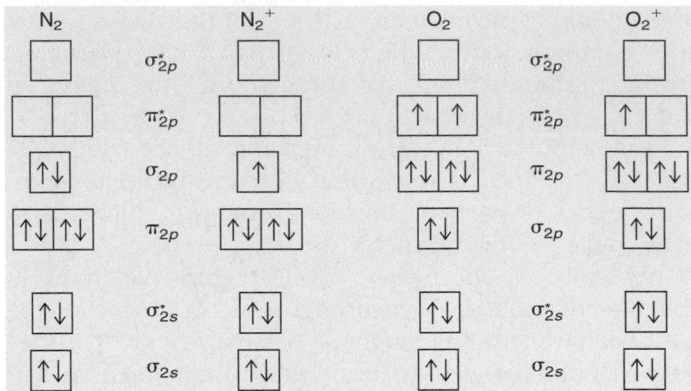

Calculating bond orders:

$$\tfrac{1}{2}(8 - 2) = 3 \qquad \tfrac{1}{2}(7 - 2) = 2.5 \qquad \tfrac{1}{2}(8 - 4) = 2 \qquad \tfrac{1}{2}(8 - 3) = 2.5$$

When N_2 forms N_2^+, a *bonding* electron is removed. Therefore, the bond order decreases, so N_2^+ has a weaker, longer bond than N_2. When O_2 forms O_2^+, an *antibonding* electron is removed. Therefore, the bond order increases, so O_2^+ has a stronger, shorter bond than O_2.

CHECK The answer makes sense in terms of the relationships among bond order, bond energy, and bond length. Check that the total number of bonding and antibonding electrons equals the number of valence electrons calculated.

Follow-up Problem 11.4 Determine the bond orders for the following species: F_2^{2-}, F_2^-, F_2, F_2^+, F_2^{2+}. List the species in order of increasing bond energy and in order of increasing bond length.

MO Description of Some Heteronuclear Diatomic Molecules

Heteronuclear diatomic molecules, those composed of two *different* atoms, have asymmetric MO diagrams because the atomic orbitals of the two atoms have unequal energies. Atoms with greater effective nuclear charge (Z_{eff}) draw their electrons closer to the nucleus and thus have atomic orbitals of lower energy (Section 8.2). Greater Z_{eff} also gives these atoms greater electronegativity. Let's apply MO theory to the bonding in HF and NO.

Bonding in HF To form the MOs in hydrogen fluoride, we combine appropriate AOs from isolated H and F atoms. The high effective nuclear charge of F holds all its electrons more tightly than the H nucleus holds its electron. As a result, *all* occupied orbitals of F have lower energy than the 1s orbital of H. Therefore, the H 1s orbital interacts only with the F 2p orbitals, and only one of the three 2p orbitals, say the $2p_x$, leads to end-on overlap. This results in a σ MO and a σ* MO. The two other p orbitals of F ($2p_y$ and $2p_z$) are not involved in bonding. They are called **nonbonding MOs** and, as shown in Figure 11.22, they have the same energy as the isolated AOs.

Since the occupied bonding MO is closer in energy to the AOs of F, we say that the F orbital contributes more to the bonding in HF than the H orbital does. Generally, in polar covalent molecules, *bonding MOs are closer in energy to the AOs of the more electronegative atom*. In effect, fluorine's greater electronegativity lowers the energy of the bonding MO and draws the bonding electrons closer to its nucleus.

Figure 11.22 The MO diagram for HF. For a polar covalent molecule, the MO diagram is asymmetric because the more electronegative atom has AOs of lower energy. In HF, the bonding MO is closer in energy to the 2p orbital of F. Electrons that are not involved in bonding occupy nonbonding MOs. (The 2s AO of F is not shown.)

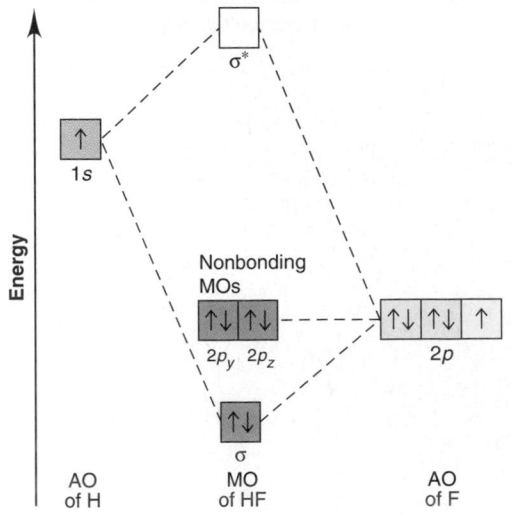

Bonding in NO Nitrogen monoxide (nitric oxide) is a highly reactive molecule because it has a lone electron. Two possible Lewis structures for NO, with formal charges (Section 10.1), are

$$\overset{0}{:}\overset{0}{\ddot{N}}=\overset{0}{\ddot{O}}: \quad \text{or} \quad \overset{-1}{:}\overset{+1}{N}=\overset{}{\ddot{O}}:$$
$$\textbf{I} \qquad\qquad \textbf{II}$$

Both structures show a double bond, but the *measured* bond energy suggests a bond order *higher* than 2. Furthermore, it is not clear where the lone electron resides, although the lower formal charges for structure I suggest that it is on the N atom.

MO theory predicts the bond order and indicates lone-electron placement with no difficulty. The MO diagram in Figure 11.23 is asymmetric, with the AOs of the more electronegative O lower in energy. The 11 valence electrons of NO enter MOs in order of increasing energy, leaving the lone electron in one of the π^*_{2p} orbitals. Eight bonding and three antibonding electrons give a bond order of $\frac{1}{2}(8 - 3) = 2.5$, more in keeping with experiment than either Lewis structure. The bonding electrons lie in MOs closer in energy to the AOs of the O atom. The lone electron occupies an antibonding orbital. Because this orbital receives a greater contribution from the $2p$ orbitals of N, the lone electron resides closer to the N atom.

MO Descriptions of Ozone and Benzene

MO theory extends to molecules with more than two atoms, but the orbital shapes and MO diagrams are too complex for a detailed treatment here. However, let's briefly discuss how the model eliminates the need for resonance forms and helps explain the effects of the absorption of energy.

Recall that we cannot draw a single Lewis structure that adequately depicts bonding in molecules such as ozone and benzene because the adjacent single and double bonds actually have identical properties. Instead, we are forced to draw more than one structure and mentally combine them into a resonance hybrid. The VB model also relies on resonance because it depicts *localized* electron-pair bonds.

In contrast, MO theory pictures a structure of delocalized σ and π bonding and antibonding MOs. Figure 11.24 shows the shapes of the π-bonding MOs of lowest energy in benzene and in ozone. Each holds one pair of electrons. The extended electron densities allow delocalization of this π-electron pair over the entire molecule, thus eliminating the need for separate resonance forms. In benzene, the upper and lower hexagonal lobes of this one π-bonding MO lie above and below all six carbon nuclei. In ozone, the two lobes of this π-bonding MO extend over and under all three oxygen nuclei.

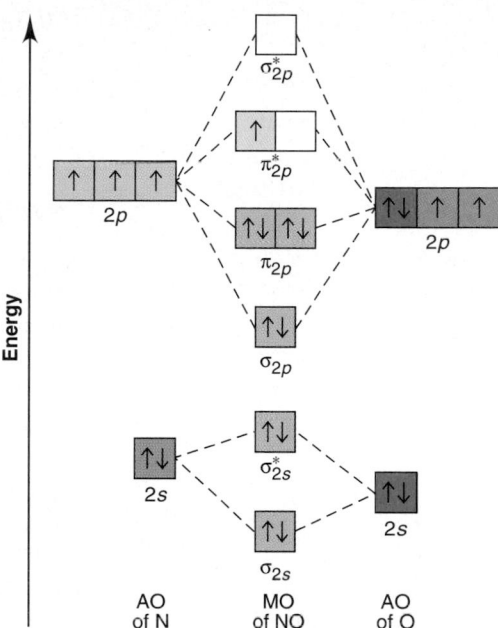

Figure 11.23 The MO diagram for NO. Eleven electrons occupy the MOs in nitric oxide. Note that the lone electron occupies an antibonding MO whose energy is closer to that of the AO of the (less electronegative) N atom.

A Benzene, C_6H_6

B Ozone, O_3

Figure 11.24 The lowest energy π-bonding MOs in benzene and ozone. MO theory eliminates the need for resonance by postulating orbitals that are highly delocalized. **A,** The most stable π-bonding MO in benzene (C_6H_6) has hexagonal lobes of electron density above and below the σ plane of the six C atoms. **B,** The most stable π-bonding MO in ozone (O_3) extends above and below the σ plane (shown as bond lines) of the three O atoms.

Another great advantage of MO theory is its ability to explain excited states and spectra of molecules. It can explain, for instance, why O_3 decomposes when it absorbs ultraviolet (UV) radiation in the stratosphere (bonding electrons are excited to enter empty antibonding orbitals), and why the UV spectrum of benzene has its characteristic absorption bands.

Section Summary

MO theory treats a molecule as a collection of nuclei with molecular orbitals delocalized over the entire structure. Atomic orbitals of comparable energy can be added and subtracted to obtain bonding and antibonding MOs, respectively. Bonding MOs have most of their electron density between the nuclei and are lower in energy than the atomic orbitals; most of the electron density of antibonding MOs does not lie between the nuclei, so these MOs are higher in energy. MOs are filled in order of their energy with electrons having opposing spins. MO diagrams show the energy levels and orbital occupancy. Those for the homonuclear diatomic molecules of Period 2 explain observed bond energy, bond length, and magnetic behavior. In heteronuclear diatomic molecules, bonding MOs have a greater contribution from the more electronegative atom. MO theory eliminates the need for resonance forms in larger molecules.

Chapter Perspective

In this chapter, you've seen that the two most important orbital-based models of covalent bonding, each with its own benefits and limitations, complement each other. Next, you'll see how the electron distribution in the bonds of molecules gives rise to the physical behavior of liquids and solids.

MO theory will come into play for a deeper understanding of metals. And, following Chapter 12 come two chapters that apply the concepts you've learned from Chapter 7 onward to the behavior of inorganic, organic, and biochemical substances.

The following learning objectives, with section and/or sample problem (SP) numbers in parentheses, can help focus your study:

Understand These Concepts

1. The main ideas of valence bond theory—orbital overlap, opposing electron spins, and hybridization as a means of rationalizing molecular shapes (11.1)
2. How orbitals mix to form hybrid orbitals with different spatial orientations (11.1)
3. The distinction between end-to-end and side-to-side overlap and the origin of sigma (σ) and pi (π) bonds in simple molecules (11.2)
4. How two modes of orbital overlap lead to single, double, and triple bonds (11.2)
5. Why π bonding restricts rotation in double bonded molecules (11.2)
6. The distinction between the localized bonding of VB theory and the delocalized bonding of MO theory (11.3)
7. How addition or subtraction of AOs form bonding or antibonding MOs (11.3)

8. Shapes of MOs formed from combinations of two s orbitals and combinations of two p orbitals (11.3)
9. How MO bond order predicts the stability of molecular species (11.3)
10. How MO theory explains the bonding and properties of the homonuclear and simple heteronuclear diatomic molecules of Period 2 (11.3)

Master These Skills

1. Using molecular shape to postulate the hybrid orbitals used by a central atom (SP 11.1)
2. Describing the orbitals and types of bonds in a molecule (SP 11.2)
3. Drawing MO diagrams, writing electron configurations, and calculating bond orders of molecular species (SP 11.3)
4. Explaining bond properties with MO diagrams (SP 11.4)

For Review and Reference

Key Terms

Section 11.1
valence bond (VB) theory
hybridization
hybrid orbital
sp hybrid orbital
sp^2 hybrid orbital

sp^3 hybrid orbital
sp^3*d* hybrid orbital
sp^3*d*^{2} hybrid orbital
Section 11.2
sigma (σ) bond
pi (π) bond

Section 11.3
molecular orbital (MO)
    theory
molecular orbital (MO)
bonding MO
antibonding MO
sigma (σ) MO

MO diagram
MO bond order
homonuclear diatomic
    molecule
pi (π) MO
nonbonding MO

Key Equations and Relationships

11.1 Calculating the MO bond order (p. 409):   Bond order = $\frac{1}{2}$[(no. of e$^-$ in bonding MO) − (no. of e$^-$ in antibonding MO)]

Highlighted Figures and Tables

These figures (F) and tables (T) provide a quick review of
key ideas.
F11.2 The *sp* hybrid orbitals in gaseous BeCl$_2$ (p. 398)
T11.1 Composition of hybrid orbitals (p. 402)
F11.8 The conceptual steps from molecular formula to hybrid orbitals (p. 402)
F11.10 The σ and π bonds of ethylene (C$_2$H$_4$) (p. 404)

F11.14 Contours and energies of the bonding and antibonding MOs in H$_2$ (p. 408)
F11.18 Contours and energies of σ and π MOs through combinations of 2*p* AOs (p. 411)
F11.20 MO occupancy and molecular properties for B$_2$ through Ne$_2$ (p. 412)

Answers to Follow-up Problems

11.1 (a) Shape is linear, so Be is *sp* hybridized.

(b) Shape is tetrahedral, so Si is *sp*^{3} hybridized.

(c) Shape is square planar, so Xe is *sp*^{3}*d*^{2} hybridized.

11.2 (a) H—C≡N:

IICN is linear, so C is *sp*
hybridized. N is also *sp*
hybridized. One *sp* of C
overlaps the 1*s* of H to form
a σ bond. The other *sp* of C over-
laps one *sp* of N to form a σ bond. The other *sp* of N holds a
lone pair. Two unhybridized *p* orbitals of N and two of C
overlap to form two π bonds.

(b) Ö=C=Ö

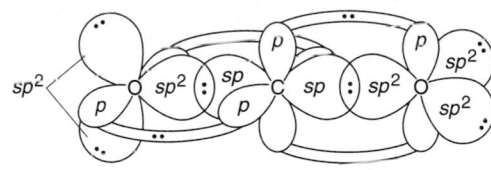

CO$_2$ is linear, so C is *sp* hybridized. Both O atoms are *sp*^{2}
hybridized. Each *sp* of C overlaps one *sp*^{2} from each O to
form two σ bonds. Each of the two unhybridized *p* orbitals of
C forms a π bond with the unhybridized *p* of one of the two
O atoms. Two *sp*^{2} on each O hold lone pairs.

11.3

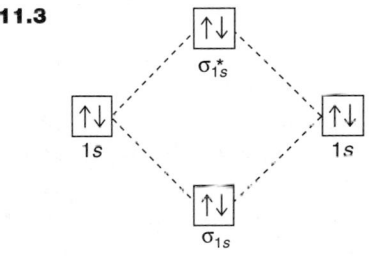

AO of H$^-$ MO of H$_2^{2-}$ AO of H$^-$

Not likely to exist. BO = $\frac{1}{2}$(2 − 2) = 0; $(\sigma_{1s})^2(\sigma_{1s}^*)^2$

11.4 Bond order: F$_2^{2-}$ = 0; F$_2^-$ = $\frac{1}{2}$; F$_2$ = 1; F$_2^+$ = 1$\frac{1}{2}$
        F$_2^{2+}$ = 2

Bond energy: F$_2^{2-}$ < F$_2^-$ < F$_2$ < F$_2^+$ < F$_2^{2+}$

Bond length: F$_2^{2+}$ < F$_2^+$ < F$_2$ < F$_2^-$; F$_2^{2-}$ has no bond

Problems

Problems with a **colored** number are answered at the back of the text. Problem sections match the text and provide the number(s) of relevant sample problems. Most offer concept review questions, skill-building exercises (written in similar pairs), and problems in a relevant context. Following these are comprehensive problems based on material from any section and/or previous chapter.

Valence Bond (VB) Theory and Orbital Hybridization
(Sample Problem 11.1)

■ Concept Review Questions

11.1 What type of central-atom orbital hybridization corresponds to each electron-group arrangement: (a) trigonal planar; (b) octahedral; (c) linear; (d) tetrahedral; (e) trigonal bipyramidal?

11.2 What is the orbital hybridization of a central atom that has one lone pair and bonds to: (a) two other atoms; (b) three other atoms; (c) four other atoms; (d) five other atoms?

11.3 How do carbon and silicon differ with regard to the *types* of orbitals available for hybridization? Explain.

11.4 How many hybrid orbitals form when four orbitals on a central atom mix during a reaction? Explain.

■ Skill-Building Exercises (paired)

11.5 Give the number and type of hybrid orbital that forms when each set of atomic orbitals mixes:
(a) two *d*, one *s*, and three *p*   (b) three *p* and one *s*

11.6 Give the number and type of hybrid orbital that forms when each set of atomic orbitals mixes:
(a) one *p* and one *s*   (b) three *p*, one *d*, and one *s*

11.7 What is the hybridization of nitrogen in (a) NO; (b) NO_2; (c) NO_2^-?

11.8 What is the hybridization of carbon in (a) CO_3^{2-}; (b) $C_2O_4^{2-}$; (c) NCO^-?

11.9 What is the hybridization of chlorine in (a) ClO_2; (b) ClO_3^-; (c) ClO_4^-?

11.10 What is the hybridization of bromine in (a) BrF_3; (b) BrO_2^-; (c) BrF_5?

11.11 Which types of atomic orbitals of the central atom mix to form hybrid orbitals in (a) $SiClH_3$; (b) CS_2?

11.12 Which types of atomic orbitals of the central atom mix to form hybrid orbitals in (a) Cl_2O; (b) $BrCl_3$?

11.13 Which types of atomic orbitals of the central atom mix to form hybrid orbitals in (a) SCl_3F; (b) NF_3?

11.14 Which types of atomic orbitals of the central atom mix to form hybrid orbitals in (a) PF_5; (b) SO_3^{2-}?

11.15 Use partial orbital diagrams to show how the atomic orbitals of the central atom lead to hybrid orbitals in (a) $GeCl_4$; (b) BCl_3; (c) CH_3^+.

11.16 Use partial orbital diagrams to show how the atomic orbitals of the central atom lead to hybrid orbitals in (a) BF_4^-; (b) PO_4^{3-}; (c) SO_3.

11.17 Use partial orbital diagrams to show how the atomic orbitals of the central atom lead to hybrid orbitals in (a) $SeCl_2$; (b) H_3O^+; (c) IF_4^-.

11.18 Use partial orbital diagrams to show how the atomic orbitals of the central atom lead to hybrid orbitals in Ö: , (a) $AsCl_3$; (b) $SnCl_2$; (c) PF_6^-.

■ Problems in Context

11.19 Methyl isocyanate, $CH_3—\ddot{N}=C=\ddot{O}:$, is an intermediate in the manufacture of many pesticides. It received notoriety in 1984 when a leak from a manufacturing plant resulted in the death of more than 2000 people in Bhopal, India. What is the hybridization of N and of the two C atoms in methyl isocyanate? Sketch the molecular shape.

The Mode of Orbital Overlap and the Types of Covalent Bonds
(Sample Problem 11.2)

■ Concept Review Questions

11.20 Are the following statements true or false? Correct any that are false.
(a) Two σ bonds comprise a double bond.
(b) A triple bond consists of one π bond and two σ bonds.
(c) Bonds formed from atomic *s* orbitals are always σ bonds.
(d) A π bond restricts rotation about the σ-bond axis.
(e) A π bond consists of two pairs of electrons.
(f) End-to-end overlap results in a bond with electron density above and below the bond axis.

■ Skill-Building Exercises (paired)

11.21 Describe the hybrid orbitals used by the central atom and the type(s) of bonds formed in (a) NO_3^-; (b) CS_2; (c) CH_2O.

11.22 Describe the hybrid orbitals used by the central atom and the type(s) of bonds formed in (a) O_3; (b) I_3^-; (c) $COCl_2$ (C is central).

11.23 Describe the hybrid orbitals used by the central atom(s) and the type(s) of bonds formed in (a) FNO; (b) C_2F_4; (c) $(CN)_2$.

11.24 Describe the hybrid orbitals used by the central atom(s) and the type(s) of bonds formed in (a) BrF_3; (b) $CH_3C≡CH$; (c) SO_2.

■ Problems in Context

11.25 2-Butene ($CH_3CH=CHCH_3$) is a starting material in the manufacture of lubricating oils and many other compounds. Draw two different structures for 2-butene, indicating the σ and π bonds in each.

Molecular Orbital (MO) Theory and Electron Delocalization
(Sample Problems 11.3 and 11.4)

■ Concept Review Questions

11.26 Two *p* orbitals from one atom and two *p* orbitals from another atom are combined to form molecular orbitals for the joined atoms. How many MOs will result from this combination? Explain.

11.27 Certain atomic orbitals on two atoms were combined to form the following MOs. Name the atomic orbitals used, the MOs formed, and explain which MO has higher energy:

11.28 How do the bonding and antibonding MOs formed from a given pair of AOs compare to each other with respect to (a) energy; (b) presence of nodes; (c) internuclear electron density?

11.29 Antibonding MOs always have at least one node. Can a bonding MO have a node? If so, draw an example.

■ Skill-Building Exercises *(paired)*

11.30 How many electrons does it take to fill (a) a σ-bonding MO; (b) a π-antibonding MO; (c) the MOs formed from combination of the $1s$ orbitals of two atoms?

11.31 How many electrons does it take to fill (a) the MOs formed from combination of the $2p$ orbitals of two atoms; (b) a σ_{2p}^* MO; (c) the MOs formed from combination of the $2s$ orbitals of two atoms?

11.32 Show the shapes of bonding and antibonding MOs formed by combination of (a) an s orbital and a p orbital; (b) two p orbitals (end to end).

11.33 Show the shapes of bonding and antibonding MOs formed by combination of (a) two s orbitals; (b) two p orbitals (side to side).

11.34 Use MO diagrams and the bond orders you obtain from them to answer the following: (a) Is Be_2^+ stable? (b) Is Be_2^+ diamagnetic? (c) What is the valence electron configuration of Be_2^+?

11.35 Use MO diagrams and the bond orders you obtain from them to answer the following: (a) Is O_2^- stable? (b) Is O_2^- paramagnetic? (c) What is the valence electron configuration of O_2^-?

11.36 Use MO diagrams to place C_2^-, C_2, and C_2^+ in order of (a) increasing bond energy; (b) increasing bond length.

11.37 Use MO diagrams to place B_2^+, B_2, and B_2^- in order of (a) decreasing bond energy; (b) decreasing bond length.

Comprehensive Problems

Problems with an asterisk (*) are more challenging.

11.38 Predict the shape, state the hybridization of the central atom, and give the ideal bond angles and any expected deviations in (a) BrO_3^-; (b) $AsCl_4^-$; (c) SeO_4^{2-}; (d) BiF_5^{2-}; (e) SbF_4^+; (f) AlF_6^{3-}; (g) IF_4^+.

11.39 Butadiene (*shown below*) is a colorless gas used to make synthetic BUNA rubber and many other compounds:

$$H-\overset{\overset{\displaystyle H}{|}}{C}=\overset{\overset{\displaystyle H}{|}}{C}-\overset{\overset{\displaystyle H}{|}}{C}=\overset{\overset{\displaystyle H}{|}}{C}-H$$

(a) How many σ bonds and π bonds does the molecule have?

(b) Are *cis/trans* structural arrangements about the double bonds possible? Explain.

11.40 Epinephrine (or adrenaline) is a naturally occurring hormone that is also manufactured commercially for use as a heart stimulant, as a nasal decongestant, and for glaucoma treatment. A valid Lewis structure is

(a) What is the hybridization of each C, O, and N atom?

(b) How many σ bonds does the molecule have?

(c) How many π electrons are delocalized in the ring?

11.41 Isoniazid is an antibacterial agent that is particularly useful against many common strains of tuberculosis. A valid Lewis structure is shown at right.

(a) How many σ bonds are in the molecule?

(b) What is the hybridization of each C and N atom?

11.42 Bond strength is greatly influenced by the mode of orbital overlap. Use VB theory to explain why the $C=C$ bond (614 kJ/mol) is *not* twice as strong as the $C-C$ bond (347 kJ/mol) and why the $C\equiv C$ bond (839 kJ/mol) is *not* three times as strong.

11.43 In each of the following equations, what hybridization change, if any, occurs at the underlined atom?

(a) $\underline{B}F_3 + NaF \longrightarrow Na^+BF_4^-$

(b) $\underline{P}Cl_3 + Cl_2 \longrightarrow PCl_5$

(c) $H\underline{C}\equiv CH + H_2 \longrightarrow H_2C=CH_2$

(d) $\underline{S}iF_4 + 2F^- \longrightarrow SiF_6^{2-}$

(e) $\underline{S}O_2 + \frac{1}{2}O_2 \longrightarrow SO_3$

11.44 Tetrazene (atom sequence H_2NNNNH_2) is a rather unstable hydride of nitrogen that decomposes above 0°C to N_2 and hydrazine (N_2H_4).

(a) What is the hybridization of N in these three compounds?

(b) Rank the three types of N-to-N bonds in terms of increasing length and strength.

(c) Draw structures for the *cis* and *trans* forms of tetrazene and predict which, if any, is polar.

11.45 Some experimental evidence unexpectedly shows that the gaseous molecules CaF_2, $SrCl_2$, and $BaCl_2$ have bent shapes.

(a) What structure would you have expected for these molecules?

(b) What property might have been measured to provide the evidence?

11.46 Use partial orbital diagrams to show how the atomic orbitals on the central atom lead to the hybrid orbitals in (a) IF_2^-; (b) ICl_3; (c) $XeOF_4$; (d) BHF_2.

11.47 Tryptophan is one of the amino acids typically found in proteins:

(a) What is the hybridization at the numbered C, N, and O atoms?

(b) How many σ bonds are present in tryptophan?

(c) Predict the bond angles at points a, b, and c.

11.48 The bond angle in NH_3 is 107.3°, whereas in PH_3 it is 93.6°. Explain these data using VB theory.

***11.49** The sulfate ion can be represented with four S—O bonds or with two S—O and two S=O bonds.

(a) Which representation is better from the standpoint of formal charges?

(b) What is the shape of the sulfate ion, and what hybrid orbitals of S are postulated for the σ bonding?

(c) In view of the answer to part (b), what S orbitals must be used for the π bonds? What O orbitals?

(d) Draw an overlap diagram to show how one atomic orbital from S and one from O combine to form a π bond.

***11.50** The hydrocarbon allene, $H_2C=C=CH_2$, is obtained indirectly from petroleum and used as a precursor for several types of plastics. What is the hybridization at each C atom in allene? Draw a bonding picture for allene with lines for σ bonds, and show the arrangement of the π bonds. Be sure to represent the geometry of the molecule in three dimensions.

11.51 Many unusual heteronuclear diatomic molecules form in hot gases. Draw an MO diagram, write the valence electron configuration, and predict the bond order for:
(a) BC; (b) OF.

***11.52** Linoleic acid *(below)* is an essential fatty acid found in many vegetable oils, such as soy, peanut, and cottonseed. A key structural feature of the molecule is the *cis* orientation around its two double bonds, where R_1 and R_2 represent two different groups that form the rest of the molecule.

(a) How many different compounds are possible, changing only the *cis/trans* arrangements around these two double bonds?

(b) How many are possible for a similar compound with three double bonds?

11.53 The molecule B_2 is paramagnetic (see Figure 11.20). How does this behavior support the order of MO energy levels arising from 2s-2p mixing? Would the magnetic behavior of B_2 differ if there were no 2s-2p mixing? Explain.

11.54 Although LiF consists of ions in the solid state, it exists as highly polar LiF molecules in the gaseous state. Based on the relative magnitudes of properties such as ionization energy, electron affinity, and electronegativity, explain why the molecules are polar. Draw an MO diagram for LiF, similar to that for HF, assuming that the Li 2s orbital interacts with the F 2p orbital.

11.55 There is unanimous concern from health-related government agencies that the American diet contains too much meat, and numerous recommendations have been made to eat more fruit and vegetables. One of the richest sources of vegetable protein is soy, available in many forms,

especially as soybean curd, or tofu. This material is a staple of many Asian diets, and recently, chemists have isolated an anticancer agent called *genistein* from tofu, which may explain the much lower incidence of cancer among people in the Far East. A valid Lewis structure for genistein is

(a) Is the hybridization of each C in the right ring the same? Explain.

(b) Is the hybridization of the O atom in the center ring the same as the O atoms in OH groups? Explain.

(c) How many carbon-oxygen σ bonds are there? How many carbon-oxygen π bonds?

(d) Do all the oxygen lone pairs occupy the same type of hybrid orbital? Explain.

***11.56** Simple proteins consist of amino acids linked together in a long chain, a small portion of which is

Experiment shows that rotation about the C—N bond *(arrow)* is somewhat restricted. Explain with resonance structures and show the types of bonding involved.

11.57 The compound 2,6-dimethylpyrazine gives chocolate its odor and is used extensively in flavorings. A valid Lewis structure is

(a) Which atomic orbitals mix to form the hybrid orbitals of N?

(b) In what type of hybrid orbital do the N lone pairs reside?

(c) Is the hybridization of C in CH_3 the same as in the ring? Explain.

11.58 Acetylsalicylic acid (aspirin), the most widely used medicine in the world, has the following Lewis structure:

(a) What is the hybridization at each central C and each O atom?

(b) How many localized π bonds are present?

(c) How many C atoms have a trigonal planar shape around them? A tetrahedral shape?

Intermolecular Forces
Liquids, Solids, and Phase Changes

12

Figure: A world of phase changes. Over much of the planet, early spring and late fall bring remarkable changes in the physical behavior of water. The magnified views depict water's three phases on the molecular scale; note the identical individual molecules in each. In this chapter, we explore the general characteristics of matter's phases and the interplay of forces that create, maintain, and change them.

Concepts and Skills to Review

before you study this chapter

- properties of gases, liquids, and solids (Section 5.1)
- kinetic-molecular theory of gases (Section 5.6)
- kinetic and potential energy (Section 6.1)
- heat capacity, enthalpy change, and Hess's law (Sections 6.2, 6.3, and 6.5)
- Coulomb's law (Section 9.2)
- chemical bonding models (Chapter 9)
- molecular polarity (Section 10.4)
- molecular orbital treatment of diatomic molecules (Section 11.3)

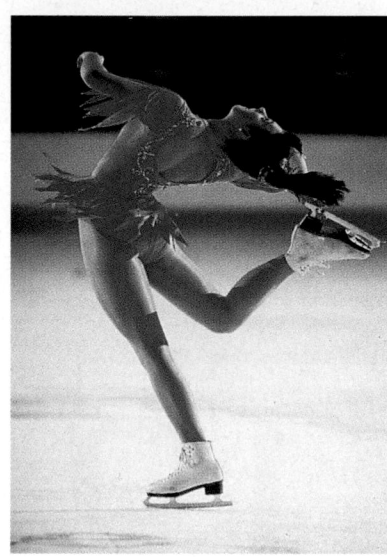

All matter occurs in one of the three physical states—gas, liquid, or solid. In fact, under specific conditions, many *pure* substances can exist in any one of the states. The states of water are most familiar: we inhale and exhale gaseous water; drink, excrete, and wash with liquid water; and slide on or cool our drinks with solid water (see photo). A careful look around reveals other examples of solids (a metal ring, salt in the kitchen), liquids (gasoline in your car, paint thinners), and gases (the air you breathe, the bubbles in a drink) that can exist in one or both of the other states.

The three states were introduced in Chapter 1 and their properties compared when we examined gases in Chapter 5. In this chapter, we turn our attention to liquids and solids. A physical state is one type of **phase,** any physically distinct, homogeneous part of a system. The water in a glass constitutes a single phase; add some ice and you have two phases. Liquids and solids are called *condensed* phases (or condensed states) because their particles are extremely close together.

The potential energy between the particles—molecules, atoms, or ions—in a sample of matter results from attractive and repulsive forces called inter-particle forces or, more commonly, **intermolecular forces.** The interplay between these forces and the kinetic energy of the particles gives rise to the properties of each state (or phase) and to **phase changes,** the changes from one phase to another.

Chapter 12 begins with an overview of the three states and their phase changes. Then we focus on phase changes at the molecular level, calculate the energy changes involved, and highlight the effects of temperature and pressure with phase diagrams. We consider next the various types of inter-molecular forces. We then discuss the properties of liquids. The next section is especially important because it combines ideas from several chapters to show how the unique properties of water arise inevitably from the electron configurations of its atoms. Then we discuss the properties of solids, emphasizing the relationship between type of bonding and intermolecular force. You will learn how solid structures are determined experimentally and, in the final section, how some exciting modern materials are produced and used.

12.1 An Overview of Physical States and Phase Changes

Imagine yourself among the particles of a molecular substance and you'll discover two types of electrostatic forces at work:

- *Intra*molecular forces (bonding forces) exist *within* each molecule (or polyatomic ion) and influence the *chemical* properties of the substance.
- *Inter*molecular forces exist *between* the molecules (or ions) and influence the *physical* properties of the substance.

Now imagine a molecular view of three states of the same substance. Take water as an example and focus on one molecule from gaseous water, one from liquid water, and one from ice. They appear identical—bent, polar H—O—H molecules. In fact, in their *chemical* behavior, the three states of water *are* identical because their molecules are held together by the same *intra*molecular covalent bonding forces. But, as you know, the *physical* behavior of these states differs greatly.

A Kinetic-Molecular View of the Three States Whether a substance is a gas, liquid, or solid depends on the interplay between the potential energy of the intermolecular attractions, which tends to draw the molecules together, and the kinetic energy of the molecules, which tends to disperse them. According to Coulomb's law, the potential energy depends on the charges of the particles and the distances between them (see Section 9.2). The average

Table 12.1 A Macroscopic Comparison of Gases, Liquids, and Solids

State	Shape and Volume	Compressibility	Ability to Flow
Gas	Conforms to shape and volume of container	High	High
Liquid	Conforms to shape of container; volume limited by surface	Very low	Moderate
Solid	Maintains its own shape and volume	Almost none	Almost none

◆ **Environmental Flow** The environment demonstrates beautifully the differences in the abilities of the three states to flow and diffuse. Atmospheric gases mix so well that the 80 km of air closest to Earth has a uniform composition. Much less mixing occurs in the oceans, and differences in composition at various depths support different species. Rocky solids (see photo) intermingle so little that adjacent strata remain separated for millions of years.

kinetic energy, which is related to their average speed, is proportional to the absolute temperature.

This interplay between potential and kinetic energies directly affects the properties that define the three states. In Table 12.1, we focus on three properties—shape, compressibility, and ability to flow—which we discussed in earlier chapters. The following *kinetic-molecular* view of the three states is an extension of the model we used to understand gases (see Section 5.6):

- *In a gas,* the energy of attraction is small relative to the energy of motion, so on average the particles are far apart. This large interparticle distance has several macroscopic consequences. A gas moves randomly throughout its container and fills it. Gases are highly compressible, and they flow and diffuse through one another easily.

- *In a liquid,* the attractions are stronger because the particles are in virtual contact. But their kinetic energy still allows them to tumble randomly over and around each other. Therefore, a liquid conforms to the shape of its container but has a surface. With very little free space between the particles, liquids resist an applied external force and thus compress only very slightly. They flow and diffuse but *much* more slowly than gases.

- *In a solid,* the attractions dominate the motion to such an extent that the particles remain in position relative to one another, jiggling in place. With the particles usually slightly closer together than in a liquid and their positions fixed, a solid has a specific shape. Consequently, solids compress even less than liquids, and their particles do not flow significantly. ◆

Types of Phase Changes Phase changes are determined by the interplay between kinetic energy and intermolecular forces also. As the temperature increases, the average kinetic energy increases as well, so the faster moving particles can overcome attractions more easily; conversely, lower temperatures allow the forces to draw the slower moving particles together.

What happens when gaseous water is cooled? First, a mist appears as the particles form tiny microdroplets that then collect into a bulk sample of liquid with a single surface. The process of a gas changing into a liquid is called **condensation;** the opposite process, changing from a liquid into a gas, is called **vaporization.** With further cooling, the particles move even more slowly and become fixed in position as the liquid solidifies in the process of **freezing;** the opposite change is called **melting,** or **fusion.** In common speech, freezing implies low temperature because we typically think of water, but many substances freeze at much higher temperatures; gold, for example, freezes (solidifies) at 1064°C. ◆

Enthalpy changes accompany these phase changes. As the molecules of a gas attract each other and come closer together in the liquid, and then become fixed in the solid, the system of particles loses energy, which is released as heat. Thus, *condensing and freezing are exothermic changes.* On the

◆ **Frozen Gold** The phase change that occurs when liquids freeze is essential for casting applications. In the preparation of a dental crown (see photo), the niches and crevices of the tooth impression are filled with a molten metal, often a gold alloy. After cooling, the metal solidifies and withstands years of high pressure from chewing. The casting of bronze statues, glass decorations, candles, and numerous plastic objects employs the same principle.

◆ A Cooling Phase Change
The evaporation of sweat has a cooling effect because heat from your body is used to vaporize the water. Many fur-covered animals achieve this cooling effect, too. Cats (and many rodents) lick themselves, transferring water from inside their bodies to the surface where it can evaporate, and dogs just open their mouths, hang out their tongues, and pant!

other hand, energy must be absorbed to overcome the attractive forces in a liquid that keep the particles together and in a solid that keep them fixed in place. Thus, *melting and vaporizing are endothermic changes.* ◆

For a pure substance, each phase change has a specific enthalpy change *per mole* (measured at 1 atm and the temperature of the change). For vaporization, it is called the **heat of vaporization (ΔH_{vap}^0),** and for fusion, it is the **heat of fusion (ΔH_{fus}^0).** In the case of water, we have

$$H_2O(l) \longrightarrow H_2O(g) \quad \Delta H = \Delta H_{vap}^0 = 40.7 \text{ kJ/mol (at } 100°C)$$
$$H_2O(s) \longrightarrow H_2O(l) \quad \Delta H = \Delta H_{fus}^0 = 6.02 \text{ kJ/mol (at } 0°C)$$

The reverse processes, condensing and freezing, have enthalpy changes of the *same magnitude but opposite sign:*

$$H_2O(g) \longrightarrow H_2O(l) \quad \Delta H = -\Delta H_{vap}^0 = -40.7 \text{ kJ/mol}$$
$$H_2O(l) \longrightarrow H_2O(s) \quad \Delta H = -\Delta H_{fus}^0 = -6.02 \text{ kJ/mol}$$

Water is typical of most pure substances in that it takes less energy to melt 1 mol of solid than to vaporize 1 mol of liquid: $\Delta H_{fus}^0 < \Delta H_{vap}^0$. Figure 12.1 shows several examples. This difference occurs because a phase change is essentially a change in intermolecular distance and freedom of motion. Thus, less energy is needed to overcome the forces holding the molecules in their fixed positions (to melt a solid) than to separate them completely from each other (to vaporize a liquid).

Figure 12.1 Heats of vaporization and fusion for several common substances. ΔH_{vap}^0 is always larger than ΔH_{fus}^0 because it takes more energy to separate particles completely than just to free them from their fixed positions in the solid.

Ice crystals on windowpane.

We are all familiar with the three states of water because they are stable under ordinary conditions. Carbon dioxide, on the other hand, exists commonly as a gas and a solid (dry ice), but liquid CO_2 occurs only at external pressures greater than 5 atm. Thus, at ordinary conditions, solid CO_2 becomes a gas without first becoming a liquid. This process is called **sublimation.** On a clear wintry day, you can dry clothes outside on a line, even though it may be too cold for ice to melt, because the ice sublimes. Freeze-dried foods are prepared by sublimation. The opposite process, changing from a gas directly into a solid, is called **deposition**—you may have seen ice crystals form on a cold window from the deposition of water vapor (see photo). The **heat of sublimation (ΔH_{subl}^0)** is the enthalpy change when 1 mol of the substance sublimes. Hess's law says that it equals the sum of the heats of fusion and vaporization:

$$
\begin{array}{ll}
\text{Solid} \longrightarrow \text{liquid} & \Delta H_{fus}^0 \\
\underline{\text{Liquid} \longrightarrow \text{gas}} & \underline{\Delta H_{vap}^0} \\
\text{Solid} \longrightarrow \text{gas} & \Delta H_{subl}^0
\end{array}
$$

Figure 12.2 Changes of state and their enthalpy changes. Each type of phase change, with its associated enthalpy change, appears on a general enthalpy diagram. Note that fusion (or melting), vaporization, and sublimation are endothermic changes (positive ΔH^0), whereas freezing, condensation, and deposition are exothermic changes (negative ΔH^0).

Figure 12.2 summarizes the terminology of the various phase changes and the enthalpy changes associated with them.

Section Summary

Because of the relative magnitudes of intermolecular forces and kinetic energy, the particles in a gas are far apart and moving randomly, those in a liquid are in contact but still moving relative to each other, and those in a solid are in contact and fixed relative to each other in a rigid structure. These molecular-level differences in the states of matter account for macroscopic differences in shape, compressibility, and ability to flow. When a solid becomes a liquid (melting, or fusion) or a liquid becomes a gas (vaporization), energy is absorbed to overcome intermolecular forces and increase the distance between particles. When particles come closer together in the reverse changes (freezing and condensation), energy is released. Sublimation is the changing of a solid directly into a gas. Each phase change is associated with a given enthalpy change under specified conditions.

12.2 Quantitative Aspects of Phase Changes

Some of the most spectacular, and familiar, phase changes occur in the daily weather. When it rains, water vapor condenses to a liquid, which changes back to a gas as puddles dry up. In the spring, snow melts and streams fill; in winter, water freezes and falls to earth. These remarkable transformations also take place whenever you make a pot of tea or a tray of ice cubes. In this section, we examine the heat absorbed or released in a phase change and the equilibrium nature of the process.

Heat Involved in Phase Changes: A Kinetic-Molecular Approach

We can apply the kinetic-molecular theory quantitatively to phase changes by means of a **heating-cooling curve,** which shows the changes that occur when heat is added or removed at a constant rate from a particular sample

Figure 12.3 **A cooling curve for the conversion of gaseous water to ice.** A plot is shown of temperature vs. heat removed as gaseous water at 130°C changes to ice at −40°C. This process occurs in five stages, with a molecular-level depiction shown for each stage. Stage 1: Gaseous water cools. Stage 2: Gaseous water condenses. Stage 3: Liquid water cools. Stage 4: Liquid water freezes. Stage 5: Solid water cools. The slopes of the lines in Stages 1, 3, and 5 reflect the magnitudes of the molar heat capacities of the phases. Although not drawn to scale, the line in Stage 2 is longer than the line in Stage 4 because ΔH^0_{vap} of water is greater than ΔH^0_{fus}. A plot of temperature vs. heat added would have the same steps but in reverse order.

of matter. As an example, the cooling process is depicted in Figure 12.3 for a 2.50-mol sample of gaseous water in a piston-cylinder assembly, with the pressure kept at 1 atm and the temperature changing from 130°C to −40°C. To an observer, the process is continuous, but we can divide it into five heat-releasing (exothermic) stages that correspond to the five portions of the curve: the gas cools, condenses to a liquid, the liquid cools, freezes to a solid, and the solid cools a bit further. For each stage, we'll think through the changes at the molecular level and then calculate the heat change that takes place.

Stage 1. Gaseous water cools. Picture a collection of water molecules behaving like a typical gas: zooming around chaotically at a range of speeds, smashing into each other and the container walls. At a high enough temperature, the most probable speed, and thus the average kinetic energy (E_k), of the molecules is high enough to overcome the potential energy (E_p) of attractions among them. As the temperature falls, the average E_k decreases, so the attractions become increasingly important.

The change is $H_2O(g)$ [130°C] $\longrightarrow$ $H_2O(g)$ [100°C]. The heat (q) is the product of the amount (number of moles, n), the molar heat capacity of *gaseous water*, $C_{water(g)}$ and the temperature change, ΔT ($T_{final} - T_{initial}$):

$$q = n \times C_{water(g)} \times \Delta T = (2.50 \text{ mol}) (33.1 \text{ J/mol} \cdot °C) (100°C - 130°C)$$
$$= -2482 \text{ J} = -2.48 \text{ kJ}$$

The minus sign indicates that heat is released. (For purposes of canceling, the molar heat capacity, C, includes °C, rather than K. The magnitude of C is not affected because the kelvin and Celsius degree represent the same temperature increment.)

Stage 2. Gaseous water condenses. At the condensation point, the slowest of the molecules are near each other long enough for intermolecular attractions to form groups of molecules, which aggregate into microdroplets and then a bulk liquid. Note that while the state is changing from gas to liquid, *the temperature remains constant,* so the average E_k is constant. This means that, even though molecules in a gas certainly move *farther* between collisions than those in a liquid, their average *speed* is the same at a given temperature. Thus, removing heat from the system involves a decrease in the average E_p (as the molecules come closer together and attract each other more strongly) but not a decrease in the average E_k. In other words, at 100°C, gaseous water and liquid water have the same average E_k, but the liquid has lower E_p.

The change is $H_2O(g)$ [100°C] $\longrightarrow$ $H_2O(l)$ [100°C]. The heat released is the product of the amount (n) and the negative of the heat of vaporization ($-\Delta H^0_{vap}$):

$$q = n(-\Delta H^0_{vap}) = (2.50 \text{ mol}) (-40.7 \text{ kJ/mol}) = -102 \text{ kJ}$$

This step contributes the *greatest portion of the total heat released* because of the decrease in potential energy that occurs with the enormous decrease in distance between molecules in a gas and those in a liquid.

Stage 3. Liquid water cools. The molecules have now condensed to the liquid state. The continued loss of heat appears as a decrease in temperature, that is, as a decrease in the most probable molecular speed and, thus, the average E_k. The temperature decreases as long as the sample remains liquid.

The change is $H_2O(l)$ [100°C] $\longrightarrow$ $H_2O(l)$ [0°C]. The heat depends on amount (n), the molar heat capacity of *liquid water,* and ΔT:

$$q = n \times C_{water(l)} \times \Delta T = (2.50 \text{ mol}) (75.4 \text{ J/mol} \cdot °C) (0°C - 100°C)$$
$$= -18850 \text{ J} = -18.8 \text{ kJ}$$

Stage 4. Liquid water freezes. At the freezing temperature of water, 0°C, intermolecular attractions overcome the motion of the molecules around one another. Beginning with the slowest, the molecules lose E_p and align themselves into the crystalline structure of ice. Molecular motion continues, but only as vibration of atoms about their fixed positions. As during condensation, the temperature and average E_k remain constant during freezing.

The change is $H_2O(l)$ [0°C] $\longrightarrow$ $H_2O(s)$ [0°C]. The heat released is n times the negative of the heat of fusion ($-\Delta H^0_{fus}$):

$$q = n(-\Delta H^0_{fus}) = (2.50 \text{ mol}) (-6.02 \text{ kJ/mol}) = -15.0 \text{ kJ}$$

Stage 5. Solid water cools. With motion restricted to jiggling in place, further cooling merely reduces the average speed of this jiggling.

The change is $H_2O(s)$ [0°C] $\longrightarrow$ $H_2O(s)$ [-40°C]. The heat released depends on n, the molar heat capacity of *solid water,* and ΔT:

$$q = n \times C_{water(s)} \times \Delta T = (2.50 \text{ mol}) (37.6 \text{ J/mol} \cdot °C) (-40°C - 0°C)$$
$$= -3760 \text{ J} = -3.76 \text{ kJ}$$

According to Hess's law, the total heat released is the sum of the heats released during the individual stages. The sum of q values for Stages 1 to 5 is −142 kJ.

Two key points stand out in this or any similar process (at constant pressure), whether exothermic or endothermic:
- *Within a phase,* a change in heat is accompanied by *a change in temperature,* which is associated with a change in average E_k as the most probable *speed* of the molecules changes. The heat lost or gained depends on the amount of substance, molar heat capacity for that phase, and change in temperature.
- *During a phase change,* a change in heat occurs at a *constant temperature,* which is associated with a change in E_p, as the average *distance* between molecules changes. Both physical states are present during a phase change. The heat lost or gained depends on the amount of substance and the enthalpy of the phase change (ΔH^0_{vap} or ΔH^0_{fus}).

The Equilibrium Nature of Phase Changes

In everyday experience, phase changes take place in open containers—the outdoors, a pot on a stove, the freezer compartment of a refrigerator—so the change is not reversible. In a closed container under controlled conditions, however, *phase changes of many substances are reversible and reach equilibrium,* just as chemical changes do.

Liquid-Gas Equilibria Picture an *open* flask containing a pure liquid at constant temperature and focus on the molecules at the surface. Within their range of molecular speeds, some are moving fast enough and in the right direction to overcome attractions, so they vaporize. Nearby molecules immediately fill the gap, and with energy supplied by the constant-temperature surroundings, the process continues until the entire liquid phase is gone.

Now picture starting with a *closed* flask at constant temperature, as in Figure 12.4A, and assume that a vacuum exists above the liquid. As before, some of the molecules at the surface have a high enough E_k to vaporize. As the number of molecules in the vapor phase increases, the pressure of the vapor increases. At the same time, some of the molecules in the vapor that collide with the surface have a low enough E_k to become attracted too strongly to leave the liquid and they condense. Since, for a given surface area, the number of molecules that make up the surface is constant, the rate of vaporization—the number of molecules leaving the surface per unit time—is also constant. On the other hand, as the vapor becomes more populated, molecules collide with the surface more often, so the rate of condensation slowly increases. As condensation continues to offset vaporization, the increase in the pressure of the vapor slows. Eventually, the rate of condensation equals the rate of vaporization, as depicted in Figure 12.4B. From this time onward, *the pressure of the vapor is constant at that temperature.* Macroscopically, the situation seems static, but at the molecular level, molecules are entering and leaving the liquid surface at equal rates. The system has reached a state of *dynamic equilibrium:*

$$\text{Liquid} \rightleftharpoons \text{gas}$$

Figure 12.4C depicts the entire process graphically.

The pressure exerted by the vapor at equilibrium is called the *equilibrium vapor pressure,* or just the **vapor pressure,** of the liquid at that temperature. If we use a larger flask, more molecules are present in the gas phase at equilibrium, but as long as some liquid remains, the vapor pressure does not change. Suppose we disturb this equilibrium system by pumping out some of the vapor at constant temperature, thereby lowering the pressure. (If this were a cylinder with piston, we could lower the pressure by increasing the volume.) The rate of condensation temporarily falls below the rate of vaporization (the backward process occurs more slowly than the forward process). Fewer molecules re-enter the liquid than leave it, so the vapor pressure rises until, after a short period, the condensation rate increases enough for equilibrium to be reached again. Similarly, if we disturb the system by pumping in additional vapor (or by decreasing the volume) at constant temperature, thereby raising the pressure, the rate of condensation temporarily exceeds the rate of vaporization. More molecules enter the liquid than leave it (the backward process is faster), but soon the condensation rate decreases, and the pressure again reaches the equilibrium value. This behavior of a pure liquid in contact with its vapor is a general one for any system and is involved in many physical and chemical changes: *when a system at equilibrium is disturbed, it counteracts the disturbance and eventually reestablishes a state of equilibrium.* We'll return to this key idea often.

The Effects of Temperature and Intermolecular Forces on Vapor Pressure
The vapor pressure of a substance depends on the temperature. Raising the temperature of a liquid *increases* the fraction of molecules moving fast enough to escape the liquid and *decreases* the fraction moving slowly enough to be

A

B

C

Figure 12.4 Liquid-gas equilibrium. A, In a closed flask at constant temperature with the air removed, the initial pressure is zero. As molecules leave the surface and enter the space above the liquid, the pressure of the vapor rises. **B,** With time, as more molecules enter the vapor phase, some collide with the surface and re-enter the liquid. At equilibrium, the same number of molecules leave as re-enter the liquid in a given time, so the pressure of the vapor reaches a constant value. **C,** A graph of pressure versus time shows that the pressure of the vapor increases as long as the rate of vaporization is greater than the rate of condensation. At equilibrium, the pressure is constant because the rates are equal. The pressure at this point is the *vapor pressure* of the liquid at that temperature.

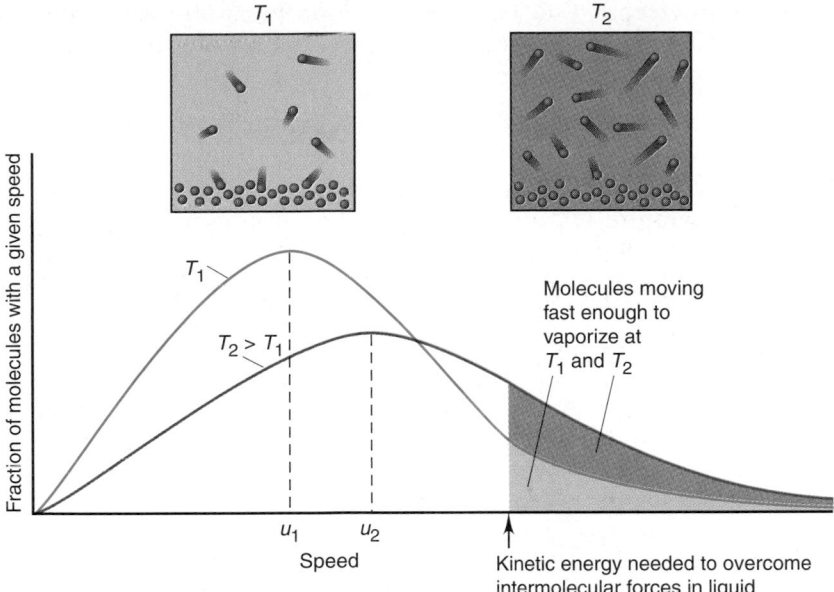

Figure 12.5 **The effect of temperature on the distribution of molecular speeds in a liquid.** With the temperature T_1 lower than T_2, the most probable molecular speed u_1 is less than u_2. (Note the similarity to Figure 5.14, p. 200.) The fraction of molecules with enough energy to escape the liquid *(shaded area)* is *greater at the higher temperature*. The molecular views show that at the higher T, equilibrium is reached with more gas molecules in the same volume and thus at a higher vapor pressure.

recaptured. This important idea is shown in Figure 12.5. In general, *the higher the temperature is, the higher the vapor pressure.*

The vapor pressure also depends on the intermolecular attractive forces present. The average E_k is the same for different substances at a given temperature. Therefore, molecules with weaker intermolecular attractions vaporize more easily. In general, *the weaker the intermolecular forces are, the higher the vapor pressure.*

Figure 12.6 shows the vapor pressure of three liquids as a function of temperature. In each case, note that the curve rises more steeply as the temperature increases. At a given temperature, the substance with the *weakest* intermolecular forces must have the *highest* vapor pressure: thus, the intermolecular forces in diethyl ether are weaker than those in ethanol, which in turn are weaker than those in water.

The nonlinear relationship between vapor pressure and temperature shown in Figure 12.6 can be expressed mathematically as a linear relationship between $\ln P$ and $1/T$:

$$\ln P = \frac{-\Delta H_{vap}}{R}\left(\frac{1}{T}\right) + C$$

$$y \;=\; m \quad x \;+\; b$$

where $\ln P$ is the natural logarithm of the vapor pressure, ΔH_{vap} is the heat of vaporization, R is the universal gas constant (8.31 J/mol · K), T is the absolute temperature, and C is a constant (not related to heat capacity). This is the **Clausius-Clapeyron equation,** which gives us a way of finding the heat of vaporization, the energy that must be supplied to vaporize 1 mol of molecules in the liquid state. A plot of $\ln P$ vs. $1/T$ has the form of a straight line, $y = mx + b$, where $y = \ln P$, $x = 1/T$, m (the slope) $= -\Delta H_{vap}/R$, and

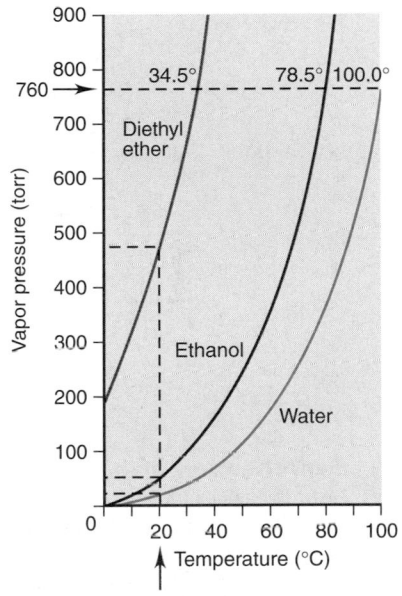

Figure 12.6 **Vapor pressure as a function of temperature and intermolecular forces.** The vapor pressures of three different liquids are plotted against temperature. At any given temperature (see the vertical dashed line at 20°C), diethyl ether has the highest vapor pressure and water the lowest, because diethyl ether has the weakest intermolecular forces and water the strongest. The horizontal dashed line at 760 torr shows the normal boiling points of the liquids, the temperature at which the vapor pressure equals atmospheric pressure at sea level.

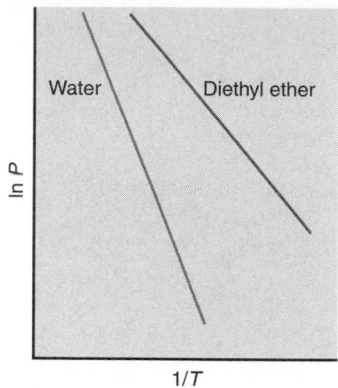

Figure 12.7 A linear plot of the vapor pressure–temperature relationship. The Clausius-Clapeyron equation gives a straight line when the natural logarithm of the vapor pressure (ln P) is plotted against the inverse of the absolute temperature (1/T). The slopes ($-\Delta H_{vap}/R$) allow determination of the heats of vaporization of the two liquids. Note that the slope is steeper for water because its ΔH_{vap} is greater.

b (the y-axis intercept) = C. Figure 12.7 shows plots for two of the liquids in Figure 12.6. A two-point version of the equation allows a nongraphical determination of ΔH_{vap}:

$$\ln \frac{P_2}{P_1} = \frac{-\Delta H_{vap}}{R}\left(\frac{1}{T_2} - \frac{1}{T_1}\right) \tag{12.1}$$

If ΔH_{vap} and P_1 at T_1 are known, we can calculate the vapor pressure (P_2) at any other temperature (T_2) or the temperature at any other pressure.

Sample Problem 12.1 Using the Clausius-Clapeyron Equation

PROBLEM The vapor pressure of ethanol is 115 torr at 34.9°C. If ΔH_{vap} of C_2H_5OH is 40.5 kJ/mol, calculate the temperature (in °C) when the vapor pressure is 760 torr.

PLAN We are given ΔH_{vap}, P_1, P_2, and T_1, so we substitute them into Equation 12.1 and solve for T_2. The value of R here is 8.31 J/mol · K, so we must convert T_1 to K to obtain T_2, and then convert T_2 to °C.

SOLUTION Substituting the values into Equation 12.1 and solving for T_2:

$$\ln \frac{P_2}{P_1} = \frac{-\Delta H_{vap}}{R}\left(\frac{1}{T_2} - \frac{1}{T_1}\right)$$

$$T_1 = 34.9°C + 273.15 = 308.0 \text{ K}$$

$$\ln \frac{760 \text{ torr}}{115 \text{ torr}} = \left(-\frac{40.5 \times 10^3 \text{ J/mol}}{8.31 \text{ J/mol} \cdot \text{K}}\right)\left(\frac{1}{T_2} - \frac{1}{308.0 \text{ K}}\right)$$

$$1.888 = (-4.87 \times 10^3)\left[\frac{1}{T_2} - (3.247 \times 10^{-3})\right]$$

$$T_2 = 350. \text{ K}$$

Converting T_2 from K to °C:

$$T_2 = 350. \text{ K} - 273.15 = \boxed{77°C}$$

CHECK Round off to check the math. The change is in the right direction: higher P should occur at higher T. As we discuss next, a substance has a vapor pressure of 760 torr at its boiling point. Checking the *CRC Handbook of Chemistry and Physics* shows that the boiling point of ethanol is 78.5°C, very close to our answer.

Follow-up Problem 12.1 At 34.1°C, the vapor pressure of water is 40.1 torr. What is the vapor pressure at 85.5°C? The ΔH_{vap} of water is 40.7 kJ/mol.

◆ **Superheating** When a liquid reaches its boiling point, bubbles of gas need a site on which to form. If the container walls are smooth and particles of dust absent, bubbles may not form and the liquid becomes *superheated:* its temperature rises above its boiling point. When boiling occurs, it does so suddenly (bumping), and the liquid spatters, a common event when heating water in a microwave oven. In the lab, a stone *boiling chip* is added before heating the liquid to provide a surface on which bubbles can form.

The Relation Between Vapor Pressure and Boiling Point In an *open* container, the atmosphere bears down on the liquid surface. As the temperature rises, molecules leave the surface more often, and they also move more quickly throughout the liquid. At some temperature, the average E_k of the molecules in the liquid is great enough for bubbles of vapor to form *in the interior,* and the liquid boils. At any lower temperature, the bubbles collapse as soon as they form because the external pressure is greater than the vapor pressure inside the bubbles. Thus, the **boiling point** is *the temperature at which the vapor pressure equals the external pressure,* usually that of the atmosphere. ◆ Once boiling begins, the temperature remains constant until the liquid phase is gone because the applied heat is used by the molecules to overcome attractions and enter the gas phase.

Since atmospheric pressure varies with elevation, so does the boiling point. At high elevations, a lower pressure is exerted on the liquid surface, so molecules in the interior need less kinetic energy to form bubbles. At low elevations, the opposite occurs. Thus, *the boiling point depends on the applied pressure.* The *normal boiling point* is observed at standard atmospheric pressure (760 torr, or 101.3 kPa). In Figure 12.6, the horizontal dashed line shows the normal boiling points of the three liquids.

Since the boiling point is the temperature at which the vapor pressure equals the external pressure, we can also interpret the curves in Figure 12.6 as a plot of external pressure vs. boiling point. For instance, the H_2O curve shows that water boils at 100°C at 760 torr (sea level), at 94°C at 610 torr (Boulder, Colorado), and at about 72°C at 270 torr (top of Mt. Everest). ◆

Solid-Liquid Equilibria At the molecular level, the particles in a crystal are continually vibrating about their fixed positions. As the temperature rises, the particles vibrate more violently, until some have enough kinetic energy to break free of their positions: melting has begun. As more molecules enter the liquid (molten) phase, some collide with the solid and become fixed again. Because the phases remain in contact, a dynamic equilibrium is established when the melting rate equals the freezing rate. The temperature at which this occurs is the **melting point;** it is the same temperature as the freezing point, differing only in the direction of the energy flow. As with the boiling point, the temperature remains at the melting point as long as both phases are present. ◆

Because liquids and solids are nearly incompressible, a change in pressure has little effect on the rate of movement to or from the solid. Therefore, in contrast to the boiling point, the melting point is affected by pressure only very slightly, and a plot of pressure (*y* axis) vs. temperature (*x* axis) for a solid-liquid phase change is typically a straight, *nearly* vertical line.

Solid-Gas Equilibria Solids generally have much lower vapor pressures than liquids. Sublimation, the process of a pure solid changing directly into a gas, is much less familiar than vaporization because the necessary conditions of pressure and temperature are uncommon for most substances. Some solids *do* have high enough vapor pressures to sublime at normal conditions, including dry ice (carbon dioxide), iodine (Figure 12.8), moth repellents, and solid room deodorizers. A substance sublimes rather than melts because the combination of intermolecular attractions and atmospheric pressure is not great enough to keep the particles near one another when they leave the solid state. The pressure vs. temperature plot for the solid-gas transition shows a large effect of temperature on pressure; that is, it resembles the liquid-gas line in curving upward at higher temperatures.

◆ **Cooking Under Low or High Pressure** People who live or hike in mountainous regions cook their meals under lower atmospheric pressure. The resulting lower boiling point of the liquid means the food takes *more* time to cook. On the other hand, in a pressure cooker, the pressure exceeds that of the atmosphere, so the temperature rises above the normal boiling point. The food becomes hotter and, thus, takes *less* time to cook.

◆ **Supercooling** When a solid is melted and then cooled slowly, it may remain liquid below its freezing point because the molecules are unable to orient themselves into a crystalline array. Like superheating, *supercooling* gives an unstable state: a stir causes the liquid to crystallize immediately, as shown for supercooled thymol in the photo.

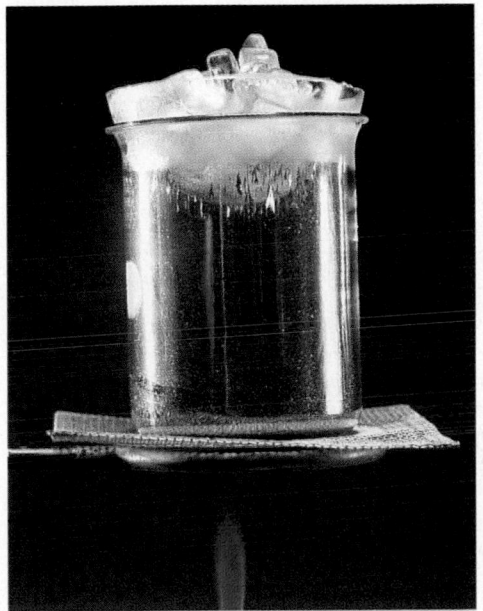

Figure 12.8 Iodine subliming. When solid iodine is heated at ordinary atmospheric pressure, it sublimes (changes directly from a solid into a gas). When the I_2 vapor comes in contact with a cold surface, it deposits I_2 crystals. Sublimation is a means of purification that, along with distillation, was probably discovered by the alchemists.

Phase Diagrams: The Effect of Pressure and Temperature on Physical State

To describe the phase changes of a substance at various conditions of temperature and pressure, we construct a **phase diagram,** which combines the liquid-gas, solid-liquid, and solid-gas curves just discussed. The shape of the phase diagram for CO_2, shown in Figure 12.9A, is typical for most substances. A phase diagram contains the following features:

1. *Regions of the diagram.* Each region corresponds to one phase of the substance. A particular phase is stable for any combination of pressure and temperature within its region. If any of the other phases is placed under those conditions, it will change to the stable phase. In general, the solid is stable at low temperature and high pressure, the gas at high temperature and low pressure, and the liquid at intermediate conditions.

2. *Lines between regions.* The lines separating the regions represent the phase-transition curves discussed earlier. Any point along a line shows the pressure and temperature at which the two phases exist in equilibrium. Note that the solid-liquid line has a *positive* slope (slants to the *right* with increasing pressure) because, for most substances, the solid is more dense than the liquid. Because the liquid occupies slightly more space than the solid, most substances expand slightly on melting. An increase in pressure favors the phase that occupies less space, which in most cases is the solid phase. (Water is the major exception, as you'll see in a moment.)

3. *The critical point.* The liquid-gas line ends at the **critical point.** Picture a liquid in a closed container. As it is heated, it expands, so its density decreases. At the same time, more liquid vaporizes, so the density of the vapor increases. The liquid and vapor densities become closer and closer to

A CO_2

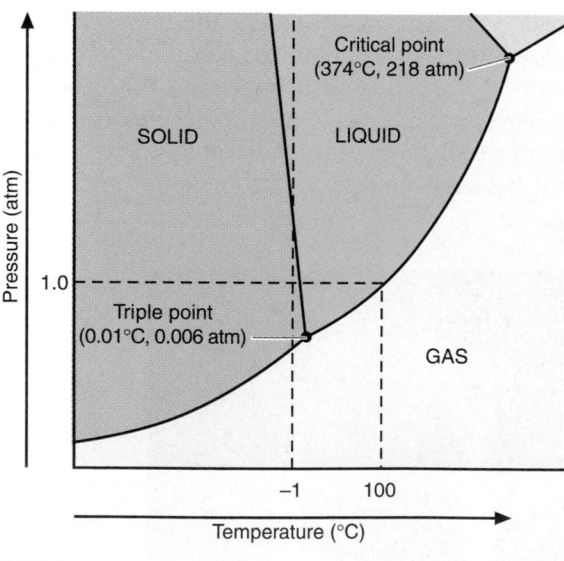

B H_2O

Figure 12.9 Phase diagrams for CO₂ and H₂O. Each region depicts the temperatures and pressures under which the phase is stable. The lines between any two regions show the conditions at which the two phases exist in equilibrium. The critical point shows the conditions beyond which separate liquid and gas phases no longer exist. Above the critical point, the liquid phase cannot exist regardless of the pressure. At the triple point, the three phases exist in equilibrium. (The axes are not linear.) **A,** The phase diagram for CO₂ is typical of most substances in that the solid-liquid line slopes to the right with increasing pressure: the solid is *more* dense than the liquid. **B,** Water is one of the few substances whose solid-liquid line slopes to the left with increasing pressure: the solid is *less* dense than the liquid. (The slopes of the solid-liquid lines in both diagrams are exaggerated.)

each other until, at the *critical temperature* (T_c), the two densities are equal and the phase boundary disappears. The pressure at this temperature is the *critical pressure* (P_c). At this point, the average E_k of the molecules is so high that the vapor cannot be condensed no matter what pressure is applied. The two most common gases in air, N_2 and O_2, have T_c values far below room temperature: O_2 does not condense above $-119°C$, nor N_2 above $-147°C$, no matter what the pressure. Beyond the critical temperature, a *supercritical fluid* exists rather than separate liquid and gaseous phases. ◆

4. *The triple point.* The three phase-transition curves meet at the **triple point:** the pressure and temperature at which three phases are in equilibrium. Phase diagrams for substances with several solid forms, such as sulfur, have more than one triple point. As strange as it sounds, at the triple point in Figure 12.9A, CO_2 is subliming and depositing, melting and freezing, and vaporizing and condensing simultaneously!

A close look at the CO_2 phase diagram clarifies a common question: why doesn't dry ice (solid CO_2) melt? The answer is that it does, but not under ordinary conditions. The triple-point pressure for CO_2 is 5.1 atm; therefore, at normal atmospheric pressure, liquid CO_2 does not occur. By following the horizontal dashed line in Figure 12.9A, you can see that when solid CO_2 is heated at 1.0 atm, it sublimes at $-78°C$ to gaseous CO_2 rather than melting. If normal atmospheric pressure were 5.2 atm, liquid CO_2 would be common.

The phase diagram for water, shown in Figure 12.9B, differs in one key respect from the general form, and reveals an extremely important property. Unlike almost every other substance, solid water is *less dense* than liquid water. Because the solid occupies *more* space than the liquid, *water expands on freezing.* This behavior results from the unique open crystal structure of ice, which we discuss in a later section. Once again, an increase in pressure favors the phase that occupies less space, but in the case of water, this is the *liquid* phase. Therefore, the solid-liquid line for water has a *negative* slope (slants to the *left* with increasing pressure): the higher the pressure, the lower the temperature at which water freezes. For example, follow the vertical dashed line at $-1°C$ to higher pressure and you see it cross the solid-liquid line, which means that at this temperature, ice melts with only an increase in pressure.

The triple point of water occurs at low pressure (0.006 atm). Therefore, when solid water is heated at 1.0 atm, the horizontal dashed line crosses the solid-liquid line (at 0°C, the normal melting point) and enters the liquid region. Thus, at ordinary pressures, ice melts rather than sublimes. As the temperature rises, the horizontal line crosses the liquid-gas curve (at 100°C, the normal boiling point) and enters the gas region.

The Remarkable Behavior of a Supercritical Fluid (SCF)

What sort of material lies beyond the familiar regions of liquid and gas? SCFs expand and contract like a gas but have the solvent properties of a liquid, properties that chemists can alter by controlling the density. Supercritical CO_2 has received the most attention so far from government and industry. It extracts nonpolar ingredients from complex mixtures, such as caffeine from coffee beans, nicotine from tobacco, and fats from potato and corn chips, while leaving taste and aroma ingredients behind, to produce healthier consumer products. Lower the pressure and it disperses immediately as a harmless gas. SCF CO_2 dissolves the fat from meat, along with pesticide and drug residues, which can then be quantified and monitored. It is currently being studied as an environmentally friendly dry cleaning agent. In an unexpected finding of great potential use, SCF H_2O was shown to dissolve nonpolar substances even though liquid water does not! Studies are under way for the large-scale removal of nonpolar organic toxins, such as PCBs, from industrial waste by their extraction into SCF H_2O; this step is followed by the introduction of O_2 gas, which oxidizes toxins to small, harmless molecules.

Section Summary

A heating-cooling curve depicts the change in temperature with heat loss or gain. Within a phase, temperature (and average E_k) change as heat is added or removed. During a phase change, temperature (and average E_k) are constant but E_p changes. The total heat change for the curve is calculated using Hess's law. In a closed container, equilibrium is established between the liquid and gas phases. Vapor pressure, the pressure of the gas at equilibrium, is related directly to temperature, and inversely to the strength of the intermolecular forces. The Clausius-Clapeyron equation uses ΔH_{vap} to relate the vapor pressure to the temperature. A liquid in an open container boils when its vapor pressure equals the external pressure. Solid-liquid equilibrium occurs at the melting point. Many solids sublime at low pressures and high

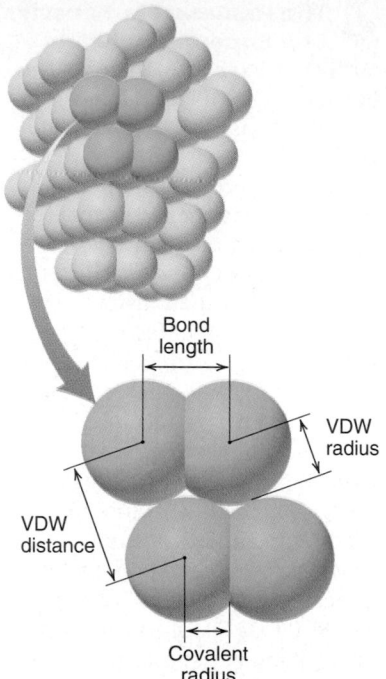

Figure 12.10 Covalent and van der Waals radii. As shown here for solid chlorine, the van der Waals radius is one-half the distance between adjacent *nonbonded* atoms ($\frac{1}{2}$ × VDW distance), and the covalent radius is one-half the distance between *bonded* atoms ($\frac{1}{2}$ × bond length).

Figure 12.11 Periodic trends in covalent and van der Waals radii (in pm). Like covalent radii (*dark blue quarter-circles and top numbers*), van der Waals radii (*light blue quarter-circles and bottom numbers*) increase down a group and decrease across a period. Note that the covalent radius of an element is *always* less than its van der Waals radius.

temperatures. A phase diagram shows the phase that exists at a given pressure and temperature and the conditions at the critical point and the triple point of a substance. Water differs from most substances in that its solid phase is less dense than its liquid phase, so its solid-liquid line has a negative slope.

12.3 Types of Intermolecular Forces

Both bonding (intramolecular) forces and intermolecular forces arise from electrostatic attractions between opposite charges. Bonding forces are due to the attraction between cations and anions (ionic bonding), nuclei and electron pairs (covalent bonding), or metal cations and delocalized valence electrons (metallic bonding). Intermolecular forces, on the other hand, are due to the attraction between molecules as a result of partial charges, or between ions and molecules. The two types of forces differ in magnitude, and Coulomb's law explains why:

- *Bonding forces are relatively strong* because they involve larger charges that are closer together.
- *Intermolecular forces are relatively weak* because they typically involve smaller charges that are farther apart.

How far apart are the charges between molecules that give rise to intermolecular forces? Consider Cl_2 as an example. When we measure the distances between two Cl nuclei in a sample of solid Cl_2, we obtain two different values, as shown in Figure 12.10. The shorter distance is between *two* **bonded** *Cl atoms in the same molecule.* It is, as you know, called the *bond length,* and one-half this distance is the *covalent radius.* The longer distance is between *two* **nonbonded** *Cl atoms in adjacent molecules.* It is called the *van der Waals distance* (named after the Dutch physicist Johannes van der Waals, who studied the effects of intermolecular forces on the behavior of real gases). This distance is the *closest* one Cl_2 molecule can approach another, the point at which intermolecular attractions balance electron-cloud repulsions. One-half this distance is the **van der Waals radius,** one-half the closest distance between the nuclei of identical *nonbonded* Cl atoms. *The van der Waals radius of an atom is always larger than its covalent radius,* but van der Waals radii decrease across a period and increase down a group, just as covalent radii do. Figure 12.11 shows these relationships for many of the nonmetals.

There are several types of intermolecular forces: ion-dipole, dipole-dipole, hydrogen bonding, dipole–induced dipole, and dispersion forces. As we discuss these *intermolecular* forces (also called van der Waals forces), look at Table 12.2, which compares them with the stronger *intramolecular* (bonding) forces and lists them in decreasing order of their relative strengths.

Ion-Dipole Forces

When an ion and a nearby polar molecule (dipole) attract each other, an **ion-dipole force** results. The most important example takes place when an ionic compound dissolves in water. The ions become separated because the attractions between the ions and the oppositely charged poles of the H_2O molecules overcome the attractions between the ions themselves. Ion-dipole forces and their associated energy are discussed fully in the context of solutions in Chapter 13.

Dipole-Dipole Forces

In Chapter 10, you saw how gaseous polar molecules are oriented by a large, external electric field. When polar molecules lie near one another, as in liquids and solids, their partial charges act as tiny electric fields that orient them and give rise to **dipole-dipole forces:** the positive pole of one molecule attracts the negative pole of another. Figure 12.12 depicts these orientations.

Table 12.2 Comparison of the Energies Associated with Bonding (Intramolecular) Forces and Intermolecular Forces

Force	Model	Basis of Attraction	Energy (kJ/mol)	Example
Intramolecular				
Ionic		Cation–anion	400–4000	NaCl
Covalent		Nuclei–shared e^- pair	150–1100	H—H
Metallic		Cations–delocalized electrons	75–1000	Fe
Intermolecular				
Ion-dipole		Ion charge–dipole charge	40–600	$Na^+ \cdots$ O⟨H H
H bond	$\delta^- \;\; \delta^+ \qquad \delta^-$ —A—H$\cdots\cdots$:B—	Polar bond to H–dipole charge (high EN of N, O, F)	10–40	:Ö—H$\cdots$:Ö—H │ │ H H
Dipole-dipole		Dipole charges	5–25	I—Cl$\cdots$I—Cl
Ion-induced dipole		Ion charge–polarizable e^- cloud	3–15	$Fe^{2+}\cdots O_2$
Dipole-induced dipole		Dipole charge–polarizable e^- cloud	2–10	H—Cl$\cdots$Cl—Cl
Dispersion (London)		Polarizable e^- clouds	0.05–40	F—F$\cdots$F—F

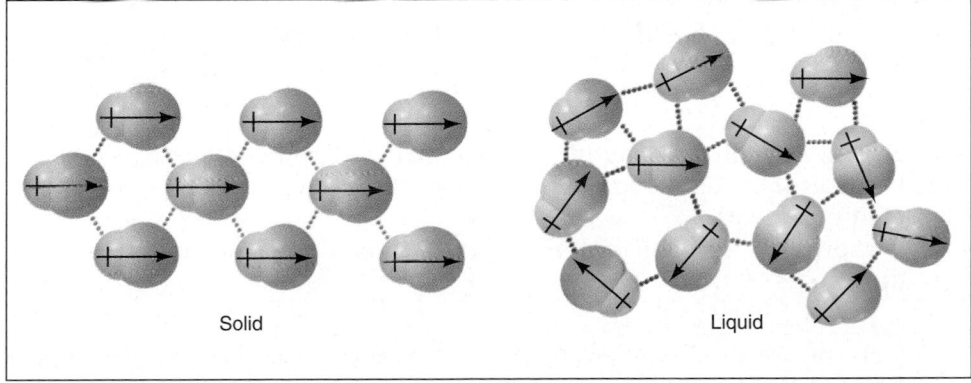

Solid   Liquid

Figure 12.12 Orientation of polar molecules because of dipole-dipole forces. In the condensed states, the polar molecules are close enough for partial charges of one molecule to attract nearby opposite charges, and the molecules become oriented. The arrangement is more orderly in the solid phase (*left*) of a substance than in the liquid (*right*) because, at the lower temperatures required for freezing, the average kinetic energy of the particles is lower. (Interparticle spaces are increased for clarity.)

Figure 12.13 Dipole moment and boiling point. For compounds of similar molar mass, the boiling point increases with increasing dipole moment. (Note the increasing color separations and intensities in the electron density models.) The greater dipole moment creates stronger dipole-dipole forces, which require higher temperatures to overcome.

| | Dipole moment (D x 100) |
| | Boiling point (K) |

Propane
$CH_3CH_2CH_3$
44.09 g/mol

Dimethyl ether
CH_3OCH_3
46.07 g/mol

Methyl chloride
CH_3Cl
50.48 g/mol

Acetaldehyde
CH_3CHO
44.05 g/mol

Acetonitrile
CH_3CN
41.05 g/mol

These are the forces that give polar *cis*-1,2-dichloroethylene a higher boiling point than the nonpolar *trans* compound (see p. 386). In fact, for molecular compounds of approximately the same size and molar mass, the greater the dipole moment, the greater the dipole-dipole force between their molecules, so the more energy it takes to separate them. Consider the boiling points of the compounds in Figure 12.13. Methyl chloride, for instance, has a smaller dipole moment than acetaldehyde, so less energy is needed to overcome the dipole-dipole forces between its molecules and it boils at a lower temperature.

The Hydrogen Bond

A special type of dipole-dipole force arises between molecules that have *an H atom bound to a small, highly electronegative atom with lone electron pairs*. The most important atoms that fit this description are nitrogen, oxygen, and fluorine. The covalent bond between H and N, O, or F is very polar, so electron density is withdrawn from H. As a result, the partially positive H of one molecule is attracted to the partially negative lone pair on the N, O, or F of another molecule, and a **hydrogen bond (H bond)** forms. Thus, the atom sequence that leads to an H bond (dotted line) is —B:····H—A— , where *both* A and B are N, O, or F. Three such examples are

$$—\ddot{F}:····H—\ddot{O}—   —\ddot{O}:····H—\ddot{N}—   —\ddot{N}:····H—\ddot{F}:$$

The small sizes of N, O, and F* are essential to H-bonding for two reasons:
1. It makes these atoms so electronegative that their covalently bonded H is highly positive.
2. It allows the lone pair on the other N, O, or F to come close enough to the H.

---

*H-bond—type interactions occur with the larger P, S, and Cl, but they are so much weaker than those with N, O, and F that they do not affect our discussion.

Sample Problem 12.2 Drawing Hydrogen Bonds Between Molecules

PROBLEM Which of the following substances exhibits H bonding? Draw the H bonds between two molecules of the substance where appropriate.

(a) C_2H_6 (b) CH_3OH (c) $CH_3\overset{\overset{O}{\|}}{C}{-}NH_2$

PLAN We examine each structure to see if it contains N, O, or F covalently bonded to H.

SOLUTION (a) For C_2H_6. No H bonds are formed.

(b) For CH_3OH. The H covalently bonded to the O in one molecule forms an H bond to the lone pair on the O of an adjacent molecule:

(c) For $CH_3\overset{\overset{O}{\|}}{C}{-}NH_2$. Two of these molecules can form one H bond from the H of N to O, or they can form two H bonds:

A third possibility (not shown) could be between an H attached to N on one molecule and the N lone pair of another molecule.

CHECK Make sure that the —B:····H—A— sequence (with A and B either N, O, or F) is present.

COMMENT Note that *H covalently bonded to C does not form H bonds* because the C is not electronegative enough to make the C—H bond very polar.

Follow-up Problem 12.2 Which of these substances exhibits H bonding? Draw the H bonds between two molecules of the substance where appropriate.

(a) $CH_3\overset{\overset{O}{\|}}{C}{-}OH$ (b) CH_3CH_2OH (c) $CH_3\overset{\overset{O}{\|}}{C}CH_3$

The Significance of H Bonding H bonding has a profound impact in many systems. Figure 12.14 shows its dramatic effect on the boiling points of Group 4A(14) through 7A(17) hydrides. For reasons that we'll discuss shortly, boiling points typically rise as molar mass increases, as you can see in the 4A hydrides CH_4 through SnH_4. In the other groups, however, the first member in each series—NH_3, H_2O, and HF—deviates enormously from this expected increase because H bonds keep these molecules together. Therefore, additional energy is required to break the H bonds before the molecules can separate and enter the gas phase. For example, on the basis of molar mass alone, we would expect water to boil about 200°C lower than it does! (The H bonds in water also have critical effects on the environment and living things; Section 12.5.)

Even though the strength of one H bond is relatively small (~5% of a typical covalent single bond energy), the combined strength of many H bonds can be large.

Figure 12.14 Hydrogen bonding and boiling point. The boiling points of the binary hydrides from Groups 4A(14) to 7A(17) are plotted against period number. The H bonds in NH_3, H_2O, and HF give them much higher boiling points than if the trend were based on molar mass, as it is for Group 4A. Thus, if not for its H bonds, water would boil almost 200°C lower than it does *(dashed line)*.

Consider the H bonds in deoxyribonucleic acid (DNA), the giant molecule in all cells that acts as a genetic "blueprint," governing the function and appearance of the entire organism. As Figure 12.15 shows, DNA consists of two molecular chains wrapped around each other in a long double helix (see also Gallery, p. 75). Strong covalent bonds link the atoms in each chain, but the two intertwining chains are joined by millions of H bonds. The total energy of the H bonds keeps the chains together during many processes, but each H bond is so weak that a few at a time break so that the chains can separate during the crucial processes of protein synthesis and cell reproduction. (We discuss these processes in Chapter 15.)

Polarizability and Charge-Induced Dipole Forces

Even though electrons are localized in bonding or lone pairs, they are in constant motion, so that we often picture them as "clouds" of negative charge. A nearby electric field can distort this cloud, pulling electron density toward a positive charge or pushing it away from a negative charge. In effect, the field *induces* a distortion in the electron cloud. For a nonpolar molecule, this distortion results in a temporary, induced dipole moment; for a polar molecule, it enhances the dipole moment that is already present. The source of the electric field can be the electrodes of a battery, the charge of a nearby ion, or even the partial charges of a nearby polar molecule.

The ease with which a particle's electron cloud can be distorted is called its **polarizability.** Smaller atoms (or ions) are less polarizable than larger ones because their electrons are closer to the nucleus and held more tightly. Thus,

- *Polarizability increases down a group* of atoms (or ions) because size increases and larger electron clouds are more easily distorted.
- *Polarizability decreases from left to right across a period* because the increasing effective nuclear charge holds the electrons more tightly.
- Cations are *less* polarizable than their parent atom because they are smaller, whereas anions are *more* polarizable because they are larger.

Ion-induced dipole and dipole–induced dipole forces are the two types of charge-induced dipole forces, but they are most important in solution, so we'll focus on them in Chapter 13. Nevertheless, the concept of polarizability is a general one that applies to all intermolecular forces.

Dispersion (London) Forces

Up to this point, we've discussed intermolecular forces that depend on an existing charge, either in an ion or a polar molecule. But what forces cause nonpolar substances like octane, chlorine, and the noble gases to condense and solidify? An attractive force must be acting between the particles, or these substances would be gases under any conditions. The intermolecular force primarily responsible for the condensed states of nonpolar substances is the **dispersion force** (or **London force,** named for Fritz London, the German physicist who first explained the quantum-mechanical basis of the attraction).

Dispersion forces are caused by *momentary oscillations of electron charge*. Over time, the electron charge within an atom is distributed uniformly around the nucleus, and the atom is nonpolar. But at any instant, this may not be the case, and the atom has an *instantaneous dipole* that can influence nearby atoms. Picture two argon atoms. When far apart, the atoms do not influence each other. When near each other, however, *the instantaneous dipole in each atom induces a dipole in its neighbor.* The result is a synchronized motion of the electrons in the two atoms, which causes an attraction between them. This process occurs with other nearby atoms and, thus, throughout the sample. At low enough temperatures, the attractions among the dipoles keep all the

Figure 12.15 Covalent bonding and H bonding in the structure of deoxyribonucleic acid (DNA). The DNA molecule consists of two chains. Each is held together by strong covalent bonds, but millions of H bonds link one chain tightly to the other to form a double helix.

Figure 12.16 Dispersion forces among nonpolar molecules. The dispersion force is responsible for the condensed states of noble gases and nonpolar molecules. **A,** Separated H_2 molecules are nonpolar. **B,** An instantaneous dipole in each molecule induces a dipole in its neighbor. These partial charges attract the molecules together. **C,** This process takes place among molecules throughout the sample.

atoms together. Thus, dispersion forces are *instantaneous dipole–induced dipole forces.* Figure 12.16 depicts the dispersion forces among nonpolar molecules.

*Dispersion forces are weak, but they exist between **any** particles.* Therefore, except for small, polar molecules with large dipole moments or those able to form H bonds, *the dispersion force is the dominant intermolecular force between identical molecules.* The relative strength of the dispersion force depends on the polarizability of the particle, which in turn depends on its size. In general terms, therefore, *dispersion forces increase with number of electrons, which correlates closely with molar mass* because particles with greater mass have more atoms and/or larger (heavier) atoms and thus more electrons. For example, Figure 12.17 shows that as molar mass increases down the halogens or noble gases, dispersion forces become greater, which is reflected in higher boiling points.

For nonpolar substances with the same molar mass, the strength of the dispersion force may be influenced by molecular shape. Shapes that allow more points of contact have more area over which electron clouds can be distorted, so stronger attractions result. Consider the hydrocarbons *n*-pentane and neopentane, which have the same formula (C_5H_{12}) but different shapes. As shown in Figure 12.18, *n*-pentane is a chain of five C atoms and is somewhat cylindrical. Neopentane has two CH_3 branches off a three-C chain and, thus, a more spherical shape. As a result, two *n*-pentane molecules make more contact with each other than do two neopentane molecules. Greater contact allows the dispersion forces to act at more points, so *n*-pentane has the higher boiling point.

Figure 12.17 **Molar mass and boiling point.** The strength of dispersion forces increases with number of electrons, which usually correlates with molar mass. One effect of this is the higher boiling points going down the groups for halogens and noble gases.

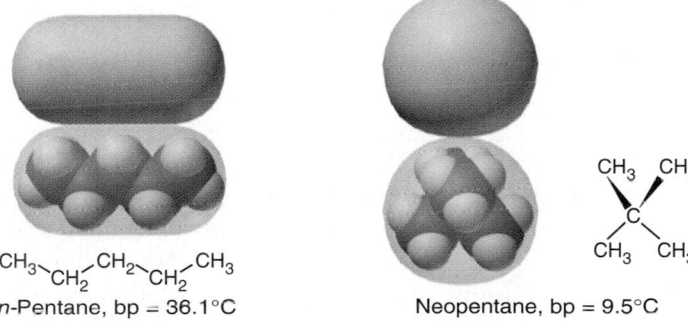

n-Pentane, bp = 36.1°C   Neopentane, bp = 9.5°C

Figure 12.18 **Molecular shape and boiling point.** The spherical neopentane molecules make less contact with each other than do the cylindrical *n*-pentane molecules, so neopentane has a lower boiling point.

Sample Problem 12.3   Predicting the Type and Relative Strength of Intermolecular Forces

PROBLEM Identify the dominant intermolecular forces for each of the following substances, and select the substance with the higher boiling point in each pair:
(a) $MgCl_2$ or PCl_3 (b) CH_3NH_2 or CH_3F
(c) CH_3OH or CH_3CH_2OH (d) Hexane or cyclohexane

PLAN We examine the formulas and picture (or draw) the structures to identify key differences between members of each pair: Are ions present? Are molecules polar or nonpolar? Is N, O, or F bonded to H? Do the molecules have different masses or shapes? To rank their strengths, we consult Table 12.2 and remember that

• Intramolecular (bonding) forces are stronger than intermolecular forces.
• Hydrogen bonding is a strong type of dipole-dipole force.
• Dispersion forces are decisive when the major difference is molar mass or molecular shape.

SOLUTION (a) $MgCl_2$ consists of Mg^{2+} and Cl^- ions held together by ionic bonding forces; PCl_3 consists of polar molecules, so intermolecular dipole-dipole forces are present. The forces in $MgCl_2$ are stronger, so it has a higher boiling point.

Cyclohexane

Hexane

(b) CH_3NH_2 and CH_3F both consist of polar molecules of about the same molar mass. CH_3NH_2 has N—H bonds, so it can form H bonds (see margin). CH_3F contains a C—F bond but no H—F bond, so dipole-dipole forces occur but not H bonds. Therefore, CH_3NH_2 has the higher boiling point.

(c) CH_3OH and CH_3CH_2OH molecules both contain an O—H bond, so they can form H bonds. CH_3CH_2OH has an additional —CH_2— group and thus a larger molar mass, which correlates with stronger dispersion forces; therefore, it has a higher boiling point.

(d) Hexane and cyclohexane are nonpolar molecules of about the same molar mass but different molecular shapes (see margin). Cylindrical hexane molecules make less intermolecular contact than disc-like cyclohexane molecules, so cyclohexane should have greater dispersion forces and a higher boiling point.

Check The actual boiling points show that our predictions are correct:

(a) $MgCl_2$ (1412°C) and PCl_3 (76°C)

(b) CH_3NH_2 (−6.3°C) and CH_3F (−78.4°C)

(c) CH_3OH (64.7°C) and CH_3CH_2OH (78.5°C)

(d) Hexane (69°C) and cyclohexane (80.7°C)

Comment Dispersion forces are *always* present, but in parts **(a)** and **(b),** they are much less significant than the other forces involved.

Follow-up Problem 12.3   In each of the following pairs, identify all the intermolecular forces present and select the substance with the higher boiling point:
(a) CH_3Br or CH_3F **(b)** $CH_3CH_2CH_2OH$ or $CH_3CH_2OCH_3$ **(c)** C_2H_6 or C_3H_8

Section Summary

The van der Waals radius determines the shortest distance over which intermolecular forces operate; it is always larger than the covalent radius. Intermolecular forces are much weaker than bonding (intramolecular) forces. Ion-dipole forces occur between ions and polar molecules. Dipole-dipole forces occur between oppositely charged poles on polar molecules. Hydrogen bonding, a special type of dipole-dipole force, occurs when H bonded to N, O, or F is attracted to the lone pair of N, O, or F on another molecule. Electron clouds can be distorted (polarized) in an electric field. Ion- and dipole-induced dipole forces arise between a charge and the dipole it induces in another molecule. Dispersion (London) forces are instantaneous dipole-induced dipole forces that occur among all particles and increase with number of electrons (molar mass). Molecular shape determines the extent of contact between molecules and thus can be a factor in the strength of dispersion forces.

12.4 Properties of the Liquid State

Of the three states of matter, the liquid state is the least understood at the molecular level. Because of the *randomness* of the particles in a gas, any region of the sample is virtually identical to any other. Also, as you'll see in Section 12.6, different regions of a crystalline solid are identical because of the *orderliness* of the particles. Liquids, however, have a combination of these attributes that changes continually and defies simple description: a region that is orderly one moment becomes random the next, and vice versa. Despite this complexity at the molecular level, the macroscopic behavior of liquids is well understood. In this section, we discuss three liquid properties—surface tension, capillarity, and viscosity—in terms of the intermolecular forces that create them.

Surface Tension

Within a liquid, intermolecular forces are at play that exert effects differently depending on a molecule's location. As Figure 12.19 shows, molecules in the interior are attracted by others on all sides, whereas molecules at the surface have others only below and to the sides. As a result, molecules at the surface experience a *net attraction* downward and move into the interior to increase attractions and, thus, become more stable. Therefore, *a liquid surface tends to have the smallest possible area,* that of a sphere, and behaves like a "taut skin" covering the interior.

To increase the surface area, molecules must move to the surface by breaking some attractions in the interior, which requires energy. The **surface tension** of a liquid is the energy required to increase the surface area by a unit amount (in SI, the units are J/m^2). Some representative values are presented in Table 12.3. By comparing these values with those in Table 12.2, you can see that, in general, *the stronger the forces are between the particles in a liquid, the greater the surface tension.* Water has a high surface tension because its molecules form multiple H bonds. *Surfactants* (surface-active agents), such as soaps, detergents, petroleum recovery agents, and biological fat emulsifiers, decrease the surface tension of water by congregating at the surface and disrupting the H bonds.

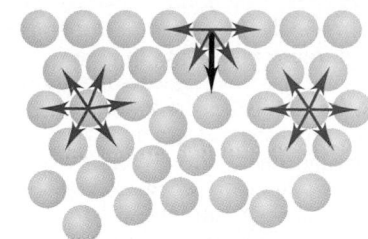

Figure 12.19 The molecular basis of surface tension. Molecules in the interior of a liquid experience intermolecular attractions in all directions. Molecules at the surface experience a net attraction downward and move into the interior. Thus, a liquid tends to minimize the number of molecules at the surface, which results in surface tension.

Table 12.3 Surface Tension and Forces Between Particles

Substance	Formula	Surface Tension (J/m^2) at 20°C	Major Force(s)
Diethyl ether	$CH_3CH_2OCH_2CH_3$	1.7×10^{-2}	Dipole-dipole; dispersion
Ethanol	CH_3CH_2OH	2.3×10^{-2}	H bonding
Butanol	$CH_3CH_2CH_2CH_2OH$	2.5×10^{-2}	H bonding; dispersion
Water	H_2O	7.3×10^{-2}	H bonding
Mercury	Hg	48×10^{-2}	Metallic bonding

Capillarity

For simple blood-screening tests, a sample may be taken by pricking the finger. A narrow tube, called a *capillary tube,* is placed against the skin opening, and the liquid rises up through the tube against the pull of gravity (see photo). This phenomenon is called capillary action, or **capillarity,** and it results from a competition between the intermolecular forces within the liquid (cohesive forces) and those between the liquid and the tube walls (adhesive forces).

Picture what occurs at the molecular level when you place a glass capillary tube in water. Glass is mostly silicon dioxide (SiO_2), so the water molecules form H bonds to the oxygen atoms of the tube's inner wall. The adhesive forces (H bonding) between the water and the wall are stronger than the cohesive forces (H bonding) within the water, so a thin film of water creeps up the wall. At the same time, the cohesive forces that give rise to surface tension pull the liquid surface taut. These adhesive and cohesive forces combine to raise the water level and produce the familiar concave meniscus seen in Figure 12.20A on the next page. The liquid rises until gravity pulling down is balanced by the adhesive forces.

On the other hand, if you place a glass capillary tube in a dish of mercury, the mercury level in the tube drops below that in the dish. Mercury has a higher surface tension than water (see Table 12.3), which means it has

Figure 12.20 **Shape of the water or mercury meniscus in glass.**
A, Water displays a concave meniscus in a glass tube because the adhesive (H bond) forces between the H_2O molecules and the O—Si—O groups of the glass are *stronger* than the cohesive (H bond) forces within the water.
B, Mercury displays a convex meniscus in a glass tube because the cohesive (metallic bonding) forces within the mercury are stronger than the adhesive (dispersion) forces between the mercury and the glass.

stronger cohesive forces (metallic bonding). The cohesive forces among the mercury atoms are stronger than the relatively weak adhesive forces (mostly dispersion) between mercury and glass, so the liquid tends to pull away from the walls. At the same time, the surface atoms are being pulled toward the interior of the mercury by its high surface tension, so the level drops. These combined forces produce the convex meniscus, shown in Figure 12.20B, that you see in a mercury barometer or manometer.

Viscosity

When a liquid flows, the molecules slide around and past each other. The extent to which intermolecular attractions resist this movement results in a liquid's **viscosity,** its resistance to flow. Both gases and liquids flow, but liquid viscosities are higher because the intermolecular forces operate over much shorter distances.

The *viscosity of a liquid decreases with heating,* as you can see for water in Table 12.4. Since molecules move faster at higher temperatures, they can overcome intermolecular forces more easily, so their resistance to flow decreases. You can see this if you put cooking oil in a cool pan, turn on the heat, and watch the oil spread out in a thin layer.

Molecular shape plays a role in a liquid's viscosity. Long molecules make more contact than spherical ones, so for the same types of forces, liquids containing longer molecules have higher viscosities. A striking example of a change in viscosity occurs during the making of syrup. Even at room temperature, a concentrated aqueous sugar solution has a higher viscosity than water because of H bonding among the many hydroxyl (—OH) groups on the ring-shaped sugar molecules. When the solution is slowly heated to boiling, the sugar molecules react with each other and link covalently, gradually forming long chains. Hydrogen bonds and dispersion forces occur at many points along the chains, and the resulting syrup is a viscous liquid that pours slowly and clings to a spoon. When a viscous syrup is cooled, it may become stiff enough to be picked up and stretched—into taffy candy. The Gallery shows other familiar examples of these three liquid properties.

Table 12.4 Viscosity of Water at Several Temperatures

Temperature (°C)	Viscosity (N · s/m²)*
20	1.00×10^{-3}
40	0.65×10^{-3}
60	0.47×10^{-3}
80	0.35×10^{-3}

*The units of viscosity are newton-seconds per square meter.

Properties of Liquids

Of the three states, only liquids combine the ability to flow with the strength that comes from intermolecular contact, and this combination appears in numerous applications.

Beaded droplets on waxy surfaces

The adhesive (dipole–induced dipole) forces between water and a nonpolar surface are much weaker than the cohesive (H-bond) forces within water. As a result, water pulls away from a nonpolar surface and forms beaded droplets. You have seen this effect when water beads on a flower petal or a freshly waxed car after a rainfall.

Minimizing a surface

In the low-gravity environment of the orbiting Space Shuttle, the tendency of a liquid to minimize its surface creates perfectly spherical droplets, unlike the elongated drops we see on Earth. For the same reason, bubbles in a soft drink are spherical because the liquid uses the minimum number of molecules needed to surround the gas. A water strider flits across a pond on widespread legs that do not exert enough pressure to exceed the surface tension.

Maintaining motor oil viscosity

To protect engine parts during long drives or in hot weather, when an oil would ordinarily become too thin, motor oils contain additives, called *polymeric viscosity index improvers,* that make the oil thicken. As the oil heats up, the additive molecules change shape from compact spheres to spaghetti-like strands and become tangled with the hydrocarbon oil molecules. As a result of the greater dispersion forces, the viscosity increases to compensate for the decrease due to heating.

Capillary action after a shower

Paper and cotton consist of fibers of cellulose, long carbon-containing molecules with many attached hydroxyl (—OH) groups. A towel dries you in two ways: First, capillary action draws the water molecules away from your body between the closely spaced cellulose molecules. Second, the water molecules themselves form adhesive H bonds to the cellulose —OH groups.

How a ballpoint pen works

The essential parts of a ballpoint pen are the moving ball and its contact with the viscous ink. The material of the ball is chosen for its strong adhesive forces with the ink. Cohesive forces within the ink are replaced by those adhesive forces when the ink "wets" the ball. As the ball rolls along the paper, the adhesive forces between ball and ink are replaced by those between ink and paper. The rest of the ink stays in the pen because of its high viscosity.

Ink

Moving ball

Paper surface

Section Summary

Surface tension is a measure of the energy required to increase a liquid's surface area. Greater intermolecular forces within the liquid create higher surface tension. Capillary action, the rise of a liquid through a narrow space, occurs when the forces between a liquid and a solid surface (adhesive) are greater than those within the liquid itself (cohesive). Viscosity, the resistance to flow, depends on molecular shape and decreases with temperature. Stronger intermolecular forces within a liquid give it higher viscosity.

12.5   The Uniqueness of Water

Water is so familiar that we take it for granted, but it has some of the most unusual properties of any substance. These properties, which are vital to our very existence, arise inevitably from the nature of the H and O atoms that make up the molecule. Each atom attains a filled outer level by sharing electrons in single covalent bonds. With two bonding pairs and two lone pairs around the O atom and a large electronegativity difference in each O—H bond, the H_2O molecule is bent and highly polar. This arrangement is important because it allows each water molecule to engage in four H bonds with its neighbors, as shown in Figure 12.21. From these fundamental atomic and molecular properties emerges remarkable macroscopic behavior.

Solvent Properties of Water

The *great solvent power* of water is the result of its polarity *and* its exceptional H-bonding ability. Water dissolves ionic compounds through ion-dipole forces that separate the ions from the solid and keep them in solution (see Figure 4.3, p. 137). Water dissolves many polar nonionic substances, such as ethanol (CH_3CH_2OH) and glucose ($C_6H_{12}O_6$), by forming H bonds to them. Water even dissolves nonpolar gases to a limited extent, such as those in the atmosphere, through dipole-induced dipole and dispersion forces. Chapter 13 highlights these solvent properties.

Because it can dissolve so many substances, water is the environmental and biological solvent, forming the complex solutions we know as oceans, rivers, lakes, and cell fluids. Aquatic animals could not survive without dissolved O_2, nor could aquatic plants survive without dissolved CO_2. The coral reefs that girdle the sea bottom in tropical latitudes are composed of carbonates made by tiny marine animals from dissolved CO_2 and HCO_3^- (Figure 12.22). Life itself is thought to have begun in a "primordial soup," a rich aqueous mixture of simple biomolecules from which emerged the larger molecules and their self-sustaining reactions that are characteristic of living things. From a chemical point of view, all organisms, from bacteria to humans, can be thought of as highly organized systems of membranes enclosing and compartmentalizing complex aqueous solutions.

Thermal Properties of Water

Water has an exceptionally *high specific heat capacity*, higher than almost any other liquid. Recall from Section 6.3 that heat capacity is a measure of the heat absorbed by a substance for a given temperature rise. When a substance is heated, some of the energy increases the average molecular speed, some increases molecular vibration and rotation, and some is used to overcome intermolecular forces. Because water has so many strong H bonds, it has a high specific heat capacity. Since oceans and seas cover 70% of the Earth's surface, heat from the Sun causes relatively small changes in daily tempera-

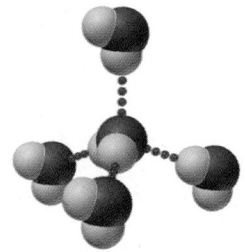

Figure 12.21   The H-bonding ability of the water molecule. Because it has two O—H bonds and two lone pairs, one H_2O molecule can engage in as many as four H bonds to surrounding H_2O molecules, which are arranged tetrahedrally.

Figure 12.22   Coral. Coral reef organisms form their carbonate-based skeletons from dissolved CO_2 and HCO_3^-. The reef is made of the skeletons of millions of these tiny animals.

tures, allowing our planet to support life. On the waterless, airless Moon, temperatures can range from 100°C (212°F) to −150°C (−238°F) in the same day. Even in Earth's deserts, where a dense atmosphere tempers these extremes, day-night temperature differences of 40°C (72°F) are common.

Numerous strong H bonds also give water an exceptionally *high heat of vaporization*. A quick calculation shows how essential this property is to our existence. When 1000 g water absorbs about 4 kJ of heat, its temperature rises 1°C. With a ΔH^0_{vap} of 2.3 kJ/g, however, less than 2 g water must evaporate to keep the temperature constant for the remaining 998 g. The average human adult has 40 kg body water and generates about 10,000 kJ of heat each day from metabolism. If this heat were used only to increase the average E_k of body water, the temperature rise would mean immediate death. Instead, the heat is converted to E_p as it breaks H bonds and evaporates sweat, resulting in a stable body temperature and minimal loss of body fluid.

The Sun's energy supplies the heat of vaporization for ocean water. Water vapor, formed in warm latitudes, moves through the atmosphere, and its potential energy is released as heat to warm cooler regions when the vapor condenses to rain. The enormous energy involved in this cycling of water powers the storms and winds of the planet.

Surface Properties of Water

The H bonds that give water its remarkable thermal properties are also responsible for its *high surface tension* and *high capillarity*. Except for some metals and molten salts, water has the highest surface tension of any liquid. This property is vital for surface aquatic life because it keeps plant debris resting on a pond surface, which provides shelter and nutrients for many fish, microorganisms, and insects. Water's high capillarity, a direct result of its high surface tension, is crucial to the survival of land plants. During dry periods, plant roots absorb deep ground water, which rises by capillary action through the tiny spaces between soil particles.

The Density of Solid and Liquid Water

As you saw in Figure 12.21, in the H bonds of water, each O atom becomes connected to as many as four other O atoms via four H atoms. Continuing this pattern through many molecules in a fixed array gives ice the hexagonal, *open structure* shown in Figure 12.23A. The symmetrical beauty of snowflakes, as shown in Figure 12.23B, reflects this hexagonal organization.

This organization explains the negative slope of the solid-liquid curve in the phase diagram for water: as pressure is applied, some H bonds break and, as a result, some water molecules enter the spaces. The crystal structure breaks down, and the sample liquefies.

The large spaces within ice give *the solid state a lower density than the liquid state*. When the surface of a lake freezes in winter, the ice floats on the liquid water below. If the solid were denser than the liquid, as is true for nearly every other substance, the surface of a lake would freeze and sink repeatedly until the entire lake was solid. Aquatic life would not survive from year to year.

The density of water changes in a complex way. When ice melts at 0°C, the tetrahedral arrangement around each O atom breaks down, and the loosened molecules pack much more closely, filling spaces in the collapsing solid structure. As a result, water is most dense (1.000 g/mL) at around 4°C (3.98°C). With more heating, the density decreases through normal thermal expansion.

A

B

Figure 12.23 **The hexagonal structure of ice. A,** As a consequence of the geometric requirements of the H bonds in H_2O, ice has an open, hexagonally shaped crystal structure. Thus, when liquid water freezes, the volume *increases*. **B,** The delicate six-pointed beauty of a snowflake reflects the hexagonal crystal structure of ice.

Figure 12.24 The expansion and contraction of water. As water freezes and thaws repeatedly, the stress can break rocks. Over geologic time, the process creates sand and soil.

This change in density is vital for freshwater life. As lake water becomes colder in the fall and early winter, it becomes more dense *before* it freezes. Similarly, in spring, less dense ice thaws to form more dense water *before* the water expands. During both these seasonal density changes, the top layer of water reaches the high-density point first and sinks. The next layer of water rises because it is slightly less dense, reaches 4°C, and likewise sinks. This sinking and rising distributes nutrients and dissolved oxygen.

The expansion and contraction of water affect the land dramatically also. When rain fills the crevices in rocks and then freezes, great outward stress is applied, to be relieved only when the ice melts. In time, this repeated freeze-thaw stress cracks the rocks apart (Figure 12.24). Over eons of geologic change, this effect has helped to produce the sand and soil of the planet.

The properties of water and their far-reaching consequences illustrate the theme that runs throughout this book: the world we know is the stepwise, macroscopic outgrowth of the atomic world we seek to know. Figure 12.25

Figure 12.25 The macroscopic properties of water and their atomic and molecular "roots."

offers a fanciful summary of water's unique properties in the form of a tree whose "roots" (atomic properties) give foundation to the base of the "trunk" (molecular properties), which strengthens the next portion (polarity), from which grows another portion (H bonding). These two portions of the trunk "branch" out to the other properties of water and their global effects.

Section Summary

The atomic properties of hydrogen and oxygen atoms result in the water molecule's bent shape, polarity, and H-bonding ability. These properties of water enable it to dissolve many ionic and polar molecular compounds. Water's hydrogen bonding results in high specific heat capacity and high heat of vaporization, which combine to give both the planet and its organisms a narrow temperature range. H bonds also confer high surface tension and capillarity, which are essential to plant and animal life. Water expands on freezing because of its H bonds, which form an open structure in ice. Seasonal density changes foster nutrient mixing in lakes. Seasonal freeze-thaw stress on rocks results eventually in soil formation.

12.6 The Solid State: Structure, Properties, and Bonding

Stroll through the mineral collection of any school or museum and you'll be struck by the extraordinary variety and beauty of solids. In this section, we first discuss the general structural features of crystalline solids and then examine a laboratory method for studying them. We survey the properties of the major types of solids and find the whole range of intermolecular forces at work. We then present a model for bonding in solids that explains many of their properties.

Structural Features of Solids

We can divide solids into two broad categories based on the orderliness of their shapes, which in turn is based on the orderliness of their particles. **Crystalline solids** generally have a well-defined shape, as shown in Figure 12.26, because their particles—atoms, molecules, or ions—occur in an orderly

Figure 12.26 **The striking beauty of crystalline solids.** The symmetry and regularity of crystals are due to the orderly arrangement of their particles. *Left to right:* beryl; barite and calcite; aragonite.

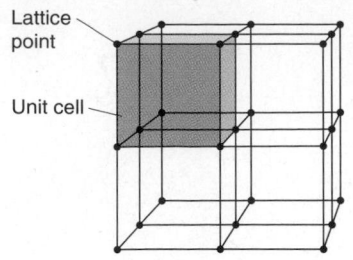

A Portion of 3-D lattice

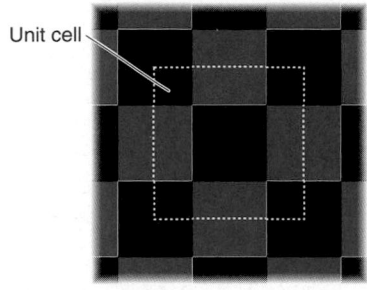

B Portion of 2-D lattice

Figure 12.27 **The crystal lattice and the unit cell. A,** A crystal lattice is an array of points that defines the positions of the particles in the crystal structure. It is shown here with the points connected by lines. A unit cell *(colored)* is the simplest array of points that produces the lattice, when repeated in all directions. A simple cubic unit cell, one of the 14 types of unit cell that occur in nature, is shown. **B,** A section of checker board is a two-dimensional analogy for a lattice.

arrangement. **Amorphous solids** have poorly defined shapes because they lack extensive molecular-level order of their particles. We focus here, for the most part, on crystalline solids.

The Crystal Lattice and the Unit Cell   If you could see the particles within a crystal, you would find them packed tightly together in an orderly, three-dimensional array. Consider the simplest case, in which all the particles are identical spheres, and imagine a point at the same location within each particle in this array, say at the center. The points form a regular pattern throughout the crystal that is called the crystal **lattice.** Thus, *the lattice consists of all points with identical surroundings.* Put another way, if you were to remove the rest of each particle, leaving only the lattice point, and were transported from one point to another, you would not be able to tell that you had moved. Keep in mind that there is no preexisting array of lattice points; rather, *the arrangement of the particle points defines the lattice.*

Figure 12.27A shows a portion of a lattice and the **unit cell,** the *smallest* portion of the crystal that, if repeated in all three directions, gives the crystal. A two-dimensional analogy for unit cell and crystal can be seen in a checkerboard (Figure 12.27B), a section of tiled floor, a piece of wallpaper, or any other pattern constructed from a repeating unit. The **coordination number** of a particle in a crystal is the number of nearest neighbors surrounding it.

There are seven crystal systems and 14 types of unit cells that occur in nature, but we will be concerned primarily with the *cubic system,* which gives rise to the cubic lattice. The solid states of a majority of metallic elements, some covalent compounds, and many ionic compounds occur in a cubic lattice. (We also describe the hexagonal unit cell a bit later.) There are three types of cubic unit cells within the cubic system:

1. In the **simple cubic unit cell,** shown in Figure 12.28A, the centers of eight particles define the corners of a cube. Attractions pull the particles together, so they touch along the cube's edges but not diagonally along its faces or through its center. The coordination number of each particle is six: four in its own layer, one in the layer above, and one in the layer below.

2. In the **body-centered cubic unit cell,** shown in Figure 12.28B, a particle lies at each corner *and* in the center of the cube. Those at the corners do not touch each other, but they all touch the one in the center. Each particle is surrounded by eight nearest neighbors, four above and four below, so the coordination number is eight.

3. In the **face-centered cubic unit cell,** shown in Figure 12.28C, a particle lies at each corner *and* in the center of each face but not in the center of the cube. Those at the corners touch those in the faces but not each other. The coordination number is 12.

One unit cell lies adjacent to another throughout the crystal, with no gaps, so a particle at a corner or face is *shared* by adjacent unit cells. As you can see from Figure 12.28 (third row), in the three cubic unit cells, the particle at each corner is part of eight adjacent cells, so one-eighth of each of these particles belongs to each cell (bottom row). There are eight corners in a cube, so each simple cubic cell contains $8 \times \frac{1}{8}$ particle = 1 particle. The body-centered cubic unit cell contains one particle from the eight corners and one in the center, or two particles; and the face-centered cubic unit cell contains four particles, one from the eight corners and three from the half-particles in the six faces.

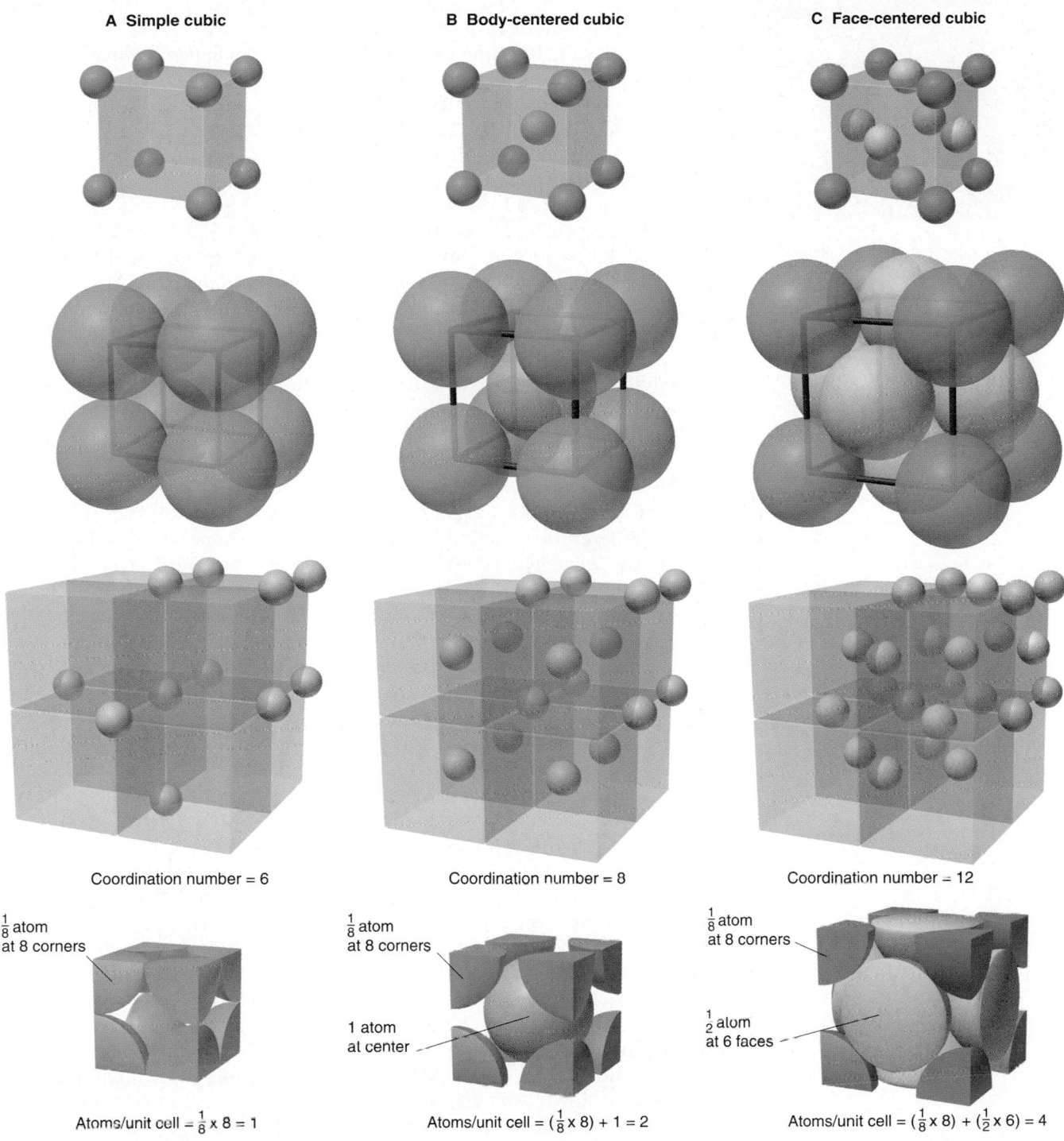

A Simple cubic

B Body-centered cubic

C Face-centered cubic

Coordination number = 6

Coordination number = 8

Coordination number = 12

$\frac{1}{8}$ atom at 8 corners

Atoms/unit cell $= \frac{1}{8} \times 8 = 1$

$\frac{1}{8}$ atom at 8 corners

1 atom at center

Atoms/unit cell $= (\frac{1}{8} \times 8) + 1 = 2$

$\frac{1}{8}$ atom at 8 corners

$\frac{1}{2}$ atom at 6 faces

Atoms/unit cell $= (\frac{1}{8} \times 8) + (\frac{1}{2} \times 6) = 4$

Figure 12.28 The three cubic unit cells. A, Simple; **B,** body-centered; and **C,** face-centered cubic unit cells. *Top row:* Cubic arrangements of atoms in expanded view. *Second row:* Space-filling view of these cubic arrangements. For clarity, corner atoms are blue, body-centered atoms pink, and face-centered atoms yellow. *Third row:* A unit cell *(shaded blue, upper right rear)* in a portion of the crystal. One particle *(dark blue in center)* surrounded by a given number of nearest neighbors shows the coordination number. *Bottom row:* Total numbers of atoms in the actual unit cells. The simple cubic has one atom, the body-centered two, and the face-centered four.

Packing Efficiency and the Creation of Unit Cells The unit cells found in nature result from the various ways atoms are packed together, which are similar to the ways macroscopic spheres—marbles, golf balls, fruit—are packed for shipping or displayed (see photo).

For particles of the same size, *the higher the coordination number of the crystal is, the greater the number of particles in a given volume.* Therefore, as the coordination numbers in Figure 12.28 indicate, a crystal structure based on the face-centered cubic cell has more particles packed into a given volume than one based on the body-centered cubic cell, which has more than one based on the simple cubic cell. Let's see how to pack spheres of the *same size* to create these unit cells and the hexagonal unit cell as well:

1. *The simple cubic cell.* Suppose we arrange the first layer of spheres as shown in Figure 12.29A. Note the large diamond-shaped spaces (cutaway portion). If we place the next layer of spheres *directly above* the first, as shown in Figure 12.29B, we obtain an arrangement based on the *simple* cubic unit cell. By calculating the **packing efficiency** of this arrangement—the percentage of the total volume occupied by the spheres themselves—we find that only 52% of the available unit-cell volume is occupied by spheres and 48% consists of the empty space between them (see Problem 12.120 at the end of the chapter). This is a very inefficient way to pack spheres, so neither fruit nor atoms are usually packed this way.

2. *The body-centered cubic cell.* Rather than placing the second layer directly above the first, a more efficient use of space would be to place the spheres (colored differently for clarity) on the diamond-shaped spaces in the first layer, as shown in Figure 12.29C. Then we pack the third layer onto these spaces in the second so that the first and third layers line up vertically. This arrangement is based on the *body-centered* cubic unit cell, and its packing efficiency is 68%—much higher than the simple cubic. Several metallic elements, including chromium, iron, and all the Group 1A(1) elements, have a crystal structure based on the body-centered cubic unit cell.

3. *The hexagonal and face-centered cubic unit cells.* Spheres can be packed even more efficiently. First we shift rows in the bottom layer such that the large diamond-shaped spaces become smaller triangular spaces. Then we place the second layer over these spaces. Figure 12.29D shows this arrangement, with the first layer labeled *a* (*orange*) and the second layer *b* (*green*).

We can place the third layer in two different ways, and how we do so gives rise to two different unit cells. If you look carefully at the spaces formed in layer *b* of Figure 12.29D, you'll see that some are orange because they lie above *spheres* in layer *a*, whereas others are white because they lie above *spaces* in layer *a*. If we place the third layer of spheres (*orange*) over the orange spaces (down and left to Figure 12.29E), they lie directly over spheres in layer *a*, and we obtain an *abab*... layering pattern because every other layer is placed identically. This gives **hexagonal closest packing,** which is based on the *hexagonal unit cell.*

On the other hand, if we place the third layer of spheres (*blue*) over the white spaces (down and right to Figure 12.29F), the spheres lie over spaces in layer *a*. This placement is different from both layers *a* and *b*, so we obtain an *abcabc*... pattern. This gives **cubic closest packing,** which is based on the *face-centered* cubic unit cell.

The packing efficiency of both hexagonal and cubic closest packing is 74%, and the coordination number of both is 12. There is no way to pack spheres of equal size more efficiently. Most metallic elements crystallize in either of

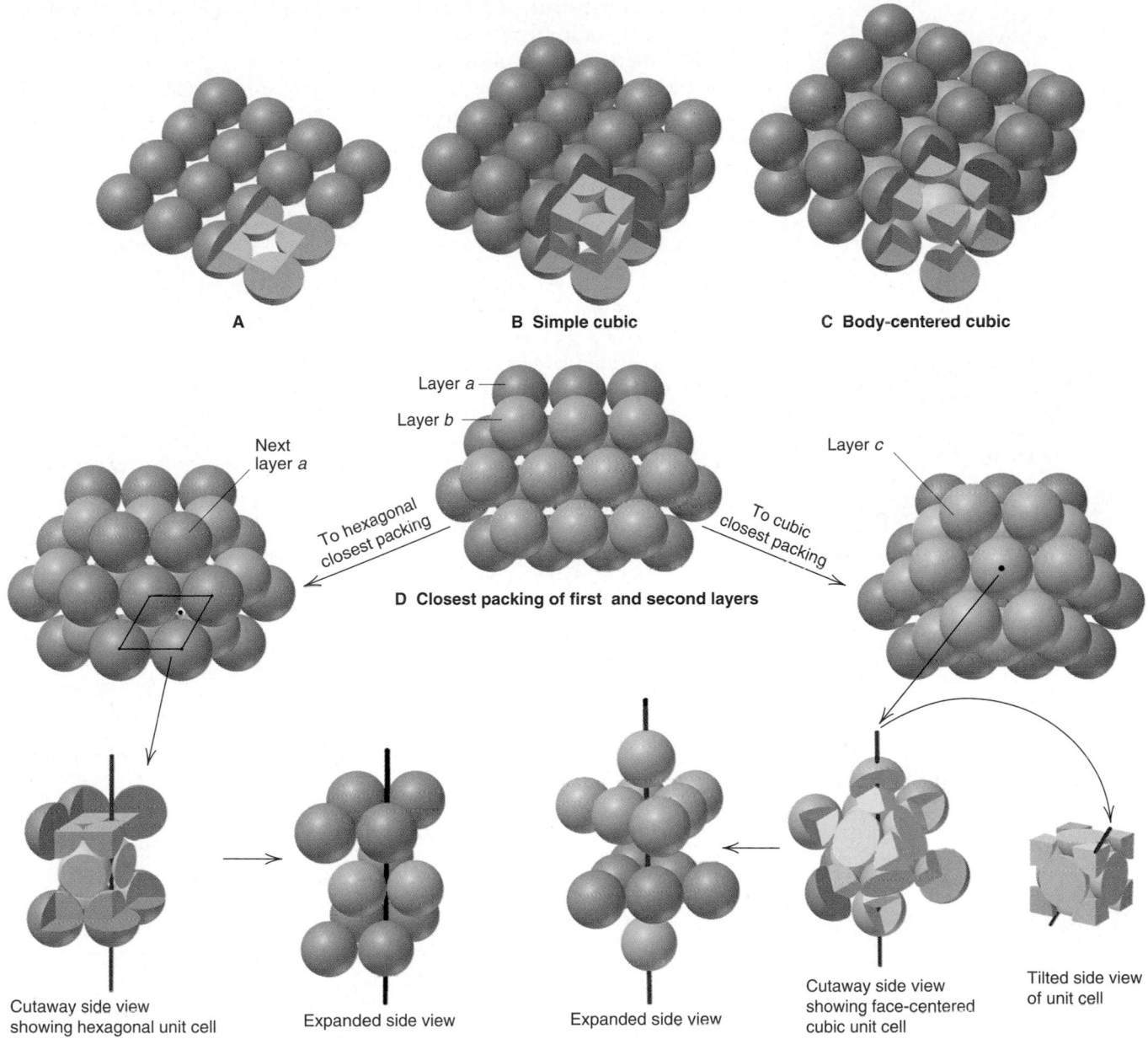

A   B Simple cubic   C Body-centered cubic

Layer *a*
Layer *b*

Next layer *a*

To hexagonal closest packing

D Closest packing of first and second layers

Layer *c*

To cubic closest packing

Cutaway side view showing hexagonal unit cell   Expanded side view

Expanded side view

Cutaway side view showing face-centered cubic unit cell

Tilted side view of unit cell

E Hexagonal closest packing (*abab*...)   F Cubic closest packing (*abcabc*...)

Figure 12.29 Packing of spheres. A, In the first layer, each sphere lies next to another horizontally and vertically; note the large diamond-shaped spaces *(cutaway)*. **B,** If the next layers lie *directly* over the first, the packing is based on the *simple cubic* unit cell *(pale orange cube, lower right corner)*. **C,** If the next layers lie in the diamond-shaped spaces of each preceding layer, the packing is based on the *body-centered cubic* unit cell *(lower right corner)*. **D,** The closest possible packing of the first layer *(a; orange)* is obtained by shifting every other row in **A,** thus reducing the diamond-shaped spaces to smaller triangular spaces. The spheres of the second layer *(b; green)* are placed above these spaces; note the orange and white spaces that result. **E,** Follow the left arrow from **D** to obtain

hexagonal closest packing. When the third layer *(a; orange)* is placed directly over the first, that is, over the orange spaces, we obtain an *abab* . . . pattern. Rotating the layers up produces the side view, with the hexagonal unit cell shown as a cutaway segment, and the expanded side view. **F,** Follow the right arrow from **D** to obtain cubic closest packing. When the third layer *(c; blue)* covers the white spaces, it lies in a different position from the first *and* second layers to give an *abcabc* . . . pattern. Rotating the layers up shows the side view, with the face-centered cubic unit cell as a cutaway, and a further tilt shows the unit cell clearly; finally, we see the expanded view.

these arrangements. Magnesium, titanium, and zinc are some elements that adopt the hexagonal structure; nickel, copper, and lead adopt the cubic structure, as do many ionic compounds and other substances, such as frozen carbon dioxide, methane, and most noble gases.

In Sample Problem 12.4, we use the density of an element and the packing efficiency of its crystal structure to calculate its atomic radius. Variations of this approach are used to find the molar mass and as one of the ways to determine Avogadro's number.

Sample Problem 12.4 Determining Atomic Radius from Crystal Structure

PROBLEM Barium is the largest nonradioactive alkaline earth metal. It has a body-centered cubic unit cell and a density of 3.62 g/cm^3. What is the atomic radius of barium? (Volume of a sphere: $V = \frac{4}{3}\pi r^3$.)

PLAN Because an atom is spherical, we can find its radius from its volume. If we multiply the reciprocal of density (volume/mass) by the molar mass (mass/mole), we find the volume of 1 mol Ba metal. Since the metal crystallizes in the body-centered cubic structure, 68% of this volume is occupied by 1 mol Ba atoms. Dividing by Avogadro's number gives the volume of one atom, from which we find the radius.

SOLUTION Combining steps to find the volume of 1 mol Ba metal:

$$\text{Volume/mole of Ba metal} = \frac{1}{\text{density}} \times \mathcal{M}$$

$$= \frac{1 \text{ cm}^3}{3.62 \text{ g Ba}} \times \frac{137.3 \text{ g Ba}}{1 \text{ mol Ba}}$$

$$= 37.9 \text{ cm}^3/\text{mol Ba}$$

Finding the volume of 1 mol Ba *atoms:*

$$\text{Volume/mole of Ba atoms} = \text{volume/mole Ba} \times \text{packing efficiency}$$
$$= 37.9 \text{ cm}^3/\text{mol Ba} \times 0.68 = 26 \text{ cm}^3/\text{mol Ba atoms}$$

Finding the volume of one Ba atom:

$$\text{Volume of Ba atom} = \frac{26 \text{ cm}^3}{1 \text{ mol Ba atoms}} \times \frac{1 \text{ mol Ba atoms}}{6.022 \times 10^{23} \text{ Ba atoms}}$$

$$= 4.3 \times 10^{-23} \text{ cm}^3/\text{Ba atom}$$

Finding the atomic radius of Ba from the volume of a sphere:

$$V \text{ of Ba atom} = \frac{4}{3}\pi r^3 \text{ and } r^3 = \frac{3V}{4\pi}$$

So

$$r = \sqrt[3]{\frac{3V}{4\pi}} = \sqrt[3]{\frac{3(4.3 \times 10^{-23} \text{ cm}^3)}{4 \times 3.14}}$$

$$= 2.2 \times 10^{-8} \text{ cm}$$

CHECK The order of magnitude is correct for an atom ($\sim 10^{-8}$ cm $\approx 10^{-10}$ m). The actual value is 2.22×10^{-8} cm (see Figure 8.12), so our answer seems correct.

Follow-up Problem 12.4 Iron crystallizes in a body-centered cubic structure. The volume of one Fe atom is 8.38×10^{-24} cm^3, and the density of Fe is 7.874 g/cm^3. Calculate an approximate value for Avogadro's number.

Density (g/cm^3) of Ba

find reciprocal and multiply by $\mathcal{M}$ (g/mol)

Volume (cm^3) per mole of Ba

multiply by packing efficiency

Volume (cm^3) per mole of Ba atoms

divide by Avogadro's number

Volume (cm^3) of Ba atom

$V = \frac{4}{3}\pi r^3$

Radius (cm) of Ba atom

Our understanding of solids is based on our "seeing" the crystal structure. Two techniques for doing so are described in the Tools of the Chemistry Laboratory essay.

Tools of the Chemistry Laboratory

X-Ray Diffraction Analysis and Scanning Tunneling Microscopy

In this chapter and in Chapter 10, we have discussed molecular shapes and crystal structures as if they have actually been seen. You may have been wondering how chemists know atomic radii, bond lengths, and bond angles when the objects exhibiting them are so incredibly minute. Various tools exist for peering into the molecular world and measuring its dimensions, but two of the most powerful are **x-ray diffraction analysis** and **scanning tunneling microscopy**.

X-Ray Diffraction Analysis

This technique has been used for decades to determine crystal structures. In Chapter 7, we discussed wave diffraction to show how interference patterns of bright and dark regions appear when light passes through slits that are spaced at the distance of the light's wavelength (see Figure 7.5). In 1912, the Swiss physicist Max von Laue suggested that, since x-ray wavelengths are about the same size as the spaces between layers of particles in many solids, the layers might diffract x-rays. (Actually, the suggestion was made to test whether x-rays were particulate or wavelike.) X-ray diffraction was soon recognized as a powerful tool for determining structure.

Let's see how this technique is used to measure a key parameter in a crystal structure: the distance (d) between layers of atoms. Figure 12.A depicts a side view of two layers in a simplified lattice. Two waves impinge on the crystal at an angle θ and are diffracted at the same angle by adjacent layers. When the first wave strikes the top layer and the second strikes the next layer, the waves are "in phase" (peaks aligned with peaks and troughs with troughs). If they are still in phase after being diffracted, a spot appears on a nearby photographic plate. Note that this will occur only if the additional distance traveled by the second wave ($DE + EF$ in the figure) is a whole number of wavelengths, $n\lambda$, where n is an integer (1, 2, 3, and so on). From trigonometry, we find that

$$n\lambda = 2d \sin \theta$$

where θ is the known angle of incoming light, λ is its known wavelength, and d is the unknown distance between layers in the crystal. This relationship is the *Bragg equation*, named for

W. H. Bragg and his son W. L. Bragg, who shared the Nobel Prize in 1915 for their work on crystal structure analysis.

Rotating the crystal changes the angle of incoming radiation and produces different sets of spots and eventually produces a complete diffraction pattern that is used to determine the distances and angles within the lattice (Figure 12.B). The diffraction pattern is not an actual picture of the structure; the pattern must be analyzed mathematically to obtain the dimensions of the crystal. Modern x-ray diffraction equipment

(continued)

Figure 12.A **Diffraction of x-rays by crystal planes.** As in-phase x-ray beams *A* and *B* pass into a crystal at angle θ, they are diffracted by interaction with the particles. Beam *B* travels the distance *DE + EF* farther than beam *A*. If this additional distance is equal to a whole number of wavelengths, the beams remain in phase and create a spot on a screen or photographic plate. From the pattern of spots and the Bragg equation, $n\lambda = 2d \sin \theta$, the distance *d* between layers of particles can be calculated.

Figure 12.B **Formation of an x-ray diffraction pattern of the protein hemoglobin. A,** The sample of crystalline hemoglobin is rotated to obtain many different angles of incoming and diffracted x-rays. **B,** A diffraction pattern is obtained as a complex series of spots. (The large white spot in the center is the shadow of part of the apparatus.) **C,** Computerized analysis relates the pattern to distances and angles within the crystal, providing data used to generate a picture of the hemoglobin molecule.

automatically rotates the crystal and measures thousands of diffractions, and a computer calculates the parameters of interest.

X-ray analysis is used to answer questions in many branches of chemistry, but its greatest impact has been in biochemistry. It has shown that DNA exists as a double helix, and it is currently helping us understand how a protein's three-dimensional structure is related to its function.

Scanning Tunneling Microscopy

This technique, a much more recent method than x-ray analysis, is used to observe surfaces on the atomic scale. It was invented in the early 1980s by Gerd Binnig and Heinrich Rohrer, two Swiss physicists who won the Nobel Prize for their work in 1986. The technique is based on the idea that an electron in an atom has a small probability of existing far from the nucleus, so given the right conditions, it can move ("tunnel") to end up closer to another atom.

In practice, the tunneling electrons create a current that can be used to image the atoms of an adjacent surface. An extremely sharp tungsten-tipped probe, the source of the tunneling electrons, is placed very close (about 0.5 nm) to the surface under study. A small potential is applied across this minute gap to increase the probability that the electrons will tunnel across it. The size of the gap is kept constant by main-

taining a constant tunneling current generated by the moving electrons. For this to occur, the probe must move tiny distances up and down, thus following the atomic contour of the surface. This movement is electronically monitored, and after many scans, a three-dimensional map of the surface is obtained. The method has revealed magnificent images of atoms and molecules coated on surfaces and is being used to study many aspects of surfaces, such as the nature of defects and the adhesion of films (Figure 12.C).

Figure 12.C Scanning tunneling micrographs. The light-sensitive semiconducting substance gallium arsenide (*left*) exhibits remarkable order (Ga, *blue*; As, *pink*). A sample of crystallized silicon (*right*) prior to recrystallization and further purification reveals many surface defects.

Types and Properties of Crystalline Solids

Now we can turn to the five most important types of solids, which are summarized in Table 12.5. Each is defined by the type of particle in the crystal, which determines the forces between them. You may want to review the bonding models (Chapter 9) because they clarify the differences in properties among the solids.

Figure 12.30 Cubic closest packing of frozen argon. Group 8A(18) elements form atomic solids and adopt cubic closest packing (face-centered cubic cell).

Figure 12.31 Cubic closest packing of frozen methane. In the solid state, methane adopts a face-centered cubic unit cell (cubic closest packing), with the C atom centered on the lattice point. Individual atoms are shown for only one CH$_4$ molecule.

Atomic Solids Individual atoms held together by dispersion forces form an **atomic solid.** The noble gases [Group 8A(18)] are the only examples, and their physical properties reflect the very weak forces among the atoms. Melting and boiling points and heats of vaporization and fusion are all very low, rising smoothly with increasing molar mass. As shown in Figure 12.30, argon crystallizes in a cubic closest packed structure. The other atomic solids do so as well.

Molecular Solids In the many thousands of **molecular solids,** the lattice points are occupied by individual molecules. For example, methane crystallizes in a face-centered cubic structure, shown in Figure 12.31, with the carbon of each molecule centered on the lattice point.

Various combinations of dipole-dipole, dispersion, and H bonding forces are at work in molecular solids, which accounts for their wide range of physical properties. Dispersion forces are the principal force acting in nonpolar substances, so melting points generally increase with molar mass

Table 12.5 Characteristics of the Major Types of Crystalline Solids

	Particle(s)	Interparticle Forces	Physical Behavior	Examples [mp °C]
Atomic	Atoms	Dispersion	Soft, very low mp, poor thermal and electrical conductors	Group 8A(18) [Ne −249 to Rn −71]
Molecular	Molecules	Dispersion, dipole-dipole, H bonds	Fairly soft, low to moderate mp, poor thermal and electrical conductors	*Nonpolar** O_2 [−219], C_4H_{10} [−138] Cl_2 [−101], C_6H_{14} [−95] P_4 [44.1] *Polar* SO_2 [−73], $CHCl_3$ [−64] HNO_3 [−42], H_2O [0.0] CH_3COOH [17]
Ionic	Positive and negative ions	Ion-ion attraction	Hard and brittle, high mp, good thermal and electrical conductors when molten	NaCl [801] CaF_2 [1423] MgO [2852]
Metallic	Atoms	Metallic bond	Soft to hard, low to very high mp, excellent thermal and electrical conductors, malleable and ductile	Na [97.8] Zn [420] Fe [1535]
Network	Atoms	Covalent bond	Very hard, very high mp, usually poor thermal and electrical conductors	SiO_2 (quartz) [1610] C(diamond) [~4000]

*Nonpolar molecular solids are arranged in order of increasing molar mass. Note the correlation with increasing melting point (mp).

(Table 12.5). Among polar molecules, dipole-dipole forces and, where possible, H bonding dominate. Except for those substances consisting of the simplest molecules, molecular solids have higher melting points than the atomic solids (noble gases). Nevertheless, intermolecular forces are still relatively weak, so the melting points are much lower than those of ionic, network covalent, and metallic solids.

Ionic Solids In crystalline **ionic solids,** the unit cell contains particles with whole, rather than partial, charges. As a result, the interparticle forces (ionic bonding forces) are *much* stronger than the van der Waals forces in atomic or molecular solids. To maximize attractions, cations are surrounded by as many anions as possible, and vice versa, with *the smaller of the two ions lying in the spaces (holes) formed by the packing of the larger.* Since the unit cell is the smallest portion of the crystal that maintains the overall spatial arrangement, it is also the smallest portion that maintains the overall chemical composition. In other words, *the unit cell has the same cation/anion ratio as the empirical formula.*

Ionic compounds adopt several different crystal structures, but many use cubic closest packing. Let's first consider two structures that have a 1:1 ratio of ions. The *sodium chloride structure* is found in many compounds, including most of the alkali [Group 1A(1)] halides and hydrides, the alkaline earth [Group 2A(2)] oxides and sulfides, several transition-metal oxides and sulfides, and most of the silver halides. To visualize this structure, first imagine Cl^- anions and Na^+ cations organized separately in face-centered cubic (cubic closest packing) arrays. The crystal structure arises when these two arrays penetrate each other such that the smaller Na^+ ions end up in the holes

Figure 12.32 The sodium chloride structure. A, In an expanded view, the sodium chloride structure can be pictured as resulting from the penetration of two face-centered cubic arrangements, in this case one of Na⁺ ions and the other of Cl⁻ ions. **B,** A space-filling view of the NaCl unit cell (central overlapped portion in **A**), which consists of four Cl⁻ ions and four Na⁺ ions.

between the larger Cl⁻ ions, as shown in Figure 12.32A. Thus, each Na⁺ is surrounded by six Cl⁻, and vice versa (coordination number = 6). Figure 12.32B is a space-filling depiction of the unit cell showing a face-centered cube of Cl⁻ ions with Na⁺ ions between them. Note the four Cl⁻ [$(8 \times \frac{1}{8})$ + $(6 \times \frac{1}{2}) = 4$ Cl⁻] and four Na⁺ [$(12 \times \frac{1}{4})$ + 1 in the center = 4 Na⁺], giving a 1:1 ion ratio.

Another structure with a 1:1 ion ratio is the *zinc blende (ZnS) structure.* It can be pictured as two face-centered cubic arrays, one of Zn²⁺ ions and the other of S²⁻ ions, penetrating each other such that each ion is tetrahedrally surrounded by four ions of opposite charge (coordination number = 4). Note the 1:1 ratio of ions in the unit cell shown in Figure 12.33. Many other compounds, including AgI, CdS, and the Cu(I) halides adopt the zinc blende structure.

The *fluorite (CaF₂) structure* is common among salts with a 1:2 cation/anion ratio. It often appears with relatively large cations and relatively small anions. In the case of CaF₂, the unit cell is a face-centered cubic array of Ca²⁺ ions with F⁻ ions occupying *all* eight available holes (Figure 12.34). This results in a Ca²⁺:F⁻ ratio of 4:8, or 1:2. SrF₂ and BaCl₂ have the fluorite structure also. The *antifluorite structure* is often seen in compounds with a cation/anion ratio of 2:1 and in which the anion is relatively large (for example, K₂S). In this structure, the cations occupy all eight holes formed by the cubic closest packing of the anions, just the opposite of the fluorite structure.

The properties of ionic solids are a direct consequence of the *fixed ion positions* and *very strong interionic forces,* which create a high lattice energy. Thus, ionic solids typically have high melting points and low electrical conductivities. When a large amount of heat is supplied and the ions gain enough kinetic energy to break free of their positions, the solid melts and the mobile

Figure 12.33 The zinc blende structure. Zinc sulfide adopts the zinc blende structure. **A,** The translucent cube shows a face-centered cubic array of four [$(8 \times \frac{1}{8})$ + $(6 \times \frac{1}{2})$ = 4] S²⁻ ions tetrahedrally surrounding four Zn²⁺ ions to give the 1:1 empirical formula. (The bond lines are shown only for clarity.) **B,** The actual unit cell slightly expanded to show the interior ions.

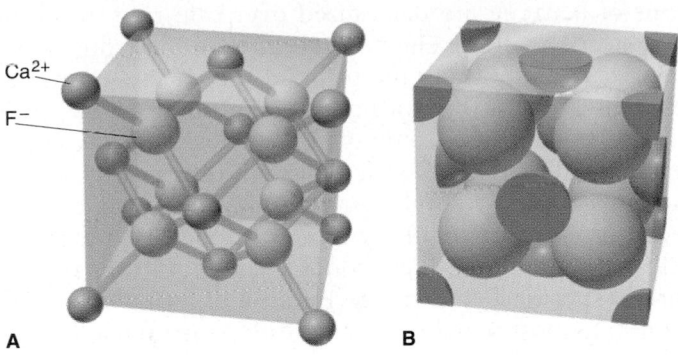

Figure 12.34 The fluorite structure. Calcium fluoride adopts the fluorite structure. **A,** The translucent cube shows a face-centered cubic array of Ca^{2+} (four Ca^{2+} ions per unit cell) tetrahedrally surrounding eight F^- ions to give the 4:8, or 1:2, ratio. **B,** The actual unit cell (slightly expanded).

ions conduct a current. Ionic compounds are hard because only a strong external force can change the relative positions of many trillions of interacting ions. If enough force *is* applied to move them, ions of like charge are brought near each other, and their repulsions crack the crystal (see Figure 9.8, p. 339).

Metallic Solids Unlike the weak dispersion forces between the atoms in atomic solids, powerful metallic bonding forces hold individual atoms together in **metallic solids.** Most metallic elements crystallize in one of the two closest packed structures (Figure 12.35).

The properties of metals—high electrical and thermal conductivity, luster, and malleability—result from the presence of delocalized electrons, the essential feature of metallic bonding (introduced in Section 9.5). Metals have a wide range of melting points and hardnesses, which are related to the packing efficiency of the crystal structure and the number of valence electrons available for bonding. For example, Group 2A metals are harder and higher melting than Group 1A metals (see Figure 9.23, p. 354), because the 2A metals have closest packed structures (except Ba) and twice as many delocalized valence electrons.

Network Covalent Solids In the final type of crystalline solid, separate particles are not present. Instead, strong covalent bonds link the atoms together throughout **network covalent solids.** As a consequence of the strong bonding, all of these substances have extremely high melting and boiling points, but their conductivity and hardness depend on the details of their bonding.

The two common crystalline forms of elemental carbon are examples of network covalent solids. Even though graphite and diamond have the same composition, their properties are strikingly different, as Table 12.6 shows. Graphite occurs as stacked flat sheets of hexagonal carbon rings with a strong σ-bond framework and delocalized π bonds, reminiscent of benzene. The arrangement of hexagons looks like chicken wire or honeycomb. Whereas

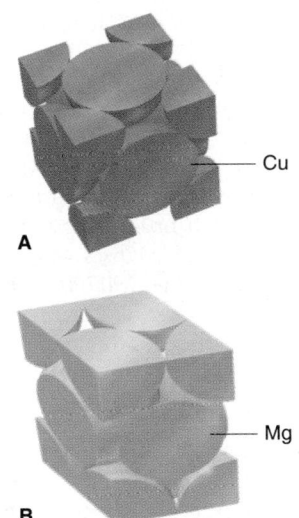

Figure 12.35 Crystal structures of metals. Most metallic elements crystallize in one of the closest packed arrangements. **A,** Copper adopts cubic closest packing. **B,** Magnesium adopts hexagonal closest packing.

Table 12.6 Comparison of the Properties of Diamond and Graphite

Property	Graphite		Diamond	
Density (g/cm^3)	2.27		3.51	
Hardness	<1 (very soft)		10 (hardest)	
Melting point (K)	4100		4100	
Color	Shiny black		Colorless transparent	
Electrical conductivity	High (along sheet)		None	
ΔH^0_{comb} (kJ/mol)	−393.5		−395.4	
ΔH^0_f (kJ/mol)	0 (standard state)		1.90	

◆ **A Diamond Film on Every Pot**   In the 1950s, synthetic diamonds were made slowly and expensively by exposing graphite to extreme temperatures (~1400°C) and pressures (50,000 atm). In the 1960s, a much cheaper method was discovered, which, in the 1990s, is being used to deposit thin films of diamond onto virtually any surface. In the process of chemical vapor deposition (CVD), a stream of methane breaks down at moderate temperatures (~600°C) and low pressures (~0.001 atm), and the carbon atoms deposit on the surface at rates of more than 100μm thickness per hour. Because of diamond's incredible hardness and high thermal conductivity, applications for diamond films are endless: scratch-proof cookware, watch crystals, hard discs, and eyeglasses; lifetime drill bits, ball bearings, and razor blades; high-temperature semiconductors. The list goes on and on.

the π electrons of benzene are delocalized over one ring, those of graphite are delocalized over the entire sheet. These mobile electrons allow graphite to conduct electricity, but only in the plane of the sheets. Graphite is a common electrode material and was once used for lightbulb filaments. The sheets interact via dispersion forces. Common impurities, such as O_2, that lodge between the sheets allow them to slide past each other easily, which explains why graphite is so soft. Diamond crystallizes in a face-centered cubic unit cell, with each carbon atom tetrahedrally surrounded by four others in one virtually endless array. Strong, single bonds throughout the crystal make diamond the hardest substance known. ◆ Because of its localized bonding electrons, diamond (like most network covalent solids) is unable to conduct electricity.

By far the most important network covalent solids are the *silicates*. They exist in a variety of bonding patterns, but nearly all consist of extended arrays of covalently bonded silicon and oxygen atoms. Quartz (SiO_2) is a common example. We'll discuss silicates, which form the structure of clays, rocks, and many minerals, when we consider the chemistry of silicon in Chapter 14.

Amorphous Solids

Amorphous solids are noncrystalline. Many have small, somewhat ordered regions connected by large disordered regions. Charcoal, rubber, and glass are some familiar examples of amorphous solids.

The process that forms quartz glass is typical of that for many amorphous solids. Crystalline quartz (SiO_2) has a cubic closest packed structure. The crystalline form is melted, and the viscous liquid is cooled rapidly to prevent it from recrystallizing. The chains of silicon and oxygen atoms cannot orient themselves quickly enough into an orderly structure, so they solidify in a distorted jumble containing many gaps and misaligned rows (Figure 12.36). The absence of regularity in the structure confers some properties of a liquid; in fact, glasses are sometimes referred to as *supercooled liquids*.

Figure 12.36 Crystalline and amorphous silicon dioxide. A, The atomic arrangement of cristobalite, one of the many crystalline forms of silica (SiO_2), shows the regularity of cubic closest packing. **B,** The atomic arrangement of a quartz glass is amorphous with a generally disordered structure.

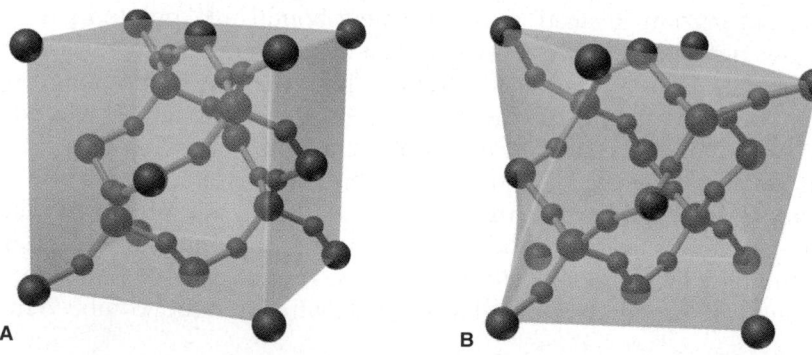

A   B

Bonding in Solids: Molecular Orbital Band Theory

Chapter 9 introduced a qualitative model of metallic bonding that pictures metal ions submerged in a "sea" of mobile, delocalized valence electrons. Quantum mechanics offers another model, an extension of molecular orbital (MO) theory, called **band theory,** that is more quantitative and therefore more useful. We'll pay special attention to bonding in metals and differences in electrical conductivity of metals, metalloids, and nonmetals.

Recall that when two atoms form a diatomic molecule, their atomic orbitals combine to form an equal number of molecular orbitals (MOs). Let's con-

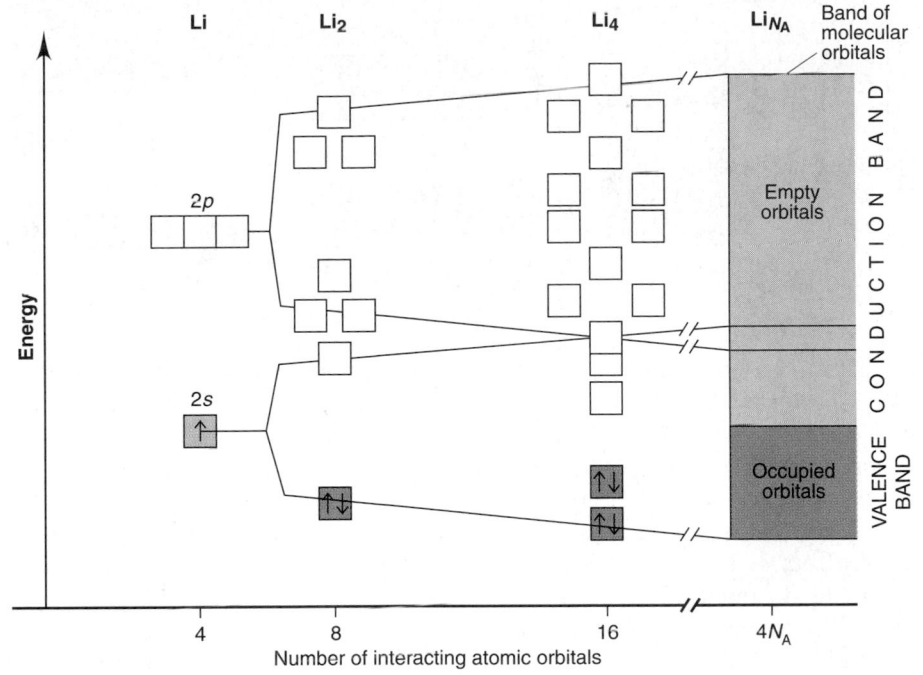

Figure 12.37 **The band of molecular orbitals in lithium metal.** Lithium atoms contain four valence orbitals, one 2s and three 2p *(left).* When two atoms combine (Li$_2$), their atomic orbitals form eight MOs within a certain range of energy. Four Li atoms (Li$_4$) form 16 MOs. A mole of Li atoms forms 4N_A MOs (N_A = Avogadro's number). The orbital energies are so close together that they form a continuous band. The valence electrons enter the lower energy portion (valence band), while the higher energy portion (conduction band) remains empty. In lithium (and other metals), the valence and conduction bands have no gap between them.

sider lithium as an example. Figure 12.37 shows the formation of MOs in lithium. In diatomic lithium, Li$_2$, each atom has four valence orbitals (one 2s and three 2p). (Recall that in Section 11.3, we focused on the 2s orbitals only.) They combine to form eight MOs, four bonding and four antibonding, spread over both atoms. If two more Li atoms combine, they form Li$_4$, a slightly larger aggregate, with 16 delocalized MOs. As more Li atoms join the cluster, more MOs are created, their energy levels lying closer and closer together. Extending this process to a 7-g sample of lithium metal (the molar mass) results in 1 mol Li atoms (Li$_{N_A}$) combining to form an extremely large number (4 × Avogadro's number) of delocalized MOs, with *energies so closely spaced that they form a continuum, or band, of MOs.* It is almost as though the entire piece of metal were one enormous Li molecule.

The band model proposes that the lower energy MOs are occupied by the valence electrons and make up the **valence band.** The empty MOs that are higher in energy make up the **conduction band.** In Li metal, the valence band is derived from the 2s orbitals, and the conduction band is derived mostly from an intermingling of the 2s and 2p orbitals. In Li$_2$, two valence electrons fill the lowest energy MO and leave the antibonding MO empty. Similarly, in Li metal, 1 mol of valence electrons fills the valence band and leaves the conduction band empty.

The key to understanding metallic properties is that *in metals, the valence and conduction bands are contiguous,* which means that electrons can jump from the filled valence band to the unfilled conduction band with an infinitesimally small quantity of energy. In other words, the electrons are completely delocalized, *free to move throughout the piece of metal.* Thus, metals conduct electricity so well because an applied electric field easily excites the highest energy electrons into empty orbitals, and they move through the sample.

Metallic luster (shininess) is another effect of the continuous band of MO energy levels. With so many closely spaced levels available, electrons can absorb and release photons of many frequencies as they move between the valence and conduction bands. Malleability and thermal conductivity also result from the completely delocalized electron orbitals. Under an externally

Figure 12.38 Electrical conductivity in a conductor, semiconductor, and insulator. Band theory explains differences in electrical conductivity in terms of the size of the energy gap between the material's valence and conduction bands. In conductors (metals), there is no gap. In semiconductors (many metalloids), electrons can jump the small gap if they are given energy, as when the sample is heated. In insulators (most nonmetals), electrons cannot jump the large energy gap.

applied force, layers of positive metal ions simply move past each other, always protected from mutual repulsions by the presence of the delocalized electrons (see Figure 9.24, p. 354). When a metal wire is heated, the highest energy electrons are excited and their extra energy is transferred as kinetic energy along the wire's length.

Large numbers of nonmetal or metalloid atoms can also combine to form bands of MOs. Metals conduct a current well (conductors), whereas most nonmetals do not (insulators), and the conductivity of metalloids lies somewhere in between (semiconductors). Band theory explains these differences in terms of the size of the energy gaps between the valence and conduction bands, as shown in Figure 12.38:

1. *Conductors (metals).* The valence and conduction bands of a **conductor** have no gap between them, so electrons flow when even a tiny electrical potential difference is applied. When the temperature is raised, greater random motion of the atoms hinders electron movement, which *decreases* the conductivity of a metal.

2. *Semiconductors (metalloids).* In a **semiconductor,** a relatively small energy gap exists between the valence and conduction bands. Thermally excited electrons can cross the gap, allowing a small current to flow. Thus, in contrast to a conductor, the conductivity of a semiconductor *increases* when it is heated.

3. *Insulators (nonmetals).* In an **insulator,** the gap between the bands is too large for electrons to jump even when the substance is heated, so no current is observed.

Another type of electrical conductivity, called **superconductivity,** has been generating greatly renewed interest for more than a decade now. When metals conduct at ordinary temperatures, electron flow is restricted by collisions with atoms vibrating in their lattice sites. Such restricted flow appears as resistive heating and represents a loss of energy. To conduct with no energy loss—to superconduct—requires extreme cooling to minimize atom movement. This remarkable phenomenon had been observed in metals only by cooling them to near absolute zero, which can be done only with liquid helium (bp = 4 K; price = $11/L).

In 1986, all this changed when new ionic oxides were synthesized that superconduct near the boiling point of liquid nitrogen (bp= 77 K; price = $0.25/L). Like metal conductors, oxide superconductors have no band gap. In the case of $YBa_2Cu_3O_7$, x-ray analysis shows that the Cu ions in the oxide lattice are aligned, which may be related to its superconducting property. In 1989, oxides with Bi and Tl instead of Y and Ba were synthesized that could superconduct at 125 K; recently, an oxide with Hg, Ba, and Ca, in addition to Cu and O, was shown to superconduct at 133 K. Engineering dreams for these materials include storage and transmission of electricity with no loss of energy; electric power plants operating far from cities; ultrasmall microchips for ultrafast computers; electromagnets to levitate superfast railway trains (Figure 12.39); and inexpensive medical diagnostic equipment with remarkable image clarity.

However, manufacturing problems must be overcome. The oxides are very brittle and fragile, but some recent developments may solve this drawback. A more fundamental concern is that when the oxide is warmed or placed in a strong magnetic field, the superconductivity may disappear and not return again on cooling. Clearly, research into superconductivity will involve chemists, physicists, and engineers for many years to come. We consider other remarkable materials in the next section.

Figure 12.39 The levitating power of a superconducting oxide. A magnet remains suspended above a cooled high-temperature superconductor. Someday, this phenomenon may be used to levitate trains above their tracks for quiet, fast travel.

Section Summary

The particles in crystalline solids lie at points that form a structure of repeating unit cells. The three unit cells in the cubic crystal system are simple, body-centered, and face centered cubic. The most efficient packing arrangements are cubic closest packing and hexagonal closest packing. Bond angles and distances in a crystal structure can be determined with x-ray diffraction analysis and scanning tunneling microscopy. Atomic solids have a closest packed structure, with atoms held together by very weak dispersion forces. Molecular solids have molecules at the lattice points, often in the cubic closest packed structure. Their intermolecular forces (dispersion, dipole, H bond) and resulting physical properties vary greatly. Ionic solids often crystallize with one ion filling holes in a cubic closest packed structure of the other. Their high melting points, hardness, and low conductivity in the solid arise from strong ionic attractions. Most metals have a closest packed structure. The atoms of network covalent solids are covalently bonded throughout the crystal. Amorphous solids have very little regularity among their particles. Band theory proposes that orbitals in the atoms of solids combine to form a continuum, or band, of molecular orbitals. Metals are electrical conductors because electrons move freely from the filled (valence band) to the empty (conduction band) portions of this energy continuum. Insulators have a large energy gap between the two portions; semiconductors have a small gap.

12.7 Advanced Materials

In the last few decades, the exciting field of materials science was born from solid-state chemistry, physics, and engineering, and it is changing our lives in astonishing ways. Objects that were once considered futuristic fantasies of science-fiction writers are here today or just a few years away: powerful, ultrafast computers no bigger than this book, connected electronically to millions of others throughout the world; cars powered by sunlight and made of nonmetallic parts stronger than steel yet lighter than aluminum; sporting goods made of the materials of space vehicles; ultrasmall machines constructed by manipulating individual atoms and molecules. In this section, we briefly discuss some of these advanced materials.

Electronic Materials

The ideal of a perfectly ordered crystal is attainable only if it is grown very slowly under carefully controlled conditions. When crystals form more rapidly, **crystal defects** inevitably form. Planes of particles are misaligned, particles are out of place or missing entirely, and foreign particles are lodged.

Although crystal defects usually weaken a substance, they are sometimes introduced intentionally to create materials with improved properties, such as increased strength or hardness or, as you'll see in a moment, to increase

◆ **Solar Cells** One of the more common types of solar cell is, in essence, a p-n junction with an n-type surface exposed to a light source. The light provides energy to free electrons from the n-type region and accelerate them through an external circuit into the p-type region, thus providing a current flow to power a calculator, light a bulb, and so on. Arrays of solar cells supply electric power to many residences and businesses, as well as to the Space Shuttle and most communications satellites (see figure).

a material's conductivity for use in electronic devices. In the process of welding two metals together, for example, *vacancies* form near the surface when atoms vaporize, and then they move deeper as atoms from lower rows rise to fill the gaps. Welding causes the two types of metal atoms to intermingle and fill each other's vacancies. Metal alloying introduces several kinds of defects, such as some atoms of a second metal occupying lattice sites of the first. Often, the alloy is harder than the pure metal, as is brass, an alloy of copper with zinc. One reason the welded metals are stronger and the alloy is harder is that the second metal contributes additional valence electrons for metallic bonding.

Doped Semiconductors The manufacture and miniaturization of doped semiconductors have revolutionized the communications, home-entertainment, and information industries. By controlling the number of valence electrons through the creation of specific types of defects, chemists and engineers can greatly increase the conductivity of a semiconductor.

Pure silicon (Si), which lies below carbon in Group 4A(14), conducts poorly at room temperature because an energy gap separates its filled valence band from its conduction band (Figure 12.40A). Its conductivity can be greatly enhanced by **doping,** adding small amounts of other elements to increase or decrease the number of valence electrons in the bands. When Si is doped with phosphorus [or another Group 5A(15) element], P atoms occupy some of the lattice sites. Since P has one more valence electron than Si, this additional electron must enter an empty orbital in the conduction band, thus bridging the energy gap and increasing conductivity. Such doping creates an *n-type semiconductor*, so called because extra *n*egative charges (electrons) are present (Figure 12.40B).

When Si is doped with gallium [or another Group 3A(13) element], Ga atoms occupy some sites (Figure 12.40C). Since Ga has one fewer valence electron than Si, some of the orbitals in the valence band are empty, which creates a positive site. Si electrons can migrate to these empty orbitals, thereby increasing conductivity. Such doping creates a *p-type semiconductor*, so called because the empty orbitals act as *p*ositive holes.

In contact with each other, an n-type and a p-type semiconductor form a *p-n junction.* ◆ When the negative terminal of a battery is connected to the n-type portion and the positive terminal to the p-type portion, electrons flow

A Pure silicon crystal   **B** n-Type doping with phosphorus   **C** p-Type doping with gallium

Figure 12.40 Crystal structures and band representations of doped semiconductors. A, Pure silicon has the diamond crystal structure but acts as a semiconductor, the energy gap between its valence and conduction bands keeping conductivity low at room temperature. **B,** Doping silicon with phosphorus *(purple)* adds additional valence electrons, which are free to move through the crystal. They enter the lower portion of the conduction band, which is adjacent to higher energy empty orbitals, thereby increasing conductivity. **C,** Doping silicon with gallium *(orange)* removes electrons from the valence band and introduces a positive "hole." Nearby Si electrons can enter these empty orbitals, thereby increasing conductivity. The orbital from which the Si electron moved now has a vacancy; in effect, the hole has moved.

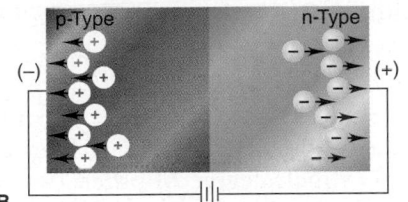

Figure 12.41 The p-n junction. Placing a p-type semiconductor adjacent to an n-type creates a p-n junction. **A,** If the negative battery terminal is on the n-type portion, electrons *(yellow sphere with minus sign)* flow toward the p-type portion, which, in effect, moves holes *(white circle with plus sign)* toward the n-type portion. The small arrows indicate the net direction of movement. Note that any hole in the n-type portion lies opposite an electron that moved to the p-type portion. **B,** If the positive battery terminal is on the n-type portion, electrons are attracted to it, so no flow takes place across the junction.

freely in the n-to-p direction, which has the simultaneous effect of moving holes in the p-to-n direction (Figure 12.41). No current flows if the terminals are reversed. Such unidirectional current flow acts as a rectifier, a device that converts alternating current into direct current. A p-n junction in a modern integrated circuit can be made smaller than a square 10μm on a side. Before the p-n junction was created, rectifiers were bulky, expensive vacuum tubes.

A modern computer chip the size of a nickel may incorporate millions of p-n junctions in the form of *transistors*. One of the most common types, an n-p-n transistor, is made by sandwiching a p-type portion between two n-type portions to form adjacent p-n junctions. The current flowing through one junction controls the current flowing through the other and results in an amplified signal. Once again, to accomplish signal amplification before the advent of doped semiconductors required large, and often unreliable, vacuum tubes. Today, minute transistors are found in every radio, TV, and computer and have made possible the multibillion-dollar electronics industry.

Manufacturing a p-n Junction Several steps are required to manufacture a simple p-n junction. The process, as shown in Figure 12.42, begins with a thin wafer made from a single crystal of n-type silicon:

1. Forming an oxide surface. In a furnace, the wafer is heated in O_2 to form a surface layer of SiO_2.
2. Covering with a photoresist. The oxide-coated wafer is covered by a light-sensitive wax or polymer film called a *photoresist.*
3. Applying the template. A template with spaces having the desired shape of the p-type region is applied. Thus, all other areas are "masked" from the subsequent treatments.
4. Exposing and removing the photoresist. Light shining on the template alters the exposed areas of photoresist so that it can be dissolved away in specific solvents, revealing the oxide surface. The template is removed.
5. Etching the oxide surface. Treatment with hydrofluoric acid etches the template-shaped area of oxide coating to expose the n-type silicon surface. Following this, the remaining photoresist is also removed.
6. Creating the p-n junction. The wafer is exposed at high temperature to vapor of a Group 3A(13) element, which diffuses into the bare areas to create a template-shaped region of p-type Si adjacent to the n-type Si. The remaining SiO_2 is removed at this point also.

Typically, these steps are repeated to create an n-type region adjacent to the newly formed p-type region, thus forming an n-p-n transistor.

Figure 12.42 Steps in manufacturing a p-n junction. Steps 1 to 5 prepare the desired shape of the p-type portion on the n-type wafer. Step 6 dopes that shape with the Group 3A(13) element.

Liquid Crystals

Incorporated in the membrane of every cell in your body and in the display of just about every digital watch, pocket calculator, and laptop computer are substances that form a unique type of advanced material. **Liquid crystal** phases flow like liquids but, like crystalline solids, pack at the molecular level with a high degree of order.

Properties, Preparation, and Types of Liquid Crystals To understand the properties of liquid crystals, let's first examine how particles are ordered in the three common physical states and how this affects their properties. The extent of order among particles distinguishes crystalline solids clearly from gases and liquids. Gases have no order and liquids have little more. Both are considered *isotropic,* which means that their physical properties are the same in every direction within the phase. For example, the viscosity of a gas or a liquid is the same regardless of direction. Glasses and other amorphous solids are also isotropic because they have no regular lattice structure.

In contrast, crystalline solids have a high degree of order among their particles. The properties of a crystal *do* depend on direction, so a crystal is *anisotropic.* The facets in a cut diamond, for instance, arise because the crystal cracks in one direction more easily than in another. Liquid crystals are also anisotropic in that several physical properties, including the electrical and optical properties that lead to their most important applications, differ with direction through the phase.

Like crystalline molecular solids, liquid crystal phases consist of individual molecules. In most cases, the molecules that form liquid crystal phases have two characteristics: a long, cylindrical shape and a structure that allows intermolecular attractions through dispersion and dipole-dipole or H-bonding forces, but inhibits perfect crystalline packing. Figure 12.43 shows the structures of two molecules that form liquid crystal phases. Note the rodlike shapes and that certain groups, in these cases the flat benzenelike ring systems, keep the molecules extended. Many of these types of molecules also have a molecular dipole associated with the long molecular axis. Like a compass needle in a magnetic field, a sufficiently strong electric field can orient these polar molecules in approximately the same direction.

The viscosity of a liquid crystal phase is lowest parallel to the long axis. Like moistened microscope slides, it is easier for the molecules to slide along each other (because the total attractive force remains the same), than it is for them to pull apart from each other sideways. As a result, the molecules tend to align while the phase flows.

Figure 12.43 Structures of two typical liquid crystal molecules. Note the long, extended shapes and the regions of high (*red*) and low (*blue*) electron density.

A Nematic   **B** Cholesteric   **C** Smectic

Figure 12.44 The three common types of liquid crystal phases.
A, Nematic phase. A rectangular volume of the phase, with expanded view, shows a closeup of the arrangement of molecules. **B,** Cholesteric phase. Note the corkscrew-like arrangement of the layers. **C,** Smectic phase. A rectangular volume of the phase shows the more orderly stacking of layers.

Liquid crystal phases can arise in two general ways and, sometimes, can arise through either way in the same substance. A *thermotropic* phase arises through a change in temperature. As a crystalline solid is heated, the molecules leave their lattice sites, but the intermolecular interactions are still strong enough to keep the molecules aligned with each other along their long axes. Like any other phase, the liquid crystal phase has sharp transition temperatures, but the phase exists over a relatively small temperature range. Further heating provides enough kinetic energy for the molecules to become disordered, as in a normal liquid. Typical ranges for liquid crystal phases of pure substances are from <1°C to around 10°C, but mixing different liquid crystal molecules can greatly extend this range. For this reason, the liquid crystal phases used within display devices, as well as those within cell membranes, consist of mixtures of molecules.

A *lyotropic* phase occurs in solution and arises through changes in concentration, but the conditions for forming the phase are not at all the same for different substances. For example, when purified, some biomolecules that exist naturally in mammalian cell membranes form lyotropic phases in water at the mild temperature that occurs within the organism. At the other extreme, Kevlar, a fiber used in bullet-proof vests and high-performance sports equipment, forms a lyotropic phase at high temperatures in concentrated H_2SO_4 solution.

Molecules that form liquid crystals can exhibit various types of order. Three common types are nematic, cholesteric, and smectic:

• In a *nematic* phase, the molecules lie in the same direction but their ends are not aligned, much like a school of fish swimming in synchrony (Figure 12.44A). The nematic phase is the least ordered class of liquid crystal phases.

• In a *cholesteric* phase, which is somewhat more ordered, the molecules lie in layers that each exhibit nematic-type ordering. Rather than stacking directly next to each other, however, each layer is rotated by a fixed angle with respect to the next layer. The result is a helical (corkscrew) arrangement, so a cholesteric phase is often called a twisted nematic phase (Figure 12.44B). ◆

• In a *smectic* phase, which is the most ordered, the molecules lie parallel to each other, *with* their ends aligned, in layers that are stacked directly over each other, much like a supermarket display of shelves filled with identical bottles (Figure 12.44C). The long molecular axis has a well-defined angle (shown in the figure as 90°) with respect to the plane of the layer. The molecules in Figure 12.43 are typical of those that form nematic or smectic phases.

◆ **Liquid Crystals in Biological Systems**
Nematic and cholesteric liquid crystalline species appear in many biological systems. The arrays of virus particles within the fluid of a tobacco leaf infected with tobacco mosaic virus (TMV; see photo) is one of many examples. Every voluntary muscle cell attains its striated appearance from the orderly arrangement of filamentous molecules of the proteins actin and myosin in the cytoplasm. And every cell membrane consists in large part of a double layer of long, thin, polar fatty molecules aligned in a nematic array. Chemical and biological agents that disrupt this alignment can cause cell leakage and dysfunction.

Current on: molecules align, light blocked, dark region

Current off: molecules not aligned, light passes, bright region

Figure 12.45 **Schematic of a liquid crystal display (LCD).** A closeup of the "2" on a wristwatch LCD reveals two polarizers sandwiching two glass plates, which sandwich an LC layer, all lying on a mirror. When light of all directions enters the first polarizer, only waves of one direction emerge to enter the LC layer. Enlarging a dark region of the numeral *(top blowup)* shows that with the current on, the LC molecules are aligned and the light cannot pass through the other polarizer to the mirror, so the viewer sees no light. Enlarging a bright region *(bottom blowup)* shows that with the current off, the LC molecules lie in a twisted nematic arrangement, which twists the plane of the light and allows it to pass through the other polarizer to the mirror. Reflecting and retracing this path (not shown), the light reaches the viewer.

In some cases, a substance that forms a given liquid crystal phase under one set of conditions forms other phases under different conditions. Thus, a given thermotropic liquid crystal substance can pass from disordered liquid through a series of distinct liquid crystal phases to an ordered crystal through a decrease in temperature. A lyotropic substance can undergo similar changes through an increase in concentration.

Applications of Liquid Crystals The ability to control the orientation of the molecules in a liquid crystal allows us to produce materials with high strength or unique optical properties.

High strength applications involve the use of extremely long molecules called *polymers*. While in a thermotropic liquid crystal phase and during their flow through the processing equipment, these molecules become highly aligned, like the fibers in wood. Cooling solidifies them into fibers, rods, and sheets that can be shaped into materials with superior mechanical properties in the direction of the long molecular axis. Sporting equipment, supersonic aircraft parts, and the sails used in the America's Cup races are fabricated from these polymeric materials. (We discuss other polymers in detail in Chapter 15.)

Far more important in today's consumer market are the liquid crystal displays (LCDs) used in watches, calculators, and computers. All depend on *changes in molecular orientation in an electric field*. The most common type, called a *twisted nematic* display, is shown schematically in Figure 12.45 in a small portion from a wristwatch LCD. The liquid crystal phase consists of layers of nematic phases sandwiched between thin glass plates that incorporate transparent electrodes. Through a special coating process, the long molecular axis lies parallel to the plane of the glass plates. The distance between the plates (6 to 8 μm) is chosen so that the molecular axis within each succeeding layer twists just enough for the molecular orientation at the bottom plate to be 90° with respect to that at the top plate. Above and below this "sandwich" are thin polarizing filters (like those used in Polaroid lenses or camera sunlight filters), which allow light waves oriented in only one direction to pass through. The filters are placed in a "crossed" arrangement, so that light passing through the top filter must twist 90° to pass through the bottom filter. The orientation and optical properties of the molecules twist the orientation of the light by exactly this amount. This whole grouping of filters, plates, and liquid crystal phase lies on a mirror. A current generated by the watch battery controls the orientation of the molecules within the phase. With the current on in one region of the display, the molecules become oriented *toward* the field, and thus block the light from passing through to the bottom filter, so that region appears dark. With the current off in another region, light passes through the molecules and bottom filter to the mirror and back again, so that region appears bright.

Cholesteric liquid crystals are used in applications that involve color changes with temperature. The helical twist in these phases "unwinds" with heating, and the extent of the unwinding determines the color. Liquid crystal thermometers that include a mixture of substances to widen their range of temperatures use this effect (Figure 12.46), as do novelty items such as "mood" rings. New and more important uses include "mapping" the area of a tumor, detecting faulty connections in electronic circuit boards, and nondestructive testing of materials under stress.

Ceramic Materials

First developed by Stone Age people, **ceramics** are defined as nonmetallic-nonpolymeric solids that are hardened by heating to high temperatures. Clay ceramics consist of silicate microcrystals suspended in a glassy, cementing

Table 12.7 Some Uses of New Ceramics and Ceramic Mixtures

Ceramic	Applications
SiC, Si_3N_4, TiB_2, Al_2O_3	Whiskers (fibers) to strengthen Al and other ceramics
Si_3N_4	Car engine parts; turbine rotors for "turbo" cars; electronic sensor units
Si_3N_4, BN, Al_2O_3	Supports or layering materials (as insulators) in electronic microchips
SiC, Si_3N_4, TiB_2, ZrO_2, Al_2O_3, BN	Cutting tools, edge sharpeners (as coatings and whole devices), scissors, surgical tools, industrial "diamond"
BN, SiC	Armor-plating reinforcement fibers (as in Kevlar composites)
ZrO_2, Al_2O_3	Surgical implants (hip and knee joints)

Figure 12.46 Cholesteric LC changing color with heat. A change in temperature affects the "turn" of the helical arrangement of layers, which affects how light passes through the layers. The result is a change in color.

medium. In "firing" a ceramic pot, for example, a kiln heats the object made of an aluminosilicate clay, such as kaolinite, to 1500°C at which temperature the clay loses water:

$$Si_2Al_2O_5(OH)_4(s) \longrightarrow Si_2Al_2O_7(s) + 2H_2O(g)$$

During the heating process, the structure rearranges to an extended network of Si-centered and Al-centered tetrahedra of O atoms (Section 14.6).

Bricks, porcelain, glazes, and other clay ceramics are useful because of their hardness and resistance to heat and chemicals. Today's generation of high-technology ceramics incorporate these traditional characteristics in addition to superior electrical and magnetic properties (Table 12.7). As just one example, consider the unusual electrical behavior of certain zinc oxide (ZnO) composites. Ordinarily a semiconductor, ZnO can be doped to become a conductor. Imbedding particles of the doped oxide into an insulating ceramic produces a variable resistor: at low voltage, the material conducts poorly, but at high voltage, it conducts well. Best of all, the changeover voltage can be "preset" by controlling the size of ZnO particles and the thickness of the insulating medium.

Preparing Modern Ceramics Among the important new ceramics are silicon carbide (SiC) and nitride (Si_3N_4), boron nitride (BN), and the superconducting oxides. They are prepared by standard chemical methods that involve driving off a volatile component during the reaction.

The SiC ceramics are made from compounds used in silicone polymer manufacture (we'll discuss their structures and uses in Section 14.6):

$$n(CH_3)_2SiCl_2(l) + 2nNa(s) \longrightarrow 2nNaCl(s) + [(CH_3)_2Si]_n(s)$$

This product is heated to 800°C to form the ceramic:

$$[(CH_3)_2Si]_n \longrightarrow nCH_4(g) + nH_2(g) + nSiC(s)$$

SiC can also be prepared by direct reaction of Si and graphite under vacuum:

$$Si(s) + C(graphite) \xrightarrow{\sim 1500°C} SiC(s)$$

The nitride is also prepared by reaction of the elements:

$$3Si(s) + 2N_2(g) \xrightarrow{>1300°C} Si_3N_4(s)$$

The formation of a BN ceramic begins with boron trichloride or boric acid reacting with ammonia:

$$B(OH)_3(s) + 3NH_3(g) \longrightarrow B(NH_2)_3(s) + 3H_2O(g)$$

Heat drives off some of the bound nitrogen as NH_3 to yield the ceramic:

$$B(NH_2)_3(s) \xrightarrow{\Delta} 2NH_3(g) + BN(s)$$

One of the common high-temperature superconducting ceramic oxides is made by heating a mixture of barium carbonate and copper and yttrium oxides, followed by further heating in the presence of O_2:

$$4BaCO_3(s) + 6CuO(s) + Y_2O_3(s) \xrightarrow{\Delta} 2YBa_2Cu_3O_{6.5}(s) + 4CO_2(g)$$

$$YBa_2Cu_3O_{6.5}(s) + \tfrac{1}{4}O_2(g) \xrightarrow{\Delta} YBa_2Cu_3O_7(s)$$

Ceramic Structures and Uses Structures of several ceramic materials are shown in Figure 12.47. Note the diamond-like structure of silicon carbide. Network covalent bonding gives the material great strength. SiC is being made into thin fibers, called *whiskers,* to reinforce other ceramics in a composite structure and prevent cracking, much like steel rods act in reinforced concrete. Silicon nitride is virtually inert chemically, retains its strength and wear resistance for extended periods above 1000°C, and is dense, hard, and an electrical insulator. Japanese and American automakers are testing it in high-efficiency car and truck engines because it allows an ideal combination of low weight, high operating temperature, and little need for lubrication.

The BN ceramics exist in two structures (Section 14.5), analogous to the common crystalline forms of carbon. In the graphite-like form, BN has extraordinary properties as an electrical insulator. At high temperature and very high pressure (1800°C and 8.5×10^4 atm), it converts to a diamond-like structure, which is extremely hard and durable. Both forms are virtually invisible to radar.

Earlier, we mentioned some potential future uses of the superconducting ceramics. In nearly every one of these materials, copper occurs in an unusual

Figure 12.47 **Unit cells of some new ceramic materials.** SiC **(A)** and the high-pressure form of BN **(B)** both have the diamond structure and are extremely hard. **C,** $YBa_2Cu_3O_7$, one of the new high-temperature superconductors.

A Silicon carbide

B Cubic BN (borazon)

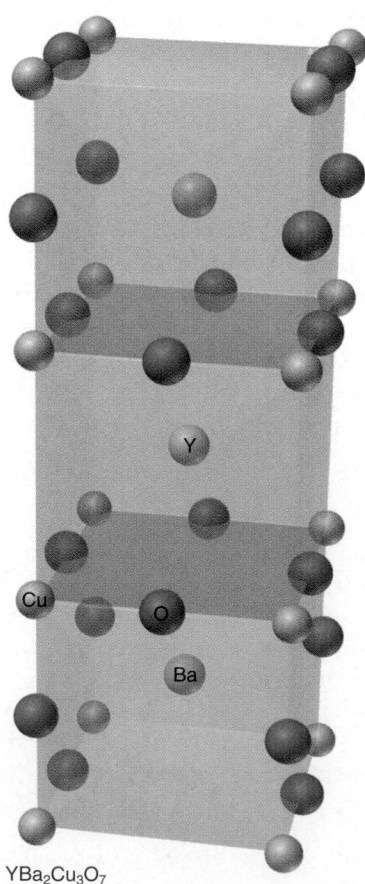

C $YBa_2Cu_3O_7$

oxidation state. In $YBa_2Cu_3O_7$, for instance, assuming oxidation states of $+3$ for Y, $+2$ for Ba, and -2 for O, the three Cu atoms have a total oxidation state of $+7$. This is divided as $Cu(II)_2Cu(III)$, with Cu in the unusual $+3$ state. X-ray crystallography indicates that a distortion in the structure makes four of the oxide ions lean toward the Y^{3+} ion, which aligns the Cu ions into chains within the crystal. It is suspected that a specific half-filled $3d$ orbital in Cu oriented toward a neighboring O^{2-} ion may be associated with super-conductivity, although the process is still poorly understood. Because of their brittleness, it has been difficult to fashion these new materials into wires, but methods for making superconducting films and ribbons have recently been developed.

Research in ceramic processing is beginning to overcome the inherent brit-tleness of this entire class of materials. The problem arises from the strength of the ionic-covalent bonding in many ceramics and their resulting inability to deform. Under stress, a microfine crystal defect widens and lengthens until the material cracks. One new method forms defect-free ceramics by the con-trolled packing and heat-treating of extremely small, uniform oxide particles coated with organic polymers. Another method arrests the widening crack by fashioning ceramics imbedded with zirconia (ZrO_2), whose crystal structure expands up to 5% under the mechanical stress of a crack tip: the moment the advancing crack reaches them, the zirconia particles effectively pinch it shut. Very recently, a third method was reported. Japanese researchers pre-pared a ceramic material made of precisely grown single crystals of Al_2O_3 and $GdAlO_3$, which become entangled during the solidification process. The mate-rial bends without cracking at temperatures above 1800 K.

Despite many remaining technical difficulties, chemical ingenuity applied to the development of new ceramic materials and research into their amaz-ing and useful properties will continue well into the next century.

Nanotechnology: Manufacturing the Smallest Possible Machines

At the frontier of interdisciplinary discovery has emerged the remarkable new field of *nanotechnology,* the manufacture of machines and other devices from atomic and molecular parts. As you've seen throughout the text so far, the macroscopic properties of a material depend ultimately on the arrangement of its atoms. Yet even though modern methods can create devices like com-puter chips the size of a penny that carry out millions of operations per sec-ond, the manufacture of each of the million p-n junctions in such a chip involves arranging billions of atoms at a time. Through the use of scanning tunneling microscopy (see Tools of the Chemistry Laboratory, p. 454) and the similar techniques of scanning probe and atomic force microscopies, pioneers of nanotechnology believe that, by arranging structures one atom at a time, they can create simple computers the size of bacteria or computers a million times more powerful than today's desktop models the size of a sugar cube! Medical devices could be made so precise that individual cells, even individ-ual genes, could be targeted surgically or pharmacologically. Minute disease monitors with multiple binding sites could circulate freely in the bloodstream measuring levels of various specific disease-related molecules. The approach could also make large-scale products lighter, stronger, and cheaper. Imagine the uses of a new class of structural materials as strong as steel that weigh $\frac{1}{50}$th as much: lightweight aircraft and spacecraft, 100-lb cars, or sofas you can lift with one hand.

The key to this futuristic technology involves two aspects of the kind of molecular manufacturing that occurs routinely in nature. The first is *self-assembly,* the ability of smaller, simpler parts to organize themselves into a larger, more complex whole. On the molecular scale, it refers to building blocks of small molecules with complementary shapes and intermolecular forces, especially dipole-dipole forces and H-bonding, that could act as "glue." Oppositely charged regions on two such molecules would connect to form a larger molecule, which in turn would form a still larger one. As you'll see in Chapter 15, self-assembly occurs all the time in biological systems during metabolism, protein synthesis, and cell division. The other is *controlled orientation,* the positioning of the two molecules near each other long enough for the intermolecular forces to take effect. Some industrial catalysts and all biological catalysts (enzymes) act this way. (Catalysts, discussed in Chapter 16, are substances that speed reactions.)

Operating on the molecular scale brings up a major problem, however, that is insignificant on the macroscopic scale: thermal disordering. In a solid, units of the crystal lattice are constantly jiggling at their sites and bonds are vibrating. The higher the temperature, the more rapid are these motions. Therefore, any structure chosen for the parts of a molecular machine must be as rigid as possible, which means the atom of choice is carbon. It has a low atomic mass and, in the form of diamond, forms four strong, tetrahedrally oriented covalent bonds per atom. Thus, diamond would form the stiffest, lightest structure possible.

Here is a possible scenario describing manipulation of a diamond surface for constructing various parts of a molecular machine. On this surface, the fourth bond of each C is attached to H. This makes the diamond surface nearly inert, like an alkane, which prevents unwanted reactions, but it prevents desired reactions as well. Thus, a nanoscale "tool kit" would prepare the surface for reaction and then proceed with construction. It would have several molecular tools, each consisting of a chemical grouping attached to a molecular "robotic arm" perhaps 100 nm long by 30 nm around and composed of a few million atoms. Many such arms would have their tips positioned within a fraction of an atomic diameter from the growing structure and build it up by sweeping back and forth, adding or removing atoms or small groups of atoms one at a time.

Each molecular tool would perform one reaction step. For example, an H-abstraction tool would be a chemical grouping that removes an H atom from the diamond surface to expose a reactive site; a C-deposition tool would be a grouping that deposits a small unit of carbon atoms, say a C=C unit, onto adjacent exposed surface sites; a C-insertion tool could insert a C atom into a double or triple bond on the growing structure; an H-deposition tool would make reactive sites inert by attaching an H atom to a fourth bonding position on a terminal C atom; a doping tool could insert atoms of other elements, such as Si, P, and S, into the growing structure to attain specific properties; and so forth. These tools would form the gears (Figure 12.48), struts, bearings, and arms needed to make diamond-based nanomachines that launch this new technology.

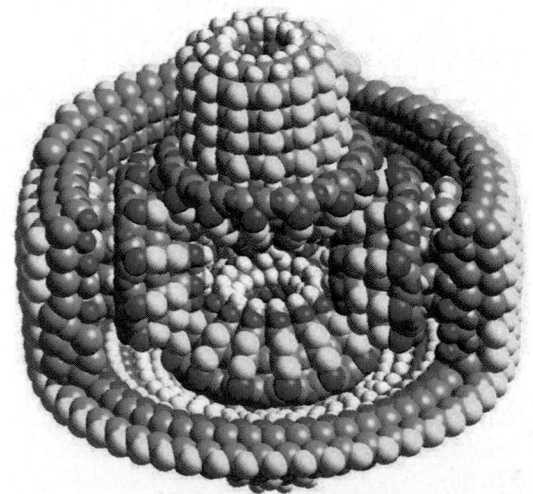

Figure 12.48 A nanoscale gear. This cutaway of a proposed design for a molecular differential gear reveals two cylindrical shafts and their facing bevel gears, along with two of the four casing-mounted side gears that mesh with both shaft gears. With the casing fixed, clockwise rotation of the top shaft drives the side gears, which in turn cause counterclockwise rotation of the bottom shaft. (In addition to the usual red for O, yellow for S, and purple for P, here C atoms are gray, H are white, and Si are orange.)

Section Summary

Doping increases the conductivity of semiconductors and is essential to modern electronic materials. Doping silicon with Group 5A atoms introduces negative sites (n-type) by adding valence electrons to the conduction band, whereas doping with Group 3A atoms adds positive holes (p-type) by emptying some orbitals in the valence band. Joining these two types of doped Si chips forms a p-n junction. Sandwiching one type between two of the other forms a transistor.

Liquid crystal phases flow like liquids but have molecules ordered like crystalline solids. Typically, the molecules have rodlike shapes, and their intermolecular forces keep them aligned. Thermotropic phases are prepared by heating the solid; lyotropic phases form when the solvent concentration is varied. The nematic, cholesteric, and smectic types of liquid crystals differ in their molecular order. Liquid crystal applications depend on our ability to control the orientation of the molecules.

Ceramics are very resistant to heat and chemicals. Most are network covalent solids formed at high temperature from simple reactants. They add lightweight strength to other materials.

Nanoscale materials could be made one atom at a time through mechanical processes involving self-assembly and complementary intermolecular forces and shapes.

Chapter Perspective

Our central focus—macroscopic behavior resulting from molecular behavior—became still clearer in this chapter, as we built on earlier ideas of bonding, molecular shape, and polarity to understand the intermolecular forces that create the properties of liquids and solids. In Chapter 13, we'll find many parallels to the key ideas in this chapter: the same intermolecular forces create solutions, temperature influences solubility as it does vapor pressure, and the equilibrium state also underlies the properties of solutions.

The following learning objectives, with section and/or sample problem (SP) numbers in parentheses, can help focus your study:

Understand These Concepts

1. How the interplay between kinetic and potential energy underlies the properties of the three states of matter and their phase changes (12.1)
2. The processes involved, both within a phase and through a phase change, when heat is added or removed from a pure substance (12.2)
3. The meaning of vapor pressure and how phase changes are dynamic equilibrium processes (12.2)
4. How temperature and intermolecular forces influence vapor pressure (12.2)
5. The relation between vapor pressure and boiling point (12.2)
6. How a phase diagram shows the phases of a substance at differing conditions of pressure and temperature (12.2)
7. The distinction between bonding and intermolecular forces on the basis of Coulomb's law and the meaning of the van der Waals radius of an atom (12.3)
8. The types and relative strengths of intermolecular forces acting in a substance (dipole-dipole, H-bonding, dispersion), the impact of H-bonding on physical properties, and the meaning of polarizability (12.3)
9. The meanings of surface tension, capillarity, and viscosity and how intermolecular forces influence their magnitudes (12.4)
10. How the important macroscopic properties of water arise from atomic and molecular properties (12.5)
11. The meaning of crystal lattice and the characteristics of the three cubic unit cells (12.6)
12. How packing of spheres gives rise to the hexagonal and cubic unit cells (12.6)
13. Types of crystalline solids and how their intermolecular forces give rise to their properties (12.6)
14. How MO band theory accounts for the properties of metals and the relative conductivities of metals, nonmetals, and metalloids (12.6)
15. The meaning of crystal defects and the functioning of advanced materials (doped semiconductors and p-n junctions, liquid crystal displays, modern ceramics, and nanostructures) on the atomic scale (12.7)

Master These Skills

1. Calculating the overall enthalpy change when heat is added to or removed from a pure substance (12.2)
2. Using the Clausius-Clapeyron equation to examine the relationship between vapor pressure and temperature (SP 12.1)
3. Using a phase diagram to predict the physical state and/or phase change of a substance (12.2)
4. Determining whether a substance can form H bonds and drawing the H-bonded structures (SP 12.2)
5. Predicting the intermolecular forces acting within a substance from its structure (SP 12.3)
6. Finding the number of particles in a unit cell (12.6)
7. Calculating atomic radius from the density and unit cell of an element (SP 12.4)

For Review and Reference

Key Terms

phase
intermolecular forces
phase change
Section 12.1
condensation
vaporization
freezing
melting (fusion)
heat of vaporization (ΔH^0_{vap})
heat of fusion (ΔH^0_{fus})
sublimation
deposition
heat of sublimation (ΔH^0_{subl})
Section 12.2
heating-cooling curve
vapor pressure
Clausius-Clapeyron
  equation

boiling point
melting point
phase diagram
critical point
triple point
Section 12.3
van der Waals radius
ion-dipole force
dipole-dipole force
hydrogen bond (H bond)
polarizability
dispersion (London) force
Section 12.4
surface tension
capillarity
viscosity

Section 12.6
crystalline solid
amorphous solid
lattice
unit cell
coordination number
simple cubic unit cell
body-centered cubic unit
  cell
face-centered cubic unit cell
packing efficiency
hexagonal closest packing
cubic closest packing
x-ray diffraction analysis
scanning tunneling
  microscopy

atomic solid
molecular solid
ionic solid
metallic solid
network covalent solid
band theory
valence band
conduction band
conductor
semiconductor
insulator
superconductivity
Section 12.7
crystal defect
doping
liquid crystal
ceramic

Key Equations and Relationships

12.1 Using the vapor pressure at one temperature to find the vapor pressure at another temperature (two-point form of the Clausius-Clapeyron equation) (p. 430):

$$\ln \frac{P_2}{P_1} = \frac{-\Delta H_{vap}}{R}\left(\frac{1}{T_2} - \frac{1}{T_1}\right)$$

Highlighted Figures and Tables

These figures (F) and tables (T) provide a quick review of key ideas.
T12.1 A macroscopic comparison of gases, liquids, and solids (p. 423)
F12.2 Changes of state and their enthalpy changes (p. 425)
F12.3 A cooling curve for the conversion of gaseous water to ice (p. 426)
F12.4 Liquid-gas equilibrium (p. 428)
F12.5 The effect of temperature on the distribution of molecular speeds in a liquid (p. 429)
F12.6 Vapor pressure as a function of temperature and intermolecular forces (p. 429)
F12.9 Phase diagrams for CO_2 and H_2O (p. 432)
F12.10 Covalent radii and van der Waals radii (p. 434)
F12.11 Periodic trends in van der Waals radii (p. 434)

T12.2 Bonding and intermolecular forces (p. 435)
F12.14 Hydrogen bonding and boiling point (p. 437)
F12.17 Molar mass and boiling point (p. 439)
F12.21 The H-bonding ability of the water molecule (p. 444)
F12.25 The macroscopic properties of water and their atomic and molecular "roots" (p. 446)
F12.27 The crystal lattice and the unit cell (p. 448)
F12.28 The three cubic unit cells (p. 449)
F12.29 Packing of spheres (p. 451)
T12.5 The major types of crystalline solids (p. 455)
F12.32 The sodium chloride structure (p. 456)
F12.37 The band of molecular orbitals in lithium metal (p. 459)
F12.38 Electrical conductivity in a conductor, semiconductor, and insulator (p. 460)

Answers to Follow-up Problems

12.1 $\ln \dfrac{P_2}{P_1} = \left(\dfrac{-40.7\times10^3 \text{ J/mol}}{8.31 \text{ J/mol}\cdot\text{K}}\right)$

$\times \left(\dfrac{1}{273.15 + 85.5 \text{ K}} - \dfrac{1}{273.15 + 34.1 \text{ K}}\right)$

$= (-4.90\times10^3 \text{ K})(-4.66\times10^{-4} \text{ K}^{-1}) = 2.28$

$\dfrac{P_2}{P_1} = 9.8$; thus, $P_2 = 40.1$ torr $\times 9.8 = 3.9\times10^2$ torr

12.2 (a)

(b)

(c) No H bonding

12.3 (a) Dipole-dipole, dispersion: CH_3Br
(b) H bonds, dipole-dipole, dispersion: $CH_3CH_2CH_2OH$
(c) Dispersion: C_3H_8

12.4 Avogadro's no. $= \dfrac{1 \text{ cm}^3}{7.874 \text{ g Fe}} \times \dfrac{55.85 \text{ g Fe}}{1 \text{ mol Fe}} \times 0.68$

$\times \dfrac{1 \text{ Fe atom}}{8.38\times10^{-24} \text{ cm}^3}$

$= 5.8\times10^{23}$ Fe atoms/mol Fe

Problems

Problems with a **colored** number are answered at the back of the text. Problem sections match the text and provide the number(s) of relevant sample problems. Most offer concept review questions, skill-building exercises (written in similar pairs), and problems in a relevant context. Following these are comprehensive problems based on material from any section and/or previous chapter.

An Overview of Physical States and Phase Changes

■ Concept Review Questions

12.1 How does the energy of attraction between particles compare with their energy of motion in a gas and in a solid? Describe two macroscopic properties that differ between a gas and a solid as part of your answer.

12.2 What types of forces, intramolecular or intermolecular, (a) prevent ice cubes from adopting the shape of their container?
(b) are overcome when ice melts?
(c) are overcome when liquid water is vaporized?
(d) are overcome when gaseous water is converted to hydrogen gas and oxygen gas?

12.3 (a) Why are gases more easily compressed than liquids?
(b) Why do liquids have a greater ability to flow than solids?

12.4 (a) Why is the heat of fusion (ΔH_{fus}) of a substance smaller than its heat of vaporization (ΔH_{vap})?
(b) Why is the heat of sublimation (ΔH_{subl}) of a substance greater than its ΔH_{vap}?
(c) At a given temperature and pressure, how does the magnitude of the heat of vaporization of a substance compare with that of its heat of condensation?

■ Skill-Building Exercises (paired)

12.5 Which of the following forces are intramolecular and which intermolecular?
(a) Those preventing oil from evaporating at room temperature
(b) Those preventing butter from melting in a refrigerator
(c) Those allowing silver to tarnish
(d) Those preventing O_2 in air from forming O atoms

12.6 Which of the following forces are intramolecular and which intermolecular?
(a) Those allowing fog to form on a cool, humid evening
(b) Those allowing water to form when H_2 is sparked
(c) Those allowing liquid benzene to crystallize when cooled
(d) Those responsible for the low boiling point of hexane

12.7 Name the phase change in each of these events:
(a) Dew appears on a lawn in the morning.
(b) Icicles change into liquid water.
(c) Wet clothes dry on a summer day.

12.8 Name the phase change in each of these events:
(a) A diamond film forms on a surface from gaseous carbon atoms in a vacuum.
(b) Mothballs in a bureau drawer disappear over time.
(c) Molten iron from a blast furnace is cast into ingots ("pigs").

■ Problems in Context

12.9 Liquid propane, a widely used fuel, is produced by compressing gaseous propane at 20°C. During the process, approximately 15 kJ of energy is released for each mole of gas liquefied. Where does this energy come from?

12.10 Many heat-sensitive and oxygen-sensitive solids, such as camphor, are purified by warming under vacuum. The solid vaporizes directly, and the vapor crystallizes on a cool surface. What phase changes are involved in this method of purifying camphor?

Quantitative Aspects of Phase Changes
(Sample Problem 12.1)

■ Concept Review Questions

12.11 Describe the changes (if any) in potential energy and in kinetic energy among the molecules when gaseous PCl_3 condenses to a liquid at a fixed temperature.

12.12 When benzene is at its melting point, two processes occur simultaneously and balance each other. Describe these processes on the macroscopic and molecular levels.

12.13 Liquid hexane (boiling point = 69°C) is placed in a closed container at room temperature. At first the pressure of the vapor phase increases, but after a short time it stops changing. Why?

12.14 Explain the effect of strong intermolecular forces on each of the following parameters: (a) critical temperature; (b) boiling point; (c) vapor pressure; (d) heat of vaporization.

12.15 Will water at a pressure of 1.1 atm boil at 100.°C? Explain.

12.16 A liquid is in equilibrium with its vapor in a closed vessel at a fixed temperature, and the vessel is connected through a stopcock to an evacuated vessel. When the stopcock is opened, will the final pressure of the vapor be different from the original value if (a) some liquid remains; (b) all the liquid is first removed? Explain.

12.17 The phase diagram for substance A has a solid-liquid curve with a positive slope, and the one for substance B has a solid-liquid line with a negative slope. What macroscopic property can distinguish A from B?

12.18 Why does water vapor at 100°C cause more severe burns than liquid water at 100°C?

■ Skill-Building Exercises (paired)

12.19 From the following data, calculate the total heat (in J) needed to convert 12.00 g ice at −5.00°C to liquid water at 0.500°C:

Melting point at 1 atm	0.0°C
c_{solid}	2.09 J/g · °C
c_{liquid}	4.21 J/g · °C
ΔH^0_{fus}	6.02 kJ/mol

12.20 From the following data, calculate the total heat (in J) needed to convert 0.333 mol ethanol gas at 300°C and 1 atm to liquid ethanol at 25.0°C and 1 atm:

Boiling point at 1 atm	78.5°C
c_{gas}	1.43 J/g · °C
c_{liquid}	2.45 J/g · °C
ΔH^0_{vap}	40.5 kJ/mol

12.21 A liquid has a heat of vaporization of 35.5 kJ/mol and a boiling point of 122°C at 1 atm. What is its vapor pressure at 109°C?

12.22 Diethyl ether has a heat of vaporization of 29.1 kJ/mol and a vapor pressure of 0.703 atm at 25.0°C. What is its vapor pressure at 95.0°C?

12.23 What is the heat of vaporization of a liquid that has a vapor pressure of 641 torr at 85.2°C and a boiling point of 95.6°C at 1 atm?

12.24 Methane (CH_4) has a boiling point of −164°C at 1 atm and a vapor pressure of 42.8 atm at −100°C. What is the heat of vaporization of CH_4?

12.25 Use the following data to sketch a qualitative phase diagram for ethylene:

Boiling point at 1 atm	−103.7°C
Melting point at 1 atm	−169.16°C
Critical point	9.9°C and 50.5 atm
Triple point	−169.17°C and 1.20×10^{-3} atm

Is solid ethylene more or less dense than liquid ethylene?

12.26 Use the following data to sketch a qualitative phase diagram for molecular hydrogen:

Melting point at 1 atm	13.96 K
Boiling point at 1 atm	20.39 K
Triple point	13.95 K and 0.07 atm
Critical point	33.2 K and 13.0 atm
Vapor pressure of solid at 10 K	0.001 atm

Does hydrogen sublime at 0.05 atm? Explain.

■ Problems in Context

12.27 In the process of freeze-drying, ice sublimes and the water vapor is removed by vacuum. In which region of the phase diagram for water (Figure 12.9B) does sublimation take place? What is the highest temperature at which water can sublime? Why does freeze-drying become difficult (or uneconomical) at very low temperatures?

12.28 Butane is a common fuel used in cigarette lighters and camping stoves. Normally supplied in metal containers under pressure, the fuel exists as a mixture of liquid and gas, so high temperatures may cause the container to explode. At 25.0°C, the vapor pressure of butane is 2.3 atm. What is the pressure in the container at 150.°C (ΔH_{vap} = 24.3 kJ/mol)?

12.29 Use Figure 12.9A to answer the following questions: (a) Carbon dioxide is sold in steel cylinders under pressures of approximately 20 atm. Is there liquid carbon dioxide in the cylinder at room temperature (~20°C)? At 40°C? At −40°C? At −120°C?
(b) Carbon dioxide is also sold as solid chunks, called "dry ice," in insulated containers. If the chunks are warmed by leaving them in an open container at room temperature, will they melt?
(c) If a container is nearly filled with dry ice and then sealed and warmed to room temperature, will the dry ice melt?
(d) If dry ice is compressed at a temperature below its triple point, will it melt?
(e) If liquid carbon dioxide is placed in a beaker at room temperature, will it boil?

Types of Intermolecular Forces
(Sample Problems 12.2 and 12.3)

■ Concept Review Questions

12.30 Why are covalent bonds typically much stronger than intermolecular forces?

12.31 Even though molecules are neutral, the dipole-dipole force is one of the most important interparticle forces that exists among them. Explain.

12.32 Both oxygen and selenium are members of Group 6A(16). Water molecules form H bonds, but H_2Se molecules do not. Explain.

12.33 In solid I_2, is the distance between the two I nuclei of one I_2 molecule longer or shorter than the distance between the two I nuclei of adjacent I_2 molecules? Explain.

12.34 Polar molecules exhibit dipole-dipole forces. Do they also exhibit dispersion forces? Explain.

12.35 Distinguish between the terms *polarizability* and *polarity*. How does each influence intermolecular forces?

12.36 How can one nonpolar molecule induce a dipole in a nearby nonpolar molecule?

■ Skill-Building Exercises *(paired)*

12.37 What is the strongest interparticle force in a sample of (a) CH_3OH; (b) CCl_4; (c) Cl_2?

12.38 What is the strongest interparticle force in a sample of (a) H_3PO_4; (b) SO_2; (c) $MgCl_2$?

12.39 What is the strongest interparticle force in a sample of (a) CH_3Br; (b) CH_3CH_3; (c) NH_3?

12.40 What is the strongest interparticle force in a sample of (a) Kr; (b) BrF; (c) H_2SO_4?

12.41 Which member of each pair of compounds forms intermolecular H bonds? Draw the H-bonded structures in each case: (a) CH_3CHCH_3 or CH_3SCH_3; (b) HF or HBr
$\qquad\quad\ |$
$\qquad\quad OH$

12.42 Which member of each pair of compounds forms intermolecular H bonds? Draw the H-bonded structures in each case:
(a) $(CH_3)_2NH$ or $(CH_3)_3N$
(b) $HOCH_2CH_2OH$ or FCH_2CH_2F

12.43 Which forces oppose vaporization of each of the following: (a) crude oil; (b) water; (c) $SiCl_4$?

12.44 Which forces oppose vaporization of each of the following: (a) Br_2; (b) SbH_3; (c) CH_3NH_2?

12.45 Which member of each pair has the greater polarizability? Explain.
(a) Br^- or I^- (b) $CH_2=CH_2$ or $CH_3—CH_3$ (c) H_2O or H_2Se

12.46 Which member of each pair has the greater polarizability? Explain.
(a) Ca^{2+} or Ca (b) CH_3CH_3 or $CH_3CH_2CH_3$ (c) CCl_4 or CF_4

12.47 Which member in each pair of liquids has the *higher* vapor pressure at a given temperature? Explain.
(a) C_2H_6 or C_4H_{10} (b) CH_3CH_2OH or CH_3CH_2F
(c) NH_3 or PH_3

12.48 Which member in each pair of liquids has the *lower* vapor pressure at a given temperature? Explain.
(a) $HOCH_2CH_2OH$ or $CH_3CH_2CH_2OH$
(b) CH_3COOH or $(CH_3)_2C=O$ (c) HF or HCl

12.49 Which member of each pair has the *higher* boiling point? Explain.
(a) LiCl or HCl (b) NH_3 or PH_3 (c) Xe or I_2

12.50 Which member of each pair has the *higher* boiling point? Explain.
(a) CH_3CH_2OH or $CH_3CH_2CH_3$ (b) NO or N_2 (c) H_2S or H_2Te

12.51 Which member of each pair has the *lower* boiling point? Explain.
(a) $CH_3CH_2CH_2CH_3$ or $CH_2—CH_2$
$\qquad\qquad\qquad\qquad\qquad\quad\ |\qquad |$
$\qquad\qquad\qquad\qquad\qquad CH_2—CH_2$
(b) NaBr or PBr_3 (c) H_2O or HBr

12.52 Which member of each pair has the *lower* boiling point? Explain.
(a) CH_3OH or CH_3CH_3 (b) FNO or ClNO
(c)

■ Problems in Context

12.53 For pairs of molecules in the gas phase, average H-bond dissociation energies are 17 kJ/mol for NH_3, 22 kJ/mol for H_2O, and 29 kJ/mol for HF. Explain this general increase in H-bond strength.

12.54 Why does motor oil have a high boiling point, even though dispersion forces are the only intermolecular forces present?

12.55 Why does the antifreeze ingredient ethylene glycol ($HOCH_2CH_2OH$; $\mathcal{M} = 62.07$ g/mol) have a boiling point of 197.6°C, whereas propanol ($CH_3CH_2CH_2OH$; $\mathcal{M} = 60.09$ g/mol), a compound with a similar molar mass, has a boiling point of only 97.4°C?

Properties of the Liquid State

■ Concept Review Questions

12.56 Before the phenomenon of surface tension was understood, physicists described the surface of water as being covered with a "skin." What causes this skinlike behavior?

12.57 Small, equal-sized drops of oil, water, and mercury lie on a waxed floor. How does each liquid behave? Explain.

12.58 Why does an aqueous solution of ethanol (CH_3CH_2OH) have a lower surface tension than water?

12.59 Why are units of energy per area (J/m^2) used for surface tension values?

12.60 Does the *strength* of the intermolecular forces in a liquid change as the liquid is heated? Explain. Why does liquid viscosity decrease with rising temperature?

■ Skill-Building Exercises *(paired)*

12.61 Rank the following in order of *increasing* surface tension at a given temperature, and explain your ranking:
(a) $CH_3CH_2CH_2OH$ (b) $HOCH_2CH(OH)CH_2OH$
(c) $HOCH_2CH_2OH$

12.62 Rank the following in order of *decreasing* surface tension at a given temperature, and explain your ranking:
(a) CH_3OH (b) CH_3CH_3 (c) $H_2C=O$

12.63 Rank the compounds in Problem 12.61 in order of *increasing* viscosity at a given temperature, and explain your ranking.

12.64 Rank the compounds in Problem 12.62 in order of *decreasing* viscosity at a given temperature, and explain your ranking.

■ Problems in Context

12.65 Are the same cohesive and adhesive forces involved when a paper towel absorbs apple juice as when it absorbs cooking oil? Explain.

12.66 Viscosity-enhancing additives increase the viscosity of a motor oil as the temperature increases. How do they work?

12.67 Pentanol ($C_5H_{11}OH$; $\mathcal{M} = 88.15$ g/mol) has nearly the same molar mass as hexane (C_6H_{14}; $\mathcal{M} = 86.17$ g/mol) but is more than 12 times as viscous at 20°C. Explain.

The Uniqueness of Water

■ Concept Review Questions

12.68 For what types of substances is water a good solvent? For what types is it a poor solvent? Explain.

12.69 The oxygen atom of a water molecule has two covalent O—H bonds but can engage in as many as four H bonds. Explain.

12.70 Warm-blooded animals maintain a narrow range of body temperature because their bodies have a high water content. Explain.

12.71 What property of water keeps plant debris on the surface of lakes and ponds? What is the ecological significance of this?

12.72 A drooping plant can be made upright by watering the ground around it. Explain.

12.73 Describe the molecular origin of the property of water responsible for the presence of ice on the surface of a frozen lake.

12.74 Describe in molecular terms what occurs when ice melts.

The Solid State: Structure, Properties, and Bonding

(Sample Problem 12.4)

■ Concept Review Questions

12.75 What is the difference between an amorphous solid and a crystalline solid on the macroscopic and molecular levels? Give an example of each.

12.76 How is the unit cell related to the crystal structure of a solid?

12.77 For structures consisting of identical atoms, how many atoms are contained in the simple, the body-centered, and the face-centered cubic unit cells? Explain how you obtained the values.

12.78 An element has a crystal structure in which the width of the cubic unit cell equals the diameter of an atom. What type of unit cell does it have?

12.79 What specific difference in the positioning of spheres gives a crystal structure based on the face-centered cubic unit cell less empty space than one based on the body-centered cubic unit cell?

12.80 Both solid Kr and solid Cu consist of individual atoms. Why do their physical properties differ so much?

12.81 What is the energy gap in band theory? How does its size compare in conductors, superconductors, semiconductors, and insulators?

12.82 Predict the effect (if any) of an increase in temperature on the electrical conductivity of (a) a conductor; (b) a semiconductor; (c) an insulator.

12.83 In addition to the type of unit cell, what atomic properties are needed to find the density of a solid consisting of identical atoms?

■ Skill-Building Exercises (paired)

12.84 For the metals listed, the number of atoms per unit cell is given in parentheses. What type of cubic lattice does each metal form:
(a) Ni (4)   (b) Cr (2)   (c) Ca (4)

12.85 Determine the number of atoms per unit cell for each of the following metals:

(a) Polonium, Po   (b) Iron, Fe   (c) Silver, Ag

12.86 Of the five major types of crystalline solid, which does each of the following form, and why: (a) Sn; (b) Si; (c) Xe?

12.87 Of the five major types of crystalline solid, which does each of the following form, and why: (a) cholesterol ($C_{27}H_{45}OH$); (b) KCl; (c) BN?

12.88 Of the five major types of crystalline solid, which does each of the following form, and why: (a) Ni; (b) F_2; (c) CH_3OH?

12.89 Of the five major types of crystalline solid, which does each of the following form, and why: (a) SiC; (b) Na_2SO_4; (c) SF_6?

12.90 Zinc oxide adopts the zinc blende crystal structure, as shown in Figure P12.90. How many Zn^{2+} ions are in the ZnO unit cell?

12.91 Calcium sulfide adopts the rock salt (NaCl) crystal structure, as shown in Figure P12.91. How many S^{2-} ions are in the CaS unit cell?

Figure P12.90   Figure P12.91

12.92 Zinc selenide (ZnSe) crystallizes in the zinc blende structure and has a density of 5.42 g/cm^3.
(a) How many Zn and Se particles are in each unit cell?
(b) What is the mass of a unit cell?
(c) What is the volume of a unit cell?
(d) What is the unit cell edge length?

12.93 An element crystallizes in a face-centered cubic lattice and has a density of 1.45 g/cm^3. The edge of its unit cell is 4.52×10^{-8} cm.
(a) How many atoms are in each unit cell?
(b) What is the volume of a unit cell?
(c) What is the mass of a unit cell?
(d) Calculate an approximate atomic mass for the element.

12.94 Classify each of the following as a conductor, insulator, or semiconductor: (a) phosphorus; (b) mercury; (c) germanium.

12.95 Classify each of the following as a conductor, insulator, or semiconductor: (a) carbon (graphite); (b) sulfur; (c) platinum.

12.96 Predict the effect (if any) of an increase in temperature on the electrical conductivity of (a) antimony, Sb; (b) tellurium, Te; (c) bismuth, Bi.

12.97 Predict the effect (if any) of a decrease in temperature on the electrical conductivity of (a) silicon, Si; (b) lead, Pb; (c) germanium, Ge.

■ Problems in Context

12.98 Polonium, the largest member of Group 6A(16), is a rare radioactive metal that is the only element with a crystal structure based on the simple cubic unit cell. Given a density of 9.142 g/cm^3, calculate an approximate atomic radius for polonium.

12.99 The coinage metals—copper, silver, and gold—crystallize in a cubic closest packed structure. Use the density of copper (8.95 g/cm^3) and its molar mass (63.55 g/mol) to calculate an approximate atomic radius for copper.

12.100 Many common rocks contain large regions of silicate networks held together by ionic interactions. What properties of rocks can be attributed to this general composition?

12.101 Semiconductors are used in many devices that measure temperature. Use band theory to explain the nature of the property that makes semiconductors suitable for this purpose.

Advanced Materials

■ Concept Review Questions

12.102 When tin is added to copper, the resulting alloy (bronze) is much harder than copper. Explain.

12.103 In the process of doping a semiconductor, certain impurities are added to increase its electrical conductivity. Explain how this occurs with regard to an n-type and a p-type semiconductor.

12.104 Silicon and germanium are both semiconducting elements from Group 4A(14) that can be doped to improve their conductivity. Predict whether each of the following would form an n-type or a p-type semiconductor:
(a) Ge doped with P   (b) Si doped with In
(c) Ge doped with As   (d) Si doped with B

12.105 State two molecular characteristics of substances that typically form liquid crystals and how each is related to function.

12.106 Distinguish between isotropic and anisotropic properties. Which describes the behavior of a liquid crystal?

12.107 How are the properties of modern ceramics the same as those of traditional clays and how are they different? Refer to specific substances in your answer.

Comprehensive Problems

Problems with an asterisk (*) are more challenging.

12.108 In many buried, iron-containing rocks, the iron is present as greenish Fe^{2+}. When the rock is mined and broken into smaller pieces, the outer few millimeters of the pieces display the brown color of Fe^{3+}, while the center remains greenish. What property of solids prevents the change of Fe^{2+} to Fe^{3+}?

***12.109** In a meteorological experiment, 4.00 L N_2 is saturated with water vapor at 22°C and then compressed to half its volume.

(a) What is the partial pressure of H_2O in the compressed gas mixture?
(b) What mass of water vapor condenses to liquid?

12.110 Which forces are overcome when the following events occur: (a) NaCl dissolves in water; (b) krypton boils; (c) water boils; (d) CO_2 sublimes?

12.111 Changes in pressure cause phase changes analogous to the changes with temperature shown in Figure 12.3.
(a) Refer to Figure 12.9B and draw a curve of pressure versus time for water similar to Figure 12.3; label the phase changes as the pressure is continuously *increased* at a constant temperature of 2°C.
(b) Refer to Figure 12.9A and draw a curve for carbon dioxide as the pressure is continuously *increased* at a constant temperature of −50°C.

12.112 Why are x-rays more useful than gamma rays or ultraviolet light for measuring the interatomic distances in crystals?

12.113 Does it take more or less heat to make a sample of ice sublime than to make the same amount of liquid water vaporize? Would the same be true for dry ice?

12.114 In making computer chips, a 5.00-kg cylindrical ingot of ultrapure n-type doped silicon that is 5.25 inches in diameter is sliced into wafers 1.02×10^{-4} m thick.
(a) Assuming no waste, how many wafers can be made from this ingot?
(b) What is the mass of a wafer? (d of Si = 2.34 g/cm^3; V of a cylinder = $\pi r^2 h$)
(c) A key step in making p-n junctions for the chip is chemical removal of the oxide layer on the wafer through treatment with gaseous hydrogen fluoride. Write a balanced equation for this reaction.
(d) If 0.750% of the Si atoms are removed during the treatment in (c), how many moles of HF are required per wafer, assuming 100% reaction yield?

12.115 Why do the densities of most liquids increase as they are cooled and solidified? How does water differ in this regard?

12.116 Methyl salicylate, $C_8H_8O_3$, the odorous constituent of oil of wintergreen and of the flavor of root beer, has a vapor pressure of 1.00 torr at 54.3°C and 10.0 torr at 95.3°C.
(a) What is its vapor pressure at 25°C?
(b) If the compound is exposed to slowly moving air at 25°C, how many liters of air must pass over its surface to vaporize 1.0 mg?

12.117 Mercury vapor is extremely toxic and is readily absorbed through the lungs. At 20.°C, mercury has a vapor pressure of 1.20×10^{-3} torr, which is high enough to be hazardous. To reduce the danger to workers who may be exposed in processing plants, mercury is cooled to lower its vapor pressure. At what temperature would the vapor pressure of mercury be at the relatively safe level of 5.0×10^{-5} torr (ΔH_{vap} = 59.1 kJ/mol)?

12.118 Use band theory to explain why electrical conductivity increases with atomic size for elements in the same group.

12.119 A greenhouse contains 216 m^3 of air at a temperature of 26°C, and a humidifier vaporizes 4.00 L water.

(a) What is the pressure of water vapor in the greenhouse, assuming that none escapes and that the air was originally completely dry? (d of H_2O = 1.00 g/mL.)

(b) What total volume of liquid water would have to be vaporized to saturate the air (i. e., achieve 100% relative humidity)? (See Table 5.4, p. 196.)

*12.120 The packing efficiency of spheres is the percentage of the total space (volume) of the unit cell occupied by the spheres:

$$\text{Packing efficiency (\%)} = \frac{\text{volume of spheres in unit cell}}{\text{volume of unit cell}} \times 100$$

Using spheres of radius r and unit-cell edge length A, calculate the packing efficiency of the following (volume of a sphere = $\frac{4}{3}\pi r^3$): (a) a simple cubic unit cell; (b) a face-centered cubic unit cell; (c) a body-centered cubic unit cell. (d) A solid consisting of identical atoms has a density of 9.0 g/cm^3 and crystallizes in a cubic closest packed structure. What is its density if the atoms are rearranged to a structure with each of the following?
(i) A body-centered cubic unit cell
(ii) A simple cubic unit cell

12.121 Consider the phase diagram for substance X:

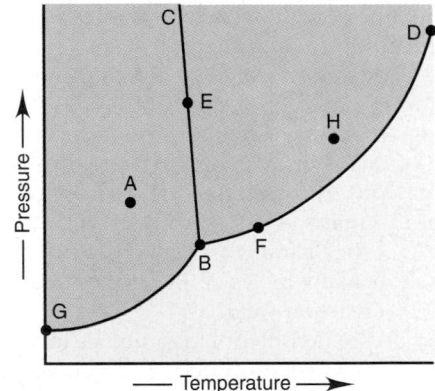

(a) What phase(s) is(are) present at point A? E? F? H? B?
(b) Which point corresponds to the critical point? Which point corresponds to the triple point?
(c) What curve corresponds to conditions at which the solid and gas are in equilibrium?
(d) Describe what happens when you start at point A and increase the temperature at constant pressure.
(e) Describe what happens when you start at point H and decrease the pressure at constant temperature.
(f) Is liquid X more or less dense than solid X?

12.122 When you step on the brake pedal of a car, the pressure of your foot is transferred smoothly and evenly from your foot through the brake lines to the brake pad. Are the brake lines filled with gas, liquid, or solid? How is this phase best suited for the function?

12.123 A capillary tube is dipped into molten paraffin wax and then allowed to drain as it cools so that the inside of the tube is coated with a thin layer of solid wax. If the tube is now dipped into a beaker of water, is the water level in the tube higher or lower than the water in the beaker? What is the shape of the meniscus? Explain.

12.124 Why do uninsulated water pipes sometimes burst in cold weather?

*12.125 The only alkali halides that do not adopt the NaCl structure are CsCl, CsBr, and CsI, formed from the largest alkali cation and the three largest halides. These crystallize in the *cesium chloride structure* (shown below for CsCl). The very existence of this structure has been used as an example of how dispersion forces can dominate even in the presence of ionic forces. Use the ideas of coordination number and polarizability to explain why the CsCl structure exists.

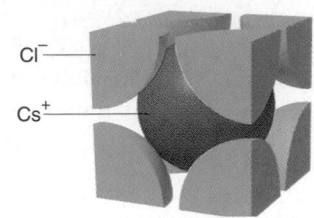

12.126 H bonding often causes individual molecules to join with others and remain together under varying conditions. Each of the following has been identified in either the gas or liquid phase. Draw structures for each showing the H bonds: (a) $(HF)_2$, dimer; (b) $(CH_3OH)_4$, cyclic; (c) $(HF)_6$, cyclic.

*12.127 Corn is not only a wonderful food source but also a valuable source of industrial chemicals. For example, furfural (*center*) is prepared from corncobs. It is an important reactant in plastics manufacture and a key solvent for the production of cellulose acetate, which is used to make everything from videotape to waterproof fabric. It can be reduced to furfuryl alcohol (*right*) or oxidized to 2-furoic acid (*left*).

(a) Which of these compounds can form H bonds? Draw structures in each case.
(b) The molecules of some substances can form an "internal" H bond, that is, an H bond within a single molecule. This takes the form of a polygon with atoms as corners and bonds as sides and an H bond as one of the sides. Which of these molecules is (are) likely to form a stable internal H bond? Draw the structure. (*Hint:* Structures with five or six atoms as corners are most stable.)

12.128 The density of solid gallium at its melting point is 5.9 g/cm^3, whereas that of liquid gallium is 6.1 g/cm^3. Is the temperature at the triple point higher or lower than the normal melting point? Is the slope of the solid-liquid curve for gallium positive or negative?

12.129 When supercooling occurs, the temperature of the liquid phase drops smoothly to a point slightly below the normal freezing point. When the first crystals of solid appear, the temperature rises sharply to the freezing point, and from then on the cooling curve appears normal. Sketch a general cooling curve, with labeled axes and regions, for a substance that changes from gas to liquid to solid and exhibits supercooling.

12.130 A chemist studying the viscosity of molten ionic compounds collects data for cesium chloride (melting point = 645°C), but a computer error jumbles the values. Assuming molten CsCl behaves like other liquids, arrange the following values correctly:

T (°C)	VISCOSITY (N · s/m²)
650.8	1.432×10^{-3}
661.3	1.371×10^{-3}
674.9	1.548×10^{-3}
688.3	1.281×10^{-3}
711.0	1.494×10^{-3}

*12.131 A 4.7-L sealed bottle containing 0.33 g ethanol, C_2H_6O, is placed in a refrigerator and reaches equilibrium with its vapor at −11°C.
(a) What mass of ethanol is present in the vapor?
(b) When the container is removed and warmed to room temperature, 20.°C, will all the ethanol vaporize?
(c) How much liquid ethanol would be present at 0.0°C? The vapor pressure of ethanol is 10. torr at −2.3°C and 40. torr at 19°C.

12.132 A cubic-type unit cell contains atoms of element A at each corner and atoms of element Z on each face. What is the empirical formula of the compound?

12.133 The boiling point of amphetamine, $C_9H_{13}N$, is 201°C at 760 torr and 83°C at 13 torr. What is the concentration (in g/m^3) of amphetamine when it is in contact with 20.°C air?

*12.134 According to band theory, application of extremely high pressures will cause a band of empty high-energy orbitals to broaden and eventually overlap a band of filled low-energy orbitals. How might this idea be used to explain the observation made by passing spacecraft that Jupiter and Saturn may have metallic hydrogen near their small, rocky cores?

12.135 Is it possible for a salt of formula AB_3 to have a face-centered cubic lattice of anions with cations in all the eight available holes? Explain.

*12.136 Substance A has the following properties:

Melting point at 1 atm	−20.°C
Boiling point at 1 atm	85°C
ΔH_{fus}	180. J/g
ΔH_{vap}	500. J/g
c_{solid}	1.0 J/g · °C
c_{liquid}	2.5 J/g · °C
c_{gas}	0.5 J/g · °C

At 1 atm, a 25-g sample of A is heated from −40.°C to 100.°C at a constant rate of 450. J/min.
(a) How many minutes does it take to heat the sample to its melting point?
(b) How many minutes does it take to melt the sample?
(c) Perform any other necessary calculations and draw a curve of temperature vs. time for the entire heating process.

*12.137 An aerospace manufacturing facility is contracted by the Department of Defense to build a prototype experimental aircraft that cannot be detected by radar. Boron nitride is chosen for incorporation into the body parts and the boric acid/ammonia method is used to prepare the ceramic material. Given 85.5% and 86.8% yields for the two reaction steps, how much boron nitride can be prepared from 1.00 t boric acid and 12.5 m^3 ammonia at 275 K and

3.07×10^3 kPa (t = metric ton)? Assume that ammonia does *not* behave ideally under these conditions and that it is recycled completely in the reaction process.

*12.138 In a body-centered cubic unit cell, the central atom lies on an internal (*body*) diagonal of the cell and touches the corner atoms.
(a) What is the length of the body diagonal in terms of the atomic radius, r?
(b) If the edge length of the cube is a, what is the length of a *face* diagonal?
(c) Derive an expression for a in terms of r.
(d) How many atoms are in this unit cell?
(e) What fraction of the volume of this unit cell is filled with spheres?

12.139 Ice is held in a cylinder by means of a piston at −10°C. What happens to the contents of the cylinder as the piston is slowly withdrawn at a constant temperature?

12.140 The simplest hydrides of N, O, and F boil at higher temperatures than those of P, S, and Cl, but the simplest hydrides of B and C boil at lower temperatures than those of Al and Si. Explain these patterns.

12.141 A 0.75-L bottle is cleaned, dried, and closed in a room where the air is 22°C and 44% relative humidity (that is, the water vapor in the air is 0.44 of the equilibrium vapor pressure at that temperature). The bottle is brought outside and stored at 0.0°C.
(a) What mass of liquid water condenses inside the bottle?
(b) Would liquid water condense at 10°C? (See Table 5.4.)

*12.142 Sodium has a crystal structure based on the body-centered cubic unit cell. What is the mass of one unit cell of sodium?

*12.143 KF has the same type of crystal structure as NaCl. The unit cell of KF has an edge length of 5.39 Å. Calculate the density of KF.

*12.144 One way of purifying gaseous H_2 is to pass it under high pressure through the holes of a metal's crystal structure. Palladium, which adopts a cubic closest packed structure, absorbs more H_2 than any other element and is one of the metals currently used for this purpose. Although the exact Pd/H interaction is unclear, it is estimated that the density of absorbed H_2 approaches that of liquid hydrogen (70.8 g/L). What volume (in L) of gaseous H_2, measured at STP, can be packed into the spaces of 1 dm^3 of palladium metal?

*12.145 On a humid day in New Orleans, the temperature is 22.0°C, and the partial pressure of water vapor in the air is 31.0 torr. The 9000-ton air-conditioning system in the Louisiana Superdome maintains an inside air temperature of 22.0°C also but a partial pressure of water vapor of 10.0 torr. The volume of air in the dome is 2.4×10^6 m^3, and the total pressure inside and outside the dome are both 1.0 atm.
(a) What mass of water (in metric tons) must be removed every time the inside air is completely replaced with outside air? (*Hint:* How many moles of gas are in the dome? How many moles of water vapor? How many moles of dry air? How many moles of outside air must be added to the air in the dome to simulate the composition of outside air?)
(b) Calculate the heat released when this mass of water condenses.

Approximate Composition of a Bacterium

Substance	Mass % of Cell	Number of Types	Number of Molecules
Water	~70	1	5×10^{10}
Ions	1	20	?
Sugars, etc.*	3	200	3×10^8
Amino acids, etc.*	0.4	100	5×10^7
Lipids, etc.*	2	50	3×10^7
Nucleotides, etc.*	0.4	200	1×10^7
Other small molecules	0.2	~200	?
Macromolecules (proteins, nucleic acids, polysaccharides)	23	~5000	6×10^6

*Includes precursors and metabolites.

13

The Properties of Mixtures
Solutions and Colloids

Figure: The Most Marvelous Mixtures. The world consists of mixtures, and the most marvelous by far are living cells, even the simplest bacterium. The table above catalogs, in broad strokes, the incredibly complex, aqueous mixture of inorganic ions, small organic molecules, and giant biomolecules that occurs in a typical bacterium, such as *Listeria monocytogenes* shown here (12,000×). Yet, this seeming molecular hodgepodge is a highly organized system that carries out the intricacies of life.

Chapter Outline

13.1 Types of Solutions: Intermolecular Forces and the Prediction of Solubility
- Intermolecular Forces in Solution
- Liquid Solutions
- Gas Solutions and Solid Solutions

13.2 Energy Changes in the Solution Process
- Heats of Solution and Solution Cycles
- Heats of Hydration
- The Tendency Toward Disorder

13.3 Solubility as an Equilibrium Process
- Effect of Temperature
- Effect of Pressure

13.4 Quantitative Ways of Expressing Concentration
- Molarity and Molality
- Parts of Solute by Parts of Solution
- Converting Units of Concentration

13.5 Colligative Properties of Solutions
- Nonvolatile Nonelectrolyte Solutions
- Solute Molar Mass
- Volatile Nonelectrolyte Solutions
- Electrolyte Solutions

13.6 The Structure and Properties of Colloids

Nearly all the gases, liquids, and solids that make up our world are *mixtures*—two or more substances physically mixed together but not chemically combined. Synthetic mixtures, such as glass and soap, usually contain relatively few components (see photo), whereas natural mixtures, such as seawater and soil, are more complex, often containing more than 50 different substances. Living mixtures, such as trees and students, are the most complex—even a simple bacterial cell contains more than 5000 different compounds.

Recall from Chapter 2 that a mixture has two defining characteristics: *its composition is variable*, and *it retains some properties of its components*. In this chapter, we focus on two common types of mixtures: solutions and colloids. *A solution is a homogeneous mixture*, one with no boundaries separating its components; thus, a solution exists as one phase. A *heterogeneous mixture* has two or more phases. The small pebbles in a slab of concrete or the bubbles in a glass of champagne indicate that these are heterogeneous mixtures. A *colloid* is a heterogeneous mixture in which one component is dispersed as fine particles in another component. Smoke and milk are colloids. The essential difference between solutions and colloids is one of particle *size:*

- In a solution, the particles are individual atoms, ions, or small molecules.
- In a colloid, the particles are typically either macromolecules or aggregations of small molecules that are not large enough to settle out.

These molecular-scale differences result in a key observable difference that we'll discuss later in the chapter.

This chapter opens with a survey of the types of solutions and the role of intermolecular forces in their formation. Predicting solubility is a major focus of the first section, in which we look at systems ranging from salts in water to antibiotics in bacterial cells. Next we investigate the reason a substance dissolves, in terms of two key factors: the enthalpy change and the disordering that occur when a solution forms. To understand the second factor, the concept of entropy changes in the solution process is introduced. Then we examine the equilibrium nature of solubility and see how temperature and pressure affect it. We discuss ways of expressing concentration and then use them to explore the differences between the physical properties of solutions and those of pure substances. An investigation of the properties of colloids follows, and the chapter closes with the application of solution and colloid chemistry to the purification of water.

Concepts and Skills to Review

before you study this chapter

- classification and separation of mixtures (Section 2.9)
- calculations involving mass percent (Section 3.1) and molarity (Section 3.5)
- electrolytes; water as a solvent (Sections 4.1 and 12.5)
- mole fraction and Dalton's law of partial pressures (Section 5.4)
- types of intermolecular forces and the concept of polarizability (Section 12.3)
- vapor pressure of liquids (Section 12.2)

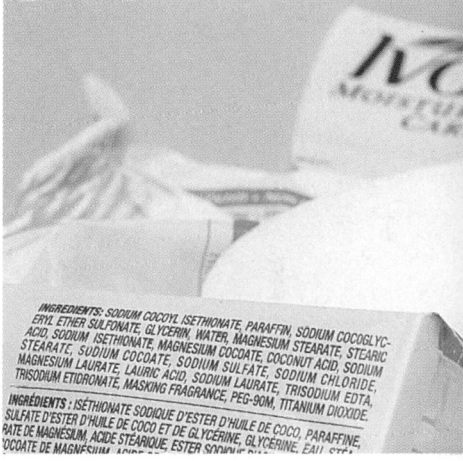

13.1 Types of Solutions: Intermolecular Forces and the Prediction of Solubility

We often describe solutions in terms of one substance dissolving in another: the **solute** dissolves in the **solvent**. Usually, the solvent is the *most abundant component* of a given solution. In some cases, however, the substances are **miscible,** that is, soluble in each other in any proportion, so it is not very meaningful to call one the solute and the other the solvent.

The **solubility (S)** of a solute is the maximum amount that dissolves in a fixed quantity of a particular solvent at a specified temperature, given that excess solute is present. Different solutes may have very different solubilities. For example, for sodium chloride (NaCl), S = 39.12 g/100. mL water at 100.°C, whereas for silver chloride (AgCl), S = 0.0021 g/100. mL water at 100.°C. Obviously, NaCl is much more soluble in water than AgCl is. (Solubility may also be expressed in other units, as you'll see later.) Although solubility has a quantitative meaning, the words *dilute* and *concentrated* are qualitative terms that refer to the *relative amounts of solute:* a dilute solution contains much less dissolved solute than a concentrated one.

From everyday experience you know that some solvents can dissolve a given solute, whereas others cannot. For example, butter does not dissolve in water, but it does in cooking oil. A major factor determining whether a solution forms is the *relative strength of the intermolecular forces within and between solute and solvent.* From a knowledge of these forces, we can often predict which solutes will dissolve in which solvents.

Intermolecular Forces In Solution

All the intermolecular forces we discussed in Chapter 12 for pure substances also occur within mixtures. Figure 13.1 summarizes these forces in order of decreasing strength.

Ion-dipole forces are a principal factor in the solubility of ionic compounds in water. When a salt dissolves, each ion on the crystal's surface attracts the oppositely charged end of the water dipole. These attractive forces overcome those between the ions and break down the crystal structure. As each ion becomes separated, more water molecules cluster around it in **hydration shells,** as shown in Figure 13.2. The closest hydration shell is hydrogen bonded to water molecules slightly farther away; those form a less structured hydration shell and are in turn H bonded to other molecules in the bulk solvent. For monatomic ions, the number of water molecules in the closest hydration shell depends on the ion's size. Four water molecules can fit tetrahedrally around small ions, such as Li^+, while larger ions, such as Na^+ and F^-, usually have six water molecules surrounding them octahedrally.

Dipole-dipole forces and the special type of dipole-dipole force known as the *H bond* are both very important in solutions. The H bond is a primary factor in water's ability to dissolve numerous O-containing and N-containing organic and biological compounds, such as alcohols, sugars, amines, and amino acids. (Recall that O and N are small, so their lone pairs can get very close to the partially positive H of H_2O.)

The two types of *charge-induced dipole forces* rely on the polarizability of the components. When an ion's charge distorts the electron cloud of a nearby nonpolar particle, an **ion-induced dipole force** results. To cite one essential biological example, this intermolecular force plays a role in the attraction between the Fe^{2+} ion in hemoglobin and an O_2 molecule in the bloodstream, which results in oxygen binding. An ion can also increase the magnitude of an existing dipole in a nearby molecule. Thus, this force contributes to the formation of any solution that contains ions—salts dissolved in water or in less polar solvents. Coulomb's law shows that a greater charge results in a stronger energy of attraction. Therefore, the ion-induced dipole force is stronger than the **dipole-induced dipole force,** which arises when the partial charges of a polar molecule distort the electron cloud of a nearby nonpolar one. The solubility in water, limited though it is, of the nonpolar atmospheric gases O_2, N_2, and the noble gases, is due in part to dipole-induced dipole forces. Paint thinners and grease solvents function through these forces also.

We must always appreciate the importance of ever-present *dispersion forces* because they contribute to the solubility of all solutes in all solvents. In fact, they are the *principal* attractive force in solutions of nonpolar substances; thus, petroleum exists as a complex homogeneous mixture because of dispersion forces.

With these intermolecular forces in mind, let's examine the types of solutions. Solutions can be gaseous, liquid, or solid. In most cases, *the physical state of the solvent determines that of the solution.* We highlight solutions in which the solvent is a liquid because they are by far the most common and important.

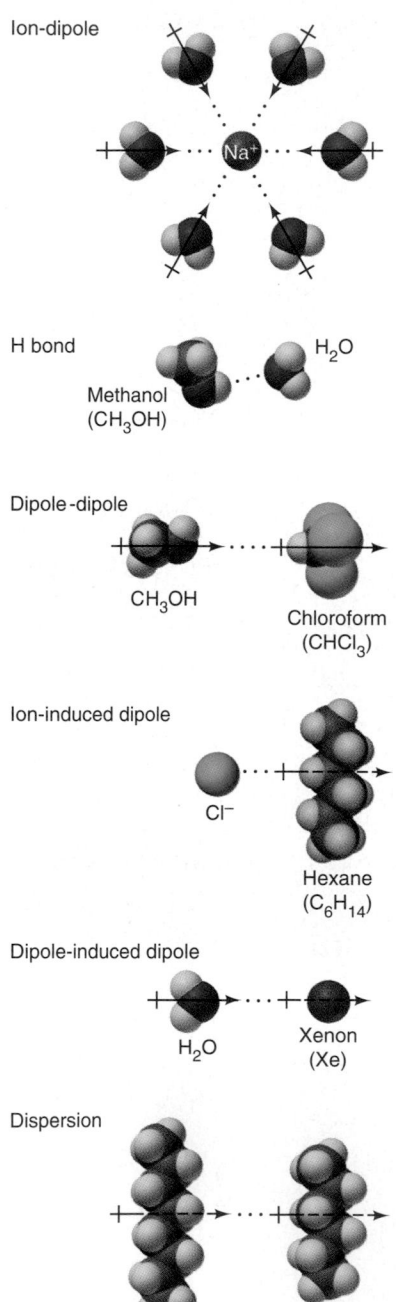

Ion-dipole

Na^+

H bond

Methanol
(CH_3OH)

H_2O

Dipole-dipole

CH_3OH

Chloroform
($CHCl_3$)

Ion-induced dipole

Cl^-

Hexane
(C_6H_{14})

Dipole-induced dipole

H_2O

Xenon
(Xe)

Dispersion

Octane
(C_8H_{18})

C_6H_{14}

Figure 13.1 The major types of intermolecular forces in solutions. Forces are listed in decreasing order of strength, and an example of each is shown with space-filling models.

Figure 13.2 **Hydration shells around an aqueous ion.** When an ionic compound dissolves in water, ion-dipole forces orient water molecules around the separated ions to form hydration shells. The cation shown here is octahedrally surrounded by six water molecules, which form H bonds to water molecules in the next hydration shell, and those form H bonds with others farther away.

Liquid Solutions and the Role of Molecular Polarity

From cytoplasm to tree sap, gasoline to cleaning fluid, iced tea to urine, solutions in which a liquid is the solvent appear throughout everyday life (see photo). Water is the most prominent liquid solvent because it is so abundant in the environment and can dissolve both ionic compounds and polar molecules. It dissolves many substances through the formation of H bonds. Nonpolar substances, such as cooking oil and car wax, do not dissolve appreciably in water but dissolve freely in less polar or nonpolar solvents.

Experience has shown that *substances with similar types of intermolecular forces dissolve in each other.* This fact is summarized in the old rule-of-thumb **like dissolves like,** which usually provides a good qualitative means of predicting solubility.

Liquid-Liquid and Solid-Liquid Solutions Water dissolves many salts because the strong ion-dipole attractions that water forms with the ions are very similar to the strong attractions between the ions themselves and, therefore, *substitute* for them. The same salts are insoluble in hexane (C_6H_{14}) because the weak ion-induced dipole forces their ions could form with this nonpolar solvent *cannot* substitute for attractions between the ions. Similarly, oil does not dissolve in water because the weak dipole-induced dipole forces between oil and water molecules cannot substitute for the strong H bonds between water molecules. Oil *does* dissolve in hexane, however, because the dispersion forces in one substitute well for the dispersion forces in the other. Thus, for a solution to form, "like dissolves like" means that the forces created between solute and solvent must be *comparable in strength* to the forces destroyed within both the solute and the solvent.

To examine this idea further, let's compare the solubilities of a series of alcohol solutes in water and in hexane, two solvents that dissolve through very different intermolecular forces. Alcohols are organic molecules with a hydroxyl (—OH) group bound to a hydrocarbon group. The simplest type of alcohol has the general formula $CH_3(CH_2)_nOH$, where $n \geq 0$; we'll consider alcohols with $n = 0$ to 5. We can view an alcohol molecule as consisting of *two* portions, the polar —OH group and the nonpolar hydrocarbon chain. The —OH portion forms strong H bonds with water and weak dipole-induced dipole forces with hexane. The hydrocarbon portion interacts through dispersion forces with hexane and through dipole-induced dipole forces with water.

Table 13.1 Solubility* of a Series of Alcohols in Water and Hexane

Alcohol	Model	Water	Hexane
CH_3OH (methanol)		∞	0.12
CH_3CH_2OH (ethanol)		∞	∞
$CH_3(CH_2)_2OH$ (propanol)		∞	∞
$CH_3(CH_2)_3OH$ (butanol)		0.11	∞
$CH_3(CH_2)_4OH$ (pentanol)		0.030	∞
$CH_3(CH_2)_5OH$ (hexanol)		0.0058	∞

*Expressed in mol alcohol/100 g solvent at 20°C.

Look at Table 13.1, which includes electron-density models of the alcohols, and consider alcohol solubility in water. In the smaller alcohols (one to three carbons), the hydroxyl group is a relatively large portion of the molecule, so the solute molecules interact with one another through H bonding, just as the water molecules do. When they mix, strong H bonding within solute and within solvent is replaced by strong H bonding *between* solute and solvent, as you see in Figure 13.3. Thus, the smaller alcohols are miscible with water.

Note that water solubility decreases dramatically from the three-carbon to the four-carbon alcohol. Those with chains longer than six carbons are virtually insoluble in water. As the nonpolar chain becomes longer, the —OH group becomes a smaller portion of the molecule. For the longer alcohols to dissolve, they must move between the water molecules and separate them by substituting weak attractions with water for the strong H bonds among the water molecules themselves. Even though the —OH portion forms H bonds to water, these cannot compensate for the significant disruption of the H bonds in pure water.

The opposite trend in solubility occurs with hexane as the solvent, as the right column of Table 13.1 shows. Now the major solute-solvent *and* solvent-solvent interactions are dispersion forces. The weak forces between the —OH

Water   Methanol   A solution of water
                                                     and methanol

Figure 13.3 **Like dissolves like: solubility of methanol in water.** The H bonds in water and in methanol are similar in type and strength, so they can substitute for one another. Thus, methanol is soluble in water; in fact, they are miscible.

group of methanol (CH_3OH) and hexane *cannot* substitute for the strong H bonding among CH_3OH molecules, so the solubility of methanol in hexane is relatively low. In the larger alcohols, however, dispersion forces become increasingly more important, and these *can* substitute for dispersion forces in pure hexane, so solubility increases. Since no strong solvent-solvent forces must be replaced by weak solute-solvent forces, even the two-carbon chain of ethanol makes strong enough solute-solvent attractions for it to be miscible in hexane.

Sample Problem 13.1   Predicting Relative Solubilities of Substances

PROBLEM Predict which solvent will dissolve more of the given solute:
(a) Sodium chloride in methanol (CH_3OH) or in propanol ($CH_3CH_2CH_2OH$)
(b) Ethylene glycol ($HOCH_2CH_2OH$) in hexane ($CH_3CH_2CH_2CH_2CH_2CH_3$) or in water
(c) Diethyl ether ($CH_3CH_2OCH_2CH_3$) in water or in ethanol (CH_3CH_2OH)
PLAN We examine the formulas of the solute and each solvent to determine the types of forces that could occur. A solute tends to be more soluble in a solvent whose intermolecular forces are similar to, and therefore can substitute for, those in the solute.
SOLUTION **(a)** Methanol. NaCl is an ionic solid that dissolves through ion-dipole forces. Both methanol and propanol contain a polar —OH group, but propanol's longer hydrocarbon chain can form only weak forces with the ions, so it is less effective at substituting for the ionic attractions in the solute.
(b) Water. Ethylene glycol molecules have two —OH groups, and the molecules interact with each other through H bonding. They are more soluble in H_2O, whose H bonds can substitute for solute H bonds better than can the dispersion forces in hexane.
(c) Ethanol. Diethyl ether molecules interact with each other through dipole and dispersion forces and can form H bonds to both H_2O and ethanol. The ether is more soluble in ethanol because that solvent can form H bonds *and* substitute for the dispersion forces in the solute. Water, on the other hand, can form H bonds with the ether, but it lacks any hydrocarbon portion, so it forms much weaker dispersion forces that can only partially substitute for those within the solute.

Follow-up Problem 13.1 Predict which solute is more soluble in the given solvent:
(a) Butanol ($CH_3CH_2CH_2CH_2OH$) or 1,4-butanediol ($HOCH_2CH_2CH_2CH_2OH$) in water
(b) Chloroform ($CHCl_3$) or carbon tetrachloride (CCl_4) in water

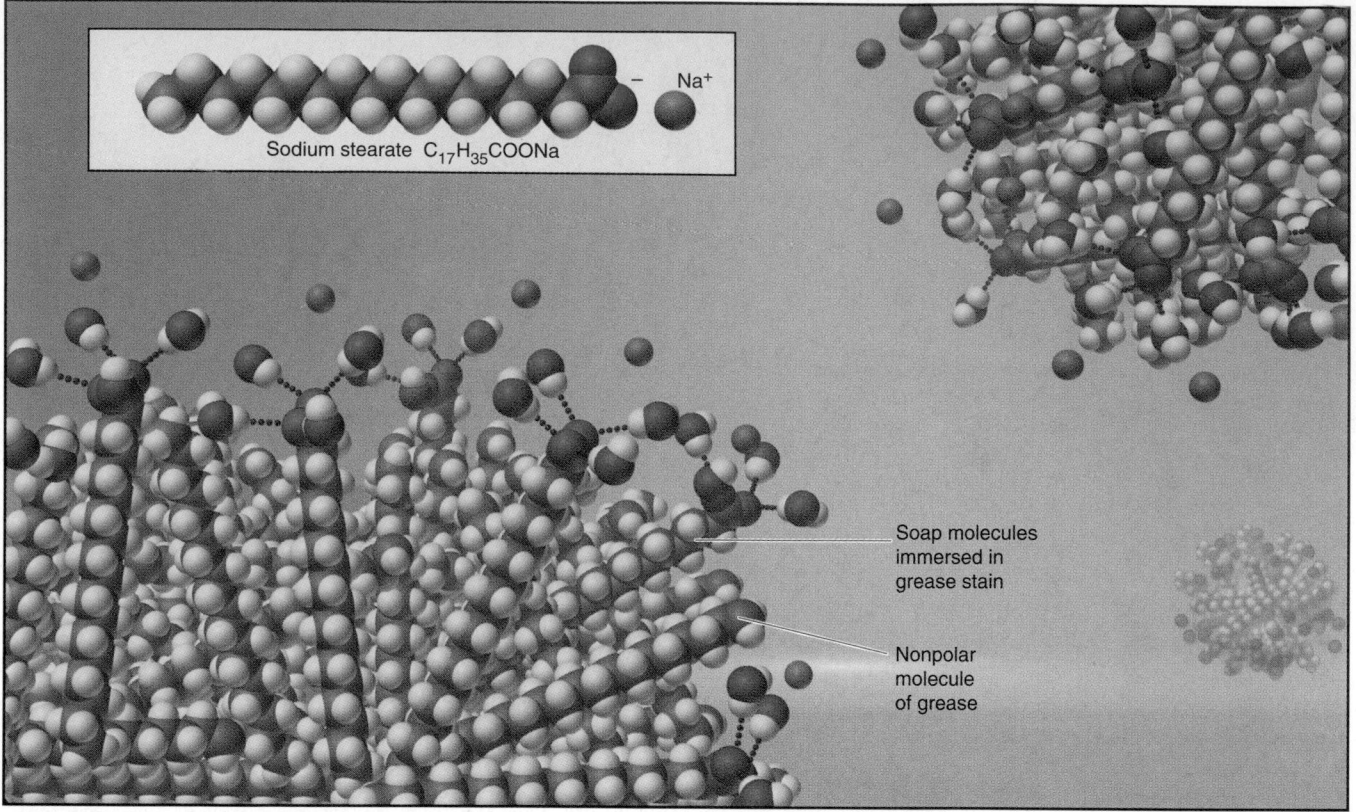

Sodium stearate C$_{17}$H$_{35}$COONa

Soap molecules immersed in grease stain

Nonpolar molecule of grease

Figure 13.4 **The structure and function of a soap.** The inset shows the structure of sodium stearate, a typical soap. Note the nonpolar tail and polar ionic head. The tails of soap molecules interact with nonpolar molecules in grease by dispersion forces, while the heads interact with water through H bonds and ion-dipole forces. Agitation breaks up the grease stain into small soap-grease aggregates, and rinsing flushes them away.

◆ Cations and the Properties of Soaps

The cation of a soap influences its properties greatly. Lithium soaps are hard and high melting and are used in car lubricants. Softer, more water-soluble sodium soaps are used as common bar soap. Potassium soaps are low melting and used as liquid soaps. The insolubility of calcium soaps explains why it is difficult to clean clothes in hard water, which typically contains Ca^{2+} ions (Chemical Connections, Section 13.6).

The Dual Polarity of Soaps   Many other organic molecules have both polar and nonpolar portions, and the predominance of one portion or the other determines the solubility of the substance in various solvents. The two polarities of some types of substances, such as soaps, detergents, and many common antibiotics, also determine their function. A **soap** is the salt of an acid-base reaction between a strong base (metal hydroxide) and a fatty acid, a molecule with a long hydrocarbon chain bonded to an organic acid group (—COOH). A typical soap molecule has a nonpolar "tail" that is 15 to 19 carbons long and a polar-ionic "head" consisting of the —COO$^-$ group and a cation. ◆ Sodium stearate [CH$_3$(CH$_2$)$_{16}$COONa], shown in the inset of Figure 13.4, is an example. The tail is soluble in oily materials and the head is soluble in water. When a grease-stained cloth is immersed in soapy water, the nonpolar tails of the soap molecules interact through dispersion forces with the nonpolar grease molecules, while the polar-ionic heads interact through ion-dipole forces and H bonds with the water. Agitation creates tiny aggregates of grease molecules enveloped by the polar-ionic heads of embedded soap molecules. These aggregates are flushed away with added water. Detergents have a similar structure of nonpolar tail and ionic head (see Figure 15.18, p. 630). Soaps and detergents are called *surfactants* (a combination of the words *surf*ace-*act*ive *agents*) because they interact with the surfaces of two phases, such as oil and water. Certain antibiotics function via dual polarities as well, as shown in the Chemical Connections essay.

Chemical Connections   Chemistry in Pharmacology

How Antibiotics Work

All cells have membranes that maintain their internal concentrations of ions in delicate balance with those in the external aqueous fluid: some ions, such as Na^+, are excluded from the cell, whereas others, such as K^+, are included. If this ionic segregation of Na^+ and K^+ is disrupted, the organism cannot survive.

Cell membranes are thin envelopes that consist mostly of a double layer of molecules. Each molecule combines two fatty acids, an alcohol, and a phosphate group. The nonpolar tails of the fatty-acid portions interact through dispersion forces within the membrane, while the charged, polar heads of the phosphate portion interact through ion-dipole forces with the watery interior and exterior fluids.

Antibiotics are natural substances produced by one microorganism to chemically destroy another. Many have been adopted by medical science as potent weapons against bacterial infection. Several classes of antibiotics function by using two molecular polarities to disrupt an organism's aqueous ionic makeup. Some antibiotics disrupt ion balance by forming a channel in the bacterial membrane through which aqueous ions can flow. Figure 13.A shows the action of the antibiotic gramicidin A. This molecule has two polarities on one tube-shaped molecule: nonpolar chemical groups on the outside of the tube and polar groups on the inside. The nonpolar outside helps the molecule dissolve into the nonpolar membrane of the target bacterium through dispersion forces, and the polar inside allows ions to enter through H bonds and ion-dipole forces. Two gramicidin A molecules lying end to end span the bacterial membrane and remain there, providing a polar passageway for ions to diffuse in and out. The cell's interior-exterior ionic segregation is disrupted, and the organism dies.

Valinomycin is a donut-shaped antibiotic molecule that works in a different way. The polar hole of the donut binds an ion, while the nonpolar rim allows the molecule to dissolve into the bacterial membrane. Rather than remaining lodged

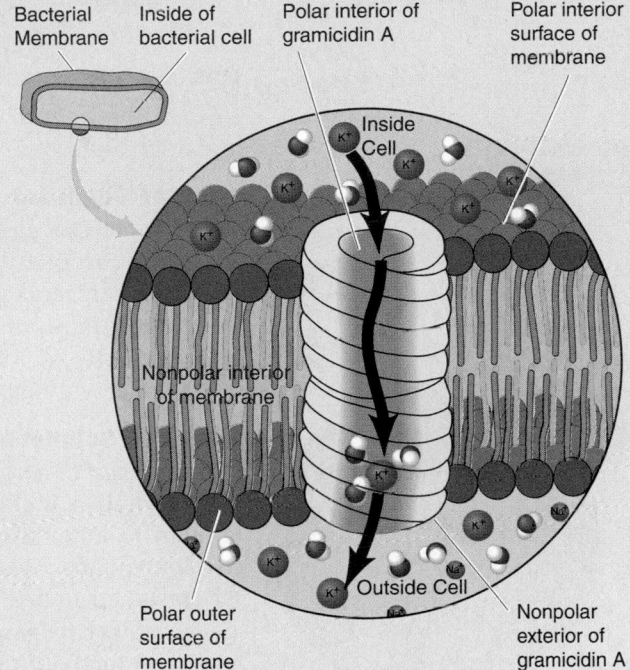

Figure 13.A The mode of action of an antibiotic. Gramicidin A is a tubelike molecule, nonpolar on the outside and polar on the inside. After dissolving into the nonpolar interior of a bacterial cell membrane via dispersion forces, pairs of gramicidin molecules aligned end to end span the membrane's thickness. Ions diffuse through the polar interior of these molecules, which destroys the cell's ionic balance and segregation of Na^+ outside and K^+ inside.

there as gramicidin A does, valinomycin moves through to the other side and releases the ion. Millions of such transits by many valinomycin molecules soon disrupt the ionic segregation, and the organism dies.

Gas-Liquid Solutions   Gases that are nonpolar, such as N_2, or nearly so, such as NO, have low boiling points because their intermolecular attractions are weak. Likewise, they are not very soluble in water because solute-solvent forces are weak. In fact, as Table 13.2 shows, for nonpolar gases, boiling point generally correlates with solubility in water.

In some cases, the small amount of a nonpolar gas that does dissolve is essential to a process. The most important environmental example is the solubility of O_2 in water. At 25°C and 1 atm, only 3.2 mL O_2 dissolves per 100. mL water, but aquatic animal life would die without the presence of this small amount. In other cases, the solubility of a gas may seem high because the gas is actually reacting with the solvent or another component. Oxygen seems much more soluble in blood than in water because the O_2 is continually bonding with hemoglobin molecules in red blood cells. Similarly, carbon dioxide, which is essential for aquatic plants and coral-reef growth, seems

Table 13.2 Correlation Between Boiling Point and Solubility in Water

Gas	Solubility (*M*)*	bp (K)
He	4.2×10^{-4}	4.2
Ne	6.6×10^{-4}	27.1
N_2	10.4×10^{-4}	77.4
CO	15.6×10^{-4}	81.6
O_2	21.8×10^{-4}	90.2
NO	32.7×10^{-4}	121.4

*At 273 K and 1 atm.

very soluble in water (~81 mL CO_2/100. mL H_2O at 25°C and 1 atm) because it is actually reacting, in addition to simply dissolving:

$$CO_2(g) + H_2O(l) \longrightarrow H^+(aq) + HCO_3^-(aq)$$

Gas Solutions and Solid Solutions

Despite the central place of liquid solutions in chemistry, gaseous solutions and solid solutions have vital importance and numerous applications.

Gas-Gas Solutions *All gases are infinitely soluble in one another.* Air is the classic example of a gaseous solution, consisting of about 18 gases in widely differing proportions. Anesthetic gas proportions are finely adjusted to the needs of the patient and the length of the surgical procedure. The ratios of components in many industrial gas mixtures, such as $CO:H_2$ in syngas production or $N_2:H_2$ in ammonia production, are controlled to optimize product yield under varying conditions of temperature and pressure.

Gas-Solid Solutions *When a gas dissolves in a solid, it occupies the spaces between the closely packed particles.* Hydrogen can be purified by passing an impure sample through a metal such as palladium. Only the H_2 molecules are small enough to enter the spaces between the Pd atoms, where they form Pd—H covalent bonds. Under high H_2 pressure, the H atoms are passed along the Pd crystal structure and emerge from the solid as H_2 molecules.

The ability of gases to penetrate a solid also has disadvantages. The electrical conductivity of copper, for example, is drastically reduced by the presence of O_2, which dissolves into the crystal structure and reacts to form copper(I) oxide. High-conductivity copper is prepared by melting and recasting the copper in an O_2-free atmosphere.

Solid-Solid Solutions Since solids diffuse so little, their mixtures are usually heterogeneous, as in gravel mixed with sand. Some solid-solid solutions can be formed by melting the solids and then mixing them and allowing them to freeze. Many **alloys,** mixtures of elements that have an overall metallic character, are examples of solid-solid solutions (although several common alloys have microscopic heterogeneous regions). In *substitutional* alloys, such as brass (Figure 13.5A) and sterling silver, atoms of another element substitute for some atoms of the main element in the structure. In *interstitial* alloys, atoms of another element (often a nonmetal) fill some of the spaces *(interstices)* between atoms of the main element. Some forms of carbon steel, shown in Figure 13.5B, for example, are interstitial alloys of iron with a small amount of carbon.

Waxes are another familiar type of solid-solid solution. Most waxes are amorphous solids that may contain small regions of crystalline regularity. A natural *wax* is a solid of biological origin that is insoluble in water but dissolves in nonpolar solvents. Many plants have waxy coatings on their leaves and fruit to prevent evaporation of interior water. ◆ (See margin opposite page.)

Section Summary

Solutions are homogeneous mixtures consisting of a solute dissolved in a solvent through the influence of intermolecular forces. The solubility of a solute in a given amount of solvent is the maximum amount, with excess solute present, that can dissolve under specified conditions of pressure and temperature. In addition to the intermolecular forces that exist in pure substances, ion-dipole, ion-induced dipole, and dipole-induced dipole forces occur in

A Brass, a substitutional alloy

B Carbon steel, an interstitial alloy

Figure 13.5 The arrangement of atoms in two types of alloys.
A, Brass is a substitutional alloy in which zinc atoms substitute for copper at many of its face-centered cubic packing sites. **B,** Some forms of carbon steel are interstitial alloys in which carbon atoms lie in the holes (interstices) of the body-centered cubic crystal structure of iron.

solution. If similar intermolecular forces occur in solute and solvent, a solution will likely form. When ionic compounds dissolve in water, the ions become surrounded by hydration shells of H-bonded water molecules. Solubility of organic molecules in water depends on their polarity and the extent of their polar and nonpolar portions. Soaps and some antibiotics act through the dual polarities of their molecules. The solubility of nonpolar gases in water is low because of weak intermolecular forces. Gases are miscible with one another and dissolve in solids by fitting into spaces in the crystal structure. Solid-solid solutions, such as alloys and waxes, form when the components are mixed while molten.

13.2 Energy Changes in the Solution Process

As a qualitative predictive tool, "like dissolves like" is helpful in many cases. As you might expect, this handy *macroscopic* rule is based on the *molecular* events that occur between solute and solvent particles. To see *why* like dissolves like, we can break down the solution process conceptually into steps and examine them in terms of changes in *enthalpy* and *entropy* of the system. We discussed enthalpy in Chapter 6 and focus on it first here. The concept of entropy is introduced at the end of this section and treated quantitatively in Chapter 20.

Heats of Solution and Solution Cycles

Picture a general solute and solvent about to form a solution. Both consist of particles attracting each other. For one substance to dissolve in another, three events must occur: (1) solute particles must separate from each other, (2) some solvent particles must separate to make room for the solute particles, and (3) solute and solvent particles must mix together. No matter what the nature of the attractions within solute and solvent, some energy is *absorbed* when particles separate, and some energy is *released* when they mix and attract each other. As a result of these changes in attractions, the solution process is typically accompanied by a change in enthalpy. We can divide the process into these three steps, each with its own enthalpy term:

Step 1. Solute particles separate from each other. This step involves overcoming intermolecular attractions, so it is *endothermic:*

$$\text{Solute (aggregated)} + heat \longrightarrow \text{solute (separated)} \qquad \Delta H_{solute} > 0$$

Step 2. Solvent particles separate from each other. This step also involves overcoming attractions, so it is *endothermic,* too:

$$\text{Solvent (aggregated)} + heat \longrightarrow \text{solvent (separated)} \qquad \Delta H_{solvent} > 0$$

Step 3. Solute and solvent particles mix. The particles attract each other, so this step is *exothermic:*

$$\text{Solute (separated)} + \text{solvent (separated)} \longrightarrow \text{solution} + heat \qquad \Delta H_{mix} < 0$$

The total enthalpy change that occurs when a solution forms from solute and solvent is the **heat of solution (ΔH_{soln}),** and we combine the three individual enthalpy changes to find it. The overall process is called a *thermochemical solution cycle* and is yet another application of Hess's law:

$$\Delta H_{soln} = \Delta H_{solute} + \Delta H_{solvent} + \Delta H_{mix} \qquad \textbf{(13.1)}$$

(In Section 9.2 we conceptually broke down the heat of formation of an ionic compound into component enthalpies in a similar way through the use of a Born-Haber cycle.) If the sum of the endothermic terms ($\Delta H_{solute} + \Delta H_{solvent}$)

Waxes for Home and Auto Beeswax, the remarkable structural material that bees secrete to build their combs, is a complex mixture of fatty acids and hydrocarbons in which some of the molecules contain chains more than 40 carbon atoms long. Carnauba wax, from a South American palm, is a mixture of compounds, each consisting of a fatty acid bound to a long-chain alcohol. It is hard and forms a thick gel in nonpolar solvents—perfect for car waxes.

A Exothermic solution process

B Endothermic solution process

Figure 13.6 Solution cycles and the enthalpy components of the heat of solution. The ΔH_{soln} can be thought of as the sum of three enthalpy changes: $\Delta H_{solvent}$ (separating the solvent; always > 0), ΔH_{solute} (separating the solute; always > 0), and ΔH_{mix} (mixing solute and solvent; always < 0). In **A**, ΔH_{mix} is larger than the sum of ΔH_{solute} and $\Delta H_{solvent}$, so ΔH_{soln} is negative (exothermic process). In **B**, ΔH_{mix} is smaller than the sum of the others, so ΔH_{soln} is positive (endothermic process).

is smaller than the exothermic term (ΔH_{mix}), ΔH_{soln} is negative, the process is exothermic, and the solution becomes warmer as it forms. Figure 13.6A shows an enthalpy diagram for the formation of such a solution. If the sum of the endothermic terms is larger than the exothermic term, ΔH_{soln} is positive, the process is endothermic, as shown in Figure 13.6B, and the solution becomes cooler. However, if ΔH_{soln} is highly positive, the solute may not dissolve to any significant extent in that solvent.

Heats of Hydration: Ionic Solids in Water

Before we discuss the entropy factor in the solution process, there is an important simplification we can make in the solution cycle for aqueous systems. The $\Delta H_{solvent}$ and ΔH_{mix} components of the heat of solution are especially difficult to measure individually. These terms combined represent the enthalpy change during **solvation,** the process of surrounding a solute particle with solvent particles. Solvation in water is called **hydration.** Thus, the enthalpy changes for separating the water molecules ($\Delta H_{solvent}$) and mixing the solute with them (ΔH_{mix}) are combined into the **heat of hydration (ΔH_{hydr}).** In water, Equation 13.1 becomes

$$\Delta H_{soln} = \Delta H_{solute} + \Delta H_{hydr}$$

The heat of hydration is a crucial factor in dissolving an ionic solid. Breaking several H bonds in water is more than compensated for when several strong ion-dipole forces form, so hydration of an ion is *always* exothermic. The ΔH_{hydr} of an ion is defined as the enthalpy change for the hydration of 1 mol of separated (gaseous) ions:

$$M^+(g) \text{ [or } X^-(g)] \xrightarrow{H_2O} M^+(aq) \text{ [or } X^-(aq)] \qquad \Delta H_{hydr \text{ of the ion}} \text{ (always < 0)}$$

Heats of hydration exhibit trends based on the **charge density** of the ion, the ratio of the ion's charge to its volume. In general, the higher the charge density is, the more negative ΔH_{hydr} is. According to Coulomb's law, the greater the ion's charge is and the closer the ion can approach the charge of the water dipole, the stronger the attraction. Therefore,

- A 2+ ion attracts H_2O molecules more strongly than a 1+ ion of similar size does.
- A small 1+ ion attracts H_2O molecules more strongly than a large 1+ ion does.

Down a group of ions, such as Li^+ to Cs^+ in Group 1A(1), the charge stays the same and the size increases, so the charge densities decrease, as do the heats of hydration. Across the periodic table from Group 1A(1) to Group 2A(2), the 2A ion has a smaller radius *and* a greater charge, so its charge density and ΔH_{hydr} are greater. Table 13.3 shows these relationships for some ionic heats of hydration.

The energy required to separate an ionic solute (ΔH_{solute}) into gaseous ions is the negative of its lattice energy ($-\Delta H_{lattice}$), so it is highly positive:

$$M^+X^-(s) \longrightarrow M^+(g) + X^-(g) \qquad \Delta H_{solute} \text{ (always} > 0) = -\Delta H_{lattice}$$

Thus, the heat of solution for ionic compounds in water combines the negative of the lattice energy (always > 0) and the combined heats of hydration of cation and anion (always < 0),

$$\Delta H_{soln} = -\Delta H_{lattice} + \Delta H_{hydr\ of\ the\ ions} \qquad \textbf{(13.2)}$$

The sizes of the individual terms determine the sign of the overall heat of solution.

Figure 13.7 shows solution enthalpy diagrams for three ionic solutes. The first, NaCl, has a small endothermic heat of solution ($\Delta H_{soln} = 3.9$ kJ/mol). Its lattice energy term is only slightly greater than the combined ionic heats of hydration, so if you dissolve NaCl in water in a flask, you do not notice any temperature change. On the other hand, if you dissolve NaOH in water, the flask feels hot. The lattice energy term for NaOH is much smaller than the combined ionic heats of hydration, so dissolving NaOH is highly exothermic ($\Delta H_{soln} = -44.5$ kJ/mol). Finally, if you dissolve NH_4NO_3 in water, the flask feels cold. In this case, the lattice energy term is much larger than the

Table 13.3 Trends in Ionic Heats of Hydration

Ion	Ionic Radius (pm)	ΔH_{hydr} (kJ/mol)
Group 1A(1)		
Li^+	76	−510
Na^+	102	−410
K^+	138	−336
Rb^+	152	−315
Cs^+	167	−282
Group 2A(2)		
Mg^{2+}	72	−1903
Ca^{2+}	100	−1591
Sr^{2+}	118	−1424
Ba^{2+}	135	−1317
Group 7A(17)		
F^-	133	−431
Cl^-	181	−313
Br^-	196	−284
I^-	220	−247

A

B

C

Figure 13.7 Enthalpy diagrams for dissolving three ionic compounds in water. The enthalpy diagram for dissolving an ionic compound in water includes the negative of the $\Delta H_{lattice}$ (ΔH_{solute}; always positive) and the combined ionic heats of hydration (ΔH_{hydr}; always negative). **A,** For NaCl, the magnitude of $\Delta H_{lattice}$ is slightly greater than that of ΔH_{hydr}, so ΔH_{soln} is small and positive. **B,** For NaOH, ΔH_{hydr} dominates, so ΔH_{soln} is large and negative. **C,** For NH_4NO_3, $\Delta H_{lattice}$ dominates, so ΔH_{soln} is large and positive.

Hot Packs, Cold Packs, and Self-Heating Soup

Strain a muscle or sprain a joint and you may obtain temporary relief by applying the right heat of solution. Hot packs and cold packs consist of a thick outer pouch containing water and a thin inner pouch containing a salt. A squeeze on the outer pouch breaks the inner pouch and the salt dissolves. Most hot packs use anhydrous $CaCl_2$ ($\Delta H_{soln} = -82.8$ kJ/mol), whereas cold packs use NH_4NO_3 ($\Delta H_{soln} = 25.7$ kJ/mol). The change in temperature can be quite large—a cold pack, for instance, can bring the solution from room temperature down to 0°C—but their usable time is limited to around half an hour. In Japan, double-walled cans of soup contain an ionic compound in a packet and water between the walls. When you open the can, the packet breaks, and the exothermic solution process, which can quickly reach about 90°C, warms the soup.

combined ionic heats of hydration, so the process is highly endothermic ($\Delta H_{soln} = 25.7$ kJ/mol). ◆

The Solution Process and the Tendency Toward Disorder

The other major factor that determines whether a substance dissolves is somewhat more abstract than the change in heat, but it must be considered along with it. This factor concerns the *natural tendency of most systems to become more disordered*. In thermodynamic terms, we say that the **entropy** of the system tends to increase. *Entropy is a measure of a system's disorder.*

Here is an obvious example of this tendency. Stack piles of nickels, dimes, and quarters heads up in a closed box. This system is very ordered, so it has low entropy. Now shake the box and look inside. The coins lie randomly in a pile, some heads up and some heads down. The disorder of the system has increased, and so has its entropy. Common sense tells you that if you shook the box for another century, the coins would not wind up in the stacks you started with. To get them that way, you must expend energy sorting and restacking them to counteract their natural tendency to become mixed up. A solution is more disordered, has greater entropy, than the pure solute and solvent. Thus, *solutions form naturally; pure solutes and solvents do not*. Water treatment plants, oil refineries, metal foundries, and many other large industrial plants expend enormous quantities of energy reversing this natural tendency and separating mixtures into pure components.

It is important to realize that *the solution process involves two factors—the change in enthalpy **and** the change in entropy*. In many cases, their *relative magnitudes* determine whether a solution forms. The increase in entropy that accompanies dissolving always *favors* solution formation. However, the change in enthalpy can work either way: a decrease in enthalpy of solution ($\Delta H_{soln} < 0$) *favors* solution formation, but an increase in enthalpy *hinders* it.

To see this interplay of enthalpy and entropy, let's consider two solute-solvent pairs. The first does *not* form a solution because its enthalpy factor outweighs its entropy factor; the second *does* form a solution because its entropy factor dominates. Sodium chloride does not dissolve in hexane, as you would predict from the dissimilar forces in the substances. As Figure 13.8A shows, separating the solvent is relatively easy because of the weak dispersion forces,

A

B

Figure 13.8 **Enthalpy diagrams for dissolving NaCl and octane in hexane. A,** Since attractions between ions and hexane molecules are weak, ΔH_{mix} is *much* smaller than ΔH_{solute}. Thus, ΔH_{soln} is so positive that NaCl does *not* dissolve in hexane.

B, Intermolecular forces in octane and in hexane are so similar that ΔH_{soln} is very small. Octane dissolves in hexane because the solution has greater entropy (more disorder) than the pure components.

but separating the ionic solute requires supplying the lattice energy. Mixing releases very little energy because the ion-induced dipole attractions between Na^+ (or Cl^-) ions and hexane are weak. Since the sum of the endothermic terms is much larger than the exothermic term, ΔH_{soln} is very positive. In this case, dissolution does not occur because the entropy increase that would occur when solute and solvent mix cannot outweigh the *large* enthalpy increase.

Now consider the second solute-solvent pair, octane (C_8H_{18}) and hexane (C_6H_{14}). Both consist of nonpolar molecules held together by dispersion forces of comparable strength. We would therefore predict that octane is soluble in hexane; in fact, they are infinitely soluble (miscible). Miscibility does not necessarily mean a great deal of heat is released, however; in this case, the heat of solution is around zero ($\Delta H_{soln} \approx 0$), as shown in Figure 13.8B. With no enthalpy change driving the process, why do these substances form a solution? Octane dissolves in hexane because *the entropy increases greatly when pure substances mix and become disordered.* Thus, in the face of little change in enthalpy, the large increase in entropy drives solution formation.

In some cases, a large enough increase in entropy can cause a solution to form even when the enthalpy increases significantly ($\Delta H_{soln} > 0$). As Figure 13.7C showed earlier, when NH_4NO_3 dissolves in water, the process is very endothermic. Nevertheless, in that case, the increase in entropy that occurs when the orderly ionic crystal breaks down and the ions mix with water molecules more than compensates for the heat absorbed. The importance of entropy in physical and chemical systems is covered in depth in Chapter 20.

Section Summary

An overall heat of solution can be obtained from a thermochemical cycle as the sum of two endothermic steps, solute separation and solvent separation, and one exothermic step, solute-solvent mixing. In aqueous solutions, the combination of solvent separation and mixing is called *hydration*. Ionic heats of hydration are always negative because of strong ion-dipole forces. Most systems have a natural tendency to increase their entropy (become disordered), and a solution has greater entropy (more disorder) than the pure solute and solvent. The combination of enthalpy and entropy changes determines whether a solution forms. A substance with a positive ΔH_{soln} dissolves *only* if the entropy increase is large enough to outweigh it.

13.3 Solubility as an Equilibrium Process

Imagine what takes place on the molecular level when an ionic solid dissolves. Ions leave the solid and become dispersed in the solvent. Some dissolved ions collide occasionally with the undissolved solute and recrystallize. As long as the rate of dissolving is greater than the rate of recrystallizing, the concentration of ions rises. Eventually, ions from the solid are dissolving at the same rate as dissolved ions are recrystallizing, as Figure 13.9 shows. At this point, even though dissolving and recrystallizing continue, there is no further change in the concentration with time. The system has reached equilibrium; that is, *excess undissolved solute is in equilibrium with the dissolved solute:*

$$\text{Solute (undissolved)} \rightleftharpoons \text{solute (dissolved)}$$

This solution is called **saturated:** it contains the maximum amount of dissolved solute at a given temperature in the presence of undissolved solute. ◆ Filter off the saturated solution and add more solute to it, and the solute will remain undissolved. A solution that contains less than this amount of dissolved solute is called **unsaturated:** add more solute, and more will dissolve until the solution becomes saturated.

Figure 13.9 Equilibrium in a saturated solution. In a saturated solution, equilibrium exists between a small piece of excess solute and the solution. At a particular temperature, the number of solute particles dissolving per unit time equals the number recrystallizing.

◆ **A Saturated Solution Is Like a Pure Liquid and Its Vapor** Equilibrium processes in a saturated solution are analogous to those of a pure liquid in a closed flask (Section 12.2). In the liquid, rates of vaporizing and condensing are equal; in the solution, rates of dissolving and recrystallizing are equal. In the liquid, particles leave the liquid to enter the vapor, and their concentration (pressure) increases until, at equilibrium, the available space is "saturated" with vapor at a given temperature. In the solution, particles leave the solid solute to enter the solvent, and their concentration increases until, at equilibrium, the available solvent is saturated with solute at a given temperature.

Figure 13.10 **Sodium acetate crystallized from a supersaturated solution.** When a seed crystal of sodium acetate is added to a supersaturated solution of the compound (**A**), solute begins to crystallize out of solution (**B**) and continues to do so until the solution remaining is saturated (**C**).

In some cases, a solution may be prepared that contains more than the equilibrium amount of dissolved solute. Such a solution is called **supersaturated.** It is unstable relative to the saturated solution, which means that if you add a "seed" crystal of solute, or just tap the container, the excess solute crystallizes immediately, leaving a saturated solution (Figure 13.10). You can often prepare a supersaturated solution of a solute that has greater solubility at a higher temperature. While warming the contents of the flask, you dissolve more than the amount of solute required to prepare a saturated solution at a lower temperature and then slowly cool the solution. If the excess solute remains dissolved, the solution is supersaturated.

Effect of Temperature on Solubility

Temperature has a major effect on the solubility of most substances. You may have noticed, for example, that not only does sugar dissolve more quickly in hot tea than in iced tea, but *more* sugar dissolves: the solubility of sugar is greater at higher temperatures. For other solutes the solubility may be lower. The key to this effect of temperature is the equilibrium nature of solubility.

As you saw in Chapter 12, when a system at equilibrium is disturbed, it adjusts itself to reestablish equilibrium. Consider a saturated solution that has a *positive* heat of solution. Since heat is absorbed to form the solution, we can think of the heat as if it were a reactant:

$$\text{Solute} + \text{solvent} + heat \rightleftharpoons \text{saturated solution}$$

If the system at equilibrium is disturbed by a temperature rise (that is, if more heat is "added"), the system absorbs some of the added heat by increasing the rate of the forward process. More solute dissolves and equilibrium becomes reestablished with *more* ions in solution. Generally, *solubility increases with temperature if the solution process is endothermic* ($\Delta H_{soln} > 0$). Figure 13.11 shows a few examples of the fact that *the solubility of most ionic compounds increases with temperature;* that is, most have *positive* heats of solution.

If a solute has a negative heat of solution, heat is given off:

$$\text{Solute} + \text{solvent} \rightleftharpoons \text{saturated solution} + heat$$

As before, the system at equilibrium will absorb some heat in response to a temperature rise. In this case, however, it does so by increasing the rate of the reverse process. Some solute crystallizes out and equilibrium becomes reestablished with *fewer* ions in solution. Generally, *solubility decreases with temperature if the solution process is exothermic* ($\Delta H_{soln} < 0$). Potassium hydroxide, sodium sulfate, and cerium sulfate (see Figure 13.11) are among the compounds that become less soluble as the temperature rises.

Figure 13.11 **The relation between solubility and temperature for several ionic compounds.** Most ionic compounds have a higher solubility at higher temperatures because their heats of solution are positive. Cerium sulfate is one of many exceptions; its heat of solution is negative, so it is less soluble at higher temperature.

Sample Problem 13.2 Predicting the Effect of Temperature on Solubility

PROBLEM From the following information, predict whether the solubility of each compound increases or decreases with an increase in temperature:
(a) ΔH_{soln} of NaOH(s) = −44.5 kJ/mol
(b) When KNO_3 dissolves in water, the solution becomes cold.
(c) CsCl(s) $\xrightleftharpoons{H_2O}$ $Cs^+(aq)$ + $Cl^-(aq)$; ΔH_{soln} = +17.8 kJ
PLAN We use the information to write an equation that includes heat being absorbed ("reactant") or released ("product"). If heat is absorbed, a temperature increase shifts the system to the right, so more solute dissolves. If heat is released, a temperature increase shifts the system to the left, so less solute dissolves.
SOLUTION (a) A negative ΔH means the process is exothermic, so when 1 mol NaOH dissolves in water, 44.5 kJ of heat is released:
$$NaOH(s) \xrightleftharpoons{H_2O} Na^+(aq) + OH^-(aq) + \text{heat}$$
A higher temperature (more heat) decreases the solubility of NaOH.
(b) When KNO_3 dissolves, the solution becomes cold, so heat is absorbed:
$$KNO_3(s) + \text{heat} \xrightleftharpoons{H_2O} K^+(aq) + NO_3^-(aq)$$
A higher temperature increases the solubility of KNO_3.
(c) The positive ΔH means heat is absorbed when CsCl dissolves:
$$CsCl(s) + \text{heat} \xrightleftharpoons{H_2O} Cs^+(aq) + Cl^-(aq)$$
A higher temperature increases the solubility of CsCl.
CHECK Be sure the sign of ΔH_{soln} corresponds with the change in solubility. In part **(a)**, the process is exothermic, so ΔH_{soln} is negative and adding heat decreases solubility. In parts **(b)** and **(c)**, the process is endothermic, so ΔH_{soln} is positive and adding heat increases solubility.

Follow-up Problem 13.2 Predict whether the solubility increases or decreases at *lower* temperature and give the sign of ΔH_{soln} for the following cases:
(a) When sodium cyanate (NaOCN) dissolves, the solution becomes cold.
(b) KF(s) $\xrightleftharpoons{H_2O}$ $K^+(aq)$ + $F^-(aq)$ + 17.7 kJ

The Special Case of Changing Temperature and Gas Solubility in Water

The ΔH_{solute} term in the solution cycle for nonpolar gases influences the effect of temperature on gas solubility. When a solid or liquid dissolves in a liquid, the solute particles must separate, so energy must be added; thus, for a solid or liquid, $\Delta H_{solute} > 0$. In contrast, gas particles start out far apart as a pure solute. Therefore, for a gas, $\Delta H_{solute} \approx 0$. Since the hydration step is exothermic ($\Delta H_{hydr} < 0$), the sum of these two terms must be negative. Thus, for all gases in water, $\Delta H_{soln} < 0$:

$$\text{Solute}(g) + \text{water}(l) \rightleftharpoons \text{saturated solution}(aq) + \text{heat}$$

This equation means that *gas solubility in water decreases with rising temperature.* The molecular-scale reason for this phenomenon is that gases have weak intermolecular forces, so there are relatively weak intermolecular forces between the gas and water. When the temperature rises, the average kinetic energy of the particles in solution increases, allowing the gas particles to easily overcome these weak forces and reenter the gas phase.

This effect of temperature on gas solubility can lead to an environmental problem known as *thermal pollution.* During many industrial processes, large amounts of water are taken from a nearby river or lake, pumped through the system to cool liquids, gases, and equipment, and then returned to the body of water at a higher temperature. The metabolic rates of fish and other aquatic animals increase in the warmer water released near the plant outlet, so their need for O_2 increases as well, but less O_2 dissolves at the higher temperature. This O_2 depletion can severely hinder these aquatic populations. Moreover, since the warmer water is less dense, it floats on the cooler water below and prevents O_2 from reaching it. Thus, creatures living at lower levels can become O_2 deprived as well. Farther from the plant, the water temperature returns to ambient levels, the O_2 solubility increases, and the temperature layering disappears. One way to lessen the problem is with cooling towers, which lower the temperature of the water exiting the plant (Figure 13.12).

Effect of Pressure on Solubility

Since liquids and solids are almost incompressible, pressure has little effect on their solubility. In contrast, it has a major effect on gas solubility. Consider the piston-cylinder assembly in Figure 13.13, with a gas above a satu-

Figure 13.12 Fighting thermal pollution. Steam billowing from cooling towers is common at large electric power plants. Hot water resulting from the cooling of gases and equipment enters near the top of the tower and cools in contact with air by evaporative cooling as it falls. The cooler water is then released back into the water source.

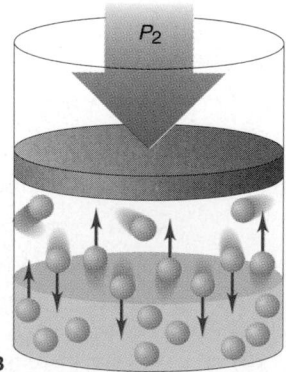

Figure 13.13 The effect of pressure on gas solubility. A, A saturated solution of a gas is in equilibrium at pressure P_1. **B,** If the pressure is increased to P_2, the volume of the gas decreases. As a result, the frequency of collisions with the surface increases and more gas is in solution when equilibrium is reestablished.

rated aqueous solution of the gas. At a given pressure, the same number of gas molecules enter and leave the solution per unit time; that is, the system is at equilibrium:

$$\text{Gas + solvent} \rightleftharpoons \text{saturated solution}$$

If you push down on the piston, the gas volume decreases, its pressure increases, and gas particles collide with the liquid surface more often. Therefore, more gas particles enter than leave the solution per unit time. Higher gas pressure disturbs the balance at equilibrium, so more gas dissolves to reduce this disturbance (the previous equation shifts to the right) until the system reestablishes equilibrium. ◆

Henry's law expresses the quantitative relationship between gas pressure and solubility: *the solubility of a gas (S_{gas}) is directly proportional to the partial pressure of the gas (P_{gas}) above the solution:*

$$S_{gas} = k_H \times P_{gas} \qquad (13.3)$$

where k_H is the Henry's law constant and is specific for each gas-solvent combination at a given temperature. With S_{gas} in mol/L and P_{gas} in atm, the units of k_H are mol/L · atm.

Sample Problem 13.3   Using Henry's Law to Calculate Gas Solubility

PROBLEM The partial pressure of CO_2 gas inside a bottle of cola is 4 atm at 25°C. What is the solubility of CO_2? Henry's law constant for CO_2 dissolved in water = 3.3×10^{-2} mol/L · atm at 25°C.
PLAN We know P_{CO_2} and the value of the Henry's law constant, k_H, so we substitute them into Equation 13.3 to find S_{CO_2}.
SOLUTION $S_{CO_2} = k_H \times P_{CO_2} = (3.3 \times 10^{-2}$ mol/L · atm$)(4$ atm$) = $ 0.1 mol/L
CHECK The units are correct for solubility. We rounded the answer to one significant figure because there is only one in the pressure value.

Follow-up Problem 13.3   What is the solubility of N_2 in water at 25°C and 1 atm if air contains 78% N_2 by volume? The k_H for N_2 in H_2O at 25°C is 7×10^{-4} mol/L · atm.

Section Summary

A solution that contains the maximum amount of dissolved solute in the presence of excess solute is saturated. A state of equilibrium exists when a saturated solution is in contact with excess solute, because particles are entering and leaving the solute at the same rate. For an endothermic solution process ($\Delta H_{soln} > 0$), a temperature rise increases solubility; for an exothermic process ($\Delta H_{soln} < 0$), a temperature rise decreases solubility. All gases have a negative aqueous ΔH_{soln}, so heating lowers gas solubility in water. Henry's law says that the solubility of a gas is directly proportional to its partial pressure.

13.4 Quantitative Ways of Expressing Concentration

Concentration is the *proportion* of a substance in a mixture, so it is an intensive property, one that does *not* depend on the quantity of mixture present: 1.0 L of 0.1 *M* NaCl has the same concentration as 1.0 mL of 0.1 *M* NaCl. Concentration is most often expressed as the ratio of the quantity of solute to the quantity of *solution*, but sometimes it is the ratio of solute to *solvent*.

◆ **Scuba Diving and Soda Pop**   Although N_2 is barely soluble in water or blood at sea level, high external pressures increase its solubility significantly. Scuba divers who breathe compressed air and dive below about 50 ft have considerably more N_2 dissolved in their blood. If they ascend quickly to lower pressures, they may be afflicted with decompression sickness ("the bends"), as the dissolved N_2 bubbles out of solution in the blood, which causes painful, sometimes fatal, blockage of capillaries. This condition can be avoided by using less soluble gases, such as He, in the breathing mixtures. In principle, the same thing happens when you open a can of a carbonated drink. In the closed can, dissolved CO_2 is at equilibrium with 4 atm of CO_2 gas in the space above it. In the open can, the dissolved CO_2 is under 1 atm of air (with $P_{CO_2} = 3 \times 10^{-4}$ atm), so CO_2 bubbles out of solution. With time, the system again reaches equilibrium but with the much lower P_{CO_2} in air: the drink goes "flat."

Table 13.4 Concentration Definitions

Concentration Term	Ratio
Molarity (M)	$\dfrac{\text{amount (mol) of solute}}{\text{volume (L) of solution}}$
Molality (m)	$\dfrac{\text{amount (mol) of solute}}{\text{mass (kg) of solvent}}$
Parts by mass	$\dfrac{\text{mass of solute}}{\text{mass of solution}}$
Parts by volume	$\dfrac{\text{volume of solute}}{\text{volume of solution}}$
Mole fraction (X)	$\dfrac{\text{amount (mol) of solute}}{\text{amount (mol) of solute} + \text{amount (mol) of solvent}}$

Since both parts of the ratio can be given in terms of mass, volume, or amount (mol), chemists employ several concentration terms, as shown in Table 13.4, including molarity, molality, and various expressions of "parts of solute per part of solution."

Molarity and Molality

Molarity (M) is defined as the *number of moles of solute dissolved in 1 L of solution:*

$$\text{Molarity} = \frac{\text{amount (mol) of solute}}{\text{volume (L) of solution}} \qquad \text{in units of} \qquad M = \frac{\text{mol solute}}{\text{L soln}} \quad \textbf{(13.4)}$$

In Chapter 3, you used molarity to convert liters of solution into moles of dissolved solute. Expressing concentration as molarity may have drawbacks, however: since volume is affected by temperature, molarity is also. A solution expands slightly when heated, so each unit volume of a hot solution contains slightly less solute than the solution when cooled, and this can be a source of error in very precise work. More importantly, because of solute-solvent interactions that are difficult to predict, *solution volumes are not necessarily additive;* that is, adding exactly 500. mL of one solution to exactly 500. mL of a different one may not give exactly 1000. mL. Therefore, in precise work, a solution with a desired molarity may not be easy to prepare.

A unit that does not contain volume in its ratio is **molality (*m*),** *the number of moles of solute dissolved in 1000 g (1 kg) of solvent:*

$$\text{Molality} = \frac{\text{amount (mol) of solute}}{\text{mass (kg) of solvent}} \qquad \text{in units of} \qquad m = \frac{\text{mol solute}}{\text{kg solvent}} \quad \textbf{(13.5)}$$

Note that molality is expressed in terms of the quantity of *solvent,* not solution. Molal solutions are prepared by measuring *masses* of solute and solvent, not solvent or solution volume. Since mass does not change with temperature, molality does not change. Moreover, masses *are* additive, unlike volumes: adding exactly 500. g of one solution to exactly 500. g of another *does* give exactly 1000. g of final solution. For these reasons, molality is a preferred unit when temperature, and hence density, is changing, as in the examination of solution physical properties. It's important to realize that, because 1 L of water has a mass of 1 kg, *molality and molarity are nearly the same for dilute aqueous solutions.*

Sample Problem 13.4 Calculating Molality

PROBLEM What is the molality of a solution prepared by dissolving 32.0 g $CaCl_2$ in 271 g water?

PLAN To use Equation 13.5, we convert mass (g) of $CaCl_2$ to amount (mol) with the molar mass (g/mol) and then divide by the mass of water (being sure to convert from grams to kilograms).

SOLUTION Converting from grams of solute to moles:

$$\text{Moles of } CaCl_2 = 32.0 \text{ g } CaCl_2 \times \frac{1 \text{ mol } CaCl_2}{110.98 \text{ g } CaCl_2} = 0.288 \text{ mol } CaCl_2$$

Finding molality:

$$\text{Molality} = \frac{\text{mol solute}}{\text{kg solvent}} = \frac{0.288 \text{ mol } CaCl_2}{271 \text{ g} \times \dfrac{1 \text{ kg}}{10^3 \text{ g}}} = \boxed{1.06 \; m \; CaCl_2}$$

CHECK The answer seems reasonable: since both moles of $CaCl_2$ and kg of H_2O are about the same numerically, their ratio is about 1.

Follow-up Problem 13.4 How many grams of glucose ($C_6H_{12}O_6$) must be dissolved in 563 g ethanol (C_2H_5OH) to prepare a 2.40×10^{-2} m solution?

Mass (g) of $CaCl_2$

↓ divide by
$\mathcal{M}$ (g/mol)

Amount (mol) of $CaCl_2$

↓ divide by
kg of water

Molality (m) of $CaCl_2$ solution

Parts of Solute by Parts of Solution

Several concentration terms are based on the number of solute (or solvent) parts present in a specific number of *solution* parts. The solution parts can be expressed in terms of mass, volume, or amount (mol).

Parts by Mass The most common of the parts-by-mass terms is **mass percent,** which you encountered in Chapter 3. The word *percent* means "per hundred," so mass percent of solute means the mass of solute dissolved in every 100. parts by mass of solution, or the mass fraction times 100:

$$\text{Mass percent} = \frac{\text{mass of solute}}{\text{mass of solute} + \text{mass of solvent}} \times 100$$

$$= \frac{\text{mass of solute}}{\text{mass of solution}} \times 100 \qquad \textbf{(13.6)}$$

Sometimes mass percent is written as **% (w/w),** the "w/w" indicating the percent is a ratio of weights (more accurately, masses). You may have seen mass percent values on bottles of solid chemicals to indicate the amounts of impurities present. Two very similar units are parts per million (ppm) by mass and parts per billion (ppb) by mass: grams of solute per million or per billion grams of solution. (In Equation 13.6, you multiply by 10^6 or by 10^9, instead of by 100.) ◆

Parts by Volume Solution parts measured by volume are also expressed as parts per hundred (percent), per million, or per billion. Thus, **volume percent** is the volume of solute in 100. volumes of solution:

$$\text{Volume percent} = \frac{\text{volume of solute}}{\text{volume of solution}} \times 100 \qquad \textbf{(13.7)}$$

A common symbol for this term is **% (v/v).** Commercial rubbing alcohol, for example, is an aqueous solution of isopropanol (a three-carbon alcohol) that contains 70 volumes of isopropanol per 100 volumes of solution, and the label indicates this as "70% (v/v)." Parts-by-volume concentrations are most often used for liquids and gases. Minor atmospheric components occur in parts per million by volume (ppmv). For example, there are about 0.05 ppmv (50 ppbv) of carbon monoxide (CO) in clean air, 1000 times as much (about

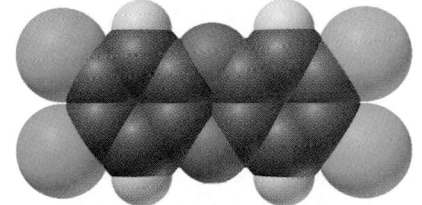

◆ Unhealthy Ultralow Concentrations Environmental toxicologists often measure extremely low concentrations of pollutants. The Centers for Disease Control and Prevention consider TCDD (*tetrachlorodibenzodioxin, above*) one of the most toxic substances known. It is a member of the dioxin family of chlorinated hydrocarbons, a byproduct of bleaching paper. TCDD is considered unsafe at soil levels above 1 ppb. From contact with air, water, and soil, it is estimated that most Americans and Canadians already have an average of 0.01 ppb TCDD in their fatty tissue. However, in a recent reassessment of TCDD, the Environmental Protection Agency found that this substance appears to be unsafe at *all* levels measured.

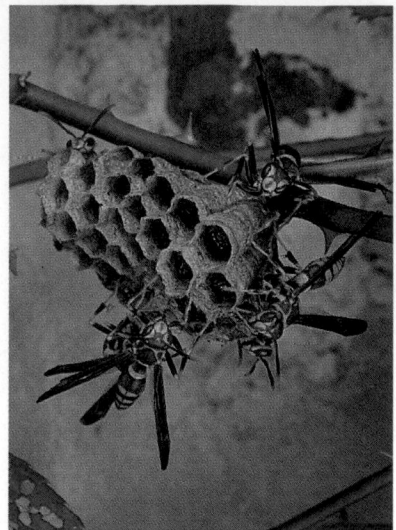

◆ **Pheromones: Rarified Calls to Action** Pheromones are organic compounds secreted by one member of a species to signal other members about food, danger, sexual readiness, and so forth. Many organisms, including dogs and monkeys, release pheromones, and researchers suspect that humans do as well. Most studies involve social insects. Wasp pheromones are active at only a few hundred molecules per milliliter of air, about 100 parts per quadrillion by volume!

50 ppmv of CO) in air over urban traffic, and 10,000 times as much (about 500 ppmv of CO) in cigarette smoke. ◆

A symbol frequently used for aqueous solutions is % (w/v), a ratio of solute *weight* (actually mass) to solution *volume*. Thus, a 1.5% (w/v) NaCl solution contains 1.5 g NaCl per 100. mL of *solution*. This unit is particularly common in medical labs and other health-related facilities. You should also be aware that several handbooks, including the *CRC Handbook of Chemistry and Physics*, cite solubility values in terms of grams of solute per 100. mL of *solvent*.

Mole Fraction The **mole fraction (X)** of solute is the ratio of number of solute moles to the total number of moles (solute plus solvent), that is, parts by moles. The *mole percent* is the mole fraction expressed as a percentage:

$$\text{Mole fraction } (X) = \frac{\text{amount (mol) of solute}}{\text{amount (mol) of solute} + \text{amount (mol) of solvent}} \quad \textbf{(13.8)}$$

$$\text{Mole percent (mol \%)} = \text{mole fraction} \times 100$$

We discussed these terms in Chapter 5 in relation to Dalton's law of partial pressures for mixtures of gases, but they apply to liquids and solids as well. Concentrations based on mole fraction give the most direct picture of the actual proportion of solute (or solvent) particles among all the particles in the solution.

Sample Problem 13.5   Expressing Concentration in Parts by Mass, Parts by Volume, and Mole Fraction

PROBLEM **(a)** Calculate the ppm by mass of calcium in a 3.50-g pill that contains 40.5 mg Ca.
(b) The label on a 0.750-L bottle of Italian chianti indicates "11.5% alcohol by volume." How many liters of alcohol does the wine contain?
(c) A sample of rubbing alcohol contains 142 g isopropanol (C_3H_7OH) and 58.0 g water. What are the mole fractions of alcohol and water?
PLAN **(a)** We convert the given mass of Ca from milligrams to grams, find the ratio of the mass of Ca to the mass of pill, and multiply by 10^6 to obtain ppm. **(b)** We know the vol % and the total volume, so we use Equation 13.7 to find the volume of alcohol. **(c)** We know the mass and formula of each component, so we convert both to amount (mol) and apply Equation 13.8 to find mole fraction.
SOLUTION **(a)** Finding parts per million by mass Ca. Combining the steps, we have

$$\text{ppm Ca} = \frac{\text{mass of Ca}}{\text{mass of pill}} \times 10^6 = \frac{40.5 \text{ mg Ca} \times \dfrac{1 \text{ g}}{10^3 \text{ mg}}}{3.50 \text{ g}} \times 10^6 = \boxed{1.16 \times 10^4 \text{ ppm Ca}}$$

(b) Finding volume (L) of alcohol:

$$\text{Volume (L) of alcohol} = \frac{\text{vol \%} \times \text{vol chianti}}{100} = \frac{11.5 \times 0.750 \text{ L}}{100} = \boxed{0.0862 \text{ L}}$$

(c) Finding mole fractions. Converting from grams to moles:

$$\text{Moles of } C_3H_7OH = 142 \text{ g } C_3H_7OH \times \frac{1 \text{ mol } C_3H_7OH}{60.09 \text{ g } C_3H_7OH} = 2.36 \text{ mol } C_3H_7OH$$

$$\text{Moles of } H_2O = 58.0 \text{ g } H_2O \times \frac{1 \text{ mol } H_2O}{18.02 \text{ g } H_2O} = 3.22 \text{ mol } H_2O$$

Calculating mole fractions:

$$X_{C_3H_7OH} = \frac{\text{moles of } C_3H_7OH}{\text{total moles}} = \frac{2.36 \text{ mol}}{2.36 \text{ mol} + 3.22 \text{ mol}} = \boxed{0.423}$$

$$X_{H_2O} = \frac{\text{moles of } H_2O}{\text{total moles}} = \frac{3.22 \text{ mol}}{2.36 \text{ mol} + 3.22 \text{ mol}} = \boxed{0.577}$$

CHECK (a) The mass ratio is about $0.04/4 = 10^{-2}$, and $10^{-2} \times 10^6 = 10^4$ ppm, so it seems correct. (b) The vol % is a bit more than 10%, so the volume of alcohol should be a bit more than 75 mL (0.075 L). (c) Always check that the *mole fractions add up to 1:* $0.423 + 0.577 = 1.000$.

Follow-up Problem 13.5 An alcohol solution contains 35.0 g propanol (C_3H_7OH) and 150.0 g ethanol (C_2H_5OH). Calculate the mass percent and the mole fraction of each alcohol.

Converting Units of Concentration

All the units we just discussed represent different ways of expressing concentration, so they are interconvertible. Keep these points in mind:

- To convert a unit based on amount (mol) to one based on mass, you need the molar mass. These conversions are similar to mass-mole conversions you've done earlier.
- To convert a unit based on mass to one based on volume, you need the solution *density*. Given the mass of a solution, the density (mass/volume) gives you the volume, or vice versa.
- Molality involves quantity of *solvent*, whereas the others involve quantity of *solution*.

Sample Problem 13.6   Converting Concentration Units

PROBLEM Hydrogen peroxide is a powerful oxidizing agent that is used in concentrated solution in rocket fuels and in dilute solution as a hair bleach. An aqueous solution of H_2O_2 is 30.0% by mass and has a density of 1.11 g/mL. Calculate its
(a) molality   **(b)** mole fraction of H_2O_2 **(c)** molarity
PLAN We know the mass % and the density. (a) For molality, we need the amount (mol) of solute and the mass (kg) of *solvent*. Assuming 100.0 g of H_2O_2 solution allows us to express the mass % directly as grams of substance. We subtract the grams of H_2O_2 to obtain the grams of solvent. To find molality, we convert grams of H_2O_2 to moles and divide by mass of solvent (converting g to kg). (b) To find the mole fraction, we use the number of moles of H_2O_2 (from part a) and convert the grams of H_2O to moles. Then we divide moles of H_2O_2 by the total moles. (c) To find molarity, we assume 100.0 g of solution and use the given solution density to find the volume. Then we divide amount (mol) of H_2O_2 (from part a) by *solution* volume (L).
SOLUTION (a) From mass % to molality. Finding mass of solvent (assuming 100.0 g of solution):

$$\text{Mass (g) of } H_2O = 100.0 \text{ g solution} - 30.0 \text{ g } H_2O_2 = 70.0 \text{ g } H_2O$$

Converting from grams of H_2O_2 to moles:

$$\text{Moles of } H_2O_2 = 30.0 \text{ g } H_2O_2 \times \frac{1 \text{ mol } H_2O_2}{34.02 \text{ g } H_2O_2} = 0.882 \text{ mol } H_2O_2$$

Calculating molality:

$$\text{Molality of } H_2O_2 = \frac{0.882 \text{ mol } H_2O_2}{70.0 \text{ g} \times \frac{1 \text{ kg}}{10^3 \text{ g}}} = 12.6 \text{ } m \text{ } H_2O_2$$

(b) From mass % to mole fraction:

$$\text{Moles of } H_2O_2 = 0.882 \text{ mol } H_2O_2 \text{ (from part a)}$$

$$\text{Moles of } H_2O = 70.0 \text{ g } H_2O \times \frac{1 \text{ mol } H_2O}{18.02 \text{ g } H_2O} = 3.88 \text{ mol } H_2O$$

$$X_{H_2O_2} = \frac{0.882 \text{ mol}}{0.882 \text{ mol} + 3.88 \text{ mol}} = 0.185$$

(c) From mass % and density to molarity. Converting from solution mass to volume:

$$\text{Volume (mL) of solution} = 100.0 \text{ g} \times \frac{1 \text{ mL}}{1.11 \text{ g}} = 90.1 \text{ mL}$$

Calculating molarity:

$$\text{Molarity} = \frac{\text{mol H}_2\text{O}_2}{\text{L soln}} = \frac{0.882 \text{ mol H}_2\text{O}_2}{90.1 \text{ mL} \times \dfrac{1 \text{ L soln}}{10^3 \text{ mL}}} = \boxed{9.79 \ M \text{ H}_2\text{O}_2}$$

CHECK The answers seem reasonable. **(a)** The ratio of ~0.9/0.07 is greater than 10. **(b)** Rounding gives ~1 mol H_2O_2/5 mol solution components = 0.2. **(c)** The ratio of moles to liters is slightly less than 10.

Follow-up Problem 13.6   A sample of commercial concentrated hydrochloric acid is 11.8 M HCl and has a density of 1.190 g/mL. Calculate the mass %, molality, and mole fraction of HCl.

Section Summary

The concentration of a solution is independent of the amount of solution and can be expressed by molarity (mol solute/L solution) and molality (mol solute/kg solvent), as well as parts by mass (mass solute/mass solution), parts by volume (volume solute/volume solution), and mole fraction [mol solute/(mol solute + mol solvent)]. The choice of units depends on convenience or the nature of the solution. If, in addition to the quantities of solute and solution, the solution density is also known, all concentration units are interconvertible.

13.5   Colligative Properties of Solutions

We might expect the presence of solute particles to make the physical properties of a solution different from those of the pure solvent. However, what we might *not* expect is that, in the case of four important solution properties, the *number* of solute particles makes the difference, *not* their chemical identity. These properties, known as **colligative properties** (*colligative* means "collective") are vapor pressure lowering, boiling point elevation, freezing point depression, and osmotic pressure. Even though most of these effects are small, they have many practical applications, including some that are vital to biological systems.

Historically, colligative properties were measured to explore the nature of a solute in aqueous solution and its extent of dissociation into ions. In Chapter 4, we classified solutes by their ability to conduct an electric current, which implies that moving ions are present. Recall that an aqueous solution of an **electrolyte** conducts a current because the solute separates into ions as it dissolves. Soluble salts, strong acids, and strong bases dissociate completely and their solutions conduct a large current, so these solutes are *strong electrolytes*. Weak acids and bases dissociate very little. They are *weak electrolytes* because their solutions conduct little current. Many compounds, such as sugar and alcohol, do not dissociate into ions at all. They are **nonelectrolytes** because their solutions do not conduct any current. Figure 13.14 shows these behaviors.

To predict the magnitude of a colligative property, we refer to the solute formula to find the number of particles in solution. Each mole of nonelectrolyte yields 1 mol of particles in solution. For example, 0.35 M glucose contains 0.35 mol of solute particles per liter. In principle, each mole of strong electrolyte dissociates into the number of moles of ions in the formula unit: 0.4 M Na_2SO_4 contains 0.8 mol Na^+ ions and 0.4 mol SO_4^{2-} ions, or 1.2 mol of particles, per liter (see Sample Problem 4.1). (We examine the equilibrium nature of the dissociation of weak electrolytes in Chapters 18 and 19.)

A Strong electrolyte

B Weak electrolyte

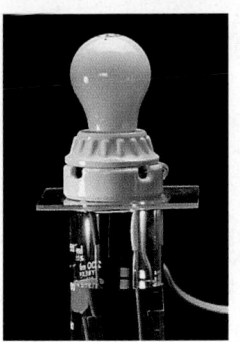

C Nonelectrolyte

Figure 13.14 The three types of electrolyte behavior. A, Strong electrolytes conduct a large current because they dissociate completely into ions. **B,** Weak electrolytes conduct a small current because they dissociate very little. **C,** Nonelectrolytes conduct no current because they do not dissociate.

Colligative Properties of Nonvolatile Nonelectrolyte Solutions

In this section, we focus most of our attention on the simplest case, the colligative properties of dilute solutions of solutes that do not dissociate into ions and have negligible vapor pressure even at the boiling point of the solvent. Such solutes are called *nonvolatile nonelectrolytes;* sucrose (table sugar) is an example. Later, we briefly explore the properties of volatile nonelectrolytes and of strong electrolytes.

Vapor Pressure Lowering Experiment shows that the vapor pressure of a solution of a nonvolatile nonelectrolyte is always *lower* than that of the pure solvent. We can understand this **vapor pressure lowering (ΔP)** if we recall that natural processes tend to occur in a direction that increases disorder. A pure solvent vaporizes because particles zooming randomly in a vapor phase are more disordered than when huddled near each other in the liquid. But a solution is already more disordered than a pure liquid, so the solvent has less tendency to vaporize for the system to attain the same degree of disorder. As a result, equilibrium is reached for the solution—the rates of vaporization and condensation become equal—at a lower vapor pressure. The molecular view in Figure 13.15 illustrates this point.

In quantitative terms, we find that the vapor pressure of solvent above the solution ($P_{solvent}$) equals the mole fraction of solvent in the solution ($X_{solvent}$) times the vapor pressure of the pure solvent ($P^0_{solvent}$). This relationship is expressed by **Raoult's law:**

$$P_{solvent} = X_{solvent} \times P^0_{solvent} \qquad \textbf{(13.9)}$$

Since $X_{solvent}$ is always less than 1, $P_{solvent}$ is always less than $P^0_{solvent}$. An **ideal solution** is one that follows Raoult's law at any concentration. However, just as most gases deviate from ideality, so do most solutions. In practice, Raoult's law gives a good approximation of the behavior of *dilute* solutions.

How does the *amount* of solute affect the *magnitude* of the vapor pressure lowering, ΔP? The solution consists of solute and solvent, so the sum of their mole fractions equals 1:

$$X_{solvent} + X_{solute} = 1 \quad \text{thus} \quad X_{solvent} = 1 - X_{solute}$$

From Raoult's law, we have

$$P_{solvent} = X_{solvent} \times P^0_{solvent} = (1 - X_{solute}) \times P^0_{solvent}$$

Multiplying through on the right side gives

$$P_{solvent} = P^0_{solvent} - (X_{solute} \times P^0_{solvent})$$

Rearranging and introducing ΔP gives

$$P^0_{solvent} - P_{solvent} = \Delta P = X_{solute} \times P^0_{solvent} \qquad \textbf{(13.10)}$$

Thus, the *magnitude* of ΔP equals the mole fraction of solute times the vapor pressure of the pure solvent.

Solvent molecules

A

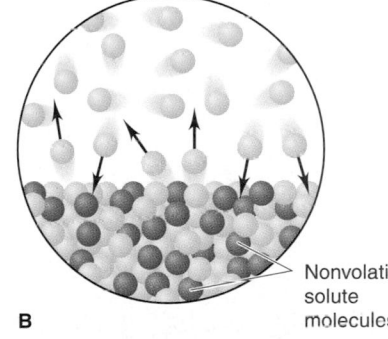

Nonvolatile solute molecules

B

Figure 13.15 The effect of solute on the vapor pressure of a solution. Vaporization occurs because of the tendency of a system to become more disordered (increase its entropy). **A,** Equilibrium is established between a pure liquid and its vapor when the numbers of molecules vaporizing and condensing in a given time are equal. **B,** The presence of a dissolved solute already increases the disorder of the system, so fewer solvent molecules vaporize in a given time. Therefore, fewer molecules need to condense to balance them, so equilibrium is established at a lower vapor pressure.

Sample Problem 13.7   Using Raoult's Law to Find the Vapor Pressure Lowering

PROBLEM Calculate the vapor pressure lowering, ΔP, when 10.0 mL glycerol ($C_3H_8O_3$) is added to 500.0 mL water at 50.°C. At this temperature, the vapor pressure of pure water is 92.5 torr and its density is 0.988 g/mL. The density of glycerol is 1.26 g/mL.

PLAN To calculate ΔP, we use Equation 13.10. Since we are given the vapor pressure of pure water, $P^0_{H_2O}$, we just need the mole fraction of glycerol, $X_{glycerol}$. We convert the given volume of glycerol to mass with the given density, find the molar mass from the formula, and convert mass (g) to amount (mol). The same procedure gives amount of H_2O. From these, we find $X_{glycerol}$ and ΔP.

SOLUTION Calculating the amount (mol) of glycerol and of water:

$$\text{Moles of glycerol} = 10.0 \text{ mL glycerol} \times \frac{1.26 \text{ g glycerol}}{1 \text{ mL glycerol}} \times \frac{1 \text{ mol glycerol}}{92.09 \text{ g glycerol}}$$

$$= 0.137 \text{ mol glycerol}$$

$$\text{Moles of } H_2O = 500.0 \text{ mL } H_2O \times \frac{0.988 \text{ g } H_2O}{1 \text{ mL } H_2O} \times \frac{1 \text{ mol } H_2O}{18.02 \text{ g } H_2O} = 27.4 \text{ mol } H_2O$$

Calculating the mole fraction of glycerol:

$$X_{glycerol} = \frac{0.137 \text{ mol}}{0.137 \text{ mol} + 27.4 \text{ mol}} = 0.00498$$

Finding the vapor pressure lowering:

$$\Delta P = X_{glycerol} \times P^0_{H_2O} = 0.00498 \times 92.5 \text{ torr} = \boxed{0.461 \text{ torr}}$$

CHECK The amounts of each component seem correct: for glycerol, ~10 × 1.25 ÷ 100 = 0.125 mol; for H_2O, ~ 500 × 1 ÷ 20 = 25 mol. The small ΔP is reasonable because the mole fraction of solute is small.

COMMENT The calculation assumes that glycerol is nonvolatile. At 1 atm, glycerol boils at 290.0°C, so the vapor pressure of glycerol at 50°C is so low it can be neglected.

Follow-up Problem 13.7   Calculate the vapor pressure lowering of a solution of 2.00 g aspirin ($\mathcal{M} = 180.15$ g/mol) in 50.0 g methanol (CH_3OH) at 21.2°C. Pure methanol has a vapor pressure of 101 torr at this temperature.

Flowchart (left margin):

Volume (mL) of glycerol (or H_2O)

↓ multiply by density (g/mL)

Mass (g) of glycerol (or H_2O)

↓ divide by $\mathcal{M}$ (g/mol)

Amount (mol) of glycerol (or H_2O)

↓ divide by total number of moles

Mole fraction (X) of glycerol

↓ multiply by $P^0_{H_2O}$

Vapor pressure lowering (ΔP)

Boiling Point Elevation   Because the vapor pressure of a solution is *lower* than that of the pure solvent at *any* temperature, *a solution boils at a higher temperature than the pure solvent.* Let's see why. The boiling point (boiling temperature, T_b) of a liquid is the temperature at which its vapor pressure equals the external pressure. Since the vapor pressure of a solution is lower than the external pressure at the solvent's boiling point, the solution does not boil. A higher temperature is needed to raise the solution's vapor pressure to equal the external pressure. We can see this **boiling point elevation (ΔT_b)** by superimposing a phase diagram for the solution on one for the pure solvent, as shown in Figure 13.16. Note that the gas-liquid curve for the solution lies *below* the pure solvent curve at any temperature and to the right of it at any pressure.

Like the vapor pressure lowering, the magnitude of the boiling point elevation is proportional to the concentration of solute particles:

$$\Delta T_b \propto m \quad \text{or} \quad \Delta T_b = K_b m \tag{13.11}$$

where m is the solution molality, K_b is the *molal boiling point elevation constant,* and ΔT_b is the boiling point elevation. We typically speak of ΔT_b as a positive value, so we subtract the lower temperature from the higher; that is, we subtract the solvent T_b from the solution T_b:

$$\Delta T_b = T_{b(solution)} - T_{b(solvent)}$$

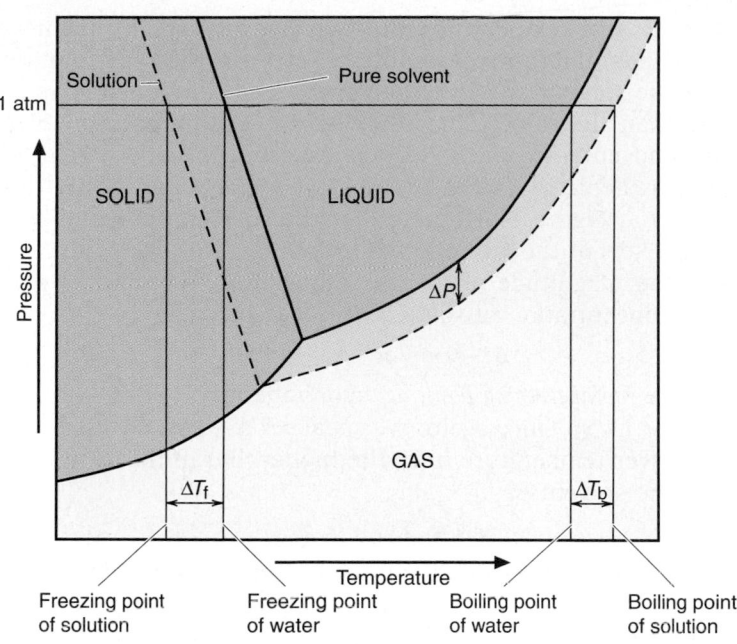

Temperature →

Freezing point of solution   Freezing point of water   Boiling point of water   Boiling point of solution

Figure 13.16 Phase diagrams of solvent and solution. Phase diagrams of an aqueous solution (*dashed lines*) and of pure water (*solid lines*) show that, by lowering the vapor pressure (ΔP), a dissolved solute elevates the boiling point and depresses the freezing point.

Molality is used as the concentration unit because it is directly related to mole fraction and thus to particles of solute. It also involves mass rather than volume of solvent, so it is not affected by temperature changes. The constant K_b has units of degrees Celsius per molal unit (°C/m) and is specific for a given solvent; Table 13.5 lists some examples.

Table 13.5 Molal Boiling Point Elevation and Freezing Point Depression Constants of Several Solvents

Solvent	Boiling Point (°C)*	K_b (°C/m)	Melting Point (°C)	K_f (°C/m)
Acetic acid	117.9	3.07	16.6	3.90
Benzene	80.1	2.53	5.5	4.90
Carbon disulfide	46.2	2.34	−111.5	3.83
Carbon tetrachloride	76.5	5.03	−23	30.
Chloroform	61.7	3.63	−63.5	4.70
Diethyl ether	34.5	2.02	−116.2	1.79
Ethanol	78.5	1.22	−117.3	1.99
Water	100.0	0.512	0.0	1.86

*At 1 atm.

Notice that for water the changes in boiling point are quite small: K_b for water is only 0.512°C/m. That is, if you dissolved 1.00 mol glucose (180. g; 1.00 mol of particles) in 1.00 kg water, or 0.500 mol NaCl (29.2 g; a strong electrolyte, so also 1.00 mol of particles) in 1.00 kg water, the boiling points of the resulting solutions at 1 atm would be only 100.512°C instead of 100.000°C.

Freezing Point Depression   As you just saw, only solvent molecules can vaporize from the solution, so the nonvolatile solute is left behind. Similarly, in many cases, *only solvent molecules can solidify,* again leaving solute molecules behind to form a slightly more concentrated solution. The freezing point of a solution is that temperature at which its vapor pressure equals that of the

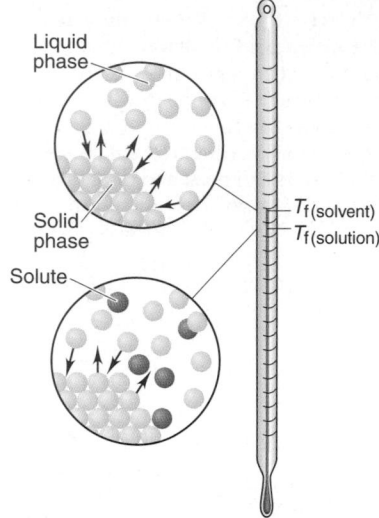

Figure 13.17 **The effect of solute on the freezing point of a solution.** In a pure solvent (*top*), equilibrium exists at the freezing point: the number of particles entering the solid per unit time equals the number leaving. Since only the solvent freezes, the presence of solute particles lowers the number of solvent particles per unit time reentering the solid (*bottom*). Thus, fewer particles must leave the solid to balance this number, and this balance occurs at a lower temperature.

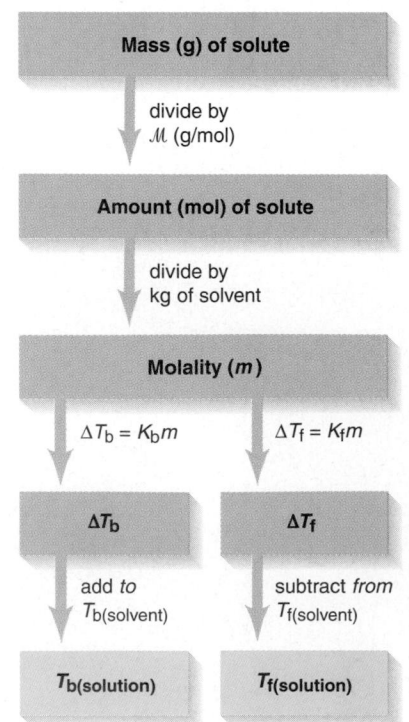

pure solvent. At this temperature, the two phases—solid solvent and liquid solution—are in equilibrium. Since the vapor pressure of the solution is lower than that of the solvent at any temperature, the solution freezes at a lower temperature than the solvent. In other words, the number of solvent particles leaving and entering the solid per unit time become equal at a lower temperature, as depicted in Figure 13.17. The **freezing point depression (ΔT_f)** is shown in Figure 13.16; note that the solid-liquid curve for the solution lies to the left of the curve for the pure solvent at any given pressure.

Like ΔT_b, the magnitude of the freezing point depression is proportional to the molal concentration of solute:

$$\Delta T_f \propto m \quad \text{or} \quad \Delta T_f = K_f m \tag{13.12}$$

where K_f is the *molal freezing point depression constant*, which also has units of °C/*m* (see Table 13.5). Once again, we speak of ΔT_f as a positive value, so we subtract the lower temperature from the higher, but in this case it is the solution T_f from the solvent T_f:

$$\Delta T_f = T_{f(\text{solvent})} - T_{f(\text{solution})}$$

Here, too, the overall effect in aqueous solution is quite small because the K_f value is small—only 1.86°C/*m*. Thus, 1 *m* glucose, 0.5 *m* NaCl, and 0.33 *m* K$_2$SO$_4$, all solutions with 1 mol of particles per kilogram of water, freeze at −1.86°C at 1 atm instead of at 0.00°C.

Sample Problem 13.8   Determining the Boiling Point Elevation and Freezing Point Depression of a Solution

PROBLEM You add 1.00 kg of the antifreeze ethylene glycol ($C_2H_6O_2$) to your car radiator, which contains 4450 g water. What are the boiling and freezing points of the solution?

PLAN To find the boiling and freezing points of the solution, we first find the molality by converting mass (kg) of solute to amount (mol) and dividing by mass (kg) of solvent. Then we calculate ΔT_b and ΔT_f from Equations 13.11 and 13.12 (using constants from Table 13.5). We add ΔT_b to the solvent boiling point and subtract ΔT_f from the solvent freezing point. The roadmap shows the steps.

SOLUTION Calculating the molality:

$$\text{Moles of } C_2H_6O_2 = 1.00 \text{ kg } C_2H_6O_2 \times \frac{10^3 \text{ g}}{1 \text{ kg}} \times \frac{1 \text{ mol } C_2H_6O_2}{62.07 \text{ g } C_2H_6O_2} = 16.1 \text{ mol } C_2H_6O_2$$

$$\text{Molality} = \frac{\text{mol solute}}{\text{kg solvent}} = \frac{16.1 \text{ mol } C_2H_6O_2}{4450 \text{ g } H_2O \times \dfrac{1 \text{ kg}}{10^3 \text{ g}}} = 3.62 \text{ } m \text{ } C_2H_6O_2$$

Finding the boiling point elevation and $T_{b(\text{solution})}$, with $K_b = 0.512$°C/*m*:

$$\Delta T_b = \frac{0.512°C}{m} \times 3.62 \text{ } m = 1.85°C$$

$$T_{b(\text{solution})} = T_{b(\text{solvent})} + \Delta T_b = 100.00°C + 1.85°C = \boxed{101.85°C}$$

Finding the freezing point depression and $T_{f(\text{solution})}$, with $K_f = 1.86$°C/*m*:

$$\Delta T_f = \frac{1.86°C}{m} \times 3.62 \text{ } m = 6.73°C$$

$$T_{f(\text{solution})} = T_{f(\text{solvent})} - \Delta T_f = 0.00°C - 6.73°C = \boxed{-6.73°C}$$

CHECK The changes in boiling and freezing points should be in the same proportion as the constants used. That is, $\Delta T_b/\Delta T_f$ should equal K_b/K_f: 1.85/6.73 = 0.275 = 0.512/1.86.

COMMENT These answers are only approximate because the concentration far exceeds that of a *dilute* solution, for which Raoult's law is most useful.

Follow-up Problem 13.8   What is the minimum concentration of ethylene glycol solution that will protect the cooling system from freezing at 0.00°F? (Assume the solution is ideal.)

Osmotic
pressure

Applied pressure needed to
prevent volume increase

Π

Pure
solvent

Solution

Net
movement
of solvent

Semipermeable
membrane

Solute
molecules
Solvent
molecules

A

B

C

Figure 13.18 The development of osmotic pressure. A, In the process of osmosis, a solution and a solvent (or solutions of different concentrations) are separated by a semipermeable membrane. Pores in the membrane allow only solvent to pass through. The molecular view (*below*) shows that more solvent molecules enter the solution than leave it in a given time. **B,** As a result, the solution volume increases, so its concentration decreases. The difference in heights of liquid in the two compartments at equilibrium creates a pressure called the *osmotic pressure* (Π). The greater height in the solution compartment exerts a backward pressure that eventually equalizes the flow of solvent in both directions. **C,** The osmotic pressure is also defined as the applied pressure required to *prevent* this volume change.

Osmotic Pressure   The fourth colligative property arises when two solutions of different concentrations are separated by a **semipermeable membrane,** one that allows solvent, but *not* solute, to pass through. The process by which this occurs is called **osmosis.** Many parts of organisms have semipermeable membranes that regulate internal concentrations by osmosis.

Consider a simple apparatus in which a membrane lies at the curve of a U tube and separates an aqueous sugar solution from pure water. The pores in the membrane allow water molecules to pass in *either* direction, but not the larger sugar molecules. As Figure 13.18A shows, because of the presence of solute, fewer water molecules lie at the membrane on the solution side, so more water molecules enter the solution in a given time than leave it. This net flow of water into the solution increases the volume of the solution and thus decreases its concentration.

As the height of the solution rises and that of the solvent falls, the resulting pressure difference pushes some water molecules *from* the solution back through the membrane. Equilibrium is reached when water molecules are pushed out of the solution at the same rate that they enter it, as shown in Figure 13.18B. The pressure difference at equilibrium is the **osmotic pressure** (symbol Greek capital *pi,* **Π**), which is defined as the applied pressure required to *prevent* the net movement of water from solvent to solution, which is shown in Figure 13.18C.

The osmotic pressure of a solution is proportional to the number of solute particles in a given *volume* of solution, that is, to the molarity (*M*):

$$\Pi \propto \frac{n_{\text{solute}}}{V_{\text{soln}}} \qquad \text{or} \qquad \Pi \propto M$$

The proportionality constant is the universal gas constant *R* times the absolute temperature *T* of the particular experiment. Thus, we have

$$\Pi = \frac{n_{\text{solute}}}{V_{\text{soln}}} RT = MRT \qquad \text{(13.13)}$$

The similarity of Equation 13.13 to the ideal gas law ($P = nRT/V$) is not surprising, since both relate the pressure of a system to its concentration and temperature. The Gallery shows some important applications of colligative properties.

Colligative Properties in Industry and Biology

Colligative properties—especially freezing point depression and osmotic pressure—have much practical relevance to everyday life. Some common applications of freezing point depression make life safer during cold winter months. Others are essential to the electronics industry. Applications of osmotic pressure are found throughout nature and the health and biosciences because, without question, the most important semipermeable membranes surround living cells.

Applications of Freezing Point Depression

Plane de-icing and car antifreezing
Ethylene glycol ($C_2H_6O_2$) is miscible with water through extensive hydrogen bonding and has a high enough boiling point for it to be essentially nonvolatile at 100°C. It is the major ingredient in airplane "de-icers." In automobile "year-round" antifreeze it lowers the freezing point of water in the radiator in the winter and raises its boiling point in the summer.

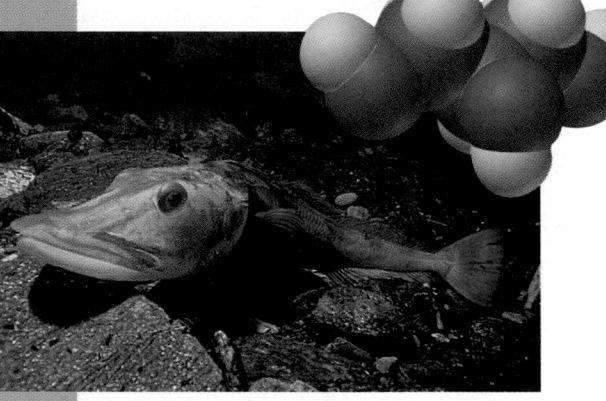

Biological antifreeze To survive in the Arctic and in northern winters, many fish and insects, including the common housefly, produce large amounts of glycerol ($C_3H_8O_3$) —a substance with a structure very similar to that of ethylene glycol and also miscible with water—which lowers the freezing point of their blood.

Salts for slippery streets
Highway crews use salts, such as mixtures of NaCl and $CaCl_2$, to melt ice on streets. A small amount of salt dissolves in the ice by lowering its freezing point and melting it. More salt dissolves, more ice melts, and so forth. An advantage of $CaCl_2$ is that it has a highly negative ΔH_{soln}, so heat is released when it dissolves, which melts more ice.

Silicon rod with impurities   Zone of molten silicon   Inert gas

Heating coil   Purer silicon

Zone refining
Manufacturing computer chips requires extremely pure starting materials. In the process of zone refining, a rod of impure silicon (or other metal or metalloid) is passed slowly through a heating coil in an inert atmosphere, and the first narrow zone of impure solid melts. As the next zone melts, the dissolved impurities from the first zone lower the freezing point of the solution, while the purer solvent refreezes. The process continues, zone by zone, throughout the entire rod. After several passes through the coil, in which each zone's impurities combine with those from other zones, the refrozen silicon becomes extremely pure—greater than 99.999999%. The ultrapure silicon is then sliced into wafers for the production of computer chips. (*Section 12.7*)

Applications of Osmotic Pressure

Controlling cell shape
The word "tonicity" refers to the tone, or firmness, of a biological cell. An *isotonic* solution has the same concentration of particles as in the cell fluid, so water enters the cell at the same rate that it leaves, thereby maintaining the cell's normal shape.

To study cell contents, biochemists rupture membranes by placing the cell in a *hypotonic* solution, one that has a lower concentration of solute particles than the cell fluid. As a result, water enters the cell faster than it leaves, causing the cell to expand and burst.

In a *hypertonic* solution, one that contains a higher concentration of solute particles than the cell fluid, the cell shrinks from the net outward flow of water.

Isotonic daily care
Contact-lens rinses consist of isotonic saline (0.15 *M* NaCl) to prevent any changes in the volume of corneal cells. Intravenous solutions for the delivery of nutrients or drugs are always isotonic.

Hypotonic watering of trees
The dissolved substances in tree sap create a more concentrated solution than the surrounding ground water. Water enters membranes in the roots and rises into the tree, creating an osmotic pressure that can exceed 20 atm in the tallest trees!

Sodium ion: the extracellular osmoregulator
Of the four major biological cations—Na^+, K^+, Mg^{2+}, and Ca^{2+}—Na^+ is essential for all animals that regulate their fluid volume (which includes you!). The Na^+ ion accounts for more than 90 mol % of all cations *outside a cell*. A high Na^+ concentration draws water out of the cell by osmosis; a low concentration leaves more inside. The primary role of Na^+ is to regulate the water volume of the body, and the primary role of the kidney is to regulate the concentration of Na^+. Changes in blood pressure (volume) activate nerves and hormones to adjust blood flow and alter kidney function.

Hypertonic food preservation Before refrigeration was common, salt was used as a preservative. The salt causes microbes on the food's surface to shrivel and die from loss of water. (Salt was so highly prized for this purpose that Roman soldiers were paid in salt, from which comes the word *salary*.) In 1772, Captain James Cook wisely brought on board his ship large amounts of cabbage as food stores and preserved them with salt, thus converting the perishable vegetable into long-lived sauerkraut. The high vitamin-C content of the pickled cabbage prevented the debilitating effects of scurvy and allowed Cook's crew to continue explorations and partake in experiments that would revolutionize longitude measurements and, thus, oceangoing navigation.

The Underlying Nature of Colligative Properties   A common thread runs through our explanations of the four colligative properties of nonvolatile solutes. Each involves the inability of solute particles to cross between two phases. They cannot enter the gas phase, which leads to vapor pressure lowering and boiling point elevation. They cannot enter the solid phase, which leads to freezing point depression. They cannot cross the semipermeable membrane, which leads to the development of osmotic pressure. Because of these factors, the presence of solute decreases the mole fraction of solvent, which lowers the number of solvent particles leaving the solution per unit time, and this lowering requires an adjustment to reach equilibrium again. The adjustment to reach the new balance in numbers of particles crossing between two phases per unit time results in the measured colligative property.

Using Colligative Properties to Find Solute Molar Mass

Each of the colligative properties relates concentration to some measurable quantity: the number of degrees the freezing point is lowered, the magnitude of osmotic pressure that is created, and so forth. From these measurements, we can determine the amount (mol) of solute particles and, for a known mass of solute, the molar mass of the solute as well.

In principle, any of the colligative properties can be used to find the solute molar mass, but in practice, some systems provide more accurate data than others. For example, to determine the molar mass of an unknown solute by freezing point depression, you would select a solvent with as large a molal freezing point depression constant as possible (see Table 13.5). If the solute is soluble in acetic acid, for instance, a 1 m solution depresses the freezing point by 3.90°C, more than twice the change in water (1.86°C).

Of the four colligative properties, osmotic pressure creates the largest changes and therefore the most precise measurements. Biological and polymer chemists estimate molar masses as great as 10^5 g/mol by measuring osmotic pressure. Because only a tiny fraction of a mole of a macromolecular solute dissolves in any solvent, it would create an impractically tiny change in the other colligative properties.

Sample Problem 13.9   Determining Molar Mass from Osmotic Pressure

PROBLEM Biochemists have discovered more than 400 mutant varieties of hemoglobin, the blood protein that carries oxygen throughout the body. A physician studying a variety associated with a fatal disease first finds its molar mass ($\mathcal{M}$). She dissolves 21.5 mg of the protein in water at 5.0°C to make 1.50 mL of solution and measures an osmotic pressure of 3.61 torr. What is the molar mass of this hemoglobin variety?

PLAN We know the osmotic pressure (Π), R, and T. We convert Π from torr to atm, and T from °C to K, and then use Equation 13.13 to solve for molarity (M). Then we calculate the amount (mol) of hemoglobin from the known volume and use the known mass to find $\mathcal{M}$.

SOLUTION Combining unit conversion steps and solving for molarity from Equation 13.13:

$$M = \frac{\Pi}{RT} = \frac{\dfrac{3.61 \text{ torr}}{760 \text{ torr/1 atm}}}{\left(0.0821 \dfrac{\text{atm} \cdot \text{L}}{\text{mol} \cdot \text{K}}\right)(273.15 \text{ K} + 5.0)} = 2.08 \times 10^{-4} \text{ M}$$

Finding amount (mol) of solute:

$$\text{Moles of solute} = M \times V = \frac{2.08 \times 10^{-4} \text{ mol}}{\text{L soln}} \times 0.00150 \text{ L soln} = 3.12 \times 10^{-7} \text{ mol}$$

Π (atm)

$M = \Pi/RT$

M (mol/L)

multiply by volume (L) of solution

Amount (mol) of solute

divide *into* mass (g) of solute

$\mathcal{M}$ (g/mol)

Calculating molar mass of hemoglobin (after changing mg to g):

$$\mathcal{M} = \frac{0.0215 \text{ g}}{3.12 \times 10^{-7} \text{ mol}} = \boxed{6.89 \times 10^4 \text{ g/mol}}$$

CHECK The answers seem reasonable: The small osmotic pressure implies a very low molarity. Since hemoglobin is a protein, a biological macromolecule, we expect a small number of moles [$(\sim 2 \times 10^{-4})$ (1.5×10^{-3}) = 3×10^{-7}] and a high molar mass $(\sim 21 \times 10^{-3}/3 \times 10^{-7} = 7 \times 10^4)$.

Follow-up Problem 13.9 A 0.30 M solution of sucrose at 37°C has approximately the same osmotic pressure as blood. What is the osmotic pressure of blood?

Colligative Properties of Volatile Nonelectrolyte Solutions

What is the effect on vapor pressure when the solute *is* volatile, that is, when the vapor consists of solute *and* solvent molecules? From Raoult's law (Equation 13.9), we know that

$$P_{\text{solvent}} = X_{\text{solvent}} \times P^0_{\text{solvent}} \quad \text{and} \quad P_{\text{solute}} = X_{\text{solute}} \times P^0_{\text{solute}}$$

where X_{solvent} and X_{solute} refer to the mole fractions in the liquid phase. According to Dalton's law of partial pressures, the total vapor pressure is the sum of the partial vapor pressures:

$$P_{\text{total}} = P_{\text{solvent}} + P_{\text{solute}} = (X_{\text{solvent}} \times P^0_{\text{solvent}}) + (X_{\text{solute}} \times P^0_{\text{solute}})$$

Just as a nonvolatile solute lowers the vapor pressure of solvent by making the mole fraction of solvent less than 1, *the presence of each volatile component lowers the vapor pressure of the other* by making each mole fraction less than 1.

Let's examine this effect in a solution of benzene (C_6H_6) and toluene (C_7H_8) that contains equal amounts (mol) of benzene and toluene: $X_{\text{ben}} = X_{\text{tol}} = 0.500$. At 25°C, the vapor pressure of pure benzene (P^0_{ben}) is 95.1 torr and that of pure toluene (P^0_{tol}) is 28.4 torr; note that benzene is more volatile than toluene. We find their partial pressures from Raoult's law:

$$P_{\text{ben}} = X_{\text{ben}} \times P^0_{\text{ben}} = 0.500 \times 95.1 \text{ torr} = 47.6 \text{ torr}$$

$$P_{\text{tol}} = X_{\text{tol}} \times P^0_{\text{tol}} = 0.500 \times 28.4 \text{ torr} = 14.2 \text{ torr}$$

As you can see, the presence of benzene lowers the vapor pressure of toluene, and vice versa.

Does the composition of the vapor differ from that of the solution? To see, let's calculate the mole fraction of each substance *in the vapor* by applying Dalton's law. Recall from Section 5.4 that $X_A = P_A/P_{\text{total}}$. Therefore, for benzene and toluene in the vapor,

$$X_{\text{ben}} = \frac{P_{\text{ben}}}{P_{\text{total}}} = \frac{47.6 \text{ torr}}{47.6 \text{ torr} + 14.2 \text{ torr}} = 0.770$$

$$X_{\text{tol}} = \frac{P_{\text{tol}}}{P_{\text{total}}} = \frac{14.2 \text{ torr}}{47.6 \text{ torr} + 14.2 \text{ torr}} = 0.230$$

The vapor composition is very different from the solution composition. The essential point to notice is that *the vapor has a higher mole fraction of the **more** volatile solution component.* The 50:50 ratio of benzene:toluene in the liquid created a 77:23 ratio of benzene:toluene in the vapor. Condense this vapor into a separate container, and that new *solution* has this 77:23 composition, and the new *vapor* above it would be enriched still further in benzene.

In the process of **fractional distillation,** this phenomenon is employed to separate a mixture of volatile components. Numerous vaporization-condensation steps continually enrich the vapor, until the vapor reaching the top of the fractionating column consists solely of the most volatile component.

Figure 13.19 **The process of fractional distillation. A,** In the laboratory, a flask containing a solution of two or more volatile components is attached to a *fractionating column* that is packed with glass beads and connected to a condenser. Expansion lines show a close-up of the glass beads within the column. As the flask is heated, the vapor mixture rises and condenses on the lowest beads, forming a liquid enriched in the more volatile component. Some of this liquid vaporizes again to form a more enriched vapor, which condenses on beads higher up. The process continues until the vapor reaching the condenser consists of the more volatile component only, which condenses to a pure liquid. **B,** In industry, this process is used to separate petroleum into many products. A fractionating tower 30 m high separates components that differ by a few tenths of a degree in their boiling points. (The illustration is a simplified version of a multipart process.)

Figure 13.19A shows the laboratory apparatus. In petroleum refining, shown schematically in Figure 13.19B, fractional distillation is used to separate the hundreds of individual compounds in crude oil into a small number of "fractions" based on boiling point range.

Colligative Properties of Electrolyte Solutions

When we consider electrolyte solutions, we must take the solute formula into account because colligative properties depend on the number of particles. For instance, the boiling point elevation (ΔT_b) of 0.050 *m* NaCl should be twice that of 0.050 *m* glucose ($C_6H_{12}O_6$), because NaCl is ionic and dissociates into two particles per formula unit. Thus, we include a multiplying factor in the equations for the colligative properties of electrolyte solutions. The *van't Hoff factor (i)*, named after the Dutch chemist Jacobus van't Hoff (1852–1911), is the ratio of the *measured* value of the colligative property in the electrolyte solution to the *expected* value for a nonelectrolyte solution:

$$i = \frac{\text{measured value for electrolyte solution}}{\text{expected value for nonelectrolyte solution}}$$

To calculate the colligative properties of electrolyte solutions, we incorporate the van't Hoff factor into the equation:

For vapor pressure lowering:　　　$\Delta P = i(X_{\text{solute}} \times P^0_{\text{solvent}})$
For boiling point elevation:　　　$\Delta T_b = i(K_b m)$
For freezing point depression:　　$\Delta T_f = i(K_f m)$
For osmotic pressure:　　　　　　$\Pi = i(MRT)$

If electrolyte solutions behaved ideally, the factor *i* would simply be the amount (mol) of particles in solution divided by the amount (mol) of solute dissolved; that is, *i* would be 2 for NaCl, 3 for $Mg(NO_3)_2$, and so forth. Careful experiment shows, however, that *most electrolyte solutions are **not** ideal*. For example, the boiling point elevation of 0.050 *m* NaCl solution compared with 0.050 *m* glucose solution gives a factor *i* of 1.9, not 2.0:

$$i = \frac{\Delta T_b \text{ of } 0.050 \ m \text{ NaCl}}{\Delta T_b \text{ of } 0.050 \ m \text{ glucose}} = \frac{0.049°C}{0.026°C} = 1.9$$

The measured value of the van't Hoff factor is typically *lower* than that expected from the formula. This deviation implies that the ions are not behaving as independent particles. Yet we know from other evidence that soluble salts dissociate completely into ions. The fact that the deviation is greater with divalent and trivalent ions provides a clue that ionic charge is somehow involved in the behavior, as the values in Figure 13.20 show.

To explain nonideal behavior, we picture ions as separate but near each other. Clustered near a positive ion are, on average, more negative ions, and vice versa. Figure 13.21 shows each ion surrounded by an **ionic atmosphere** of net opposite charge. Through these electrostatic associations, each type of ion behaves as if it were "tied up," so its concentration seems *lower* than it actually is. Thus, we often speak of an *effective* concentration, obtained by multiplying *i* by the *stoichiometric* concentration based on the formula. The greater the charge, the stronger these associations, so the deviation from ideal behavior is greater for compounds that dissociate into multivalent ions.

At ordinary conditions and concentrations, nonideal behavior in solutions is much more common, and the deviations much larger, than nonideal behavior in gases, because the particles are so much closer together. Nevertheless, the two systems exhibit some interesting similarities. Gases display nearly ideal behavior at low pressures because the distances between particles are large. Similarly, van't Hoff (*i*) factors approach their ideal values as the solution becomes more dilute, that is, as the distance between ions increases. In gases, attractions between particles cause deviations from the expected pressure. In solutions, attractions between particles cause deviations from the expected size of a colligative property. Finally, for both real gases and real solutions, we use empirically determined numbers (van der Waals constants or van't Hoff factors) to transform simple theories (the ideal gas law or Raoult's law) into more useful ones.

Section Summary

Colligative properties of solutions are related to the number of dissolved solute particles, not their chemical nature. Compared with the pure solvent, a solution of a nonvolatile nonelectrolyte has a lower vapor pressure (Raoult's law), an elevated boiling point, a depressed freezing point, and an osmotic pressure. Colligative properties can be used to determine the solute molar mass. When solute *and* solvent are volatile, the vapor pressure of each is lowered by the presence of the other. The vapor pressure of the more volatile component is always higher. Electrolyte solutions exhibit nonideal behavior because ionic interactions reduce the effective concentration of the ions.

13.6 The Structure and Properties of Colloids

Stir a handful of fine sand into a glass of water and wait a moment. The sand particles are suspended at first but then gradually settle to the bottom. Sand in water is an example of a **suspension,** a *heterogeneous* mixture containing particles large enough to be seen with the naked eye and clearly distinct from the surrounding fluid. In contrast, stirring sugar into water forms a solution, a *homogeneous* mixture in which the particles are individual molecules distributed evenly throughout the surrounding fluid.

Between the extremes of suspensions and solutions is a large group of mixtures called *colloidal dispersions,* or simply **colloids,** in which a dispersed (solute-like) substance is distributed throughout a dispersing (solvent-like) substance. Colloidal particles are larger than simple molecules but small enough to remain distributed and not settle out. They have a range of diameters between 1 and 1000 nm (10^{-9} to 10^{-6} m). A colloidal particle may

Figure 13.20 Nonideal behavior of electrolyte solutions. The van't Hoff factors *(i)* for various ionic solutes in dilute (0.05 *m*) aqueous solution show that the observed value *(dark blue)* is always *lower* than the expected value *(light blue)*. This deviation is due to ionic interactions that, in effect, reduce the number of free ions in solution. The deviation is greatest for multivalent ions.

Figure 13.21 An ionic atmosphere model for nonideal behavior of electrolyte solutions. Hydrated anions cluster near cations, and vice versa, to form ionic atmospheres of net opposite charge. Since ions do not behave independently, their concentrations are effectively *less* than expected. Such interactions cause deviations from the ideal behavior expressed by Raoult's law.

Table 13.6 Types of Colloids

Colloid Type	Dispersed Substance	Dispersing Medium	Example
Aerosol	Liquid	Gas	Fog
Aerosol	Solid	Gas	Smoke
Foam	Gas	Liquid	Whipped cream
Solid foam	Gas	Solid	Marshmallow
Emulsion	Liquid	Liquid	Milk
Solid emulsion	Liquid	Solid	Butter
Sol	Solid	Liquid	Paint; cell fluid
Solid sol	Solid	Solid	Opal

◆ **"Soaps" in Your Small Intestine**   In the small intestine, fats are digested by *bile salts,* soaplike molecules with smaller polar and larger nonpolar portions (sodium taurocholate is shown). Secreted by the liver, stored in the gallbladder, and released in the intestine, bile salts emulsify fats just as soap emulsifies grease: fatty aggregates are broken down into colloid-sized particles and dispersed in the watery fluid. Only in this form can the fats be broken down further and transported into the blood for further metabolism.

consist of a single macromolecule (such as a protein or synthetic polymer) or an aggregate of many atoms, ions, or molecules. Whatever their composition, as a result of their small particle size, colloids have an enormous total surface area. Consider this: a cube with 1-cm sides has a total surface area of 6 cm^2. If it were divided equally into 10^{12} cubes, the cubes would be the size of large colloidal particles and have a total surface area of 60,000 cm^2, or 6 m^2. This enormous surface area allows many more interactions to exert a great total adhesive force, which attracts other particles and gives rise to some of the practical uses of colloids.

Colloids are classified in Table 13.6 according to whether the dispersed and dispersing substances are gases, liquids, or solids. Many familiar commercial products and natural objects are colloids. For example, whipped cream is a *foam,* a gas dispersed in a liquid. Firefighting foams, such as those used in emergency airplane landings, are liquid mixtures of proteins in water made frothy with fine jets of air. Most biological fluids are aqueous *sols,* solids dispersed in water. Within a typical cell, colloid-sized proteins and nucleic acids are dispersed in an aqueous solution of ions and small molecules. The action of soaps and detergents occurs by the formation of an *emulsion,* a liquid (soap dissolved in grease) dispersed in another liquid (water). ◆

Most colloids are cloudy or opaque, but some are transparent to the naked eye. When light passes through a colloid, it is scattered randomly by the dispersed particles because their sizes are similar to the wavelengths of visible light (400 to 700 nm). Viewed from the side, the scattered light beam is visible and broader than one passing through a solution. This light-scattering phenomenon is known as the **Tyndall effect** and is shown in Figure 13.22.

A   **B**

Figure 13.22 Light scattering and the Tyndall effect.
A, When a beam of light passes through a solution (*left*), its path remains narrow and barely visible. When it passes through a colloid (*right*), it is scattered and broadened by the particles and thus easily visible. **B,** Sunlight is scattered as it shines through misty air in a forest.

Dust in air displays this effect when sunlight shines through it, as does mist pierced by headlights at night.

Under low magnification, you can see colloidal particles exhibit *Brownian motion,* a characteristic movement in which the particles change speed and direction erratically. This motion results from the colloidal particles being pushed this way and that by molecules of the dispersing medium. These collisions are primarily responsible for keeping colloidal particles from settling, although convection also helps suspend larger particles. (Einstein's explanation of Brownian motion in 1905 was a principal factor in the acceptance of the molecular nature of matter.)

Why don't colloidal particles aggregate into still larger particles and settle out? Interparticle forces provide the explanation. Water-dispersed colloids remain distributed because the particles have charged surfaces that interact strongly with the water through ion-dipole forces. Soap molecules form spherical *micelles,* with the charged heads forming the micelle exterior and the nonpolar tails interacting via dispersion forces in the interior. Aqueous proteins are typically spherical and mimic this micellar arrangement, with charged amino acid groups facing the water and uncharged groups buried within the molecule. Nonpolar oily particles can be dispersed in water by introducing ions, which are adsorbed onto their surfaces. Figure 13.23 shows that charge repulsions between adsorbed ions of like charge prevent the particles from adhering to each other when they collide.

Despite these forces, various methods can coagulate the particles and "destroy" the colloid. Heating a colloid makes the particles move faster and collide more often and with enough force to coalesce into heavier particles that settle out. Adding an electrolyte solution introduces oppositely charged ions that neutralize the particles' surface charges, which allows the particles to coagulate and settle. ◆ Uncharged colloidal particles in smokestack gases are removed by creating ions that become adsorbed on the particles, which are then attracted to the charged plates of a Cottrell precipitator. Such precipitators are installed in the smokestacks of coal-burning power plants (Figure 13.24) and collect about 90% of colloidal smoke particulates, thus preventing their release into the air.

The upcoming Chemical Connections essay applies solution and colloid chemistry to the purification of water for residential and industrial use.

Figure 13.23 The charged surfaces of water-dispersed, nonpolar colloids. Nonpolar particles can be dispersed in water only if ions are adsorbed on their surfaces. Because like charges repel, the similarly charged colloidal particles repel one another during collisions and remain dispersed.

① Hot gases pass through discharge area and some molecules are ionized

② Gaseous ions are adsorbed by suspended smoke particles

Outlet for clean gases

③ Charged smoke particles are attracted to oppositely charged electrode

Plate electrode

④ Charged particles are neutralized, fall, and are discarded

High DC voltage

Wire

Smoke inlet

Figure 13.24 A Cottrell precipitator for removing particulates from industrial flue gases.

◆ From Colloid to Civilization At times, civilizations have been born where colloids are coagulated by electrolyte solutions. At the mouths of rivers, where salt concentrations increase near an ocean or sea, the clay particles dispersed in the river water come together to form muddy deltas, such as those of the Nile (*reddish area in photo*) and the Mississippi. The ancient Egyptian empire and the city of New Orleans are the results of this global colloid chemistry.

Solutions and Colloids in Water Purification

Clean water is a priceless and limited resource that we've begun to treasure only recently, after decades of pollution and waste. Because of the natural tendency of systems to become disordered, it requires energy to remove dissolved, dispersed, and suspended particles from water to make it clean enough for humans to use.

Most water destined for human use comes from lakes, rivers, or reservoirs that may serve also as the final sink after the water is used. Many mineral ions, such as NO_3^- and Fe^{3+}, may be present in high concentrations. Dissolved organic compounds, some of them toxic, may be present as well. Fine clay particles and a whole spectrum of microorganisms occur dispersed in colloidal form. Larger particles and debris of every variety may be present in suspension.

Water Treatment Plants

As a sample of water moves from the natural source into a water treatment facility, the largest particles are physically removed at the intake site by screens (Figure 13.B, Step 1). Finer particles, including microorganisms, are removed in large settling tanks by treatment with lime (CaO) and alum $[Al_2(SO_4)_3]$ (Step 2), which react to form a fluffy, gel-like mass of $Al(OH)_3$:

$$3CaO(s) + 3H_2O(l) + Al_2(SO_4)_3(s) \longrightarrow$$
$$2Al(OH)_3(colloidal\ gel) + 3CaSO_4(aq)$$

The fine particles are trapped within or adsorbed onto the enormous surface area of the gel, which coagulates, settles out, and is filtered through a sand bed (Step 3).

With suspended and colloidal particles removed, the water sample is aerated in large sprayers to saturate the water with oxygen, which speeds the oxidation of dissolved organic compounds (Step 4). The water is then sterilized, usually by treat-ment with Cl_2 gas and/or aqueous solutions of hypochlorite ion, ClO^- (Step 5), which may give the water an unpleasant odor. Chlorine can also form toxic chlorinated hydrocarbons, but these can be removed by adsorption onto activated charcoal particles. These steps through the treatment facility dispose of debris and grit, colloidal clay, microorganisms, and much of the oxidizable organic matter, but dissolved ions remain. Many of these can be removed by water softening and reverse osmosis.

Water Softening via Ion Exchange

Water that contains large amounts of divalent cations, such as Ca^{2+}, Mg^{2+}, and Fe^{2+}, is called **hard water.** These cations cause several problems. During cleaning, they combine with the fatty-acid anions in soaps to produce insoluble deposits on clothes, washing machine parts, and sinks:

$$Ca^{2+}(aq) + 2C_{17}H_{35}COONa(aq) \longrightarrow$$
$$\underset{soap}{} \quad \underset{deposit}{(C_{17}H_{35}COO)_2Ca(s)} + 2Na^+(aq)$$

When a large amount of bicarbonate (HCO_3^-) is present in the water, the hard-water cations cause a buildup of *scale* within boilers and hot-water pipes, insoluble carbonate deposits that interfere with the transfer of heat and damage plumbing:

$$Ca^{2+}(aq) + 2HCO_3^-(aq) \xrightarrow{\Delta} CaCO_3(s) + CO_2(g) + H_2O(l)$$

The removal of hard-water ions, called **water softening,** solves these problems. It is accomplished by exchanging "soft-water" Na^+ ions for the hard-water ions. A typical domestic **ion-exchange** system contains an *ion-exchange resin*, an insoluble polymer with covalently bound anion groups, such as $-SO_3^-$ or $-COO^-$, with Na^+ ions attached to balance the charge (Figure 13.C). The divalent cations in hard water are

Figure 13.B The steps in a typical municipal water treatment plant. Before water is sent to users, (1) it is filtered to remove large debris, (2) the finer particles are trapped in an $Al(OH)_3$ gel, (3) the gel is filtered through sand, (4) the filtrate is aerated to oxidize organic compounds, and (5) the water is disinfected with chlorine.

⑤ *Sterilization and disinfection*

Storage tank

Chlorine added

④ *Aeration and oxidation of organics*

To users

CaO and $Al_2(SO_4)_3$ added

Valve

Settling tanks

② *Fine particle trapping in gel*

Water intake

① *Coarse filtration and screening*

③ *Sand filtration*

Figure 13.C Ion exchange for removal of hard-water ions. A, A commercial ion-exchange column is installed in a household water system. **B,** In a typical ion-exchange resin, negatively charged groups are covalently bound to resin beads, with Na^+ ions present to keep the material neutral. Hard-water ions, such as Ca^{2+}, exchange with the Na^+ ions, which are displaced into the flowing water.

Resin bead with negative groups

attracted to the resin's anionic groups and displace the Na^+ ions into the water: one type of ion is exchanged for another. The resin is replaced when all the resin sites are occupied, or it can be "regenerated" by treating it with a very concentrated Na^+ solution, which exchanges Na^+ ions for the bound Ca^{2+}.

Reverse Osmosis

Another way to remove ions and other dissolved substances from water is by **reverse osmosis.** In osmosis, water moves from a dilute to a concentrated solution through a semipermeable membrane. The resulting difference in water volumes creates an osmotic pressure. In reverse osmosis, water moves out of the concentrated solution when a pressure *greater* than the osmotic pressure is *applied* to the solution, forcing the water back through the membrane and leaving the ions behind—in a sense, filtering out the ions at the molecular level.

In domestic water systems, reverse osmosis is used to remove toxic ions, such as the *heavy-metal ions* Pb^{2+}, Cd^{2+}, and Hg^{2+}, present at concentrations too low for removal by ion exchange. On a much larger scale, reverse osmosis is used in **desalination** plants, which remove large amounts of ions from seawater (Figure 13.D). Reverse osmosis plants find increasing use in arid regions, such as the Middle East. Seawater is pumped under high pressure into tubes containing millions of hollow fiber membranes, each the thickness of a human hair. Water molecules, but not ions, pass through the membranes into the fiber to be collected. Seawater containing about 40,000 ppm of total dissolved solids can be purified to 400 ppm (suitable for drinking) in one pass through such a system.

Water Treatment after Use

Used water is called **wastewater,** or *sewage,* and it must be treated before being returned to the ground water, river, or lake. Sewage treatment is especially important for industrial wastewater, which may contain toxic components. In *primary* sewage treatment, wastewater undergoes the same steps as the water coming into the system. Most municipalities now also include *secondary* sewage treatment. In this stage, bacteria biologically degrade the organic compounds and some microorganisms still present in solution or in the solids from the settling tanks. In certain cases, secondary treatment may be supplemented by *tertiary* treatment in a process tailored to the specific pollutant involved. Heavy-metal ion contamination, for instance, can be eliminated by a precipitation step before primary and secondary treatment. Tertiary methods also exist for phosphate, nitrate, and toxic organic substances.

Permeator

Hollow fibers of semipermeable membrane

Water molecules   Solute particles

Pure water to collector

High *P*

Figure 13.D Reverse osmosis for removal of ions. A, A section of a coiled reverse-osmosis permeator. **B,** Each permeator contains a bundle of thin, hollow fibers of semipermeable membrane. **C,** Seawater is pumped through the permeator at high pressure. Most of the ions are removed, so much purer water enters the fibers and is collected.

Section Summary

Colloidal particles are smaller than those in a suspension and larger than those in a solution. Colloids are classified by the physical state of the dispersed and dispersing substances and are formed from many combinations of gas, liquid, and solid. Colloids have extremely large surface areas, exhibit random (Brownian) motion, and scatter incoming light (Tyndall effect). Colloidal particles in water have charged surfaces that keep them dispersed, but they can be coagulated by heating or by the addition of ions.

Chapter Perspective

In Chapter 12, you saw how pure liquids and solids behave, and here you've seen how their behaviors change when they are mixed together. Two features of these systems reappear in later chapters: their equilibrium nature in Chapters 17 to 19, and their tendency toward disorder in Chapter 20.

This chapter completes our general discussion of atomic and molecular properties and their influence on the properties of matter. Immediately following is an Interchapter feature that reviews these properties in a pictorial format and helps pre-view their application in upcoming chapters. In Chapter 14, we travel through the main groups of the periodic table, applying the ideas you've learned so far to the chemical and physical behavior of the elements. Then, in Chapter 15, we focus on the atomic properties of carbon and compare them with those of carbon's neighbors to see how these properties create the fascinating world of organic substances, including biomolecules and synthetic polymers.

The following learning objectives, with section and/or sample problem (SP) numbers in parentheses, can help focus your study:

Understand These Concepts

1. The quantitative meaning of solubility (13.1)
2. The major types of intermolecular forces in solution and their relative strengths (13.1)
3. How the "like-dissolves-like" rule depends on intermolecular forces (13.1)
4. Why gases have relatively low solubilities in water (13.1)
5. General characteristics of solutions formed by various combinations of gases, liquids, and solids (13.1)
6. The enthalpy components of a solution cycle and their effect on ΔH_{soln} (13.2)
7. The dependence of ΔH_{hydr} on ionic charge density and the factors that determine exothermic or endothermic ionic solution processes (13.2)
8. The meaning of entropy and how the balance between the change in enthalpy and the change in entropy governs the solution process (13.2)
9. The distinctions among saturated, unsaturated, and supersaturated solutions and the equilibrium nature of a saturated solution (13.3)
10. The effect of temperature on solubility and its relation to the sign of ΔH_{soln} (13.3)
11. Why the solubility of gases in water decreases with a rise in temperature (13.3)
12. The effect of pressure on solubility and its quantitative expression as Henry's law (13.3)

13. The meaning of molarity, molality, mole fraction, and parts by mass or by volume (13.4)
14. The distinction between electrolytes and nonelectrolytes in solution (13.5)
15. The four colligative properties and their dependence on number of dissolved particles (13.5)
16. Ideal solutions and the importance of Raoult's law (13.5)
17. How the phase diagram of a solution differs from that of the pure solvent (13.5)
18. Why the vapor over a solution of volatile nonelectrolyte is richer in the more volatile component (13.5)
19. Why electrolyte solutions are not ideal and the meanings of the van't Hoff factor and the ionic-atmosphere concept (13.5)
20. How particle size distinguishes suspensions, colloids, and solutions (13.6)
21. How colloidal behavior is demonstrated by Brownian motion and the Tyndall effect (13.6)

Master These Skills

1. Predicting relative solubilities from intermolecular forces (SP 13.1)
2. Predicting the effect of temperature on relative solubility of a substance (SP 13.2)
3. Using Henry's law to calculate the solubility of a gas (SP 13.3)

4. Expressing concentration in terms of molarity, molality, and parts by mass, parts by volume, and mole fraction (SPs 13.4 and 13.5)
5. Interconverting the various ways of expressing concentration (SP 13.6)
6. Using Raoult's law to calculate the vapor pressure lowering of a solution (SP 13.7)

7. Using a colligative property to calculate the molar mass of a solute (SP 13.9)
8. Calculating the composition of vapor over a solution of volatile nonelectrolyte (13.5)
9. Calculating the van't Hoff factor i from the magnitude of a colligative property (13.5)

For Review and Reference

Key Terms

Section 13.1
solute
solvent
miscible
solubility (S)
hydration shell
ion-induced dipole force
dipole-induced dipole force
like-dissolves-like rule
soap
alloy
Section 13.2
heat of solution (ΔH_{soln})
solvation

hydration
heat of hydration (ΔH_{hydr})
charge density
entropy
Section 13.3
saturated solution
unsaturated solution
supersaturated solution
Henry's law
Section 13.4
molality (m)
mass percent [% (w/w)]
volume percent [% (v/v)]
mole fraction (X)

Section 13.5
colligative property
electrolyte
nonelectrolyte
vapor pressure lowering (ΔP)
Raoult's law
ideal solution
boiling point elevation (ΔT_b)
freezing point depression (ΔT_f)
semipermeable membrane
osmosis
osmotic pressure (Π)

fractional distillation
ionic atmosphere
Section 13.6
suspension
colloid
Tyndall effect
hard water
water softening
ion exchange
reverse osmosis
desalination
wastewater

Key Equations and Relationships

13.1 Dividing the general heat of solution into component enthalpies (p. 489):

$$\Delta H_{soln} = \Delta H_{solute} + \Delta H_{solvent} + \Delta H_{mix}$$

13.2 Dividing the heat of solution of an ionic compound in water into component enthalpies (p. 491):

$$\Delta H_{soln} = -\Delta H_{lattice} + \Delta H_{hydr\ of\ the\ ions}$$

13.3 Relating gas solubility to its partial pressure (Henry's law) (p. 497):

$$S_{gas} = k_H \times P_{gas}$$

13.4 Defining concentration in terms of molarity (p. 498):

$$\text{Molarity } (M) = \frac{\text{amount (mol) of solute}}{\text{volume (L) of solution}}$$

13.5 Defining concentration in terms of molality (p. 498):

$$\text{Molality } (m) = \frac{\text{amount (mol) of solute}}{\text{mass (kg) of solvent}}$$

13.6 Defining concentration in terms of mass percent (p. 499):

$$\text{Mass percent [\% (w/w)]} = \frac{\text{mass of solute}}{\text{mass of solution}} \times 100$$

13.7 Defining concentration in terms of volume percent (p. 499):

$$\text{Volume percent [\% (v/v)]} = \frac{\text{volume of solute}}{\text{volume of solution}} \times 100$$

13.8 Defining concentration in terms of mole fraction (p. 500):

Mole fraction (X)

$$= \frac{\text{amount (mol) of solute}}{\text{amount (mol) of solute} + \text{amount (mol) of solvent}}$$

13.9 Expressing the relationship between the vapor pressure of solvent above a solution and its mole fraction in the solution (Raoult's law) (p. 503):

$$P_{solvent} = X_{solvent} \times P^0_{solvent}$$

13.10 Calculating the vapor pressure lowering due to solute (p. 503):

$$\Delta P = X_{solute} \times P^0_{solvent}$$

13.11 Calculating the boiling point elevation of a solution (p. 504):

$$\Delta T_b = K_b m$$

13.12 Calculating the freezing point depression of a solution (p. 506):

$$\Delta T_f = K_f m$$

13.13 Calculating the osmotic pressure of a solution (p. 507):

$$\Pi = \frac{n_{solute}}{V_{soln}} RT = MRT$$

Highlighted Figures and Tables

These figures (F) and tables (T) provide a quick review of key ideas.

F13.1 Major types of intermolecular forces in solutions (p. 482)

F13.2 Hydration shells around an aqueous ion (p. 483)

F13.6 Solution cycles and the components of ΔH_{soln} (p. 490)

T13.3 Trends in ionic heats of hydration (p. 491)

F13.7 Enthalpy diagrams for dissolving three ionic compounds in water (p. 491)

F13.9 Equilibrium in a saturated solution (p. 493)

F13.13 Effect of pressure on gas solubility (p. 496)

T13.4 Concentration definitions (p. 498)

F13.15 Effect of solute on vapor pressure of a solution (p. 503)

F13.16 Phase diagrams of solvent and solution (p. 505)

F13.17 Effect of solute on freezing point of a solution (p. 506)

F13.18 Development of osmotic pressure (p. 507)

F13.20 Nonideal behavior of electrolyte solutions (p. 513)

T13.6 Types of colloids (p. 514)

Answers to Follow-up Problems

13.1 (a) 1,4-Butanediol is more soluble in water because it can form more H bonds.

(b) Chloroform is more soluble in water because it can form dipole-dipole forces.

13.2 (a) $NaOCN(s) + heat \xrightleftharpoons{H_2O} Na^+(aq) + OCN^-(aq)$

$\Delta H_{soln} > 0$; at lower T, solubility decreases.

(b) $\Delta H_{soln} < 0$; at lower T, solubility increases.

13.3 $S_{N_2} = (7\times10^{-4} \text{ mol/L} \cdot \text{atm}) (0.78 \text{ atm})$

$= 5\times10^{-4} \text{ mol/L}$

13.4 Mass (g) of glucose

$= 563 \text{ g ethanol} \times \dfrac{1 \text{ kg}}{10^3 \text{ g}}$

$\times \dfrac{2.40\times10^{-2} \text{ mol glucose}}{1 \text{ kg ethanol}} \times \dfrac{180.16 \text{ g glucose}}{1 \text{ mol glucose}}$

$= 2.43 \text{ g glucose}$

13.5 Mass % $C_3H_7OH = \dfrac{35.0 \text{ g}}{35.0 \text{ g} + 150.0 \text{ g}} \times 100$

$= 18.9 \text{ mass \%}$

Mass % $C_2H_5OH = 100.0 - 18.9 = 81.1 \text{ mass \%}$

$X_{C_3H_7OH} = \dfrac{35.0 \text{ g } C_3H_7OH \times \dfrac{1 \text{ mol } C_3H_7OH}{60.09 \text{ g } C_3H_7OH}}{\left(35.0 \text{ g } C_3H_7OH \times \dfrac{1 \text{ mol } C_3H_7OH}{60.09 \text{ g } C_3H_7OH}\right) + \left(150.0 \text{ g } C_2H_5OH \times \dfrac{1 \text{ mol } C_2H_5OH}{46.07 \text{ g } C_2H_5OH}\right)} = 0.152$

$X_{C_2H_5OH} = 1.000 - 0.152 = 0.848$

13.6 Mass % HCl $= \dfrac{\text{mass of HCl}}{\text{mass of soln}} \times 100$

$= \dfrac{\dfrac{11.8 \text{ mol HCl}}{1 \text{ L soln}} \times \dfrac{36.46 \text{ g HCl}}{1 \text{ mol HCl}}}{\dfrac{1.190 \text{ g}}{1 \text{ mL soln}} \times \dfrac{10^3 \text{ mL}}{1 \text{ L}}} \times 100$

$= 36.2 \text{ mass \% HCl}$

Mass (kg) of soln $= 1 \text{ L soln} \times \dfrac{1.190\times10^{-3} \text{ kg soln}}{1\times10^{-3} \text{ L soln}}$

$= 1.190 \text{ kg soln}$

Mass (kg) of HCl $= 11.8 \text{ mol HCl} \times \dfrac{36.46 \text{ g HCl}}{1 \text{ mol HCl}} \times \dfrac{1 \text{ kg}}{10^3 \text{ g}}$

$= 0.430 \text{ kg HCl}$

Molality of HCl $= \dfrac{\text{mol HCl}}{\text{kg water}} = \dfrac{\text{mol HCl}}{\text{kg soln} - \text{kg HCl}}$

$= \dfrac{11.8 \text{ mol HCl}}{0.760 \text{ kg } H_2O} = 15.5 \text{ } m \text{ HCl}$

$X_{HCl} = \dfrac{\text{mol HCl}}{\text{mol HCl} + \text{mol } H_2O}$

$= \dfrac{11.8 \text{ mol}}{11.8 \text{ mol} + \left(760 \text{ g } H_2O \times \dfrac{1 \text{ mol}}{18.02 \text{ g } H_2O}\right)}$

$= 0.219$

13.7 $\Delta P = X_{aspirin} \times P^0_{methanol}$

$= \dfrac{\dfrac{2.00 \text{ g}}{180.15 \text{ g/mol}}}{\dfrac{2.00 \text{ g}}{180.15 \text{ g/mol}} + \dfrac{50.00 \text{ g}}{32.04 \text{ g/mol}}} \times 101 \text{ torr}$

$= 0.713 \text{ torr}$

13.8 $m = \dfrac{(0.00°F - 32°F)\left(\dfrac{5°C}{9°F}\right)}{1.86°C/m} = 9.56 \text{ } m$

13.9 $\Pi = MRT$

$= 0.30 \text{ mol/L} \left(0.0821 \dfrac{\text{atm} \cdot \text{L}}{\text{mol} \cdot \text{K}}\right) (273.15 \text{ K} + 37)$

$= 7.6 \text{ atm}$

Problems

Problems with a **colored** number are answered at the back of the text. Problem sections match the text and provide the number(s) of relevant sample problems. Most offer concept review questions, skill-building exercises (written in similar pairs), and problems in a relevant context. Following these are comprehensive problems based on material from any section and/or previous chapter.

Types of Solutions: Intermolecular Forces and the Prediction of Solubility

(Sample Problem 13.1)

■ Concept Review Questions

13.1 Use the properties of seawater to describe the two characteristics that define mixtures.

13.2 What types of intermolecular forces give rise to hydration shells in an aqueous solution of sodium chloride?

13.3 Acetic acid is miscible with water. Would you expect carboxylic acids, general formula $CH_3(CH_2)_nCOOH$, to become more or less water soluble as n increases? Explain.

13.4 Which would you expect to be more effective as a soap, sodium acetate or sodium stearate? Explain.

13.5 Hexane and methanol are miscible as gases but only slightly soluble in each other as liquids. Explain.

13.6 Hydrogen chloride (HCl) gas is much more soluble than propane gas (C_3H_8) in water, even though HCl has a lower boiling point. Explain.

■ Skill-Building Exercises (paired)

13.7 Which gives the more concentrated solution, (a) KNO_3 in H_2O or (b) KNO_3 in carbon tetrachloride (CCl_4)? Explain.

13.8 Which gives the more concentrated solution, (a) stearic acid [$CH_3(CH_2)_{16}COOH$] in H_2O or (b) stearic acid in CCl_4? Explain.

13.9 What is the strongest type of intermolecular force between solute and solvent in each solution?
(a) $CsCl(s)$ in $H_2O(l)$
(b) $CH_3\overset{\displaystyle O}{\overset{\displaystyle \|}{C}}CH_3(l)$ in $H_2O(l)$
(c) $CH_3OH(l)$ in $CCl_4(l)$

13.10 What is the strongest type of intermolecular force between solute and solvent in each solution?
(a) $Cu(s)$ in $Ag(s)$
(b) $CH_3Cl(g)$ in $CH_3OCH_3(g)$
(c) $CH_3CH_3(g)$ in $CH_3CH_2CH_2NH_2(l)$

13.11 What is the strongest type of intermolecular force between solute and solvent in each solution?
(a) $CH_3OCH_3(g)$ in $H_2O(l)$
(b) $Ne(g)$ in $H_2O(l)$
(c) $N_2(g)$ in $C_4H_{10}(g)$

13.12 What is the strongest type of intermolecular force between solute and solvent in each solution?
(a) $C_6H_{14}(l)$ in $C_8H_{18}(l)$
(b) $H_2C{=}O(g)$ in $CH_3OH(l)$
(c) $Br_2(l)$ in $CCl_4(l)$

13.13 Which member of each pair is more soluble in diethyl ether? Why?
(a) $NaCl(s)$ or $HCl(g)$
(b) $H_2O(l)$ or $CH_3\overset{\displaystyle O}{\overset{\displaystyle \|}{C}}H(l)$
(c) $MgBr_2(s)$ or $CH_3CH_2MgBr(s)$

13.14 Which member of each pair is more soluble in water? Why?
(a) $CH_3CH_2OCH_2CH_3(l)$ or $CH_3CH_2OCH_3(g)$
(b) $CH_2Cl_2(l)$ or $CCl_4(l)$
(c)

cyclohexane   or   tetrahydropyran

■ Problems in Context

13.15 The dictionary defines "homogeneous" as "uniform in composition throughout." River water is a mixture of dissolved compounds, such as calcium bicarbonate, and suspended soil particles. Is river water homogeneous? Explain.

13.16 Gluconic acid is a derivative of glucose used in cleaners and in the dairy and brewing industries. Caproic acid is a short-chain fatty acid used in the flavoring industry. Although both are six-carbon acids (see structures), gluconic acid is soluble in water and nearly insoluble in hexane, whereas caproic acid has the opposite solubility behavior. Explain.

gluconic acid

caproic acid

Energy Changes in the Solution Process

■ Concept Review Questions

13.17 What is the relationship between solvation and hydration?

13.18 For a general solvent, which enthalpy terms in the solution cycle are combined to obtain $\Delta H_{solvation}$?

13.19 (a) What is the charge density of an ion, and what two properties of an ion affect it?
(b) Arrange the following in order of increasing charge density:

(c) How do the two properties in part (a) affect the ionic heat of hydration, ΔH_{hydr}?

13.20 For ΔH_{soln} to be zero (or very small), what quantities must be nearly equal in magnitude? Would their signs be the same or opposite?

13.21 Aside from stacks of coins being shaken, as mentioned in the text, describe three common systems undergoing an increase in entropy.

13.22 A flask containing solid NH_4Cl becomes colder as water is added and the salt dissolves.
(a) Is the dissolving of NH_4Cl in water exothermic or endothermic?
(b) Is the magnitude of $\Delta H_{lattice}$ of NH_4Cl larger or smaller than the ΔH_{hydr} of the ions? Explain.
(c) Given the answer to part (a), why does NH_4Cl dissolve in water?

13.23 An ionic compound has a highly negative heat of solution in water. Would you expect it to be very soluble or nearly insoluble in water? Explain in terms of enthalpy and entropy changes.

■ Skill-Building Exercises (paired)

13.24 Sketch a qualitative enthalpy diagram for the process of dissolving $KCl(s)$ in H_2O (endothermic).

13.25 Sketch a qualitative enthalpy diagram for the process of dissolving $NaI(s)$ in H_2O (exothermic).

13.26 Which ion in each pair has the greater charge density? Explain.
(a) Na^+ or Cs^+ (b) Sr^{2+} or Rb^+
(c) Na^+ or Cl^- (d) O^{2-} or F^-
(e) OH^- or SH^-

13.27 Which ion has the lower ratio of charge to ionic volume? Explain.
(a) Br^- or I^- (b) Sc^{3+} or Ca^{2+}
(c) Br^- or K^+ (d) S^{2-} or Cl^-
(e) Sc^{3+} or Al^{3+}

13.28 Which ion in each pair of Problem 13.26 has the *larger* ΔH_{hydr}?

13.29 Which ion in each pair of Problem 13.27 has the *smaller* ΔH_{hydr}?

13.30 (a) Use the following data to calculate the combined heats of hydration for the ions in potassium bromate ($KBrO_3$):

$$\Delta H_{lattice} = -745 \text{ kJ/mol} \qquad \Delta H_{soln} = 41.1 \text{ kJ/mol}$$

(b) Which ion do you think contributes more to the answer to part (a)? Why?

13.31 (a) Use the following data to calculate the combined heats of hydration for the ions in sodium acetate ($NaC_2H_3O_2$):

$$\Delta H_{lattice} = -763 \text{ kJ/mol} \qquad \Delta H_{soln} = 17.3 \text{ kJ/mol}$$

(b) Which ion do you think contributes more to the answer to part (a)? Why?

13.32 State whether the entropy of the system increases or decreases in each of the following processes:
(a) A glass vase is shattered.
(b) Gold is extracted and purified from its ore.
(c) Ethanol (CH_3CH_2OH) dissolves in propanol ($CH_3CH_2CH_2OH$).
(d) "Bugs" in a computer program are eliminated.

13.33 State whether the entropy of the system increases or decreases in each of the following processes:
(a) Pure gases are mixed to prepare an anesthetic.
(b) Electronic-grade silicon is prepared from sand.
(c) Dry ice (solid CO_2) sublimes.
(d) Gasoline is burned in a car engine.

■ Problems in Context

13.34 Silver nitrate is used industrially to produce silver halides for photographic film and in forensic science to accomplish a similar task. The sodium chloride left behind in the sweat of a fingerprint is treated with silver nitrate solution to form silver chloride. This precipitate is then developed to show the black-and-white fingerprint. Given that the lattice energy of silver nitrate is -822 kJ/mol and its heat of hydration is -799 kJ/mol, calculate its heat of solution.

Solubility as an Equilibrium Process
(Sample Problems 13.2 and 13.3)

■ Concept Review Questions

13.35 You are given a bottle of solid X and three aqueous solutions of X, one saturated, one unsaturated, and one supersaturated. How would you determine which solution is which?

13.36 Potassium permanganate ($KMnO_4$) has a solubility of 6.4 g/100 g H_2O at 20°C and a positive heat of solution. How would you prepare a supersaturated solution of $KMnO_4$?

13.37 Why does the solubility of any gas in water decrease with rising temperature?

■ Skill-Building Exercises (paired)

13.38 The heat of solution for NaI in water is -7.5 kJ/mol. Is NaI more soluble at 20°C or at 60°C? Why?

13.39 Cesium bromide has a heat of solution of 26.0 kJ/mol. How does its solubility in water at 50°C compare with that at 25°C? Why?

13.40 Consider the following solubility data (in units of g solute/100 g H_2O):

SOLUTE	10°C	20°C
$AgNO_3$	170	222
Li_2CO_3	1.43	1.33
O_2	0.0054	0.0044

(a) What is the sign of ΔH_{soln} for each solute?
(b) Write a reaction for dissolution of each solute, with heat as reactant or product.

13.41 Consider the following solubility data (in units of g solute/100 g H_2O):

SOLUTE	0°C	50°C
$AgC_2H_3O_2$	0.72	1.6
$CO_2(g)$ at 1.0 atm	0.35	0.08
Valine	8.34	9.62

(a) State whether each solution process is exothermic or endothermic.

(b) Write a reaction for dissolution of each solute, showing heat absorbed or released.

13.42 For a saturated aqueous solution of each of the following at 20°C and 1 atm, will the solubility increase, decrease, or stay the same when the indicated change occurs?

(a) $O_2(g)$, increase P

(b) $N_2(g)$, increase V

(c) $KCl(s)$ ($\Delta H_{soln} > 0$), decrease T

13.43 For a saturated aqueous solution of each of the following at 20°C and 1 atm, will the solubility increase, decrease, or stay the same when the indicated change occurs?

(a) $He(g)$, decrease T

(b) $NaOH(s)$ ($\Delta H_{soln} < 0$), increase T

(c) $RbI(s)$ ($\Delta H_{soln} > 0$), increase P

13.44 The Henry's law constant (k_H) for O_2 in water at 20°C is 1.28×10^{-3} mol/L · atm.

(a) How many grams of O_2 will dissolve in 2.00 L H_2O that is in contact with pure O_2 at 1.00 atm?

(b) How many grams of O_2 will dissolve in 2.00 L H_2O that is in contact with air, in which the partial pressure of O_2 is 0.209 atm?

13.45 Argon makes up 0.93% by volume of the atmosphere. Calculate its solubility (mol/L) in water at 20°C and 1.0 atm. The Henry's law constant for Ar under these conditions is 1.5×10^{-3} mol/L · atm.

■ Problems in Context

13.46 Caffeine is about 10 times as soluble in hot water as in cold water.

(a) Is ΔH_{soln} of caffeine in water positive or negative?

(b) A chemist puts a hot-water extract of caffeine into an ice bath, and some caffeine crystallizes. Is the remaining solution saturated, unsaturated, or supersaturated?

13.47 The partial pressure of CO_2 gas above the liquid in a bottle of champagne at 20°C is 5.5 atm. What is the solubility of CO_2 in champagne? Assume that the Henry's law constant is the same for champagne as for water; at 20°C, $k_H = 3.7\times10^{-2}$ mol/L · atm.

13.48 Individuals with respiratory problems are often treated with devices that deliver air with a higher partial pressure of O_2 than normal air. Why?

Quantitative Ways of Expressing Concentration

(Sample Problems 13.4 to 13.6)

■ Concept Review Questions

13.49 Explain the difference between molarity and molality. Under what circumstances would molality be a more accurate measure of the prepared concentration of a solution than molarity? Why?

13.50 Which of the different ways of expressing concentration include the following: (a) volume of solution; (b) mass of solution; (c) mass of solvent?

13.51 A solute has a solubility in water of 21 g/kg solvent. Is this value the same as 21 g/kg solution? Explain.

13.52 You want to convert among molarity, molality, and mole fraction of a solution. You know the masses of solute and solvent and the volume of solution. Is this enough information to carry out all the conversions? Explain.

13.53 When a solution is heated, which of the values for the different ways of expressing concentration change? Which remain unchanged? Explain.

■ Skill-Building Exercises (paired)

13.54 Calculate the molarity of the following aqueous solutions:

(a) 42.3 g table sugar ($C_{12}H_{22}O_{11}$) in 100. mL solution

(b) 5.50 g $LiNO_3$ in 505 mL solution

13.55 Calculate the molarity of the following aqueous solutions:

(a) 0.82 g ethanol (C_2H_5OH) in 10.5 mL solution

(b) 1.22 g gaseous NH_3 dissolved in water to make 33.5 mL solution

13.56 Calculate the molarity of the following aqueous solutions:

(a) 75.0 mL of 0.250 M NaOH diluted to 0.250 L with water

(b) 35.5 mL of 1.3 M HNO_3 diluted to 0.150 L with water

13.57 Calculate the molarity of the following aqueous solutions:

(a) 25.0 mL of 6.15 M HCl diluted to 0.500 L with water

(b) 8.55 mL of 2.00×10^{-2} M KI diluted to 10.0 mL with water

13.58 How would you prepare the following aqueous solutions?

(a) 355 mL of 8.74×10^{-2} M KH_2PO_4 from solid KH_2PO_4

(b) 425 mL of 0.315 M NaOH from 1.25 M NaOH

13.59 How would you prepare the following aqueous solutions?

(a) 3.5 L of 0.55 M NaCl from solid NaCl

(b) 17.5 L of 0.3 M urea [$(NH_2)_2C{=}O$] from 2.2 M urea

13.60 How would you prepare the following aqueous solutions?

(a) 1.50 L of 0.257 M KBr from solid KBr

(b) 355 mL of 0.0956 M $LiNO_3$ from 0.244 M $LiNO_3$

13.61 How would you prepare the following aqueous solutions?

(a) 67.5 mL of 1.33×10^{-3} M $Cr(NO_3)_3$ from solid $Cr(NO_3)_3$

(b) 6.8×10^3 m^3 of 1.55 M NH_4NO_3 from 3.00 M NH_4NO_3

13.62 Calculate the molality of the following:

(a) A solution containing 88.4 g glycine (NH_2CH_2COOH) dissolved in 1.250 kg H_2O

(b) A solution containing 8.89 g glycerol ($C_3H_8O_3$) in 75.0 g ethanol (C_2H_6O)

13.63 Calculate the molality of the following:

(a) A solution containing 164 g HCl in 753 g H_2O

(b) A solution containing 16.5 g naphthalene ($C_{10}H_8$) in 53.3 g benzene (C_6H_6)

13.64 What is the molality of a solution consisting of 34.0 mL benzene (C_6H_6; $d = 0.877$ g/mL) in 187 mL hexane (C_6H_{14}; $d = 0.660$ g/mL)?

13.65 What is the molality of a solution consisting of 2.77 mL carbon tetrachloride (CCl_4; $d = 1.59$ g/mL) in 79.5 mL methylene chloride (CH_2Cl_2; $d = 1.33$ g/mL)?

13.66 How would you prepare the following aqueous solutions?
(a) 3.00×10^2 g of 0.115 m ethylene glycol ($C_2H_6O_2$) from ethylene glycol and water
(b) 1.00 kg of 2.00 mass % HNO_3 from 62.0 mass % HNO_3

13.67 How would you prepare the following aqueous solutions?
(a) 1.00 kg of 0.0555 m ethanol (C_2H_5OH) from ethanol and water
(b) 475 g of 15.0 mass % HCl from 37.1 mass % HCl

13.68 A solution of isopropanol (C_3H_7OH) is made by dissolving 0.30 mol isopropanol in 0.80 mol water.
(a) What is the mole fraction of isopropanol?
(b) What is the mass percent of isopropanol?
(c) What is the molality of isopropanol?

13.69 A solution is made by dissolving 0.100 mol NaCl in 8.60 mol water.
(a) What is the mole fraction of NaCl?
(b) What is the mass percent of NaCl?
(c) What is the molality of NaCl?

13.70 What mass of cesium chloride must be added to 0.500 L water to produce a 0.400 m solution? What are the mole fraction and the mass percent of CsCl? (Assume d of $H_2O = 1.00$ g/mL.)

13.71 What are the mole fraction and the mass percent of a solution made by dissolving 0.30 g KBr in 0.400 L water? ($d = 1.00$ g/mL.)

13.72 An 8.00 mass % aqueous solution of ammonia has a density of 0.9651 g/mL. Calculate the molality, molarity, and mole fraction of NH_3.

13.73 A 28.8 mass % aqueous solution of iron(III) chloride has a density of 1.280 g/mL. Calculate the molality, molarity, and mole fraction of $FeCl_3$.

■ **Problems in Context**

13.74 Wastewater from a cement factory contains 0.22 g Ca^{2+} ion and 0.066 g Mg^{2+} ion per 100.0 L solution. The solution density is 1.001 g/mL. Calculate the Ca^{2+} and Mg^{2+} concentrations in ppm (by mass).

13.75 An automobile antifreeze mixture is made by mixing equal volumes of ethylene glycol ($d = 1.114$ g/mL; $\mathcal{M} = 62.07$ g/mol) and water ($d = 1.00$ g/mL) at 20°C. The density of the mixture is 1.070 g/mL. Express the concentration of ethylene glycol in each of the following:
(a) volume percent
(b) mass percent
(c) molarity
(d) molality
(e) mole fraction

Colligative Properties of Solutions
(Sample Problems 13.7 to 13.9)

■ **Concept Review Questions**

13.76 The composition (chemical formula) of a solute does *not* affect the extent of the solution's colligative properties. What characteristic of a solute *does* affect these properties? Name a physical property of a solution that *is* affected by the composition of the solute.

13.77 What is a nonvolatile nonelectrolyte? Why does this type of solute provide the simplest case for examining colligative properties?

13.78 In what sense is a strong electrolyte "strong"? What property of the substance makes it a strong electrolyte?

13.79 Express Raoult's law in words. Is Raoult's law valid for a solution of a volatile solute? Explain.

13.80 What are the most important differences between the phase diagram of a pure solvent and the phase diagram of a solution of that solvent?

13.81 Is the composition of the vapor at the top of a fractionating column different from the composition at the bottom? Explain.

13.82 Is the boiling point of 0.01 m KF(aq) higher or lower than that of 0.01 m glucose(aq)? Explain.

13.83 Which aqueous solution has a boiling point closer to its predicted value, 0.050 m NaF or 0.50 m KCl? Explain.

13.84 Which aqueous solution has a freezing point closer to its predicted value, 0.01 m NaBr or 0.01 m $MgCl_2$? Explain.

13.85 The freezing point depression constants of the solvents cyclohexane and naphthalene are 20.1°C/m and 6.94°C/m, respectively. Which would give a more accurate determination by freezing point depression of the molar mass of a substance that is soluble in either solvent? Why?

■ **Skill-Building Exercises (paired)**

13.86 Classify the following substances as strong electrolytes, weak electrolytes, or nonelectrolytes:
(a) hydrogen chloride (HCl)
(b) potassium nitrate (KNO_3)
(c) glucose ($C_6H_{12}O_6$)
(d) ammonia (NH_3)

13.87 Classify the following substances as strong electrolytes, weak electrolytes, or nonelectrolytes:
(a) sodium permanganate ($NaMnO_4$)
(b) acetic acid (CH_3COOH)
(c) methanol (CH_3OH)
(d) calcium acetate [$Ca(C_2H_3O_2)_2$]

13.88 How many moles of solute particles are present in 1 L of the following aqueous solutions?
(a) 0.2 M KI
(b) 0.070 M HNO_3
(c) 10^{-4} M K_2SO_4
(d) 0.07 M ethanol (C_2H_5OH)

13.89 How many moles of solute particles are present in 1 mL of the following aqueous solutions?
(a) 0.01 M $CuSO_4$
(b) 0.005 M $Ba(OH)_2$

(c) 0.06 M pyridine (C_5H_5N)

(d) 0.05 M (NH_4)$_2CO_3$

13.90 Which of the following solutions has the lower freezing point?

(a) 10.0 g CH_3OH in 100. g H_2O *or*

20.0 g CH_3CH_2OH in 200. g H_2O

(b) 10.0 g H_2O in 1.00 kg CH_3OH *or*

10.0 g CH_3CH_2OH in 1.00 kg CH_3OH

13.91 Which of the following solutions has the higher boiling point?

(a) 35.0 g $C_3H_8O_3$ in 250. g ethanol   *or*

35.0 g $C_2H_6O_2$ in 250. g ethanol

(b) 20. g $C_2H_6O_2$ in 0.50 kg H_2O *or*

20. g NaCl in 0.50 kg H_2O

13.92 Rank the following aqueous solutions

(I)   0.100 m $NaNO_3$

(II) 0.200 m glucose

(III) 0.100 m $CaCl_2$

in order of increasing (a) osmotic pressure; (b) boiling point; (c) freezing point; (d) vapor pressure at 50°C.

13.93 Rank the following aqueous solutions

(I)   0.04 m urea [(NH_2)$_2$C=O]

(II) 0.02 m $AgNO_3$

(III) 0.02 m $CuSO_4$

in order of decreasing (a) osmotic pressure; (b) boiling point; (c) freezing point; (d) vapor pressure at 298 K.

13.94 Calculate the vapor pressure of a solution of 44.0 g glycerol ($C_3H_8O_3$) in 500.0 g water at 25°C. The vapor pressure of water at 25°C is 23.76 torr. (Assume ideal behavior.)

13.95 Calculate the vapor pressure of a solution of 0.39 mol cholesterol in 5.4 mol toluene at 32°C. Pure toluene has a vapor pressure of 41 torr at this temperature. (Assume ideal behavior.)

13.96 What is the freezing point of 0.111 m urea in water?

13.97 What is the boiling point of 0.200 m lactose in water?

13.98 The boiling point of ethanol (C_2H_5OH) is 78.5°C. What is the boiling point of a solution of 3.4 g vanillin ($\mathcal{M}$ = 152.14 g/mol) in 50.0 g ethanol? (K_b of ethanol = 1.22°C/m.)

13.99 The freezing point of benzene is 5.5°C. What is the freezing point of a solution of 5.00 g naphthalene ($C_{10}H_8$) in 444 g benzene? (K_f of benzene = 4.90°C/m.)

13.100 What is the minimum mass of ethylene glycol ($C_2H_6O_2$) that must be dissolved in 14.5 kg water to prevent the solution from freezing at −10.0°F? (Assume ideal behavior.)

13.101 What is the minimum mass of glycerol ($C_3H_8O_3$) that must be dissolved in 11.0 mg water to prevent the solution from freezing at −25°C? (Assume ideal behavior.)

13.102 Calculate the molality and van't Hoff factor i for the following aqueous solutions:

(a) 1.00 mass % NaCl, freezing point = −0.593°C

(b) 0.500 mass % CH_3COOH, freezing point = −0.159°C

13.103 Calculate the molality and van't Hoff factor i for the following aqueous solutions:

(a) 0.500 mass % KCl, freezing point = −0.234°C

(b) 1.00 mass % H_2SO_4, freezing point = −0.423°C

■ **Problems in Context**

13.104 Wastewater discharged into a stream by a sugar refinery contains sucrose ($C_{12}H_{22}O_{11}$) as its main impurity. The solution contains 3.42 g sucrose/L. A government-industry project is designed to test the feasibility of removing the sugar by reverse osmosis. What pressure must be applied to the apparatus at 20°C to produce pure water?

13.105 In a study designed to prepare new gasoline-resistant coatings, a polymer chemist dissolves 6.053 g poly(vinyl alcohol) in enough water to make 100.0 mL solution. At 25°C, the osmotic pressure of this solution vs. pure water is 0.272 atm. What is the molar mass of the polymer sample?

13.106 The U.S. Food and Drug Administration lists dichloromethane (CH_2Cl_2) and carbon tetrachloride (CCl_4) among the many chlorinated organic compounds that are carcinogenic. What are the partial pressures of these substances in the vapor above a solution of 1.50 mol CH_2Cl_2 and 1.00 mol CCl_4 at 23.5°C? The vapor pressures of pure CH_2Cl_2 and CCl_4 at this temperature are 352 torr and 118 torr, respectively. (Assume ideal behavior.)

The Structure and Properties of Colloids

■ **Concept Review Questions**

13.107 Is the fluid inside a bacterial cell considered a solution, a colloid, or both? Explain.

13.108 What type of colloid is each of the following?

(a) milk

(b) fog

(c) shaving cream

13.109 What is Brownian motion, and what causes it?

13.110 In a movie theater, you can often see the beam of projected light. What phenomenon does this exemplify? Why does it occur?

13.111 Why don't soap micelles coagulate and form large globules? Is soap a more effective cleaner in freshwater or in seawater? Why?

Comprehensive Problems

Problems with an asterisk (*) are more challenging.

13.112 Nitrous oxide (N_2O) is used in whipped cream containers as the gas that makes the cream foam. Some experiments to use carbon dioxide (CO_2) instead have proven unsuccessful. What does this suggest about the relative sizes of the Henry's law constant for N_2O and CO_2 in cream? Explain.

13.113 An aqueous solution is 10.% glucose by mass (d = 1.039 g/mL at 20°C). Calculate its freezing point, boiling point at 1 atm, and osmotic pressure.

13.114 Gramicidin A is a common antibiotic. If the molecule were polar on the outside and nonpolar on the inside, would its function be affected? Explain.

13.115 Which of the following simple depictions best represents a molecular view of an ionic compound in aqueous solution? Explain.

(a) (b) (c)

13.116 Solutes elevate the boiling point of a solvent but depress the freezing point. Explain in molecular terms.

13.117 Gold occurs in seawater at an average concentration of 1.1×10^{-2} ppb. How many liters of seawater must be processed to recover 1 troy ounce of gold, assuming 79.5% efficiency? (d of seawater = 1.025 g/mL; 1 troy ounce = 31.1 g.)

13.118 Use atomic properties to explain why xenon is more than 25 times as soluble as helium in water at 0°C.

13.119 The text points out that molality and molarity are nearly the same for dilute aqueous solutions. Is this true for nonaqueous solvents as well? Explain.

13.120 Pyridine (see structure) is an essential portion of many biologically active compounds, such as nicotine and vitamin B_6. Like ammonia, it has a lone pair on N, which makes it act as a weak base. Because it is miscible in a wide range of solvents, from water to benzene, pyridine is one of the most important bases and solvents in organic syntheses. Account for its solubility behavior in terms of intermolecular forces.

pyridine

13.121 The solubility of a particular ionic compound increases with rising temperature. Is the lattice energy larger or smaller than the heat of hydration? Explain.

13.122 A mixture of solid NaCl and saturated NaCl solution at 2°C is warmed slowly with constant stirring. The solid is completely dissolved at 10°C. The solution is cooled slowly to 5°C and no solid appears. What will happen if a crystal of NaCl is added to this solution? What will happen to the temperature?

13.123 Is a solution that is 50% by mass of methanol in ethanol different from one that is 50% by mass of ethanol in methanol? Explain.

13.124 An industrial chemist is studying small organic compounds for their potential use as an auto antifreeze. When 0.243 g of a compound is dissolved in 25.0 mL water, the freezing point of the solution is −0.201°C.
(a) Calculate the molar mass of the compound. (d of water = 1.00 g/mL at the temperature of the experiment.)
(b) Compositional analysis of the compound gives 53.31 mass % C and 11.18 mass % H, the remainder being O.

Calculate the empirical and molecular formulas of the compound.
(c) Draw two possible Lewis structures for a compound with this formula, one that forms H bonds and one that does not.

13.125 Use the concept of osmotic pressure to explain why drinking seawater does not quench your thirst.

13.126 Give brief answers for each of the following:
(a) Why are lime (CaO) and alum [$Al_2(SO_4)_3$] added during water purification?
(b) Why is water that contains large amounts of Ca^{2+}, Mg^{2+}, or Fe^{2+} difficult to use for cleaning?
(c) What is the meaning of "reverse" in reverse osmosis?
(d) Why might a water treatment plant use ozone as the final disinfectant instead of chlorine, even though ozone is more expensive?
(e) How does passing a saturated NaCl solution through a "spent" ion-exchange resin regenerate the resin?

13.127 Which ion in each pair has the *larger* ΔH_{hydr}?
(a) Mg^{2+} or Ba^{2+}
(b) Mg^{2+} or Na^+
(c) NO_3^- or CO_3^{2-}
(d) SO_4^{2-} or ClO_4^-
(e) Fe^{3+} or Fe^{2+}
(f) Ca^{2+} or K^+

13.128 β-Pinene ($C_{10}H_{16}$) and α-terpineol ($C_{10}H_{18}O$) are two of the many compounds used in perfumes and cosmetics to provide a "fresh pine" scent. At 367 K, the pure substances have vapor pressures of 100.3 torr and 9.8 torr, respectively. What is the composition of the vapor (in terms of mole fractions) above a solution containing equal masses of these compounds at 367 K? (Assume ideal behavior.)

*13.129 A solution is prepared by dissolving 1.50 g of a compound in 25.0 mL H_2O at 25°C. The boiling point of the solution is 100.45°C.
(a) What is the molar mass of the compound if it is a nonvolatile nonelectrolyte and the solution behaves ideally? (d of H_2O at 25°C = 0.997 g/mL.)
(b) Independent conductivity measurements indicate that the compound is actually ionic with general formula AB_2 or A_2B. What is the molar mass of the compound if the solution behaves ideally?
(c) Compositional analysis indicates an empirical formula of CaN_2O_6. Explain the difference between the actual formula mass and that calculated from the boiling point elevation experiment.
(d) Calculate the van't Hoff factor i for this solution.

*13.130 A pharmaceutical preparation made with ethanol (C_2H_5OH) is contaminated with methanol (CH_3OH). A sample of vapor above the liquid mixture is found to contain a 97:1 mass ratio of $C_2H_5OH:CH_3OH$. What is the mass ratio of these alcohols in the liquid? At the temperature of the liquid, the vapor pressures of C_2H_5OH and CH_3OH are 60.5 torr and 126.0 torr, respectively.

13.131 The conversion of NaCl(s) to $Na^+(g)$ and $Cl^-(g)$ in Figure 13.7A requires a very large quantity of energy and, of course, does not actually occur when table salt dissolves in water. Why, then, does it appear in the solution cycle?

13.132 A saturated Na_2CO_3 solution is prepared, and a small excess of solid is present. A seed crystal of $Na_2{}^{14}CO_3$ is introduced (^{14}C is a radioactive isotope of ^{12}C), and the radioactivity is measured over time (see figure).

Excess solid Na_2CO_3 — Saturated Na_2CO_3 soln — Seed crystal of radioactive $Na_2{}^{14}CO_3$

(a) Would you expect to find radioactivity in the solution? Explain.
(b) Would you expect to find radioactivity in all the solid or just in the seed crystal? Explain.

13.133 A biochemical engineer isolates a bacterial gene fragment and dissolves a 10.0-mg sample of the material in enough water to make 30.0 mL solution. The osmotic pressure of the solution is 0.340 torr at 25°C.
(a) What is the molar mass of the gene fragment?
(b) If the solution density is 0.997 g/mL, how large is the freezing point depression for this solution? (K_f of water = 1.86°C/m.)

13.134 A river is contaminated with 0.75 mg/L of dichloroethylene ($C_2H_2Cl_2$). What is the concentration of dichloroethylene (in ng/L) at 21°C in the air breathed by the people sitting along the riverbank? The Henry's law constant for dichloroethylene in water is 0.033 mol/L · atm.

13.135 A simple device used for estimating the concentration of total dissolved solids in an aqueous solution works by measuring the electrical conductivity of the solution. The method assumes that equal concentrations of different solids give approximately the same conductivity, and that the conductivity is proportional to concentration. The table below gives some actual electrical conductivities (in arbitrary units) for solutions of selected solids at the indicated concentrations (in ppm by mass):

SAMPLE	CONDUCTIVITY		
	0 ppm	5.00×10³ ppm	10.00×10³ ppm
$CaCl_2$	0.0	8.0	16.0
K_2CO_3	0.0	7.0	14.0
Na_2SO_4	0.0	6.0	11.0
Seawater (dil.)	0.0	8.0	15.0
Sucrose ($C_{12}H_{22}O_{11}$)	0.0	0.0	0.0
Urea [$(NH_2)_2C{=}O$]	0.0	0.0	0.0

(a) Comment on the reliability of these measurements for estimating concentrations of dissolved solids.
(b) For what types of substances is this method likely to be seriously in error? Why?
(c) Based on this method, an aqueous $CaCl_2$ solution has a conductivity of 14.0 units. Calculate its mole fraction and molality.

*13.136 Two beakers are placed in a closed container (see figure, left). One beaker contains water, the other a concentrated aqueous sugar solution. With time, the solution volume increases and the water volume decreases (right). Explain on the molecular level.

time

Water — Sugar solution — Water — Sugar solution

13.137 Sulfur dioxide is a major air pollutant that forms from the combustion of high-sulfur coal. It becomes oxidized to sulfur trioxide in the atmosphere and falls as acid rain in contact with water. Unlike most other nonpolar gases, sulfur trioxide is very soluble in water. Write a balanced equation that demonstrates this fact.

13.138 How would you prepare 250. g of 0.150 m aqueous $NaHCO_3$?

13.139 Tartaric acid can be produced from crystalline residues found in wine vats. It is used in baking powders and as an additive in foods. Analysis shows that it contains 32.3 mass % carbon and 3.97 mass % hydrogen; the balance is oxygen. When 0.981 g tartaric acid is dissolved in 11.23 g water, the solution freezes at −1.26°C. Use these data to find the empirical and molecular formulas of tartaric acid.

13.140 A chemist purifying crude potassium chlorate ($KClO_3$) by recrystallization prepares a saturated solution of the salt in boiling water, filters any undissolved solids, and cools the filtrate to 20°C. Pure $KClO_3$ crystallizes out.
(a) Use the solubility data of Figure 13.11 to predict the % recovery for the recrystallization process. (In this context, the % recovery is 100. times the mass of salt recovered divided by the original mass of salt that dissolved in the hot solvent.)
(b) If the original sample of $KClO_3$ weighs 15.0 g, what mass can be recovered in this process?
(c) Referring again to Figure 13.11, suggest how the chemist might recrystallize $Ce_2(SO_4)_3$ from water.
(d) Is the solution process for $KClO_3$ exothermic or endothermic? What is the sign of ΔH_{soln} for $Ce_2(SO_4)_3$?

13.141 Carbon dioxide is less soluble in dilute HCl(aq) than in dilute NaOH(aq). Explain.

*13.142 Derive a general equation that expresses the relationship between the molarity and the molality of a solution, and use it to explain why the numerical values of these two terms are approximately equal for very dilute aqueous solutions.

*13.143 A florist prepares a solution of nitrogen-phosphorus fertilizer by dissolving 5.66 g NH_4NO_3 and 4.42 g $(NH_4)_3PO_4$ in enough water to make 20.0 L solution. What are the molarities of $NH_4{}^+$ and of $PO_4{}^{3-}$ in the solution?

13.144 Urea is a white crystalline solid that has uses as a fertilizer, in the pharmaceutical industry, and in the manufacture of certain polymer resins. Analysis of urea reveals

that it is 20.1% carbon, 6.7% hydrogen, 46.5% nitrogen, by mass, and the balance oxygen.
(a) Calculate the empirical formula of urea.
(b) A 5.0 g/L solution of urea in water has an osmotic pressure of 2.04 atm, measured at 25°C. What is the molar mass and molecular formula of urea?

13.145 The survival of fish in natural waters depends on the solubility of air in the water, which is 0.147 cm^3 of air (measured at STP) per gram of water at 20.°C and 0.10 MPa (megapascal) pressure.
(a) What is the solubility in a mountain stream where the pressure is 0.060 MPa?
(b) Calculate k_H of air in water at 20.°C.
(c) At 20.°C and 0.50 MPa, the solubility is 0.825 cm^3 of air (at STP) per gram of water. What solubility would be calculated from Henry's law? Calculate the error, as a percent of the measured solubility, from relying on Henry's law at this high pressure.

13.146 When making ice cream, the temperature of the ingredients is kept below the freezing point of water with a surrounding ice bath that contains a large amount of salt.
(a) Assuming that it dissolves completely and forms an ideal solution, what mass of NaCl is needed to lower the melting point of 5.5 kg ice to −5.0°C?
(b) Making the same assumptions, calculate the mass of $CaCl_2$ needed.

13.147 Several different ionic compounds are each being recrystallized by the following procedure:
1. A saturated aqueous solution of the compound is prepared at 50°C.

2. The mixture is filtered to remove undissolved compound.
3. The filtrate is cooled to 0°C.
4. The crystals that form are filtered, dried, and weighed.
(a) Using Figure 13.11, which of the following compounds would have the highest % recovery and which the lowest: KNO_3, $KClO_3$, KCl, NaCl? Explain.
(b) Given 100. g of each compound in your answer to
(a), how many grams of each can be recovered?

13.148 An automobile radiator antifreeze must prevent the radiator fluid from freezing in winter and boiling in summer. Ethylene glycol is currently used as an antifreeze, but it is poisonous.
(a) What properties are necessary for a useful antifreeze?
(b) Is ethanol (C_2H_6O) a suitable substitute? Explain.
(c) If glycerol ($C_3H_8O_3$) were used under the same conditions as in Sample Problem 13.8, what would be the freezing and boiling points of the solution? Based on this result, would glycerol be a suitable substitute?

*13.149 The phase diagram of water in Figure 12.9B (p. 432) describes the phase changes when only water is present. Consider how the diagram would change if air were also present at normal atmospheric pressure (about 1 atm) and dissolved in the water.
(a) Would the three phases of water still attain equilibrium at some temperature? Explain.
(b) Would that temperature be higher, lower, or the same as the triple point for pure water? Explain.
(c) Would ice sublime at a few degrees below the freezing point under this pressure? Explain.
(d) Would the liquid have the same vapor pressure at 100°C as that shown in Figure 12.9B? At 120°C?

The dramatic chemical change that occurs when sodium reacts with water is just one example of the countless reactions of the main-group elements. As you have seen, these changes are based on atomic and molecular properties, which we revisit in the overview presented in the upcoming pages.

A Perspective on the Properties of the Elements

Topics

1 **The Key Atomic Properties**
2 **Characteristics of Chemical Bonding**
3 **Metallic Behavior**

4 **Acid-Base Behavior of the Element Oxides**
5 **Redox Behavior of the Elements**
6 **Physical States and Changes of State**

Chemistry has a central, underlying principle: *The behavior of a sample of matter emerges from the properties of its component atoms.* This illustrated Interchapter reviews many ideas about these properties from earlier chapters so that you can see in upcoming chapters how they lead to the behavior of the main-group elements. Keep in mind that, despite our categories, clear dividing lines rarely appear in nature: instead, the periodic properties of matter display gradual changes from one substance to another.

The Key Atomic Properties

Four atomic properties are critical to the behavior of an element: *electron configuration, atomic size, ionization energy,* and *electronegativity.*

Electron configuration ($nl^{\#}$) is the distribution of electrons in the energy levels and sublevels of an atom *(Sections 7.4 and 8.3):*

- The n value (positive integer) indicates the *energy* and *relative distance* from the nucleus of orbitals in a level.
- The l value (and its more commonly used letter designation s, p, d, f) indicates the *shape* of orbitals in the sublevel *(right).*
- The superscript ($^{\#}$) tells the *number* of electrons in the sublevel.

The periodic table above shows the sublevel blocks of elements and the ground-state (lowest energy), outer (valence-level) electron configuration of the main-group (s and p block) elements. Note that

- The **s block** lies to the left of the transition elements and the **p block** lies to the right. [Although H is not an alkali metal, like the elements in Group 1A(1), and He belongs in Group 8A(18), both are part of the s block.]
- Outer electron configurations are *similar within a group.*
- Outer electron configurations are *different within a period.*
- Outer electrons occupy the ns and np sublevels (n = period number).
- Four valence-level orbitals (one ns + three np) occur among the main-group elements.
- Outer electrons *are* the valence electrons of the main-group elements.
- The A-group number (**1A** to **8A**) equals the number of valence electrons.

Electrons in the same and, especially, inner levels *shield* outer electrons from the full nuclear charge. Shielding reduces the attraction they experience to a much lower *effective nuclear charge* (Z_{eff}) *(Section 8.2).* Within a level, electrons that *penetrate* more (spend more time near the nucleus) shield others more effectively. The extent of penetration is in the order $s > p > d > f$. The radial probability distribution curves *(right)* show that

- Inner ($n = 1$) electrons shield outer ($n = 2$) electrons very effectively.
- $2s$ electrons shield $2p$ electrons somewhat because $2s$ electrons spend more time near the nucleus.

Z_{eff} greatly influences atomic properties. In general,

- Z_{eff} increases significantly *across* a period.
- Z_{eff} increases slightly *down* a group.

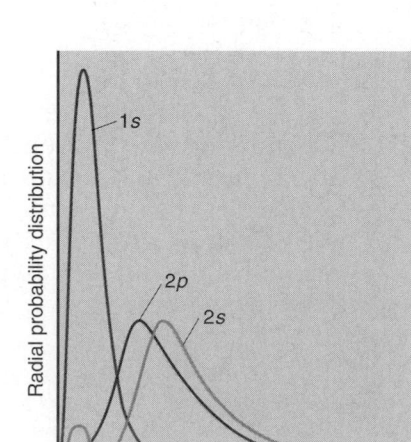

Radial probability distribution

Distance from nucleus

Atomic size is based on atomic radius, one-half the distance between nuclei of identical, bonded atoms *(Section 8.4)*. The small red periodic table shows the trends in atomic size among the main-group elements. Note that

- Atomic size generally *decreases across a period:* increasing Z_{eff} pulls outer electrons closer.
- Atomic size generally *increases down a group:* outer electrons in higher periods lie farther from the nucleus.

Ionization energy (IE) is the energy required to remove the highest energy electron from 1 mol of gaseous atoms *(Section 8.4)*. The relative magnitude of the IE influences the types of bonds an atom forms: an element with a *low IE* is more likely to *lose* electrons, and one with a *high IE* is more likely to *share (or gain)* electrons (excluding the noble gases). From the small yellow periodic table, note that

- IE generally *increases across a period:* higher Z_{eff} holds electrons tighter.
- IE generally *decreases down a group:* greater distance from the nucleus lowers the attraction for electrons.

Thus, the trends in IE are *opposite* those in atomic size: it is easier to remove an electron (lower IE) that is farther from the nucleus (larger atomic size).

Electronegativity (EN) is a number that refers to the relative ability of an atom in a covalent bond to attract shared electrons *(Section 9.4)*. From the small green periodic table, note that

- EN generally *increases across a period:* higher Z_{eff} and shorter distance from the nucleus strengthen the attraction for the shared pair.
- EN generally *decreases down a group:* greater distance from the nucleus weakens the attraction for the shared pair. (Group 8A is not shaded because the noble gases form few compounds.)

Thus, the trends in EN are *opposite* those in atomic size and the *same* as those in IE.

The graph shows simplified plots of atomic size *(red)*, ionization energy *(yellow)*, and electronegativity *(green)* versus atomic number. Note that

- Atomic size decreases gradually within a period *(vertical grey band)* and then increases suddenly at the beginning of the next period.
- IE and EN display the opposite pattern, increasing within a period and decreasing at the beginning of the next period.

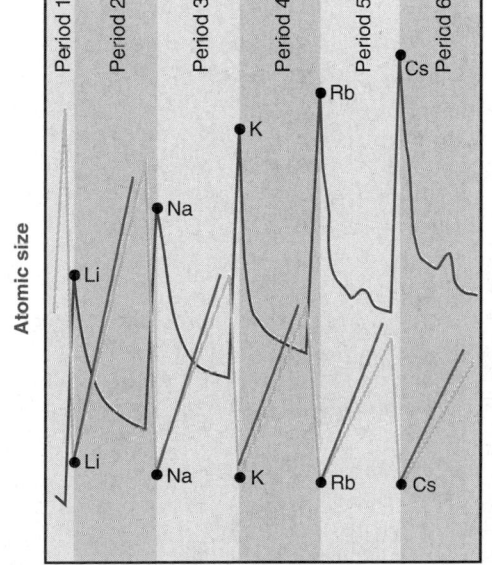

The difference in electronegativity (ΔEN) between the atoms in a bond greatly influences physical and chemical behavior of the compound, as the block diagram shows.

Characteristics of Chemical Bonding

Chemical bonds are the forces that hold atoms (or ions) together in an element or compound. The type of bonding, bond properties, nature of orbital overlap, and number of bonds determine physical and chemical behavior.

Types of Bonding

There are three idealized bonding models: *ionic, covalent,* and *metallic.*

Covalent bonding results from the attraction between two nuclei and a localized electron pair. The bond arises through electron sharing between atoms with a small ΔEN (usually two nonmetals) and leads to discrete molecules with specific shapes or to extended networks *(Section 9.3).*

Ionic bonding results from the attraction between positive and negative ions. The ions arise through electron transfer between atoms with a large ΔEN (from metal to nonmetal). This bonding leads to crystalline solids with ions packed tightly in regular arrays *(Section 9.2).*

Metallic bonding results from the attraction between the cores of metal atoms (metal cations) and their delocalized valence electrons. This bonding arises through the shared pooling of valence electrons from many atoms and leads to crystalline solids *(Sections 9.5 and 12.6).*

The actual bonding in real substances usually lies between these distinct models *(Section 9.4).* The electron density depictions show that electron clouds overlap slightly even in ionic bonding (NaCl). They overlap significantly in polar covalent bonding (an SiCl bond from $SiCl_4$) and completely in nonpolar covalent bonding (Cl_2).

NaCl

SiCl bond in $SiCl_4$

Cl_2

The triangular diagram shows the continuum of bond types among all the Period 3 main-group elements:

- Along the left leg of the triangle, compounds of each element with chlorine display a gradual change from ionic to covalent bonding and a *decrease* in bond polarity.

- Along the right leg, the elements themselves display a gradual change from covalent to metallic bonding.

- Along the base, compounds of each element with sodium display a gradual change from ionic to metallic bonding and, once again, a *decrease* in bond polarity.

Bond Properties

There are two important properties of a covalent bond *(Section 9.3):*

Bond length is the distance between the nuclei of bonded atoms.

Bond energy (bond strength) is the enthalpy change required to break a given bond in 1 mol of gaseous molecules.

Among similar compounds, these bond properties are related to each other and to reactivity, as shown in the graph for the carbon tetrahalides (CX_4). Note that

- *As bond length increases, bond energy decreases:* shorter bonds are stronger bonds.
- *As bond energy decreases, reactivity increases.*

Nature of Orbital Overlap

In a covalent bond, the shared electrons reside in the entire region composed of the overlapping orbitals of the two atoms. The diagram depicts the bonding in ethylene (C_2H_4).

Bond order is one-half the number of electrons shared. Bond orders of 1 (single bond) and 2 (double bond) are common; a bond order of 3 (triple bond) is much less common. Fractional bond orders occur when there are resonance structures for species with adjacent single and double bonds *(Sections 9.3 and 10.1).*

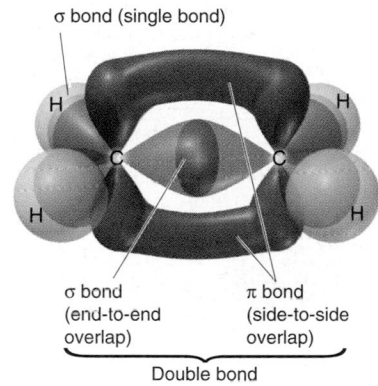

σ bond (single bond)

σ bond (end-to-end overlap) π bond (side-to-side overlap)

Double bond

Orbitals overlap in two ways, which leads to two types of bonds *(Section 11.2):*

- **End-to-end overlap** (of *s*, *p*, and hybrid atomic orbitals) leads to a sigma (σ) bond, one with electron density distributed symmetrically along the bond axis. A single bond is a σ bond.
- **Side-to-side overlap** (of *p* with *p*, or sometimes *d*, orbitals) leads to a pi (π) bond, one with electron density distributed above and below the bond axis. A double bond consists of one σ bond and one π bond. A π bond restricts rotation around the bond axis, allowing for different spatial arrangements of the atoms and, therefore, different molecules. Pi bonds are often sites of reactivity; for example,

$$CH_2{=}CH_2(g) + H{-}Cl(g) \longrightarrow CH_3{-}CH_2{-}Cl(g)$$
$$CH_3{-}CH_3(g) + H{-}Cl(g) \longrightarrow \text{no reaction}$$

Number of Bonds and Molecular Shape

The shape of a molecule is defined by the positions of the nuclei of the bonded atoms. According to VSEPR theory *(Section 10.3),* the number of electron groups in the valence level of a central atom, which is based on the number of bonding and lone pairs, is the key factor that determines molecular shape. The small periodic table shows that

- *The elements in Period 2 cannot form more than four bonds* because they have a maximum of four (one *s* and three *p*) valence orbitals. (Only carbon forms four bonds routinely.) Molecular shapes *(small circle)* are based on linear, trigonal planar, and tetrahedral electron-group arrangements.
- *Many elements in Period 3 or higher can form more than four bonds* by including empty *d* orbitals and, thus, expanding their valence levels. Shapes include those above and others based on trigonal bipyramidal and octahedral electron-group arrangements *(large circle).*

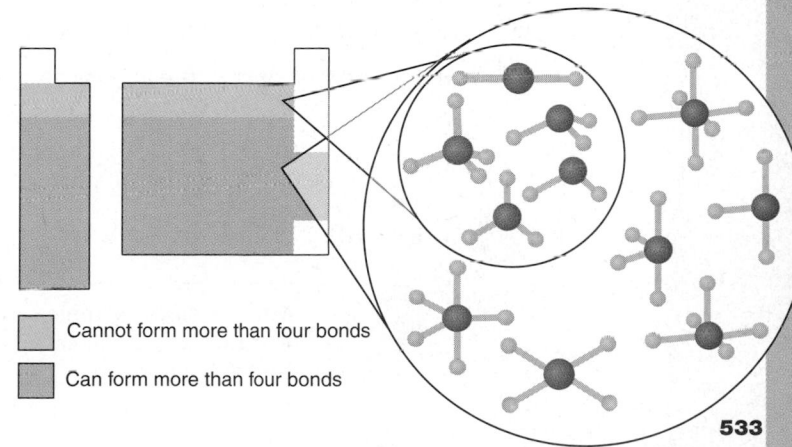

Cannot form more than four bonds

Can form more than four bonds

533

Metallic Behavior

The elements are often classified as metals, metalloids, or nonmetals. Although exceptions exist, this table contrasts the general atomic, physical, and chemical properties of metals with those of nonmetals (*Section 8.5*).

	Metals	Nonmetals
Atomic Properties	Have fewer valence electrons (in period) Have larger atomic size Have lower ionization energies Have lower electronegativities	Have more valence electrons (in period) Have smaller atomic size Have higher ionization energies Have higher electronegativities
Physical Properties	Occur as solids at room temperature Conduct electricity and heat well Are malleable and ductile	Occur in all three physical states Conduct electricity and heat poorly Are not malleable or ductile
Chemical Properties	Lose electron(s) to become cations React with nonmetals to form ionic compounds Mix with other metals to form solutions (alloys)	Gain electron(s) to become anions React with metals to form ionic compounds React with other nonmetals to form covalent compounds

This small periodic table shows the location of metals, metalloids, and nonmetals among the main-group elements. Note that

- Metals lie in the lower left portion of the table.
- Nonmetals lie in the upper right portion of the table.
- Metalloids lie between the metals and nonmetals. These elements have intermediate values of atomic size, IE, and EN and display an intermediate metallic character: shiny solids with low conductivity; cation-like with nonmetals (e.g., AsF_3) and anion-like with metals (e.g., Na_3As).

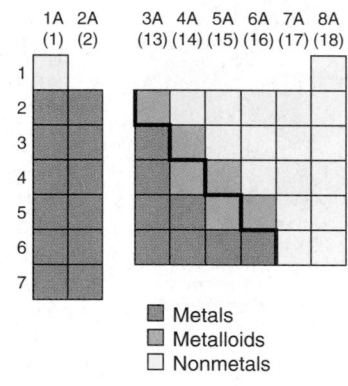

From the blue, shaded periodic table, note that

- *Metallic behavior* changes gradually among the elements.
- *Metallic behavior parallels atomic size:* Larger members of a group *(bottom)* or period *(left)* are more metallic; smaller members are less metallic.

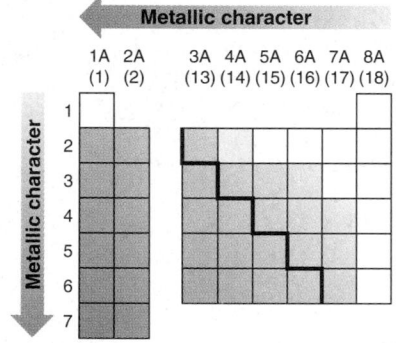

Metals and nonmetals typically form crystalline ionic compounds when they react with each other, and ionic size and charge determine the packing in these solids. Monatomic ions exhibit clear size trends:

- Cations are smaller than their parent atoms, and anions are larger.
- Ionic size *increases down* a group.
- Ionic size *decreases across* a period, but anions are much larger than cations.

Within an isoelectronic series of ions, such as the anions of Period 2 and the cations of Period 3, size decreases in the following order:

$$N^{3-} > O^{2-} > F^- > Na^+ > Mg^{2+} > Al^{3+}$$

Acid-Base Behavior of the Element Oxides

Oxides are known for almost every element. The metallic behavior of an element correlates with the acid-base behavior of its oxide in water *(Section 8.5)*. Recall that

- An acid reacts with water to increase the H^+ concentration, and with a base to form a salt and water.
- A base reacts with water to increase the OH^- concentration, and with an acid to form a salt and water.

This chart shows that the electronegativity and metallic behavior of an element (E) determine the type of bonding (E-to-O) in the oxide and, therefore, the acid-base behavior of the dissolved oxide.

Basic Oxide (Ionic E-to-O)	+ H_2O $\longrightarrow$	more OH^-
	+ acid $\longrightarrow$	salt (E cation) + H_2O
Amphoteric Oxide	+ acid $\longrightarrow$	salt (E cation) + H_2O
	+ base $\longrightarrow$	salt (E oxoanion) + H_2O
Acidic Oxide (Covalent E-to-O)	+ base $\longrightarrow$	salt (E oxoanion) + H_2O
	+ H_2O $\longrightarrow$	more H^+

(Metallic behavior of E — increasing; Electronegativity of E — increasing)

Note that, among the main groups,

- *Elements with low EN (metals) form basic oxides.* The E-to-O bonding is ionic. The O^{2-} ion is the basic species:

$$O^{2-}(s) + H_2O(l) \longrightarrow 2OH^-(aq)$$

For example, barium forms the basic oxide BaO:

  Reacts with water: $BaO(s) + H_2O(l) \longrightarrow Ba^{2+}(aq) + 2OH^-(aq)$

  Reacts with acid: $BaO(s) + 2H^+(aq) \longrightarrow Ba^{2+}(aq) + H_2O(l)$

- *Elements with high EN (nonmetals) form acidic oxides.* The E-to-O bonding is covalent. Water bonds to E of the oxide to form an acid, which releases H^+. For example, sulfur forms the acidic oxide SO_2:

  Reacts with water: $SO_2(g) + H_2O(l) \rightleftharpoons H_2SO_3(aq) \rightleftharpoons H^+(aq) + HSO_3{}^-(aq)$

  Reacts with base: $SO_2(g) + 2OH^-(aq) \longrightarrow SO_3{}^{2-}(aq) + H_2O(l)$

- *Elements with intermediate EN (some metalloids and metals) form amphoteric oxides, which react with acid and base.* For example, Al_2O_3 is an amphoteric oxide:

  Reacts with acid: $Al_2O_3(s) + 6H^+(aq) \longrightarrow 2Al^{3+}(aq) + 3H_2O(l)$

  Reacts with base: $Al_2O_3(s) + 2OH^-(aq) + 3H_2O(l) \longrightarrow 2Al(OH)_4{}^-(aq)$

1A (1)	2A (2)	3A (13)	4A (14)	5A (15)	6A (16)	7A (17)	8A (18)
Li_2O	BeO	B_2O_3	CO_2	N_2O_5 / N_2O_3			
Na_2O	MgO	Al_2O_3	SiO_2	P_4O_{10} / P_4O_6	SO_3 / SO_2	Cl_2O_7 / Cl_2O	
K_2O	CaO	Ga_2O_3	GeO_2	As_2O_5 / As_4O_6	SeO_3 / SeO_2	Br_2O	
Rb_2O	SrO	In_2O_3 / In_2O	SnO_2 / SnO	Sb_2O_5 / Sb_4O_6	TeO_3 / TeO_2	I_2O_5	
Cs_2O	BaO	Tl_2O	PbO_2 / PbO	Bi_2O_3	PoO_2 / PoO		
Fr_2O	RaO						

- ☐ Strongly basic
- ☐ Weakly basic
- ☐ Amphoteric
- ☐ Strongly acidic
- ☐ Moderately acidic
- ☐ Weakly acidic

The periodic table shows the acid-base behavior of many main-group oxides in water. Note that

- *Oxide acidity increases across a period and decreases down a group,* which is *opposite* the trend in metallic behavior (and atomic size).
- When an element forms two oxides, *the more acidic oxide has the element in a higher oxidation state* (see also Topic 5). Thus, for example, SO_2 forms the weak acid H_2SO_3, whereas SO_3 forms the strong acid H_2SO_4.

Redox Behavior of the Elements

The relative ability of an element to lose or gain electrons (or electron charge) when reacting with other elements defines its redox (oxidation-reduction) behavior *(Section 4.3):*

- *The oxidation state (or oxidation number, O.N.)* of an atom in an element is zero. In a compound, the O.N. is the number of electrons that have shifted away from the atom (positive O.N.) or toward it (negative O.N.). O.N. values are determined by a set of rules *(Section 4.3).*
- *A redox reaction* occurs when the O.N. values of any atoms in the reactants are different from those in the products.
- Among the countless redox reactions are all those that involve *an elemental substance as reactant or product.* These include all combustion reactions and all formation reactions, such as this one between potassium and chlorine:

Reducing and Oxidizing Agents

All redox reactions involve a reducing *and* an oxidizing agent among the reactants. This chart shows that

- The reducing agent gives electrons *to* (reduces) the oxidizing agent and becomes oxidized (more positive O.N.).
- The oxidizing agent removes electrons *from* (oxidizes) the reducing agent and becomes reduced (more negative O.N.).

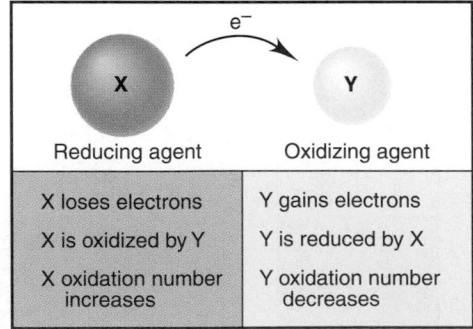

Reducing agent	Oxidizing agent
X loses electrons	Y gains electrons
X is oxidized by Y	Y is reduced by X
X oxidation number increases	Y oxidation number decreases

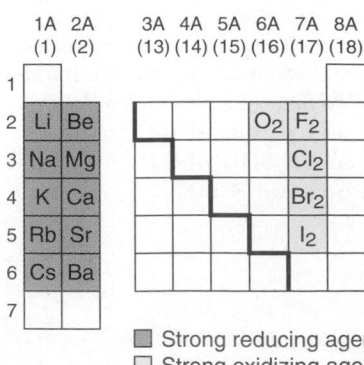

■ Strong reducing agent
☐ Strong oxidizing agent

The periodic table shows that oxidizing and reducing ability are related to atomic properties:

- Elements with low IE and low EN [Groups 1A(1) and 2A(2)] are *strong reducing agents.*
- Elements with high IE and high EN [Group 7A(17) and oxygen in Group 6A(16)] are *strong oxidizing agents.*

Oxidation States of the Main-Group Elements

The periodic table below shows some oxidation states (most common states in **bold** type) of the elements in their compounds. Note that

- *The highest (most positive) state in a group equals the A-group number.* It occurs when all of an atom's outer (valence) electrons shift toward a *more* electronegative atom.
- *Among nonmetals, the lowest (most negative) state equals the A-group number minus eight.* It occurs when a nonmetal atom fills its outer level with electrons that shift away from a *less* electronegative atom.
- *Nonmetals have more oxidation states than metals* in the same group or period. (Oxygen and fluorine are exceptions.)
- Odd-numbered groups generally have odd-numbered states and even-numbered groups have even-numbered states. *Oxidation states differ by units of two* because electrons are lost (or gained) in pairs *(Section 14.9)*.
- For many metals and metalloids with more than one oxidation state [Groups 3A(13) to 5A(15)], *the lower state becomes more common down the group.* This state results when *np* electrons only are lost *(Section 8.5)*.
- An element with more than one oxidation state exhibits *greater metallic behavior in its lower state.* For example, arsenic(III) oxide is more basic, more like a metal oxide, than is arsenic(V) oxide (see Topic 4).

Legend:
- Metals
- Metalloids
- Nonmetals

Group	1A (1)	2A (2)	3A (13)	4A (14)	5A (15)	6A (16)	7A (17)	8A (18)
1	H −1, +1							He
2	Li +1	Be +2	B +3	C −4, +4, +2	N −3, +5, +4, +3, +2, +1	O −1, −2	F −1	Ne
3	Na +1	Mg +2	Al +3	Si −4, +4, +2	P −3, +5, +3	S −2, +6, +4, +2	Cl −1, +7, +5, +3, +1	Ar
4	K +1	Ca +2	Ga +3, +1	Ge +4, +2	As −3, +5, +3	Se −2, +6, +4, +2	Br −1, +7, +5, +1	Kr +2
5	Rb +1	Sr +2	In +3, +1	Sn +4, +2	Sb −3, +5, +3	Te −2, +6, +4, +2	I −1, +7, +5, +1	Xe +8, +6, +4, +2
6	Cs +1	Ba +2	Tl +1	Pb +4, +2	Bi +3	Po +4, +2	At −1	Rn +2
7	Fr +1	Ra +2						

Physical States and Changes of State

Physical state and the heat of a phase change reflect the relative strengths of the bonding and/or intermolecular forces between the atoms, ions, or molecules that make up an element or compound *(Sections 12.2, 12.3, and 12.6).*

Physical States of the Elements

The large periodic table shows the type of particle or structure *(shape in box)*, physical state *(color of shape)*, and dominant interparticle force *(background color of box)* in the most common form of each of the main-group elements at room temperature. Note that

- *Metals (left and bottom) are solids:* strong metallic bonding holds the atoms in their crystal structures.
- *Metalloids (along staircase line) and carbon are solids:* strong covalent bonding holds the atoms together in extensive networks.
- *Lighter nonmetals and Group 8A(18) (right and top) are gases:* dispersion forces are weak between molecules (H_2, N_2, O_2, F_2, Cl_2) or atoms with smaller, less polarizable electron clouds.
- *Heavier nonmetals are liquid (Br_2) or soft solids (P_4, S_8, and I_2):* dispersion forces are stronger between molecules with larger, more polarizable electron clouds.

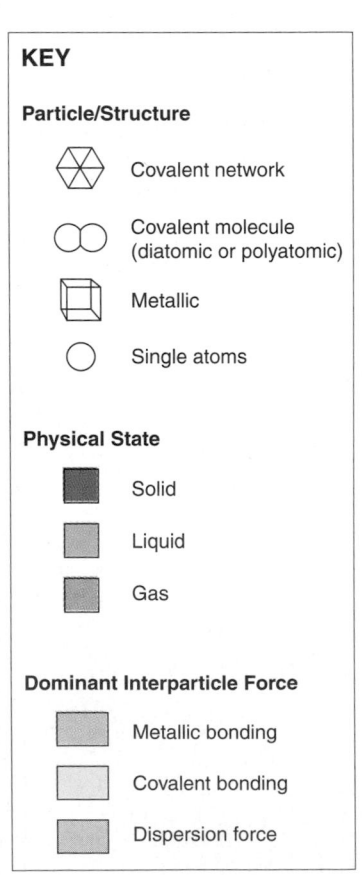

Phase Changes of the Elements

The small periodic table shows trends in melting point, boiling point, ΔH_{fus}, and ΔH_{vap} for Groups 1A(1), 7A(17), and 8A(18):

- In Group 1A(1), these properties generally *increase up* the group: smaller atom cores attract delocalized electrons more strongly, which leads to stronger metallic bonding.
- In Groups 7A(17) and 8A(18), these properties generally *increase down* the group: dispersion forces become stronger with larger, more polarizable atoms.
- In Groups 3A(13) to 6A(16), these properties reflect changes in interparticle forces down the group: lower values for molecular nonmetals, higher values for covalent networks of metalloids (and carbon), and intermediate values for metals.

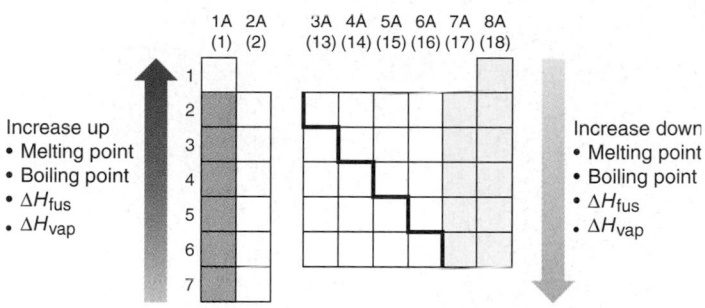

Increase up
- Melting point
- Boiling point
- ΔH_{fus}
- ΔH_{vap}

Increase down
- Melting point
- Boiling point
- ΔH_{fus}
- ΔH_{vap}

Physical Properties of Compounds

Compounds have physical properties based on the types of bonding and intermolecular forces.

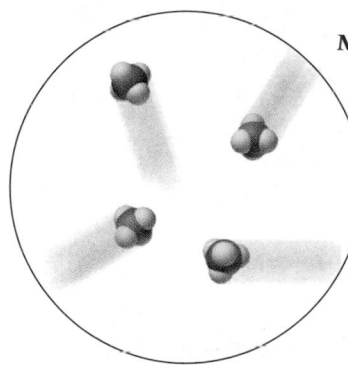

Molecular compounds, such as methane, have a physical state that depends on intermolecular forces. For polar compounds, dipole-dipole forces dominate; for nonpolar compounds, dispersion forces are most important. Most of these substances are gases, liquids, or low-melting solids at room temperature.

Hydrogen bonding arises when H is bonded to N, O, or F. It has a major effect on physical properties. For example, despite similar molar masses, H bonding in H_2O (18.02 g/mol) gives it a much higher melting point, boiling point, ΔH_{fus}, and ΔH_{vap} than CH_4 (16.04 g/mol). Water's unusually high specific heat capacity, surface tension, and viscosity also result from H bonding *(Section 12.5)*.

Network covalent compounds, such as silica, have extremely high melting points, boiling points, ΔH_{fus}, and ΔH_{vap}.

Ionic compounds, such as sodium chloride, have very high melting points, boiling points, ΔH_{fus}, and ΔH_{vap}.

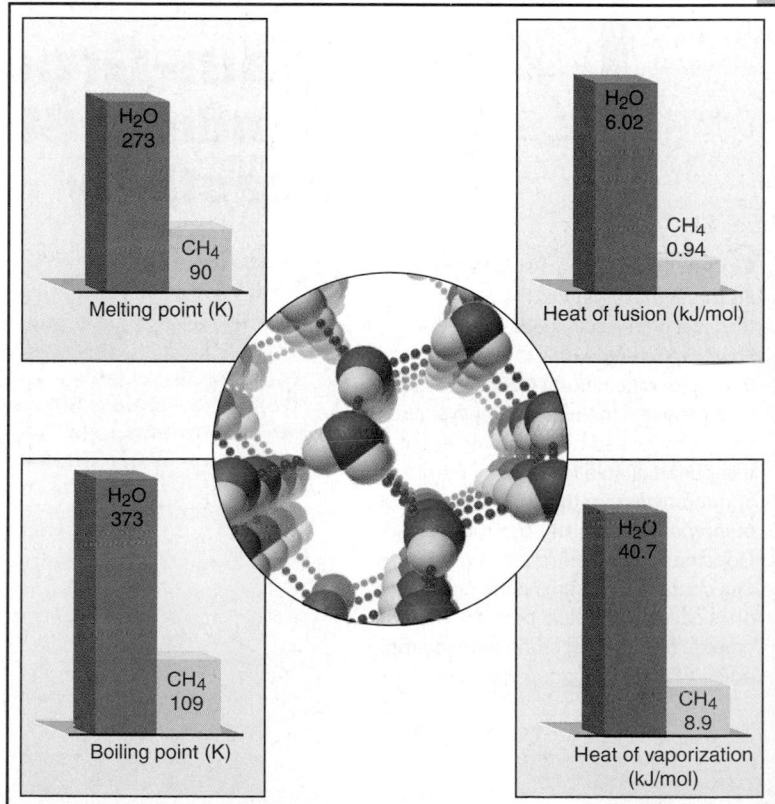

H_2O 273 / CH_4 90 — Melting point (K)

H_2O 6.02 / CH_4 0.94 — Heat of fusion (kJ/mol)

H_2O 373 / CH_4 109 — Boiling point (K)

H_2O 40.7 / CH_4 8.9 — Heat of vaporization (kJ/mol)

14 Periodic Patterns in the Main-Group Elements
Bonding, Structure, and Reactivity

Figure: Periodic patterns in nature. From the movement of the planets to the arrangement of seeds in a sunflower, recurring patterns appear throughout the natural world. The regular increase in the spiral of the *Nautilus* shell is mimicked by the arrangement of this periodic table (colored by period and redrawn from the 1905 text *Outline of Inorganic Chemistry* by Frank Austin Gooch and Claude Frederic Walker). In this chapter, we examine the patterns in physical and chemical behavior that emerge from the recurring atomic properties of the main-group elements.

Chapter Outline

14.1 Hydrogen, the Simplest Atom
• Highlights of Hydrogen Chemistry

14.2 Trends Across the Periodic Table: The Period 2 Elements

14.3 Group 1A(1): The Alkali Metals

14.4 Group 2A(2): The Alkaline Earth Metals

14.5 Group 3A(13): The Boron Family
• Highlights of Boron Chemistry

14.6 Group 4A(14): The Carbon Family
• Highlights of Carbon Chemistry
• Highlights of Silicon Chemistry

14.7 Group 5A(15): The Nitrogen Family
• Highlights of Nitrogen Chemistry
• Highlights of Phosphorus Chemistry

14.8 Group 6A(16): The Oxygen Family
• Highlights of Oxygen Chemistry
• Highlights of Sulfur Chemistry

14.9 Group 7A(17): The Halogens
• Highlights of Halogen Chemistry

14.10 Group 8A(18): The Noble Gases

n your study of chemistry so far, you've learned how to name compounds, balance equations, and calculate reaction yields. You've seen how heat is related to chemical and physical change, how electron configuration influences atomic properties, how atoms bond to form compounds, and how the arrangement of bonding and lone pairs accounts for molecular shapes. Most recently, you've seen how atomic and molecular properties give rise to the macroscopic properties of gases, liquids, solids, and solutions.

The purpose of this knowledge, of course, is to make sense of the magnificent diversity of chemical and physical behavior around you. Therefore, in this chapter, we apply these ideas to understand the bonding, structure, and reactivity of the main-group elements and to see how their behavior correlates with their position in the periodic table. We begin with hydrogen, the simplest and, in some ways, most important of all the elements, and then use Period 2 to survey the general changes *across* the periodic table. Each of the remaining sections deals with one of the eight families of main-group elements. (If you haven't already read the illustrated Interchapter feature preceding this chapter, now is the perfect time to do so. It reviews the major ideas and trends seen throughout the periodic table in preparation for the upcoming discussion.)

The periodic table was derived from chemical facts observed in countless hours of 18th- and 19th-century research. One of the greatest achievements in science is 20th-century quantum theory, which provides a theoretical foundation for the periodic table's arrangement. But bear in mind that one theory can rarely account for *all* the facts. Therefore, be amazed by the predictive powers of patterns in the table, but do not be concerned if occasional exceptions to these patterns occur. After all, our models are simple, but nature is complex.

Concepts and Skills to Review
before you study this chapter

- see Interchapter feature

14.1 Hydrogen, the Simplest Atom

A hydrogen atom consists of a nucleus with a single positive charge, surrounded by a single electron. Despite this simple structure, or perhaps because of it, hydrogen may be the most important element of all. In the Sun, hydrogen (H) nuclei combine to form helium (He) nuclei in a process that provides nearly all the energy on Earth. About 90% of all the atoms in the universe are H atoms, making it the most abundant element by far. On Earth, only tiny amounts of the free element occur naturally (as H_2), but hydrogen is abundant in combination with oxygen in water. Because of its simple structure and low molar mass, nonpolar gaseous H_2 is colorless and odorless, and its extremely weak dispersion forces result in very low melting ($-259°C$) and boiling points ($-253°C$).

Where Does Hydrogen Fit in the Periodic Table?

Hydrogen has no perfectly suitable position in the periodic table (Figure 14.1). Because of its single valence electron and common +1 oxidation state, it might almost fit in Group 1A(1). However, unlike the alkali metals, hydrogen *shares* its electron with nonmetals rather than losing it to them. Like a nonmetal, it has a relatively high ionization energy (IE = 1311 kJ/mol)—much higher than that of lithium (IE = 520 kJ/mol), which is the highest in Group 1A—and a much higher electronegativity as well (EN of H = 2.1; EN of Li = 1.0).

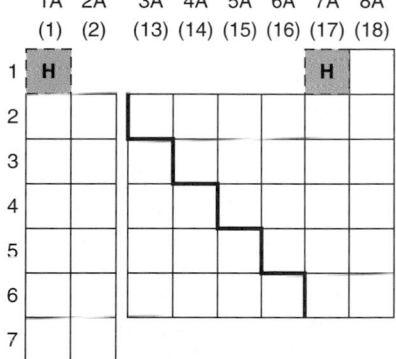

Figure 14.1 Where does hydrogen belong? Hydrogen's small size confers properties that are not entirely consistent with the members of any one periodic group. Depending on the property, hydrogen may fit better in Group 1A(1) or in 7A(17).

On the other hand, hydrogen might almost fit in Group 7A(17). Like the halogens, it occurs as diatomic molecules and fills its outer shell either by electron sharing or by gaining an electron from a metal to form a monatomic anion, the hydride ion (H^-; O.N. = -1). However, hydrogen has a lower EN than any of the halogens and lacks their three valence electron pairs. Moreover, the H^- ion is rare and reactive, whereas halide ions are common and stable.

Hydrogen's unique behavior is due to its tiny size. It has a high IE because its electron is very close to the nucleus, with no core electrons to shield it from the positive charge. It has a low EN (for a nonmetal) because it has only one proton to attract bonded electrons. In this chapter, hydrogen will appear in either Group 1A(1) or 7A(17) depending on the property being considered.

Highlights of Hydrogen Chemistry

In Chapters 12 and 13, we discussed hydrogen bonding and its impact on physical properties (melting and boiling points, heats of fusion and vaporization, and specific heat capacities) and solubilities. You learned that H bonding plays a critical part in stabilizing the Earth's climate as well as your body temperature, and you glimpsed its role in the functioning of biomolecules. In Chapter 6, we considered some possible future uses for hydrogen as a fuel, and later in the text we'll see how hydrogen is used to recover some metals from their ores. Hydrogen is very reactive, combining with nearly every element, so we focus here on the three types of hydrides.

Ionic (Saltlike) Hydrides With very reactive metals, such as those in Groups 1A(1) and the larger members of 2A(2) (Ca, Sr, and Ba), hydrogen forms *saltlike hydrides:* white, crystalline solids composed of the metal cation and the hydride ion:

$$2Li(s) + H_2(g) \longrightarrow 2LiH(s)$$
$$Ca(s) + H_2(g) \longrightarrow CaH_2(s)$$

In water, H^- is a strong base that pulls H^+ from surrounding H_2O molecules to form H_2 and OH^-:

$$NaH(s) + H_2O(l) \longrightarrow Na^+(aq) + OH^-(aq) + H_2(g)$$

The hydride ion is also a powerful reducing agent; for example, it reduces Ti(IV) to the free metal:

$$TiCl_4(l) + 4LiH(s) \longrightarrow Ti(s) + 4LiCl(s) + 2H_2(g)$$

Covalent (Molecular) Hydrides Hydrogen reacts with nonmetals to form many *covalent hydrides*, such as CH_4, NH_3, H_2O, and HF. Most are gases consisting of small molecules, but many hydrides of boron and carbon are liquids or solids consisting of much larger molecules. In most covalent hydrides, hydrogen has an oxidation number of $+1$ because the other nonmetal has a higher electronegativity.

Conditions for preparing the covalent hydrides depend on the reactivity of the other nonmetal. For example, with stable, triple-bonded N_2, hydrogen reacts at high temperatures ($\sim$400°C) and pressures ($\sim$250 atm), and the reaction needs a catalyst to proceed at any practical speed:

$$N_2(g) + 3H_2(g) \xrightarrow{\text{catalyst}} 2NH_3(g) \qquad \Delta H^0_{rxn} = -91.8 \text{ kJ}$$

Industrial facilities throughout the world use this reaction to produce millions of tons of ammonia each year for fertilizers, explosives, and synthetic fibers. On the other hand, hydrogen combines rapidly with reactive, single-bonded F_2, even at extremely low temperatures ($-196°C$):

$$F_2(g) + H_2(g) \longrightarrow 2HF(g) \qquad \Delta H^0_{rxn} = -546 \text{ kJ}$$

Metallic (Interstitial) Hydrides Many transition elements form *metallic (interstitial) hydrides,* in which H_2 molecules (and H atoms) occupy the holes in the metal's crystal structure. Thus, such hydrides are *not* compounds but gas-solid solutions. Also, unlike ionic and covalent hydrides, interstitial hydrides, such as $TiH_{1.7}$, typically lack a single formula because the metal can incorporate variable amounts of hydrogen, depending on the pressure and temperature of the gas. ◆

14.2 Trends Across the Periodic Table: The Period 2 Elements

Table 14.1 on the next two pages presents the trends in atomic properties of the Period 2 elements, lithium through neon, and the physical and chemical properties that emerge from them. In general, these trends apply to the other periods as well. Note the following points:

- Electrons fill the one *ns* and the three *np* orbitals according to the Pauli exclusion principle and Hund's rule.
- As a result of increasing nuclear charge and electrons being added to orbitals of the same energy level (same *n* value), atomic size generally decreases, whereas first ionization energy and electronegativity generally increase (see bar graphs on p. 545).
- Metallic character decreases with increasing nuclear charge as elements change from metals to metalloids to nonmetals.
- Reactivity is highest at the left and right ends of the period, except for the inert noble gas.
- Bonding between atoms of an element changes from metallic to covalent in networks to covalent in individual molecules to none between separate atoms. As expected, physical properties change abruptly at the network/molecule boundary, which occurs in Period 2 between carbon (solid) and nitrogen (gas).
- Bonding between each element and an active nonmetal changes from ionic to polar covalent to covalent. Bonding between each element and an active metal changes from metallic to polar covalent to ionic.
- The acid-base behavior of the common oxides in water changes from basic to amphoteric to acidic as the bond between the element and oxygen becomes more covalent.
- Reducing strength decreases through the metals, and oxidizing strength increases through the nonmetals. In Period 2, common oxidation numbers (O.N.s) equal the A-group number for Li and Be and the A-group number minus eight for O and F. Boron has several O.N.s, Ne has none, and C and N show all possible O.N.s for their groups.

One point we'll be seeing often that is not shown in Table 14.1 is the anomalous behavior of the Period 2 elements within their groups. These elements display some behavior that is *not* representative of their groups because of their relatively *small size* and *small number of orbitals* within the energy level.

Pd   H H_2

◆ **Fill 'Er Up with Hydrogen? Not Likely** Dreams of a future hydrogen economy had included using metallic hydrides as "storage containers" for hydrogen fuel in cars. Just drive up to your local refueling station, insert a cylinder of H-packed metal in your car, and zip away again! It is true that metals, such as palladium (see figure) and niobium, and some alloys, such as $LaNi_5$, store large amounts of hydrogen. However, research over the past 15 years has brought out some serious problems. The main ones are that the metals that store the most hydrogen are expensive, heavy, and hold it tightest, releasing it only at very high temperatures. Thus, in 1996, U.S. government funding for the research stopped. Some groups are keeping the dream alive, however, in studies of carbon nanotubes, which store large amounts of H_2, and of an Na-Al alloy that is light-weight, stores 5% H_2 by mass, and releases it below 200°C. Only time and careful testing will tell!

Table 14.1 Trends in Atomic, Physical, and Chemical Properties of the Period 2 Elements

Group: Element/At. No.:	1A(1) Lithium (Li) $Z = 3$	2A(2) Beryllium (Be) $Z = 4$	3A(13) Boron (B) $Z = 5$	4A(14) Carbon (C) $Z = 6$
Atomic Properties				
Condensed electron configuration; partial orbital box diagram	[He] $2s^1$	[He] $2s^2$	[He] $2s^2 2p^1$	[He] $2s^2 2p^2$
Physical Properties Appearance				
Metallic character	Metal	Metal	Metalloid	Nonmetal
Hardness	Soft	Hard	Very hard	Graphite: soft Diamond: extremely hard
Melting point/ boiling point	Low mp for a metal	High mp	Extremely high mp	Extremely high mp
Chemical Properties				
General reactivity	Reactive	Low reactivity at room temperature	Low reactivity at room temperature	Low reactivity at room temperature; graphite more reactive
Bonding among atoms of element	Metallic	Metallic	Network covalent	Network covalent
Bonding with nonmetals	Ionic	Polar covalent	Polar covalent	Covalent (π bonds common)
Bonding with metals	Metallic	Metallic	Polar covalent	Polar covalent
Acid/base behavior of common oxide	Strongly basic	Amphoteric	Very weakly acidic	Very weakly acidic
Redox behavior (O.N.)	Strong reducing agent (+1)	Moderately strong reducing agent (+2)	Complex hydrides good reducing agents (+3, −3)	Every oxidation state from +4 to −4
Relevance/Uses of Element and Compounds	Li soaps for auto grease; thermonuclear bombs; high-voltage, low-weight batteries; manic-depressive treatment (Li_2CO_3)	Rocket nose cones; alloys for springs and gears; nuclear reactor parts; x-ray tubes	Cleaning agent (borax); eyewash, antiseptic (boric acid); armor (B_4C); borosilicate glass; plant nutrient	Graphite: lubricant, structural fiber; diamond: jewelry, cutting tools, protective films; limestone ($CaCO_3$); organic compounds (drugs, fuels, textiles, etc.)

5A(15) Nitrogen (N) $Z = 7$	6A(16) Oxygen (O) $Z = 8$	7A(17) Fluorine (F) $Z = 9$	8A(18) Neon (Ne) $Z = 10$
[He] $2s^2 2p^3$	[He] $2s^2 2p^4$	[He] $2s^2 2p^5$	[He] $2s^2 2p^6$
Nonmetal —	Nonmetal —	Nonmetal —	Nonmetal —
Very low mp and bp	Very low mp and bp	Very low mp and bp	Extremely low mp and bp
Inactive at room temperature	Very reactive	Extremely reactive	Chemically inert
Covalent N_2 molecules	Covalent O_2 (or O_3) molecules	Covalent F_2 molecules	None; separate atoms
Covalent (π bonds common)	Covalent (π bonds common)	Covalent	None
Ionic/polar covalent; anions with active metals	Ionic	Ionic	None
Strongly acidic (NO_2)	—	Acidic	None
Every oxidation state from +5 to −3	O_2 (and O_3) very strong oxidizing agents (−2)	Strongest oxidizing agent (−1)	None
Component of proteins; ammonia for fertilizers, explosives; oxides involved in manufacturing and air pollution (smog, acid rain)	Final oxidizer in residential, industrial, and biological energy production	In manufacture of coatings (Teflon); glass etching (HF); refrigerants involved in ozone depletion (CFCs); dental protection (NaF, SnF_2)	Electrified gas in advertising signs

Atomic radius (pm)

	Li 152	Be 112	B 85	C 77	N 75	O 73	F 72	Ne 71
1A (1)	2A (2)	3A (13)	4A (14)	5A (15)	6A (16)	7A (17)	8A (18)

First ionization energy (kJ/mol)

Li 520	Be 899	B 800	C 1086	N 1402	O 1314	F 1681	Ne 2080
1A (1)	2A (2)	3A (13)	4A (14)	5A (15)	6A (16)	7A (17)	8A (18)

Electronegativity

Li 1.0	Be 1.5	B 2.0	C 2.5	N 3.0	O 3.5	F 4.0	
1A (1)	2A (2)	3A (13)	4A (14)	5A (15)	6A (16)	7A (17)	8A (18)

14.3 Group 1A(1): The Alkali Metals

The first group of elements in the periodic table is named for the alkaline (basic) nature of their oxides and for the basic solutions the elements form in water. Group 1A(1) provides a perfect example of regular trends with no significant exceptions. All the elements in the group—lithium (Li), sodium (Na), potassium (K), rubidium (Rb), cesium (Cs), and rare, radioactive francium (Fr)—are very reactive metals. The Family Portrait of Group 1A(1) elements, on pages 548 and 549, is the first in a series that provides an overview of each of the main groups. Atomic and physical properties are summarized on the left-hand page; representative reactions and some important compounds appear on the right-hand page. Refer to these family portraits during the discussions because they present supporting information.

Why Are the Alkali Metals Soft, Low Melting, and Lightweight?

Unlike most metals, the alkali metals are soft: Na has the consistency of cold butter, and K can be squeezed like clay. The alkali metals also have lower melting and boiling points than any other group of metals. Except for Li, they all melt below 100°C, and Cs melts a few degrees above room temperature. They also have lower densities than most metals: Li floats on lightweight household oil (see Sample Problem 1.5, p. 23).

The unusual physical behavior of the alkali metals can be traced to their atomic size, the largest in their respective periods, and to the ns^1 electron configuration. Because the single valence electron is relatively far from the nucleus, there is only a weak attraction between the delocalized electrons and the atom cores. This weak metallic bonding means that the alkali metal crystal structure can be easily deformed or broken down, which results in a soft consistency and low melting point. These elements also have the lowest molar masses in their periods, so with their large atomic radii, they have relatively low densities.

Why Are the Alkali Metals So Reactive?

The alkali metals are extremely reactive elements. They are *powerful reducing agents* and, thus, always occur in nature as 1+ cations rather than as free metals. (As we discuss in Section 22.4, highly endothermic reduction processes are required to prepare the free metals industrially from their molten salts.) The alkali metals reduce the halogens and form ionic solids in reactions that release large quantities of heat. They reduce the hydrogen in water, reacting vigorously (Rb and Cs explosively) to form H_2 and metal hydroxide solutions. They reduce O_2 in the air, so they tarnish rapidly. Because of this reactivity, Na and K are usually kept under mineral oil (an unreactive liquid) in the laboratory, and Rb and Cs are handled with gloves under an inert argon atmosphere.

The ns^1 configuration, which you saw is the basis for their physical properties, is also the reason these metals form salts so readily. In a Born-Haber cycle of the reaction between an alkali metal and a nonmetal, for example, the solid metal separates into gaseous atoms, each of the atoms transfers its outer electron to the nonmetal, and the resulting cations attract the anions into an ionic solid (Section 9.2). Several properties based on the ns^1 configuration relate to each of these steps.

1. *Low heat of atomization* (ΔH^0_{atom}). Consistent with the alkali metals' low melting and boiling points, their weak metallic bonding leads to low values

for ΔH^0_{atom} (the energy needed to convert the solid into individual gaseous atoms), which decrease down the group:

$$E(s) \longrightarrow E(g) \qquad \Delta H_{atom} \ (Li > Na > K > Rb > Cs)*$$

2. *Low IE and high charge density.* Each alkali metal has the largest size and lowest IE in its period. A great *decrease* in size occurs when the outer electron is lost: the volume of the Li^+ ion is less than 13% that of the Li atom! Thus, E^+ ions are small spheres with high charge density.

3. *High lattice energy.* The small cations can come close to the anions and release large amounts of energy as they crystallize. Thus, the endothermic atomization and ionization steps are easily outweighed by the highly exothermic formation of the solid. For a given anion, the trend in lattice energy is the inverse of the trend in cation size: *as the cation becomes larger, the lattice energy becomes smaller (less negative).* The steady decrease in the magnitude of the lattice energy within the Group 1A(1) and 2A(2) chlorides is shown in Figure 14.2.

Despite the strong ionic attractions in the solid, *nearly all Group 1A salts are water soluble.* The high charge density attracts water molecules to create a highly exothermic heat of hydration (ΔH_{hydr}), and a large increase in disorder arises when ions in the organized crystal become randomized and hydrated in solution; together, these factors outweigh the high lattice energy.

The magnitude of the hydration energy *decreases* as ionic size increases:

$$E^+(g) \longrightarrow E^+(aq) \qquad \Delta H = -\Delta H_{hydr} \ (Li^+ > Na^+ > K^+ > Rb^+ > Cs^+)$$

Interestingly, the *smaller* ions attract water molecules strongly enough to form *larger hydrated ions.* This size trend has a major effect on the function of nerves, kidneys, and cell membranes because the *sizes* of $Na^+(aq)$ and $K^+(aq)$, the most common cations in cell fluids, influence their movement in and out of cells.

The Anomalous Behavior of Lithium

As we noted in discussing Table 14.1, all the Period 2 elements display some anomalous (unrepresentative) behavior within their groups. Even within the regular, predictable trends of Group 1A(1), Li has some atypical properties. It is the only member that forms a simple oxide and nitride, Li_2O and Li_3N, on reaction with O_2 and N_2 in air. Only Li forms molecular compounds with hydrocarbon groups from organic halides:

$$2Li(s) + CH_3CH_2Cl(g) \longrightarrow CH_3CH_2Li(s) + LiCl(s)$$

Organolithium compounds, such as CH_3CH_2Li, are liquids or low-melting solids that dissolve in nonpolar solvents and contain polar covalent $^{\delta-}C-Li^{\delta+}$ bonds. They are important reactants in the synthesis of organic compounds.

Because of its small size and thus high charge density, the Li^+ ion can deform nearby electron clouds, which gives many lithium salts significant covalent bond character (Figure 14.3). Thus, LiCl, LiBr, and LiI, for example, are much more soluble in polar organic solvents, such as ethanol and acetone, than are the halides of Na and K, because the lithium halide dipole interacts with these solvents through dipole-dipole forces. The relatively high charge density of Li^+ makes separation of salts into ions more difficult in water; thus, the fluoride, carbonate, hydroxide, and phosphate of Li are much less soluble in water than those of Na and K.

---

*Throughout the chapter, we use E to represent any element in a group.

Figure 14.2 Lattice energies of the Group 1A(1) and 2A(2) chlorides. Lattice energies decrease regularly in both groups of metal chlorides as the cations become larger. Lattice energies for the 2A chlorides are greater because the 2A cations have higher charge and smaller size.

Figure 14.3 The effect of Li^+ charge density on a nearby electron cloud. The ability of the Li^+ ion to deform nearby electron clouds gives rise to many anomalous properties for a Group 1A(1) element. In this case, Li^+ polarizes an I^- ion, which gives some covalent character to lithium iodide, LiI.

Key Atomic and Physical Properties

KEY

Atomic No.
Symbol
Atomic mass
Valence e⁻ configuration
Common oxidation states

GROUP 1A(1)

3	
Li	
6.941	
$2s^1$	
+1	

11	
Na	
22.99	
$3s^1$	
+1	

19	
K	
39.10	
$4s^1$	
+1	

37	
Rb	
85.47	
$5s^1$	
+1	

55	
Cs	
132.9	
$6s^1$	
+1	

87	
Fr	
(223)	
$7s^1$	
+1	

No sample available

Atomic Properties

Atomic radius (pm)		Ionic radius (pm)
Li 152		Li⁺ 76
Na 186		Na⁺ 102
K 227		K⁺ 138
Rb 248		Rb⁺ 152
Cs 265		Cs⁺ 167
Fr (~270)		Fr⁺ 180

Group electron configuration is ns^1. All members have the +1 oxidation state and form an E⁺ ion.

Atoms have the largest size and lowest IE and EN in their periods.

Down the group, atomic and ionic size increase, while IE and EN decrease.

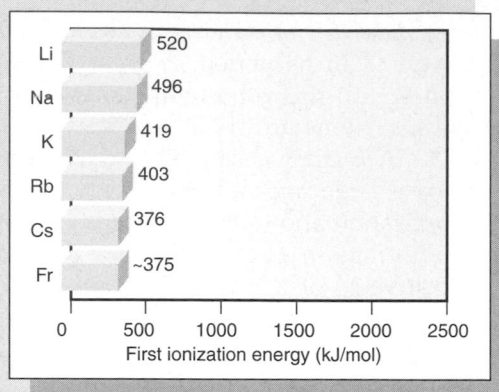

First ionization energy (kJ/mol)

Li	520
Na	496
K	419
Rb	403
Cs	376
Fr	~375

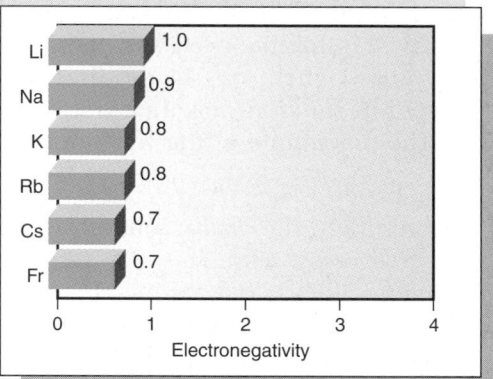

Electronegativity

Li	1.0
Na	0.9
K	0.8
Rb	0.8
Cs	0.7
Fr	0.7

Physical Properties

Metallic bonding is relatively weak because there is only one valence electron. Therefore, these metals are soft with relatively low melting and boiling points. These values decrease down the group because larger atom cores attract delocalized electrons less strongly.

Temperature (°C)

	MP	BP
Li	181	1347
Na	98	881
K	63	766
Rb	39	688
Cs	28	705
Fr		

■ BP ☐ MP

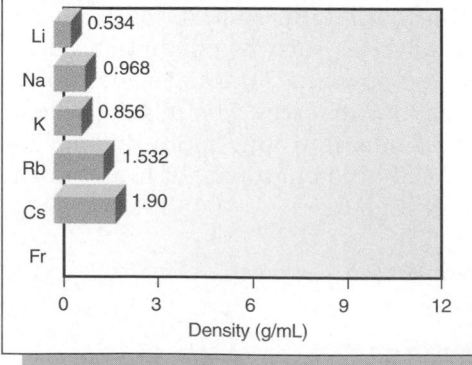

Density (g/mL)

Li	0.534
Na	0.968
K	0.856
Rb	1.532
Cs	1.90
Fr	

Large atomic size and low atomic mass result in low density, which generally increases down the group because mass increases more than size.

Some Reactions and Compounds

Important Reactions

The reducing power of the alkali metals (E) is shown in reactions 1 to 4. Some industrial applications of 1A(1) compounds are shown in reactions 5 to 7.

1. The alkali metals reduce H in H_2O from the $+1$ to the zero oxidation state:

$$2E(s) + 2H_2O(l) \longrightarrow 2E^+(aq) + 2OH^-(aq) + H_2(g)$$

The reaction becomes more vigorous down the group (*see photo*).

Potassium reacting with water

2. The alkali metals reduce oxygen, but the product depends on the metal. Li forms the oxide, Li_2O; Na forms the peroxide, Na_2O_2; K, Rb, and Cs form the superoxide, EO_2:

$$4Li(s) + O_2(g) \longrightarrow 2Li_2O(s)$$
$$K(s) + O_2(g) \longrightarrow KO_2(s)$$

In emergency breathing units, KO_2 reacts with H_2O and CO_2 in exhaled air to release O_2.

3. The alkali metals reduce hydrogen to form ionic (saltlike) hydrides:

$$2E(s) + H_2(g) \longrightarrow 2EH(s)$$

NaH is an industrial base and reducing agent that is used to prepare other reducing agents, such as $NaBH_4$.

4. The alkali metals reduce halogens to form ionic halides:

$$2E(s) + X_2 \longrightarrow 2EX(s) \qquad (X = F, Cl, Br, I)$$

5. Sodium chloride is the most important alkali halide.
(a) In the Downs process for the production of sodium metal (*Section 22.4*), reaction 4 is reversed by supplying electricity to molten NaCl:

$$2NaCl(l) \xrightarrow{\text{electricity}} 2Na(l) + Cl_2(g)$$

(b) In the chlor-alkali process (*Section 22.5*), NaCl(aq) is electrolyzed to form several key industrial chemicals:

$$2NaCl(aq) + 2H_2O(l) \longrightarrow 2NaOH(aq) + H_2(g) + Cl_2(g)$$

(c) In its reaction with sulfuric acid, NaCl forms two major products:

$$2NaCl(s) + H_2SO_4(aq) \longrightarrow Na_2SO_4(aq) + 2HCl(g)$$

Sodium sulfate is important in the paper industry; HCl is essential in steel, plastics, textiles, and food production.

6. Sodium hydroxide is used in the formation of bleaching solutions:

$$2NaOH(aq) + Cl_2(g) \longrightarrow NaClO(aq) + NaCl(aq) + H_2O(l)$$

7. In an ion-exchange process (*Chemical Connections, Section 13.6*), water is "softened" by removal of dissolved "hard-water" ions, which displace Na^+ from a resin:

$$M^{2+}(aq) + Na_2Z(s) \longrightarrow MZ(s) + 2Na^+(aq)$$
$$(M = Mg, Ca; Z = resin)$$

Important Compounds

1. Lithium chloride and lithium bromide, LiCl and LiBr. Because the Li^+ ion is so small, Li salts have a high affinity for H_2O and yet a positive heat of solution. Thus, they are used in dehumidifiers and air-cooling units.

2. Lithium carbonate, Li_2CO_3. Used to make porcelain enamels and toughened glasses and as a drug in the treatment of manic-depressive disorders.

3. Sodium chloride, NaCl. Millions of tons used in the industrial production of Na, NaOH, $Na_2CO_3/NaHCO_3$, Na_2SO_4, HCl, and purified for use as table salt.

4. Sodium carbonate and sodium hydrogen carbonate, Na_2CO_3 and $NaHCO_3$. Carbonate used as an industrial base and to make glass. Hydrogen carbonate, which releases CO_2 at low temperatures (50° to 100°C), used in baking powder and in fire extinguishers.

5. Sodium hydroxide, NaOH. Most important industrial base; used to make bleach, sodium phosphates, and alcohols.

6. Potassium nitrate, KNO_3. Powerful oxidizing agent used in gunpowder and fireworks (*see photo*).

◆ **Versatile Magnesium**
Magnesium, second of the alkaline earths, can be rolled, forged, welded, and riveted into virtually any shape, and it forms strong, low-density alloys: some weigh 25% as much as steel but are just as strong. A tough, adherent oxide coating prevents further reaction in air. Alloyed with aluminum and zinc, magnesium is used for everyday objects, such as camera bodies, luggage, and the "mag" wheels of bicycles and sports cars. Alloyed with the lanthanides (first series of inner transition elements), it is used in objects that require great strength at high temperature, such as auto engine blocks and missile parts.

◆ **Lime: The Most Useful Metal Oxide** Calcium oxide (lime) is a slightly soluble, basic oxide that is among the five most heavily produced industrial compounds in the world; it is made by roasting limestone to high temperatures [Group 2A(2) Family Portrait, reaction 7]. It has essential roles in steelmaking, water treatment, and flue "scrubbing." Lime reacts with carbon to form calcium carbide, which is used to make acetylene, and with arsenic acid (H_3AsO_4) to make insecticides for treating cotton, tobacco, and potato plants. Most glass contains about 12% lime by mass. The paper industry uses lime to prepare the bleach [$Ca(ClO)_2$] that whitens paper. Farmers "dust" fields with lime to "sweeten" acidic soil (see photo). The food industry uses it to neutralize compounds in milk to make cream and butter and to neutralize impurities in crude sugar.

14.4 Group 2A(2): The Alkaline Earth Metals

The Group 2A(2) elements are called *alkaline earth metals* because their oxides give basic (alkaline) solutions and melt at such high temperatures that they remained as solids ("earths") in the alchemists' fires. The group includes a fascinating collection of elements: rare beryllium (Be), common magnesium (Mg) and calcium (Ca), less familiar strontium (Sr) and barium (Ba), and radioactive radium (Ra). The Group 2A(2) Family Portrait (pp. 552 and 553) presents an overview of these elements.

How Do the Physical Properties of the Alkaline Earth and Alkali Metals Compare?

In general terms, the elements in Groups 1A(1) and 2A(2) behave as close cousins. Whatever differences occur between the groups are those of degree, not kind, and are due to the change in electron configuration: ns^2 vs. ns^1. Two electrons are available for metallic bonding, and the nucleus contains one additional positive charge. These factors make the attraction between delocalized electrons and atom cores greater. Consequently, 2A melting and boiling points are much higher than for the corresponding 1A metals; in fact, the 2A elements melt at around the same temperatures that the 1A elements boil! Compared with transition metals, such as iron and chromium, the 2A elements are soft and lightweight, but they are much harder and more dense than their alkali metal neighbors. ◆

How Do the Chemical Properties of the Alkaline Earth and Alkali Metals Compare?

The alkaline earth metals display a wider range of chemical behavior than the alkali metals, largely because of the behavior of beryllium, as you'll see shortly. Since the second valence electron lies in the same sublevel as the first, it is not shielded from the additional nuclear charge very well, so Z_{eff} is greater. Therefore, Group 2A(2) elements have smaller atomic radii and higher ionization energies than Group 1A(1) elements. Despite the higher IEs, *all the alkaline earths (except Be) form ionic compounds* as 2+ cations. Beryllium behaves differently because so much energy is needed to remove two electrons from this tiny atom that it never forms discrete Be^{2+} ions, and its compounds are polar covalent.

Like the alkali metals, the alkaline earth metals are *strong reducing agents*. The elements reduce O_2 in air to form the oxide (Ba also forms the peroxide, BaO_2). Except for Be and Mg, which form adherent oxide coatings, they reduce H_2O at room temperature to form H_2. And, except for Be, they reduce the halogens, N_2, and H_2 to form ionic compounds. The oxides are strongly basic (except for amphoteric BeO) and react with acidic oxides to form salts, such as sulfites and carbonates; for example,

$$SrO(s) + CO_2(g) \longrightarrow SrCO_3(s)$$

Natural carbonates, such as limestone and marble, are major structural materials and the commercial sources for most 2A compounds. ◆

The alkaline earth metals are reactive because the high lattice energies of their compounds more than compensate for the large total IE needed to form the 2+ cation (Section 9.2). Group 2A salts have much higher lattice energies than those of Group 1A (see Figure 14.2) because the 2A cations are smaller and doubly charged.

One of the main differences between the two groups is the lower solubility of 2A salts in water. Their ions are smaller and more highly charged than 1A ions, resulting in much higher charge densities. Even though this increases heats of hydration, it increases lattice energies even more. In fact, most 2A fluorides, carbonates, phosphates, and sulfates are considered insoluble, unlike the corresponding 1A compounds. Nevertheless, the ion-dipole attraction of 2+ ions for water is so strong that many slightly soluble 2A salts crystallize as hydrates; two examples are Epsom salt, $MgSO_4 \cdot 7H_2O$, used as a soak for inflammations, and gypsum, $CaSO_4 \cdot 2H_2O$, used as the bonding material between the paper sheets in wallboard and as the cement in surgical casts.

The Anomalous Behavior of Beryllium

As the numerous exceptions just mentioned indicate, the Period 2 element Be displays many examples of anomalous behavior, far more than does Li in Group 1A(1). The high charge density of a possible Be^{2+} ion would polarize nearby electron clouds very strongly and cause extensive orbital overlap. In fact, *all Be compounds exhibit covalent bonding.* Even BeF_2, the most ionic Be compound, has a relatively low melting point and, when melted, a low electrical conductivity.

Since Be has only two valence electrons, it does not attain an octet in its simple gaseous compounds (Section 10.1). When it bonds to an electron-rich atom, however, this electron deficiency is overcome as the gas condenses. Consider beryllium chloride ($BeCl_2$) (Figure 14.4). At temperatures greater than 900°C, it consists of linear molecules in which two sp hybrid orbitals hold four electrons around the central Be. As it cools, the molecules bond together, solidifying in long chains, with each Be sp^3 hybridized to finally attain an octet.

Figure 14.4 Overcoming electron deficiency in beryllium chloride. A, At high temperatures, $BeCl_2$ occurs as a gaseous molecule with only four electrons around Be. **B,** In the solid state, $BeCl_2$ occurs in long chains with each Cl bridging two Be atoms, which gives each Be an octet.

Diagonal Relationships: Lithium and Magnesium

One of the clearest ways in which atomic properties influence chemical behavior appears in the **diagonal relationships** of the periodic table, similarities between a Period 2 element and one in Period 3 diagonally down and to the right (Figure 14.5).

The first of these relationships occurs between lithium and magnesium and reflects similarities in atomic and ionic size. Note that *one period down increases atomic (or ionic) size and one group to the right decreases it.* Thus, Li has a radius of 152 pm and Mg has a radius of 160 pm; the Li^+ radius is 76 pm and that of Mg^{2+} is 72 pm. From these similar atomic properties emerge remarkably similar chemical properties. Both elements form nitrides with N_2, hydroxides and carbonates that decompose easily with heat, organic compounds with a polar covalent bond from the metal atom to a hydrocarbon group, and salts with similar solubilities. We will discuss the other two diagonal relationships shown in Figure 14.5—the one between Be and Al, and the one between B and Si—in later sections.

Figure 14.5 Three diagonal relationships in the periodic table. Certain Period 2 elements exhibit behaviors that are very similar to those of Period 3 elements immediately below and to the right. Three such diagonal relationships exist: Li and Mg, Be and Al, and B and Si.

Looking Backward and Forward: Groups 1A(1), 2A(2), and 3A(13)

Throughout this chapter, comparing the previous, current, and upcoming groups (Figure 14.6) will help you to keep horizontal trends in mind while examining vertical groups. Not much changes from 1A to 2A, and the elements behave as metals both physically and chemically. With smaller atomic sizes and stronger metallic bonding, 2A elements are harder, higher melting, and denser than those in 1A. Nearly all 1A and most 2A compounds are ionic. The higher ionic charge in Group 2A (2+ vs. 1+) leads to higher lattice energies and less soluble salts. The range of behavior in 2A is wider than that in 1A because of Be and is widened much further in Group 3A from metalloid boron to metallic thallium.

Figure 14.6 **Standing in Group 2A(2), looking backward to 1A(1) and forward to 3A(13).**

Key Atomic and Physical Properties

KEY

Atomic No.
Symbol
Atomic mass
Valence e⁻ configuration
Common oxidation states

ns^2

GROUP 2A(2)

4	
Be	
9.012	
$2s^2$	
+2	

12	
Mg	
24.30	
$3s^2$	
+2	

20	
Ca	
40.08	
$4s^2$	
+2	

38	
Sr	
87.62	
$5s^2$	
+2	

56	
Ba	
137.3	
$6s^2$	
+2	

88	
Ra	
(226)	No sample available
$7s^2$	
+2	

	Atomic radius (pm)		Ionic radius (pm)
Be	112		
Mg	160	Mg²⁺	72
Ca	197	Ca²⁺	100
Sr	215	Sr²⁺	118
Ba	222	Ba²⁺	135
Ra	(~220)	Ra²⁺	148

Atomic Properties

Group electron configuration is ns^2 (filled ns sublevel). All members have the +2 oxidation state and, except for Be, form compounds with an E²⁺ ion.

Atomic and ionic sizes increase down the group but are smaller than for the corresponding 1A(1) element.

IE and EN decrease down the group but are higher than for the corresponding 1A(1) element.

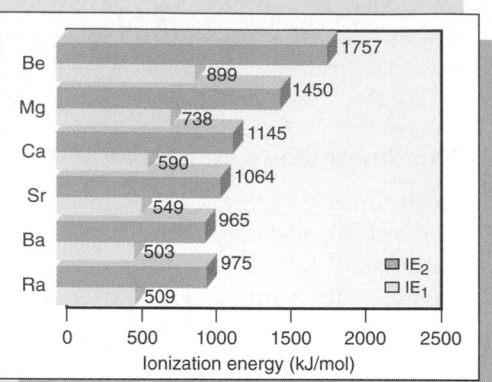

Ionization energy (kJ/mol)

	IE₁	IE₂
Be	899	1757
Mg	738	1450
Ca	590	1145
Sr	549	1064
Ba	503	965
Ra	509	975

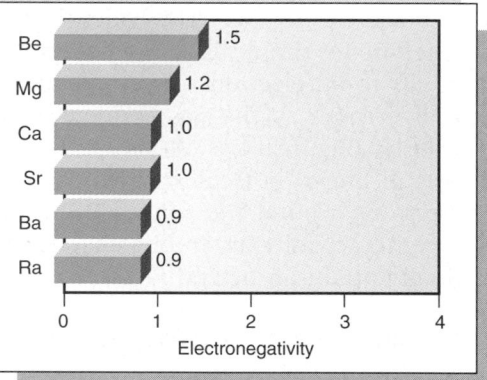

Electronegativity

Be	1.5
Mg	1.2
Ca	1.0
Sr	1.0
Ba	0.9
Ra	0.9

Physical Properties

Metallic bonding involves two valence e⁻. These metals are still relatively soft but are much harder than the 1A(1) metals.

Temperature (°C)

	MP	BP
Be	1287	~2500
Mg	649	1105
Ca	839	1494
Sr	768	1381
Ba	727	1850
Ra	700	1700

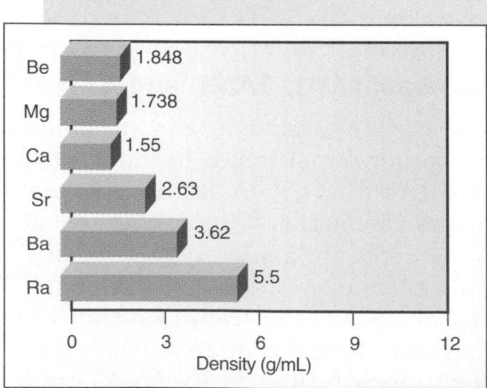

Density (g/mL)

Be	1.848
Mg	1.738
Ca	1.55
Sr	2.63
Ba	3.62
Ra	5.5

Melting and boiling points generally decrease, and densities generally increase down the group. These values are much higher than for 1A(1), and the trend is not as regular.

Some Reactions and Compounds

Important Reactions

The elements (E) act as reducing agents in reactions 1 to 5; note the similarity to reactions of Group 1A(1). Reaction 6 shows the general basicity of the oxides; reaction 7 shows the general instability of the carbonates at high temperature.

1. The metals reduce O_2 to form the oxide:

$$2E(s) + O_2(g) \longrightarrow 2EO(s)$$

Ba also forms the peroxide, BaO_2.

Magnesium ribbon burning

2. The larger metals reduce water to form hydrogen gas:

$$E(s) + 2H_2O(l) \longrightarrow E^{2+}(aq) + 2OH^-(aq) + H_2(g)$$
$$(E = Ca, Sr, Ba)$$

Be and Mg form an adherent oxide coating that allows only slight reaction.

3. The metals reduce halogens to form ionic halides:

$$E(s) + X_2 \longrightarrow EX_2(s) \qquad (X = F, Cl, Br, I)$$

4. Most of the elements reduce hydrogen to form ionic hydrides:

$$E(s) + H_2(g) \longrightarrow EH_2(s) \qquad (E = all \ except \ Be)$$

5. Most of the elements reduce nitrogen to form ionic nitrides:

$$3E(s) + N_2(g) \longrightarrow E_3N_2(s) \qquad (E = all \ except \ Be)$$

6. Except for amphoteric BeO, the oxides are basic:

$$EO(s) + H_2O(l) \longrightarrow E^{2+}(aq) + 2OH^-(aq)$$

$Ca(OH)_2$ is a component of cement and mortar.

7. All carbonates undergo thermal decomposition to the oxide:

$$ECO_3(s) \xrightarrow{\Delta} EO(s) + CO_2(g)$$

This reaction is used to produce CaO (lime) in huge amounts from naturally occurring limestone (*see Margin Note, p. 550*).

Important Compounds

1. Beryl, $Be_3Al_2Si_6O_{18}$. Beryl, the industrial source of Be metal, also occurs as a gemstone with a variety of colors (*see photo*). It is chemically identical to emerald, except for the trace of Cr^{3+} that gives emerald its green color.

2. Magnesium oxide, MgO. Because of its high melting point (2852°C), MgO is used as a refractory material for furnace brick (*see photo*) and wire insulation.

Industrial kiln

3. Alkylmagnesium halides, RMgX (R = hydrocarbon group; X = halogen). These compounds, called *Grignard reagents*, are used to synthesize many organic compounds. Organotin agricultural fungicides are made by treating RMgX with $SnCl_4$:

$$3RMgCl + SnCl_4 \longrightarrow 3MgCl_2 + R_3SnCl$$

4. Calcium carbonate, $CaCO_3$. Occurs as enormous natural deposits of limestone, marble, chalk, and coral. Used as a building material, to make lime, and, in high purity, as a toothpaste abrasive and an antacid (*see photo*).

Antacid tablet   Limestone

14.5 Group 3A(13): The Boron Family

The third family of main-group elements contains some unusual members and some familiar ones, some exotic bonding, and some strange physical properties. Boron (B) heads the family, but, as you'll see, its properties certainly do not represent the other members. Metallic aluminum (Al) has properties that are more typical of the group, but its great abundance and importance contrast with the rareness of gallium (Ga), indium (In), and thallium (Tl). The atomic, physical, and chemical properties of these elements are summarized in the Group 3A(13) Family Portrait (pp. 556 and 557).

How Do the Transition Elements Influence Group 3A(13) Properties?

Group 3A(13) is the first of the *p* block. If you look at the main groups only, the elements of this group seem to be just one group away from those of Group 2A(2). In Period 4 and higher, however, a large gap separates the two groups (see Figure 8.10). The gap holds 10 transition elements (*d* block) each in Periods 4, 5, and 6 and an additional 14 inner transition elements (*f* block) in Period 6. Recall from Section 8.2 that *d* and *f* electrons penetrate very little and spend very little time near the nucleus. Thus, the heavier 3A members—Ga, In, and Tl—have nuclei with many more protons, but their outer (*s* and *p*) electrons are only partially shielded from the much higher positive charge, so these elements have greater Z_{eff} than the two lighter members.

Many properties of these heavier 3A elements are influenced by this stronger nuclear attraction. Figure 14.7 compares several properties of Group 3A(13) with those of Group 3B(3) (the first group of transition elements), in which the additional protons of the *d* block and *f* block have *not* been added. Note the regular changes exhibited by the 3B elements in contrast to the irregular patterns for those in 3A. The deviations for Ga reflect the *d*-block *contraction in size* and can be explained by limited shielding by the *d* electrons of the 10 additional protons of the first transition series. Similarly, the deviations for Tl reflect the *f*-block (lanthanide) contraction and can be explained by limited shielding by the *f* electrons of the 14 additional protons of the first inner transition series.

Physical properties are influenced by the type of bonding that occurs in the element. Boron is a network covalent metalloid—black, hard, and very high melting. The other group members are metals—shiny and relatively soft and low melting. Aluminum's low density and three valence electrons make it an exceptional conductor: for a given mass, aluminum conducts a current twice as effectively as copper. Gallium has the largest liquid temperature range of any element: it melts in your hand but does not boil until 2403°C (see Figure 9.22). Its metallic bonding is too weak to keep the Ga atoms fixed when the solid is warmed, but it is strong enough to keep them from escaping the molten metal until it is very hot. ◆

What New Features Appear in the Chemical Properties of Group 3A(13)?

Looking down Group 3A(13), we see a wide range of chemical behavior. Boron, the anomalous member from Period 2, is the first metalloid we've encountered so far and the only one in the group. It is much less reactive at room temperature than the other members and forms covalent bonds exclusively. Although aluminum acts like a metal physically, its halides exist in the gas phase as covalent dimers—molecules formed by joining two identical smaller molecules (Figure 14.8)—and its oxide is amphoteric rather than basic. Most of the other 3A compounds are ionic, but they have more covalent character than similar 2A compounds. Because the 3A ions are smaller

◆ **Gallium Arsenide: The Next Wave of Semiconductors** An important modern use of gallium is in the production of gallium arsenide (GaAs) semiconductors. One of the factors limiting the efficiency of computer chips is the speed with which electrons can move, and they move 10 times faster through GaAs than through Si-based chips. GaAs chips also have novel optical properties: absorbing light creates a current and, conversely, supplying a current emits light. GaAs devices are already used in light-powered calculators, wristwatches, and solar panels. In addition, GaAs-based lasers are much smaller and more powerful than normal types.

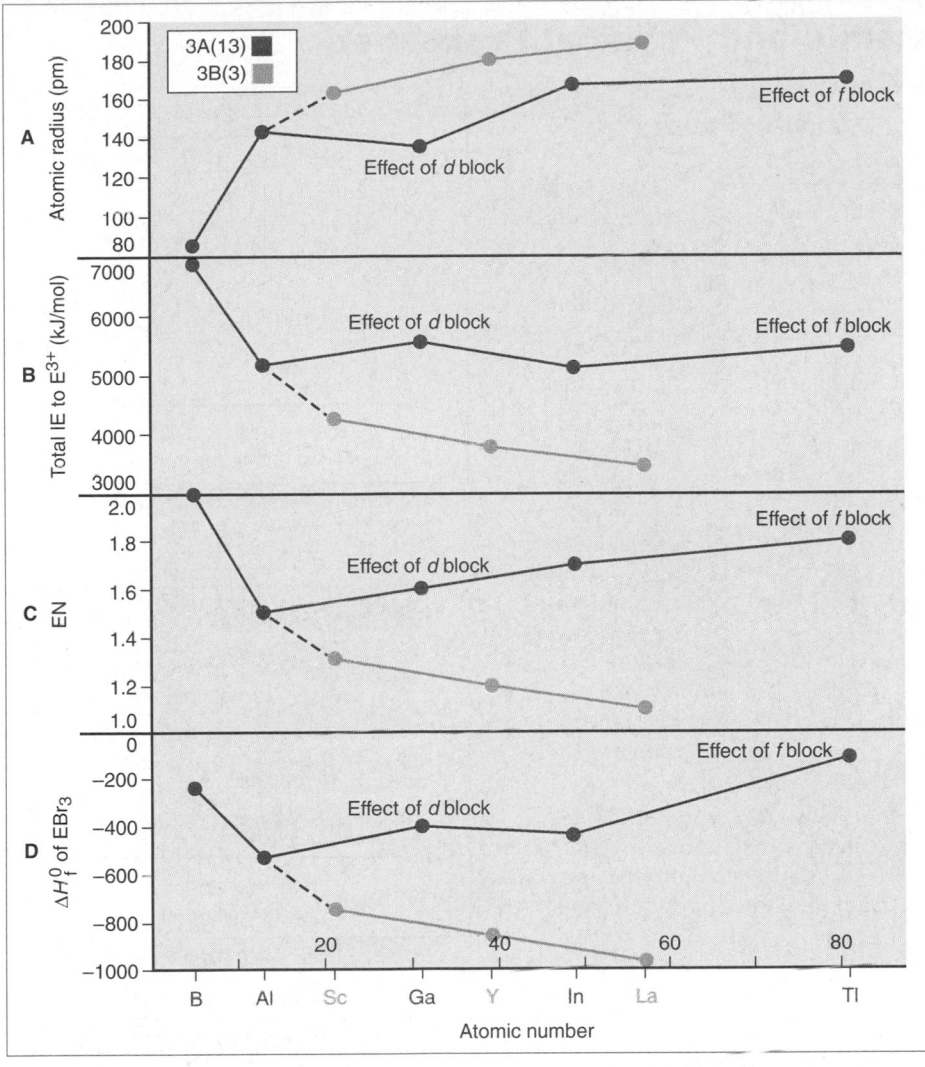

Figure 14.7 The effect of transition elements on properties: Group 3B(3) vs. Group 3A(13). The additional protons in the nuclei of transition elements exert an exceptionally strong attraction because *d* and *f* electrons shield the nuclear charge poorly. This greater effective nuclear charge affects the *p*-block elements in Periods 4 to 6, as can be seen by comparing properties of Group 3B(3), the first group after the *s* block, with 3A(13), the first group after the *d* block. **A,** Atomic size. In Group 3B, size increases smoothly, whereas in 3A, Ga and Tl are smaller than expected. **B,** Total ionization energy for E^{3+}. The deviations in size lead to deviations in total IE ($IE_1 + IE_2 + IE_3$). Note the regular decrease for Group 3B and the unexpectedly higher values for Ga and Tl in 3A. **C,** Electronegativity. The deviations in size also make Ga and Tl more electronegative than expected. **D,** Heat of formation of EBr_3. The higher IE values for Ga and Tl mean less heat is released upon ionic-compound formation, thus the smaller-than-expected ΔH_f^0 values for $GaBr_3$ and $TlBr_3$.

and more highly charged, they polarize the anion electron cloud more effectively.

Our first glimpse of multiple oxidation states occurs in this group, and it provides a chance to note some general principles that appear in Groups 3A(13) to 6A(16):

1. *Increasing prominence of the lower oxidation state.* When a group exhibits more than one oxidation state, *the lower state becomes more prominent down the group.* In Group 3A(13), for instance, all members exhibit the +3 state, but the +1 state first appears with some compounds of gallium and becomes the only important state of thallium.

2. *Explanation of the inert-pair effect.* Many of the larger elements in these groups also have an important oxidation state *two lower than the A-group number.* The lower state occurs when the atoms lose their *np* electrons, but not their two *ns* electrons. This fact is often called the *inert-pair effect* (Section 8.5), but it has nothing to do with any inertness of *ns* electrons; in fact, the 6*s* electrons in Tl are lost *more* easily than the 4*s* electrons in Ga. The reason for the common appearance of the lower state involves bond energies of the compounds. Bond energy decreases as atomic size, and therefore bond length, increases. Since the Tl—Cl bond, for instance, is relatively long and weak, it takes more energy to remove the two 6*s* electrons from Tl^+ to make Tl^{3+}

Figure 14.8 The dimeric structure of gaseous aluminum chloride. Despite its name, aluminum trichloride actually exists in the gas phase as a dimer of separate Al_2Cl_6 molecules.

Key Atomic and Physical Properties

ns^2np^1

GROUP 3A(13)

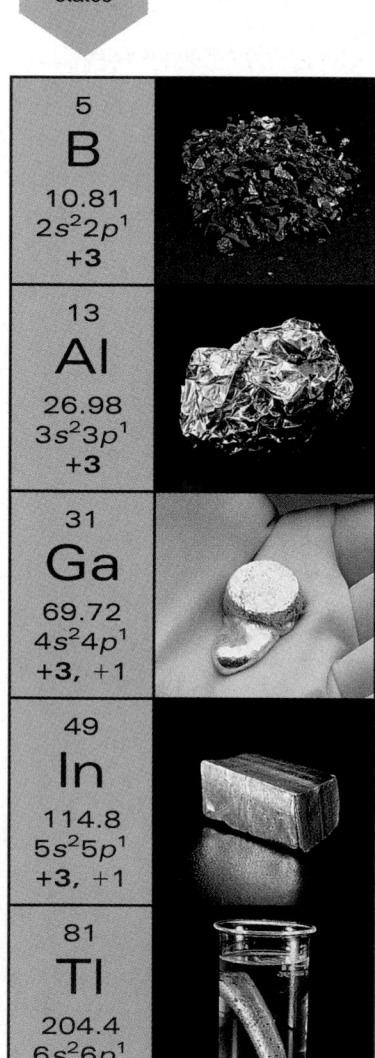

| 5 |
| B |
| 10.81 |
| $2s^2 2p^1$ |
| +3 |

| 13 |
| Al |
| 26.98 |
| $3s^2 3p^1$ |
| +3 |

| 31 |
| Ga |
| 69.72 |
| $4s^2 4p^1$ |
| +3, +1 |

| 49 |
| In |
| 114.8 |
| $5s^2 5p^1$ |
| +3, +1 |

| 81 |
| Tl |
| 204.4 |
| $6s^2 6p^1$ |
| +1 |

Atomic Properties

	Atomic radius (pm)	Ionic radius (pm)
B	85	
Al	143	Al^{3+} 54
Ga	135	Ga^{3+} 62
In	167	In^{3+} 80
Tl	170	Tl^+ 150

Group electron configuration is ns^2np^1. All except Tl commonly display the +3 oxidation state. The +1 state becomes more common down the group.

Atomic size is smaller and EN is higher than for 2A(2) elements; but IE is lower because it is easier to remove e⁻ from the higher energy p sublevel.

Atomic size, IE, and EN do not change as expected down the group because there are intervening transition and inner transition elements.

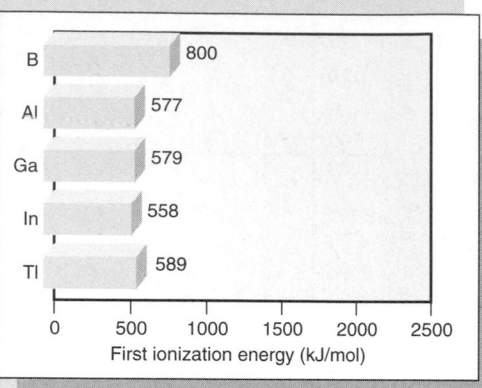

First ionization energy (kJ/mol): B 800, Al 577, Ga 579, In 558, Tl 589

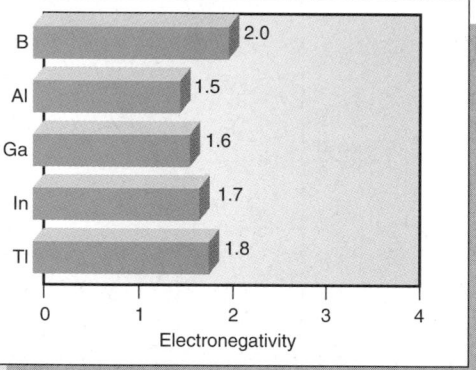

Electronegativity: B 2.0, Al 1.5, Ga 1.6, In 1.7, Tl 1.8

Physical Properties

Bonding changes from network covalent in B to metallic in rest of group. Thus, B has a much higher melting point than the others, but there is no overall trend. Boiling points decrease down the group.

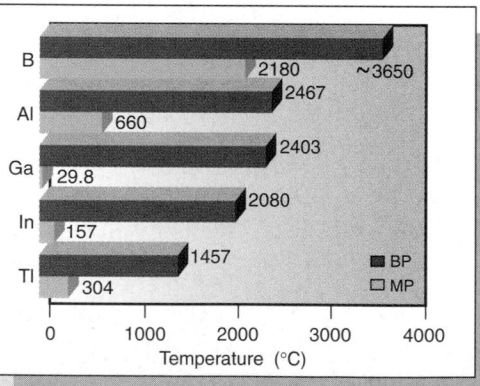

Temperature (°C) — BP / MP:
B 2180, ~3650
Al 660, 2467
Ga 29.8, 2403
In 157, 2080
Tl 304, 1457

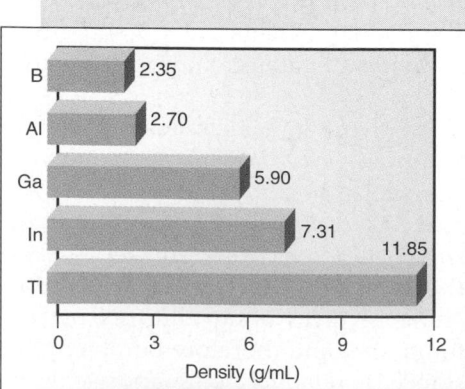

Density (g/mL): B 2.35, Al 2.70, Ga 5.90, In 7.31, Tl 11.85

Densities increase down the group.

Some Reactions and Compounds

Important Reactions

In reactions 1 to 3, note that the elements (E) usually require higher temperatures to react than those of Groups 1A(1) and 2A(2); note the lower oxidation state of Tl. Reactions 4 to 6 show some compounds in key industrial processes.

1. The elements react sluggishly, if at all, with water:

$$2Ga(s) + 6H_2O(hot) \longrightarrow 2Ga^{3+}(aq) + 6OH^-(aq) + 3H_2(g)$$

$$2Tl(s) + 2H_2O(steam) \longrightarrow 2Tl^+(aq) + 2OH^-(aq) + H_2(g)$$

Al becomes covered with a layer of Al_2O_3 that prevents further reaction (see photo).

Electron micrograph of oxide coating on Al surface

2. When strongly heated in pure O_2, all members form oxides:

$$4E(s) + 3O_2(g) \xrightarrow{\Delta} 2E_2O_3(s)$$

$$(E = B, Al, Ga, In)$$

$$4Tl(s) + O_2(g) \xrightarrow{\Delta} 2Tl_2O(s)$$

Oxide acidity decreases down the group: B_2O_3 (weakly acidic) $> Al_2O_3 > Ga_2O_3 > In_2O_3 > Tl_2O$ (strongly basic), and the +1 oxide is more basic than the +3 oxide.

3. All members reduce halogens (X_2):

$$2E(s) + 3X_2 \longrightarrow 2EX_3 \qquad (E = B, Al, Ga, In)$$

$$2Tl(s) + X_2 \longrightarrow 2TlX(s)$$

BX_3 are volatile covalent molecules. Trihalides of Al, Ga, and In are (mostly) ionic solids but occur as covalent dimers in the gas phase; in this way, the 3A atom attains a filled outer level.

4. Acid treatment of Al_2O_3 is important in water purification:

$$Al_2O_3(s) + 3H_2SO_4(l) \longrightarrow Al_2(SO_4)_3(s) + 3H_2O(l)$$

In water, $Al_2(SO_4)_3$ and CaO form a colloid that aids in removing suspended particles.

5. The overall reaction in the production of aluminum metal is a redox process:

$$2Al_2O_3(s) + 3C(s) \longrightarrow 4Al(s) + 3CO_2(g)$$

This process is carried out electrochemically in the presence of cryolite (Na_3AlF_6), which lowers the melting point of the reactant mixture and takes part in the change (Section 22.4).

6. A displacement reaction produces gallium arsenide, GaAs (see Margin Note, p. 554):

$$(CH_3)_3Ga(g) + AsH_3(g) \longrightarrow 3CH_4(g) + GaAs(s)$$

Important Compounds

1. Boron oxide, B_2O_3. Used in the production of borosilicate glass (see Margin Note, p. 558).

2. Borax, $Na_2[B_4O_5(OH)_4] \cdot 8H_2O$. Major mineral source of boron compounds and B_2O_3. Used as a fireproof insulation material and as a washing powder (20-Mule Team Borax).

3. Boric acid, H_3BO_3 [or $B(OH)_3$]. Used as external disinfectant, eyewash, and insecticide.

4. Diborane, B_2H_6. A powerful reductant for possible use as a rocket fuel. Used to synthesize higher boranes, compounds that led to new theories of chemical bonding.

5. Aluminum sulfate (alum), $Al_2(SO_4)_3 \cdot 18H_2O$. Used in purifying water, tanning leather, sizing paper, as a fixative for dyeing cloth (see photo), and as an antiperspirant.

6. Aluminum oxide, Al_2O_3. Major compound in natural source (bauxite) of Al metal. Used as abrasive in sandpaper, sanding and cutting tools, and toothpaste. Large crystals with metal ion impurities often of gemstone quality (see photo). Inert support for chromatography. In fibrous forms, woven into heat-resistant fabrics; also used to strengthen ceramics and metals.

Ruby

7. $Tl_2Ba_2Ca_2Cu_3O_{10}$. Becomes a high-temperature superconductor at 125 K, which is readily attained with liquid N_2 (see photo).

Magnet levitated by superconductor

than is released when two more weak Tl—Cl bonds form in TlCl$_3$. In fact, TlCl$_3$ is so unstable that it decomposes readily to Cl$_2$ gas and TlCl.

3. *Relative basicity of oxides.* In general, *lower state oxides are more basic than higher state oxides.* A good example in Group 3A is that In$_2$O is more basic than In$_2$O$_3$. In general, when an element has more than one oxidation state, *it acts more like a metal in its lower state,* and this, too, is related to ionic charge density. In this case, the lower charge of In$^+$ does not polarize the O^{2-} ion as much as the higher charge of In^{3+} does. Thus, in compounds of general formula E$_2$O, the E-to-O bonding is more ionic than in E$_2$O$_3$, so the O^{2-} ion is more available to act as a base (Interchapter, Topic 4).

Highlights of Boron Chemistry

Like the other Period 2 members, the chemical behavior of boron is strikingly different from that of the other members of its group. As pointed out earlier, *all boron compounds are covalent,* and unlike the other 3A(13) members, boron forms network covalent compounds or large molecules with metals, H, O, N, and C. The unifying feature of many B compounds is their *electron deficiency,* but B adopts two strategies to fill its outer level: accepting a bonding pair from an electron-rich atom and forming bridge bonds with electron-poor atoms.

Accepting a Bonding Pair from an Electron-Rich Atom In gaseous boron trihalides (BX$_3$), the B atom is electron deficient, with only six electrons around it (Section 10.1). To attain an octet, the B atom accepts a lone pair of electrons from an electron-rich atom and forms a covalent bond:

$$BF_3(g) + :NH_3(g) \longrightarrow F_3B—NH_3(g)$$

(Such reactions, in which one reactant accepts an electron pair from another to form a covalent bond, are very widespread in inorganic, organic, and biochemical processes. They are known as *Lewis acid-base reactions,* and we'll discuss them in Chapters 18 and 23 and see examples of them throughout the second half of the text.)

Similarly, B has only six electrons in boric acid, B(OH)$_3$ (sometimes written as H$_3$BO$_3$). In water, the acid itself does not release a proton. Rather it accepts an electron pair from the O in H$_2$O, forming a fourth bond and releasing an H$^+$ ion:

$$B(OH)_3(s) + H_2O(l) \rightleftharpoons B(OH)_4^-(aq) + H^+(aq)$$

Boron's outer shell is filled in the wide variety of borate salts, such as the mineral borax (sodium borate), Na$_2$[B$_4$O$_5$(OH)$_4$]·8H$_2$O, used for decades as a household cleaning agent. ◆

Boron also attains an octet in several nitrogen compounds whose structures are amazingly similar to that of elemental carbon and some of its organic compounds (Figure 14.9). These similarities are due to the fact that the size, IE, and EN of C are between those of B and N (see Table 14.1). Moreover, C has four valence electrons, whereas B has three and N has five, so the $\cdot\ddot{C}—\ddot{C}\cdot$ and $\cdot\ddot{B}—\dot{N}\cdot$ groupings have the same number of valence electrons. Therefore, H$_3$C—CH$_3$ (ethane) and H$_3$B—NH$_3$ are isoelectronic, as are benzene and borazine (Figure 14.9A and B). Boron nitride (Figure 14.9C) has a structure consisting of hexagons fused into sheets very similar to that of graphite. However, its π electrons are localized into separate double bonds, whereas the π electrons in graphite are highly delocalized through resonance. As a result, boron nitride is an electrical insulator, whereas graphite is an electrical conductor. At high pressure and temperature, boron nitride forms borazon (Figure 14.9D), which has a crystal structure like that of diamond and is extremely hard and abrasive.

◆ **Borates in Your Labware**
Strong heating of boric acid (or borate salts) drives off water molecules and gives molten boron oxide: 2B(OH)$_3$(s) ⟶ B$_2$O$_3$(l) + 3H$_2$O(g). The molten oxide dissolves metal oxides to form borate glasses. When mixed with silica (SiO$_2$), it forms borosilicate glass. Its transparency and small change in size when heated or cooled make borosilicate glass useful in cookware and in the glassware you use in the lab.

Figure 14.9 **Similarities between substances with C—C bonds and those with B—N bonds.** Note that in each case, B attains an octet of electrons by bonding with electron-rich N. **A,** Ethane and its BN analog. **B,** Benzene and borazine, which is often referred to as "inorganic" benzene. **C,** Graphite and the similar extended hexagonal structure of boron nitride. **D,** Diamond and borazon have the same crystal structure and are among the hardest substances known.

Forming Bridge Bonds with Electron-Poor Atoms In elemental boron and its many hydrides (boranes), there is no electron-rich atom to supply boron with electrons. In these substances, boron attains an octet through some unusual bonding. In diborane (B_2H_6) and many larger boranes, for example, two types of B—H bonds exist. The first type is a typical electron-pair bond. The valence bond picture in Figure 14.10 shows an sp^3 orbital of B overlapping the H $1s$ orbital in each of the four terminal B—H bonds, using two of the three electrons in the valence shell of each B atom.

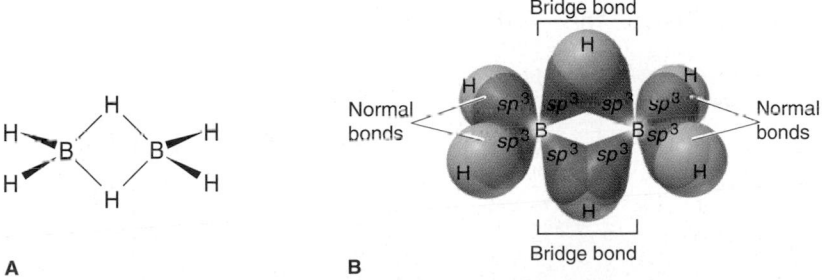

Figure 14.10 **The two types of covalent bonding in diborane. A,** A perspective diagram of B_2H_6 shows the unusual B—H—B bridge bond and the tetrahedral arrangement around each B atom. **B,** A valence bond depiction shows sp^3-hybridized B forming normal covalent bonds at the four terminal B—H bonds and bridge bonds, in which two electrons bind three atoms, at the two central B—H—B groupings.

A B_{12} unit

B B_5H_9

Figure 14.11 **The boron icosa-hedron and a larger borane. A,** The icosahedron structural unit of elemental boron. **B,** The structure of B_5H_9, one of many boranes.

The other type of bond is a hydride **bridge bond** (or three-center, two-electron bond), in which *each B—H—B grouping is held together by only two electrons.* An sp^3 orbital from *each* B overlaps an H $1s$ orbital between them. Two electrons move through this extended bonding orbital—one from one of the B atoms and the other from the H atom—and join the two B atoms via the H atom bridge. Notice that *each B atom is surrounded by eight electrons:* four from the two normal B—H bonds and four from the two B—H—B bridge bonds. In many boranes and in elemental boron (Figure 14.11), one B atom bridges two others in a three-center, two-electron B—B—B bond.

Diagonal Relationships: Beryllium and Aluminum

Beryllium in Group 2A(2) and aluminum in Group 3A(13) are the next pair of diagonally related elements. Both form oxoanions in strong base: beryllate, $Be(OH)_4^{2-}$, and aluminate, $Al(OH)_4^-$. Both have bridge bonds in their hydrides and chlorides. Both form oxide coatings impervious to reaction with water, and both oxides are amphoteric, extremely hard, and high melting. Although their atomic and ionic sizes differ, the small, highly charged Be^{2+} and Al^{3+} ions polarize nearby electron clouds strongly. Therefore, some Al compounds and all Be compounds have significant covalent character.

14.6 Group 4A(14): The Carbon Family

The whole range of elemental behavior occurs within Group 4A(14): non-metallic carbon (C) leads off, followed by the metalloids silicon (Si) and germanium (Ge), with metallic tin (Sn) and lead (Pb) at the bottom of the group. Information about the compounds of C and of Si fills libraries: organic chemistry, most polymer chemistry, and biochemistry are based on carbon, whereas geochemistry is based on silicon. There are also some extremely important polymer and electronic technologies based on silicon. The Group 4A(14) Family Portrait (pp. 562 and 563) summarizes atomic, physical, and chemical properties.

How Does the Bonding in an Element Affect Physical Properties?

The elements of Group 4A(14) and their neighbors in Groups 3A(13) and 5A(15) illustrate how physical properties, such as melting point and heat of fusion (ΔH_{fus}^0), depend on the type of bonding in an element (Table 14.2). Within Group 4A, the large decrease in melting point between the C and Si covalent networks is due to longer, weaker bonds in the Si structure; the

Table 14.2 Bond Type and the Melting Process in Groups 3A(13) to 5A(15)

Period	Group 3A(13)				Group 4A(14)				Group 5A(15)				Key:	
	Element	Bond Type	Melting Point (°C)	ΔH_{fus} (kJ/mol)	Element	Bond Type	Melting Point (°C)	ΔH_{fus} (kJ/mol)	Element	Bond Type	Melting Point (°C)	ΔH_{fus} (kJ/mol)		Metallic
2	B	⬡	2180	23.6	C	⬡	4100	Very high	N	∞	−210	0.7		Covalent network
3	Al	⬛	660	10.5	Si	⬡	1420	50.6	P	∞	44.1	2.5		Covalent molecule
4	Ga	⬛	30	5.6	Ge	⬡	945	36.8	As	⬡	816	27.7		Metal
5	In	⬛	157	3.3	Sn	⬛	232	7.1	Sb	⬡	631	20.0		Metalloid
6	Tl	⬛	304	4.3	Pb	⬛	327	4.8	Bi	⬛	271	10.5		Nonmetal

large decrease between Ge and Sn is due to the change from covalent network to metallic bonding. Similarly, looking horizontally, the large increases in melting point and ΔH_{fus}^0 across a period between Al and Si and between Ga and Ge reflect the change from metallic bonding to covalent networks. Note the abrupt rises in these properties from the values for metallic Al, Ga, and Sn to those for the network-covalent metalloids Si, Ge, and Sb, and note the abrupt drops from the covalent networks of C and Si to the individual molecules of N and P in Group 5A.

Allotropism: Different Forms of an Element   Striking changes in physical properties often appear among **allotropes,** different crystalline or molecular forms of a substance. One allotrope is usually more stable than another at a particular pressure and temperature. Group 4A provides the first dramatic example of allotropism, in the forms of carbon. It is difficult to imagine two substances made entirely of the same atom that are more different than graphite and diamond. Graphite is a black electrical conductor that is soft and "greasy," whereas diamond is a colorless electrical insulator that is extremely hard. Graphite is the standard state of carbon, the more stable form at ordinary temperature and pressure, as the phase diagram in Figure 14.12 shows. Fortunately for jewelry owners, diamond changes to graphite at a negligible rate under normal conditions.

In the mid-1980s, interest arose about a newly discovered allotrope of carbon. Mass spectrometric analysis of soot had shown evidence for a soccer ball–shaped molecule of formula C_{60} (Figure 14.13A; see also the Gallery, p. 383). More recent findings reveal the molecule in geological samples formed by meteorite impact, even the one that occurred around the time the dinosaurs became extinct. The molecule has been dubbed *buckminsterfullerene* (informally called a *bucky ball*) after the architect-engineer R. Buckminster Fuller, who designed structures with similar shapes. Excitement rose in 1990, when scientists learned how to prepare multigram quantities of C_{60} and related fullerenes, enough to study macroscopic behavior and possible applications. Since then, metal atoms have been incorporated into the structure and compounds have been prepared with many different groups attached (fluorine, hydroxyl, sugars, etc.) that have a range of useful properties.

Then, in 1991, scientists passed an electric discharge through graphite rods sealed in a container with helium gas and obtained extremely thin (~1 nm in diameter) graphite-like tubes with fullerene ends (Figure 14.13B). These "nanotubes" are rigid and, on a mass basis, much stronger than steel along their long axis. They also conduct electricity along this axis because of the delocalized electrons. Reports about fullerenes and nanotubes appear almost daily in scientific journals. With potential applications in ultraminiature electronics, catalysis, polymers, and medicine, fullerene and nanotube chemistry will receive increasing attention well into the next century.

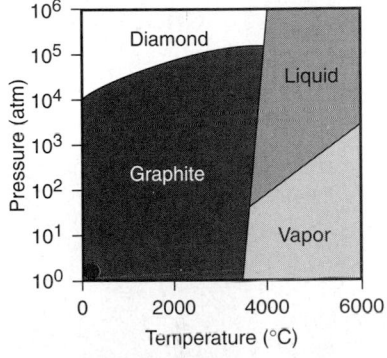

Figure 14.12 Phase diagram of carbon. Graphite is the more stable form at ordinary conditions (*small red circle at extreme lower left*). Diamond is more stable at very high pressure.

Figure 14.13 Buckyballs and nanotubes. A, Crystals of buckminsterfullerene (C_{60}) are shown leading to a ball-and-stick model. The parent of the fullerenes, the "bucky ball," is a soccer ball–shaped molecule of 60 carbon atoms. **B,** Nanotubes are single or, as shown in this electron micrograph, concentric graphite-like tubes with fullerene ends (see the Gallery, p. 383).

A

B

Key Atomic and Physical Properties

KEY

Atomic No.

Symbol

Atomic mass

Valence e⁻
configuration

Common
oxidation
states

ns^2np^2

GROUP 4A(14)

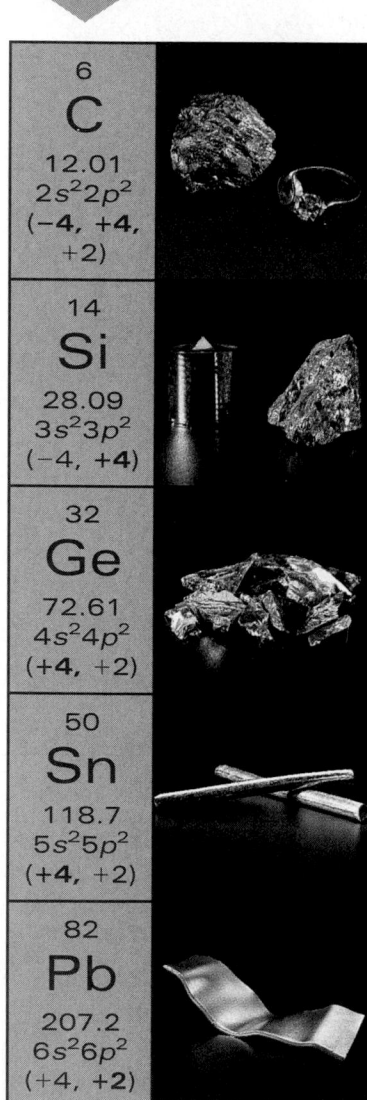

6
C
12.01
$2s^22p^2$
(**−4**, **+4**, +2)

14
Si
28.09
$3s^23p^2$
(−4, **+4**)

32
Ge
72.61
$4s^24p^2$
(**+4**, +2)

50
Sn
118.7
$5s^25p^2$
(**+4**, +2)

82
Pb
207.2
$6s^26p^2$
(+4, **+2**)

Atomic Properties

Atomic radius (pm)		Ionic radius (pm)
C 77		
Si 118		
Ge 122		
Sn 140		Sn^{2+} 118
Pb 146		Pb^{2+} 119

Group electron configuration is ns^2np^2. Down the group, the number of oxidation states decreases, and the lower (+2) state becomes more common.

Down the group, size increases, as IE and EN generally decrease; but deviations occur for Ge and Pb because of intervening transition and inner transition elements.

First ionization energy (kJ/mol)

C 1086
Si 786
Ge 761
Sn 708
Pb 715

Electronegativity

C 2.5
Si 1.8
Ge 1.8
Sn 1.8
Pb 1.9

Physical Properties

Trends in properties, such as decreasing hardness and melting point, are due to changes in types of bonding within the solid: covalent network in C, Si, and Ge; metallic in Sn and Pb (*see text*).

Temperature (°C)

	BP	MP
C	Unstable	4100
Si	~3280	1420
Ge	2850	945
Sn	2623	232
Pb	1751	327

Density (g/mL)

C 2.27
Si 2.34
Ge 5.32
Sn 7.26
Pb 11.34

Down the group, density increases because of several factors, including differences in crystal packing.

Some Reactions and Compounds

Oxyacetylene torch

Important Reactions

Reactions 1 and 2 pertain to all the elements (E); reactions 3 to 7 concern industrial uses for compounds of C and Si.

1. The elements are oxidized by halogen:

$$E(s) + 2X_2 \longrightarrow EX_4 \qquad (E = C, Si, Ge)$$

The +2 halides are more stable for tin and lead, SnX_2 and PbX_2.

2. The elements are oxidized by O_2:

$$E(s) + O_2(g) \longrightarrow EO_2 \qquad (E = C, Si, Ge, Sn)$$

Pb forms the +2 oxide, PbO. Oxides become more basic down the group. The reaction of CO_2 and H_2O provides the weak acidity of natural unpolluted waters:

$$CO_2(g) + H_2O(l) \rightleftharpoons [H_2CO_3(aq)] \rightleftharpoons H^+(aq) + HCO_3^-(aq)$$

3. Air and steam passed over hot coke produce gaseous fuel mixtures (producer gas and water gas):

$$C(s) + air(g) + H_2O(g) \longrightarrow CO(g) + CO_2(g) + N_2(g) + H_2(g)$$
[not balanced]

4. Hydrocarbons react with O_2 to form CO_2 and H_2O. The reaction for methane is adapted to yield heat or electricity:

$$CH_4(g) + 2O_2(g) \longrightarrow CO_2(g) + 2H_2O(g)$$

5. Certain metal carbides react with water to produce acetylene:

$$CaC_2(s) + 2H_2O(l) \longrightarrow Ca(OH)_2(aq) + C_2H_2(g)$$

The gas is used to make other organic compounds and as a fuel in welding (*see photo*).

6. Freons (chlorofluorocarbons) are formed by fluorinating carbon tetrachloride:

$$CCl_4(l) + HF(g) \longrightarrow CFCl_3(g) + HCl(g)$$

Production of trichlorofluoromethane (Freon-11), the major refrigerant in the world, is being eliminated because of its severe effects on the environment (*see Margin Note, p. 565*).

7. Silica is reduced to form elemental silicon:

$$SiO_2(s) + 2C(s) \longrightarrow Si(s) + 2CO(g)$$

This crude silicon is made ultrapure through zone refining (*see Gallery, Section 13.5*) for manufacture of computer chips (*see photo*).

Computer chip

Important Compounds

1. Carbon monoxide, CO. Used as a gaseous fuel, as a precursor for one-carbon organic compounds, and as a reactant in the purification of nickel. Formed in internal combustion engines and released as a toxic air pollutant.

2. Carbon dioxide, CO_2. Atmospheric component used by photosynthetic plants to make carbohydrates and O_2. The final oxidation product of all C-based fuels; its increase in the atmosphere may lead to global warming. Used industrially as a refrigerant gas, blanketing gas in fire extinguishers, and effervescent gas in beverages (*see photo*). Combined with NH_3 to form urea for fertilizers and plastics manufacture.

3. Methane, CH_4. Used as a fuel and in the production of many organic compounds. Major component of natural gas. Formed by anaerobic decomposition of plants (swamp gas) and by microbes in termites and certain mammals. May contribute to global warming.

4. Silicon dioxide, SiO_2. Occurs in many amorphous (glassy) and crystalline forms, quartz being the most common. Used to make glass and as an inert chromatography support material.

5. Silicon carbide, SiC. Known as carborundum, a major industrial abrasive and a highly refractory ceramic for tough, high-temperature uses. Can be doped to form a high-temperature semiconductor.

6. Organotin compounds, R_4Sn. Used to stabilize PVC, poly(vinyl chloride) plastics (*see photo*), and to cure silicone rubbers. Agricultural biocide for insects, fungi, and weeds.

7. Tetraethyl lead, $(C_2H_5)_4Pb$. Once used as a gasoline additive to improve fuel efficiency, but now removed because of its inactivation of auto catalytic converters. Major source of lead as a toxic air pollutant.

Figure 14.14 The greater metallic character of tin and lead in the lower oxidation state. Metals with more than one oxidation state exhibit more metallic behavior in the lower state. Tin(II) and lead(II) chlorides are white, crystalline, saltlike solids. In contrast, tin(IV) and lead(IV) chlorides are volatile liquids, indicating the presence of individual molecules.

Tin has two allotropes. White β-tin is stable at room temperature and above, whereas gray α-tin is the more stable form below 13°C (56°F). When white tin is kept for long periods at a low temperature, some converts to microcrystals of gray tin. The random formation and growth of these regions of gray tin, which has a different crystal structure, weaken the metal and make it crumble. In the unheated cathedrals of medieval northern Europe, tin pipes of magnificent organs sometimes crumbled as a result of "tin disease" caused by this allotropic transition from white to gray tin.

How Does the Type of Bonding Change in Group 4A(14) Compounds?

The 4A(14) elements display a wide range of chemical behavior, from the covalent compounds of carbon to the ionic compounds of lead. Carbon's intermediate EN of 2.5 ensures that it virtually always forms covalent bonds, but the larger members of Group 4A form bonds with increasing ionic character. With nonmetals, Si and Ge form strong polar covalent bonds, such as the Si—O bond, one of the strongest of any Period 3 element (368 kJ/mol). This bond is responsible for the physical and chemical stability of the Earth's solid surface, as we discuss later in this section. Although individual ions rarely exist, Sn and Pb bonding to nonmetals has more ionic character.

The patterns of elements with more than one oxidation state that we first observed in Group 3A(13) appear here as well. After silicon, the shift to greater importance of the lower oxidation state occurs: Si compounds of the +4 state are much more stable than those of the +2 state, whereas Pb compounds of the +2 state are more stable than those of the +4 state. The elements also behave more like metals in the lower state. Consider the chlorides and oxides of Sn and Pb. Figure 14.14 shows that the +2 chlorides $SnCl_2$ and $PbCl_2$ are white, relatively high-melting, water-soluble crystals—typical properties of a salt. In contrast, $SnCl_4$ is a volatile, benzene-soluble liquid, and $PbCl_4$ is a thermally unstable oil. The +2 oxides SnO and PbO are more basic than the +4 oxides SnO_2 and PbO_2 because the +2 metals are less able to polarize the O^{2-} ion, so the E-to-O bonding is more ionic.

Highlights of Carbon Chemistry

Like the other Period 2 elements, carbon is an anomaly in its group; indeed it may be an anomaly in the entire periodic table. Carbon forms bonds with the smaller Group 1A(1) and 2A(2) metals, many transition metals, the halogens, and its neighbors B, Si, N, O, P, and S. This versatile element exhibits every oxidation state possible for its group, from +4 in CO_2 and halides like CCl_4 through −4 in CH_4.

Figure 14.15 Three of the several million known organic compounds of carbon. A, Acrylonitrile (precursor of acrylic fibers). **B,** One of numerous PCBs (polychlorinated biphenyls). **C,** Lysine (an amino acid).

A Acrylonitrile   **B PCB**   **C Lysine**

Two features stand out in the chemistry of carbon: its ability to bond to itself, a process known as *catenation*, and its ability to form multiple bonds. As a result of its small size and its capacity for four bonds, carbon can form chains, branches, and rings that lead to myriad structures. Add a lot of H, some O and N, a bit of S, P, halogen, and a few metals, and you have the whole organic world! Figure 14.15 shows three of the several million organic compounds known. Multiple bonding is common in carbon structures because the C—C bond is short enough for sideways overlap of half-filled $2p$ orbitals to form p,p-π bonds. (In Chapter 15, we discuss in detail how the atomic properties of carbon give rise to the diverse structure and reactivity of organic compounds.)

Because the other 4A members are larger, E—E bonds become longer and weaker down the group; thus, in terms of bond strength, C—C > Si—Si > Ge—Ge. The empty d orbitals of these larger atoms make the chains much more susceptible to chemical attack. Thus, some compounds with long Si chains are known but they are very reactive, and the longest Ge chain has only eight atoms. Moreover, longer bonds do not typically allow sufficient overlap for p,p-π bonding. Only very recently have compounds with π bonds between Si atoms and between Ge atoms been prepared, but they too are extremely reactive.

In contrast to its organic compounds, carbon's inorganic compounds are simple. Metal carbonates are the main mineral form. Marble, limestone, chalk, coral, and several other types are found in enormous deposits throughout the world. Many of these compounds are remnants of fossilized marine organisms. Carbonates are used in several common antacids because they react with the HCl in stomach acid [see Group 2A(2) Family Portrait, compound 4]:

$$CaCO_3(s) + 2HCl(aq) \longrightarrow CaCl_2(aq) + CO_2(g) + H_2O(l)$$

Identical net ionic reactions with sulfuric and nitric acids protect lakes bounded by limestone deposits from the harmful effects of acid rain.

Unlike the solid network or ionic oxides of the other 4A members, carbon forms two common gaseous oxides, CO_2 and CO. Carbon dioxide is essential to all life as the primary source of carbon in plants and animals through its role in photosynthesis. Its aqueous solution is the cause of acidity in natural waters. However, its atmospheric buildup from deforestation and excessive use of fossil fuels may severely affect the global climate. Carbon monoxide forms when carbon or its compounds burn in an inadequate supply of O_2:

$$2C(s) + O_2(g) \longrightarrow 2CO(g)$$

Carbon monoxide is a key component of syngas fuels (see Chemical Connections, p. 247) and is widely used in the production of methanol, formaldehyde, and other major industrial compounds.

CO binds strongly to many transition metals. When inhaled in cigarette smoke or polluted air, it enters the blood and binds strongly to the Fe(II) in hemoglobin, preventing the normal binding of O_2, and to other iron-containing proteins. The cyanide ion (CN^-) is *isoelectronic* with CO:

$$[:C{\equiv}N:]^- \quad \text{same electronic structure as} \quad :C{\equiv}O:$$

Cyanide binds to many of the same iron-containing proteins and is also toxic.

Monocarbon halides (or halomethanes) are tetrahedral molecules whose stability to heat and light decreases as the size of the halogen atom increases and the C—X bond becomes longer (weaker) (see Interchapter, Topic 2). The chlorofluorocarbons (CFCs, or Freons) have important industrial uses, but their short, strong carbon-halogen bonds are exceptionally stable, and the environmental persistence of these compounds has created major problems. ◆

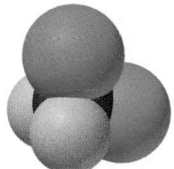

◆ **CFCs: The Good, the Bad, and the Strong**
The strengths of the C—F and C—Cl bonds make CFCs, such as Freon-12 shown here, both useful and harmful. Chemically and thermally stable, nontoxic, and nonflammable, they are excellent cleaners for electronic parts, coolants in refrigerators and air conditioners, and propellants in aerosol cans. However, these bond strengths also mean they decompose *very* slowly near the Earth's surface. In the lower atmosphere, they contribute to climate warming, absorbing infrared radiation 16,000 times as effectively as CO_2. Once in the stratosphere, however, they are bombarded by ultraviolet (UV) photons, which break the otherwise stable C—Cl bonds, releasing free Cl atoms that initiate ozone-destroying reactions (Chapter 16).

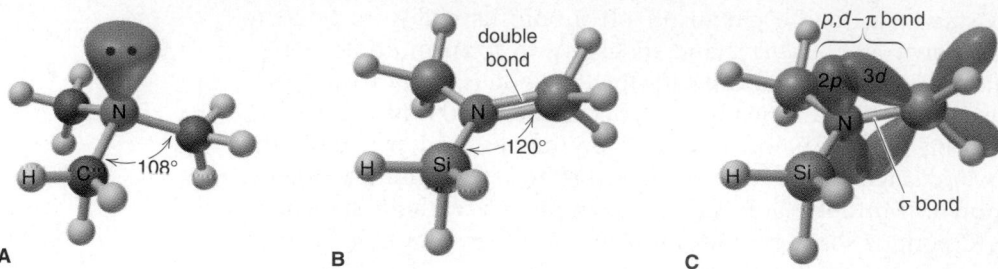

Figure 14.16 The impact of *p,d*-π bonding on the structure of trisilylamine. **A,** The molecular shape of trimethylamine is trigonal *pyramidal*, as in ammonia. **B,** Trisilylamine, the silicon analog, has a trigonal *planar* shape because of the formation of a double bond between N and Si. The ball-and-stick model shows one of three resonance forms. **C,** The lone pair in an unhybridized *p* orbital of N overlaps with an empty *d* orbital of Si to give a *p,d*-π bond. In the resonance hybrid, a *d* orbital on each Si is involved in the π bond.

Highlights of Silicon Chemistry

Silicon halides are more reactive than carbon halides because Si has empty *d* orbitals that are available for chemical attack. Surprisingly, the Si halides have longer yet *stronger* bonds than the corresponding C halides (see Tables 9.2 and 9.3). One explanation for this unusual strength is that the Si—X bond has some double-bond character because of the presence of a σ bond *and* a different type of π bond, called a *p,d*-π *bond*. This bond arises from sideways overlap of an Si *d* orbital and a halogen *p* orbital. A similar type of *p,d*-π bonding leads to the trigonal planar molecular shape of trisilylamine, in contrast to the trigonal pyramidal shape of trimethylamine, shown in Figure 14.16.

To a great extent, the chemistry of silicon is the chemistry of the *silicon-oxygen bond*. Just as carbon forms unending C—C chains, the —Si—O— grouping repeats itself endlessly in a wide variety of **silicates,** the most important minerals on the planet, and in **silicones,** synthetic polymers with many applications:

1. *Silicate minerals.* From common sand and clay to semiprecious amethyst and carnelian, silicate minerals are the dominant form of matter in the nonliving world. Oxygen, the most abundant element on Earth, and silicon, the next most abundant, compose these minerals and thus account for four of every five atoms on the surface of the planet!

The silicate building unit is the *orthosilicate* grouping, —SiO_4—, a tetrahedral arrangement of four oxygens around a central silicon. Several well-known minerals contain SiO_4^{4-} ions or small groups of them linked together. The gemstone zircon ($ZrSiO_4$) contains one unit; hemimorphite [$Zn_4(OH)_2Si_2O_7 \cdot H_2O$] contains two units linked through an oxygen corner; and beryl ($Be_3Al_2Si_6O_{18}$), the major source of beryllium, contains six units joined into a cyclic ion (Figure 14.17). As you'll see in a moment, in addition to these separate ions, SiO_4 units are linked more extensively to create much of the planet's mineral structure.

2. *Silicone polymers.* Unlike the naturally occurring silicates, silicone polymers are manufactured substances consisting of alternating Si and O atoms with two organic groups bound to the Si atoms. A key starting material is formed by the reaction of silicon with methyl chloride:

$$Si(s) + 2CH_3Cl(g) \xrightarrow[\sim 300°C]{\text{Cu catalyst}} (CH_3)_2SiCl_2(g)$$

Figure 14.17 Structures of the silicate anions in some minerals.

SiO_4^{4-}

$Si_2O_7^{6-}$

$Si_6O_{18}^{12-}$

A Silicate ion in zircon

B Silicate ion in hemimorphite

C Silicate ion in beryl

Although the corresponding carbon compound [$(CH_3)_2CCl_2$] is inert in water, the empty d orbitals in Si make this compound reactive:

$$(CH_3)_2SiCl_2(l) + 2H_2O(l) \longrightarrow (CH_3)_2Si(OH)_2(l) + 2HCl(g)$$

The product reacts with itself to form water and a silicone chain molecule called a *polydimethylsiloxane:*

$$n(CH_3)_2Si(OH)_2 \longrightarrow \left[O - \underset{\underset{CH_3}{|}}{\overset{\overset{CH_3}{|}}{Si}} \right]_n + nH_2O$$

Silicones have properties of both plastics and minerals. The organic groups give them the flexibility and weak intermolecular forces between chains of a plastic, while the O—Si—O backbone confers the thermal stability and non-flammability of a mineral. In the upcoming Gallery, note the structural similarities of silicates and silicones.

Diagonal Relationships: Boron and Silicon

The final diagonal relationship that we consider occurs between the metalloids B and Si. Both exhibit the electrical properties of a semiconductor (Section 12.6). Both elements and their mineral oxoanions, borates and silicates, occur in extended covalent networks. Both boric acid [$B(OH)_3$] and silicic acid [$Si(OH)_4$] are weakly acidic and occur in layers with widespread H bonding. Both elements form flammable, low-melting compounds with hydrogen—the boranes and silanes—that act as reducing agents.

Looking Backward and Forward: Groups 3A(13), 4A(14), and 5A(15)

Standing in Group 4A(14), we look back at Group 3A(13) as the transition from the s block of metals to the p block of mostly metalloids and nonmetals (Figure 14.18). Major changes occur in physical behavior as we move across from metals to covalent networks. Changes in chemical behavior occur as well, as cations give way to covalent tetrahedra. Looking ahead to Group 5A(15), we find covalent bonding and (as ENs increase) the expanded valence shells of nonmetals occurring more often, as well as the first appearance of monatomic anions.

Figure 14.18 Standing in Group 4A(14), looking backward to 3A(13) and forward to 5A(15).

Silicate Minerals and Silicone Polymers

The silicates and silicones show beautifully how organization at the molecular level manifests itself in the properties of macroscopic substances. Interestingly, the major types of both materials exhibit the same three structural classes: chains, sheets, and frameworks.

Silicate Minerals

Chain Silicates

The simplest structural class occurs when each SiO_4 unit shares two O corners and links into a chain. Two chains can link laterally into a ribbon, the most common having repeating $Si_4O_{11}^{6-}$ units. Metal ions bind the polyanionic ribbons together into neutral sheaths. With only weak intermolecular forces between sheaths, the material occurs in fibrous strands, as in the family of asbestos minerals.

Portion of ribbon

$Si_4O_{11}^{6-}$ unit

Asbestos

Sheet (Layer) Silicates

The next structural class arises when each SiO_4 unit shares three of its four O corners to form a sheet; double sheets arise when the fourth O is shared with another sheet. In talc, the softest mineral, the sheets interact through weak forces, so talcum powder feels slippery. If Al substitutes for some Si, or if $Al(OH)_3$ layers interleave with silicate sheets, an aluminosilicate results, such as the clay kaolinite. Different substitutions and/or interlayering of ions give the micas. In muscovite mica, ions lie between aluminosilicate double layers. Mica flakes when the ionic attractions are overcome.

$-SiO_4$
K^+
$-SiO_4$
OH^-
Al^{3+}
OH^-
$-SiO_4$
K^+
$-SiO_4$

Muscovite mica

Framework Silicates

The final structural class arises when SiO_4 units share all four O corners to give a three-dimensional framework silicate, such as silica (SiO_2), which occurs most often as α-quartz. Some of silica's 12 crystalline forms exist as semiprecious gems. Feldspars, which comprise 60% of the Earth's crust, result when some Si is replaced by Al; granite consists of microcrystals of feldspar, mica, and quartz. Eons of weathering convert feldspars into clays. Zeolites have open frameworks of polyhedra that give rise to minute tunnels. Synthetic zeolites are made with cavities of specific sizes to trap particular molecules; they are used to dry gas mixtures, separate hydrocarbons, and prepare catalysts.

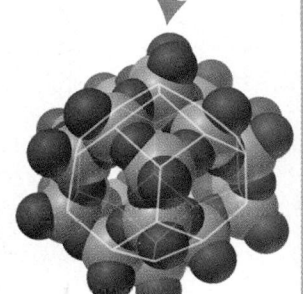

Zeolite bead

Quartz

Silicone Polymers

Polymer Chemistry

The design, synthesis, and production of polymers forms one of the largest branches of modern chemical science. Nearly half of all industrial chemists and chemical engineers are involved in this pursuit. A major branch of polymer chemistry is devoted to exploring the properties and countless uses of silicones.

chain repeating unit

chain terminating unit

Chain Silicones: Oils and Greases

The simplest structural class is the polysiloxane chain, in which each $(CH_3)_2Si(OH)_2$ unit uses both OH groups to link two others. A chain-terminating compound with a third organic group, such as $(CH_3)_3SiOH$, is added to control chain length. Polysiloxanes are unreactive, oily liquids with high viscosity and low surface tension. They are used as hydraulic oils and lubricants, as anti-foam agents in frying potato chips, and as components of suntan oil, car polish, digestive aids, and makeup.

569

Sheet Silicones: Elastomers

In the next class, the third OH group of an added bridging compound, such as $CH_3Si(OH)_3$, reacts to condense chains laterally into gummy sheets that are made into elastomers (rubbers), which are flexible, elastic, and stable from −100°C to 250°C. These are used in gaskets, rollers, cable insulation, space suits, contact lenses, and dentures.

The actor Dustin Hoffman applying makeup consisting of chain and sheet silicones.

Framework Silicones: Resins

In the final structural class, reactions that free OH groups, while substituting larger organic groups for some CH_3 groups, interlink sheets to produce strong, thermally stable resins. These are used as insulating laminates on printed circuit boards, and as nonstick coatings on cookware. Sheet and framework silicones have revolutionized modern surgical practice by providing numerous parts that can be implanted permanently in a patient to replace damaged ones. Some of these (indicated by dots on Leonardo's man) are artificial skin, bone, joints, blood vessels, and organ parts.

14.7 Group 5A(15): The Nitrogen Family

The first two elements of Group 5A(15), gaseous nonmetallic nitrogen (N) and solid nonmetallic phosphorus (P), will occupy most of our attention. The industrial and environmental significance of their compounds is matched only by their importance in the structure and function of biomolecules. Below them are two metalloids, arsenic (As) and antimony (Sb), followed by the sole metal, bismuth (Bi), the last nonradioactive element in the periodic table. The Group 5A(15) Family Portrait (pp. 572 and 573) provides an overview.

What Accounts for the Wide Range of Physical Behavior in Group 5A(15)?

Group 5A(15) displays the widest range of physical behavior we've seen so far because of large changes in bonding and intermolecular forces. Nitrogen occurs as a gas consisting of N_2 molecules, which interact through such weak dispersion forces that it *boils* more than 200°C below room temperature. Elemental phosphorus exists most commonly as tetrahedral P_4 molecules. However, because P is heavier and more polarizable than N, stronger dispersion forces are present and the element melts about 25°C above room temperature. Arsenic consists of extended, puckered sheets in which each As is covalently bonded to three others and forms nonbonding interactions with three nearest neighbors in adjacent sheets. This arrangement gives As the highest melting point in the group. A similar covalent network for Sb gives it a much higher melting point than Bi below it, which has metallic bonding.

Phosphorus has several allotropes. The white and red forms have very different properties because of the way the atoms are linked. The highly reactive white form is prepared as a gas and condensed to a whitish, waxy solid under cold water to prevent it from igniting in air. It consists of tetrahedral molecules of four P atoms bonded *to each other*, with no atom in the center (Figure 14.19A). Each P atom uses its half-filled $3p$ orbitals to bond to the other three. Whereas the $3p$ orbitals of an isolated P atom lie 90° apart, the bond angles in P_4 are 60°. With the smaller angle comes poor orbital overlap and a P—P bond strength only about 80% that of a normal P—P bond (Figure 14.19B). Weaker bonds break more easily, so they contribute to the white allotrope's high reactivity. Heating the white form in the absence of air breaks one of the P—P bonds in each tetrahedron, and those orbitals overlap with others to form the chains of P_4 units that make up the red form (Figure 14.19C). Individual molecules in white P make it highly reactive, low melting (44.1°C), and soluble in nonpolar solvents; the chains in red P make it much less reactive, high melting (~600°C), and insoluble.

Figure 14.19 Two allotropes of phosphorus. A, White phosphorus exists as individual P_4 molecules, with the P—P bonds forming the edges of a tetrahedron. **B,** The reactivity of P_4 is due in part to the strained bonds that arise from the 60° bond angle. Note how *p,p* overlap is decreased because it is not directly end to end (shown here for only three of the P—P bonds), which makes the bonds easier to break. **C,** In red phosphorus, one of the P—P bonds of the white form has broken and links the tetrahedra together. Lone pairs (not shown) reside in *s* orbitals in both allotropes.

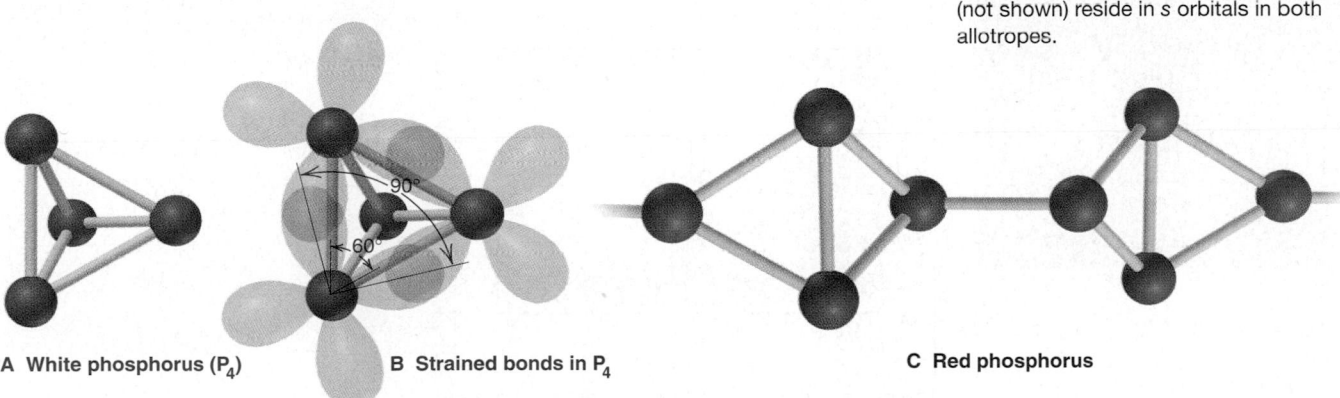

A White phosphorus (P_4) **B** Strained bonds in P_4 **C** Red phosphorus

Key Atomic and Physical Properties

KEY
Atomic No.
Symbol
Atomic mass
Valence e⁻
configuration
Common
oxidation
states

ns^2np^3

GROUP 5A(15)

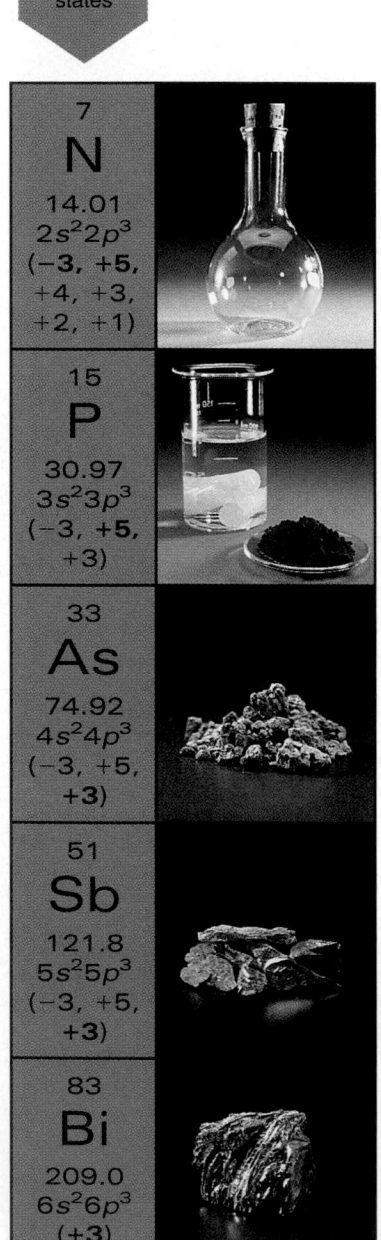

7	
N	
14.01	
$2s^2 2p^3$	
(**−3, +5,** +4, +3, +2, +1)	
15	
P	
30.97	
$3s^2 3p^3$	
(**−3, +5,** +3)	
33	
As	
74.92	
$4s^2 4p^3$	
(**−3, +5,** +3)	
51	
Sb	
121.8	
$5s^2 5p^3$	
(**−3, +5,** +3)	
83	
Bi	
209.0	
$6s^2 6p^3$	
(**+3**)	

Atomic Properties

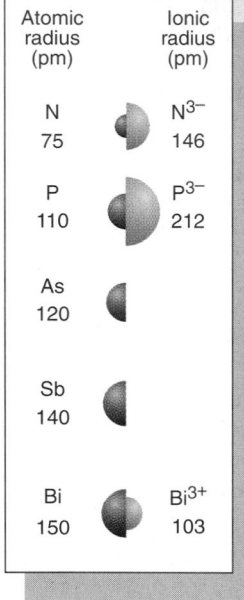

Atomic radius (pm)		Ionic radius (pm)
N 75		N^{3-} 146
P 110		P^{3-} 212
As 120		
Sb 140		
Bi 150		Bi^{3+} 103

Group electron configuration is ns^2np^3. The np sublevel is half-filled, with each p orbital containing one electron. The number of oxidation states decreases down the group, and the lower (+3) state becomes more common.

Atomic properties follow generally expected trends. The large (~50%) increase in size from N to P correlates with the much lower IE and EN of P.

First ionization energy (kJ/mol): N 1402, P 1012, As 947, Sb 834, Bi 703

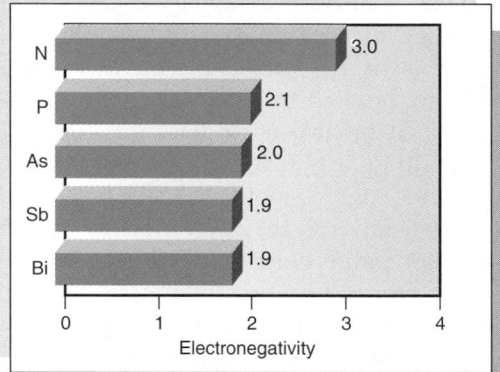

Electronegativity: N 3.0, P 2.1, As 2.0, Sb 1.9, Bi 1.9

Physical Properties

Physical properties reflect the change from individual molecules (N, P) to covalent network (As, Sb) to metal (Bi). Thus, melting points increase and then decrease. Densities of the elements as solids increase steadily.

Temperature (°C): ■ BP □ MP
N −196, −210; P 280, 44.1; As 615 (subl), 816 (at 39 atm); Sb 1587, 631; Bi 1564, 271

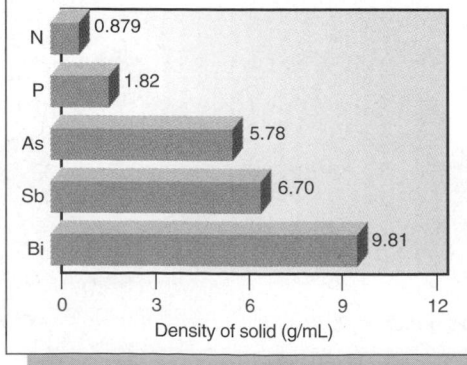

Density of solid (g/mL): N 0.879, P 1.82, As 5.78, Sb 6.70, Bi 9.81

Large atomic size and low atomic mass result in low density, which generally increases down the group because mass increases more than size.

Some Reactions and Compounds

Important Reactions

General group behavior is shown in reactions 1 to 3, whereas phosphorus chemistry is the theme in reactions 4 and 5.

1. Nitrogen is "fixed" industrially in the Haber process:

$$N_2(g) + 3H_2(g) \rightleftharpoons 2NH_3(g)$$

Further reactions convert NH_3 to NO, NO_2, and HNO_3 (see *Highlights of Nitrogen Chemistry*). Some other group hydrides are formed from reaction in water (or H_3O^+) of a metal phosphide, arsenide, and so forth:

$$Ca_3P_2(s) + 6H_2O(l) \longrightarrow 2PH_3(g) + 3Ca(OH)_2(aq)$$

2. Halides are formed by direct combination of the elements:

$$2E(s) + 3X_2 \longrightarrow 2EX_3 \quad \text{(E = all except N)}$$
$$EX_3 + X_2 \longrightarrow EX_5 \quad \text{(E = all except N and Bi)}$$

3. Oxoacids are formed from the halide in a reaction with water that is common to many nonmetal halides:

$$EX_3 + 3H_2O(l) \longrightarrow H_3EO_3(aq) + 3HX(aq)$$
$$\text{(E = all except N)}$$
$$EX_5 + 4H_2O(l) \longrightarrow H_3EO_4(aq) + 5HX(aq)$$
$$\text{(E = all except N and Bi)}$$

Note that the oxidation number of E does *not* change.

4. Phosphate ions are dehydrated to form polyphosphates:

$$3NaH_2PO_4(s) \longrightarrow Na_3P_3O_9(s) + 3H_2O(g)$$

5. When P_4 reacts in basic solution, its oxidation state both decreases *and* increases (disproportionation):

$$P_4(s) + 3OH^-(aq) + 3H_2O(l) \longrightarrow PH_3(g) + 3H_2PO_2^-(aq)$$

Analogous reactions are typical of many nonmetals, such as S_8 and X_2 (halogens).

Important Compounds

1. Ammonia, NH_3. First substance formed when atmospheric N_2 is used to make N-containing compounds. Annual multimillion-ton production for use in fertilizers, explosives, rayon, and polymers such as nylon, urea-formaldehyde resins, and acrylics.

Detonation of explosives

2. Hydrazine, N_2H_4 (see *Margin Note, p. 574*).

3. Nitric oxide (NO), nitrogen dioxide (NO_2), and nitric acid (HNO_3). Oxides are intermediates in HNO_3 production. Acid used in fertilizer manufacture, nylon production, metal etching, and explosives industry (see *Highlights of Nitrogen Chemistry*).

4. Amino acids, H_3N^+—CH(R)—COO$^-$ (R = one of 20 different organic groups). Occur in every organism, both free and linked together into proteins. Essential to the growth and function of all cells. Synthetic amino acids used as dietary supplements.

5. Phosphorus trichloride, PCl_3. Used to form many organic phosphorus compounds, including oil and fuel additives, plasticizers, flame retardants, and insecticides. Also used to make PCl_5, $POCl_3$, and other important P-containing compounds.

6. Tetraphosphorus decaoxide (P_4O_{10}) and phosphoric acid (H_3PO_4) (see *Highlights of Phosphorus Chemistry*).

7. Sodium tripolyphosphate, $Na_5P_3O_{10}$. As a water-softening agent (Calgon), combines with hard-water Mg^{2+} and

Algal growth in polluted lake

Ca^{2+} ions, preventing them from reacting with soap anions, and thus improves cleaning action. Use curtailed in the United States because it pollutes lakes and streams by causing excessive algal growth (see photo).

8. Adenosine triphosphate (ATP) and other biophosphates. ATP acts to transfer chemical energy in the cell; necessary for all biological processes requiring energy. Phosphate groups occur in sugars, fats, proteins, and nucleic acids.

9. Bismuth subsalicylate, $BiO(C_7H_5O_3)$. The active ingredient in Pepto-Bismol (see photo), a widely used remedy for diarrhea and nausea. (The pink color is not due to this white compound.)

What Patterns Appear in the Chemical Behavior of Group 5A(15)?

The same general pattern of chemical behavior that we discussed for Group 4A(14) appears again in this group, reflecting the change from nonmetallic N to metallic Bi. The overwhelming majority of 5A(15) compounds have *covalent bonds*. Whereas N can form no more than four bonds, the next three members can expand their valence shells by using empty *d* orbitals.

For a 5A(15) element to form an ion with a noble gas core, it must *gain* three electrons, the last two in endothermic steps. Nevertheless, the enormous lattice energy released when such highly charged anions attract cations drives their formation, but this only occurs with N in compounds with active metals, such as Li_3N and Mg_3N_2 (and perhaps with P in Na_3P). Metallic Bi forms mostly covalent compounds but becomes a cation in a few compounds, such as BiF_3 and $Bi(NO_3)_3 \cdot 5H_2O$, by *losing* its three valence *p* electrons.

Again, we see the patterns first seen in Groups 3A and 4A as we move down the group. Fewer oxidation states occur, with the lower state becoming more prominent: N exhibits every state possible for a 5A element, from +5 to −3; only the +5 and +3 states are common for P, As, and Sb; and +3 is the only common state of Bi. The acid-base behavior of the oxides changes from acidic to amphoteric to basic, reflecting the increase in metallic character. In addition, the lower oxide of an element is more basic than the higher oxide, reflecting the greater ionic character of the E-to-O bonding in the lower oxide.

All the Group 5A(15) elements form gaseous hydrides of formula EH_3. Except for NH_3, they are extremely reactive and poisonous and are synthesized by reaction of a metal phosphide, arsenide, and so forth, which acts as a strong base in water or aqueous acid. For example,

$$Ca_3As_2(s) + 6H_2O(l) \longrightarrow 2AsH_3(g) + 3Ca(OH)_2(aq)$$

Ammonia is made industrially by direct combination of the elements at high pressure and moderately high temperature:

$$N_2(g) + 3H_2(g) \rightleftharpoons 2NH_3(g)$$

Molecular properties of the hydrides reveal some interesting bonding and structure patterns:

- Despite its much lower molar mass, NH_3 melts and boils at higher temperatures than the other 5A hydrides as a result of *H bonding*.
- Bond angles decrease from 107.3° for NH_3 to around 90° for the others, which suggests that the larger atoms use unhybridized *p* orbitals.
- E—H bond lengths increase down the group, so bond strength and thermal stability decrease: AsH_3 decomposes at 250°C, SbH_3 at 20°C, and BiH_3 at −45°C.

We'll see these three features—H bonding for the smallest member, change in bond angles, change in bond energies—in the hydrides of Group 6A(16) as well. ◆

All Group 5A(15) elements form trihalides (EX_3), and some form pentahalides (EX_5). Nitrogen forms the trihalide only, because it cannot expand its valence shell; bismuth forms the trihalide because it exhibits only the +3 state. Most trihalides are prepared by direct combination:

$$P_4(s) + 6Cl_2(g) \longrightarrow 4PCl_3(l)$$

The pentahalides form with excess halogen:

$$PCl_3(l) + Cl_2(g) \longrightarrow PCl_5(s)$$

As with the hydrides, the thermal stability of the halides decreases as the E—X bond becomes longer. Among the nitrogen halides, for example, NF_3 is a stable, rather unreactive gas. NCl_3 is explosive and reacts rapidly with water. (The chemist who first prepared it lost three fingers and an eye!) NBr_3 can

◆ **Hydrazine, Nitrogen's Other Hydride** Aside from NH_3, the most important 5A(15) hydride is hydrazine, N_2H_4. Like NH_3, it is a weak base, forming $N_2H_5^+$ and $N_2H_6^{2+}$ ions with acids. Hydrazine is also used to make antituberculin drugs, plant growth regulators, and fungicides, and organic hydrazine derivatives are used in rocket and missile fuels. We might expect the lone pairs in the structure to lie opposite each other and give a symmetrical molecule with no dipole moment. However, repulsions between each lone pair and the bonding pairs on the other atom force the lone pairs to lie below the N—N bond (see model), giving a large dipole moment ($\mu = 1.85$ D in the gas phase). A similar arrangement occurs in hydrogen peroxide (H_2O_2), the analogous hydride of oxygen.

only be made below $-87°C$. NI_3 has never even been prepared, but an ammoniated product ($NI_3 \cdot NH_3$) explodes at the slightest touch.

In an aqueous reaction pattern *typical of many nonmetal halides,* the 5A halides react with water to yield the hydrogen halide and the oxoacid with E in the *same* oxidation state as in the original halide. For example, PX_5 (O.N. of P = +5) produces phosphoric acid (O.N. of P = +5) and HX:

$$PCl_5(s) + 4H_2O(l) \longrightarrow H_3PO_4(l) + 5HCl(g)$$

Highlights of Nitrogen Chemistry

Surely the most obvious highlight of nitrogen chemistry is the inertness of N_2 itself. Nearly four-fifths of the atmosphere consists of N_2, and the other fifth is nearly all O_2, a very strong oxidizing agent. Nevertheless, the searing temperature of a lightning bolt is required for significant amounts of atmospheric nitrogen oxides to form. Thus, despite its inertness at moderate temperatures, N_2 reacts at high temperatures with H_2, Li, Group 2A(2) members, B, Al, C, Si, Ge, O_2, and many transition elements. In fact, nearly every element in the periodic table forms bonds to N. Here we focus on the oxides and the oxoacids and their salts.

Nitrogen Oxides Nitrogen is remarkable for having six stable oxides, each with a *positive* heat of formation because of the great strength of the $N≡N$ bond (945 kJ/mol). Their structures and some properties are shown in Table 14.3. Unlike the hydrides and halides of nitrogen, the oxides are planar.

Table 14.3 Structures and Properties of the Nitrogen Oxides

Formula	Name	Space-filling Model	Lewis Structure	Oxidation State of N	ΔH_f^0 at 298 K (kJ/mol)	Comment
N_2O	Dinitrogen monoxide (dinitrogen oxide; nitrous oxide)		$:N≡N—\ddot{O}:$	+1 (0, +2)	82.0	Colorless gas; used as dental anesthetic ("laughing gas") and aerosol propellant
NO	Nitrogen monoxide (nitrogen oxide; nitric oxide)		$:\dot{N}=\ddot{O}:$	+2	90.3	Colorless, paramagnetic gas; biochemical messenger; air pollutant
N_2O_3	Dinitrogen trioxide			+3 (+2, +4)	83.7	Reddish brown gas (reversibly dissociates to NO and NO_2)
NO_2	Nitrogen dioxide			+4	33.2	Orange-brown, paramagnetic gas formed in HNO_3 manufacture; poisonous air pollutant
N_2O_4	Dinitrogen tetraoxide			+4	9.16	Colorless to yellow liquid (reversibly dissociates to NO_2)
N_2O_5	Dinitrogen pentaoxide			+5	11.3	Colorless, volatile solid consisting of NO_2^+ and NO_3^-; gas consists of N_2O_5 molecules

Nitrogen displays all its positive oxidation states in these compounds, and in N_2O and N_2O_3 the two N atoms have different states.

Dinitrogen monoxide (N_2O; also called dinitrogen oxide or nitrous oxide) is the dental anesthetic "laughing gas" and the propellant in canned whipped cream. It is a linear molecule with an electronic structure best described by three resonance forms (note formal charges; see Problem 10.96):

$$\overset{0 \quad +1 \quad -1}{:N\equiv N-\ddot{O}:} \longleftrightarrow \overset{-1 \quad +1 \quad 0}{:\ddot{N}=N=\ddot{O}:} \longleftrightarrow \overset{-2 \quad +1 \quad +1}{:\ddot{N}-N\equiv O:}$$
$$\text{most important} \qquad\qquad\qquad\qquad\qquad \text{least important}$$

Nitrogen monoxide (NO; also called nitrogen oxide or nitric oxide) is an odd-electron molecule with a vital biochemical function. ◆ In Section 11.3, we used MO theory to explain its bond properties. The commercial preparation of NO occurs as a first step in the production of nitric acid through the oxidation of ammonia:

$$4NH_3(g) + 5O_2(g) \longrightarrow 4NO(g) + 6H_2O(g)$$

It is also produced whenever air is heated to high temperatures, as in a car engine or a lightning storm:

$$N_2(g) + O_2(g) \xrightarrow{\text{high } T} 2NO(g)$$

Heating converts NO to two other oxides:

$$3NO(g) \xrightarrow{\Delta} N_2O(g) + NO_2(g)$$

This type of redox reaction is called a **disproportionation.** It occurs when a substance *acts as both an oxidizing and a reducing agent in a reaction.* In the process, an atom with an intermediate oxidation state in the reactant occurs in the products in both lower and higher states: the oxidation state of N in NO (+2) is intermediate between that in N_2O (+1) and that in NO_2 (+4).

Nitrogen dioxide (NO_2), a brown poisonous gas, also forms when NO reacts with additional oxygen:

$$2NO(g) + O_2(g) \longrightarrow 2NO_2(g)$$

Like NO, NO_2 is also an odd-electron molecule, but the electron is more localized on the N atom, so NO_2 dimerizes reversibly to dinitrogen tetraoxide:

$$O_2N\cdot(g) + \cdot NO_2(g) \rightleftharpoons O_2N-NO_2(g) \quad \text{(or } N_2O_4\text{)}$$

Thunderstorms form NO and NO_2 and carry them down to the soil, where they act as natural fertilizers. In urban traffic, however, their formation leads to *photochemical smog* (Figure 14.20). During the morning commute, NO forms in car and truck (especially diesel) engines and is then oxidized in air to NO_2. As the Sun climbs higher, radiant energy breaks down some NO_2:

$$NO_2(g) \xrightarrow{\text{sunlight}} NO(g) + O(g)$$

The O atoms collide with O_2 molecules and form ozone, O_3, a powerful oxidizing agent that damages synthetic rubber and plastic, as well as plant and animal tissue:

$$O_2(g) + O(g) \longrightarrow O_3(g)$$

A complex series of reactions between NO_2, O_3, and unburned hydrocarbons in gasoline fumes forms *peroxyacylnitrates* (PANs), a group of potent nose and eye irritants. The outcome of this fascinating atmospheric chemistry is choking, brown smog.

Figure 14.20 **The formation of photochemical smog.** Concentrations of the precursor components of smog change during the day. In early morning traffic, NO and hydrocarbon levels increase from auto exhaust, followed by increases in NO_2 as NO reacts with air. Ozone peaks later as NO_2 breaks down in stronger sunlight and releases O atoms that react with O_2. By midafternoon, all the components for production of peroxyacylnitrates (PANs) are present and photochemical smog results.

Nitrogen Oxoacids and Oxoanions The two common nitrogen oxoacids are nitric acid and nitrous acid (Figure 14.21). The first two steps in the *Ostwald process* for the production of nitric acid—the oxidations of NH_3 to NO and of NO to NO_2—have been shown. The final step is a disproportionation, as the oxidation numbers show:

$$\overset{+4}{3NO_2(g)} + H_2O(l) \longrightarrow \overset{+5}{2HNO_3(aq)} + \overset{+2}{NO(g)}$$

The NO is recycled to make more NO_2.

Figure 14.21 **The structures of nitric and nitrous acids and their oxoanions.**
A, Nitric acid loses an H^+ to form the trigonal planar nitrate ion (one of three resonance forms is shown). **B,** Nitrous acid, a much weaker acid, forms the planar nitrite ion. Note the effect of the lone pair in reducing the ideal 120° bond angle to 115° (one of two resonance forms is shown). Lone pairs are shown on N only.

In nitric acid, as in all oxoacids, *the acidic H is attached to one of the O atoms.* In the laboratory, nitric acid is used as a strong oxidizing acid. The products of its reaction with metals vary with the metal's reactivity and the HNO_3 concentration. In the following examples, notice from the net ionic equations that *the NO_3^- ion is the oxidizing agent.* Nitrate ion that is not reduced is a spectator ion and does not appear in the net ionic equations.

- With an active metal, such as Al, and dilute acid, N is reduced from the $+5$ state all the way to the -3 state in the ammonium ion:

$$8Al(s) + 30HNO_3(aq;\ 1\ M) \longrightarrow 8Al(NO_3)_3(aq) + 3NH_4NO_3(aq) + 9H_2O(l)$$
$$8Al(s) + 30H^+(aq) + 3NO_3^-(aq) \longrightarrow 8Al^{3+}(aq) + 3NH_4^+(aq) + 9H_2O(l)$$

- With a less reactive metal, such as Cu, and more concentrated acid, N is reduced to the $+2$ state in NO:

$$3Cu(s) + 8HNO_3(aq;\ 3\ to\ 6\ M) \longrightarrow 3Cu(NO_3)_2(aq) + 4H_2O(l) + 2NO(g)$$
$$3Cu(s) + 8H^+(aq) + 2NO_3^-(aq) \longrightarrow 3Cu^{2+}(aq) + 4H_2O(l) + 2NO(g)$$

- With more concentrated acid, N is reduced only to the $+4$ state in NO_2 (see photo):

$$Cu(s) + 4HNO_3(aq;\ 12\ M) \longrightarrow Cu(NO_3)_2(aq) + 2H_2O(l) + 2NO_2(g)$$
$$Cu(s) + 4H^+(aq) + 2NO_3^-(aq) \longrightarrow Cu^{2+}(aq) + 2H_2O(l) + 2NO_2(g)$$

Nitrates form when HNO_3 reacts with metals and with their hydroxides, oxides, or carbonates. *All nitrates are soluble in water.*

Nitrous acid, HNO_2, a much weaker acid than HNO_3, forms when metal nitrites are treated with a strong acid:

$$NaNO_2(aq) + HCl(aq) \longrightarrow HNO_2(aq) + NaCl(aq)$$

These two acids reveal a *general pattern in relative acid strength among oxoacids:* the more O atoms bound to the central nonmetal, the stronger the acid. Thus, HNO_3 is stronger than HNO_2. The O atoms pull electron density from the N atom, which in turn pulls electron density from the O of the O—H bond, facilitating the release of the H^+ ion. The O atoms also act to stabilize the resulting oxoanion by delocalizing its negative charge. The same pattern occurs in the oxoacids of sulfur and the halogens; we'll discuss the pattern quantitatively in Chapter 18.

Copper metal in 12 *M* HNO_3.

A P_4O_6

B P_4O_{10}

Figure 14.22 Important oxides of phosphorus. A, P_4O_6. **B,** P_4O_{10}.

The Countless Uses of Phosphates

Phosphates have an amazing array of applications in home and industry. Na_3PO_4 is a paint stripper and grease remover and is still used in cleaning powders in other countries. Na_2HPO_4 is a laxative ingredient and is used to adjust the acidity of boiler water. The potassium salts have other uses. K_3PO_4 is used to stabilize latex for synthetic rubber; K_2HPO_4 is a radiator corrosion inhibitor. The ammonium salts are used as fertilizers and as flame retardants on curtains and paper costumes. The various calcium phosphates are used in baking powders and toothpastes, as mineral supplements in stock feed, and (on the hundred-million-ton scale) as fertilizers throughout the world.

Highlights of Phosphorus Chemistry: Oxides and Oxoacids

Phosphorus forms two important oxides, P_4O_6 and P_4O_{10}. Tetraphosphorus hexaoxide, P_4O_6, has P in its +3 oxidation state and forms when white P_4 reacts with limited oxygen:

$$P_4(s) + 3O_2(g) \longrightarrow P_4O_6(s)$$

P_4O_6 has the tetrahedral orientation of the P atoms in P_4, with an O atom between each pair of P atoms (Figure 14.22A). It reacts with water to form phosph*orous* acid (note the spelling):

$$P_4O_6(s) + 6H_2O(l) \longrightarrow 4H_3PO_3(l)$$

The formula H_3PO_3 is misleading because the acid has only two acidic H atoms; the third is bound to the central P and does not dissociate. Phosphorous acid is a weak acid in water but reacts completely in two steps with excess strong base:

Salts of phosphorous acid contain the phosphite ion, HPO_3^{2-}.

In tetraphosphorus decaoxide, P_4O_{10}, P is in the +5 oxidation state. Commonly known as "phosphorus pentoxide" from the empirical formula (P_2O_5), it forms when P_4 burns in excess O_2:

$$P_4(s) + 5O_2(g) \longrightarrow P_4O_{10}(s)$$

Its structure can be viewed as P_4O_6 with another O atom bonded to each of the four corner P atoms (Figure 14.22B). It is a powerful drying agent and, in a vigorous exothermic reaction with water, forms phosphoric acid (H_3PO_4), one of the "Top-10" most important compounds in chemical manufacturing:

$$P_4O_{10}(s) + 6H_2O(l) \longrightarrow 4H_3PO_4(l)$$

The presence of many H bonds makes pure H_3PO_4 syrupy and more than 75 times as viscous as water. The laboratory-grade concentrated acid is an 85 mass % aqueous solution. H_3PO_4 is a weak triprotic acid; in water, it loses one proton in the following equilibrium reaction:

$$H_3PO_4(l) + H_2O(l) \rightleftharpoons H_2PO_4^-(aq) + H_3O^+(aq)$$

In excess strong base, however, the three protons dissociate completely in three steps to give the three phosphate oxoanions:

dihydrogen phosphate ion   hydrogen phosphate ion   phosphate ion

Phosphoric acid has a central role in fertilizer production, but it is also used as a polishing agent for aluminum car trim and as an additive in soft drinks to give a touch of tartness. The various phosphate salts have numerous essential applications. ◆

Polyphosphates are formed by heating hydrogen phosphates, which lose water as they form P—O—P linkages. This type of reaction, in which an H_2O molecule is lost for every pair of OH groups that join, is called a **dehydration-condensation;** it occurs frequently in the formation of polyoxoanion

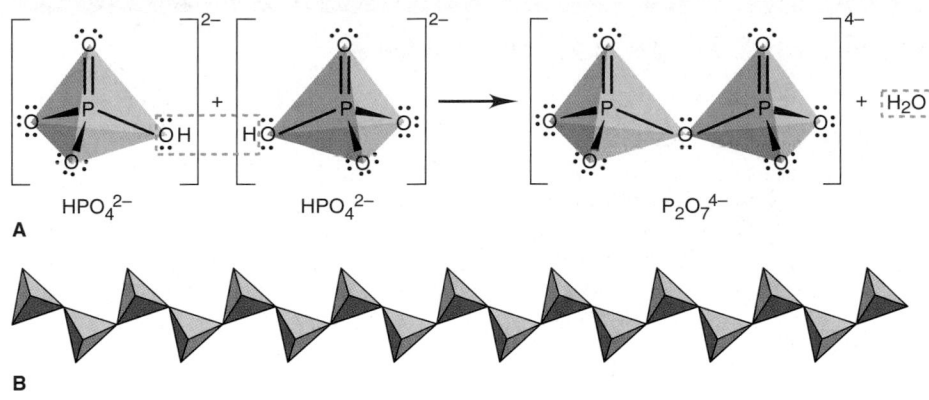

A

B

Figure 14.23 **The diphosphate ion and polyphosphates. A,** When two hydrogen phosphate ions undergo a dehydration-condensation reaction, they lose a water molecule and join through a shared O atom to form a diphosphate ion. **B,** Polyphosphates consist of many such tetrahedral PO_4 units. Chain shapes depend on the orientation of the individual units. Note the similarity to silicate chains (see Gallery, Section 14.6).

chains and other polymeric structures, both synthetic and natural. For example, sodium diphosphate, $Na_4P_2O_7$, is prepared by heating sodium hydrogen phosphate:

$$2Na_2HPO_4(s) \xrightarrow{\Delta} Na_4P_2O_7(s) + H_2O(g)$$

The diphosphate ion, the smallest of the polyphosphates, consists of two PO_4 units "fused" through an oxygen corner (Figure 14.23A). Its reaction with water, the reverse of the previous reaction, generates heat:

$$P_2O_7^{4-}(aq) + H_2O(l) \longrightarrow 2HPO_4^-(aq) + heat$$

A similar process is put to great use by organisms, when a third PO_4 unit fused to diphosphate creates the triphosphate grouping, part of the all-important high-energy biomolecule adenosine triphosphate (ATP). In Chapters 20 and 21, we discuss the central role of ATP in biological energy production. Extended polyphosphate chains consist of tetrahedral PO_4 units (Figure 14.23B) and are structurally similar to silicate chains. As a final look at the chemical versatility of phosphorus, consider some of its numerous important compounds with sulfur and with nitrogen. ◆

14.8 Group 6A(16): The Oxygen Family

The first two members of this family—gaseous nonmetallic oxygen (O) and solid nonmetallic sulfur (S)—are among the most important elements in industry, the environment, and living things. Two metalloids, selenium (Se) and tellurium (Te), appear below them, and the lone metal, radioactive polonium (Po), ends the group. The Group 6A(16) Family Portrait (pp. 580 and 581) displays the features of these elements.

How Do the Oxygen and Nitrogen Families Compare Physically?

Group 6A(16) resembles Group 5A(15) in many respects, so let's look at some common themes. The pattern of physical properties we saw in Group 5A appears again in this group. Like nitrogen, oxygen occurs as a low-boiling diatomic gas. Like phosphorus, sulfur occurs as a polyatomic molecular solid. Like arsenic, selenium commonly occurs as a gray metalloid. Like antimony, tellurium is slightly more metallic than the preceding group member but still displays network bonding. Finally, like bismuth, polonium has a metallic crystal structure. As we expect by comparison with the 5A elements, electrical conductivities increase steadily down the group as bonding changes from individual molecules (insulators) to metalloid networks (semiconductors) to metallic solid (conductor).

Fuel lines

O rings

Shock absorbers

Fuel pump parts

Helicopter rotor gaskets

◆ **Match Heads, Bug Sprays, and O-Rings** Phosphorus forms many sulfides and nitrides. P_4S_3 is used in "strike-anywhere" match heads; P_4S_{10} is used in the manufacture of organophosphorus pesticides, such as malathion. Polyphosphazenes have properties similar to those of silicones. Indeed, the $—(R_2)P{=}N—$ unit is isoelectronic with the silicone $—(R_2)Si—O—$ unit. Polyphosphazene sheets, films, fibers, and foams are water repellent, flame and solvent resistant, and flexible at low temperature—perfect for gaskets and O-rings (see photo) in spacecraft and polar vehicles.

Key Atomic and Physical Properties

KEY

Atomic No.
Symbol
Atomic mass
Valence e⁻
configuration
Common
oxidation
states

ns^2np^4

GROUP 6A(16)

Atomic Properties

Atomic radius (pm)		Ionic radius (pm)
O 73		O^{2-} 140
S 103		S^{2-} 184
Se 119		Se^{2-} 198
Te 142		
Po 168		Po^{4+} 94

Group electron configuration is ns^2np^4. As with Groups 3A(13) and 5A(15), a lower (+4) oxidation state becomes more common down the group.

Down the group, atomic and ionic size increase, and IE and EN decrease.

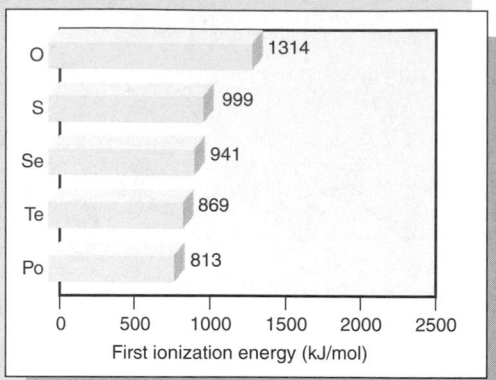

First ionization energy (kJ/mol)
- O 1314
- S 999
- Se 941
- Te 869
- Po 813

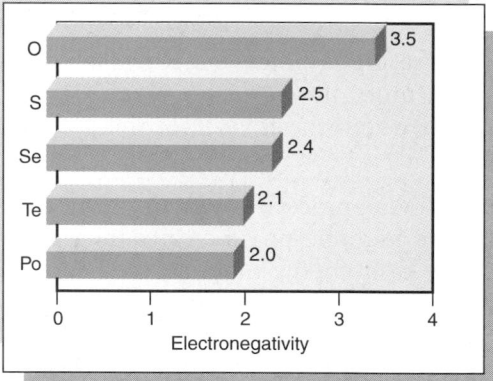

Electronegativity
- O 3.5
- S 2.5
- Se 2.4
- Te 2.1
- Po 2.0

Physical Properties

Melting points increase through Te, which has covalent bonding, and then decrease for Po, with its metallic bonding.

Temperature (°C) — BP ■ / MP □
- O −183 / −219
- S 445 / 113
- Se 685 / 217
- Te 990 / 452
- Po 962 / 254

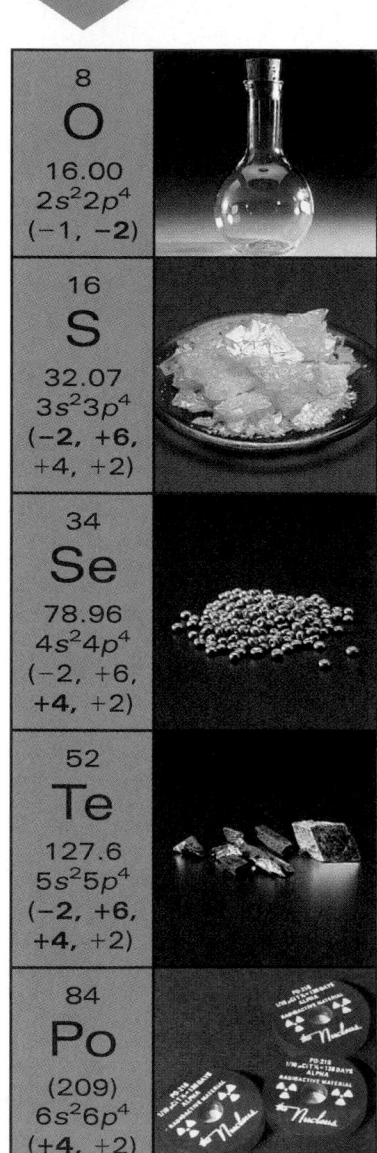

8	
O	
16.00	
$2s^22p^4$	
(−1, **−2**)	

16
S
32.07
$3s^23p^4$
(**−2, +6, +4, +2**)

34
Se
78.96
$4s^24p^4$
(−2, +6, **+4, +2**)

52
Te
127.6
$5s^25p^4$
(**−2, +6, +4,** +2)

84
Po
(209)
$6s^26p^4$
(**+4,** +2)

Density of solid (g/mL)
- O 1.50
- S 2.07
- Se 4.28
- Te 6.25
- Po 9.14

Densities of the elements as solids increase steadily.

Some Reactions and Compounds

Important Reactions

General halogenation and oxidation appears in reactions 1 and 2, and sulfur chemistry in reactions 3 and 4.

1. Halides are formed by direct combination:

$$E(s) + X_2(g) \longrightarrow \text{various halides}$$
$$(E = S, Se, Te; X = F, Cl)$$

2. The other elements in the group are oxidized by O_2:

$$E(s) + O_2(g) \longrightarrow EO_2 \quad (E = S, Se, Te, Po)$$

SO_2 is oxidized further, and the product is used in the final step of H_2SO_4 manufacture (*see Highlights of Sulfur Chemistry*):

$$2SO_2(g) + O_2(g) \longrightarrow 2SO_3(g)$$

3. Sulfur is recovered when hydrogen sulfide is oxidized:

$$8H_2S(g) + 4O_2(g) \longrightarrow S_8(s) + 8H_2O(g)$$

This reaction is used to obtain sulfur when natural deposits are not available.

4. The thiosulfate ion is formed when an alkali sulfite reacts with sulfur, as in the preparation of photographer's "hypo":

$$S_8(s) + 8Na_2SO_3(aq) \longrightarrow 8Na_2S_2O_3(aq)$$

Important Compounds

1. Water, H_2O. The single most important compound on Earth (*Section 12.5*).

2. Hydrogen peroxide, H_2O_2. Used as an oxidizing agent, disinfectant, bleach, and in the production of peroxy compounds for polymerization (*see Margin Note, p. 583*).

3. Hydrogen sulfide, H_2S. Vile-smelling toxic gas formed during anaerobic decomposition of plant and animal matter, in volcanoes, and in deep-sea thermal vents. Used as a sulfur source and in the manufacture of paper. Atmospheric traces cause silver to tarnish through formation of black Ag_2S (*see photo*).

4. Sulfur dioxide, SO_2. Colorless, choking gas formed in volcanoes (*see photo*) or whenever an S-containing compound (coal, oil, metal sulfide ores, and so on) is burned. More than 90% of SO_2 produced is used to make sulfuric acid. Also used as a fumigant and preservative of fruit, syrups, and wine. As a reducing agent, removes excess Cl_2 from industrial waste water, removes O_2 from petroleum handling tanks, and prepares ClO_2 for bleaching paper. Atmospheric pollutant in acid rain.

5. Sulfur trioxide (SO_3) and sulfuric acid (H_2SO_4). SO_3, formed from SO_2 over a V_2O_5 catalyst, is then converted to sulfuric acid. The acid is the cheapest strong acid and is so widely used in industry that its production level is an indicator of a nation's economic strength. Strong dehydrating agent that removes water from any organic source (*see Highlights of Sulfur Chemistry*).

6. Sulfur hexafluoride, SF_6. Extremely inert gas used as an electrical insulator.

Figure 14.24 **The cyclo-S$_8$ molecule.** The most stable form of sulfur consists of octatomic (8-membered) cyclic molecules called cyclo-S$_8$. **A,** Top view of a space-filling model of the cyclo-S$_8$ molecule. **B,** Side-view ball-and-stick model of the molecule; note the crownlike shape.

◆ **Liquid and Plastic Sulfur**

Sulfur undergoes remarkable changes when heated. At 112°C, the α-S$_8$ form melts to a yellow, flowing liquid. By 160°C, it darkens to red-orange and then deep red-brown. S$_8$ rings break, and the —S· ends are free radicals that attack other rings and link into growing chains. These chains cross-link and increase the viscosity. By 200°C, chains of 6×10^5 S atoms occur, and the liquid barely flows. With further heating, chains break faster than they form, so that at the boiling point (445°C), the liquid flows more easily. When poured into cold water, the syrupy liquid becomes plastic sulfur, an amorphous mass of long, cross-linked S helices that impart a rubberiness.

◆ **Selenium and Xerography**

Photocopying was invented in the 1930s and 1940s as a rapid, inexpensive, dry means of copying documents (xerography, Greek "dry writing"). The process is based on the ability of selenium to conduct a current when illuminated. A film of amorphous Se is deposited on an aluminum drum and electrostatically charged. Exposure to a document produces an "image" of low and high positive charges that correspond to the document's bright areas and dark lines. Negatively charged black, dry ink (toner) particles are attracted to the regions of high charge more than to those of low charge. This pattern of black particles is transferred electrostatically to print paper, and the particles are fused by heat or solvent. Excess toner is removed from the Se film, the charges are "erased" by exposure to light, and the film is ready for the next page.

Allotropism is more common in Group 6A(16) than in Group 5A(15). Oxygen has two allotropes: life-giving dioxygen (O_2), and poisonous triatomic ozone (O_3). Oxygen gas is colorless, odorless, paramagnetic, and thermally stable. In contrast, ozone gas is bluish, has a pungent odor, is diamagnetic, and decomposes in heat and especially in ultraviolet (UV) light:

$$2O_3(g) \xrightarrow{\text{UV}} 3O_2(g)$$

This ability to absorb high-energy photons makes stratospheric ozone vital to life. A thinning of the ozone layer, recently observed above the North and especially the South Poles, means that more UV light will reach the Earth's surface, with potentially hazardous effects. (We'll discuss the chemical causes of ozone depletion in Chapter 16.)

Sulfur is the allotrope "champion" of the periodic table, with more than 10 forms. The S atom's ability to bond to other S atoms creates numerous rings and chains, with S—S bond lengths that range from 180 pm to 260 pm and bond angles from 90° to 180°. At room temperature, the sulfur molecule is a crown-shaped ring of eight atoms, called *cyclo-S$_8$* (Figure 14.24). The most stable allotrope is orthorhombic α-S$_8$, which consists entirely of these molecules; all other S allotropes eventually revert to this one. ◆

Selenium also has several allotropes, some consisting of crown-shaped Se$_8$ molecules. Gray Se is composed of layers of helical chains. Its electrical conductivity in visible light has revolutionized the photocopying industry. ◆ When molten glass, cadmium sulfide, and gray Se are mixed and heated in the absence of air, a ruby-red glass forms, which you see whenever you stop at a traffic light.

How Do the Oxygen and Nitrogen Families Compare Chemically?

Changes in chemical behavior are also similar to those in the previous group. Even though O and S occur as anions much more often than do N and P, like N and P, they bond covalently with almost every other nonmetal. Covalent bonds appear in the compounds of Se and Te (as in those of As and Sb), whereas Po behaves like a metal (as does Bi) in some of its saltlike compounds. In contrast to nitrogen, oxygen has few common oxidation states, but the earlier pattern returns with the other members: the +6, +4, and −2 states occur most often, with the lower positive (+4) state becoming more common in Te and Po [as is the lower positive (+3) state in Sb and Bi].

The range in atomic properties is wider in this group than in 5A(15) because of oxygen's high EN (3.5) and great oxidizing strength, second only to that of fluorine. As in 5A and earlier groups, the behavior of the Period 2 element stands out. In fact, aside from a similar outer electron configuration, the larger 6A members behave very little like oxygen: they are much less electronegative, form anions much less often (S^{2-} occurs with active metals), and their hydrides exhibit no H bonding.

Except for O, all the 6A(16) elements form foul-smelling, poisonous, gaseous hydrides (H_2E) by treatment with acid of the metal sulfide, selenide, and so forth. For example,

$$FeSe(s) + 2HCl(aq) \longrightarrow H_2Se(g) + FeCl_2(aq)$$

Hydrogen sulfide also forms naturally in swamps from the breakdown of organic matter. It is as toxic as HCN, and even worse, it anesthetizes your olfactory nerves, so that as its concentration increases, you smell it less! The other hydrides are about 100 times *more* toxic.

In their bonding and thermal stability, these hydrides have several features in common with those of Group 5A:

- Only water can form H bonds, so it melts and boils much higher than the other H_2E compounds (see Figure 12.14). (Oxygen's other hydride, H_2O_2, is also extensively H bonded.) ◆
- Bond angles drop from the nearly tetrahedral value for H_2O (104.5°) to around 90° for the larger hydrides, suggesting that the central atom uses unhybridized *p* orbitals.
- E—H bond length increases (bond energy decreases) down the group. Thus, H_2Te decomposes above 0°C, and H_2Po can be made only in extreme cold because thermal energy from the radioactive Po decomposes it. Another result of longer (weaker) bonds is that the 6A hydrides are acids in water, and their acidity increases from H_2S to H_2Po.

Except for O, the Group 6A elements form a wide range of halides, whose structure and reactivity patterns depend on the *sizes of the central atom and the surrounding halogens:*

- Sulfur forms many fluorides, a few chlorides, one bromide, but no stable iodides.
- As the central atom becomes larger, the halides become more stable. Thus, tetrachlorides and tetrabromides of Se, Te, and Po are known, as are tetraiodides of Te and Po. Hexafluorides are known only for S, Se, and Te.

The inverse relationship between bond length and bond strength that we've seen previously does not account for this pattern. Rather, it is based on the effect of electron repulsions due to crowding of lone pairs and halogen (X) atoms around the central 6A atom. With S, the larger X atoms become too crowded, which explains why sulfur iodides do not occur. With increasing size of E and therefore length of E—X bonds, however, lone pairs and X atoms do not crowd each other as much, and a greater number of stable halides form.

Two sulfur fluorides illustrate clearly how crowding and orbital availability affect reactivity. Sulfur tetrafluoride (SF_4) is extremely reactive. It forms SO_2 and HF when exposed to moisture and is commonly used to fluorinate many compounds:

$$3SF_4(g) + 4BCl_3(g) \longrightarrow 4BF_3(g) + 3SCl_2(l) + 3Cl_2(g)$$

In contrast, sulfur hexafluoride (SF_6) is almost as inert as a noble gas! It is odorless, tasteless, nonflammable, nontoxic, and insoluble. Hot metals, boiling HCl, molten KOH, and high-pressure steam have no effect on it. It is used as an insulating gas in high-voltage generators, withstanding over 10^6 volts across electrodes only 50 mm apart. A look at the structures of these two fluorides provides the key to these astounding differences (Figure 14.25). Sulfur tetrafluoride can form bonds to another atom either by donating its lone electron pair or by accepting a lone pair into one of its empty *d* orbitals. On the other hand, SF_6 has no central lone pair, and the six F atoms form an octahedral sheath around the central S atom that blocks chemical attack.

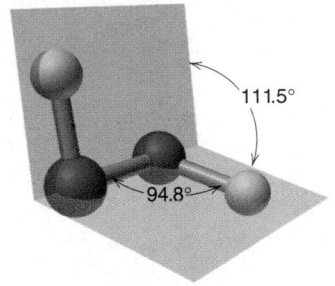

111.5°
94.8°

◆ Hydrogen Peroxide: Hydrazine's Cousin

Oxygen forms another hydride called hydrogen peroxide, H_2O_2 (HO—OH). Like hydrazine (H_2N—NH_2), the related hydride of nitrogen in Group 5A(15), it has a skewed shape. It is a colorless liquid with a high density, viscosity, and boiling point because of extensive H bonding. In peroxides, O is in the -1 oxidation state, midway between that in O_2 (zero) and in oxides (-2); thus, H_2O_2 readily disproportionates:

$$H_2O_2(l) \longrightarrow H_2O(l) + \tfrac{1}{2}O_2(g)$$
$$\Delta H^0 = -98 \text{ kJ}$$

Aside from its familiar use as a hair bleach and disinfectant, more than 70% of the half-million tons of H_2O_2 produced each year is used to bleach paper pulp, textiles, straw, and leather and to make other chemicals. H_2O_2 is now also used in tertiary sewage treatment (Section 13.6) to oxidize foul-smelling effluents and restore O_2 to wastewater.

Sulfur tetrafluoride (SF_4)

Sulfur hexafluoride (SF_6)

Figure 14.25 Structural differences between SF_4 and SF_6. SF_4 has a lone pair and empty *d* orbitals that can become involved in bonding. SF_6 already has the maximum number of bonds that can be formed by S, and the closely packed F atoms envelop the central S atom, rendering SF_6 chemically inert.

Highlights of Oxygen Chemistry: Range of Oxide Properties

Oxygen is the most abundant element on the Earth's surface, occurring both as the free element and in innumerable oxides, silicates, carbonates, and phosphates, as well as in water. Virtually all free O_2 has a biological origin, having been formed for billions of years by photosynthetic algae and multi-cellular plants in an overall equation that looks deceptively simple:

$$n H_2O(l) + n CO_2(g) \xrightarrow{\text{light}} n O_2(g) + (CH_2O)_n \text{ (carbohydrates)}$$

The reverse process occurs during combustion and respiration. Through these O_2-forming and O_2-utilizing processes, the 1.5×10^9 km^3 of water on Earth is, on average, used and remade every 2 million years!

Every element (except He, Ne, and Ar) forms at least one oxide, many by direct combination. A broad spectrum of properties characterizes these compounds. Some oxides are gases that condense at very low temperatures, such as CO (bp = $-192°$C); others are solids that melt at extremely high temperatures, such as BeO (mp = $2530°$C). They cover the full range of conductivity: insulators (MgO), semiconductors (NiO), conductors (ReO$_3$), and superconductors (YBa$_2$Cu$_3$O$_7$). Some have endothermic heats of formation (ΔH_f^0 of NO = $+90.3$ kJ/mol), whereas others have exothermic ones (ΔH_f^0 of CO_2 = -393.5 kJ/mol). They may be thermally stable (CaO) or unstable (HgO), and may be chemically reactive (Li$_2$O) or inert (Fe$_2$O$_3$).

Given this vast range of behavior, another useful way to classify element oxides is by their acid-base properties (see Interchapter, Topic 4). The oxides of Group 6A(16) exhibit expected trends in acidity, with SO$_3$ the most acidic and PoO$_2$ the most basic.

Highlights of Sulfur Chemistry: Oxides, Oxoacids, and Sulfides

Like phosphorus, sulfur forms two important oxides, sulfur dioxide (SO_2) and sulfur trioxide (SO_3). Sulfur is in its $+4$ oxidation state in SO_2, a colorless, choking gas that forms whenever S, H_2S, or a metal sulfide burns in air: ◆

$$2H_2S(g) + 3O_2(g) \longrightarrow 2H_2O(g) + 2SO_2(g)$$
$$4FeS_2(s) + 11O_2(g) \longrightarrow 2Fe_2O_3(s) + 8SO_2(g)$$

Most SO_2 is used to produce sulfuric acid.

In water, sulfur dioxide forms sulfurous acid, which exists in equilibrium with hydrated SO_2 rather than as isolable H_2SO_3 molecules:

$$SO_2(aq) + H_2O(l) \rightleftharpoons [H_2SO_3(aq)] \rightleftharpoons H^+(aq) + HSO_3^-(aq)$$

(Similarly, carbonic acid occurs in equilibrium with hydrated CO_2 and cannot be isolated as H_2CO_3 molecules.) Sulfurous acid is weak and has two acidic protons, forming the hydrogen sulfite (bisulfite, HSO$_3^-$) and sulfite (SO$_3^{2-}$) ions with strong base. Because the S in SO$_3^{2-}$ is in the $+4$ state and easily oxidized to the $+6$ state, sulfites are good reducing agents and are used to preserve foods and wine by eliminating undesirable products of air oxidation.

En route to sulfuric acid, SO_2 is first oxidized to SO_3 (S in the $+6$ state) by heating in O_2 over a catalyst:

$$SO_2(g) + \tfrac{1}{2}O_2(g) \underset{}{\overset{\text{V}_2\text{O}_5/\text{K}_2\text{O catalyst}}{\rightleftharpoons}} SO_3(g)$$

(We discuss how catalysts work in Chapter 16 and how H_2SO_4 is produced in Chapter 22.) The SO_3 is absorbed into concentrated H_2SO_4 and treated with additional H_2O:

$$SO_3(\text{in concentrated } H_2SO_4) + H_2O(l) \longrightarrow H_2SO_4(l)$$

With more than 40 million tons produced each year in the United States alone, H_2SO_4 ranks first among all industrial chemicals. Fertilizer production,

◆ **Acid from the Sky**

Awareness of SO_2 as a major air pollutant is now widespread. Even though enormous amounts of SO_2 form during volcanic and other geothermal activity, they are dwarfed by the amounts formed by human sources: coal-based power plants, petroleum refineries, and metal-ore smelters. In the atmosphere, SO_2 reacts with O_2 and water to form sulfuric acid, which rains, snows, and dusts down on animals, plants, buildings, and lakes. The destructive effects of acid precipitation are being intensively studied, and remedial action is increasingly under way (Chapter 19).

Figure 14.26 **The dehydration of carbohydrates by sulfuric acid.** The protons of concentrated H_2SO_4 combine exothermically with water, dehydrating many organic materials. When table sugar is treated with sulfuric acid, the components of water are removed from the carbohydrate molecules $(CH_2O)_n$. Steam forms, and the remaining carbon expands to a porous mass.

metal, pigment, and textile processing, and soap and detergent manufacturing are just a few of the major industries that depend on sulfuric acid.

Concentrated laboratory-grade sulfuric acid is a viscous, colorless liquid that is 98% H_2SO_4 by mass. Like other strong acids, H_2SO_4 dissociates completely in water, forming the hydrogen sulfate (or bisulfate) ion, which is a much weaker acid:

hydrogen sulfate ion   sulfate ion

Most common hydrogen sulfates and sulfates are water soluble but those of Group 2A(2) (except $MgSO_4$), Pb^{2+}, and Hg_2^{2+} are not.

Concentrated sulfuric acid is an excellent dehydrating agent. Its loosely held proton transfers to water in a highly exothermic formation of hydronium ions. This process can occur even when the reacting substance contains no free water. For example, H_2SO_4 dehydrates wood, natural fibers, and many other organic substances by removing the components of water from the molecular structure, leaving behind a carbonaceous mass (Figure 14.26).

Thiosulfuric acid ($H_2S_2O_3$) is a structural analog of sulfuric acid in which a second S substitutes for one of the O atoms (*thio-* means S in place of O). The thiosulfate ion ($S_2O_3^{2-}$) is an important reducing agent in chemical analysis. However, its largest commercial use is in photography, where sodium thiosulfate pentahydrate ($Na_2S_2O_3 \cdot 5H_2O$), known as "hypo," is involved in fixing the image (Section 23.3).

Many metals combine directly with S to form *metal sulfides*. Indeed, naturally occurring sulfides are ores, which are mined for the extraction of many metals, including copper, zinc, lead, and silver. Aside from the sulfides of Groups 1A(1) and 2A(2), most metal sulfides do not have discrete S^{2-} ions. Several transition metals, such as chromium, iron, and nickel, form covalent, alloylike, nonstoichiometric compounds with S, such as $Cr_{0.88}S$ or $Fe_{0.86}S$. Some important minerals contain S_2^{2-} units in the structure, such as iron pyrite, or "fool's gold" (FeS_2) (Figure 14.27). We discuss the metallurgy of ores in Chapter 22.

Figure 14.27 **A common sulfide mineral.** Pyrite (FeS_2), or fool's gold, is a beautiful but relatively cheap mineral that contains the S_2^{2-} ion, but no gold.

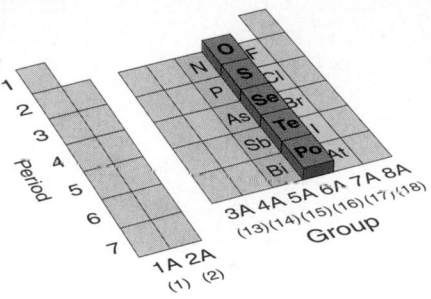

Figure 14.28 Standing in Group 6A(16), looking backward to Group 5A(15) and forward to Group 7A(17).

Looking Backward and Forward: Groups 5A(15), 6A(16), and 7A(17)

Groups 5A(15) and 6A(16) are very similar in their physical and chemical trends and in the versatility of phosphorus and sulfur (Figure 14.28). Their greatest difference is the sluggish behavior of N_2 compared with the striking reactivity of O_2. In both groups, metallic character appears only in the largest members. From here on, metals and even metalloids are left behind: all the 7A(17) elements are reactive nonmetals. Anion formation, which was rare in 5A and more common in 6A, is one of the dominant features of 7A. Another feature of Group 7A elements is the number of covalent compounds they form with oxygen *and* with each other.

14.9 Group 7A(17): The Halogens

Our last chance to view elements of great reactivity occurs in Group 7A(17). The halogens begin with fluorine (F), the strongest electron "grabber" of all. Chlorine (Cl), bromine (Br), and iodine (I) also form compounds with most elements, and even extremely rare astatine (At) is thought to be reactive. The key features of the halogens are presented in the Group 7A(17) Family Portrait (pp. 588 and 589).

What Accounts for the Regular Change in the Halogens' Physical Properties?

Like the alkali metals at the other end of the periodic table, the halogens display regular trends in their physical properties. However, whereas melting and boiling points and heats of fusion and vaporization *decrease* down Group 1A(1), these properties *increase* down Group 7A(17) (see Interchapter, Topic 6). The reason for these opposite trends is the different type of bonding in the elements. The alkali metals consist of atoms held together by metallic bonding, which *decreases* in strength as the atoms become larger. The halogens, on the other hand, exist as diatomic molecules that interact through dispersion forces, which *increase* in strength as the atoms become larger and more easily polarized; thus, F_2 is a very pale yellow gas, Cl_2 a yellow-green gas, Br_2 a brown-orange liquid, and I_2 a purple-black solid.

Why Are the Halogens So Reactive?

The Group 7A(17) elements react with most metals and nonmetals to form many ionic and covalent compounds: metal and nonmetal halides, halogen oxides, and oxoacids. The reason for halogen reactivity is the same as that for alkali metal reactivity—an electron configuration one electron away from that of a noble gas. Whereas a 1A metal atom must *lose* one electron to attain a filled outer shell, *a 7A nonmetal atom must gain one electron to fill its outer shell.* It accomplishes this filling in either of two ways:

1. Gaining an electron from a metal atom, thus forming a negative ion as the metal forms a positive one.
2. Sharing an electron pair with a nonmetal atom, thus forming a covalent bond.

Down the group, reactivity reflects the decrease in electronegativity: F_2 is the most reactive and I_2 the least. The exceptional reactivity of elemental F_2 is also related to the weakness of the F—F bond. Since F is small, the bond is short, but the lone pairs on each F atom repel those on the other, which weakens the bond (Figure 14.29). As a result of these factors, F_2 reacts with every element (except He, Ne, and Ar), in many cases explosively.

The halogens display the largest range in electronegativity of any group, but all are electronegative enough to behave as nonmetals. They act as *oxi-*

Figure 14.29 Bond energies and bond lengths of the halogens. A, In keeping with the increase in atomic size down the group, bond lengths increase steadily. **B,** The halogens show a general decrease in bond energy as bond length increases. However, F_2 deviates from this trend because its small, close, electron-rich atoms repel each other, thereby lowering its bond energy.

dizing agents in the majority of their reactions, and halogens higher in the group can oxidize halide ions lower down:

$$F_2(g) + 2X^-(aq) \longrightarrow 2F^-(aq) + X_2(aq) \qquad (X = Cl, Br, I)$$

Thus, the oxidizing ability of X_2 *decreases* down the group: the lower the EN, the less strongly it pulls electrons. Similarly, the reducing ability of X^- *increases* down the group: the larger the ion, the more easily it gives up its electron (Figure 14.30).

The halogens undergo some important aqueous redox chemistry. Fluorine is such a powerful oxidizing agent that it tears water apart, oxidizing the O to produce O_2, some O_3, and HFO (hypofluorous acid). The other halogens undergo disproportionations (note the oxidation numbers):

$$\overset{0}{X_2} + H_2O(l) \rightleftharpoons \overset{-1}{H}X(aq) + \overset{+1}{H}XO(aq) \qquad (X = Cl, Br, I)$$

At equilibrium, very little product is present unless excess OH^- ion is added, which reacts with the HX and HXO and drives the reaction to completion:

$$X_2 + 2OH^-(aq) \longrightarrow X^-(aq) + XO^-(aq) + H_2O(l)$$

When X is Cl, the product mixture acts as a bleach: household bleach is a dilute solution of sodium hypochlorite (NaClO). Heating causes XO^- to disproportionate further, creating oxoanions with X in a higher oxidation state:

$$\overset{+1}{3XO^-}(aq) \overset{\Delta}{\longrightarrow} \overset{-1}{2X^-}(aq) + \overset{+5}{XO_3^-}(aq)$$

$$Cl_2(aq) + 2I^-(aq) \longrightarrow 2Cl^-(aq) + I_2(\text{in } CCl_4)$$

Figure 14.30 The relative oxidizing ability of the halogens. A, Halogen redox behavior is based on atomic properties such as electron affinity, ionic charge density, and electronegativity. A halogen (X_2) higher in the group can oxidize a halide ion (X^-) lower down. **B,** As an example, when aqueous Cl_2 is added to a solution of I^- (*top layer*), it oxidizes the I^- to I_2, which dissolves in the CCl_4 solvent (*bottom layer*) to give a purple solution.

Key Atomic and Physical Properties

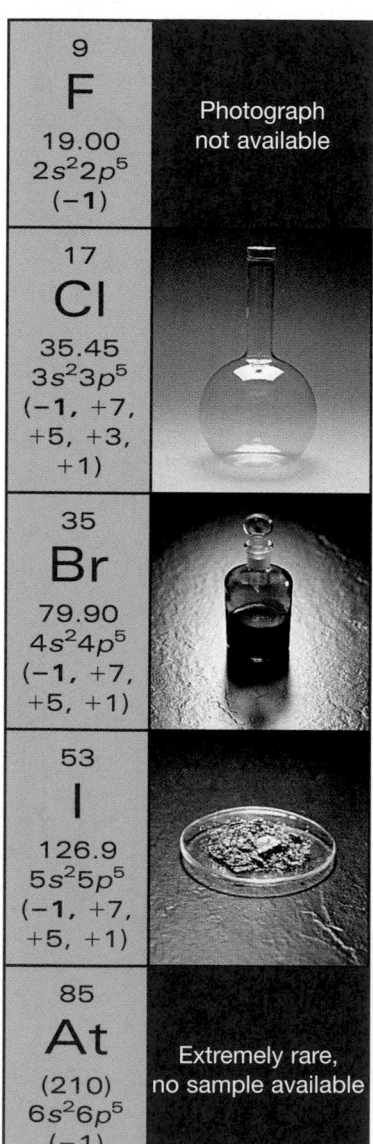

9	
F	Photograph not available
19.00 $2s^22p^5$ (−1)	

17
Cl
35.45 $3s^23p^5$ (−1, +7, +5, +3, +1)

35
Br
79.90 $4s^24p^5$ (−1, +7, +5, +1)

53
I
126.9 $5s^25p^5$ (−1, +7, +5, +1)

85	
At	Extremely rare, no sample available
(210) $6s^26p^5$ (−1)	

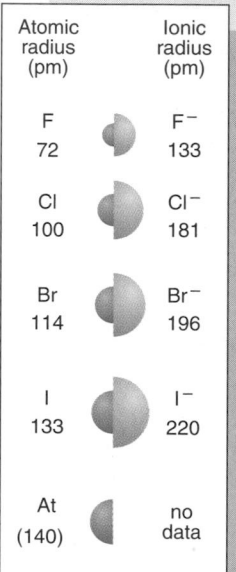

Atomic radius (pm)		Ionic radius (pm)
F 72		F⁻ 133
Cl 100		Cl⁻ 181
Br 114		Br⁻ 196
I 133		I⁻ 220
At (140)		no data

Atomic Properties

Group electron configuration is ns^2np^5; elements lack one e⁻ to complete their outer shell. The −1 oxidation state is the most common for all members. Except for F, the halogens exhibit all odd-numbered states (+7 through −1).

Down the group, atomic and ionic size increase steadily, as IE and EN decrease.

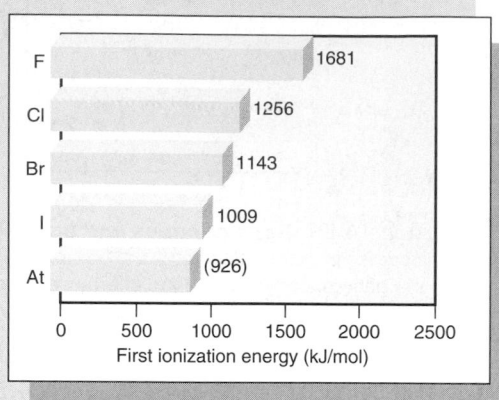

First ionization energy (kJ/mol)

- F — 1681
- Cl — 1256
- Br — 1143
- I — 1009
- At — (926)

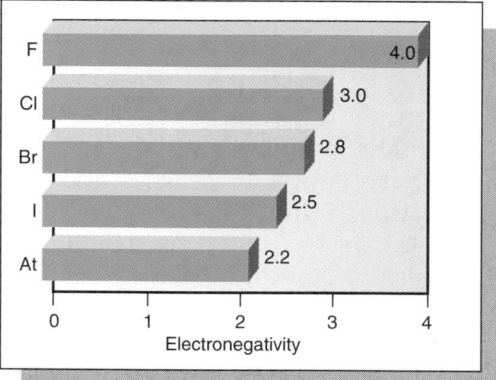

Electronegativity

- F — 4.0
- Cl — 3.0
- Br — 2.8
- I — 2.5
- At — 2.2

Physical Properties

Phase-change temperatures and enthalpies exhibit smooth trends. Down the group, melting and boiling points increase as a result of stronger dispersion forces between heavier molecules.

Temperature (°C)

- F: BP −188, MP −219
- Cl: BP −34.0, MP −101
- Br: BP 59.5, MP −7.2
- I: BP 185, MP 114
- At

■ BP □ MP

The densities of the elements as liquids (at given T) increase steadily with molar mass.

Density of liquid (g/mL)

- F 1.51 (−188°C)
- Cl 1.66 (−70°C)
- Br 3.19 (0°C)
- I 3.96 (120°C)
- At

Group 7A(17): The Halogens   Family Portrait

Some Reactions and Compounds

Important Reactions

Oxidizing strength and aqueous redox chemistry are shown in reactions 1 and 2 and industrial processes involving fluorine in reactions 3 and 4.

1. The halogens (X_2) oxidize many metals and nonmetals. The reaction with hydrogen, although not used commercially for HX production (except for high-purity HCl), is characteristic of these strong oxidizing agents:

$$X_2 + H_2(g) \longrightarrow 2HX(g)$$

2. The halogens disproportionate in water:

$$X_2 + H_2O(l) \rightleftharpoons HX(aq) + HXO(aq)$$
$$(X = Cl, Br, I)$$

In aqueous base, the reaction goes to completion to form hypohalites (*see text*) and, at higher temperatures, halates; for example:

$$3Cl_2(g) + 6OH^-(aq) \xrightarrow{\Delta} ClO_3^-(aq) + 5Cl^-(aq) + 3H_2O(l)$$

3. F_2 is produced electrolytically at moderate temperature:

$$2HF \text{ (as a soln of KF in HF)} \xrightarrow[90°C]{electrolysis} H_2(g) + F_2(g)$$

A major use of F_2 is in the preparation of UF_6 for nuclear fuel.

4. Glass (amorphous silica) is etched with HF:

$$SiO_2(s) + 6HF(g) \longrightarrow H_2SiF_6(aq) + 2H_2O(l)$$

Space shuttle

Important Compounds

1. Fluorspar (fluorite), CaF_2. Widely distributed mineral used as a flux in steel making and in the production of HF (*see photo*).

Fluorite

2. Hydrogen fluoride, HF. Colorless, extremely toxic gas used to make F_2, organic fluorine compounds, and polymers. Also used in aluminum manufacture and in glass etching (*see Margin Note, p. 590*).

3. Hydrogen chloride, HCl. Extremely water-soluble gas that forms hydrochloric acid, which occurs naturally in stomach juice of mammals (humans produce 1.5 L of 0.1 *M* HCl daily) and in volcanic gases (from reaction of H_2O on sea salt). Made by reaction of NaCl and H_2SO_4 and as a by-product of plastics (PVC) production. Used in the "pickling" of steel (removal of adhering oxides) and in the production of syrups, rayon, and plastic.

4. Sodium hypochlorite, NaClO, and calcium hypochlorite, $Ca(ClO)_2$. Oxidizing agents used to bleach wood pulp and textiles, and disinfect swimming pools, foods, and sewage (also used to disinfect the Apollo 11 on return from the moon). Household bleach is 5.25% NaClO by mass in water.

5. Ammonium perchlorate, NH_4ClO_4. Strong oxidizing agent used in the Space Shuttle program (*see photo*).

6. Potassium iodide, KI. Most common soluble iodide. Table salt additive to prevent thyroid disease (goiter). Used in chemical analysis because it is easily oxidized to I_2, which provides a colored end point.

7. Polychlorinated biphenyls, PCBs. Mixture of chlorinated organic compounds used as nonflammable insulating liquids in electrical transformers. Production discontinued because of persistence in the environment, where they become concentrated in fish, birds, and mammals, and cause reproductive disturbances and possibly cancer.

HF: Unusual Structure, Familiar Uses At room temperature, all the hydrogen halides except HF are diatomic gases. Because of extensive H bonding, gaseous HF becomes H bonded into short chains or rings of formula $(HF)_n$; liquid HF boils at 19.5°C, more than 50 degrees higher than even the much heavier HI; and solid HF exists as an H-bonded polymer. HF has many uses, including the synthesis of cryolite (Na_3AlF_6) for aluminum production, fluorocarbons for refrigeration, and NaF for water fluoridation. HF is also used in nuclear fuel processing and for glass etching in the manufacture of lightbulbs, transistors, and TV tubes.

Highlights of Halogen Chemistry

In this section, we examine the compounds that the halogens form with hydrogen and with each other, as well as the oxides, oxoanions, and oxoacids.

The Hydrogen Halides The halogens form gaseous hydrogen halides (HX) through direct combination with H_2 or through the action of a concentrated acid on the metal halide (a nonoxidizing acid is used for HBr and HI): ◆

$$CaF_2(s) + H_2SO_4(l) \longrightarrow CaSO_4(s) + 2HF(g)$$
$$3NaBr(s) + H_3PO_4(l) \longrightarrow Na_3PO_4(s) + 3HBr(g)$$

Commercially, most HCl is formed as a by-product in the chlorination of hydrocarbons for plastics production:

$$CH_2{=}CH_2(g) + Cl_2(g) \longrightarrow ClCH_2CH_2Cl(l) \xrightarrow{500°C} CH_2{=}CHCl(g) + HCl(g)$$
$$\text{vinyl chloride}$$

In this case, the vinyl chloride reacts in a separate process to form poly(vinyl chloride), a polymer used extensively in modern plumbing pipes.

In water, gaseous HX molecules form a *hydrohalic acid*. Only HF, with its relatively short, strong bond, forms a weak acid:

$$HF(g) + H_2O(l) \rightleftharpoons H_3O^+(aq) + F^-(aq)$$

The others dissociate completely to form the stoichiometric amount of hydronium ions:

$$HBr(g) + H_2O(l) \longrightarrow H_3O^+(aq) + Br^-(aq)$$

(We saw reactions similar to these in Chapter 4. They involve transfer of a proton from acid to H_2O and are classified as *Brønsted-Lowry acid-base reactions.* We discuss them thoroughly in Chapter 18 and examine the relation between bond length and acidity of the larger HX molecules there as well.)

Interhalogen Compounds: The "Halogen Halides" Halogens react exothermically with one another to form many **interhalogen compounds.** The simplest are diatomic molecules, such as ClF or BrCl. Every binary combination of the four common halogens is known. The more electronegative halogen is in the -1 oxidation state, and the less electronegative is in the $+1$ state. Interhalogens of general formula XY_n ($n = 3, 5, 7$) form when the larger members (X) use d orbitals to expand their valence shells. In every case, the central atom has the *lower electronegativity* and a positive oxidation state.

The commercially useful interhalogens are powerful *fluorinating agents,* some of which react with metals, nonmetals, and oxides—even wood and asbestos:

$$Sn(s) + ClF_3(l) \longrightarrow SnF_2(s) + ClF(g)$$
$$P_4(s) + 5ClF_3(l) \longrightarrow 4PF_3(g) + 3ClF(g) + Cl_2(g)$$
$$2B_2O_3(s) + 4BrF_3(l) \longrightarrow 4BF_3(g) + 2Br_2(l) + 3O_2(g)$$

Their reactions with water are nearly explosive and yield HF and *the oxoacid in which the central halogen has the same oxidation state.* For example,

$$3H_2O(l) + \overset{+5}{BrF_5}(l) \longrightarrow 5HF(g) + \overset{+5}{HBrO_3}(aq)$$

The Oddness and Evenness of Oxidation States Topic 5 of the Interchapter shows that odd-numbered groups exhibit odd-numbered oxidation states and even-numbered groups exhibit even-numbered states. The reason for this general behavior is that *almost all stable molecules have paired electrons,* either as bonding or lone pairs. Therefore, *when bonds form or break, two electrons are involved, so the oxidation state changes by two.*

Consider the case of the interhalogens. Four general formulas are XY, XY$_3$, XY$_5$, and XY$_7$; examples are shown in Figure 14.31. With Y in the -1 state, X must be in the $+1$, $+3$, $+5$, and $+7$ state, respectively. The -1 state arises when Y fills its valence level; the $+7$ state arises when the central halogen (X) is completely oxidized, that is, all seven valence electrons have shifted away from it to the more electronegative surrounding Y atoms.

Let's examine the iodine fluorides to see why the oxidation states jump by two units. When I$_2$ reacts with F$_2$, IF forms (we focus on the oxidation number, O.N., of I):

$$I_2 + F_2 \longrightarrow 2\overset{+1}{I}F$$

In IF$_3$, I uses *two* more valence electrons to form *two* more bonds:

$$\overset{+1}{I}F + F_2 \longrightarrow \overset{+3}{I}F_3$$

Otherwise, an unstable lone-electron species containing two fluorines would form. With more fluorine, another jump of two units occurs and the penta-fluoride forms:

$$\overset{+3}{I}F_3 + F_2 \longrightarrow \overset{+5}{I}F_5$$

With still more fluorine, the heptafluoride forms:

$$\overset{+5}{I}F_5 + F_2 \longrightarrow \overset{+7}{I}F_7$$

An element in an even-numbered group, such as sulfur in Group 6A(16), shows the same tendency for its compounds to have paired electrons. Ele-mental sulfur (O.N. = 0) gains or shares two electrons to complete its shell (O.N. = -2). It uses two electrons to react with fluorine, for example, and form SF$_2$ (O.N. = $+2$), two more electrons for SF$_4$ (O.N. = $+4$), and two more for SF$_6$ (O.N. = $+6$). Thus, an element with one even state typically has all even states, and an element with one odd state typically has all odd states. To reiterate the main point, *successive oxidation states differ by two units because stable molecules have electrons in pairs around their atoms.*

Halogen Oxides, Oxoacids, and Oxoanions The Group 7A(17) elements form many oxides that are *powerful oxidizing agents and acids in water.* Dichlo-rine monoxide (Cl$_2$O) and especially chlorine dioxide (ClO$_2$) are used to bleach paper (Figure 14.32). ClO$_2$ is unstable to heat and shock, so it is pre-pared on site, and more than 100,000 tons are used annually:

$$2NaClO_3(s) + SO_2(g) + H_2SO_4(aq) \longrightarrow 2ClO_2(g) + 2NaHSO_4(aq)$$

Note that the dioxide has an unpaired electron and Cl in the unusual $+4$ oxidation state.

XY
Linear
ClF

XY$_3$
T-shaped
88°
ClF$_3$

XY$_5$
Square pyramidal
86°
BrF$_5$

XY$_7$
Pentagonal bipyramidal
90°
IF$_7$

Figure 14.31 Molecular shapes of the main types of interhalogen compounds.

A   Dichlorine monoxide (Cl$_2$O)

Lone e$^-$

Chlorine dioxide (ClO$_2$)

Dichlorine heptaoxide (Cl$_2$O$_7$)

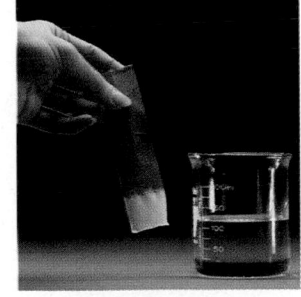

B

Figure 14.32 Chlorine oxides. A, Dichlorine monoxide and chlorine dioxide are bent molecules; note the lone electron in ClO$_2$. Dichlorine heptaoxide can be viewed as two ClO$_4$ tetrahedra joined through an O corner. (The ball-and-stick models are drawn so each

atom has its lowest formal charge. Lone pairs are shown on the central atoms only.) **B,** Several chlorine oxides are important reac-tants in the bleaching of paper. Here, a piece of brown paper bag has been bleached.

Table 14.4 The Known Halogen Oxoacids*

Central Atom	Hypohalous Acid (HOX)	Halous Acid (HOXO)	Halic Acid (HOXO$_2$)	Perhalic Acid (HOXO$_3$)
Fluorine	HOF	—	—	—
Chlorine	HOCl	HOClO	HOClO$_2$	HOClO$_3$
Bromine	HOBr	(HOBrO)?	HOBrO$_2$	HOBrO$_3$
Iodine	HOI	—	HOIO$_2$	HOIO$_3$, (HO)$_5$IO
Oxoanion	Hypohalite	Halite	Halate	Perhalate

*Lone pairs are shown only on the halogen atom.

◆ Pyrotechnic Perchlorates
Thousands of tons of perchlorates are made each year for use in explosives and fireworks. The white flash and thundering boom of a fireworks display are caused by KClO$_4$ reacting with powdered sulfur and aluminum. In rock concerts and other theatrical productions (see photo), mixtures of KClO$_4$ and Mg are often used for special effects.

Cl is in its highest (+7) oxidation state in dichlorine heptaoxide, Cl$_2$O$_7$, which is a symmetrical molecule formed when two HClO$_4$ (HO—ClO$_3$) molecules undergo a dehydration-condensation reaction:

$$O_3Cl—O\boxed{H + HO}—ClO_3 \longrightarrow O_3Cl—O—ClO_3(l) + H_2O(l)$$

The halogen oxoacids and oxoanions are produced from reaction of the halogens and their oxides with water. Most of the oxoacids are stable only in solution. Table 14.4 shows ball-and-stick models of the acids with each atom having its lowest formal charge; note the formulas, which emphasize that H is bonded to O. The hypohalites (XO$^-$), halites (XO$_2^-$), and halates (XO$_3^-$) are oxidizing agents formed by aqueous disproportionation reactions [see Group 7A(17) Family Portrait, Reaction 2]. You may have heated solid alkali chlorates in the laboratory to form small amounts of O$_2$:

$$2MClO_3(s) \xrightarrow{\Delta} 2MCl(s) + 3O_2(g)$$

Potassium chlorate is the oxidizer in "safety" matches.

Several perhalates are also strong oxidizing agents. ◆ Ammonium perchlorate, prepared from sodium perchlorate, is the oxidizing agent for the aluminum powder in the solid-fuel booster rocket of the Space Shuttle; each launch uses more than 700 tons of NH$_4$ClO$_4$:

$$10Al(s) + 6NH_4ClO_4(s) \longrightarrow 4Al_2O_3(s) + 12H_2O(g) + 3N_2(g) + 2AlCl_3(g)$$

The relative strengths of the halogen oxoacids depend on two factors:

1. *Electronegativity of the halogen.* Among oxoacids in the same oxidation state, such as the halic acids, HXO$_3$ (or HOXO$_2$), acid strength decreases as the halogen EN decreases:

$$HOClO_2 > HOBrO_2 > HOIO_2$$

The more electronegative the halogen, the more electron density it removes from the O—H bond, and the more easily the proton is lost.

2. *Oxidation state of the halogen.* Among oxoacids of a given halogen, such as chlorine, acid strength decreases as the oxidation state of the halogen decreases:

$$HOClO_3 > HOClO_2 > HOClO > HOCl$$

The higher the oxidation state (number of bound O atoms) of the halogen, the more electron density it pulls from the O—H bond. We consider these trends quantitatively in Chapter 18.

14.10 Group 8A(18): The Noble Gases

The last main group consists of individual atoms too "noble" to interact with others. The Group 8A(18) elements display regular trends in physical properties and very low, if any, reactivity. The group consists of helium (He), the second most abundant element in the universe, neon (Ne) and argon (Ar), krypton (Kr) and xenon (Xe), the only members for which compounds are known, and finally, radioactive radon (Rn). The noble gases make up about 1% by volume of the atmosphere, primarily due to the high abundance of Ar. Their properties appear in the Group 8A(18) Family Portrait (p. 594).

How Can Noble Gases Form Compounds?

Lying at the far right side of the periodic table, the Group 8A(18) elements consist of individual atoms with filled outer levels and the smallest radii in their periods: even Li, the smallest alkali metal (152 pm), is bigger than Rn, the largest noble gas (141 pm). These elements come as close to behaving as ideal gases as any other substances. Only at very low temperatures do they condense and solidify. In fact, He is the only substance that does *not* solidify by a reduction in temperature alone; it requires an increase in pressure as well. Helium has the lowest melting point known ($-272.2°C$ at 25 atm), only one degree above 0 K ($-273.15°C$), and it boils only about three degrees higher. Weak dispersion forces hold these elements in condensed states, with melting and boiling points that increase, as expected, with molar mass.

Figure 14.33 **Crystals of xenon tetrafluoride (XeF$_4$).**

Ever since their discovery in the late 19th century, these elements had been considered, and even formerly named, the "inert" gases. Atomic theory and, more important, all laboratory experience had supported this idea. Then, in 1962, all this changed when the first noble gas compound was prepared. Nevertheless, we must ask how, with filled outer levels and extremely high ionization energies, *can* noble gases react?

The discovery of noble gas reactivity is a classic example of clear thinking in the face of an unexpected event. At the time, a young inorganic chemist named Neil Bartlett was studying platinum fluorides, known to be strong oxidizing agents. When he accidentally exposed PtF$_6$ to air, its deep-red color lightened slightly, and analysis showed that the PtF$_6$ had oxidized O$_2$ to form the ionic compound $[O_2]^+[PtF_6]^-$. Knowing that the ionization energy of the oxygen molecule ($O_2 \longrightarrow O_2^+ + e^-$; IE = 1175 kJ/mol) is very close to IE$_1$ of xenon (1170 kJ/mol), Bartlett reasoned that PtF$_6$ might be able to oxidize xenon. Shortly thereafter, he prepared XePtF$_6$, an orange-yellow solid. Within a few months, the white crystalline XeF$_2$ and XeF$_4$ (Figure 14.33) were also prepared. In addition to the +2 and +4 oxidation states, Xe occurs in the +6 state in several compounds, such as XeF$_6$, and in the +8 state in the unstable oxide, XeO$_4$. A few compounds of Kr have also been made. The xenon fluorides react rapidly in water to form HF and various other products, including different xenon compounds.

Looking Backward and Forward: Groups 7A(17), 8A(18), and 1A(1)

With the disappearance of metallic behavior, a host of 7A anions, covalent oxides, and oxoanions appear, which change oxidation states readily in a rich aqueous chemistry. The vigorous reactivity of the halogens is in stark contrast to the inertness of their 8A neighbors. Filled outer levels render these lone 8A atoms largely inert, despite a limited ability to react with the most electronegative elements, fluorine and oxygen. The least reactive family in the periodic table stands between the two most reactive: the halogens, which need one more electron to fill their outer level, and the alkali metals, which need one fewer (Figure 14.34). As you know, atomic, physical, and chemical properties change dramatically from Group 8A(18) to Group 1A(1).

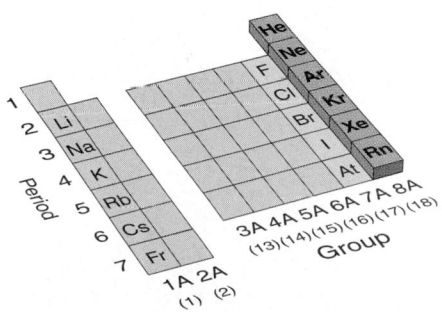

Figure 14.34 **Standing in Group 8A(18), looking backward at the halogens, Group 7A(17), and ahead to the alkali metals, Group 1A(1).**

Key Atomic and Physical Properties

ns^2np^6

GROUP 8A(18)

2	
He	
4.003	
$1s^2$	
(none)	

| 10 |
| **Ne** |
| 20.18 |
| $2s^22p^6$ |
| (none) |

| 18 |
| **Ar** |
| 39.95 |
| $3s^23p^6$ |
| (none) |

| 36 |
| **Kr** |
| 83.80 |
| $4s^24p^6$ |
| (+2) |

| 54 |
| **Xe** |
| 131.3 |
| $5s^25p^6$ |
| (+8, +6, +4, +2) |

| 86 |
| **Rn** |
| (222) |
| $6s^26p^6$ |
| (+2) |

Mass spectral peak

Atomic Properties

Atomic radius (pm)	
He	31
Ne	71
Ar	98
Kr	112
Xe	131
Rn	(140)

Group electron configuration is $1s^2$ for He; ns^2np^6 for others. The valence shell is filled. Only Kr and Xe (and perhaps Rn) are known to form compounds. The more reactive Xe exhibits all even oxidation states (+2 to +8).

This group contains the smallest atoms with the highest IE in their periods. Down the group, atomic size increases and IE decreases steadily. (EN values are given only for Kr and Xe.)

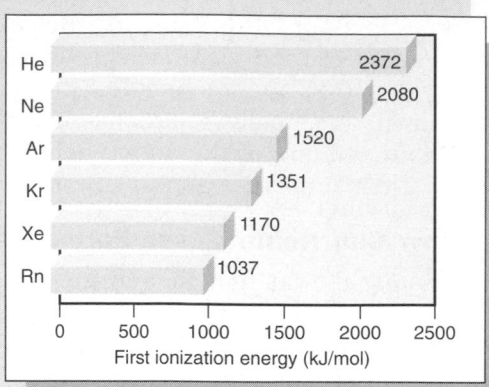

First ionization energy (kJ/mol): He 2372; Ne 2080; Ar 1520; Kr 1351; Xe 1170; Rn 1037

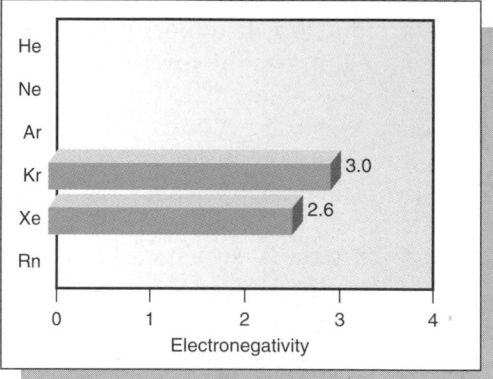

Electronegativity: Kr 3.0; Xe 2.6

Physical Properties

Melting and boiling points of these gaseous elements are extremely low but increase down the group because of stronger dispersion forces. Note the extremely small liquid ranges.

Temperature (°C) — BP / MP:
He −269; Ne −246, −249; Ar −186, −189; Kr −153, −157; Xe −108, −112; Rn −62, −71

Densities (at STP) increase steadily, as expected.

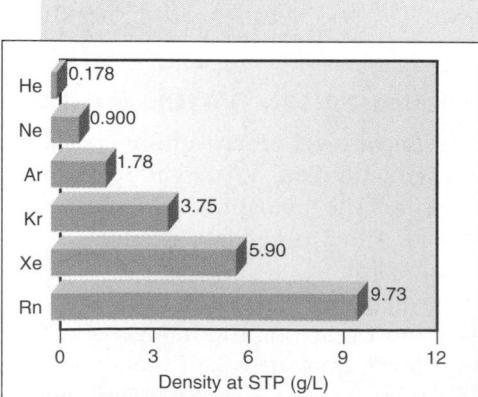

Density at STP (g/L): He 0.178; Ne 0.900; Ar 1.78; Kr 3.75; Xe 5.90; Rn 9.73

Chapter Perspective

Our excursion through the bonding and reactivity patterns of the elements has come full circle, but we've only been able to touch on some of the most important features. Clearly, the properties of the atoms and the resultant physical and chemical behaviors of the elements are magnificent testimony to nature's diversity. In Chapter 15, we continue with our theme of macroscopic behavior emerging from atomic properties in an investigation of the marvelously complex organic compounds of carbon. In Chapter 22, we revisit the most important main-group elements to see how they occur in nature and how we isolate and use them.

The following learning objectives, with section numbers in parentheses, can help focus your study:

Understand These Concepts

Note: Many characteristic reaction types appear in the "Important Reactions" sections within each group's Family Portrait.

1. How hydrogen is similar to, yet different from, alkali metals and halogens; the differences between saltlike and covalent hydrides (Section 14.1)

2. Key horizontal trends in atomic properties, types of bonding, oxide acid-base properties, and redox behavior of the elements as they change from metal to nonmetal (Section 14.2)

3. How the ns^1 configuration accounts for the physical and chemical properties of the alkali metals (Section 14.3)

4. How small atomic size and limited number of valence orbitals account for the anomalous behavior of the Period 2 member of each group (see each section for details)

5. How the ns^2 configuration accounts for the key differences between Groups 1A and 2A (Section 14.4)

6. The basis of the three important diagonal relationships (Li/Mg, Be/Al, B/Si) (Sections 14.4 to 14.6)

7. How the presence of inner $(n-1)d$ electrons affects properties in Group 3A (Section 14.5)

8. Patterns among larger members of Groups 3A to 6A: two common oxidation states (inert-pair effect), lower state more important down the group, and more basic lower oxide (Sections 14.5 to 14.8)

9. How boron attains an octet of electrons (Section 14.5)

10. The effect of bonding on the physical behavior of Groups 4A to 6A (Section 14.6)

11. Allotropism in carbon, phosphorus, and sulfur (Sections 14.6 to 14.8)

12. How atomic properties lead to catenation and multiple bonding in organic compounds (Section 14.6)

13. Varieties of structure and properties of the silicates and silicones (Section 14.6)

14. Patterns of behavior among hydrides and halides of Groups 5A and 6A; reactions of nonmetal halides with water (Sections 14.7 to 14.9)

15. Structure and chemistry of the nitrogen oxides and oxoacids (Section 14.7)

16. Structure and chemistry of the phosphorus oxides and oxoacids (Section 14.7)

17. Dehydration-condensation reactions and polymeric structures (Section 14.7)

18. Structure and chemistry of the sulfur oxides and oxoacids (Section 14.8)

19. How ns^2np^5 configuration accounts for halogen reactivity with metals (Section 14.9)

20. The meaning of disproportionation and its importance in halogen aqueous chemistry (Section 14.9)

21. Why the oxidation states of an element change by two units (Section 14.9)

22. Structure and chemistry of the halogen oxides and oxoacids (Section 14.9)

23. How ns^2np^6 configuration accounts for relative inertness of noble gases (Section 14.10)

For Review and Reference

Key Terms

Section 14.4
diagonal relationship

Section 14.5
bridge bond

Section 14.6
allotrope
silicate
silicone

Section 14.7
disproportionation reaction
dehydration-condensation
  reaction

Section 14.9
interhalogen compound

Highlighted Figures and Tables

These figures (F) and tables (T) provide a quick review of key ideas.

Problems

Problems with a colored number are answered at the back of the text. Problem sections match the text and provide the number(s) of relevant sample problems. Most offer concept review questions, skill-building exercises (written in similar pairs), and problems in a relevant context. Following these are comprehensive problems based on material from any section and/or previous chapter.
Note: This set begins with problems based on material from the Interchapter.

Interchapter Review

■ Concept Review Questions

14.1 (a) Define the four atomic properties that are reviewed in the Interchapter.
(b) To what do the three parts of the electron configuration ($nl^{\#}$) correlate?
(c) Which part of the electron configuration is primarily associated with the size of the atom?
(d) What is the major distinction between outer electron configurations in a group compared with those in a period?
(e) What correlation, if any, exists between the group number and the number of valence electrons?

14.2 (a) What trends, if any, exist for Z_{eff} across a period and down a group?
(b) How does Z_{eff} influence atomic size, IE_1, and EN across a period of elements?

14.3 Iodine monochloride and elemental bromine have nearly the same molar mass and liquid density but very different boiling points.
(a) What molecular property is primarily responsible for this difference in boiling point? What atomic property gives rise to it? Explain.
(b) Which substance has a higher boiling point? Why?

14.4 How does the trend in atomic size differ from the trend in ionization energy? Explain.

14.5 How are bond energy, bond length, and reactivity related for similar compounds?

14.6 How are covalent and metallic bonding similar? How are they different?

14.7 If the leftmost element in a period combined with each of the others in the period, how would the type of bonding change from left to right? Explain in terms of atomic properties.

14.8 Why is rotation about the bond axis possible for single-bonded atoms but not double-bonded atoms?

14.9 Atomic size tends to decrease smoothly across a period, but ionic size exhibits a major irregularity. With what is this irregularity associated?

14.10 Would you expect S^{2-} to be larger or smaller than Cl^-? Would you expect Mg^{2+} to be larger or smaller than Na^+? Explain.

14.11 (a) How does the type of bonding in element oxides correlate with the electronegativity of the elements?
(b) How does the acid-base behavior of element oxides correlate with the electronegativity of the elements?

14.12 (a) How does the metallic character of an element correlate with the *acidity* of its oxide?
(b) What trends, if any, exist in oxide *basicity* across a period and down a group?

14.13 How are atomic size, IE_1, and EN related to redox behavior of the elements in Groups 1A(1), 2A(2), 6A(16), and 7A(17)?

14.14 How do the physical properties of a network covalent solid and a molecular covalent solid differ? Why?

■ Skill-Building Exercises (paired)

14.15 Rank the following elements in order of *increasing*
(a) atomic size: Ba, Mg, Sr
(b) IE_1: P, Na, Al
(c) EN: Br, Cl, Se
(d) number of valence electrons: Bi, Ga, Sn

14.16 Rank the following elements in order of *decreasing*
(a) atomic size: N, Si, P
(b) IE_1: Kr, K, Ar
(c) EN: In, Rb, I
(d) number of valence electrons: Sb, S, Cs

14.17 Which of the following pairs react to form *ionic* compounds: (a) Cl and Br; (b) Na and Br; (c) P and Se; (d) H and Ba?

14.18 Which of the following pairs react to form *covalent* compounds: (a) Be and C; (b) Sr and O; (c) Ca and Cl; (d) P and F?

14.19 Draw a Lewis structure for a compound with a bond order of 2 throughout the molecule.

14.20 Draw a Lewis structure for a polyatomic ion with a fractional bond order throughout the molecule.

14.21 Rank the following in order of *increasing* bond length: $SiCl_4$, CF_4, $GeBr_4$.

14.22 Rank the following in order of *decreasing* bond energy: NF_3, NI_3, NCl_3.

14.23 Rank the following in order of *increasing* radius: (a) O^{2-}, F^-, Na^+; (b) S^{2-}, P^{3-}, Cl^-.

14.24 Rank the following in order of *decreasing* radius: (a) Ca^{2+}, K^+, Ga^{3+}; (b) Br^-, Sr^{2+}, Rb^+.

14.25 Rank O^-, O^{2-}, and O in order of *increasing* size.

14.26 Rank Tl^{3+}, Tl, and Tl^+ in order of *decreasing* size.

14.27 Which member of each pair gives the more *basic* solution in water: (a) CaO or SO_3; (b) BeO or BaO; (c) CO_2 or NO_2; (d) P_4O_{10} or K_2O? For the pair in (a), write an equation for each oxide to support your answer.

14.28 Which member of each pair gives the more *acidic* solution in water: (a) NO_2 or SrO; (b) SnO or SnO_2; (c) Cl_2O or Na_2O; (d) SO_2 or MgO? For the pair in (a), write an equation for each oxide to support your answer.

14.29 Which member of each pair has more *covalent* character in its bonds: (a) LiCl or KCl; (b) $AlCl_3$ or PCl_3; (c) NCl_3 or $AsCl_3$?

14.30 Which member of each pair has more *ionic* character in its bonds: (a) BeF_2 or CaF_2; (b) PbF_2 or PbF_4; (c) GeF_4 or PF_3?

14.31 Rank the following in order of *increasing* (a) melting point: Na, Si, Ar   (b) ΔH_{fus}: Rb, Cs, Li

14.32 Rank the following in order of *decreasing* (a) boiling point: O_2, Br_2, $As(s)$ (b) ΔH_{vap}: Cl_2, Ar, I_2

Hydrogen, the Simplest Atom

■ Concept Review Questions

14.33 Hydrogen has only one proton but its IE_1 is much greater than that of lithium, which has three protons. Explain.

14.34 Sketch a periodic table and label the areas containing elements that give rise to the three types of hydrides discussed in the text.

■ Skill-Building Exercises *(paired)*

14.35 Draw Lewis structures for the following compounds, and predict which member of each pair will form hydrogen bonds: (a) NF_3 or NH_3; (b) CH_3OCH_3 or CH_3CH_2OH.

14.36 Draw Lewis structures for the following compounds, and predict which member of each pair will form hydrogen bonds: (a) NH_3 or AsH_3; (b) CH_4 or H_2O.

14.37 Complete and balance the following equations: (a) An active metal reacting with acid,

$$Al(s) + HCl(aq) \longrightarrow$$

(b) A saltlike (alkali metal) hydride reacting with water,

$$LiH(s) + H_2O(l) \longrightarrow$$

14.38 Complete and balance the following equations: (a) A saltlike (alkaline earth metal) hydride reacting with water,

$$CaH_2(s) + H_2O(l) \longrightarrow$$

(b) Reduction by hydrogen to form a metal,

$$PdCl_2(aq) + H_2(g) \longrightarrow$$

■ Problems in Context

14.39 Compounds such as $NaBH_4$, $Al(BH_4)_3$, and $LiAlH_4$ are called complex hydrides and are used as reducing agents in many chemical syntheses.

(a) Give the oxidation number of each element in these three compounds.

(b) Write a Lewis structure for the polyatomic anion in $NaBH_4$ and predict its shape.

14.40 Unlike the F^- ion, which has an ionic radius close to 133 pm in all alkali metal fluorides, the H^- ionic radius varies from 137 pm in LiH to 152 pm in CsH. Suggest an explanation for the large variability in H^- but not in F^-.

Trends Across the Periodic Table

■ Concept Review Questions

14.41 How does the maximum oxidation state vary across a period for the main groups? Is the pattern in Period 2 different?

14.42 What correlation, if any, exists for the Period 2 elements between group number and the number of covalent bonds the element typically forms? How is the correlation different for elements in higher periods?

14.43 Each of the chemically active Period 2 elements forms stable compounds that have bonds to fluorine.

(a) What are the names and formulas of the substances formed?

(b) Does ΔEN increase or decrease from left to right?

(c) Does percent ionic character increase or decrease from left to right?

(d) Draw Lewis structures for those compounds with predominantly covalent bonding.

14.44 Period 6 is unusual in several ways.

(a) It is the longest period in the table. How many elements belong to Period 6? How many metals?

(b) It contains no metalloids. Where is the metal-nonmetal boundary in Period 6?

14.45 An element forms an oxide E_2O_3 and a fluoride EF_3.

(a) Of what two groups might E be a member?

(b) How does the group to which E belongs affect the properties of the oxide and the fluoride?

14.46 Fluorine lies between oxygen and neon in Period 2. Whereas atomic sizes and ionization energies of these three elements change smoothly, their electronegativities display a dramatic change. What is this change and how do their electron configurations explain it?

Group 1A(1): The Alkali Metals

■ Concept Review Questions

14.47 Lithium salts are often much less soluble in water than the corresponding salts of other alkali metals. For example, at 18°C the concentration of a saturated LiF solution is 1.0×10^{-2} *M*, whereas that of KF is 1.6 *M*. How would you explain this behavior?

14.48 The alkali metals play virtually the same general chemical role in all their reactions. (a) What is this role? (b) How is it based on atomic properties? (c) Using sodium, write two balanced equations that exhibit this role.

14.49 How do atomic properties account for the low densities of the Group 1A(1) elements?

■ Skill-Building Exercises *(paired)*

14.50 Each of the following properties shows regular trends in Group 1A(1). Predict whether each increases or decreases *down* the group: (a) density; (b) ionic size; (c) E—E bond energy; (d) IE_1; (e) magnitude of ΔH_{hydr} of E^+ ion.

14.51 Each of the following properties shows regular trends in Group 1A(1). Predict whether each increases or decreases *up* the group: (a) melting point; (b) E—E bond length; (c) hardness; (d) molar volume; (e) lattice energy of EBr.

14.52 Write a balanced equation for the formation from its elements of sodium peroxide, an industrial bleach for fabric and paper.

14.53 Write a balanced equation for the formation of rubidium bromide through a neutralization reaction of a strong acid and a strong base.

■ **Problems in Context**

14.54 Although the alkali halides can be prepared directly from the elements, the far less expensive industrial route is through treatment of the carbonate or hydroxide with aqueous hydrohalic acid (HX) followed by recrystallization. Balance the reaction between potassium carbonate and aqueous hydriodic acid.

14.55 The total terrestrial abundance of francium ($Z = 87$) is estimated at 2×10^{-18} ppm, or about 15 g Fr in the top kilometer of the Earth's crust. Nevertheless, it has been predicted that if a weighable quantity of Fr could be obtained, it would be a liquid at room temperature. What is the basis of this prediction?

Group 2A(2): The Alkaline Earth Metals

■ **Concept Review Questions**

14.56 How do Groups 1A(1) and 2A(2) compare with respect to reaction of the metals with water?

14.57 Alkaline earth metals are involved in two key diagonal relationships in the periodic table. (a) Give the two pairs of elements in these diagonal relationships. (b) For each pair, cite two similarities that demonstrate the relationship. (c) Why are the members of each pair so similar in behavior?

14.58 The melting points of alkaline earth metals are many times higher than those of the alkali metals. Explain this difference on the basis of atomic properties. Name three other physical properties for which Group 2A(2) metals have higher values than the corresponding 1A(1) metals.

■ **Skill-Building Exercises (paired)**

14.59 Write a balanced equation for each reaction:
(a) "Slaking" of lime (treatment with water)
(b) Combustion of calcium in air

14.60 Write a balanced equation for each reaction:
(a) Thermal decomposition of witherite (barium carbonate)
(b) Neutralization of stomach acid, HCl, by milk of magnesia (magnesium hydroxide)

■ **Problems in Context**

14.61 Lime (CaO) is one of the most abundantly produced chemicals in the world. Write balanced equations for
(a) The preparation of lime from natural sources
(b) The use of slaked lime to remove SO_2 from flue gases
(c) The reaction of lime with arsenic acid (H_3AsO_4) to manufacture the insecticide calcium arsenate
(d) The regeneration of NaOH in the paper industry by reaction of lime with aqueous sodium carbonate

14.62 In some reactions, Be behaves like a typical alkaline earth metal, whereas in others, it does not. Complete and balance the following equations:

(a) $BeO(s) + H_2O(l) \longrightarrow$
(b) $BeCl_2(l) + Cl^-(l;$ from molten NaCl$) \longrightarrow$
In which reaction does Be behave like the other Group 2A(2) members?

Group 3A(13): The Boron Family

■ **Concept Review Questions**

14.63 How do the transition metals in Period 4 affect the pattern of ionization energies in Group 3A(13)? How does this pattern compare with that of Group 3B(3)?

14.64 How do the aqueous acidities of Tl_2O and Tl_2O_3 compare with each other? Explain.

14.65 Despite the expected decrease in atomic size, there is an unexpected drop in the first ionization energy between Groups 2A(2) and 3A(13) in Periods 2 through 4 (e.g., Be to B). Explain this pattern in terms of electron configuration and orbital energies.

14.66 Many compounds of Group 3A(13) elements have chemical behavior that reflects an electron deficiency.
(a) What is the meaning of "electron deficiency"?
(b) Give two reactions that illustrate this behavior.

14.67 Boron chemistry is not typical of its group.
(a) Cite three ways in which boron and its compounds differ significantly from the other 3A(13) members.
(b) What is the reason for these differences?

■ **Skill-Building Exercises (paired)**

14.68 Rank the following oxides in order of increasing aqueous *acidity:* Ga_2O_3, Al_2O_3, In_2O_3.

14.69 Rank the following hydroxides in order of increasing aqueous *basicity:* TlOH, $B(OH)_3$, $In(OH)_3$.

14.70 Thallium forms the compound TlI_3. What is the apparent oxidation state of Tl in this compound? Given that the anion is I_3^-, what is the actual oxidation state of Tl? Draw the shape of the anion, giving its VSEPR class and bond angles. Propose a reason why the compound does not exist as $(Tl^{3+})(I^-)_3$.

14.71 Very stable "dihalides" of the Group 3A(13) metals are known. What is the apparent oxidation state of Ga in $GaCl_2$? Given that $GaCl_2$ consists of a Ga^+ cation and a $GaCl_4^-$ anion, what are the actual oxidation states of Ga? Draw the shape of the anion, giving its VSEPR class and bond angles.

■ **Problems in Context**

14.72 Give the name and formula of a Group 3A(13) element or compound that fits each description or use:
(a) Component of heat-resistant (Pyrex-type) glass
(b) Manufacture of high-speed computer chips
(c) Largest temperature range for liquid state of an element
(d) Elementary substance with three-center, two-electron bonds
(e) Metal protected from oxidation by adherent oxide coat
(f) Mild antibacterial agent (e.g., for eye infections)
(g) Toxic metal that lies in the periodic table between two other toxic metals.

14.73 Many compounds of Groups 3A(13) and 5A(15) are technologically important as semiconductors. They can be prepared from the elements at high pressure and temperature, but must be kept encased to prevent decomposition in moist air to the 3A hydroxide and the 5A hydride.

(a) Write a balanced equation for the formation of indium(III) arsenide.

(b) Write a balanced equation for the decomposition of gallium antimonide in moist air.

14.74 Use VSEPR theory to draw structures, with ideal bond angles, for boric acid and the anion it forms in reaction with water.

14.75 Halides of Al, Ga, and In occur as dimers in the gas and liquid phases (those of the larger halogens form dimeric solids also). Use VSEPR theory to draw the structure, with ideal bond angles, of the $GaBr_3$ dimer.

Group 4A(14): The Carbon Family

■ Concept Review Questions

14.76 How does the basicity of SnO_2 in water compare with that of CO_2? Explain.

14.77 Nearly every compound of silicon has the element in the $+4$ oxidation state. In contrast, most compounds of lead have the element in the $+2$ state.

(a) What general observation do these facts illustrate?

(b) What is the explanation for these facts in terms of atomic and molecular properties?

(c) Give an analogous example from the chemistry of Group 3A(13).

14.78 The sum of IE_1 through IE_4 for Group 4A(14) elements shows a decrease from C to Si, a slight increase from Si to Ge, a decrease from Ge to Sn, and an increase from Sn to Pb. (a) What is the expected trend for ionization energy down a group? (b) Suggest an explanation for the deviations from the expected trend. (c) Which group might you expect to show even greater deviations?

14.79 Give explanations for the large drops in melting point from C to Si and from Ge to Sn.

14.80 What is an allotrope? Name two Group 4A(14) elements that exhibit allotropy and name two of their allotropes.

14.81 Even though EN values vary relatively little down Group 4A(14), the elements change from nonmetal to metal. Explain.

14.82 How do atomic properties account for the enormous number of carbon compounds? Why don't other Group 4A(14) elements behave similarly?

■ Skill-Building Exercises (paired)

14.83 Draw a Lewis structure for

(a) The cyclic silicate ion $Si_4O_{12}^{8-}$

(b) A cyclic hydrocarbon with formula C_4H_8

14.84 Draw a Lewis structure for

(a) The cyclic silicate ion $Si_6O_{18}^{12-}$

(b) A cyclic hydrocarbon with formula C_6H_{12}

14.85 Show three units of a linear silicone polymer made from $(CH_3)_2Si(OH)_2$ with some $(CH_3)_3SiOH$ added to end the chain.

14.86 Show two chains of three units each of a sheet silicone polymer made from $(CH_3)_2Si(OH)_2$ with $CH_3Si(OH)_3$ added to crosslink the chains.

■ Problems in Context

14.87 Although it is often stated that double bonding is limited to compounds of Period 2 elements, compounds of Period 3 elements also contain double bonds.

(a) What types of atomic orbitals are used for the π bond in $C{=}O$?

(b) Why are the same types of orbitals not satisfactory for an $Si{=}O$ π bond?

(c) What orbital type could be used for an $Si{=}O$ π bond?

(d) Which atom(s) would supply the electrons in such a π bond?

14.88 Give the name and formula of a Group 4A(14) element or compound that fits each description or use:

(a) Hardest known substance

(b) Medicinal antacid

(c) Atmospheric gas implicated in greenhouse effect

(d) Waterproofing polymer based upon silicon

(e) Synthetic abrasive composed entirely of Group 4A elements

(f) Product formed when coke burns in a limited supply of air

(g) Toxic metal found in gasoline, plumbing, and paints

14.89 One similarity between B and Si is the explosive combustion of their hydrides in air. Write balanced equations for the combustion of B_2H_6 and of Si_4H_{10}.

Group 5A(15): The Nitrogen Family

■ Concept Review Questions

14.90 Which Group 5A(15) elements form trihalides? Pentahalides? Explain.

14.91 As you move down Group 5A(15), the melting points of the elements increase and then decrease. Explain.

14.92 (a) What is the range of oxidation states shown by the elements of Group 5A(15) as you move down the group? (b) How does this range illustrate the general rule for the range of oxidation states in groups on the right side of the periodic table?

14.93 Bismuth(V) compounds are such powerful oxidizing agents that they have not been prepared in pure form. How is this fact consistent with the location of Bi in the periodic table?

14.94 Rank the following oxides in order of increasing acidity in water: Sb_2O_3, Bi_2O_3, P_4O_{10}, Sb_2O_5.

■ Skill-Building Exercises (paired)

14.95 Assuming that acid strength relates directly to electronegativity of the central atom, rank H_3PO_4, HNO_3, and H_3AsO_4 in order of *increasing* acid strength.

14.96 Assuming that acid strength relates directly to number of O atoms on the central atom, rank $H_2N_2O_2$ [or $(HON)_2$]; HNO_3 (or $HONO_2$); and HNO_2 (or $HONO$) in order of *decreasing* acid strength.

14.97 Complete and balance the following:

(a) $As(s) + \text{excess } O_2(g) \longrightarrow$

(b) $Bi(s) + \text{excess } F_2(g) \longrightarrow$

(c) $Ca_3As_2(s) + H_2O(l) \longrightarrow$

14.98 Complete and balance the following:

(a) $\text{Excess } Sb(s) + Br_2(l) \longrightarrow$

(b) $HNO_3(aq) + MgCO_3(s) \longrightarrow$

(c) $K_2HPO_4(s) \xrightarrow{\text{heat}}$

14.99 Complete and balance the following:

(a) $N_2(g) + Al(s) \xrightarrow{\text{heat}}$

(b) $PF_5(g) + H_2O(l) \longrightarrow$

14.100 Complete and balance the following:
(a) $AsCl_3(l) + H_2O(l) \longrightarrow$
(b) $Sb_2O_3(s) + NaOH(aq) \longrightarrow$

14.101 Based on the relative sizes of F and Cl, predict the structure of PF_2Cl_3.

14.102 Use the VSEPR model to predict the structure of the cyclic ion $P_3O_9^{3-}$.

■ **Problems in Context**

14.103 The white and red allotropes of phosphorus differ dramatically in toxicity. One is relatively unreactive in the body, whereas the other is quite poisonous. Suggest how their structures lead to a difference in toxicity and name the nontoxic allotrope.

14.104 Give the name and formula of a Group 5A(15) element or compound that fits each of the following descriptions or uses:
(a) Hydride produced at multimillion-ton level
(b) Element(s) essential in plant nutrition
(c) Hydride used in the manufacture of rocket propellants and drugs
(d) Odd-electron molecule (two examples)
(e) Amphoteric hydroxide with 5A element in its +3 state
(f) P-containing water softener
(g) Element that is an electrical conductor

14.105 Would you expect hydrazine (N_2H_4) to form H bonds? Explain with structures.

14.106 Nitrous oxide (N_2O), the "laughing gas" used as an anesthetic by dentists, is made by thermal decomposition of solid NH_4NO_3. Write a balanced equation for this reaction. What are the oxidation states of N in NH_4NO_3 and in N_2O?

14.107 Write balanced equations for the thermal decomposition of potassium nitrate (O_2 is also formed in both cases):
(a) at low temperature to the nitrite; (b) at high temperature to the metal oxide and nitrogen.

Group 6A(16): The Oxygen Family

■ **Concept Review Questions**

14.108 Rank the following in order of increasing electrical conductivity and explain your ranking: Po, S, Se.

14.109 The oxygen and nitrogen families have some obvious similarities and differences.
(a) State two general physical similarities between Group 5A(15) and 6A(16) elements.
(b) State two general chemical similarities between Group 5A and 6A elements.
(c) State two chemical similarities between P and S.
(d) State two physical similarities between N and O.
(e) State two chemical differences between N and O.

14.110 A molecular property of the Group 6A(16) hydrides changes abruptly down the group. This change has been explained in terms of a change in hybridization.
(a) Between what periods does the change occur?
(b) What is the change in the molecular property?
(c) What is the change in hybridization?
(d) What other group displays a similar change?

■ **Skill-Building Exercises (paired)**

14.111 Complete and balance the following:
(a) $NaHSO_4(aq) + NaOH(aq) \longrightarrow$
(b) $S_8(s) + excess\ F_2(g) \longrightarrow$

(c) $FeS(s) + HCl(aq) \longrightarrow$
(d) $Te(s) + I_2(s) \longrightarrow$

14.112 Complete and balance the following:
(a) $H_2S(g) + O_2(g) \longrightarrow$
(b) $SO_3(g) + H_2O(l) \longrightarrow$
(c) $SF_4(g) + H_2O(l) \longrightarrow$
(d) $Al_2Se_3(s) + H_2O(l) \longrightarrow$

14.113 Is each oxide basic, acidic, or amphoteric in water:
(a) SeO_2; (b) N_2O_3; (c) K_2O; (d) BeO; (e) BaO?

14.114 Is each oxide basic, acidic, or amphoteric in water:
(a) MgO; (b) N_2O_5; (c) CaO; (d) CO_2; (e) TeO_2?

14.115 Rank the following hydrides in order of *increasing* acid strength: H_2S, H_2O, H_2Te.

14.116 Rank the following species in order of *decreasing* acid strength: H_2SO_4, H_2SO_3, HSO_3^-.

■ **Problems in Context**

14.117 Describe the physical changes observed when solid sulfur is heated from room temperature to 440°C and then poured quickly into cold water. Explain the molecular changes responsible for the macroscopic changes.

14.118 Give the name and formula of a Group 6A(16) element or compound that fits each of the following descriptions or uses:
(a) Unreactive gas used as an electrical insulator
(b) Unstable allotrope of oxygen
(c) Oxide having sulfur in the same oxidation state as in sulfuric acid
(d) Air pollutant produced by burning sulfur-containing coal
(e) Powerful dehydrating agent
(f) Compound used in solution in the photographic process
(g) Trace gas that tarnishes silver

14.119 In addition to the monatomic sulfide anion S^{2-}, sulfur forms a variety of polyatomic sulfide anions, S_n^{2-}. The simplest, S_2^{2-}, is found in pyrite ores, such as FeS_2, and others through S_6^{2-} are known.
(a) Name and draw a Lewis structure for the oxygen anion that is analogous to S_2^{2-}.
(b) Predict the shape and bond angle of the anion in BaS_3.

14.120 Disulfur decafluoride is intermediate in reactivity between SF_4 and SF_6. It disproportionates at 150°C to these monosulfur fluorides. Write a balanced equation for this reaction and give the oxidation state of S in each compound.

Group 7A(17): The Halogens

■ **Concept Review Questions**

14.121 (a) What is the physical state and color of each of the halogens at STP?
(b) Explain the change in physical state down the group in terms of molecular properties.

14.122 (a) What are the common oxidation states of the halogens?
(b) Give an explanation based on electron configuration for the range and values of the oxidation states of chlorine.
(c) Why is fluorine an exception to the pattern of oxidation states found for the other group members?

14.123 How many electrons does a halogen atom need to complete its octet? Give examples of the different ways that a Cl atom can do so.

14.124 Select the stronger bond in each pair:
(a) Cl—Cl or Br—Br; (b) Br—Br or I—I; (c) F—F or Cl—Cl. Why doesn't the F—F bond strength follow the group trend?

14.125 In addition to interhalogen compounds, many polyatomic interhalogen ions exist. Would you expect interhalogen ions with a 1+ or a 1− charge to have an even or odd number of atoms? Explain.

14.126 (a) A halogen (X_2) disproportionates in base in several steps to X^- and XO_3^-. Write the overall equation for the disproportionation of Br_2 to Br^- and BrO_3^-.
(b) Write a balanced equation for the reaction of ClF_5 with aqueous base (by analogy with the reaction of BrF_5 shown in text).

▥ Skill-Building Exercises *(paired)*

14.127 Complete and balance the following equations. If no reaction occurs, write NR:
(a) $Rb(s) + Br_2(l) \longrightarrow$ (b) $I_2(s) + H_2O(l) \longrightarrow$
(c) $Br_2(l) + I^-(aq) \longrightarrow$ (d) $CaF_2(s) + H_2SO_4(l) \longrightarrow$

14.128 Complete and balance the following equations. If no reaction occurs, write NR:
(a) $H_3PO_4(l) + NaI(s) \longrightarrow$ (b) $Cl_2(g) + I^-(aq) \longrightarrow$
(c) $Br_2(l) + Cl^-(aq) \longrightarrow$ (d) $ClF(g) + F_2(g) \longrightarrow$

14.129 Rank the following acids in order of *increasing* acid strength: $HClO$, $HClO_2$, $HBrO$, HIO.

14.130 Rank the following acids in order of *decreasing* acid strength: $HBrO_3$, $HBrO_4$, HIO_3, $HClO_4$.

▥ Problems in Context

14.131 Give the name and formula of a Group 7A(17) element or compound that fits each description or use:
(a) Used in etching glass
(b) Naturally occurring source (ore) of fluorine
(c) Oxide used in bleaching paper pulp and textiles
(d) Weakest hydrohalic acid
(e) Compound used as food additive to prevent goiter (thyroid disorder)
(f) Element that is produced in the largest quantity
(g) Organic chloride used to make plastics

14.132 An industrial chemist treats solid NaCl with concentrated H_2SO_4 and obtains gaseous HCl and $NaHSO_4$. When she substitutes solid NaI for NaCl, gaseous H_2S, solid I_2, and S_8 are obtained but no HI.
(a) What type of reaction did the H_2SO_4 undergo with NaI?
(b) Why does NaI, but not NaCl, cause this type of reaction?
(c) To produce $HI(g)$ by the reaction of NaI with an acid, how does the acid have to differ from sulfuric acid?

14.133 Rank the larger halogens in order of increasing oxidizing strength based on their products with metallic Re: $ReCl_6$, $ReBr_5$, ReI_4. Explain your ranking.

Group 8A(18): The Noble Gases

14.134 Which noble gas is the most abundant in the universe? In the atmosphere?

14.135 What oxidation states does Xe show in its compounds?

14.136 Why do the noble gases have such low boiling points?

14.137 Explain why Xe, and to a limited extent Kr, form compounds, whereas He, Ne, and Ar do not.

14.138 (a) Why do the stable xenon fluorides have an even number of fluorine atoms?

(b) Why do the ionic species XeF_3^+ and XeF_7^- have odd numbers of F atoms?
(c) Predict the shape of XeF_3^+.

Comprehensive Problems

Problems with an asterisk (*) are more challenging.

14.139 Sodium hydride is used to prepare sodium dithionate ($Na_2S_2O_4$), used in bleaching paper pulp:

$$NaH(s) + SO_2(l) \longrightarrow Na_2S_2O_4(s) + H_2(g)$$

(a) Balance the equation and give the O.N. of each element.
(b) How many liters of hydrogen gas measured at 758 torr and −45°C can form when exactly 1 metric ton NaH reacts with 1 metric ton SO_2?

14.140 Given the following information,

$$H^+(g) + H_2O(g) \longrightarrow H_3O^+(g); \Delta H = -720 \text{ kJ}$$
$$H^+(g) + H_2O(l) \longrightarrow H_3O^+(aq); \Delta H = -1090 \text{ kJ}$$
$$H_2O(l) \longrightarrow H_2O(g); \Delta H = 40.7 \text{kJ}$$

calculate the heat of solution of the hydronium ion:

$$H_3O^+(g) \xrightarrow{H_2O} H_3O^+(aq)$$

14.141 The electronic transition in Na from $3p^1$ to $3s^1$ gives rise to a bright yellow-orange emission at 589.2 nm. What is the energy of this transition?

14.142 Unlike the other Group 2A(2) metals, beryllium acts like aluminum and zinc in reacting with concentrated aqueous base to release hydrogen gas and form oxoanions of formula $M(OH)_4^{n-}$. Write equations for the reaction of these metals with NaOH.

14.143 Just as boron nitride is isoelectronic with carbon, other compounds of Groups 3A(13) and 5A(15) are isoelectronic with elements in Group 4A(14). What element is isoelectronic with (a) aluminum phosphide; (b) gallium arsenide?

14.144 Cyclopropane (C_3H_6), the smallest cyclic hydrocarbon, is reactive for the same reason that white phosphorus is. Use bond properties and valence bond theory to explain the high reactivity of C_3H_6.

14.145 Thionyl chloride ($SOCl_2$) is a sulfur oxohalide that is used industrially to dehydrate metal halide hydrates.
(a) Write a balanced equation for its reaction with magnesium chloride hexahydrate, in which SO_2 and HCl form along with the metal halide.
(b) Draw the Lewis structure of thionyl chloride with the lowest formal charges.

14.146 The main reason that alkali metal dihalides (MX_2) do *not* form is the high IE_2 of the metal.
(a) Why is the IE_2 so high for alkali metals?
(b) The IE_2 for Cs is 2255 kJ/mol, low enough for CsF_2 to form exothermically ($\Delta H_f^0 = -125$ kJ/mol). This compound cannot be synthesized, however, because CsF forms with a much greater release of heat ($\Delta H_f^0 = -530$ kJ/mol). Thus, the breakdown of CsF_2 to CsF happens readily. Write the equation for this breakdown and calculate the heat of reaction per mole of CsF.

14.147 Semiconductors made from elements in Groups 3A and 5A are typically prepared by direct reaction of the elements at high temperature. An engineer treats 32.5 g molten gallium with 20.4 L white phosphorus vapor at 515 K and 195 kPa. If purification losses are 7.2% by mass, how many grams of gallium phosphide can be prepared?

*14.148 Two substances with the empirical formula HNO are hyponitrous acid ($\mathcal{M}$ = 62.04 g/mol) and nitroxyl ($\mathcal{M}$ = 31.02 g/mol).
(a) What is the molecular formula of each species?
(b) Draw the Lewis structure with the lowest formal charges for each species. (*Hint:* Hyponitrous acid has an N=N bond.)
(c) Predict the shape of each species around the N atoms.
(d) When hyponitrous acid loses two protons, it forms the hyponitrite ion. Draw *cis* and *trans* forms of this ion.

14.149 The species CO, CN$^-$, and C$_2^{2-}$ are isoelectronic.
(a) Draw their Lewis structures.
(b) Draw their MO diagrams (assume 2s-2p mixing as in N$_2$), and give the bond order and electron configuration for each.

*14.150 The Ostwald process is a series of three main reactions used for the industrial production of nitric acid from ammonia.
(a) Write out the series of balanced equations for the Ostwald process.
(b) If NO is *not* recycled, how many moles of NH$_3$ are consumed per mole of HNO$_3$ produced?
(c) In a typical industrial unit, the process is very efficient, with a 96% yield for the first step. Assuming 100% yields for the subsequent steps, what volume of nitric acid (60.% by mass; d = 1.37 g/mL) can be prepared per cubic meter of a gas mixture that is 90.% air and 10.% NH$_3$ by volume at the industrial conditions of 5.0 atm and 850.°C?

*14.151 Organolithium compounds such as LiCH$_3$ are important reagents in organic synthesis. The compounds are not simple substances, as the formula suggests, but exist in the solid state, and in solution with nonpolar solvents, as tetramers [e.g., methyllithium is Li$_4$(CH$_3$)$_4$].
(a) How many electrons are available for bonding among the four lithium atoms and the four methyl groups?
(b) Considering this number of available electrons and the total number of atoms bonded in the cluster, what unusual type of bonding might you expect to occur in some of the bonds in methyllithium?

14.152 Perhaps surprisingly, some pure liquid interhalogen fluorides have high electrical conductivity. The explanation is that one molecule transfers a fluoride ion to another molecule. Write the equation that would explain the high electrical conductivity of bromine trifluoride.

14.153 Solid PCl$_5$ exists not as molecules but rather as two ions, PCl$_4^+$ and PCl$_6^-$. Similarly, solid PBr$_5$ exists as ions, but in this case as PBr$_4^+$ and Br$^-$. Suggest a reason for this difference in solid state structure.

*14.154 Producer gas is a fuel formed by passing air over red-hot coke (amorphous carbon). It consists of approximately 25% CO, 5.0% CO$_2$, and 70.% N$_2$ by mass. What mass of producer gas can be formed from 1.75 metric tons of coke, assuming an 87% yield?

14.155 Hypofluorous acid (HFO, or more correctly HOF) was first prepared in weighable amounts as recently as 1971. The synthesis required treatment of fluorine with ice followed by rapid removal of the oxoacid to prevent the formation of oxygen difluoride through its reaction with more F$_2$.
(a) Write balanced equations for these reactions.
(b) What is the O.N. of O in HOF and in OF$_2$?
(c) Predict the shapes of HOF and OF$_2$.

14.156 What is a disproportionation reaction, and which of the following fit the description?
(a) $I_2(s) + KI(aq) \longrightarrow KI_3(aq)$
(b) $2ClO_2(g) + H_2O(l) \longrightarrow HClO_3(aq) + HClO_2(aq)$
(c) $Cl_2(g) + 2NaOH(aq) \longrightarrow$
$$NaCl(aq) + NaClO(aq) + H_2O(l)$$
(d) $NH_4NO_2(s) \longrightarrow N_2(g) + 2H_2O(g)$
(e) $3MnO_4^{2-}(aq) + 2H_2O(l) \longrightarrow$
$$2MnO_4^-(aq) + MnO_2(s) + 4OH^-(aq)$$
(f) $3AuCl(s) \longrightarrow AuCl_3(s) + 2Au(s)$

14.157 Explain the following observations:
(a) Phosphorus forms PCl$_5$ in addition to the expected PCl$_3$, but nitrogen forms only NCl$_3$.
(b) Carbon tetrachloride is stable toward reaction with water, but silicon tetrachloride reacts rapidly and completely. (To give what?)
(c) The oxygen-sulfur bond in SO$_4^{2-}$ is shorter than expected for an S—O single bond.
(d) Chlorine forms ClF$_3$ and ClF$_5$, but ClF$_4$ is unknown.

14.158 Which group(s) of the periodic table is(are) described by the following general statements?
(a) The elements form neutral compounds of VSEPR class AX$_3$E.
(b) The free elements are strong oxidizing agents and form monatomic ions and oxoanions.
(c) The valence shell allows the atoms to form compounds by combining with two atoms that donate one electron each.
(d) The free elements are strong reducing agents, show only one nonzero oxidation state, and form mainly ionic compounds.
(e) The elements can form stable compounds with only three bonds, but as a central atom, they can accept a pair of electrons from a fourth atom without expanding their valence shell.
(f) Only larger members of the group are known to be chemically active.

14.159 Diiodine pentaoxide (I$_2$O$_5$) was discovered by Gay-Lussac in 1813, but its structure was unknown until 1970! Like Cl$_2$O$_7$, it can be prepared by the dehydration-condensation of the corresponding oxoacid.
(a) Name the precursor oxoacid, write a reaction for formation of the oxide, and draw a likely Lewis structure.
(b) Data show that the bonds to the terminal O are shorter than the bonds to the bridging O. Why?
(c) I$_2$O$_5$ is one of the few chemicals that can oxidize CO rapidly and completely; elemental iodine forms in the process. Write a balanced equation for this reaction.

14.160 An important starting material for the manufacture of polyphosphazenes is the cyclic molecule (NPCl$_2$)$_3$. The molecule has a symmetrical six-membered ring of alternating N and P atoms, with the Cl atoms bound to the P atoms. The N—P bond length is significantly less than that expected for an N—P single bond.
(a) Draw a likely Lewis structure for the molecule.
(b) How many lone pairs of electrons appear on the ring atoms?
(c) What is the order of the N—P bond?

14.161 Grignard reagents have remarkable versatility in organic syntheses. Recently some of the solvated intermediates have been crystallized and their structure determined.

Draw a Lewis structure for the species in which Mg is surrounded by CH_3, Br, and two molecules of ethyl ether (CH_3CH_2—O—CH_2CH_3). Predict the shape around the Mg atom. Predict the shape around the O atom in each ether group.

14.162 What are the molecular formulas for the most common allotrope of oxygen and of sulfur? Why are these formulas so different?

14.163 Account for the following facts:
(a) Ca^{2+} and Na^+ have very nearly the same radii.
(b) CaF_2 is insoluble, but NaF is quite soluble.
(c) Molten $BeCl_2$ is a poor electrical conductor, whereas molten $CaCl_2$ is an excellent conductor.

14.164 Alum (aluminum sulfate) is used as a "flocculating agent" in water purification. The "floc" is a gelatinous precipitate of aluminum hydroxide that carries down small suspended particles and bacteria for removal by filtration.
(a) The hydroxide is formed by the reaction of the aluminum ion with water. Write the equation for this reaction.
(b) The acidity from this reaction is partially neutralized by the sulfate ion. Write an equation for this reaction.

14.165 Three of the hardest substances known are diamond, silicon carbide (SiC), and borazon (BN).
(a) What common structural feature do these materials possess?
(b) Explain electronically how BN resembles the other two, whose elements come from Group 4A(14).

14.166 H_2 may act as a reducing agent or an oxidizing agent, depending upon the substance reacting with it. Using, in turn, sodium and chlorine as the other reactant, write balanced equations for the two reactions and characterize the redox role of hydrogen in each.

14.167 P_4 is prepared by heating phosphate rock [principally $Ca_3(PO_4)_2$] with sand and coke:

$$Ca_3(PO_4)_2(s) + SiO_2(s) + C(s) \longrightarrow$$
$$CaSiO_3(s) + CO(g) + P_4(g) \text{ [unbalanced]}$$

How many kilograms of phosphate rock will be needed to produce 315 mol P_4, assuming that the conversion is 90.% efficient?

14.168 Assume you can use either NH_4NO_3 or N_2H_4 as fertilizer. Which contains more moles of N per mole of compound? Which contains the higher mass of N per gram of compound?

14.169 From its formula, one might expect CO to be quite polar, but its dipole moment is actually low (0.11 D).
(a) Draw the Lewis structure for CO.
(b) Calculate the formal charges.
(c) Based on (a) and (b), explain why the dipole moment is so low.

*14.170 In addition to Al_2Cl_6, aluminum forms other species with bridging halide ions to two aluminum atoms. One such unit is the ion $Al_2Cl_7^-$. The ion is symmetrical, with a linear Al—Cl—Al bond.
(a) What orbitals does Al use to bond the Cl atoms?
(b) What is the shape around each Al?
(c) What is the hybridization of the central Cl?
(d) What do the shape and hybridization suggest about the presence of lone pairs of electrons on the central chlorine?

14.171 The best method for synthesizing SF_4 is the reaction of an alkali metal fluoride with SCl_2 in a nonaqueous solvent. Some SCl_2 is converted to S_2Cl_2 and the alkali metal fluoride is converted to the chloride.
(a) Using NaF, write the balanced equation for the production of SF_4.
(b) Draw Lewis structures for the three sulfur-containing compounds.

14.172 The bond angles in the nitrite ion, nitrogen dioxide, and the nitronium ion (NO_2^+) are 115°, 134°, and 180°, respectively. Rationalize these values using Lewis structures and VSEPR theory.

14.173 A common method for producing a gaseous hydride is to treat a salt containing the anion of the volatile hydride with a strong acid.
(a) Write an equation for each of the following examples:
(1) the production of HF from CaF_2; (2) the production of HCl from NaCl; (3) the production of H_2S from FeS.
(b) In some cases even a weak acid such as water will suffice if the salt anion has a sufficiently strong attraction for protons. An example is the production of PH_3 from Ca_3P_2 and water. Write the equation for this reaction.
(c) By analogy, predict the products and write the equation for the reaction of Al_4C_3 with water.

14.174 A former use of chlorine trifluoride in the United States was the production of uranium hexafluoride for the nuclear industry:

$$U(s) + 3ClF_3(l) \longrightarrow UF_6(l) + 3ClF(g)$$

How many grams of UF_6 can form from 1.00 metric ton of uranium ore that is 1.55% by mass uranium and 12.75 L chlorine trifluoride ($d = 1.88$ g/mL)?

*14.175 Chlorine is used to make household bleach solutions containing 5.25% (by mass) NaClO. Assuming 100% yield in the reaction producing NaClO from Cl_2, how many liters of $Cl_2(g)$ at STP will be needed to make 1000. L bleach solution ($d = 1.07$ g/mL)?

14.176 The triatomic molecular ion H_3^+ was first detected and characterized by J. J. Thomson using mass spectrometry. Use the bond energy of H_2 (432 kJ/mol) and the proton affinity of H_2 ($H_2 + H^+ \longrightarrow H_3^+$; $\Delta H = -337$ kJ/mol) to calculate the heat of reaction for $H + H + H^+ \longrightarrow H_3^+$.

14.177 Carbon monoxide can be used as a fuel. Use the heats of reaction (see Appendix B) for the following processes to compute the heat of combustion of CO:

$$C(s) + O_2(g) \longrightarrow CO_2(g)$$
$$C(s) + \tfrac{1}{2}O_2(g) \longrightarrow CO(g)$$

14.178 In aqueous HF solution, an important species is the ion HF_2^-, which has the bonding arrangement FHF^-. Draw the Lewis structure for this ion and explain how it arises.

14.179 Which of the following oxygen ions are paramagnetic: O^+, O^-, O^{2-}, O^{2+}?

*14.180 Hydrogen peroxide can act as either an oxidizing agent or a reducing agent. (a) When H_2O_2 is treated with aqueous KI, I_2 forms. In which role is H_2O_2 acting? What is the oxygen-containing product formed? (b) When H_2O_2 is treated with aqueous $KMnO_4$, the purple color of MnO_4^- disappears and a gas forms. In which role is H_2O_2 acting? What is the oxygen-containing product formed?

15 Organic Compounds and the Atomic Properties of Carbon

Figure: Crystals of an organic compound. This color-enhanced micrograph of crystalline hippuric acid (with model hovering over it), a key amino-acid metabolite, shows one of the millions of organic compounds studied by chemists. Each of these substances either occurs in a living source, from which it is extracted and purified, or is synthesized in the laboratory. Whatever the origin, the behavior of organic compounds obeys the same chemical principles that govern all substances. Fuels, medicines, and polymers consist of organic compounds. In this chapter, you'll see that their physical and chemical properties depend on the properties of the carbon atom.

A living cell is a remarkable chemical system. Through elegantly controlled mechanisms, it oxidizes food for energy, maintains the concentrations of thousands of aqueous components, interacts continuously with its environment, synthesizes both simple and complex molecules for its survival and growth, and even reproduces itself. With all our technological prowess, no human-made system even approaches the cell for sheer artistry of function. This amazing chemical machine consumes, creates, and consists largely of *organic compounds*. Except for a few inorganic salts and ever-present water, everything you put into or on your body—food, medicine, cosmetics, and clothing—consists of organic compounds. Organic fuels warm our homes, cook our meals, and power our society. Major industries are devoted to producing organic compounds, such as polymers, pharmaceuticals, and insecticides.

What *is* an organic compound? Dictionaries define it as "a compound of carbon," but that definition would include carbonates, cyanides, carbides, cyanates, and other carbon-containing ionic compounds most chemists would classify as inorganic. Here is a practical, working definition: all **organic compounds** contain carbon, nearly always bonded to itself and to hydrogen, and often to other elements as well.

The word *organic* has a biological connotation arising from a major misconception that stifled research into the chemistry of living systems for many decades. In the early 19th century, many prominent thinkers believed that an unobservable spiritual energy, a "vital force," existed *within* the compounds of living things, making them impossible to synthesize and fundamentally different from compounds of the mineral world. This idea of *vitalism* was challenged in 1828, when the young German chemist Friedrich Wöhler heated ammonium cyanate, a "mineral-world" compound, and produced urea, a "living-world" compound:

$$NH_4OCN \xrightarrow{\Delta} H_2N-\overset{\overset{\textstyle O}{\|}}{C}-NH_2$$

Although Wöhler did not appreciate the significance of this reaction—he was more interested by the fact that two compounds had the same molecular formula—his experiment is considered a key event in the origin of organic chemistry. Chemists soon synthesized methane, acetic acid, acetylene, and many other organic compounds from inorganic sources. ◆ Today we know that *the same chemical principles govern organic and inorganic systems* because the behavior of a compound arises from the properties of its elements, no matter how marvelous that behavior may be.

In this brief introduction to an enormous and ever-growing field, we continue the text's central theme—how the structure and reactivity of organic molecules emerge naturally from the properties of the component atoms, in this case carbon and its handful of bonding partners. First, we review the rather special atomic properties of carbon and see how they relate to organic molecules. We focus on hydrocarbons initially to give you a feel for writing and naming organic compounds. Then we classify the main types of organic reactions and, in the central portion of the chapter, apply them to the major families of organic compounds. Finally, we extend these ideas to the giant molecules of commerce and life—synthetic and natural polymers.

15.1 The Special Nature of Carbon and the Characteristics of Organic Molecules

Although there is nothing mystical about organic molecules, their indispensible role in biology and industry leads us to ask if carbon has some extraordinary attributes that give it a special chemical "personality." Of course,

Concepts and Skills to Review

before you study this chapter

- naming simple alkanes (Section 2.8)
- electronegativity difference and bond polarity (Section 9.4)
- resonance structures (Section 10.1)
- VSEPR theory of molecular shape (Section 10.3)
- σ and π bonding; bond rotation (Section 11.2)
- types of intermolecular forces (Sections 12.3 and 13.1)
- properties of the Period 2 elements (Section 14.2)
- properties of the Group 4A(14) elements (Section 14.6)

urea

◆ **Organic Chemistry Is Enough to Drive One Mad** The vitalists did not change their beliefs overnight. Indeed, organic compounds do seem different from inorganic compounds because of their complex structures and compositions. Imagine the consternation of the 19th-century chemist accustomed to studying compounds with formulas such as $CaCO_3$, $Ba(NO_3)_2$, and $CuSO_4 \cdot 5H_2O$, who isolated white crystals from a gallstone and found their empirical formula to be $C_{27}H_{46}O$ (cholesterol). Even Wöhler later said, "Organic chemistry . . . is enough to drive one mad. It gives me the impression of a primeval tropical forest, full of the most remarkable things, a monstrous and boundless thicket, with no way of escape, into which one may well dread to enter."

605

each element has its own specific properties, and carbon is no more unique than sodium, hafnium, or any other. But the atomic properties of carbon do give it bonding capabilities beyond those of any other element, which in turn lead to the two obvious characteristics of organic molecules: structural complexity and chemical diversity.

The Structural Complexity of Organic Molecules

Most organic molecules have much more complex structures than most inorganic molecules, and a quick review of carbon's atomic properties and bonding behavior shows why:

1. *Electron configuration, electronegativity, and covalent bonding.* Carbon's ground-state electron configuration of [He] $2s^2 2p^2$—four electrons more than He and four fewer than Ne—means that the formation of carbon ions is energetically impossible under ordinary conditions: to form a C^{4+} cation requires energy equal to the sum of IE_1 through IE_4, and a C^{4-} anion requires the sum of EA_1 through EA_4, the last three steps being endothermic. Carbon's position in the periodic table (Figure 15.1) gives it an electronegativity midway between the most metallic and nonmetallic elements of Period 2: Li = 1.0, C = 2.5, F = 4.0. Therefore, *carbon shares electrons to attain a filled shell,* bonding covalently in all its elemental forms and compounds.

2. *Bond properties, catenation, and molecular shape.* The *number* and *strength* of carbon's bonds lead to its outstanding ability to *catenate* (bond to itself), by which it forms a multitude of chemically and thermally stable chain, ring, and branched compounds. Through the process of hybridization (Section 11.1), *carbon forms four bonds in virtually all its compounds* and they point in as many as four directions at once. Because it is small, *carbon forms relatively short, strong bonds,* which allows close approach to another atom and thus greater orbital overlap. The C—C bond is short enough to allow sideways overlap of half-filled, unhybridized *p* orbitals and the formation of *multiple bonds,* which restrict rotation of attached groups. These features add more possibilities for the shapes of carbon compounds (see Figure 11.12, p. 406).

3. *Molecular stability.* Although silicon and several other elements also catenate, none can compete with carbon. Atomic and bonding properties confer three crucial differences between C and Si chains that explain why C chains are so stable and therefore common:

- Atomic size and bond strength. As atomic size increases down Group 4A(14), bonds between identical atoms become longer and weaker. Figure 15.2 shows that a C—C bond is much stronger than an Si—Si bond.
- Relative bond energy. Figure 15.2 also shows that a C—C bond is nearly as strong as a C—O bond, so relatively little energy is released when a C chain reacts and one bond replaces the other. This lack of a significant energy change removes a major driving force for a C chain to react. In contrast, Si—O bonds are much stronger than Si—Si bonds, so a large quantity of energy is released when an Si chain reacts similarly.
- Orbitals available for reaction. Unlike C, Si has low-energy *d* orbitals that can be attacked (occupied) by the lone pairs of incoming reactants. Thus, for example, ethane (CH_3—CH_3) is stable in water and does not react in air unless sparked, whereas disilane (SiH_3—SiH_3) breaks down in water and ignites spontaneously in air.

The Chemical Diversity of Organic Molecules

In addition to their elaborate geometries, organic compounds are noted for their sheer number and diverse chemical behavior. Look in any compendium of known compounds, such as the *CRC Handbook of Chemistry and Physics,* and

Figure 15.1 The position of carbon in the periodic table. Carbon lies at the center of Period 2, so it has an intermediate electronegativity (EN), and at the top of Group 4A(14), so it is relatively small. Other elements common in organic compounds are H, N, O, P, S, and the halogens.

Figure 15.2 Bond energy and the stability of carbon chains. The C—C bond is stronger than the Si—Si bond, so long carbon chains are more stable than long silicon chains. Carbon chains are less easily oxidized than silicon chains because much less energy is released: C—C bond energy ≈ C—O bond energy, but Si—Si bond energy << Si—O bond energy.

you'll find that the number of organic compounds dwarfs the number of inorganic compounds of all the other elements combined! Several million organic compounds are known, and thousands more are discovered or synthesized each year.

This incredible diversity is also founded on atomic and bonding behavior and is due to three interrelated factors:

1. *Bonding to heteroatoms.* Carbon frequently forms bonds to **heteroatoms,** atoms other than C or H. The most common heteroatoms are N and O, but S, P, and the halogens are common also, and organic compounds with other elements are known as well. To get an idea of the diversity created by a heteroatom, look at Figure 15.3, which shows that 23 different molecular structures are produced by various arrangements of four C atoms singly bonded to each other, the necessary number of H atoms, and just one O atom (either singly or doubly bonded).

2. *Electron density and reactivity.* Most reactions start—that is, a new bond begins to form—*when a region of high electron density on one molecule meets a region of low electron density on another.* These regions may be due to the presence of a multiple bond or to the partial charges that occur in carbon-heteroatom bonds. For example, consider four common bonds found in organic molecules:

- The C—C bond. When C is singly bonded to itself, as it is in portions of nearly every organic molecule, the EN values are equal and the bond is nonpolar. Therefore, in general, *C—C bonds are unreactive.*

- The C—H bond. This bond, which also occurs in nearly every organic molecule, is very nearly nonpolar because it is short (109 pm) and the EN values of H (2.1) and C (2.5) are close. Thus, *C—H bonds are largely unreactive* as well.

- The C—O bond. In contrast to the previous two bonds, this bond, which occurs in many types of organic molecules, is highly polar ($\Delta EN = 1.0$), with the O end of the bond electron rich (δ^-) and the C end electron poor (δ^+). As a result of this imbalance in electron density, *the C—O bond is reactive* and, given appropriate conditions, reaction will occur there.

- Bonds to other heteroatoms. Even when a carbon-heteroatom bond has a small ΔEN, as in C—Br ($\Delta EN = 0.3$), or none at all, as in C—S ($\Delta EN = 0$), because the heteroatoms are large, their bonds to carbon are long, weak, and thus reactive.

3. *Nature of functional groups.* One of the most important concepts in organic chemistry is that of the **functional group,** a specific combination of bonded atoms that reacts in a *characteristic* way no matter in which molecule it occurs. In nearly every case, *the reaction of an organic compound takes place at the functional group.* In fact, as you'll see, we often substitute a general symbol for the rest of the molecule because it does not usually change when the functional group undergoes a reaction. Functional groups vary from a carbon multiple bond to any combination of carbon-heteroatom bonds. In other words, any bonded grouping of atoms other than C—C and C—H constitutes a functional group, and each has its own pattern of reactivity. A particular bond may be a functional group or part of one or more functional groups. For example, the C—O bond occurs in four functional groups, three of which we discuss in this chapter: the alcohol group (—C—Ö—H), the carboxylic acid

group (—C—Ö—H), and the ester group (—C—Ö—C—).
(with :O: double bonds shown above the carbons)

Figure 15.3 The chemical diversity of organic compounds. Different arrangements of chains, branches, rings, and heteroatoms give rise to many structures. There are 23 different compounds possible from just four C atoms with single bonds between them, one O atom, and the necessary H atoms.

Section Summary

The structural complexity of organic compounds arises from carbon's small size, intermediate EN, four bonding orbitals, ability to form π bonds, and non-expandable valence shell. These factors lead to chains, branches, and rings of C atoms joined by strong, chemically resistant bonds that point in as many as four directions. The chemical diversity of organic compounds arises from C's ability to bond to itself and to many other elements and to form multiple bonds to itself and to O and N. These factors lead to compounds that contain functional groups, portions of molecules that react in characteristic ways.

15.2 The Structures and Classes of Hydrocarbons

A fanciful, anatomical analogy can be made between an organic molecule and an organism. The carbon-carbon bonds form the skeleton, with the longest continual chain the backbone and any branches the limbs. Covering the skeleton is a skin of hydrogen atoms, with functional groups protruding at specific locations, like chemical fingers ready to grab an incoming reactant.

In this section, we "dissect" one group of compounds down to their skeletons and see how to name and draw them. **Hydrocarbons,** the simplest type of organic compound, are a large group of substances containing only H and C atoms. Some common fuels, such as natural gas and gasoline, are hydrocarbon mixtures. Hydrocarbons are also important *feedstocks,* precursor reactants used to make other compounds. Ethylene, acetylene, and benzene, for example, are feedstocks for hundreds of other substances (see photo).

Carbon Skeletons and Hydrogen Skins

Let's begin by examining the possible bonding arrangements of C atoms only (we'll leave off the H atoms at first) in simple skeletons without multiple bonds or rings. To distinguish different arrangements, focus on the *sequence* of C atoms (that is, the successive linkage one after another) and keep in mind that *groups bonded to single (sigma) bonds are relatively free to rotate* (Section 11.2).

Structures with one, two, or three carbons can be arranged in only one way. Whether you draw three C atoms in a line or with a bend, the *sequence* is the same. Four C atoms, however, have two possible arrangements: a four-C chain or a three-C chain with a one-C branch at the central C:

Even when we show the chain more realistically with the bends due to the tetrahedral shape around the C atoms, as in the ball-and-stick models, the situation is the same. Notice that if the branch is added to either end of the three-C chain, it is simply a bend in a four-C chain, *not* a different arrangement. Similarly, if the branch points down instead of up, it represents the same arrangement because groups bonded to single bonds rotate.

As the total number of C atoms increases, the number of different arrangements increases as well. Five C atoms have 3 arrangements; 6 C atoms can be arranged in 5 ways, 7 C atoms in 9 ways, 10 C atoms in 75 ways, and 20 C atoms in more than 300,000 ways! If we consider multiple bonds and rings,

Plastic toys made from organic feedstocks.

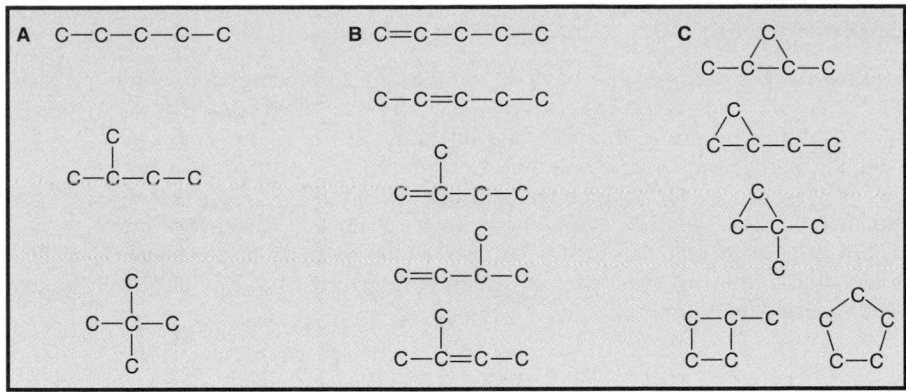

Figure 15.4 Some five-carbon skeletons. A, Three five-C skeletons are possible with only single bonds. **B,** Five more skeletons are possible with one C=C bond present. **C,** Five more skeletons are possible with one ring present. Even more would be possible with a ring *and* a double bond.

the number of arrangements increases further. For example, including one C=C bond in the five-C skeletons creates 5 more arrangements, and including one ring creates 5 more (Figure 15.4).

When determining the number of different skeletons, remember that

• Each C can form a *maximum* of four single bonds, or two single and one double bond, or one single and one triple bond.
• The *arrangement* of C atoms determines the skeleton, so a straight chain and a bent chain represent the same skeleton.
• Groups attached to single bonds can *rotate*, so a branch pointing down is the same as one pointing up. (Recall that a double bond restricts rotation.)

If we put a hydrogen "skin" on a carbon skeleton, we obtain a hydrocarbon. Figure 15.5 shows that the skeleton has the correct number of H atoms when each C has four bonds. Sample Problem 15.1 provides practice in drawing hydrocarbons

Figure 15.5 Adding the H-atom skin to the C-atom skeleton. In a hydrocarbon molecule, each carbon atom bonds to as many hydrogen atoms as needed to give the carbon a total of four bonds.

Sample Problem 15.1   Drawing Hydrocarbons

PROBLEM Draw structures that have different atom arrangements for hydrocarbons with

(a) Six C atoms, no multiple bonds, and no rings

(b) Four C atoms, one double bond, and no rings

(c) Four C atoms, no multiple bonds, and one ring

PLAN In each case, we draw the longest carbon chain and then work down to smaller chains with branches at different points along them. The process typically involves trial and error. Then we add H atoms to give each C a total of four bonds.

SOLUTION **(a)** Compounds with six C atoms:

6-C chain:

```
      H  H  H  H  H  H
      |  |  |  |  |  |
  H — C— C— C— C— C— C —H
      |  |  |  |  |  |
      H  H  H  H  H  H
```

5-C chains:

```
      H  H  H  H  H                          H
      |  |  |  |  |                          |
  H — C— C— C— C— C —H                    H— C—H
      |  |  |  |  |               H  H     |   H   H
      H  H  |  H  H               |  |     |   |   |
            C                 H — C— C— C— C— C —H
          H—|—H                   |  |   |  |   |
            H                      H  H   H  H   H
```

4-C chains:

```
          H                              H
          |                              |
        H—C—H                          H—C—H
      H   |   H  H                 H  H  |   H
      |   |   |  |                 |  |  |   |
  H — C— C— C— C —H            H — C— C— C— C —H
      |   |   |  H                 |  |  |   |
      H   |   H                    H  |  H   H
        H—C—H                         H—C—H
          |                             |
          H                             H
```

(b) Compounds with four C atoms and one double bond:

```
      H  H  H  H                H  H  H  H
      |  |  |  |                |  |  |  |
4-C chains: H—C—C=C—C—H     H—C—C—C=C—H
      |     |  |                |  |  |
      H     H  H                H  H  H
```

```
                 H       H
                 |       |
3-C chains: H—C—C=C—H
                 |
               H—C—H
                 |
                 H
```

(c) Compounds with four C atoms and one ring:

```
            H  H
            |  |
4-C ring: H—C——C—H
            |  |
          H—C——C—H
            |  |
            H  H
```

```
                    H   H
                     \ /
                      C
3-C ring:           /   \     H
                 H—C—————C—C—H
                   |     |  |
                   H     H  H
```

CHECK Be sure each skeleton has the correct number of C atoms and bonds and that no arrangements are repeated or omitted; remember that a double bond counts as two bonds.

COMMENT Avoid some common mistakes:

```
                                        C
                                        |
In (a):  C—C—C—C—C  is the same skeleton as  C—C—C—C—C
             |
             C


            C                           C  C
            |                           |  |
       C—C—C—C  is the same skeleton as  C—C—C—C
          |
          C
```

In **(b)**: C—C—C=C is the same skeleton as C=C—C—C

Since the double bond restricts rotation, another possible structure is

$$H-\overset{\overset{\displaystyle H}{|}}{\underset{\underset{\displaystyle H}{|}}{C}}-\overset{\overset{\displaystyle H}{|}}{C}=\overset{\overset{\displaystyle H}{}}{C}-\overset{\overset{\displaystyle H}{|}}{\underset{\underset{\displaystyle H}{|}}{C}}-H$$

Too many bonds in

$$H-\overset{\overset{\displaystyle H}{|}}{\underset{\underset{\displaystyle H}{|}}{C}}-\overset{\overset{\displaystyle H}{|}}{\underset{\underset{\displaystyle H-\overset{\overset{\displaystyle H}{|}}{\underset{\underset{\displaystyle H}{|}}{C}}-H}{|}}{C}}=\overset{\overset{\displaystyle H}{}}{C}-H$$

5 bonds

In **(c)**: Too many bonds in

$$H-\overset{\overset{\displaystyle H}{|}}{\underset{\underset{\displaystyle H}{|}}{C}}-\overset{\overset{\displaystyle C}{}}{\underset{\underset{\displaystyle H}{|}}{C}}-\overset{\overset{\displaystyle H}{}}{\underset{\underset{\displaystyle H}{|}}{C}}-H$$

5 bonds

Follow-up Problem 15.1 Draw all hydrocarbons that have different atom arrangements with
(a) Seven C atoms, no multiple bonds, and no rings (nine arrangements)
(b) Five C atoms, one triple bond, and no rings (three arrangements)

The enormous number of hydrocarbons can be classified into four main groups. For the remainder of this section, we examine some structural features and physical properties of each group. Later, we discuss the chemical behavior of the hydrocarbons.

Alkanes: Hydrocarbons with Only Single Bonds

A hydrocarbon that contains only single bonds is an **alkane** (general formula C_nH_{2n+2}, where n is an integer). For example, if $n = 5$, the formula is $C_5H_{[(2\times5)+2]}$, or C_5H_{12}. These compounds comprise a **homologous series,** one in which each member differs from the next by a —CH_2— (methylene) group. In alkanes, each C is sp^3 hybridized. Since each C is bonded to the *maximum number of other atoms* (C or H), alkanes are referred to as **saturated hydrocarbons.**

Naming Alkanes You learned the names of the first ten unbranched alkanes in Chapter 2 (see Table 2.7). Here we discuss general rules for naming any alkane and, by extension, other organic compounds as well. The key point to remember is that *each chain, branch, or ring has a name based on the **number** of C atoms*. The entire name of the compound has three portions:

PREFIX + ROOT + SUFFIX

- *Root:* the root tells the number of C atoms in the longest *continuous* chain in the molecule. The roots are shown in Table 15.1. Recall that there are special roots for compounds of one to four C atoms; roots of longer chains are based on Greek numbers.
- *Prefix:* each prefix tells the *group attached to the main chain* and the number of the carbon to which it is attached. Prefix names are the same as root names (Table 15.1) but take a *-yl* ending. Each prefix is placed *before* the root.
- *Suffix:* the suffix tells the *type of organic compound* to which the molecule belongs, that is, the functional group the molecule possesses. The suffix is generally placed *after* the root.

Table 15.1 Numerical Roots for Carbon Chains and Branches

Root	Number of C Atoms
meth-	1
eth-	2
prop-	3
but-	4
pent-	5
hex-	6
hept-	7
oct-	8
non-	9
dec-	10

Chapter 15 Organic Compounds and the Atomic Properties of Carbon

For example, in the name 2-methylbutane, "2-methyl" is the prefix (a methyl group is attached to C-2 of the main chain), "but" is the root (the main chain has four C atoms), and "ane" is the suffix (the compound is an alk*ane*).

The alkanes are used here to demonstrate this general approach to naming; other organic compounds are named in the same way, with a variety of other prefixes and suffixes (see Table 15.5, p. 627). In addition to the *systematic* names introduced here, many compounds are still known by *common* names, so we'll note the most important of them. To obtain the systematic name of a compound,

1. Name the longest chain (root).
2. Add the compound type (suffix).
3. Name any branches (prefix).

Table 15.2 presents the rules for naming an organic compound and applies them to an alkane component of gasoline.

Table 15.2 Rules for Naming an Organic Compound

1. Naming the longest chain (root)
   (a) Find the longest *continuous* chain of C atoms.
   (b) Select the root that corresponds to the number of C atoms in this chain.
2. Naming the compound type (suffix)
   (a) For alkanes, add the suffix *-ane* to the chain root. (Other suffixes appear in Table 15.5 with their functional group and compound type.)
   (b) If the chain forms a ring, the name is preceded by *cyclo-*.
3. Naming the branches (prefix)
   (a) Each branch name consists of a subroot (number of C atoms) and the ending *-yl* to signify that it is not part of the main chain.
   (b) Branch names precede the chain name. When two or more branches are present, name them in *alphabetical* order.
   (c) To specify where the branch occurs along the chain, number the main-chain C atoms consecutively, starting at the end *closer* to a branch, to achieve the *lowest* numbers for the branches. Precede each branch name with the number of the chain C to which that branch is attached.
   (d) If the compound has no branches, the name consists of the root and suffix.

$$CH_3-CH-CH_2-CH_2-CH_3$$ with CH_3 on top and CH_2-CH_3 below the second carbon

6 carbons $\Longrightarrow$ hex-

hex- + -ane $\Longrightarrow$ hexane

CH_3 methyl on top; $CH_3-CH-CH_2-CH_2-CH_3$; CH_2-CH_3 ethyl below

ethylmethylhexane

$$\overset{1}{CH_3}-\overset{2}{CH}-\overset{3}{CH}-\overset{4}{CH_2}-\overset{5}{CH_2}-\overset{6}{CH_3}$$ with CH_3 on top of C-2 and CH_2-CH_3 below C-3

3-ethyl-2-methylhexane

Depicting Alkanes with Formulas and Models Nowhere is it more important—or useful—to visualize a molecule than in discussions of organic compounds, so chemists use several ways of depicting these complex structures. On the two-dimensional surface of a page or blackboard, expanded and condensed structural formulas are the easiest to draw. With molecular model kits or computer software, three-dimensional models make the actual molecular shapes vivid.

The *expanded formula* shows each atom and bond; this type appears in Sample Problem 15.1. A common type of *condensed formula* groups the H atoms with the C atom to which they are bound. Figure 15.6 shows the expanded and condensed formulas, together with ball-and-stick and space-filling models, of the compound named in Table 15.2.

Expanded formula

Condensed formula

Figure 15.6 Formulas and models of alkanes. The expanded formula shows every bond. The condensed formula combines each C with its bonded H atoms. Ball-and-stick and space-filling models show the molecule in three-dimensional space.

Cyclic Hydrocarbons A **cyclic hydrocarbon** contains one or more rings in its structure. When a straight-chain alkane (C_nH_{2n+2}) forms a ring, two H atoms are lost as the C—C bond forms to join the two ends. Thus, *cycloalkanes* have the general formula C_nH_{2n}. Cyclic hydrocarbons are often drawn with a shorthand method that shows *only* C—C bond lines. Each corner of the ring is understood to be *a C atom with the correct number of H atoms* attached to give a total of four bonds; expanded and shorthand structures for some cycloalkanes, together with the three-dimensional models, are shown in Figure 15.7. Note that, except for three-C rings, *cycloalkanes are nonplanar*. This structural feature arises from the tetrahedral shape around each C atom. As a result, electron repulsions between adjacent H atoms are minimized and orbital overlap of adjacent C atoms is maximized. The most stable form of cyclohexane (Figure 15.7D) is called the *chair conformation*. Each C is bonded to an *axial* H atom, which points above or below the ring, and an *equatorial* H atom, which points out from the ring.

A Cyclopropane   B Cyclobutane   C Cyclopentane   D Cyclohexane

Figure 15.7 Depicting cycloalkanes. Cycloalkanes are usually drawn as regular polygons. Each side is a C—C bond, and each corner represents a C atom with its required number of H atoms. The expanded formulas show each bond in the molecule. The ball-and-stick and space-filling models show that, except for cyclopropane, the rings are not planar. These arrangements minimize repulsions between adjacent H atoms. Cyclohexane **(D)** is shown in its more stable "chair" conformation (axial H atoms point up and down; equatorial H atoms point to the side).

Constitutional Isomerism and the Physical Properties of Alkanes

Two or more compounds with the same molecular formula but different properties are called **isomers.** Those with *different arrangements of bonded atoms* are **constitutional (or structural) isomers;** alkanes with a given number of C atoms but different skeletons are examples. The smallest alkane to exhibit constitutional isomerism has four C atoms: two different compounds have the formula C_4H_{10} (Table 15.3). The unbranched one is butane (common name, *n*-butane; *n*- stands for "normal," or straight chain), and the other is 2-methylpropane (common name, *iso*butane). Similarly, three compounds have the formula C_5H_{12}. The unbranched isomer is pentane (common name, *n*-pentane); the one with a methyl group at C-2 of a four-C chain is 2-methylbutane (common name, *iso*pentane). The third isomer has two methyl branches off C-2 of a three-C chain, so its name is 2,2-dimethylpropane (common name, *neo*pentane).

Because alkanes are nearly nonpolar, we expect their physical properties to be determined by dispersion forces, and the boiling points in Table 15.3 certainly bear this out. The four-C alkanes boil lower than the five-C compounds. Moreover, within each group of isomers, the more spherical member (isobutane or neopentane) boils lower than the more elongated one (*n*-butane or *n*-pentane). As you saw in Chapter 12, this trend occurs because a spherical shape makes less intermolecular contact, and thus exerts a lower total dispersion force, than does an elongated shape.

Table 15.3 The Constitutional Isomers of C_4H_{10} and C_5H_{12}

Systematic Name (Common Name)	Condensed Formula	Expanded Formula	Space-filling Model	Density (g/mL)	Boiling Point (°C)
Butane (*n*-butane)	$CH_3-CH_2-CH_2-CH_3$			0.579	−0.5
2-Methylpropane (isobutane)	$CH_3-CH-CH_3$ | CH_3			0.549	−11.6
Pentane (*n*-pentane)	$CH_3-CH_2-CH_2-CH_2-CH_3$			0.626	36.1
2-Methylbutane (isopentane)	$CH_3-CH-CH_2-CH_3$ | CH_3			0.620	27.8
2,2-Dimethylpropane (neopentane)	$CH_3-\underset{\underset{CH_3}{\mid}}{\overset{\overset{CH_3}{\mid}}{C}}-CH_3$			0.614	9.5

Figure 15.8 Boiling points of the first 10 unbranched alkanes. Boiling point increases smoothly with chain length because dispersion forces increase. Each entry includes the name, molar mass ($\mathcal{M}$, in g/mol), abbreviated formula, and boiling point at 1 atm pressure.

A particularly clear example of the effect of dispersion forces on physical properties occurs among the unbranched alkanes (*n*-alkanes). Among these compounds, boiling points increase steadily with chain length: the longer the chain, the greater the contact, the stronger the dispersion forces, and the higher the boiling point (Figure 15.8). Pentane (five C atoms) is the smallest *n*-alkane that exists as a liquid at room temperature. The solubility of alkanes, and of all hydrocarbons, is easy to predict from the like-dissolves-like rule (Section 13.1). Alkanes are miscible in each other and in other nonpolar solvents, such as benzene, but nearly insoluble in water. The solubility of pentane in water, for example, is only 0.36 g/L at room temperature.

Chiral Molecules and Optical Isomerism

Another type of isomerism that we see in some alkanes and many other organic (as well as some inorganic) compounds is called **stereoisomerism.** It occurs in molecules with the same arrangement of atoms *but different orientations of groups in space.* **Optical isomerism** is one type of stereoisomerism: *when two objects are mirror images of each other and cannot be superimposed, they are optical isomers,* also called *enantiomers.* To use a familiar example, your right hand is an optical isomer of your left. Look at your right hand in a mirror and you will see that the *image* is identical to your left hand (Figure 15.9). No matter how you twist your arms around, however, your hands cannot lie on top of each other with all parts superimposed. They are not superimposable because each is *asymmetric:* there is no plane of symmetry that divides your hand into two identical parts.

An asymmetric molecule is called **chiral** (Greek *cheir,* "hand"). In most cases, *an organic molecule is chiral if it contains a C atom that is bonded to four different groups.* This C atom is called a *chiral center* or an asymmetric carbon. In 3-methylhexane, for example, C-3 is a chiral center because it is bonded to four different groups: H—, CH_3—, CH_3—CH_2—, and CH_3—CH_2—CH_2— (Figure 15.10A). The central C atom in the amino acid alanine is also a chiral center. The two forms in Figure 15.10B are mirror images and cannot be superimposed on each other: when two of the groups are superimposed, the other two are opposite each other. Thus, the two forms are optical isomers. (Molecular models make this fact easier to see.)

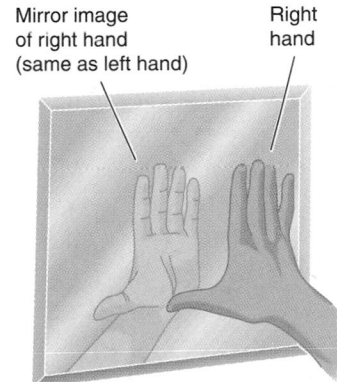

Figure 15.9 An analogy for optical isomers. The reflection of your right hand looks like your left hand. Because each hand is asymmetric, you cannot superimpose one on the other.

A 3-Methylhexane

B Optical isomers of alanine

Figure 15.10 Two chiral molecules. A, A molecule of 3-methylhexane is chiral because C-3 is bonded to four different groups. Only one of the two optical isomers is shown. **B,** The central C in the amino acid alanine is also bonded to four different groups. These two models of alanine are mirror images that cannot be superimposed on each other, so they are optical isomers (enantiomers).

Figure 15.11 The rotation of plane-polarized light by an optically active substance. The source emits light moving in all planes. When the light passes through the first polarizing filter, light moving in only one plane emerges. The plane-polarized beam enters the sample compartment, which contains a known concentration of an optical isomer, and the plane rotates as it passes through the solution. For the experimenter to see the light, it must pass through a second polarizing filter (called the *analyzer*), which is attached to a movable ring calibrated in degrees that is used to measure the angle of rotation.

◆ Chiral Medicines

The fields of stereoselective synthesis and separation are exploding in the pharmaceutical industry. Many drugs are chiral molecules of which one optical isomer is biologically active and the other has either a different type of activity or none at all. Naproxen, the common pain reliever and anti-inflammatory agent, is an example; one isomer (*model*) is active as an antiarthritic agent, and the other is a potent liver toxin that must be removed from the synthetic mixture. The notorious drug thalidomide is another example. One optical isomer is active against depression, whereas the other causes fetal mutations and deaths. Tragically, the drug was marketed in the 1950s as the racemic mixture and caused limb malformations in many children whose mothers had it prescribed to relieve "morning sickness" during pregnancy. Designing an organic synthesis or separation procedure to yield only the desired isomer can create many useful medicinal products.

Unlike constitutional isomers, optical isomers are identical in all but two respects:

1. In their physical properties, *optical isomers differ only in the direction that each isomer rotates the plane of polarized light.* A **polarimeter** is used to measure the angle that the plane is rotated (Figure 15.11). A beam of light consists of waves moving in all planes. A polarizing filter blocks all waves except those in one plane, so the light emerging through the filter is *plane-polarized.* An optical isomer is **optically active** because it rotates the plane of this polarized light. (Liquid-crystal displays incorporate polarizing filters and optically active compounds; see Figure 12.45, p. 466.) The *dextrorotatory* isomer (designated *d* or +) rotates the plane of light clockwise; the *levorotatory* isomer (designated *l* or −) is the mirror image of the first and rotates the plane counterclockwise. An equimolar mixture of the two isomers (called a *racemic mixture*) does not rotate the plane at all because the dextrorotation cancels the levorotation. The *specific rotation* is a characteristic, measurable property of the isomer at a certain temperature, concentration, and wavelength of light.

2. In their chemical properties, *optical isomers differ only in a chiral (asymmetric) chemical environment,* one that distinguishes "right-handed" from "left-handed" molecules. As an analogy, your right hand fits in your right glove but not in your left glove. Similarly, an optical isomer interacts only with a corresponding optical isomer. Typically, one isomer of an optically active reagent is added to a mixture of optical isomers of another compound. For example, when the anion *d*-lactate is added to a mixture of *d*-alanine and *l*-alanine in their cationic forms, the *d* isomer of alanine crystallizes as the *d*-lactate/*d*-alanine salt, but the *l*-alanine isomer remains in solution.

Optical isomerism plays a vital role in living cells. Nearly all carbohydrates and amino acids are optically active, but only one of the isomers is biologically usable. For example, *d*-glucose is metabolized for energy, but *l*-glucose is excreted unused. Similarly, *l*-alanine is incorporated naturally into proteins, but *d*-alanine is not. ◆ The organism distinguishes one optical isomer from the other through its enzymes, large molecules that speed virtually every reaction in the cell by binding to the reactants. A specific portion of the enzyme provides the asymmetric environment, so only one of the isomers can bind there and undergo reaction (Figure 15.12).

Alkenes: Hydrocarbons with Double Bonds

A hydrocarbon that contains at least one C=C bond is called an **alkene.** Since two H atoms are removed to make the double bond, alkenes have the general formula, C_nH_{2n}. The double-bonded C atoms are sp^2 hybridized. Since their carbon atoms bond fewer than the maximum of four atoms each, alkenes are considered **unsaturated hydrocarbons.**

Alkene names differ from those of alkanes in two respects:

1. The root chain *must* contain both C atoms of the double bond, even if it is not the longest chain. The chain is numbered from the end *closer* to the C=C bond, and the position of the bond is indicated by the number of the *first* C atom in it.

2. The suffix for alkenes is *-ene*.

For example, there are three four-C alkenes (C_4H_8), two unbranched and one branched (see part b of Sample Problem 15.1). The branched isomer is 2-methylpropene; the unbranched isomer with the C=C bond between C-1 and C-2 is 1-butene; the unbranched isomer with the C=C bond between C-2 and C-3 is 2-butene. As you'll see next, there are two isomers of 2-butene, but they are of a different sort than we have discussed so far.

The C=C Bond and Geometric (*cis-trans*) Isomerism There are two major structural differences between alkenes and alkanes. First, alkanes have a *tetrahedral* geometry (~109.5°) around each C atom, whereas the double-bonded C atoms in alkenes are *trigonal planar* (~120°). Second, the C—C bond *allows* rotation of bonded groups, so the atoms in an alkane continually change their relative positions. In contrast, the π bond of the C=C bond *restricts* rotation, which fixes the relative positions of the atoms bonded to it.

This rotational restriction leads to another type of stereoisomerism. **Geometric isomers** (also called ***cis-trans* isomers** and *diastereomers*) have different orientations of groups around a double bond (or similar structural feature). Table 15.4 shows the two geometric isomers of 2-butene (also see Comment, Sample Problem 15.1). One isomer, *cis*-2-butene, has the CH_3 groups on the *same* side of the C=C bond, whereas the other isomer, *trans*-2-butene, has them on *opposite* sides of the C=C bond. In general, a *cis* isomer has the *larger portions of the main chain on the same side* of the double bond, and a *trans* isomer has them on opposite sides. (This type of geometric isomerism is also called *cis-trans isomerism*. It also occurs in many transition metal compounds, which have a different structural feature that restricts rotation, as we discuss in Chapter 23.) To have geometric isomers, *each C atom in the C=C bond must be bonded to two different groups.* Like all isomers, geometric isomers have different properties. Note in Table 15.4 that the two 2-butenes are quite different in molecular shape *and* physical properties. The *cis* molecule has a bend in the chain that the *trans* compound lacks. In Chapters 10 and 12, you saw how such a difference affects molecular polarity and physical properties, which arise from differing strengths of intermolecular attractions. The upcoming Chemical Connections essay shows how this simple difference in geometry has profound effects in biological systems as well.

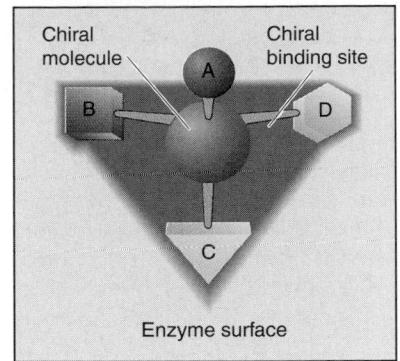

Figure 15.12 The binding site of an enzyme. Organisms can utilize only one of a pair of optical isomers because their enzymes have binding sites with shapes that are chiral (asymmetric). The shape of the mirror image of this molecule does not allow it to bind at this site.

Table 15.4 The Geometric Isomers of 2-Butene

Systematic Name	Condensed Formula	Space-filling Model	Density (g/mL)	Boiling Point (°C)

cis-2-Butene	CH₃ CH₃
	  \ /
	  C=C
	  / \
	 H H
			0.621	3.7

trans-2-Butene	CH₃ H
	  \ /
	  C=C
	  / \
	 H CH₃
			0.604	0.9

Geometric Isomers and the Chemistry of Vision

Of all our senses, sight provides the most information about the external world. Light bouncing off objects enters the lens of the eye and is focused on the retina. From there, molecular signals are converted to mechanical signals and then to electrical signals that are transmitted to the brain. This remarkable sequence is one of the few physiological processes that we understand thoroughly at the molecular level. The first step relies on the different shapes of geometric isomers.

The molecule responsible for receiving the light energy is *retinal*. It is derived from retinol (vitamin A), which we obtain mostly from β-carotene in yellow and green vegetables. Retinal is a 20-C compound consisting of a 15-C chain and five 1-C branches. As you can see from the ball-and-stick structure in Figure 15.A, the chain includes five C=C bonds, a six-C ring at one end, and a C=O bond at the other. There are two biologically occurring isomers of retinal. The all-*trans* isomer, shown on the right, has a *trans* orientation around all five double bonds. The 11-*cis* isomer, shown on the left, has a *cis* orientation around the C=C bond between C-11 and C-12. Note the significant difference in shape between the two isomers.

Certain cells of the retina are densely packed with *rhodopsin*, which consists of the relatively small 11-*cis*-retinal covalently bonded to a large protein. The initial chemical event in vision occurs when rhodopsin absorbs a photon of visible light. The energy of visible photons (between 165 and 293 kJ/mol) lies in the range needed to break a C=C π bond (~250 kJ/mol). Retinal is bonded to the protein in such a way that the 11-*cis* π bond is the most susceptible to breakage. The photon is absorbed in a few trillionths of a second, the *cis* π bond breaks, the groups attached to the intact σ bond rotate, and a π bond re-forms to produce all-*trans*-retinal in another few millionths of a second. In effect, light energy is converted into the mechanical energy of the moving molecular chain.

This rapid and relatively large change in the shape of retinal causes the protein portion of rhodopsin to change shape as well, a process that breaks the bond to retinal. The change in protein shape triggers a flow of ions into the retina cells, initiating electrical impulses to the optic nerve, which leads to the brain. Meanwhile, the free all-*trans*-retinal diffuses away and is changed back to the *cis* form, which binds to the protein portion again.

Retinal must be ideally suited to its function because it has been selected through evolution as a photon absorber in organisms as different as purple bacteria, mollusks, insects, and vertebrates. The features that make it the perfect choice are its strong absorption in the visible region, the efficiency with which light converts the *cis* to the *trans* form, and the large structural change it undergoes when this takes place.

Figure 15.A The initial chemical event in vision. In rhodopsin, the geometric isomer 11-*cis*-retinal is bonded to (*shown here as lying on*) a large protein. A photon absorbed by the retinal breaks the 11-*cis* π bond. The two parts of the retinal chain rotate around the σ bond (*shown in circle*), and the π bond forms again but with a *trans* orientation. This change in retinal shape changes the protein shape, causing it to release the all-*trans*-retinal.

Alkynes: Hydrocarbons with Triple Bonds

Hydrocarbons that contain at least one C≡C bond are called **alkynes.** Their general formula is C_nH_{2n-2} because they have two H atoms fewer than alkenes of the same length. Since a carbon in a C≡C bond can bond to only one other atom, the geometry around each C atom is linear (180°): each C is *sp* hybridized. Alkynes are named in the same way as alkenes, except that the suffix is *-yne.* Because of their localized π electrons, C=C and C≡C bonds are electron rich and act as functional groups. Thus, alkenes and alkynes are much more reactive than alkanes, as we'll discuss in Section 15.4.

Sample Problem 15.2 brings together many ideas about hydrocarbon names and isomers.

Sample Problem 15.2   Naming and Drawing Alkanes, Alkenes, and Alkynes

PROBLEM Give the systematic name for each of the following, indicate the chiral center in part **(d),** and draw two geometric isomers for part **(e):**

(a)
```
        CH3
         |
CH3 — C — CH2 — CH3
         |
        CH3
```

(b)
```
CH3 — CH2 — CH — CH — CH3
                    |
                   CH2
                    |
                   CH3
```

(c)
```
   ⬠ — CH3
       CH2 — CH3
```

(d)
```
        CH3
         |
CH3 — CH2 — CH — CH = CH2
```

(e)
```
                  CH3
                   |
CH3 — CH2 — CH = C — CH — CH3
                   |
                  CH3
```

PLAN For **(a)** to **(c),** we refer to Table 15.2. We first name the longest chain (root- + -ane). Then we find the *lowest* branch numbers by counting C atoms from the end *closer* to a branch. Finally, we name each branch (root-+-yl) and put them alphabetically before the chain name. For **(d)** and **(e),** the longest chain that *includes* the multiple bond is numbered from the end closer to it. For **(d),** the chiral center is the C atom bonded to four different groups. In **(e),** the *cis* isomer has larger groups on the same side of the double bond, and the *trans* isomer has them on opposite sides.

SOLUTION

(a)
```
          methyl
     ┌──(CH3)
     │      butane
 ┌─CH3 — C — CH2 — CH3─┐
 │ 1     2    3    4   │
 └───(CH3)─────────────┘
       methyl
```

2,2-dimethylbutane

When a type of branch appears more than once, we group the chain numbers and indicate the number of branches with a numerical prefix, such as 2,2-*di*methyl.

(b)
```
                    methyl
              ┌──(CH3)
hexane
 ┌CH3 — CH2 — CH — CH┤(CH3)
 │ 6     5     4    3│
 │                  2│CH2
 │                  1│CH3
 └───────────────────┘
```

3,4-dimethylhexane

In this case, we can number the chain from either end because the branches are the same and are attached to the two central C atoms.

(c)
```
 cyclopentane
            methyl
   3  ┌(CH3)
 4    2
   5  1
      (CH2 — CH3)─ ethyl
```

1-ethyl-2-methylcyclopentane

We number the ring C atoms so that a branch is attached to C-1.

(d)
```
                methyl
          ┌──(CH3)
          │      1-pentene
 ┌CH3 — CH2 — CH — CH = CH2┐
 │ 5     4    3    2    1  │
 └─────────────────────────┘
        chiral center
```

3-methyl-1-pentene

(e)
```
   H          CH3   methyl
    \    ┌───/
CH3 — CH2  C = C   CH — CH3   3-hexene
    6    5       4   3   2   1
              (CH3) methyl
```

cis-**2,3-dimethyl-3-hexene**

trans-**2,3-dimethyl-3-hexene**

CHECK A good check (and excellent practice) is to reverse the process by drawing structures for the names to see if you come up with the structure in the problem.
COMMENT Note that in **(b),** C-3 and C-4 are also chiral centers, as are C-1 and C-2 in **(c).** However, in **(b)** the molecule is not chiral: it has a plane of symmetry between C-3 and C-4, so one half of the molecule rotates light opposite to that of the other half. Avoid these common mistakes: In **(b),** 2-ethyl-3-methylpentane is wrong: the longest chain is *hexane.* In **(c),** 1-methyl-2-ethylcyclopentane is wrong: the branches are named *alphabetically.*

Follow-up Problem 15.2   Draw condensed formulas for the compounds with the following names: **(a)** 3-ethyl-3-methyloctane; **(b)** 1-ethyl-3-propylcyclohexane; **(c)** 3,3-diethyl-l-hexyne; **(d)** *trans*-3-methyl-3-heptene.

Aromatic Hydrocarbons: Cyclic Molecules with Delocalized π Electrons

Unlike the cycloalkanes, **aromatic hydrocarbons** are planar molecules, usually with one or more rings of six C atoms, and are often drawn with alternating single and double bonds. As you learned for benzene (Section 10.1), however, all the ring bonds are identical, with values of length and strength *between* those of a C—C and a C=C bond. To indicate this, benzene is also shown as a resonance hybrid, with a circle (or dashed circle) representing the delocalized character of the π electrons (Figure 15.13A). An orbital picture shows the two lobes of the delocalized π cloud above and below the hexagonal σ-bond plane of C atoms (Figure 15.13B).

Figure 15.13 Representations of benzene. A, Benzene is often drawn with two resonance forms, showing alternating single and double bonds in different positions. The molecule is more correctly depicted as the resonance hybrid, with the delocalized electrons shown as a full or dashed circle. **B,** The delocalized π cloud and the σ-bond plane of benzene.

A   **B**

The systematic naming of simple aromatic compounds is quite straightforward. Usually, benzene is the parent compound, and attached groups, or *substituents,* are named as prefixes. However, many common names are still in use. For example, benzene with one methyl group is systematically named *methylbenzene* but is better known by its common name *toluene.* With only one substituent present in toluene, we do not number the ring C atoms, but when two or more groups are attached, we number in such a way that one of the groups is attached to ring C-1. Thus, toluene and the three structural isomers with two methyl groups attached are

methylbenzene
(toluene)
bp = 110.6°C

1,2-dimethylbenzene
(*o*-xylene)
bp = 144.4°C

1,3-dimethylbenzene
(*m*-xylene)
bp = 139.1°C

1,4-dimethylbenzene
(*p*-xylene)
bp = 138.3°C

The positions of two groups in common names are indicated by *o-* (ortho) for groups on adjacent ring C atoms, *m-* (meta) for groups separated by one ring C atom, and *p-* (para) for groups on opposite ring C atoms. The dimethylbenzenes (commonly known as *xylenes*) are important solvents and feedstocks for polyester fibers and dyes. ◆

The number of isomers increases with more than two groups. For example, there are six isomers for a compound with one methyl and three nitro ($-NO_2$) groups attached to a benzene ring; the explosive TNT is only one,

2,4,6-trinitromethylbenzene
(**t**rin**i**trot**o**luene, TNT)

One of the most important methods for determining the structures of organic molecules is discussed in the upcoming Tools of the Chemistry Laboratory essay.

Variations on a Theme: Catenated Inorganic Hydrides

In short discussions called *Variations on a Theme* found throughout this chapter, we examine similarities between organic and inorganic compounds. From this perspective, you'll see that the behavior of carbon is remarkable, but not unique, in the chemistry of the elements.

Although no element approaches carbon in the variety and complexity of its hydrides, catenation occurs frequently in the periodic table, and many ring, chain, and cage structures are known. Some of the most fascinating belong to the boron hydrides, or boranes (Section 14.5). Although their shapes rival even those of the hydrocarbons, the weakness of their unusual bridge bonds renders most of them thermally and chemically unstable.

An obvious structural similarity exists between alkanes and the silicon hydrides, or silanes (Section 14.6). Silanes even have an analogous general formula (Si_nH_{2n+2}). Branched silanes are also known, but no cyclic or unsaturated ($Si=Si$) compounds had been prepared until very recently. Unlike alkanes, silanes are unstable thermally and ignite spontaneously in air.

Sulfur's ability to catenate is second only to carbon's, and many chains and rings occur among its allotropes (Section 14.8). A large series of sulfur hydrides, or polysulfanes, is known. However, these molecules are unbranched chains with H atoms at the ends only ($H-S_n-H$). Like the silanes, the polysulfanes are oxidized easily and decompose readily to sulfur's only stable hydride, H_2S, and its most stable allotrope, cyclo-S_8.

Section Summary

Hydrocarbons contain only C and H atoms, so their physical properties depend on the strength of dispersion forces. The names of the organic compounds have a root for the longest chain, a prefix for any attached group, and a suffix for the type of compound. Alkanes (C_nH_{2n+2}) have only single bonds. Cycloalkanes (C_nH_{2n}) have nonplanar ring structures. Alkenes (C_nH_{2n}) have at least one C=C bond. Alkynes (C_nH_{2n-2}) have at least one C≡C bond. Aromatic hydrocarbons have at least one planar ring with delocalized π electrons.

Naphthalene

Benzo[*a*]pyrene

◆ **Aromatic Carcinogens**
Polycyclic aromatic compounds have "fused" ring systems, two or more rings sharing one or more sides. The simplest is naphthalene, a feedstock for dyes. Many of these compounds (and benzene itself) have been shown to have carcinogenic (cancer-causing) activity. One of the most potent, benzo[*a*]pyrene, is found in soot, cigarette smoke, car exhaust, and even the smoke from barbecue grills!

Tools of the Chemistry Laboratory

Nuclear Magnetic Resonance (NMR) Spectroscopy

Chemists rely on a battery of instrumental methods to determine the complex structures of organic molecules. Earlier we discussed mass spectrometry (Chapter 2) and infrared (IR) spectroscopy (Chapter 9). One of the most useful tools is **nuclear magnetic resonance (NMR) spectroscopy,** which measures the environments of certain nuclei in a molecule to elucidate its structure.

In Chapter 8, we saw that an electron can spin in either of two directions, each of which creates a tiny magnetic field. Several types of nuclei behave in a similar way. The most important of these are ^1H, ^{13}C, ^{19}F, and ^{31}P. In this discussion we focus primarily on the proton, ^1H, the nucleus of the most common isotope of hydrogen, and therefore refer to ^1H-NMR spectroscopy. Generally, the magnetic fields of all the protons in a sample of compound are oriented randomly. When placed in a strong external magnetic field (H_0), however, the proton fields become aligned with it (parallel) or against it (antiparallel). The parallel orientation is slightly lower in energy, with the energy difference (ΔE) between the two energy states (spin states) lying in the radio frequency (rf) region of the spectrum.

The protons in the sample oscillate rapidly between the two spin states, and in a process known as *resonance*, the rf value is varied until it matches the frequency of this oscillation. At this point, the protons are "in resonance" with the rf radiation and they absorb and reemit the energy, which is detected by the rf receiver of the NMR spectrometer (Figure 15.B). If all the protons in a sample required the same ΔE for resonance, an NMR spectrum would have only one peak and be useless. However, the ΔE between the two states depends on the *actual* magnetic field felt by each proton, which is affected by the tiny magnetic fields of the *electrons* on atoms adjacent to that proton. Thus, the ΔE of each proton depends on the electrons in the adjacent atoms—C atoms, electronegative atoms, multiple bonds, and aromatic rings—in other words,

Figure 15.B The basis of proton spin resonance. The randomly oriented magnetic fields of protons in a sample become aligned in a strong external field (H_0), with slightly more protons in the lower spin state. In a process called *resonance*, the spin flips when the proton absorbs a photon with energy equal to ΔE (radio frequency region).

on the specific molecular environment. Therefore, the NMR spectrum is *unique* to that compound.

The NMR spectrum of a compound is a series of peaks that represents the resonance of each proton as a function of changing magnetic field. The *chemical shift* is the frequency at which resonance occurs for a given proton, that is, where a peak appears. The chemical shifts are shown relative to that of an added standard, tetramethylsilane $[(CH_3)_4Si$, TMS], which has 12 protons bonded to four C atoms that are bonded to one Si atom. Because the shape of TMS is tetrahedral around the Si, the protons are in identical environments, so they produce one peak. Figure 15.C shows the ^1H-NMR spectrum of acetone. The six protons of acetone also have identical environments—bonded to two C atoms that are bonded to the C atom in a C=O bond—so they also produce one peak, but at a different position from that of TMS. (The axes need not concern us.) The spectrum of dimethoxymethane in Figure 15.D shows *two* peaks in addition to the TMS peak. The taller one is due to the six CH_3 protons, and the shorter is due to the two

Isomers are compounds with the same molecular formula but different properties. Structural isomers have different atom arrangements. Stereoisomers (optical and geometric) have the same arrangement of atoms, but their atoms are oriented differently in space. Optical isomers cannot be superimposed on each other because they are asymmetric, with four different groups bonded to the C that is the chiral center. They have identical physical and chemical properties except in their rotation of plane-polarized light and their reaction with chiral reactants. Geometric (*cis-trans*) isomers have groups oriented differently around a C=C bond, which restricts rotation. Light converts *cis*-retinal to *trans*-retinal, which initiates the visual response. ^1H-NMR spectroscopy indicates the relative numbers of H atoms in the various environments within an organic molecule.

Figure 15.C The ¹H-NMR spectrum of acetone. Since the six CH_3 protons are in identical environments, they produce one peak, which has a different chemical shift from the 12 protons of the TMS standard.

Figure 15.D The ¹H-NMR spectrum of dimethoxymethane. The two peaks represent the chemical shifts of protons in two different environments. The area under each peak is proportional to the number of protons in each environment.

CH_2 protons. The area under each peak (given here in units of chart-paper spaces) is proportional to *the number of protons in a given environment* and is determined by the instrument. Note that the area ratio is $20.3:6.8 \approx 3:1$, the same as the ratio of six CH_3 protons:two CH_2 protons. Thus, by analyzing the chemical shifts and peak areas, the chemist learns the type and number of each ¹H in the compound.

Newer NMR methods measure the resonance of other nuclei and have many applications in biochemistry and medicine. ¹³C-NMR is used to monitor changes in protein and nucleic acid shape and function, and ³¹P-NMR can determine the health of various organs. For example, the extent of damage from a heart attack can be learned by using ³¹P-NMR to measure the concentrations of specific phosphate-containing molecules involved in energy utilization by cardiac muscle tissue.

Most recently, computer-aided magnetic resonance imaging (MRI) has allowed visualization of damage to organs and greatly assists physicians in medical diagnosis. For example, an MRI scan of the head (Figure 15.E) can show various levels of metabolic activity in different regions of the brain.

Figure 15.E Magnetic resonance imaging (MRI) of a human head. Colors indicate a range from high (*red*) to low (*blue*) metabolic activity.

15.3 Some Important Classes of Organic Reactions

In Chapter 4, we classified chemical reactions based on the chemical process involved (precipitation, acid-base, or redox) and then briefly included a classification based on the number of reactants and products (combination, decomposition, or displacement). We take a similar approach here with organic reactions.

From here on, we use the notation of an upper-case R with a single bond, R—, to signify a general organic group attached to the atoms shown; you can usually picture R— as an **alkyl group,** a saturated hydrocarbon chain with one bond available. Thus, R—CH_2—Br has an alkyl group attached to a CH_2 group bearing a Br atom; R—CH=CH_2 is an alkene with an alkyl group attached to one of the carbons in the double bond; and so forth. (Often, when more than one R group is present, we write R, R′, R″ to indicate that these groups may be different.)

Types of Organic Reactions

Most organic reactions are examples of three broad types that can be identified by comparing the *number of bonds to C* in the reactants and products:

1. An **addition reaction** occurs when an unsaturated reactant becomes a saturated product:

$$R{-}CH{=}CH{-}R \ + \ X{-}Y \longrightarrow R{-}\overset{\overset{\displaystyle X}{|}}{C}H{-}\overset{\overset{\displaystyle Y}{|}}{C}H{-}R$$

Note that the C atoms are bonded to *more* atoms in the product than in the reactant.

The C=C and C≡C bonds and the C=O bond commonly undergo addition reactions. In each case, the π bond breaks, leaving the σ bond intact. In the product, the C atoms (or C and O) form two additional σ bonds. Let's examine the standard heat of reaction (ΔH^{0}_{rxn}) for a typical addition reaction to see why these reactions occur. Consider the reaction between ethene (common name, ethylene) and HCl:

$$CH_2{=}CH_2 \ + \ H{-}Cl \longrightarrow H{-}CH_2{-}CH_2{-}Cl$$

REACTANTS (bonds broken)	PRODUCT (bonds formed)
1 C=C = 614 kJ	1 C—C = −347 kJ
4 C—H = 1652 kJ	5 C—H = −2065 kJ
1 H—Cl = 427 kJ	1 C—Cl = −339 kJ
Total = 2693 kJ	Total = −2751 kJ

And $\Delta H^{0}_{rxn} = \Delta H^{0}_{bonds\ broken} + \Delta H^{0}_{bonds\ formed} = 2693\ \text{kJ} + (-2751\ \text{kJ}) = -58\ \text{kJ}$

The reaction is exothermic. By looking at the *net* change in bonds, we see that the driving force for many additions is the formation of two σ bonds (in this case, C—H and C—Cl) from one σ bond (in this case, H—Cl) and one relatively weak π bond. An addition reaction is the basis of a color test for the presence of C=C bonds (Figure 15.14).

2. **Elimination reactions** are the opposite of addition reactions. They occur when a saturated reactant becomes an unsaturated product:

$$R{-}\overset{\overset{\displaystyle Y}{|}}{C}H{-}\overset{\overset{\displaystyle X}{|}}{C}H_2 \longrightarrow R{-}CH{=}CH_2 \ + \ X{-}Y$$

Note that the C atoms are bonded to *fewer* atoms in the product than in the reactant. Pairs of halogen atoms, an H atom and a halogen atom, or an H atom and an —OH group are typically eliminated, but C atoms are not. Thus, the driving force for many elimination reactions is the loss of a small, stable molecule, such as HCl(*g*) or H$_2$O, which increases the entropy (disorder) of the system (Section 13.2):

$$CH_3{-}\overset{\overset{\displaystyle OH}{|}}{C}H{-}\overset{\overset{\displaystyle H}{|}}{C}H_2 \ \xrightarrow{\ H_2SO_4\ } \ CH_3{-}CH{=}CH_2 \ + \ H_2O$$

3. A **substitution reaction** occurs when an atom (or group) from an added reagent substitutes for one in the organic reactant:

$$R{-}\overset{\displaystyle |}{\underset{\displaystyle |}{C}}{-}X \ + \ :Y \longrightarrow R{-}\overset{\displaystyle |}{\underset{\displaystyle |}{C}}{-}Y \ + \ :X$$

Note that the C atom is bonded to the *same number* of atoms in the product as in the reactant. The C atom may be saturated or unsaturated, and X and Y can be many different atoms, but generally *not* C. The main flavor ingre-

A   **B**

Figure 15.14 A color test for C=C bonds. A, When Br$_2$ (in pipet) is mixed with a compound that has a C=C bond (in test tube), it adds to the bond and its orange-brown color disappears:

$$\overset{\diagdown}{\underset{\diagup}{}}C{=}C\overset{\diagup}{\underset{\diagdown}{}} \ + \ Br_2 \longrightarrow {-}\overset{\overset{\displaystyle Br}{|}}{C}{-}\overset{\underset{\displaystyle Br}{|}}{C}{-}$$

B, The substance in this test tube has no C=C bond, so the Br$_2$ does not react and it remains orange-brown.

dient in banana oil, for instance, forms through a substitution reaction; note that the O substitutes for the Cl:

$$CH_3—\overset{\overset{O}{\|}}{C}—Cl \ + \ HO—CH_2—CH_2—\overset{\overset{CH_3}{|}}{CH}—CH_3 \ \longrightarrow \ CH_3—\overset{\overset{O}{\|}}{C}—O—CH_2—CH_2—\overset{\overset{CH_3}{|}}{CH}—CH_3 \ + \ HCl$$

Sample Problem 15.3   Recognizing the Type of Organic Reaction

PROBLEM State whether each of the following reactions is an addition, elimination, or substitution:

(a) $CH_3—CH_2—CH_2—Br \ \longrightarrow \ CH_3—CH{=}CH_2 \ + \ HBr$

(b) $+ \ H_2 \ \longrightarrow$

(c) $CH_3—CH_2—CH_2—Br \ + \ CH_3—ONa \ \longrightarrow \ CH_3—CH_2—CH_2—O—CH_3 \ + \ NaBr$

PLAN We determine the type of reaction by examining the change in number of atoms bonded to C:
- More atoms bonded to C is an *addition.*
- Fewer atoms bonded to C is an *elimination.*
- Same number of atoms bonded to C is a *substitution.*

SOLUTION

(a) Elimination: two bonds in the reactant, C—H and C—Br, are absent in the product, so fewer atoms are bonded to C.

(b) Addition: two more C—H bonds form in the product, so more atoms are bonded to C.

(c) Substitution: the reactant C—Br bond becomes a C—O bond in the product, so the same number of atoms are bonded to C.

COMMENT Sodium methoxide, $CH_3—ONa$, appears in part (c) as a substituting reactant that supplies the $CH_3—O^-$ ion. It also appears in part (c) of the follow-up problem in the role of a strong base that removes a proton from 2-chloropropane.

Follow-up Problem 15.3   Write a balanced equation for the following:
(a) An addition reaction between 2-butene and H_2O
(b) A substitution reaction between $CH_3—CH_2—CH_2—Br$ and OH^-
(c) The elimination of HCl from $CH_3—CHCl—CH_3$ by $CH_3—ONa$

The Redox Process in Organic Reactions

An important process in many organic reactions is *oxidation-reduction.* But chemists do not usually monitor the change in oxidation numbers of the various C atoms in a reaction. Rather, they note the movement of electron density around a C atom by counting the number of bonds to more electronegative atoms (usually O) or to less electronegative atoms (usually H). A more electronegative atom takes some electron density from the C, whereas a less electronegative atom gives some electron density to the C. Moreover, even though a redox reaction always involves both an oxidation and a reduction, organic chemists typically *focus on the organic reactant only.* Therefore,
- When a C atom in the organic reactant forms more bonds to O or fewer bonds to H, the reactant is oxidized and the reaction is an *oxidation.*
- When a C atom in the organic reactant forms fewer bonds to O or more bonds to H, the reactant is reduced and the reaction is a *reduction.*

The most dramatic redox reactions are combustion reactions. All organic compounds that contain C and H atoms burn in excess O_2 to form CO_2 and H_2O. For ethane, the reaction is

$$2CH_3—CH_3 \ + \ 7O_2 \ \longrightarrow \ 4CO_2 \ + \ 6H_2O$$

Obviously, when ethane converts to CO_2 and H_2O, each of its C atoms has more bonds to O and fewer bonds to H, so the ethane is oxidized and this reaction is referred to as an *oxidation*, even though the O_2 is reduced as well.

Most oxidations do not involve such a total breaking apart of the molecule, however. When 2-propanol reacts with potassium dichromate in acidic solution, a common oxidizing agent in organic reactions, the organic product is 2-propanone:

$$CH_3-\underset{\underset{OH}{|}}{C}H-CH_3 \longrightarrow CH_3-\underset{\underset{O}{||}}{C}-CH_3$$
$$\text{2-propanol} \qquad\qquad \text{2-propanone}$$

Note that C-2 in 2-propanone has one fewer bond to H and one more bond to O than it does in 2-propanol. Thus, the 2-propanol was oxidized, so this is an *oxidation*. Don't forget, however, that the dichromate ion is reduced at the same time:

$$Cr_2O_7^{2-} + 14H^+ + 6e^- \longrightarrow 2Cr^{3+} + 7H_2O$$

The addition of H_2 to an alkene is referred to as a *reduction:*

$$CH_2{=}CH_2 + H_2 \xrightarrow{\text{Pd}} CH_3-CH_3$$

Note that each C has more bonds to H in ethane than it has in ethene, so the ethene is reduced. (The H_2 is oxidized in the process and the palladium shown over the arrow acts as a catalyst to speed up the reaction.)

Section Summary

In an addition reaction, a π bond breaks and the two C atoms bond to more atoms. In an elimination, a π bond forms and the two C atoms bond to fewer atoms. In a substitution, one atom replaces another atom, but the total number of atoms bonded to C does not change. In an organic redox process, the organic reactant is oxidized if a C atom in the compound forms more bonds to O atoms (or fewer bonds to H atoms), and it is reduced if a C atom forms more bonds to H (or fewer bonds to O).

15.4 Properties and Reactivity of Common Functional Groups

The central organizing principle of organic reaction chemistry is the *functional group*. To predict how an organic compound might react, we narrow our focus there because *the distribution of electron density in the functional group affects the reactivity*. The electron density can be high, as in the $C{=}C$ and $C{\equiv}C$ bonds, or it can be low at one end of a bond and high at the other, as in the $C-Cl$ and $C-O$ bonds. Such bond sites enhance dipoles in the other reactant. As a result, the reactants attract each other and begin a sequence of bond-forming and bond-breaking steps that lead to product. Thus, *the intermolecular forces that affect physical properties and solubility also affect reactivity*. Table 15.5 lists some of the important functional groups in organic compounds.

When we classify functional groups by bond order (single, double, and so forth), in most cases they follow certain patterns of reactivity:

- Single-bonded functional groups undergo substitution or elimination.
- Double- and triple-bonded functional groups undergo addition.
- Functional groups with both single and double bonds undergo substitution.

Table 15.5 Important Functional Groups in Organic Compounds

Functional Group	Compound Type	Suffix or Prefix of Name	Example	Systematic Name (Common Name)
C=C	alkene	-ene	H₂C=CH₂	ethene (ethylene)
—C≡C—	alkyne	-yne	H—C≡C—H	ethyne (acetylene)
—C—Ö—H	alcohol	-ol	H—C—Ö—H	methanol (methyl alcohol)
—C—Ẍ: (X=halogen)	haloalkane	halo-	H—C—C̈l:	chloromethane (methyl chloride)
—C—N̈—	amine	-amine	H—C—C—N̈—H	ethylamine
—C—H with :O:	aldehyde	-al	H—C—C—H with :O:	ethanal (acetaldehyde)
—C—C—C— with :O:	ketone	-one	H—C—C—C—H with :O:	2-propanone (acetone)
—C—Ö—H with :O:	carboxylic acid	-oic acid	H—C—C—Ö—H with :O:	ethanoic acid (acetic acid)
—C—Ö—C— with :O:	ester	-oate	H—C—C—Ö—C—H with :O:	methyl ethanoate (methyl acetate)
—C—N̈— with :O:	amide	-amide	H—C—C—N̈—H with :O:	ethanamide (acetamide)
—C≡N:	nitrile	-nitrile	H—C—C≡N:	ethanenitrile (acetonitrile, methyl cyanide)

Methanol (methyl alcohol)
By-product in coal gasification; de-icing agent; gasoline substitute; precursor of organic compounds

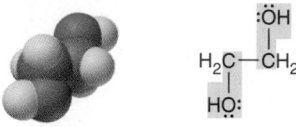

1,2-Ethanediol (ethylene glycol)
Main component of auto antifreeze

Serine
Amino acid found in most proteins

Cholesterol
Major sterol in animals; essential for cell membranes; precursor of steroid hormones

Figure 15.15 **Some molecules with the alcohol functional group.**

Functional Groups with Single Bonds

The most common single-bonded functional groups are alcohols, haloalkanes, and amines.

Alcohols The **alcohol** functional group consists of carbon bonded to an —OH group, —C—Ö—H, and the general formula of an alcohol is R—OH.

Alcohols are named by dropping the final *-e* from the parent hydrocarbon name and adding the suffix *-ol*. Thus, the two-carbon alcohol is ethanol (ethan- + -ol). The common name is the hydrocarbon *root-* + *-yl*, followed by "alcohol"; thus, the common name of ethanol is ethyl alcohol. (This substance, obtained from fermented grain, has been consumed by people as an intoxicant in beverages since ancient times; today, it is recognized as the most abused drug in the world.) Alcohols are important laboratory reagents, and the functional group occurs in many biomolecules, including carbohydrates, sterols, and some amino acids. Figure 15.15 shows the names, structures, and uses of some important compounds that contain the alcohol group.

You can think of an alcohol as a water molecule with an R group in place of one of the H atoms. In fact, alcohols react with very active metals, such as the alkali metals [Group 1A(1)], in a manner similar to water:

$$2Na + 2HOH \longrightarrow 2NaOH + H_2$$

$$2Na + 2CH_3—CH_2—OH \longrightarrow 2CH_3—CH_2—ONa + H_2$$

Water forms the hydroxide ion, and alcohols form the *alkoxide ion* (RO^-), in this case the ethoxide ion, $CH_3—CH_2—O^-$. The physical properties of the smaller alcohols are also similar to those of water. They have high melting and boiling points as a result of hydrogen bonding, and they dissolve polar molecules and some salts. (Substitution of R groups for both H atoms of water gives *ethers*, R—O—R.)

Alcohols undergo elimination and substitution reactions. Dehydration, the elimination of H and OH, requires acid and forms alkenes:

cyclohexanol   cyclohexene

Elimination of two H atoms requires inorganic oxidizing agents, such as $K_2Cr_2O_7$ in aqueous H_2SO_4. As we saw in Section 15.3, the reaction is an oxidation and produces the C=O group:

2-butanol   2-butanone

For alcohols with an OH group at the end of the chain (R—CH_2—OH), another oxidation occurs. Wine turns sour, for example, when the ethanol in contact with air is oxidized to acetic acid:

Substitution yields products with other single-bonded functional groups. With hydrohalic acids, many alcohols give haloalkanes:

$$R_2CH—OH + HBr \longrightarrow R_2CH—Br + HOH$$

As you'll see below, *the C atom undergoing the change in a substitution is bonded to a more electronegative element*, which makes it partially positive and readily attacked by an incoming negative group.

Haloalkanes A *halogen* atom (X) bonded to C gives the **haloalkane** functional group, $-\overset{|}{\underset{|}{C}}-\ddot{\underset{\cdot\cdot}{X}}:$, and compounds have the general formula R—X.

Haloalkanes (common name, **alkyl halides**) are named with the halogen as a prefix to the parent hydrocarbon, numbering the C atom to which it is attached, as in bromomethane, 2-chloropropane, or 1,3-diiodohexane.

Just as many alcohols undergo substitution to alkyl halides with halide ions in acid, the opposite change occurs in base. For example, OH⁻ attacks the positive C end of the C—X bond and displaces X⁻:

$$CH_3-CH_2-CH_2-CH_2-Br + OH^- \longrightarrow CH_3-CH_2-CH_2-CH_2-OH + Br^-$$

1-bromobutane   1-butanol

Substitution by groups such as —CN, —SH, —OR, and —NH₂ allows chemists to convert alkyl halides to a host of other compounds.

Just as addition of HX *to* an alkene produces haloalkanes, elimination of HX *from* a haloalkane by reaction with a strong base, such as potassium ethoxide, produces an alkene:

$$\underset{\substack{\text{2-chloro-2-methyl-}\\\text{propane}}}{CH_3-\overset{\overset{\displaystyle CH_3}{|}}{\underset{\underset{\displaystyle Cl}{|}}{C}}-CH_3} + \underset{\substack{\text{potassium}\\\text{ethoxide}}}{CH_3-CH_2-OK} \longrightarrow \underset{\text{2-methylpropene}}{CH_3-\overset{\overset{\displaystyle CH_3}{|}}{C}=CH_2} + KCl + CH_3-CH_2-OH$$

Haloalkanes have many important uses, but many are carcinogenic in mammals and have severe neurological effects in humans. Their stability has made them notorious environmental contaminants. ◆

Amines The **amine** functional group is $-\overset{|}{\underset{|}{C}}-\overset{|}{N}:$. Chemists classify amines as derivatives of ammonia, with R groups in place of one or more H atoms. *Primary* (1°) amines are RNH₂, *secondary* (2°) amines are R₂NH, and *tertiary* (3°) amines are R₃N. Common names are usually used, and the suffix *-amine* follows the name of the alkyl group; thus, methylamine has one methyl group attached to N, diethylamine has two ethyl groups attached, and so forth. Figure 15.16 shows that the amine functional group occurs in many biomolecules.

Pollutants in the Food Chain Until recently, halogenated aromatics, such as the *polychlorinated biphenyls* (*PCBs;* one of 209 different compounds is shown), were used as insulating fluids in electrical transformers and then discharged in wastewater. Because of their low solubility and high stability, they accumulate for decades in river and lake sediment and are eaten by microbes and invertebrates. Fish eat the invertebrates, and birds and mammals, including humans, eat the fish. PCBs become increasingly concentrated in body fat at each stage. As a result of their health risks, PCBs in natural waters present an enormous cleanup problem. The halogenated pesticide DDT, banned in the United States years ago, is still used freely in Central and South America. Like the PCBs, it accumulates in the food chain and continues to ravage several bird species, such as the California condor.

Lysine (primary amine)
Amino acid found in most proteins

Adenine (primary amine)
Component of nucleic acids

Epinephrine (adrenaline; secondary amine)
Neurotransmitter in brain; hormone released during stress

Cocaine (tertiary amine)
Brain stimulant; widely abused drug

Figure 15.16 **Some biomolecules with the amine functional group.**

Figure 15.17 **General structures of amines.** Amines have a trigonal pyramidal shape and are classified by the number of R groups bonded to N. The N lone pair is the key to amine reactivity.

Benzylcetyldimethyl-ammonium chloride

Figure 15.18 **Structure of a cationic detergent.** Quaternary ammonium salts are used as detergents. The charged portion dissolves in water, and the hydrocarbon portion dissolves in grease.

Primary and secondary amines can form H bonds, so they have higher melting and boiling points than hydrocarbons and alkyl halides of similar molar mass. For example, dimethylamine ($\mathcal{M}$ = 45.09 g/mol) boils 45°C higher than ethyl fluoride ($\mathcal{M}$ = 48.06 g/mol). Trimethylamine has a greater molar mass than dimethylamine, but it melts more than 20°C *lower* because trimethylamine molecules are not H bonded.

Like ammonia, amines have trigonal pyramidal shapes and a lone pair of electrons on a partially negative N atom (Figure 15.17). Amines of low molar mass are fishy smelling, water soluble, and weakly basic. The reaction with water proceeds only slightly to the right to reach equilibrium:

$$CH_3-\overset{..}{N}H_2 + H_2O \rightleftharpoons CH_3-\overset{+}{N}H_3 + OH^-$$

Amines undergo substitution reactions in which the N lone pair attacks the partially positive C in alkyl halides to displace X^- and form a larger amine:

$$2CH_3-CH_2-\overset{..}{N}H_2 + CH_3-CH_2-Cl \longrightarrow CH_3-CH_2-\underset{\underset{CH_3-CH_2}{|}}{\overset{..}{N}H} + CH_3-CH_2-\overset{+}{N}H_3Cl^-$$

ethylamine   chloroethane   diethylamine   ethylammonium chloride

(One molecule of ethylamine participates in the substitution, while the other binds the released H^+ and prevents it from remaining on the diethylamine product.)

Four R groups bonded to an N atom give an ionic compound called a *quaternary (4°) ammonium salt*:

$$4NH_3 + 4RCl \longrightarrow 3NH_4Cl + R_4N^+Cl^- \text{(a quaternary ammonium chloride)}$$

Many common liquid detergents are concentrated aqueous solutions of quaternary ammonium salts with large R groups (Figure 15.18). As with soaps (Section 13.1), the ionic portion makes such detergents water soluble, and the R groups allow them to dissolve in grease.

Variations on a Theme: Inorganic Compounds with Single Bonds to O, X, and N The —OH group occurs frequently in inorganic compounds. All oxoacids contain at least one —OH, usually bonded to a relatively electronegative nonmetal atom, which in most cases is bonded to other O atoms. Oxoacids are acidic in water because these other O atoms pull electron density from the central nonmetal, which pulls electron density from the O—H bond, releasing an H^+ ion and stabilizing the oxoanion through resonance. Alcohols are *not* acidic in water because they lack the additional O atoms and the electronegative nonmetal.

Halides of nearly every nonmetal are known, and many undergo substitution reactions in base. As in the case of an alkyl halide, the process involves an attack on the partially positive central atom by OH^-:

Thus, alkyl halides undergo the same general reaction as other nonmetal halides, such as BCl_3, SiF_4, and PCl_5.

The bonds from nitrogen to larger nonmetals, such as Si, P, and S, have significant double-bond character, which affects structure and reactivity. For example, trisilylamine, the Si analog of trimethylamine (see Figure 14.16, p. 566), is planar, rather than trigonal pyramidal, partially as a result of p,d-π bonding. The N lone pair is delocalized in this π bond, so trisilylamine is not basic.

Sample Problem 15.4   Predicting the Reactions of Alcohols, Alkyl Halides, and Amines

PROBLEM Determine the reaction type and predict the product(s) in the following:

(a) $CH_3—CH_2—CH_2—I + NaOH \longrightarrow$

(b) $CH_3—CH_2—Br + 2CH_3—CH_2—CH_2—NH_2 \longrightarrow$

(c) $CH_3—\underset{\underset{OH}{|}}{CH}—CH_3 \xrightarrow[\text{H}_2\text{SO}_4]{\text{Cr}_2\text{O}_7^{2-}}$

PLAN We first determine the functional group of the reactant(s) and then examine any inorganic reagent(s) to decide on the possible reaction type, keeping in mind that, in general, these functional groups undergo substitution or elimination. In **(a),** the reactant is an alkyl halide, so the OH^- of the inorganic reagent substitutes for the —I. In **(b),** the reactants are an amine and an alkyl halide, so the N: of the amine substitutes for the —Br. In **(c),** the reactant is an alcohol, the inorganic reagents form a strong oxidizing agent, and alcohols undergo elimination to carbonyl compounds.

SOLUTION

(a) Substitution: The products are $CH_3—CH_2—CH_2—OH + NaI$

(b) Substitution: The products are $CH_3—CH_2—CH_2—\underset{\underset{CH_2—CH_3}{|}}{N}H + CH_3—CH_2—CH_2—\overset{+}{N}H_3Br^-$

(c) Elimination (oxidation): The product is $CH_3—\underset{\underset{O}{||}}{C}—CH_3$

CHECK The only changes should be at the functional group.

Follow-up Problem 15.4   Fill in the blank in the following reactions. (*Hint:* Examine any inorganic compounds and the organic product to determine the organic reactant.)

(a) _____ $+ CH_3—ONa \longrightarrow CH_3—CH=\underset{\underset{CH_3}{|}}{C}—CH_3 + NaCl + CH_3—OH$

(b) _____ $\xrightarrow[\text{H}_2\text{SO}_4]{\text{Cr}_2\text{O}_7^{2-}} CH_3—CH_2—\overset{\overset{O}{||}}{C}—OH$

Functional Groups with Double Bonds

The most important double-bonded functional groups are the $C=C$ bond of alkenes and the $C=O$ bond of aldehydes and ketones. Both appear in many organic and biological molecules.

Comparing the Reactivity of Alkenes and Aromatic Compounds   The $C=C$ bond is the essential portion of the alkene functional group, $\overset{\displaystyle \diagdown}{\underset{\displaystyle \diagup}{C}}=\overset{\displaystyle \diagup}{\underset{\displaystyle \diagdown}{C}}$. Although they can be unsaturated further to alkynes, *alkenes typically undergo addition.* The electron-rich double bond is readily attracted to the partially positive H atoms of hydronium ions and hydrohalic acids, yielding alcohols and alkyl halides, respectively:

2-methylpropene   2-methyl-2-propanol

propene   2-chloropropane

The *localized* unsaturation of alkenes is very different from the *delocalized* unsaturation of benzene. Since benzene does *not* have double bonds, despite the structures of its resonance forms, it does *not* behave like an alkene. Benzene, for example, does not decolorize bromine because there are no isolated π-electron pairs to bond with Br_2.

In general, aromatic rings are much *less* reactive than alkenes because delocalized π electrons stabilize the ring, making it *lower* in energy than one with localized π electrons. Data indicate that benzene is about 150 kJ/mol more stable than a six-C ring with three $C=C$ bonds would be; in other words, benzene requires about 150 kJ/mol more energy to react.

An *addition* reaction with benzene, therefore, requires additional energy to break up the delocalized π system. Benzene does undergo many *substitution* reactions, however, in which the delocalization is retained when a ring H atom is replaced by another group:

benzene   bromobenzene

Aldehydes and Ketones   The $C=O$ bond, or **carbonyl group,** is one of the most chemically versatile. In the **aldehyde** functional group, the carbonyl C is bonded to H (and often C), so it always occurs *at the end of a chain,* $R-\overset{\displaystyle H}{\underset{\displaystyle |}{C}}=O$. Aldehyde names drop the final *-e* from the parent alkane and add *-al.* For example, the three-C aldehyde is propanal. In the **ketone** functional group, the carbonyl C is bonded to two other C atoms, $-\overset{|}{C}-\overset{\displaystyle \overset{:O:}{\|}}{C}-\overset{|}{C}-$, so it occurs *within the chain.* Ketones, $R-\overset{\displaystyle \overset{O}{\|}}{C}-R'$, are named by numbering the carbonyl C, dropping the final *-e* from the alkane, and adding *-one.* For example, the unbranched, five-C ketone with the carbonyl C as C-2 in the chain is named 2-pentanone. Figure 15.19 shows some common carbonyl compounds.

Methanal (formaldehyde)
Used to make resins in plywood, dishware, countertops; biological preservative

Ethanal (acetaldehyde)
Narcotic product of ethanol metabolism; used to make perfumes, flavors, plastics, other chemicals

Benzaldehyde
Artificial almond flavoring

2-Propanone (acetone)
Solvent for fat, rubber, plastic, varnish, lacquer; chemical feedstock

2-Butanone (methyl ethyl ketone)
Important solvent

Figure 15.19 Some common aldehydes and ketones.

Like the C=C bond, the C=O bond is *electron rich;* unlike the C=C bond, it is *highly polar* (ΔEN = 1.0). Figure 15.20 emphasizes this polarity with an electron density model and a charged resonance form. Aldehydes and ketones are formed by the oxidation of alcohols:

$$CH_3-CH_2-OH \xrightarrow{\text{oxidation}} CH_3-\overset{O}{\underset{}{\overset{\|}{C}}}-H$$

ethanol → ethanal (common name, acetaldehyde)

$$CH_3-CH_2-\overset{OH}{\underset{}{\overset{|}{CH}}}-CH_3 \xrightarrow{\text{oxidation}} CH_3-CH_2-\overset{O}{\underset{}{\overset{\|}{C}}}-CH_3$$

2-butanol → 2-butanone

Conversely, as a result of their unsaturation, they can undergo *addition* and be reduced to alcohols:

cyclobutanone $\xrightarrow{\text{reduction}}$ cyclobutanol

As a result of bond polarity, addition often occurs with an electron-rich group bonding to the carbonyl C and an electron-poor group bonding to the carbonyl O. **Organometallic compounds,** which have a metal attached to an R group through a polar covalent bond (Section 14.3), take part in an important example of this type of reaction. They convert carbonyl compounds to alcohols with *different carbon skeletons.* In the following reaction, for example, the electron-rich C of ethyllithium, CH_3CH_2—Li, attacks the electron-poor carbonyl C of 2-propanone, adding its ethyl group; at the same time, the Li adds to the carbonyl O. Treating the mixture with water forms the C—OH group:

$$CH_3-\overset{\delta^+}{\underset{\delta^-}{CH_2}} + \overset{\delta^-}{\underset{\delta^+}{C}}\overset{Li}{\underset{CH_3}{\overset{O}{\|}}}-CH_3 \longrightarrow CH_3-CH_2-\overset{O^-Li^+}{\underset{CH_3}{\overset{|}{C}}}-CH_3 \xrightarrow{H_2O} CH_3-CH_2-\overset{OH}{\underset{CH_3}{\overset{|}{C}}}-CH_3 + LiOH$$

Note that the product skeleton combines the two reactant skeletons. The field of *organic synthesis* often employs organometallic compounds to create molecules with different skeletons and, thus, new compounds.

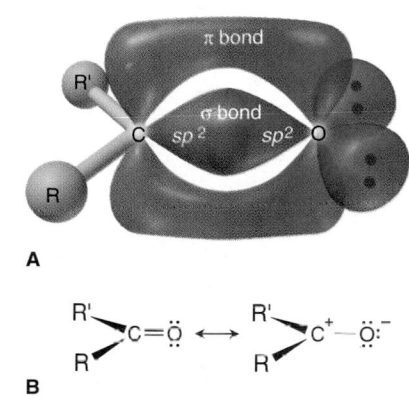

A

B

Figure 15.20 The carbonyl group. A, An orbital depiction of the σ bond and π bond that make up the C=O bond of the carbonyl group. **B,** The C=O bond is polar (ΔEN = 1.0), which is indicated by the charged resonance form.

Sample Problem 15.5 Predicting the Steps in an Organic Reaction Sequence

PROBLEM Fill in the blanks in the following reaction sequence:

$$CH_3-CH_2-\underset{\underset{Br}{|}}{CH}-CH_3 \xrightarrow{OH^-} \underline{\hspace{1cm}} \xrightarrow[H_2SO_4]{Cr_2O_7{}^{2-}} \underline{\hspace{1cm}} \xrightarrow{CH_3-Li} \xrightarrow{H_2O} \underline{\hspace{1cm}}$$

PLAN For each step, we examine the functional group of the reactant and the reagent above the yield arrow to decide on the most likely product.

SOLUTION The sequence starts with an alkyl halide reacting with OH^-. Substitution gives an alcohol. Oxidation of this alcohol with acidic dichromate gives a ketone. Finally, a two-step reaction of a ketone with CH_3-Li and then water forms an alcohol with a carbon skeleton that has the CH_3 group attached to the carbonyl C:

$$CH_3-CH_2-\underset{\underset{Br}{|}}{CH}-CH_3 \xrightarrow{OH^-} CH_3-CH_2-\underset{\underset{OH}{|}}{CH}-CH_3 \xrightarrow[H_2SO_4]{Cr_2O_7{}^{2-}} CH_3-CH_2-\underset{\underset{O}{\parallel}}{C}-CH_3 \xrightarrow{CH_3-Li} \xrightarrow{H_2O} CH_3-CH_2-\underset{\underset{CH_3}{|}}{\overset{\overset{OH}{|}}{C}}-CH_3$$

2-bromobutane   2-butanol   2-butanone   2-methyl-2-butanol

CHECK In this case, make sure that the first two reactions alter the functional group only and that the final steps change the C skeleton.

Follow-up Problem 15.5 Choose reactants to obtain the following products:

(a) $\underline{\hspace{1cm}} \xrightarrow[H_2SO_4]{Cr_2O_7{}^{2-}}$

(b) $\underline{\hspace{1cm}} \xrightarrow{CH_3-CH_2-Li} \xrightarrow{H_2O} CH_3-CH_2-\underset{\underset{OH}{|}}{CH}-$

Variations on a Theme: Inorganic Compounds with Double Bonds

Homonuclear (same atom) double bonds are rare among atoms other than C, but we've seen many double bonds to O with other nonmetals, as in the oxides of S, N, and halogens. Like carbonyl compounds, these substances undergo addition reactions. In its reaction with SO_3, for example, the partially negative O of water attacks the partially positive S to form sulfuric acid:

S bonds to 3 atoms   S bonds to 4 atoms

Functional Groups with Both Single and Double Bonds

A family of three functional groups contains C double bonded to O (a carbonyl group) *and* single bonded to O or N. The parent of the family is the **carboxylic acid** group, $-\overset{\overset{:O:}{\parallel}}{C}-\ddot{O}H$, also called the *carboxyl group* and written $-COOH$. *The most important reaction type of the family is substitution from one member to another.* Substitution for the $-OH$ by the $-OR$ of alcohols gives the **ester** group, $-\overset{\overset{:O:}{\parallel}}{C}-\ddot{O}-R$; substitution by the $-\overset{|}{\underset{\cdot\cdot}{N}}-$ of amines gives the **amide** group, $-\overset{\overset{:O:}{\parallel}}{C}-\overset{|}{\underset{\cdot\cdot}{N}}-$.

Figure 15.21 **Some molecules with the carboxylic acid functional group.**

Carboxylic Acids Carboxylic acids, R—C—OH, are named by dropping the -*e* from the parent alkane and adding -*oic acid;* however, many common names are used. For example, the four-C acid is butanoic acid (the carboxyl C is counted in the root); its common name is butyric acid. Figure 15.21 shows some important carboxylic acids. The carboxyl C already has three bonds, so it forms only one other. In formic acid (methanoic acid), it bonds to an H, but all other carboxylic acids contain chains or rings.

Carboxylic acids are weak acids in water:

$$CH_3-\overset{O}{\overset{||}{C}}-OH(l) + H_2O(l) \rightleftharpoons CH_3-\overset{O}{\overset{||}{C}}-O^-(aq) + H_3O^+(aq)$$
ethanoic acid
(acetic acid)

At equilibrium in acid solutions of typical concentration, more than 99% of the acid molecules are undissociated at any given moment. In strong base, however, they are neutralized completely to form a salt and water:

$$CH_3-\overset{O}{\overset{||}{C}}-OH(l) + NaOH(aq) \longrightarrow CH_3-\overset{O}{\overset{||}{C}}-O^-(aq) + Na^+(aq) + H_2O(l)$$

The anion is the *carboxylate ion,* named by dropping -*oic acid* and adding -*oate;* the sodium salt of butanoic acid, for instance, is sodium butanoate.

Carboxylic acids with long hydrocarbon chains are **fatty acids,** an essential group of compounds found in all cells. Animal fatty acids have saturated chains, whereas many from vegetable sources are unsaturated, usually with the C=C bonds in the *cis* configuration. The double bond renders them much easier to metabolize. Nearly all fatty acid skeletons have an even number of C atoms—16 and 18 carbons are very common—because they are made in the cell from two-C pieces. Fatty acid salts are soaps, with the cation usually from Group 1A(1) or 2A(2) (Section 13.1).

Substitution occurs through a two-step sequence: *addition plus elimination equals substitution.* Addition to the trigonal planar shape of the carbonyl group gives an unstable tetrahedral intermediate, which immediately undergoes elimination to give a trigonal planar product again:

$$\underset{R}{\overset{O}{\overset{||}{C}}}\diagdown_X + Z-Y \xrightarrow{\text{addition}} \left[\underset{R}{\overset{O-Z}{\overset{|}{\underset{Y}{C}}}}-X \right] \xrightarrow{\text{elimination}} \underset{R}{\overset{O}{\overset{||}{C}}}\diagdown_Y + Z-X$$

Strong heating of carboxylic acids forms an **acid anhydride** through a *dehydration-condensation* reaction, in which two molecules condense into one with loss of water:

$$R-C(=O)-OH + HO-C(=O)-R \xrightarrow{\Delta} R-C(=O)-O-C(=O)-R + HOH$$

Esters *An alcohol and a carboxylic acid form an ester.* The first part of an ester name designates the alcohol portion and the second the acid portion (named in the same way as the carboxylate ion). For example, the ester formed between ethanol and ethanoic acid is ethyl ethanoate (common name, ethyl acetate), a solvent for nail polish and model glue.

The ester group occurs commonly in **lipids,** a large group of fatty biological substances. Most dietary fats are *triglycerides,* esters composed of three fatty acids linked to the alcohol 1,2,3-trihydroxypropane (common name, glycerol), which function as energy stores. Some important lipids are shown in Figure 15.22.

Figure 15.22 **Some lipid molecules with the ester functional group.**

Tristearin A typical dietary fat used as an energy store in animals

Lecithin A phospholipid found in all cell membranes

Cetyl palmitate The most common fat in whale blubber

Esters, like acid anhydrides and several other organic (and inorganic) compounds, form through a dehydration-condensation reaction:

$$R-C(=O)-OH + H-O-R' \underset{}{\overset{H^+}{\rightleftharpoons}} R-C(=O)-O-R' + HOH$$

Studies of the reaction with ^{18}O isotope-labeling show that the alcohol O is attracted to the carboxyl C and becomes bonded to it in the ester, and the —OH of the acid becomes part of the product water (Figure 15.23). Thus,

Figure 15.23 Which reactant contributes which group to the ester? An ester forms when a carboxylic acid reacts with an alcohol. To determine which reactant supplies the ester O, the acid and alcohol were prepared by labeling with the isotope ^{18}O. **A,** When R—^{18}OH reacts with the unlabeled acid, the ester contains ^{18}O but the water does not.

B, When R—C(=O)—^{18}OH reacts with the unlabeled alcohol, the water contains ^{18}O. Thus, the alcohol supplies the —OR' portion of the ester, and the acid supplies the RC=O portion.

A $R-C(=O)-\ddot{O}H + R'-^{18}\ddot{O}H \rightleftharpoons R-C(=O)-^{18}\ddot{O}-R' + H-\ddot{O}-H$

B $R-C(=O)-^{18}\ddot{O}H + R'-\ddot{O}H \rightleftharpoons R-C(=O)-\ddot{O}-R' + H-^{18}\ddot{O}-H$

the acid supplies the RC=O portion of the ester, and the alcohol supplies the —OR′ portion. (We discuss this multistep reaction in Chapter 16.) ◆

Note that the reaction is reversible. The opposite of dehydration-condensation is called **hydrolysis,** in which the O atom of water is attracted to the partially positive ester C, cleaving (lysing) the molecule into two parts. One part receives the water's —OH, and the other part receives the water's other H. In soap manufacture, which began in ancient times, ester bonds in animal or vegetable fats are hydrolyzed with strong base in the process of *saponification* (Latin *sapon*, "soap"):

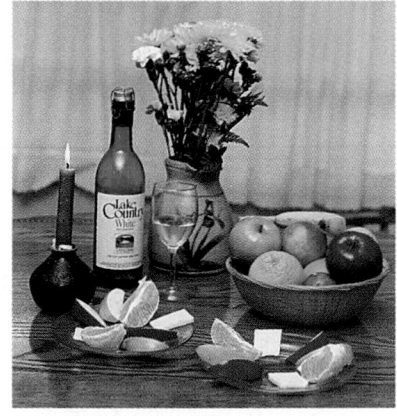

Amides The product of a substitution between an amine (or NH_3) and an ester is an amide. The partially negative N is attracted to the partially positive ester C, an alcohol (ROH) is lost, and an amide forms:

Amides are named by denoting the amine portion with *N-* and replacing *-oic acid* with *-amide*. In the amide from the previous reaction, the ethyl group comes from the amine, and the acid portion comes from ethanoic acid (acetic acid). Some amides are shown in Figure 15.24.

Amides are hydrolyzed in hot water (or base) to a carboxylic acid and an amine, so even though amides are not normally formed in the following way, they can be viewed as the result of a reversible dehydration-condensation:

The most important example of the amide group is in the *peptide bond*, which links amino acids in a protein, as you'll see shortly.

Acetaminophen
Active ingredient
in nonaspirin
pain relievers; used
to make dyes and
photographic chemicals

N,N-Dimethylmethanamide (dimethylformamide)
Major organic solvent;
used in production of
synthetic fibers

Lysergic acid diethylamide (LSD-25)
A potent hallucinogen

Figure 15.24 **Some molecules with the amide functional group.**

The carboxylic acid family undergoes reactions to form other functional groups. For example, certain inorganic reducing agents convert acids and esters to alcohols, and amides to amines:

$$R-\overset{\overset{\displaystyle O}{\|}}{C}-OH \text{ (or } O-R') \xrightarrow{\text{reduction}} R-CH_2-OH + HOH \text{ (or } R'-OH)$$

$$R-\overset{\overset{\displaystyle O}{\|}}{C}-NH-R' \xrightarrow{\text{reduction}} R-CH_2-NH-R' + H_2O$$

Sample Problem 15.6 Predicting the Reactions of the Carboxylic Acid Family

PROBLEM Predict the product(s) of the following reactions:

(a) $CH_3-CH_2-CH_2-\overset{\overset{\displaystyle O}{\|}}{C}-OH + CH_3-\overset{\overset{\displaystyle OH}{|}}{CH}-CH_3 \underset{}{\overset{H^+}{\rightleftharpoons}}$

(b) $CH_3-\overset{\overset{\displaystyle CH_3}{|}}{CH}-CH_2-CH_2-\overset{\overset{\displaystyle O}{\|}}{C}-NH-CH_2-CH_3 \xrightarrow[H_2O]{NaOH}$

PLAN We discussed substitution (including addition-elimination and dehydration-condensation) and hydrolysis. In **(a)**, a carboxylic acid and alcohol react, so it must be a substitution to form an ester and water. In **(b)**, an amide reacts with OH^-, so it is hydrolyzed to an amine and a sodium carboxylate.

SOLUTION

(a) Formation of an ester: $CH_3-CH_2-CH_2-\overset{\overset{\displaystyle O}{\|}}{C}-O-\overset{\overset{\displaystyle CH_3}{|}}{CH}-CH_3 + H_2O$

(b) Basic hydrolysis of an amide:

$CH_3-\overset{\overset{\displaystyle CH_3}{|}}{CH}-CH_2-CH_2-\overset{\overset{\displaystyle O}{\|}}{C}-O^- + Na^+ + H_2N-CH_2-CH_3$

CHECK Note that in **(b)**, the carboxylate ion forms, rather than the acid, because aqueous NaOH is present, which will react with the acid.

Follow-up Problem 15.6 Fill in the blanks in the following reactions:

(a) _____ + $CH_3-OH \overset{H^+}{\rightleftharpoons}$ ⬡$-CH_2-\overset{\overset{\displaystyle O}{\|}}{C}-O-CH_3 + H_2O$

(b) _____ + _____ $\longrightarrow CH_3-CH_2-CH_2-\overset{\overset{\displaystyle O}{\|}}{C}-NH-CH_2-CH_3 + CH_3-OH$

Variations on a Theme: Oxoacids, Esters, and Amides of Other Nonmetals
A nonmetal both double and single bonded to O occurs in most inorganic oxoacids, such as phosphoric, sulfuric, and chlorous acids. Those with additional O atoms are stronger acids than carboxylic acids.

Diphosphoric and disulfuric acids are acid anhydrides formed by dehydration-condensation reactions, just as the carboxylic acid anhydride is formed (Figure 15.25). Inorganic oxoacids form esters and amides that are part of many biological molecules. We already saw that certain lipids are phosphate esters (see Figure 15.22). The first compound formed when glucose is digested is a phosphate ester (Figure 15.26A), and a similar phosphate ester is a major structural feature of nucleic acids, as you'll see shortly. Amides of organic S-containing oxoacids, called sulfonamides, are potent antibiotics (Figure 15.26B). More than 10,000 different sulfonamides have been synthesized.

Figure 15.25 **Formation of carboxylic, phosphoric, and sulfuric acid anhydrides.**

A Glucose-6-phosphate   **B Sulfanilamide**

Figure 15.26 **An ester and an amide of other nonmetals. A,** Glucose-6-phosphate contains a phosphate ester group. **B,** Sulfanilamide, an important grouping in many antibiotics, contains an amide group.

Functional Groups with Triple Bonds

There are only two important triple-bonded functional groups. *Alkynes,* with their electron-rich $-C\equiv C-$ groups, undergo addition (by H_2O, H_2, HX, X_2, and so forth) to form double-bonded or saturated compounds:

$$CH_3-C\equiv CH \xrightarrow{H_2} CH_3-CH=CH_2 \xrightarrow{H_2} CH_3-CH_2-CH_3$$
propyne   propene   propane

Nitriles ($R-C\equiv N$) contain the **nitrile** group ($-C\equiv N\!:$) and are made by substituting a CN^- (cyanide) ion for X^- in a reaction with an alkyl halide:

$$CH_3-CH_2-Cl + NaCN \longrightarrow CH_3-CH_2-C\equiv N + NaCl$$

This reaction is useful because it *increases the chain by one C atom.* Nitriles can be reduced to amines or hydrolyzed to carboxylic acids:

$$CH_3-CH_2-CH_2-NH_2 \xleftarrow{reduction} \boxed{CH_3-CH_2-C\equiv N} \xrightarrow[\text{hydrolysis}]{H_3O^+,\, H_2O} CH_3-CH_2-\overset{\displaystyle O}{\overset{\|}{C}}-OH + NH_4{}^+$$

Variations on a Theme: Inorganic Compounds with Triple Bonds Triple bonds are as scarce in the inorganic world as in the organic world. Carbon monoxide ($:C\equiv O:$), elemental nitrogen ($:N\equiv N:$), and the cyanide ion ($[:C\equiv N:]^-$) are the only common examples.

You've seen quite a few functional groups by this time, and it is especially important that you can recognize them in a complex organic molecule. Sample Problem 15.7 provides some practice.

Sample Problem 15.7 Recognizing Functional Groups

PROBLEM Circle and name the functional groups in the following molecules:

(a)

(b)

(c)

PLAN We use Table 15.5 to identify the various functional groups.

SOLUTION

Follow-up Problem 15.7   Circle and name the functional groups in the following molecules:

(a)

⬡—CH=CH—C(=O)—H

(b)

H_2N—C(=O)—CH_2—CH—CH_3
                              |
                              Br

Figure 15.27 provides a summarizing overview of the names, structures, and interconversions of the functional groups we've discussed. Note the remarkable versatility of organic functional groups.

Figure 15.27 **A summary of the interconversions among the major organic functional groups.** Organic functional groups can be interconverted by reactions with specific reagents. Each arrow identifies the reaction type. Oxidizing and reducing agents are not shown. Changes in R group are not indicated (see text for details).

Section Summary

Organic reactions are initiated when regions of high and low electron density of different reactant molecules attract each other. Single-bonded groups— alcohols, amines, and alkyl halides—take part in substitution and elimination reactions. Multiple-bonded groups—alkenes, aldehydes, ketones, alkynes, and nitriles—generally take part in addition reactions. Aromatic compounds typically undergo substitution, rather than addition, because electron delocalization stabilizes the ring π system. Groups with both double and single bonds—carboxylic acids, esters, and amides—generally take part in substitution reactions. Many reactions change one functional group to another, but some change the C skeleton, especially reactions with organometallic reactants and with the cyanide ion.

15.5 The Monomer-Polymer Theme I: Synthetic Macromolecules

Polymers (Greek, "many parts"), or *macromolecules,* are extremely large molecules that result from the covalent linking of many simpler molecular units called **monomers** (Greek, "one part"). *Synthetic polymers,* in the form of plastics, fibers, films, rubbers, and so forth, have revolutionized everyday life. More than half of all industrial chemists work in polymer-related fields. There are probably dozens of these materials in your home, and there will be many more in the future. Some of these products are nearly indestructible in the environment, however, so their manufacture has created a critical waste disposal problem.

The two major types of synthetic polymers are named for the reaction processes that form them—addition and condensation.

Addition Polymers

When monomers add together, **addition polymers** form. These are also called *chain-reaction (or chain-growth) polymers* because as each monomer joins the chain, it forms a new reactive site to continue the process. The monomers of most addition polymers have the $\overset{\diagdown}{\underset{\diagup}{C}}=\overset{\diagdown}{\underset{\diagup}{C}}$ grouping.

The *free-radical polymerization* of ethene (ethylene, $CH_2{=}CH_2$) to polyethylene is the simplest example of the process. In Figure 15.28, the monomer becomes a *free radical,* a species with an unpaired electron, that seeks another electron from the next monomer to form a covalent bond. The process begins when an *initiator,* usually a peroxide, generates a free radical that attacks the π bond of an ethylene unit, forming a σ bond with one of the p electrons and leaving the other unpaired. This new free radical then attacks the π bond of another ethylene, and the polymer chain grows. As each ethylene adds, it leaves an unpaired electron on the growing end to find an electron "mate" and make the chain one unit longer. This process stops when two free radicals form a covalent bond or when a very stable free radical is formed by addition of an *inhibitor* molecule. In a similar method, the polymerization is initiated by the formation of a cation (or anion) instead of a free radical. The cationic (or anionic) monomer attacks the π bond of the next monomer to form another cationic (or anionic) end, and the process continues.

The most important polymerization reactions take place under relatively mild conditions through the use of catalysts that incorporate transition metals. In 1963, Karl Ziegler and Giulio Natta received a Nobel Prize for *Ziegler-Natta catalysts,* which employ an organoaluminum compound, such as $Al(C_2H_5)_3$, and the tetrachloride of titanium or vanadium. These *stereoselective* catalysts create polymers with groups oriented spatially in a particular way.

Through the use of these catalysts, polyethylene chains with molar masses of 10^4 to 10^5 g/mol are made by varying conditions and reagents. One form has high density and strength as a result of extensive dispersion forces between long, unbranched chains. A lower density form has some branches that prevent the chains from packing as well, which confers flexibility and transparency. Similarly, polypropylenes, $\text{+CH}_2\text{—CH+}_n$ can be made that
   $|$
   CH_3

Figure 15.28 Steps in the free-radical polymerization of ethylene. In this polymerization method, free radicals initiate, propagate, and terminate the formation of an addition polymer. An initiator ($Y{-}O{-}O{-}Y$) is split to form two molecules of a free radical ($Y{-}O\cdot$). The free radical attacks the π bond of a monomer and creates another free radical ($Y{-}O{-}CH_2{-}CH_2\cdot$). The process proceeds and the chain grows (propagates) until an inhibitor is added (not shown) or two free radicals combine.

Table 15.6 Some Major Addition Polymers

$$n \; \begin{matrix} R_1 \\ \\ R_2 \end{matrix} C = C \begin{matrix} R_3 \\ \\ R_4 \end{matrix} \longrightarrow \left[\begin{matrix} R_1 & R_2 \\ | & | \\ C - C \\ | & | \\ R_3 & R_4 \end{matrix} \right]_n$$

Monomer	Polymer	Applications
$\begin{matrix} H \\ \\ H \end{matrix} C = C \begin{matrix} H \\ \\ H \end{matrix}$	polyethylene	Plastic bags; bottles; toys
$\begin{matrix} F \\ \\ F \end{matrix} C = C \begin{matrix} F \\ \\ F \end{matrix}$	polytetrafluoroethylene	Cooking utensils (e.g., Teflon)
$\begin{matrix} H \\ \\ H \end{matrix} C = C \begin{matrix} H \\ \\ CH_3 \end{matrix}$	polypropylene	Carpeting (indoor-outdoor); bottles
$\begin{matrix} H \\ \\ H \end{matrix} C = C \begin{matrix} H \\ \\ Cl \end{matrix}$	poly(vinyl chloride)	Plastic wrap; garden hose; indoor plumbing
$\begin{matrix} H \\ \\ H \end{matrix} C = C \begin{matrix} H \\ \\ \bigcirc \end{matrix}$	polystyrene	Insulation; furniture; packing materials
$\begin{matrix} H \\ \\ H \end{matrix} C = C \begin{matrix} H \\ \\ CN \end{matrix}$	polyacrylonitrile	Yarns; fabrics; wigs (e.g., Orlon, Acrilon)
$\begin{matrix} H \\ \\ H \end{matrix} C = C \begin{matrix} H \\ \\ O-\overset{O}{\overset{\|}{C}}-CH_3 \end{matrix}$	poly(vinyl acetate)	Adhesives; paints; textile coatings; computer disks
$\begin{matrix} H \\ \\ H \end{matrix} C = C \begin{matrix} Cl \\ \\ Cl \end{matrix}$	poly(vinylidene chloride)	Food wrap (e.g., Saran)
$\begin{matrix} H \\ \\ H \end{matrix} C = C \begin{matrix} CH_3 \\ \\ \underset{O}{\overset{\|}{C}}-O-CH_3 \end{matrix}$	poly(methyl methacrylate)	Glass substitute (e.g., Lucite, Plexiglas); bowling balls; paint

have all the monomer CH_3 groups either on one side of the chain or on alternating sides. The different orientations lead to different packing efficiencies of the chains and thus differences in density, rigidity, elasticity, and so forth.

Variations on these reactions, such as using isobutylene $CH_3 - \overset{CH_3}{\underset{}{C}} = CH_2$ or styrene $\bigcirc - CH = CH_2$, give rise to many familiar products. Other substituted monomers are vinyl chloride $CH_2 = CH - Cl$, used to form PVC [poly(vinyl chloride)], and tetrafluoroethene $CF_2 = CF_2$, used to form Teflon. Table 15.6 shows the monomers used for the most important addition polymers. Note that the general chain is identical in all of them. Thus, the essential chemical differences between an acrylic sweater, a plastic grocery bag, and a bowling ball are the different groups attached to the main chain.

Condensation Polymers

The monomers of **condensation polymers** must have two functional groups. Most commonly, they link when a group on one unit undergoes a dehydration-condensation reaction with a group on another. Most condensation polymers are *copolymers* made from two or more different monomers. Condensation of carboxylic acid and amine units forms *polyamides (nylons)*, whereas carboxylic acid and alcohol units form *polyesters.*

One of the most common polyamides is *nylon-66,* manufactured by mixing equimolar amounts of a six-C diamine (1,6-diaminohexane) and a six-C diacid (1,6-hexanedioic acid). The basic amine reacts with the acid to form a "nylon salt." Heating drives off water and forms the amide bonds:

$$n\text{HO}-\overset{\overset{\text{O}}{\|}}{\text{C}}-(\text{CH}_2)_4-\overset{\overset{\text{O}}{\|}}{\text{C}}-\text{OH} \ + \ n\text{H}_2\text{N}-(\text{CH}_2)_6-\text{NH}_2 \ \xrightarrow[-n\text{H}_2\text{O}]{\Delta} \ \left[\overset{\overset{\text{O}}{\|}}{\text{C}}-(\text{CH}_2)_4-\overset{\overset{\text{O}}{\|}}{\text{C}}-\text{NH}-(\text{CH}_2)_6-\text{NH}\right]_{n-1}$$

In the laboratory, this nylon is made without heating by using a more reactive acid component (Figure 15.29). Covalent bonds in the chain give nylons great strength, and H bonds between chains give them great flexibility (see Gallery, p. 75). About half of all nylons are made to reinforce automobile tires, the remainder being used for rugs, clothing, fishing line, and so forth.

Dacron, a popular polyester fiber, is woven from polymer strands formed when equimolar amounts of 1,4-benzcnedicarboxylic acid and 1,2-ethanediol react. Blending these polyester fibers with various cotton products gives fabrics that are durable, easily dyed, and crease resistant. Extremely thin Mylar films, used for recording tape and food packaging, are also made from this polymer.

Variations on a Theme: Inorganic Polymers You already know that some synthetic polymers are not organic. In Chapter 14, we discussed the silicones, polymers with a repeating —Si(R$_2$)—O— unit. Depending on the chain cross-links and the R groups, silicones range from oily liquids to elastic sheets to rigid solids and have applications that include stopcock grease, artificial limbs, and spacesuits. We also mentioned the polyphosphazenes, whose repeating —P(R$_2$)=N— unit exists as a flexible chain even at low temperatures.

Figure 15.29 The formation of nylon-66. Nylons are formed industrially by the reaction of diamine and diacid monomers. In this laboratory demonstration, the more reactive six-C diacid chloride monomer is used; the polyamide forms between the phases.

Section Summary

Polymers are extremely large molecules made of many smaller monomers. Addition polymers have unsaturated units that commonly link through free-radical reactions. Most condensation polymers have two types of monomer that link through dehydration-condensation reactions. By varying reaction conditions, catalysts, and monomer groups, polymers with different properties can be made.

15.6 The Monomer-Polymer Theme II: Biological Macromolecules

The monomer-polymer theme was being played out in nature eons before humans employed it to such great advantage. Biological macromolecules are nothing more than condensation polymers created by nature's reaction chemistry and improved through evolution. These remarkable molecules are the greatest proof of the versatility of carbon and its handful of atomic partners.

Natural polymers are the "stuff of life"—polysaccharides, proteins, and nucleic acids. Some have structures that make wood strong, hair curly, fingernails hard, and wool flexible. Others speed up the myriad reactions that occur in every cell or defend us against infection. Still others possess the genetic information needed to forge other biomolecules. Remarkable as these giant molecules are, the functional groups of their monomers and the reactions that link them are identical to those of other, smaller organic molecules.

Sugars and Polysaccharides

In essence, the same overall chemical change occurs when you burn a piece of wood or eat a piece of bread. Both wood and bread are mixtures of carbohydrate molecules, substances that provide energy through oxidation, which is their major metabolic role in the natural world.

Monomer Structure and Linkage Glucose and other simple sugars, from the three-C *trioses* to the seven-C *heptoses,* are called **monosaccharides.** They consist of carbon chains with attached hydroxyl and carbonyl groups. In addition to their roles as individual molecules primarily engaged in energy metabolism, they serve as the monomer units of **polysaccharides.** Most natural polysaccharides are formed from five- and six-C units. In aqueous solution, an alcohol group and the aldehyde (or ketone) group of the *same* sugar molecule react with each other to form a cyclic molecule with either a five- or six-membered ring. The ring structure of glucose is shown in Figure 15.30A. When two of these cyclic units undergo a dehydration-condensation reaction, a **disaccharide** forms. For example, sucrose (table sugar) is a disaccharide of glucose and fructose (Figure 15.30B); lactose (milk sugar) is a disaccharide of glucose and galactose; maltose, used in brewing and as a sweetener, is a disaccharide of two glucose units.

A   **B**

Glucose   Fructose   Sucrose

Cyclic form of glucose

$-H_2O$

Figure 15.30 The structure of glucose in aqueous solution and the formation of a disaccharide.
A, A molecule of glucose undergoes an internal addition reaction between the aldehyde group of C-1 and the alcohol group of C-5 to form a cyclic monosaccharide. **B,** Two monosaccharides, glucose and fructose, undergo a dehydration-condensation reaction to form the disaccharide sucrose (table sugar) and a water molecule.

Types of Polysaccharides A polysaccharide consists of *many* monosaccharide units linked together. The three major natural polysaccharides—cellulose, starch, and glycogen—consist entirely of glucose units, but they differ in the ring positions of the links, in bond orientation, and in the extent of cross-linking. Some polysaccharides also contain nitrogen in their attached groups. ◆

Cellulose is the most abundant organic chemical on Earth. More than 50% of the carbon in plants occurs in the cellulose of stems and leaves; wood is largely cellulose, and cotton is more than 90% cellulose. This polymer consists of long chains of glucose monomers. The great strength of wood is due largely to the H bonds between cellulose chains. The monomers are linked in a particular way from C-1 in one unit to C-4 in the next. Humans lack the enzymes to break this link, so we cannot digest cellulose (unfortunately!), but microorganisms in the digestive tracts of some animals, such as cows, sheep, and termites, can.

Starch is a mixture of glucose polysaccharides that serves as an *energy store* in plants. When a plant needs energy, some starch is broken down by hydrolysis of the bonds between units, and the released glucose is oxidized through a multistep metabolic pathway. Starch occurs in plant cells as insoluble granules of amylose, a helical molecule of several thousand glucose units, and amylopectin, a highly branched, bushlike molecule of up to a million glucose units. Most of the glucose units are linked by C-1 to C-4 bonds, as in cellulose, but a different bond orientation allows our digestive enzymes to break starch down into monomers. A C-6 to C-1 branch cross-links chains every 24 to 30 units.

Glycogen functions as the energy storage molecule in animals. It occurs in liver and muscle cells as large, insoluble granules consisting of glycogen molecules made from 1000 to more than 500,000 glucose units. In glycogen, the glucose units are linked by C-1 to C-4 bonds also, but the molecule is more highly cross-linked than starch, with C-6 to C-1 cross-links every 8 to 12 units (Figure 15.31).

◆ **Polysaccharide Skeletons of Lobsters and Roaches**
The variety of polysaccharide properties that arises from simple changes in the monomers is amazing. For example, substituting an —NH$_2$ group for the —OH group at C-2 in glucose produces *glucosamine*. The amide of glucosamine with acetic acid (*N*-acetylglucosamine) is the monomer of *chitin* (pronounced "KY-tin"), a polysaccharide that is the main component of the tough, brittle, external skeletons of insects and crustaceans.

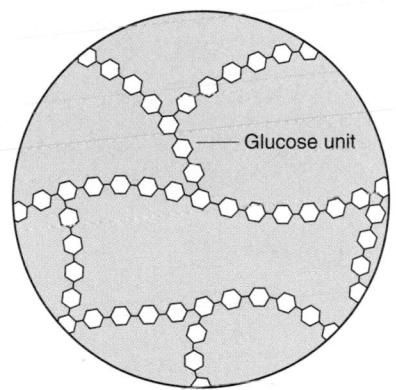

Figure 15.31 **Glycogen, the major storage polysaccharide in animals.** This tiny portion of a tangled glycogen granule shows the highly branched polymer made of glucose units.

Amino Acids and Proteins

As you saw in the previous section, synthetic polyamides (such as nylon-66) are formed from two monomers, one with a carboxyl group at each end and another with an amine group at each end. **Proteins,** the polyamides of nature, are unbranched polymers formed from monomers called **amino acids.** *Each* amino acid monomer has a carboxyl end and an amine end.

Monomer Structure and Linkage   An amino acid has both a carboxyl group and an amine group attached to the *α-carbon,* the second C atom in the chain. In the aqueous cell fluid, these groups are charged because the carboxyl group transfers an H^+ ion to H_2O to form H_3O^+, which transfers the H^+ to the amine group. The overall process is, in effect, an intramolecular acid-base reaction:

Figure 15.32 The common amino acids. About 20 different amino acids occur in proteins. The R groups are screened yellow, and the α-carbons (*boldface*), with carboxyl and amino groups, are screened grey. Here the amino acids are charged as they are under physiological conditions. They are grouped by polarity, acid-base character, and presence of an aromatic ring. The R groups play a major role in the shape and function of the protein.

As you can see, an H atom is the third group bonded to the α-carbon, and the fourth is the R group (also called the *side chain*). Proteins are made up of about 20 different types of amino acids, each with its own particular R group, ranging from an H atom to a polycyclic N-containing aromatic structure, as shown in Figure 15.32.

Figure 15.33 Portion of a polypeptide chain. The peptide bond holds the monomers together in a protein. Three peptide bonds (*orange*) joining four amino acids (*grey*) occur in this portion of a polypeptide chain. Note the repeating pattern of the chain: peptide bond—α-carbon—peptide bond—α-carbon—and so on. Also note that the R groups dangle off the chain.

Each amino acid is linked to the next by a *peptide* (amide) bond in a dehydration-condensation reaction by which the carboxyl group of one monomer reacts with the amine group of the next. Therefore, the repeating unit of the polypeptide chain, the "backbone" of the protein, is an *α-carbon bonded to an amide group bonded to the next α-carbon bonded to the next amide group,* and so on (Figure 15.33). The various R groups dangle from the α-carbons on alternate sides of the chain.

Proteins range in length from about 50 amino acids ($\mathcal{M} \approx 5 \times 10^3$ g/mol) to several thousand ($\mathcal{M} \approx 5 \times 10^5$ g/mol). Even for a relatively small protein of 100 amino acids, the number of possible sequences of the 20 types of amino acids is virtually limitless ($20^{100} \approx 10^{130}$) from a purely mathematical point of view. Only a tiny fraction of these possibilities occur, however; for example, in a species as complex as a human being, there are about 10^5 different types of protein.

Proteins: Composition, Sequence, Shape, and Function *Each type of protein has its own amino acid composition,* the specific number and proportion of the different amino acids. However, it is not the composition that defines the protein's role in the cell; rather, *the sequence of amino acids determines the protein's shape and function.* Shapes vary from long rods to undulating sheets, from baskets with deep crevices to Y-shaped blobs; many proteins have regions of different shapes. The forces responsible for protein shapes are *the same bonding and intermolecular forces that operate for all molecules.* Because proteins are so large, however, these forces often act between distant regions of the same molecule.

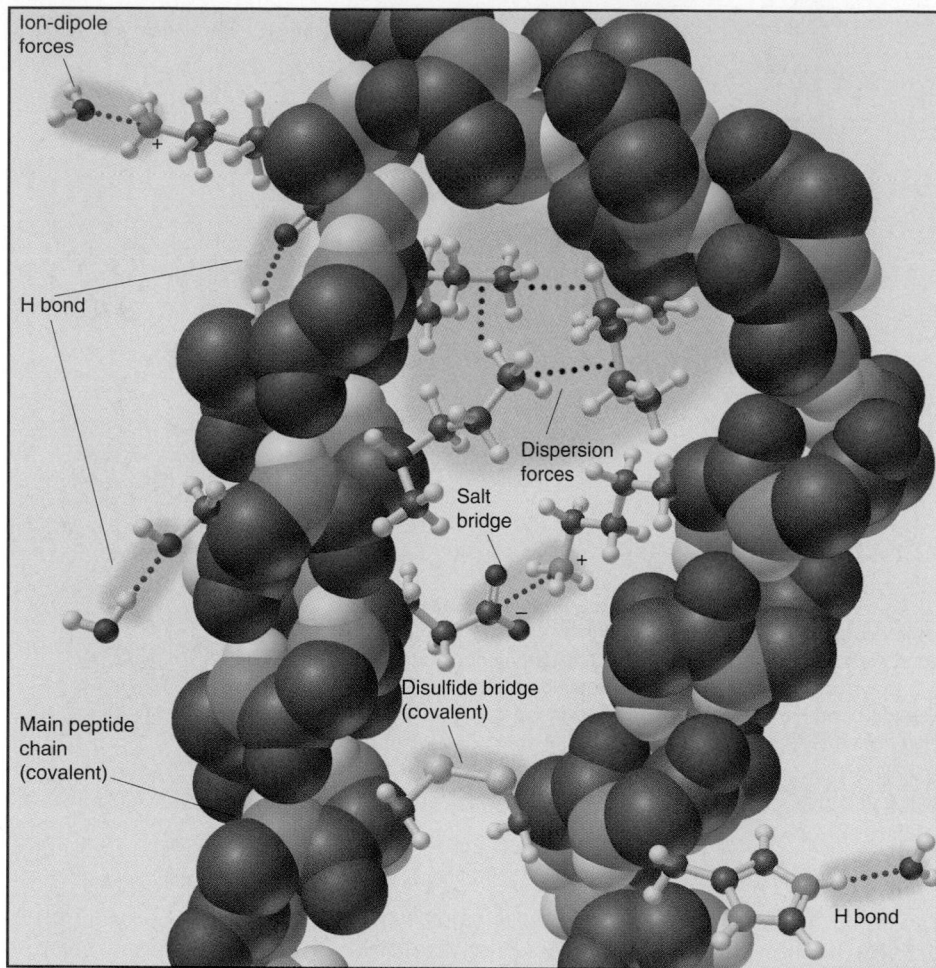

Figure 15.34 The forces that maintain protein structure. In this schematic of a portion of a general protein, ball-and-stick R groups are attached to a space-filling polypeptide chain. A combination of covalent, ionic, and intermolecular forces is responsible for the overall protein shape, which in turn determines the function.

Figure 15.34 is a schematic depiction of the forces operating in many proteins. The covalent peptide bonds create the chain (backbone). The —SH ends of two cysteine R groups (see Figure 15.32) often form an —S—S— bond, a covalent *disulfide bridge* that brings distant parts of the chain together. Polar and ionic R groups usually protrude into the surrounding aqueous fluid, interacting with water through ion-dipole forces and H bonds. Sometimes ionic groups secure the chain's bends through an acidic (—COO⁻) R group lying near a basic (—NH₃⁺) one to form an electrostatic *salt bridge*. Helical and sheetlike segments arise from *H bonds between the C=O of one peptide bond and the N—H of another*. Other H bonds between peptide bond atoms or R groups act to keep distant portions of the chain near each other. Nonpolar R groups usually congregate through dispersion forces within the nonaqueous protein interior.

Two broad classes of proteins differ in the complexity of their amino acid compositions and sequences, and, therefore, in their shape and function:

1. *Fibrous proteins* have relatively simple amino acid compositions, with structures shaped like extended helices or sheets. They are key components of hair, wool, skin, and connective tissue—materials that require strength and flexibility. Like synthetic polymers, these proteins have a small number of

Figure 15.35 **The shapes of fibrous proteins.** Fibrous proteins have largely structural roles in an organism, and their amino acid sequence is relatively simple. **A,** The triple helix of a collagen molecule has a glycine as every third amino acid along the chain. **B,** The "pleated sheet" structure of silk fibroin has a repeating sequence of glycine at every other position with alanine or serine in between. The sheet sections interact through dispersion forces.

different R groups in a repeating sequence. For example, collagen (Figure 15.35A), the most common animal protein, is found in tendons and skin; more than 30% of the R groups come from glycine (G) and another 20% come from proline (P) to create a long, triple helix with the sequence —G—X—P—G—X—P— and so on (where X is another amino acid). In silk fibroin, a protein secreted by the silk moth caterpillar, more than 85% of the R groups come from glycine, serine, and alanine (Figure 15.35B). Fibroin chain segments hydrogen bond to one another to form a "pleated sheet." Stacks of sheets interact through dispersion forces, which make fibroin strong and flexible but not very extendable—perfect for a silkworm's cocoon.

2. *Globular proteins* have much more complex amino acid compositions, often containing varying proportions of all 20 different R groups. As the name implies, globular proteins are typically more rounded and compact, with a wide variety of shapes and a correspondingly wide range of functions: defenders against bacterial invasion, messengers that trigger cell actions, catalysts of chemical change, membrane gatekeepers that maintain aqueous concentrations, and many others. Particular R groups occur at locations crucial to the protein's function. For example, in catalytic proteins, a few R groups form a crevice that closely matches the shapes of reactant molecules. These groups hold the reactants through bonding and intermolecular forces and speed their reaction by bringing them together and twisting and stretching their bonds to form products. Experiment has shown repeatedly that a slight change in one of these critical R groups decreases function dramatically. This fact supports the essential idea that the protein's amino acid sequence determines its structure, which in turn determines its function:

$$\text{SEQUENCE} \Longrightarrow \text{STRUCTURE} \Longrightarrow \text{FUNCTION}$$

As you'll see next, the sequence of amino acids in every protein of every organism is prescribed by the genetic information held within the organism's nucleic acids.

Nucleotides and Nucleic Acids

The chemical information that guides the design, construction, and function of all proteins is contained in **nucleic acids.**

Monomer Structure and Linkage   Nucleic acids are unbranched polymers that consist of monomers called **mononucleotides,** each of which is itself a dehydration-condensation product made from three parts: an N-containing base, a sugar, and a phosphate group (Figure 15.36A). The two types of nucleic acid, *ribonucleic acid* (RNA) and *deoxyribonucleic acid* (DNA), differ in the sugar portions of their mononucleotides. RNA contains *ribose,* a five-C monosaccharide, and DNA contains *deoxyribose,* in which —H substitutes for —OH on the C-2 of ribose.

Dehydration-condensation reactions create phosphate ester links between mononucleotides to give a polynucleotide chain. Therefore, the repeating pattern of the nucleic acid backbone is *sugar linked to phosphate linked to sugar linked to phosphate,* and so on (Figure 15.36B). Attached to each sugar is one of four N-containing bases, either a pyrimidine (six-membered ring) or a purine (six- and five-membered rings sharing a side). The pyrimidines are thymine (T) and cytosine (C); the purines are guanine (G) and adenine (A); in RNA, uracil (U) substitutes for thymine. The bases dangle off the sugar-phosphate chain, much like the R groups dangle off the polypeptide chain of a protein.

Figure 15.36 Mononucleotide monomers and their linkage.
A, Each mononucleotide consists of a base (structure not shown), a sugar, and a phosphate group. In RNA, the sugar is ribose; in DNA, it is 2-deoxyribose (note the absence of an —OH group on C-2 of the ring). **B,** A tiny segment of the polynucleotide chain of DNA shows the phosphate ester link from one sugar portion to the next formed through a dehydration-condensation. Dangling off the chain are the N-containing bases.

Phosphate group

Mononucleotide of ribonucleic acid (RNA)

Mononucleotide of deoxyribonucleic acid (DNA)

A

Portion of DNA polynucleotide chain

B

The Central Importance of Base Pairing In the nucleus of the cell, DNA exists as two chains wrapped around each other in a **double helix** (Figure 15.37). The negatively charged sugar-phosphate backbones face the aqueous surroundings, and each base in one chain "pairs" with a base in the other through H bonding. A double-helical DNA molecule contains hundreds of thousands of H-bonded bases in prescribed pairs. Two features of these **base pairs** are crucial to the structure and function of DNA:

- A pyrimidine and a purine are always paired, which gives the double helix a constant diameter.
- Each base is always paired with the same partner: A with T and G with C. Thus, *the base sequence on one chain is the complement of the base sequence on the other.* For example, the sequence A—C—T on one chain is *always* paired with the sequence T—G—A on the other: A with T, C with G, and T with A.

Each of the DNA molecules is folded into a tangled mass that forms one of the cell's *chromosomes.* The DNA molecule is amazingly long and thin: if the largest human chromosome were stretched out, it would be 4 cm long, although it is crumpled into a structure only 5 nm long—8 million times shorter! Within a chromosome, linear segments of the DNA molecule act as *genes,* chemical blueprints for synthesizing the organism's proteins.

Figure 15.37 The double helix of DNA. In DNA, shown with a short segment of space-filling model (*left*) whose length matches the schematic drawing (*center*), the polar sugar-phosphate backbone faces the watery outside, and the nonpolar bases form H bonds to each other in the DNA core. A pyrimidine and a purine always form H-bonded pairs to maintain the double helix width (*right*), and the members of the pairs are always the same: A with T and G with C.

An Outline of Protein Synthesis   *The information content of a gene resides in its base sequence.* In the **genetic code,** each base acts as a "letter," each three-base sequence as a "word," and *each word codes for a specific amino acid.* For example, the sequence C—A—C codes for the amino acid histidine, A—A—G codes for lysine, and so on. Through a complex series of interactions, greatly simplified in Figure 15.38, one amino acid at a time is positioned and linked to the next in the process of protein synthesis. To fully appreciate just this aspect of the chemical basis of biology, try to keep in mind that *this amazingly complex process occurs largely through H bonding between base pairs.*

Here is an outline of the process of *protein synthesis.* DNA occurs in the cell nucleus, but the genetic message is decoded outside it, so the information must be sent to the synthesis site. RNA serves in this messenger role, as well as in several others. A portion of the DNA is temporarily unwound and acts as a *template* for the formation of a complementary chain of *messenger RNA* made by linking together individual mononucleotides; thus, the DNA code words are transcribed into RNA code words through base pairing. The messenger leaves the nucleus and binds, again through base pairing, to an RNA-rich particle in the cell called a *ribosome.* The words (three-base sequences) in the RNA message are then decoded by molecules of *transfer RNA.* These smaller nucleic acid "shuttles" have two key portions on opposite ends of their structures:

- A three-base sequence that is complementary with a word on the messenger RNA
- A binding site for the amino acid coded by that word

The ribosome moves along the bound messenger, one word at a time, while transfer RNAs bind and position their amino acids near one another in preparation for peptide bond formation. In effect, the message of three-base words is translated into a sequence of amino acids that are then linked to make a protein. Thus, the essence of the process is

DNA BASE SEQUENCE $\Longrightarrow$ RNA BASE SEQUENCE $\Longrightarrow$ PROTEIN AMINO ACID SEQUENCE

① *Portion of DNA unwinds and mRNA is transcribed*

DNA

Amino acids

② *tRNA binds a specific amino acid*

Nucleus

tRNA

④ *Peptide bond forms, adding amino acid to growing chain*

③ *Loaded tRNA binds to complementary bases on ribosome-bound mRNA*

⑤ *Ribosome moves along mRNA and sequence of 3-base words is translated into amino acid sequence in protein*

mRNA

Ribosome

Figure 15.38 **The key stages in protein synthesis.**

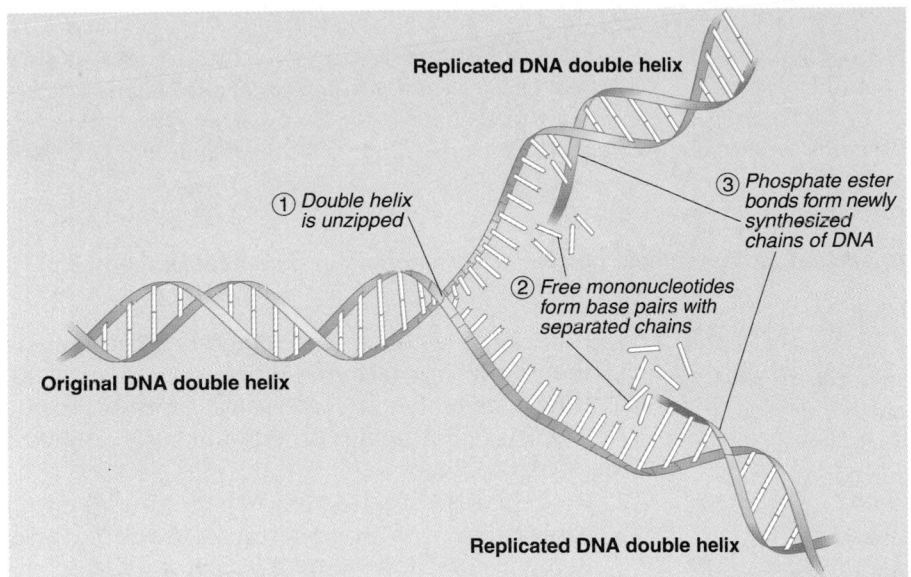

Figure 15.39 **The key stages in DNA replication.**

An Outline of DNA Replication Another complex series of interactions allows *DNA replication*, the ability of DNA to copy itself. When a cell divides, its chromosomes are replicated, or reproduced, ensuring that the new cells have the same number and types of chromosomes. In this process, a small portion of the double helix is "unzipped," and each DNA chain acts as a template for the base pairing of monomers (Figure 15.39). As the next portion unzips, monomers in the first portion are covalently linked together to make a chain. Gradually, each of these new chains forms the complementary half of a double helix, leading to *two* double helices. Because a given base always pairs with its complement, the original double helix is copied and the genetic makeup of the cells is maintained.

The biopolymers provide striking evidence for the folly of vitalism, the idea with which we began the chapter, that there exists some sort of vital force that is found only in substances from living systems. No unknowable force exclusive to living things is required to explain the marvels of the living world. The same atomic properties that give rise to covalent bonds, molecular shape, and intermolecular forces provide the means for all life forms to flourish.

Section Summary

The three natural polymers—polysaccharides, proteins, and nucleic acids—are formed by dehydration-condensation reactions. Polysaccharides are formed from cyclic monosaccharides, such as glucose. Cellulose, starch, and glycogen have structural or energy-storage roles. Proteins are polyamides formed from as many as 20 different types of amino acids. Fibrous proteins have extended shapes and structural roles. Globular proteins have compact shapes and metabolic, immunologic, and hormonal roles. The amino acid sequence of a protein determines its shape and function. Nucleic acids (DNA and RNA) are polynucleotides formed from four different mononucleotides. The base sequence of the DNA chain determines the sequence of amino acids in an organism's proteins. Hydrogen bonding between specific base pairs is the key to protein synthesis and gene replication.

Chapter Perspective

The amazing diversity of organic compounds highlights the importance of atomic properties in chemical and biological behavior. While gaining an appreciation for the special properties of carbon, you've seen similar types of bonding, shapes, intermolecular forces, and reactivity in organic and inorganic compounds. Upcoming chapters focus on the dynamic aspects of all reactions—their speed, extent, and direction—as we explore the kinetics, equilibrium, and thermodynamics of chemical and physical change. We'll have many opportunities to exemplify these topics with organic compounds and biochemical systems.

The following learning objectives, with section and/or sample problem (SP) numbers in parentheses, can help focus your study:

Understand These Concepts

1. How carbon's atomic properties give rise to its ability to form four strong covalent bonds, multiple bonds, and bonds to itself, which results in the great structural diversity of organic compounds (Section 15.1)
2. How carbon's atomic properties give rise to its ability to bond heteroatoms, which creates regions of charge imbalance that result in functional groups (Section 15.1)
3. Structures and names of alkanes, alkenes, and alkynes (Section 15.2)
4. The distinctions among constitutional, optical, and geometric isomers (Section 15.2)
5. The importance of optical isomerism in organisms (Section 15.2)
6. The effect of restricted rotation around a π bond on alkene structure and properties (Section 15.2)
7. The nature of organic addition, elimination, and substitution reactions (Section 15.3)
8. The properties and reaction types of the various functional groups (Section 15.4):
   - Substitution and elimination for alcohols, alkyl halides, and amines
   - Addition for alkenes, alkynes, and aldehydes and ketones
   - Substitution for the carboxylic acid family (acids, esters, amides)
9. Why electron delocalization leads to lower reactivity of aromatic rings compared to alkenes (Section 15.4)
10. The polarity of the carbonyl bond and the importance of organometallic compounds in their addition reactions (Section 15.4)
11. How addition plus elimination lead to substitution in the reactions of the carboxylic acid family (Section 15.4)
12. How addition and condensation polymers form (Section 15.5)
13. The three types of natural biopolymers and their monomers (Section 15.6)
14. How the nature of amino acid R groups and intermolecular forces influence the shape of a protein (Section 15.6)

15. How amino acid sequence determines protein shape, which determines function (Section 15.6)
16. How complementary base-pairing controls the processes of protein synthesis and DNA replication (Section 15.6)
17. How the DNA base sequence determines the RNA base sequence, which determines the amino acid sequence (Section 15.6)

Master These Skills

1. Determining hydrocarbon structures given the number of C atoms, multiple bonds, and rings (SP 15.1)
2. Naming hydrocarbons and drawing expanded and condensed formulas (Section 15.2 and SP 15.2)
3. Drawing geometric isomers and identifying chiral centers of molecules (SP 15.2)
4. Recognizing the type of reaction from the structures of reactants and products (SP 15.3)
5. Recognizing a reaction as an oxidation or reduction from the structures of reactants and products (Section 15.3)
6. Determining the reactants and products of the reactions of alcohols, alkyl halides, and amines (SP 15.4 and Follow-up)
7. Determining the products in a stepwise reaction sequence (SP 15.5)
8. Determining the reactants of the reactions of aldehydes and ketones (Follow-up to SP 15.5)
9. Determining the reactants and products of the reactions of the carboxylic acid family (SP 15.6 and Follow-up)
10. Recognizing and naming the functional groups in an organic molecule (SP 15.7)
11. Drawing an abbreviated synthetic polymer structure based on monomer structures (Section 15.5)
12. Drawing small peptides from amino acid structures (Section 15.6)
13. Using the base-paired sequence of one DNA strand to predict the sequence of the other (Section 15.6)

For Review and Reference

Key Terms

organic compound
Section 15.1
heteroatom
functional group
Section 15.2
hydrocarbon
alkane (C_nH_{2n+2})
homologous series
saturated hydrocarbon
cyclic hydrocarbon
isomers
constitutional (structural) isomers
stereoisomers
optical isomers
chiral molecule
polarimeter

optically active
alkene (C_nH_{2n})
unsaturated hydrocarbon
geometric (*cis-trans*) isomers
alkyne (C_nH_{2n-2})
aromatic hydrocarbon
nuclear magnetic resonance (NMR) spectroscopy
Section 15.3
alkyl group
addition reaction
elimination reaction
substitution reaction
Section 15.4
alcohol
haloalkane (alkyl halide)
amine

carbonyl group
aldehyde
ketone
organometallic compound
carboxylic acid
ester
amide
fatty acid
acid anhydride
lipid
hydrolysis
nitrile
Section 15.5
polymer
monomer
addition polymer
condensation polymer

Section 15.6
monosaccharide
polysaccharide
disaccharide
protcin
amino acid
nucleic acid
mononucleotide
double helix
base pair
genetic code

Highlighted Figures and Tables

These figures (F) and tables (T) provide a quick review of key ideas.
F15.5 Adding H atoms to the C-atom skeleton (p. 609)
T15.1 Roots for carbon chains and branches (p. 611)
T15.2 Naming an organic compound (p. 612)

T15.5 Important functional groups (p. 627)
F15.27 Interconversions of functional groups (p. 640)
F15.33 Portion of polypeptide chain (p. 647)
F15.34 Forces that maintain protein structure (p. 648)
F15.36 The monomers of RNA and DNA (p. 650)

Answers to Follow-up Problems

5.1 (a)

(b)

Answers to Follow-up Problems *(continued)*

15.2 (a) $CH_3-CH_2-CH_2-CH_2-CH_2-\underset{\underset{CH_3}{|}}{\overset{\overset{CH_2-CH_3}{|}}{C}}-CH_2-CH_3$

(b)

CH$_2$—CH$_2$—CH$_3$

CH$_2$—CH$_3$

(c) $HC\equiv C-\underset{\underset{CH_2-CH_3}{|}}{\overset{\overset{CH_2-CH_3}{|}}{C}}-CH_2-CH_2-CH_3$

(d)

$\underset{CH_3}{\overset{CH_3-CH_2}{\diagdown}}C=C\underset{CH_2-CH_2-CH_3}{\overset{H}{\diagup}}$

15.3 (a) $CH_3-CH=CH-CH_3 + H_2O \xrightarrow{H^+}$

$\underset{\underset{OH}{|}}{CH_3-\overset{|}{CH}-CH_2-CH_3}$

(b) $CH_3-CH_2-CH_2-Br + OH^- \longrightarrow$

$CH_3-CH_2-CH_2-OH + Br^-$

(c) $CH_3-\underset{\underset{Cl}{|}}{CH}-CH_3 + CH_3-ONa \longrightarrow$

$CH_3-CH=CH_2 + NaCl + CH_3-OH$

15.4 (a) $CH_3-\underset{\underset{Cl}{|}}{CH}-CH-CH_3$ or $CH_3-CH_2-\underset{\underset{Cl}{|}}{\overset{\overset{CH_3}{|}}{C}}-CH_3$

(b) $CH_3-CH_2-CH_2-OH$

15.5 (a)

OH

CH$_3$

(b)

$\overset{O}{\overset{||}{C}}-H$

15.6 (a)

$CH_2-\overset{O}{\overset{||}{C}}-OH$

(b) $CH_3-CH_2-CH_2-\overset{O}{\overset{||}{C}}-O-CH_3 + CH_3-CH_2-NH_2$

15.7 (a)

$CH=CH$ $\overset{O}{\overset{||}{C}}-H$

alkene   aldehyde

(b) $H_2N-\overset{O}{\overset{||}{C}}-CH_2-\underset{\underset{Br}{|}}{CH}-CH_3$

amide

haloalkane

Problems

Problems with a **colored** number are answered at the back of the text. Problem sections match the text and provide the number(s) of relevant sample problems. Most offer concept review questions, skill-building exercises (written in similar pairs), and problems in a relevant context. Following these are comprehensive problems based on material from any section and/or previous chapter.

The Special Nature of Carbon and the Characteristics of Organic Molecules

■ **Concept Review Questions**

15.1 Give the name and formula of two carbon compounds that are organic and two that are inorganic.

15.2 Through the first quarter of the 19th century, the idea of vitalism proposed that a key difference existed between substances isolated from animate sources and those from inanimate sources. What was the central notion of vitalism? Give an example of a finding that led to its eventual downfall.

15.3 Explain each statement in terms of atomic properties:
(a) Carbon engages in covalent rather than ionic bonding.
(b) Carbon has four bonds in all its organic compounds.

(c) Carbon forms neither stable cations, like many metals, nor stable anions, like many nonmetals.
(d) Carbon bonds to itself more extensively than does any other element.
(e) Carbon forms stable multiple bonds.

15.4 Carbon bonds to many elements other than itself.
(a) Name six elements that commonly bond to carbon in organic compounds.
(b) Which of these elements are heteroatoms?
(c) Which of these elements are more electronegative than carbon? Less electronegative?
(d) How does bonding of carbon to heteroatoms increase the number of organic compounds?

15.5 Silicon lies just below carbon in Group 4A(14) and also forms four covalent bonds. Why aren't there as many silicon compounds as carbon compounds?

15.6 What is the range of oxidation states for carbon? Name a compound in which carbon has its highest oxidation state and one in which it has its lowest.

15.7 Which of the following bonds to carbon would you expect to be relatively reactive: C—H, C—C, C—I, C=O, C—Li? Explain.

The Structures and Classes of Hydrocarbons
(Sample Problems 15.1 and 15.2)

■ Concept Review Questions

15.8 (a) What structural feature is associated with each of the following hydrocarbons: an alkane; a cycloalkane; an alkene; an alkyne?
(b) Give the general formula for each.
(c) Which are considered "saturated"?

15.9 Define each of the following types of isomers: (a) constitutional; (b) geometric; (c) optical. Which types of isomers are stereoisomers?

15.10 Among alkenes, alkynes, and aromatic hydrocarbons, only alkenes exhibit *cis-trans* isomerism. Explain why the others do not.

15.11 Which objects are asymmetric (have no plane of symmetry): (a) a circular clock face; (b) a football; (c) a dime; (d) a brick; (e) a hammer; (f) a spring?

15.12 Explain briefly how a polarimeter works and what it measures.

15.13 How does an aromatic hydrocarbon differ from a cycloalkane in terms of its bonding? How does this difference affect structure?

■ Skill-Building Exercises (paired)

15.14 Draw all possible skeletons for a 7-C compound with
(a) A 6-C chain and 1 double bond
(b) A 5-C chain and 1 double bond
(c) A 5-C ring and no double bonds

15.15 Draw all possible skeletons for a 6-C compound with
(a) A 5-C chain and 2 double bonds
(b) A 5-C chain and 1 triple bond
(c) A 4-C ring and no double bonds

15.16 Add the correct number of hydrogens to each of the skeletons in Problem 15.14.

15.17 Add the correct number of hydrogens to each of the skeletons in Problem 15.15.

15.18 Draw correct structures, by making a single change, for any that are incorrect:

(a) $CH_3-CH-CH_2-CH_3$ with CH_3 above and CH_3 below

(b) $CH_3=CH-CH_2-CH_3$

(c) $CH\equiv C-CH_2-CH_3$ with CH_2 and CH_3 below

(d) CH_3- ⟨benzene ring⟩ $-CH_3$

15.19 Draw correct structures, by making a single change, for any that are incorrect:
(a) $CH_3-CH=CH-CH_2-CH_3$

(b) cyclopentene ring with CH_3 and CH_3

(c) $CH_3-C\equiv CH-CH_2-CH_3$

(d) $CH_3-CH_2-\overset{\overset{\displaystyle CH_3}{|}}{C}-CH_2-CH_2-CH_3$

15.20 Draw the structure or give the name of the following:
(a) 2,3-dimethyloctane
(b) 1-ethyl-3-methylcyclohexane

(c) $CH_3-CH_2-\overset{\overset{\displaystyle CH_3}{|}}{CH}-\overset{\overset{\displaystyle }{|}}{CH}-CH_2$ with CH_3 and CH_2-CH_3 below

(d) $CH_3-\overset{\overset{\displaystyle CH_3}{|}}{\underset{\underset{\displaystyle CH_3\,CH_3}{|}}{C}}-CH_2$

15.21 Draw the structure or give the name of the following:

(a) $CH_3-\overset{\overset{\displaystyle CH_3}{|}}{CH}-CH_2-CH_3$

(b) H_3C ⟨cyclohexane ring⟩ with CH_3, CH_3

(c) 1,2-diethylcyclopentane
(d) 2,4,5-trimethylnonane

15.22 Each of the following names is wrong. Draw structures based on them and correct the names:
(a) 4-methylhexane   (b) 2-ethylpentane
(c) 2-methylcyclohexane   (d) 3,3-methyl-4-ethyloctane

15.23 Each of the following names is wrong. Draw structures based on them and correct the names:
(a) 3,3-dimethylbutane   (b) 1,1,1-trimethylheptane
(c) 1,4-diethylcyclopentane (d) 1-propylcyclohexane

15.24 Each of the following compounds can exhibit optical activity. Circle the chiral center(s) in each:

(a) structure with H, H, C, Cl, H, H
(b) structure

15.25 Each of the following compounds can exhibit optical activity. Circle the chiral center(s) in each:

(a) cyclopentene structure

(b)

15.26 Draw structures from the following names and determine which compounds are optically active:
(a) 3-bromohexane
(b) 3-chloro-3-methylpentane
(c) 1,2-dibromo-2-methylbutane

15.27 Draw structures from the following names and determine which compounds are optically active:
(a) 1,3-dichloropentane
(b) 3-chloro-2,2,5-trimethylhexane
(c) 1-bromo-1-chlorobutane

15.28 Which of the following structures exhibit geometric isomerism? Draw and name the two isomers in each case:

(a) CH_3—CH_2—CH=CH—CH_3 (b) ⬡—CH=CH—CH_3

(c) CH_3—$\overset{\overset{\displaystyle CH_3}{|}}{C}$=$CH$—$\overset{\overset{\displaystyle CH_3}{|}}{CH}$—$CH_2$—$CH_3$

15.29 Which of the following structures exhibit geometric isomerism? Draw and name the two isomers in each case:

(a) CH_3—$\overset{\overset{\displaystyle CH_3}{|}}{\underset{\underset{\displaystyle CH_3}{|}}{C}}$—$CH$=$CH$—$CH_3$ (b) CH_3—$\overset{\overset{\displaystyle CH_3}{|}}{C}$=$CH$—$CH_3$

(c) Cl—CH_2—CH=$\overset{\overset{\displaystyle CH_3}{|}}{C}$—$CH_2$—$CH_2$—$CH_2$—$CH_3$

15.30 Which compounds exhibit geometric isomerism? Draw and name the two isomers in each case:
(a) propene
(b) 3-hexene
(c) 1,1-dichloroethene
(d) 1,2-dichloroethene

15.31 Which compounds exhibit geometric isomerism? Draw and name the two isomers in each case:
(a) 1-pentene
(b) 2-pentene
(c) 1-chloropropene
(d) 2-chloropropene

15.32 Draw and name all the constitutional isomers of dichlorobenzene.

15.33 Draw and name all the constitutional isomers of trimethylbenzene.

▪ Problems in Context

15.34 "Butylated hydroxytoluene" (BHT) is a common preservative added to cereals and other dry foods. Its systematic name is 1-hydroxy-2,6-di-*tert*-butyl-4-methylbenzene (where "*tert*-butyl" is 1,1-dimethylethyl). Draw the structure of BHT.

15.35 There are two compounds with the name 2-methyl-3-hexene, but only one with the name 2-methyl-2-hexene. Explain with structures.

15.36 The explosive TNT is one of six isomers of trinitrotoluene (see p. 621). Draw and name the other five.

15.37 Ethanol and dimethyl ether are constitutional isomers with the molecular formula C_2H_6O.
(a) Draw their structures.
(b) Aside from the TMS peak, how many peaks representing different proton environments appear in the ^1H NMR spectrum of each isomer?

Some Important Classes of Organic Reactions

(Sample Problem 15.3)

▪ Concept Review Questions

15.38 In terms of numbers of reactant and product substances, which organic reaction type corresponds to

(a) a combination reaction, (b) a decomposition reaction, (c) a displacement reaction?

15.39 The same bond type is broken in an addition reaction and formed in an elimination reaction. Name the bond type.

15.40 Can a redox reaction also be an addition, elimination, or substitution reaction? Explain with examples.

Skill-Building Exercises (*paired*)

15.41 Determine the type of each of the following reactions:

(a) CH_3—CH_2—$\overset{\overset{\displaystyle Br}{|}}{CH}$—$CH_3$ $\xrightarrow[\Delta]{NaOH}$
CH_3—CH=CH—CH_3 + $NaBr$ + H_2O

(b) CH_3—CH=CH—CH_2—CH_3 + H_2 $\xrightarrow{Pt}$
CH_3—CH_2—CH_2—CH_2—CH_3

15.42 Determine the type of each of the following reactions:

(a) CH_3—$\overset{\overset{\displaystyle O}{||}}{CH}$ + HCN $\longrightarrow$ CH_3—$\overset{\overset{\displaystyle OH}{|}}{CH}$—$CN$

(b) CH_3—$\overset{\overset{\displaystyle O}{||}}{C}$—$O$—$CH_3$ + CH_3—NH_2 $\xrightarrow{H^+}$
CH_3—$\overset{\overset{\displaystyle O}{||}}{C}$—$NH$—$CH_3$ + CH_3—OH

15.43 Write equations for the following:
(a) An addition reaction between H_2O and 3-hexene (H^+ is a catalyst)
(b) An elimination reaction between 2-bromopropane and hot potassium ethoxide, CH_3—CH_2—OK
(c) A light-induced substitution reaction between Cl_2 and ethane to form 1,1-dichloroethane

15.44 Write equations for the following:
(a) A substitution reaction between 2-bromopropane and KI
(b) An addition reaction between cyclohexene and Cl_2
(c) An addition reaction between 2-propanone and H_2 (Ni metal is a catalyst)

15.45 Based on the number of bonds and the nature of the bonded atoms, state whether each of the following changes is an oxidation or a reduction:
(a) =CH_2 becomes —CH_2—OH
(b) =CH— becomes —CH_2—
(c) ≡C— becomes —CH_2—

15.46 Based on the number of bonds and the nature of the bonded atoms, state whether each of the following changes is an oxidation or a reduction:

(a) —$\overset{\overset{\displaystyle |}{}}{\underset{\underset{\displaystyle |}{}}{C}}$—$OH$ becomes —C=O

(b) —CH_2—OH becomes =CH_2

(c) —$\overset{\overset{\displaystyle O}{||}}{C}$—$\overset{\overset{\displaystyle O}{||}}{\underset{\underset{\displaystyle |}{}}{C}}$— becomes —$\overset{\overset{\displaystyle O}{||}}{C}$—$O$—

15.47 Is the organic reactant oxidized, reduced, or neither in each of the following reactions?

(a) 2-hexene $\xrightarrow[\text{cold } OH^-]{KMnO_4}$ 2,3-dihydroxyhexane

(b) cyclohexane $\xrightarrow[\text{catalyst}]{\Delta}$ benzene + $3H_2$

15.48 Is the organic reactant oxidized, reduced, or neither in each of the following reactions?

(a) 1-butyne + H_2 $\xrightarrow{\text{Pt}}$ 1-butene

(b) toluene $\xrightarrow[\text{H}_3\text{O}^+, \Delta]{\text{KMnO}_4}$ benzoic acid

Problems in Context

15.49 Phenylethylamine is a natural substance that resembles amphetamine structurally. It is found in sources as diverse as almond oil and human urine, where it occurs at elevated concentrations due to stress and certain forms of schizophrenia. One method of synthesis for pharmacological and psychiatric studies involves two steps:

Classify each step as an addition, elimination, or substitution.

Properties and Reactivity of Common Functional Groups
(Sample Problems 15.4 to 15.7)

■ Concept Review Questions

15.50 Compounds with nearly identical molar masses often have very different physical properties. Choose the compound with the higher value for each of the following properties, and explain your choice:
(a) Solubility in water: chloroethane or methylethylamine
(b) Melting point: diethyl ether or 1-butanol
(c) Boiling point: trimethylamine or propylamine

15.51 Fill in each blank with a general formula for the type of compound formed:

15.52 Of the three major types of organic reactions, which do *not* occur readily with benzene? Why?

15.53 Why does the C=O group react differently from the C=C group? Show an example of the difference.

15.54 Many substitution reactions involve an initial electrostatic attraction between reactants. Show this attraction in the formation of an amide from an amine and an ester.

15.55 Although carboxylic acids and alcohols both contain an —OH group, one is acidic in water and the other is not. Explain.

15.56 What reaction type is common to the formation of esters and acid anhydrides? What is the other product?

15.57 Alcohols and carboxylic acids both undergo substitution, but the processes are very different. Explain.

Skill-Building Exercises (paired)

15.58 Name the type of organic compound from the following description of its functional group:
(a) Polar single-bonded group that does not include O or N
(b) Triple-bonded group that is polar

(c) Single- and double-bonded group that is acidic in water
(d) Double-bonded group that must be at the end of a carbon chain

15.59 Name the type of organic compound from the following description of its functional group:
(a) N-containing single- and double-bonded group
(b) Double-bonded group that is not polar
(c) Polar double-bonded group that cannot be at the end of a carbon chain
(d) Single-bonded group that is basic in water

15.60 In each of the following, circle and name the functional group(s):

15.61 In each of the following, circle and name the functional group(s):

15.62 Draw all possible alcohols with the formula $C_5H_{12}O$.

15.63 Draw all possible aldehydes and ketones with the formula $C_5H_{10}O$.

15.64 Draw all possible amines with the formula $C_4H_{11}N$.

15.65 Draw all possible carboxylic acids with the formula $C_5H_{10}O_2$.

15.66 Draw the product resulting from mild oxidation of
(a) 2-butanol; (b) 2-methylpropanal; (c) cyclopentanol.

15.67 Draw the alcohol you would oxidize to produce
(a) 2-methylpropanal; (b) 2-pentanone; (c) 3-methylbutanoic acid.

15.68 Draw the organic product formed when the following compounds undergo a substitution reaction:
(a) Acetic acid and methylamine
(b) Butanoic acid and 2-propanol
(c) Formic acid and 2-methyl-1-propanol

15.69 Draw the organic product formed when the following compounds undergo a substitution reaction:
(a) Acetic acid and 1-hexanol
(b) Propanoic acid and dimethylamine
(c) Ethanoic acid and diethylamine

15.70 Draw structures for the carboxylic acid and alcohol portions of the following esters:

(a) $CH_3-(CH_2)_4-\overset{\overset{\displaystyle O}{\|}}{C}-O-CH_2-CH_3$

(b) $\overset{\overset{\displaystyle O}{\|}}{C}-O-CH_2-CH_2-CH_3$

(c) $CH_3-CH_2-O-\overset{\overset{\displaystyle O}{\|}}{C}-CH_2-CH_2-$

15.71 Draw structures for the carboxylic acid and amine portions of the following amides:

(a) H_3C- $-CH_2-\overset{\overset{\displaystyle O}{\|}}{C}-NH_2$

(b) $CH_3-\overset{\overset{\displaystyle CH_3}{|}}{CH}-\overset{\overset{\displaystyle O}{\|}}{C}-\underset{\underset{\displaystyle CH_3}{|}}{N}-CH_2-CH_3$

(c) $H\overset{\overset{\displaystyle O}{\|}}{C}-NH-$

15.72 Fill in the expected organic products:

(a) $CH_3-CH_2-Br \xrightarrow{OH^-} \underline{\quad} \xrightarrow[H^+]{CH_3-CH_2-\overset{\overset{\displaystyle O}{\|}}{C}-OH} \underline{\quad}$

(b) $CH_3-CH_2-\overset{\overset{\displaystyle Br}{|}}{CH}-CH_3 \xrightarrow{CN^-} \underline{\quad} \xrightarrow{H_3O^+, H_2O} \underline{\quad}$

15.73 Fill in the expected organic products:

(a) $CH_3-CH_2-CH=CH_2 \xrightarrow{H^+, H_2O} \underline{\quad} \xrightarrow{Cr_2O_7^{2-}, H^+} \underline{\quad}$

(b) $CH_3-CH_2-\overset{\overset{\displaystyle O}{\|}}{C}-CH_3 \xrightarrow{CH_3-CH_2-Li} \xrightarrow{H_2O} \underline{\quad}$

15.74 Supply the missing organic and/or inorganic substances:

(a) $CH_3-CH_2-OH + \underline{\quad ? \quad} \xrightarrow{?} CH_3-CH_2-O-\overset{\overset{\displaystyle O}{\|}}{C}-CH_2-CH_3$

(b) $CH_3-\overset{\overset{\displaystyle O}{\|}}{C}-O-CH_3 \xrightarrow{?} CH_3-CH_2-NH-\overset{\overset{\displaystyle O}{\|}}{C}-CH_3$

15.75 Supply the missing organic and/or inorganic substances:

(a) $CH_3-\overset{\overset{\displaystyle Cl}{|}}{CH}-CH_3 \xrightarrow{?} CH_3-CH=CH_2 \xrightarrow{?} CH_3-\overset{\overset{\displaystyle Br}{|}}{CH}-\overset{\overset{\displaystyle Br}{|}}{CH_2}$

(b) $CH_3-CH_2-CH_2-OH \xrightarrow{?} CH_3-CH_2-\overset{\overset{\displaystyle O}{\|}}{C}-OH + \underline{\quad ? \quad} \xrightarrow{?}$

$CH_3-CH_2-\overset{\overset{\displaystyle O}{\|}}{C}-O-CH_2-$

■ **Problems in Context**

15.76 Which of the following compounds is highly soluble in water? Explain.

(a) $CH_3-CH_2-CH=CH_2$ (b) $CH_3-CH_2-CH_2-OH$

(c) $CH_3-CH_2-CH_2-NH_2$ (d) $CH_3-CH_2-\overset{\overset{\displaystyle O}{\|}}{C}-OH$

(e) $CH_3-(CH_2)_6-\overset{\overset{\displaystyle O}{\|}}{C}-OH$ (f) $CH_3-CH_2-\overset{\overset{\displaystyle Br}{|}}{CH}-CH_3$

15.77 Ethyl formate $(H\overset{\overset{\displaystyle O}{\|}}{C}-O-CH_2-CH_3)$ is commonly added to foods to give them the flavoring of rum. How would you synthesize ethyl formate from ethanol, methanol, and any inorganic reagents?

The Monomer-Polymer Theme I: Synthetic Macromolecules

■ **Concept Review Questions**

15.78 Name the reaction processes that lead to the two types of synthetic polymers.

15.79 Which functional group is common to the monomers that make up addition polymers? What makes these polymers different from one another?

15.80 What is a free radical? How is it involved in polymer formation?

15.81 Which intermolecular force is primarily responsible for the different types of polyethylene? Explain.

15.82 Which of the two types of synthetic polymer is more similar chemically to biopolymers? Explain.

15.83 Which two functional groups react to form nylons? Polyesters?

■ **Skill-Building Exercises** *(paired)*

15.84 Draw an abbreviated structure for the following polymers, with brackets around the repeating unit:

(a) Poly(vinyl chloride) (PVC) from $\overset{\overset{\displaystyle H}{\diagup}}{\underset{\underset{\displaystyle H}{\diagdown}}{}}C=C\overset{\overset{\displaystyle H}{\diagdown}}{\underset{\underset{\displaystyle Cl}{\diagup}}{}}$

(b) Polypropylene from $\overset{\overset{\displaystyle H}{\diagup}}{\underset{\underset{\displaystyle H}{\diagdown}}{}}C=C\overset{\overset{\displaystyle H}{\diagdown}}{\underset{\underset{\displaystyle CH_3}{\diagup}}{}}$

15.85 Draw an abbreviated structure for the following polymers, with brackets around the repeating unit:

(a) Teflon from $\overset{\overset{\displaystyle F}{\diagup}}{\underset{\underset{\displaystyle F}{\diagdown}}{}}C=C\overset{\overset{\displaystyle F}{\diagdown}}{\underset{\underset{\displaystyle F}{\diagup}}{}}$

(b) Polystyrene from $\overset{\overset{\displaystyle H}{\diagup}}{\underset{\underset{\displaystyle H}{\diagdown}}{}}C=C\overset{\overset{\displaystyle H}{\diagdown}}{\underset{\underset{\displaystyle \text{C}_6\text{H}_5}{\diagup}}{}}$

15.86 Write a balanced equation for the reaction between 1,4-benzenedicarboxylic acid and 1,2-dihydroxyethane to form the polyester Dacron. Draw an abbreviated structure for the polymer, with brackets around the repeating unit.

15.87 Write a balanced equation for the reaction of dihydroxydimethylsilane,

$$HO—\overset{\overset{\displaystyle CH_3}{|}}{\underset{\underset{\displaystyle CH_3}{|}}{Si}}—OH$$

to form the condensation polymer popularly known as Silly Putty.

The Monomer-Polymer Theme II: Biological Macromolecules

■ Concept Review Questions

15.88 Which type of polymer is formed from each of the following monomers: (a) amino acids; (b) alkenes; (c) simple sugars; (d) mononucleotides?

15.89 What is the key structural difference between fibrous and globular proteins? How is it related, in general, to the amino acid composition?

15.90 Protein shape, function, and amino acid sequence are interrelated. Arrange them in order of which determines which.

15.91 What type of functional group bonds the monomers to each other in each strand of DNA?

15.92 What is base pairing? How does it pertain to the structure of DNA?

15.93 RNA base sequence, protein amino acid sequence, and DNA base sequence are interrelated. Arrange them in order of which determines which in the process of protein synthesis.

■ Skill-Building Exercises (paired)

15.94 Draw the structure of the R group of (a) alanine; (b) histidine; (c) methionine.

15.95 Draw the structure of the R group of (a) glycine; (b) isolcucine; (c) tyrosine.

15.96 Draw the structure of the following tripeptides:
(a) Aspartic acid-histidine-tryptophan
(b) Glycine-cysteine-tyrosine with the charges that exist in cell fluid

15.97 Draw the structure of the following tripeptides:
(a) Lysine-phenylalanine-threonine
(b) Alanine-leucine-valine with the charges that exist in cell fluid

15.98 Write the sequence of the complementary DNA strand that pairs with each of the following DNA base sequences:
(a) TTAGCC; (b) AGACAT.

15.99 Write the sequence of the complementary DNA strand that pairs with each of the folowing DNA base sequences:
(a) GGTTAC; (b) CCCGAA.

15.100 Write the base sequence of DNA template from which the following RNA sequence was derived: UGUUACGGA. How many amino acids are coded for in this sequence?

15.101 Write the base sequence of DNA template from which the following RNA sequence was derived:

GUAUCAAUGAACUUG. How many amino acids are coded for in this sequence?

■ Problems in Context

15.102 Protein shapes are maintained by a variety of forces that arise through interaction between the amino acid R groups. Name the amino acid that possesses the R group and tell the force that could arise in each of the following interactions:

(a) —CH$_2$—SH with HS—CH$_2$—

(b) —(CH$_2$)$_4$—NH$_3^+$ with $\overset{\displaystyle O}{\overset{\|}{^-O—C—CH_2—}}$

(c) —CH$_2$—$\overset{\overset{\displaystyle O}{\|}}{C}$—NH$_2$ with HO—CH$_2$—

(d) —$\overset{\overset{\displaystyle CH_3}{|}}{CH}$—CH$_3$ with ⬡—CH$_2$—

15.103 What force is responsible for the helix and pleated sheet structures seen in so many proteins? From which groups do they arise?

Comprehensive Problems

Problems with an asterisk (*) are more challenging.

*15.104 Starting with the given organic reactant and any necessary inorganic reagents, explain how you would perform each of the following syntheses:
(a) Starting with CH$_3$—CH$_2$—CH$_2$—OH , make

$$CH_3—\overset{\overset{\displaystyle Br}{|}}{CH}—CH_2—Br$$

(b) Starting with CH$_3$—CH$_2$—OH , make

$$CH_3—\overset{\overset{\displaystyle O}{\|}}{C}—O—CH_2—CH_3$$

*15.105 Ethers (general formula, R—O—R′) have many important uses. Methyl *tert*-butyl ether (MTBE, see structure) has been shown to be an excellent octane booster and clean fuel additive for gasoline. It increases the oxygen content of the fuel, which reduces CO emissions during winter months in accord with the Clean Air Act. MTBE is synthesized by reacting 2-methylpropene with methanol.

(a) Write a balanced equation for the synthesis of MTBE. (*Hint:* Alcohols add to alkenes in a manner similar to water.)
(b) If the government requires that auto fuel mixtures contain 2.7% by mass oxygen to reduce CO emissions, how many grams of MTBE must be added to each 100. g gasoline?
(c) How many liters of MTBE are present in each liter of fuel mixture? The density of both gasoline and MTBE is 0.740 g/mL.

(d) How many liters of air, which is approximately 21% O_2 by volume, are needed at 24°C and 1.00 atm to fully combust 1.00 L MTBE?

15.106 Compound X has the formula C_4H_8O and reacts readily with $K_2Cr_2O_7$ in H_2SO_4 to yield a carboxylic acid. X is synthesized from 2-methyl-l-propanol. Give a structure of compound X.

*15.107 Some of the most useful compounds for organic synthesis are Grignard reagents, for the development of which Victor Grignard and Paul Sabatier were awarded the Nobel Prize in 1912. These compounds (general formula R—MgX, where X is a halogen) are made from R—X with Mg in ether solvent and used to change the carbon skeleton of the starting carbonyl reactant in a reaction similar to those with R—Li:

(a) What is the product, after a final reaction step with water, of the reaction between ethanal and the Grignard reagent of bromobenzene?

(b) What is the product, after a final step with water, of the reaction between 2-butanone and the Grignard reagent of 2-bromopropane?

(c) There are often two (or more) combinations of Grignard reagent and carbonyl compound that will give the same product. Choose another pair of reactants to give the product in (a).

(d) What carbonyl compound must react with a Grignard reagent to obtain the —OH group at the *end* of the carbon chain?

(e) What Grignard reagent and carbonyl compound would you use to prepare 2-methyl-2-butanol?

15.108 A synthesis of 2-butanol was performed by treating 2-bromobutane with hot sodium hydroxide solution. The yield was 60%, indicating that a significant portion of the reactant was converted into a second product. Predict what this other product might be. What simple test would support your prediction?

15.109 The "octane number" of a gasoline sample is determined by comparing its combustion characteristics to a pure compound called "isooctane." The systematic name for isooctane is 2,2,4-trimethylpentane. Draw its structure.

15.110 Pyrethrins, such as jasmolin II (shown below), are a group of natural compounds that are synthesized by pyrethrum flowers to act as insecticides. (a) Circle and name the functional groups in jasmolin II. (b) What is the hybridization of the numbered carbons? (c) Which, if any, of the numbered carbons are chiral centers?

15.111 Taste can often be affected by relatively small changes in a molecule. For example, Compound A (shown below) tastes 4000 times sweeter than glucose, whereas Compound B has no taste. If the —NH_2 group is attached to ring carbon 1, aminobenzene is called "aniline," and CH_3—CH_2—CH_2—O is called a "propoxy" group, name Compounds A and B.

*15.112 Benzophenone is a ketone with two benzene rings as R groups. It is used as a fixative for perfumes and soaps, and in the manufacture of antihistamines. Suggest a method for its synthesis, starting with benzene, benzaldehyde, and any inorganic reagents. (*Hint:* Make an organometallic compound.)

15.113 Following Wöhler's synthesis of urea from an inorganic compound, many other organic substances were similarly synthesized. Explain how the reaction between calcium carbide (CaC_2) and water violates the notion of vitalism.

15.114 Which features of retinal make it so useful as a photon absorber in the visual systems of organisms?

*15.115 Cadaverine (1,5-diaminopentane) and putrescine (1,4-diaminobutane) are two compounds formed by bacterial action that are responsible for the odor of rotting flesh. Draw their structures. Suggest a series of reactions to synthesize putrescine from 1,2-dibromoethane and any inorganic reagents.

15.116 The polypeptide chain in proteins does not rotate freely because of partial double-bond character of the peptide bond. Explain this fact with resonance structures.

*15.117 Although other nonmetals form many compounds that are structurally analogous to those of carbon, the inorganic compounds are usually more reactive. Predict any missing products and write balanced equations for each of the following:

(a) The decomposition and chlorination of diborane to boron trichloride

(b) The combustion of pentaborane (B_5H_9) in O_2

(c) The addition of water to the double bonds of borazine ($B_3N_3H_6$, Figure 14.9). (*Hint:* The —OH group bonds to B.)

(d) The hydrolysis of trisilane (Si_3H_8) to silica (SiO_2) and H_2

(e) The complete halogenation of disilane with Cl_2

(f) The thermal decomposition of H_2S_5 to hydrogen sulfide and sulfur molecules

(g) The hydrolysis of PCl_5

*15.118 The genetic code consists of a series of three-base words that each code for a given amino acid.

(a) Using the selections from the genetic code shown below, determine the amino acid sequence coded by the following segment of RNA:

UCCACAGCCUAUAUGGCAAACUUGAAG

AUG = methionine	CCU = proline	CAU = histidine
UGG = tryptophan	AAG = lysine	UAU = tyrosine
GCC = alanine	UUG = leucine	CGG = arginine
UGU = cysteine	AAC = asparagine	ACA = threonine
UCC = serine	GCA = alanine	UCA = serine

(b) What is the complementary DNA sequence from which this RNA sequence was made?

*15.119 Citral, the main odor constituent in oil of lemon grass, is used extensively in the flavoring and perfume industries. It occurs naturally as a mixture of the geometric isomers geranial (the *trans* isomer) and neral (the *cis* isomer). Its systematic name is 3,7-dimethyl-2,6-octadienal ("dien" refers to two C=C groups). Draw the structures of geranial and neral.

*15.120 Complete hydrolysis of a 100.00-g sample of a peptide gave the following amounts of individual amino acids (molar masses appear in parentheses): 3.00 g glycine (75.07); 0.90 g alanine (89.10); 3.70 g valine (117.15); 6.90 g proline (115.13); 7.30 g serine (105.10); and 86.00 g arginine (174.21).

(a) Why does the total mass of amino acids exceed the mass of peptide?

(b) What are the relative numbers of amino acids in the peptide?

(c) What is the minimum molar mass of the peptide?

15.121 Thiols (or mercaptans) are the sulfur analogs of alcohols; that is, S appears in the molecule in place of O. Many occur naturally, and all have very disagreeable odors.

They are named by adding the suffix "thiol" to the entire parent hydrocarbon name or by using "mercapto" as a prefix.

(a) Draw the structure of a compound in skunk musk, 3-methyl-1-butanethiol.

(b) Write a reaction to convert 3-mercapto-1-propene (found in garlic) to propanethiol (found in onion).

*15.122 2-Butanone is reduced by hydride ion donors, such as sodium borohydride ($NaBH_4$), to the alcohol 2-butanol. Even though the alcohol has a chiral center, the product isolated from the redox reaction is not optically active. Explain.

*15.123 Sodium propanoate (CH_3—CH_2—$\overset{\overset{\displaystyle O}{\|}}{C}$—ONa) is a common preservative found in breads, cheeses, and pies. How would you synthesize sodium propanoate from 1-propanol and any inorganic reagents?

15.124 It has been said that "the hydrogen bond is the most important intermolecular force in nature." Give five cases to support this statement.

15.125 Because of the behavior of their R groups in water, lysine is classified as a basic amino acid and aspartic acid as an acidic amino acid. Write balanced equations that demonstrate this behavior.

16

Kinetics
Rates and Mechanisms of Chemical Reactions

Figure: Reaction rate and survival. Evidence continues to mount that, unlike modern reptiles, many dinosaurs, such as the speedy predator *Velociraptor*, could generate sufficient body heat to maintain metabolic reactions at high rates. In this chapter, you'll see how the rates of reactions are influenced by several factors, including temperature, and how chemists have learned to control them.

Throughout the natural and industrial worlds, wherever chemical reactions are taking place, matter and energy are changing continuously. Until now we've taken a rather simple approach to reactions: reactants mix and products form. A balanced equation is a convenient shorthand for a reaction and an essential quantitative tool for calculating product yields from reactant amounts. However, an equation tells us nothing about three dynamic aspects of the reaction, which are essential to understanding chemical change and which we examine in the next several chapters:

- How fast is the reaction proceeding at a given moment?
- What will the reactant and product concentrations be when the reaction is complete?
- Will the reaction proceed by itself and release energy, or will it require energy to proceed?

In this chapter, we address the first of these questions and focus on the field of *kinetics,* which deals with the speed of a reaction and its mechanism, the stepwise changes reactants undergo in their conversion to products. Chapters 17 through 19 are concerned with *equilibrium,* the dynamic balance between forward and reverse reactions and how external influences alter reactant and product concentrations. Chapters 20 and 21 present *thermodynamics* and its application to electrochemistry; there, we investigate why a reaction occurs and how we can put it to use. These central subdisciplines of chemistry apply to all physical and chemical change and, thus, are essential to our understanding of modern technology, the environment, and our own biology.

Chemical kinetics is the study of *reaction rates,* the changes in concentrations of reactants (or products) as a function of time (Figure 16.1).

Figure 16.1 Reaction rate: the central focus of chemical kinetics. The rate at which reactant becomes product is the underlying theme of chemical kinetics. As time elapses, reactant *(purple) decreases* and product *(green) increases.*

Reactions, as you probably realize, occur at a wide range of rates (Figure 16.2, next page). Some, like a neutralization, a precipitation, or an explosive redox process, seem to be over as soon as the reactants make contact—in a fraction of a second. Others, such as the reactions involved in cooking or rusting, take a moderate length of time, from minutes to months. Still others take much longer: the reactions that make up the human aging process continue for decades, and those in the formation of coal from dead plants take hundreds of millions of years.

A

B

C

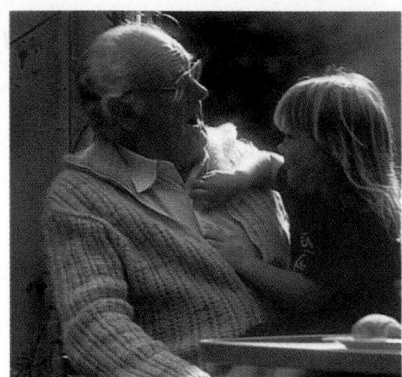

D

Figure 16.2 **The wide range of reaction rates.** Reaction processes occur at a wide range of rates. An explosion **(A)** is much faster than the process of ripening **(B)**, which is much faster than the process of rusting **(C)**, which is much faster than the process of human aging **(D)**.

Knowing how fast a chemical change occurs can be extremely important. How quickly a medicine acts or blood clots can make the difference between life and death. How long it takes for cement to harden, polyethylene to form, or a fabric to be dyed can make the difference between profit and loss. In general, the rates of these diverse processes depend on the same variables, most of which chemists can manipulate to maximize yields within a given time or to slow down an unwanted reaction.

We begin with a qualitative overview of the factors affecting reaction rate. Then we see how to express a rate quantitatively in the form of a *rate law*, how the components of a rate law are experimentally determined, and how concentration and temperature affect the rate. Next, we examine the models that explain those effects. Only then can we take apart the overall reaction, see the stages it may go through, and picture the structure that exists fleetingly at the moment the reactant bonds are breaking and the product bonds are forming. The chapter ends with a discussion of how catalysts increase reaction rates, highlighting the role of catalysts in two vital areas of nature—the depletion of atmospheric ozone and the reactions of a living cell.

16.1   Factors That Influence Reaction Rate

Let's begin our study of kinetics with a qualitative look at the key factors that affect how fast a reaction proceeds. Under any given set of conditions, *each reaction has its own characteristic rate*, which is determined by the chemical nature of the reactants. At room temperature, for example, hydrogen reacts explosively with fluorine but extremely slowly with nitrogen:

$$H_2(g) + F_2(g) \longrightarrow 2HF(g) \qquad \text{[very fast]}$$
$$3H_2(g) + N_2(g) \longrightarrow 2NH_3(g) \qquad \text{[very slow]}$$

Iron reacts slowly with oxygen and water but much more quickly than does aluminum:

$$2Fe(s) + \tfrac{3}{2}O_2(g) + nH_2O(l) \longrightarrow Fe_2O_3 \cdot nH_2O(s; \text{ rust}) \qquad \text{[slow but measurable]}$$
$$2Al(s) + \tfrac{3}{2}O_2(g) + nH_2O(l) \longrightarrow Al_2O_3 \cdot nH_2O(s) \qquad \text{[too slow to measure]}$$

Thus, one key aspect of the diverse chemical behavior of the elements is the variation in the rates of their reactions with other substances.

We can control four factors that affect the rate of a given reaction: the concentrations of reactants, the physical state of reactants, the temperature at which the reaction occurs, and the use of a catalyst. We'll consider the first three factors here and discuss the fourth later in the chapter.

1. *Concentration: molecules must collide to react.* A major factor influencing the rate of a given reaction is reactant concentration. Consider the reaction between ozone and nitric oxide that occurs in the stratosphere, where the oxide is released in the exhaust gases of supersonic aircraft:

$$NO(g) + O_3(g) \longrightarrow NO_2(g) + O_2(g)$$

Imagine what this reaction might look like at the molecular level if the reactants were confined in a reaction vessel. Nitric oxide and ozone molecules zoom every which way, crashing into each other and the vessel walls. A reaction between NO and O_3 cannot occur from a distance: it can occur only when the molecules collide. The more molecules present in the container, the more frequently they collide, and therefore the more often a reaction occurs. Thus, *reaction rate is proportional to the concentration of reactants:*

$$\text{Rate} \propto \text{collision frequency} \propto \text{concentration}$$

In this case, we're looking at a very simple reaction, one in which reactant molecules collide and form product molecules in one step, but even the rates of complex reactions depend on reactant concentration.

2. *Physical state: molecules must mix to collide.* The frequency of collisions between molecules also depends on the physical states of the reactants. When the reactants are in the same phase, as in aqueous solution, thermal motion brings them into contact. When they are in different phases, contact can occur only at the interface, so vigorous stirring and grinding may be needed. In these cases, the degree to which the reactant material is divided affects the rate significantly: *the more finely divided a solid or liquid reactant, the greater its surface area per unit volume, the more contact it makes with the other reactant, and the faster the reaction.* Figure 16.3 shows a steel nail heated in oxygen glowing feebly, but finely divided steel wool bursting into flame. The oil-burner nozzle of a furnace produces a fine spray of oil because small droplets make greater contact with the incoming air. Likewise, you start a campfire with wood chips and thin branches, not logs.

A   B

Figure 16.3 **The effect of surface area on reaction rate. A,** A nail heated and then thrust into O_2 just glows. **B,** Finely divided steel treated the same way bursts into flame. The steel wool has more surface area per unit volume than the nail, so more metal makes contact with O_2 and the reaction is faster.

Figure 16.4 **Collision energy and reaction rate.** Although many NO-O₃ collisions occur, relatively few have enough energy to cause reaction. At this temperature, only collision *a* is energetic enough to lead to product; the reactant molecules in collisions *b*, *c*, and *d* just bounce off each other unchanged.

3. *Temperature: molecules must collide with enough energy to react.* Temperature usually has a major effect on the speed of a reaction. Recall that molecules in a sample of gas have a range of speeds, with the most probable speed dependent on the temperature (see Figure 5.14, p. 200). Thus, *at a higher temperature, more collisions occur in a given time.* Even more important, however, is the fact that temperature affects the kinetic energy of the molecules, and thus the *energy* of the collisions. In the jumble of molecules in the NO-O₃ reaction mentioned previously, most collisions simply result in the molecules recoiling, like billiard balls, with no reaction taking place. However, some collisions occur with such force that the molecules react (Figure 16.4). At a higher temperature, more collisions occur with *enough energy* to react. Thus, *raising the temperature increases the reaction rate by increasing the number and, especially, the energy of the collisions:*

$$\text{Rate} \propto \text{collision energy} \propto \text{temperature}$$

Two familiar kitchen appliances employ this effect: a refrigerator slows down chemical processes that spoil food, whereas an oven speeds up other chemical processes that cook it.

The qualitative idea that reaction rate is influenced by the frequency and energy of reactant collisions leads to several quantitative questions: How can we describe the dependence of rate on reactant concentration mathematically? Do all changes in concentration affect the rate to the same extent? Do all rates increase to the same extent by a given rise in temperature? How do reactant molecules use the energy of collision to form product molecules, and is there a way to determine this energy? What do the reactants look like as they are turning into products? We address these questions in the following sections.

Section Summary

Chemical kinetics deals with reaction rates and the stepwise molecular events by which a reaction occurs. Under a given set of conditions, each reaction has its own rate. Concentration affects rate by influencing the frequency of collisions between reactant molecules. Physical state affects rate by determining the surface area per unit volume of reactants. Temperature affects rate by influencing the frequency but, even more importantly, the energy of the collisions.

16.2 Expressing the Reaction Rate

Before we can deal quantitatively with the effects of concentration and temperature on reaction rate, we must be able to express the rate mathematically. A rate is a change in some variable per unit of time. The most common examples relate to the rate of motion (speed) of an object, which is the change in its position divided by the change in time. Suppose, for instance, we measure a racehorse's starting position (x_1) and time (t_1) and its final position (x_2) and time (t_2). The horse's average speed is given by

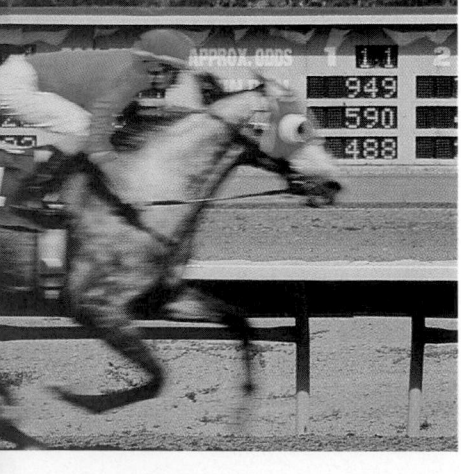

$$\text{Rate of motion} = \frac{\text{change in position}}{\text{change in time}} = \frac{x_2 - x_1}{t_2 - t_1} = \frac{\Delta x}{\Delta t}$$

In the case of a chemical change, we are concerned with the **reaction rate,** the changes in concentrations of reactants or products per unit time: *reactant concentrations decrease while product concentrations increase.* Consider a general reaction, A ⟶ B. We measure the starting reactant concentration (conc A₁) at t_1, allow the reaction to proceed, and then measure the reactant concentration again (conc A_2) at t_2. The change in concentration divided by the change in time gives the *average* rate:

$$\text{Rate of reaction} = -\frac{\text{change in concentration of A}}{\text{change in time}}$$

$$= -\frac{\text{conc } A_2 - \text{conc } A_1}{t_2 - t_1} = -\frac{\Delta(\text{conc A})}{\Delta t}$$

Note the minus sign. By convention, reaction rate is a *positive* number, but conc A_2 will always be *lower* than conc A_1, so the *change in (final − initial) concentration of reactant A is always negative*. We use the minus sign simply to convert the negative change in reactant concentration to a positive value for the rate. Suppose the concentration of A changes from 1.2 mol/L (conc A_1) to 0.75 mol/L (conc A_2) over a 125-s period. The average rate is

$$\text{Rate} = -\frac{0.75 \text{ mol/L} - 1.2 \text{ mol/L}}{125 \text{ s} - 0 \text{ s}} = 3.6 \times 10^{-3} \text{ mol/L} \cdot \text{s}$$

We use *square brackets [ ] to express concentration in moles per liter*. Thus, [A] is the concentration of A in mol/L, so the rate expressed in terms of A is

$$\text{Rate} = -\frac{\Delta[A]}{\Delta t} \qquad \textbf{(16.1)}$$

The rate has units of moles per liter per second (mol/L · s), or whatever time unit is convenient for the reaction under study (minutes, years, and so on).

If instead we measure the product to determine the reaction rate, we find its concentration *increasing* over time. That is, conc B_2 is always *higher* than conc B_1, so the *change* in product concentration, $\Delta[B]$, is *positive* and the reaction rate for A $\longrightarrow$ B expressed in terms of B is

$$\text{Rate} = \frac{\Delta[B]}{\Delta t}$$

Average, Instantaneous, and Initial Reaction Rates

Examining the rate of a real reaction reveals an important point: *the rate itself varies with time as the reaction proceeds.* Consider the reversible gas-phase reaction between ethylene and ozone, one of many possible reactions in the formation of photochemical smog:

$$C_2H_4(g) + O_3(g) \rightleftharpoons C_2H_4O(g) + O_2(g)$$

For now, we consider only reactant concentrations. You can see from the equation coefficients that for every molecule of C_2H_4 that reacts, a molecule of O_3 reacts with it. In other words, the concentrations of both reactants decrease at the same rate in this particular reaction:

$$\text{Rate} = -\frac{\Delta[C_2H_4]}{\Delta t} = -\frac{\Delta[O_3]}{\Delta t}$$

By experimentally monitoring the concentration of either reactant, we can follow the rate of the reaction as it proceeds.

Suppose we have a known concentration of O_3 in a closed reaction vessel kept at 30°C (303 K). Table 16.1 shows the concentration of O_3 at various times during the first minute after we introduce C_2H_4 gas into the vessel. The rate over the entire 60.0 s is the total change in concentration divided by the change in time:

$$\text{Rate} = -\frac{\Delta[O_3]}{\Delta t} = -\frac{(1.10 \times 10^{-5} \text{ mol/L}) - (3.20 \times 10^{-5} \text{ mol/L})}{60.0 \text{ s} - 0.0 \text{ s}}$$

$$= 3.50 \times 10^{-7} \text{ mol/L} \cdot \text{s}$$

Table 16.1 O_3 Concentration at Various Times in Its Reaction with C_2H_4 at 303 K

Time (s)	Concentration of O_3 (mol/L)
0.0	3.20×10^{-5}
10.0	2.42×10^{-5}
20.0	1.95×10^{-5}
30.0	1.63×10^{-5}
40.0	1.40×10^{-5}
50.0	1.23×10^{-5}
60.0	1.10×10^{-5}

This calculation gives us the **average rate** over that period; that is, during the first 60.0 s of the reaction, ozone concentration decreases an *average* of 3.50×10^{-7} mol/L each second. However, the average rate does not show that the rate is changing, and it tells us nothing about how fast the ozone concentration is decreasing *at any given instant.*

We can see that the rate changes during the reaction by calculating the average rate over two shorter periods—one earlier and one later. Between the starting time 0.0 s and 10.0 s, the average rate is

$$\text{Rate} = -\frac{\Delta[O_3]}{\Delta t} = -\frac{(2.42 \times 10^{-5} \text{ mol/L}) - (3.20 \times 10^{-5} \text{ mol/L})}{10.0 \text{ s} - 0.0 \text{ s}}$$
$$= 7.80 \times 10^{-7} \text{ mol/L} \cdot \text{s}$$

During the last 10.0 s, between 50.0 s and 60.0 s, the average rate is

$$\text{Rate} = -\frac{\Delta[O_3]}{\Delta t} = -\frac{(1.10 \times 10^{-5} \text{ mol/L}) - (1.23 \times 10^{-5} \text{ mol/L})}{60.0 \text{ s} - 50.0 \text{ s}}$$
$$= 1.30 \times 10^{-7} \text{ mol/L} \cdot \text{s}$$

The earlier rate is six times as fast as the later rate. Thus, *the rate decreased during the course of the reaction.* This makes perfect sense from a molecular point of view: as O_3 molecules are used up, fewer of them are present to collide with C_2H_4, so the rate decreases.

The change in rate can also be seen by plotting the concentrations vs. the times at which they were measured (Figure 16.5). A curve is obtained, which

Figure 16.5 The concentration of O_3 vs. time during its reaction with C_2H_4. A plot of the data in Table 16.1 gives a curve because the rate changes as the reaction proceeds. The *average* rate over a given period is the slope of a line joining any two points along the curve. The slope of line *b* is the average rate over the first 60.0 s of the reaction. The slopes of lines *c* and *e* give the average rate over the first and last 10.0-s intervals, respectively. Line *c* is steeper than line *e* because the average rate over the earlier period is higher. The *instantaneous* rate at 35.0 s is the slope of line *d*, the tangent to the curve at $t = 35.0$ s. The *initial* rate is the slope of line *a*, the tangent to the curve at $t = 0.0$ s.

means that the rate changes. *The slope of the line ($\Delta y/\Delta x$, that is, $\Delta[O_3]/\Delta t$) joining any two points gives the average rate over that period.*

The shorter the time period we choose, the closer we come to the **instantaneous rate,** the rate at a particular instant during the reaction. *The slope of a line tangent to the curve at a particular point gives the instantaneous rate at that time.* For example, the rate of the reaction 35.0 s after it began is 2.50×10^{-7} mol/L · s, the slope of the line drawn tangent to the curve through the point at which $t = 35.0$ s (line *d* in Figure 16.5). In general, we use the term "reaction rate" to mean the *instantaneous* reaction rate.

As a reaction continues, the product concentrations increase, so the reverse reaction proceeds more quickly. To find the overall (net) rate, we would have to take both forward and reverse reactions into account and calculate the difference between their rates. A common way to avoid this complication for many reactions is to measure the **initial rate,** the instantaneous rate at the moment the reactants are mixed. Under these conditions, the product concentrations are negligible, so the reverse rate is negligible. Moreover, we know the reactant concentrations simply from the concentrations and volumes of the solutions we mix together. The initial rate is measured by determining the slope of the line tangent to the curve at $t = 0$. In Figure 16.5, the initial rate is 10.0×10^{-7} mol/L · s (line *a*). Unless stated otherwise, we will use initial rate data to determine other kinetic parameters.

Expressing Rate in Terms of Reactant and Product Concentrations

So far, in our discussion of the O_3-C_2H_4 reaction, we've expressed the rate in terms of the decreasing concentration of O_3. The rate is the same in terms of C_2H_4, but it is exactly the opposite in terms of the products: their concentrations are *increasing* as the reaction proceeds. From the balanced equation, we see that one molecule of C_2H_4O and of O_2 appears for every molecule of C_2H_4 and of O_3 that disappears. We can express the rate in terms of any of the four substances involved:

$$\text{Rate} = -\frac{\Delta[C_2H_4]}{\Delta t} = -\frac{\Delta[O_3]}{\Delta t} = +\frac{\Delta[C_2H_4O]}{\Delta t} = +\frac{\Delta[O_2]}{\Delta t}$$

Again, note the negative values for the reactants and the positive values for the products (usually written without the plus sign). Figure 16.6 shows a plot of the simultaneous monitoring of one reactant and one product. Because, in this case, product concentration increases at the same rate that reactant concentration decreases, the curves have the same shapes but are inverted.

In the reaction between ethylene and ozone, the reactants disappear and the products appear at the same rate because all the coefficients in the balanced equation equal one. Consider next the reaction between hydrogen and iodine to form hydrogen iodide:

$$H_2(g) + I_2(g) \longrightarrow 2HI(g)$$

For every molecule of H_2 that disappears, one molecule of I_2 disappears and *two* molecules of HI appear. In other words, the rate of [H_2] decrease is the same as the rate of [I_2] decrease, but both are only half the rate of [HI] increase. By referring the change in [I_2] and [HI] to the change in [H_2], we have

$$\text{Rate} = -\frac{\Delta[H_2]}{\Delta t} = -\frac{\Delta[I_2]}{\Delta t} = \frac{1}{2}\frac{\Delta[HI]}{\Delta t}$$

If we refer the change in [H_2] and [I_2] to the change in [HI] instead, we obtain

$$\text{Rate} = \frac{\Delta[HI]}{\Delta t} = -2\frac{\Delta[H_2]}{\Delta t} = -2\frac{\Delta[I_2]}{\Delta t}$$

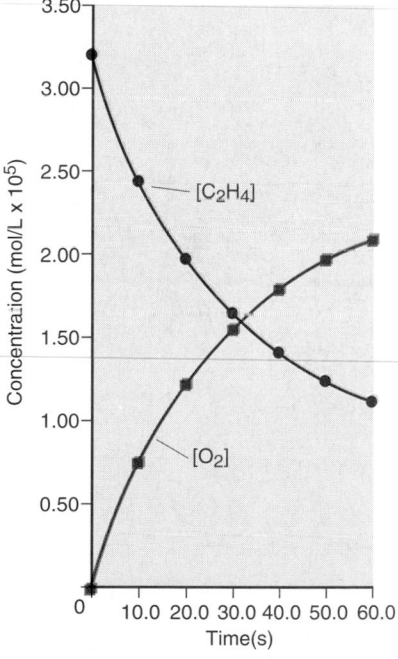

Figure 16.6 Plots of [C₂H₄] and [O₂] vs. time. In this reaction, simultaneous monitoring of reactant [C_2H_4] and product [O_2] gives curves of identical shape changing in opposite directions. The steep upward (positive) slope of [O_2] early in the reaction mirrors the steep downward (negative) slope of [C_2H_4] because the faster C_2H_4 is used up, the faster O_2 is formed. The curve shapes are identical in this case because the equation coefficients are identical.

Notice that this expression is just a rearrangement of the previous one; also note that it gives a numerical value for the rate that is double the previous value. Thus, the mathematical expression for the rate of a particular reaction and *the numerical value of the rate depend on which substance serves as the reference*.

We can summarize these results for any reaction:

$$aA + bB \longrightarrow cC + dD$$

where *a*, *b*, *c*, and *d* are coefficients of the balanced equation. In general, the rate is related to reactant or product concentrations as follows:

$$\text{Rate} = -\frac{1}{a}\frac{\Delta[A]}{\Delta t} = -\frac{1}{b}\frac{\Delta[B]}{\Delta t} = \frac{1}{c}\frac{\Delta[C]}{\Delta t} = \frac{1}{d}\frac{\Delta[D]}{\Delta t} \qquad \textbf{(16.2)}$$

Sample Problem 16.1   Expressing Rate in Terms of Changes in Concentration with Time

PROBLEM Because of its non-polluting product gases, hydrogen gas is used for fuel aboard the Space Shuttle and may be used in Earth-bound engines of the future:

$$2H_2(g) + O_2(g) \longrightarrow 2H_2O(g)$$

(a) Express the rate of this reaction in terms of changes in $[H_2]$, $[O_2]$, and $[H_2O]$ with time.
(b) When $[O_2]$ is decreasing at 0.23 mol/L · s, at what rate is $[H_2O]$ increasing?
PLAN **(a)** Of the three substances in the equation, let's choose O_2 as the reference because its coefficient is 1. For every molecule of O_2 that disappears, two molecules of H_2 disappear, so the rate of $[O_2]$ decrease is one-half the rate of $[H_2]$ decrease. By similar reasoning, we see that the rate of $[O_2]$ decrease is one-half the rate of $[H_2O]$ increase. **(b)** Because $[O_2]$ is decreasing, the change in its concentration must be negative. We substitute the negative value into the expression and solve for $\Delta[H_2O]/\Delta t$.
SOLUTION **(a)** Expressing the rate in terms of each component:

$$\text{Rate} = -\frac{1}{2}\frac{\Delta[H_2]}{\Delta t} = -\frac{\Delta[O_2]}{\Delta t} = \frac{1}{2}\frac{\Delta[H_2O]}{\Delta t}$$

(b) Calculating the rate of change of $[H_2O]$:

$$\frac{1}{2}\frac{\Delta[H_2O]}{\Delta t} = -\frac{\Delta[O_2]}{\Delta t} = -(-0.23 \text{ mol/L} \cdot \text{s})$$

$$\frac{\Delta[H_2O]}{\Delta t} = 2 \times 0.23 \text{ mol/L} \cdot \text{s} = \boxed{0.46 \text{ mol/L} \cdot \text{s}}$$

CHECK **(a)** A good check is to use the rate expression to obtain the balanced equation: $[H_2]$ changes twice as fast as $[O_2]$, so two H_2 react for each O_2. $[H_2O]$ changes twice as fast as $[O_2]$, so two H_2O form from each O_2. From this reasoning, we get $2H_2 + O_2 \longrightarrow 2H_2O$. The $[H_2]$ and $[O_2]$ decrease, so they take minus signs; $[H_2O]$ increases, so it takes a plus sign. Another check is to use Equation 16.2, where we have A = H_2, *a* = 2; B = O_2, *b* = 1; C = H_2O, *c* = 2. Thus,

$$\text{Rate} = -\frac{1}{a}\frac{\Delta[A]}{\Delta t} = -\frac{1}{b}\frac{\Delta[B]}{\Delta t} = \frac{1}{c}\frac{\Delta[C]}{\Delta t}$$

or $$\text{Rate} = -\frac{1}{2}\frac{\Delta[H_2]}{\Delta t} = -\frac{\Delta[O_2]}{\Delta t} = \frac{1}{2}\frac{\Delta[H_2O]}{\Delta t}$$

(b) Given the rate expression, it makes sense for the numerical value of the rate of $[H_2O]$ increase to be twice that of $[O_2]$ decrease.
COMMENT Thinking through this type of problem at the molecular level is the best approach, but use Equation 16.2 to confirm your answer.

Follow-up Problem 16.1   **(a)** Balance the following equation and express the rate in terms of changes in concentration with time for each substance: $NO(g) + O_2(g) \longrightarrow N_2O_3(g)$.
(b) How fast is $[O_2]$ decreasing when $[NO]$ is decreasing at 1.60×10^{-4} mol/L · s?

Section Summary

The average reaction rate is the change in reactant (or product) concentration over a change in time, Δt. The rate slows as reactants are used up. The instantaneous rate at time t is obtained from the slope of the tangent to a concentration-time curve at time t. The initial rate, the instantaneous rate at $t = 0$, occurs when reactants are just mixed and before any product accumulates. The expression for a reaction rate and its value depend on which reaction component is being monitored.

16.3 The Rate Law and Its Components

The centerpiece of any kinetic study is the **rate law** (or **rate equation**) for the reaction in question. The rate law expresses the rate as a function of reactant concentrations, product concentrations, and temperature. Since the rate law is based on experimental fact, any hypothesis we make about how the reaction occurs on the molecular level must conform to it.

In our discussion, we'll generally consider only reactions for which the products are not involved in the rate law. In these cases, *the reaction rate depends only on reactant concentrations and temperature*. In this section, we consider the effect of concentration on rate for reactions occurring at a fixed temperature. For a general reaction,

$$a\text{A} + b\text{B} + \cdots \longrightarrow c\text{C} + d\text{D} + \cdots$$

the rate law has the form

$$\text{Rate} = k[\text{A}]^m[\text{B}]^n \ldots \tag{16.3}$$

The proportionality constant k, called the **rate constant,** is specific for a given reaction at a given temperature; it does *not* change as the reaction proceeds. (As you'll see later, k *does* change with temperature and therefore determines how temperature affects the rate.) The exponents m and n, called the **reaction orders,** define how the rate is affected by the concentration of each reactant. For example, if the rate doubles when [A] doubles, the rate depends on [A] raised to the first power, $[\text{A}]^1$, so $m = 1$; if the rate quadruples when [B] doubles, the rate depends on [B] raised to the second power, $[\text{B}]^2$, so $n = 2$. Keep in mind that the coefficients a and b in the general balanced equation are *not* necessarily related in any way to the reaction orders m and n.

A key point to remember is that *the components of the rate law—rate, reaction orders, and rate constant—must be found by experiment;* they *cannot* be deduced from the reaction stoichiometry. So let's take an experimental approach to finding the components by

1. Using concentration measurements to find the *initial rate.*
2. Using initial rates from several experiments to find the *reaction orders.*
3. Using these values to calculate the *rate constant.*

Once we know the rate law, we can use it to *predict* the rate for any initial reactant concentrations.

Determining the Initial Rate

In the last section, we showed how initial rates are determined from a plot of concentration vs. time. Since we use initial rate data to determine the reaction orders and rate constant, an accurate experimental method for measuring concentration at various times during the reaction is the key to constructing the rate law. A few of the many techniques used for measuring changes in reactant or product concentration over time are presented in the following Tools of the Chemistry Laboratory essay.

Tools of the Chemistry Laboratory

Measuring Reaction Rates

Speculation about how a reaction occurs at the molecular level must be based on measurement of reaction rates. There are many experimental approaches, but all must obtain the results quickly and reproducibly. We consider four common methods, with specific examples.

Spectrometric Methods

These methods are used to measure the concentration of a reactant or product that absorbs (or emits) light of a narrow range of wavelengths. The reaction is typically performed *within* the sample compartment of a spectrometer set to measure a wavelength characteristic of one of the species (Figure 16.A; see also Tools of the Chemistry Laboratory, pp. 271–272). For example, in the NO-O_3 reaction, only NO_2 has a color:

$$NO(g, \text{colorless}) + O_3(g, \text{colorless}) \longrightarrow$$
$$O_2(g, \text{colorless}) + NO_2(g, \text{brown})$$

Known amounts of reactants are injected into a gas sample tube of known volume, and the rate of NO_2 formation is measured by monitoring the color over time. Reactions in aqueous solution are studied similarly.

Conductometric Methods

When non-ionic reactants form ionic products, or vice versa, the change in conductivity of the solution over time can be used to measure the rate. Electrodes are immersed in the reaction mixture, and the increase (or decrease) in conductivity correlates with the formation of product (Figure 16.B). Consider the reaction between an organic halide, such as 2-bromo-2-methylpropane, and water:

$$(CH_3)_3C—Br(l) + H_2O(l) \longrightarrow$$
$$(CH_3)_3C—OH(l) + H^+(aq) + Br^-(aq)$$

The HBr that forms is a strong acid in water, so it dissociates completely into ions. As time passes, more ions form, so the conductivity of the reaction mixture increases.

Figure 16.A Spectrometric monitoring of a reaction. The investigator adds the reactant(s) to the sample tube and immediately places it in the spectrometer. For a reactant that is colored, rate data is determined from a plot of light absorbed vs. time.

Reaction Order Terminology

Before we see how reaction orders are determined from initial rate data, let's discuss the meaning of reaction order and some important terminology. We speak of the reaction as having an order "with respect to" or "in" each reactant. For example, for the reaction between nitric oxide and ozone,

$$NO(g) + O_3(g) \longrightarrow NO_2(g) + O_2(g)$$

the rate law has been experimentally determined to be

$$\text{Rate} = k[NO][O_3]$$

This reaction is first order with respect to NO (or "first order in NO"), which means that the rate depends on NO concentration raised to the first power, that is, $[NO]^1$ (although the exponent "1" is not written in the rate law). It is also first order with respect to O_3, or $[O_3]^1$. The sum of the individual orders gives the *overall* reaction order; this reaction is second order overall.

Now consider a different gas-phase reaction:

$$2NO_2(g) + F_2(g) \longrightarrow 2NO_2F(g)$$

for which the rate law has been determined to be

$$\text{Rate} = k[NO_2][F_2]$$

Figure 16.B Conductometric monitoring of a reaction. When a reactant mixture differs in conductivity from the product mixture, the change in conductivity is proportional to the reaction rate. It is usually easier to monitor a nonionic reactant forming an ionic product.

Figure 16.C Manometric monitoring of a reaction. When a reaction results in a change in the number of moles of gas, the change in pressure with time corresponds to a change in reaction rate. The rate of formation of NO_2 from N_2O_4 is being studied here.

Manometric Methods

If a reaction involves a change in the number of moles of gas, the rate can be determined from the change in pressure (at constant volume and temperature) over time. In practice, a manometer is attached to a reaction vessel of known volume that is immersed in a constant-temperature bath. For example, the reaction between zinc and acetic acid can be monitored by this method:

$$Zn(s) + 2CH_3COOH(aq) \longrightarrow$$
$$Zn^{2+}(aq) + 2CH_3COO^-(aq) + H_2(g)$$

As H_2 forms, the pressure increases. Thus, the reaction rate is directly proportional to the rate of increase of pressure. In Figure 16.C, this method is being used to study a different reaction.

Direct Chemical Methods

Rates of slow reactions, or of those that can be easily slowed, are often studied by direct chemical methods. A small, measured portion (called an *aliquot*) of the reaction mixture is removed, and the reaction in this portion is stopped, usually by rapid cooling. The concentration of reactant or product in the aliquot is measured, while the bulk of the reaction mixture continues to react and is sampled later. For example, the earlier reaction between an organic halide and water can also be studied by titration. The reaction rate in an aliquot is slowed by quickly transferring it to a chilled flask in an ice bath. HBr concentration in the aliquot is determined by titrating with standardized NaOH solution. To determine the change in HBr concentration with time, the procedure is repeated at regular intervals during the reaction.

This reaction is first order in NO_2 and first order in F_2. Overall, this is also a second-order reaction.

Finally, for the hydrolysis of 2-bromo-2-methylpropane, which we looked at in the Tools of the Chemistry Laboratory essay,

$$(CH_3)_3C—Br(l) + H_2O(l) \longrightarrow (CH_3)_3C—OH(l) + HBr(aq)$$

the rate law has been found to be

$$Rate = k[(CH_3)_3CBr]$$

This reaction is first order in 2-bromo-2-methylpropane. Note that the concentration of H_2O does not even appear in the rate law. Thus, the reaction is zero order with respect to H_2O ($[H_2O]^0$). This means that the rate does not depend on the concentration of H_2O, which is true for any aqueous reaction in which H_2O is a reactant. We can also write the rate law as

$$Rate = k[(CH_3)_3CBr][H_2O]^0$$

Overall, this is a first-order reaction.

These examples demonstrate a major point: *reaction orders **cannot** be deduced from the balanced equation.* In the reaction between NO_2 and F_2 and in the hydrolysis of 2-bromo-2-methylpropane, the reaction orders in the rate laws

675

do *not* correspond to the coefficients of the balanced equations. Reaction orders *must* be determined from rate data.

Reaction orders are usually positive integers or zero, but they can also be fractional or negative. For the reaction

$$CHCl_3(g) + Cl_2(g) \longrightarrow CCl_4(g) + HCl(g)$$

a fractional order appears in the rate law:

$$Rate = k[CHCl_3][Cl_2]^{1/2}$$

This order means that the reaction rate depends on the square root of the Cl_2 concentration. For example, if the initial Cl_2 concentration is increased by a factor of 4, while the initial $CHCl_3$ concentration is kept the same, the rate increases by a factor of 2, the square root of the change in $[Cl_2]$. A negative exponent means that the rate *decreases* when the concentration of that component increases. Negative orders are often seen for reactions whose rate laws include products. For example, for the atmospheric reaction

$$2O_3(g) \rightleftharpoons 3O_2(g)$$

the rate law has been shown to be

$$Rate = k[O_3]^2[O_2]^{-1}, \text{ or } k\frac{[O_3]^2}{[O_2]}$$

If the O_2 concentration doubles, the reaction proceeds half as fast.

Sample Problem 16.2   Determining Reaction Order from the Rate Law

PROBLEM For each of the following reactions, determine the reaction order with respect to each reactant and the overall order from the given rate law:
(a) $2NO(g) + O_2(g) \longrightarrow 2NO_2(g)$; rate = $k[NO]^2[O_2]$
(b) $CH_3CHO(g) \longrightarrow CH_4(g) + CO(g)$; rate = $k[CH_3CHO]^{3/2}$
(c) $H_2O_2(aq) + 3I^-(aq) + 2H^+(aq) \longrightarrow I_3^-(aq) + 2H_2O(l)$; rate = $k[H_2O_2][I^-]$
PLAN We inspect the exponents in the rate law, *not* the coefficients of the balanced equation, to find the individual orders, and then take their sum to obtain the overall reaction order.
SOLUTION (a) The exponent of [NO] is 2, so the reaction is second order with respect to NO, first order with respect to O_2, and third order overall.
(b) The reaction is $\frac{3}{2}$ order in CH_3CHO and $\frac{3}{2}$ order overall.
(c) The reaction is first order in H_2O_2, first order in I^-, and second order overall.
The reactant H^+ does not appear in the rate law, so the reaction is zero order in H^+.
CHECK Be sure each reactant has an order and the sum of the individual orders gives the overall order.

Follow-up Problem 16.2   Experiment shows that the reaction
$$5Br^-(aq) + BrO_3^-(aq) + 6H^+(aq) \longrightarrow 3Br_2(l) + 3H_2O(l)$$
obeys this rate law: rate = $k[Br^-][BrO_3^-][H^+]^2$. What are the reaction orders in each reactant and the overall reaction order?

Determining Reaction Orders

Sample Problem 16.2 shows how to find the reaction orders from a known rate law. Now let's see how they are determined from data *before* the rate law is known. Suppose we are studying the reaction between oxygen and nitric oxide, a key step in the formation of acid rain and in the industrial production of nitric acid:

$$O_2(g) + 2NO(g) \longrightarrow 2NO_2(g)$$

The rate law, expressed in general form, is

$$Rate = k[O_2]^m[NO]^n$$

Table 16.2 Initial Rates for a Series of Experiments in the Reaction Between O_2 and NO

Experiment	Initial Reactant Concentrations (mol/L)		Initial Rate (mol/L · s)
	O_2	NO	
1	1.10×10^{-2}	1.30×10^{-2}	3.21×10^{-3}
2	2.20×10^{-2}	1.30×10^{-2}	6.40×10^{-3}
3	1.10×10^{-2}	2.60×10^{-2}	12.8×10^{-3}
4	3.30×10^{-2}	1.30×10^{-2}	9.60×10^{-3}
5	1.10×10^{-2}	3.90×10^{-2}	28.8×10^{-3}

To find the reaction orders, *we run a series of experiments, each of which starts with a different set of reactant concentrations, and from each we obtain an initial rate.* As Table 16.2 shows, the experiments are designed to change one reactant concentration while keeping the other constant. If we compare the values in experiments 1 and 2, we see the effect of doubling $[O_2]$ on the rate. First, we take the ratio of their rate laws:

$$\frac{\text{Rate 2}}{\text{Rate 1}} = \frac{k[O_2]_2^m[NO]_2^n}{k[O_2]_1^m[NO]_1^n}$$

where $[O_2]_2$ is the O_2 concentration for experiment 2, $[NO]_1$ is the NO concentration for experiment 1, and so forth. Since k is a constant and $[NO]$ does not change between these two experiments, these quantities cancel:

$$\frac{\text{Rate 2}}{\text{Rate 1}} = \frac{[O_2]_2^m}{[O_2]_1^m} = \left(\frac{[O_2]_2}{[O_2]_1}\right)^m$$

Substituting the values from Table 16.2, we obtain

$$\frac{6.40 \times 10^{-3} \text{ mol/L} \cdot \text{s}}{3.21 \times 10^{-3} \text{ mol/L} \cdot \text{s}} = \left(\frac{2.20 \times 10^{-2} \text{ mol/L}}{1.10 \times 10^{-2} \text{ mol/L}}\right)^m$$

Dividing, we obtain

$$1.99 = (2.00)^m$$

Rounding to one significant figure gives

$$2 = 2^m; \text{ therefore, } m = 1$$

The reaction is first order in O_2: when $[O_2]$ doubles, the rate doubles.

To find the order with respect to NO, we compare experiments 3 and 1, in which $[O_2]$ is held constant and $[NO]$ is doubled:

$$\frac{\text{Rate 3}}{\text{Rate 1}} = \frac{k[O_2]_3^m[NO]_3^n}{k[O_2]_1^m[NO]_1^n}$$

As before, k is constant and $[O_2]$ does not change in this pair of experiments, so these quantities cancel:

$$\frac{\text{Rate 3}}{\text{Rate 1}} = \left(\frac{[NO]_3}{[NO]_1}\right)^n$$

The actual values give

$$\frac{12.8 \times 10^{-3} \text{ mol/L} \cdot \text{s}}{3.21 \times 10^{-3} \text{ mol/L} \cdot \text{s}} = \left(\frac{2.60 \times 10^{-2} \text{ mol/L}}{1.30 \times 10^{-2} \text{ mol/L}}\right)^n$$

Dividing, we obtain

$$3.99 = (2.00)^n$$

Rounding gives

$$4 = 2^n; \text{ therefore, } n = 2$$

The reaction is second order in NO: when [NO] doubles, the rate quadruples. Thus, the rate law is

$$\text{Rate} = k[O_2][NO]^2$$

You may want to use experiment 1 in combination with experiments 4 and 5 to check this result.

Sample Problem 16.3   Determining Reaction Orders from Initial Rate Data

PROBLEM Many gaseous reactions take place in a car engine and exhaust system. One of these is

$$NO_2(g) + CO(g) \longrightarrow NO(g) + CO_2(g); \quad \text{rate} = k[NO_2]^m[CO]^n$$

Use the following data to determine the individual and overall reaction orders:

EXPERIMENT	INITIAL RATE (mol/L · s)	INITIAL [NO₂] (mol/L)	INITIAL [CO] (mol/L)
1	0.0050	0.10	0.10
2	0.080	0.40	0.10
3	0.0050	0.10	0.20

PLAN We need to solve the general rate law for the reaction orders m and n. To solve for each exponent, we proceed as in the text, taking the ratio of the rate laws for two experiments in which only the reactant in question changes.

SOLUTION Calculating m in $[NO_2]^m$: We take the ratio of the rate laws for experiments 1 and 2, in which [NO₂] varies but [CO] is constant,

$$\frac{\text{Rate 2}}{\text{Rate 1}} = \frac{k[NO_2]_2^m[CO]_2^n}{k[NO_2]_1^m[CO]_1^n} = \left(\frac{[NO_2]_2}{[NO_2]_1}\right)^m; \text{ or } \frac{0.080 \text{ mol/L} \cdot \text{s}}{0.0050 \text{ mol/L} \cdot \text{s}} = \left(\frac{0.40 \text{ mol/L}}{0.10 \text{ mol/L}}\right)^m$$

Since $16 = 4.0^m$, $m = 2.0$. The reaction is second order in NO₂.

Calculating n in $[CO]^n$: We take the ratio of the rate laws for experiments 1 and 3, in which [CO] varies but [NO₂] is constant,

$$\frac{\text{Rate 3}}{\text{Rate 1}} = \frac{k[NO_2]_3^2[CO]_3^n}{k[NO_2]_1^2[CO]_1^n} = \left(\frac{[CO]_3}{[CO]_1}\right)^n; \text{ or } \frac{0.0050 \text{ mol/L} \cdot \text{s}}{0.0050 \text{ mol/L} \cdot \text{s}} = \left(\frac{0.20 \text{ mol/L}}{0.10 \text{ mol/L}}\right)^n$$

Since $1.0 = (2.0)^n$, $n = 0$. The rate does not change when [CO] varies, so the reaction is zero order in CO.

Therefore, the rate law is

$$\text{Rate} = k[NO_2]^2[CO]^0 = k[NO_2]^2(1) = k[NO_2]^2$$

The reaction is second order overall.

CHECK A good check is to reason through the orders. If $m = 1$, quadrupling [NO₂] would quadruple the rate; but the rate *more* than quadruples, so $m > 1$. If $m = 2$, quadrupling [NO₂] would increase the rate by a factor of 16 (4^2). The ratio of rates is $0.080/0.005 = 16$, so $m = 2$. In contrast, increasing [CO] has no effect on the rate, which can happen only if $[CO]^n = 1$, so $n = 0$.

Follow-up Problem 16.3   Find the rate law and the overall reaction order for the reaction $H_2 + I_2 \longrightarrow 2HI$ from the following data at 450°C:

EXPERIMENT	INITIAL RATE (mol/L · s)	INITIAL [H₂] (mol/L)	INITIAL [I₂] (mol/L)
1	1.9×10^{-23}	0.0113	0.0011
2	1.1×10^{-22}	0.0220	0.0033
3	9.3×10^{-23}	0.0550	0.0011
4	1.9×10^{-22}	0.0220	0.0056

Determining the Rate Constant

With the rate, reactant concentrations, and reaction orders known, the sole remaining unknown in the rate law is the rate constant, k. The rate constant is specific for a particular reaction *at a particular temperature*. Since the experiments in the O_2-NO series that we are considering were conducted at the same temperature, we can use the data from any one of them to solve for k. From experiment 1 in Table 16.2, for instance, we obtain

$$k = \frac{\text{rate 1}}{[O_2]_1[NO]_1^2} = \frac{3.21\times10^{-3}\,\text{mol/L}\cdot\text{s}}{(1.10\times10^{-2}\,\text{mol/L})(1.30\times10^{-2}\,\text{mol/L})^2}$$

$$= \frac{3.21\times10^{-3}\,\text{mol/L}\cdot\text{s}}{1.86\times10^{-6}\,\text{mol}^3/\text{L}^3} = 1.73\times10^3\,\text{L}^2/\text{mol}^2\cdot\text{s}$$

Always check that the values of k in the same series are constant within experimental error. To three significant figures, the average value of k for the five experiments in Table 16.2 is $1.72\times10^3\,\text{L}^2/\text{mol}^2\cdot\text{s}$.

Note the units for the rate constant. Since concentrations are in mol/L and the reaction rate is in units of mol/L · time, the units for k will depend on the order of the reaction and, of course, the time unit. The units for k here, $\text{L}^2/\text{mol}^2\cdot\text{s}$, are required to give a rate with units of mol/L · s:

$$\frac{\text{mol}}{\text{L}\cdot\text{s}} = \frac{\text{L}^2}{\text{mol}^2\cdot\text{s}} \times \frac{\text{mol}}{\text{L}} \times \left(\frac{\text{mol}}{\text{L}}\right)^2$$

The rate constant will *always* have these units for an overall third-order reaction with the time unit in seconds. Table 16.3 shows the units of k for some common overall reaction orders, but you can always determine the units mathematically.

Table 16.3 Units of the Rate Constant k for Several Overall Reaction Orders

Overall Reaction Order	Units of k (t in seconds)
0	$\text{mol/L}\cdot\text{s}$ (or $\text{mol L}^{-1}\,\text{s}^{-1}$)
1	$1/\text{s}$ (or s^{-1})
2	$\text{L/mol}\cdot\text{s}$ (or $\text{L mol}^{-1}\,\text{s}^{-1}$)
3	$\text{L}^2/\text{mol}^2\cdot\text{s}$ (or $\text{L}^2\,\text{mol}^{-2}\,\text{s}^{-1}$)

General formula:

$$\text{Units of } k = \frac{\left(\dfrac{\text{L}}{\text{mol}}\right)^{\text{order}-1}}{t}$$

Section Summary

An experimentally determined rate law of a reaction shows how the rate depends on concentration. If we consider only initial rates, the rate law often takes the form, rate $= k[A]^m[B]^n$ .... With an accurate method for obtaining initial rates, reaction orders are determined by comparing rates for different initial concentrations. To do this, using several experiments, we vary the concentration of one reactant at a time to see its effect on the rate. With rate, concentrations, and reaction orders known, the rate constant is the only remaining unknown in the rate law, so it can be calculated.

16.4 Integrated Rate Laws: Concentration Changes over Time

Notice that the rate laws we've developed so far do not include time as a variable. They tell us the rate or concentration at a given instant, allowing us to answer the critical question, "How fast is the reaction proceeding at the moment when y moles per liter of A are reacting with z moles per liter of B?" However, by employing different forms of the rate laws, called **integrated rate laws,** we can consider the time factor and answer other questions, such as "How long will it take for x moles per liter of A to be used up?" or "What is the concentration of A after y minutes of reaction?"

Integrated Rate Laws for First-Order and Second-Order Reactions

Consider a simple first-order reaction, A $\longrightarrow$ B. As we discussed previously, the rate can be expressed as the change in the concentration of A divided by the change in time:

$$\text{Rate} = -\frac{\Delta[A]}{\Delta t}$$

It can also be expressed in terms of the rate law:

$$\text{Rate} = k[A]$$

Setting these different expressions equal to each other gives

$$-\frac{\Delta[A]}{\Delta t} = k[A]$$

Through the methods of calculus, this expression is integrated over time to obtain the integrated rate law for a first-order reaction:

$$\ln\frac{[A]_0}{[A]_t} = kt \qquad \text{(first-order reaction; rate} = k[A]) \qquad \textbf{(16.4)}$$

where ln is the natural logarithm, $[A]_0$ is the concentration of A at $t = 0$, and $[A]_t$ is the concentration of A at any time t during an experiment. Since $\ln\frac{a}{b} = \ln a - \ln b$, we have

$$\ln[A]_0 - \ln[A]_t = kt$$

For a general second-order rate law, the expression including time can become complex, so let's consider only the simplest case, one in which the rate law contains only one reactant. Setting the rate expressions equal to each other gives

$$\text{Rate} = -\frac{\Delta[A]}{\Delta t} = k[A]^2$$

Integrating over time gives the integrated rate law for a second-order reaction involving one reactant:

$$\frac{1}{[A]_t} - \frac{1}{[A]_0} = kt \qquad \text{(second-order reaction; rate} = k[A]^2) \qquad \textbf{(16.5)}$$

Sample Problem 16.4 presents one way in which these integrated rate laws are applied.

Sample Problem 16.4   Determining the Reactant Concentration at a Given Time

PROBLEM Cyclobutane (C_4H_8) decomposes at 1000°C to two molecules of ethylene (C_2H_4) with a very high first-order rate constant, 87 s^{-1}.
(a) If the initial concentration of cyclobutane is 2.00 M, what is the concentration after 0.010 s?
(b) What fraction of cyclobutane has decomposed in this time?
PLAN (a) We must find the concentration of cyclobutane at time t, $[C_4H_8]_t$. The problem tells us this is a first-order reaction, so we use the integrated first-order rate law:

$$\ln\frac{[C_4H_8]_0}{[C_4H_8]_t} = kt$$

We know k, t, and $[C_4H_8]_0$, so we can solve for $[C_4H_8]_t$. **(b)** The fraction decomposed is the concentration that has decomposed divided by the initial concentration:

$$\text{Fraction decomposed} = \frac{[C_4H_8]_0 - [C_4H_8]_t}{[C_4H_8]_0}$$

SOLUTION (a) Substituting the data into the integrated rate law:

$$\ln\frac{2.00 \text{ mol/L}}{[C_4H_8]_t} = (87 \text{ s}^{-1})(0.010 \text{ s}) = 0.87$$

Taking the antilog of both sides:

$$\frac{2.00 \text{ mol/L}}{[C_4H_8]_t} = e^{0.87} = 2.4$$

Solving for $[C_4H_8]_t$:

$$[C_4H_8]_t = \frac{2.00 \text{ mol/L}}{2.4} = \boxed{0.83 \text{ mol/L}}$$

(b) Finding the fraction that has decomposed after 0.010 s:

$$\frac{[C_4H_8]_0 - [C_4H_8]_t}{[C_4H_8]_0} = \frac{2.00 \text{ mol/L} - 0.83 \text{ mol/L}}{2.00 \text{ mol/L}} = \boxed{0.58}$$

CHECK The concentration remaining after 0.010 s (0.83 mol/L) is less than the starting concentration (2.00 mol/L), which makes sense. Raising e to an exponent slightly less than 1 should give a number (2.4) slightly less than the value of e (2.718). Moreover, the final result makes sense: a high rate constant indicates a fast reaction, so it's not surprising that so much decomposes in such a short time.

COMMENT Integrated rate laws are also used to solve for the time it takes to reach a certain reactant concentration, as in Follow-up Problem 16.4.

Follow-up Problem 16.4 At 25°C, hydrogen iodide breaks down very slowly to hydrogen and iodine: rate = $k[HI]^2$. The rate constant at 25°C is 2.4×10^{-21} L/mol · s. If 0.0100 mol HI(g) is placed in a 1.0-L container, how long will it take for the concentration of HI to reach 0.00900 mol/L (10.0% reacted)?

Determining the Reaction Order from the Integrated Rate Law

Suppose you do not know the rate law for a reaction and do not have the initial rate data needed to determine the reaction orders (as we did in Sample Problem 16.3). Another method for finding reaction orders is a graphical technique that uses concentration-time data directly.

Integrated rate laws can be rearranged into the form of an equation for a straight line, $y = mx + b$, where m is the slope and b is the y-axis intercept. For a first-order reaction, we have

$$\ln [A]_0 - \ln [A]_t = kt$$

Rearranging and changing signs gives

$$\ln [A]_t = -kt + \ln [A]_0$$
$$y \;\;\; = mx + \;\; b$$

Thus, a plot of $\ln [A]_t$ vs. t gives a straight line with slope $= -k$ and y intercept $= \ln [A]_0$ (Figure 16.7A).

For a simple second-order reaction, we have

$$\frac{1}{[A]_t} - \frac{1}{[A]_0} = kt$$

Rearranging gives

$$\frac{1}{[A]_t} = kt + \frac{1}{[A]_0}$$
$$y \;\; = mx + \;\; b$$

In this case, a plot of $1/[A]_t$ vs. t gives a straight line with slope $= k$ and y intercept $= 1/[A]_0$ (Figure 16.7B).

To find the reaction order from the concentration-time data, some trial-and-error graphical plotting is required:

- If you obtain a straight line when you plot $\ln$ [reactant] vs. time, the reaction is *first order* with respect to that reactant.
- If you obtain a straight line when you plot $1/$[reactant] vs. time, the reaction is *second order* with respect to that reactant.

A First order   Time

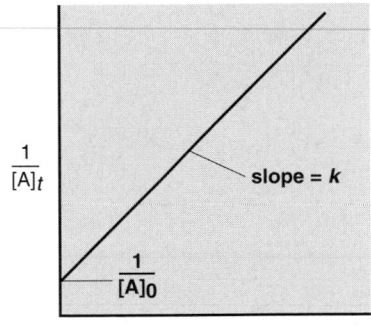

B Second order   Time

Figure 16.7 Integrated rate laws and reaction order. A, A plot of $\ln [A]_t$ vs. t gives a straight line for a reaction that is first order in A. **B,** A plot of $1/[A]_t$ vs. t gives a straight line for a reaction that is second order in A.

Time (min)	[N₂O₅]	ln [N₂O₅]	1/[N₂O₅]
0	0.0165	−4.104	60.6
10	0.0124	−4.390	80.6
20	0.0093	−4.68	1.1×10^2
30	0.0071	−4.95	1.4×10^2
40	0.0053	−5.24	1.9×10^2
50	0.0039	−5.55	2.6×10^2
60	0.0029	−5.84	3.4×10^2

A

Figure 16.8 Graphical determination of the reaction order for the decomposition of N₂O₅.
A, Time and concentration data for determining reaction order. **B,** A plot of ln [N₂O₅] vs. time gives a straight line, indicating that the reaction is first order in N₂O₅. **C,** A plot of 1/[N₂O₅] vs. time is curved, indicating that the reaction is *not* second order in N₂O₅, which supports the conclusion in part B.

B

C

Figure 16.8 shows how this approach is used to determine the order for the decomposition of N_2O_5. Since a plot of ln $[N_2O_5]$ *is* linear and the plot of $1/[N_2O_5]$ *is not,* the decomposition of N_2O_5 must be first order in N_2O_5.

Reaction Half-Life

The **half-life ($t_{1/2}$)** of a reaction is the time required for the reactant concentration to reach half its initial value. Half-lives are expressed in time units appropriate for a given reaction and are characteristic of that reaction at a given temperature.

At fixed conditions, *the half-life of a first-order reaction is a constant, independent of reactant concentration.* For example, the half-life for the first-order decomposition of N_2O_5 at 45°C is 24.0 min. The half-life means that if we start with, say, 0.0600 mol/L N_2O_5 at 45°C, after 24 min (one half-life), 0.0300 mol/L has been consumed and 0.0300 mol/L remains; after 48 min (two half-lives), 0.0150 mol/L remains; after 72 min (three half-lives), 0.0075 mol/L remains, and so forth (Figure 16.9).

We can see why the half-life of a first-order reaction is constant from the integrated rate law:

$$\ln \frac{[A]_0}{[A]_t} = kt$$

After one half-life, $t = t_{1/2}$, and $[A]_t = \frac{1}{2}[A]_0$. Substituting, we obtain

$$\ln \frac{[A]_0}{\frac{1}{2}[A]_0} = kt_{1/2}$$

Thus, $$\ln 2 = kt_{1/2}$$

Then, solving for $t_{1/2}$, we have

$$t_{1/2} = \frac{\ln 2}{k} = \frac{0.693}{k} \qquad \text{(first-order process; rate} = k[A]) \qquad \textbf{(16.6)}$$

As you can see, the time to reach one-half the starting concentration in a first-order reaction does not depend on what that starting concentration is.

Radioactive decay of an unstable nucleus is another example of a first-order process. For example, the half-life for the decay of uranium-235 is 7.1×10^8 yr. After 710 million years, a 1-kg sample of uranium-235 will contain 0.5 kg uranium-235; after the same amount of time, a 1-mg sample will contain 0.5 mg. Whether we consider a molecule or a radioactive nucleus, the *decomposition of each particle in a first-order process is independent of the number of other particles present.*

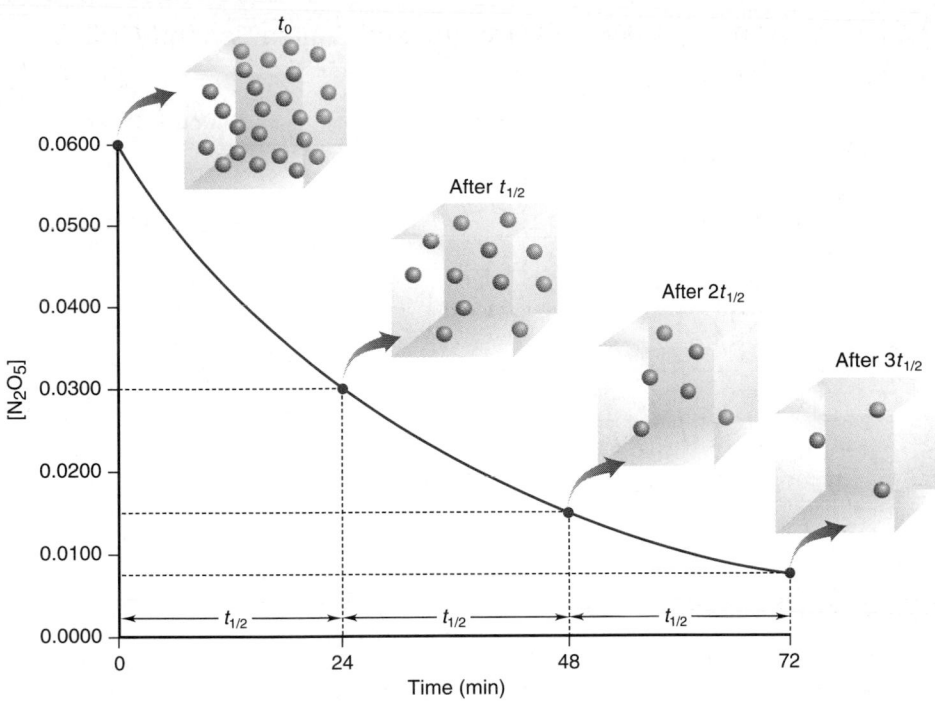

Figure 16.9 **A plot of [N₂O₅] vs. time for three half-lives.** During each half-life, the concentration is halved. $T = 45°C$ and $[N_2O_5]_0 = 0.0600$ mol/L. The blowup volumes, with N_2O_5 molecules as colored spheres, show that after three half-lives, $\frac{1}{2} \times \frac{1}{2} \times \frac{1}{2} = \frac{1}{8}$ of the original concentration remains.

Sample Problem 16.5   Determining the Half-Life of a First-Order Reaction

PROBLEM Cyclopropane is the smallest cyclic hydrocarbon. Because its 60° bond angles allow only poor orbital overlap, its bonds are weak. As a result, it is thermally unstable and rearranges to propene at 1000°C via the following first-order reaction:

$$H_2C-CH_2(g) \xrightarrow{\Delta} CH_3-CH=CH_2(g)$$

The rate constant is 9.2 s^{-1}. How long does it take for the initial concentration of cyclopropane to decrease by one-half?

PLAN We have to find the time it takes for one-half of the cyclopropane to react, that is, the half-life. Since the reaction is first order, we use Equation 16.6, substitute for k, and solve for $t_{1/2}$.

SOLUTION Solving for $t_{1/2}$:

$$t_{1/2} = \frac{\ln 2}{k} = \frac{0.693}{9.2 \text{ s}^{-1}} = \boxed{0.075 \text{ s}}$$

It takes 0.075 s for half the cyclopropane to form propene at this temperature.

CHECK Rounding, we have 0.7/9 = 0.08, so the answer seems correct.

Follow-up Problem 16.5   Iodine-123 is used to study thyroid gland function. This radioactive isotope breaks down in a first-order process with a half-life of 13.1 h. What is the rate constant for the process?

In contrast to the half-life of a first-order reaction, the half-life of a second-order reaction *does* depend on reactant concentration:

$$t_{1/2} = \frac{1}{k[A]_0} \quad \text{(second-order process; rate} = k[A]^2)$$

Note that here *the half-life is **inversely** proportional to the initial reactant concentration.* This result means that a second-order reaction with a high initial reactant concentration has a shorter half-life, and one with a low initial reactant

Table 16.4 An Overview of First-Order and Simple Second-Order Reactions

	First Order	Second Order
Rate law	rate = $k[A]$	rate = $k[A]^2$
Units for k	$1/s$	$L/mol \cdot s$
Integrated rate law in straight-line form	$\ln [A]_t = -kt + \ln [A]_0$	$1/[A]_t = kt + 1/[A]_0$
Plot for straight line	$\ln [A]_t$ vs. t	$1/[A]_t$ vs. t
Slope, y intercept	$-k$, $\ln [A]_0$	k, $1/[A]_0$
Half-life	$(\ln 2)/k$	$1/k[A]_0$

concentration has a longer half-life. Therefore, *as a second-order reaction proceeds, the half-life increases.* Table 16.4 summarizes the essential features of first- and second-order reactions.

Section Summary

Integrated rate laws are used to find the time needed to reach a certain concentration or the concentration present after a given time. Rearrangements of the integrated rate laws allow us to determine reaction orders and rate constants graphically. The half-life is the time needed to consume half the reactant; for first-order reactions, it is independent of concentration.

16.5 The Effect of Temperature on Reaction Rate

Temperature often has a major effect on reaction rate. As Figure 16.10A shows for a common organic reaction (hydrolysis, or reaction with water, of an ester), when reactant concentrations are held constant, the rate nearly doubles with each rise in temperature of 10 K (or 10°C). In fact, for many reactions near room temperature, an increase of 10°C causes a doubling or tripling of the rate.

How does the rate law express this effect of temperature? If we collect concentration-time data for the same reaction run at *different* temperatures, and then solve each of the rate expressions for k, we find that k increases as the temperature (T) increases. In other words, *temperature affects the rate by affecting the rate constant.* A plot of k vs. T gives a curve that increases exponentially, as shown in Figure 16.10B.

Expt	[Ester]	[H_2O]	T (K)	Rate (mol/L · s)	k (L/mol · s)
1	0.100	0.200	288	1.04×10^{-3}	0.0521
2	0.100	0.200	298	2.02×10^{-3}	0.101
3	0.100	0.200	308	3.68×10^{-3}	0.184
4	0.100	0.200	318	6.64×10^{-3}	0.332

A

B

Figure 16.10 Dependence of the rate constant on temperature.
A, In the hydrolysis of an ester, when reactant concentrations are held constant and temperature increases, the rate and rate constant increase. Note the approximate doubling of k with each 10 K (10°C) temperature rise.
B, A plot of the rate constant vs. temperature for this reaction shows a smoothly increasing curve.

These results are consistent with studies made in 1889 by the Swedish chemist Svante Arrhenius, who discovered a key relationship between temperature and the rate constant. In its modern form, the **Arrhenius equation** is

$$k = Ae^{-E_a/RT} \tag{16.7}$$

where k is the rate constant, e is the base of natural logarithms, T is the absolute temperature, and R is the universal gas constant. We'll discuss the meaning of A, which is related to the orientation of the colliding molecules, in the next section. The E_a term is the **activation energy** of the reaction, which Arrhenius considered the *minimum energy* the molecules must have to react; we discuss its meaning further in the next section as well. This negative exponential relationship between temperature and the rate constant means that *as the temperature increases, the negative exponent becomes smaller, so the value of k becomes larger, which means that the rate increases:*

Higher $T \Longrightarrow$ larger $k \Longrightarrow$ increased rate

We can calculate E_a from the Arrhenius equation by taking the natural logarithm of both sides and recasting the equation into the form of an equation for a straight line:

$$\ln k = \ln A - \frac{E_a}{R}\left(\frac{1}{T}\right)$$
$$y \quad = \quad b \quad + \quad mx$$

A plot of $\ln k$ vs. $1/T$ gives a straight line whose slope is $-E_a/R$ and y intercept is $\ln A$ (Figure 16.11). Therefore, since we know the constant R, we can determine E_a graphically from a series of k values at different temperatures.

Because the relationship between $\ln k$ and $1/T$ is linear, we can use an even simpler method for finding E_a if we know the rate constant at two different temperatures, T_2 and T_1:

$$\ln k_2 = \ln A - \frac{E_a}{R}\left(\frac{1}{T_2}\right) \qquad \ln k_1 = \ln A - \frac{E_a}{R}\left(\frac{1}{T_1}\right)$$

When we subtract $\ln k_1$ from $\ln k_2$, the "$\ln A$" term drops out and the other terms can be rearranged to give

$$\ln \frac{k_2}{k_1} = -\frac{E_a}{R}\left(\frac{1}{T_2} - \frac{1}{T_1}\right) \tag{16.8}$$

From this, we can solve for E_a. ◆

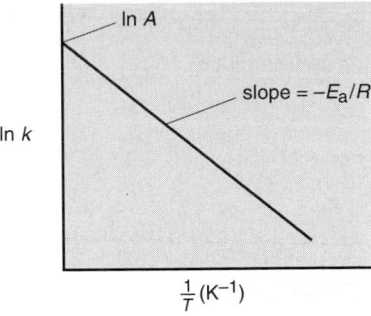

Figure 16.11 Graphical determination of the activation energy. A plot of $\ln k$ vs. $1/T$ gives a straight line with slope $-E_a/R$.

◆ **The Significance of R**
As you can see, the importance of R extends beyond the study of gases (or osmotic pressure). By expressing pressure, P, and volume, V, in more fundamental quantities, we obtain the dimensions for energy, E:

$$P = \frac{\text{force}}{\text{area}} = \frac{\text{force}}{(\text{length})^2}$$

and $V = (\text{length})^3$

Thus,

$$PV = \frac{\text{force}}{(\text{length})^2} \times (\text{length})^3$$
$$= \text{force} \times \text{length}$$

Energy is involved when an object is moved, that is, when a force acts over a distance. Thus, $E = \text{force} \times$ distance (or length), so

$$PV = \text{force} \times \text{length} = E$$

Solving for R in the ideal gas law and substituting for PV, we obtain

$$R = \frac{PV}{nT} = \frac{E}{\text{amount} \times T}$$

Therefore, R is the proportionality constant that relates the energy, amount (mol) of substance, and temperature of any chemical system. We'll use R in this context many times in the remainder of the text.

Sample Problem 16.6 Determining the Energy of Activation

PROBLEM The decomposition of hydrogen iodide, $2HI(g) \longrightarrow H_2(g) + I_2(g)$, has rate constants of 9.51×10^{-9} L/mol · s at 500. K and 1.10×10^{-5} L/mol · s at 600. K. Find E_a.
PLAN We are given the rate constants, k_1 and k_2, at two temperatures, T_1 and T_2, so we substitute into Equation 16.8 and solve for E_a.
SOLUTION Rearranging Equation 16.8 to solve for E_a:

$$\ln \frac{k_2}{k_1} = -\frac{E_a}{R}\left(\frac{1}{T_2} - \frac{1}{T_1}\right)$$

$$E_a = -R\left(\ln \frac{k_2}{k_1}\right)\left(\frac{1}{T_2} - \frac{1}{T_1}\right)^{-1}$$

$$= -(8.31 \text{ J/mol} \cdot \text{K})\left(\ln \frac{1.10\times10^{-5} \text{ L/mol} \cdot \text{s}}{9.51\times10^{-9} \text{ L/mol} \cdot \text{s}}\right)\left(\frac{1}{600. \text{ K}} - \frac{1}{500. \text{ K}}\right)^{-1}$$

$$= 1.76\times10^5 \text{ J/mol} = \boxed{1.76\times10^2 \text{ kJ/mol}}$$

COMMENT Be sure to retain the same number of significant figures in $1/T$ as you have in T, or a significant error could be introduced. Round to the correct number of significant figures only at the final answer. On most pocket calculators, the expression $(1/T_2 - 1/T_1)$ is entered as "$(T_2)(1/x) - (T_1)(1/x) =$".

Follow-up Problem 16.6   The reaction $2NOCl(g) \longrightarrow 2NO(g) + Cl_2(g)$ has an E_a of 1.00×10^2 kJ/mol and a rate constant of 0.286 s^{-1} at 500. K. What is the rate constant at 490. K?

In this section and the previous two, we discussed a series of experimental and mathematical methods for the study of reaction kinetics. Figure 16.12 is a useful summary of this information. Note that the integrated rate law provides an alternative method for obtaining reaction orders and the rate constant.

Figure 16.12 **Information sequence to determine the kinetic parameters of a reaction.** Note that the integrated rate law does not depend on the method of initial rates and is also used to determine reaction orders and rate constant.

Section Summary

As the Arrhenius equation shows, rate increases with temperature because a temperature rise increases the rate constant. The activation energy, E_a, the minimum energy needed for a reaction to occur, can be determined graphically from k values at different T values.

16.6 Explaining the Effects of Concentration and Temperature

The Arrhenius equation was developed empirically from the observations of many reactions. It took more than 30 years for models to appear that could explain the effects of concentration and temperature on reaction rate. The two major models we consider here are distinct but completely compatible, each highlighting different aspects of the reaction process. **Collision theory** views the reaction rate as the result of particles colliding with a certain frequency and minimum energy. **Transition state theory** offers a close-up view of how this energy converts reactant to product.

Collision Theory: Basis of the Rate Law

The basic tenet of collision theory is that reactant particles—atoms, molecules, and ions—must collide with each other to react. Therefore, the number of collisions per unit time provides an upper limit on how fast a reaction can take place. The model restricts itself to simple one-step reactions in which two particles collide and form products: A + B $\longrightarrow$ products. With its emphasis on collisions between three-dimensional particles, it elegantly explains why reactant concentrations are multiplied together in the rate law, how temperature affects the rate, and what influence molecular structure has on rate.

Why Concentrations Are Multiplied in the Rate Law   If particles must collide to react, the laws of probability tell us why the rate depends on the *product* of the reactant concentrations, not their sum. Imagine that you have only two particles of A and two of B confined in a reaction vessel. Figure 16.13 shows that four A-B collisions are possible. If you add another particle of A, there can be six A-B collisions (3×2), not five ($3 + 2$); add another particle of B and there can be nine A-B collisions (3×3), not six ($3 + 3$). Thus, the collision model is consistent with the observation that concentrations are *multiplied* in the rate law.

How Temperature Affects Rate: The Importance of Activation Energy
Increasing the temperature of a reaction increases the average speed of particles and therefore their collision frequency. But, collision frequency cannot be the only factor affecting rate, or every gaseous reaction would be over instantaneously: after all, at 1 atm and 20°C, the molecules in a milliliter of

gas experience about 10^{27} collisions per second, or about 4×10^7 collisions/molecule, so the reaction would be over in less than one ten-millionth of a second! In fact, *in the vast majority of collisions, the molecules rebound without reacting.*

Arrhenius proposed that every reaction has an *energy threshold* that the colliding molecules must exceed in order to react. (An analogy might be an athlete who must exceed the height of the bar to accomplish a high jump.) This minimum collision energy is the *activation energy (E_a)*, the energy required to activate the molecules into a state from which reactant bonds can change into product bonds. Recall that at any given temperature, molecules have a range of kinetic energies; thus, their collisions have a range of energies as well. According to collision theory, *only those collisions with enough energy to exceed E_a can lead to reaction.*

We said earlier that many reactions near room temperature approximately double or triple their rates with a 10°C rise in temperature. Is the rate increase due to a higher number of collisions? Actually, this has only a minor effect. Calculations show that a 10°C rise increases the average molecular speed by only 2%. If an increase in speed were the only effect of temperature and the speed of each colliding molecule increases by 2%, we would expect only a 4% increase in rate. Far more important is that *the temperature rise enlarges the fraction of collisions with enough energy to exceed the activation energy.* This key point is shown in Figure 16.14.

At a given temperature, the fraction f of molecular collisions with energy greater than or equal to the activation energy E_a is given by

$$f = e^{-E_a/RT}$$

where e is the base of natural logarithms, T is the absolute temperature, and R is the universal gas constant. [Notice that the right side of this equation is the central component in the Arrhenius equation (Equation 16.7).] *The magnitudes of both E_a and T affect the fraction of sufficiently energetic collisions.* In the top portion of Table 16.5, you can see the effect of increasing E_a at a fixed temperature on this fraction of collisions. Note how much the fraction shrinks with a 25-kJ/mol increase in activation energy. (As the height of the bar is raised, fewer athletes can accomplish the jump.) In the bottom portion you can see the effect of T on the fraction for a fixed E_a of 50 kJ/mol, a typical value for many reactions. Note that the fraction nearly doubles for a 10°C increase. Doubling the fraction doubles the rate constant, which doubles the reaction rate.

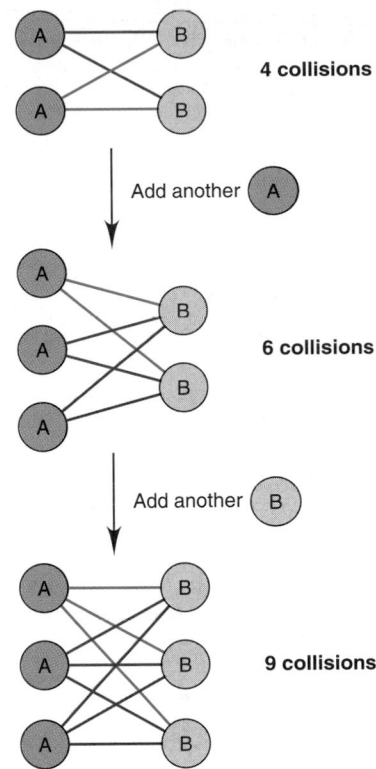

Figure 16.13 The dependence of collision number on the product of reactant concentrations. Concentrations are multiplied, not added, in the rate law because the number of possible collisions is the *product*, not the sum, of the numbers of particles present.

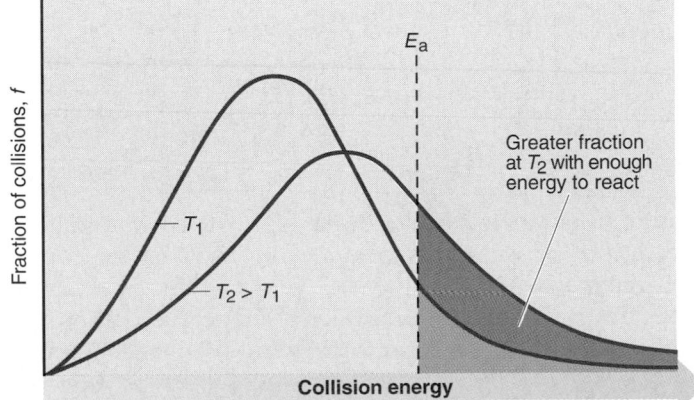

Figure 16.14 The effect of temperature on the distribution of collision energies. At the higher temperature, T_2, a larger fraction of collisions occur with enough energy to exceed E_a.

Table 16.5 The Effect of E_a and T on the Fraction (f) of Collisions with Sufficient Energy to Allow Reaction

E_a (kJ/mol)	f (at T = 298 K)
50	1.70×10^{-9}
75	7.03×10^{-14}
100	2.90×10^{-18}

T	f (at E_a = 50 kJ/mol)
25°C (298 K)	1.70×10^{-9}
35°C (308 K)	3.29×10^{-9}
45°C (318 K)	6.12×10^{-9}

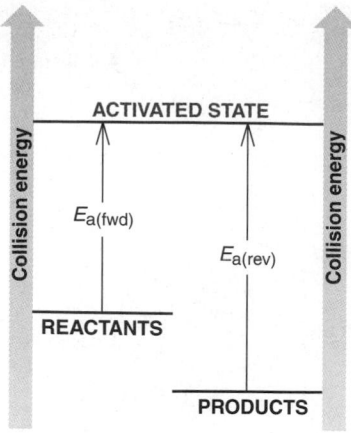

Figure 16.15 Energy-level diagram for a reaction. For molecules to react, they must collide with enough energy to reach an activated state. This minimum collision energy is the energy of activation, E_a. Because a reaction can occur in either direction, the diagram shows two activation energies. In the case shown, the forward reaction is exothermic because $E_{a(fwd)} < E_{a(rev)}$.

A reversible reaction has two activation energies (Figure 16.15). The activation energy for the forward reaction [$E_{a(fwd)}$] is the energy difference between the activated state and the reactants; the activation energy for the reverse reaction [$E_{a(rev)}$] is the energy difference between the activated state and the products. The figure shows an energy-level diagram for an exothermic reaction, so the products are at a lower energy than the reactants, and $E_{a(fwd)}$ is less than $E_{a(rev)}$.

By reorienting the collision-energy distribution curve of Figure 16.14 vertically and aligning it on both sides of Figure 16.15, we obtain Figure 16.16, which shows how temperature affects the fraction of collisions that exceed the activation energy for both the forward and reverse reactions. Several ideas are illustrated in this composite figure:

- In both reaction directions, a larger fraction of collisions exceeds the activation energy at the higher temperature, T_2; thus, higher T increases reaction rate.
- For an exothermic process (forward reaction here) at any temperature, the fraction of reactant collisions with energy exceeding $E_{a(fwd)}$ is *larger* than the fraction of product collisions with energy exceeding $E_{a(rev)}$; for this reason, the forward reaction is faster. On the other hand, in an endothermic process (reverse reaction here), $E_{a(fwd)}$ is greater than $E_{a(rev)}$, so the fraction of product collisions with energy exceeding $E_{a(rev)}$ is larger, and the reverse reaction is faster.

These conclusions are consistent with the Arrhenius equation; that is, *the larger the E_a, the smaller the k, and the slower the reaction:*

$$\text{Larger } E_a \Longrightarrow \text{smaller } k \Longrightarrow \text{decreased rate}$$

Figure 16.16 An energy-level diagram of the fraction of collisions exceeding E_a. A composite of Figure 16.14 aligned vertically on the left and right axes of Figure 16.15 shows that

- In either direction, the fraction of collisions exceeding E_a is greater at a higher temperature.
- In an *exothermic* reaction at any temperature, the fraction of collisions exceeding $E_{a(fwd)}$ is greater than the fraction exceeding $E_{a(rev)}$.

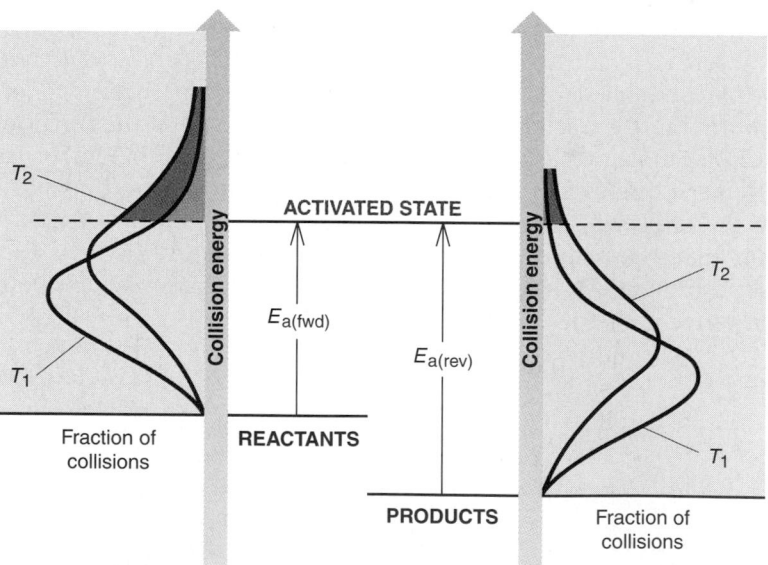

How Molecular Structure Affects Rate You've seen that the enormous number of collisions per second is greatly reduced when we count only those with enough energy to react. However, even this tiny fraction of the total collisions does not reveal the true number of **effective collisions,** those that actually lead to product. In addition to colliding with enough energy, *the molecules must collide such that the reacting atoms make contact.* In other words, a collision must have enough energy *and* a particular *molecular orientation* to be an effective collision.

In the Arrhenius equation, the effect of molecular orientation is contained in the factor A:

$$k = Ae^{-E_a/RT}$$

This term is called the **frequency factor,** the product of the collision frequency Z and an *orientation probability factor p,* which is specific for each reaction: $A = pZ$. The factor p is related to the structural complexity of the colliding particles. You can think of it as the ratio of effectively oriented collisions to all possible collisions. For example, Figure 16.17 shows a few of the possible collision orientations for the following simple gaseous reaction:

$$NO(g) + NO_3(g) \longrightarrow 2NO_2(g)$$

Of the five collisions shown, only one has an orientation in which the N of NO collides with an O of NO_3. Actually, the probability factor (p value) for this reaction is 0.006: only 6 collisions in every thousand (1 in 167) have an orientation that leads to reaction.

Collisions between individual atoms have p values near 1: almost no matter how they hit, so long as the collision has enough energy, the particles react. In such cases, the rate constant depends only on the frequency and energy of the collisions. At the other extreme are biochemical reactions, in which the reactants are often two small molecules that can react only when they collide with a specific tiny region of a giant molecule—a protein or nucleic acid. The orientation factor for these reactions is often less than 10^{-6}: fewer than one in a million sufficiently energetic collisions leads to product. The fact that countless such biochemical reactions are occurring right now as you read this sentence helps make the point that the number of collisions per second is truly astounding.

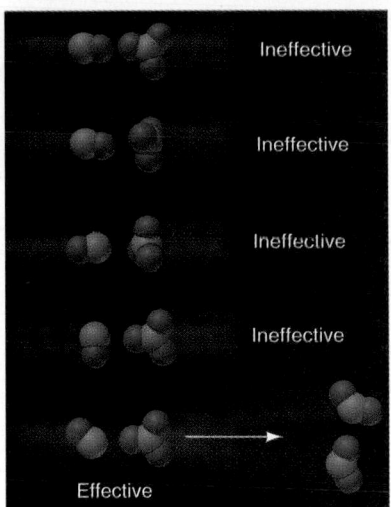

Figure 16.17 The importance of molecular orientation to an effective collision. Only one of the five orientations shown for the collision between NO and NO_3 has the correct orientation to lead to product. In the effective orientation, collision occurs between the atoms that will become bonded in the product.

Transition State Theory: Molecular Nature of the Activated State

Collision theory is a simple model that is easy to visualize, but it provides no insight about why the activation energy is needed and what the activated molecules look like. To understand these aspects of the process, we turn to transition state theory.

Visualizing the Transition State Recall from our discussions of energy changes (Chapter 6) that the internal energy of a system is the sum of its kinetic and potential energies. Two molecules that are far apart but speeding toward each other have high kinetic energy and low potential energy. As the molecules become closer, some kinetic energy is converted to potential energy as the electron clouds repel each other. At the moment of a head-on collision, the molecules stop, and their kinetic energy is converted to the potential energy of the collision. *If this potential energy is less than the activation energy, the molecules recoil,* bouncing off each other like billiard balls. Repulsions decrease, speeds increase, and the molecules zoom apart without reacting.

The tiny fraction of molecules that are oriented effectively *and* moving at the highest speed behave differently. *Their kinetic energy pushes them together with enough force to overcome repulsions and react.* Nuclei in one atom attract electrons in another; atomic orbitals overlap and electron density shifts; some bonds lengthen and weaken while others start to form. If we could watch this process in slow motion, we would see the reactant molecules gradually change their bonds and shapes as they turn into product molecules. At some point during this smooth transformation, what exists is *neither reactant nor product but a transitional species with partial bonds.* This species is extremely unstable (has very high potential energy) and exists only at the instant when the reacting system is highest in energy. It is called the **transition state,** or **activated complex,** of the reaction, and it forms only if the molecules

Figure 16.18 Nature of the transition state in the reaction between CH₃Br and OH⁻. Note the partial (elongated) C—O and C—Br bonds and the trigonal bipyramidal shape of the transition state of this reaction.

collide in an effective orientation *and* the energy of the collision is equal to or greater than the activation energy. Thus, *the activation energy is needed to stretch and deform bonds in order to reach the transition state.* Because they *cannot* be isolated, our knowledge of transition states is indirect only, coming through reasoning and studies of analogous, more stable species.

Consider the reaction between methyl bromide and hydroxide ion:

$$CH_3Br + OH^- \longrightarrow CH_3OH + Br^-$$

The electronegative bromine makes the carbon of methyl bromide partially positive. If the reactants are moving toward each other fast enough and oriented effectively when they collide, the negative oxygen in OH⁻ approaches the carbon with enough energy to begin forming a C—O bond, which causes the C—Br bond to weaken. In the transition state (Figure 16.18), the carbon is surrounded by five atoms in a trigonal bipyramidal shape, which never occurs in stable carbon compounds. This high-energy species consists of three normal C—H bonds and two partial bonds, one to O and the other to Br; there are *never* five normal bonds to carbon.

Reaching the transition state is no guarantee that the reaction will proceed to products; once in the transition state, the system can change in either direction. If the C—O bond continues to shorten and strengthen, products will form; however, if the C—Br bond becomes shorter and stronger again, the transition state will decompose back to reactants.

Depicting the Change with Reaction Energy Diagrams   A useful way to depict the events we just described is with a **reaction energy diagram,** which shows the potential energy of the system during the reaction as a smooth curve. Figure 16.19 shows the reaction energy diagram for the methyl bromide–hydroxide ion reaction, with a perspective (wedge) structure and

Figure 16.19 Reaction energy diagram for the reaction between CH₃Br and OH⁻. A plot of energy vs. reaction progress shows the relative energy levels of reactants, products, and transition state joined by a curved line, as well as the activation energies of the forward and reverse steps and the heat of reaction. The structures and molecular-level views depict the change at five points. Note the gradual bond forming and bond breaking as the system goes through the transition state.

molecular view at various points during the change. The horizontal axis, labeled "reaction progress" (or reaction coordinate), means that reactants change to products as we move from left to right. The reaction is exothermic, so the reactants are higher in energy than the products. This energy difference is due to differences in bond energy, which appear as the heat of reaction, ΔH_{rxn}. The diagram also shows the activation energies for the forward and reverse reactions; in this case, $E_{a(fwd)}$ is less than $E_{a(rev)}$.

Transition state theory proposes that *every reaction (and every step in an overall reaction) goes through its own transition state,* from which point it can continue in either direction. Thus, according to this model, *all reactions are reversible.* We can imagine how the transition state in many reactions might look by examining the reactant and product bonds that undergo change. Figure 16.20 depicts reaction energy diagrams for three simple reactions. Note that the shape of the postulated transition state in each case is based on a collision between atoms that become bonded in the product.

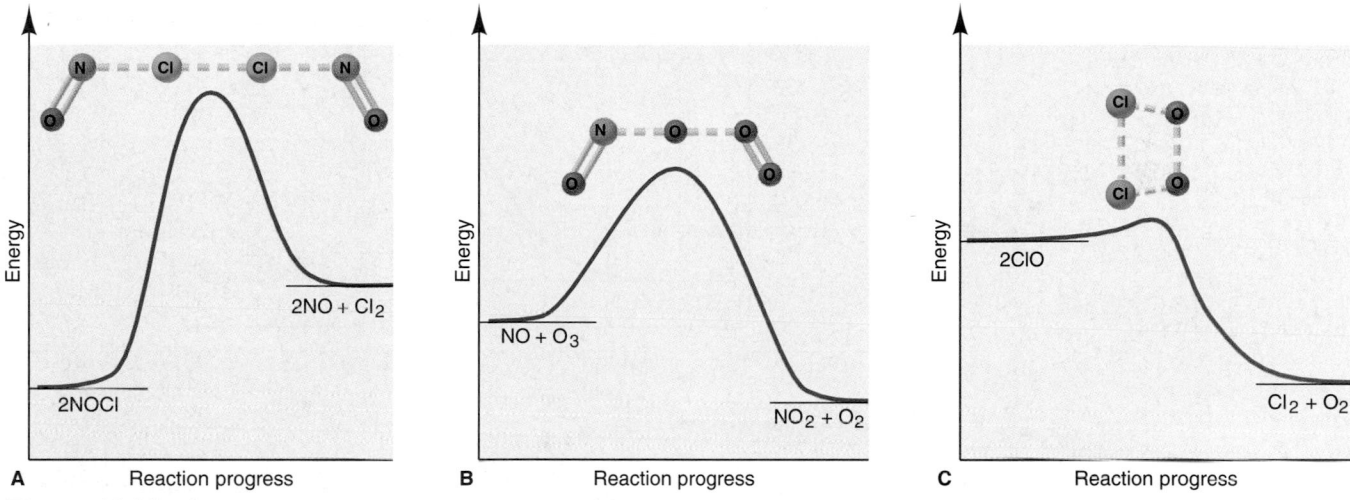

Figure 16.20 Reaction energy diagrams and possible transition states for three reactions.
A, $2NOCl(g) \longrightarrow 2NO(g) + Cl_2(g)$
(despite the formula NOCl, the atom sequence is ClNO).

B, $NO(g) + O_3(g) \longrightarrow NO_2(g) + O_2(g)$.
C, $2ClO(g) \longrightarrow Cl_2(g) + O_2(g)$.
Note that reaction **A** is endothermic, **B** and **C** are exothermic, and **C** has a very small $E_{a(fwd)}$.

Sample Problem 16.7 Drawing Reaction Energy Diagrams and Transition States

PROBLEM A key reaction in the upper atmosphere is

$$O_3(g) + O(g) \longrightarrow 2O_2(g)$$

The $E_{a(fwd)}$ is 19 kJ, and the ΔH_{rxn} for the reaction as written is -392 kJ. Draw a reaction energy diagram for this reaction, postulate a transition state, and calculate $E_{a(rev)}$.

PLAN Since the reaction is highly exothermic, the products are much lower in energy than the reactants. The small $E_{a(fwd)}$ means that the energy of the reactants lies slightly below that of the transition state. To reach the transition state from the products would require energy equal to ΔH_{rxn} plus $E_{a(fwd)}$; thus, $E_{a(rev)} = \Delta H_{rxn} + E_{a(fwd)}$. To postulate the transition state, we sketch the species and note that one of the bonds in O_3 weakens, and this partially bonded O begins forming a bond to the separate O atom.

SOLUTION The reaction energy diagram (not drawn to scale), with the transition state depicted, is

CHECK Rounding to find $E_{a(rev)}$ gives ~ 390 + 20 = 410.

Follow-up Problem 16.7   The following reaction energy diagram depicts another key atmospheric reaction. Label the axes, $E_{a(fwd)}$, $E_{a(rev)}$, and ΔH_{rxn}, draw and label the transition state, and calculate $E_{a(rev)}$ for the reaction.

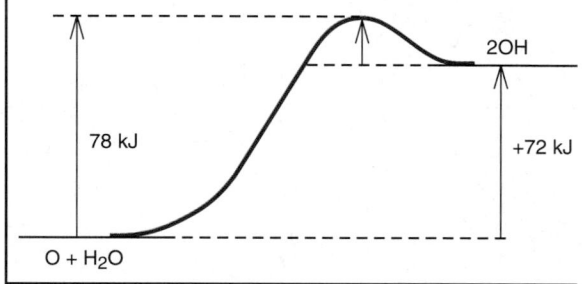

Section Summary

According to collision theory, reactant particles must collide to react, and the number of collisions depends on the product of the reactant concentrations. At higher temperatures, more collisions have enough energy to exceed the activation energy (E_a). The relative sizes of E_a for the forward and the reverse reactions depend on whether the overall reaction is exothermic or endothermic. Molecules must collide with an effective orientation for reaction to occur, so structural complexity decreases rate.

Transition state theory pictures the kinetic energy of the particles changing to potential energy during a collision. Given sufficient collision energy and an effective molecular orientation, the reactant species become an unstable transition state, which decomposes to either reactant or product. Reaction energy diagrams depict the changing energy of the chemical system as it progresses from reactants through transition state(s) to products.

16.7   Reaction Mechanisms: Steps in the Overall Reaction

Imagine trying to figure out how a car works just by examining the body, wheels, and dashboard. It can't be done—you need to look under the hood, peer inside the engine, and see how the parts fit together and function. Similarly, since our main purpose is to know how a reaction works *at the molecular level*, examining the overall balanced equation is not much help—we must "look under the yield arrow and peer inside the reaction" to see how reactants change into products.

When we do so, we find that most reactions occur through a **reaction mechanism,** a sequence of single reaction steps that sum to the overall reaction. For example, a possible mechanism for the overall reaction

$$2A + B \longrightarrow E + F$$

might involve these three simpler steps:

(1) $A + B \longrightarrow C$
(2) $C + A \longrightarrow D$
(3) $\quad\quad D \longrightarrow E + F$

Adding them together and canceling common substances, we get the overall equation:

$$A + B + \cancel{C} + A + \cancel{D} \longrightarrow \cancel{C} + \cancel{D} + E + F \quad\quad \text{or} \quad\quad 2A + B \longrightarrow E + F$$

Chemists *propose* a reaction mechanism to explain how a given reaction might occur and then *test* it. This section focuses on the nature of the individual steps and how they fit together to give a rate law consistent with experiment.

Elementary Reactions and Molecularity

The individual steps, which together make up the proposed reaction mechanism, are called **elementary reactions** (or **elementary steps**). Each describes a *single molecular event,* such as one particle decomposing or two particles colliding and combining. *An elementary step is **not** made up of simpler steps.*

An elementary step is characterized by its **molecularity,** the number of *reactant* particles involved in the step. Consider the mechanism for the breakdown of ozone in the stratosphere. The overall reaction is

$$2O_3(g) \longrightarrow 3O_2(g)$$

A two-step mechanism has been proposed for this reaction. Note that the two steps sum to the overall reaction. The first elementary step is a **unimolecular reaction,** one that involves the decomposition or rearrangement of a single particle:

(1) $O_3(g) \longrightarrow O_2(g) + O(g)$

The second step is a **bimolecular reaction,** one in which two particles react:

(2) $O_3(g) + O(g) \longrightarrow 2O_2(g)$

Some *termolecular* elementary steps occur, but they are rare because the probability of three particles colliding simultaneously with enough energy and with an effective orientation is small. Higher molecularities are not known. Unless evidence exists to the contrary, it makes good chemical sense to propose only unimolecular or bimolecular reactions as elementary steps in a mechanism.

The rate law for an elementary reaction, unlike that of an overall reaction, *can* be deduced from the reaction stoichiometry. Since an elementary reaction occurs in one step, its rate must be proportional to the product of the reactant concentrations. Therefore, *we use the equation coefficients as the reaction orders in the rate law for an elementary step; that is, reaction order equals molecularity* (Table 16.6). Remember that this statement holds *only* when we know that the reaction is elementary; you've already seen that for an overall reaction, the reaction orders must be determined experimentally.

Table 16.6 Rate Laws for General Elementary Steps

Elementary Step	Molecularity	Rate Law
A $\longrightarrow$ product	Unimolecular	Rate = $k[A]$
2A $\longrightarrow$ product	Bimolecular	Rate = $k[A]^2$
A + B $\longrightarrow$ product	Bimolecular	Rate = $k[A][B]$
2A + B $\longrightarrow$ product	Termolecular	Rate = $k[A]^2[B]$

Sample Problem 16.8 Determining Molecularity and Rate Laws for Elementary Steps

PROBLEM The following two reactions are proposed as elementary steps in the mechanism for an overall reaction:

(1) $NO_2Cl(g) \longrightarrow NO_2(g) + Cl(g)$

(2) $NO_2Cl(g) + Cl(g) \longrightarrow NO_2(g) + Cl_2(g)$

(a) Write the overall balanced equation.
(b) Determine the molecularity of each step.
(c) Write the rate law for each step.

PLAN We find the overall equation from the sum of the elementary steps. The molecularity of each step equals the total number of reactant particles. We write the rate law for each step using the molecularities as reaction orders.

SOLUTION **(a)** Writing the overall equation:

$$NO_2Cl(g) \longrightarrow NO_2(g) + Cl(g)$$
$$\underline{NO_2Cl(g) + Cl(g) \longrightarrow NO_2(g) + Cl_2(g)}$$
$$NO_2Cl(g) + NO_2Cl(g) + \cancel{Cl(g)} \longrightarrow NO_2(g) + \cancel{Cl(g)} + NO_2(g) + Cl_2(g)$$
$$2NO_2Cl(g) \longrightarrow 2NO_2(g) + Cl_2(g)$$

(b) Determining the molecularity of each step: The first elementary step has only one reactant, NO_2Cl, so it is unimolecular. The second elementary step has two reactants, NO_2Cl and Cl, so it is bimolecular.
(c) Writing rate laws for the elementary reactions:
(1) $Rate_1 = k_1[NO_2Cl]$
(2) $Rate_2 = k_2[NO_2Cl][Cl]$

CHECK In **(a)**, be sure the equation is balanced; in **(c)**, be sure the substances in brackets are the reactants of each elementary step.

Follow-up Problem 16.8 The following elementary steps constitute a proposed mechanism for a reaction:

(1) $2NO(g) \longrightarrow N_2O_2(g)$

(2) $2[H_2(g) \longrightarrow 2H(g)]$

(3) $N_2O_2(g) + H(g) \longrightarrow N_2O(g) + HO(g)$

(4) $2[HO(g) + H(g) \longrightarrow H_2O(g)]$

(5) $H(g) + N_2O(g) \longrightarrow HO(g) + N_2(g)$

(a) Write the balanced equation for the overall reaction.
(b) Determine the molecularity of each step.
(c) Write the rate law for each step.

◆ Sleeping Through the Rate-Determining Step
Baking provides a tasty, macroscopic example of a rate-limiting step. Five steps in making a loaf of French bread are (1) mixing the ingredients (15 min), (2) kneading the dough (10 min), (3) letting the dough rise in a refrigerator (400 min), (4) shaping the loaf (2 min), and (5) baking the loaf (25 min). Obviously, the dough-rising step limits how fast a baker can produce a loaf because it is so much slower than the other steps. Keenly aware of the baking "reaction mechanism," bakers let the dough rise overnight, thereby sleeping through the rate-determining step.

The Rate-Determining Step of a Reaction Mechanism

All the elementary steps in a mechanism do not have the same rate. Usually, one of the steps is much slower than the others, so it limits how fast the overall reaction proceeds. This step is called the **rate-determining step** (or **rate-limiting step**). ◆

Because the rate-determining step limits the rate of the overall reaction, its rate law represents the rate law for the overall reaction. Consider the reaction between nitrogen dioxide and carbon monoxide:

$$NO_2(g) + CO(g) \longrightarrow NO(g) + CO_2(g)$$

If the overall reaction were an elementary reaction—that is, if the mechanism consisted of only one step—we could immediately write the overall rate law as

$$Rate = k[NO_2][CO]$$

However, as you saw in Sample Problem 16.3, experiment shows that the actual rate law is

$$Rate = k[NO_2]^2$$

From this, we know immediately that the reaction shown cannot be elementary.

A proposed two-step mechanism is

(1) $NO_2(g) + NO_2(g) \longrightarrow NO_3(g) + NO(g)$ [slow; rate determining]

(2) $NO_3(g) + CO(g) \longrightarrow NO_2(g) + CO_2(g)$ [fast]

Rate laws for these elementary steps are

(1) Rate $= k_1[NO_2][NO_2] = k_1[NO_2]^2$

(2) Rate $= k_2[NO_3][CO]$

Note that if $k_1 = k$, *the rate law for the rate-determining step (step 1) is identical to the experimental rate law.* The first step is so slow compared with the second that the overall reaction takes essentially as long as the first step.

It is also important to consider what happens to NO_3 in this mechanism. It is a product in step 1 and a reactant in step 2. Therefore, it functions here as a **reaction intermediate,** a substance that is formed and used up during the overall reaction. It does not appear in the overall balanced equation, and its existence is temporary; nevertheless, its presence is absolutely necessary for the reaction to occur. Reaction intermediates are usually unstable relative to the reactants and products but are far more stable than transition states (activated complexes). They are molecules with normal bonds and are sometimes stable enough to be isolated.

Correlating the Mechanism with the Rate Law

Conjuring up a reasonable reaction mechanism is one of the most exciting aspects of chemical kinetics and can be a classical example of the scientific method. We use observations and data from rate experiments to hypothesize what the individual steps might be and then test our hypothesis by gathering further evidence. If the evidence supports it, we continue to apply that mechanism; if not, we propose a new one. However, *we can never prove, just from data, that a particular mechanism represents the actual chemical change.*

Regardless of the elementary steps that are proposed for the mechanism, they must obey three criteria:

1. *The elementary steps must add up to the overall equation.* We cannot wind up with more (or fewer) reactants or products than are present in the balanced equation.
2. *The elementary steps must be physically reasonable.* As we noted, most steps should involve one reactant particle (unimolecular) or two (bimolecular). Steps with three reactant particles (termolecular) are very unlikely.
3. *The mechanism must correlate with the rate law.* Most importantly, a mechanism must support the experimental facts shown by the rate law, not the other way around.

Let's see how the mechanisms of several reactions conform to these criteria and how the elementary steps fit together.

Mechanisms with a Slow Initial Step We've already seen one mechanism with a rate-determining first step in the NO_2-CO reaction shown previously. Another example is the reaction between nitrogen dioxide and fluorine gas:

$$2NO_2(g) + F_2(g) \longrightarrow 2NO_2F(g)$$

The experimental rate law is first order in NO_2 and in F_2:

$$\text{Rate} = k[NO_2][F_2]$$

The accepted mechanism for the reaction is

(1) $NO_2(g) + F_2(g) \longrightarrow NO_2F(g) + F(g)$ [slow; rate determining]

(2) $NO_2(g) + F(g) \longrightarrow NO_2F(g)$ [fast]

Molecules of reactant and product appear in both elementary steps. The free fluorine atom is a reaction intermediate.

Does this mechanism meet the three crucial criteria?

1. The elementary reactions sum to the balanced equation:

$$NO_2(g) + NO_2(g) + F_2(g) + \cancel{F(g)} \longrightarrow NO_2F(g) + NO_2F(g) + \cancel{F(g)}$$

Or $$2NO_2(g) + F_2(g) \longrightarrow 2NO_2F(g)$$

2. Both steps are bimolecular, so they are chemically reasonable.

3. The mechanism gives the rate law of the overall equation. To show this, we write the rate laws for the elementary steps:

(1) $Rate_1 = k_1[NO_2][F_2]$

(2) $Rate_2 = k_2[NO_2][F]$

Step 1 is the rate-determining step and therefore gives the overall rate law, with $k_1 = k$. Since the second molecule of NO_2 appears in the step that follows the rate-determining step, it does not appear in the overall rate law. Thus, we see that *the overall rate law includes only species active in the reaction up to and including those in the rate-determining step*. We also saw this point in the NO_2-CO mechanism earlier. Carbon monoxide was absent from the overall rate law because it appeared *after* the rate-determining step.

Figure 16.21 shows a reaction energy diagram for the NO_2-F_2 reaction. Notice that

- *Each step in the mechanism has its own transition state.* (Note that only one molecule of NO_2 is involved in step 1, and only the first transition state is depicted.)

- The F atom intermediate is a reactive, unstable species (as you know from halogen chemistry), so it is higher in energy than reactants or product.

- The first step is slower (rate limiting), so its activation energy is *larger* than that of the second.

- The overall reaction is exothermic, so the product is lower in energy than the reactants.

Figure 16.21 Reaction energy diagram for the two-step NO_2-F_2 reaction. Each step in the mechanism has its own transition state. The proposed transition state is shown for step 1. Reactants for the second step are the F atom intermediate and the second molecule of NO_2. Note that the first step is slower (higher E_a). The overall reaction is exothermic ($\Delta H_{rxn} < 0$).

Mechanisms with a Fast Initial Step   If the rate-limiting step in a mechanism is *not* the initial step, it acts as a bottleneck later in the reaction sequence. As a result, the product of a fast initial step builds up and starts reverting to reactant, while waiting for the slow step to remove it. With time, the product of the initial step is changing back to reactant as fast as it is forming. In other words, the *fast initial step reaches equilibrium*. As you'll see, this situation allows us to fit the mechanism to the overall rate law.

Consider once again the oxidation of nitric oxide:

$$2NO(g) + O_2(g) \longrightarrow 2NO_2(g)$$

The experimentally determined rate law is

$$Rate = k[NO]^2[O_2]$$

and a proposed mechanism is

(1) $NO(g) + O_2(g) \rightleftharpoons NO_3(g)$ [fast, reversible]

(2) $NO_3(g) + NO(g) \longrightarrow 2NO_2(g)$ [slow; rate determining]

Note that, with cancellation of the intermediate NO_3, the first criterion is met because the sum of the steps gives the overall equation. Also note that the second criterion is met because both steps are bimolecular.

To meet the third criterion (the mechanism conforms to the overall rate law), we first write rate laws for the elementary steps:

(1) $Rate_{1(fwd)} = k_1[NO][O_2]$

  $Rate_{1(rev)} = k_{-1}[NO_3]$

where k_{-1} is the rate constant for the reverse reaction.

(2) $Rate_2 = k_2[NO_3][NO]$

Now we must show that the rate law for the rate-determining step (step 2) gives the overall rate law. As written it does not, because it contains the intermediate NO_3, and *an overall rate law can include only reactants (and products)*. Therefore, we must eliminate $[NO_3]$ from the step 2 rate law. To do so, we express $[NO_3]$ in terms of reactants. Step 1 reaches equilibrium when the forward and reverse rates are equal:

$$\text{Rate}_{1(fwd)} = \text{rate}_{1(rev)}$$

Or
$$k_1[NO][O_2] = k_{-1}[NO_3]$$

To express $[NO_3]$ in terms of reactants, we isolate it algebraically:

$$[NO_3] = \frac{k_1}{k_{-1}}[NO][O_2]$$

Then, substituting for $[NO_3]$ in the rate law for step 2, we obtain

$$\text{Rate}_2 = k_2[NO_3][NO] = k_2\left(\frac{k_1}{k_{-1}}[NO][O_2]\right)[NO] = \frac{k_2 k_1}{k_{-1}}[NO]^2[O_2]$$

Thus, this rate law is identical to the overall rate law, with $k = \dfrac{k_2 k_1}{k_{-1}}$.

To summarize the approach for a mechanism with a fast initial, reversible step:

1. Write rate laws for both directions of the fast step and for the slow step.
2. Show that the slow step's rate law is equivalent to the overall rate law, by *expressing the [intermediate] in terms of the [reactant]:* set the forward rate law of the fast, reversible step equal to the reverse rate law, and solve for [intermediate].
3. Substitute the expression for the [intermediate] into the rate law for the slow step to obtain the overall rate law.

Several end-of-chapter problems, including 16.72 and 16.73, provide additional examples of this approach.

Section Summary

The mechanisms of most common reactions consist of two or more elementary steps, reactions that occur in one step and depict a single chemical change. The molecularity of an elementary step equals the number of reactant particles and is the same as the reaction order of its rate law. Unimolecular and bimolecular steps are common. The rate-determining, or rate-limiting (slowest), step determines how fast the overall reaction occurs, and its rate law represents the overall rate law. Intermediates are species that form in one step and react in a later one. The steps in a proposed mechanism must add up to the overall reaction, be physically reasonable, and conform to the overall rate law. If a fast step precedes the slow step, the fast step reaches equilibrium, and the concentrations of intermediates in the rate law of the slow step must be expressed in terms of reactants.

16.8 Catalysis: Speeding Up a Chemical Reaction

There are many situations in which the rate of a reaction must be increased for it to be useful. In an industrial process, for example, a higher rate often determines whether a new product can be made economically. Sometimes, we can speed up a reaction sufficiently with a higher temperature, but energy is costly and many substances are heat sensitive and easily decomposed. Alternatively, we can often employ a **catalyst,** a substance that increases the rate *without* being consumed in the reaction. Because catalysts are not consumed, very small, nonstoichiometric quantities are generally all that are required. Nevertheless, these substances are employed in so many important processes that over three million tons of industrial catalysts are produced annually in the United States alone! Nature is the master designer and user of catalysts. Even the simplest bacterial cell employs thousands of biological catalysts, known as *enzymes,* to speed up its cellular reactions. Every organism relies on enzymes to sustain life.

Each catalyst has its own specific way of functioning, but in general, *a catalyst lowers the activation energy, which in turn makes the rate constant larger and the rate higher.* Two important points stand out in Figure 16.22:

- A catalyst speeds up the forward *and* reverse reactions. A reaction with a catalyst *does not yield more product* than one without a catalyst, but it yields the product *more quickly.*
- A catalyst *lowers the activation energy* by providing a *different mechanism* for the reaction, a new lower-energy pathway.

Figure 16.22 Reaction energy diagram of a catalyzed and an uncatalyzed process. A catalyst speeds a reaction by providing a new lower energy path, in this case by replacing the one-step mechanism with a two-step mechanism. Both forward and reverse rates are increased to the same extent, so *a catalyst does not affect the overall reaction yield.* (The only activation energy shown for the catalyzed reaction is the larger one for the forward direction.)

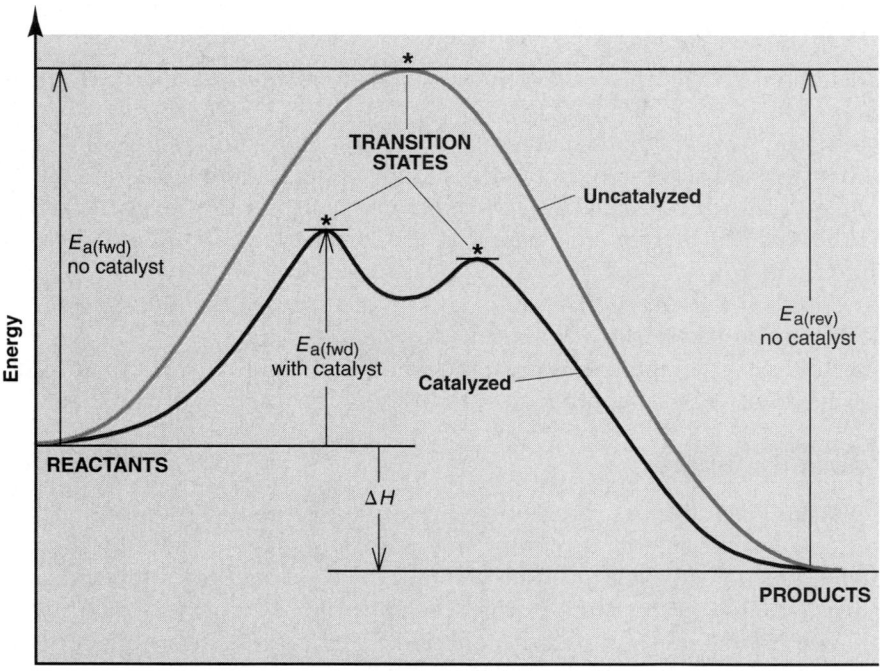

Reaction progress

Consider a general *uncatalyzed* reaction that proceeds by a one-step mechanism involving a bimolecular collision:

$$A + B \longrightarrow \text{product} \quad \text{[slower]}$$

In the *catalyzed* reaction, the reactants interact with the catalyst, so the mechanism might involve a two-step pathway:

$$A + \text{catalyst} \longrightarrow C \quad \text{[faster]}$$
$$C + B \longrightarrow \text{product} + \text{catalyst} \quad \text{[faster]}$$

Note that *the catalyst is not consumed,* as its definition requires. Rather, it is used and then regenerated, and the activation energies of both steps are lower than the activation energy of the uncatalyzed path.

There are two broad categories of catalyst—homogeneous and heterogeneous—depending on whether the catalyst is in the same phase as the reactant and product.

Homogeneous Catalysis

A **homogeneous catalyst** exists in solution with the reaction mixture. All homogeneous catalysts are gases, liquids, or soluble solids. Some industrial processes that employ these catalysts are shown in Table 16.7 *(top)*.

A thoroughly studied example of homogeneous catalysis is the hydrolysis of an organic ester (RCOOR'), a reaction we examined in Section 15.4:

$$R-\overset{O}{\underset{\|}{C}}-O-R' + H_2O \rightleftharpoons R-\overset{O}{\underset{\|}{C}}-OH + R'-OH$$

Here R and R' are hydrocarbon groups, $R-\overset{O}{\underset{\|}{C}}-OH$ is an organic acid, and R'—OH is an alcohol. The reaction rate is low at room temperature but can be increased by adding a small amount of strong inorganic acid, which provides H^+ ion, the catalyst in the reaction.

In the first step of the catalyzed reaction (Figure 16.23), the H^+ ion forms a bond to the O atom that was double bonded to the C atom. This makes the C atom more positive, which *increases its attraction* for the partially negative O atom of water, thus enhancing their bonding, which is the rate-determining step. Several steps later, H^+ returns to solution. Thus, H^+ acts as a catalyst because it speeds up the reaction but is not itself consumed: it is used up in one step and re-formed in another. The Chemical Connections essay provides a troubling example of homogeneous catalysis in our atmosphere that has become a major societal concern.

Heterogeneous Catalysis

A **heterogeneous catalyst** speeds up a reaction that occurs in a separate phase. The catalyst is most often a solid interacting with gaseous or liquid reactants. Since reaction occurs on the solid's surface, heterogeneous catalysts usually have enormous areas for contact, between 1 and 500 m^2/g. Table 16.7 *(bottom)* lists some polymer manufacturing processes that employ heterogeneous catalysts.

Step 1

Step 2

Step 3

Figure 16.23 Mechanism for the catalyzed hydrolysis of an organic ester. In step 1, the catalytic H^+ ion binds to the electron-rich oxygen, making the C atom more positive than it would ordinarily be. This enhanced charge on C attracts the partially negative O of water more strongly, increasing the fraction of effective collisions and thus speeding step 2, the rate-limiting step. Loss of R'OH and release of H^+ occur in a final series of fast steps.

Table 16.7 Some Modern Processes Based on Catalysis

Reactants	Catalyst	Product	Use
Homogeneous			
Propylene, oxidizer	Mo(VI) complexes	Propylene oxide	Polyurethane foams; polyesters
Methanol, CO	$[Rh(CO)_2I_2]^-$	Acetic acid	Poly(vinyl acetate) coatings; poly(vinyl alcohol)
Butadiene, HCN	Ni/P compounds	Adiponitrile	Nylons (fibers, plastics)
α-Olefins, CO, H_2	Rh/P compounds	Aldehydes	Plasticizers, lubricants
Heterogeneous			
Ethylene, O_2	Silver, cesium chloride on alumina	Ethylene oxide	Polyesters, ethylene glycol, lubricants
Propylene, NH_3, O_2	Bismuth molybdates	Acrylonitrile	Plastics, fibers, resins
Ethylene	Organochromium and titanium halides on silica	High-density polyethylene	Molded products

Chemical Connections
Chemistry in Atmospheric Science

Depletion of the Earth's Ozone Layer

Homogeneous catalysis takes part in one of the most serious environmental problems of our time: the depletion of ozone from the stratosphere. The stratospheric ozone layer is vital to life on Earth because ozone absorbs short-wavelength ($\sim 3 \times 10^{-7}$ m) ultraviolet (UV) radiation from the Sun:

$$O_3(g) \xrightarrow{\text{UV photon}} O_2(g) + O(g)$$

This radiation has enough energy to break bonds in deoxyribonucleic acid (DNA) and thereby damage genes. Were large amounts of UV radiation to reach the Earth's surface, mutations and cancers would increase dramatically, and the planet's food chain could be disrupted.

Under normal conditions, the stratospheric ozone concentration varies seasonally but remains nearly constant annually through a complex series of atmospheric reactions. Two reactions that maintain a balance in ozone concentration are

$$O_2(g) + O(g) \longrightarrow O_3(g) \quad \text{[formation]}$$
$$O_3(g) + O(g) \longrightarrow 2O_2(g) \quad \text{[breakdown]}$$

However, based on the ground-breaking research by Paul Crutzen, Mario J. Molina, and F. Sherwood Rowland, for which they received the Nobel Prize in 1995, we now understand that release of industrially produced chlorofluorocarbons (CFCs) has shifted this balance by catalyzing the breakdown reaction.

The CFCs are employed as air-conditioner refrigerants, plastic foam reagents, and aerosol propellants, uses that lead ultimately to large quantities being released into the atmosphere. They are chemically inert and very stable in the lower atmosphere. While there, the ozone layer shields them from high-energy, molecule-splitting UV photons. However, once the CFCs reach the stratosphere, they absorb UV photons and release Cl atoms:

$$CF_2Cl_2(g) \xrightarrow{\text{UV photon}} \cdot CF_2Cl(g) + \cdot Cl(g)$$

The dots ($\cdot$) represent unpaired electrons resulting from bond breakage.

Like many species with unpaired electrons, atomic chlorine is very reactive. The Cl atoms react with stratospheric ozone to produce the intermediate chlorine monoxide ($\cdot$ClO), which then reacts with free O atoms to regenerate Cl atoms:

$$O_3(g) + \cdot Cl(g) \longrightarrow \cdot ClO(g) + O_2(g)$$
$$\cdot ClO(g) + O(g) \longrightarrow \cdot Cl(g) + O_2(g)$$

The sum of these two elementary reactions yields the overall reaction of ozone breakdown:

$$O_3(g) + \cancel{\cdot Cl(g)} + \cancel{\cdot ClO(g)} + O(g) \longrightarrow$$
$$\cancel{\cdot ClO(g)} + O_2(g) + \cancel{\cdot Cl(g)} + O_2(g)$$

or
$$O_3(g) + O(g) \longrightarrow 2O_2(g)$$

Note that the Cl atom acts here as a typical homogeneous catalyst: it exists in the same phase as the reactants, speeds up a process via a different mechanism, and is regenerated to continue this role. Measurements of high [ClO] over Antarc-

Figure 16.D **The increasing size of the Antarctic ozone "hole."** These satellite images show changes in ozone concentration over the South Pole for several years from October 1990 through 1998. Note the "hole" in the ozone layer *(purple)* and its darkening center. More recent data show a similar thinning, though not yet as severe, over the North Pole.

tica are consistent with this mechanism, but more recent data suggest that it represents a simplified version of the actual situation. The current proposed mechanism is far more complex and involves nitrogen-containing species and ice microcrystals in high-altitude clouds. Nevertheless, the crux of the problem remains the same: each Cl atom has a stratospheric lifetime of about 2 years, during which time it speeds the destruction of about 100,000 ozone molecules.

Atmospheric scientists have documented more than 80% ozone depletion over the South Pole during certain times of the year (Figure 16.D), and there is now strong evidence of ozone thinning over the North Pole as well.

Beginning in 1995, data from NASA indicate a thinning of ozone over the temperate zones during summer months, when people are lightly clothed and outdoors. Worldwide, more than 1 million tons of CFCs are released from air conditioners and spray cans each year. As a result of international agreements, CFC production in industrial countries has been virtually phased out, but this situation brings up other questions: Can we get along with less air conditioning? Are other refrigerants (NH_3, hydrofluorocarbons) good alternatives?

Even though CFC production has stopped, smuggling of existing stockpiles is thriving and estimates are that the amounts already released that have not yet reached the stratosphere will continue ozone depletion (we hope less severely) for the next 100 years!

① H_2 and C_2H_4 approach and adsorb to metal surface.

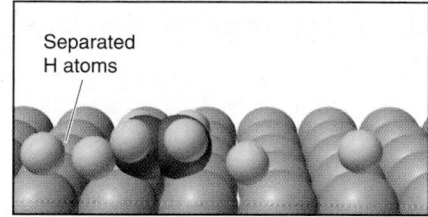

② Rate-limiting step is H—H bond breakage.

③ One H atom bonds to adsorbed C_2H_4.

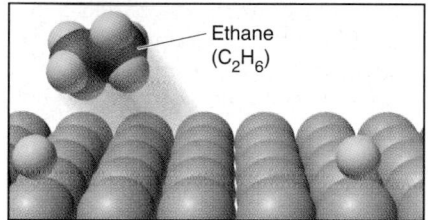

④ Another C—H bond forms and C_2H_6 leaves the surface.

Figure 16.24 **The metal-catalyzed hydrogenation of ethylene.**

One of the most important examples of heterogeneous catalysis is the *cis*-addition of hydrogen to the C=C bonds of organic compounds to form C—C bonds. The petroleum, plastics, and food industries use such catalytic **hydrogenation** to change a wide variety of compounds into more useful substances. The conversion of vegetable oil into margarine is one example.

The simplest hydrogenation converts ethylene to ethane:

$$H_2C{=}CH_2(g) + H_2(g) \longrightarrow H_3C{-}CH_3(g)$$

In the absence of a catalyst, the reaction occurs very slowly. At high H_2 pressure in the presence of finely divided nickel, palladium, or platinum, the reaction becomes rapid even at ordinary temperatures. These Group 8B(10) metals catalyze by *chemically adsorbing the reactants onto their surface* (Figure 16.24). Once there, H_2 splits into separate H atoms chemically bound to the solid catalyst's metal atoms (catM):

$$H{-}H(g) + 2catM(s) \longrightarrow 2catM{-}H \text{ (H atoms bound to metal surface)}$$

The H atoms migrate over the surface, eventually collide with a bound C_2H_4 molecule, and the reaction takes place. The H—H bond breakage is the rate-determining step in the overall process, and interaction with the catalyst's surface provides the low–activation energy step as part of an alternative reaction mechanism. ◆ The next Chemical Connections essay introduces the remarkable abilities of the heterogeneous catalysts inside you.

Section Summary

A catalyst is a substance that increases the rate of a reaction without being consumed. It accomplishes this by providing an alternative mechanism with a lower activation energy. Homogeneous catalysts function in the same phase as the reactants. Gaseous chlorine atoms derived from CFC molecules that catalyze the breakdown of stratospheric ozone are an example. Heterogeneous catalysts act in a different phase from the reactants. The hydrogenation of carbon double bonds takes place on a solid catalyst, which speeds the breakage of the H—H bond in H_2. Enzymes are biological catalysts with spectacular efficiency and specificity.

◆ **Catalytically Cleaning Your Car's Exhaust**

A heterogeneous catalyst you use every day, but rarely see, is the catalytic converter in your car's exhaust system. It is designed to convert polluting exhaust gases into nontoxic ones. In a single pass through the catalyst bed, CO and unburned gasoline are oxidized to CO_2 and H_2O, while NO is reduced to N_2. As in the hydrogenation mechanism, the catalyst lowers the activation energy of the rate-determining step by adsorbing the molecules, thereby weakening their bonds. Mixtures of transition metals and their oxides embedded in inert supports convert as much exhaust gas as possible in the shortest time. It is estimated, for example, that an NO molecule is adsorbed and split into catalyst-bound N and O atoms in less than $2{\times}10^{-12}$ second!

Kinetics and Function of Biological Catalysts

Within every living cell, thousands of individual reactions occur. Many involve complex chemical changes, yet they take place in dilute solution at ordinary temperatures and pressures. The rate of each reaction responds smoothly to momentary or permanent changes in other reaction rates, various signals from other cells, and environmental stresses. Virtually every reaction in this marvelous chemical harmony is catalyzed by its own specific **enzyme,** a protein catalyst whose function has been perfected through evolution.

Enzymes have complex three-dimensional shapes and molar masses ranging from about 15,000 to 1,000,000 g/mol

(Section 15.6). At a specific region on an enzyme's surface is its **active site,** a molecular crevice whose shape results from the shapes of the amino acid side chains directly involved in catalyzing the reaction (also see Figure 10.D, p. 388). When the reactant molecules, called the **substrates** of the reaction, collide with the active site, the chemical change is initiated. The active site makes up only a small part of the enzyme's surface—like a tiny hollow carved into a mountainside—and often includes amino acid groups from distant regions of the protein that exist near each other because of the folding of the protein backbone (Figure 16.E). In most cases, *substrates bind*

Figure 16.E The widely separated amino acid groups that form an active site. The amino acids in chymotrypsin, a digestive enzyme, are shown as linked spheres and numbered consecutively from the beginning of the chain. The R groups of the active-site amino acids 57 (histidine, His), 102 (aspartic acid, Asp), and 195 (serine, Ser) are shown because they play a crucial role in the enzyme-catalyzed reaction. Part of the substrate lies within a binding pocket to anchor it during reaction. (Copyright Irving Geis; The estate of Irving Geis.)

to the active site through intermolecular forces: H bonds, dipole forces, and other weak attractions.

An enzyme has features of both a homogeneous and a heterogeneous catalyst. Most enzymes are enormous compared with their substrates, and they are often found embedded within membranes of larger cell parts. Thus, like a heterogeneous catalyst, an enzyme provides an active surface on which a reactant is immobilized temporarily, waiting for its reaction partner to land nearby. Like a homogeneous catalyst, the enzyme's amino acid groups interact actively with the substrates in multistep sequences involving intermediates.

Enzymes are incredibly *efficient* catalysts. Consider the hydrolysis of urea as an example:

$$(NH_2)_2C = O(aq) + 2H_2O(l) + H^+(aq) \longrightarrow$$
$$2NH_4^+(aq) + HCO_3^-(aq)$$

In water at room temperature, the rate constant for the uncatalyzed reaction is approximately 3×10^{-10} s^{-1}. Under the same conditions in the presence of the enzyme *urease* (pronounced "*yur*-ee-ase"), the rate constant is 3×10^4 s^{-1}, a 10^{14}-fold increase! Enzymes increase rates by 10^8 to 10^{20} times, values that industrial chemists who design catalysts can only dream of.

Enzymes are also extremely *specific,* in that each reaction is generally catalyzed by a particular enzyme. Urease catalyzes *only* the hydrolysis of urea, and none of the several thousand other enzymes present in the cell catalyzes that reaction. This remarkable specificity results from the particular groups that comprise the active site. Two models of enzyme action are illustrated in Figure 16.F. According to the **lock-and-key model,** when the "key" (substrate) fits the "lock" (active site), the chemical change begins. However, modern x-ray crystallographic and spectroscopic methods show that, in many cases, *the enzyme changes shape when the substrate lands at the active site.* This **induced-fit model** of enzyme action pictures the substrate inducing the active site to adopt a perfect fit.

Rather than a rigidly shaped lock and key, therefore, we might picture a hand in a glove, in which the "glove" (active site) does not attain its functional shape until the "hand" (substrate) moves into place.

The kinetics of enzyme catalysis has many features in common with ordinary catalysis. In an uncatalyzed reaction, the rate is affected by the concentrations of the reactants; in a catalyzed reaction, the rate is affected by the *concentration of reactant bound to catalyst.* In the enzyme-catalyzed case, substrate (S) and enzyme (E) form an intermediate **enzyme-substrate complex (ES),** whose concentration determines the rate of product (P) formation. The steps common to virtually all enzyme-catalyzed reactions are

(1) E + S $\rightleftharpoons$ ES   [fast, reversible]
(2)   ES $\longrightarrow$ E + P   [slow; rate-determining]
Thus, rate = k[ES].

Enzymes employ a variety of catalytic mechanisms. In some cases, the active site groups bring the reacting atoms of the bound substrates closer together. In other cases, the groups move apart slightly, stretching the substrate bond that is to be broken in the process. Some enzyme groups are acidic and thus are able to provide H$^+$ ions that increase the speed of a rate-determining step. *Hydrolases* are a class of enzymes that cleave bonds by such *acid catalysis.* For example, lysozyme, an enzyme found in tears, hydrolyzes bacterial cell walls, thus protecting the eyes from microbes; chymotrypsin, an enzyme in the small intestine, hydrolyzes proteins into smaller molecules during digestion.

No matter what their specific mode of action, *all enzymes function by stabilizing the reaction's transition state.* For instance, in the lysozyme-catalyzed reaction, the transition state is a sugar molecule with bonds twisted and stretched into unusual lengths and angles, but it fits the lysozyme active site perfectly. By stabilizing the transition state through binding it effectively, lysozyme lowers the activation energy of the reaction and thus increases the rate.

A Lock-and-key model

B Induced-fit model

Figure 16.F Two models of enzyme action. A, In the lock-and-key model, the active site is thought to be an exact fit for the substrate shapes. **B,** In the induced-fit model, the active site is thought to change shape to fit the substrates. Most enzyme-catalyzed reactions proceed through a fast, reversible formation of an enzyme-substrate(s) complex, followed by a slow conversion to product(s) and free enzyme.

Chapter Perspective

With this introduction to chemical kinetics, we have begun to explore the dynamic inner workings of chemical change. Variations in reaction rate are observed through concentration and temperature changes, which operate on the molecular level through the frequency and energetics of particle collisions and the details of reactant structure. Kinetics allows us to speculate about the molecular pathway of a reaction. Modern industry and biochemistry depend on its principles. However, speed and yield are very different aspects of a reaction. In Chapter 17, you'll see how opposing reaction rates give rise to the equilibrium state and examine how much product has formed once the net reaction has stopped.

The following learning objectives, with section and/or sample problem (SP) numbers in parentheses, can help focus your study:

Understand These Concepts

1. How reaction rate depends on concentration, particle size, and temperature (Section 16.1)
2. The meaning of reaction rate in terms of changing concentrations over time (Section 16.2)
3. How the rate can be expressed in terms of reactant or product concentrations (Section 16.2)
4. The distinction between average and instantaneous rate and why the instantaneous rate changes during the reaction (Section 16.2)
5. The interpretation of reaction rate in terms of reactant and product concentrations (Section 16.2)
6. The experimental basis of the rate law and the information needed to determine it—initial rate data, reaction orders, and rate constant (Section 16.3)
7. The importance of reaction order in determining the rate (Section 16.3)
8. How reaction order is determined from initial rates at different concentrations (Section 16.3)
9. How integrated rate laws show the dependence of concentration on time (Section 16.4)
10. The meaning of half-life and why it is constant for a first-order reaction (Section 16.4)
11. Activation energy and the effect of temperature on the rate constant (Arrhenius equation) (Section 16.5)
12. Why concentrations are multiplied in the rate law (Section 16.6)
13. How temperature affects rate by influencing collision energy and, thus, the fraction of collisions exceeding the activation energy (Section 16.6)
14. Why molecular orientation and complexity influence the number of effective collisions and the rate (Section 16.6)
15. How the transition state represents the momentary species between reactants and products and how the activation energy is needed to form it (Section 16.6)
16. How an elementary step represents a single molecular event and its molecularity equals the number of colliding particles (Section 16.7)

17. How a reaction mechanism consists of several elementary steps, with the slowest step determining the overall rate (Section 16.7)
18. The criteria for a valid mechanism (Section 16.7)
19. How a catalyst speeds a reaction by lowering the activation energy (Section 16.8)
20. The distinction between homogeneous and heterogeneous catalysis (Section 16.8)

Master These Skills

1. Calculating instantaneous rate from the slope of a tangent to a concentration vs. time plot (Section 16.2)
2. Expressing rate in terms of changes in concentration over time and calculating the instantaneous rate (SP 16.1)
3. Determining reaction order from a known rate law (SP 16.2)
4. Determining reaction order from changes in initial rate with concentration (SP 16.3)
5. Calculating the rate constant and its units (Section 16.3)
6. Using an integrated rate law to find concentration at a given time or the time to reach a given concentration (SP 16.4)
7. Determining reaction order graphically with a rearranged integrated rate law (Section 16.4)
8. Determining the half-life of a first-order reaction (SP 16.5)
9. Using the Arrhenius equation to calculate the activation energy or the rate constant (SP 16.6)
10. Using reaction energy diagrams to depict the energy changes during a reaction (SP 16.7)
11. Postulating a transition state for a simple reaction (SP 16.7)
12. Determining the molecularity of an elementary step (SP 16.8)
13. Constructing a mechanism with either a slow or a fast initial step (Section 16.7)

For Review and Reference

Key Terms

chemical kinetics
Section 16.2
reaction rate
average rate
instantaneous rate
initial rate
Section 16.3
rate law (rate equation)
rate constant
reaction orders
Section 16.4
integrated rate law
half-life ($t_{1/2}$)

Section 16.5
Arrhenius equation
activation energy (E_a)
Section 16.6
collision theory
transition state theory
effective collision
frequency factor
transition state (activated complex)
reaction energy diagram

Section 16.7
reaction mechanism
elementary reaction (elementary step)
molecularity
unimolecular reaction
bimolecular reaction
rate-determining (rate-limiting) step
reaction intermediate

Section 16.8
catalyst
homogeneous catalyst
heterogeneous catalyst
hydrogenation
enzyme
active site
substrate
lock-and-key model
induced-fit model
enzyme-substrate complex (ES)

Key Equations and Relationships

16.1 Expressing reaction rate in terms of reactant A (p. 669):

$$\text{Rate} = -\frac{\Delta[A]}{\Delta t}$$

16.2 Expressing the rate of a general reaction (p. 672):

$$aA + bB \longrightarrow cC + dD$$

$$\text{Rate} = -\frac{1}{a}\frac{\Delta[A]}{\Delta t} = -\frac{1}{b}\frac{\Delta[B]}{\Delta t} = \frac{1}{c}\frac{\Delta[C]}{\Delta t} = \frac{1}{d}\frac{\Delta[D]}{\Delta t}$$

16.3 Writing a general rate law (for a case not involving products) (p. 673):

$$\text{Rate} = k[A]^m[B]^n \ldots$$

16.4 Calculating the time to reach a given [A] in a first-order reaction (rate = $k[A]$) (p. 680):

$$\ln\frac{[A]_0}{[A]_t} = kt$$

16.5 Calculating the time to reach a given [A] in a simple second-order reaction (rate = $k[A]^2$) (p. 680):

$$\frac{1}{[A]_t} - \frac{1}{[A]_0} = kt$$

16.6 Finding the half-life of a first-order process (p. 682):

$$t_{1/2} = \frac{\ln 2}{k} = \frac{0.693}{k}$$

16.7 Relating the rate constant to the temperature (Arrhenius equation) (p. 685):

$$k = Ae^{-E_a/RT}$$

16.8 Calculating the activation energy (rearranged Arrhenius equation in two-point form) (p. 685):

$$\ln\frac{k_2}{k_1} = -\frac{E_a}{R}\left(\frac{1}{T_2} - \frac{1}{T_1}\right)$$

Highlighted Figures and Tables

These figures (F) and tables (T) provide a quick review of important ideas.
F16.1 Reaction rate (p. 665)
F16.5 The concentration of O_3 vs. time (p. 670)
T16.3 Units of k for overall reaction orders (p. 679)
F16.7 Integrated rate laws and reaction order (p. 681)
F16.8 Graphical determination of reaction order (p. 682)
F16.9 [N_2O_5] vs. time for three half-lives (p. 683)
T16.4 First- and second-order reactions (p. 684)
F16.10 Dependence of the rate constant on temperature (p. 684)
F16.11 Graphical determination of E_a (p. 685)

F16.12 Kinetic parameters of a reaction (p. 686)
T16.5 Effect of E_a and T on the fraction (f) of energetic collisions (p. 687)
F16.14 Effect of temperature on distribution of collision energies (p. 687)
F16.15 Energy-level diagram for a reaction (p. 688)
F16.16 The fraction of collisions exceeding E_a (p. 688)
F16.19 Reaction energy diagram for the reaction of CH_3Br and OH^- (p. 690)
T16.6 Rate laws for elementary steps (p. 693)
F16.22 Reaction energy diagram for catalyzed and uncatalyzed processes (p. 698)

Answers to Follow-up Problems

16.1 (a) $4NO(g) + O_2(g) \longrightarrow 2N_2O_3(g)$;

$$\text{rate} = -\frac{\Delta[O_2]}{\Delta t} = -\frac{1}{4}\frac{\Delta[NO]}{\Delta t} = \frac{1}{2}\frac{\Delta[N_2O_3]}{\Delta t}$$

(b) $-\dfrac{\Delta[O_2]}{\Delta t} = -\dfrac{1}{4}\dfrac{\Delta[NO]}{\Delta t}$

$= -\dfrac{1}{4}(-1.60\times10^{-4}\ \text{mol/L}\cdot\text{s}) = 4.00\times10^{-5}\ \text{mol/L}\cdot\text{s}$

16.2 1st order in Br^-, 1st order in BrO_3^-, 2nd order in H^+, 4th order overall.

16.3 Rate $= k[H_2]^m[I_2]^n$. From experiments 1 and 3, $m = 1$. From experiments 2 and 4, $n = 1$. Therefore, rate $= k[H_2][I_2]$; 2nd order overall.

16.4 $1/[HI]_1 - 1/[HI]_0 = kt$;
$111\ \text{L/mol} - 100\ \text{L/mol} = (2.4\times10^{-21}\ \text{L/mol}\cdot\text{s})(t)$
$t = 4.6\times10^{21}\ \text{s (or } 1.5\times10^{14}\ \text{yr)}$

16.5 $t_{1/2} = \ln 2/k$; $k = 0.693/13.1\ \text{h} = 5.29\times10^{-2}\ \text{h}^{-1}$

16.6 $\ln\dfrac{0.286\ \text{s}^{-1}}{k_1}$

$= -\dfrac{1.00\times10^5\ \text{J/mol}}{8.31\ \text{J/mol}\cdot\text{K}} \times \left(\dfrac{1}{500.\ \text{K}} - \dfrac{1}{490.\ \text{K}}\right) = 0.491$

$k_1 = 0.175\ \text{s}^{-1}$

16.7

16.8 (a) Balanced equation:
$2NO(g) + 2H_2(g) \longrightarrow N_2(g) + 2H_2O(g)$
(b) Step 2 is unimolecular. All others are bimolecular.
(c) $\text{Rate}_1 = k_1[NO]^2$; $\text{rate}_2 = k_2[H_2]$; $\text{rate}_3 = k_3[N_2O_2][H]$;
$\text{rate}_4 = k_4[HO][H]$; $\text{rate}_5 = k_5[H][N_2O]$.

Problems

Problems with a **colored** number are answered at the back of the text. Problem sections match the text and provide the number(s) of relevant sample problems. Most offer concept review questions, skill-building exercises (written in similar pairs), and problems in a relevant context. Following these are comprehensive problems based on material from any section and/or previous chapter.

Factors That Influence Reaction Rate

■ Concept Review Questions

16.1 What variable of a chemical reaction is measured over time to obtain the reaction rate?

16.2 How does an increase in pressure affect the rate of a gas-phase reaction? Explain.

16.3 A reaction is carried out with water as the solvent. How does the addition of more water to the reaction vessel affect the reaction rate? Explain.

16.4 How does an increase in surface area of a solid affect the rate of its reaction with a gas? Explain.

16.5 How does an increase in temperature affect the rate of a reaction? Explain the two factors involved.

16.6 In a kinetics experiment, a chemist places crystals of I_2 in a closed reaction vessel, introduces a given quantity of H_2 gas, and obtains data to calculate the rate of HI formation. In a second experiment, she uses the same amounts of I_2 and H_2 but first warms the flask to 130°C, at which temperature the I_2 sublimes. In which experiment does the reaction proceed at a higher rate? Why?

Expressing the Reaction Rate

(Sample Problem 16.1)

■ Concept Review Questions

16.7 Define reaction rate. Assuming constant temperature and a closed reaction vessel, why does rate change with time?

16.8 (a) What is the difference between an average rate and an instantaneous rate? (b) What is the difference between an initial rate and an instantaneous rate?

16.9 Give two reasons for measuring initial rates in a kinetic study.

16.10 For the reaction $A(g) \longrightarrow B(g)$, sketch two curves on the same set of axes that show
(a) The formation of product as a function of time
(b) The consumption of reactant as a function of time

16.11 For the reaction $C(g) \longrightarrow D(g)$, a plot of [C] versus time is shown below.

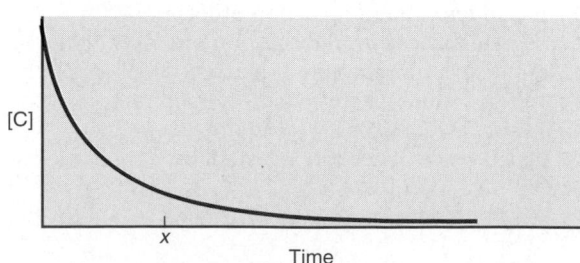

How do you determine
(a) The average rate over the entire experiment
(b) The reaction rate at time x
(c) The initial reaction rate
(d) Would the values in (a), (b), and (c) be different if you plotted [D] versus time? Explain.

■ Skill-Building Exercises *(paired)*

16.12 The compound AX_2 decomposes according to the equation, $2AX_2(g) \longrightarrow 2AX(g) + X_2(g)$. In one experiment, $[AX_2]$ was measured at various times and the following data were obtained:

t (s)	$[AX_2]$ (mol/L)
0	0.0500
2.0	0.0448
6.0	0.0300
8.0	0.0249
10.0	0.0209
20.0	0.0088

(a) Find the average rate over the entire experiment.
(b) Is the initial rate higher or lower than the rate in part (a)? Use graphical methods to estimate the initial rate.

16.13 (a) Use the data from Problem 16.12 to calculate the average rate from 8.0 to 20.0 s.
(b) Is the rate at exactly 5.0 s higher or lower than the rate in part (a)? Use graphical methods to estimate the rate at 5.0 s.

16.14 Express the rate of reaction in terms of the change in concentration of each of the reactants and products:
$$2A(g) \longrightarrow B(g) + C(g)$$
When [C] is increasing at 2 mol/L · s, how fast is [A] decreasing?

16.15 Express the rate of reaction in terms of the change in concentration of each of the reactants and products:
$$D(g) \longrightarrow \tfrac{3}{2}E(g) + \tfrac{5}{2}F(g)$$
When [E] is increasing at 0.25 mol/L · s, how fast is [F] increasing?

16.16 Express the rate of reaction in terms of the change in concentration of each of the reactants and products:
$$A(g) + 2B(g) \longrightarrow C(g)$$
When [B] is decreasing at 0.5 mol/L · s, how fast is [A] decreasing?

16.17 Express the rate of reaction in terms of the change in concentration of each of the reactants and products:
$$2D(g) + 3E(g) + F(g) \longrightarrow 2G(g) + H(g)$$
When [D] is decreasing at 0.1 mol/L · s, how fast is [H] increasing?

16.18 The rate of a reaction is expressed in terms of changes in concentration of reactants and products. Write a balanced equation for the reaction:
$$\text{Rate} = -\frac{1}{2}\frac{\Delta[N_2O_5]}{\Delta t} = \frac{1}{4}\frac{\Delta[NO_2]}{\Delta t} = \frac{\Delta[O_2]}{\Delta t}$$

16.19 The rate of a reaction is expressed in terms of changes in concentration of reactants and products. Write a balanced equation for the reaction:
$$\text{Rate} = -\frac{\Delta[CH_4]}{\Delta t} = -\frac{1}{2}\frac{\Delta[O_2]}{\Delta t} = \frac{1}{2}\frac{\Delta[H_2O]}{\Delta t} = \frac{\Delta[CO_2]}{\Delta t}$$

■ Problems in Context

16.20 The decomposition of nitrosyl bromide is followed manometrically because the number of moles of gas changes, but it cannot be followed colorimetrically because both NOBr and Br_2 are reddish brown:
$$2NOBr(g) \longrightarrow 2NO(g) + Br_2(g)$$
Given the data below,
(a) Determine the average rate over the entire experiment.
(b) Determine the average rate between 2.00 and 4.00 s.
(c) Use graphical methods to estimate the initial reaction rate.
(d) Use graphical methods to estimate the rate at 7.00 s.
(e) At what time does the instantaneous rate equal the average rate over the entire experiment?

t (s)	[NOBr] (mol/L)
0.00	0.0100
2.00	0.0071
4.00	0.0055
6.00	0.0045
8.00	0.0038
10.00	0.0033

16.21 The formation of ammonia is one of the most important processes in the chemical industry:
$$N_2(g) + 3H_2(g) \longrightarrow 2NH_3(g)$$
Express the reaction rate in terms of changes in $[N_2]$, $[H_2]$, and $[NH_3]$.

16.22 Just as the depletion of stratospheric ozone today threatens life on Earth, its accumulation was one of the crucial steps that allowed life to develop in prehistoric times:
$$3O_2(g) \longrightarrow 2O_3(g)$$
(a) Express the reaction rate in terms of $[O_2]$ and $[O_3]$.
(b) At a given instant, the rate in terms of $[O_2]$ is 2.17×10^{-5} mol/L · s. What is it in terms of $[O_3]$?

The Rate Law and Its Components
(Sample Problems 16.2 and 16.3)

■ Concept Review Questions

16.23 The rate law for the general reaction
$$aA + bB + \cdots \longrightarrow cC + dD + \cdots$$
is rate $= k\,[A]^m[B]^n \ldots$
(a) Explain the meaning of k.
(b) Explain the meanings of m and n. Does $m = a$ and $n = b$? Explain.
(c) If the reaction is first order in A and second order in B, and time is measured in minutes (min), what are the units for k?

16.24 You are studying the reaction
$$A_2(g) + B_2(g) \longrightarrow 2AB(g)$$
to determine its rate law. Assuming that you have a valid experimental procedure for obtaining $[A_2]$ and $[B_2]$ at various times, explain how you determine (a) the initial rate; (b) the reaction orders; (c) the rate constant.

16.25 By what factor does the rate change in each of the following cases (assume constant temperature)?
(a) A reaction is first order with respect to reactant A and [A] is doubled.

(b) A reaction is second order with respect to reactant B and [B] is halved.
(c) A reaction is second order with respect to reactant C and [C] is tripled.

■ **Skill-Building Exercises (paired)**

16.26 Give the individual reaction orders for each substance and the overall reaction order for the following rate law:

$$\text{rate} = k\,[BrO_3{}^-][Br^-][H^+]^2$$

16.27 Give the individual reaction orders for each substance and the overall reaction order for the following rate law:

$$\text{rate} = k\frac{[O_3]^2}{[O_2]}$$

16.28 By what factor does the rate in Problem 16.26 change if each of the following changes occurs: (a) $[BrO_3{}^-]$ is doubled; (b) $[Br^-]$ is halved; (c) $[H^+]$ is quadrupled?

16.29 By what factor does the rate in Problem 16.27 change if each of the following changes occurs: (a) $[O_3]$ is doubled; (b) $[O_2]$ is doubled; (c) $[O_2]$ is halved?

16.30 Give the individual reaction orders for each substance and the overall reaction order for the rate law:

$$\text{rate} = k\,[NO_2]^2[Cl_2]$$

16.31 Give the individual reaction orders for each substance and the overall reaction order for the rate law:

$$\text{rate} = k\frac{[HNO_2]^4}{[NO]^2}$$

16.32 By what factor does the rate in Problem 16.30 change if each of the following changes occurs: (a) $[NO_2]$ is tripled; (b) $[NO_2]$ and $[Cl_2]$ are doubled; (c) $[Cl_2]$ is halved?

16.33 By what factor does the rate in Problem 16.31 change if each of the following changes occurs: (a) $[HNO_2]$ is doubled; (b) $[NO]$ is doubled; (c) $[HNO_2]$ is halved?

16.34 For the reaction

$$4A(g) + 3B(g) \longrightarrow 2C(g)$$

the following data were obtained at constant temperature:

TRIAL	INITIAL [A] (mol/L)	INITIAL [B] (mol/L)	INITIAL RATE (mol/L · min)
1	0.100	0.100	5.00
2	0.300	0.100	45.0
3	0.100	0.200	10.0
4	0.300	0.200	90.0

(a) What is the order with respect to each reactant?
(b) Write the rate law.
(c) Calculate k (using, for example, trial 1 data).

16.35 For the reaction

$$A(g) + B(g) + C(g) \longrightarrow D(g)$$

the following data were obtained at constant temperature:

TRIAL	INITIAL [A] (mol/L)	INITIAL [B] (mol/L)	INITIAL [C] (mol/L)	INITIAL RATE (mol/L · s)
1	0.0500	0.0500	0.0100	6.25×10^{-3}
2	0.1000	0.0500	0.0100	1.25×10^{-2}
3	0.1000	0.1000	0.0100	5.00×10^{-2}
4	0.0500	0.0500	0.0200	6.25×10^{-3}

(a) What is the order with respect to each reactant?
(b) Write the rate law.
(c) Calculate k (using, for example, trial 1 data).

16.36 Without consulting Table 16.3, give the units of the rate constants for reactions with the following overall orders: (a) first order; (b) second order; (c) third order; (d) $\frac{5}{2}$ order.

16.37 Give the overall reaction order that corresponds to rate constants with the following units:
(a) mol/L · s; (b) yr^{-1}; (c) $(mol/L)^{1/2} \cdot s^{-1}$;
(d) $(mol/L)^{-5/2} \cdot min^{-1}$.

■ **Problems in Context**

16.38 Phosgene is a toxic gas prepared by the reaction of carbon monoxide with chlorine:

$$CO(g) + Cl_2(g) \longrightarrow COCl_2(g)$$

The following data were obtained in a kinetic study of its formation:

TRIAL	INITIAL [CO] (mol/L)	INITIAL [Cl₂] (mol/L)	INITIAL RATE (mol/L · s)
1	1.00	0.100	1.29×10^{-29}
2	0.100	0.100	1.33×10^{-30}
3	0.100	1.00	1.30×10^{-29}
4	0.100	0.0100	1.32×10^{-31}

(a) Write the rate law for the formation of phosgene.
(b) Calculate the average value of the rate constant.

Integrated Rate Laws: Concentration Changes over Time

(Sample Problems 16.4 and 16.5)

■ **Concept Review Questions**

16.39 How are integrated rate laws used to determine reaction order? What is the order in reactant if a plot of
(a) The natural logarithm of [reactant] versus time is linear?
(b) The inverse of [reactant] versus time is linear?
(c) [Reactant] versus time is linear?

16.40 Define the half-life of a reaction. Explain on the molecular level why the half-life of a first-order reaction is a constant value.

■ **Skill-Building Exercises (paired)**

16.41 For the simple decomposition reaction

$$AB(g) \longrightarrow A(g) + B(g)$$

rate $= k[AB]^2$ and $k = 0.2$ L/mol · s. How long will it take for [AB] to reach one-third of its initial concentration of 1.50 M?

16.42 For the reaction in Problem 16.41, what is [AB] after 10.0 s?

16.43 In a first-order decomposition reaction, 50.0% of a compound decomposes in 10.5 min.
(a) What is the rate constant of the reaction?
(b) How long does it take for 75.0% of the compound to decompose?

16.44 A decomposition reaction has a rate constant of 0.0012 yr^{-1}.
(a) What is the half-life of the reaction?
(b) How long does it take for [reactant] to reach 12.5% of its original value?

■ Problems in Context

16.45 During a study of ammonia production, an industrial chemist discovers that the compound decomposes to its elements N_2 and H_2 in a first-order process. She collects the following data:

Time (s)	0	1.000	2.000
$[NH_3]$ (mol/L)	4.000	3.986	3.974

(a) Use graphical methods to determine the rate constant.
(b) What is the half-life of ammonia decomposition?

The Effect of Temperature on Reaction Rate
(Sample Problem 16.6)

■ Concept Review Questions

16.46 Use the exponential term in the Arrhenius equation to explain how temperature affects reaction rate.
16.47 How is the activation energy determined from the Arrhenius equation?
16.48 (a) Sketch a graph to show the relationship between k (y axis) and T (x axis).
(b) Sketch a graph to show the relationship between ln k (y axis) and $1/T$ (x axis). How is the activation energy determined from this graph?

■ Skill-Building Exercises (paired)

16.49 The rate constant of a reaction is 4.7×10^{-3} s^{-1} at 25°C and the activation energy is 33.6 kJ/mol. What is the value of k at 75°C?
16.50 The rate constant of a reaction is 4.50×10^{-5} L/mol · s at 195°C and 3.20×10^{-3} L/mol · s at 258°C. What is the activation energy of the reaction?

■ Problems in Context

16.51 Understanding the high-temperature formation and breakdown of the nitrogen oxides is essential for controlling the pollutants generated by car engines. The second-order breakdown of nitric oxide to its elements has rate constants of 0.0796 L/mol · s at 737°C and 0.0815 L/mol · s at 947°C. What is the activation energy of this reaction?

Explaining the Effects of Concentration and Temperature
(Sample Problem 16.7)

■ Concept Review Questions

16.52 What is the central idea of collision theory? How does this idea explain the effect of concentration on reaction rate?
16.53 Is collision frequency the only factor affecting reaction rate? Explain.
16.54 Arrhenius proposed that each reaction has an energy threshold that must be reached for the particles to react. The kinetic theory of gases proposes that the average kinetic energy of the particles in a sample is proportional to the absolute temperature. Explain how these concepts relate to the effect of temperature on reaction rate.
16.55 (a) For a reaction with a given E_a, how does an increase in T affect the rate?
(b) For a reaction at a given T, how does a decrease in E_a affect the rate?
16.56 In the reaction AB + CD $\rightleftharpoons$ EF, 4×10^{-5} mol AB collide with 4×10^{-5} mol CD. Will 4×10^{-5} mol EF form? Explain.

16.57 Assuming the activation energies are equal, which of the following reactions will occur at a higher rate at 50°C? Explain:

$$NH_3(g) + HCl(g) \longrightarrow NH_4Cl(s)$$
$$N(CH_3)_3(g) + HCl(g) \longrightarrow (CH_3)_3NHCl(s)$$

■ Skill-Building Exercises (paired)

16.58 For the reaction A(g) + B(g) $\longrightarrow$ AB(g), how many unique collisions between A and B are possible if there are four particles of A and three particles of B present in the vessel?
16.59 For the reaction A(g) + B(g) $\longrightarrow$ AB(g), how many unique collisions between A and B are possible if 1.01 mol A(g) and 2.12 mol B(g) are present in the vessel?

16.60 At 25°C, what is the fraction of collisions with energy equal to or greater than an activation energy of 100. kJ/mol?
16.61 If the temperature in Problem 16.60 is increased to 50.°C, by what factor does the fraction of collisions with energy equal to or greater than the activation energy change?

16.62 For the reaction ABC + D $\rightleftharpoons$ AB + CD, $\Delta H_{rxn}^0 = -55$ kJ/mol and $E_{a(fwd)} = 215$ kJ/mol. Assuming the reaction occurs in one step,
(a) Draw a reaction energy diagram.
(b) Calculate $E_{a(rev)}$.
(c) Sketch a possible transition state if A—B—C is V-shaped.
16.63 For the reaction $A_2 + B_2 \longrightarrow$ 2AB, $E_{a(fwd)} =$ 125 kJ/mol and $E_{a(rev)} = 85$ kJ/mol. Assuming the reaction occurs in one step,
(a) Draw a reaction energy diagram.
(b) Calculate ΔH_{rxn}^0.
(c) Sketch a possible transition state.

■ Problems in Context

16.64 Aqua regia, a mixture of hydrochloric and nitric acids, has been used since alchemical times as a solvent for many metals, including gold. Its orange color is due to the presence of nitrosyl chloride. Consider this one-step gaseous reaction for the formation of this compound:

$$NO(g) + Cl_2(g) \longrightarrow NOCl(g) + Cl(g) \quad \Delta H^0 = 83 \text{ kJ}$$

(a) Draw a reaction energy diagram for the reaction, given that $E_{a(fwd)}$ is 86 kJ/mol.
(b) Calculate $E_{a(rev)}$.
(c) Sketch a possible transition state for the reaction. (Hint: The atom sequence of nitrosyl chloride is Cl—N—O.)

Reaction Mechanisms: Steps in the Overall Reaction
(Sample Problem 16.8)

■ Concept Review Questions

16.65 Is the rate of an overall reaction lower, higher, or equal to the average rate of the individual steps? Explain.
16.66 Explain why the coefficients of an elementary step equal the reaction orders of its rate law but those of an overall reaction do not.
16.67 Is it possible for more than one mechanism to be consistent with the rate law of a given reaction? Explain.
16.68 What is the difference between a reaction intermediate and a transition state?

16.69 Why is a bimolecular step more reasonable physically than a termolecular step?

16.70 If a slow step precedes a fast step in a two-step mechanism, do the substances in the fast step appear in the rate law? Explain.

16.71 If a fast step precedes a slow step in a two-step mechanism, how is the fast step affected? How is this effect used to determine the validity of the mechanism?

■ **Skill-Building Exercises** *(paired)*

16.72 The proposed mechanism for a reaction is
(1) $A(g) + B(g) \rightleftharpoons X(g)$ [fast]
(2) $X(g) + C(g) \longrightarrow Y(g)$ [slow]
(3) $Y(g) \longrightarrow D(g)$ [fast]
(a) What is the overall equation?
(b) Identify the intermediate(s), if any.
(c) What is the molecularity and rate law for each step?
(d) Is the mechanism consistent with the actual rate law: rate = $k[A][B][C]$?
(e) Is the following one-step mechanism equally valid: $A(g) + B(g) + C(g) \longrightarrow D(g)$?

16.73 Consider the following mechanism:
(1) $ClO^-(aq) + H_2O(l) \rightleftharpoons HClO(aq) + OH^-(aq)$ [fast]
(2) $I^-(aq) + HClO(aq) \longrightarrow HIO(aq) + Cl^-(aq)$ [slow]
(3) $OH^-(aq) + HIO(aq) \longrightarrow H_2O(l) + IO^-(aq)$ [fast]
(a) What is the overall equation?
(b) Identify the intermediates, if any.
(c) What is the molecularity and the rate law for each step?
(d) Is the mechanism consistent with the actual rate law: rate = $k[ClO^-][I^-]$?

■ **Problems in Context**

16.74 In a study of nitrosyl halides, a chemist proposes the following mechanism for the synthesis of nitrosyl bromide:
$$NO(g) + Br_2(g) \rightleftharpoons NOBr_2(g) \quad \text{[fast]}$$
$$NOBr_2(g) + NO(g) \longrightarrow 2NOBr(g) \quad \text{[slow]}$$
If the rate law is rate = $k[NO]^2[Br_2]$, is the proposed mechanism valid? Explain by showing that it satisfies the three criteria for validity.

16.75 Kinetic studies of hydrogen halide formation show that the rate law for HBr formation, $H_2(g) + Br_2(g) \longrightarrow 2HBr(g)$, is rate = $k[H_2][Br_2]^{1/2}$. Which of the following mechanisms is consistent with the rate law?

I $H_2(g) + Br_2(g) \longrightarrow 2HBr(g)$
II $H_2(g) \rightleftharpoons 2H(g)$ [fast]
    $H(g) + Br_2(g) \longrightarrow HBr(g) + Br(g)$ [slow]
    $Br(g) + H(g) \longrightarrow HBr(g)$ [fast]
III $Br_2(g) \rightleftharpoons 2Br(g)$ [fast]
    $Br(g) + H_2(g) \longrightarrow HBr(g) + H(g)$ [slow]
    $H(g) + Br(g) \longrightarrow HBr(g)$ [fast]

Catalysis: Speeding Up a Chemical Reaction

■ **Concept Review Questions**

16.76 Consider the reaction $N_2O(g) \xrightarrow{\text{Au}} N_2(g) + \frac{1}{2}O_2(g)$.
(a) Is the gold acting as a homogeneous or a heterogeneous catalyst?
(b) On the same set of axes, sketch the reaction energy diagrams for the catalyzed and the uncatalyzed reactions.

16.77 Does a catalyst increase reaction rate by the same means as a rise in temperature does? Explain.

16.78 In a popular classroom demonstration, hydrogen gas and oxygen gas are mixed in a balloon. Although the mixture is stable under normal conditions, when a spark is applied to the mixture or a small amount of powdered metal is dropped into it, the mixture explodes. (a) Is the spark acting as a catalyst? Explain. (b) Is the metal acting as a catalyst? Explain.

16.79 Describe three common examples of catalyzed reactions that occur around you daily.

Comprehensive Problems

Problems with an asterisk (*) are more challenging.

16.80 Consider the following reaction energy diagram:

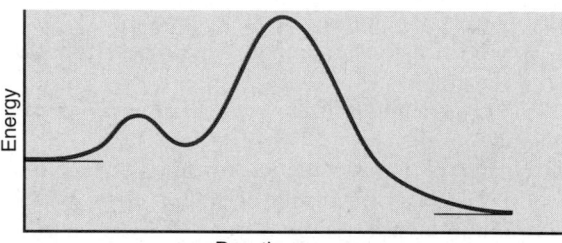

Reaction progress

(a) How many elementary steps are in the reaction mechanism?
(b) Which step is rate limiting?
(c) Is the overall reaction exothermic or endothermic?

16.81 Reactions between certain organic (alkyl) halides and water produce alcohols. Consider the overall reaction of *t*-butyl bromide (2-bromo-2-methylpropane):
$$(CH_3)_3CBr(aq) + H_2O(l) \longrightarrow$$
$$(CH_3)_3COH(aq) + H^+(aq) + Br^-(aq)$$
The experimental rate law is rate = $k[(CH_3)_3CBr]$. The accepted mechanism for the reaction is
(1) $(CH_3)_3C-Br(aq) \longrightarrow (CH_3)_3C^+(aq) + Br^-(aq)$ [slow]
(2) $(CH_3)_3C^+(aq) + H_2O(l) \longrightarrow (CH_3)_3C-OH_2^+(aq)$ [fast]
(3) $(CH_3)_3C-OH_2^+(aq) \longrightarrow H^+(aq) + (CH_3)_3C-OH(aq)$
                                                                                [fast]
(a) Why doesn't H_2O appear in the rate law?
(b) Write rate laws for the elementary steps.
(c) What intermediates appear in the mechanism?
(d) Show that the mechanism is consistent with the experimental rate law.

16.82 A student is measuring the rate of a reaction with a stopwatch but finds that the rate is too fast to obtain reproducible results. In each of the following cases, describe two ways to slow the reaction:
(a) The reactants are gases.
(b) The reactants are in solution.

16.83 When studying atmospheric or other gaseous reactions, chemists find it useful to express the rate law in terms of pressure. How do you express the general rate law in terms of pressure? If a reaction rate has units of torr/s, what are the units of k for a first- and a second-order reaction?

16.84 In the environment, many pollutants react slowly with the water in rivers and lakes and are gradually broken down to harmless end products. Measurements taken by environmental chemists of decreasing pollutant concentrations indicate that the process appears to be first order. Given that H_2O is required for the reaction, how can the process be first order?

16.85 High-flying supersonic transports release NO into the stratosphere. NO catalyzes ozone depletion by a mechanism analogous to the action of Cl. Write the reactions in the mechanism and show why NO acts as a catalyst.

16.86 Archeologists can determine the approximate age of artifacts made of wood or bone by measuring the concentration of the radioactive isotope carbon-14 present in the object. The amount of isotope decreases in a first-order process. If 15.5% of the original amount of carbon-14 is present in a wooden tool at the time of analysis, what is the age of the artifact? The half-life of carbon-14 is 5730 yr.

16.87 A slightly bruised apple will rot extensively in about 4 days at room temperature (20°C). If it is kept in the refrigerator at 0°C, the same extent of rotting takes about 16 days. What is the activation energy for the rotting reaction?

16.88 Benzoyl peroxide, the substance most widely used against acne, has a half-life of 9.8×10^3 days when refrigerated. How long will it take to lose 5% of its potency (95% remaining)?

16.89 How do each of the following changes affect the reaction rate (increase, decrease, no effect):
(a) Decreasing the pressure of a gas-liquid reaction
(b) Increasing the concentration of a reactant that occurs in a step preceding the rate-limiting step
(c) Increasing the concentration of a reactant that occurs in a step following the rate-limiting step
(d) Grinding up a solid reactant in a gas-solid reaction
(e) Rapidly stirring a reaction between immiscible liquids

16.90 Enzymes are remarkably efficient catalysts that can increase reaction rates by as many as 20 orders of magnitude.
(a) How do enzymes affect the transition state of a reaction, and how does this effect increase the reaction rate?
(b) What characteristics of enzymes give them this tremendous effectiveness as catalysts?

16.91 Biacetyl, the flavoring that makes margarine taste "just like butter," is extremely stable at room temperature, but at 200°C it undergoes a first-order breakdown with a half-life of 9.0 min. An industrial flavor-enhancing process requires that a butter-flavored food be heated briefly at 200°C. How long can the food be heated and retain 85% of its buttery flavor?

16.92 Biochemists consider the citric acid cycle to be the central reaction sequence in metabolism. One of the key steps is an oxidation catalyzed by the enzyme isocitrate dehydrogenase and the oxidizing agent NAD^+. Under certain conditions, the reaction in yeast obeys 11th-order kinetics:

Rate = k[enzyme][isocitrate]^4[AMP]^2[NAD$^+$]^m[Mg^{2+}]^2

What is the order with respect to NAD^+?

16.93 Nitrogen oxides undergo numerous decomposition and combination reactions in both industry and the environment. One of the most thoroughly studied is the decomposition of dinitrogen pentaoxide:

$$2N_2O_5(g) \longrightarrow 4NO_2(g) + O_2(g)$$

At a given instant, $[N_2O_5]$ is decreasing at the rate of 3.15 mol/L · s. What is the rate of the reaction in terms of $[NO_2]$?

16.94 Enzymes in human liver catalyze a large number of reactions that degrade ingested toxic chemicals. By what factor is the rate of a detoxification reaction changed if a liver enzyme lowers the activation energy by 5 kJ/mol at 37°C?

16.95 Experiment shows that the rate of formation of carbon tetrachloride from chloroform,

$$CHCl_3(g) + Cl_2(g) \longrightarrow CCl_4(g) + HCl(g),$$

is first order in $CHCl_3$, $\frac{1}{2}$ order in Cl_2, and $\frac{3}{2}$ order overall. Show that the following mechanism is consistent with the overall rate law:
(1) $Cl_2(g) \rightleftharpoons 2Cl(g)$ [fast]
(2) $Cl(g) + CHCl_3(g) \longrightarrow HCl(g) + CCl_3(g)$ [slow]
(3) $CCl_3(g) + Cl(g) \longrightarrow CCl_4(g)$ [fast]

16.96 A biochemist studying the breakdown in soil of the insecticide DDT finds that it decays by a first-order reaction with a half-life of 12 yr. How long does it take DDT to decay from 275 ppbm to 10. ppbm in a soil sample ("ppbm" is parts per billion by mass)?

16.97 Under certain conditions, the rate of a reaction is 0.192 mol/L · min.
(a) What is the rate in units of mol/L · s?
(b) What is the rate in units of mol · dm^{-3} · s^{-1}?
(c) What is the rate expressed in SI base units?

16.98 For the reaction

$$A(g) + B(g) \longrightarrow AB(g)$$

the rate is 0.20 mol/L · s, when $[A]_0 = [B]_0 = 1.0$ mol/L. If the reaction is first order in B and second order in A, what is the rate when $[A]_0 = 2.0$ mol/L and $[B]_0 = 3.0$ mol/L?

*16.99 The hydrolysis of table sugar (sucrose) occurs by the following overall reaction:

$$C_{12}H_{22}O_{11}(s) + H_2O(l) \longrightarrow C_6H_{12}O_6(aq) + C_6H_{12}O_6(aq)$$
     sucrose   glucose   fructose

A nutritional biochemist studies the kinetics of the process and obtains the following data:

[SUCROSE] (mol/L)	TIME (h)
0.501	0
0.451	0.50
0.404	1.00
0.363	1.50
0.267	3.00

(a) Use the data to determine the rate constant and the half-life of the reaction.
(b) How long does it take to hydrolyze 75% of the sucrose?
(c) Other studies have shown that this reaction is actually second order overall but appears to follow first-order kinetics. (Such a reaction is termed a *pseudo first-order reaction.*) Suggest a reason for this apparent first-order behavior.

16.100 Is each of the following statements true? If not, explain why.
(a) At a given temperature, all molecules possess the same kinetic energy.
(b) Halving the pressure of a gaseous reaction doubles the reaction rate.

(c) The higher the activation energy of a reaction is, the lower the reaction rate.

(d) A temperature increase of 10°C doubles the rate of any reaction.

(e) If reactant molecules collide with greater energy than the activation energy, they change into product molecules.

(f) The activation energy of a reaction depends on the temperature.

(g) The rate of a reaction increases as the reaction proceeds.

(h) The activation energy of a reaction depends on collision frequency.

(i) A catalyst increases the rate by increasing collision frequency.

(j) Exothermic reactions have higher rates than endothermic ones.

(k) Temperature has no effect on the value of the Arrhenius factor, A.

(l) The activation energy of a reaction is lowered by a catalyst.

(m) For most common reactions, the enthalpy change is lowered by a catalyst.

(n) The probability factor p is near unity for reactions between single atoms.

(o) The initial rate of a reaction is its maximum rate.

(p) A bimolecular reaction is generally twice as fast as a unimolecular reaction.

(q) The molecularity of an elementary reaction is proportional to the molecular complexity of the reactant(s).

16.101 For the decomposition of gaseous dinitrogen pentaoxide, $2N_2O_5(g) \longrightarrow 4NO_2(g) + O_2(g)$, the rate constant is $k = 2.8 \times 10^{-3} \, s^{-1}$ at 60°C. If the initial concentration of N_2O_5 is 1.58 mol/L,

(a) What is $[N_2O_5]$ after 5.00 min?

(b) What fraction of the N_2O_5 has decomposed after 5.00 min?

16.102 Even when a mechanism is consistent with the rate law, later experimentation may show it to be incorrect or only one of several alternatives. As an example, the reaction between hydrogen and iodine has the following rate law: rate = $k[H_2][I_2]$. The long-accepted mechanism proposed a single bimolecular step; that is, the overall reaction was thought to be elementary:

$$H_2(g) + I_2(g) \longrightarrow 2HI(g)$$

In the 1960s, however, spectroscopic evidence showed the presence of free I atoms during the reaction. Kineticists have since proposed a three-step mechanism

(1) $I_2(g) \rightleftharpoons 2I(g)$ [fast]
(2) $H_2(g) + I(g) \rightleftharpoons H_2I(g)$ [fast]
(3) $H_2I(g) + I(g) \longrightarrow 2HI(g)$ [slow]

Show that this mechanism is consistent with the rate law.

16.103 Suggest an experimental method for measuring the change in concentration with time for each of the following reactions:

(a) $CH_3CH_2Br(l) + H_2O(l) \longrightarrow CH_3CH_2OH(l) + HBr(aq)$

(b) $2NO(g) + Cl_2(g) \longrightarrow 2NOCl(g)$

*16.104 An atmospheric chemist fills a gas-reaction container with gaseous dinitrogen pentaoxide to a pressure of 125 kPa, and the gas decomposes to nitrogen dioxide and oxygen. What is the partial pressure of nitrogen dioxide, P_{NO_2}, (in kPa) when the total pressure is 178 kPa?

16.105 Several studies have shown that small doses of aspirin are effective against the formation of blood clots in arteries. Therefore, elderly people with this form of cardiovascular disease are advised to take half a tablet each day as a precaution against stroke. Aspirin (and many other drugs) is broken down in the body by a first-order process. The half-life of aspirin in elderly humans is 3.7 h.

(a) How much aspirin remains in the bloodstream from a 160-mg dose after 24 hours?

(b) In young humans, the half-life is 2.4 h. How much aspirin remains in a young person 24 hours after the same dose?

*16.106 Iodide ion reacts with chloroform to displace chloride ion in a common organic substitution reaction:

$$I^- + CH_3Cl \longrightarrow CH_3I + Cl^-$$

(a) Draw a wedge structure of chloroform and indicate the most effective direction of I^- attack.

(b) The analogous reaction with 2-chlorobutane [Figure P16.106(b)] results in a major change in specific rotation as measured by polarimetry. Explain, showing a wedge structure of the product.

(c) Under different conditions, 2-chlorobutane loses Cl^- in a rate-determining step to form a planar intermediate [Figure P16.106(c)]. This cationic species reacts with HI and then loses H^+ to form a product that exhibits no optical activity. Explain, showing wedge structures.

Figure P16.106(b)   Figure P16.106(c)

16.107 A pile of flour on your kitchen counter does not ignite with a match, but flour dust in a mill or silo can react explosively. Explain.

16.108 The chlorination of ethane is one of several synthetic routes to producing chloroethanes, a group of major industrial solvents. An example of this type of reaction is $C_2H_6(g) + 4Cl_2(g) \longrightarrow C_2H_2Cl_4(l) + 4HCl(g)$. Express the reaction rate in terms of changes in concentration of each reactant and product.

16.109 Acetone is one of the most important solvents in organic chemistry, used to dissolve everything from fats and waxes to airplane glue and nail polish. At high temperatures, it decomposes in a first-order process to methane and ketene ($CH_2=C=O$). At 600°C, the rate constant is $8.7 \times 10^{-3} \, s^{-1}$.

(a) What is the half-life of the reaction?

(b) How much time is required for 40.% of a sample of acetone to decompose?

(c) How much time is required for 90.% of a sample of acetone to decompose?

*16.110 In the lower troposphere, ozone is one of the components of photochemical smog. It is generated in air when nitrogen dioxide, formed by the oxidation of nitric oxide from car exhaust, reacts by the following mechanism:

$$(1)\ NO_2(g) \xrightarrow{k_1} NO(g) + O(g)$$
$$(2)\ O(g) + O_2(g) \xrightarrow{k_2} O_3(g)$$

Assuming the rate of formation of atomic oxygen in step (1) equals the rate of its consumption in step (2), use the data below to calculate
(a) The concentration of atomic oxygen [O]
(b) The rate of ozone formation

$$k_1 = 6.0\times10^{-3}\ s^{-1};\ [NO_2] = 4.0\times10^{-9}\ M$$
$$k_2 = 1.0\times10^6\ L/mol \cdot s;\ [O_2] = 1.0\times10^{-2}\ M$$

16.111 The reaction and rate law for the gas-phase decomposition of dinitrogen pentaoxide are

$$2N_2O_5(g) \longrightarrow 4NO_2(g) + O_2(g)\quad rate = k[N_2O_5]$$

Which of the following are valid mechanisms for the reaction?

I	One-step collision	
II	$2[N_2O_5(g) \longrightarrow NO_3(g) + NO_2(g)]$	[slow]
	$2[NO_3(g) \longrightarrow NO_2(g) + O(g)]$	[fast]
	$2O(g) \longrightarrow O_2(g)$	[fast]
III	$N_2O_5(g) \rightleftharpoons NO_3(g) + NO_2(g)$	[fast]
	$NO_2(g) + N_2O_5(g) \longrightarrow 3NO_2(g) + O(g)$	[slow]
	$NO_3(g) + O(g) \longrightarrow NO_2(g) + O_2(g)$	[fast]
IV	$2N_2O_5(g) \rightleftharpoons 2NO_2(g) + N_2O_3(g) + 3O(g)$	[fast]
	$N_2O_3(g) + O(g) \longrightarrow 2NO_2(g)$	[slow]
	$2O(g) \longrightarrow O_2(g)$	[fast]
V	$2N_2O_5(g) \longrightarrow N_4O_{10}(g)$	[slow]
	$N_4O_{10}(g) \longrightarrow 4NO_2(g) + O_2(g)$	[fast]

16.112 Carbon disulfide is a poisonous, flammable liquid that is an excellent solvent for phosphorus, sulfur, and several other nonmetals. A kinetic study of its gaseous decomposition reveals the following data:

TRIAL	INITIAL [CS$_2$] (mol/L)	INITIAL RATE (mol/L · s)
1	0.100	2.7×10^{-7}
2	0.080	2.2×10^{-7}
3	0.055	1.5×10^{-7}
4	0.044	1.2×10^{-7}

(a) Write the rate law for the decomposition of CS$_2$.
(b) Calculate the average value of the rate constant.

*16.113 In a "clock" reaction, a dramatic color change occurs at a time determined by concentration and temperature. One of the most famous is the iodine-clock reaction. The overall equation is

$$2I^-(aq) + S_2O_8{}^{2-}(aq) \longrightarrow I_2(aq) + 2SO_4{}^{2-}(aq)$$

As I$_2$ forms, it is immediately consumed by its reaction with a fixed amount of added S$_2$O$_3{}^{2-}$:

$$I_2(aq) + 2S_2O_3{}^{2-}(aq) \longrightarrow 2I^-(aq) + S_4O_6{}^{2-}(aq)$$

Once the S$_2$O$_3{}^{2-}$ is consumed, the excess I$_2$ forms a blue-black product with starch solution present in the mixture:

$$I_2 + starch \longrightarrow starch \cdot I_2\ (blue\text{-}black)$$

The rate of the reaction is also influenced by the total concentration of ions, so KCl and (NH$_4$)$_2$SO$_4$ are added to maintain a constant value. Use the data below to determine
(a) The average rate for each trial
(b) The order with respect to each reactant
(c) The rate constant at 23°C
(d) The rate law for the overall reaction

	TRIAL 1	TRIAL 2	TRIAL 3
0.200 M KI (mL)	10.0	20.0	20.0
0.100 M Na$_2$S$_2$O$_8$ (mL)	20.0	20.0	10.0
0.0050 M Na$_2$S$_2$O$_3$ (mL)	10.0	10.0	10.0
0.200 M KCl (mL)	10.0	0	0
0.100 M (NH$_4$)$_2$SO$_4$ (mL)	0	0	10.0
Time to color (s)	29.0	14.5	14.5

16.114 The rate law for $2NO(g) + O_2(g) \longrightarrow 2NO_2(g)$ is rate = $k[NO]^2[O_2]$. In addition to the mechanism in the text, the following ones have been proposed:

I	$2NO(g) + O_2(g) \longrightarrow 2NO_2(g)$	
II	$2NO(g) \rightleftharpoons N_2O_2(g)$	[fast]
	$N_2O_2(g) + O_2(g) \longrightarrow 2NO_2(g)$	[slow]
III	$2NO(g) \rightleftharpoons N_2(g) + O_2(g)$	[fast]
	$N_2(g) + 2O_2(g) \longrightarrow 2NO_2(g)$	[slow]

(a) Which of these mechanisms is consistent with the rate law?
(b) Which is most reasonable chemically? Why?

16.115 The rate law for the reaction

$$CO(g) + NO_2(g) \longrightarrow CO_2(g) + NO(g)$$

is rate = $k\ [NO_2]^2$, and one possible mechanism was shown on p. 695.
(a) Draw a reaction energy diagram for the in-text mechanism, given that $\Delta H^0_{overall} = -226$ kJ/mol.
(b) The following alternative mechanism has been proposed:
(1) $2NO_2(g) \longrightarrow N_2(g) + 2O_2(g)$ [slow]
(2) $2CO(g) + O_2(g) \longrightarrow 2CO_2(g)$ [fast]
(3) $N_2(g) + O_2(g) \longrightarrow 2NO(g)$ [fast]
Is the alternative mechanism consistent with the rate law? Is one mechanism more reasonable physically? Explain.

16.116 The mathematics of the first-order rate law can be applied to any situation in which a quantity decreases by a constant fraction per unit of time (or any other variable).
(a) As light moves through a solution, its intensity decreases per unit length of solution. Show that

$$\ln \left(\frac{\text{intensity of light leaving the solution}}{\text{intensity of light entering the solution}} \right)$$
$$= -\text{fraction of light removed per unit of length} \times \text{length of solution}$$

(b) The value of your savings declines under conditions of constant inflation. Show that

$$\ln(\text{value remaining}) = -\text{fraction lost per unit of time} \times \text{time of saving}$$

17

Equilibrium
The Extent of Chemical Reactions

Figure: The dynamic equilibrium of juggling. The objects passing back and forth between these two jugglers, like reactants and products changing back and forth into one another, demonstrate the dynamic nature of the equilibrium process. The objects are continuously moving from one juggler to the other, and the rates of movement in either direction are equal. Therefore, at any moment, each juggler holds the same number of objects that he held the previous moment and will hold the next moment. This chapter is the first of three to focus on equilibrium, the universal condition of chemical change.

In this chapter, we turn to the second central question in the dynamics of reaction chemistry: How much product will form under a given set of starting concentrations and conditions? Whereas chemical kinetics, the topic of Chapter 16, tells us how fast reactant and product concentrations are changing, chemical equilibrium tells us what those concentrations are once they've stopped changing. Furthermore, studies of equilibrium provide the information we need to affect these final concentrations by altering conditions.

Just as reactions vary greatly in their speed, they also vary in their extent. These two aspects are *not* the same. A fast reaction may go a long way or barely at all toward products. Consider the dissociation of an acidic molecule in water, for example. In 1 *M* HCl, virtually all the hydrogen chloride molecules are dissociated into ions. In 1 *M* CH₃COOH, fewer than 1% of the acetic acid molecules are dissociated at any given time. Yet both reactions take less than a second to reach completion. Similarly, some slow reactions eventually yield a large amount of product, whereas others yield very little. After several years at ordinary temperatures, a steel water-storage tank will rust, and given enough time will do so completely, but no matter how long you wait, the water inside will not decompose to its elements.

The point is that the principles of kinetics and of equilibrium apply to different aspects of a reaction:

- Kinetics applies to the *speed* of a reaction, the concentration of product that is appearing per unit time.
- Equilibrium applies to the *extent* of a reaction, the concentration of product that has appeared given unlimited time, or when no further change is observed.

Knowing how much product will form in a given reaction is often crucial information. How much of a new drug or industrial polymer can you obtain from a particular reaction? Is another reactant mixture that yields more product at a higher temperature a wiser choice? If a slow reaction has a good yield, will a catalyst speed it up enough to make the reaction useful?

This chapter opens with a description of the equilibrium state at the macroscopic and molecular levels and then focuses on the equilibrium constant and its relation to the balanced equation. You'll see how to express the equilibrium condition in terms of concentrations or pressures and how to determine whether a reaction mixture is proceeding toward products or reactants. We apply equilibrium concepts to a series of common quantitative problems, and then examine how reaction conditions affect the equilibrium state. We end with a discussion of equilibrium in two areas of applied chemistry: the industrial production of ammonia and the reaction pathways in living cells. This introduction to equilibrium principles covers mostly systems of gases and pure liquids and solids; we discuss solution equilibria in the next two chapters.

17.1 The Dynamic Nature of the Equilibrium State

Countless experiments with chemical systems have shown that, in a state of equilibrium, *the concentrations of reactants and products no longer change with time.* This apparent cessation of chemical activity occurs because *all reactions are reversible.* Let's examine a reacting chemical system at the macroscopic and molecular levels to see how reversibility gives rise to the equilibrium state. The system consists of two gases, colorless dinitrogen tetraoxide and brown nitrogen dioxide:

$$N_2O_4(g; \text{colorless}) \rightleftharpoons 2NO_2(g; \text{brown})$$

If we introduce a small amount of $N_2O_4(l)$ into a sealed flask kept at 100°C, the liquid immediately vaporizes (bp = 21°C) and the gas begins to turn pale brown. The color slowly darkens, but after a few moments, no further color change can be seen (Figure 17.1).

As we close in on the molecular level, a much more active scene unfolds. The N_2O_4 molecules fly wildly throughout the flask, some splitting into two NO_2 molecules. As time passes, more N_2O_4 molecules decompose and the concentration of NO_2 rises. As observers in the macroscopic world, we see the flask contents darken because NO_2 is reddish-brown. As the number of N_2O_4 molecules decreases, N_2O_4 decomposition slows. At the same time, increasing numbers of NO_2 molecules collide and combine, so N_2O_4 re-formation speeds up. Eventually, N_2O_4 molecules decompose as fast as NO_2 molecules combine. The system has reached equilibrium: *reactant and product concentrations stop changing because the forward and reverse rates have become equal,*

$$\text{At equilibrium: rate}_{fwd} = \text{rate}_{rev} \qquad \textbf{(17.1)}$$

Thus, a system at equilibrium continues to be dynamic at the molecular level, but we see no further *net* change because changes in one direction are balanced by changes in the other.

At a particular temperature, the product and reactant concentrations do not change when the system reaches equilibrium. Therefore, the ratio of their concentrations must be a constant. We'll use the rate laws for the N_2O_4-NO_2 system to derive this constant. At equilibrium, we have

$$\text{rate}_{fwd} = \text{rate}_{rev}$$

Since, in this case, both forward and reverse reactions are elementary steps (Section 16.7), we can use the balanced equation to write rate laws for them:

$$k_{fwd}[N_2O_4] = k_{rev}[NO_2]^2$$

where k_{fwd} and k_{rev} are the forward and reverse rate constants, respectively. By rearranging, we set the ratio of the rate constants equal to the ratio of the concentration terms:

$$\frac{k_{fwd}}{k_{rev}} = \frac{[NO_2]^2}{[N_2O_4]}$$

Figure 17.1 Reaching equilibrium on the macroscopic and molecular levels. A, When the experiment begins, the reaction mixture consists mostly of colorless N_2O_4. **B,** As N_2O_4 decomposes to reddish brown NO_2, the color of the mixture becomes pale brown. **C,** When equilibrium is reached, the concentrations of NO_2 and N_2O_4 are constant, and the color reaches its final color. **D,** Because the reaction continues in the forward and reverse directions at equal rates, the concentrations (and color) remain constant.

The ratio of constants gives rise to a new overall constant called the **equilibrium constant (K):**

$$K = \frac{k_{fwd}}{k_{rev}} = \frac{[NO_2]^2}{[N_2O_4]} \qquad (17.2)$$

The equilibrium constant K is a *number* whose value is equal to the ratio of rate constants. In addition, and most importantly, *K is equal to a particular ratio of equilibrium product and reactant concentration terms at a particular temperature.* We examine this idea closely in the next section and show that it holds as well for overall reactions made up of several elementary steps.

Although the concentrations of reactants and products are constant in a system at equilibrium, this does *not* mean that the system contains 50% products and 50% reactants. It is the opposing *rates* that are equal at equilibrium, not necessarily the concentrations. Indeed, different reactions, even at the same temperature, have a wide range of concentrations at equilibrium—from almost all reactant to almost all product—and therefore, they have a wide range of equilibrium constants (Figure 17.2). Here are three specific examples:

1. *Small K.* If a reaction goes very little toward product before reaching equilibrium, K will be small. For example, the oxidation of nitrogen barely proceeds at 1000 K:*

$$N_2(g) + O_2(g) \rightleftharpoons 2NO(g) \quad K = 1 \times 10^{-30}$$

2. *Large K.* Conversely, if the reaction reaches equilibrium with virtually no reactant remaining, we say it "goes to completion" and has a large K. The oxidation of carbon monoxide goes to completion at 1000 K:

$$2CO(g) + O_2(g) \rightleftharpoons 2CO_2(g) \quad K = 2.2 \times 10^{22}$$

3. *Intermediate K.* Significant amounts of both reactant and product are present at equilibrium. When bromine monochloride breaks down to its elements at 1000 K, the equilibrium constant has an intermediate value:

$$2BrCl(g) \rightleftharpoons Br_2(g) + Cl_2(g) \quad K = 5$$

Section Summary

Kinetics and equilibrium are distinct aspects of a reacting system; that is, rate and yield are not necessarily related. When the forward and reverse reactions occur at the same rate, the system has reached dynamic equilibrium and concentrations no longer change. The equilibrium constant (K) is a number based on a particular ratio of product and reactant terms. K is small for reactions that reach equilibrium with a high concentration of reactants and large for reactions that reach equilibrium with a low concentration of reactants.

17.2 The Reaction Quotient and the Equilibrium Constant

In 1864, two Norwegian chemists, Cato Guldberg and Peter Waage, observed from experiment that *at a given temperature, a chemical system reaches a state in which a particular ratio of reactant and product concentration terms has a constant value.* This is one way of stating the **law of chemical equilibrium,** or the **law of mass action.** Note that no mention of rates appears in this statement. Indeed, the law of mass action was stated many years before the principles of kinetics had been developed. Although kinetic theory later showed

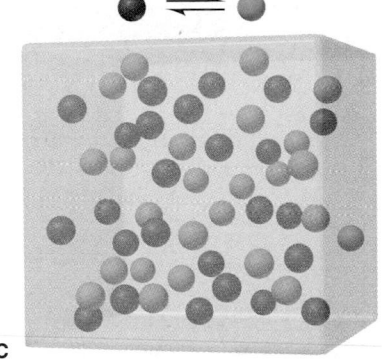

Figure 17.2 The range of equilibrium constants. A, A system that reaches equilibrium with very little product has a small K. For this reaction, $K = \frac{1}{49} = 0.020$. **B,** A system that reaches equilibrium with nearly all product has a large K. For this reaction, $K = \frac{49}{1} = 49$. **C,** A system that reaches equilibrium with significant concentrations of reactant and product has an intermediate K. For this reaction, $K = \frac{25}{25} = 1.0$.

*To distinguish the equilibrium constant from the Kelvin temperature unit, the equilibrium constant is written with an upper case italic K, whereas the kelvin is an upper case roman K. Also, since the kelvin is a unit, it always follows a number.

Table 17.1 Initial and Equilibrium Concentrations for the N_2O_4-NO_2 System at 100°C

Initial		Equilibrium		Ratio
$[N_2O_4]$	$[NO_2]$	$[N_2O_4]$	$[NO_2]$	$[NO_2]^2/[N_2O_4]$
0.1000	0.0000	0.0491	0.1018	0.211
0.0000	0.1000	0.0185	0.0627	0.212
0.0500	0.0500	0.0332	0.0837	0.211
0.0750	0.0250	0.0411	0.0930	0.210

that K could be obtained from a ratio of rate constants, as you saw in the previous section, *the law of mass action does not depend on a knowledge of rates.* To make this point even more emphatic, none of the principles of equilibrium that we discuss in this and subsequent chapters depend on the principles of kinetics.

Guldberg and Waage studied many reactions in which reactant and product concentrations varied widely and found that the law of mass action has a major implication: *for a particular system and temperature, the same equilibrium state is attained regardless of how the reaction is run.* Table 17.1 shows that, for the N_2O_4-NO_2 system at 100°C, we can start the reaction by introducing pure N_2O_4, pure NO_2, or any mixture of NO_2 and N_2O_4, and given enough time, the particular ratio of concentration terms, $[NO_2]^2/[N_2O_4]$, attains the same value (within experimental error). The essential point to note is that this *ratio* of equilibrium concentration terms is fixed even though the *individual* equilibrium concentrations are different in each case.

The particular ratio (quotient) of terms that we write for a given reaction is called the **reaction quotient (*Q*, or mass-action expression)**. For the N_2O_4-NO_2 system, the reaction quotient is

$$Q = \frac{[NO_2]^2}{[N_2O_4]}$$

Although the reactant and product concentration *terms* we use to write Q remain the same, the numerical *values* of those terms change during the reaction, so the *numerical value of Q changes.* When the system reaches equilibrium at a given temperature, the value of Q no longer changes and equals K at that temperature:

At equilibrium: $Q = K$ **(17.3)**

The curves in Figure 17.3 show the case of the first row of values in Table 17.1. Note that, as indicated by the curves, $[N_2O_4]$ and $[NO_2]$ change during the course of the reaction and, thus, so does the value of Q. Once the system reaches equilibrium, the concentrations no longer change and Q equals K. In other words, for a given chemical system, *K is a special value of Q that occurs when the reactant and product terms have their equilibrium values.*

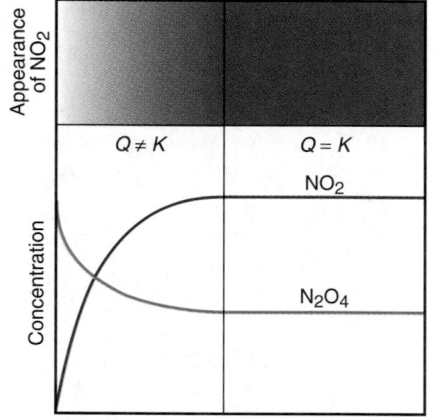

Figure 17.3 The change in *Q* during the N_2O_4-NO_2 reaction. The curved plots and the darkening brown screen above them show that $[N_2O_4]$ and $[NO_2]$, and therefore the value of Q, change with time. Before equilibrium is reached, the concentrations are changing continuously, so $Q \neq K$. Once equilibrium is reached *(vertical line)* and any time thereafter, $Q = K$.

Writing the Reaction Quotient

Recall that the rate law for an overall reaction cannot be written from the balanced equation, but must be determined from rate data. In contrast, as you'll see in the upcoming discussion, the reaction quotient *can* be written directly from the balanced equation: *Q is a ratio made up of product concentration terms multiplied together divided by reactant concentration terms multiplied together, with each term raised to the power of its stoichiometric coefficient.*

The most common form of the reaction quotient shows reactant and product terms as concentrations in moles per liter (*M*), which is designated by square brackets, [ ]. In these cases, which include those you've seen so far, K is the *equilibrium constant based on concentrations*, which we designate from now on as K_c. Similarly, we designate the reaction quotient based on concentrations as Q_c. For the general equation

$$aA + bB \rightleftharpoons cC + dD$$

where a, b, c, and d are the stoichiometric coefficients, the reaction quotient is

$$Q_c = \frac{[C]^c[D]^d}{[A]^a[B]^b} \tag{17.4}$$

(Another form of the reaction quotient that we discuss later shows gaseous reactant and product terms as pressures.)

For any reaction, *write the balanced equation first and then use it to construct the reaction quotient.* For the formation of ammonia from its elements, for example, the balanced equation is

$$N_2(g) + 3H_2(g) \rightleftharpoons 2NH_3(g)$$

To obtain the reaction quotient, the product term goes in the numerator and the reactant terms go in the denominator multiplied by each other, and each term is raised to the power of its balancing coefficient:

$$Q_c = \frac{[NH_3]^2}{[N_2][H_2]^3}$$

Let's practice this essential skill.

Sample Problem 17.1   Writing the Reaction Quotient from the Balanced Equation

PROBLEM Write the reaction quotient for each of the following reactions:
(a) The decomposition of dinitrogen pentaoxide, $N_2O_5(g) \rightleftharpoons NO_2(g) + O_2(g)$
(b) The combustion of propane gas, $C_3H_8(g) + O_2(g) \rightleftharpoons CO_2(g) + H_2O(g)$
PLAN We balance the equations and then construct the reaction quotient as described by Equation 17.4.

SOLUTION (a) $2N_2O_5(g) \rightleftharpoons 4NO_2(g) + O_2(g)$ $\quad Q_c = \dfrac{[NO_2]^4[O_2]}{[N_2O_5]^2}$

(b) $C_3H_8(g) + 5O_2(g) \rightleftharpoons 3CO_2(g) + 4H_2O(g)$ $\quad Q_c = \dfrac{[CO_2]^3[H_2O]^4}{[C_3H_8][O_2]^5}$

CHECK Always be sure that the exponents in Q are the same as the balancing coefficients. A good check is to reverse the process: turn the numerator into products and the denominator into reactants and change the exponents to coefficients.

Follow-up Problem 17.1   Write a reaction quotient for each of the following reactions (unbalanced):
(a) The first step in nitric acid production, $NH_3(g) + O_2(g) \rightleftharpoons NO(g) + H_2O(g)$
(b) The disproportionation of nitric oxide, $NO(g) \rightleftharpoons N_2O(g) + NO_2(g)$

Variations in the Form of the Reaction Quotient

As you'll see in the upcoming discussion, the reaction quotient Q is a collection of terms based on the balanced equation *exactly as written* for a given reaction. Therefore, the value of Q, which varies during the reaction, and the value of K, the constant value of Q when the system has reached equilibrium, also depend on how the balanced equation is written.

In this text (and most others), *the values of Q and K are shown as unitless numbers.* This is because each term in the reaction quotient represents the *ratio* of the measured quantity of the substance (molar concentration or pressure) to the thermodynamic standard state quantity of the substance. Recall from Section 6.6 that these standard states are 1 M for a substance in solution, 1 atm for gases, and the pure substance for a liquid or solid. Thus, a concentration of 1.20 M becomes $\dfrac{1.20\ M}{1\ M} = 1.20$; similarly, a pressure of 0.53 atm becomes $\dfrac{0.53\ \text{atm}}{1\ \text{atm}} = 0.53$. (As you'll see, the molar "concentration" of a pure liquid or solid, that is, the number of moles per liter of the substance, is a constant, and the term does not appear in Q at all.) With these quantity terms unitless, the ratio of terms we use to find the value of Q (or K) is also unitless.

Form of Q for an Overall Reaction Notice that we've been writing reaction quotients without knowing whether an equation represents an individual reaction step or an overall multistep reaction. We can do this because we obtain the same expression for the overall reaction as we do when we combine the expressions for the individual steps. That is, *if an overall reaction is the **sum** of two or more reactions, the overall reaction quotient (or equilibrium constant) is the **product** of the reaction quotients (or equilibrium constants) for the steps:*

$$Q_{\text{overall}} = Q_1 \times Q_2 \times Q_3 \times \cdots$$

and

$$K_{\text{overall}} = K_1 \times K_2 \times K_3 \times \cdots \tag{17.5}$$

Sample Problem 17.2 demonstrates this point.

Sample Problem 17.2   Writing the Reaction Quotient for an Overall Reaction

PROBLEM At the high temperatures reached during the explosive combustion of gasoline within the cylinders of an auto engine, some of the N_2 and O_2 present form nitric oxide, which combines with more O_2 to form nitrogen dioxide, a toxic pollutant that contributes to photochemical smog (see photo):

(1) $N_2(g) + O_2(g) \rightleftharpoons 2NO(g)$ $K_{c1} = 4.3 \times 10^{-25}$
(2) $2NO(g) + O_2(g) \rightleftharpoons 2NO_2(g)$ $K_{c2} = 6.4 \times 10^9$

(a) Show that the overall Q_c for this reaction sequence is the same as the product of the Q_c's for the individual reactions.
(b) Calculate K_c for the overall reaction.

PLAN In **(a)**, we first write the overall reaction by adding the individual reactions and then write the overall Q_c. Then, we write the Q_c for each reaction. Since we *add* the individual steps, we *multiply* their Q_c's and cancel common terms to obtain the overall Q_c. In **(b)**, we multiply the individual K_c values to find $K_{c(\text{overall})}$.

SOLUTION (a) Writing the overall reaction and its reaction quotient:

$$
\begin{array}{ll}
(1) & N_2(g) + O_2(g) \rightleftharpoons \cancel{2NO(g)} \\
(2) & \cancel{2NO(g)} + O_2(g) \rightleftharpoons 2NO_2(g) \\
\hline
\text{Overall:} & N_2(g) + 2O_2(g) \rightleftharpoons 2NO_2(g)
\end{array}
$$

$$Q_{c(\text{overall})} = \frac{[NO_2]^2}{[N_2][O_2]^2}$$

Writing the reaction quotients for the individual steps:

For step (1),
$$Q_{c1} = \frac{[NO]^2}{[N_2][O_2]}$$

For step (2),
$$Q_{c2} = \frac{[NO_2]^2}{[NO]^2[O_2]}$$

Multiplying the individual reaction quotients and canceling:

$$Q_{c1} \times Q_{c2} = \frac{\cancel{[NO]^2}}{[N_2][O_2]} \times \frac{[NO_2]^2}{\cancel{[NO]^2}[O_2]} = \frac{[NO_2]^2}{[N_2][O_2]^2} = Q_{c(\text{overall})}$$

(b) Calculating the overall K_c:

$$K_{c(overall)} = K_{c1} \times K_{c2} = (4.3\times10^{-25})(6.4\times10^{9}) = 2.8\times10^{-15}$$

CHECK Round off and check the calculation in **(b)**:

$$K_c \approx (4\times10^{-25})(6\times10^{9}) = 24\times10^{-16} = 2.4\times10^{-15}$$

Follow-up Problem 17.2 The following sequence of individual steps has been proposed for the overall reaction between H_2 and Br_2 to form HBr:

(1) $Br_2(g) \rightleftharpoons 2Br(g)$
(2) $Br(g) + H_2(g) \rightleftharpoons HBr(g) + H(g)$
(3) $H(g) + Br_2(g) \rightleftharpoons HBr(g) + Br(g)$
(4) $2Br(g) \rightleftharpoons Br_2(g)$

Write the overall equation and show that the overall Q_c is the product of the Q_c's for the individual steps.

Form of Q for a Forward and Reverse Reaction The form of the reaction quotient depends on the *direction* in which the balanced equation is written. Consider, for example, the oxidation of sulfur dioxide to sulfur trioxide, a key step in acid rain formation and sulfuric acid production (see photo):

$$2SO_2(g) + O_2(g) \rightleftharpoons 2SO_3(g)$$

The reaction quotient for this equation *as written* is

$$Q_{c(fwd)} = \frac{[SO_3]^2}{[SO_2]^2[O_2]}$$

If we had written the reverse reaction, the decomposition of sulfur trioxide,

$$2SO_3(g) \rightleftharpoons 2SO_2(g) + O_2(g)$$

the reaction quotient would be the *reciprocal* of $Q_{c(fwd)}$:

$$Q_{c(rev)} = \frac{[SO_2]^2[O_2]}{[SO_3]^2} = \frac{1}{Q_{c(fwd)}}$$

Thus, *a reaction quotient (or equilibrium constant) for a forward reaction is the **reciprocal** of the reaction quotient (or equilibrium constant) for the reverse reaction:*

$$Q_{c(fwd)} = \frac{1}{Q_{c(rev)}} \quad \text{and} \quad K_{c(fwd)} = \frac{1}{K_{c(rev)}} \quad \textbf{(17.6)}$$

The K_c values for these reactions at 1000 K are

$$K_{c(fwd)} = 261 \quad \text{and} \quad K_{c(rev)} = \frac{1}{K_{c(fwd)}} = \frac{1}{261} = 3.83\times10^{-3}$$

These values make sense: if the forward reaction goes far to the right (high K_c), the reverse reaction does not (low K_c).

A sulfuric acid manufacturing plant.

Form of Q for a Reaction with Coefficients Multiplied by a Common Factor Multiplying all the coefficients of the equation by some factor also changes the form of Q. For example, multiplying all the coefficients in the previous equation for the formation of SO_3 by $\frac{1}{2}$ gives

$$SO_2(g) + \tfrac{1}{2}O_2(g) \rightleftharpoons SO_3(g)$$

For this equation, the reaction quotient is

$$Q'_{c(fwd)} = \frac{[SO_3]}{[SO_2][O_2]^{1/2}}$$

Notice that Q_c for the halved equation equals Q_c for the original equation raised to the $\frac{1}{2}$ power:

$$Q'_{c(fwd)} = Q_{c(fwd)}{}^{1/2} = \left(\frac{[SO_3]^2}{[SO_2]^2[O_2]}\right)^{1/2} = \frac{[SO_3]}{[SO_2][O_2]^{1/2}}$$

Once again, the same property holds for the equilibrium constants. Relating the halved reaction to the original, we have

$$K'_{c(fwd)} = K_{c(fwd)}^{1/2} = (261)^{1/2} = 16.2$$

Similarly, if you double coefficients, the reaction quotient is the original expression squared; if you triple coefficients, it is the original expression cubed, and so on. It may seem that we have changed the extent of the reaction, as indicated by a change in K, merely by changing the balancing coefficients of the equation, but this clearly cannot be true. *A particular K has meaning only in relation to a particular balanced equation.* In this case, $K_{c(fwd)}$ and $K'_{c(fwd)}$ relate to different equations and thus cannot be compared directly.

In general, *if all the coefficients of the balanced equation are multiplied by some factor, that factor becomes the exponent for relating the reaction quotients and the equilibrium constants.* For a multiplying factor n, which we can write as

$$n(aA + bB \rightleftharpoons cC + dD)$$

the reaction quotient is

$$Q' = \left(\frac{[C]^c[D]^d}{[A]^a[B]^b}\right)^n \quad \text{and} \quad K' = (K)^n \qquad \textbf{(17.7)}$$

Sample Problem 17.3   Determining the Equilibrium Constant for an Equation Multiplied by a Common Factor

PROBLEM For the ammonia-formation reaction,

$$N_2(g) + 3H_2(g) \rightleftharpoons 2NH_3(g)$$

the equilibrium constant, K_c, is 2.4×10^{-3} at 1000 K. If we change the coefficients of this equation, which we'll call the reference (ref) equation, what are the values of K_c for the following balanced equations?
(a) $\frac{1}{3}N_2(g) + H_2(g) \rightleftharpoons \frac{2}{3}NH_3(g)$ **(b)** $NH_3(g) \rightleftharpoons \frac{1}{2}N_2(g) + \frac{3}{2}H_2(g)$
PLAN We compare each equation with the reference equation to see how the direction and coefficients have changed. In **(a)**, the equation is the reference equation multiplied by $\frac{1}{3}$, so K_c equals $K_{c(ref)}$ raised to the $\frac{1}{3}$ power. In **(b)**, the equation is one-half the *reverse* of the reference equation, so K_c is the reciprocal of $K_{c(ref)}$ raised to the $\frac{1}{2}$ power.

SOLUTION The reaction quotient for the reference equation is $Q_{c(ref)} = \dfrac{[NH_3]^2}{[N_2][H_2]^3}$.

(a)
$$Q_c = Q_{c(ref)}^{1/3} = \left(\frac{[NH_3]^2}{[N_2][H_2]^3}\right)^{1/3} = \frac{[NH_3]^{2/3}}{[N_2]^{1/3}[H_2]}$$

Thus,
$$K_c = K_{c(ref)}^{1/3} = (2.4\times10^{-3})^{1/3} = 0.13$$

(b)
$$Q_c = \left(\frac{1}{Q_{c(ref)}}\right)^{1/2} = \left(\frac{1}{\frac{[NH_3]^2}{[N_2][H_2]^3}}\right)^{1/2} = \frac{[N_2]^{1/2}[H_2]^{3/2}}{[NH_3]}$$

Thus,
$$K_c = \left(\frac{1}{K_{c(ref)}}\right)^{1/2} = \left(\frac{1}{2.4\times10^{-3}}\right)^{1/2} = 20.$$

CHECK A good check is to work the math backward. For **(a)**, $(0.13)^3 = 2.2\times10^{-3}$, within rounding of 2.4×10^{-3}. The reaction goes in the same direction, so at equilibrium, it should be mostly reactants, as the $K_c < 1$ indicates. For **(b)**, $1/(20.)^2 = 2.5\times10^{-3}$, again within rounding. At equilibrium, the reverse reaction should contain mostly products, as $K_c > 1$ indicates.

Follow-up Problem 17.3   At 1200 K, the reaction of hydrogen and chlorine to form hydrogen chloride is

$$H_2(g) + Cl_2(g) \rightleftharpoons 2HCl(g) \quad K_c = 7.6\times10^8$$

Calculate K_c for the following reactions:
(a) $\frac{1}{2}H_2(g) + \frac{1}{2}Cl_2(g) \rightleftharpoons HCl(g)$ **(b)** $\frac{4}{3}HCl(g) \rightleftharpoons \frac{2}{3}H_2(g) + \frac{2}{3}Cl_2(g)$

Form of *Q* for a Reaction Involving Pure Liquids and Solids Until now, we've looked at gaseous reactions only. If the components of the reaction are in the same phase, the system reaches *homogeneous* equilibrium. If they are in different phases, the system reaches *heterogeneous* equilibrium. In the latter case, one or more of the components is a liquid or solid.

Consider the decomposition of limestone to lime and carbon dioxide as an example of a system reaching heterogeneous equilibrium:

$$CaCO_3(s) \rightleftharpoons CaO(s) + CO_2(g)$$

Based on the rules we have been using for writing the reaction quotient, the expression for this reaction is

$$Q_c = \frac{[CaO][CO_2]}{[CaCO_3]}$$

A pure solid, however, such as $CaCO_3$ or CaO, always has the same *concentration* at a given temperature, that is, the same number of moles per liter of the solid, just as it has the same density at a given temperature. Moreover, since a solid's volume changes very little with temperature, its concentration also changes very little. For all intents and purposes, therefore, the concentration of a pure solid is constant. The same argument applies to the concentration of a pure liquid.

Because we are concerned only with concentrations that *change* as they approach equilibrium, *we eliminate the terms for pure liquids and solids from the reaction quotient* by incorporating their constant concentrations into a rearranged reaction quotient, Q_c'. We multiply both sides of the equation by $[CaCO_3]$ and divide both sides by $[CaO]$. Thus, the only substance whose concentration can change is the gaseous CO_2:

$$Q_c' = Q_c \frac{[CaCO_3]}{[CaO]} = [CO_2]$$

No matter how much CaO and $CaCO_3$ are in the reaction vessel, so long as some of each is present, the reaction quotient for the reaction equals the CO_2 concentration (Figure 17.4).

Table 17.2 on the next page summarizes the various ways of writing the reaction quotient.

T = 650°C

Same [CO₂]

Same K

CaCO₃

CaO

CaO

CaCO₃

Figure 17.4 **The reaction quotient for a heterogeneous system.** Even though the two containers have different amounts of the two solids, as long as both solids are present, at a given temperature, the containers have the same [CO₂] at equilibrium.

Table 17.2   Ways of Expressing the Reaction Quotient, Q

Form of Chemical Equation	Form of Q	Value of K
Reference reaction: A $\rightleftharpoons$ B	$Q_{(ref)} = \dfrac{[B]}{[A]}$	$K_{(ref)} = \dfrac{[B]_{eq}}{[A]_{eq}}$
Reverse reaction: B $\rightleftharpoons$ A	$Q = \dfrac{1}{Q_{(ref)}} = \dfrac{[A]}{[B]}$	$K = \dfrac{1}{K_{(ref)}}$
Reaction as sum of two steps: (1) A $\rightleftharpoons$ C	$Q_1 = \dfrac{[C]}{[A]}$; $Q_2 = \dfrac{[B]}{[C]}$	
(2) C $\rightleftharpoons$ B	$Q_{overall} = Q_1 \times Q_2 = Q_{(ref)}$ $= \dfrac{[\cancel{C}]}{[A]} \times \dfrac{[B]}{[\cancel{C}]} = \dfrac{[B]}{[A]}$	$K_{overall} = K_1 \times K_2$ $= K_{(ref)}$
Coefficients multiplied by n	$Q = Q_{(ref)}^n$	$K = K_{(ref)}^n$
Reaction with pure solid or liquid component, such as A(s)	$Q' = Q_{(ref)}[A] = [B]$	$K' = K_{(ref)}[A] = [B]$

Section Summary

The reaction quotient, Q, is a particular ratio of product to reactant terms. Substituting experimental values into this expression gives the value of Q, which changes as the reaction proceeds. When the system reaches equilibrium at a particular temperature, the value of $Q = K$. If a reaction is the sum of two or more reactions, the overall Q (or K) is the product of the individual Q's (or K's). The *form* of Q is based directly on the balanced equation for the reaction, so it changes if the equation is reversed or multiplied by some factor, and K changes accordingly. Pure liquids or solids do not appear in Q because their concentrations are constant.

17.3 Expressing Equilibria with Pressure Units: Relation Between K_c and K_p

It is easier to measure the pressure of a gas than its concentration and, as long as the gas behaves ideally under the conditions of the experiment, the ideal gas law (Section 5.3) allows us to relate these variables to each other:

$$PV = nRT, \qquad \text{so} \qquad P = \frac{n}{V}RT \qquad \text{or} \qquad \frac{P}{RT} = \frac{n}{V}$$

where P is the pressure of a gas and n/V is its molar concentration (M). Thus, since R is a constant and T is kept constant, *pressure is directly proportional to molar concentration.* When substances in the reaction are gases, we can express the reaction quotient and calculate its value in terms of partial pressures instead of concentrations, as the derivation below shows. For example, in the reaction between NO and O_2,

$$2NO(g) + O_2(g) \rightleftharpoons 2NO_2(g)$$

the reaction quotient based on partial pressures, Q_p, is

$$Q_p = \frac{P_{NO_2}^2}{P_{NO}^2 \times P_{O_2}}$$

The equilibrium constant obtained when all species are present at their equilibrium partial pressures is designated K_p, the *equilibrium constant based on pressures.* In many cases, K_p has a different value from K_c, but the two constants are related, so that if you know one, you can calculate the other by noting the *change in amount (mol) of gas, Δn_{gas},* in the balanced equation. Let's see their relationship by converting the terms in Q_c for the NO-O$_2$ reaction to those in Q_p:

$$2NO(g) + O_2(g) \rightleftharpoons 2NO_2(g)$$

The change in amount (mol) of gas is

$$3 \text{ mol gaseous reactants} \rightleftharpoons 2 \text{ mol gaseous products}$$

$$\Delta n_{gas} = \text{moles of gaseous product} - \text{moles of gaseous reactant} = 2 - 3 = -1$$

Keep this value of Δn_{gas} in mind because it appears at a crucial place in the algebraic conversion that follows. The reaction quotient based on concentrations is

$$Q_c = \frac{[NO_2]^2}{[NO]^2[O_2]}$$

Based on the ideal gas law, we write this expression with the concentration terms as n/V and then convert them to partial pressures:

$$Q_c = \frac{\dfrac{n_{NO_2}^2}{V^2}}{\dfrac{n_{NO}^2}{V^2} \times \dfrac{n_{O_2}}{V}} = \frac{\dfrac{P_{NO_2}^2}{(RT)^2}}{\dfrac{P_{NO}^2}{(RT)^2} \times \dfrac{P_{O_2}}{RT}}$$

Collecting the RT terms, we obtain

$$Q_c = \frac{P_{NO_2}^2}{P_{NO}^2 \times P_{O_2}} \times \frac{\dfrac{1}{(RT)^2}}{\dfrac{1}{(RT)^2} \times \dfrac{1}{RT}} = \frac{P_{NO_2}^2}{P_{NO}^2 \times P_{O_2}} \times RT$$

The right side of this expression is the reaction quotient based on partial pressures, which we wrote earlier, multiplied by RT: $Q_c = Q_p(RT)$. Also, for this reaction at equilibrium, $K_c = K_p(RT)$; thus, $K_p = \dfrac{K_c}{RT}$, or $K_c(RT)^{-1}$.

Notice that *the exponent of the RT term equals the change in the amount (mol) of gas (Δn_{gas}) from the balanced equation*, −1. Thus, in general, we have

$$K_p = K_c(RT)^{\Delta n_{gas}} \tag{17.8}$$

The units for the partial pressure terms in K_p will be atmospheres, pascals, torr, etc. raised to some power, so the units of R must be consistent with those units. As Equation 17.8 shows, for those reactions in which the amount (mol) of gas does not change, $\Delta n_{gas} = 0$, so $K_p = K_c$.

Sample Problem 17.4   Converting Between K_c and K_p

PROBLEM Calculate K_c for the following reaction:

$$CaCO_3(s) \rightleftharpoons CaO(s) + CO_2(g) \qquad K_p = 2.1 \times 10^{-4} \text{ (at 1000. K)}$$

PLAN In this case, we know K_p. To convert between K_p and K_c, we must first determine Δn_{gas} from the balanced equation. Then we rearrange Equation 17.8. R is 0.0821 atm · L/mol · K.

SOLUTION Determining Δn_{gas}: There is 1 mol of gaseous product and none of gaseous reactant, so $\Delta n_{gas} = 1$.

Rearranging Equation 17.8 and calculating K_c:

$$K_p = K_c(RT)^1 \qquad \text{so} \qquad K_c = K_p(RT)^{-1}$$

$$K_c = (2.1 \times 10^{-4})\left(0.0821 \frac{\text{atm} \cdot \text{L}}{\text{mol} \cdot \text{K}} \times 1000. \text{ K}\right)^{-1} = \boxed{2.6 \times 10^{-6}}$$

CHECK Round off and work backward to see if you obtain the given K_p:
$K_p \approx (3 \times 10^{-6})(0.08 \times 1000) = 2.4 \times 10^{-4}$, within rounding of 2.1×10^{-4}.

Follow-up Problem 17.4   Calculate K_p for the following reaction:

$$PCl_3(g) + Cl_2(g) \rightleftharpoons PCl_5(g) \qquad K_c = 1.67 \text{ (at 500. K)}$$

The reaction quotient and the equilibrium constant can be expressed in terms of concentration (Q_c and K_c) and, for gases, in terms of partial pressure (Q_p and K_p). The values of K_p and K_c are related by using the ideal gas law: $K_p = K_c(RT)^{\Delta n_{gas}}$.

17.4 Reaction Direction: Comparing *Q* and *K*

Suppose you start a reaction with a mixture of reactants and products and you know the equilibrium constant at the temperature of the reaction. How do you know if the reaction has reached equilibrium? And, if it hasn't, how do you know in which direction it is progressing to reach equilibrium? Since the value of Q can change, at any particular time during the reaction, Q can be smaller than K, larger than K, or, when the system reaches equilibrium, equal to K. By comparing the value of Q at a particular time with the known K, you can tell whether the reaction has attained equilibrium or, if not, in which direction it is progressing. Since product terms are in the numerator of Q and reactant terms in the denominator, *more product makes the ratio of terms larger and more reactant makes the ratio smaller.*

The three possible comparisons of Q and K are shown in Figure 17.5.

- $Q < K$. If the value of Q is smaller than K, the denominator (reactants) is large relative to the numerator (products). For Q to become equal to K, the denominator must decrease and the numerator increase. In other words, the reaction will progress to the right, toward products, until equilibrium is reached:

$$\text{If } Q < K, \text{ reactants} \longrightarrow \text{products}$$

- $Q > K$. If Q is larger than K, the numerator (products) will decrease and the denominator (reactants) increase until equilibrium is reached. Therefore, the reaction will progress to the left, toward reactants:

$$\text{If } Q > K, \text{ reactants} \longleftarrow \text{products}$$

- $Q = K$. This situation exists only when the reactant and product concentrations (or pressures) have attained their equilibrium values. Thus, despite the dynamic processes occurring at the molecular level, no further net change occurs:

$$\text{If } Q = K, \text{ reactants} \rightleftharpoons \text{products}$$

Figure 17.5 Reaction direction and the relative sizes of *Q* and *K*. When Q_c is less than K_c, the equilibrium system shifts to the right, that is, toward products. When Q_c is more than K_c, the equilibrium system shifts to the left. Both shifts continue until $Q_c = K_c$. Note that the size of K_c remains the same throughout.

Sample Problem 17.5 Comparing Q and K to Determine Reaction Direction

PROBLEM For the reaction $N_2O_4(g) \rightleftharpoons 2NO_2(g)$, $K_c = 0.21$ at 100°C. At a point during the reaction, $[N_2O_4] = 0.12\ M$ and $[NO_2] = 0.55\ M$. Is the reaction at equilibrium? If not, in which direction is it progressing?

PLAN We write the expression for Q_c, find its value by substituting the given concentrations, and then compare its value with the given K_c.

SOLUTION Writing the reaction quotient and solving for Q_c:

$$Q_c = \frac{[NO_2]^2}{[N_2O_4]} = \frac{0.55^2}{0.12} = 2.5$$

Since $Q_c > K_c$, the reaction is not at equilibrium and will proceed to the left until $Q_c = K_c$.

CHECK With $[NO_2] > [N_2O_4]$, we expect to obtain a value for Q_c that is greater than 0.21. If $Q_c > K_c$, the denominator will increase until $Q_c = K_c$, so the reaction proceeds toward reactants.

Follow-up Problem 17.5 Chloromethane forms by the reaction

$$CH_4(g) + Cl_2(g) \rightleftharpoons CH_3Cl(g) + HCl(g)$$

At 1500 K, the equilibrium constant $K_p = 1.6 \times 10^4$. In the reaction mixture, $P_{CH_4} = 0.13$ atm, $P_{Cl_2} = 0.035$ atm, $P_{CH_3Cl} = 0.24$ atm, and $P_{HCl} = 0.47$ atm. Is CH_3Cl or CH_4 forming?

Section Summary

We compare the values of Q and K to see the direction a reaction will proceed toward equilibrium. If $Q_c < K_c$, more product forms; if $Q_c > K_c$, more reactant forms; if $Q_c = K_c$, there is no net change.

As you've seen in this and the previous sections, three criteria define a system at equilibrium:
- Reactant and product concentrations are constant over time.
- The forward reaction rate equals the reverse reaction rate.
- The reaction quotient equals the equilibrium constant: $Q = K$.

17.5 How to Solve Equilibrium Problems

Many kinds of equilibrium problems arise in the real world, as well as on chemistry exams, but we can group most of them into two types:
1. In one type, we are given equilibrium quantities (concentrations or partial pressures) and solve for K.
2. In the other type, we are given K and initial quantities and solve for the equilibrium quantities.

Using Quantities to Determine the Equilibrium Constant

There are two common variations of the type of equilibrium problem in which we solve for K: one involves a straightforward substitution of quantities, the other requires first finding some of the quantities.

Substituting Given Equilibrium Quantities into Q to find K The straightforward case occurs when we are given the equilibrium quantities and must calculate K.

Suppose, for example, that equal amounts of gaseous hydrogen and iodine are injected into a 1.50-L reaction flask at a fixed temperature. In time, the following equilibrium is attained:

$$H_2(g) + I_2(g) \rightleftharpoons 2HI(g)$$

At equilibrium, analysis shows that the flask contains 1.80 mol H_2, 1.80 mol I_2, and 0.520 mol HI. Since these are equilibrium amounts, we calculate K_c by finding the concentrations and substituting them into the reaction quotient. From the balanced equation, we write the reaction quotient:

$$Q_c = \frac{[HI]^2}{[H_2][I_2]}$$

We first have to convert the amounts (mol) to concentrations (mol/L), using the flask volume of 1.50 L:

$$[H_2] = \frac{1.80 \text{ mol}}{1.50 \text{ L}} = 1.20 \ M$$

Similarly, $[I_2] = 1.20 \ M$, and $[HI] = 0.347 \ M$. Substituting these values into the Q_c expression gives K_c:

$$K_c = \frac{(0.347)^2}{1.20 \times 1.20} = 8.36 \times 10^{-2}$$

Using a Reaction Table to Determine Equilibrium Quantities and Find *K*
When some values are not given, we determine them first from stoichiometry and then find K. In the following example, pay close attention to a valuable device being introduced: *the reaction table.*

In a study of carbon oxidation, an evacuated vessel containing a small amount of powdered graphite is heated to 1080 K, and then CO_2 is added to a pressure of 0.458 atm. Once the CO_2 is added, the system starts to produce CO. After equilibrium is reached, the total pressure inside the vessel is 0.757 atm. Calculate K_p.

As always, we start by writing the balanced equation and the reaction quotient:

$$CO_2(g) + C(graphite) \rightleftharpoons 2CO(g)$$

Since the data are given in atmospheres and we must find K_p, we write Q in terms of partial pressures (note the absence of the solid, C):

$$Q_p = \frac{P_{CO}^2}{P_{CO_2}}$$

We are given the initial P_{CO_2} and P_{total} at equilibrium. To find K_p, we must find the equilibrium pressures, which requires solving a stoichiometry problem, and then substitute them into the expression for Q_p.

Let's stop for a moment before we begin the calculations to think through what happened in the vessel. An unknown portion of the CO_2 reacted with graphite to form an unknown amount of CO. We know the *relative* amounts of CO_2 and CO from the balanced equation: for 1 mol CO_2 that reacts, 2 mol CO forms, which means that when x atm CO_2 reacts, $2x$ atm CO forms:

$$x \text{ atm } CO_2 \longrightarrow 2x \text{ atm CO}$$

From the data given, we already know something about the size of K_p. If it were very large, almost all the CO_2 would be converted to CO, so the final (total) pressure would be twice the initial pressure ($\sim$0.5 atm $\times$ 2 $\approx$ 1 atm). On the other hand, if K_p were very small, almost no CO would form, so the final pressure would be close to the initial pressure, $\sim$0.5 atm. Since the final pressure (0.757 atm) is between these extremes, K_p must have an intermediate value. The pressure of CO_2 at equilibrium, $P_{CO_2(eq)}$, is the initial pressure, $P_{CO_2(init)}$, *minus* the pressure of the CO_2 that reacts, x:

$$P_{CO_2(init)} - x = P_{CO_2(eq)}$$

Similarly, the pressure of CO at equilibrium, $P_{CO(eq)}$, is the initial pressure, $P_{CO(init)}$, *plus* the pressure of the CO_2 that forms, $2x$. Since $P_{CO(init)}$ is zero at the beginning of the reaction, we have

$$P_{CO(init)} + 2x = 2x = P_{CO(eq)}$$

A useful way to summarize this information is with a reaction table that shows the balanced equation and what we know about
- the *initial* quantities (concentrations or pressures) of reactants and products
- the *changes* in these quantities during the reaction
- the *equilibrium* quantities

PRESSURE (atm)	$CO_2(g)$	+	C(graphite)	$\rightleftharpoons$	$2CO(g)$
Initial	0.458		—		0
Change	$-x$		—		$+2x$
Equilibrium	$0.458 - x$		—		$2x$

Be sure to note that we *add the initial value to the change to obtain the equilibrium value* in each column. Note also that we include data only for those substances whose concentrations change; in this case, the graphite column is blank. We use reaction tables in many of the equilibrium problems here and in later chapters.

To solve for K_p, we must substitute values into the reaction quotient, so we have to find the value of x. To do so, we use the other piece of given information, P_{total}. According to Dalton's law of partial pressures and using the quantities from the reaction table,

$$P_{total} = 0.757 \text{ atm} = P_{CO_2(eq)} + P_{CO(eq)} = (0.458 \text{ atm} - x) + 2x$$

Thus,

$$0.757 \text{ atm} = 0.458 \text{ atm} + x, \quad \text{and} \quad x = 0.299 \text{ atm}$$

With x known, we determine the equilibrium partial pressures:

$$P_{CO_2(eq)} = 0.458 \text{ atm} - x = 0.458 \text{ atm} - 0.299 \text{ atm} = 0.159 \text{ atm}$$

$$P_{CO(eq)} = 2x = 2 \times 0.299 \text{ atm} = 0.598 \text{ atm}$$

Now, we can substitute these values into the expression for Q_p to find K_p:

$$Q_p = \frac{P^2_{CO(eq)}}{P_{CO_2(eq)}} = \frac{(0.598)^2}{0.159} = 2.25 = K_p$$

As we predicted, K_p is neither very large nor very small.

Sample Problem 17.6   Calculating K_c from Concentration Data

PROBLEM In a study of hydrogen halide decomposition, a researcher fills an evacuated 2.00-L flask with 0.200 mol HI gas and allows the reaction to proceed at 453°C:

$$2HI(g) \rightleftharpoons H_2(g) + I_2(g)$$

At equilibrium, [HI] = 0.078 M. Calculate K_c.

PLAN To calculate K_c, we need the equilibrium concentrations. We can find the initial [HI] and are given [HI] at equilibrium. The balanced equation shows that when $2x$ mol HI react, x mol H_2 and x mol I_2 form. We set up a reaction table, use the known equilibrium [HI] to solve for x, the amount (mol) of H_2 or I_2 that forms, and substitute the concentrations into Q_c.

SOLUTION Calculating initial [HI]:

$$[HI] = \frac{0.200 \text{ mol}}{2.00 \text{ L}} = 0.100 \ M$$

Setting up the reaction table, with x = [H_2] and [I_2] that forms and $2x$ = [HI] that reacts:

CONCENTRATION (M)	$2HI(g)$	$\rightleftharpoons$	$H_2(g)$	+	$I_2(g)$
Initial	0.100		0		0
Change	$-2x$		$+x$		$+x$
Equilibrium	$0.100 - 2x$		x		x

Solving for x, using the known [HI] at equilibrium:

$$[HI] = 0.100 \ M - 2x = 0.078 \ M$$
$$x = 0.011 \ M$$

Therefore, the equilibrium concentrations are

$$[H_2] = [I_2] = 0.011 \ M \quad \text{and} \quad [HI] = 0.078 \ M$$

Substituting into the reaction quotient:

$$Q_c = \frac{[H_2][I_2]}{[HI]^2}$$

Thus,

$$K_c = \frac{0.011 \times 0.011}{(0.078)^2} = \boxed{0.020}$$

CHECK Rounding gives $\sim 0.01^2 / 0.08^2 = 0.02$. Since the initial [HI] of 0.100 M was reduced slightly to 0.078 M at equilibrium, relatively little product formed, so we expect $K_c < 1$.

Follow-up Problem 17.6   The atmospheric oxidation of nitric oxide, $2NO(g) + O_2(g) \rightleftharpoons 2NO_2(g)$, was studied at 184°C with initial pressures of 1.000 atm NO and 1.000 atm O_2. At equilibrium, $P_{O_2} = 0.506$ atm. Calculate K_p.

Using the Equilibrium Constant to Determine Quantities

Like the type of problem that involves finding K, there are several variations of the type that involves finding equilibrium concentrations (or pressures). Sample Problem 17.7 is one variation, in which we know K and some of the equilibrium concentrations and must find another equilibrium concentration.

Sample Problem 17.7   Determining Equilibrium Concentrations from K_c

PROBLEM In a study of the conversion of methane to other fuels, a chemical engineer mixes gaseous CH_4 and H_2O in a 0.32-L flask at 1200 K. At equilibrium, the flask contains 0.26 mol CO, 0.091 mol H_2, and 0.041 mol CH_4. What is $[H_2O]$ at equilibrium? $K_c = 0.26$ for the equation

$$CH_4(g) + H_2O(g) \rightleftharpoons CO(g) + 3H_2(g)$$

PLAN First, we use the balanced equation to write the reaction quotient. We can calculate the equilibrium concentrations from the given numbers of moles and the flask volume. Substituting these into Q_c, and setting it equal to the given K_c, we solve for the unknown equilibrium concentration, $[H_2O]$.

SOLUTION Writing the reaction quotient:

$$CH_4(g) + H_2O(g) \rightleftharpoons CO(g) + 3H_2(g) \qquad Q_c = \frac{[CO][H_2]^3}{[CH_4][H_2O]}$$

Determining the equilibrium concentrations:

$$[CH_4] = \frac{0.041 \ \text{mol}}{0.32 \ \text{L}} = 0.13 \ M$$

Similarly, $[CO] = 0.81 \ M$ and $[H_2] = 0.28 \ M$.

Calculating $[H_2O]$ at equilibrium: Since $Q_c = K_c$, rearranging gives

$$[H_2O] = \frac{[CO][H_2]^3}{[CH_4]K_c} = \frac{0.81 \times (0.28)^3}{0.13 \times 0.26} = \boxed{0.53 \ M}$$

CHECK Always check by substituting the concentrations into Q_c to confirm K_c:

$$Q_c = \frac{[CO][H_2]^3}{[CH_4][H_2O]} = \frac{0.81 \times (0.28)^3}{0.13 \times 0.53} = 0.26 = K_c$$

Follow-up Problem 17.7   The equilibrium between nitric oxide, oxygen, and nitrogen is described by the following equation: $2NO(g) \rightleftharpoons N_2(g) + O_2(g)$; $K_c = 2.3 \times 10^{30}$ at 298 K. In the atmosphere, $P_{O_2} = 0.209$ atm and $P_{N_2} = 0.781$ atm. What is the equilibrium partial pressure of NO in the air we breathe?

In a somewhat more involved variation, you know K and *initial* quantities and must find equilibrium quantities, for which you use a reaction table. A special case appears in the upcoming sample problem because it allows us to apply a math shortcut and, thus, focus more easily on the overall approach.

Sample Problem 17.8   Determining Equilibrium Concentrations from Initial Concentrations and K_c

PROBLEM Fuel engineers use the extent of the change from CO and H_2O to CO_2 and H_2 to regulate the proportions of syngas fuel mixtures. If 0.250 mol CO and 0.250 mol H_2O are placed in a 125-mL flask at 900 K, what is the composition of the equilibrium mixture? At this temperature, K_c is known to be 1.56 for the equation $CO(g) + H_2O(g) \rightleftharpoons CO_2(g) + H_2(g)$.

PLAN We have to find the "composition" of the equilibrium mixture, in other words, the equilibrium concentrations. As always, we use the balanced equation to write the reaction quotient. We find the initial [CO] and [H_2O] from the given amount (mol) and volume (L), use the balanced equation to define x and set up a reaction table, substitute into Q_c, and solve for x, from which we calculate the concentrations.

SOLUTION Writing the reaction quotient:

$$CO(g) + H_2O(g) \rightleftharpoons CO_2(g) + H_2(g) \qquad Q_c = \frac{[CO_2][H_2]}{[CO][H_2O]}$$

Calculating initial reactant concentrations:

$$[CO] = [H_2O] = \frac{0.250 \text{ mol}}{0.125 \text{ L}} = 2.00 \ M$$

Setting up the reaction table, with x = [CO] and [H_2O] that reacts:

CONCENTRATION (M)	CO(g)	+	H₂O(g)	⇌	CO₂(g)	+	H₂(g)
Initial	2.00		2.00		0		0
Change	$-x$		$-x$		$+x$		$+x$
Equilibrium	$2.00 - x$		$2.00 - x$		x		x

Substituting into the reaction quotient and solving for x:

$$Q_c = \frac{[CO_2][H_2]}{[CO][H_2O]} = \frac{(x)(x)}{(2.00 - x)(2.00 - x)} = \frac{x^2}{(2.00 - x)^2}$$

At equilibrium, we have

$$Q_c = K_c = 1.56 = \frac{x^2}{(2.00 - x)^2}$$

We can apply a math shortcut in this case *but not in general*: since the right side of the equation is a perfect square, we take the square root of both sides:

$$\sqrt{1.56} = \frac{x}{2.00 - x} = \pm 1.25$$

A positive number (1.56) has a positive *and* a negative square root, but *only the positive root has any chemical meaning*, so we ignore the negative root:*

$$1.25 = \frac{x}{2.00 - x} \qquad \text{or} \qquad 2.50 - 1.25x = x$$

So

$$2.50 = 2.25x; \text{ therefore, } x = 1.11 \ M$$

---

*The negative root gives $-1.25 = \dfrac{x}{2.00 - x}$, or $-2.50 + 1.25x = x$.

So $\qquad\qquad\qquad -2.50 = -0.25x$, and $x = 10. \ M$

This value has no chemical meaning because we started with 2.00 M of each reactant, so it is impossible for 10. M to react. Moreover, the square root of an equilibrium constant is another equilibrium constant, which cannot have a negative value.

Calculating equilibrium concentrations:

$$[CO] = [H_2O] = 2.00\ M - x = 2.00\ M - 1.11\ M = \boxed{0.89\ M}$$
$$[CO_2] = [H_2] = x = \boxed{1.11\ M}$$

CHECK From the intermediate size of K_c, it makes sense that the changes in concentration are moderate. It's a good idea to check that the sign of x in the reaction table makes sense—only reactants were initially present, so the change had to proceed to the right: x is negative for reactants and positive for products. Also check that the equilibrium concentrations give the known K_c: $\dfrac{1.11 \times 1.11}{0.89 \times 0.89} = 1.56$.

Follow-up Problem 17.8   The decomposition of HI at low temperature was studied by injecting 2.50 mol HI into a 10.32-L vessel at 25°C. What is $[H_2]$ at equilibrium for the reaction $2HI(g) \rightleftharpoons H_2(g) + I_2(g)$; $K_c = 1.26 \times 10^{-3}$?

Using the Quadratic Formula to Solve for the Unknown   The shortcut that allowed us to simplify the math in Sample Problem 17.8 is a special case that occurs when the numerator and denominator of the reaction quotient are perfect squares. It worked because we started with equal concentrations of the two reactants, but that is not ordinarily the case.

Suppose, for example, we had started the reaction in the sample problem with 2.00 M CO and 1.00 M H_2O. The reaction table is

CONCENTRATION (M)	CO(g)	+	H₂O(g)	⇌	CO₂(g)	+	H₂(g)
Initial	2.00		1.00		0		0
Change	$-x$		$-x$		$+x$		$+x$
Equilibrium	$2.00 - x$		$1.00 - x$		x		x

Substituting these values into Q_c, we obtain

$$Q_c = \frac{[CO_2][H_2]}{[CO][H_2O]} = \frac{(x)(x)}{(2.00 - x)(1.00 - x)} = \frac{x^2}{x^2 - 3.00x + 2.00}$$

At equilibrium, we have

$$1.56 = \frac{x^2}{x^2 - 3.00x + 2.00}$$

To solve for x in this case, we rearrange the previous expression into the form of a *quadratic equation*: $ax^2 + bx + c = 0$. Carrying out the arithmetic gives

$$0.56x^2 - 4.68x + 3.12 = 0$$

where $a = 0.56$, $b = -4.68$, and $c = 3.12$. Then we can find x with the quadratic formula (Appendix A):

$$x = \frac{-b \pm \sqrt{b^2 - 4ac}}{2a}$$

The "$\pm$" sign means that we obtain two possible values for x:

$$x = \frac{4.68 \pm \sqrt{(-4.68)^2 - 4(0.56)(3.12)}}{2(0.56)}$$

$$x = 7.6\ M \qquad \text{and} \qquad x = 0.73\ M$$

Note that only one of the values for x makes sense chemically. The larger value gives negative concentrations at equilibrium (for example, $2.00\ M - 7.6\ M = -5.6\ M$), which have no meaning. Therefore, $x = 0.73\ M$ and we have

$$[CO] = 2.00\ M - x = 2.00\ M - 0.73\ M = 1.27\ M$$
$$[H_2O] = 1.00\ M - x = 0.27\ M$$
$$[CO_2] = [H_2] = x = 0.73\ M$$

Checking to see if these values give the known K_c, we have

$$K_c = \frac{0.73 \times 0.73}{1.27 \times 0.27} = 1.6, \text{ within rounding of } 1.56$$

Simplifying Assumptions for Finding an Unknown Quantity In many cases, we can use chemical "common sense" to make an assumption that avoids the use of the quadratic formula to find x. In general, *if a reaction has a relatively small K and a relatively large initial reactant concentration, the concentration change (x) can often be neglected* without introducing significant error. This assumption does not mean that $x = 0$, because then there would be no reaction. It means that if a reaction proceeds very little (small K) and if you start with a high reactant concentration, very little will be used up, so at equilibrium, the reactant concentration will have hardly changed:

$$[\text{reactant}]_{\text{init}} - x = [\text{reactant}]_{\text{eq}} \approx [\text{reactant}]_{\text{init}}$$

You can imagine a similar situation in everyday life. On a bathroom scale, you weigh 158 lb. Take off your wristwatch, and you still weigh 158 lb. Within the precision of the measurement, the weight of the wristwatch is so small compared with your weight that it can be neglected:

$$\text{Initial body weight} - \text{weight of watch} = \text{final body weight} \approx \text{initial body weight}$$

Similarly, if the initial concentration of reactant A is, for example, 0.500 M and, because of a small K_c, the concentration that reacts is 0.002 M, we can assume that

$$[A]_{\text{init}} - [A]_{\text{reacting}} = [A]_{\text{eq}} \approx [A]_{\text{init}} \tag{17.9}$$
$$0.500\ M - 0.002\ M = 0.498\ M \approx 0.500\ M$$

For the assumption that x is negligible to be justified, you must check that the error introduced is not significant. But how much is "significant"? One commonly used criterion is *if the assumption results in a change (error) in a concentration that is less than 5%, the error is not significant, and the assumption is justified*. This approach may seem a bit vague at this point, so let's go through a sample problem and make this assumption to see how it simplifies the math, and then we'll see if the assumption is justified in the case of two different initial concentrations. We make this assumption often in Chapters 18 and 19.

Sample Problem 17.9 Calculating Equilibrium Concentrations with Simplifying Assumptions

PROBLEM Phosgene is a potent chemical warfare agent that is now outlawed by international agreement. It decomposes by the reaction

$$COCl_2(g) \rightleftharpoons CO(g) + Cl_2(g) \quad K_c = 8.3 \times 10^{-4} \text{ (at 360°C)}$$

Calculate [CO], [Cl$_2$], and [COCl$_2$], when the following amounts of phosgene decompose and reach equilibrium in a 10.0-L flask:
(a) 5.00 mol COCl$_2$ **(b)** 0.100 mol COCl$_2$

PLAN We know from the balanced equation that when x mol COCl$_2$ decomposes, x mol CO and x mol Cl$_2$ form. We convert amount (mol) to concentration, define x and set up the reaction table, and substitute the values into Q_c. Before using the quadratic formula, we simplify the calculation by assuming that x is negligibly small. After solving for x, we check the assumption and find the concentrations. If the assumption is not justified, we must use the quadratic formula to find x.

SOLUTION **(a)** For 5.00 mol COCl$_2$. Writing the reaction quotient:

$$Q_c = \frac{[CO][Cl_2]}{[COCl_2]}$$

Calculating the initial $[COCl_2]$:

$$[COCl_2]_{init} = \frac{5.00 \text{ mol}}{10.0 \text{ L}} = 0.500 \, M$$

Setting up the reaction table, with $x = [COCl_2]_{reacting}$:

CONCENTRATION (M)	$COCl_2(g)$	$\rightleftharpoons$	$CO(g)$	+	$Cl_2(g)$
Initial	0.500		0		0
Change	$-x$		$+x$		$+x$
Equilibrium	$0.500 - x$		x		x

If we use these values directly in Q_c, at equilibrium we obtain

$$Q_c = \frac{[CO][Cl_2]}{[COCl_2]} = \frac{x^2}{0.500 - x} = K_c = 8.3 \times 10^{-4}$$

Since K_c is small, the reaction does not proceed very far to the right, so let's assume that x (the $[COCl_2]$ that reacts) is so much smaller than the initial concentration, 0.500 M, that the equilibrium concentration is nearly the same. Therefore,

$$0.500 \, M - x \approx 0.500 \, M$$

Using this assumption, we substitute and solve for x:

$$K_c = 8.3 \times 10^{-4} \approx \frac{x^2}{0.500}$$

$$x^2 \approx (8.3 \times 10^{-4})(0.500), \quad \text{so } x \approx 2.0 \times 10^{-2}$$

Checking the assumption by finding the percent error:

$$\frac{2.0 \times 10^{-2}}{0.500} \times 100 = 4\% \text{ is less than 5\%, so the assumption is justified.}$$

Solving for the equilibrium concentrations:

$$[CO] = [Cl_2] = x = \boxed{2.0 \times 10^{-2} \, M}$$

$$[COCl_2] = 0.500 \, M - x = \boxed{0.480 \, M}$$

(b) For 0.100 mol $COCl_2$. This calculation is the same, except $[COCl_2]_{init} = 0.100 \text{ mol}/10.0 \text{ L} = 0.0100 \, M$. Thus, at equilibrium, we have

$$Q_c = \frac{[CO][Cl_2]}{[COCl_2]} = \frac{x^2}{0.0100 - x} = K_c = 8.3 \times 10^{-4}$$

Making the assumption that $0.0100 \, M - x \approx 0.0100 \, M$ and solving for x:

$$K_c = 8.3 \times 10^{-4} \approx \frac{x^2}{0.0100}$$

$$x \approx 2.9 \times 10^{-3}$$

Checking the assumption:

$$\frac{2.9 \times 10^{-3}}{0.0100} \times 100 = 29\% \text{ is more than 5\%, so the assumption is } not \text{ justified.}$$

We must solve the quadratic equation, $x^2 + (8.3 \times 10^{-4})x - (8.3 \times 10^{-6}) = 0$, for which the only meaningful value of x is 2.5×10^{-3}.
Solving for the equilibrium concentrations:

$$[CO] = [Cl_2] = \boxed{2.5 \times 10^{-3} \, M}$$

$$[COCl_2] = 1.00 \times 10^{-2} \, M - x = \boxed{7.5 \times 10^{-3} \, M}$$

CHECK Once again, the best check is to use the calculated values to be sure you obtain the given K_c.
COMMENT Note that, at the high initial concentration, the assumption was justified, but at the low initial concentration, it was *not*.

Follow-up Problem 17.9 In a study of halogen bond strengths, 0.50 mol I_2 was heated in a 2.5-L vessel, and the following reaction occurred: $I_2(g) \rightleftharpoons 2I(g)$.
(a) Calculate $[I_2]$ and $[I]$ at equilibrium at 600 K; $K_c = 2.94 \times 10^{-10}$.
(b) Calculate $[I_2]$ and $[I]$ at equilibrium at 2000 K; $K_c = 0.209$.

Problems Involving Mixtures of Reactants and Products: Determining Reaction Direction In the problems we've worked so far, the direction of the reaction was obvious: since only reactants were present, the reaction had to go toward products. Thus, in the reaction tables, we knew that the unknown change in reactant concentration had a negative sign ($-x$) and that the change in product concentration had a positive sign ($+x$). Suppose, however, we start with a *mixture* of reactants and products. Whenever the reaction direction is not obvious, we first *compare Q with K to find the direction* in which the reaction proceeds to reach equilibrium. This tells us whether the unknown change in concentration, x, is positive or negative. (In order to focus on this idea, the upcoming sample problem includes data that eliminate the need for the quadratic formula.)

Sample Problem 17.10   Predicting Reaction Direction and Calculating Equilibrium Concentrations

PROBLEM The research and development unit of a chemical company is studying the reaction of CH_4 and H_2S, two components of natural gas:

$$CH_4(g) + 2H_2S(g) \rightleftharpoons CS_2(g) + 4H_2(g)$$

In one experiment, 1.00 mol CH_4, 1.00 mol CS_2, 2.00 mol H_2S, and 2.00 mol H_2 are mixed in a 250-mL vessel at 960°C. At this temperature, $K_c = 0.036$.
(a) In which direction will the reaction proceed to reach equilibrium?
(b) If $[CH_4] = 5.56\ M$ at equilibrium, what are the concentrations of the other substances?
PLAN **(a)** To find the direction, we convert the given initial amounts to concentrations, calculate Q_c, and compare it with K_c. **(b)** Based on the results from (a), we determine the sign of each concentration change for the reaction table and then use the known $[CH_4]$ at equilibrium to determine the value of x and the other equilibrium concentrations.
SOLUTION **(a)** Calculating the initial concentrations:

$$[CH_4] = \frac{1.00\ \text{mol}}{0.250\ \text{L}} = 4.00\ M$$

Similarly, $[H_2S] = 8.00\ M$, $[CS_2] = 4.00\ M$, and $[H_2] = 8.00\ M$.
Calculating the value of Q_c:

$$Q_c = \frac{[CS_2][H_2]^4}{[CH_4][H_2S]^2} = \frac{4.00 \times (8.00)^4}{4.00 \times (8.00)^2} = 64.0$$

Comparing Q_c and K_c: $Q_c > K_c$ (64.0 > 0.036), so the reaction goes to the left. Therefore, reactants increase and products decrease their concentrations.
(b) Setting up the reaction table, with $x = [CS_2]$ that reacts, which equals the $[CH_4]$ that forms:

CONCENTRATION (M)	$CH_4(g)$	+	$2H_2S(g)$	$\rightleftharpoons$	$CS_2(g)$	+	$4H_2(g)$
Initial	4.00		8.00		4.00		8.00
Change	$+x$		$+2x$		$-x$		$-4x$
Equilibrium	$4.00 + x$		$8.00 + 2x$		$4.00 - x$		$8.00 - 4x$

Solving for x: At equilibrium,

$$[CH_4] = 5.56\ M = 4.00\ M + x$$

So,

$$x = 1.56\ M$$

Thus,

$$[H_2S] = 8.00\ M + 2x = 8.00\ M + 2(1.56\ M) = 11.12\ M$$

$$[CS_2] = 4.00\ M - x = 2.44\ M$$

$$[H_2] = 8.00\ M - 4x = 1.76\ M$$

Check The comparison of Q_c and K_c showed the reaction moving to the left. The given data from part (b) confirm this because [CH_4] increases from 4.00 M to 5.56 M during the reaction. Check that the concentrations give the known K_c:

$$\frac{2.44 \times (1.76)^4}{5.56 \times (11.12)^2} = 0.0341, \text{ which is close to } 0.036$$

Follow-up Problem 17.10   An inorganic chemist studying the reactions of phosphorus halides mixes 0.1050 mol PCl_5 with 0.0450 mol Cl_2 and 0.0450 mol PCl_3 in a 0.5000-L flask at 250°C: $PCl_5(g) \rightleftharpoons PCl_3(g) + Cl_2(g)$; $K_c = 4.2 \times 10^{-2}$. **(a)** In which direction will the reaction proceed? **(b)** If [PCl_5] = 0.2065 M at equilibrium, what are the equilibrium concentrations of the other components?

By this time, you've seen quite a few variations on the type of equilibrium problem in which you know K and some initial quantities and must find the equilibrium quantities. Figure 17.6 summarizes the steps involved in solving these problems by grouping them into three overall parts.

Section Summary

In most equilibrium problems, we use quantities (concentrations or pressures) of reactants and products to find K, or we use K to find quantities. We use a reaction table to summarize the initial quantities, how they change, and what the equilibrium quantities are. When K is small and the initial quantity of reactant is large, we assume the unknown quantity of material that reacts (x) is so much smaller than the initial quantity that it can be neglected when added to or subtracted from the initial quantity. If this assumption is not justified (error > 5%), we use the quadratic formula to find x.

17.6 Reaction Conditions and the Equilibrium State: Le Châtelier's Principle

The most remarkable feature of a system at equilibrium is its ability to return to equilibrium after a change in conditions moves it away from that state. This drive to reattain equilibrium is stated in **Le Châtelier's principle:** when a chemical system in a state of equilibrium is disturbed, it reattains equilibrium by undergoing a net reaction that reduces the effect of the disturbance.

Two phrases in this statement need further explanation. First, what does it mean to "disturb" a system in a state of equilibrium? At equilibrium, Q equals K. When a change in conditions forces the system temporarily out of equilibrium ($Q \neq K$), we say the system has been stressed, or disturbed. Three such common disturbances are a change in concentration of a component, a change in pressure (caused by a change in volume), or a change in temperature. The "net reaction" that the system undergoes is often referred to as a shift in its *equilibrium position,* those specific concentrations (or pressures) that make up Q when it equals K. Thus, when a disturbance occurs, the equilibrium position shifts: *concentrations (or pressures) change in a way that reduces the disturbance, and the system attains a new equilibrium* ($Q = K$ again).

Le Châtelier's principle allows us to predict the direction of the shift in position (change in concentrations or pressures) and thus to create conditions that maximize yields. Let's examine each of these three kinds of disturbances to see how a system at equilibrium responds and then note the effect, if any, of a catalyst. In the following discussion, we focus on the reversible reaction between phosphorus trichloride and chlorine to produce phosphorus pentachloride:

$$PCl_3(g) + Cl_2(g) \rightleftharpoons PCl_5(g)$$

SOLVING EQUILIBRIUM PROBLEMS

PRELIMINARY SETTING UP

1. Write the balanced equation
2. Write the reaction quotient, Q
3. Convert all amounts into the correct units (M or atm)

WORKING ON THE REACTION TABLE

4. When reaction direction is not known, compare Q with K
5. Construct a reaction table

✓ Check the sign of x, the change in the quantity

SOLVING FOR x AND EQUILIBRIUM QUANTITIES

6. Substitute the quantities into Q
7. To simplify the math, assume that x is negligible
   ($[A]_{init} - x = [A]_{eq} \approx [A]_{init}$)
8. Solve for x

✓ Check that assumption is justified (< 5% error)

9. Find the equilibrium quantities

✓ Check to see that calculated values give the known K

Figure 17.6 How to solve equilibrium problems. These nine steps, grouped into three tasks, present a useful approach to calculating equilibrium quantities (concentrations or pressures), given initial quantities and K.

However, the principles hold for any system at equilibrium, whether in the natural or social sciences. ◆

The Effect of a Change in Concentration

When a system at equilibrium is disturbed by a change in concentration of one of the components, the system reacts in the direction that reduces the change:

- If the concentration increases, the system reacts to consume some of it.
- If the concentration decreases, the system reacts to produce some of it.
  At 523 K, the PCl_3-Cl_2-PCl_5 system reaches equilibrium when

$$Q_c = \frac{[PCl_5]}{[PCl_3][Cl_2]} = 24.0 = K_c$$

What happens if we now inject some Cl_2 gas? The $[Cl_2]$ term increases, so the value of Q_c immediately falls as the denominator becomes larger; thus, the system is no longer at equilibrium. As a result of this disturbance, some of the added Cl_2 reacts with some of the PCl_3 present and produces more PCl_5. The denominator becomes smaller once again, the numerator larger, and eventually Q_c again equals K_c. The concentrations of the components have changed, however: the concentrations of Cl_2 and PCl_5 are higher than in the original equilibrium position, and the concentration of PCl_3 is lower. Nevertheless, the ratio of values gives the same K_c. We describe this change by saying that *the equilibrium position shifts to the right when a component on the left is added:*

$$PCl_3 + Cl_2(\text{added}) \longrightarrow PCl_5$$

What happens if, instead of adding Cl_2, we could remove some PCl_3? The $[PCl_3]$ term decreases, the denominator becomes smaller, and the value of Q_c rises above K_c. As a result of the removal, some PCl_5 decomposes to PCl_3 and Cl_2. The numerator decreases and the denominator increases until Q_c equals K_c again. Once again, the concentrations are different from those of the original equilibrium position but K_c is not. We say that *the equilibrium position shifts to the left when a component on the left is removed:*

$$PCl_3(\text{removed}) + Cl_2 \longleftarrow PCl_5$$

To summarize the effects of concentration changes:

- The equilibrium position shifts to the *right* if a reactant is added or a product is removed.
- The equilibrium position shifts to the *left* if a reactant is removed or a product is added.

In general, whenever the concentration of a component changes, *the equilibrium system reacts to consume some of the added substance or produce some of the removed substance.* In this way, the system "reduces the effect of the disturbance." The effect is not completely eliminated, however, as you can see next from a quantitative comparison of original and new equilibrium positions.

Consider the case in which we added Cl_2 to the system at equilibrium. Suppose the original equilibrium position was established with the following concentrations: $[PCl_3] = 0.200\ M$, $[Cl_2] = 0.125\ M$, and $[PCl_5] = 0.600\ M$. Thus,

$$Q_c = \frac{[PCl_5]}{[PCl_3][Cl_2]} = \frac{0.600}{0.200 \times 0.125} = 24.0 = K_c$$

Now we add enough Cl_2 to increase its concentration by $0.075\ M$. Before any reaction occurs, this addition creates a new set of initial concentrations. Then the system reacts and comes to a new equilibrium position. From Le Châtelier's principle, we predict that adding more reactant will produce more product, that is, shift the equilibrium position to the right. Experiment shows that the new $[PCl_5]$ at equilibrium is $0.637\ M$.

◆ The Universality of Le Châtelier's Principle
Although Le Châtelier limited the scope of his principle to physical and chemical systems, its application is much wider. Ecologists and economists, for example, see it at work often. On the African savannah, the numbers of herbivores (antelope, wildebeest, zebra) and carnivores (lion, cheetah) are in delicate balance. Any disturbance (drought, disease) causes shifts in the relative numbers until they attain a new balance. In its purest form, the economic principle of supply-and-demand is another example of this equilibrium principle. A given demand-supply balance for a product establishes a given price. If either demand or supply is disturbed, it causes a shift in the other and, therefore, in the prevailing price until a new balance is attained.

Table 17.3 The Effect of Added Cl_2 on the PCl_3-Cl_2-PCl_5 System

Concentration (M)	$PCl_3(g)$	+	$Cl_2(g)$	$\rightleftharpoons$	$PCl_5(g)$
Original equilibrium	0.200		0.125		0.600
Disturbance			+0.075		
New initial	0.200		0.200		0.600
Change	$-x$		$-x$		$+x$
New equilibrium	$0.200 - x$		$0.200 - x$		$0.600 + x$
					$(0.637)^*$

*Experimentally determined value.

Table 17.3 shows a reaction table of the entire process: the original equilibrium position, the disturbance, the (new) initial concentrations, the size and direction of the change needed to reattain equilibrium, and the new equilibrium position. From Table 17.3,

$$[PCl_5] = 0.600\ M + x = 0.637\ M, \qquad \text{so } x = 0.037\ M$$

Also, $\qquad\qquad [PCl_3] = [Cl_2] = 0.200\ M - x = 0.163\ M$

Therefore, at equilibrium,

$$K_{c(\text{original concentration})} = \frac{0.600}{0.200 \times 0.125} = 24.0$$

$$K_{c(\text{new concentration})} = \frac{0.637}{0.163 \times 0.163} = 24.0$$

There are several key points to notice about the new equilibrium concentrations that exist after Cl_2 is added:

- As we predicted, $[PCl_5]$ (0.637 M) is higher than its original concentration (0.600 M).
- $[Cl_2]$ (0.163 M) is higher than its original equilibrium concentration (0.125 M), but lower than its initial concentration just after the addition (0.200 M); thus, the disturbance (addition of Cl_2) is *reduced but not eliminated.*
- $[PCl_3]$ (0.163 M), the other left-hand component, is lower than its original concentration (0.200 M) because some reacted with the added Cl_2.
- Most importantly, although the position of equilibrium shifted to the right, K_c *remains the same.*

Be sure to note that the system adjusts by changing concentrations, but the value of Q_c *at equilibrium* is the same as in the original system. In other words, *at a given temperature, K_c does not change with a change in concentration.*

Sample Problem 17.11 Predicting the Effect of a Change in Concentration on the Position of Equilibrium

PROBLEM To improve air quality and obtain a useful product, sulfur is often removed from coal and natural gas by treating the fuel contaminant hydrogen sulfide with O_2:

$$2H_2S(g) + O_2(g) \rightleftharpoons 2S(s) + 2H_2O(g)$$

What happens to
(a) $[H_2O]$ if O_2 is added?   (b) $[H_2S]$ if O_2 is added?
(c) $[O_2]$ if H_2S is removed?   (d) $[H_2S]$ if sulfur is added?

PLAN We write the reaction quotient to see how Q_c is affected by each disturbance relative to K_c. This effect tells us the direction in which the reaction proceeds for the system to reattain equilibrium and how each concentration changes.

SOLUTION Writing the reaction quotient: $Q_c = \dfrac{[H_2O]^2}{[H_2S]^2[O_2]}$

(a) When O_2 is added, the denominator of Q_c increases, so $Q_c < K_c$. The reaction proceeds to the right until $Q_c = K_c$ again, so $[H_2O]$ increases.

(b) As in part **(a),** when O_2 is added, $Q_c < K_c$. Some H_2S reacts with the added O_2 as the reaction proceeds to the right, so [H_2S] decreases.

(c) When H_2S is removed, the denominator of Q_c decreases, so $Q_c > K_c$. As the reaction proceeds to the left to re-form H_2S, more O_2 is produced as well, so [O_2] increases.

(d) Since the concentration of solid S is unchanged as long as some is present, it does not appear in the reaction quotient. Adding more S has no effect, so [H_2S] is unchanged.

CHECK Apply Le Châtelier's principle to see that the reaction proceeds in the direction that lowers the increased concentration or raises the decreased concentration.

COMMENT As you know, sulfur exists most commonly as S_8, so Q_c would be

$\dfrac{[H_2O]^8}{[H_2S]^8[O_2]^4}$. The value of K_c is different for this equation, but the changes described in the problem have the same effects.

Follow-up Problem 17.11 In a study of the chemistry of glass etching, an inorganic chemist examines the reaction between sand (SiO_2) and hydrogen fluoride at a temperature above the boiling point of water:

$$SiO_2(s) + 4HF(g) \rightleftharpoons SiF_4(g) + 2H_2O(g)$$

Predict the effect on [SiF_4] when **(a)** $H_2O(g)$ is removed; **(b)** some liquid water is added; **(c)** HF is removed; **(d)** some sand is removed.

The Effect of a Change in Pressure (Volume)

Changes in pressure have significant effects only on equilibrium systems with gaseous components. Aside from phase changes, a change in pressure has a negligible effect on liquids and solids because they are nearly incompressible. Pressure changes can occur in three ways:

- Changing the concentration of a gaseous component
- Adding an inert gas (one that does not take part in the reaction)
- Changing the volume of the reaction vessel

We just considered the effect of changing the concentration of a component, and that reasoning holds here. Next, let's see why *adding an inert gas has no effect on the equilibrium position*. Since adding an inert gas does not change the volume, all *reactant and product concentrations remain the same*. In other words, since the volume and number of moles of the reactant and product gases do not change, their *partial pressures do not change*. Since we use these (unchanged) partial pressures in the reaction quotient, the equilibrium position cannot change.

On the other hand, changing the pressure by changing the volume often causes a large change in the equilibrium position, but it does so by a means we've already discussed. Note that *a change in volume causes a change in concentration*, the number of moles per liter of container volume: a decrease in container volume raises the concentration, and an increase in volume lowers the concentration.

Suppose we let the PCl_3-Cl_2-PCl_5 system come to equilibrium in a cylinder-piston assembly. Recall that $Q_c = \dfrac{[PCl_5]}{[PCl_3][Cl_2]}$. Now we press down on the piston to halve the volume. The concentrations double, but the denominator of Q_c is the product of two concentrations, so it quadruples while the numerator only doubles. Thus, Q_c becomes less than K_c. As a result, the reaction shifts toward formation of PCl_5. The denominator then becomes smaller and the numerator larger as the system moves toward a new equilibrium position. Because it is just another way to change the concentration, *a change in pressure due to a change in volume does not alter K_c.*

A key point to notice is how the system responded to this particular disturbance: higher pressure created *less volume*, which moved the reaction toward the side with *fewer moles of gas*. Two moles were used to make one:

$$2 \text{ mol gas} \longrightarrow 1 \text{ mol gas} \qquad PCl_3(g) + Cl_2(g) \longrightarrow PCl_5(g)$$

The disturbance, the crowding created by the compression, was reduced by lowering the total number of gas molecules. Thus, according to Le Châtelier's principle, when a system at equilibrium that contains gases undergoes a change in pressure *as a result of a change in volume*, the equilibrium position shifts to reduce the effect of the change:

- If the volume is lower (pressure is higher), the total number of gas molecules decreases.
- If the volume is higher (pressure is lower), the total number of gas molecules increases.

These effects occur only if the number of moles of gas, n_{gas}, changes during the reaction. In many cases, however, $\Delta n_{gas} = 0$. For example,

$$2 \text{ mol gas} \longrightarrow 2 \text{ mol gas} \qquad H_2(g) + I_2(g) \rightleftharpoons 2HI(g)$$

Q_c has the same number of terms in the numerator and denominator:

$$Q_c = \frac{[HI]^2}{[H_2][I_2]} = \frac{[HI][HI]}{[H_2][I_2]}$$

Therefore, a change in volume has the same effect on the numerator and denominator. Thus, *if $\Delta n_{gas} = 0$, there is no effect on the equilibrium position.*

Sample Problem 17.12   Predicting the Effect of a Change in Volume (Pressure) on the Position of Equilibrium

PROBLEM How would you change the volume of each of the following reactions to *increase* the yield of the products?
(a) $CaCO_3(s) \rightleftharpoons CaO(s) + CO_2(g)$ **(b)** $S(s) + 3F_2(g) \rightleftharpoons SF_6(g)$
(c) $Cl_2(g) + I_2(g) \rightleftharpoons 2ICl(g)$

PLAN A change in volume causes a change in concentration. If the volume decreases (pressure increases), the equilibrium position shifts to relieve the pressure by reducing the number of moles of gas. A volume increase (pressure decrease) has the opposite effect.

SOLUTION (a) The only gas is the product CO_2. To make the system produce more CO_2, we increase the volume (decrease the pressure).

(b) With 3 mol of gas on the left and only 1 mol on the right, we decrease the volume (increase the pressure) to form more SF_6.

(c) The number of moles of gas is the same on both sides of the equation, so a change in volume (pressure) will have no effect on the yield of ICl.

CHECK Let's predict the relative values of Q_c and K_c. In **(a)**, $Q_c = [CO_2]$, so increasing the volume will make $Q_c < K_c$, and the system will make more CO_2. In **(b)**, $Q_c = [SF_6]/[F_2]^3$. Lowering the volume increases $[F_2]$ and $[SF_6]$ proportionately, but Q_c decreases because of the difference in exponents. To make $Q_c = K_c$ again, $[SF_6]$ must increase. In **(c)**, $Q_c = [ICl]^2/[Cl_2][I_2]$. A change in volume (pressure) affects the numerator (2 mol) and denominator (2 mol) equally, so it will have no effect.

Follow-up Problem 17.12 How would you change the pressure (via a volume change) of the following reaction mixtures to *decrease* the yield of products?
(a) $2SO_2(g) + O_2(g) \rightleftharpoons 2SO_3(g)$ **(b)** $4NH_3(g) + 5O_2(g) \rightleftharpoons 4NO(g) + 6H_2O(g)$
(c) $CaC_2O_4(s) \rightleftharpoons CaCO_3(s) + CO(g)$

The Effect of a Change in Temperature

Of the three types of disturbances—change in concentration, pressure, or temperature—*only temperature changes alter K*. To see why, we must take the heat of reaction into account:

$$PCl_3(g) + Cl_2(g) \rightleftharpoons PCl_5(g) \qquad \Delta H^0_{rxn} = -111 \text{ kJ}$$

The forward reaction is exothermic (releases heat; $\Delta H^0 < 0$), so the reverse reaction is endothermic (absorbs heat; $\Delta H^0 > 0$):

$$PCl_3(g) + Cl_2(g) \longrightarrow PCl_5(g) + \textit{heat} \text{ (exothermic)}$$
$$PCl_3(g) + Cl_2(g) \longleftarrow PCl_5(g) + \textit{heat} \text{ (endothermic)}$$

If we consider *heat as a component of the equilibrium system,* a rise in temperature "adds" heat to the system and a drop in temperature "removes" heat from the system. As with a change in any other component, the system shifts to reduce the effect of the change. Therefore, *a temperature increase favors the endothermic (heat-absorbing) direction and a temperature decrease favors the exothermic (heat-releasing) direction.*

If we start with the system at equilibrium, Q_c equals K_c. Increase the temperature, and the system responds by absorbing the added heat, so some PCl_5 decomposes to PCl_3 and Cl_2. The denominator of Q_c becomes larger and the numerator smaller, so the system reaches a new equilibrium position at a smaller ratio of concentration terms, that is, a lower K_c. Similarly, the system responds to a drop in temperature by releasing more heat, so some PCl_3 and Cl_2 form more PCl_5. The numerator of Q_c becomes larger, the denominator smaller, and the new equilibrium position has a higher K_c. Thus,

- A temperature rise will increase K_c for a system with a positive ΔH^0_{rxn}.
- A temperature rise will decrease K_c for a system with a negative ΔH^0_{rxn}.

Let's take a kinetic point of view to see *why* the equilibrium constant changes. An increase in temperature increases both forward and reverse reaction rates but not equally: it increases the rate of the endothermic reaction (decompositon of PCl_5 in this case) *more* than it does the rate of the exothermic reaction (formation of PCl_5). As the Arrhenius equation shows (see Equation 16.7), this increase in temperature acts by increasing the rate constant for the endothermic reaction more than for the exothermic reaction. Thus, since K is the ratio of rate constants, its value changes.

Sample Problem 17.13 Predicting the Effect of a Change in Temperature on the Position of Equilibrium

PROBLEM How does an *increase* in temperature affect the equilibrium concentration of the underlined substance and K_c for the following reactions?
(a) $CaO(s) + H_2O(l) \rightleftharpoons \underline{Ca(OH)_2(aq)}$ $\Delta H^0 = -82$ kJ
(b) $CaCO_3(s) \rightleftharpoons CaO(s) + \underline{CO_2(g)}$ $\Delta H^0 = 178$ kJ
(c) $\underline{SO_2(g)} \rightleftharpoons S(s) + O_2(g)$ $\Delta H^0 = 297$ kJ
PLAN We write each equation to show heat as a reactant or product. Increasing the temperature adds heat, so the system shifts to absorb the heat; that is, the endothermic reaction occurs. K_c will increase if the forward reaction is endothermic and decrease if it is exothermic.
SOLUTION (a) $CaO(s) + H_2O(l) \rightleftharpoons Ca(OH)_2(aq) + \textit{heat}$
Adding heat shifts the system to the left: $[Ca(OH)_2]$ and K_c will decrease.
(b) $CaCO_3(s) + \textit{heat} \rightleftharpoons CaO(s) + CO_2(g)$
Adding heat shifts the system to the right: $[CO_2]$ and K_c will increase.
(c) $SO_2(g) + \textit{heat} \rightleftharpoons S(s) + O_2(g)$
Adding heat shifts the system to the right: $[SO_2]$ will decrease and K_c will increase.
CHECK You might check by going through the reasoning for a *decrease* in temperature: heat is removed and the exothermic direction is favored. All the answers should be opposite.

Follow-up Problem 17.13 How does a *decrease* in temperature affect the partial pressure of the underlined substance and K_p for the following reactions?
(a) $C(graphite) + 2H_2(g) \rightleftharpoons \underline{CH_4(g)}$ $\Delta H^0 = -75$ kJ
(b) $\underline{N_2(g)} + O_2(g) \rightleftharpoons 2NO(g)$ $\Delta H^0 = 181$ kJ
(c) $P_4(s) + 10Cl_2(g) \rightleftharpoons \underline{4PCl_5(g)}$ $\Delta H^0 = -1528$ kJ

◆ **Temperature-Dependent Systems** There is a striking similarity among expressions for the temperature dependence of K, k (rate constant), and P (equilibrium vapor pressure):

$$\ln \frac{K_2}{K_1} = -\frac{\Delta H^0_{rxn}}{R}\left(\frac{1}{T_2} - \frac{1}{T_1}\right)$$

$$\ln \frac{k_2}{k_1} = -\frac{E_a}{R}\left(\frac{1}{T_2} - \frac{1}{T_1}\right)$$

$$\ln \frac{P_2}{P_1} = -\frac{\Delta H_{vap}}{R}\left(\frac{1}{T_2} - \frac{1}{T_1}\right)$$

Each concentration-related term—K, k, or P—is dependent on T through an energy term—ΔH^0_{rxn}, E_a, or ΔH_{vap}, respectively—divided by R. The similarities arise because the equations express the same relationship. K equals a ratio of rate constants and $E_{a(fwd)} - E_{a(rev)} = \Delta H^0_{rxn}$. In the vapor pressure case, for the phase change, $A(l) \rightleftharpoons A(g)$, the heat of reaction is the heat of vaporization: $\Delta H_{vap} = \Delta H^0_{rxn}$. Moreover, the equilibrium constant equals the equilibrium vapor pressure: $K_p = P_A$.

◆ **Catalysts and Perpetual Motion?** The engine shown consists of a piston attached to a flywheel, whose rocker arm, holding a catalyst, moves in and out of the reaction in the cylinder. What if the catalyst had the impossible property of increasing the rate of PCl_5 breakdown but not of its formation? When in the cylinder, the catalyst would speed up the breakdown of PCl_5 to PCl_3 and Cl_2— 1 mol of gas to 2 mol—increasing gas pressure and pushing the piston out. With the catalyst out of the cylinder, PCl_3 and Cl_2 would re-form PCl_5, lowering gas pressure, and the piston would move in. The process would supply power with no external input of energy. If a catalyst *did* shift the position of equilibrium, we could design truly amazing machines!

The van't Hoff Equation: Changes in K with Changes in T The *van't Hoff equation* shows mathematically how the equilibrium constant is affected by changes in temperature:

$$\ln \frac{K_2}{K_1} = -\frac{\Delta H^0_{rxn}}{R}\left(\frac{1}{T_2} - \frac{1}{T_1}\right) \qquad (17.10)$$

where K_1 is the equilibrium constant at T_1, K_2 is the equilibrium constant at T_2, and R is the universal gas constant. If we know ΔH^0_{rxn} and K at one temperature, the van't Hoff equation allows us to determine K at any other temperature (or to find ΔH^0_{rxn}, given the K's at two temperatures). Equation 17.10 confirms the qualitative prediction from Le Châtelier's principle: If $T_2 > T_1$, then $(1/T_2 - 1/T_1) < 0$. Therefore,

- For an endothermic reaction ($\Delta H^0_{rxn} > 0$), $\ln (K_2/K_1) > 0$, so $K_2 > K_1$
- For an exothermic reaction ($\Delta H^0_{rxn} < 0$), $\ln (K_2/K_1) < 0$, so $K_2 < K_1$ ◆

(For practice with applying the van't Hoff equation, see Problems 17.73 and 17.74.)

The Lack of Effect of a Catalyst

Let's briefly consider a final external change to the reacting system that we can cause: adding a catalyst. Recall from Chapter 16 that a catalyst speeds up a reaction by lowering the activation energy, thereby increasing the forward *and* reverse rates to the same extent. In other words, it shortens the time needed for the *final* reactant and product concentrations to be attained. Thus, *a catalyst shortens the time the system takes to reach equilibrium but has **no** effect on the equilibrium position.* ◆

If, for instance, we add a catalyst to a mixture of PCl_3 and Cl_2 at 523 K, the system will attain the *same* equilibrium concentrations of PCl_3, Cl_2, and PCl_5 *more quickly* than it did without the catalyst. As you'll see in a moment, however, catalysts often play key roles in optimizing reaction systems. The upcoming Chemical Connections essays highlight two areas that apply equilibrium principles: the first concerns a major industrial process, and the second examines metabolic processes in organisms.

Table 17.4 summarizes the effects of changing conditions on the position of equilibrium. Note that all changes except the addition of a catalyst change the equilibrium position, but only temperature changes affect the value of the equilibrium constant.

Table 17.4 Effect of Various Disturbances on an Equilibrium System

Disturbance	Net Direction of Reaction	Effect on Value of K
Concentration		
Increase [reactant]	Toward formation of product	None
Decrease [reactant]	Toward formation of reactant	None
Pressure (volume)		
Increase P	Toward formation of lower amount (mol) of gas	None
Decrease P	Toward formation of higher amount (mol) of gas	None
Temperature		
Increase T	Toward absorption of heat	Increases if $\Delta H^0_{rxn} > 0$ Decreases if $\Delta H^0_{rxn} < 0$
Decrease T	Toward release of heat	Increases if $\Delta H^0_{rxn} < 0$ Decreases if $\Delta H^0_{rxn} > 0$
Catalyst added	None; rates of forward and reverse reactions increase equally	None

Chemical Connections   Chemistry in Industrial Production

The Haber Process for the Synthesis of Ammonia

Nitrogen occurs in many essential natural and synthetic compounds. By far the richest source of nitrogen is the atmosphere, where four of every five molecules are N_2. Despite this abundance, the supply of *usable* nitrogen for biological and manufacturing processes is limited because of the low chemical reactivity of N_2. Because of the strong triple bond holding the two N atoms together, the nitrogen atom is very difficult to "fix," that is, to combine with other atoms.

Natural nitrogen fixation is accomplished either through the elegant specificity of certain enzymes found in bacteria that live on plant roots or through the brute force of lightning storms. Nearly 13% of all the nitrogen fixation on Earth is accomplished industrially through the **Haber process** for the formation of ammonia from its elements:

$$N_2(g) + 3H_2(g) \rightleftharpoons 2NH_3(g) \qquad \Delta H^0_{rxn} = -91.8 \text{ kJ}$$

The process was developed by the German chemist Fritz Haber and first used in 1913. From its humble beginnings in a plant with a capacity of 12,000 tons a year, world production of ammonia has exploded to a current value of more than 110 million tons a year. On a mole basis, more ammonia is produced industrially than any other compound. Over 80% of this ammonia is used in fertilizer applications. In fact, the most common form of fertilizer is compressed anhydrous, liquid NH_3 injected directly into the soil (Figure 17.A). Other uses of NH_3 include the production of explosives, via the formation of HNO_3, and the making of nylons and other polymers. Smaller amounts are used as refrigerants, rubber stabilizers, household cleaners, and in the synthesis of pharmaceuticals and other organic chemicals.

The Haber process provides an excellent opportunity to apply equilibrium principles and see the compromises needed to make an industrial process economically worthwhile. From inspection of the balanced equation, we can see three ways to maximize the yield of ammonia:

Table 17.A Effect of Temperature on K_c for Ammonia Synthesis

T (K)	K_c
200.	7.17×10^{15}
300.	2.69×10^{8}
400.	3.94×10^{4}
500.	1.72×10^{2}
600.	4.53×10^{0}
700.	2.96×10^{-1}
800.	3.96×10^{-2}

1. Decrease $[NH_3]$. Since ammonia is the product, removing it as it forms will make the system produce more in a continual drive to reattain equilibrium.
2. Decrease volume (increase pressure). Since 4 mol of gas react to form 2 mol of gas, decreasing the volume will shift the equilibrium position toward fewer moles of gas, that is, toward ammonia formation.
3. Decrease temperature. Since the formation of ammonia is exothermic, decreasing the temperature (removing heat) will shift the equilibrium position toward the product, thereby increasing K_c (Table 17.A).

Therefore, the ideal conditions for maximizing the yield of ammonia are continual removal of NH_3 as it forms, high pressure, and low temperature. Figure 17.B shows the percent yield of ammonia at various conditions of pressure and temperature. Note the almost complete conversion (98.3%) to ammonia at 1000 atm and the relatively low temperature of 473 K (200.°C).

Figure 17.A Liquid ammonia used as fertilizer.

Figure 17.B Percent yield of ammonia vs. temperature (°C) at five different operating pressures. At very high pressure and low temperature *(top left)*, the yield is high, but the rate of formation is low. Industrial conditions *(circle)* are between 200 and 300 atm at about 400°C.

Chemical Connections *(continued)*

Unfortunately, a problem arises that clearly highlights the distinction between the principles of equilibrium and kinetics. Although the *yield* is favored by low temperature, the *rate* of formation is not. In fact, ammonia forms so slowly at low temperature that the process becomes uneconomical. In practice, a compromise is achieved that optimizes yield *and* rate. High pressure and continuous removal are used to increase yield, but the temperature is raised to a moderate level and a catalyst is employed to increase the rate. Achieving the same rate without a catalyst requires much higher temperatures and results in a much lower yield.

Stages in the industrial production of ammonia are shown schematically in Figure 17.C. To extend equipment life and minimize cost, modern ammonia plants operate at pressures of about 200 to 300 atm and temperatures of around 673 K (400.°C). The catalyst consists of 5-mm to 10-mm chunks of iron crystals embedded in a fused mixture of MgO, Al_2O_3, and SiO_2. The stoichiometric ratio of compressed reactant gases ($N_2:H_2 = 1:3$ by volume) is injected into the heated, pressurized reaction chamber, where it flows over the catalyst beds. Some of the heat needed is supplied by the enthalpy change of the reaction. The emerging equilibrium mixture, which contains about 35% NH_3 by volume, is cooled by refrigeration coils until the NH_3 condenses (boiling point, -33.4°C) and is removed. Since the boiling points of N_2 and H_2 are much lower, they remain gaseous and are recycled by pumps back into the reaction chamber to continue the process.

Figure 17.C Key stages in the Haber synthesis of ammonia.

Section Summary

Le Châtelier's principle states that if an equilibrium system is disturbed, it undergoes a net reaction that reduces the disturbance, and it reattains equilibrium. Changes in concentration cause a net reaction away from the added component or toward the removed component. For a reaction that involves a change in number of moles of gas, an increase in pressure (decrease in volume) causes a net reaction toward fewer moles of gas, and a decrease in pressure causes the opposite change. Although the equilibrium concentrations of components change as a result of concentration and volume changes, K does not change. A temperature change *does* change K by causing a net reaction to replace removed heat (exothermic direction) or to absorb added heat (endothermic direction). A catalyst does not affect the equilibrium position; it only causes the system to reach equilibrium more quickly by speeding forward and reverse reactions equally. Ammonia is produced in a process favored by high pressure, low temperature, and continual removal of product. To make the process economical, an intermediate temperature and a catalyst are used. A metabolic pathway is a cellular reaction sequence in which each step is shifted completely toward product. Its overall yield is controlled by product inhibition of certain key enzymes.

Chemical Connections Chemistry in Cellular Metabolism

Design and Control of a Metabolic Pathway

Biological cells are microscopic wizards of chemical change. From the simplest bacterium to the most specialized nerve, every cell performs thousands of individual reactions that allow it to grow and reproduce, feed and excrete, move and communicate. Taken together, these chemical reactions constitute the cell's *metabolism*. These myriad feats of biochemical breakdown, synthesis, and energy flow are organized into reaction sequences called **metabolic pathways.** Some pathways disassemble the biopolymers in food into monomer building blocks: sugars, amino acids, and nucleotides. Others extract energy from these small molecules and then use much of the energy to assemble molecules with other functions, such as hormones, neurotransmitters, defensive toxins, and the cell's own biopolymers.

In principle, *each step in a metabolic pathway is a reversible reaction catalyzed by a specific enzyme* (Section 16.8). As you'll see, however, *equilibrium is never reached* in a pathway, even though the principles we discussed earlier apply. As with other multistep reaction sequences, the product of the first reaction becomes the reactant of the second, the product of the second becomes the reactant of the third, and so on. Consider, for example, the five-step pathway shown in Figure 17.D, in which one amino acid, threonine, is converted into another, isoleucine, in the cells of a bread mold. Threonine, supplied from a different region of the cell, forms ketobutyrate through the catalytic action of the first enzyme (reaction 1). The equilibrium position of reaction 1 continuously shifts to the right because the ketobutyrate is continuously removed as the reactant in reaction 2. Similarly, reaction 2 shifts to the right as its product is used in reaction 3. Each subsequent reaction shifts the equilibrium position of the previous reaction in the direction of product. The final product, isoleucine, is typically removed to make proteins in another region of the cell. Thus, *the entire pathway operates in one direction.*

This continuous shift in equilibrium position results in two major features of metabolic pathways. First, *each step proceeds with nearly 100% yield*. That is, virtually every molecule of threonine that enters this region of the cell eventually changes to ketobutyrate, every molecule of ketobutyrate to the next product, and so on.

Second, *reactant and product concentrations remain constant,* or vary within extremely narrow limits, even though the system never attains equilibrium. This situation, called a *steady state,* is different in a basic way from those we have studied so far. In equilibrium systems, equal reaction rates in *opposing* directions give rise to constant concentrations of reactants and products. In steady-state systems, on the other hand, the rates of reactions in *one* direction—into, through, and out of the system—give rise to nearly constant concentrations of intermediates. Ketobutyrate, for example, is formed via reaction 1 just as fast as it is used via reaction 2, so its concentration is kept constant. (You can establish a steady-state amount of water by filling a sink and then opening the faucet and drain so that water enters just as fast as it leaves.)

It is absolutely critical that a cell regulate the concentration of the final product of a pathway. Recall from Chapter 16 that an enzyme catalyzes a reaction when the substrate (reactant) occupies the *active site.* However, substrate concentrations are so much higher than enzyme concentrations that, if no other factors were involved, the active sites on all the enzyme molecules would always be occupied and all cellular reactions would occur at their maximum rates. Although this might be ideal for an industrial process, it could be catastrophic for an organism. To regulate overall product formation, the rates of certain key steps are controlled by *regulatory enzymes,* which contain an *inhibitor site* on their surface in addition to an active site. The enzyme's three-dimensional structure is such that when the inhibitor site is occupied, the shape of the active site

(continued)

Figure 17.D The metabolic pathway for the biosynthesis of isoleucine from threonine. Isoleucine is synthesized from threonine in a sequence of five enzyme-catalyzed reactions. As indicated by the unequal equilibrium arrows, each step is reversible but is shifted toward product because each product becomes the reactant of the subsequent step. When the cell's need for isoleucine is temporarily satisfied, this synthesis slows through end-product feedback inhibition: the concentration of isoleucine, the end product, builds up and inhibits the catalytic activity of threonine dehydratase, the first enzyme in the pathway.

Chemical Connections *(continued)*

is deformed and the reaction cannot be catalyzed (Figure 17.E).

In the simplest case of metabolic control (see Figure 17.D), *the final product of the pathway is also the inhibitor molecule, and the regulatory enzyme catalyzes the first step.* Suppose, for instance, that the cell is temporarily making less protein, so the isoleucine synthesized by the pathway is not being removed as quickly. As its concentration rises, the chance increases that isoleucine molecules will land on the inhibitor site of molecules of the first enzyme in the pathway, gradually inhibiting its own production. This process is called *end-product feedback inhibition.* More complex pathways have more elaborate regulatory schemes, but many operate through similar types of inhibitory feedback (see Problem 17.108). The exquisitely detailed regulation of a cell's numerous metabolic pathways arises directly from the principles of chemical kinetics and equilibrium.

Figure 17.E **The effect of inhibitor binding on the shape of the active site. A,** When the inhibitor site is *not* occupied, the enzyme catalyzes the reaction. **B,** When the inhibitor site *is* occupied, that molecule of enzyme does not function.

Chapter Perspective

The equilibrium phenomenon is central to all natural systems. In this introduction, we discussed the nature of equilibrium on the observable and molecular levels, ways to solve relevant problems, and how conditions affect equilibrium systems. In the next two chapters, we apply these ideas to acids and bases *and to other aqueous ionic systems. Then we examine the fundamental relationship between the equilibrium constant and the energy change that accompanies a reaction to understand why chemical reactions occur.*

The following learning objectives, with section and/or sample problem (SP) numbers in parentheses, can help focus your study:

Understand These Concepts

1. The distinction between the rate and the extent of a reaction (Intro)
2. Why a system attains dynamic equilibrium when forward and reverse reaction rates are equal (Section 17.1)
3. The equilibrium constant as a number equal to a particular ratio of rate constants and of concentration terms (Section 17.1)
4. How the magnitude of K refers to the extent of the reaction (Section 17.1)
5. How the same equilibrium condition is reached no matter what the starting concentrations of the reacting system (Section 17.2)
6. How the reaction quotient (Q) changes continuously until the system reaches equilibrium, at which point $Q = K$ (Section 17.2)
7. Why the form of Q is based exactly on the balanced equation *as written* (Section 17.2)
8. How the *sum* of reaction steps gives the overall reaction, and the *product* of Q's (or K's) gives the overall Q (or K) (Section 17.2)
9. Why pure solids and liquids do not appear in Q (Section 17.2)
10. How the interconversion of K_c and K_p is based on the ideal gas law and Δn_{gas} (Section 17.3)
11. How the reaction direction depends on the relative values of Q and K (Section 17.4)
12. How a reaction table is used to find an unknown quantity (concentration or pressure) (Section 17.5)
13. How assuming that the change in [reactant] is relatively small simplifies finding equilibrium quantities (Section 17.5)
14. How Le Châtelier's principle explains the effects of a change in concentration, pressure (volume), and temperature on a system at equilibrium and on K (Section 17.6)
15. Why a change in temperature *does* affect K (Section 17.6)
16. Why addition of a catalyst does *not* affect K (Section 17.6)

Master These Skills

1. Writing the reaction quotient (Q) from a balanced equation (SP 17.1)
2. Writing Q and calculating K for a reaction consisting of several steps (SP 17.2)
3. Writing Q for a reverse reaction and for a reaction multiplied by a common factor (SP 17.3)
4. Writing Q for heterogeneous equilibria (Section 17.2)
5. Converting between K_c and K_p (SP 17.4)

6. Comparing Q and K to determine reaction direction (SP 17.5)
7. Substituting quantities (concentrations or pressures) into Q to find K (Section 17.5)
8. Using a reaction table to determine quantities and find K (SP 17.6)
9. Finding one equilibrium quantity from other equilibrium quantities and K (SP 17.7)
10. Finding an equilibrium quantity from initial quantities and K (SP 17.8)
11. Solving a quadratic equation for an unknown equilibrium quantity (Section 17.5)
12. Assuming that the change in [reactant] is relatively small to find equilibrium quantities and checking the assumption (SP 17.9)

13. Comparing the values of Q and K to find reaction direction and sign for x, the unknown change in the quantity (SP 17.10)
14. Using the relative values of Q and K to predict the effect of a change in concentration on the equilibrium position and on K (SP 17.11)
15. Using Le Châtelier's principle and Δn_{gas} to predict the effect of a change in pressure (volume) on the equilibrium position and on K (SP 17.12)
16. Using Le Châtelier's principle and ΔH^0 to predict the effect of a change in temperature on the equilibrium position and on K (SP 17.13)
17. Using the van't Hoff equation to calculate K at one temperature given K at another temperature (Section 17.6)

For Review and Reference

Key Terms

Section 17.1
equilibrium constant (K)

Section 17.2
law of chemical equilibrium (law of mass action)

reaction quotient (Q) (mass-action expression)

Section 17.6
Le Châtelier's principle
Haber process
metabolic pathway

Key Equations and Relationships

17.1 Defining equilibrium in terms of reaction rates (p. 716):

$$\text{At equilibrium: rate}_{fwd} = \text{rate}_{rev}$$

17.2 Defining the equilibrium constant for the reaction $A \rightleftharpoons 2B$ (p. 717):

$$K = \frac{k_{fwd}}{k_{rev}} = \frac{[B]^2}{[A]}$$

17.3 Defining the equilibrium constant in terms of the reaction quotient (p. 718):

$$\text{At equilibrium: } Q = K$$

17.4 Expressing Q_c for the reaction $aA + bB \rightleftharpoons cC + dD$ (p. 719):

$$Q_c = \frac{[C]^c[D]^d}{[A]^a[B]^b}$$

17.5 Finding the overall K for a reaction sequence (p. 720):

$$K_{overall} = K_1 \times K_2 \times K_3 \times \cdots$$

17.6 Finding K of a process from K of the reverse process (p. 721):

$$K_{fwd} = \frac{1}{K_{rev}}$$

17.7 Finding K of a reaction multiplied by a factor n (p. 722):

$$K' = (K)^n$$

17.8 Relating K based on pressures to K based on concentrations (p. 725):

$$K_p = K_c(RT)^{\Delta n_{gas}}$$

17.9 Assuming that the concentration reacting introduces insignificant error (p. 733):

$$[A]_{init} - [A]_{reacting} = [A]_{eq} \approx [A]_{init}$$

17.10 Finding K at one temperature given K at another (van't Hoff equation) (p. 742):

$$\ln \frac{K_2}{K_1} = -\frac{\Delta H^0_{rxn}}{R}\left(\frac{1}{T_2} - \frac{1}{T_1}\right)$$

Highlighted Figures and Tables

These figures (F) and tables (T) provide a quick review of key ideas.
F17.2 The range of equilbrium constants (p. 717)
F17.3 The change in Q during a reaction (p. 718)
T17.2 Ways of expressing Q (p. 724)
F17.5 Reaction direction and the relative sizes of Q and K (p. 726)

F17.6 Steps in solving equilibrium problems (p. 736)
T17.3 The effect of added Cl_2 on the PCl_3-Cl_2-PCl_5 system (p. 738)
T17.4 Effect of various disturbances on an equilibrium system (p. 742)

Answers to Follow-up Problems

17.1 (a) $Q_c = \dfrac{[NO]^4[H_2O]^6}{[NH_3]^4[O_2]^5}$

(b) $Q_c = \dfrac{[N_2O][NO_2]}{[NO]^3}$

17.2 $H_2(g) + Br_2(g) \rightleftharpoons 2HBr(g);$

$Q_{c(overall)} = \dfrac{[HBr]^2}{[H_2][Br_2]}$

$Q_{c(overall)} = Q_{c1} \times Q_{c2} \times Q_{c3} \times Q_{c4}$

$= \dfrac{\cancel{[Br]^2}}{[Br_2]} \times \dfrac{[HBr]\cancel{[H]}}{\cancel{[Br]}[H_2]} \times \dfrac{[HBr]\cancel{[Br]}}{\cancel{[H]}\cancel{[Br_2]}} \times \dfrac{\cancel{[Br_2]}}{\cancel{[Br]^2}}$

$= \dfrac{[HBr]^2}{[H_2][Br_2]}$

17.3 (a) $K_c = K_{c(ref)}^{1/2} = 2.8 \times 10^4$

(b) $K_c = \left(\dfrac{1}{K_{c(ref)}}\right)^{2/3} = 1.2 \times 10^{-6}$

17.4 $K_p = K_c(RT)^{-1} = 1.67\left(0.0821 \dfrac{atm \cdot L}{mol \cdot K} \times 500.\ K\right)^{-1}$

$= 4.07 \times 10^{-2}$

17.5 $Q_p = \dfrac{(P_{CH_3Cl})(P_{HCl})}{(P_{CH_4})(P_{Cl_2})} = \dfrac{0.24 \times 0.47}{0.13 \times 0.035} = 25;$

$Q_p < K_p$, so CH_3Cl is forming.

17.6 From the reaction table for $2NO + O_2 \rightleftharpoons 2NO_2$,
$P_{O_2} = 1.000$ atm $- x = 0.506$ atm; $x = 0.494$ atm
Also, $P_{NO} = 0.012$ atm and $P_{NO_2} = 0.988$ atm, so

$K_p = \dfrac{0.988^2}{0.012^2 \times 0.506} = 1.3 \times 10^4$

17.7 Since $\Delta n_{gas} = 0$, $K_p = K_c = 2.3 \times 10^{30} = \dfrac{0.781 \times 0.209}{P_{NO}^2}$

$P_{NO} = 2.7 \times 10^{-16}$ atm

17.8 From the reaction table, $[H_2] = [I_2] = x$ and
$[HI] = 0.242 - 2x$.

Therefore, $K_c = 1.26 \times 10^{-3} = \dfrac{x^2}{(0.242 - 2x)^2}$

Taking the square root of both sides, neglecting the negative
root, and solving gives $x = [H_2] = 8.02 \times 10^{-3}$ M.

17.9 (a) Based on the reaction table and assuming that
$0.20\ M - x \approx 0.20\ M$,

$K_c = 2.94 \times 10^{-10} \approx \dfrac{4x^2}{0.20}; x \approx 3.8 \times 10^{-6}$

Error $= 1.9 \times 10^{-3}\%$, so assumption is justified; so, at equilibrium, $[I_2] = 0.20\ M$ and $[I] = 7.6 \times 10^{-6}$ M.
(b) Based on the same reaction table and assumption,
$x \approx 0.10$; error is 50%, so assumption is *not* justified. Solve
equation:

$4x^2 + 0.209x - 0.042 = 0; x = 0.080\ M$

Therefore, at equilibrium, $[I_2] = 0.12\ M$ and $[I] = 0.16\ M$.

17.10 (a) $Q_c = \dfrac{0.0900 \times 0.0900}{0.2100} = 3.86 \times 10^{-2}; Q_c < K_c,$

so reaction proceeds to the right.
(b) From the reaction table,

$[PCl_5] = 0.2100\ M - x = 0.2065\ M; x = 0.0035\ M$

So $[Cl_2] = [PCl_3] = 0.0900\ M + x = 0.0935\ M$.

17.11 (a) Increases; (b) decreases; (c) decreases; (d) no effect.
17.12 (a) Decrease P; (b) increase P; (c) increase P.
17.13 (a) P_{H_2} will decrease; K_p will increase; (b) P_{N_2} will
increase; K_p will decrease; (c) P_{PCl_5} will increase; K_p will
increase.

Problems

Problems with a **colored** number are answered at the back of
the text. Problem sections match the text and provide the
number(s) of relevant sample problems. Most offer concept
review questions, skill-building exercises (written in similar
pairs), and problems in a relevant context. Following these are
comprehensive problems based on material from any section
and/or previous chapter.

The Dynamic Nature of the Equilibrium State

■ Concept Review Questions

17.1 A change in reaction conditions increases the rate of a
forward reaction more than that of the reverse reaction.
What is the effect on the equilibrium constant and the concentrations of reactants and products at equilibrium?
17.2 When a chemical company employs a new reaction to
manufacture a product, the chemists consider its rate (kinetics) and yield (equilibrium). How do each of these affect the
usefulness of a manufacturing process?

17.3 If there is no change in concentrations, why is the
equilibrium state considered dynamic?
17.4 Is K very large or very small for a reaction that goes
essentially to completion? Explain.
17.5 Does the following reaction energy diagram depict a
reaction in which K is small or large? Explain.

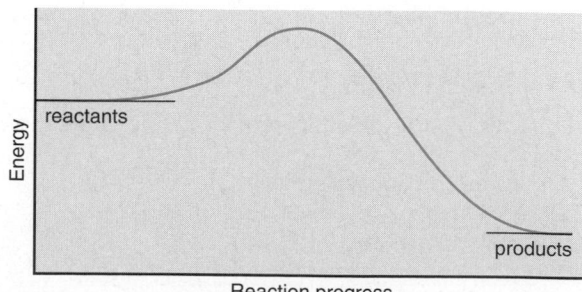

The Reaction Quotient and the Equilibrium Constant

(Sample Problems 17.1 to 17.3)

■ Concept Review Questions

17.6 For a given reaction at a given temperature, the value of K is constant. Is the value of Q always constant also? Explain.

17.7 In a series of experiments on the thermal decomposition of lithium peroxide,

$$2Li_2O_2(s) \rightleftharpoons 2Li_2O(s) + O_2(g)$$

a chemist finds that, as long as enough Li_2O_2 is present so that some remains at the end of the experiment, the amount of O_2 obtained in a given container at a given T reaches the same value. Explain.

17.8 In a study of the formation of HI from its elements,

$$H_2(g) + I_2(g) \rightleftharpoons 2HI(g)$$

equal amounts of H_2 and I_2 were placed in a container, which was then sealed and heated.

(a) On one set of axes, sketch concentration vs. time curves for H_2 and HI and explain how the value of Q changes as a function of time.

(b) Is the value of Q different if $[I_2]$ is plotted instead of $[H_2]$?

17.9 Explain the difference between a heterogeneous and a homogeneous equilibrium reaction. Give an example of each.

17.10 Does Q for the formation of 1 mol NO from its elements differ from Q for the decomposition of 1 mol NO to its elements? Explain and give the relationship between the two reaction quotients.

17.11 Does Q for the formation of 1 mol NH_3 from H_2 and N_2 differ from Q for the formation of NH_3 from H_2 and 1 mol N_2? Explain and give the relationship between the two reaction quotients.

■ Skill-Building Exercises (paired)

17.12 Balance each of the following and write its reaction quotient, Q_c:

(a) $NO(g) + O_2(g) \rightleftharpoons N_2O_3(g)$
(b) $SF_6(g) + SO_3(g) \rightleftharpoons SO_2F_2(g)$
(c) $SClF_5(g) + H_2(g) \rightleftharpoons S_2F_{10}(g) + HCl(g)$

17.13 Balance each of the following and write its reaction quotient, Q_c:

(a) $C_2H_6(g) + O_2(g) \rightleftharpoons CO_2(g) + H_2O(g)$
(b) $CH_4(g) + F_2(g) \rightleftharpoons CF_4(g) + HF(g)$
(c) $SO_3(g) \rightleftharpoons SO_2(g) + O_2(g)$

17.14 Balance each of the following and write its reaction quotient, Q_c:

(a) $NO_2Cl(g) \rightleftharpoons NO_2(g) + Cl_2(g)$
(b) $POCl_3(g) \rightleftharpoons PCl_3(g) + O_2(g)$
(c) $NH_3(g) + O_2(g) \rightleftharpoons N_2(g) + H_2O(g)$

17.15 Balance each of the following and write its reaction quotient, Q_c:

(a) $O_2(g) \rightleftharpoons O_3(g)$
(b) $NO(g) + O_3(g) \rightleftharpoons NO_2(g) + O_2(g)$
(c) $N_2O(g) + H_2(g) \rightleftharpoons NH_3(g) + H_2O(g)$

17.16 At a particular temperature, $K_c = 1.6 \times 10^{-2}$ for the equation

$$2H_2S(g) \rightleftharpoons 2H_2(g) + S_2(g)$$

Calculate K_c for each of the following equations:

(a) $\frac{1}{2}S_2(g) + H_2(g) \rightleftharpoons H_2S(g)$
(b) $5H_2S(g) \rightleftharpoons 5H_2(g) + \frac{5}{2}S_2(g)$

17.17 At a particular temperature, $K_c = 6.5 \times 10^2$ for the equation

$$2NO(g) + 2H_2(g) \rightleftharpoons N_2(g) + 2H_2O(g)$$

Calculate K_c for each of the following equations:

(a) $NO(g) + H_2(g) \rightleftharpoons \frac{1}{2}N_2(g) + H_2O(g)$
(b) $2N_2(g) + 4H_2O(g) \rightleftharpoons 4NO(g) + 4H_2(g)$

17.18 Balance each of the following examples of heterogeneous equilibria and write its reaction quotient, Q_c:

(a) $Na_2O_2(s) + CO_2(g) \rightleftharpoons Na_2CO_3(s) + O_2(g)$
(b) $H_2O(l) \rightleftharpoons H_2O(g)$
(c) $NH_4Cl(s) \rightleftharpoons NH_3(g) + HCl(g)$

17.19 Balance each of the following examples of heterogeneous equilibria and write its reaction quotient, Q_c:

(a) $H_2O(l) + SO_3(g) \rightleftharpoons H_2SO_4(aq)$
(b) $KNO_3(s) \rightleftharpoons KNO_2(s) + O_2(g)$
(c) $S_8(s) + F_2(g) \rightleftharpoons SF_6(g)$

17.20 Balance each of the following examples of heterogeneous equilibria and write its reaction quotient, Q_c:

(a) $NaHCO_3(s) \rightleftharpoons Na_2CO_3(s) + CO_2(g) + H_2O(g)$
(b) $SnO_2(s) + H_2(g) \rightleftharpoons Sn(s) + H_2O(g)$
(c) $H_2SO_4(l) + SO_3(g) \rightleftharpoons H_2S_2O_7(l)$

17.21 Balance each of the following examples of heterogeneous equilibria and write its reaction quotient, Q_c:

(a) $Al(s) + NaOH(aq) + H_2O(l) \rightleftharpoons$
$$Na[Al(OH)_4](aq) + H_2(g)$$

(b) $CO_2(s) \rightleftharpoons CO_2(g)$
(c) $N_2O_5(s) \rightleftharpoons NO_2(g) + O_2(g)$

■ Problems in Context

17.22 White phosphorus, P_4, is produced by the reduction of phosphate rock, $Ca_3(PO_4)_2$. If exposed to oxygen, the waxy, white solid bursts into smoke and flames, and releases a large quantity of heat. Does the reaction

$$P_4(g) + 5O_2(g) \rightleftharpoons P_4O_{10}(s)$$

have an equilibrium constant with a large or small value? Explain.

17.23 The interhalogen ClF_3 is prepared in a two-step fluorination of chlorine gas:

$$Cl_2(g) + F_2(g) \rightleftharpoons ClF(g)$$
$$ClF(g) + F_2(g) \rightleftharpoons ClF_3(g)$$

(a) Balance each step and write the overall equation.
(b) Show that the overall Q_c equals the product of the Q_c's for the individual steps.

Expressing Equilibria with Pressure Units: Relation Between K_c and K_p

(Sample Problem 17.4)

■ Concept Review Questions

17.24 Guldberg and Waage proposed the original definition of the equilibrium constant as a particular ratio of *concentrations*. What relationship allows us to use a particular ratio of *partial pressures* (for a gaseous reaction) to obtain an equilibrium constant? Explain.

17.25 In which cases are K_c and K_p equal, and in which cases are they not equal?

17.26 A reaction at equilibrium has more moles of gaseous products than reactants.
(a) Is K_c larger or smaller than K_p?
(b) Write a general statement about the relative sizes of K_c and K_p for any gaseous equilibria.

■ **Skill-Building Exercises (paired)**

17.27 Determine Δn_{gas} for each of the following equations:
(a) $2KClO_3(s) \rightleftharpoons 2KCl(s) + 3O_2(g)$
(b) $2PbO(s) + O_2(g) \rightleftharpoons 2PbO_2(s)$
(c) $I_2(s) + 3XeF_2(s) \rightleftharpoons 2IF_3(s) + 3Xe(g)$

17.28 Determine Δn_{gas} for each of the following equations:
(a) $MgCO_3(s) \rightleftharpoons MgO(s) + CO_2(g)$
(b) $2H_2(g) + O_2(g) \rightleftharpoons 2H_2O(l)$
(c) $HNO_3(l) + ClF(g) \rightleftharpoons ClONO_2(g) + HF(g)$

17.29 Calculate K_c for the following equilibria:
(a) $CO(g) + Cl_2(g) \rightleftharpoons COCl_2(g)$; $K_p = 3.9 \times 10^{-2}$ at 1000. K
(b) $S_2(g) + C(s) \rightleftharpoons CS_2(g)$; $K_p = 28.5$ at 500. K

17.30 Calculate K_c for the following equilibria:
(a) $H_2(g) + I_2(g) \rightleftharpoons 2HI(g)$; $K_p = 49$ at 730. K
(b) $2SO_2(g) + O_2(g) \rightleftharpoons 2SO_3(g)$; $K_p = 2.5 \times 10^{10}$ at 500. K

17.31 Calculate K_p for the following equilibria:
(a) $N_2O_4(g) \rightleftharpoons 2NO_2(g)$; $K_c = 6.1 \times 10^{-3}$ at 298 K
(b) $N_2(g) + 3H_2(g) \rightleftharpoons 2NH_3(g)$; $K_c = 2.4 \times 10^{-3}$ at 1000. K

17.32 Calculate K_p for the following equilibria:
(a) $H_2(g) + CO_2(g) \rightleftharpoons H_2O(g) + CO(g)$; $K_c = 0.77$ at 1020. K
(b) $3O_2(g) \rightleftharpoons 2O_3(g)$; $K_c = 1.8 \times 10^{-56}$ at 570. K

Reaction Direction: Comparing Q and K

(Sample Problem 17.5)

■ **Concept Review Questions**

17.33 When the numerical value of Q is less than K, in which direction does the reaction proceed to reach equilibrium? Explain.

17.34 State three criteria that characterize a chemical system at equilibrium.

■ **Skill-Building Exercises (paired)**

17.35 At 425°C, $K_p = 4.18 \times 10^{-9}$ for the reaction
$$2HBr(g) \rightleftharpoons H_2(g) + Br_2(g)$$
In one experiment, 0.20 atm HBr(g), 0.010 atm $H_2(g)$, and 0.010 atm $Br_2(g)$ are introduced into a reaction vessel. Is the reaction at equilibrium? If not, in which direction will it proceed?

17.36 At 100°C, $K_p = 60.6$ for the reaction
$$2NOBr(g) \rightleftharpoons 2NO(g) + Br_2(g)$$
In a given experiment, 0.10 atm of each component is placed in a container. Is the system at equilibrium? If not, in which direction will it proceed?

■ **Problems in Context**

17.37 The water-gas shift reaction plays a central role in the chemical methods for obtaining cleaner fuels from coal:
$$CO(g) + H_2O(g) \rightleftharpoons CO_2(g) + H_2(g)$$
At a given temperature, $K_p = 2.7$. If 0.13 mol CO, 0.56 mol H_2O, 0.62 mol CO_2, and 0.43 mol H_2 are introduced into a 2.0-L flask, in which direction must the reaction proceed to reach equilibrium?

How to Solve Equilibrium Problems

(Sample Problems 17.6 to 17.10)

■ **Concept Review Questions**

17.38 In the 1980s, CFC-11 was one of the most heavily produced chlorofluorocarbons. The last step in its formation is
$$CCl_4(g) + HF(g) \rightleftharpoons CFCl_3(g) + HCl(g)$$
If you start the reaction with equal concentrations of CCl_4 and HF, you obtain equal concentrations of $CFCl_3$ and HCl at equilibrium. Are the concentrations of $CFCl_3$ and HCl equal if you start with unequal concentrations of CCl_4 and HF? Explain.

17.39 In a problem involving the catalyzed reaction of methane and steam, the following reaction table was prepared:

PRESSURE (atm)	$CH_4(g)$	+	$2H_2O(g)$	$\rightleftharpoons$	$CO_2(g)$	+	$4H_2(g)$
Initial	0.30		0.40		0		0
Change	$-x$		$-2x$		$+x$		$+4x$
Equilibrium	$0.30 - x$		$0.40 - 2x$		x		$4x$

Explain the entries in the "Change" and "Equilibrium" rows.

17.40 (a) Explain the basis of the approximation made to avoid using the quadratic formula when finding an equilibrium concentration.
(b) Describe a situation in which this approximation *cannot* be made.

■ **Skill-Building Exercises (paired)**

17.41 In an experiment to study the formation of HI(g),
$$H_2(g) + I_2(g) \rightleftharpoons 2HI(g)$$
$H_2(g)$ and $I_2(g)$ were placed in a sealed container at a certain temperature. At equilibrium, $[H_2] = 6.50 \times 10^{-5}$ M, $[I_2] = 1.06 \times 10^{-3}$ M, and $[HI] = 1.87 \times 10^{-3}$ M. Calculate K_c for the reaction at this temperature.

17.42 Gaseous ammonia was introduced into a sealed container and heated to a certain temperature:
$$2NH_3(g) \rightleftharpoons N_2(g) + 3H_2(g)$$
At equilibrium, $[NH_3] = 0.0225$ M, $[N_2] = 0.114$ M, and $[H_2] = 0.342$ M. Calculate K_c for the reaction at this temperature.

17.43 Gaseous PCl_5 decomposes according to the reaction
$$PCl_5(g) \rightleftharpoons PCl_3(g) + Cl_2(g)$$
In one experiment, 0.15 mol $PCl_5(g)$ was introduced into a 2.0-L container. Construct the reaction table for this process.

17.44 Hydrogen fluoride, HF, can be made from the reaction
$$H_2(g) + F_2(g) \rightleftharpoons 2HF(g)$$
In one experiment, 0.10 mol $H_2(g)$ and 0.050 mol $F_2(g)$ are introduced into a 0.50-L container. Construct the reaction table for this process.

17.45 For the following reaction, $K_p = 6.5 \times 10^4$ at 308 K:
$$2NO(g) + Cl_2(g) \rightleftharpoons 2NOCl(g)$$
At equilibrium, $P_{NO} = 0.35$ atm and $P_{Cl_2} = 0.10$ atm. What is the equilibrium partial pressure of NOCl(g)?

17.46 For the following reaction, $K_p = 0.262$ at 1000°C:
$$C(s) + 2H_2(g) \rightleftharpoons CH_4(g)$$

At equilibrium, P_{H_2} is 1.22 atm. What is the equilibrium partial pressure of $CH_4(g)$?

17.47 Ammonium hydrogen sulfide decomposes according to the following reaction, for which $K_p = 0.11$ at 250°C:

$$NH_4HS(s) \rightleftharpoons H_2S(g) + NH_3(g)$$

If 55.0 g $NH_4HS(s)$ is placed in a sealed 5.0-L container, what is the partial pressure of $NH_3(g)$ at equilibrium?

17.48 Hydrogen sulfide decomposes according to the following reaction, for which $K_c = 9.30\times10^{-8}$ at 700°C:

$$2H_2S(g) \rightleftharpoons 2H_2(g) + S_2(g)$$

If 0.45 mol H_2S is placed in a 3.0-L container, what is the equilibrium concentration of $H_2(g)$ at 700°C?

17.49 Even at high temperature, the formation of nitric oxide is not favored:

$$N_2(g) + O_2(g) \rightleftharpoons 2NO(g) \qquad K_c = 4.10\times10^{-4} \text{ at } 2000°C$$

What is the equilibrium concentration of $NO(g)$ when a mixture of 0.20 mol $N_2(g)$ and 0.15 mol $O_2(g)$ are allowed to come to equilibrium in a 1.0-L container at this temperature?

17.50 Nitrogen dioxide decomposes according to the reaction:

$$2NO_2(g) \rightleftharpoons 2NO(g) + O_2(g)$$

where $K_p = 4.48\times10^{-13}$ at a certain temperature. A pressure of 0.75 atm of NO_2 is introduced into a container and allowed to come to equilibrium. What are the equilibrium partial pressures of $NO(g)$ and $O_2(g)$?

17.51 Hydrogen iodide decomposes according to the reaction

$$2HI(g) \rightleftharpoons H_2(g) + I_2(g)$$

A sealed 1.50-L container initially holds 0.00623 mol H_2, 0.00414 mol I_2, and 0.0244 mol HI at 703 K. When equilibrium is reached, the equilibrium concentration of $H_2(g)$ is 0.00467 M. What are the equilibrium concentrations of $HI(g)$ and $I_2(g)$?

17.52 Compound A decomposes according to the equation

$$A(g) \rightleftharpoons 2B(g) + C(g)$$

A sealed 1.00-L reaction vessel initially contains 1.75×10^{-3} mol $A(g)$, 1.25×10^{-3} mol $B(g)$, and 6.50×10^{-4} mol $C(g)$ at 100°C. When equilibrium is reached, the concentration of $A(g)$ is 2.15×10^{-3} M. What are the equilibrium concentrations of $B(g)$ and $C(g)$?

■ **Problems in Context**

17.53 In an analysis of interhalogen reactivity, 0.500 mol ICl was placed in a 5.00-L flask and allowed to decompose at high temperature:

$$2ICl(g) \rightleftharpoons I_2(g) + Cl_2(g)$$

Calculate the equilibrium concentrations of I_2, Cl_2, and ICl. $K_c = 0.110$ at this temperature.

17.54 A United Nations toxicologist studying the properties of mustard gas [$S(CH_2CH_2Cl)_2$], a blistering agent used in warfare, prepares a mixture of 0.675 M SCl_2 and 0.973 M C_2H_4 and allows it to react at room temperature (20.0°C):

$$SCl_2(g) + 2C_2H_4(g) \rightleftharpoons S(CH_2CH_2Cl)_2(g)$$

At equilibrium, 0.350 M $S(CH_2CH_2Cl)_2$ is present. Calculate K_p.

17.55 The first step in industrial nitric acid production is the catalyzed oxidation of ammonia. Without a catalyst, a different reaction predominates:

$$4NH_3(g) + 3O_2(g) \rightleftharpoons 2N_2(g) + 6H_2O(g)$$

When 0.0150 mol $NH_3(g)$ and 0.0150 mol $O_2(g)$ are placed in a 1.00-L container at a certain temperature, the N_2 concentration at equilibrium is 1.96×10^{-3} M. Calculate K_c for the reaction at this temperature.

17.56 One of the key steps in the extraction of iron from its ore is

$$FeO(s) + CO(g) \rightleftharpoons Fe(s) + CO_2(g) \quad K_p = 0.403 \text{ at } 1000°C$$

This step occurs in the 700° to 1200°C zone within a blast furnace. What are the equilibrium partial pressures of $CO(g)$ and $CO_2(g)$ when 1.00 atm $CO(g)$ and excess $FeO(s)$ react in a sealed container at 1000°C?

Reaction Conditions and the Equilibrium State: Le Châtelier's Principle
(Sample Problems 17.11 to 17.13)

■ **Concept Review Questions**

17.57 What is meant by the word *disturbance* in the statement of Le Châtelier's principle?

17.58 The three molecular scenes shown below represent the following reaction at three temperatures:

$$NH_4Cl(s) \rightleftharpoons NH_3(g) + HCl(g) \qquad \Delta H^0_{rxn} = 176 \text{ kJ}$$

A   **B**   **C**

(a) Which best represents the mixture at the highest temperature? Explain.

(b) Which best represents the mixture at the lowest temperature? Explain.

17.59 What is the difference between the equilibrium position and the equilibrium constant of a reaction? Which changes as a result of a change in reactant concentration?

17.60 What is implied by the word *constant* in the term *equilibrium constant*? Give two reaction parameters that can be changed without changing the value of an equilibrium constant.

17.61 Le Châtelier's principle is related ultimately to the rates of the forward and reverse steps in a reaction. Use this idea to explain

(a) Why an increase in reactant concentration shifts the equilibrium position to the right but does not change the equilibrium constant.

(b) Why a decrease in volume shifts the equilibrium position toward fewer moles of gas but does not change the equilibrium constant.

(c) Why a rise in temperature shifts the equilibrium position of an exothermic reaction toward reactants and also changes the equilibrium constant.

17.62 Le Châtelier's principle predicts that a rise in the temperature of an endothermic reaction from T_1 to T_2 results in K_2 larger than K_1. Explain.

■ **Skill-Building Exercises (paired)**

17.63 Consider the equilibrium system

$$CO(g) + Fe_3O_4(s) \rightleftharpoons CO_2(g) + 3FeO(s)$$

How does the equilibrium position shift as a result of each of the following disturbances?
(a) CO is added.
(b) CO_2 is removed by adding solid NaOH.
(c) Additional $Fe_3O_4(s)$ is added to the system.
(d) Dry ice is added at constant T.

17.64 Sodium bicarbonate undergoes thermal decomposition according to the reaction

$$2NaHCO_3(s) \rightleftharpoons Na_2CO_3(s) + CO_2(g) + H_2O(g)$$

How does the equilibrium position shift as a result of each of the following disturbances?
(a) 0.20 atm argon gas is added.
(b) $NaHCO_3(s)$ is added.
(c) $Mg(ClO_4)_2(s)$ is added as a drying agent to remove H_2O.
(d) Dry ice is added at constant T.

17.65 Predict the effect of *increasing* the container volume on the amounts of each reactant and product in the following:
(a) $F_2(g) \rightleftharpoons 2F(g)$
(b) $2CH_4(g) \rightleftharpoons C_2H_2(g) + 3H_2(g)$

17.66 Predict the effect of *increasing* the container volume on the amounts of each reactant and product in the following:
(a) $CH_3OH(l) \rightleftharpoons CH_3OH(g)$
(b) $CH_4(g) + NH_3(g) \rightleftharpoons HCN(g) + 3H_2(g)$

17.67 Predict the effect of *decreasing* the container volume on the amounts of each reactant and product in the following:
(a) $H_2(g) + Cl_2(g) \rightleftharpoons 2HCl(g)$
(b) $2H_2(g) + O_2(g) \rightleftharpoons 2H_2O(l)$

17.68 Predict the effect of *decreasing* the container volume on the amounts of each reactant and product in the following:
(a) $C_3H_8(g) + 5O_2(g) \rightleftharpoons 3CO_2(g) + 4H_2O(l)$
(b) $4NH_3(g) + 3O_2(g) \rightleftharpoons 2N_2(g) + 6H_2O(g)$

17.69 How would you adjust the *volume* of the reaction vessel in order to maximize product yield in the following reactions?
(a) $Fe_3O_4(s) + 4H_2(g) \rightleftharpoons 3Fe(s) + 4H_2O(g)$
(b) $2C(s) + O_2(g) \rightleftharpoons 2CO(g)$

17.70 How would you adjust the *volume* of the reaction vessel in order to maximize product yield in the following reactions?
(a) $Na_2O_2(s) \rightleftharpoons 2Na(l) + O_2(g)$
(b) $C_2H_2(g) + 2H_2(g) \rightleftharpoons C_2H_6(g)$

17.71 Predict the effect of *increasing* the temperature on the amounts of products in the following reactions:
(a) $CO(g) + 2H_2(g) \rightleftharpoons CH_3OH(g)$; $\Delta H_{rxn}^0 = -90.7$ kJ
(b) $C(s) + H_2O(g) \rightleftharpoons CO(g) + H_2(g)$; $\Delta H_{rxn}^0 = 131$ kJ
(c) $2NO_2(g) \rightleftharpoons 2NO(g) + O_2(g)$ (endothermic)
(d) $2C(s) + O_2(g) \rightleftharpoons 2CO(g)$ (exothermic)

17.72 Predict the effect of *decreasing* the temperature on the amounts of reactants in the following reactions:
(a) $C_2H_2(g) + H_2O(g) \rightleftharpoons CH_3CHO(g)$; $\Delta H_{rxn}^0 = -151$ kJ
(b) $CH_3CH_2OH(l) + O_2(g) \rightleftharpoons CH_3CO_2H(l) + H_2O(g)$;
$$\Delta H_{rxn}^0 = -451 \text{ kJ}$$
(c) $2C_2H_4(g) + O_2(g) \rightleftharpoons 2CH_3CHO(g)$ (exothermic)
(d) $N_2O_4(g) \rightleftharpoons 2NO_2(g)$ (endothermic)

17.73 Deuterium (D or ^{2}H) is an isotope of hydrogen. The molecule D_2 undergoes an exchange reaction with ordinary H_2 that leads to isotopic equilibrium:

$$D_2(g) + H_2(g) \rightleftharpoons 2DH(g) \qquad K_p = 1.80 \text{ at } 298 \text{ K}$$

If ΔH_{rxn}^0 is 0.32 kJ/mol DH, calculate K_p at 500. K.

17.74 The formation of methanol is an important industrial reaction in the processing of new fuels. At 298 K, $K_p = 2.25 \times 10^4$ for the reaction

$$CO(g) + 2H_2(g) \rightleftharpoons CH_3OH(l)$$

If $\Delta H_{rxn}^0 = -128$ kJ/mol CH_3OH, calculate K_p at 0°C.

■ **Problems in Context**

17.75 Lime (CaO) is used primarily in the manufacture of steel, glass, and high-quality paper. It is produced in an endothermic reaction by the thermal decomposition of limestone:

$$CaCO_3(s) \rightleftharpoons CaO(s) + CO_2(g)$$

How would you control reaction conditions to produce the maximum amount of lime?

17.76 The oxidation of SO_2 to SO_3 is one of the most important industrial reactions because it is the key step in sulfuric acid production:

$$SO_2(g) + \tfrac{1}{2}O_2(g) \rightleftharpoons SO_3(g) \qquad \Delta H_{rxn}^0 = -99.2 \text{ kJ}$$

(a) What qualitative combination of T and P maximizes SO_3 yield?
(b) How does addition of O_2 affect Q? K?
(c) Suggest a reason that catalysis is used for this reaction in the manufacture of H_2SO_4.

Comprehensive Problems

Problems with an asterisk (*) are more challenging.

17.77 The "filmstrip" represents five molecular-level scenes of a gaseous mixture as it reaches equilibrium over time:

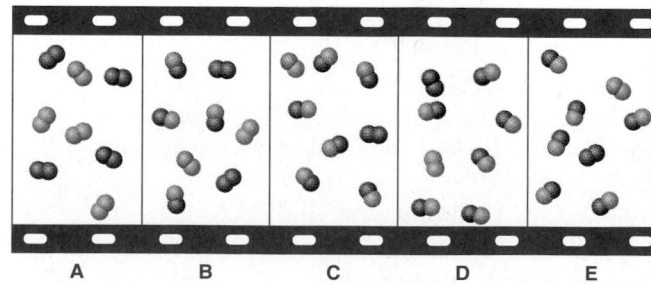

A   B   C   D   E

X is purple and Y is orange. The equation is

$$X_2(g) + Y_2(g) \rightleftharpoons 2XY(g)$$

(a) Write the reaction quotient, Q, for this reaction.
(b) If each particle represents 0.1 mol of particles, calculate Q for each scene.
(c) If $K > 1$, is time increasing right-to-left or left-to-right? Explain.

(d) Calculate K at this temperature.

(e) If $\Delta H^0_{rxn} < 0$, which scene, if any, best represents the mixture at a higher temperature? Explain.

(f) Which scene, if any, best represents the mixture at a higher pressure (lower volume)? Explain.

17.78 The powerful chlorinating agent sulfuryl dichloride (SO_2Cl_2) can be prepared by the following two-step sequence:

$$H_2S(g) + O_2(g) \rightleftharpoons SO_2(g) + H_2O(g)$$

$$SO_2(g) + Cl_2(g) \rightleftharpoons SO_2Cl_2(g)$$

(a) Balance each step and write the overall equation.

(b) Show that the overall Q_c equals the product of the Q_c's for the individual steps.

17.79 A mixture of 5.00 volumes N_2 and 1.00 volume O_2 passes through a heated furnace and reaches equilibrium at 900. K and 5.00 atm pressure:

$$N_2(g) + O_2(g) \rightleftharpoons 2NO(g) \qquad K_p = 6.70 \times 10^{-10}$$

(a) What is the partial pressure of NO?

(b) What is the concentration in micrograms per liter ($\mu g/L$) of NO in the mixture?

17.80 Consider the following equilibrium system in a piston-cylinder:

$$A(g) + 3B(s) \rightleftharpoons 5D(l) + E(g) \qquad \Delta H^0 < 0$$

In which direction will the equilibrium position shift as a result of each of the following changes?

(a) Raise the temperature.

(b) Add more B.

(c) Reduce the volume of the container.

(d) Add a catalyst.

(e) Remove some E.

*17.81 Ammonium carbamate (NH_2COONH_4) is a salt of carbamic acid that is found in the blood and urine of mammals. At 250.°C, $K_c = 1.58 \times 10^{-8}$ for the following equilibrium:

$$NH_2COONH_4(s) \rightleftharpoons 2NH_3(g) + CO_2(g)$$

If 7.80 g NH_2COONH_4 is introduced into a 0.500-L evacuated container, what is the total pressure inside the container at equilibrium?

17.82 A study of the water-gas shift reaction (see Problem 17.37) was made in which equilibrium was reached with $[CO] = [H_2O] = [H_2] = 0.10\ M$ and $[CO_2] = 0.40\ M$. After 0.60 mol H_2 is added to the 2.0-L container and equilibrium is reestablished, what are the new concentrations of all the components?

17.83 The Group 8B(10) elements Ni, Pd, and Pt are used as industrial catalysts. Isolation and purification of these metals involve a series of steps. In the case of nickel, for example, the sulfide ore Ni_3S_2 is roasted in air:

$$Ni_3S_2(s) + O_2(g) \rightleftharpoons NiO(s) + SO_2(g)$$

The metal oxide is reduced by the H_2 in water gas (CO + H_2) to impure Ni:

$$NiO(s) + H_2(g) \rightleftharpoons Ni(s) + H_2O(g)$$

The CO in water gas then reacts with the metal in the Mond process to form gaseous nickel carbonyl:

$$Ni(s) + CO(g) \rightleftharpoons Ni(CO)_4(g)$$

which is subsequently decomposed to the metal.

(a) Balance each of the three steps and obtain an overall balanced equation for the conversion of Ni_3S_2 to $Ni(CO)_4$.

(b) Show that the overall Q_c is the product of the Q_c's for the individual reactions.

17.84 One of the most important industrial sources of ethanol is the exothermic reaction of steam with ethene derived from crude oil:

$$C_2H_4(g) + H_2O(g) \rightleftharpoons C_2H_5OH(g)$$

$$\Delta H^0_{rxn} = -47.8\ kJ \qquad K_c = 9 \times 10^3 \text{ at } 600.\ K$$

(a) At equilibrium, $P_{C_2H_5OH} = 200.$ atm and $P_{H_2O} = 400.$ atm. Calculate $P_{C_2H_4}$.

(b) Is the highest yield of ethanol obtained at high or low pressures? High or low temperatures?

(c) Calculate K_c at 450. K.

(d) In the manufacture of ammonia, the yield of ammonia is increased by condensing it to a liquid and removing it from the vessel. Would condensing the C_2H_5OH work in this process? Explain.

17.85 The Group 5A(15) hydrides react with boron trihalides in a reversible Lewis acid-base reaction (discussed thoroughly in the next chapter). When 0.15 mol $PH_3BCl_3(s)$ is introduced into a 3.0-L container at a certain temperature, 8.4×10^{-3} mol PH_3 is present at equilibrium:

$$PH_3BCl_3(s) \rightleftharpoons PH_3(g) + BCl_3(g)$$

(a) Calculate K_c for the reaction at this temperature.

(b) Draw a Lewis structure for the reactant.

*17.86 An industrial chemist introduces 2.0 atm H_2 and 2.0 atm CO_2 into a 1.00-L container at 25.0°C and then raises the temperature to 700.°C, at which $K_c = 0.534$:

$$H_2(g) + CO_2(g) \rightleftharpoons H_2O(g) + CO(g)$$

How many grams of H_2 are present after equilibrium is established?

17.87 As an EPA scientist studying catalytic converters and urban smog, you want to find K_c for the following reaction:

$$2NO_2(g) \rightleftharpoons N_2(g) + 2O_2(g) \qquad K_c = ?$$

Use the following data to find the unknown K_c:

$$\tfrac{1}{2}N_2(g) + \tfrac{1}{2}O_2(g) \rightleftharpoons NO(g) \qquad K_c = 4.8 \times 10^{-10}$$

$$2NO_2(g) \rightleftharpoons 2NO(g) + O_2(g) \qquad K_c = 1.1 \times 10^{-5}$$

17.88 An inorganic chemist places 1 mol BrCl in container A and 0.5 mol Br_2 and 0.5 mol Cl_2 in container B. She seals the containers and heats them to 300°C. Measurement shows that, with time, both containers hold identical mixtures of BrCl, Br_2, and Cl_2.

(a) Write a balanced equation for the reaction taking place in container A.

(b) Write the reaction quotient, Q, for this reaction.

(c) How do the values of Q in A compare with those in B over time?

(d) Explain on the molecular level how it is possible for both containers to end up with identical mixtures.

17.89 A quality control engineer examining the conversion of SO_2 to SO_3 in the manufacture of sulfuric acid determines that $K_c = 1.7 \times 10^8$ at 600. K for the reaction

$$2SO_2(g) + O_2(g) \rightleftharpoons 2SO_3(g)$$

(a) At equilibrium, $P_{SO_3} = 300.$ atm and $P_{O_2} = 100.$ atm. Calculate P_{SO_2}.

(b) The engineer places a mixture of 0.0040 mol $SO_2(g)$ and 0.0028 mol $O_2(g)$ in a 1.0-L container and raises the temperature to 1000 K. At equilibrium, 0.0020 mol $SO_3(g)$ is present. Calculate K_c and P_{SO_2} for this reaction at 1000. K.

17.90 Phosgene ($COCl_2$) is an extremely toxic substance that forms readily from carbon monoxide and chlorine at elevated temperatures:

$$CO(g) + Cl_2(g) \rightleftharpoons COCl_2(g)$$

If 0.350 mol of each reactant is placed in a 0.500-L flask at 600 K, what are the concentrations of each substance at equilibrium? $K_c = 4.95$ at this temperature.

17.91 When 0.100 mol $CaCO_3(s)$ and 0.100 mol $CaO(s)$ are placed in an evacuated sealed 10.0-L container and heated to 385 K, $P_{CO_2} = 0.220$ atm after equilibrium is established:

$$CaCO_3(s) \rightleftharpoons CaO(s) + CO_2(g)$$

An additional 0.300 atm $CO_2(g)$ is then pumped into the container. What is the total mass (in g) of $CaCO_3$ after equilibrium is reestablished?

17.92 Use each of the following reaction quotients to write the balanced equation:

(a) $Q = \dfrac{[CO_2]^2[H_2O]^2}{[C_2H_4][O_2]^3}$ (b) $Q = \dfrac{[NH_3]^4[O_2]^7}{[NO_2]^4[H_2O]^6}$

17.93 Hydrogenation of C=C bonds is a major reaction in the petroleum and food industries. The conversion of acetylene to ethylene is a simple example of the process:

$$C_2H_2(g) + H_2(g) \rightleftharpoons C_2H_4(g) \qquad K_c = 2.9 \times 10^8 \text{ at 2000. K}$$

The process is usually performed at much lower temperatures with the aid of a catalyst. Use ΔH values from Appendix B to calculate K_c for this reaction at 300. K.

17.94 In combustion studies of H_2 as an alternative fuel, you find evidence that the hydroxyl radical (HO) is formed in flames by the reaction

$$H(g) + \tfrac{1}{2}O_2(g) \rightleftharpoons HO(g)$$

Use the following data to calculate K_c for the reaction:

$$\tfrac{1}{2}H_2(g) + \tfrac{1}{2}O_2(g) \rightleftharpoons HO(g) \qquad K_c = 0.58$$
$$\tfrac{1}{2}H_2(g) \rightleftharpoons H(g) \qquad K_c = 1.6 \times 10^{-3}$$

*17.95 Highly toxic disulfur decafluoride decomposes by a free-radical process:

$$S_2F_{10}(g) \rightleftharpoons SF_4(g) + SF_6(g)$$

In a study of the decomposition, S_2F_{10} was placed in a 2.0-L flask and heated to 100°C; $[S_2F_{10}]$ was 0.50 M at equilibrium. More S_2F_{10} was added and when equilibrium was reattained, $[S_2F_{10}]$ was 2.5 M. How did $[SF_4]$ and $[SF_6]$ change from the original equilibrium position to the new equilibrium position after the addition of more S_2F_{10}?

17.96 Aluminum is one of the most versatile metals. It is produced by the Hall-Heroult process, in which molten cryolite, Na_3AlF_6, is used as a solvent for the aluminum ore. Cryolite undergoes very slight decomposition with heat to produce a tiny amount of F_2, which escapes into the atmosphere above the solvent. K_c is 2×10^{-104} at 1300 K for the reaction:

$$Na_3AlF_6(l) \rightleftharpoons 3Na(l) + Al(l) + 3F_2(g)$$

What is the concentration of F_2 over a bath of molten cryolite at this temperature?

17.97 An equilibrium mixture of car exhaust gases consisting of 10.0 volumes CO_2, 1.00 volume unreacted O_2, and 50.0 volumes unreacted N_2 leaves the engine at 4.0 atm pressure and 800. K.
(a) Given the following equilibrium, what is the partial pressure of CO?

$$2CO_2(g) \rightleftharpoons 2CO(g) + O_2(g) \qquad K_p = 1.4 \times 10^{-28} \text{ at 800. K}$$

(b) Assuming the mixture has enough time to reach equilibrium, what is the concentration in picograms per liter (pg/L) of CO in the exhaust gas?
(The actual concentration of CO in car exhaust is much higher because the gases do *not* reach equilibrium in the short transit time through the engine and exhaust system.)

*17.98 Consider the following reaction:

$$3Fe(s) + 4H_2O(g) \rightleftharpoons Fe_3O_4(s) + 4H_2(g)$$

(a) What are the apparent oxidation states of Fe and of O in Fe_3O_4?
(b) Fe_3O_4 is a compound of iron in which Fe occurs in two oxidation states. What are the oxidation states of Fe in Fe_3O_4?
(c) At 900°C, K_c for the reaction is 5.1. If 0.050 mol $H_2O(g)$ and 0.100 mol Fe(s) are placed in a 1.0-L container at 900°C, how many grams of Fe_3O_4 are present when equilibrium is established?

The synthesis of ammonia is a major process throughout the industrialized world. Problems 17.99 to 17.105 refer to various aspects of this all-important reaction:

$$N_2(g) + 3H_2(g) \rightleftharpoons 2NH_3(g) \qquad \Delta H^0_{rxn} = -91.8 \text{ kJ}$$

17.99 When ammonia is made industrially, the mixture of N_2, H_2, and NH_3 that emerges from the reaction chamber is far from equilibrium. Why does the plant supervisor use reaction conditions that produce less than the maximum yield of ammonia?

*17.100 The following reaction is sometimes used to produce the H_2 needed for the synthesis of ammonia:

$$CH_4(g) + CO_2(g) \rightleftharpoons 2CO(g) + 2H_2(g)$$

(a) What is the percent yield of H_2 when an equimolar mixture of CH_4 and CO_2 at 20.0 atm reaches equilibrium at 1200. K, at which $K_p = 3.548 \times 10^6$?
(b) What is the percent yield at 1300. K, at which $K_p = 2.626 \times 10^7$?

*17.101 The methane used to obtain H_2 for manufacturing NH_3 is impure and usually contains some higher hydrocarbons as well, such as propane, C_3H_8. Imagine the reaction of propane occurring in two steps:

$$C_3H_8(g) + 3H_2O(g) \rightleftharpoons 3CO(g) + 7H_2(g)$$
$$K_p = 8.175 \times 10^{15} \text{ at 1200. K}$$
$$CO(g) + H_2O(g) \rightleftharpoons CO_2(g) + H_2(g)$$
$$K_p = 0.6944 \text{ at 1200. K}$$

(a) Write the overall equation for the reaction of propane and steam to produce carbon dioxide and hydrogen.
(b) Calculate the equilibrium constant, K_p, for the overall process at 1200. K.
(c) When 1.00 volume C_3H_8 and 4.00 volumes H_2O each at 1200. K and 5.0 atm are mixed in a container, what is the final pressure? Assume the total volume remains constant,

that the reaction is essentially complete, and that the gases behave ideally.

(d) What percentage of the C_3H_8 remains unreacted?

*17.102 Using methane and steam as a source of H_2 for ammonia synthesis requires high temperatures. Rather than burning CH_4 separately to heat the mixture, a more efficient strategy is to inject some oxygen into the reaction mixture. All of the H_2 is thus released for the synthesis, and the heat of combustion of CH_4 helps maintain the required temperature. Imagine the reaction occurring in two steps:

$$2CH_4(g) + O_2(g) \rightleftharpoons 2CO(g) + 4H_2(g)$$
$$K_p = 9.34 \times 10^{28} \text{ at } 1000. \text{ K}$$

$$CO(g) + H_2O(g) \rightleftharpoons CO_2(g) + H_2(g)$$
$$K_p = 1.374 \text{ at } 1000. \text{ K}$$

(a) Write the overall equation for the reaction of methane, steam, and oxygen to form carbon dioxide and hydrogen.

(b) What is K_p for the overall reaction?

(c) What is K_c for the overall reaction?

(d) A mixture of 2.0 mol CH_4, 1.0 mol O_2, and 2.0 mol steam with a total pressure of 30. atm reacts at 1000. K in a container of constant volume. Assuming the reaction is essentially complete and the ideal gas law is a valid approximation, what is the final pressure?

*17.103 A mixture of 3.00 volumes H_2 and 1.00 volume N_2 reacts at 344°C to form ammonia. The equilibrium mixture at 110. atm contains 41.49% NH_3 by volume. Calculate K_p for the reaction assuming that the gases behave ideally.

*17.104 One mechanism for the synthesis of ammonia proposes that nitrogen and hydrogen molecules catalytically dissociate into atoms:

$$N_2(g) \rightleftharpoons 2N(g) \qquad \log K_p = -43.10$$
$$H_2(g) \rightleftharpoons 2H(g) \qquad \log K_p = -17.30$$

(a) What is the partial pressure of N in N_2 at 1000. K and 200. atm?

(b) What is the partial pressure of H in H_2 at 1000. K and 600. atm?

(c) How many atoms of N and of H are present per liter of mixture?

(d) Based on these answers, which of the following is a more reasonable step to continue the mechanism after the catalytic dissociation? Explain.

$$N(g) + H(g) \longrightarrow NH(g)$$
$$N_2(g) + H(g) \longrightarrow NH(g) + N(g)$$

*17.105 You are a member of a research team of industrial chemists who are discussing the plans to operate an ammonia processing plant:

$$N_2(g) + 3H_2(g) \rightleftharpoons 2NH_3(g)$$

(a) The plant operates at close to 700 K, at which K_p is 1.00×10^{-4}, and employs the stoichiometric 1:3 ratio of $N_2:H_2$. At equilibrium the partial pressure of NH_3 product is 50. atm. Calculate the partial pressures of each reactant and the total pressure under these operating conditions.

(b) One member of the team makes the following suggestion: since the partial pressure of H_2 is cubed in the reaction quotient, the plant could produce the same amount of NH_3 if the reactants were in a 1:6 ratio of $N_2:H_2$ instead and do so at a lower pressure, which would lower operating costs and, thus, increase profitability. Calculate the partial pressure of each reactant and the total pressure under these operating conditions, assuming an unchanged partial pressure of 50. atm for NH_3. Is the team member's argument valid?

17.106 Pitchblende is the principal mineral source of uranium used for nuclear reactors. In pitchblende, uranium decays to radium, which decays to radon. Consequently, the concentration of radium in the mineral remains nearly constant. Is the constant concentration of radium in pitchblende an example of equilibrium or of steady state? Explain.

17.107 When isopentyl alcohol and acetic acid react, they form the pleasant-smelling compound isopentyl acetate, the essence of banana oil:

$$C_5H_{11}OH(aq) + CH_3COOH(aq) \rightleftharpoons$$
$$CH_3COOC_5H_{11}(aq) + H_2O(l)$$

A student adds a drying agent to remove H_2O in an attempt to increase the yield of banana oil. Is this approach reasonable? Explain.

17.108 Many essential metabolites are products in branched pathways, such as the one shown below:

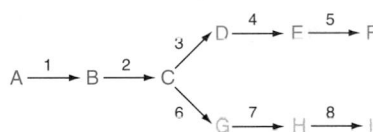

One method of control of these pathways occurs through inhibition of the first enzyme specific for a branch.

(a) Which enzyme is inhibited by F?

(b) Which enzyme is inhibited by I?

(c) What disadvantage would there be if F inhibited Enzyme 1?

(d) What disadvantage would there be if F inhibited Enzyme 6?

18 Acid-Base Equilibria

Figure: Acid-base soil. Home gardeners and agribusinesses alike test their soil before planting and adjust the acidity to optimize yield. The *Hydrangea* plant contains a substance in its extracellular fluids that changes color depending on the acidity of the soil: basic gives pink flowers, and acidic gives blue. The exploration in this chapter of acids and bases and their equilibria highlights our ever-widening understanding of these important substances.

Acids and bases have been used as laboratory chemicals since the time of the alchemists. With exotic names such as oil of vitriol (sulfuric acid), aqua fortis (nitric acid), and spirits of hartshorn (ammonia), these substances found early uses in everything from fraudulent "gold-forming" recipes to the practical metallurgy of gold, silver, and copper. In the 15th century, artists etched copper plates with nitric acid to create their works. To make glass, sand was treated with the strongly basic potash (K_2CO_3) that formed among wood ashes. In modern times, acids and bases are everyday chemicals in the home and in industry (Figure 18.1) and still play an indispensable role in the chemistry laboratory.

Table 18.1 on the next page shows some common acids and bases and their familiar uses. Notice that some of the acids (e.g., acetic and citric) have a sour taste. In fact, since the 17th century, sourness had been one of the defining properties of acids. An acid was any substance that had a sour taste; reacted with active metals, such as aluminum and zinc, to produce hydrogen gas; and turned certain organic compounds characteristic colors. (We discuss these compounds, known as *indicators*, later and in Chapter 19.) A base, on the other hand, was any substance that had a bitter taste and slippery feel and turned the same organic compounds different characteristic colors.* Moreover, it was commonly known that *when acids and bases react, each cancels the properties of the other in a process called neutralization.* ◆

Evolving definitions are common in science. As more phenomena are understood, an early description becomes too limited and is replaced by a broader one. Even though these very early definitions of acids and bases described some distinctive properties, they inevitably gave way to definitions based on the molecular nature of acid-base behavior.

In this chapter, we develop in succession three definitions of acids and bases that allow us to understand ever-increasing numbers of reactions. In the process, you'll see how the principles of chemical equilibrium apply to this essential group of substances. After presenting the classical (Arrhenius) acid-base definition, we examine acid dissociation as an equilibrium process to see why acids vary in strength. Then we introduce the pH scale as a means of comparing the acidity or basicity of aqueous solutions. Next, we see how the Brønsted-Lowry definition greatly expands the meaning of "base" and,

---

*Despite what 17th-century chemists may have done, you should *NEVER* taste or touch laboratory chemicals. Many of them, including common acids and bases, are harmful and can cause severe burns. To satisfy your curiosity, put some vinegar or lemon juice on your next salad and note the sour taste of an acid.

Concepts and Skills to Review
before you study this chapter

- role of water as solvent (Section 4.1)
- writing total and net ionic equations (Section 4.2)
- acids, bases, and acid-base reactions (Section 4.2)
- proton transfer in acid-base reactions (Section 4.2)
- properties of an equilibrium constant (Section 17.2)
- solving equilibrium problems (Section 17.5)

◆ **Pioneers of Acid-Base Chemistry** Three 17th-century chemists laid the early foundations of acid-base chemistry. Johann Glauber (1604–1668) became renowned for his ability to prepare acids and their salts. Glauber's salt ($Na_2SO_4 \cdot 10H_2O$) is still used today for preparing dyes and printing textiles. Otto Tachenius (c. 1620–1690) is credited with first recognizing that a salt is the product of the reaction between an acid and a base. Robert Boyle (1627–1691), in addition to his studies of gas behavior, fostered the use of spot tests, flame colors, fume odors, and precipitates to analyze reactions. He was the first to associate the color change in syrup of violets (an organic dye) with the acidic or basic nature of the test solution.

Figure 18.1 Etching with acids. A, The insides of "frosted" bulbs have been etched with hydrofluoric acid. **B,** Acid is used to remove unwanted oxides of silicon and metals during the process of manufacturing computer chips.

Table 18.1 Some Common Acids and Bases and Their Household Uses

Substance	Formula	Use
Acids		
Acetic acid (vinegar)	CH_3COOH (or $HC_2H_3O_2$)	Flavoring, preservative
Citric acid	$H_3C_6H_5O_7$	Flavoring
Phosphoric acid	H_3PO_4	Rust remover
Boric acid	$B(OH)_3$ (or H_3BO_3)	Mild antiseptic; insecticide
Aluminum salts	$NaAl(SO_4)_2 \cdot 12H_2O$	In baking powder, with sodium hydrogen carbonate
Hydrochloric acid (muriatic acid)	HCl	Brick and ceramic tile cleaner
Bases		
Sodium hydroxide (lye)	NaOH	Oven cleaner, unblocking plumbing
Ammonia	NH_3	Household cleaner
Sodium carbonate	Na_2CO_3	Water softener, grease remover
Sodium hydrogen carbonate	$NaHCO_3$	Fire extinguisher, rising agent in cake mixes (baking soda), mild antacid
Trisodium phosphate	Na_3PO_4	Cleaner for surfaces before painting or wallpapering

with it, the chemical changes we include as acid-base reactions. We investigate the molecular structures of acids and bases to rationalize variations in strength and then see that the very designations "acid" and "base" depend on their relative strengths and on the solvent in which the reaction occurs. Finally, we examine the Lewis acid-base definition, which expands the meaning of "acid" and what we consider to be acid-base behavior even further.

18.1 Acids and Bases in Water

Although water is not an essential participant in all modern acid-base definitions, most of your laboratory work with acids and bases involves water, as do most important environmental, biological, and industrial applications. You know from our introductory discussion in Chapter 4 that *water is a product in all reactions between strong acids and strong bases:*

$$HCl(aq) + NaOH(aq) \longrightarrow NaCl(aq) + H_2O(l)$$

Indeed, as the net ionic equation of this reaction shows, water is *the* product:

$$H^+(aq) + OH^-(aq) \longrightarrow H_2O(l)$$

Furthermore, whenever an acid dissociates in water, solvent molecules participate in the reaction:

$$HA(g \text{ or } l) + H_2O(l) \longrightarrow A^-(aq) + H_3O^+(aq)$$

As you saw in that earlier discussion, water surrounds the proton to form H-bonded species with the general formula $H(H_2O)_n^+$. Because the proton is so small, its charge density is very high, so its attraction to water is especially strong. The proton bonds covalently to one of the lone electron pairs of a water molecule's O atom to form a **hydronium ion, H_3O^+,** which forms H bonds to several other water molecules; the $H(H_2O)_3{}^+$ ion is shown in Figure 18.2. To emphasize the active role of water in aqueous acid-base chemistry and the nature of the proton-water interaction, the hydrated proton is shown generally in the text as $H_3O^+(aq)$, although in some cases this hydrated species is shown more simply as $H^+(aq)$.

Proton/Hydroxide Release and the Classical Acid-Base Definition

The earliest and simplest definition of acids and bases that reflects their chemical nature on the molecular scale was suggested by Svante Arrhenius, whose work on the rate constant we encountered in Chapter 16. In the **classical** (or **Arrhenius**) **acid-base definition,** acids and bases are classified in terms of their formulas and their behavior *in water:*

- An *acid* is a substance that contains hydrogen and dissociates in water to yield H_3O^+.
- A *base* is a substance that contains the hydroxyl group and dissociates in water to yield OH^-.

Some typical Arrhenius acids are HCl, HNO_3, and HCN, and some typical bases are NaOH, KOH, and $Ba(OH)_2$. Although Arrhenius bases contain discrete OH^- ions in their structures, Arrhenius acids *never* contain H^+ ions. On the contrary, these acids contain *covalently bonded H atoms that ionize in water.*

When an acid and a base react, they undergo **neutralization.** As we said, 17th-century scientists also observed this ability of an acid to cancel, or neutralize, the properties of the base, and vice versa. The meaning of acid-base reactions has changed along with the definitions of acid and base, but in the Arrhenius sense, neutralization occurs when *the H^+ ion from the acid and the OH^- ion from the base combine to form H_2O.* This description explains an observation that puzzled many of Arrhenius's colleagues. They observed that all neutralization reactions between what we now call strong acids and strong bases (those that dissociate completely in water) had the same heat of reaction. No matter which strong acid and base reacted, and no matter which salt formed, ΔH^0_{rxn} was about -56 kJ per mole of water that formed. Arrhenius suggested that the heat of reaction was always the same because the actual reaction was always the same—a hydrogen ion and a hydroxide ion formed water:

$$H^+(aq) + OH^-(aq) \longrightarrow H_2O(l) \quad \Delta H^0_{rxn} = -55.9 \text{ kJ}$$

The dissolved salt that formed along with the water, for example, NaCl in the reaction of sodium hydroxide with hydrochloric acid,

$$Na^+(aq) + OH^-(aq) + H^+(aq) + Cl^-(aq) \longrightarrow Na^+(aq) + Cl^-(aq) + H_2O(l)$$

did not affect the ΔH^0_{rxn} but consisted of hydrated spectator ions.

Despite its importance at the time, limitations in the classical definition soon became apparent. Arrhenius and many others realized that some substances that do *not* contain OH in their formulas *do* behave as bases. For example, NH_3 and K_2CO_3 also yield OH^- in water. As you'll see shortly, broader acid-base definitions are required to include these species.

Variation in Acid Strength: The Acid-Dissociation Constant (K_a)

Acids and bases differ greatly in their *strength* in water, that is, in the amount of H_3O^+ or OH^- produced per mole of substance dissolved. We generally classify acids and bases as either strong or weak, according to the extent of their dissociation into ions in water (see Table 4.2, p. 143). It's important to remember, however, that a *gradation* in strength exists, as we examine quantitatively in a moment. Acids and bases are electrolytes in water, so this classification of acid and base strength correlates with our earlier classification of

Figure 18.2 The nature of the hydrated proton. When an acid dissolves in water, the proton that is released forms a hydronium ion (H_3O^+) by bonding covalently to a water molecule. The H_3O^+ ion hydrogen bonds to other water molecules, forming a mixture of species with the general formula $H(H_2O)_n{}^+$. The $H(H_2O)_3{}^+$ (or $H_7O_3{}^+$) ion is shown here.

A Strong acid: HA(*g* or *l*) + H₂O(*l*) ⟶ H₃O⁺(*aq*) + A⁻(*aq*)

B Weak acid: HA(*aq*) + H₂O(*l*) ⇌ H₃O⁺(*aq*) + A⁻(*aq*)

Figure 18.3 The extent of dissociation for strong and weak acids. The bar graphs show the relative numbers of moles of species before *(left)* and after *(right)* acid dissociation occurs. **A,** When a strong acid dissolves in water, it dissociates completely, yielding H₃O⁺(*aq*) and A⁻(*aq*) ions; virtually no HA molecules are present. **B,** In contrast, when a weak acid dissolves in water, it remains mostly undissociated, yielding relatively few H₃O⁺(*aq*) and A⁻(*aq*) ions.

electrolyte strength: *strong electrolytes dissociate completely, and weak electrolytes dissociate partially:*

- *Strong acids dissociate completely into ions in water* (Figure 18.3A):

$$\text{HA}(g \text{ or } l) + \text{H}_2\text{O}(l) \longrightarrow \text{H}_3\text{O}^+(aq) + \text{A}^-(aq)$$

In a dilute solution of a strong acid, *virtually no HA molecules are present;* that is, $[\text{H}_3\text{O}^+] \approx [\text{HA}]_{\text{init}}$. In other words, $[\text{HA}]_{\text{eq}} \approx 0$, so the value of K_c is extremely large:

$$Q_c = \frac{[\text{H}_3\text{O}^+][\text{A}^-]}{[\text{HA}][\text{H}_2\text{O}]} \qquad \text{At equilibrium, } Q_c = K_c \gg 1$$

Because the reaction is essentially complete, it is not very useful to express it as an equilibrium process. In a dilute aqueous nitric acid solution, for example, there are virtually no undissociated nitric acid molecules:

$$\text{HNO}_3(l) + \text{H}_2\text{O}(l) \longrightarrow \text{H}_3\text{O}^+(aq) + \text{NO}_3^-(aq)$$

- *Weak acids dissociate very slightly into ions in water* (Figure 18.3B):

$$\text{HA}(aq) + \text{H}_2\text{O}(l) \rightleftharpoons \text{H}_3\text{O}^+(aq) + \text{A}^-(aq)$$

In a dilute solution of a weak acid, *the great majority of HA molecules are undissociated.* Thus, $[\text{H}_3\text{O}^+] \ll [\text{HA}]_{\text{init}}$. In other words, $[\text{HA}]_{\text{eq}} \approx [\text{HA}]_{\text{init}}$, so the value of K_c is very small. Hydrocyanic acid is an example of a weak acid:

$$HCN(aq) + H_2O(l) \rightleftharpoons H_3O^+(aq) + CN^-(aq)$$

$$Q_c = \frac{[H_3O^+][CN^-]}{[HCN][H_2O]} \qquad \text{At equilibrium, } Q_c = K_c \ll 1$$

(From here on, square brackets without a subscript are used to mean molar concentration *at equilibrium;* that is, [X] means $[X]_{eq}$. Since we deal with systems *at equilibrium* in this chapter, instead of presenting Q and stating that Q equals K at equilibrium, we will express K directly as a collection of equilibrium concentration terms.)

Because of the effect of concentration on rate (Section 16.6), this dramatic difference in $[H_3O^+]$ causes a dramatic difference in the reaction rate, when equal concentrations of a strong or a weak acid react with an active metal, such as zinc (Figure 18.4):

$$Zn(s) + 2H_3O^+(aq) \longrightarrow Zn^{2+}(aq) + 2H_2O(l) + H_2(g)$$

In a strong acid, such as 1 M HCl, zinc reacts rapidly, forming bubbles of H_2 vigorously. In a weak acid, such as 1 M CH_3COOH, zinc reacts slowly, forming bubbles of H_2 sluggishly on the metal piece. The strong acid has a high $[H_3O^+]$, so much more H_3O^+ is available at any given moment for reaction with the metal. The weak acid, on the other hand, has a low $[H_3O^+]$, so much less H_3O^+ is available.

The Meaning of K_a There is a *specific* equilibrium constant for acid dissociation that highlights the species whose concentrations change. The expression for the dissociation of a general *weak acid, HA,* in water is

$$K_c = \frac{[H_3O^+][A^-]}{[HA][H_2O]}$$

The amount of water is so large that its concentration changes negligibly when reaction occurs and it is considered constant. Therefore, as you saw in Section 17.2, we simplify this expression by including the constant $[H_2O]$ term with the value of K_c to define a new equilibrium constant, the **acid-dissociation constant, K_a** (or **acid-ionization constant**):

$$K_c[H_2O] = K_a = \frac{[H_3O^+][A^-]}{[HA]} \qquad \textbf{(18.1)}$$

Like any equilibrium constant, K_a is a number that is temperature dependent, whose magnitude tells how far to the right the reaction has proceeded to reach equilibrium. Thus, *the stronger the acid, the higher the $[H_3O^+]$ at equilibrium, the larger the K_a:*

$$\text{Stronger acid} \Longrightarrow \text{higher } [H_3O^+] \Longrightarrow \text{larger } K_a$$

The range of K_a values for weak acids extends over many orders of magnitude. Here are some benchmark K_a values for typical weak acids to give you an idea of the fraction of HA molecules that dissociates into ions:

- For a weak acid with a relatively high K_a ($\sim 10^{-2}$), a 1 M solution has $\sim 10\%$ of the HA molecules dissociated. The K_a of chlorous acid ($HClO_2$) is 1.12×10^{-2}, and 1 M $HClO_2$ is 10.6% dissociated.
- For a weak acid with a moderate K_a ($\sim 10^{-5}$), a 1 M solution has $\sim 0.3\%$ of the HA molecules dissociated. The K_a of acetic acid (CH_3COOH) is 1.8×10^{-5}, and 1 M CH_3COOH is 0.42% dissociated.
- For a weak acid with a relatively low K_a ($\sim 10^{-10}$), a 1 M solution has $\sim 0.001\%$ of the HA molecules dissociated. The K_a of HCN is 6.2×10^{-10}, and 1 M HCN is 0.0025% dissociated.

Thus, for solutions of the same initial HA concentration, *the smaller the K_a, the lower the percent dissociation of HA:*

$$\text{Smaller } K_a \Longrightarrow \text{lower \% HA dissociated} \Longrightarrow \text{weaker acid}$$

Figure 18.4 Reaction of zinc with a strong and a weak acid. In the reaction of zinc with a strong acid, such as 1 M HCl (*left*), the higher concentration of H_3O^+ results in rapid formation of H_2 (bubbles). In a weak acid, such as 1 M CH_3COOH (*right*), the H_3O^+ concentration is much lower, so the formation of H_2 is much slower.

Table 18.2 K_a Values for Some Monoprotic Acids at 25°C

Name (Formula)	Lewis Structure*	K_a
Iodic acid (HIO_3)	H—Ö—Ï=Ö ∥ :O:	1.6×10^{-1}
Chlorous acid ($HClO_2$)	H—Ö—Çl=Ö	1.12×10^{-2}
Nitrous acid (HNO_2)	H—Ö—N̈=Ö	7.1×10^{-4}
Hydrofluoric acid (HF)	H—F̈:	6.8×10^{-4}
Formic acid (HCOOH)	:O: ∥ H—C—Ö—H	1.8×10^{-4}
Benzoic acid (C_6H_5COOH)	:O: ∥ ⬡—C—Ö—H	6.3×10^{-5}
Acetic acid (CH_3COOH)	H :O: ∣ ∥ H—C—C—Ö—H ∣ H	1.8×10^{-5}
Propanoic acid (CH_3CH_2COOH)	H H :O: ∣ ∣ ∥ H—C—C—C—Ö—H ∣ ∣ H H	1.3×10^{-5}
Hypochlorous acid (HClO)	H—Ö—Çl:	2.9×10^{-8}
Hypobromous acid (HBrO)	H—Ö—B̈r:	2.3×10^{-9}
Hydrocyanic acid (HCN)	H—C≡N:	6.2×10^{-10}
Phenol (C_6H_5OH)	⬡—Ö—H	1.0×10^{-10}
Hypoiodous acid (HIO)	H—Ö—Ï:	2.3×10^{-11}

ACID STRENGTH ↑

*Red type indicates the ionizable proton; structures have zero formal charge.

Table 18.2 lists K_a values of some weak *monoprotic* acids (those with one ionizable proton) in water. Strong acids are absent because they do not have meaningful K_a values. Note that the ionizable H atom in organic acids is attached to oxygen in the —COOH grouping; the H atoms bonded to the C atoms in these acids do *not* ionize. In Section 18.4, we discuss the behavior of polyprotic acids (those with more than one ionizable proton).

Classifying the Relative Strengths of Acids and Bases

Using a table of acid-dissociation constants is the surest way to quantify relative acid strength, but you can often classify acids and bases qualitatively as strong or weak just from their formulas:

- *Strong acids.* Two types of strong acids, with examples that *you should memorize*, are
  1. The hydrohalic acids HCl, HBr, and HI
  2. Oxoacids in which the number of O atoms exceeds the number of ionizable H atoms by two or more, such as HNO_3, H_2SO_4, and $HClO_4$

- *Weak acids.* There are many *more* weak acids than strong ones. Four types, with examples, are
  1. The hydrohalic acid HF
  2. Those acids in which H is not bonded to O or to halogen, such as HCN and H_2S
  3. Oxoacids in which the number of O atoms equals or exceeds by one the number of ionizable H atoms, such as HClO, HNO_2, and H_3PO_4
  4. Organic acids (general formula RCOOH), such as CH_3COOH and C_6H_5COOH
- *Strong bases.* Soluble compounds containing O^{2-} or OH^- ions are strong bases. The cations are usually those of the most active metals:
  1. M_2O or MOH, where M = Group 1A(1) metal (Li, Na, K, Rb, Cs)
  2. MO or $M(OH)_2$, where M = Group 2A(2) metal (Ca, Sr, Ba)
     [MgO and $Mg(OH)_2$ are only slightly soluble, but the soluble portion dissociates completely.]
- *Weak bases.* Many compounds with an electron-rich nitrogen are weak bases (none are Arrhenius bases). The common structural feature is an N atom that has a lone electron pair in its Lewis structure:
  1. Ammonia ($\ddot{N}H_3$)
  2. Amines (general formula $R\ddot{N}H_2$, $R_2\ddot{N}H$, $R_3\ddot{N}$), such as $CH_3CH_2\ddot{N}H_2$, $(CH_3)_2\ddot{N}H$, $(C_3H_7)_3\ddot{N}$, and $C_5H_5\ddot{N}$

Sample Problem 18.1 Classifying Acid and Base Strength from the Chemical Formula

PROBLEM Classify each of the following compounds as a strong acid, weak acid, strong base, or weak base:
(a) H_2CrO_4 (b) $(CH_3)_2CHCOOH$ (c) KOH   (d) $(CH_3)_2CHNH_2$
PLAN We examine the formula and classify each acid or base, using the previous descriptions. Particular points to note for acids are the numbers of O atoms relative to H atoms and the presence of the COOH group. For bases, note the nature of the cation and the presence of an N atom that has a lone pair.
SOLUTION (a) Strong acid: H_2CrO_4 is an oxoacid in which the number of O atoms exceeds the number of ionizable H atoms by two.
(b) Weak acid: $(CH_3)_2CHCOOH$ is an organic acid, as indicated by the —COOH group.
(c) Strong base: KOH is one of the Group 1A(1) hydroxides.
(d) Weak base: $(CH_3)_2CHNH_2$ has a lone pair on the N and is an amine.

Follow-up Problem 18.1 Which of the following is the stronger acid or base: (a) HClO or $HClO_3$; (b) HCl or CH_3COOH; (c) NaOH or CH_3NH_2?

Section Summary

Acids and bases are essential substances in home, industry, and the environment. In aqueous solution, water combines with the proton released from an acid to form the hydrated species represented by $H_3O^+(aq)$. In the classical (Arrhenius) definition, acids contain H and yield H_3O^+ in water, bases contain OH and yield OH^- in water, and an acid-base reaction (neutralization) is the reaction of H^+ and OH^- to form H_2O. Acid strength depends on $[H_3O^+]$ relative to [HA] in aqueous solution. Strong acids dissociate completely and weak acids slightly. The extent of dissociation is expressed by the acid-dissociation constant, K_a. Weak acids have K_a values ranging from about 10^{-1} to 10^{-12}. Acids and bases can be classified qualitatively as strong or weak based on their formulas.

18.2 Autoionization of Water and the pH Scale

Before we discuss the next major definition of acid-base behavior, let's examine a crucial property of water that enables us to quantify $[H_3O^+]$ in any aqueous system: *water is an extremely weak electrolyte*. The electrical conductivity of tap water is due almost entirely to dissolved ions, but even water that has been distilled and deionized repeatedly exhibits a tiny conductance. The reason is that water itself dissociates into ions very slightly in an equilibrium process known as **autoionization** (or self-ionization):

$$H_2O(l) \qquad H_2O(l) \qquad H_3O^+(aq) \qquad OH^-(aq)$$

The Equilibrium Nature of Autoionization: The Ion-Product Constant for Water, K_w

Like any equilibrium system, the autoionization of water is described quantitatively by an equilibrium constant:

$$K_c = \frac{[H_3O^+][OH^-]}{[H_2O]^2}$$

Since the concentration of H_2O is essentially constant here, we simplify this equilibrium expression by including the constant $[H_2O]^2$ term with the value of K_c to obtain a new equilibrium constant, the **ion-product constant for water, K_w**:

$$K_c[H_2O]^2 = K_w = [H_3O^+][OH^-] = 1.0 \times 10^{-14} \text{ (at 25°C)} \qquad \textbf{(18.2)}$$

Notice that *one H_3O^+ ion and one OH^- ion appear for each H_2O molecule that dissociates*. Therefore, in pure water, we find that

$$[H_3O^+] = [OH^-] = \sqrt{1.0 \times 10^{-14}} = 1.0 \times 10^{-7} \ M \text{ (at 25°C)}$$

Pure water has a concentration of about 55.5 M $\left(\text{that is, } \dfrac{1000 \text{ g/L}}{18.02 \text{ g/mol}}\right)$, so these equilibrium concentrations are attained when only one in 555 million water molecules dissociates reversibly into ions!

Autoionization of water has two major consequences for aqueous acid-base chemistry:

1. *A change in $[H_3O^+]$ causes an inverse change in $[OH^-]$*, and vice versa:

higher $[H_3O^+] \Longrightarrow$ lower $[OH^-]$ \qquad and \qquad higher $[OH^-] \Longrightarrow$ lower $[H_3O^+]$

Recall from our discussion of Le Châtelier's principle that a change in concentration of either ion shifts the equilibrium position, but it does *not* change the equilibrium constant. Therefore, if some acid is added, $[H_3O^+]$ increases, so $[OH^-]$ must decrease; if some base is added, $[OH^-]$ increases, so $[H_3O^+]$ must decrease. However, these additions of H_3O^+ or OH^- merely lead to the formation of H_2O, so the value of K_w is maintained.

2. *Both ions are present in all aqueous systems*. Thus, all acidic solutions contain a low concentration of OH^- ions, and all basic solutions contain a low concentration of H_3O^+ ions. The equilibrium nature of autoionization allows us to define "acidic" and "basic" solutions in terms of relative magnitudes of $[H_3O^+]$ and $[OH^-]$:

In an *acidic* solution, \qquad $[H_3O^+] > [OH^-]$

In a *basic* solution, \qquad $[H_3O^+] < [OH^-]$

In a *neutral* solution, \qquad $[H_3O^+] = [OH^-]$

Moreover, if you know the value of K_w at a particular temperature and the concentration of one of these ions, you can easily calculate the concentration of the other ion:

$$[H_3O^+] = \frac{K_w}{[OH^-]} \qquad \text{or} \qquad [OH^-] = \frac{K_w}{[H_3O^+]}$$

Sample Problem 18.2 Calculating $[H_3O^+]$ and $[OH^-]$ in Aqueous Solutions

PROBLEM A research chemist adds a measured amount of HCl gas to pure water at 25°C and obtains a solution with $[H_3O^+] = 3.0 \times 10^{-4}$ M. Calculate $[OH^-]$. Is the solution neutral, acidic, or basic?

PLAN We use the known value of K_w at 25°C (1.0×10^{-14}) and the given $[H_3O^+]$ to solve for $[OH^-]$. Then we compare $[H_3O^+]$ with $[OH^-]$ to determine whether the solution is acidic, basic, or neutral. This calculation is very common, so a simple roadmap is shown.

SOLUTION Calculating $[OH^-]$:

$$[OH^-] = \frac{K_w}{[H_3O^+]} = \frac{1.0 \times 10^{-14}}{3.0 \times 10^{-4}} = 3.3 \times 10^{-11} \ M$$

Since $[H_3O^+] > [OH^-]$, the solution is acidic.

CHECK It makes sense that adding an acid to water results in an acidic solution. Moreover, since $[H_3O^+]$ is greater than 10^{-7} M, $[OH^-]$ must be less than 10^{-7} M to give a constant K_w.

Follow-up Problem 18.2 Calculate $[H_3O^+]$ in a solution at 25°C whose $[OH^-] = 6.7 \times 10^{-2}$ M. Is the solution neutral, acidic, or basic?

Expressing the Hydronium Ion Concentration: The pH Scale

In aqueous solutions, $[H_3O^+]$ can vary over an enormous range: from about 10 M to 10^{-15} M. To handle numbers with negative exponents more conveniently in calculations, we convert them to positive numbers using a numerical system called a *p-scale,* the negative of the common (base-10) logarithm of the number. ◆ Applying this numerical system to $[H_3O^+]$ gives **pH,** the negative logarithm of $[H^+]$ (or $[H_3O^+]$):

$$pH = -\log [H_3O^+] \tag{18.3}$$

What is the pH of 10^{-12} M H_3O^+ solution?

$$pH = -\log [H_3O^+] = -\log 10^{-12} = (-1)(-12) = 12$$

Similarly, a 10^{-3} M H_3O^+ solution has a pH of 3, and a 5.4×10^{-4} M solution has a pH of 3.27:

$$pH = -\log [H_3O^+] = (-1)(\log 5.4 + \log 10^{-4}) = 3.27$$

As with any measurement, the number of significant figures in the pH reflects the precision with which the concentration is known. However, since it is a logarithm, recall that the number of significant figures in the concentration equals the number of digits *to the right of the decimal point* (see Appendix A). In this case, 5.4×10^{-4} M has two significant figures, so its negative logarithm, 3.27, has two digits to the right of the decimal point.

Note in particular that *the higher the pH, the lower the $[H_3O^+]$.* Therefore, *an acidic solution has a lower pH (higher $[H_3O^+]$) than a basic solution.* At 25°C in pure water, $[H_3O^+]$ is 1.0×10^{-7} M, so

$$pH \text{ of a neutral solution} = 7.00$$
$$pH \text{ of an acidic solution} < 7.00$$
$$pH \text{ of a basic solution} \quad > 7.00$$

◆ Logarithmic Scales in Sound and Seismology
The p-scale is not the only logarithmic scale used in scientific measurements. The decibel scale measures the power of an acoustic signal, and the Richter scale measures the energy of ground movement. Urban planners study noise "pollution" by measuring decibel levels in different city locations at various times of the day. Seismologists record ground movement at stations around the world and try to predict the onset of earthquakes (see photo).

Figure 18.5 The pH values of some familiar aqueous solutions.

Figure 18.5 shows that the pH of some familiar aqueous solutions falls within a range of 0 to 14.

Another important point arises when we compare $[H_3O^+]$ in different solutions. Because the pH scale is logarithmic, a solution of pH 1.0 has an $[H_3O^+]$ that is 10 times higher than that of a pH 2.0 solution, 100 times higher than that of a pH 3.0 solution, and so forth. To find the $[H_3O^+]$ from the pH, you perform the opposite arithmetic process; that is, you find the negative antilog of pH:

$$[H_3O^+] = 10^{-pH}$$

A p-scale is used to express other quantities as well:
- Hydroxide ion concentration can be expressed as pOH:

$$pOH = -\log [OH^-]$$

Acidic solutions have a higher pOH (lower [OH⁻]) than basic solutions.
- Equilibrium constants can be expressed as pK:

$$pK = -\log K$$

A low pK corresponds to a high K. A reaction that reaches equilibrium with mostly products (proceeds far to the right) has a low pK (high K), whereas one that has mostly reactants at equilibrium has a high pK (low K). Table 18.3 shows this relationship for some weak acids.

Table 18.3 The Relationship Between K_a and pK_a

Acid Name (Formula)	K_a at 25°C	pK_a
Hydrogen sulfate ion (HSO_4^-)	1.02×10^{-2}	1.991
Nitrous acid (HNO_2)	7.1×10^{-4}	3.15
Acetic acid (CH_3COOH)	1.8×10^{-5}	4.74
Hypobromous acid (HBrO)	2.3×10^{-9}	8.64
Phenol (C_6H_5OH)	1.0×10^{-10}	10.00

The Relations Among pH, pOH, and pK_w Taking the negative log of both sides of the K_w expression gives a very useful relationship among pK_w, pH, and pOH:

$$K_w = [H_3O^+][OH^-] = 1.0 \times 10^{-14} \text{ (at 25°C)}$$
$$-\log K_w = (-\log [H_3O^+]) + (-\log [OH^-]) = -\log (1.0 \times 10^{-14})$$
$$pK_w = pH + pOH = 14.00 \quad \text{(at 25°C)} \tag{18.4}$$

Thus, the sum of pH and pOH is 14.00 in any aqueous solution at 25°C. Since pH, pOH, $[H_3O^+]$, and $[OH^-]$ are interrelated through K_w, knowing any one of the values allows us to determine the others (Figure 18.6).

Sample Problem 18.3   Calculating $[H_3O^+]$, pH, $[OH^-]$, and pOH

PROBLEM In an art restoration project, a conservator prepares copper-plate etching solutions by diluting concentrated HNO_3 to 2.0 M, 0.30 M, and 0.0063 M HNO_3. Calculate $[H_3O^+]$, pH, $[OH^-]$, and pOH of the three solutions at 25°C.

PLAN We know from its formula that HNO_3 is a strong acid, so it dissociates completely in water; thus, $[H_3O^+] = [HNO_3]_{init}$. We use the given concentrations and the value of K_w to calculate $[OH^-]$ and then use these concentrations to calculate pH and pOH.

	[H$_3$O$^+$]	pH	[OH$^-$]	pOH
BASIC	1.0 x 10^{-15}	15.00	1.0 x 10^1	−1.00
	1.0 x 10^{-14}	14.00	1.0 x 10^0	0.00
	1.0 x 10^{-13}	13.00	1.0 x 10^{-1}	1.00
	1.0 x 10^{-12}	12.00	1.0 x 10^{-2}	2.00
	1.0 x 10^{-11}	11.00	1.0 x 10^{-3}	3.00
	1.0 x 10^{-10}	10.00	1.0 x 10^{-4}	4.00
	1.0 x 10^{-9}	9.00	1.0 x 10^{-5}	5.00
	1.0 x 10^{-8}	8.00	1.0 x 10^{-6}	6.00
NEUTRAL	1.0 x 10^{-7}	7.00	1.0 x 10^{-7}	7.00
	1.0 x 10^{-6}	6.00	1.0 x 10^{-8}	8.00
	1.0 x 10^{-5}	5.00	1.0 x 10^{-9}	9.00
	1.0 x 10^{-4}	4.00	1.0 x 10^{-10}	10.00
	1.0 x 10^{-3}	3.00	1.0 x 10^{-11}	11.00
ACIDIC	1.0 x 10^{-2}	2.00	1.0 x 10^{-12}	12.00
	1.0 x 10^{-1}	1.00	1.0 x 10^{-13}	13.00
	1.0 x 10^0	0.00	1.0 x 10^{-14}	14.00
	1.0 x 10^1	−1.00	1.0 x 10^{-15}	15.00

Figure 18.6 The relations among [H$_3$O$^+$], pH, [OH$^-$], and pOH. Because K_w is constant, [H$_3$O$^+$] and [OH$^-$] are interdependent, and change in opposite directions as the acidity or basicity of the aqueous solution increases. The pH and pOH are interdependent in the same way. Note that at 25°C, the product of [H$_3$O$^+$] and [OH$^-$] is 1.0×10^{-14}, and the sum of pH and pOH is 14.00.

SOLUTION Calculating the values for 2.0 M HNO$_3$:

$$[H_3O^+] = \boxed{2.0\ M}$$

$$pH = -\log [H_3O^+] = -\log 2.0 = \boxed{-0.30}$$

$$[OH^-] = \frac{K_w}{[H_3O^+]} = \frac{1.0\times10^{-14}}{2.0} = \boxed{5.0\times10^{-15}\ M}$$

$$pOH = -\log (5.0\times10^{-15}) = \boxed{14.30}$$

Calculating the values for 0.30 M HNO$_3$:

$$[H_3O^+] = \boxed{0.30\ M}$$

$$pH = -\log [H_3O^+] = -\log 0.30 = \boxed{0.52}$$

$$[OH^-] = \frac{K_w}{[H_3O^+]} = \frac{1.0\times10^{-14}}{0.30} = \boxed{3.3\times10^{-14}\ M}$$

$$pOH = -\log (3.3\times10^{-14}) = \boxed{13.48}$$

Calculating the values for 0.0063 M HNO$_3$:

$$[H_3O^+] = \boxed{6.3\times10^{-3}\ M}$$

$$pH = -\log [H_3O^+] = -\log (6.3\times10^{-3}) = \boxed{2.20}$$

$$[OH^-] = \frac{K_w}{[H_3O^+]} = \frac{1.0\times10^{-14}}{6.3\times10^{-3}} = \boxed{1.6\times10^{-12}\ M}$$

$$pOH = -\log (1.6\times10^{-12}) = \boxed{11.80}$$

CHECK As the solution becomes more dilute, [H$_3$O$^+$] decreases, so pH increases, as we expect. Since an [H$_3$O$^+$] greater than 1.0 M, as in 2.0 M HNO$_3$, gives a positive log, it results in a negative pH. The arithmetic seems correct because pH + pOH = 14.00 in each case.

COMMENT On most calculators, finding the pH requires several keystrokes. For example, to find the pH of 6.3×10^{-3} M HNO$_3$ solution, you enter "6.3, EXP, 3, +/−, log, +/−".

Follow-up Problem 18.3 A solution of NaOH has a pH of 9.52. What is its pOH, [H$_3$O$^+$], and [OH$^-$] at 25°C?

A

B

Figure 18.7 **Methods for measuring the pH of an aqueous solution. A,** A few drops of the solution are placed on a strip of pH paper, and the color is compared with the color chart. **B,** The electrodes of a pH meter immersed in the test solution measure $[H_3O^+]$. (In this equipment, two electrodes are housed in one probe.)

Measuring pH In the laboratory, pH values are usually obtained with an acid-base indicator or, more precisely, with an instrument called a pH meter. **Acid-base indicators** are organic molecules whose colors depend on the acidity or basicity of the solution in which they are dissolved. The pH of a solution is estimated quickly with *pH paper,* a paper strip impregnated with one or a mixture of indicators. A drop of test solution is placed on the paper strip, and the color of the strip is compared with a color chart, as shown in Figure 18.7A.

The *pH meter* measures $[H_3O^+]$ by means of two electrodes immersed in the test solution. One electrode provides a stable reference voltage; the other has an extremely thin, conducting, glass membrane that separates a known internal $[H_3O^+]$ from the unknown external $[H_3O^+]$. The difference in $[H_3O^+]$ creates a voltage difference across the membrane, which is measured and displayed in pH units (Figure 18.7B).

Section Summary

Pure water has a low conductivity because it autoionizes to a small extent. This process is described by an equilibrium reaction whose equilibrium constant is the ion-product constant for water, K_w (1.0×10^{-14} at 25°C). Thus, $[H_3O^+]$ and $[OH^-]$ are inversely related. In acidic solution, $[H_3O^+]$ is greater than $[OH^-]$, the reverse is true in basic solution, and the two are equal in neutral solution. To express small $[H_3O^+]$ values more simply, we use the pH scale (pH = $-\log [H_3O^+]$). A high pH represents a low $[H_3O^+]$. Similarly, pOH = $-\log [OH^-]$, and pK = $-\log K$. In acidic solutions, pH < 7.00; in basic solutions, pH > 7.00; and in neutral solutions, pH = 7.00. The sum of pH and pOH equals pK_w (14.00 at 25°C).

18.3 Proton Transfer and the Brønsted-Lowry Acid-Base Definition

Earlier we noted a major shortcoming of the classical (Arrhenius) definition: many substances that yield OH^- ions when they dissolve in water do not contain OH in their formulas. Examples include ammonia, the amines, and many salts of weak acids, such as NaF. Another limitation of the Arrhenius definition was that water had to be the solvent for acid-base reactions. In the early 20th century, J. N. Brønsted and T. M. Lowry suggested definitions that remove these limitations. (Recall that we discussed their ideas briefly in Section 4.2.) According to the **Brønsted-Lowry acid-base definition,**

- *An acid is a **proton donor,** any species that donates an H^+ ion.* An acid must contain H in its formula; HNO_3 and $H_2PO_4^-$ are two of many examples. All Arrhenius acids are Brønsted-Lowry acids.

- *A base is a **proton acceptor,** any species that accepts an H^+ ion.* A base must contain a lone pair of electrons to bind the H^+ ion; a few examples are NH_3, CO_3^{2-}, F^-, as well as OH^-. Brønsted-Lowry bases are not Arrhenius bases, but all Arrhenius bases contain the Brønsted-Lowry base OH^-.

From the Brønsted-Lowry perspective, the only requirement for an acid-base reaction is that *one species donate a proton and another species accept it: an acid-base reaction is a proton transfer process.* Acid-base reactions can occur between gases, in nonaqueous solutions, and in heterogeneous mixtures, as well as in aqueous solutions.

An acid and a base always work together in the transfer of a proton. In other words, one species behaves as an acid only if another species *simultaneously* behaves as a base, and vice versa. Even when an acid or a base merely dissolves in water, an acid-base reaction occurs because water acts as the other partner. Consider two typical acidic and basic solutions:

Figure 18.8 Proton transfer as the essential feature of a Brønsted-Lowry acid-base reaction. A, When HCl dissolves in water, it acts as an acid by donating a proton to water, which acts as a base by accepting it. **B,** When NH_3 dissolves in water, it acts as a base by accepting a proton from water, which acts as an acid by donating it. Thus, in the Brønsted-Lowry sense, an acid-base reaction occurs in both cases.

1. *Acid donates a proton to water* (Figure 18.8A). When HCl dissolves in water, an H^+ ion (a proton) is transferred from HCl to H_2O, where it becomes attached to a lone pair of electrons on the O atom and forms H_3O^+. In effect, HCl (the acid) has *donated* the H^+ and H_2O (the base) has *accepted* it:

$$HCl(g) + H_2\ddot{O}(l) \longrightarrow Cl^-(aq) + H_3\ddot{O}^+(aq)$$

2. *Base accepts a proton from water* (Figure 18.8B). When ammonia dissolves in water, proton transfer also occurs. An H^+ from H_2O attaches to the N atom's lone pair and forms NH_4^+. With one fewer H^+, the water molecule becomes an OH^- ion:

$$\ddot{N}H_3(g) + H_2O(l) \rightleftharpoons NH_4^+(aq) + OH^-(aq)$$

In this case, H_2O (the acid) has *donated* the H^+ and NH_3 (the base) has *accepted* it. Thus, H_2O is *amphoteric:* it acts as a base in one case and as an acid in the other. As you'll see, many other species are amphoteric.

The Conjugate Acid-Base Pair

The Brønsted-Lowry definition provides a new way to look at acid-base reactions because it focuses on the reactants *and* the products. For example, let's examine the reaction between hydrogen sulfide and ammonia:

$$H_2S + NH_3 \rightleftharpoons HS^- + NH_4^+$$

In the forward reaction, H_2S acts as an acid by donating an H^+ to NH_3, which acts as a base. The reverse reaction involves another acid-base pair. The ammonium ion, NH_4^+, acts as an acid by donating an H^+ to the hydrogen sulfide ion, HS^-, which acts as a base. Notice that the acid, H_2S, becomes a base, HS^-, and the base, NH_3, becomes an acid, NH_4^+.

In Brønsted-Lowry terminology, H_2S and HS^- are a **conjugate acid-base pair:** HS^- is the conjugate base of the acid H_2S. Similarly, NH_3 and NH_4^+ form a conjugate acid-base pair: NH_4^+ is the conjugate acid of the base NH_3. *Every acid has a conjugate base, and every base has a conjugate acid.* Thus, for any conjugate acid-base pair,

• The conjugate base of the pair has one *fewer* H and one *more* negative charge than the acid.
• The conjugate acid of the pair has one *more* H and one *fewer* negative charge than the base.

A Brønsted-Lowry acid-base reaction occurs when *an acid and a base react to form their conjugate base and conjugate acid, respectively:*

$$acid_1 + base_2 \rightleftharpoons base_1 + acid_2$$

Table 18.4 The Conjugate Pairs in Some Acid-Base Reactions

	Conjugate Pair					
	Acid	**+**	**Base**	$\rightleftharpoons$	**Base**	**+**	**Acid**

Conjugate Pair

	Acid	+	Base	$\rightleftharpoons$	Base	+	Acid
Reaction 1	HF	+	H_2O	$\rightleftharpoons$	F^-	+	H_3O^+
Reaction 2	HCOOH	+	CN^-	$\rightleftharpoons$	$HCOO^-$	+	HCN
Reaction 3	NH_4^+	+	CO_3^{2-}	$\rightleftharpoons$	NH_3	+	HCO_3^-
Reaction 4	$H_2PO_4^-$	+	OH^-	$\rightleftharpoons$	HPO_4^{2-}	+	H_2O
Reaction 5	H_2SO_4	+	$N_2H_5^+$	$\rightleftharpoons$	HSO_4^-	+	$N_2H_6^{2+}$
Reaction 6	HPO_4^{2-}	+	SO_3^{2-}	$\rightleftharpoons$	PO_4^{3-}	+	HSO_3^-

Table 18.4 shows some Brønsted-Lowry acid-base reactions. Notice that
- Each reaction has an acid and a base as reactants *and* as products, and these comprise two conjugate acid-base pairs.
- Acids and bases can be neutral, cationic, or anionic.
- The same species can be an acid or a base, depending on the other species reacting. Water behaves this way in Reactions 1 and 4, and HPO_4^{2-} does so in Reactions 4 and 6.

Sample Problem 18.4   Identifying Conjugate Acid-Base Pairs

PROBLEM The following reactions are important environmental processes. Identify the conjugate acid-base pairs.
(a) $H_2PO_4^-(aq) + CO_3^{2-}(aq) \rightleftharpoons HCO_3^-(aq) + HPO_4^{2-}(aq)$
(b) $H_2O(l) + SO_3^{2-}(aq) \rightleftharpoons OH^-(aq) + HSO_3^-(aq)$
PLAN To find the conjugate pairs, we find the species that donated an H^+ (acid) and the species that accepted it (base). The acid (or base) on the left becomes its conjugate base (or conjugate acid) on the right. Remember, the conjugate acid has one more H and a charge that is 1+ greater than that of its conjugate base.
SOLUTION (a) $H_2PO_4^-$ has one more H^+ than HPO_4^{2-}; CO_3^{2-} has one fewer H^+ than HCO_3^-. Therefore, $H_2PO_4^-$ and HCO_3^- are the acids, and HPO_4^{2-} and CO_3^{2-} are the bases. The conjugate acid-base pairs are
$H_2PO_4^-/HPO_4^{2-}$ and HCO_3^-/CO_3^{2-}.
(b) H_2O has one more H^+ than OH^-; SO_3^{2-} has one fewer H^+ than HSO_3^-. The acids are H_2O and HSO_3^-; the bases are OH^- and SO_3^{2-}. The conjugate acid-base pairs are H_2O/OH^- and HSO_3^-/SO_3^{2-}.

Follow-up Problem 18.4   Identify the conjugate acid-base pairs in the following reactions:
(a) $CH_3COOH(aq) + H_2O(l) \rightleftharpoons CH_3COO^-(aq) + H_3O^+(aq)$
(b) $H_2O(l) + F^-(aq) \rightleftharpoons OH^-(aq) + HF(aq)$

Relative Acid-Base Strength and the Net Direction of Reaction

The net *direction* of an acid-base reaction depends on the relative strengths of the acids and bases involved. *A reaction proceeds to the greater extent in the direction in which a stronger acid and stronger base form a weaker acid and weaker base.* If the stronger acid and base are written on the left, the net direction is to the right, so $K_c > 1$. The net direction of the H_2S-NH_3 reaction is to the right ($K_c > 1$) because H_2S is a stronger acid than NH_4^+, the other acid present, and NH_3 is a stronger base than HS^-, the other base:

$$H_2S + NH_3 \rightleftharpoons HS^- + NH_4^+$$

stronger acid + stronger base $\longrightarrow$ weaker base + weaker acid

You might think of the process as *a competition for the proton between the two bases*, NH_3 and HS^-, in which NH_3 wins.

Similarly, the extent of acid (HA) dissociation in water depends on a competition for the proton between the two bases, A^- and H_2O. When the acid, HNO_3, dissolves in water, it transfers an H^+ to the base, H_2O, forming the conjugate base of HNO_3, NO_3^-, and the conjugate acid of H_2O, H_3O^+:

$$HNO_3 \quad + \quad H_2O \quad \longrightarrow \quad NO_3^- \quad + \quad H_3O^+$$
stronger acid + stronger base $\longrightarrow$ weaker base + weaker acid

(In this case, the net direction is so far to the right that it would be inappropriate to show an equilibrium arrow.) HNO_3 is a stronger acid than H_3O^+, and H_2O is a stronger base than NO_3^-. Thus, for strong acids such as HNO_3, the H_2O wins the competition for the proton because A^- (NO_3^-) is a much weaker base. On the other hand, for weak acids such as HF, the A^- (F^-) wins because it is a stronger base than H_2O:

$$HF \quad + \quad H_2O \quad \rightleftharpoons \quad F^- \quad + \quad H_3O^+$$
weaker acid + weaker base $\longleftarrow$ stronger base + stronger acid

From many such reactions, we can rank conjugate pairs in terms of the ability of the acid to transfer its proton (Figure 18.9). Note, especially, that *a weaker acid has a stronger conjugate base*. This makes perfect sense: the acid gives up its proton less readily because its conjugate base holds it more strongly. We can use this list to predict the direction of a reaction between any two pairs, that is, whether the equilibrium position lies predominantly to the right ($K_c > 1$) or to the left ($K_c < 1$). *An acid-base reaction proceeds to the right if the acid reacts with a base that is lower on the list* because this combination produces a weaker conjugate base and a weaker conjugate acid.

Figure 18.9 Strengths of conjugate acid-base pairs. The stronger the acid is, the weaker its conjugate base. The strongest acid appears on the top left and the strongest base on the bottom right. When an acid reacts with a base farther down the list, the reaction proceeds to the right ($K_c > 1$).

Sample Problem 18.5   Predicting the Net Direction of an Acid-Base
Reaction

PROBLEM Predict the net direction and whether K_c is greater or less than one for
each of the following reactions (assume equal initial concentrations of all species):
(a) $H_2PO_4^-(aq) + NH_3(aq) \rightleftharpoons NH_4^+(aq) + HPO_4^{2-}(aq)$
(b) $H_2O(l) + HS^-(aq) \rightleftharpoons OH^-(aq) + H_2S(aq)$
PLAN We first identify the conjugate acid-base pairs. To predict the direction, we
consult Figure 18.9 to see which acid and base are stronger. The stronger acid and
base form the weaker acid and base, so the reaction proceeds in that net direction.
If the reaction *as written* proceeds to the right, then [products] is higher than [reac-
tants], and $K_c > 1$.
SOLUTION (a) The conjugate pairs are $H_2PO_4^-/HPO_4^{2-}$ and NH_4^+/NH_3. Since
$H_2PO_4^-$ is higher on the list of acids, it is stronger than NH_4^+; since NH_3 is lower
on the list of bases, it is stronger than HPO_4^{2-}. Therefore,

$$H_2PO_4^-(aq) + NH_3(aq) \rightleftharpoons NH_4^+(aq) + HPO_4^{2-}(aq)$$
$$\text{stronger acid} + \text{stronger base} \longrightarrow \text{weaker acid} + \text{weaker base}$$

The net direction is right, so $K_c > 1$.
(b) The conjugate pairs are H_2O/OH^- and H_2S/HS^-. Since H_2S is higher on the list
of acids and OH^- is lower on the list of bases, we have

$$H_2O(l) + HS^-(aq) \rightleftharpoons OH^-(aq) + H_2S(aq)$$
$$\text{weaker acid} + \text{weaker base} \longleftarrow \text{stronger base} + \text{stronger acid}$$

The net direction is left, so $K_c < 1$.

Follow-up Problem 18.5   Explain with balanced equations, in which you
show the net direction of the reaction, each of the following observations:
(a) You smell ammonia when NH_3 dissolves in water.
(b) The odor goes away when you add an excess of HCl to the solution in **(a)**.
(c) The odor returns when you add an excess of NaOH to the solution in **(b)**.

Section Summary

The Brønsted-Lowry acid-base definition does not require that bases contain
OH or that acids and bases react in water. It defines an acid as a species that
donates a proton and a base as one that accepts it. Acids and bases act
together in proton transfer. When an acid donates its proton, it becomes a
conjugate base; when a base accepts a proton, it becomes a conjugate acid.
In an acid-base reaction, acids and bases form their conjugates. A stronger
acid has a weaker conjugate base, and vice versa. Thus, the reaction proceeds
in the net direction in which a stronger acid and base form a weaker base
and acid.

18.4 Solving Problems Involving Weak-Acid Equilibria

Just as you saw in the problems in Chapter 17, there are two general types
of equilibrium problems involving weak acids and their conjugate bases:
 1. Given equilibrium concentrations, find K_a.
 2. Given K_a and some concentration information, find the other equilib-
    rium concentrations.
For all of these problems, we'll apply the same problem-solving approach,
notation system, and assumptions:
- *The problem-solving approach.* As always, start with what is given in the
   problem statement and move logically toward what you want to find.

Make a habit of applying the following steps:

1. Write the balanced equation and K_a expression; these will tell you what to find.
2. Define x as the unknown concentration that changes during the reaction. Frequently, $x = [HA]_{dissoc}$, the concentration of HA that dissociates, which, through the use of certain assumptions, also equals $[H_3O^+]$ and $[A^-]$ at equilibrium.
3. Construct a reaction table that incorporates the unknown.
4. Make assumptions that simplify the calculation, usually that x is very small relative to the initial concentration.
5. Substitute the values into the K_a expression and solve for x.
6. Check that the assumptions are justified. (We apply the 5% test that was introduced in Sample Problem 17.9, p. 733.) If they are not justified, use the quadratic formula to find x.

- *The notation system.* As always, the molar concentration of each species is shown with brackets. A subscript refers to where the species comes from or when it occurs in the reaction process. For example, $[H_3O^+]_{from\ HA}$ is the molar concentration of H_3O^+ that comes from HA dissociation; $[HA]_{init}$ is the initial molar concentration of HA, that is, before the dissociation occurs; $[HA]_{dissoc}$ is the molar concentration of HA that dissociates; and so forth. Recall that *brackets with no subscript refer to the molar concentration of the species at equilibrium.*

- *The assumptions.* Two key assumptions we make to simplify the arithmetic are

  1. The $[H_3O^+]$ from the autoionization of water is negligible. In fact, it is so much smaller than $[H_3O^+]$ from the HA dissociation that we can neglect it:

     $$[H_3O^+] = [H_3O^+]_{from\ HA} + [H_3O^+]_{from\ H_2O} \approx [H_3O^+]_{from\ HA}$$

     Indeed, Le Châtelier's principle tells us that $[H_3O^+]_{from\ HA}$ *decreases* the extent of autoionization of water, so $[H_3O^+]_{from\ H_2O}$ in the HA solution is even less than $[H_3O^+]$ in pure water. Moreover, each HA that dissociates forms one H_3O^+ and one A^-, so $[A^-] = [H_3O^+]$.

  2. A weak acid has a small K_a. Therefore, it dissociates to such a small extent that we can neglect the change in its concentration to find its equilibrium concentration:

     $$[HA] = [HA]_{init} - [HA]_{dissoc} \approx [HA]_{init}$$

Finding K_a Given Concentrations

This problem type involves finding the acid-dissociation constant, K_a, of a weak acid:

$$HA(aq) + H_2O(l) \rightleftharpoons H_3O^+(aq) + A^-(aq)$$

$$K_a = \frac{[H_3O^+][A^-]}{[HA]}$$

A common laboratory approach is to prepare an aqueous solution of HA and measure its pH. You prepared the solution, so you know $[HA]_{init}$. You can calculate $[H_3O^+]$ from the measured pH and determine $[A^-]$ and $[HA]$ at equilibrium from the assumptions you make. Then you substitute into the K_a expression and solve for K_a. We'll go through the entire approach in Sample Problem 18.6 and then simplify later problems by omitting some of the recurring steps.

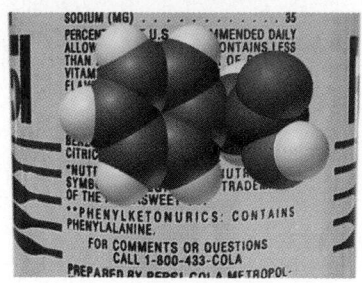

Phenylalanine, one of the amino acids that make up aspartame, is metabolized to phenylacetic acid (model).

Sample Problem 18.6   Finding the K_a of a Weak Acid from the pH of Its Solution

PROBLEM Phenylacetic acid ($C_6H_5CH_2COOH$, simplified here to HPAc; see photo) builds up in the blood of persons with phenylketonuria, an inherited disorder that, if untreated, causes mental retardation and death. A study of the acid shows that the pH of 0.12 M HPAc is 2.60. What is the K_a of phenylacetic acid?

PLAN We are given $[HPAc]_{init}$ and the pH and must find K_a. We first write the reaction and the expression for K_a to see which values we need to find:

$$HPAc(aq) + H_2O(l) \rightleftharpoons H_3O^+(aq) + PAc^-(aq)$$

$$K_a = \frac{[H_3O^+][PAc^-]}{[HPAc]}$$

- To find $[H_3O^+]$: We know the pH, so we can find $[H_3O^+]$. Since pH 2.60 is over four pH units (10^4-fold) *lower* than that of pure water (pH = 7.0), we can assume that $[H_3O^+]_{from\ HPAc} \gg [H_3O^+]_{from\ H_2O}$.
  Thus, $[H_3O^+]_{from\ HPAc} + [H_3O^+]_{from\ H_2O} \approx [H_3O^+]_{from\ HPAc} \approx [H_3O^+]$.
- To find $[PAc^-]$: Since each HPAc that dissociates forms one H_3O^+ and one PAc^-, $[H_3O^+] \approx [PAc^-]$.
- To find $[HPAc]$: We know $[HPAc]_{init}$. Since HPAc is a weak acid, we assume that very little dissociates, so $[HPAc]_{init} - [HPAc]_{dissoc} = [HPAc] \approx [HPAc]_{init}$.

We set up a reaction table, make the assumptions, substitute the equilibrium values, solve for K_a, and then check the assumptions.

SOLUTION Calculating $[H_3O^+]$:

$$[H_3O^+] = 10^{-pH} = 10^{-2.60} = 2.5 \times 10^{-3}\ M$$

Setting up the reaction table, with $x = [HPAc]_{dissoc} = [H_3O^+]_{from\ HPAc} = [PAc^-] \approx [H_3O^+]$:

CONCENTRATION (M)	HPAc(aq)	+	H₂O(l)	$\rightleftharpoons$	H₃O⁺(aq)	+	PAc⁻(aq)
Initial	0.12		—		1×10^{-7}		0
Change	$-x$		—		$+x$		$+x$
Equilibrium	$0.12 - x$		—		$x + {<}1 \times 10^{-7}$		x

Making the assumptions:
1. The calculated $[H_3O^+]$ ($2.5 \times 10^{-3}\ M$) $\gg [H_3O^+]_{from\ H_2O}$ ($<1 \times 10^{-7}\ M$), so we assume that $[H_3O^+] \approx [H_3O^+]_{from\ HPAc} = x$.
2. Since HPAc is weak, we assume that $[HPAc] = 0.12\ M - x \approx 0.12\ M$.

Solving for the equilibrium concentrations:

$$x \approx [H_3O^+] = [PAc^-] = 2.5 \times 10^{-3}\ M$$

$[HPAc] = 0.12\ M - x = 0.12\ M - (2.5 \times 10^{-3}\ M) \approx 0.12\ M$ (to 2 significant figures)

Substituting these values into K_a:

$$K_a = \frac{[H_3O^+][PAc^-]}{[HPAc]} \approx \frac{(2.5 \times 10^{-3})(2.5 \times 10^{-3})}{0.12} = \boxed{5.2 \times 10^{-5}}$$

Checking the assumptions by finding the percent error in concentration:

1. For $[H_3O^+]_{from\ H_2O}$: $\dfrac{1 \times 10^{-7}\ M}{2.5 \times 10^{-3}\ M} \times 100 = 4 \times 10^{-3}\% < 5\%$; assumption is justified.

2. For $[HPAc]_{dissoc}$: $\dfrac{2.5 \times 10^{-3}\ M}{0.12\ M} \times 100 = 2.1\% < 5\%$; assumption is justified. We had already shown above that, to two significant figures, the concentration had not changed, so this check was not really necessary.

CHECK The $[H_3O^+]$ makes sense: pH 2.60 should give an $[H_3O^+]$ between 10^{-2} and $10^{-3}\ M$. The K_a calculation also seems in the correct range: $(10^{-3})^2/10^{-1} = 10^{-5}$, and this value seems reasonable for a weak acid.

COMMENT The $[H_3O^+]_{from\ H_2O}$ is so small relative to $[H_3O^+]_{from\ HA}$ that we will disregard it and no longer show it in reaction tables.

Follow-up Problem 18.6 The conjugate acid of ammonia, NH_4^+, is a weak acid. If a 0.2 M NH₄Cl solution has a pH of 5.0, what is the K_a of NH_4^+?

Finding Concentrations Given K_a

The second type of problem gives some concentration data and the K_a value and asks for the equilibrium concentration of some component. Such problems are very similar to those we solved in Chapter 17 in which a substance with a given initial concentration reacted to an unknown extent (see Sample Problems 17.8 to 17.10).

Sample Problem 18.7   Determining Concentrations from K_a and Initial [HA]

PROBLEM Propanoic acid (CH_3CH_2COOH, which we simplify as HPr) is an organic acid whose salts are used to retard mold growth in foods. What is the $[H_3O^+]$ of 0.10 M HPr? $K_a = 1.3 \times 10^{-5}$.

PLAN We need to find $[H_3O^+]$. First we write the balanced equation and the expression for K_a:

$$HPr(aq) + H_2O(l) \rightleftharpoons H_3O^+(aq) + Pr^-(aq)$$

$$K_a = \frac{[H_3O^+][Pr^-]}{[HPr]} = 1.3 \times 10^{-5}$$

We know $[HPr]_{init}$ but not $[HPr]$. If we let $x = [HPr]_{dissoc}$, x is also $[H_3O^+]_{from\ HPr}$ and $[Pr^-]$ because each HPr that dissociates yields one H_3O^+ and one Pr^-. With this information, we can set up a reaction table. In solving for x, we assume that, since HPr has a small K_a, it dissociates very little; therefore, $[HPr]_{init} - x = [HPr] \approx [HPr]_{init}$. Then we find x and check the assumption.

SOLUTION Setting up the reaction table, with $x = [HPr]_{dissoc} = [H_3O^+]_{from\ HPr} = [Pr^-] = [H_3O^+]$:

CONCENTRATION (M)	HPr(aq)	+	H₂O(l)	⇌	H₃O⁺(aq)	+	Pr⁻(aq)
Initial	0.10		—		0		0
Change	$-x$		—		$+x$		$+x$
Equilibrium	$0.10 - x$		—		x		x

Making the assumption:
Since K_a is small, x is small compared with $[HPr]_{init}$, so 0.10 $M - x \approx 0.10$ M. Substituting into the K_a expression and solving for x:

$$K_a = \frac{[H_3O^+][Pr^-]}{[HPr]} = 1.3 \times 10^{-5} \approx \frac{(x)(x)}{0.10}$$

$$x \approx \sqrt{(0.10)(1.3 \times 10^{-5})} = \boxed{1.1 \times 10^{-3}\ M = [H_3O^+]}$$

Checking the assumption:

For $[HPr]_{dissoc}$: $\dfrac{1.1 \times 10^{-3}\ M}{0.10\ M} \times 100 = 1.1\% < 5\%$; assumption is justified.

CHECK The $[H_3O^+]$ seems reasonable for a dilute solution of a weak acid with a moderate K_a. By reversing the calculation, we can check the math: $(1.1 \times 10^{-3})^2/0.10 = 1.2 \times 10^{-5}$, which is within rounding of the given K_a.

COMMENT In these problems, we assume that since K_a is relatively small, the amount that dissociates (x) can be neglected. However, this is true only if $[HA]_{init}$ is relatively large. A simple benchmark shows when the assumption is justified:

- If $\dfrac{[HA]_{init}}{K_a} > 400$, the assumption is justified: neglecting $[HA]_{dissoc}$ introduces an error < 5%.

- If $\dfrac{[HA]_{init}}{K_a} < 400$, the assumption is *not* justified, so we solve a quadratic equation to find x.

The latter situation occurs in the follow-up problem.

Follow-up Problem 18.7   Cyanic acid (HOCN) is an extremely acrid, unstable substance. What is the $[H_3O^+]$ and pH of 0.10 M HOCN? K_a of cyanic acid is 3.5×10^{-4}.

The Effect of Concentration on the Extent of Acid Dissociation

If we repeat the calculation in Sample Problem 18.7, but start with a lower [HPr], we observe a very interesting fact about the extent of dissociation of a weak acid. Suppose the initial concentration of HPr is 0.010 M rather than 0.10 M. After filling in the reaction table and making the same assumptions, we find that

$$x = [\text{HPr}]_{\text{dissoc}} = 3.6 \times 10^{-4} \ M$$

Now let's compare the percent of HPr molecules dissociated at the two different initial acid concentrations, with the relationship

$$\text{Percent HA dissociated} = \frac{[\text{HA}]_{\text{dissoc}}}{[\text{HA}]_{\text{init}}} \times 100 \qquad \textbf{(18.5)}$$

Case 1: $[\text{HPr}]_{\text{init}} = 0.10 \ M$

$$\text{Percent dissociated} = \frac{1.1 \times 10^{-3} \ M}{1.0 \times 10^{-1} \ M} \times 100 = 1.1\%$$

Case 2: $[\text{HPr}]_{\text{init}} = 0.010 \ M$

$$\text{Percent dissociated} = \frac{3.6 \times 10^{-4} \ M}{1.0 \times 10^{-2} \ M} \times 100 = 3.6\%$$

As the initial acid concentration decreases, the percent dissociation of the acid increases. Don't confuse the *concentration* of HA dissociated with the *percent* HA dissociated. The $[\text{HA}]_{\text{dissoc}}$ is lower in the diluted HA solution because the actual *number* of dissociated HA molecules is smaller. It is the *fraction* (and thus the *percent*) of HA molecules that dissociate that increases with dilution.

This phenomenon is analogous to a change in container volume (pressure) for gases at equilibrium (Section 17.6). In that case, an increase in volume shifts the equilibrium position to favor more moles of gas. In HA dissociation, an increase in available volume, as solvent is added and the solution is diluted, shifts the equilibrium position to favor more moles of ions.

The Behavior of Polyprotic Acids

Acids with more than one ionizable proton are **polyprotic acids.** In a solution of a polyprotic acid, one proton at a time dissociates from the acid molecule, and each dissociation step has a different K_a. For example, phosphoric acid is a triprotic acid, so it has three K_a values:

$$\text{H}_3\text{PO}_4(aq) + \text{H}_2\text{O}(l) \rightleftharpoons \text{H}_2\text{PO}_4^-(aq) + \text{H}_3\text{O}^+(aq)$$

$$K_{a1} = \frac{[\text{H}_2\text{PO}_4^-][\text{H}_3\text{O}^+]}{[\text{H}_3\text{PO}_4]} = 7.2 \times 10^{-3}$$

$$\text{H}_2\text{PO}_4^-(aq) + \text{H}_2\text{O}(l) \rightleftharpoons \text{HPO}_4^{2-}(aq) + \text{H}_3\text{O}^+(aq)$$

$$K_{a2} = \frac{[\text{HPO}_4^{2-}][\text{H}_3\text{O}^+]}{[\text{H}_2\text{PO}_4^-]} = 6.3 \times 10^{-8}$$

$$\text{HPO}_4^{2-}(aq) + \text{H}_2\text{O}(l) \rightleftharpoons \text{PO}_4^{3-}(aq) + \text{H}_3\text{O}^+(aq)$$

$$K_{a3} = \frac{[\text{PO}_4^{3-}][\text{H}_3\text{O}^+]}{[\text{HPO}_4^{2-}]} = 4.2 \times 10^{-13}$$

As you can see from the relative K_a values, H_3PO_4 is a much stronger acid than H_2PO_4^-, which is much stronger than HPO_4^{2-}. Table 18.5 lists some common polyprotic acids and their K_a values. Notice that, in every case, the first proton comes off to a much greater extent than the second and, where applicable, the second to a much greater extent than the third:

$$K_{a1} > K_{a2} > K_{a3}$$

This trend makes sense: it is more difficult for an H^+ ion to leave a singly charged anion (such as H_2PO_4^-) than a neutral molecule (such as H_3PO_4) and more difficult still to leave a doubly charged anion (HPO_4^{2-}). Successive

Table 18.5 Successive K_a Values for Some Polyprotic Acids at 25°C

Name (Formula)	Lewis Structure*	K_{a1}	K_{a2}	K_{a3}
Oxalic acid ($H_2C_2O_4$)		5.6×10^{-2}	5.4×10^{-5}	
Phosphorous acid (H_3PO_3)		3×10^{-2}	1.7×10^{-7}	
Sulfurous acid (H_2SO_3)		1.4×10^{-2}	6.5×10^{-8}	
Phosphoric acid (H_3PO_4)		7.2×10^{-3}	6.3×10^{-8}	4.2×10^{-13}
Arsenic acid (H_3AsO_4)		6×10^{-3}	1.1×10^{-7}	3×10^{-12}
Citric acid ($H_3C_6H_5O_7$)		7.5×10^{-4}	1.7×10^{-5}	4.0×10^{-7}
Carbonic acid (H_2CO_3)		4.5×10^{-7}	4.7×10^{-11}	
Hydrosulfuric acid (H_2S)		9×10^{-8}	1×10^{-17}	

ACID STRENGTH

*Red type indicates the ionizable protons.

acid dissociation constants typically differ by several orders of magnitude. This fact greatly simplifies pH calculations involving polyprotic acids because *we can usually neglect the H_3O^+ coming from the subsequent dissociations.*

Sample Problem 18.8 Calculating Equilibrium Concentrations for a Polyprotic Acid

PROBLEM Ascorbic acid ($H_2C_6H_6O_6$; H_2Asc for this problem), known as vitamin C, is a diprotic acid ($K_{a1} = 1.0 \times 10^{-5}$ and $K_{a2} = 5 \times 10^{-12}$) found in citrus fruit (see photo). Calculate $[H_2Asc]$, $[HAsc^-]$, $[Asc^{2-}]$, and the pH of 0.050 M H_2Asc.
PLAN We must calculate the equilibrium concentrations of all species and convert $[H_3O^+]$ to pH. We first write the equations and K_a expressions:

$$H_2Asc(aq) + H_2O(l) \rightleftharpoons HAsc^-(aq) + H_3O^+(aq)$$

$$K_{a1} = \frac{[HAsc^-][H_3O^+]}{[H_2Asc]} = 1.0 \times 10^{-5}$$

$$HAsc^-(aq) + H_2O(l) \rightleftharpoons Asc^{2-}(aq) + H_3O^+(aq)$$

$$K_{a2} = \frac{[Asc^{2-}][H_3O^+]}{[HAsc^-]} = 5 \times 10^{-12}$$

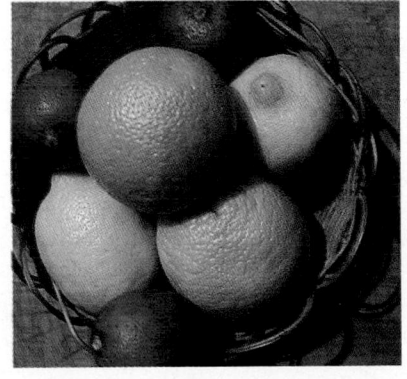

Then we assume that

1. Since $K_{a1} \gg K_{a2}$, the first dissociation produces almost all the H_3O^+:
   $$[H_3O^+]_{\text{from } H_2Asc} \gg [H_3O^+]_{\text{from } HAsc^-}$$
2. Since K_{a1} is small, the amount that dissociates can be neglected relative to the initial concentration: $[H_2Asc]_{\text{init}} \approx [H_2Asc]$.

We set up a reaction table for the first dissociation, with x equal to the concentration of H_2Asc that dissociates, then solve for $[H_3O^+]$ and $[HAsc^-]$. Because the second dissociation is so much less than the first, we can substitute values from the first directly to find $[Asc^{2-}]$ of the second.

SOLUTION Setting up a reaction table with $x = [H_2Asc]_{\text{dissoc}} = [HAsc^-] \approx [H_3O^+]$:

CONCENTRATION (M)	$H_2Asc(aq)$	+	$H_2O(l)$	$\rightleftharpoons$	$H_3O^+(aq)$	+	$HAsc^-(aq)$
Initial	0.050		—		0		0
Change	$-x$		—		$+x$		$+x$
Equilibrium	$0.050 - x$		—		x		x

Making the assumptions:

1. Since $K_{a2} \ll K_{a1}$, $[H_3O^+]_{\text{from } HAsc^-} \ll [H_3O^+]_{\text{from } H_2Asc}$. Therefore,
   $$[H_3O^+]_{\text{from } H_2Asc} \approx [H_3O^+]$$
2. Since K_{a1} is small, $[H_2Asc]_{\text{init}} - x = [H_2Asc] \approx [H_2Asc]_{\text{init}}$

Thus, $[H_2Asc] = 0.050\ M - x \approx \boxed{0.050\ M}$

Substituting into the expression for K_{a1} and solving for x:

$$K_{a1} = \frac{[H_3O^+][HAsc^-]}{[H_2Asc]} = 1.0 \times 10^{-5} \approx \frac{x^2}{0.050}$$

$$x = [HAsc^-] \approx [H_3O^+] \approx \boxed{7.1 \times 10^{-4}\ M}$$

$$pH = -\log [H_3O^+] = -\log (7.1 \times 10^{-4}) = \boxed{3.15}$$

Checking the assumptions:

1. $[H_3O^+]_{\text{from } HAsc^-} \ll [H_3O^+]_{\text{from } H_2Asc}$: Based on any second dissociation,
   $$[H_3O^+]_{\text{from } HAsc^-} \approx \sqrt{[HAsc^-] \times K_{a2}} = \sqrt{(7.1 \times 10^{-4})(5 \times 10^{-12})} = 6 \times 10^{-8}\ M;$$
   this is even less than $[H_3O^+]_{\text{from } H_2O}$, so the assumption is justified.

2. $[H_2Asc]_{\text{dissoc}} \ll [H_2Asc]_{\text{init}}$: $\dfrac{7.1 \times 10^{-4}\ M}{0.050\ M} \times 100 = 1.4\% < 5\%$; assumption
   is justified. Also, from the Comment in Sample Problem 18.7, note that
   $$\frac{[H_2Asc]_{\text{init}}}{K_{a1}} = \frac{0.050}{1.0 \times 10^{-5}} = 5000 > 400.$$

Calculating $[Asc^{2-}]$:

$$K_{a2} = \frac{[H_3O^+][Asc^{2-}]}{[HAsc^-]} \quad \text{and} \quad [Asc^{2-}] = \frac{K_{a2} \times [HAsc^-]}{[H_3O^+]}$$

$$[Asc^{2-}] = \frac{(5 \times 10^{-12})(7.1 \times 10^{-4})}{7.1 \times 10^{-4}} = \boxed{5 \times 10^{-12}\ M}$$

CHECK Since $K_{a1} \gg K_{a2}$, it makes sense that $[HAsc^-] \gg [Asc^{2-}]$ because Asc^{2-} is produced only in the second (much weaker) dissociation. Since both K_a's are small, all concentrations except $[H_2Asc]$ should be much lower than the original $0.050\ M$.

Follow-up Problem 18.8 Oxalic acid (HOOC—COOH, or $H_2C_2O_4$) is the simplest organic diprotic acid. Its commercial uses include bleaching straw and leather and removing rust and ink stains. Calculate $[H_2C_2O_4]$, $[HC_2O_4^-]$, $[C_2O_4^{2-}]$, and the pH of a $0.150\ M$ $H_2C_2O_4$ solution. Use K_a values from Table 18.5.

Section Summary

Two common types of weak-acid equilibrium problems involve finding K_a from concentrations and finding concentrations from K_a. We summarize the information in a reaction table, and we simplify the arithmetic by assuming (1) $[H_3O^+]_{from\ H_2O}$ is so small relative to $[H_3O^+]_{from\ HA}$ that it can be neglected, and (2) weak acids dissociate so little that $[HA]_{init} \approx [HA]$ at equilibrium. The *fraction* of weak acid molecules that dissociates is greater in more dilute solution, even though the total $[H_3O^+]$ is less. Polyprotic acids have more than one ionizable proton, but we assume that the first dissociation provides virtually all the H_3O^+.

18.5 Weak Bases and Their Relation to Weak Acids

By focusing on where the proton comes from and goes to, the Brønsted-Lowry concept expands the definition of a base to encompass a host of species that the Arrhenius definition excludes: a base is any species that accepts a proton, and to do so, *the base must have a lone electron pair.* (The lone electron pair plays the central role in the Lewis acid-base definition, as you'll see later in this chapter.)

Now let's examine the equilibrium system for a weak base and focus, as we did for weak acids, on aqueous solutions. When a base (B) dissolves, it accepts a proton from H_2O, which acts here as an acid, leaving behind an OH^- ion:

$$B(aq) + H_2O(aq) \rightleftharpoons BH^+(aq) + OH^-(aq)$$

This general reaction for a base in water is described by the following equilibrium expression:

$$K_c = \frac{[BH^+][OH^-]}{[B][H_2O]}$$

Based on our earlier reasoning that $[H_2O]$ is treated as a constant in aqueous reactions, we include $[H_2O]$ in the value of K_c and obtain the **base-dissociation constant, K_b**:

$$K_b = \frac{[BH^+][OH^-]}{[B]} \qquad \textbf{(18.6)}$$

Despite the term "base-dissociation constant," *no base dissociates in the process,* as you can see from the reaction. In aqueous solution, the two large classes of weak bases are nitrogen-containing molecules, such as ammonia and the amines, and the anions of weak acids. ◆

Molecules as Bases: Ammonia and the Amines

Ammonia is the simplest member of a family of nitrogen-containing compounds that act as weak bases in water:

$$NH_3(aq) + H_2O(l) \rightleftharpoons NH_4^+(aq) + OH^-(aq) \qquad K_b = 1.76 \times 10^{-5} \text{ (at 25°C)}$$

Despite labels on reagent bottles that read "ammonium hydroxide," an aqueous solution of ammonia consists largely of *intact* NH_3 molecules, as you can see from the small K_b value. In a 1.0 M NH_3 solution, for example, $[OH^-] = [NH_4^+] = 4.2 \times 10^{-3}$ M. Table 18.6 on the next page shows the K_b values for some common molecular bases.

◆ **Ammonia's Picturesque Past** One of today's key industrial chemicals has a long, vivid past. The name *ammonia* derives from an Egyptian god, whom the Romans called Ammon. Sacrificial wastes were piled outside temples (see photo), where they decomposed; the remaining mineral salts were called *salts of Ammon*. Later, the name *ammon* was retained for the volatile portion of these substances. In the late 15th century and for some time thereafter, ammonia was obtained from animal protein through the distillation of horns and hoofs and was called *spirits of hartshorn*.

Table 18.6 K_b Values for Some Molecular (Amine) Bases at 25°C

Name (Formula)	Lewis Structure*	K_b
Diethylamine [$(CH_3CH_2)_2NH$]		8.6×10^{-4}
Dimethylamine [$(CH_3)_2NH$]		5.9×10^{-4}
Triethylamine [$(CH_3CH_2)_3N$]		5.2×10^{-4}
Methylamine (CH_3NH_2)		4.4×10^{-4}
Ethanolamine ($HOCH_2CH_2NH_2$)		3.2×10^{-5}
Ammonia (NH_3)		1.76×10^{-5}
Pyridine (C_5H_5N)		1.7×10^{-9}
Aniline ($C_6H_5NH_2$)		4.0×10^{-10}

BASE STRENGTH ↑

*Blue type indicates the basic nitrogen and its lone pair.

If one or more of the H atoms in NH_3 is replaced by an organic group (designated as R), an *amine* results: RNH_2, R_2NH, or R_3N (Section 15.4; see Figure 15.17). The key structural feature of these organic compounds, as in all Brønsted-Lowry bases, is *a lone pair of electrons that can bind the proton donated by the acid.* Figure 18.10 depicts this process for methylamine, the simplest of the amines. Solving equilibrium problems that involve molecular weak bases is very similar to solving problems involving weak acids.

Figure 18.10 Abstraction of a proton from water by methylamine. The amines are organic derivatives of ammonia. Methylamine, the simplest amine, acts as a base in water by abstracting a proton, thereby increasing the [OH^-].

Sample Problem 18.9 Determining pH from K_b and Initial [B]

PROBLEM Dimethylamine, $(CH_3)_2NH$ (see margin), a key intermediate in detergent manufacture, has a K_b of 5.9×10^{-4}. What is the pH of 1.5 M $(CH_3)_2NH$?

PLAN The amine reacts with water to form OH^-, so we find $[OH^-]$ and then calculate $[H_3O^+]$ and pH. The balanced equation and K_b expression are

$$(CH_3)_2NH(aq) + H_2O(l) \rightleftharpoons (CH_3)_2NH_2^+(aq) + OH^-(aq)$$

$$K_b = \frac{[(CH_3)_2NH_2^+][OH^-]}{[(CH_3)_2NH]}$$

Since $K_b \gg K_w$, the $[OH^-]$ from the autoionization of water is negligible, and we disregard it. Therefore, $[OH^-]_{from\ base} = [(CH_3)_2NH_2^+] = [OH^-]$. Since K_b is small, we assume that the amount of amine reacting is small, so $[(CH_3)_2NH]_{init} - [(CH_3)_2NH]_{reacting} = [(CH_3)_2NH] \approx [(CH_3)_2NH]_{init}$. We proceed as usual, setting up a reaction table, making the assumption, and solving for x. Then we check the assumption and convert $[OH^-]$ to $[H_3O^+]$ with K_w, and then to pH.

SOLUTION Setting up the reaction table, with $x = [(CH_3)_2NH]_{reacting} = [(CH_3)_2NH_2^+] = [OH^-]$:

CONCENTRATION (M)	$(CH_3)_2NH(aq)$	+	$H_2O(l)$	$\rightleftharpoons$	$(CH_3)_2NH_2^+(aq)$	+	$OH^-(aq)$
Initial	1.5		—		0		0
Change	$-x$		—		$+x$		$+x$
Equilibrium	$1.5 - x$		—		x		x

Making the assumption: Since K_b is small, $[(CH_3)_2NH]_{init} \approx [(CH_3)_2NH]$; thus $1.5\ M - x \approx 1.5\ M$.

Substituting into the K_b expression and solving for x:

$$K_b = \frac{[(CH_3)_2NH_2^+][OH^-]}{[(CH_3)_2NH]} = 5.9\times10^{-4} \approx \frac{x^2}{1.5}$$

$$x = [OH^-] \approx 3.0\times10^{-2}\ M$$

Checking the assumption:

$$\frac{3.0\times10^{-2}\ M}{1.5\ M} \times 100 = 2.0\% < 5\%;\ \text{assumption is justified}$$

Note that the Comment from Sample Problem 18.7 applies to weak bases as well:

$$\frac{[B]_{init}}{K_b} = \frac{1.5}{5.9\times10^{-4}} = 2.5\times10^3 > 400$$

Calculating pH:

$$[H_3O^+] = \frac{K_w}{[OH^-]} = \frac{1.0\times10^{-14}}{3.0\times10^{-2}} = 3.3\times10^{-13}\ M$$

$$pH = -\log(3.3\times10^{-13}) = \boxed{12.48}$$

CHECK The value of x seems reasonable: $\sqrt{(\sim6\times10^{-4})(1.5)} = \sqrt{9\times10^{-4}} = 3\times10^{-2}$. Since $(CH_3)_2NH$ is a weak base, the pH should be several pH units greater than 7.

Follow-Up Problem 18.9 Pyridine (C_5H_5N, see margin), a major solvent and base in organic syntheses, has a pK_b of 8.77. What is the pH of 0.10 M pyridine?

Dimethylamine

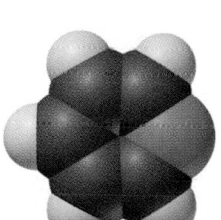
Pyridine

Anions of Weak Acids as Bases

The other large group of Brønsted-Lowry bases consists of the anions of weak acids:*

$$A^-(aq) + H_2O(l) \rightleftharpoons HA(aq) + OH^-(aq) \qquad K_b = \frac{[HA][OH^-]}{[A^-]}$$

---

*This equation and equilibrium expression are sometimes referred to as a *hydrolysis reaction* and a *hydrolysis constant*, K_h, because water is dissociated (hydrolyzed), and its parts end up in the products. Actually, it is the same as the proton abstraction process we saw with molecular bases such as ammonia, except for the charge on the base, so a new term and new equilibrium constant are unnecessary. Thus, K_h is just another symbol for K_b, so we'll use K_b throughout.

For example, F^-, the anion of the weak acid HF, acts as a weak base:

$$F^-(aq) + H_2O(l) \rightleftharpoons HF(aq) + OH^-(aq)$$

$$K_b = \frac{[HF][OH^-]}{[F^-]}$$

Why is a solution of HA acidic and a solution of A^- basic? Let's approach the question by examining the relative concentrations of species present in 1 M HF and in 1 M NaF:

1. *The acidity of HA(aq).* Since HF is a weak acid, most of the HF exists undissociated. A small fraction of the HF molecules do dissociate, donating their protons to H_2O and yielding small concentrations of H_3O^+ and F^-. The equilibrium position of the system lies far to the left:

$$HF(aq) + H_2O(l) \underset{\longleftarrow}{\rightleftharpoons} H_3O^+(aq) + F^-(aq)$$

Water molecules also contribute a minute amount of H_3O^+ and OH^-, but their concentrations are extremely small:

$$2H_2O(l) \underset{\longleftarrow}{\rightleftharpoons} H_3O^+(aq) + OH^-(aq)$$

Of all the species present—HF, H_2O, H_3O^+, F^-, and OH^-—the two that can influence the acidity of the solution are H_3O^+, predominantly from HF, and OH^- from water. Since $[H_3O^+]_{\text{from HF}} >> [OH^-]_{\text{from H}_2\text{O}}$, the solution is acidic.

2. *The basicity of A^-(aq).* Now, consider the species present in 1 M NaF. The salt dissociates completely to yield a relatively large concentration of F^-. The Na^+ ion behaves as a spectator, but some F^- reacts with water to produce small amounts of HF and OH^-:

$$F^-(aq) + H_2O(l) \underset{\longleftarrow}{\rightleftharpoons} HF(aq) + OH^-(aq)$$

As before, water dissociation contributes minute amounts of H_3O^+ and OH^-. Thus, in addition to the Na^+ ion, the species present are the same as in the HF solution: HF, H_2O, H_3O^+, F^-, and OH^-. The two species that affect the acidity are OH^-, predominantly from the F^- reaction with water, and H_3O^+ from water. In this case, $[OH^-]_{\text{from F}^-} >> [H_3O^+]_{\text{from H}_2\text{O}}$, so the solution is basic.

To summarize, *the factor that determines the relative acidity of an HA solution or an A^- solution is the relative concentrations of HA and of A^- in each solution:*

- In an HA solution, $[HA] >> [A^-]$ and $[H_3O^+]_{\text{from HA}} >> [OH^-]_{\text{from H}_2\text{O}}$, so the solution is acidic.
- In an A^- solution, $[A^-] >> [HA]$ and $[OH^-]_{\text{from A}^-} >> [H_3O^+]_{\text{from H}_2\text{O}}$, so the solution is basic.

The Relation Between K_a and K_b of a Conjugate Acid-Base Pair

An important relationship exists between the K_a of HA and the K_b of A^-, which we can see by treating the two dissociation reactions as a reaction sequence and adding them together:

$$\begin{aligned}\cancel{HA} + H_2O &\rightleftharpoons H_3O^+ + \cancel{A^-} \\ \cancel{A^-} + H_2O &\rightleftharpoons \cancel{HA} + OH^- \\ \hline 2H_2O &\rightleftharpoons H_3O^+ + OH^-\end{aligned}$$

The sum of the two dissociation reactions is the autoionization of water. Recall from Chapter 17 that, for a reaction that is the *sum* of two or more reactions, the overall equilibrium constant is the *product* of the individual equilibrium constants. Therefore, writing the expressions for each reaction gives

$$\frac{[H_3O^+]\cancel{[A^-]}}{\cancel{[HA]}} \times \frac{\cancel{[HA]}[OH^-]}{\cancel{[A^-]}} = [H_3O^+][OH^-]$$

or

$$K_a \quad \times \quad K_b \quad = \quad K_w \qquad \textbf{(18.7)}$$

This relationship allows us to find K_a of the acid in a conjugate pair given K_b of the base, and vice versa. Let's use this relationship to obtain a key piece of data for solving equilibrium problems. Reference tables typically have K_a and K_b values for molecular species only. The K_b for F^- ion or the K_a for $CH_3NH_3^+$, for example, do not appear in standard tables, but you can calculate them simply by looking up the values of the molecular conjugate species and relating them to K_w. For the K_b value of F^-, for instance, we look up the K_a value for HF and relate it to K_w:

$$K_a \text{ of HF} = 6.8 \times 10^{-4} \text{ (from Table 18.2)}$$

So, we have

$$K_a \text{ of HF} \times K_b \text{ of } F^- = K_w$$

or,

$$K_b \text{ of } F^- = \frac{K_w}{K_a \text{ of HF}} = \frac{1.0 \times 10^{-14}}{6.8 \times 10^{-4}} = 1.5 \times 10^{-11}$$

Then we use this calculated K_b value to solve the rest of the problem.

Sample Problem 18.10 Determining the pH of a Solution of A^-

PROBLEM Sodium acetate (CH_3COONa, or NaAc for this problem) has applications in photographic development and textile dyeing. What is the pH of 0.25 M NaAc? K_a of acetic acid (HAc) $= 1.8 \times 10^{-5}$.

PLAN We have to find the pH of a solution of acetate ion, Ac^-, which acts as a base in water:

$$Ac^-(aq) + H_2O(l) \rightleftharpoons HAc(aq) + OH^-(aq)$$

$$K_b = \frac{[HAc][OH^-]}{[Ac^-]}$$

If we calculate $[OH^-]$, we can find $[H_3O^+]$ and convert to pH. To solve for $[OH^-]$, we need K_b of Ac^-, which we obtain from the K_a of HAc and K_w. All sodium salts are soluble, so we know that $[Ac^-] = 0.25$ M. Our usual assumption is that $[Ac^-]_{init} \approx [Ac^-]$.

SOLUTION Setting up the reaction table, with $x = [Ac^-]_{reacting} = [HAc] = [OH^-]$:

CONCENTRATION (M)	$Ac^-(aq)$	+	$H_2O(l)$	$\rightleftharpoons$	$HAc(aq)$	+	$OH^-(aq)$
Initial	0.25		—		0		0
Change	$-x$		—		$+x$		$+x$
Equilibrium	$0.25 - x$		—		x		x

Solving for K_b:

$$K_b = \frac{K_w}{K_a} = \frac{1.0 \times 10^{-14}}{1.8 \times 10^{-5}} = 5.6 \times 10^{-10}$$

Making the assumption: Since K_b is small, $0.25 \text{ M} - x \approx 0.25$ M.

Substituting into the expression for K_b and solving for x:

$$K_b = \frac{[HAc][OH^-]}{[Ac^-]} = 5.6 \times 10^{-10} \approx \frac{x^2}{0.25}$$

$$x = [OH^-] \approx 1.2 \times 10^{-5} \text{ M}$$

Checking the assumption:

$$\frac{1.2 \times 10^{-5} \text{ M}}{0.25 \text{ M}} \times 100 = 4.8 \times 10^{-3} \% < 5\%; \text{ assumption is justified}$$

Note that

$$\frac{0.25}{5.6 \times 10^{-10}} = 4.5 \times 10^8 > 400$$

Solving for pH:

$$[H_3O^+] = \frac{K_w}{[OH^-]} = \frac{1.0\times10^{-14}}{1.2\times10^{-5}} = 8.3\times10^{-10}\ M$$

$$pH = -\log(8.3\times10^{-10}) = \boxed{9.08}$$

CHECK The K_b calculation seems reasonable: $\sim 10\times10^{-15}/2\times10^{-5} = 5\times10^{-10}$. Since Ac^- is a weak base, $[OH^-] > [H_3O^+]$; so the pH > 7, which makes sense.

Follow-up Problem 18.10 Sodium hypochlorite (NaClO) is the active ingredient in household laundry bleach. What is the pH of 0.20 M NaClO?

Section Summary

The extent to which a weak base abstracts a proton from water to form OH^- is expressed by a base-dissociation constant K_b. Brønsted-Lowry bases include NH_3, the amines, and anions of weak acids. All produce basic solutions by accepting H^+ from water, which makes $[H_3O^+] < [OH^-]$. A solution of HA is acidic because $[HA] >> [A^-]$, so $[H_3O^+] > [OH^-]$. A solution of A^- is basic because $[A^-] >> [HA]$, so $[OH^-] > [H_3O^+]$. By multiplying the expressions for K_a of HA and K_b of A^-, we obtain K_w. This relationship allows us to calculate K_a of BH^+, the cationic conjugate acid of a molecular weak base B, or K_b of A^-, the anionic conjugate base of a molecular weak acid HA.

18.6 Molecular Properties and Acid Strength

The strength of an acid depends on its ability to donate a proton, which in molecular terms depends in turn on the strength of the bond to the acidic proton. In this section, we apply trends in atomic and bond properties to determine the trends in acid strength of nonmetal hydrides and oxoacids and discuss the acidity of hydrated metal ions.

Trends in Acid Strength of Nonmetal Hydrides

Two factors determine how easily a proton is released from a binary non-metal hydride: the electronegativity of the central nonmetal (E) and the strength of the E—H bond. Figure 18.11 displays two periodic trends:

1. *Across a period, nonmetal hydride acid strength increases.* Across a period, the electronegativity of the nonmetal E determines the trend. As E becomes more electronegative, electron density around the H is withdrawn, and the E—H bond becomes more polar. As a result, the H^+ is released more easily to an O atom of a surrounding water molecule. In aqueous solution, the hydrides of Groups 3A(13) to 5A(15) do not behave as acids, but an increase in acid strength is seen in Groups 6A(16) and 7A(17). Thus, HCl is a stronger acid than H_2S because Cl is more electronegative (EN = 3.0) than S (EN = 2.5). The same relationship holds across each period.

2. *Down a group, nonmetal hydride acid strength increases.* Down a group, E—H bond strength determines the trend. As E becomes larger, the E—H bond becomes longer and weaker, so H^+ comes off more easily.* Thus, the hydrohalic acids increase in strength down the group:

$$HF << HCl < HBr < HI$$

A similar trend in increasing acid strength is seen down Group 6A(16). (The trend in hydrohalic acid strength is not seen in aqueous solution, where HCl,

Electronegativity increases, acidity increases →

Bond strength decreases, acidity increases ↓

6A(16)	7A(17)
H_2O	HF
H_2S	HCl
H_2Se	HBr
H_2Te	HI

Figure 18.11 The effect of atomic and molecular properties on nonmetal hydride acidity. As the electronegativity of the nonmetal (E) bonded to the ionizable proton increases *(left to right)*, the acidity increases. As the length of the E—H bond increases *(top to bottom)*, the bond strength decreases, so the acidity increases. (In water, HCl, HBr, and HI are equally strong, for reasons discussed in Section 18.8.)

---

*Actually, bond energy refers to bond breakage that forms an H atom, whereas acidity refers to bond breakage that forms an H^+ ion, so the two processes are not the same. Nevertheless, the magnitudes of the two types of bond breakage parallel each other.

HBr, and HI are all equally strong; we discuss how this trend is observed in Section 18.8.)

Trends in Acid Strength of Oxoacids

All oxoacids have the acidic hydrogen bound to an oxygen atom, so bond strength (length) is not a factor as it is with the binary nonmetal hydrides. Rather, as you saw in Section 14.7, two factors determine the acid strength of oxoacids: the electronegativity of the central nonmetal (E) and the number of O atoms.

1. *For oxoacids with the **same** number of oxygens around E, acid strength increases with the electronegativity of E.* Consider the hypohalous acids (written here as HOE, where E is a halogen atom). The more electronegative E is, the more electron density it pulls from the O—H bond, so the more polar the O—H bond becomes, and the more easily H^+ is lost (Figure 18.12A). Because electronegativity decreases down the group, we predict that acid strength decreases: HOCl > HOBr > HOI. Our prediction is confirmed by the K_a values:

K_a of HOCl = 2.9×10^{-8} K_a of HOBr = 2.3×10^{-9} K_a of HOI = 2.3×10^{-11}

We also predict (correctly) that in Group 6A(16), H_2SO_4 is stronger than H_2SeO_4; in Group 5A(15), H_3PO_4 is stronger than H_3AsO_4, and so forth.

2. *For oxoacids with **different** numbers of oxygens around a given E, acid strength increases with number of O atoms.* The electronegative O atoms pull electron density away from E, which makes the O—H bond more polar. The more O atoms that are present, the greater the shift in electron density, and the more easily the H^+ ion comes off (Figure 18.12B). Therefore we predict, for instance, that chlorine oxoacids (written here as $HOClO_n$, with n from 0 to 3) increase in strength in the order HOCl < HOClO < $HOClO_2$ < $HOClO_3$. Once again, the K_a values support the prediction:

K_a of HOCl (hypochlorous acid) = 2.9×10^{-8}
K_a of $HClO_2$ (chlorous acid)   = 1.12×10^{-2}
K_a of $HOClO_2$ (chloric acid)   ≈ 1
K_a of $HOClO_3$ (perchloric acid) = $>10^7$

It follows from this that HNO_3 is stronger than HNO_2, that H_2SO_4 is stronger than H_2SO_3, and so forth.

Figure 18.12 The relative strengths of oxoacids. A, Among the hypohalous acids (HOE, where E is a halogen), HOCl is the strongest and HOI the weakest. Because Cl is the most electronegative of these halogen atoms, it withdraws electron density (indicated by thickness of green arrow) from the O—H bond most effectively, making that bond most polar in HOCl (indicated by the relative sizes of the δ symbols). **B,** Among the chlorine oxoacids, the O atoms in $HOClO_3$ pull electron density from the O—H bond, making the bond much more polar than in HOCl.

Acidity of Hydrated Metal Ions

The aqueous solutions of certain metal ions are acidic because the *hydrated* metal ion transfers an H^+ ion to water. Consider a general metal nitrate, $M(NO_3)_n$, as it dissolves in water. The ions separate and become bound to a specific number of surrounding H_2O molecules. The following equation shows the hydration of the cation (M^{n+}) with H_2O molecules; hydration of the anion (NO_3^-) is indicated by (*aq*):

$$M(NO_3)_n(s) + xH_2O(l) \longrightarrow M(H_2O)_x^{n+}(aq) + nNO_3^-(aq)$$

Table 18.7 K_a Values of Some Hydrated Metal Ions at 25°C

Ion	K_a
$Fe^{3+}(aq)$	6×10^{-3}
$Sn^{2+}(aq)$	4×10^{-4}
$Cr^{3+}(aq)$	1×10^{-4}
$Al^{3+}(aq)$	1×10^{-5}
$Be^{2+}(aq)$	4×10^{-6}
$Cu^{2+}(aq)$	3×10^{-8}
$Pb^{2+}(aq)$	3×10^{-8}
$Zn^{2+}(aq)$	1×10^{-9}
$Co^{2+}(aq)$	2×10^{-10}
$Ni^{2+}(aq)$	1×10^{-10}

ACID STRENGTH ↑

If the metal ion, M^{n+}, is *small and highly charged*, it has a high charge density and withdraws sufficient electron density from the O—H bonds of the bound water molecules for a proton to be released. Thus, the hydrated cation, $M(H_2O)_x^{n+}$, acts as a typical Brønsted-Lowry acid. In the process, the bound H_2O molecule that releases the proton becomes a bound OH^- ion:

$$M(H_2O)_x^{n+}(aq) + H_2O(l) \rightleftharpoons M(H_2O)_{x-1}OH^{(n-1)+}(aq) + H_3O^+(aq)$$

Each type of hydrated metal ion that releases a proton has a characteristic K_a value. Table 18.7 shows some common examples.

Aluminum ion, for example, has the small size and high positive charge needed to produce an acidic solution. When an aluminum salt, such as $Al(NO_3)_3$, dissolves in water, the following steps occur:

$$Al(NO_3)_3(s) + 6H_2O(l) \longrightarrow Al(H_2O)_6^{3+}(aq) + 3NO_3^-(aq)$$
[dissolution and hydration]

$$Al(H_2O)_6^{3+}(aq) + H_2O(l) \rightleftharpoons Al(H_2O)_5OH^{2+}(aq) + H_3O^+(aq) \quad \text{[acid dissociation]}$$

Notice the formulas of the hydrated metal ions in the second step. When the H^+ ion is released, the number of bound H_2O molecules decreases by one (from 6 to 5) and the number of bound OH^- ions increases by one (from 0 to 1), which reduces the ion's positive charge by one (from 3 to 2). This process is shown in Figure 18.13.

Figure 18.13 The acidic behavior of the hydrated Al³⁺ ion. When a metal ion enters water, it is hydrated as the solvent bonds to it. If the ion is small and multiply charged, as is the Al³⁺ ion, it pulls sufficient electron density from the O—H groups of attached water to make them more polar, and an H⁺ ion is transferred to a nearby water molecule.

Electron density drawn toward Al³⁺   Nearby H₂O acts as base

$Al(H_2O)_6^{3+}$ H_2O $Al(H_2O)_5OH^{2+}$ H_3O^+

Through its ability to withdraw electron density from the O—H bonds of the bound water molecules, a small, highly charged central metal ion behaves like a central electronegative atom in an oxoacid. Like salts of the Al^{3+} ion, salts of most M^{2+} and M^{3+} ions yield acidic aqueous solutions.

Section Summary

The strength of an acid depends on the ease with which the ionizable proton is released. For binary nonmetal hydrides, acid strength increases across a period, with electronegativity of the nonmetal (E), and down a group, with length of E—H. For oxoacids with the same number of O atoms, acid strength increases with electronegativity of E; for oxoacids with the same E, acid strength increases with number of O atoms. Small, highly charged metal ions are acidic in water because they withdraw electron density from O—H bonds of bound H_2O molecules, releasing an H^+ ion to the solution.

18.7   Acid-Base Properties of Salt Solutions

Up to now you've seen that cations of weak bases (such as NH_4^+) are acidic, anions of weak acids (such as CN^-) are basic, and small, highly charged metal cations (such as Al^{3+}) are acidic. Therefore, when salts containing these ions dissolve in water, the pH of the solution is affected. You can predict the relative acidity of a salt solution from the relative ability of the cation and/or anion to react with water. Let's examine the ionic makeup of salts that yield neutral, acidic, or basic solutions.

Salts That Yield Neutral Solutions

A salt consisting of the anion of a strong acid and the cation of a strong base yields a neutral solution because the ions do not react with water. To see why the ions don't react, consider the dissociation of the parent acid and base. When a strong acid such as HNO_3 dissolves, complete dissociation takes place:

$$HNO_3(l) + H_2O(l) \longrightarrow NO_3^-(aq) + H_3O^+(aq)$$

H_2O is a much stronger base than NO_3^-, so the reaction proceeds essentially to completion. The same argument can be made for any strong acid: *the anion of a strong acid is a much weaker base than water.* Therefore, a strong acid anion is hydrated, but nothing further happens.

Now consider the dissociation of a strong base, such as NaOH:

$$NaOH(s) \xrightarrow{H_2O} Na^+(aq) + OH^-(aq)$$

The Na^+ ion has a relatively large size and low charge and therefore does not bond strongly with the water molecules around it. When Na^+ enters water, it becomes hydrated but nothing further happens. *The cations of all strong bases behave this way.*

The anions of strong acids are the halide ions, except F^-, and those of strong oxoacids, such as NO_3^-, ClO_4^-, and HSO_4^-. The cations of strong bases are those from Group 1A(1) and Ca^{2+}, Sr^{2+}, and Ba^{2+} from Group 2A(2). Salts containing only these ions, such as NaCl and $Ba(NO_3)_2$, *yield neutral solutions because no reaction with water takes place.*

Salts That Yield Acidic Solutions

A salt consisting of the anion of a strong acid and the cation of a weak base yields an acidic solution because the cation acts as a weak acid, and the anion does not react. For example, NH_4Cl produces an acidic solution because the NH_4^+ ion, the cation that forms from the weak base NH_3, is a weak acid, and the Cl^- ion, the anion of a strong acid, does not react:

$$NH_4Cl(s) \xrightarrow{H_2O} NH_4^+(aq) + Cl^-(aq) \qquad \text{[dissolution and hydration]}$$
$$NH_4^+(aq) + H_2O(l) \rightleftharpoons NH_3(aq) + H_3O^+(aq) \qquad \text{[dissociation of weak acid]}$$

As you saw earlier, *small, highly charged metal ions* are another group of cations that yield H_3O^+ in solution. For example, $Fe(NO_3)_3$ produces an acidic solution because the hydrated Fe^{3+} ion acts as a weak acid, whereas the NO_3^- ion, the anion of a strong acid, does not react:

$$Fe(NO_3)_3(s) + 6H_2O(l) \xrightarrow{H_2O} Fe(H_2O)_6^{3+}(aq) + 3NO_3^-(aq)$$
$$\text{[dissolution and hydration]}$$
$$Fe(H_2O)_6^{3+}(aq) + H_2O(l) \rightleftharpoons Fe(H_2O)_5OH^{2+}(aq) + H_3O^+(aq)$$
$$\text{[dissociation of weak acid]}$$

Salts That Yield Basic Solutions

A salt consisting of the anion of a weak acid and the cation of a strong base yields a basic solution in water because the anion acts as a weak base, and the cation does not react. The anion of a weak acid abstracts a proton from water to yield OH^- ion. Sodium acetate, for example, yields a basic solution because the Na^+ ion, the cation of a strong base, does not react with water, and the CH_3COO^- ion, the anion of the weak acid CH_3COOH, acts as a weak base:

$$CH_3COONa(s) \xrightarrow{H_2O} Na^+(aq) + CH_3COO^-(aq) \quad \text{[dissolution and hydration]}$$
$$CH_3COO^-(aq) + H_2O(l) \rightleftharpoons CH_3COOH(aq) + OH^-(aq) \qquad \text{[reaction of weak base]}$$

Table 18.8 The Behavior of Salts in Water

Salt Solution (Examples)	pH	Nature of Ions	Ion That Reacts with Water	
Neutral [NaCl, KBr, Ba(NO$_3$)$_2$]	7.0	Cation of strong base Anion of strong acid	None	
Acidic [NH$_4$Cl, NH$_4$NO$_3$, CH$_3$NH$_3$Br]	<7.0	Cation of weak base Anion of strong acid	Cation	
Acidic [Al(NO$_3$)$_3$, CrCl$_3$, FeBr$_3$]	<7.0	Small, highly charged cation Anion of strong acid	Cation	
Basic [CH$_3$COONa, KF, Na$_2$CO$_3$]	>7.0	Cation of strong base Anion of weak acid	Anion	

Table 18.8 displays the acid-base behavior of the various types of salts in water.

Sample Problem 18.11   Predicting the Relative Acidity of Salt Solutions

PROBLEM Write reactions to predict whether aqueous solutions of the following salts are acidic, basic, or neutral:
(a) Potassium perchlorate, KClO$_4$
(b) Sodium benzoate, C$_6$H$_5$COONa
(c) Chromium trichloride, CrCl$_3$

PLAN We examine the formulas to determine the cations and anions. Depending on the nature of these ions, the solution will be neutral (strong-acid anion and strong-base cation), acidic (weak-base cation and strong-acid anion or highly charged metal cation), or basic (weak-acid anion and strong-base cation).

SOLUTION (a) Neutral. The ions are K$^+$ and ClO$_4^-$. The K$^+$ ion is from the strong base KOH, and the ClO$_4^-$ anion is from the strong acid HClO$_4$. Neither ion reacts with water.

(b) Basic. The ions are Na$^+$ and C$_6$H$_5$COO$^-$. Na$^+$ is the cation of the strong base NaOH and does not react with water. The benzoate ion, C$_6$H$_5$COO$^-$, is from the weak acid benzoic acid, so it reacts to produce OH$^-$ ion:

$$C_6H_5COO^-(aq) + H_2O(l) \rightleftharpoons C_6H_5COOH(aq) + OH^-(aq)$$

(c) Acidic. The ions are Cr^{3+} and Cl$^-$. Cl$^-$ is the anion of the strong acid HCl, so it does not react with water. Cr^{3+} is a small ion with a high positive charge, so the hydrated ion, Cr(H$_2$O)$_6^{3+}$, reacts with water to produce H$_3$O$^+$:

$$Cr(H_2O)_6^{3+}(aq) + H_2O(l) \rightleftharpoons Cr(H_2O)_5OH^{2+}(aq) + H_3O^+(aq)$$

Follow-up Problem 18.11   Write equations to predict whether solutions of the following salts are acidic, basic, or neutral: (a) KClO$_2$; (b) CH$_3$NH$_3$NO$_3$; (c) CsI.

Salts Composed of Weakly Acidic Cations and Weakly Basic Anions

The only salts left to consider are those consisting of a cation that acts as a weak acid *and* an anion that acts as a weak base. In these cases, and there are quite a few, both ions react with water. It makes sense, then, that the overall acidity of the solution will depend on the relative acid strength or base strength of the separated ions, which can be determined by comparing their equilibrium constants.

For example, will an aqueous solution of ammonium hydrogen sulfide, NH_4HS, be acidic or basic? First, we write equations for any reactions that occur between the separated ions and water. Ammonium ion is the conjugate acid of a weak base, so it acts as a weak acid:

$$NH_4^+(aq) + H_2O(l) \rightleftharpoons NH_3(aq) + H_3O^+(aq)$$

Hydrogen sulfide ion is the anion of the weak acid H_2S, so it acts as a weak base:

$$HS^-(aq) + H_2O(l) \rightleftharpoons H_2S(aq) + OH^-(aq)$$

The reaction that goes farther to the right will have the greater influence on the pH of the solution, so we must compare the K_a of NH_4^+ with the K_b of HS^-. Recall that only molecular compounds are listed in K_a and K_b tables, so we have to calculate these values for the ions:

$$K_a \text{ of } NH_4^+ = \frac{K}{K_b \text{ of } NH_3} = \frac{1.0 \times 10^{-14}}{1.76 \times 10^{-5}} = 5.7 \times 10^{-10}$$

$$K_b \text{ of } HS^- = \frac{K_w}{K_{a1} \text{ of } H_2S} = \frac{1.0 \times 10^{-14}}{9 \times 10^{-8}} = 1 \times 10^{-7}$$

The difference in magnitude of the equilibrium constants ($K_b \approx 200 \times K_a$) tells us that the abstraction of a proton from H_2O by HS^- proceeds further than the release of a proton to H_2O by NH_4^+. In other words, since K_b of $HS^- > K_a$ of NH_4^+, the NH_4HS solution is basic.

Sample Problem 18.12   Predicting the Relative Acidity of Salt Solutions from K_a and K_b of the Ions

PROBLEM Determine whether an aqueous solution of iron(III) nitrite, $Fe(NO_2)_3$, is acidic, basic, or neutral.

PLAN The formula consists of the small, highly charged, and therefore weakly acidic, Fe^{3+} cation and the weakly basic NO_2^- anion of the weak acid HNO_2. To determine the relative acidity of the solution, we write equations that show the reactions of the ions with water, and then find K_a and K_b of the ions to see which ion reacts to a greater extent.

SOLUTION Writing the reactions with water:

$$Fe(H_2O)_6^{3+}(aq) + H_2O(l) \rightleftharpoons Fe(H_2O)_5OH^{2+}(aq) + H_3O^+(aq)$$

$$NO_2^-(aq) + H_2O(l) \rightleftharpoons HNO_2(aq) + OH^-(aq)$$

Obtaining K_a and K_b of the ions: From Table 18.7, K_a of $Fe^{3+}(aq) = 6 \times 10^{-3}$. From Table 18.2, we obtain K_a of HNO_2 and solve for K_b of NO_2^-:

$$K_b \text{ of } NO_2^- = \frac{K_w}{K_a \text{ of } HNO_2} = \frac{1.0 \times 10^{-14}}{7.1 \times 10^{-4}} = 1.4 \times 10^{-11}$$

Since K_a of $Fe^{3+} > K_b$ of NO_2^-, the solution is acidic.

Follow-up Problem 18.12   Determine whether solutions of the following salts are acidic, basic, or neutral: **(a)** $Cu(CH_3COO)_2$; **(b)** NH_4F.

Section Summary

Salts that yield a neutral solution consist of ions that do not react with water. Salts that yield an acidic solution contain an unreactive anion and a cation that releases a proton to water. Salts that yield a basic solution contain an unreactive cation and an anion that abstracts a proton from water. If both cation and anion react with water, the ion that reacts to the greater extent (higher K) determines the acidity of the salt solution.

18.8 Generalizing the Brønsted-Lowry Concept: The Leveling Effect

We conclude our focus on the Brønsted-Lowry concept with an important principle that holds for acid-base behavior in any solvent. Notice that, in H_2O, all Brønsted-Lowry acids yield H_3O^+ and all Brønsted-Lowry bases yield OH^-—the ions that form when the solvent autoionizes. In general, *an acid yields the cation and a base yields the anion of solvent autoionization.*

This idea lets us examine a question you may have been wondering about: why are all strong acids and strong bases *equally* strong in water? The answer is that *in water, the strongest acid possible is H_3O^+ and the strongest base possible is OH^-.* The moment we put some gaseous HCl in water, it reacts with the base H_2O and forms H_3O^+. The same holds for HNO_3, H_2SO_4, and any strong acid. All strong acids are equally strong in water because they dissociate *completely* to form H_3O^+. Given that the strong acid is no longer present, we are actually observing the acid strength of H_3O^+.

Similarly, strong bases, such as $Ba(OH)_2$, dissociate completely in water to yield OH^-. Even those that do not contain hydroxide ions in the solid, such as K_2O, do so. The oxide ion, which is a stronger base than OH^-, immediately abstracts a proton from water to form OH^-:

$$2K^+(aq) + O^{2-}(aq) + H_2O(l) \longrightarrow 2K^+(aq) + 2OH^-(aq)$$

No matter what species we try, any acid stronger than H_3O^+ simply donates its proton to H_2O, and any base stronger than OH^- accepts a proton from H_2O. Thus, water exerts a **leveling effect** on any strong acid or base by reacting with it to form the products of water's autoionization. Acting as a base, water levels the strength of all strong acids by making them appear equally strong, and acting as an acid, it levels the strength of all strong bases as well.

To rank strong acids in terms of relative strength, we must dissolve them in a solvent that is a *weaker* base than water, one that accepts their protons less readily. For example, you saw in Figure 18.11 that the hydrohalic acids increase in strength as the halogen becomes larger, as a result of the longer, weaker H—X bond. In water, HF is weaker than the other hydrogen halides, but HCl, HBr, and HI appear equally strong because water causes them to dissociate completely. When we dissolve them in pure acetic acid, however, *the acetic acid acts as the base* and accepts a proton from the acids:

$$\underset{\text{acid}}{HCl(g)} + \underset{\text{base}}{CH_3COOH(l)} \rightleftharpoons \underset{\text{base}}{Cl^-(acet)} + \underset{\text{acid}}{CH_3COOH_2^+(acet)}$$

$$HBr(g) + CH_3COOH(l) \rightleftharpoons Br^-(acet) + CH_3COOH_2^+(acet)$$

$$HI(g) + CH_3COOH(l) \rightleftharpoons I^-(acet) + CH_3COOH_2^+(acet)$$

[The use of (*acet*) instead of (*aq*) indicates solvation by CH_3COOH.] However, since acetic acid is a *weaker base* than water, the three acids protonate it to *different* extents. Measurements show that HI protonates the solvent to a greater extent than HBr, and HBr does so more than HCl; that is, in pure acetic acid, $K_{HI} > K_{HBr} > K_{HCl}$. Therefore, HCl is a weaker acid than HBr, which is weaker than HI. Similarly, the relative strength of strong bases is determined in a solvent that is a weaker acid than H_2O, such as liquid NH_3.

Section Summary

Strong acids (or strong bases) dissociate completely to yield H_3O^+ (or OH^-) in water; in effect, water equalizes (levels) their strengths. Acids that are equally strong in water show differences in strength when dissolved in a solvent that is a weaker base than water, such as acetic acid.

18.9 Electron-Pair Donation and the Lewis Acid-Base Definition

The final acid-base concept we consider was developed by Gilbert N. Lewis, whose contribution to understanding the importance of valence electron pairs in molecular bonding we discussed in Chapter 9. Whereas the Brønsted-Lowry concept focuses on the proton in defining a species as an acid or a base, the Lewis concept highlights the role of the *electron pair*. The **Lewis acid-base definition** holds that

- A *base* is any species that *donates* an electron pair.
- An *acid* is any species that *accepts* an electron pair.

The Lewis definition, like the Brønsted-Lowry definition, requires that a base have an electron pair to donate, so it does not expand the classes of bases. However, *it greatly expands the classes of acids*. Many species, such as CO_2 and Cu^{2+}, that do not contain H in their formula (and thus cannot be Brønsted-Lowry acids) function as Lewis acids by accepting an electron pair in their reactions. Lewis stated his objection to the proton as the defining feature of an acid this way: "To restrict the group of acids to those substances which contain hydrogen interferes as seriously with the systematic understanding of chemistry as would the restriction of the term oxidizing agent to those substances containing oxygen." Moreover, in the Lewis sense, the proton itself functions as an acid because it accepts the electron pair donated by a base:

$$B: + H^+ \rightleftharpoons B-H^+$$

Thus, *all Brønsted-Lowry acids donate the Lewis acid* H^+.

The product of any Lewis acid-base reaction is *called an **adduct**, a single species that contains a new covalent bond:*

$$A + :B \rightleftharpoons A-B \text{ (adduct)}$$

Thus, the Lewis concept broadens the idea of acid-base reactions radically. What to Arrhenius was the formation of H_2O from H^+ and OH^- became, to Brønsted and Lowry, the transfer of a proton from a stronger acid to a stronger base to form a weaker base and weaker acid. To Lewis, the same process became *the donation and acceptance of an electron pair to form a covalent bond in an adduct.*

As we've seen, the key feature of a *Lewis base is a lone pair of electrons to donate*. The key feature of a *Lewis acid is a vacant orbital* (or the ability to rearrange its bonds to form one) to accept that lone pair and form a new bond. A variety of neutral molecules and positively charged ions satisfy this requirement.

Molecules as Lewis Acids

Many neutral molecules function as Lewis acids. In every case, the atom that accepts the electron pair is low in electron density because of either an electron deficiency or a polar multiple bond.

Lewis Acids with Electron-Deficient Atoms   Some molecular Lewis acids contain a central atom that is *electron deficient,* one surrounded by fewer than eight valence electrons. The most important are covalent compounds of the Group 3A(13) elements boron and aluminum. As noted in Chapters 9 and 14, these compounds react vigorously to complete their octet. For example, boron trifluoride accepts an electron pair from ammonia to form a covalent bond in a gaseous Lewis acid-base reaction:

Unexpected solubility behavior is sometimes due to adduct formation. Aluminum chloride, for instance, dissolves freely in relatively nonpolar diethyl ether because of a Lewis acid-base reaction, in which the ether O atom donates an electron pair to Al to form a covalent bond:

This acidic behavior of boron and aluminum halides is put to use in many organic syntheses. For example, toluene, an important solvent and organic reagent, can be made by the action of CH_3Cl on benzene in the presence of $AlCl_3$. The Lewis acid $AlCl_3$ abstracts the Lewis base Cl^- from CH_3Cl to form an adduct that has a reactive CH_3^+ group, which attacks the benzene ring:

$$CH_3Cl \; + \; AlCl_3 \rightleftharpoons [CH_3]^+[Cl{-}AlCl_3]^-$$

base   acid   adduct

$$C_6H_6 \; + \; [CH_3]^+[Cl{-}AlCl_3]^- \rightleftharpoons C_6H_5CH_3 \; + \; AlCl_3 \; + \; HCl$$

benzene   toluene

Lewis Acids with Polar Multiple Bonds   Molecules that contain a polar double bond also function as Lewis acids. As the electron pair on the Lewis base approaches the partially positive end of the double bond, one of the bonds breaks to form the new bond in the adduct. For example, consider the reaction that occurs when SO_2 dissolves in water. The electronegative O atoms in SO_2 withdraw electron density from the central S, so it is partially positive. The oxygen atom of water donates a lone pair to the S, breaking one of the π bonds and forming an S—O bond, and a proton is transferred from water to the O of that bond. The resulting adduct is sulfurous acid and the overall process is

In the formation of carbonates from a metal oxide and carbon dioxide, an analogous reaction occurs in a nonaqueous heterogeneous system. The O^{2-} ion (shown below from CaO) donates an electron pair to the partially positive C in CO_2, a π bond breaks, and the CO_3^{2-} ion forms as the adduct:

Metal Cations as Lewis Acids

Earlier we saw that certain hydrated metal ions act as Brønsted-Lowry acids. In the Lewis sense, the hydration process itself is an acid-base reaction; thus, *any metal ion acts as a Lewis acid when it dissolves in water.* The hydrated cation is the adduct, as lone electron pairs of the O atoms of water form covalent bonds to the positively charged ion:

$$\underset{\text{acid}}{M^{2+}} \quad \underset{\text{base}}{4H_2O(l)} \quad \underset{\text{adduct}}{M(H_2O)_4{}^{2+}(aq)}$$

Ammonia is a stronger Lewis base than water because it displaces H_2O from a hydrated ion when aqueous NH_3 is added:

$$\underset{\text{hydrated adduct}}{Ni(H_2O)_6{}^{2+}(aq)} + \underset{\text{base}}{6NH_3(aq)} \rightleftharpoons \underset{\text{ammoniated adduct}}{Ni(NH_3)_6{}^{2+}(aq)} + 6H_2O(l)$$

We discuss the equilibrium nature of these acid-base reactions in greater detail in Chapter 19, and we investigate the structures of these ions in Chapter 23.

Many essential biomolecules are Lewis adducts with central metal ions. Most often, O and N atoms of organic groups, with their lone pairs, serve as the Lewis base. Chlorophyll is a Lewis adduct of a central Mg^{2+} and the four N atoms of an organic tetrapyrrole ring system (Figure 18.14). Vitamin B_{12} has a similar structure with a central Co^{3+}, as does heme with a central Fe^{2+}. Several other metal ions, such as Zn^{2+}, Mo^{2+}, and Cu^{2+}, are bound at the active sites of enzymes and participate in the catalytic action by virtue of their Lewis acidity.

Sample Problem 18.13   Identifying Lewis Acids and Bases

PROBLEM Identify the Lewis acids and Lewis bases in the following reactions:
(a) $H^+ + OH^- \rightleftharpoons H_2O$
(b) $Cl^- + BCl_3 \rightleftharpoons BCl_4{}^-$
(c) $K^+ + 6H_2O \rightleftharpoons K(H_2O)_6{}^+$
PLAN We examine the formulas to see which species accepts the electron pair (Lewis acid) and which donates it (Lewis base) in forming the adduct.
SOLUTION (a) The H^+ accepted an electron pair from the OH^- in forming a bond. H^+ is the acid and OH^- is the base.
(b) The Cl^- ion has four lone pairs and uses one to form a new bond to the central B. Therefore, BCl_3 is the acid and Cl^- is the base.
(c) The K^+ ion has no valence electrons to provide, so the bond is formed when electron pairs from O atoms of water enter empty orbitals on K^+. Thus, K^+ is the acid and H_2O is the base.
CHECK The Lewis acids (H^+, BCl_3, and K^+) each have an unfilled valence shell that can accept an electron pair from the Lewis bases (OH^-, Cl^-, and H_2O).

Follow-up Problem 18.13   Identify the Lewis acids and Lewis bases in the following reactions:
(a) $OH^- + Al(OH)_3 \rightleftharpoons Al(OH)_4{}^-$
(b) $SO_3 + H_2O \rightleftharpoons H_2SO_4$
(c) $Co^{3+} + 6NH_3 \rightleftharpoons Co(NH_3)_6{}^{3+}$

Figure 18.14 The Mg^{2+} ion as a Lewis acid in the chlorophyll molecule. Many biomolecules contain metal ions that act as Lewis acids. In chlorophyll, Mg^{2+} accepts electron pairs from surrounding N atoms that are part of the large organic portion of the molecule.

An Overview of Acid-Base Definitions

By looking closely at the essential chemical change involved, chemists can see a common theme in reactions as diverse as the way a standardized base is used to analyze an unknown fatty acid, or the way baking soda functions in making bread, or even the way oxygen binds to hemoglobin in a blood cell. From this wider perspective, the diversity of reactions takes on more unity. Let's stand back and survey the scope of the three acid-base definitions and see how they fit together.

The *classical (Arrhenius) definition*, the first attempt at observing acids and bases on the molecular level, is the most limited and narrow of the three definitions. It applies only to species that contain H or OH groups in their structure, which are released as ions when the species dissolve in water. Since relatively few species have these prerequisites, Arrhenius acid-base reactions are relatively few in number, and all such reactions result in formation of H_2O.

The *Brønsted-Lowry definition* is more general, seeing acid-base reactions as proton transfer processes and eliminating the requirement that they occur in water. Whereas a Brønsted-Lowry acid still must have an H, like an Arrhenius acid, a Brønsted-Lowry base is defined as any species with an electron pair available to accept the transferred proton. This definition includes a great many more classes of base. Furthermore, it defines the acid-base reaction in terms of conjugate acid-base pairs with an acid and a base on both sides of the reaction. The system reaches an equilibrium state based on the relative strengths of the acid, the base, and their conjugates.

The *Lewis definition* has the widest scope of the three. The defining event of an acid-base reaction is the donation and acceptance of an electron pair to form a new covalent bond. Lewis bases still must have an electron pair to donate, but Lewis acids—electron-pair acceptors—can be very different from the species encompassed by the other two definitions, including electron-deficient compounds, compounds with polar double bonds, metal ions, and the proton itself.

Section Summary

The Lewis acid-base definition focuses on the donation or acceptance of an electron pair to form a new covalent bond in an adduct, the product of an acid-base reaction. Lewis bases donate the electron pair, and Lewis acids accept it. Thus, many non–H-containing species are Lewis acids. Molecules with polar double bonds act as Lewis acids, as do those with electron-deficient atoms. Metal ions act as Lewis acids when they dissolve in water, which acts as a Lewis base, to form the adduct, a hydrated cation. Many metal ions function as Lewis acids in biomolecules.

Chapter Perspective

In this chapter, we extended the principles of equilibrium to acids and bases. We also investigated one direction in which the science of chemistry matured, as narrow definitions of acids and bases progressively widened to encompass different species, physical states, solvent systems, and reaction types. Acids and bases, by whatever definition, are an extremely important group of substances. In Chapter 19, we continue our discussion of these systems and apply many of the ideas developed here to other aqueous equilibria.

The following learning objectives, with section and/or sample problem (SP) numbers in parentheses, can help focus your study:

Understand These Concepts

1. Why the proton exists bound to a water molecule, as H_3O^+, in all aqueous acid-base reactions (Section 18.1)
2. The classical (Arrhenius) definitions of an acid and a base (Section 18.1)
3. Why all reactions of a strong acid and a strong base have the same ΔH^0_{rxn} (Section 18.1)
4. How the strength of an acid (or base) relates to the extent of its dissociation into ions in water (Section 18.1)
5. How relative acid strength is expressed by the acid-dissociation constant K_a (Section 18.1)
6. Why water is a very weak electrolyte and how its autoionization is expressed by K_w (Section 18.2)
7. Why $[H_3O^+]$ is inversely related to $[OH^-]$ in any aqueous solution (Section 18.2)
8. How the relative magnitudes of $[H_3O^+]$ and $[OH^-]$ define whether a solution is acidic, basic, or neutral (Section 18.2)
9. The Brønsted-Lowry definitions of an acid and a base and how an acid-base reaction is a proton transfer process (Section 18.3)
10. How water acts as a base (or as an acid) when an acid (or a base) dissolves in it (Section 18.3)
11. How a conjugate acid-base pair differs by a proton (Section 18.3)
12. How a Brønsted-Lowry acid-base reaction consists of two conjugate acid-base pairs (Section 18.3)
13. Why a stronger acid and base react ($K_c > 1$) to form a weaker base and acid (Section 18.3)
14. How percent dissociation of a weak acid increases as its concentration decreases (Section 18.4)
15. How a polyprotic acid dissociates in two or more steps and why only the first step supplies significant $[H_3O^+]$ (Section 18.4)
16. How weak bases in water accept a proton rather than dissociate; the meaning of K_b and pK_b (Section 18.5)
17. How amines and weak-acid anions act as weak bases in water (Section 18.5)
18. Why relative concentrations of HA and A^- determine the acidity of their solution (Section 18.5)
19. The relationship of the K_a and K_b of a conjugate acid-base pair to K_w (Section 18.5)
20. The effects of electronegativity, bond polarity, and bond energy on acid strength (Section 18.6)
21. Why aqueous solutions of small, highly charged metal ions are acidic (Section 18.6)
22. The various combinations of cations and anions that lead to acidic, basic, or neutral salt solutions (Section 18.7)
23. Why the strengths of strong acids are leveled in water but differentiated in a less basic solvent (Section 18.8)
24. The Lewis definitions of an acid and a base and how a Lewis acid-base reaction is the donation and acceptance of an electron pair to form a covalent bond (Section 18.9)
25. How Group 3A(13) halides, molecules with polar multiple bonds, and metal cations act as Lewis acids (Section 18.9)

Master These Skills

1. Classifying strong and weak acids and bases from their formulas (SP 18.1)
2. Using K_w to calculate $[H_3O^+]$ and $[OH^-]$ in an aqueous solution (SP 18.2)
3. Using p-scales to express $[H_3O^+]$, $[OH^-]$, and K (Section 18.2)
4. Interconverting pH, pOH, $[H_3O^+]$, and $[OH^-]$ (SP 18.3)
5. Identifying conjugate acid-base pairs (SP 18.4)
6. Using relative acid strengths to predict the net direction of an acid-base reaction (SP 18.5)
7. Calculating K_a from pH (SP 18.6)
8. Calculating $[H_3O^+]$ (and, thus, pH) from K_a and $[HA]_{init}$ (SP 18.7)
9. Applying the quadratic equation to find concentrations (Follow-up to SP 18.7)
10. Calculating the percent dissociation of a weak acid (Section 18.4)
11. Calculating $[H_3O^+]$ and other concentrations for a polyprotic acid (SP 18.8)
12. Calculating pH from K_b and $[B]_{init}$ (SP 18.9)
13. Finding K_b of A^- from K_a of HA and K_w (Section 18.5 and SP 18.10)
14. Calculating pH from K_b of A^- and $[A^-]_{init}$ (SP 18.10)
15. Predicting the relative acid strength of nonmetal hydrides and oxoacids (Section 18.6)
16. Predicting the relative acidity of a salt solution from the nature of the cation and anion (SPs 18.11 and 18.12)
17. Identifying Lewis acid, base, and adduct (SP 18.13)

For Review and Reference

Key Terms

Section 18.1
hydronium ion, H_3O^+
classical (Arrhenius) acid-base definition
neutralization
acid-dissociation (acid-ionization) constant (K_a)

Section 18.2
autoionization
ion-product constant for water (K_w)
pH
acid-base indicator

Section 18.3
Brønsted-Lowry acid-base definition
proton donor
proton acceptor
conjugate acid-base pair

Section 18.4
polyprotic acid

Section 18.5
base-dissociation constant (K_b)

Section 18.8
leveling effect

Section 18.9
Lewis acid-base definition
adduct

Key Equations and Relationships

18.1 Defining the acid-dissociation constant (p. 761):

$$K_a = \frac{[H_3O^+][A^-]}{[HA]}$$

18.2 Defining the ion-product constant for water (p. 764):
$$K_w = [H_3O^+][OH^-] = 1.0 \times 10^{-14} \text{ (at 25°C)}$$

18.3 Defining pH (p. 765):

$$pH = -\log [H_3O^+]$$

18.4 Relating pK_w to pH and pOH (p. 766):

$$pK_w = pH + pOH = 14.00 \text{ (at 25°C)}$$

18.5 Finding the percent dissociation of HA (p. 776):

$$\text{Percent HA dissociated} = \frac{[HA]_{dissoc}}{[HA]_{init}} \times 100$$

18.6 Defining the base-dissociation constant (p. 779):

$$K_b = \frac{[BH^+][OH^-]}{[B]}$$

18.7 Expressing the relationship among K_a, K_b, and K_w (p. 782):

$$K_a \times K_b = K_w$$

Highlighted Figures and Tables

These figures (F) and tables (T) provide a quick review of key ideas. Entries in color contain frequently used data.
F18.3 Extent of dissociation for strong and weak acids (p. 760)
T18.2 K_a of some monoprotic acids at 25°C (p. 762)
F18.6 Relations among $[H_3O^+]$, pH, $[OH^-]$, and pOH (p. 767)
F18.8 Proton transfer in acid-base reactions (p. 769)

T18.4 Some conjugate acid-base pairs (p. 770)
F18.9 Strengths of conjugate acid-base pairs (p. 771)
T18.5 K_a of some polyprotic acids at 25°C (p. 777)
T18.6 K_b of some amines at 25°C (p. 780)
F18.11 Trends in nonmetal hydride acidity (p. 784)
F18.12 Relative strengths of oxoacids (p. 785)
T18.7 K_a of hydrated metal ions at 25°C (p. 786)
T18.8 The behavior of salts in water (p. 788)

Answers to Follow-up Problems

18.1 (a) $HClO_3$; (b) HCl; (c) NaOH

18.2 $[H_3O^+] = \dfrac{1.0 \times 10^{-14}}{6.7 \times 10^{-2}} = 1.5 \times 10^{-13}\ M$; basic

18.3 $pOH = 14.00 - 9.52 = 4.48$
$[H_3O^+] = 10^{-9.52} = 3.0 \times 10^{-10}\ M$
$[OH^-] = \dfrac{1.0 \times 10^{-14}}{3.0 \times 10^{-10}} = 3.3 \times 10^{-5}\ M$

18.4 (a) CH_3COOH/CH_3COO^- and H_3O^+/H_2O
(b) H_2O/OH^- and HF/F^-

18.5 (a) $NH_3(g) + H_2O(l) \rightleftharpoons NH_4^+(aq) + OH^-(aq)$
(b) $NH_3(g) + H_3O^+(aq; \text{from HCl}) \longrightarrow NH_4^+(aq) + H_2O(l)$
(c) $NH_4^+(aq) + OH^-(aq; \text{from NaOH}) \longrightarrow NH_3(g) + H_2O(l)$

18.6 $NH_4^+(aq) + H_2O(l) \rightleftharpoons NH_3(aq) + H_3O^+(aq)$
$[H_3O^+] = 10^{-pH} = 10^{-5.0} = 1 \times 10^{-5}\ M = [NH_3]$

From reaction table, $K_a = \dfrac{[NH_3][H_3O^+]}{[NH_4^+]} = \dfrac{(x)(x)}{0.2 - x}$

$$\approx \frac{(1 \times 10^{-5})^2}{0.2} = 5 \times 10^{-10}$$

18.7 $K_a = \dfrac{[H_3O^+][OCN^-]}{[HOCN]} = \dfrac{(x)(x)}{0.10 - x} = 3.5 \times 10^{-4}$

Since $\dfrac{[HOCN]_{init}}{K_a} = \dfrac{0.10}{3.5 \times 10^{-4}} = 286 < 400$, must solve

quadratic equation: $x^2 + (3.5 \times 10^{-4})x - 3.5 \times 10^{-5} = 0$
$x = [H_3O^+] = 5.7 \times 10^{-3}\ M$; pH = 2.24

18.8 $K_{a1} = \dfrac{[HC_2O_4^-][H_3O^+]}{[H_2C_2O_4]} = \dfrac{x^2}{0.150 - x} = 5.6 \times 10^{-2}$

Since $\dfrac{[H_2C_2O_4]_{init}}{K_{a1}} < 400$, must solve quadratic equation:

$x^2 + (5.6 \times 10^{-2})x - (8.4 \times 10^{-3}) = 0$

$x = [H_3O^+] = 0.068\ M$; pH = 1.17

$x = [HC_2O_4^-] = 0.068\ M$; $[H_2C_2O_4] = 0.150\ M - x = 0.082\ M$

$[C_2O_4^{2-}] = \dfrac{K_{a2} \times [HC_2O_4^-]}{[H_3O^+]} = \dfrac{(5.4 \times 10^{-5})(0.068)}{0.068}$

$= 5.4 \times 10^{-5}\ M$

18.9 $K_b = \dfrac{[C_5H_5NH^+][OH^-]}{[C_5H_5N]} = 10^{-8.77} = 1.7 \times 10^{-9}$

Assuming 0.10 M $x \approx 0.10\ M$, $K_b = 1.7 \times 10^{-9} \approx \dfrac{(x)(x)}{0.10}$;

$x = [OH^-] \approx 1.3 \times 10^{-5}\ M$; $[H_3O^+] = 7.7 \times 10^{-10}\ M$; pH = 9.11

18.10 K_b of $ClO^- = \dfrac{K_w}{K_a \text{ of HClO}} = \dfrac{1.0 \times 10^{-14}}{2.9 \times 10^{-8}} = 3.4 \times 10^{-7}$

Assuming 0.20 $M - x \approx 0.20\ M$,

$K_b = 3.4 \times 10^{-7} = \dfrac{[HClO][OH^-]}{[ClO^-]} \approx \dfrac{x^2}{0.20}$;

$x = [OH^-] \approx 2.6 \times 10^{-4}\ M$; $[H_3O^+] = 3.8 \times 10^{-11}\ M$; pH = 10.42

18.11 (a) Basic:

$ClO_2^-(aq) + H_2O(l) \rightleftharpoons HClO_2(aq) + OH^-(aq)$

K^+ is from strong base KOH.

(b) Acidic:

$CH_3NH_3^+(aq) + H_2O(l) \rightleftharpoons CH_3NH_2(aq) + H_3O^+(aq)$

NO_3^- is from strong acid HNO_3.

(c) Neutral: Cs^+ is from strong base CsOH; I^- is from strong acid HI.

18.12 (a) K_a of $Cu^{2+} = 3 \times 10^{-8}$;

K_b of $CH_3COO^- = \dfrac{K_w}{K_a \text{ of } CH_3COOH} = 5.6 \times 10^{-10}$

Since $K_a > K_b$, $Cu(CH_3COO)_2(aq)$ is acidic.

(b) K_a of $NH_4^+ = \dfrac{K_w}{K_b \text{ of } NH_3} = 5.7 \times 10^{-10}$;

K_b of $F^- = \dfrac{K_w}{K_a \text{ of HF}} = 1.5 \times 10^{-11}$;

since $K_a > K_b$, $NH_4F(aq)$ is acidic.

18.13 (a) OH^- is the Lewis base; $Al(OH)_3$ is the Lewis acid.

(b) H_2O is the Lewis base; SO_3 is the Lewis acid.

(c) NH_3 is the Lewis base; Co^{3+} is the Lewis acid.

Problems

Problems with a **colored** number are answered at the back of the text. Problem sections match the text and provide the number(s) of relevant sample problems. Most offer concept review questions, skill-building exercises (written in similar pairs), and problems in a relevant context. Following these are comprehensive problems based on material from any section and/or previous chapter.

[Note: Unless stated otherwise, all problems refer to aqueous solutions at 298 K (25°C).]

Acids and Bases in Water

(Sample Problem 18.1)

■ Concept Review Questions

18.1 Describe the role of water in the classical (Arrhenius) acid-base definition.

18.2 What characteristics do all Arrhenius acids have in common? What characteristics do all Arrhenius bases have in common? Explain neutralization in terms of the Arrhenius acid-base definition. What quantitative finding led Arrhenius to propose this idea of neutralization?

18.3 Why is the Arrhenius acid-base definition considered too limited? Give an example of a case in which the Arrhenius definition does not apply.

18.4 What is meant by the words "strong" and "weak" in terms of acids and bases? Weak acids have K_a values that vary over more than 10 orders of magnitude. What do they have in common that classifies them as "weak"?

■ Skill-Building Exercises (paired)

18.5 Which of the following are Arrhenius acids?
(a) H_2O (b) $Ca(OH)_2$ (c) H_3PO_3 (d) HI

18.6 Which of the following are Arrhenius acids?
(a) $NaHSO_4$ (b) CH_4 (c) NaH (d) H_3N

18.7 Which of the following are Arrhenius bases?
(a) H_3AsO_4 (b) $Ba(OH)_2$ (c) HClO (d) KOH

18.8 Which of the following are Arrhenius bases?
(a) CH_3COOH (b) HOH (c) CH_3OH (d) H_2NNH_2

18.9 Write the K_a expression for each of the following:
(a) HCN (b) HCO_3^- (c) HCOOH

18.10 Write the K_a expression for each of the following:
(a) $CH_3NH_3^+$ (b) HClO (c) H_2S

18.11 Write the K_a expression for each of the following:
(a) HNO_2 (b) CH_3COOH (c) $HBrO_2$

18.12 Write the K_a expression for each of the following:
(a) $H_2PO_4^-$ (b) H_3PO_2 (c) HSO_4^-

18.13 Use Table 18.2 to rank the following in order of *increasing* acid strength: HIO_3, HI, CH_3COOH, HF.

18.14 Use Table 18.2 to rank the following in order of *decreasing* acid strength: HClO, HCl, HCN, HNO_2.

18.15 Classify each of the following as a strong or weak acid or base: (a) H_3AsO_4; (b) $Sr(OH)_2$; (c) HIO; (d) $HClO_4$.

18.16 Classify each of the following as a strong or weak acid or base: (a) CH_3NH_2; (b) K_2O; (c) HI; (d) HCOOH.

18.17 Classify each of the following as a strong or weak acid or base: (a) RbOH; (b) HBr; (c) H_2Te; (d) HClO.

18.18 Classify each of the following as a strong or weak acid or base: (a) $HOCH_2CH_2NH_2$; (b) H_2SeO_4; (c) HS^-; (d) $B(OH)_3$.

Autoionization of Water and the pH Scale
(Sample Problems 18.2 and 18.3)

■ Concept Review Questions

18.19 What is an autoionization reaction? Write equations for the autoionization reactions of H_2O and of H_2SO_4.

18.20 What is the difference between K_c and K_w for the autoionization reaction of water?

18.21 (a) What is the change in pH when $[OH^-]$ increases by a factor of 10?
(b) What is the change in $[H_3O^+]$ when the pH decreases by two units?

18.22 Which of the following solutions has the higher pH? Explain.
(a) A 0.1 M solution of an acid with $K_a = 1 \times 10^{-4}$ or one with $K_a = 4 \times 10^{-5}$
(b) A 0.1 M solution of an acid with $pK_a = 3.0$ or one with $pK_a = 3.5$
(c) A 0.1 M solution of a weak acid or a 0.01 M solution of the same acid
(d) A 0.1 M solution of a weak acid or a 0.1 M solution of a strong acid
(e) A 0.1 M solution of an acid or a 0.1 M solution of a base
(f) A solution of pOH 6.0 or one of pOH 8.0

■ Skill-Building Exercises (paired)

18.23 (a) What is the pH of 0.0111 M NaOH? Is the solution neutral, acidic, or basic?
(b) What is the pOH of 1.23×10^{-3} M HCl? Is the solution neutral, acidic, or basic?

18.24 (a) What is the pH of 0.0333 M HNO_3? Is the solution neutral, acidic, or basic?
(b) What is the pOH of 0.0347 M KOH? Is the solution neutral, acidic, or basic?

18.25 (a) What is the pH of 5.04×10^{-3} M HI? Is the solution neutral, acidic, or basic?
(b) What is the pOH of 2.55 M $Ba(OH)_2$? Is the solution neutral, acidic, or basic?

18.26 (a) What is the pH of 7.52×10^{-4} M CsOH? Is the solution neutral, acidic, or basic?
(b) What is the pOH of 1.59×10^{-3} M $HClO_4$? Is the solution neutral, acidic, or basic?

18.27 (a) What are $[H_3O^+]$, $[OH^-]$, and pOH in a solution of pH 9.78?
(b) What are $[H_3O^+]$, $[OH^-]$, and pH in a solution of pOH 10.43?

18.28 (a) What are $[H_3O^+]$, $[OH^-]$, and pOH in a solution of pH 3.47?
(b) What are $[H_3O^+]$, $[OH^-]$, and pH in a solution of pOH 4.33?

18.29 (a) What are $[H_3O^+]$, $[OH^-]$, and pOH in a solution of pH 2.77?
(b) What are $[H_3O^+]$, $[OH^-]$, and pH in a solution of pOH 5.18?

18.30 (a) What are $[H_3O^+]$, $[OH^-]$, and pOH in a solution of pH 8.97?
(b) What are $[H_3O^+]$, $[OH^-]$, and pH in a solution of pOH 11.27?

18.31 How many moles of H_3O^+ or OH^- must you add per liter of HA solution to adjust its pH from 3.25 to 3.65? Assume a negligible volume change.

18.32 How many moles of H_3O^+ or OH^- must you add per liter of HA solution to adjust its pH from 9.33 to 9.07? Assume a negligible volume change.

18.33 How many moles of H_3O^+ or OH^- must you add to 6.5 L of HA solution to adjust its pH from 4.82 to 5.22? Assume a negligible volume change.

18.34 How many moles of H_3O^+ or OH^- must you add to 87.5 mL of HA solution to adjust its pH from 8.92 to 6.33? Assume a negligible volume change.

■ Problems in Context

18.35 Although the text asserts that water is almost nonconducting, parents commonly warn their children of the danger of swimming in a pool or lake during a lightning storm. Explain this apparent contradiction.

18.36 Like any equilibrium constant, K_w changes with temperature.
(a) If autoionization is an endothermic process, does K_w increase or decrease at higher T? Explain with a reaction that includes heat as reactant or product.
(b) In many medical applications, the value of K_w at 37°C (body temperature) may be more appropriate than the 25°C value of 1.0×10^{-14}. The pH of pure water at 37°C is 6.80. Calculate K_w, pOH, and $[OH^-]$ at this temperature.

Proton Transfer and the Brønsted-Lowry Acid-Base Definition
(Sample Problems 18.4 and 18.5)

■ Concept Review Questions

18.37 How do the Arrhenius and Brønsted-Lowry definitions of an acid and a base differ? How are they similar? Name two Brønsted-Lowry bases that are not considered Arrhenius bases. Can you do the same for acids? Explain.

18.38 What is a conjugate acid-base pair? What is the relationship between the two members of the pair?

18.39 A Brønsted-Lowry acid-base reaction proceeds in the net direction by which a stronger acid and stronger base form a weaker acid and weaker base. Explain.

18.40 What is an amphoteric species? Name one and write balanced equations that show why it is amphoteric.

■ Skill-Building Exercises (paired)

18.41 Write balanced equations and K_a expressions for these Brønsted-Lowry acids in water:
(a) H_3PO_4 (b) C_6H_5COOH (c) HSO_4^-

18.42 Write balanced equations and K_a expressions for these Brønsted-Lowry acids in water:
(a) HCOOH   (b) $HClO_3$ (c) $H_2AsO_4^-$

18.43 Give the formula of the conjugate base of each of the following: (a) HCl; (b) H_2CO_3; (c) H_2O.

18.44 Give the formula of the conjugate base of each of the following: (a) HPO_4^{2-}; (b) NH_4^+; (c) HS^-.

18.45 Give the formula of the conjugate acid of each of the following: (a) NH_3; (b) NH_2^-; (c) nicotine, $C_{10}H_{14}N_2$.

18.46 Give the formula of the conjugate acid of each of the following: (a) O^{2-}; (b) SO_4^{2-}; (c) H_2O.

18.47 In each of the following equations, label the acids, bases, and conjugate acid-base pairs:
(a) $HCl + H_2O \rightleftharpoons Cl^- + H_3O^+$
(b) $HClO_4 + H_2SO_4 \rightleftharpoons ClO_4^- + H_3SO_4^+$
(c) $HPO_4^{2-} + H_2SO_4 \rightleftharpoons H_2PO_4^- + HSO_4^-$

18.48 In each of the following equations, label the acids, bases, and conjugate acid-base pairs:
(a) $NH_3 + HNO_3 \rightleftharpoons NH_4^+ + NO_3^-$
(b) $O^{2-} + H_2O \rightleftharpoons OH^- + OH^-$
(c) $NH_4^+ + BrO_3^- \rightleftharpoons NH_3 + HBrO_3$

18.49 In each of the following equations, label the acids, bases, and conjugate acid-base pairs:
(a) $NH_3 + H_3PO_4 \rightleftharpoons NH_4^+ + H_2PO_4$
(b) $CH_3O^- + NH_3 \rightleftharpoons CH_3OH + NH_2^-$
(c) $HPO_4^{2-} + HSO_4^- \rightleftharpoons H_2PO_4^- + SO_4^{2-}$

18.50 In each of the following equations, label the acids, bases, and conjugate acid-base pairs:
(a) $NH_4^+ + CN^- \rightleftharpoons NH_3 + HCN$
(b) $H_2O + HS^- \rightleftharpoons OH^- + H_2S$
(c) $HSO_3^- + CH_3NH_2 \rightleftharpoons SO_3^{2-} + CH_3NH_3^+$

18.51 Write balanced net-ionic equations for the following reactions and label the conjugate acid-base pairs:
(a) $NaOH(aq) + NaH_2PO_4(aq) \rightleftharpoons H_2O(l) + Na_2HPO_4(aq)$
(b) $KHSO_4(aq) + K_2CO_3(aq) \rightleftharpoons K_2SO_4(aq) + KHCO_3(aq)$

18.52 Write balanced net-ionic equations for the following reactions and label the conjugate acid-base pairs:
(a) $HNO_3(aq) + Li_2CO_3(aq) \rightleftharpoons LiNO_3(aq) + LiHCO_3(aq)$
(b) $2NH_4Cl(aq) + Ba(OH)_2(aq) \rightleftharpoons$
$$2H_2O(l) + BaCl_2(aq) + 2NH_3(aq)$$

18.53 The following aqueous species constitute two conjugate acid-base pairs. Use them to write one acid-base reaction with $K_c > 1$ and another with $K_c < 1$: HS^-, Cl^-, HCl, and H_2S.

18.54 The following aqueous species constitute two conjugate acid-base pairs. Use them to write one acid-base reaction with $K_c > 1$ and another with $K_c < 1$: NO_3^-, F^-, HF, and HNO_3.

18.55 Use Figure 18.9 to determine which reactions have $K_c > 1$:
(a) $HCl + NH_3 \rightleftharpoons NH_4^+ + Cl^-$
(b) $H_2SO_3 + NH_3 \rightleftharpoons HSO_3^- + NH_4^+$

18.56 Use Figure 18.9 to determine which reactions have $K_c > 1$:
(a) $OH^- + HS^- \rightleftharpoons H_2O + S^{2-}$
(b) $HCN + HCO_3^- \rightleftharpoons H_2CO_3 + CN^-$

18.57 Use Figure 18.9 to determine which reactions have $K_c < 1$:
(a) $NH_4^+ + HPO_4^{2-} \rightleftharpoons NH_3 + H_2PO_4^-$
(b) $HSO_3^- + HS^- \rightleftharpoons H_2SO_3 + S^{2-}$

18.58 Use Figure 18.9 to determine which reactions have $K_c < 1$:

(a) $H_2PO_4^- + F^- \rightleftharpoons HPO_4^{2-} + HF$
(b) $CH_3COO^- + HSO_4^- \rightleftharpoons CH_3COOH + SO_4^{2-}$

Solving Problems Involving Weak-Acid Equilibria
(Sample Problems 18.6 to 18.8)

■ Concept Review Questions

18.59 In each of the following cases, would you expect the concentration of acid before and after dissociation to be nearly the same or very different? Explain your reasoning.
(a) A concentrated solution of a strong acid
(b) A concentrated solution of a weak acid
(c) A dilute solution of a weak acid
(d) A dilute solution of a strong acid

18.60 A sample of 0.0001 M HCl has close to the same $[H_3O^+]$ as a sample of 0.1 M CH_3COOH. Are acetic acid and hydrochloric acid equally strong in these samples? Explain.

18.61 In which of the following solutions will $[H_3O^+]$ be approximately equal to $[CH_3COO^-]$ (a) 0.1 M CH_3COOH; (b) 1×10^{-7} M CH_3COOH; (c) a solution containing both 0.1 M CH_3COOH and 0.1 M CH_3COONa? Explain.

18.62 Why do successive acid-dissociation constants decrease in all polyprotic acids?

■ Skill-Building Exercises *(paired)*

18.63 A 0.15 M solution of butanoic acid, $CH_3CH_2CH_2COOH$, contains 1.51×10^{-3} M H_3O^+. What is the K_a of butanoic acid?

18.64 A 0.035 M solution of a weak acid (HA) has a pH of 4.88. What is the K_a of the acid?

18.65 Nitrous acid, HNO_2, has a K_a of 7.1×10^{-4}. What are $[H_3O^+]$, $[NO_2^-]$, and $[OH^-]$ in 0.50 M HNO_2?

18.66 Hydrofluoric acid, HF, has a K_a of 6.8×10^{-4}. What are $[H_3O^+]$, $[F^-]$, and $[OH^-]$ in 0.75 M HF?

18.67 Chloroacetic acid, $ClCH_2COOH$, has a pK_a of 2.87. What are $[H_3O^+]$, pH, $[ClCH_2COO^-]$, and $[ClCH_2COOH]$ in 1.05 M $ClCH_2COOH$?

18.68 Hypochlorous acid, HClO, has a pK_a of 7.54. What are $[H_3O^+]$, pH, $[ClO^-]$, and $[HClO]$ in 0.115 M HClO?

18.69 A 0.25 M solution of a weak acid is 3.0% dissociated.
(a) Calculate the $[H_3O^+]$, pH, $[OH^-]$, and pOH of the solution.
(b) Calculate K_a of the acid.

18.70 A 0.735 M solution of a weak acid is 12.5% dissociated.
(a) Calculate the $[H_3O^+]$, pH, $[OH^-]$, and pOH of the solution.
(b) Calculate K_a of the acid.

18.71 A 0.250-mol sample of HX is dissolved in enough H_2O to form 655 mL of solution. If the pH of the solution is 3.44, what is the K_a of HX?

18.72 A 4.85×10^{-3} mol sample of HY is dissolved in enough H_2O to form 0.095 L of solution. If the pH of the solution is 2.68, what is the K_a of HY?

18.73 The weak acid HZ has a K_a of 1.55×10^{-4}.
(a) Calculate the pH of 0.075 M HZ.
(b) Calculate the pOH of 0.045 M HZ.

18.74 The weak acid HQ has a pK_a of 4.89.
(a) Calculate the $[H_3O^+]$ of 3.5×10^{-2} M HQ.
(b) Calculate the $[OH^-]$ of 0.65 M HQ.

18.75 (a) Calculate the pH of 0.175 M HY, if $K_a = 1.00 \times 10^{-4}$.
(b) Calculate the pOH of 0.175 M HX, if $K_a = 1.00 \times 10^{-2}$.
18.76 (a) Calculate the pH of 0.553 M KHCO$_3$; K_a of
HCO$_3^-$ = 4.7×10^{-11}.
(b) Calculate the pOH of 0.044 M HIO$_3$; K_a of HIO$_3$ = 0.16.

18.77 Use Table 18.2 to calculate the percent dissociation of
0.25 M benzoic acid, C$_6$H$_5$COOH.
18.78 Use Table 18.2 to calculate the percent dissociation of
0.050 M CH$_3$COOH.

18.79 Use Table 18.5 to calculate [H$_2$S], [HS$^-$], [S^{2-}],
[H$_3$O$^+$], pH, [OH$^-$], and pOH in a 0.10 M solution of the
diprotic acid hydrosulfuric acid.
18.80 Use Table 18.5 to calculate [H$_2$C$_2$O$_4$], [HC$_2$O$_4^-$],
[C$_2$O$_4^{2-}$], [H$_3$O$^+$], pH, [OH$^-$], and pOH in a 0.200 M solution of the diprotic acid oxalic acid.

■ **Problems in Context**
18.81 Acetylsalicylic acid (aspirin), HC$_9$H$_7$O$_4$, is the most
widely used pain reliever and fever reducer in the world.
Determine the pH of a 0.018 M aqueous solution of aspirin;
$K_a = 3.2 \times 10^{-4}$.
18.82 Formic acid, HCOOH, the simplest carboxylic acid, has
many uses in the textile and rubber industries. It is an extremely caustic liquid that is secreted as a defense by many
species of ants (family *Formicidae*). Calculate the percent
dissociation of 0.50 M HCOOH.

Weak Bases and Their Relation to Weak Acids
(Sample Problems 18.9 and 18.10)

■ **Concept Review Questions**
18.83 What is the essential structural feature of all Brønsted-Lowry bases? How does this feature function in an acid-
base reaction?
18.84 Why are most anions basic in H$_2$O? Give formulas of
four anions that are not basic.
18.85 Except for the Na$^+$ spectator ion and neglecting H$_2$O,
aqueous solutions of CH$_3$COOH and CH$_3$COONa contain the
same species.
(a) What are the species?
(b) Why is 0.1 M CH$_3$COOH acidic and 0.1 M CH$_3$COONa
basic?

■ **Skill-Building Exercises (paired)**
18.86 Write balanced equations and K_b expressions for these
Brønsted-Lowry bases in water:
(a) pyridine, C$_5$H$_5$N   (b) CO$_3^{2-}$
18.87 Write balanced equations and K_b expressions for these
Brønsted-Lowry bases in water:
(a) benzoate ion, C$_6$H$_5$COO$^-$ (b) (CH$_3$)$_3$N

18.88 Write balanced equations and K_b expressions for these
Brønsted-Lowry bases in water:
(a) hydroxylamine, HO—NH$_2$ (b) HPO$_4^{2-}$
18.89 Write balanced equations and K_b expressions for these
Brønsted-Lowry bases in water:
(a) guanidine, (H$_2$N)$_2$C═NH (the doubly bonded N is the
most basic)
(b) acetylide ion, HC≡C$^-$

18.90 What is the pH of 0.050 M dimethylamine?
18.91 What is the pH of 0.12 M diethylamine?

18.92 What is the pH of 0.15 M ethanolamine?
18.93 What is the pH of 0.26 M aniline?

18.94 (a) What is K_b of the acetate ion?
(b) What is K_a of the anilinium ion, C$_6$H$_5$NH$_3^+$?
18.95 (a) What is K_b of the benzoate ion, C$_6$H$_5$COO$^-$?
(b) What is K_a of the 2-hydroxyethylammonium ion,
HOCH$_2$CH$_2$NH$_3^+$? (pK_b of HOCH$_2$CH$_2$NH$_2$ = 4.49.)

18.96 (a) What is pK_b of ClO$_2^-$?
(b) What is pK_a of the dimethylammonium ion,
(CH$_3$)$_2$NH$_2^+$?
18.97 (a) What is the pK_b of NO$_2^-$?
(b) What is the pK_a of the hydrazinium ion, H$_2$N—NH$_3^+$
(K_b of hydrazine = 8.5×10^{-7}.)

18.98 (a) What is the pH of 0.050 M KCN?
(b) What is the pH of 0.30 M triethylammonium chloride,
(CH$_3$CH$_2$)$_3$NHCl?
18.99 (a) What is the pH of 0.100 M sodium phenolate, the
sodium salt of phenol, C$_6$H$_5$ONa?
(b) What is the pH of 0.15 M methylammonium bromide,
CH$_3$NH$_3$Br? (K_b of CH$_3$NH$_2$ = 4.4×10^{-4}.)

18.100 (a) What is the pH of 0.53 M potassium formate,
HCOOK?
(b) What is the pH of 1.22 M NH$_4$Br?
18.101 (a) What is the pH of 0.75 M NaF?
(b) What is the pH of 0.88 M pyridinium chloride,
C$_5$H$_5$NHCl?

■ **Problems in Context**
18.102 Sodium hypochlorite solution is sold as "chlorine
bleach" and is recognized as a potentially dangerous household solution. The dangers arise from its basicity and from
ClO$^-$, the active bleaching ingredient. What is [OH$^-$] in an
aqueous solution that is 5.0% NaClO by mass? What is the
pH of the solution? (Assume d of solution = 1.0 g/mL.)
18.103 Codeine (C$_{18}$H$_{21}$NO$_3$) is a narcotic pain reliever that
forms a salt with HCl. What is the pH of 0.050 M codeine
hydrochloride? (pK_b of codeine is 5.80.)

Molecular Properties and Acid Strength

■ **Concept Review Questions**
18.104 How does the electronegativity of a nonmetal affect
the acidity of its binary hydride?
18.105 How does the atomic size of a nonmetal affect the
acidity of its binary hydride?
18.106 Is it reasonable that a strong acid has a weak bond to
its acidic proton, whereas a weak acid has a strong bond to
its acidic proton? Explain.
18.107 Perchloric acid, HClO$_4$, is the strongest of the halogen oxoacids, and hypoiodous acid, HIO, is the weakest.
What two factors govern this difference in acid strength?

■ **Skill-Building Exercises (paired)**
18.108 Choose the *stronger* acid in each of the following pairs:
(a) H$_2$SeO$_3$ or H$_2$SeO$_4$ (b) H$_3$PO$_4$ or H$_3$AsO$_4$ (c) H$_2$S or H$_2$Te
18.109 Choose the *weaker* acid in each of the following pairs:
(a) HBr or H$_2$Se   (b) HClO$_4$ or H$_2$SO$_4$ (c) H$_2$SO$_3$ or H$_2$SO$_4$

18.110 Choose the *stronger* acid in each of the following pairs:
(a) H$_2$Se or H$_3$As (b) B(OH)$_3$ or Al(OH)$_3$ (c) HBrO$_2$ or HBrO

18.111 Choose the *weaker* acid in each of the following pairs:
(a) HI or HBr   (b) H_3AsO_4 or H_2SeO_4 (c) HNO_3 or HNO_2

18.112 Use Table 18.7 to choose the solution with the *lower* pH:
(a) 0.1 M $CuSO_4$ or 0.05 M $Al_2(SO_4)_3$
(b) 0.1 M $ZnCl_2$ or 0.1 M $PbCl_2$

18.113 Use Table 18.7 to choose the solution with the *lower* pH:
(a) 0.1 M $FeCl_3$ or 0.1 M $AlCl_3$
(b) 0.1 M $BeCl_2$ or 0.1 M $CaCl_2$

18.114 Use Table 18.7 to choose the solution with the *higher* pH:
(a) 0.1 M $Ni(NO_3)_2$ or 0.1 M $Co(NO_3)_2$
(b) 0.1 M $Al(NO_3)_3$ or 0.1 M $Cr(NO_3)_3$

18.115 Use Table 18.7 to choose the solution with the *higher* pH:
(a) 0.1 M $NiCl_2$ or 0.1 M NaCl
(b) 0.1 M $Sn(NO_3)_2$ or 0.1 M $Co(NO_3)_2$

Acid-Base Properties of Salt Solutions
(Sample Problems 18.11 and 18.12)

■ Concept Review Questions

18.116 What determines whether an aqueous solution of a salt will be acidic, basic, or neutral? Give an example of each type of salt.

18.117 Why is a solution of NaF basic, whereas an NaCl solution is neutral?

18.118 The NH_4^+ ion forms acidic solutions and the $C_2H_3O_2^-$ ion forms basic solutions. However, a solution of ammonium acetate is almost neutral. Do all of the ammonium salts of weak acids form neutral solutions? Explain your answer.

■ Skill-Building Exercises (paired)

18.119 Explain with equations and calculations, when necessary, whether an aqueous solution of each of the following salts is acidic, basic, or neutral:
(a) KBr   (b)NH_4I (c) KCN

18.120 Explain with equations and calculations, when necessary, whether an aqueous solution of each of the following salts is acidic, basic, or neutral:
(a) $Cr(NO_3)_3$ (b) NaHS   (c) $Zn(CH_3COO)_2$

18.121 Explain with equations and calculations, when necessary, whether an aqueous solution of each of the following salts is acidic, basic, or neutral:
(a) Na_2CO_3 (b) $CaCl_2$ (c) $Cu(NO_3)_2$

18.122 Explain with equations and calculations, when necessary, whether an aqueous solution of each of the following salts is acidic, basic, or neutral:
(a) CH_3NH_3Cl (b) $KClO_4$ (c) CoF_2

18.123 Explain with equations and calculations, when necessary, whether an aqueous solution of each of the following salts is acidic, basic, or neutral:
(a) $SrBr_2$ (b) $Ba(CH_3COO)_2$ (c) $(CH_3)_2NH_2Br$

18.124 Explain with equations and calculations, when necessary, whether an aqueous solution of each of the following salts is acidic, basic, or neutral:
(a) $Fe(HCOO)_3$ (b) $KHCO_3$ (c) K_2S

18.125 Explain with equations and calculations, when necessary, whether an aqueous solution of each of the following salts is acidic, basic, or neutral:
(a) $(NH_4)_3PO_4$ (b) Na_2SO_4 (c) LiClO

18.126 Explain with equations and calculations, when necessary, whether an aqueous solution of each of the following salts is acidic, basic, or neutral:
(a) $Pb(CH_3COO)_2$ (b) $Cr(NO_2)_3$ (c) CsI

18.127 Rank the following salts in order of *increasing* pH of their 0.1 M aqueous solutions:
(a) KNO_3, K_2SO_3, K_2S, $Fe(NO_3)_2$
(b) NH_4NO_3, $NaHSO_4$, $NaHCO_3$, Na_2CO_3

18.128 Rank the following salts in order of *decreasing* pH of their 0.1 M aqueous solutions:
(a) $FeCl_2$, $FeCl_3$, $MgCl_2$, $KClO_2$
(b) NH_4Br, $NaBrO_2$, NaBr, $NaClO_2$

Generalizing the Brønsted-Lowry Concept: The Leveling Effect

■ Concept Review Questions

18.129 The methoxide ion, CH_3O^-, and amide ion, NH_2^-, are very strong bases that are "leveled" by water. What does this mean? Write the reactions that occur in the leveling process. What species do the two leveled solutions have in common?

18.130 Explain the differing extents of dissociation of H_2SO_4 in CH_3COOH, H_2O, and NH_3.

18.131 In H_2O, HF is weak and the other hydrohalic acids are equally strong. In NH_3, however, all the hydrohalic acids are equally strong. Explain.

Electron-Pair Donation and the Lewis Acid-Base Definition
(Sample Problem 18.13)

■ Concept Review Questions

18.132 What feature must a molecule or ion possess for it to act as a Lewis base? As a Lewis acid? Explain the roles of these features.

18.133 How do Lewis acids differ from Brønsted-Lowry acids? How are they similar? Do Lewis bases differ from Brønsted-Lowry bases? Explain.

18.134 (a) Is a weak Brønsted-Lowry base necessarily a weak Lewis base? Explain with an example.
(b) Identify the Lewis bases in the following reaction:

$$Cu(H_2O)_4^{2+}(aq) + 4CN^-(aq) \rightleftharpoons Cu(CN)_4^{2-}(aq) + 4H_2O(l)$$

(c) Given that $K_c > 1$ in (b), which Lewis base is stronger?

18.135 In which of the three concepts of acid-base behavior discussed in the text can water be a product of an acid-base reaction? In which is it the only product?

18.136 (a) Give an example of a *substance* that is a base in two of the three acid-base definitions, but not in the third.
(b) Give an example of a *substance* that is an acid in one of the three acid-base definitions, but not in the other two.

■ Skill-Building Exercises (paired)

18.137 Which of the following are Lewis acids and which are Lewis bases?
(a) Cu^{2+} (b) Cl^- (c) $SnCl_2$ (d) OF_2

18.138 Which of the following are Lewis acids and which are Lewis bases?
(a) Na^+ (b) NH_3 (c) CN^- (d) BF_3

18.139 Which of the following are Lewis acids and which are Lewis bases?
(a) BF_3 (b) S^{2-} (c) SO_3^{2-} (d) SO_3

18.140 Which of the following are Lewis acids and which are Lewis bases?
(a) Mg^{2+} (b) OH^- (c) SiF_4 (d) $BeCl_2$

18.141 Identify the Lewis acid and the Lewis base in each of the following equations:
(a) $Na^+ + 6H_2O \rightleftharpoons Na(H_2O)_6^+$
(b) $CO_2 + H_2O \rightleftharpoons H_2CO_3$
(c) $F^- + BF_3 \rightleftharpoons BF_4^-$

18.142 Identify the Lewis acid and the Lewis base in each of the following equations:
(a) $Fe^{3+} + 2H_2O \rightleftharpoons FeOH^{2+} + H_3O^+$
(b) $H_2O + H^- \rightleftharpoons OH^- + H_2$
(c) $4CO + Ni^{2+} \rightleftharpoons Ni(CO)_4$

18.143 Classify the following as Arrhenius, Brønsted-Lowry, and Lewis acid-base reactions. A reaction may fit all, two, one, or none of the categories:
(a) $Ag^+ + 2NH_3 \rightleftharpoons Ag(NH_3)_2^+$
(b) $H_2SO_4 + NH_3 \rightleftharpoons HSO_4^- + NH_4^+$
(c) $2HCl \rightleftharpoons H_2 + Cl_2$
(d) $AlCl_3 + Cl^- \rightleftharpoons AlCl_4^-$

18.144 Classify the following as Arrhenius, Brønsted-Lowry, and Lewis acid-base reactions. A reaction may fit all, two, one, or none of the categories:
(a) $Cu^{2+} + 4Cl^- \rightleftharpoons CuCl_4^{2-}$
(b) $Al(OH)_3 + 3HNO_3 \rightleftharpoons Al^{3+} + 3H_2O + 3NO_3^-$
(c) $N_2 + 3H_2 \rightleftharpoons 2NH_3$
(d) $CN^- + H_2O \rightleftharpoons HCN + OH^-$

Comprehensive Problems

Problems with an asterisk (*) are more challenging.

18.145 Pantothenic acid, $C_9H_{17}NO_5$, also called *vitamin B$_3$*, has the structure shown below. The biologically active molecule is an optical isomer that behaves like a monoprotic Brønsted-Lowry acid in water.

(a) Use the molecular formula to write the equation for the reaction of pantothenic acid with water and the K_a expression.
(b) Use the model to determine which C atom is the chiral center.

18.146 The pK_a of acetic acid is 4.76 in pure water and 4.53 in seawater. Is it a stronger acid in one solvent than in the other? If so, in which?

18.147 Bodily processes in humans maintain the pH of blood within a narrow range. In fact, a condition called

acidosis occurs if the blood pH goes below 7.35 and another called *alkalosis* occurs if the pH goes above 7.45. Given that the pK_w of blood is 13.63 at 37°C (body temperature), what is the normal range of $[H_3O^+]$ and of $[OH^-]$ in blood?

18.148 Phenol, C_6H_5OH, is used as a disinfectant (known as *carbolic acid*). In water, its pK_a is 10.0, but in pure methanol it is 14.4.
(a) Why are the values different?
(b) Use these two values to decide whether methanol is a stronger or weaker base than water.
(c) Write the dissociation reaction of carbolic acid in methanol.
(d) Write an expression that defines the autoionization constant of methanol.

*18.149 When carbon dioxide dissolves in water, it undergoes a multistep equilibrium process, with $K_{overall} = 4.5 \times 10^{-7}$, which is simplifed to the following:

$$CO_2(g) + H_2O(l) \rightleftharpoons H_2CO_3(aq)$$

$$H_2CO_3(aq) + H_2O(l) \rightleftharpoons HCO_3^-(aq) + H_3O^+(aq)$$

(a) Classify each step as a Lewis or a Brønsted-Lowry acid-base reaction.
(b) What is the pH of nonpolluted rainwater in equilibrium with clean air? P_{CO_2} in clean air = 3.2×10^{-4} atm. Henry's law constant for CO_2 at 25°C is 0.033 mol/L · atm.
(c) What is the $[CO_3^{2-}]$ in rainwater? K_a of HCO_3^- = 4.7×10^{-11}.
(d) If the partial pressure of CO_2 doubles in the next few decades, what will the pH of rainwater become?

18.150 Seashells are mostly calcium carbonate, which reacts with H_3O^+ according to the equation

$$CaCO_3(s) + H_3O^+(aq) \rightleftharpoons Ca^{2+}(aq) + HCO_3^-(aq) + H_2O(l)$$

If the extent of autoionization of water increases at higher pressure, will seashells dissolve more rapidly near the surface or at great depths? Explain.

18.151 Many compounds with central atoms from Period 3 or higher take part in Lewis acid-base reactions in which they expand their valence shells. For example, $SnCl_4$ reacts with $(CH_3)_3N$ as follows:

(a) Identify the Lewis acid and Lewis base in the reaction.
(b) Give the *nl* designation of the sublevel in the acid that accepts the lone pair.

*18.152 A chemist makes four successive 1:10 dilutions of 1.0×10^{-5} *M* HCl. Calculate the pH of the original solution and of each dilution (through 1.0×10^{-9} *M* HCl).

18.153 At 25°C, the pK_w of seawater is 13.22; this value is lower than that for pure water as a result of the dissolved salts. If the pH of a sample of seawater is 7.54, what is pOH of the sample?

18.154 Chlorobenzene, C_6H_5Cl, is a key intermediate in the manufacture of many aromatic compounds, including aniline dyes and chlorinated pesticides. It is made by the $FeCl_3$-catalyzed chlorination of benzene in the following series of steps:

Step 1: $Cl_2 + FeCl_3 \rightleftharpoons FeCl_5$ (or $Cl^+FeCl_4^-$)

Step 2: $C_6H_6 + Cl^+FeCl_4^- \rightleftharpoons C_6H_6Cl^+ + FeCl_4^-$

Step 3: $C_6H_6Cl^+ \rightleftharpoons C_6H_5Cl + H^+$

Step 4: $H^+ + FeCl_4^- \rightleftharpoons HCl + FeCl_3$

(a) Which of the steps is/are Lewis acid-base reactions?

(b) Identify the Lewis acids and Lewis bases in each of those steps.

*18.155 Hydrogen peroxide, H_2O_2 ($pK_a = 11.75$), is commonly used as a bleaching agent and an antiseptic. The product sold in stores is 3% H_2O_2 by mass and contains 0.001% phosphoric acid by mass to stabilize the solution. Which contributes more H_3O^+ to this commercial solution, the H_2O_2 or the H_3PO_4?

18.156 The strengths of acids and bases are directly related to their strengths as electrolytes (Section 4.2).

(a) Is the electrical conductivity of 0.1 M HCl higher, lower, or the same as that of 0.1 M CH_3COOH? Explain.

(b) Is the electrical conductivity of 1×10^{-7} M HCl higher, lower, or the same as that of 1×10^{-7} M CH_3COOH? Explain.

18.157 Esters, RCOOR', are compounds formed by the reaction of carboxylic acids, RCOOH, and alcohols, R'OH, where R and R' are hydrocarbon groups. Many esters are active ingredients in the odors of fruit and, thus, have important uses in the food and cosmetics industries. The mechanism of ester formation is catalyzed by H^+. The first two steps are Lewis acid-base reactions:

Identify the Lewis acids and Lewis bases in these two steps.

18.158 The metallic radius of aluminum (143 pm) is similar to that of lithium (152 pm), and the ionic radius of the aluminum ion (54 pm) is similar to that of the lithium ion (76 pm). Why is an aqueous solution of aluminum nitrate acidic but one of lithium nitrate neutral?

18.159 The corrosion of iron-containing objects has a major economic impact (discussed in Chapter 21). In an investigation of corrosion of stainless steel by hydrochloric acid, some 0.010 M HCl is heated in a closed stainless steel container to 200°C, which increases the pressure to 10^4 atm. Under these conditions, pK_w is 9.25. What is $[OH^-]$ in the stainless steel container?

*18.160 Many substances undergo autoionization in a manner analogous to water. For example, the autoionization of liquid ammonia is

$$2NH_3(l) \rightleftharpoons NH_4^+(am) + NH_2^-(am)$$

where *am* refers to solvation by ammonia.

(a) Write a K_{am} expression for the autoionization of ammonia that is analogous to the K_w expression for water.

(b) What are the strongest acid and strongest base that can exist in liquid ammonia?

(c) For water, a solution with $[OH^-] > [H_3O^+]$ is basic and one with $[OH^-] < [H_3O^+]$ is acidic. What are the analogous relationships in liquid ammonia?

(d) The acids HNO_3 and HCOOH are leveled in liquid NH_3. Explain what this means and show equations.

(e) Pure liquid sulfuric acid also undergoes autoionization. The bases hydroxide, OH^-, and methoxide, CH_3O^-, are leveled in pure liquid H_2SO_4. Explain what this means and show equations.

*18.161 Autoionization (see Problem 18.160) occurs in methanol (CH_3OH) and in ethylenediamine ($NH_2CH_2CH_2NH_2$).

(a) The autoionization constant of methanol (K_{met}) is 2×10^{-17}. What is $[CH_3O^-]$ in pure CH_3OH?

(b) The concentration of $NH_2CH_2CH_2NH_3^+$ in pure $NH_2CH_2CH_2NH_2$ is 2×10^{-8} M. What is the autoionization constant of ethylenediamine (K_{en})?

*18.162 Some drugs are such weak bases that titration with strong acid to determine concentration is incomplete in water. Industrial pharmacologists titrate many of these drugs using pure acetic acid as the solvent instead of water. How does this procedure aid in the titration?

18.163 Tris(hydroxymethyl)aminomethane, commonly known as TRIS or THAM, is a water-soluble base with industrial applications in the synthesis of surfactants and pharmaceuticals, as an emulsifying agent in cosmetic creams and lotions, and as a component of various cleaning and polishing mixtures for textiles and leather. In biomedical research, its solutions are used to maintain nearly constant pH for the study of enzymes and other cellular components. Given that its pK_b is 5.91, calculate the pH of 0.060 M TRIS.

18.164 When iron(III) salts are dissolved in water, the solution becomes yellow and acidic due to the formation of $Fe(H_2O)_5OH^{2+}$ and H_3O^+. The overall process involves both Lewis and Brønsted-Lowry acid-base reactions. Write the equations for the process.

18.165 Vinegar is a 5.0% (w/v) solution of acetic acid in water. For culinary use, it is flavored with apples, herbs, wine, and so forth. What is the pH of vinegar?

18.166 Explain how to differentiate between a strong and a weak monoprotic acid in the results of the following procedures:

(a) Electrical conductivity of equimolar solutions of each acid is measured.

(b) Equal moles of each are dissolved in water and tested with pH paper.

(c) Zinc metal is added to acid solutions of equal concentration.

18.167 At 50°C and 1 atm, $K_w = 5.19 \times 10^{-14}$. Calculate parts (a)–(c) under these conditions:

(a) $[H_3O^+]$ in pure water

(b) $[H_3O^+]$ in 0.010 M NaOH

(c) $[OH^-]$ in 0.0010 M $HClO_4$

(d) Calculate $[H_3O^+]$ in 0.0100 M KOH at 100°C and 1000 atm pressure ($K_w = 1.10 \times 10^{-12}$).

(e) Calculate the pH of pure water at 100°C and 1000 atm.

18.168 The catalytic efficiency of an enzyme is called its *activity* and refers to the rate at which it catalyzes the conversion of reactants into products. Most enzymes have optimum activity over a relatively narrow range of pH values, which is related to the pH of the local cellular fluid in which the reaction occurs. The pH profiles of three digestive enzymes are shown.

Salivary amylase begins digestion of starches in the mouth and has a pH optimum of 6.8; pepsin begins protein digestion in the stomach and has a pH optimum of 2.0; and trypsin, released in pancreatic juices, continues protein digestion in the small intestine and has a pH optimum of 9.5. Calculate $[H_3O^+]$ in the cellular environments for each of these enzymes.

18.169 Sodium phosphate has industrial uses ranging from clarifying crude sugar to manufacturing paper. It is sold commercially as TSP and is used in solution to remove boiler scale and to wash painted brick and concrete. The label usually has a warning that TSP is harmful to the skin and eyes. What is the pH of a solution containing 33 g Na_3PO_4 per liter? What is $[OH^-]$ of this solution?

*18.170 For most polyprotic acids, K_{a1} is significantly larger than K_{a2}, but for the acid $HO_2C(CH_2)_6CO_2H$, the difference in K_a values is insignificant. Explain.

18.171 The autoionization constant of HF is 1×10^{-11} at 25°C. What is the concentration of F^- in pure HF? What other ion is present with molarity equal to that of F^-?

18.172 The advent of the modern supermarket has made extended shelf life of products a major concern of consumers and scientists in the food and drug industries. Calcium propionate [calcium propanoate, $Ca(CH_3CH_2COO)_2$] is one of the more common mold inhibitors in food, tobacco, and pharmaceuticals. (a) Use balanced equations to show whether an aqueous solution of calcium propionate is acidic, basic, or neutral. (b) Use Table 18.2 to find the pH of a solution that is made by dissolving 7.05 g $Ca(CH_3CH_2COO)_2$ in water to give 0.500 L of solution.

18.173 What is an acidic oxide? Which is the acidic oxide in the Lewis acid-base reaction between CaO and CO_2? Are all

reactions between acidic and basic oxides Lewis acid-base reactions?

18.174 Aqueous solutions of beryllium compounds are quite acidic, but the acidity of aqueous solutions of other Group 2A(2) salts is insignificant. Explain.

18.175 How are H_3O^+ and OH^- ions produced in pure water? Why do the concentrations of these ions remain constant? Why do the concentrations of these ions decrease when the temperature decreases? What happens to the ions that are "lost" at lower temperature?

18.176 Amine bases are notorious for having foul odors. Putrescine ($NH_2CH_2CH_2CH_2CH_2NH_2$), once thought to be found only in rotting animal tissue, is now known to be a component of all cells and essential for their normal and abnormal (cancerous) growth. It also plays a key role in formation of GABA, one of the brain's neurotransmitters. A 0.10 M aqueous solution of putrescine has $[OH^-] = 2.1\times10^{-3}$. What is its K_b?

*18.177 Quinine ($C_{20}H_{24}N_2O_2$; see structure) is a natural product that was originally extracted from the bark of cinchona trees but is now synthesized by the pharmaceutical industry. Its antimalarial properties are responsible for saving thousands of lives during construction of the Panama Canal, and, thus, it stands as a classic example of the untold chemical wealth of the forests of Central and South America. Both N atoms are basic, but the tertiary amine N (colored) is far more basic ($pK_b = 5.1$) than the N within the aromatic ring system ($pK_b = 9.7$).

(a) Quinine is not very soluble in water: a saturated solution is only 1.6×10^{-3} M. What is the pH of this solution?
(b) Show that the aromatic N contributes negligibly to the pH of the solution.
(c) Because of its low solubility as a free base, quinine is often administered as an amine salt. Quinine hydrochloride ($C_{20}H_{24}N_2O_2 \cdot HCl$), for example, is about 120 times more soluble in water than quinine. What is the pH of 0.53 M quinine hydrochloride?
(d) What is the pH of a solution ($d = 1.0$ g/mL) that is 1.5% quinine hydrochloride by mass, a typical antimalarial concentration?

Ionic Equilibria in Aqueous Systems

19

Figure: Aqueous equilibria seen from outer space. Natural waters cover three-quarters of the Earth and interact physically and chemically with the solid, gaseous, and living domains of the planet through complex aqueous equilibria. In this chapter, we investigate three examples of ionic equilibria that occur in aqueous systems.

Recent observations of Europa, one of Jupiter's many moons, caused great excitement, for the icy surface revealed hints that vast oceans of liquid water may lie beneath. Speculation arose immediately about the possibility of life there. No doubt some Europan astronomer viewing Earth would make the same speculation. Every astronaut has felt a sense of awe upon viewing our "beautiful blue orb" from space. A biologist peering at the fabulous watery world of a living cell probably feels the same way. A chemist is in awe of the principles of equilibrium and their universal application to aqueous solutions wherever they occur in the external and internal worlds.

Consider just a few cases of aqueous equilibria. The magnificent formations in limestone caves and the vast expanses of oceanic coral reefs (see photo) result from subtle shifts in carbonate solubility equilibria. Carbonates also influence soil pH and prevent acidification of lakes by acid rain. Equilibria involving carbon dioxide and phosphates help organisms maintain cellular pH within narrow limits. Equilibria involving clays found in soil control the availability of ionic nutrients for plants. The principles of ionic equilibrium also govern how water is softened, how substances are purified by precipitating unwanted ions, and even how the weak acids in wine and vinegar influence the delicate taste of a fine French sauce.

In this chapter, we explore three key aqueous ionic equilibrium systems: acid-base buffers, slightly soluble salts, and complex ions. Our discussion of buffers introduces the common-ion effect, an important phenomenon in many ionic equilibria. The discussion includes why buffers are important, how they work, and how to prepare them. We take a closer look at acid-base titrations and how buffers are involved in that process. Then we examine slightly soluble salts in the laboratory and in nature to see how conditions influence their solubility. Next, we investigate complex ions and how they form and change from one type to another. Finally, we see how these aqueous equilibria are employed in chemical analysis. There are few new ideas in this chapter, but there are many opportunities to apply earlier ideas in new ways.

19.1 Equilibria of Acid-Base Buffer Systems

Why do some lakes become acidic when showered by acid rain, while others remain unaffected? How does blood maintain a constant pH in contact with countless cellular acid-base reactions? How can a chemist sustain a nearly constant $[H_3O^+]$ in reactions that consume or produce H_3O^+ or OH^-? The answer in each case is through the presence of a buffer.

In everyday language, a buffer is something that lessens the impact of an external force. An **acid-base buffer** is a solution that *lessens changes in $[H_3O^+]$ from the addition of acid or base*. Figure 19.1 shows that when a small amount of H_3O^+ or OH^- ions is added to an unbuffered solution, *the change in pH is much larger* than the change that results from the same addition to a buffered solution.

To withstand the addition of strong acid or strong base without significantly changing its pH, a buffer must contain an acidic component that can react with added OH^- ion *and* a basic component that can react with added H_3O^+ ion. However, these buffer components cannot be just any acid and base because they would neutralize each other. Most commonly, *the components of a buffer are the conjugate acid-base pair of a weak acid*. In Figure 19.1C and D, for example, the buffer is a mixture of acetic acid (CH_3COOH) and acetate ion (CH_3COO^-).

Figure 19.1 The effect of addition of acid or base to unbuffered or buffered solutions. A, A 100-mL sample of an unbuffered solution of dilute HCl is adjusted to pH 5.00. **B,** After the addition of 1 mL of 1 *M* HCl (*left*) or of 1 *M* NaOH (*right*), the pH change is large. **C,** A 100-mL sample of a buffered solution, made by mixing 1 *M* CH₃COOH with 1 *M* CH₃COONa, is adjusted to pH 5.00. **D,** After the addition of 1 mL of 1 *M* HCl (*left*) or of 1 *M* NaOH (*right*), the pH change is negligible.

How a Buffer Works: The Common-Ion Effect

Buffers work through a phenomenon known as the **common-ion effect.** An example of this effect occurs when acetic acid dissociates in water and some sodium acetate is added. As you know, acetic acid dissociates only slightly in water:

$$CH_3COOH(aq) + H_2O(l) \rightleftharpoons CH_3COO^-(aq) + H_3O^+(aq)$$

From Le Châtelier's principle (Section 17.6), we know that if some CH_3COO^- ion is added, the equilibrium position shifts to the left; $[H_3O^+]$ decreases, in effect lowering the extent of acid dissociation:

$$CH_3COOH(aq) + H_2O(l) \overset{\longleftarrow}{\rightleftharpoons} CH_3COO^-(aq; \text{ added}) + H_3O^+(aq)$$

Similarly, if we dissolve acetic acid in a sodium acetate solution, the acetate ion already present combines with some H_3O^+ as it dissociates from the acid, which lowers the $[H_3O^+]$. Acetate ion is called *the common ion* in this case because it is "common" to both the acetic acid and sodium acetate solutions; that is, acetate ion is added to a solution in which it is already present. *The common-ion effect occurs when a reactant containing a given ion is added to an equilibrium mixture that already contains that ion and the position of equilibrium shifts away from forming more of it.*

Table 19.1 shows the percent dissociation and the pH of an acetic acid solution containing different concentrations of acetate ion (supplied by adding solid sodium acetate). Note that the *common ion,* CH_3COO^-, *suppresses the percent dissociation of* CH_3COOH, which makes the solution less acidic (higher pH).

Table 19.1 The Effect of Added Acetate Ion on the Dissociation of Acetic Acid

[CH₃COOH]	[CH₃COO⁻]ₐddₑd	% Dissociation*	pH
0.10	0.00	1.3	2.89
0.10	0.050	0.036	4.44
0.10	0.10	0.018	4.74
0.10	0.15	0.012	4.92

*% Dissociation $= \dfrac{[CH_3COOH]_{dissoc}}{[CH_3COOH]_{init}} \times 100$

The Essential Feature of a Buffer   In the previous case, we prepared a buffer by mixing a weak acid (CH$_3$COOH) and its conjugate base (CH$_3$COO$^-$). *How* does this solution resist pH changes when H$_3$O$^+$ or OH$^-$ is added? The essential feature of a buffer is that it consists of *high concentrations* of the acidic (HA) and basic (A$^-$) components. When small amounts of H$_3$O$^+$ or OH$^-$ ions are added to the buffer, they cause *a small amount of one buffer component to convert into the other*, which changes the *relative* concentrations of the buffer components. As long as the amount of H$_3$O$^+$ or OH$^-$ added is much *smaller* than the amounts of HA and A$^-$ present originally, *the added ions have little effect on the pH because they are consumed by one or the other buffer component:* the A$^-$ consumes added H$_3$O$^+$, and the HA consumes added OH$^-$.

Consider what happens to a solution containing high [CH$_3$COOH] and [CH$_3$COO$^-$] when we add small amounts of strong acid or base. The expression for HA dissociation at equilibrium is

$$K_a = \frac{[CH_3COO^-][H_3O^+]}{[CH_3COOH]}$$

Solving for [H$_3$O$^+$], we obtain

$$[H_3O^+] = K_a \times \frac{[CH_3COOH]}{[CH_3COO^-]}$$

Note that since K_a is constant, *the [H$_3$O$^+$] of the solution depends directly on the buffer-component concentration ratio,* $\dfrac{[CH_3COOH]}{[CH_3COO^-]}$:

- If the ratio [HA]/[A$^-$] goes up, [H$_3$O$^+$] goes up.
- If the ratio [HA]/[A$^-$] goes down, [H$_3$O$^+$] goes down.

When we add a small amount of strong acid, the increased amount of H$_3$O$^+$ reacts with a nearly *stoichiometric amount* of acetate ion in the buffer to form more acetic acid:

$$H_3O^+(aq; \text{added}) + CH_3COO^-(aq) \longrightarrow CH_3COOH(aq) + H_2O(l)$$

As a result, [CH$_3$COO$^-$] goes down by that amount and [CH$_3$COOH] goes up by that amount, which increases the buffer-component ratio, as you can see in Figure 19.2. The [H$_3$O$^+$] increases also but only very slightly.

Adding a small amount of strong base produces the opposite result. It supplies OH$^-$ ions, which react with a nearly *stoichiometric amount* of CH$_3$COOH in the buffer, forming that much more CH$_3$COO$^-$:

$$CH_3COOH(aq) + OH^-(aq; \text{added}) \longrightarrow CH_3COO^-(aq) + H_2O(l)$$

The buffer-component ratio decreases, which decreases [H$_3$O$^+$], but once again, the change is very slight.

Thus, the components consume virtually all the added H$_3$O$^+$ or OH$^-$. To reiterate, as long as the amount of added H$_3$O$^+$ or OH$^-$ is small compared with the amounts of the buffer components, *the conversion of one component into the other produces a small change in the buffer-component ratio and, consequently,*

Figure 19.2 How a buffer works. A buffer consists of high concentrations of a conjugate acid-base pair, in this case acetic acid (CH$_3$COOH) and acetate ion (CH$_3$COO$^-$). When a small amount of H$_3$O$^+$ is added (*left*), that same amount of CH$_3$COO$^-$ combines with it, which increases the amount of CH$_3$COOH slightly. Similarly, when a small amount of OH$^-$ is added (*right*), that amount of CH$_3$COOH combines with it, which increases the amount of CH$_3$COO$^-$ slightly. In both cases, the relative changes in buffer components are small, so their concentration ratio, and therefore the pH, changes very little.

a small change in $[H_3O^+]$ and in pH. Sample Problem 19.1 demonstrates how small these pH changes actually are in a typical case. Note that the latter two parts of the problem combine a stoichiometry portion, like the problems in Chapter 3, and a weak-acid dissociation portion, like those in Chapter 18.

Sample Problem 19.1 Calculating the Effect of Added H_3O^+ and OH^- on Buffer pH

PROBLEM Calculate the pH:
(a) Of a buffer solution consisting of 0.50 M CH_3COOH and 0.50 M CH_3COONa
(b) After adding 0.020 mol solid NaOH to 1.0 L of the buffer solution in **(a)**
(c) After adding 0.020 mol HCl to 1.0 L of the buffer solution in **(a)**
K_a of CH_3COOH = 1.8×10^{-5}. (Assume the additions cause negligible volume changes.)
PLAN In each case, we know, or can find, $[CH_3COOH]_{init}$ and $[CH_3COO^-]_{init}$ and we need to find $[H_3O^+]$ at equilibrium and convert it to pH. In **(a)**, we use the given concentrations of buffer components as the initial values. As in earlier problems, we assume that x, the $[CH_3COOH]$ that dissociates, and which equals $[H_3O^+]$, is so small relative to $[CH_3COOH]_{init}$ that it can be neglected. We set up a reaction table, solve for x, and check the assumption. In **(b)** and **(c)**, we assume that the added OH^- or H_3O^+ reacts completely with the buffer components to yield new $[CH_3COOH]_{init}$ and $[CH_3COO^-]_{init}$, which then dissociate to an unknown extent. We set up two reaction tables. The first summarizes the stoichiometry of adding strong base or acid. The second summarizes the dissociation of the new HA concentrations, so we proceed as in **(a)** to find the new $[H_3O^+]$.
SOLUTION (a) The original pH: $[H_3O^+]$ in the original buffer.
Setting up a reaction table with $x = [CH_3COOH]_{dissoc} = [H_3O^+]$ (as in Chapter 18, we assume that the $[H_3O^+]$ from H_2O is negligible and disregard it):

CONCENTRATION (M)	$CH_3COOH(aq)$	+	$H_2O(l)$	$\rightleftharpoons$	$CH_3COO^-(aq)$	+	$H_3O^+(aq)$
Initial	0.50		—		0.50		0
Change	$-x$		—		$+x$		$+x$
Equilibrium	$0.50 - x$		—		$0.50 + x$		x

Making the assumption and finding the equilibrium $[CH_3COOH]$ and $[CH_3COO^-]$:
Since K_a is small, x is small; so we assume

$[CH_3COOH] = 0.50\ M - x \approx 0.50\ M$ and $[CH_3COO^-] = 0.50\ M + x \approx 0.50\ M$

Solving for x ($[H_3O^+]$ at equilibrium):

$$x = [H_3O^+] = K_a \times \frac{[CH_3COOH]}{[CH_3COO^-]} \approx (1.8 \times 10^{-5}) \times \frac{0.50}{0.50} = 1.8 \times 10^{-5}\ M$$

Checking the assumption:

$$\frac{1.8 \times 10^{-5}\ M}{0.50\ M} \times 100 = 3.6 \times 10^{-3}\% < 5\%$$

The assumption is justified, and we will use the same assumption in parts **(b)** and **(c)**.
Calculating pH:

$$pH = -\log [H_3O^+] = -\log (1.8 \times 10^{-5}) = \boxed{4.74}$$

(b) The pH after adding base (0.020 mol NaOH to 1.0 L buffer). Finding $[OH^-]_{added}$:

$$[OH^-]_{added} = \frac{0.020\ mol\ OH^-}{1.0\ L\ soln} = 0.020\ M\ OH^-$$

Setting up a reaction table for the *stoichiometry* of adding OH^- to CH_3COOH:

CONCENTRATION (M)	$CH_3COOH(aq)$	+	$OH^-(aq)$	$\longrightarrow$	$CH_3COO^-(aq)$	+	$H_2O(aq)$
Before addition	0.50		—		0.50		—
Addition	—		0.020		—		—
After addition	0.48		0		0.52		—

Setting up a reaction table for the *acid dissociation*, using these new initial concentrations. As in part **(a)**, $x = [CH_3COOH]_{dissoc} = [H_3O^+]$:

CONCENTRATION (M)	CH₃COOH(aq)	+	H₂O(l)	⇌	CH₃COO⁻(aq)	+	H₃O⁺(aq)
Initial	0.48		—		0.52		0
Change	−x		—		+x		+x
Equilibrium	0.48 − x		—		0.52 + x		x

Making the assumption that x is small, and solving for x:

$$[CH_3COOH] = 0.48\ M - x \approx 0.48\ M \quad \text{and} \quad [CH_3COO^-] = 0.52\ M + x \approx 0.52\ M$$

$$[H_3O^+] = K_a \times \frac{[CH_3COOH]}{[CH_3COO^-]} \approx (1.8\times10^{-5}) \times \frac{0.48}{0.52} = 1.7\times10^{-5}\ M$$

Calculating the pH:

$$pH = -\log\,[H_3O^+] = -\log\,(1.7\times10^{-5}) = \boxed{4.77}$$

The addition of strong base increased the concentration of the basic buffer component at the expense of the acidic buffer component. Note especially that the pH *increased only slightly,* from 4.74 to 4.77.

(c) The pH after adding acid (0.020 mol HCl to 1.0 L buffer). Finding $[H_3O^+]_{added}$:

$$[H_3O^+]_{added} = \frac{0.020\ \text{mol}\ H_3O^+}{1.0\ \text{L soln}} = 0.020\ M\ H_3O^+$$

Now we proceed as in part **(b)** by first setting up a reaction table for the *stoichiometry* of adding H_3O^+ to CH_3COO^-:

CONCENTRATION (M)	CH₃COO⁻(aq)	+	H₃O⁺(aq)	⟶	CH₃COOH(aq)	+	H₂O(l)
Before addition	0.50		—		0.50		—
Addition	—		0.020		—		—
After addition	0.48		0		0.52		—

Now we set up the reaction table for the acid dissociation, with $x = [CH_3COOH]_{dissoc} = [H_3O^+]$:

CONCENTRATION (M)	CH₃COOH(aq)	+	H₂O(l)	⇌	CH₃COO⁻(aq)	+	H₃O⁺(aq)
Initial	0.52		—		0.48		0
Change	−x		—		+x		+x
Equilibrium	0.52 − x		—		0.48 + x		x

Making the assumption that x is small, and solving for x:

$$[CH_3COOH] = 0.52\ M - x \approx 0.52\ M \quad \text{and} \quad [CH_3COO^-] = 0.48\ M + x \approx 0.48\ M$$

$$x = [H_3O^+] = K_a \times \frac{[CH_3COOH]}{[CH_3COO^-]} \approx (1.8\times10^{-5}) \times \frac{0.52}{0.48} = 2.0\times10^{-5}\ M$$

Calculating the pH:

$$pH = -\log\,[H_3O^+] = -\log\,(2.0\times10^{-5}) = \boxed{4.70}$$

The addition of strong acid increased the concentration of the acidic buffer component at the expense of the basic component and *lowered* the pH only slightly, from 4.74 to 4.70.

CHECK The changes in $[CH_3COOH]$ and $[CH_3COO^-]$ occur in opposite directions in parts **(b)** and **(c)**, which makes sense. The additions were of equal amounts, so the pH increase in **(b)** should equal the pH decrease in **(c)**, within rounding.

COMMENT In part **(a)**, we justified our assumption that x can be neglected. Therefore, in parts **(b)** and **(c)**, we can use the "after addition" values in the last line of the stoichiometry table directly for the ratio of buffer components and dispense with the reaction table for the dissociation. In later problems, we follow this simplified approach.

Follow-up Problem 19.1 Calculate the pH of a buffer consisting of 0.50 *M* HF and 0.45 *M* F⁻ **(a)** before and **(b)** after addition of 0.40 g NaOH to 1.0 L of the buffer (K_a of HF = 6.8×10^{-4}).

The Henderson-Hasselbalch Equation

For any weak acid, HA, the equation and K_a expression for the acid dissociation at equilibrium are

$$HA + H_2O \rightleftharpoons H_3O^+ + A^- \qquad K_a = \frac{[H_3O^+][A^-]}{[HA]}$$

A simple mathematical rearrangement turns this expression into a more useful form for buffer calculations. Remember that the key variable determining $[H_3O^+]$ is the concentration *ratio* of acid species to base species. Isolating $[H_3O^+]$ gives

$$[H_3O^+] = K_a \times \frac{[HA]}{[A^-]}$$

Taking the negative logarithm (base 10) of both sides gives

$$-\log [H_3O^+] = -\log K_a - \log \left(\frac{[HA]}{[A^-]}\right)$$

from which we obtain

$$pH = pK_a + \log \left(\frac{[A^-]}{[HA]}\right)$$

(Note the inversion of the buffer-component concentration ratio when the sign of the logarithm is changed.) A key point that we'll note again later is that when $[A^-] = [HA]$, their ratio becomes 1; then the log term becomes 0, and thus $pH = pK_a$.

Generalizing the previous equation for any conjugate acid-base pair gives the **Henderson-Hasselbalch equation:**

$$pH = pK_a + \log \left(\frac{[base]}{[acid]}\right) \qquad \textbf{(19.1)}$$

This relationship allows us to solve directly for pH instead of calculating $[H_3O^+]$ first. For instance, in part (b) of Sample Problem 19.1, we could have found the pH of the buffer after addition of NaOH from

$$pH = pK_a + \log \left(\frac{[CH_3COO^-]}{[CH_3COOH]}\right) = 4.74 + \log \left(\frac{0.52}{0.48}\right) = 4.77$$

(We just derived the Henderson-Hasselbalch equation from fundamental definitions and simple algebra, so there's no need to memorize it.)

Buffer Capacity and Buffer Range

As you've seen, buffers resist a pH change as long as the concentrations of buffer components are *large* compared with the amount of strong acid or base added. **Buffer capacity** depends on the component concentrations and is a measure of the ability to resist pH change: *the more concentrated the components of a buffer, the greater the buffer capacity.* In other words, you must add more H_3O^+ or OH^- to a high-capacity (concentrated) buffer than to a low-capacity (dilute) buffer to obtain a given pH change. Conversely, adding the same amount of H_3O^+ or OH^- to buffers of different capacities produces a smaller pH change in the higher capacity buffer, as shown in Figure 19.3. This makes sense because the more concentrated buffer exhibits a smaller change in the ratio of its component concentrations on addition of a given amount of H_3O^+ or OH^-. It's important to realize that *the pH of a buffer is distinct from its buffer capacity.* A buffer made of equal volumes of 1.0 *M* CH_3COOH and 1.0 *M* CH_3COO^- has the same pH (4.74) as a buffer that is made of equal volumes of 0.10 *M* CH_3COOH and 0.10 *M* CH_3COO^-, but it has a much larger capacity for resisting a pH change.

Buffer capacity is also affected by the *relative* concentrations of the buffer components. As a buffer functions, the concentration of one component

Figure 19.3 The relation between buffer capacity and pH change. The four bars represent acetic acid/acetate buffers with the same initial pH (4.74) but different concentrations (*labeled on or near each bar*). When a given amount of strong base is added to each buffer, the pH increases. The length of the bar corresponds to the pH increase. Note that the more concentrated the buffer, the greater its capacity, and the smaller the pH change.

increases relative to the other. Since the ratio of these concentrations determines the pH, the less the ratio changes, the less the pH changes. *For a given addition of acid or base, the concentration ratio changes less for similar buffer-component concentrations than for different concentrations.* To illustrate this point, we must keep the sum of the acidic and basic components constant. Suppose we have a buffer in which $[HA] = [A^-] = 1.000$ *M*. When we add 0.010 mol OH^- to 1.00 L of buffer, $[A^-]$ becomes 1.010 *M* and $[HA]$ becomes 0.990 *M*:

$$\frac{[A^-]_{init}}{[HA]_{init}} = \frac{1.000\ M}{1.000\ M} = 1.000 \qquad \frac{[A^-]_{final}}{[HA]_{final}} = \frac{1.010\ M}{0.990\ M} = 1.02$$

$$\text{Percent change} = \frac{1.02 - 1.000}{1.000} \times 100 = 2\%$$

Now suppose the buffer concentrations are $[HA] = 0.250$ *M* and $[A^-] = 1.750$ *M*. The same addition of 0.010 mol OH^- to 1.00 L of buffer gives $[HA] = 0.240$ *M* and $[A^-] = 1.760$ *M*, so the ratios are

$$\frac{[A^-]_{init}}{[HA]_{init}} = \frac{1.750\ M}{0.250\ M} = 7.00 \qquad \frac{[A^-]_{final}}{[HA]_{final}} = \frac{1.760\ M}{0.240\ M} = 7.33$$

$$\text{Percent change} = \frac{7.33 - 7.00}{7.00} \times 100 = 4.7\%$$

As you can see, the change in the buffer-component ratio is much larger when the initial component concentrations are very different.

It follows that *a buffer has the highest capacity when the component concentrations are equal,* that is, when $[A^-]/[HA] = 1$:

$$pH = pK_a + \log\left(\frac{[A^-]}{[HA]}\right) = pK_a + \log 1 = pK_a + 0 = pK_a$$

Note this important result: for a given concentration, *a buffer whose pH is equal to or near the pK_a of its acid component has the highest buffer capacity.*

The **buffer range** is the pH range over which the buffer acts effectively. The further the buffer-component concentration ratio is from 1, the less effective the buffering action (that is, the lower the buffer capacity). In practice, we find that if the $[A^-]/[HA]$ ratio is greater than 10 or less than 0.1—that is, if one component is more than 10 times as concentrated as the other—buffering action is poor. Since $\log 10 = +1$ and $\log 0.1 = -1$, we find that *buffers have a usable range within ± 1 pH unit of the pK_a:*

$$pH = pK_a + \log\left(\frac{10}{1}\right) = pK_a + 1 \qquad \text{and} \qquad pH = pK_a + \log\left(\frac{1}{10}\right) = pK_a - 1$$

Preparing a Buffer

Any large chemical supply-house catalog lists many common buffers available in a variety of pH values and concentrations. So, you might ask, why learn how to prepare a buffer? In many cases, a common buffer is simply not available with the desired pH or concentration, and you have to make it yourself. In many modern medical or biological research applications, a buffer of unusual composition may be required to simulate a cell system or stabilize a fragile biological macromolecule. Even the most sophisticated, automated laboratory frequently relies on personnel versed in wet chemical techniques with a good knowledge of basic chemistry to prepare a buffer.

Several steps are required to prepare a buffer of a desired pH, so let's go through them with an actual example:

1. *Choose the conjugate acid-base pair.* First, decide on the chemical composition of the buffer, that is, the conjugate acid-base pair. This choice is determined to a large extent by the desired pH. Remember that a buffer is most effective when the ratio of component concentrations is close to 1, in which case the pH $\approx pK_a$ of the acid.

Suppose you need a buffer whose pH is 3.90: the pK_a of the acid component should be as close to 3.90 as possible; or $K_a = 10^{-3.90} = 1.3 \times 10^{-4}$. Scanning a table of acid-dissociation constants (see Table 18.2) shows that formic acid ($K_a = 1.8 \times 10^{-4}$; $pK_a = 3.74$) is a good choice. Therefore, the buffer components will be formic acid, HCOOH, and formate ion, $HCOO^-$, supplied by a soluble salt, such as sodium formate, HCOONa.

2. *Calculate the ratio of buffer components.* Next, find the ratio of $[A^-]/[HA]$ that gives the desired pH. With the Henderson-Hasselbalch equation, we have

$$pH = pK_a + \log\left(\frac{[A^-]}{[HA]}\right) \quad \text{or} \quad 3.90 = 3.74 + \log\left(\frac{[HCOO^-]}{[HCOOH]}\right)$$

$$\log\left(\frac{[HCOO^-]}{[HCOOH]}\right) = 0.16 \quad \text{so} \quad \left(\frac{[HCOO^-]}{[HCOOH]}\right) = 10^{0.16} = 1.4$$

Thus, for every 1.0 mol HCOOH in a given volume of solution, you need 1.4 mol HCOONa.

3. *Determine the buffer concentration.* Next, decide how concentrated the buffer should be. Remember that the higher the concentrations of components, the greater the buffer capacity. For most laboratory-scale applications, concentrations of about 0.50 *M* are suitable, but often the decision is based on availability of stock solutions.

Suppose you have a large stock of 0.40 *M* HCOOH and you need approximately 1.0 L of final buffer. A mole-to-gram calculation gives the amount (mol) of sodium formate you will need:

$$\text{Moles of HCOOH} = 1.0 \text{ L soln} \times \frac{0.40 \text{ mol HCOOH}}{1.0 \text{ L soln}} = 0.40 \text{ mol HCOOH}$$

$$\text{Moles of HCOONa} = 0.40 \text{ mol HCOOH} \times \frac{1.4 \text{ mol HCOONa}}{1.0 \text{ mol HCOOH}} = 0.56 \text{ mol HCOONa}$$

$$\text{Mass (g) of HCOONa} = 0.56 \text{ mol HCOONa} \times \frac{68.01 \text{ g HCOONa}}{1 \text{ mol HCOONa}} = 38 \text{ g HCOONa}$$

4. *Mix the solution and adjust the pH.* The buffer is prepared by thoroughly dissolving 38 g solid sodium formate in 0.40 *M* HCOOH to a total volume of 1.0 L. Due to the behavior of nonideal solutions (Section 13.5) and other ionic phenomena, a buffer prepared this way may vary from the desired pH by as much as several tenths of a pH unit. Therefore, after making up the solution, *adjust the buffer pH* to the desired value by adding strong acid or strong base, while monitoring the solution with a pH meter. The following sample problem does not refer to the Henderson-Hasselbalch equation.

Sample Problem 19.2 Preparing a Buffer

PROBLEM An environmental chemist needs a carbonate buffer of pH 10.00 to study the effects of the acidification of limestone-rich soils. How many grams of Na_2CO_3 must she add to 1.5 L of freshly prepared 0.20 *M* $NaHCO_3$ to make the buffer? K_a of $HCO_3^- = 4.7 \times 10^{-11}$.

PLAN The conjugate pair is already chosen, HCO_3^- (acid) and CO_3^{2-} (base), as are the volume and concentration of HCO_3^-, so we must find the component ratio that gives pH 10.00 and the mass of Na_2CO_3 to dissolve. We first convert pH to $[H_3O^+]$ and use the K_a expression from the equation to solve for the $[CO_3^{2-}]$ required. Multiplying by the volume of solution gives the amount (mol) of CO_3^{2-} required, and then we use the molar mass to find the mass (g) of Na_2CO_3.

SOLUTION Calculating $[H_3O^+]$: $[H_3O^+] = 10^{-pH} = 10^{-10.00} = 1.0 \times 10^{-10} M$
Solving for the $[CO_3^{2-}]$ in the component ratio:

$$HCO_3^-(aq) + H_2O(l) \rightleftharpoons H_3O^+(aq) + CO_3^{2-}(aq) \quad K_a = \frac{[H_3O^+][CO_3^{2-}]}{[HCO_3^-]}$$

So

$$[CO_3^{2-}] = \frac{K_a \times [HCO_3^-]}{[H_3O^+]} = \frac{(4.7 \times 10^{-11})(0.20)}{1.0 \times 10^{-10}} = 0.094 M$$

Calculating the amount (mol) of CO_3^{2-} needed for the given volume:

$$\text{Moles of } CO_3^{2-} = 1.5 \text{ L soln} \times \frac{0.094 \text{ mol } CO_3^{2-}}{1 \text{ L soln}} = 0.14 \text{ mol } CO_3^{2-}$$

Calculating the mass (g) of Na_2CO_3 needed:

$$\text{Mass (g) of } Na_2CO_3 = 0.14 \text{ mol } Na_2CO_3 \times \frac{105.99 \text{ g } Na_2CO_3}{1 \text{ mol } Na_2CO_3} = \boxed{15 \text{ g } Na_2CO_3}$$

We dissolve 15 g Na_2CO_3 into 1.3 L of 0.20 M $NaHCO_3$ and add 0.20 M $NaHCO_3$ to make 1.5 L. Using a pH meter, we adjust the pH to 10.00 with strong acid or base.
CHECK For a useful buffer range, the acidic component, $[HCO_3^-]$, must be within a factor of 10 of the basic component, $[CO_3^{2-}]$. We have 1.5 L × 0.20 M HCO_3^-, or 0.30 mol HCO_3^-, and 0.14 mol CO_3^{2-}; 0.30:0.14 = 2.1, so this seems fine. Make sure the relative amounts of components seem reasonable: since we want a pH lower than the pK_a of HCO_3^- (10.33), it makes sense that we have more of the acidic than the basic species.

Follow-up Problem 19.2 How would you prepare a benzoic acid/benzoate buffer with pH = 4.25, starting with 5.0 L of 0.050 M sodium benzoate (C_6H_5COONa) solution and adding the acidic component? K_a of benzoic acid (C_6H_5COOH) = 6.3×10^{-5}.

Another way to prepare a buffer is to form one of the components during the final mixing step by *partial neutralization* of the other component. For example, you can prepare an $HCOOH/HCOO^-$ buffer by mixing appropriate amounts of $HCOOH$ solution and $NaOH$ solution. As the OH^- ions react with the $HCOOH$ molecules, neutralization of part of the total $HCOOH$ present produces the $HCOO^-$ needed:

$HCOOH$ (HA total) + OH^- (amt added) $\longrightarrow$
$\qquad$ $HCOOH$ (HA total − OH^- amt added) + $HCOO^-$ (OH^- amt added) + H_2O

This method of preparing a buffer is based on the same chemical process that occurs when a weak acid is titrated with a strong base, as you'll see in the next section.

Section Summary

A buffered solution exhibits a much smaller change in pH when H_3O^+ or OH^- is added than does an unbuffered solution. A buffer consists of relatively high concentrations of the components of a conjugate weak acid-base pair. The buffer-component concentration ratio determines the pH, and the ratio and pH are related by the Henderson-Hasselbalch equation. As H_3O^+ or OH^- is added, one buffer component reacts with it and is converted into the other component, so the buffer-component ratio, and thus the free $[H_3O^+]$ (and pH), changes only slightly. A concentrated buffer undergoes smaller changes in pH than a dilute buffer. When the buffer pH equals the pK_a of the acid component, the buffer has its highest capacity. A buffer has an effective range of $pK_a \pm 1$ pH unit. When preparing a buffer, you choose the conjugate acid-base pair, calculate the ratio of buffer components, determine the buffer concentration, and adjust the final solution to the desired pH.

19.2 Acid-Base Titration Curves

In Chapter 4, we discussed acid-base titrations as a common analytical method. Let's reexamine this method, this time tracking the change in pH with an **acid-base titration curve,** a plot of pH vs. volume of titrant added. The behavior of an acid-base indicator and its role in the titration are described first. To better understand the titration process, we apply the principles of the acid-base behavior of salt solutions (Section 18.7) and, later in the section, the principles of buffer action.

Acid-Base Indicators and the Measurement of pH

The two common devices for measuring pH in the laboratory are pH meters and acid-base indicators. (We discuss the operation of pH meters in Chapter 21.) An **acid-base indicator** is a weak organic acid (which we denote here as HIn) that has a different color than its conjugate base (In$^-$), with the color change occurring over a specific and relatively narrow pH range. Typically, one or both of the forms are intensely colored, so only a tiny amount of indicator is needed, far too little to affect the pH of the test solution.

Indicators are used for estimating the pH of a solution and for approximate monitoring of pH in acid-base titrations and in reactions. Figure 19.4 shows the colors and the pH range for the color change of some common acid-base indicators. Selecting an indicator requires that you know the approximate pH of the titration end point, which in turn requires that you know the ionic species present. You'll see how this is known shortly, in our discussion of acid-base titration curves.

Since the indicator molecule is a weak acid, the ratio of the two forms is governed by the [H$_3$O$^+$] of the test solution:

$$\text{HIn}(aq) + \text{H}_2\text{O}(l) \rightleftharpoons \text{H}_3\text{O}^+(aq) + \text{In}^-(aq) \qquad K_a \text{ of HIn} = \frac{[\text{H}_3\text{O}^+][\text{In}^-]}{[\text{HIn}]}$$

Therefore,
$$\frac{[\text{HIn}]}{[\text{In}^-]} = \frac{[\text{H}_3\text{O}^+]}{K_a}$$

How we perceive colors has a major influence on the use of indicators. Typically, the experimenter will see the HIn color if the [HIn]/[In$^-$] ratio is 10:1 or greater and the In$^-$ color if the [HIn]/[In$^-$] ratio is 1:10 or less. Between these extremes, the colors of the two forms are merged into an

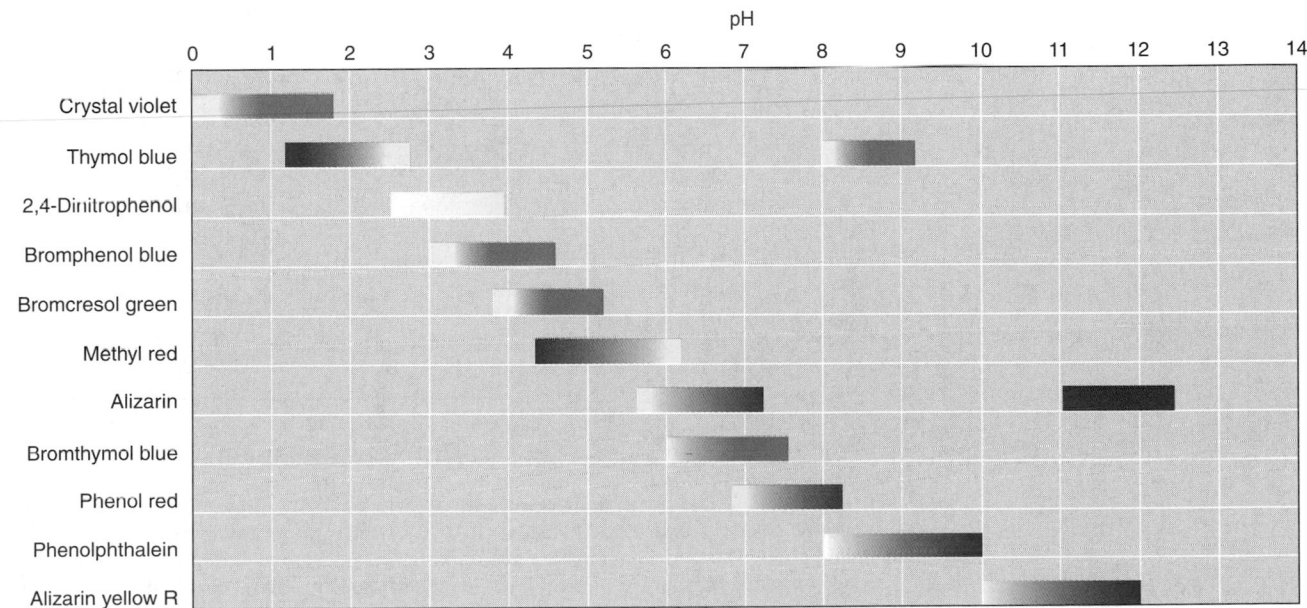

Figure 19.4 **Colors and approximate pH range of some common acid-base indicators.** Most indicators have a pH range of about two units, in keeping with a useful buffer range of about two units (p$K_a \pm 1$). (The specific pH range depends to some extent on the solvent used to prepare the indicator.)

Figure 19.5 The color change of the indicator bromthymol blue. Indicators are weak organic acids whose acidic and basic forms have different colors. The color change takes place over a pH range of about two units. The acidic form of bromthymol blue is yellow (*left*) and the basic form is blue (*right*). Over the pH range when the indicator is changing, both forms are present, so the mixture appears greenish (*center*).

intermediate hue. Therefore, an indicator has a *color range* that reflects a 100-fold range in the [HIn]/[In] ratio, which means that an *indicator changes color over a range of about two pH units.* For example, as you can see in Figure 19.4, bromthymol blue has a pH range of about 6.0 to 7.6, and as Figure 19.5 shows, it is yellow below that range, blue above it, and greenish in between.

Strong Acid–Strong Base Titration Curves

A typical curve for the titration of a strong acid with a strong base appears in Figure 19.6, along with the data used to construct it. There are three distinct regions of the curve, which correspond to three major changes in slope:
1. The pH starts out low, reflecting the high $[H_3O^+]$ of the strong acid, and increases gradually as acid is neutralized by the added base.
2. Suddenly, the pH rises steeply. This rise begins when the moles of OH^- that have been added nearly equal the moles of H_3O^+ originally present in the acid. An additional drop or two of base neutralizes the final tiny excess of acid and introduces a tiny excess of base, so the pH jumps 6 to 8 units.
3. Beyond this steep portion, the pH increases slowly again as more base is added.

The **equivalence point,** which occurs within the nearly vertical portion of the curve, is the point at which the *number of moles of added OH⁻ equals the number of moles of H₃O⁺ originally present.* At the equivalence point of a strong acid–strong base titration, *the solution consists of the anion of a strong acid and the cation of a strong base.* Recall from Chapter 18 that *these ions do not react with*

Volume of NaOH added (mL)	pH
00.00	1.00
10.00	1.22
20.00	1.48
30.00	1.85
35.00	2.18
39.00	2.89
39.50	3.20
39.75	3.50
39.90	3.90
39.95	4.20
39.99	4.90
40.00	7.00
40.01	9.40
40.05	9.80
40.10	10.40
40.25	10.50
40.50	10.79
41.00	11.09
45.00	11.76
50.00	12.05
60.00	12.30
70.00	12.43
80.00	12.52

A

B

Figure 19.6 Curve for a strong acid–strong base titration. A, Data obtained from the titration of 40.00 mL of 0.1000 *M* HCl with 0.1000 *M* NaOH are plotted in **B** to give an acid-base titration curve. The pH increases gradually at first. When the amount (mol) of OH⁻ added is slightly less than the amount (mol) of H₃O⁺ originally present, a large pH change accompanies a small addition of OH⁻. The equivalence point occurs when amount (mol) OH⁻ added = amount (mol) H₃O⁺ originally present. Note that, for a strong acid–strong base titration, pH = 7.00 at the equivalence point. Added before the titration begins, either methyl red or phenolphthalein is a suitable indicator in this case because each changes color on the steep portion of the curve, as shown by the color strips. Photos of the color changes from 1–2 drops of indicator appear nearby. Beyond this point, added OH⁻ causes a gradual pH increase again.

water, so the solution is neutral, pH = 7.00. The volume and concentration of base needed to reach the equivalence point allow us to calculate the amount of acid originally present (see Sample Problem 4.5, p. 145).

Before the titration begins, we add a few drops of an appropriate indicator to the acid solution to signal when we reach the equivalence point. The **end point** of the titration occurs when the indicator changes color. *We choose an indicator with an end point close to the equivalence point,* one that changes color in the pH range on the steep vertical portion of the curve. Figure 19.6 shows the color changes for two indicators that are suitable for a strong acid–strong base titration. Methyl red changes from red at pH 4.2 to yellow at pH 6.3, whereas phenolphthalein changes from colorless at pH 8.3 to pink at pH 10.0. Even though neither color change occurs *at* the equivalence point (pH 7.00), both occur on the vertical portion of the curve, where a single drop of base causes a large pH change: when methyl red turns yellow, or when phenolphthalein turns pink, we know we are within a fraction of a drop from the equivalence point. For example, in going from 39.90 to 39.99 mL, one to two drops, the pH changes one whole unit. For all practical purposes, then, the *visible* change in color of the indicator (end point) signals the *invisible* point at which moles of added base equal the original moles of acid (equivalence point).

By knowing the chemical species present during the titration, we can calculate the pH at various points along the way. In Figure 19.6, 40.00 mL of 0.1000 M HCl is titrated with 0.1000 M NaOH. Since a strong acid is completely dissociated, [HCl] = [H_3O^+] = 0.1000 M. Therefore, the initial pH is*

$$pH = -\log{[H_3O^+]} = -\log{(0.1000)} = 1.00$$

As soon as we start adding titrant, two changes occur that we must keep in mind and incorporate into the pH calculations: (1) some acid is neutralized, and (2) the volume of solution is increased. To find the pH at various points during the titration, we find the amount (mol) of H_3O^+ (or OH^-) present and then use the change in volume to calculate the [H_3O^+] (or [OH^-]) and convert to pH. As an example, let's calculate the pH at three points along the titration curve:

1. *Before the equivalence point.* After adding 20.00 mL of 0.1000 M NaOH:
- *Find the moles of H_3O^+ remaining.* Subtracting the number of moles of H_3O^+ reacted from the number originally present gives the number remaining. Moles of H_3O^+ reacted equals moles of OH^- added, so

$$
\begin{array}{ll}
\text{Initial moles of } H_3O^+ = 0.04000 \text{ L} \times 0.1000\ M = 0.004000 \text{ mol } H_3O^+ \\
-\text{Moles of } OH^- \text{ added} = 0.02000 \text{ L} \times 0.1000\ M = 0.002000 \text{ mol } OH^- \\
\hline
\text{Moles of } H_3O^+ \text{ remaining} = \qquad\qquad\qquad\qquad 0.002000 \text{ mol } H_3O^+
\end{array}
$$

- *Calculate [H_3O^+], taking the total volume into account.* We add one solution to another in a titration, so *the volume increases.* To find the ion concentrations, we use the *total volume* because the water of one solution dilutes the ions of the other:

$$[H_3O^+] = \frac{\text{amount (mol) of } H_3O^+ \text{ remaining}}{\text{original volume of acid} + \text{volume of added base}}$$

$$= \frac{0.002000 \text{ mol } H_3O^+}{0.04000 \text{ L} + 0.02000 \text{ L}} = 0.03333\ M \qquad pH = 1.48$$

Given the moles of OH^- added, we are halfway to the equivalence point; but we are still on the initial slow rise of the curve, so the pH is still very low. Similar calculations give values up to the equivalence point.

---

*In acid-base titrations, volumes and concentrations are usually known to four significant figures, but pH is generally reported to no more than two digits to the right of the decimal point.

2. *At the equivalence point.* After adding 40.00 mL of 0.1000 M NaOH: When the equivalence point is reached, all the H_3O^+ from the acid has been neutralized, and the solution contains Na^+ and Cl^-, neither of which reacts with water. Because of the autoionization of water, however,

$$[H_3O^+] = 1.0\times10^{-7}\ M \qquad pH = 7.00$$

In this example 0.004000 mol OH^- reacted with 0.004000 mol H_3O^+ to reach the equivalence point.

3. *After the equivalence point.* After adding 50.00 mL of 0.1000 M NaOH: From the equivalence point on, the pH calculation is based on the moles of *excess* OH^- present. After adding 50.00 mL of NaOH, we have

$$\begin{array}{rl} \text{Total moles of } OH^- \text{ added} = & 0.05000\ L \times 0.1000\ M = 0.005000\ \text{mol } OH^- \\ -\text{Moles of } H_3O^+ \text{ consumed} = & 0.04000\ L \times 0.1000\ M = 0.004000\ \text{mol } H_3O^+ \\ \hline \text{Moles of excess } OH^- = & 0.001000\ \text{mol } OH^- \end{array}$$

$$[OH^-] = \frac{0.001000\ \text{mol } OH^-}{0.04000\ L + 0.05000\ L} = 0.01111\ M \qquad pOH = 1.95$$

$$pH = pK_w - pOH = 14.00 - 1.95 = 12.05$$

Weak Acid–Strong Base Titration Curves

Now let's turn to the titration of a weak acid with a strong base. Figure 19.7 shows the curve obtained when we use 0.1000 M NaOH to titrate 40.00 mL of 0.1000 M propanoic acid, a weak organic acid (CH_3CH_2COOH; $K_a = 1.3\times10^{-5}$). (We abbreviate the acid as HPr and the conjugate base, $CH_3CH_2COO^-$, as Pr^-.) When we compare this weak acid–strong base titration curve with the strong acid–strong base titration curve (dotted curve portion in Figure 19.7 corresponds to the bottom half of the curve in Figure 19.6), three major differences appear:

- *The initial pH is higher.* Because the weak acid (HPr) dissociates only slightly, less H_3O^+ is present than with a strong acid of the same concentration.
- *A gradually rising portion of the curve, called the buffer region, appears before the steep rise to the equivalence point.* As HPr reacts with the strong base, a significant amount of the conjugate base (Pr^-) forms, which creates an HPr/Pr^- buffer. Note, especially, the midpoint of the buffer region. At this point, *half the original HPr has reacted*, so [HPr] = [Pr^-], or [Pr^-]/[HPr] = 1. Therefore, *at the midpoint of the buffer region, the pH equals the pK_a:*

$$pH = pK_a + \log\left(\frac{[Pr^-]}{[HPr]}\right) = pK_a + \log 1 = pK_a$$

In fact, observing the pH at the midpoint of the buffer region is a common experimental method for estimating the pK_a of an unknown acid.

- *The pH at the equivalence point is greater than 7.00.* The solution contains the strong-base cation Na^+, which does not react with water, and the weak-acid anion Pr^-, which acts as a weak base to accept a proton from H_2O and yield OH^-.

Our choice of indicator is more limited here than in a strong acid–strong base titration because the steep rise occurs over a smaller pH range. Phenolphthalein is suitable because its color change lies within this range (Figure 19.7). However, the figure shows that methyl red, our other choice for the strong acid–strong base titration, changes color earlier and slowly over a

Titration of 40.00 mL of 0.1000 M HPr with 0.1000 M NaOH

Figure 19.7 Curve for a weak acid–strong base titration. The curve for the titration of 40.00 mL of 0.1000 M CH$_3$CH$_2$COOH (HPr) with 0.1000 M NaOH is shown and compared with that for the strong acid HCl (*dotted curve portion*). The initial pH is higher than for a strong acid because HPr dissociates only slightly. At the midpoint of the buffer region, [HPr] = [Pr^-], so pH = pK_a. The pH at the equivalence point is greater than 7.00 because the solution contains the weak base Pr^-. Phenolphthalein (*photo*) is a suitable indicator for this titration, but methyl red is not because its color changes over a large volume range.

large volume (~10 mL) of titrant, thereby giving a vague and false indication of the equivalence point.

The calculation procedure for the weak acid–strong base titration is different from the previous case because we have to consider the partial dissociation of the weak acid and the reaction of the conjugate base with water. There are four key regions of the titration curve, each of which requires a different type of calculation to find $[H_3O^+]$:

1. *Solution of HA.* Before base is added, the $[H_3O^+]$ is that of a weak-acid solution, so we find $[H_3O^+]$ as in Section 18.4: we set up a reaction table with $x = [HPr]_{dissoc}$, assume $[H_3O^+] = [HPr]_{dissoc} \ll [HPr]_{init}$, and solve for x. That is,

$$K_a = \frac{[H_3O^+][Pr^-]}{[HPr]} \approx \frac{x^2}{[HPr]}$$

Therefore, $\qquad x = [H_3O^+] \approx \sqrt{K_a \times [HPr]_{init}}$

2. *Solution of HA and added base.* As soon as we add NaOH, it reacts with HPr to form Pr^-. This means that up to the equivalence point, we have a mixture of acid and conjugate base, and a buffer solution exists over much of that interval. Therefore, we find $[H_3O^+]$ by the relationship

$$[H_3O^+] = K_a \times \frac{[HPr]}{[Pr^-]}$$

(Of course, we can find pH directly with the Henderson-Hasselbalch equation, which is just an alternative form of this relationship.) Note that in this calculation we do *not* have to consider the new total volume because *the volumes cancel in the ratio of concentrations.* That is, $[HPr]/[Pr^-]$ = moles of HPr/moles of Pr^-, so we need not calculate concentrations.

3. *Equivalent amounts of HA and added base.* At the equivalence point, the original amount of HPr has reacted, so the flask contains a solution of Pr^-, a weak base that reacts with water to form OH^-:

$$Pr^-(aq) + H_2O(l) \rightleftharpoons HPr(aq) + OH^-(aq)$$

Therefore, as mentioned previously, in a weak acid–strong base titration, the solution at the equivalence point is slightly basic, pH > 7.00. We calculate $[H_3O^+]$ as in Section 18.5: we first find K_b of Pr^- from K_a of HPr, set up a reaction table (assume $[Pr^-] \gg [Pr^-]_{reacting}$), and solve for $[OH^-]$. Since we need a single concentration, $[Pr^-]$, to solve for $[OH^-]$, we *do* need the total volume. Then, we convert to $[H_3O^+]$. These two steps are

(1) $[OH^-] \approx \sqrt{K_b \times [Pr^-]}$, where $K_b = \dfrac{K_w}{K_a}$ and $[Pr^-] = \dfrac{\text{moles of } HPr_{init}}{\text{total volume}}$

(2) $[H_3O^+] = \dfrac{K_w}{[OH^-]}$

Combining them into one step gives

$$[H_3O^+] \approx \frac{K_w}{\sqrt{K_b \times [Pr^-]}}$$

4. *Solution of excess added base.* Beyond the equivalence point, we are just adding excess OH^- ion, so the calculation is the same as for the strong acid–strong base titration:

$$[H_3O^+] = \frac{K_w}{[OH^-]}, \qquad \text{where } [OH^-] = \frac{\text{moles of excess } OH^-}{\text{total volume}}$$

Sample Problem 19.3 shows the overall approach.

Sample Problem 19.3 Calculating the pH During a Weak Acid–Strong Base Titration

PROBLEM Calculate the pH during the titration of 40.00 mL of 0.1000 M propanoic acid (HPr; $K_a = 1.3 \times 10^{-5}$) after adding the following volumes of 0.1000 M NaOH:
(a) 0.00 mL **(b)** 30.00 mL **(c)** 40.00 mL **(d)** 50.00 mL

PLAN (a) 0.00 mL: Since no base has been added, this is a weak-acid solution. Thus, we calculate the pH as we did in Section 18.4. **(b)** 30.00 mL: A mixture of Pr⁻ and HPr is present. We find the amount (mol) of each, substitute into the K_a expression to solve for [H₃O⁺], and convert to pH. **(c)** 40.00 mL: The amount (mol) of NaOH added equals the initial amount (mol) of HPr, so a solution of the weak base Pr⁻ exists. We calculate the pH as we did in Section 18.5, except that we need *total* volume to find [Pr⁻]. **(d)** 50.00 mL: Excess NaOH is added, so we calculate the amount (mol) of excess OH⁻ in the total volume, convert to [H₃O⁺] and then pH.

SOLUTION (a) 0.00 mL of 0.1000 M NaOH added. Following the approach used in Sample Problem 18.7 and just described in text, we obtain

$$[H_3O^+] \approx \sqrt{K_a \times [\text{HPr}]_{\text{init}}} = \sqrt{(1.3 \times 10^{-5})(0.1000)} = 1.1 \times 10^{-3} \ M$$

$$\text{pH} = 2.96$$

(b) 30.00 mL of 0.1000 M NaOH added. Calculating the ratio of moles of HPr to moles of Pr⁻:

Original moles of HPr = 0.04000 L × 0.1000 M = 0.004000 mol HPr
Moles of NaOH added = 0.03000 L × 0.1000 M = 0.003000 mol OH⁻

Since 1 mol NaOH reacts to form 1 mol Pr⁻, we construct the following reaction table for the stoichiometry:

AMOUNT (mol)	HPr(*aq*)	+	OH⁻(*aq*)	⟶	Pr⁻(*aq*)	+	H₂O(*l*)
Before addition	0.004000		—		0		—
Addition	—		0.003000		—		—
After addition	0.001000		0		0.003000		—

The last line of this table shows the new initial amounts of HPr and Pr⁻ that will react to attain a new equilibrium. However, since x is very small, we assume that the [HPr]/[Pr⁻] ratio at equilibrium is essentially equal to the ratio of these new initial amounts (see Comment in Sample Problem 19.1). Thus,

$$\frac{[\text{HPr}]}{[\text{Pr}^-]} = \frac{0.001000 \ \text{mol}}{0.003000 \ \text{mol}} = 0.3333$$

Solving for [H₃O⁺]:

$$[H_3O^+] = K_a \times \frac{[\text{HPr}]}{[\text{Pr}^-]} = (1.3 \times 10^{-5})(0.3333) = 4.3 \times 10^{-6} \ M$$

$$\text{pH} = 5.37$$

(c) 40.00 mL of 0.1000 M NaOH added. Calculating [Pr⁻] after all HPr has reacted:

$$[\text{Pr}^-] = \frac{0.004000 \ \text{mol}}{0.04000 \ \text{L} + 0.04000 \ \text{L}} = 0.05000 \ M$$

Calculating K_b:

$$K_b = \frac{K_w}{K_a} = \frac{1.0 \times 10^{-14}}{1.3 \times 10^{-5}} = 7.7 \times 10^{-10}$$

Solving for [H₃O⁺] as described in text:

$$[H_3O^+] \approx \frac{K_w}{\sqrt{K_b \times [\text{Pr}^-]}} = \frac{1.0 \times 10^{-14}}{\sqrt{(7.7 \times 10^{-10})(0.05000)}} = 1.6 \times 10^{-9} \ M$$

$$\text{pH} = 8.80$$

(d) 50.00 mL of 0.1000 M NaOH added.
Moles of excess OH⁻ = 0.1000 M × (0.05000 L − 0.04000 L) = 0.001000 mol

$$[\text{OH}^-] = \frac{\text{moles of excess OH}^-}{\text{total volume}} = \frac{0.001000 \ \text{mol}}{0.09000 \ \text{L}} = 0.01111 \ M$$

$$[H_3O^+] = \frac{K_w}{[\text{OH}^-]} = \frac{1.0 \times 10^{-14}}{0.01111} = 9.0 \times 10^{-13} \ M$$

$$\text{pH} = 12.05$$

CHECK As expected from the continuous addition of base, the pH increases through the four stages. Be sure to round off and check the arithmetic along the way.

Follow-up Problem 19.3 When 20.00 mL of 0.2000 M HBrO is titrated with 0.1000 M NaOH, what is the pH **(a)** before any base is added; **(b)** when [HBrO] = [BrO$^-$]; **(c)** at the equivalence point; **(d)** when the moles of OH$^-$ added is twice the moles of HBrO originally present? **(e)** Sketch the titration curve. K_a of HBrO = 2.3×10^{-9}.

Weak Base–Strong Acid Titration Curves

In the previous case, we titrated a weak acid with a strong base. The opposite process is the titration of a weak base (NH$_3$) with a strong acid (HCl), shown in Figure 19.8. Note that *the curve has the same shape as the weak acid–strong base curve* (Figure 19.7), *but it is inverted.* Thus, the regions of the curve have the same features, but *the pH decreases* throughout the process:

1. The initial solution is that of a weak base, so *the pH starts out above 7.00.*
2. The pH decreases gradually in the buffer region, where significant amounts of base (NH$_3$) and conjugate acid (NH$_4^+$) exist. At the midpoint of the buffer region, *the pH equals the pK$_a$ of the ammonium ion.*
3. After the buffer region, the curve drops vertically to the equivalence point, at which all the NH$_3$ has reacted and the solution contains only NH$_4^+$ and Cl$^-$. Note that *the pH at the equivalence point is below 7.00* because Cl$^-$ does not react with water and NH$_4^+$ is acidic:

$$NH_4^+(aq) + H_2O(l) \rightleftharpoons NH_3(aq) + H_3O^+(aq)$$

4. Beyond the equivalence point, the pH decreases slowly as *excess H$_3$O$^+$* is added.

In this titration, we must also be more careful in the choice of indicator than for a strong acid–strong base titration. Phenolphthalein changes color too soon and too slowly to indicate the equivalence point. Methyl red, on the other hand, lies on the steep portion of the curve and straddles the equivalence point, so it is a perfect choice.

Titration Curves for Polyprotic Acids

As we discussed in Section 17.4, polyprotic acids have more than one ionizable proton. Except for sulfuric acid, the common polyprotic acids are all weak. The successive K_a values for a polyprotic acid differ by several orders of magnitude, which means that the first H$^+$ is lost much more easily than subsequent ones, as these values for sulfurous acid show:

$$H_2SO_3(aq) + H_2O(l) \rightleftharpoons HSO_3^-(aq) + H_3O^+(aq)$$
$$K_{a1} = 1.4 \times 10^{-2} \quad \text{and} \quad pK_{a1} = 1.85$$
$$HSO_3^-(aq) + H_2O(l) \rightleftharpoons SO_3^{2-}(aq) + H_3O^+(aq)$$
$$K_{a2} = 6.5 \times 10^{-8} \quad \text{and} \quad pK_{a2} = 7.19$$

In a titration of a diprotic acid such as H$_2$SO$_3$, 2 OH$^-$ ions are required to completely remove both ionizable H$^+$ ions from 1 molecule of acid. Because of the large difference in K_a values, for calculation purposes, each mole of H$^+$ is titrated separately; that is, we can assume that all the H$_2$SO$_3$ molecules lose one H$^+$ ion before any of the HSO$_3^-$ ions lose one:

$$H_2SO_3 \xrightarrow{\text{1 mol OH}^-} HSO_3^- \xrightarrow{\text{1 mol OH}^-} SO_3^{2-}$$

Titration of 40.00 mL of 0.1000 M NH$_3$ with 0.1000 M HCl

[NH$_3$] = [NH$_4^+$]

Buffer region

Phenolphthalein

pK$_a$ of NH$_4^+$ = 9.25

Methyl red

pH = 5.27 at equivalence point

Volume of HCl added (mL)

Figure 19.8 Curve for a weak base–strong acid titration. Titrating 40.00 mL of 0.1000 M NH$_3$ with a solution of 0.1000 M HCl leads to a curve whose shape is the same as that of the weak acid–strong base curve in Figure 19.7 but inverted. The midpoint of the buffer region occurs when [NH$_3$] = [NH$_4^+$]; the pH at this point equals the pK$_a$ of NH$_4^+$. The pH of the equivalence point is below 7.00 because the solution contains the weak acid NH$_4^+$. Methyl red (*photo*) is a suitable indicator here, but phenolphthalein is not because its color changes over a large volume range.

Figure 19.9 Curve for the titration of a weak polyprotic acid.
Titrating 40.00 mL of 0.1000 M H_2SO_3 with 0.1000 M NaOH leads to a curve with two buffer regions and two equivalence points. Because the K_a values are separated by several orders of magnitude, in effect the titration curve looks like two weak acid–strong base curves attached. The pH of the first equivalence point is below 7.00 because the solution contains HSO_3^-, which is a stronger acid than it is a base (K_a of $HSO_3^- = 6.5\times10^{-8}$; K_b of $HSO_3^- = 7.1\times10^{-13}$).

Titration of 40.00 mL of 0.1000 M H_2SO_3 with 0.1000 M NaOH

$pK_{a2} = 7.19$

$[HSO_3^-] = [SO_3^{2-}]$

Buffer region

pH = 9.86 at second equivalence point

pH = 4.25 at first equivalence point

$[H_2SO_3] = [HSO_3^-]$

$pK_{a1} = 1.85$

Buffer region

Volume of NaOH added (mL)

◆ **Polyprotic Proteins and Human Disease** If a red blood cell were enlarged 300 million times, it would be the approximate size and shape of the Rose Bowl piled high with 280 million grapefruit-sized molecules of hemoglobin, the oxygen-carrying protein. Two amino acids in hemoglobin are particularly critical to the molecules' ability to move around each other while packed so tightly, and this freedom of movement contributes to the cell's normal shape (*rounded cells in photo*). These two amino acids have negatively charged (—COO$^-$) R groups. In the inherited mutation that causes sickle cell anemia, abnormal hemoglobin molecules have uncharged (—CH$_3$) groups replacing the two charged ones. This change in just 2 of hemoglobin's 574 amino acids lowers charge repulsions between hemoglobin molecules enough for them to clump together into fiber-like structures, which leads to the sickle shape of the blood cell (*elongated cells in photo*). The clumped cells block capillaries, and the painful course of sickle cell anemia usually ends in early death.

Figure 19.9 shows the titration curve for sulfurous acid with strong base. As you can see, the loss of each mole of H$^+$ shows up as a separate equivalence point and buffer region. Like the curve for a weak monoprotic acid, the pH at the midpoint of the buffer region is equal to the pK_a of that acidic species. Note also that the same volume of added base (in this case, 40.00 mL of 0.1000 M OH$^-$) is required to remove each mole of H$^+$.

Amino acids, the compounds that link together to form proteins (Section 15.6), have the general formula NH$_2$—CH(R)—COOH, where R can be one of about 20 different groups. At low pH, both the amino group (—NH$_2$) and the acid group (—COOH) are protonated: $^+$NH$_3$—CH(R)—COOH. Thus, in this form the amino acid behaves like a polyprotic acid in a titration. In the case of glycine (R = H), the simplest amino acid, the dissociation reactions and pK_a values are

$$^+NH_3CH_2COOH(aq) + H_2O(l) \rightleftharpoons {}^+NH_3CH_2COO^-(aq) + H_3O^+(aq) \qquad pK_{a1} = 2.35$$

$$^+NH_3CH_2COO^-(aq) + H_2O(l) \rightleftharpoons NH_2CH_2COO^-(aq) + H_3O^+(aq) \qquad pK_{a2} = 9.78$$

The pK_a values show that the —COOH group is much more acidic than the —NH$_3^+$ group. As with H$_2$SO$_3$, the protons are titrated separately, so virtually all the —COOH protons are removed before any —NH$_3^+$ protons are:

1 mol OH$^-$ 1 mol OH$^-$

zwitterion

Thus, at physiological pH ($\sim$7), *glycine exists predominantly as* $^+$NH$_3$CH$_2$COO$^-$ (middle structure above). This form is called a *zwitterion,* a species with opposite charges on the same molecule (German *zwitter,* "double"). Among the 20 different R groups of the amino acids found in proteins, several have *additional* —COO$^-$ or —NH$_3^+$ groups at pH 7. When amino acids are linked into proteins, these charged R groups give the protein its overall charge and sometimes play a major role in its function. ◆

An acid-base (pH) indicator is a weak acid with differently colored acidic and basic forms that change color over about two pH units. In a strong acid–strong base titration, the pH starts out low, rises slowly, then shoots up near the equivalence point (pH = 7). In a weak acid–strong base titration, the pH starts out higher than in the strong acid titration, rises slowly in the buffer region (pH = pK_a at the midpoint), then rises more quickly near the equivalence point (pH > 7). A weak base–strong acid titration is the inverse of this, with its pH decreasing to the equivalence point (pH < 7). Polyprotic acids have two or more acidic protons, and each is titrated separately.

19.3 Equilibria of Slightly Soluble Ionic Compounds

The next type of aqueous equilibrium we explore is that of slightly soluble ionic compounds. In Chapter 13, we found that most solutes, even those called "soluble," have a limited solubility in a particular solvent. Add more than this amount, and some solute remains undissolved. In a saturated solution at a particular temperature, equilibrium exists between the undissolved and dissolved solute. Slightly soluble (often called "insoluble") ionic compounds have a relatively low solubility, so they reach equilibrium with relatively little solute dissolved. At this point, it would be a good idea for you to review the solubility rules in Table 4.1 (p. 141).

When a soluble ionic compound dissolves in water, it dissociates completely into ions. In this discussion, we will assume that the small amount of a slightly soluble ionic compound that dissolves in water dissociates completely into ions also. In reality, however, this is not the case. Solutions of slightly soluble salts, particularly those of many transition metals and heavy main-group metals, often contain other species that are partially dissociated or undissociated. For example, when lead(II) chloride is thoroughly stirred in water (see photo), the solution contains not only the expected $Pb^{2+}(aq)$ and $Cl^-(aq)$ ions, but also undissociated molecules of $PbCl_2(aq)$ and $PbCl^+(aq)$ ions. More advanced courses address these complexities, but we will only hint at some of them in the sample problem Comments. Keep in mind, however, that our simple calculations based on complete dissociation are best treated as first approximations.

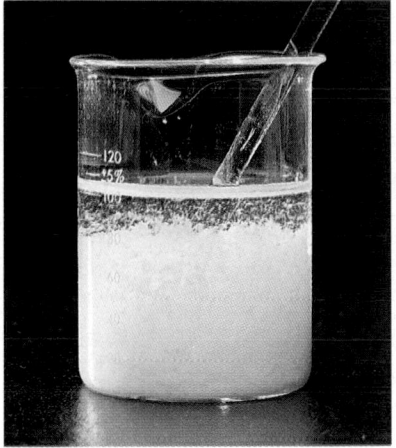

$PbCl_2$, a slightly soluble ionic compound.

The Ion-Product Expression (Q_{sp}) and the Solubility-Product Constant (K_{sp})

Making the assumption of complete dissociation for slightly soluble ionic compounds, *equilibrium exists between solid solute and dissolved ions*. For example, lead(II) sulfate dissolves only to the extent of 0.04 g/L water at 25°C, but whatever dissolves exists as separated lead(II) ions and sulfate ions:

$$PbSO_4(s) \rightleftharpoons Pb^{2+}(aq) + SO_4^{2-}(aq)$$

As with all the other equilibrium systems we've looked at, the equilibrium condition for a saturated solution can be expressed by a reaction quotient. For the lead(II) sulfate case, we have

$$Q_c = \frac{[Pb^{2+}][SO_4^{2-}]}{[PbSO_4]}$$

As in previous cases, we combine the constant value of $[PbSO_4]$ with the value of Q_c and eliminate it. This gives the ion-product expression, Q_{sp}:

$$Q_{sp} = Q_c[PbSO_4] = [Pb^{2+}][SO_4^{2-}]$$

When solid $PbSO_4$ attains equilibrium with Pb^{2+} and SO_4^{2-} ions, that is, when the solution reaches saturation, the numerical value of Q_{sp} attains a constant value. This new equilibrium constant is called the **solubility-product constant, K_{sp}.** The value of K_{sp} for $PbSO_4$ at 25°C, for example, is 1.6×10^{-8}.

As with other equilibrium constants, a particular K_{sp} value depends only on the temperature, not on the individual ion concentrations. Suppose, for example, you add some lead(II) nitrate, a soluble lead salt, to increase the solution's $[Pb^{2+}]$. The equilibrium position shifts to the left, and $[SO_4^{2-}]$ goes down as more $PbSO_4$ precipitates; so the K_{sp} value is maintained.

The form of K_{sp} is identical to that of the other reaction quotients we have written: each ion concentration is raised to an exponent equal to the coefficient in the balanced equation, which in this case also *equals the subscript in the compound's formula.* Thus, in general, for a saturated solution of a slightly soluble ionic compound, M_pX_q, composed of the ions M^{n+} and X^{z-}, the equilibrium condition is

$$Q_{sp} = [M^{n+}]^p[X^{z-}]^q = K_{sp} \tag{19.2}$$

Since, at saturation, the concentration terms represent equilibrium concentrations, from here on, we write the ion-product expression directly as K_{sp}. For example, the equation and ion-product expression that describes a saturated solution of $Cu(OH)_2$ is

$$Cu(OH)_2(s) \rightleftharpoons Cu^{2+}(aq) + 2OH^-(aq) \qquad K_{sp} = [Cu^{2+}][OH^-]^2$$

Insoluble metal sulfides present a somewhat different case. The sulfide ion, S^{2-}, is so basic that it never exists in water. Instead, it reacts completely with water to form the hydrogen sulfide ion (HS^-) and the hydroxide ion. For instance, when manganese(II) sulfide is shaken with water, the solution contains Mn^{2+}, HS^-, and OH^- ions. Although the sulfide ion does not exist as such in water, you can imagine the dissolution process as the sum of two steps:

$$MnS(s) \rightleftharpoons Mn^{2+}(aq) + S^{2-}(aq)$$
$$\underline{S^{2-}(aq) + H_2O(l) \longrightarrow HS^-(aq) + OH^-(aq)}$$
$$MnS(s) + H_2O(l) \rightleftharpoons Mn^{2+}(aq) + HS^-(aq) + OH^-(aq)$$

Therefore, the ion-product expression is

$$K_{sp} = [Mn^{2+}][HS^-][OH^-]$$

Sample Problem 19.4   Writing Ion-Product Expressions for Slightly Soluble Ionic Compounds

PROBLEM Write the ion-product expression for **(a)** magnesium carbonate; **(b)** iron(II) hydroxide; **(c)** calcium phosphate; **(d)** silver sulfide.

PLAN We write an equation that describes a saturated solution and then write the ion-product expression, K_{sp}, according to Equation 19.2, noting the sulfide in **(d)**.

SOLUTION **(a)** Magnesium carbonate:

$$MgCO_3(s) \rightleftharpoons Mg^{2+}(aq) + CO_3^{2-}(aq) \qquad K_{sp} = [Mg^{2+}][CO_3^{2-}]$$

(b) Iron(II) hydroxide:

$$Fe(OH)_2(s) \rightleftharpoons Fe^{2+}(aq) + 2OH^-(aq) \qquad K_{sp} = [Fe^{2+}][OH^-]^2$$

(c) Calcium phosphate:

$$Ca_3(PO_4)_2(s) \rightleftharpoons 3Ca^{2+}(aq) + 2PO_4^{3-}(aq) \qquad K_{sp} = [Ca^{2+}]^3[PO_4^{3-}]^2$$

(d) Silver sulfide:

$$Ag_2S(s) + H_2O(l) \rightleftharpoons 2Ag^+(aq) + HS^-(aq) + OH^-(aq) \qquad K_{sp} = [Ag^+]^2[HS^-][OH^-]$$

CHECK Except for **(d)**, you can check by reversing the process to see if you obtain the formula of the compound from K_{sp}.

COMMENT In **(d)**, we include H_2O as reactant to obtain a balanced equation.

Follow-up Problem 19.4 Write the ion-product expressions for **(a)** calcium sulfate; **(b)** chromium(III) carbonate; **(c)** magnesium hydroxide; **(d)** arsenic(III) sulfide.

The value of K_{sp} is a measure of how far to the right the dissolution proceeds at equilibrium (saturation). We'll use it later to compare solubilities. Table 19.2 presents K_{sp} values of many slightly soluble ionic compounds. Note that, even though the K_{sp} values are all quite low, they range over many orders of magnitude.

Table 19.2 Solubility-Product Constants (K_{sp}) of Some Ionic Compounds at 25°C

Name, Formula	K_{sp}	Name, Formula	K_{sp}
Carbonates		Cobalt(II) hydroxide, $Co(OH)_2$	1.3×10^{-15}
Barium carbonate, $BaCO_3$	2.0×10^{-9}	Copper(II) hydroxide, $Cu(OH)_2$	2.2×10^{-20}
Cadmium carbonate, $CdCO_3$	1.8×10^{-14}	Iron(II) hydroxide, $Fe(OH)_2$	4.1×10^{-15}
Calcium carbonate, $CaCO_3$	3.3×10^{-9}	Iron(III) hydroxide, $Fe(OH)_3$	1.6×10^{-39}
Cobalt(II) carbonate, $CoCO_3$	1.0×10^{-10}	Magnesium hydroxide, $Mg(OH)_2$	6.3×10^{-10}
Copper(II) carbonate, $CuCO_3$	3×10^{-12}	Manganese(II) hydroxide, $Mn(OH)_2$	1.6×10^{-13}
Lead(II) carbonate, $PbCO_3$	7.4×10^{-14}	Nickel(II) hydroxide, $Ni(OH)_2$	6×10^{-16}
Magnesium carbonate, $MgCO_3$	3.5×10^{-8}	Zinc hydroxide, $Zn(OH)_2$	3×10^{-16}
Mercury(I) carbonate, Hg_2CO_3	8.9×10^{-17}		
Nickel(II) carbonate, $NiCO_3$	1.3×10^{-7}	**Iodates**	
Strontium carbonate, $SrCO_3$	5.4×10^{-10}	Barium iodate, $Ba(IO_3)_2$	1.5×10^{-9}
Zinc carbonate, $ZnCO_3$	1.0×10^{-10}	Calcium iodate, $Ca(IO_3)_2$	7.1×10^{-7}
		Lead(II) iodate, $Pb(IO_3)_2$	2.5×10^{-13}
Chromates		Silver iodate, $AgIO_3$	3.1×10^{-8}
Barium chromate, $BaCrO_4$	2.1×10^{-10}	Strontium iodate, $Sr(IO_3)_2$	3.3×10^{-7}
Calcium chromate, $CaCrO_4$	1×10^{-8}	Zinc iodate, $Zn(IO_3)_2$	3.9×10^{-6}
Lead(II) chromate, $PbCrO_4$	2.3×10^{-13}		
Silver chromate, Ag_2CrO_4	2.6×10^{-12}	**Oxalates**	
		Barium oxalate dihydrate, $BaC_2O_4\cdot2H_2O$	1.1×10^{-7}
Cyanides		Calcium oxalate monohydrate,	
Mercury(I) cyanide, $Hg_2(CN)_2$	5×10^{-40}	$CaC_2O_4\cdot H_2O$	2.3×10^{-9}
Silver cyanide, $AgCN$	2.2×10^{-16}	Strontium oxalate monohydrate,	
		$SrC_2O_4\cdot H_2O$	5.6×10^{-8}
Halides			
Fluorides		**Phosphates**	
Barium fluoride, BaF_2	1.5×10^{-6}	Calcium phosphate, $Ca_3(PO_4)_2$	1.2×10^{-29}
Calcium fluoride, CaF_2	3.2×10^{-11}	Magnesium phosphate, $Mg_3(PO_4)_2$	5.2×10^{-24}
Lead(II) fluoride, PbF_2	3.6×10^{-8}	Silver phosphate, Ag_3PO_4	2.6×10^{-18}
Magnesium fluoride, MgF_2	7.4×10^{-9}		
Strontium fluoride, SrF_2	2.6×10^{-9}	**Sulfates**	
		Barium sulfate, $BaSO_4$	1.1×10^{-10}
Chlorides		Calcium sulfate, $CaSO_4$	2.4×10^{-5}
Copper(I) chloride, $CuCl$	1.9×10^{-7}	Lead(II) sulfate, $PbSO_4$	1.6×10^{-8}
Lead(II) chloride, $PbCl_2$	1.7×10^{-5}	Magnesium sulfate, $MgSO_4$	5.9×10^{-3}
Silver chloride, $AgCl$	1.8×10^{-10}	Radium sulfate, $RaSO_4$	2×10^{-11}
		Silver sulfate, Ag_2SO_4	1.5×10^{-5}
Bromides		Strontium sulfate, $SrSO_4$	3.2×10^{-7}
Copper(I) bromide, $CuBr$	5×10^{-9}		
Silver bromide, $AgBr$	5.0×10^{-13}	**Sulfides**	
		Cadmium sulfide, CdS	1.0×10^{-24}
Iodides		Copper(II) sulfide, CuS	8×10^{-34}
Copper(I) iodide, CuI	1×10^{-12}	Iron(II) sulfide, FeS	8×10^{-16}
Lead(II) iodide, PbI_2	7.9×10^{-9}	Lead(II) sulfide, PbS	3×10^{-25}
Mercury(I) iodide, Hg_2I_2	4.7×10^{-29}	Manganese(II) sulfide, MnS	3×10^{-11}
Silver iodide, AgI	8.3×10^{-17}	Mercury(II) sulfide, HgS	2×10^{-50}
		Nickel(II) sulfide, NiS	3×10^{-16}
Hydroxides		Silver sulfide, Ag_2S	8×10^{-48}
Aluminum hydroxide, $Al(OH)_3$	3×10^{-34}	Tin(II) sulfide, SnS	1.3×10^{-23}
Calcium hydroxide, $Ca(OH)_2$	6.5×10^{-6}	Zinc sulfide, ZnS	2.0×10^{-22}

Calculations Involving the Solubility-Product Constant

In Chapters 17 and 18, we described two types of equilibrium problems. In one type, we use concentrations to find K, and in the other, we use K to find concentrations. Here we encounter the same two types.

Determining K_{sp} from Solubility The solubilities of ionic compounds are determined experimentally, and several chemical handbooks tabulate them. Most solubility values are given in units of grams of solute dissolved in 100 grams of H_2O. Since the mass of compound in solution is small, a negligible error is introduced if we assume that "100 g of water" is equal to "100 mL of solution." We then convert the solubility from grams of solute/100 mL of solution to **molar solubility,** the amount (mol) of dissolved solute per liter of solution (that is, the molarity of the compound). Then, we use the balanced equation to find the molarity of each ion and substitute the values into the ion-product expression to find K_{sp}.

Sample Problem 19.5   Determining K_{sp} from Solubility

PROBLEM **(a)** Lead(II) sulfate ($PbSO_4$) is used as a white pigment in paints and as a key component in common lead-acid car batteries. Its solubility in water at 25°C is 4.25×10^{-3} g/100 mL solution. What is the K_{sp} of $PbSO_4$?
(b) When lead(II) fluoride (PbF_2) is shaken with pure water at 25°C, the solubility is found to be 0.64 g/L. Calculate K_{sp} of PbF_2.
PLAN For each part, we write an equation for the dissolution of the compound to see the number of moles of each ion that forms, and then write the ion-product expression. We convert the known solubility to molar solubility, find the molarity of each ion, and substitute them into the ion-product expression to find K_{sp}.
SOLUTION **(a)** For $PbSO_4$. Writing the equation and ion-product (K_{sp}) expression:

$$PbSO_4(s) \rightleftharpoons Pb^{2+}(aq) + SO_4^{2-}(aq) \qquad K_{sp} = [Pb^{2+}][SO_4^{2-}]$$

Converting solubility to molar solubility:

$$\text{Molar solubility of } PbSO_4 = \frac{0.00425 \text{ g } PbSO_4}{100 \text{ mL soln}} \times \frac{1000 \text{ mL}}{1 \text{ L}} \times \frac{1 \text{ mol } PbSO_4}{303.3 \text{ g } PbSO_4}$$

$$= 1.40\times10^{-4} \text{ } M \text{ } PbSO_4$$

Determining molarities of the ions: Since 1 mol Pb^{2+} and 1 mol SO_4^{2-} form when 1 mol $PbSO_4$ dissolves, $[Pb^{2+}] = [SO_4^{2-}] = 1.40\times10^{-4}$ M.
Calculating K_{sp}:

$$K_{sp} = [Pb^{2+}][SO_4^{2-}] = (1.40\times10^{-4})^2 = \boxed{1.96\times10^{-8}}$$

(b) For PbF_2. Writing the equation and K_{sp} expression:

$$PbF_2(s) \rightleftharpoons Pb^{2+}(aq) + 2F^-(aq) \qquad K_{sp} = [Pb^{2+}][F^-]^2$$

Converting solubility to molar solubility:

$$\text{Molar solubility of } PbF_2 = \frac{0.64 \text{ g } PbF_2}{1 \text{ L soln}} \times \frac{1 \text{ mol } PbF_2}{245.2 \text{ g } PbF_2} = 2.6\times10^{-3} \text{ } M \text{ } PbF_2$$

Determining molarities of the ions: Since 1 mol Pb^{2+} and 2 mol F^- form when 1 mol PbF_2 dissolves,

$$[Pb^{2+}] = 2.6\times10^{-3} \text{ } M \qquad \text{and} \qquad [F^-] = 2(2.6\times10^{-3} \text{ } M) = 5.2\times10^{-3} \text{ } M$$

Calculating K_{sp}:

$$K_{sp} = [Pb^{2+}][F^-]^2 = (2.6\times10^{-3})(5.2\times10^{-3})^2 = \boxed{7.0\times10^{-8}}$$

CHECK The low solubilities are consistent with K_{sp} values being small. In **(a)**, the molar solubility seems about right: $\sim \dfrac{4\times10^{-2} \text{ g/L}}{3\times10^2 \text{ g/mol}} \approx 1.3\times10^{-4}$ M. Squaring this number gives 1.7×10^{-8}, close to the calculated K_{sp}. In **(b)**, we check the final step: $\sim(3\times10^{-3})(5\times10^{-3})^2 = 7.5\times10^{-8}$, close to the calculated K_{sp}.

COMMENT 1. In **(b)**, the formula PbF_2 means that $[F^-]$ is twice $[Pb^{2+}]$. Then we square this value of $[F^-]$. Always follow the ion-product expression explicitly.
2. Note that the K_{sp} values for these compounds in Table 19.2 are lower than our calculated values. For PbF_2, for instance, the tabulated value is 3.6×10^{-8}, but we calculated 7.0×10^{-8} from solubility data. The discrepancy arises because we assumed that the PbF_2 in solution dissociates completely to Pb^{2+} and F^-. Here is an example of the complexity pointed out at the beginning of this section. Actually, about a third of the PbF_2 dissolves as $PbF^+(aq)$ and a small amount as undissociated $PbF_2(aq)$. The solubility (0.64 g/L) is determined experimentally and includes these other species, which we did not include in our simple calculation. In general, it is best to treat K_{sp} values calculated this way as approximations.

Fluorite.

Follow-up Problem 19.5   Fluorite (CaF_2; see photo) is a mineral source of fluorine used extensively in the manufacture of steel and glass. When powdered fluorite is shaken with pure water at 18°C, 1.5×10^{-4} g dissolves for every 10.0 mL of solution. Calculate the K_{sp} of CaF_2 at 18°C.

Determining Solubility from K_{sp}   The reverse of the previous problem type involves finding the solubility of a compound based on its formula and K_{sp} value. A sound approach is to define the unknown molar solubility as S, define the ion concentrations in terms of this unknown, and solve for S.

Sample Problem 19.6   Determining Solubility from K_{sp}

PROBLEM Calcium hydroxide (slaked lime) is a major component of mortar, plaster, and cement (see photo). Solutions of $Ca(OH)_2$ are used in industry as a cheap, strong base. Calculate the solubility of $Ca(OH)_2$ in water if the K_{sp} is 6.5×10^{-6}.
PLAN We write the dissolution equation and the ion-product expression. Letting S = molar solubility, we set up a reaction table to express $[Ca^{2+}]$ and $[OH^-]$ in terms of S, substitute into the ion-product expression, and solve for S.
SOLUTION Writing the equation and ion-product expression:

$$Ca(OH)_2(s) \rightleftharpoons Ca^{2+}(aq) + 2OH^-(aq) \qquad K_{sp} = [Ca^{2+}][OH^-]^2 = 6.5 \times 10^{-6}$$

Setting up a reaction table, with S = molar solubility:

CONCENTRATION (M)	$Ca(OH)_2(s)$	$\rightleftharpoons$	$Ca^{2+}(aq)$	+	$2OH^-(aq)$
Initial	—		0		0
Change	—		$+S$		$+2S$
Equilibrium	—		S		$2S$

Pouring cement.

Substituting into the ion-product expression and solving for S:

$$K_{sp} = [Ca^{2+}][OH^-]^2 = S \times (2S)^2 = S \times 4S^2 = 4S^3 = 6.5 \times 10^{-6}$$

$$S = \sqrt[3]{\frac{6.5 \times 10^{-6}}{4}} = \boxed{1.2 \times 10^{-2}\ M}$$

CHECK We expect a low solubility from a slightly soluble salt. If we reverse the calculation, we should obtain the given K_{sp}: $4(1.2 \times 10^{-2})^3 = 6.9 \times 10^{-6}$, within rounding of 6.5×10^{-6}.
COMMENT 1. Note that we did not double and *then* square $[OH^-]$. $2S$ *is* the $[OH^-]$, so we just squared it, as the ion-product expression required.
2. Once again, we assumed that the solid dissociates completely. Actually, the solubility is increased by the reaction $Ca(OH)_2(s) \rightleftharpoons CaOH^+(aq) + OH^-(aq)$ to about $2.0 \times 10^{-2}\ M$. Our calculated answer is only approximate because we do not take this other species into account.

Follow-up Problem 19.6   A suspension of $Mg(OH)_2$ in water is sold as "milk of magnesia" to alleviate minor stomach disorders by neutralizing stomach acid. The $[OH^-]$ is too low to harm the mouth and throat, but the suspension dissolves in the acidic stomach juices. What is the molar solubility of $Mg(OH)_2$ in pure water? $K_{sp} = 6.3 \times 10^{-10}$.

Table 19.3 Relationship Between K_{sp} and Solubility at 25°C

No. of Ions	Formula	Cation:Anion	K_{sp}	Solubility (M)
2	$MgCO_3$	1:1	3.5×10^{-8}	1.9×10^{-4}
2	$PbSO_4$	1:1	1.6×10^{-8}	1.3×10^{-4}
2	$BaCrO_4$	1:1	2.1×10^{-10}	1.4×10^{-5}
3	$Ca(OH)_2$	1:2	6.5×10^{-6}	1.2×10^{-2}
3	BaF_2	1:2	1.5×10^{-6}	7.2×10^{-3}
3	CaF_2	1:2	3.2×10^{-11}	2.0×10^{-4}
3	Ag_2CrO_4	2:1	2.6×10^{-12}	8.7×10^{-5}

Using K_{sp} Values to Compare Solubilities K_{sp} values are a guide to *relative* solubility, as long as we compare compounds whose formulas contain the *same total number of ions*. In such cases, *the higher the K_{sp}, the greater the solubility*. Table 19.3 shows this point for several compounds. Note that for compounds that form three ions, the relationship holds whether the cation:anion ratio is 1:2 or 2:1, because the mathematical expression containing S is the same ($4S^3$) in the calculation (see Sample Problem 19.6).

The Effect of a Common Ion on Solubility

The presence of a common ion decreases the solubility of a slightly soluble ionic compound. As we saw in the case of acid-base systems, Le Châtelier's principle helps explain this effect. Let's examine the equilibrium condition for a saturated solution of lead(II) chromate:

$$PbCrO_4(s) \rightleftharpoons Pb^{2+}(aq) + CrO_4^{2-}(aq) \qquad K_{sp} = [Pb^{2+}][CrO_4^{2-}] = 2.3 \times 10^{-13}$$

At a given temperature, K_{sp} depends only on the product of the ion concentrations. If the concentration of either ion goes up, the other must go down to maintain the constant K_{sp} value. Suppose we add Na_2CrO_4, a very soluble salt, to the saturated $PbCrO_4$ solution. The concentration of the common ion, CrO_4^{2-}, increases, and some of it combines with Pb^{2+} ion to form more solid $PbCrO_4$ (Figure 19.10). The overall effect is a shift in the position of equilibrium to the left:

$$PbCrO_4(s) \overset{\longleftarrow}{\rightleftharpoons} Pb^{2+}(aq) + CrO_4^{2-}(aq; \text{ added})$$

Figure 19.10 The effect of a common ion on solubility. When a common ion is added to a saturated solution of an ionic compound, the solubility is lowered and more of the compound precipitates. **A,** Lead(II) chromate, a slightly soluble salt, forms a saturated aqueous solution. **B,** When Na_2CrO_4 solution is added, the amount of $PbCrO_4(s)$ increases, indicating a lower solubility in the presence of the common ion, CrO_4^{2-}.

$PbCrO_4(s) \rightleftharpoons Pb^{2+}(aq) + CrO_4^{2-}(aq)$	$PbCrO_4(s) \overset{\longleftarrow}{\rightleftharpoons} Pb^{2+}(aq) + CrO_4^{2-}(aq; \text{ added})$
A	**B**

After the addition, $[CrO_4^{2-}]$ is higher, but $[Pb^{2+}]$ is lower. Since $[Pb^{2+}]$ represents the amount of $PbCrO_4$ dissolved, the solubility of $PbCrO_4$ has decreased. The same result is obtained if we dissolve $PbCrO_4$ in a Na_2CrO_4 solution. We also obtain this result by adding a soluble lead(II) salt, such as $Pb(NO_3)_2$. The added Pb^{2+} ion combines with some $CrO_4^{2-}(aq)$, thus lowering the amount of dissolved $PbCrO_4$.

Sample Problem 19.7   Calculating the Effect of a Common Ion on Solubility

PROBLEM In Sample Problem 19.6, we calculated the solubility of $Ca(OH)_2$ in water. What is its solubility in 0.10 M $Ca(NO_3)_2$? K_{sp} of $Ca(OH)_2$ = 6.5×10^{-6}.
PLAN From the equation and the ion-product expression for $Ca(OH)_2$, we predict that the addition of Ca^{2+} ion will lower the solubility. We set up a reaction table with $[Ca^{2+}]_{init}$ coming from $Ca(NO_3)_2$ and S equal to $[Ca^{2+}]_{from\ Ca(OH)_2}$. To simplify the math, we assume that, since K_{sp} is low, S is so small relative to $[Ca^{2+}]_{init}$ that it can be neglected. Then we solve for S and check the assumption.
SOLUTION Writing the equation and ion-product expression:

$$Ca(OH)_2(s) \rightleftharpoons Ca^{2+}(aq) + 2OH^-(aq) \qquad K_{sp} = [Ca^{2+}][OH^-]^2 = 6.5\times10^{-6}$$

Setting up the reaction table, with $S = [Ca^{2+}]_{from\ Ca(OH)_2}$:

CONCENTRATION (M)	$Ca(OH)_2(s)$	$\rightleftharpoons$	$Ca^{2+}(aq)$	+	$2OH^-(aq)$
Initial	—		0.10		0
Change	—		$+S$		$+2S$
Equilibrium	—		$0.10 + S$		$2S$

Making the assumption: K_{sp} is small, so $S \ll 0.10\ M$; thus, $0.10\ M + S \approx 0.10\ M$. Substituting into the ion-product expression and solving for S:

$$K_{sp} = [Ca^{2+}][OH^-]^2 = 6.5\times10^{-6} \approx (0.10)(2S)^2$$

Therefore, $4S^2 \approx \dfrac{6.5\times10^{-6}}{0.10}$ so $S \approx \sqrt{\dfrac{6.5\times10^{-5}}{4}} = \boxed{4.0\times10^{-3}\ M}$

Checking the assumption: $\dfrac{4.0\times10^{-3}\ M}{0.10\ M} \times 100 = 4.0\% < 5\%$

CHECK In Sample Problem 19.6, the solubility of $Ca(OH)_2$ was 0.012 M. Here, it is 0.0040 M, so the solubility *decreased* in the presence of added Ca^{2+}, the common ion, as we predicted.

Follow-up Problem 19.7   To improve the quality of x-ray photos used in the diagnosis of intestinal disorders, the patient drinks an aqueous suspension of $BaSO_4$ before the x-ray procedure (see photo). The Ba^{2+} in the suspension is opaque to x-rays, but it is also toxic, so the Ba^{2+} concentration is lowered by the addition of dilute Na_2SO_4. What is the solubility of $BaSO_4$ in **(a)** pure water and **(b)** 0.10 M Na_2SO_4? K_{sp} of $BaSO_4$ = 1.1×10^{-10}.

$BaSO_4$ imaging of human large intestine.

The Effect of pH on Solubility

The hydronium ion concentration can have a profound effect on the solubility of an ionic compound. *If the compound contains the anion of a weak acid, addition of H_3O^+ (from a strong acid) increases its solubility.* Once again, Le Châtelier's principle explains why. In a saturated solution of calcium carbonate, for example, we have

$$CaCO_3(s) \rightleftharpoons Ca^{2+}(aq) + CO_3^{2-}(aq)$$

Figure 19.11 Test for the presence of a carbonate. When a mineral that contains carbonate ion is treated with strong acid, the added H_3O^+ shifts the equilibrium position of the carbonate solubility. More carbonate dissolves, and the carbonic acid formed breaks down to water and gaseous CO_2.

Adding some strong acid introduces a large amount of H_3O^+, which immediately reacts with CO_3^{2-} to form the weak acid HCO_3^-:

$$CO_3^{2-}(aq) + H_3O^+(aq) \longrightarrow HCO_3^-(aq) + H_2O(l)$$

If enough H_3O^+ is added, further reaction occurs to form carbonic acid, which decomposes immediately to H_2O and CO_2:

$$HCO_3^-(aq) + H_3O^+(aq) \longrightarrow H_2CO_3(aq) + H_2O(l) \longrightarrow CO_2(g) + 2H_2O(l)$$

Thus, the net effect of added H_3O^+ is a shift in the equilibrium position to the right, and more $CaCO_3$ dissolves:

$$CaCO_3(s) \xrightleftharpoons{} Ca^{2+} + CO_3^{2-} \xrightarrow{H_3O^+} HCO_3^- \xrightarrow{H_3O^+} H_2CO_3 \longrightarrow$$
$$CO_2(g) + H_2O + Ca^{2+}$$

This particular case illustrates a qualitative field test for carbonate minerals because the CO_2 bubbles vigorously (Figure 19.11).

In contrast, adding H_3O^+ to a saturated solution of a compound with a strong-acid anion, such as silver chloride, has no effect on the equilibrium position:

$$AgCl(s) \rightleftharpoons Ag^+(aq) + Cl^-(aq)$$

Because Cl^- ion is the conjugate base of a strong acid (HCl), it ordinarily coexists in solution with high $[H_3O^+]$. Since Cl^- is not removed from the system, the equilibrium position is not affected.

Sample Problem 19.8   Predicting the Effect on Solubility of Adding Strong Acid

PROBLEM Write balanced equations to explain whether addition of H_3O^+ from a strong acid affects the solubility of
(a) Lead(II) bromide
(b) Copper(II) hydroxide
(c) Iron(II) sulfide
PLAN We write the balanced dissolution equation and note the anion: weak-acid anions react with H_3O^+ and shift the equilibrium position toward more dissolution. Strong-acid anions do not react, so added H_3O^+ has no effect.
SOLUTION (a) $PbBr_2(s) \rightleftharpoons Pb^{2+}(aq) + 2Br^-(aq)$
No effect. Since Br^- is the anion of HBr, a strong acid, it is a very weak base and H_3O^+ does not react with it.
(b) $Cu(OH)_2(s) \rightleftharpoons Cu^{2+}(aq) + 2OH^-(aq)$
Increases solubility. OH^- is the anion of H_2O, a very weak acid, so it reacts with the added H_3O^+:

$$OH^-(aq) + H_3O^+(aq) \longrightarrow 2H_2O(l)$$

(c) $FeS(s) + H_2O(l) \rightleftharpoons Fe^{2+}(aq) + HS^-(aq) + OH^-(aq)$
Increases solubility. We noted earlier that the S^{2-} ion reacts immediately with water to form HS^-. The added H_3O^+ reacts with both weak-acid anions, HS^- and OH^-:

$$HS^-(aq) + H_3O^+(aq) \longrightarrow H_2S(aq) + H_2O(l)$$
$$OH^-(aq) + H_3O^+(aq) \longrightarrow 2H_2O(l)$$

Follow-up Problem 19.8   Write balanced equations to show how addition of $HNO_3(aq)$ affects the solubility of **(a)** calcium fluoride; **(b)** zinc sulfide; **(c)** silver iodide.

Many principles of ionic equilibria are manifested in natural formations, as the upcoming Chemical Connections essay illustrates.

Creation of a Limestone Cave

Limestone caves and the detailed structures within them provide striking evidence of the workings of aqueous ionic equilibria (Figure 19.A). The spires and vaults of these natural cathedrals are the products of reactions between carbonate rocks and the water that has run through them for millennia. Limestone is predominantly calcium carbonate ($CaCO_3$), a slightly soluble ionic compound with a K_{sp} of 3.3×10^{-9}. This rocky material began accumulating in the Earth over 400 million years ago, and a relatively young cave, such as Howe Caverns in eastern New York State, began forming about 800,000 years ago.

Two key facts help us understand how limestone caves form:

1. Gaseous CO_2 is in equilibrium with aqueous CO_2 in natural waters:

$$CO_2(g) \xrightleftharpoons{H_2O(l)} CO_2(aq) \qquad \text{[Equation 1]}$$

The concentration of CO_2 in the water is proportional to the partial pressure of $CO_2(g)$ in contact with the water (Henry's law; Section 13.3):

$$[CO_2(aq)] \propto P_{CO_2}$$

Because of the continual release of CO_2 from within the Earth (outgassing), the P_{CO_2} in soil-trapped air is *higher* than P_{CO_2} in the atmosphere.

2. As we just discussed in the main text, the presence of $H_3O^+(aq)$ increases the solubility of ionic compounds that contain the anion of a weak acid. The reaction of CO_2 with water produces H_3O^+,

$$CO_2(aq) + 2H_2O(l) \rightleftharpoons H_3O^+(aq) + HCO_3^-(aq)$$

Thus, the presence of $CO_2(aq)$ forms H_3O^+, which increases the solubility of $CaCO_3$:

$$CaCO_3(s) + CO_2(aq) + H_2O(l) \rightleftharpoons Ca^{2+}(aq) + 2HCO_3^-(aq)$$
$$\text{[Equation 2]}$$

Here is an overview of the cave-forming process. As surface water trickles through cracks in the ground, it meets soil-trapped air with its high P_{CO_2}. As a result, $[CO_2(aq)]$ increases (Equation 1 shifts to the right), and the solution becomes more acidic. When this CO_2-rich water contacts limestone, more $CaCO_3$ dissolves (Equation 2 shifts to the right). As a result, more rock is carved out, more water flows in, more rock is carved out, and so on. Centuries pass as a cave slowly begins to form.

Eating its way through underground tunnels, some of the aqueous solution, largely dissolved $Ca(HCO_3)_2$, passes through the ceiling of the growing cave. As it drips, it meets air, which has a lower P_{CO_2} than that of the soil, so some $CO_2(aq)$ comes out of solution (Equation 1 shifts to the left). This causes some $CaCO_3$ to precipitate on the ceiling and on the floor below, where the drops land (Equation 2 shifts to the left). Decades pass and the ceiling bears an "icicle" of $CaCO_3$, called a *stalactite,* while a spike of $CaCO_3$, called a *stalagmite,* grows upward from the cave floor. Given enough time, they meet to form a column of precipitated limestone.

The same chemical process can lead to many different shapes. Standing pools of $Ca(HCO_3)_2$ solution form limestone "lily pads" or "corals." Cascades of solution form delicate limestone "draperies" on a cave wall, with fabulous colors arising from trace metal ions, such as iron (reddish brown) or copper (bluish green).

Figure 19.A   A view inside Carlsbad Caverns, New Mexico. The marvelous formations within this limestone cave (shown under colored lights) result from subtle shifts in carbonate ionic equilibria acting over millions of years.

Predicting the Formation of a Precipitate: Q_{sp} vs. K_{sp}

In Chapter 17, we compared the values of Q and K to see if a reaction had reached equilibrium, and if not, in which net direction it would move until it did. Now we use the same approach to see if a precipitate will form and what concentrations of ions will cause it to do so.

As you know, $Q_{sp} = K_{sp}$ when the solution is saturated. If Q_{sp} is greater than K_{sp}, the solution is momentarily supersaturated, and some solid precipitates until the remaining solution becomes saturated ($Q_{sp} = K_{sp}$). If Q_{sp} is less than K_{sp}, the solution is unsaturated, and no precipitate forms at that temperature (more solid can dissolve). To summarize,

- $Q_{sp} = K_{sp}$: solution is saturated and no change occurs.
- $Q_{sp} > K_{sp}$: precipitate forms until solution is saturated.
- $Q_{sp} < K_{sp}$: solution is unsaturated and no precipitate forms.

Sample Problem 19.9   Predicting Whether a Precipitate Will Form

PROBLEM A common laboratory method for preparing a precipitate is to mix solutions of the component ions. Does a precipitate form when 0.100 L of 0.30 M $Ca(NO_3)_2$ is mixed with 0.200 L of 0.060 M NaF?

PLAN First, we must decide whether the ions present create a slightly soluble salt and, if so, look up its K_{sp} value in Table 19.2. To find the initial ion concentrations, we calculate the amount (mol) of each ion and divide by the *total* volume, since one solution dilutes the other. Then we find Q_{sp} and compare it with K_{sp}.

SOLUTION The ions present are Ca^{2+}, Na^+, F^-, and NO_3^-. All sodium and all nitrate salts are soluble (Table 4.1), so the only possibility is CaF_2 ($K_{sp} = 3.2 \times 10^{-11}$). Calculating the ion concentrations:

$$\text{Moles of } Ca^{2+} = 0.30 \ M \ Ca^{2+} \times 0.100 \ L = 0.030 \ \text{mol } Ca^{2+}$$

$$[Ca^{2+}]_{init} = \frac{0.030 \ \text{mol } Ca^{2+}}{0.100 \ L + 0.200 \ L} = 0.10 \ M \ Ca^{2+}$$

$$\text{Moles of } F^- = 0.060 \ M \ F^- \times 0.200 \ L = 0.012 \ \text{mol } F^-$$

$$[F^-]_{init} = \frac{0.012 \ \text{mol } F^-}{0.100 \ L + 0.200 \ L} = 0.040 \ M \ F^-$$

Substituting into the ion-product expression and comparing Q_{sp} with K_{sp}:

$$Q_{sp} = [Ca^{2+}]_{init}[F^-]^2_{init} = (0.10)(0.040)^2 = 1.6 \times 10^{-4}$$

Since $Q_{sp} > K_{sp}$, CaF_2 will precipitate until $Q_{sp} = 3.2 \times 10^{-11}$.

CHECK Don't forget to round off and quickly check the math. For example, $Q_{sp} = (1 \times 10^{-1})(4 \times 10^{-2})^2 = 1.6 \times 10^{-4}$. Since K_{sp} is so low, CaF_2 must have a low solubility, and with the sizable concentrations being mixed, we expect CaF_2 to precipitate.

Follow-up Problem 19.9 Phosphate in natural waters often precipitates as insoluble salts, such as $Ca_3(PO_4)_2$. In a certain river, $[Ca^{2+}]_{init} = [PO_4^{3-}]_{init} = 1.0 \times 10^{-9} \ M$. Will $Ca_3(PO_4)_2$ precipitate? K_{sp} of $Ca_3(PO_4)_2 = 1.2 \times 10^{-29}$.

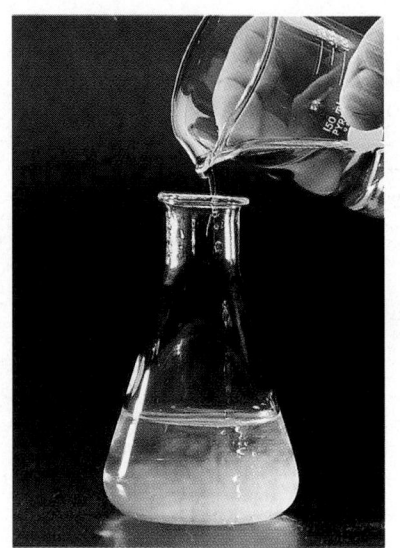

Precipitation of CaF_2.

As the upcoming Chemical Connections essay demonstrates, the principles of ionic equilibria often help us understand the chemical basis of complex environmental problems and may provide ways to solve them.

Chemical Connections   Chemistry in Environmental Science

The Acid-Rain Problem

The conflict between industrial society and the environment is very clear in the problem of acidic precipitation—rain, snow, or fog made unnaturally acidic by human action. Acidic precipitation has been recorded in all parts of the United States, in Canada, Mexico, the Amazon basin, throughout Europe and Russia, and even at the North and South Poles. We've addressed several aspects of this problem in earlier chapters; now, armed with an understanding of ionic equilibria, let's examine some effects of acidic precipitation on aqueous, biological, and mineral systems. There are several troublesome chemical culprits:

1. *Sulfurous acid.* Sulfur dioxide (SO_2), formed primarily by the burning of high-sulfur coal, forms sulfurous acid (H_2SO_3) when it comes in contact with water.

2. *Sulfuric acid.* Sulfur trioxide (SO_3) forms through the atmospheric oxidation of SO_2 by ozone or by O_2 in a reaction catalyzed by dust:

$$SO_2(g) + O_3(g) \rightleftharpoons SO_3(g) + O_2(g)$$

$$2SO_2(g) + O_2(g) \xrightarrow{dust} 2SO_3(g)$$

Sulfur trioxide forms sulfuric acid (H_2SO_4) in contact with water.

3. *Nitric acid.* Nitrogen oxides (collectively known as NO_x) form in the reaction of N_2 and O_2. NO is formed by combustion, primarily in car engines, and it forms NO_2 in air. Rainwater converts NO_x to HNO_2 and HNO_3. The strong acids H_2SO_4 and HNO_3 cause the greatest concern (Figure 19.B).

How does the pH of acidic precipitation compare with that of natural waters? *Normal rainwater is weakly acidic* because it contains dissolved CO_2 from the air:

$$CO_2(g) + 2H_2O(l) \rightleftharpoons H_3O^+(aq) + HCO_3^-(aq)$$

Based on the volume percent of CO_2 in air, the solubility of CO_2 in water, and the K_{a1} of H_2CO_3, the pH of normal rainwater is about 5.6 (see Problem 19.148 at the end of the chapter). In stark contrast, the *average* pH of rainfall in many parts of the eastern United States was 4.2 as long ago as 1984, representing about 25 times as much H_3O^+. Worldwide, rain in Sweden and in Pennsylvania share second prize with a pH of 2.7, about the same as vinegar. Rain in Wheeling, West Virginia, wins first prize with a pH of 1.8, between that of lemon juice and stomach acid! Acidic fog in California sometimes has a pH of 1.6.

These 10- to 10,000-fold excesses of $[H_3O^+]$ are very destructive to living things. Most fish and shellfish die at pH values between 4.5 and 5.0. With tens of thousands of rivers and lakes around the world becoming acidified, the loss of fish became a major concern long ago. In addition, millions of

(continued)

Figure 19.B Formation of acidic precipitation. A complex interplay of human activities, atmospheric chemistry, and environmental distribution leads to acidic precipitation and its harmful effects. Car exhaust and factory waste gases produce lower oxides of nitrogen and sulfur. These are oxidized in the atmosphere by O_2 (or O_3, not shown) to higher oxides (NO_2, SO_3), which react with moisture to form acidic rain, snow, and fog. In contact with acidic precipitation, many lakes become acidified, whereas limestone-bounded lakes form a carbonate buffer that prevents acidification.

Chemical Connections   *(continued)*

Figure 19.C A forest damaged by acid rain.

1944   1994

Figure 19.D The effect of acid rain on marble statuary.
The calcium carbonate that is the major component of marble and limestone is slowly decomposed by acid rain. These photos of the same statue of George Washington, Washington Square Park, New York City, were taken 50 years apart.

acres of forest and crops have been harmed by the acid, which removes protective waxes from leaf surfaces (Figure 19.C).

Many principles of aqueous equilibria bear directly on the effects of acid rain. The aluminosilicates that make up most soils are extremely insoluble in water. In these materials, the Al^{3+} is bonded to OH^- and O^{2-} ions in complex structures (see Gallery in Section 14.6). Continual contact with the H_3O^+ in acid rain causes these anions to react, and this dissolves some of the bound Al^{3+}, which is toxic to fish. Along with the solubilized Al^{3+} ions, the acid carries away ions that serve as nutrients for plant and animal.

Acid rain also dissolves the calcium carbonate in the marble and limestone of buildings and monuments (Figure 19.D). Ironically, the same chemical process that destroys these structures is responsible for saving those lakes that lie on and are bounded by older, limestone-rich soil. As acid rain falls,

the H_3O^+ reacts with the dissolved carbonate ion in the lake to form bicarbonate:

$$CO_3^{2-}(aq) + H_3O^+(aq) \longrightarrow HCO_3^-(aq) + H_2O(l)$$

In essence, limestone-grounded lakes become enormous CO_3^{2-}/HCO_3^- buffer solutions, absorbing the additional H_3O^+ and maintaining a relatively stable pH. In fact, lakes, rivers, and ground water in limestone-rich soils actually remain mildly basic.

For lakes and rivers in contact with limestone-poor soils, society's choices at present are few and expensive. A direct attack on the symptoms is the so-called *liming* of lakes and rivers (treating with limestone). Sweden has spent tens of millions of dollars during the 1990s to neutralize slightly more than 3000 lakes by adding limestone. In Canada, adding limestone costs more than $50 per acre, so treatment for a single large lake can cost several thousand dollars. This approach is, at best, only a stopgap because within several years the lakes are acidic again. Two longer range options aim at preventing the problem. Burning low-sulfur coal reduces SO_2 formation, but such coal deposits are rare and expensive to mine. Alternatively, coal can be converted into gaseous and liquid low-sulfur fuels (see the Chemical Connections essay, Section 6.6).

Section Summary

As a first approximation, the dissolved portion of a slightly soluble salt dissociates completely into ions. In a saturated solution, the ions are in equilibrium with the solid, and the product of the ion concentrations, each raised to the power of its subscript in the formula, has a constant value ($Q_{sp} = K_{sp}$). The value of K_{sp} can be obtained from the solubility, and vice versa. Adding a common ion lowers a compound's solubility. Adding H_3O^+ (lowering the pH) increases a compound's solubility if the anion of the compound is that of a weak acid. If $Q_{sp} > K_{sp}$ for a compound, a precipitate forms when two solutions are mixed. Limestone caves result from shifts in the $CaCO_3/CO_2$ equilibrium system. Lakes with limestone bedrock form a buffer system that prevents harmful acidification.

19.4 Equilibria Involving Complex Ions

The final type of aqueous ionic equilibrium we consider involves a different type of ion than we've examined up to now. Simple ions, such as Na^+ or SO_4^{2-}, consist of one or a few bound atoms, with an excess or deficit of electrons. A **complex ion** consists of a central metal ion covalently bonded to two or more anions or molecules, called **ligands.** Hydroxide, chloride, and cyanide ions are common ionic ligands; water, carbon monoxide, and ammonia are common molecular ligands. In the complex ion $Cr(NH_3)_6^{3+}$, for example, Cr^{3+} is the central metal ion and six NH_3 molecules are the ligands to give an overall 3+ charge (Figure 19.12).

As we discussed in Section 18.9, *all complex ions are Lewis adducts.* The metal ion acts as a Lewis acid (accepts an electron pair) and the ligand acts as a Lewis base (donates an electron pair). The acidic hydrated metal ions that we discussed in Section 18.6 are complex ions with water molecules as ligands. In Chapter 23, we discuss the transition metals and the structures and properties of the numerous complex ions they form. Our focus here is on equilibria of hydrated ions with ligands other than water.

Figure 19.12 $Cr(NH_3)_6^{3+}$, **a typical complex ion.** A complex ion consists of a central metal ion, such as Cr^{3+}, covalently bonded to a specific number of ligands, such as NH_3.

Formation of Complex Ions

Whenever a metal ion enters water, a complex ion forms, with water as the ligand. In many cases, when this hydrated cation is treated with a solution of another ligand, the bound water molecules exchange for the other ligand. For example, a hydrated M^{2+} ion, $M(H_2O)_4^{2+}$, forms the complex ion $M(NH_3)_4^{2+}$ in aqueous NH_3:

$$M(H_2O)_4^{2+}(aq) + 4NH_3(aq) \rightleftharpoons M(NH_3)_4^{2+}(aq) + 4H_2O(l)$$

At equilibrium, this system is expressed by a ratio of concentration terms whose form follows that of any other equilibrium expression:

$$K_c = \frac{[M(NH_3)_4^{2+}][H_2O]^4}{[M(H_2O)_4^{2+}][NH_3]^4}$$

Once again, since the concentration of water is essentially constant in aqueous reactions, we incorporate it into K_c and obtain the expression for a new equilibrium constant, the **formation constant K_f:**

$$K_f = \frac{K_c}{[H_2O]^4} = \frac{[M(NH_3)_4^{2+}]}{[M(H_2O)_4^{2+}][NH_3]^4}$$

At the molecular level, the actual process is stepwise, with ammonia molecules replacing water molecules one at a time to give a series of intermediate species, each with its own formation constant:

$$M(H_2O)_4^{2+}(aq) + NH_3(aq) \rightleftharpoons M(H_2O)_3(NH_3)^{2+}(aq) + H_2O(l)$$

$$K_{f1} = \frac{[M(H_2O)_3(NH_3)^{2+}]}{[M(H_2O)_4^{2+}][NH_3]}$$

$$M(H_2O)_3(NH_3)^{2+}(aq) + NH_3(aq) \rightleftharpoons M(H_2O)_2(NH_3)_2^{2+}(aq) + H_2O(l)$$

$$K_{f2} = \frac{[M(H_2O)_2(NH_3)_2^{2+}]}{[M(H_2O)_3(NH_3)^{2+}][NH_3]}$$

$$M(H_2O)_2(NH_3)_2^{2+}(aq) + NH_3(aq) \rightleftharpoons M(H_2O)(NH_3)_3^{2+}(aq) + H_2O(l)$$

$$K_{f3} = \frac{[M(H_2O)(NH_3)_3^{2+}]}{[M(H_2O)_2(NH_3)_2^{2+}][NH_3]}$$

$$M(H_2O)(NH_3)_3^{2+}(aq) + NH_3(aq) \rightleftharpoons M(NH_3)_4^{2+}(aq) + H_2O(l)$$

$$K_{f4} = \frac{[M(NH_3)_4^{2+}]}{[M(H_2O)(NH_3)_3^{2+}][NH_3]}$$

$$M(H_2O)_4{}^{2+}(aq) + NH_3(aq) \rightleftharpoons M(H_2O)_3(NH_3)^{2+}(aq) \xrightarrow[\text{3 more steps}]{3NH_3} M(NH_3)_4{}^{2+}(aq) + 4H_2O(l)$$

Figure 19.13 **The stepwise exchange of NH₃ for H₂O in M(H₂O)₄²⁺.** The ligands of a complex ion can exchange for other ligands. When ammonia is added to a solution of the hydrated M^{2+} ion, $M(H_2O)_4{}^{2+}$, NH_3 molecules replace the bound H_2O molecules one at a time to form the $M(NH_3)_4{}^{2+}$ ion. The molecular views show the first exchange and the fully ammoniated ion.

The *sum* of the equations gives the overall equation, so the *product* of the individual formation constants gives the overall formation constant:

$$K_f = K_{f1} \times K_{f2} \times K_{f3} \times K_{f4}$$

Figure 19.13 summarizes the process on the molecular level. In this case, the K_f for each step is much larger than one because ammonia is a stronger Lewis base than water. Therefore, if we add an excess of ammonia to the $M(H_2O)_4{}^{2+}$ solution, the H_2O ligands are replaced and essentially all the M^{2+} ion exists as $M(NH_3)_4{}^{2+}$.

Table 19.4 shows the formation constants of some complex ions. Notice that the K_f values are all 10^6 or greater, which means that these ions form very readily. Because of this behavior, complex-ion formation is employed to retrieve a metal from its ore, to eliminate a toxic or unwanted metal ion from a solution, or to convert the metal ion to a different form, as Sample Problem 19.10 shows for the zinc ion.

Table 19.4 Formation Constants (K_f) of Some Complex Ions at 25°C

Complex Ion	K_f
$Ag(CN)_2{}^-$	3.0×10^{20}
$Ag(NH_3)_2{}^+$	1.7×10^7
$Ag(S_2O_3)_2{}^{3-}$	4.7×10^{13}
$AlF_6{}^{3-}$	4×10^{19}
$Al(OH)_4{}^-$	3×10^{33}
$Be(OH)_4{}^{2-}$	4×10^{18}
$CdI_4{}^{2-}$	1×10^6
$Co(OH)_4{}^{2-}$	5×10^9
$Cr(OH)_4{}^-$	8.0×10^{29}
$Cu(NH_3)_4{}^{2+}$	5.6×10^{11}
$Fe(CN)_6{}^{4-}$	3×10^{35}
$Fe(CN)_6{}^{3-}$	4.0×10^{43}
$Hg(CN)_4{}^{2-}$	9.3×10^{38}
$Ni(OH)_4{}^{2-}$	2×10^{28}
$Pb(OH)_3{}^-$	8×10^{13}
$Sn(OH)_3{}^-$	3×10^{25}
$Zn(CN)_4{}^{2-}$	4.2×10^{19}
$Zn(NH_3)_4{}^{2+}$	7.8×10^8
$Zn(OH)_4{}^{2-}$	3×10^{15}

Sample Problem 19.10 Calculating the Concentrations of Complex Ions

PROBLEM An industrial chemist converts $Zn(H_2O)_4{}^{2+}$ to the more stable $Zn(NH_3)_4{}^{2+}$ by mixing 50.0 L of 0.0020 M $Zn(H_2O)_4{}^{2+}$ and 25.0 L of 0.15 M NH_3. What is the final $[Zn(H_2O)_4{}^{2+}]$? K_f of $Zn(NH_3)_4{}^{2+}$ = 7.8×10^8.

PLAN We write the equation and the K_f expression. As always, we use a reaction table to calculate the equilibrium concentrations. To set up the table, we first must find $[Zn(H_2O)_4{}^{2+}]_{init}$ and $[NH_3]_{init}$. We are given the individual volumes and molar concentrations, so we find the moles and divide by the *total* volume, since the solutions are mixed. With the large excess of NH_3 and high K_f, we assume that almost all the $Zn(H_2O)_4{}^{2+}$ is converted to $Zn(NH_3)_4{}^{2+}$. Since $[Zn(H_2O)_4{}^{2+}]$ at equilibrium is quite small, we use x to represent it.

SOLUTION Writing the equation and the K_f expression:

$$Zn(H_2O)_4{}^{2+}(aq) + 4NH_3(aq) \rightleftharpoons Zn(NH_3)_4{}^{2+}(aq) + 4H_2O(l)$$

$$K_f = \frac{[Zn(NH_3)_4{}^{2+}]}{[Zn(H_2O)_4{}^{2+}][NH_3]^4}$$

Finding the initial reactant concentrations:

$$[Zn(H_2O)_4{}^{2+}]_{init} = \frac{50.0 \text{ L} \times 0.0020 \ M}{50.0 \text{ L} + 25.0 \text{ L}} = 1.3 \times 10^{-3} \ M$$

$$[NH_3]_{init} = \frac{25.0 \text{ L} \times 0.15 \ M}{50.0 \text{ L} + 25.0 \text{ L}} = 5.0 \times 10^{-2} \ M$$

Setting up a reaction table: We assume that nearly all the $Zn(H_2O)_4^{2+}$ is converted to $Zn(NH_3)_4^{2+}$, so we set up the table with $x = [Zn(H_2O)_4^{2+}]$ at equilibrium. Since 4 mol NH_3 are needed per mole of $Zn(H_2O)_4^{2+}$, the change in $[NH_3]$ is

$$[NH_3]_{reacted} \approx 4(1.3\times10^{-3}\ M) = 5.2\times10^{-3}\ M$$

And, $\qquad [Zn(NH_3)_4^{2+}] \approx 1.3\times10^{-3}\ M$

CONCENTRATION (M)	$Zn(H_2O)_4^{2+}(aq)$ +	$4NH_3(aq)$	$\rightleftharpoons$	$Zn(NH_3)_4^{2+}(aq)$ +	$4H_2O(l)$
Initial	1.3×10^{-3}	5.0×10^{-2}		0	—
Change	$\sim(-1.3\times10^{-3})$	$\sim(-5.2\times10^{-3})$		$\sim(+1.3\times10^{-3})$	—
Equilibrium	x	4.5×10^{-2}		1.3×10^{-3}	—

Solving for x, the $[Zn(H_2O)_4^{2+}]$ remaining at equilibrium:

$$K_f = \frac{[Zn(NH_3)_4^{2+}]}{[Zn(H_2O)_4^{2+}][NH_3]^4} = 7.8\times10^8 \approx \frac{1.3\times10^{-3}}{x(4.5\times10^{-2})^4}$$

$$x = [Zn(H_2O)_4^{2+}] \approx \boxed{4.1\times10^{-7}\ M}$$

CHECK Since the K_f is large, we expect the $[Zn(H_2O)_4^{2+}]$ remaining to be very low.

Follow-up Problem 19.10 Cyanide ion is toxic because it forms stable complex ions with the Fe^{3+} in certain iron-containing proteins engaged in energy production. To study this effect, a biochemist mixes 25.5 mL of $3.1\times10^{-2}\ M$ $Fe(H_2O)_6^{3+}$ with 35.0 mL of 1.5 M NaCN. What is the final $[Fe(H_2O)_6^{3+}]$? K_f of $Fe(CN)_6^{3-} = 4.0\times10^{43}$.

Complex Ions and the Solubility of Precipitates

In Section 19.3, you saw that H_3O^+ increases the solubility of a slightly soluble ionic compound if its anion is that of a weak acid. Similarly, *a ligand increases the solubility of a slightly soluble ionic compound if it forms a complex ion with the cation.* For example, zinc sulfide is very slightly soluble:

$$ZnS(s) + H_2O(l) \rightleftharpoons Zn^{2+}(aq) + HS^-(aq) + OH^-(aq) \qquad K_{sp} = 2.0\times10^{-22}$$

When we add some 1.0 M NaCN, the CN^- ions act as ligands and react with the small amount of $Zn^{2+}(aq)$ to form the following complex ion:

$$Zn^{2+}(aq) + 4CN^-(aq) \rightleftharpoons Zn(CN)_4^{2-}(aq) \qquad K_f = 4.2\times10^{19}$$

To see the effect of complex ion formation on the solubility of ZnS, we add the equations and, therefore, multiply their equilibrium constants:

$$ZnS(s) + 4CN^-(aq) + H_2O(l) \rightleftharpoons Zn(CN)_4^{2-}(aq) + HS^-(aq) + OH^-(aq)$$

$$K_{overall} = K_{sp} \times K_f = (2.0\times10^{-22})(4.2\times10^{19}) = 8.4\times10^{-3}$$

The overall equilibrium constant increased by more than a factor of 10^{19} in the presence of the ligand; this reflects the increased amount of ZnS in solution.

Sample Problem 19.11 Calculating the Effect of Complex-Ion Formation on Solubility

PROBLEM A critical step in black-and-white film developing (see photo) is the removal of excess AgBr from the film negative by "hypo," an aqueous solution of sodium thiosulfate ($Na_2S_2O_3$), through formation of the complex ion $Ag(S_2O_3)_2^{3-}$. Calculate the solubility of AgBr in **(a)** H_2O; **(b)** 1.0 M hypo. K_f of $Ag(S_2O_3)_2^{3-} = 4.7\times10^{13}$ and K_{sp} of AgBr $= 5.0\times10^{-13}$.

PLAN (a) After writing the equation and the ion-product expression, we use the given K_{sp} to solve for S, the molar solubility. **(b)** In hypo, the free (hydrated) Ag^+ ion forms a complex with the $S_2O_3^{2-}$ ion, which shifts the dissolution to the right. We write the complex-ion equation, add it to the equation for the dissolution to obtain the overall equation for the dissolution in hypo, and multiply K_{sp} by K_f to find $K_{overall}$. To find the solubility of AgBr in hypo, we set up a reaction table, with $S = [Ag(S_2O_3)_2^{3-}]$, substitute into the expression for $K_{overall}$, and solve for S.

SOLUTION **(a)** Solubility in water. Writing the equation for the saturated solution and the ion-product expression:

$$AgBr(s) \rightleftharpoons Ag^+(aq) + Br^-(aq) \qquad K_{sp} = [Ag^+][Br^-]$$

Solving for solubility (S) directly from the equation: We know that

$$S = [AgBr]_{dissolved} = [Ag^+] = [Br^-]$$

Thus, $\qquad K_{sp} = [Ag^+][Br^-] = S^2 = 5.0 \times 10^{-13}$, so $S = \boxed{7.1 \times 10^{-7} \ M}$

(b) Solubility in 1.0 M hypo. Writing the overall equation:

$$AgBr(s) \rightleftharpoons \cancel{Ag^+(aq)} + Br^-(aq)$$
$$\cancel{Ag^+(aq)} + 2S_2O_3^{2-}(aq) \rightleftharpoons Ag(S_2O_3)_2^{3-}(aq)$$
$$\overline{AgBr(s) + 2S_2O_3^{2-}(aq) \rightleftharpoons Ag(S_2O_3)_2^{3-}(aq) + Br^-(aq)}$$

Calculating $K_{overall}$:

$$K_{overall} = \frac{[Ag(S_2O_3)_2^{3-}][Br^-]}{[S_2O_3^{2-}]^2} = K_{sp} \times K_f = (5.0 \times 10^{-13})(4.7 \times 10^{13}) = 24$$

Setting up a reaction table, with $S = [AgBr]_{dissolved} = [Ag(S_2O_3)_2^{3-}]$:

CONCENTRATION (M)	AgBr(s)	+	2S$_2$O$_3^{2-}$(aq)	$\rightleftharpoons$	Ag(S$_2$O$_3$)$_2^{3-}$(aq)	+	Br$^-$(aq)
Initial	—		1.0		0		0
Change	—		$-2S$		$+S$		$+S$
Equilibrium	—		$1.0 - 2S$		S		S

Substituting the values into $K_{overall}$ and solving for S:

$$K_{overall} = \frac{[Ag(S_2O_3)_2^{3-}][Br^-]}{[S_2O_3^{2-}]^2} = \frac{S^2}{(1.0 \ M - 2S)^2} = 24$$

Taking the square root of both sides gives

$$\frac{S}{1.0 \ M - 2S} = \sqrt{24} = 4.9 \qquad [Ag(S_2O_3)_2^{3-}] = \boxed{S = 0.45 \ M}$$

CHECK **(a)** From the number of ions in the formula of AgBr, we know that $S = \sqrt{K_{sp}}$, so the order of magnitude seems right: $\sim\sqrt{10^{-14}} = 10^{-7}$. **(b)** The $K_{overall}$ seems correct: the exponents cancel and $5 \times 5 = 25$. Most importantly, the answer makes sense because the photographic process requires the remaining AgBr to be washed off the film and the large $K_{overall}$ confirms that. We can check S by rounding and working backward to find $K_{overall}$: from the reaction table, we find that

$$[(S_2O_3)^{2-}] = 1.0 \ M - 2S = 1.0 \ M - 0.90 \ M = 0.1 \ M$$

so $K_{overall} \approx (0.45)^2/(0.1)^2 = 20$, within rounding of the calculated value.

Follow-up Problem 19.11 How does the solubility of AgBr in 1.0 M NH$_3$ compare with its solubility in hypo? K_f of Ag(NH$_3$)$_2^+$ = 1.7×10^7.

Complex Ions of Amphoteric Hydroxides

The same metals that form amphoteric oxides (Section 8.4 and Interchapter Topic 4) also form slightly soluble *amphoteric hydroxides,* compounds that dissolve very little in water but to a much greater extent in both acidic and basic solutions. Aluminum hydroxide is an example:

$$Al(OH)_3(s) \rightleftharpoons Al^{3+}(aq) + 3OH^-(aq)$$

It is effectively insoluble in water ($K_{sp} = 3 \times 10^{-34}$), but

- It dissolves in acid because H_3O^+ reacts with the OH$^-$ anion (Section 19.3),

$$3H_3O^+(aq) + 3OH^-(aq) \longrightarrow 6H_2O(l)$$

to give the overall equation,

$$Al(OH)_3(s) + 3H_3O^+(aq) \longrightarrow Al^{3+}(aq) + 6H_2O(l)$$

- It dissolves in base through the formation of a complex ion:

$$Al(OH)_3(s) + OH^-(aq) \longrightarrow Al(OH)_4^-(aq)$$

Figure 19.14 The amphoteric behavior of aluminum hydroxide. When solid $Al(OH)_3$ is treated with H_3O^+ (*left*) or with OH^- (*right*), it dissolves as a result of the formation of soluble complex ions. The molecular views show that $Al(OH)_3$ is actually the neutral species $Al(H_2O)_3(OH)_3$. (The extensive OH bridging that occurs between Al^{3+} ions throughout the solid is not shown.) Addition of OH^- (*right*) forms the soluble $Al(H_2O)_2(OH)_4^-$ ion; addition of H_3O^+ (*left*) forms the soluble $Al(H_2O)_6^{3+}$ ion.

Figure 19.14 shows this amphoteric behavior but includes some unexpected formulas for the species. Let's see how these species arise. When we dissolve a soluble aluminum salt, such as $Al(NO_3)_3$, in water and then slowly add a strong base, a white precipitate first forms and then dissolves as more base is added. What reactions are occurring? The formula for the hydrated Al^{3+} ion is $Al(H_2O)_6^{3+}(aq)$. It acts as a weak polyprotic acid and reacts with OH^- ions in a stepwise manner:

$$Al(H_2O)_6^{3+}(aq) + OH^-(aq) \rightleftharpoons Al(H_2O)_5OH^{2+}(aq) + H_2O(l)$$
$$Al(H_2O)_5OH^{2+}(aq) + OH^-(aq) \rightleftharpoons Al(H_2O)_4(OH)_2^+(aq) + H_2O(l)$$
$$Al(H_2O)_4(OH)_2^+(aq) + OH^-(aq) \rightleftharpoons Al(H_2O)_3(OH)_3(s) + H_2O(l)$$

At this point, the white precipitate has formed. It is the insoluble hydroxide $Al(H_2O)_3(OH)_3(s)$, often written as $Al(OH)_3(s)$. (It exists as a solid because of extensive bridging from one Al^{3+} ion to another by OH^- ions.) Now you can see that the precipitate is actually the hydrated Al^{3+} ion with an H^+ removed from each of three bound H_2O molecules. Addition of H_3O^+ protonates the OH groups and re-forms the hydrated Al^{3+} ion.

Further addition of OH^- removes a fourth H^+ and forms the soluble ion $Al(H_2O)_2(OH)_4^-(aq)$, which we usually write as $Al(OH)_4^-(aq)$:

$$Al(H_2O)_3(OH)_3(s) + OH^-(aq) \rightleftharpoons Al(H_2O)_2(OH)_4^-(aq) + H_2O(l)$$

In other words, this complex ion is not created by ligands substituting for bound water molecules but through an acid-base reaction in which added OH^- ions titrate bound water molecules.

Several other slightly soluble hydroxides, such as those of Cr^{3+}, Zn^{2+}, Pb^{2+}, and Sn^{2+}, are amphoteric and exhibit similar reactions:

$$Zn(H_2O)_2(OH)_2(s) + OH^-(aq) \rightleftharpoons Zn(H_2O)(OH)_3^-(aq) + H_2O(l)$$

In contrast, the water-insoluble hydroxides of Fe^{2+}, Fe^{3+}, and Ca^{2+} dissolve in acid, but *not* in base, because the remaining bound water molecules are not acidic enough:

$$Fe(H_2O)_3(OH)_3(s) + 3H_3O^+(aq) \longrightarrow Fe(H_2O)_6^{3+}(aq) + 3H_2O(l)$$

$$Fe(H_2O)_3(OH)_3(s) + OH^-(aq) \longrightarrow \text{no reaction}$$

The difference in solubility in base between $Al(OH)_3$ and $Fe(OH)_3$ is the key to an important separation step in the production of aluminum metal, so we'll see it again in Section 22.4. We also employ it in the next section in analyzing a mixture of ions.

Section Summary

A complex ion consists of a central metal ion covalently bonded to two or more negative or neutral ligands. Its formation is described by a formation constant K_f. A hydrated metal ion is a complex ion with water molecules as ligands. Other ligands can displace the water in a stepwise process. In most cases, the K_f value of each step is large, so the fully substituted complex ion forms almost completely in the presence of excess ligand. A ligand solution increases the solubility of an ionic precipitate if the cation forms a complex ion with the ligand. Amphoteric metal hydroxides dissolve in acid and base due to acid-base reactions that form soluble complex ions.

19.5 Application of Ionic Equilibria to Chemical Analysis

Many of the ideas we've discussed in this chapter are used to analyze the ions in a mixture. In this brief introduction to an extensive and time-honored field, we discuss how control of the precipitating-ion concentration is used to selectively precipitate one metal ion in the presence of another and how complex mixtures of ions are separated into smaller groups and each ion identified.

Selective Precipitation

We can often separate one ion in a solution from another by exploiting differences in the solubility of their compounds with a given precipitating ion. In the process of **selective precipitation,** we add a solution of precipitating ion until the Q_{sp} of the *more soluble* compound is almost equal to its K_{sp}. This method ensures that the K_{sp} of the *less soluble* compound is exceeded as much as possible. As a result, the maximum amount of the less soluble compound precipitates, but none of the more soluble compound does.

Sample Problem 19.12   Separating Ions by Selective Precipitation

PROBLEM A solution consists of 0.20 M $MgCl_2$ and 0.10 M $CuCl_2$. Calculate the $[OH^-]$ that would separate the metal ions as their hydroxides. K_{sp} of $Mg(OH)_2$ = 6.3×10^{-10}; K_{sp} of $Cu(OH)_2$ = 2.2×10^{-20}.

PLAN Since the two hydroxides have the same formula type (1:2) (see Section 19.3), we compare their K_{sp} values and see that $Mg(OH)_2$ is about 10^{10} times *more* soluble than $Cu(OH)_2$. Thus, $Cu(OH)_2$ precipitates first. We solve for the $[OH^-]$ that will just give a saturated solution of $Mg(OH)_2$ because this $[OH^-]$ will precipitate the greatest amount of Cu^{2+} ion. As a confirmation, we calculate the $[Cu^{2+}]$ remaining to see if the separation was accomplished.

SOLUTION Writing the equations and ion-product expressions:

$$Mg(OH)_2(s) \rightleftharpoons Mg^{2+}(aq) + 2OH^-(aq) \qquad K_{sp} = [Mg^{2+}][OH^-]^2$$

$$Cu(OH)_2(s) \rightleftharpoons Cu^{2+}(aq) + 2OH^-(aq) \qquad K_{sp} = [Cu^{2+}][OH^-]^2$$

Calculating the [OH$^-$] that gives a saturated Mg(OH)$_2$ solution:

$$[OH^-] = \sqrt{\frac{K_{sp}}{[Mg^{2+}]}} = \sqrt{\frac{6.3\times10^{-10}}{0.20}} = \boxed{5.6\times10^{-5}\ M}$$

This is the maximum [OH$^-$] that will *not* precipitate Mg^{2+} ion.
Calculating the [Cu^{2+}] remaining in the solution with this [OH$^-$]:

$$[Cu^{2+}] = \frac{K_{sp}}{[OH^-]^2} = \frac{2.2\times10^{-20}}{(5.6\times10^{-5})^2} = 7.0\times10^{-12}\ M$$

Since the initial [Cu^{2+}] was 0.10 M, virtually all the Cu^{2+} ion is precipitated.

CHECK Rounding, we find the [OH$^-$] seems right: $\sim\sqrt{(6\times10^{-10})/0.2} = 5\times10^{-5}$.
The [Cu^{2+}] remaining also seems correct: $200\times10^{-22}/(5\times10^{-5})^2 = 8\times10^{-12}$.

COMMENT There is often more than one approach to accomplishing the same analytical step. Another possibility in this case is to add excess ammonia to make the solution basic enough to precipitate both hydroxides,

$$Mg^{2+}(aq) + 2NH_3(aq) + 2H_2O(l) \rightleftharpoons Mg(OH)_2(s) + 2NH_4^+(aq)$$

$$Cu^{2+}(aq) + 2NH_3(aq) + 2H_2O(l) \rightleftharpoons Cu(OH)_2(s) + 2NH_4^+(aq)$$

Then the Cu(OH)$_2$ dissolves in excess NH$_3$ by forming a soluble complex ion:

$$Cu(OH)_2(s) + 4NH_3(aq) \rightleftharpoons Cu(NH_3)_4^{2+}(aq) + 2OH^-(aq)$$

Follow-up Problem 19.12   A solution of alkaline earth ions is made from 0.050 M BaCl$_2$ and 0.025 M CaCl$_2$. What concentration of SO$_4^{2-}$ must be present to leave 99.99% of only one of the cations in solution? K_{sp} of BaSO$_4$ = 1.1×10^{-10} and K_{sp} of CaSO$_4$ = 2.4×10^{-5}.

Sometimes two or more types of ionic equilibria are controlled simultaneously to precipitate ions selectively. This approach is used commonly to separate ions as their sulfides, so the HS$^-$ ion is the precipitating ion. In the manner used in Sample Problem 19.12, we control the [HS$^-$] to exceed the K_{sp} of one metal sulfide but not another. We exert this control on the [HS$^-$] by controlling H$_2$S dissociation because H$_2$S is the source of HS$^-$; we control H$_2$S dissociation by adjusting the [H$_3$O$^+$]:

$$H_2S(aq) + H_2O(l) \rightleftharpoons H_3O^+(aq) + HS^-(aq)$$

These interactions are controlled in the following way. If we add strong acid to the solution, [H$_3$O$^+$] is high, so H$_2$S dissociation shifts to the left, which decreases [HS$^-$]. With a low [HS$^-$], the *less* soluble sulfide precipitates. Conversely, if we add strong base, [H$_3$O$^+$] is low, so H$_2$S dissociation shifts to the right, which increases [HS$^-$], and then the *more* soluble sulfide precipitates. In essence, what we have done is shift one equilibrium system (H$_2$S dissociation) by adjusting a second (H$_2$O ionization) to control a third (metal sulfide solubility).

Qualitative Analysis: Identifying Ions in Complex Mixtures

The practice of inorganic **qualitative analysis,** the separation and identification of the ions in a mixture, was once an essential part of a chemist's skills. Today, many of these wet chemical techniques have been replaced by instrumental methods. Nevertheless, they provide an excellent means for studying ionic equilibria, including some of the very ones utilized by modern analytical instruments. In this discussion, we apply the principles of solubility and complex-ion equilibria to separate and characterize a mixture of cations; similar procedures exist for anions. Rather than a fixed series of steps for identifying a set of ions, the design of the procedure often depends on the analyst's ingenuity.

Figure 19.15 **The general procedure for separating ions in qualitative analysis.** A precipitating ion is added to a mixture of ions, the precipitate is separated by centrifugation, and the remaining dissolved ions are treated with another precipitating ion. The process is repeated until the ions are separated into ion groups.

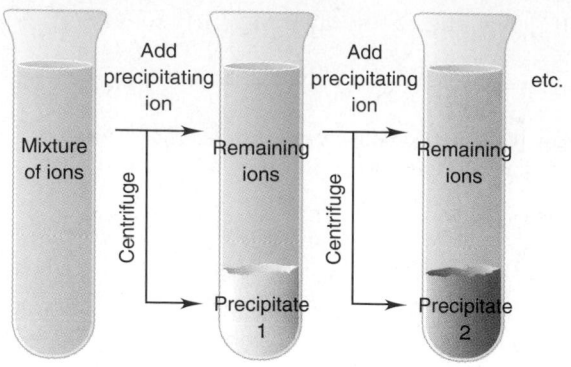

Separation into Ion Groups The general approach begins by separating the unknown solution into *ion groups*. (Ion groups have *nothing* to do with periodic table groups.) Figure 19.15 depicts the laboratory steps. The mixture of metal ions is treated with a solution that precipitates a certain group of them and leaves the others in solution. Filtration or centrifugation (the rapid spinning of the tube to collect the solid in a compact pellet at the bottom) separates the compounds containing the precipitated metal ions. The ions remaining in solution are decanted (poured off) and treated with a solution that precipitates a different group of ions. These steps are repeated until the original mixture has been separated into specific ion groups. In an actual analysis, a *known solution* (one that contains all the ions under study) and a *blank* of distilled water are treated in exactly the same way as the unknown solution, thereby making it much easier to judge a positive or negative result.

Figure 19.16 shows one common scheme for separating cations into ion groups.

Ion group 1: Insoluble chlorides. The entire mixture of soluble ions is treated with 6 *M* HCl. Since most metal chlorides are soluble, only those few ions that form insoluble chlorides precipitate in this step. If a precipitate appears, it consists of chlorides of any of the following:

$$Ag^+, Hg_2^{2+}, Pb^{2+}$$

If none appears, no ions from ion group 1 are present in the mixture. If a precipitate forms, the tube is centrifuged, and the solution is carefully decanted.

Ion group 2: Acid-insoluble sulfides. The decanted solution is already acidic from the previous treatment with HCl. The pH is adjusted to 0.5 and the solution treated with aqueous H_2S. The H_3O^+ present keeps the $[HS^-]$ very low, so any precipitate contains one or more of the least soluble sulfides, which are those of

$$Cu^{2+}, Cd^{2+}, Hg^{2+}, As^{3+}, Sb^{3+}, Bi^{3+}, Sn^{2+}, Sn^{4+}, Pb^{2+}$$

($PbCl_2$ is slightly soluble in water, so a small amount of Pb^{2+} remains in solution after addition of HCl and appears in ion groups 1 *and* 2.) If no precipitate forms under these conditions, no members of ion group 2 are present. The tube is centrifuged and the solution decanted.

Ion group 3: Base-insoluble sulfides and hydroxides. The decanted solution is made slightly basic with a buffer of NH_3/NH_4^+. The OH^- present increases the $[HS^-]$, which causes precipitation of the more soluble sulfides and some hydroxides. The cations included are

$$Zn^{2+}, Mn^{2+}, Ni^{2+}, Fe^{2+}, Co^{2+} \text{ as sulfides, and } Al^{3+}, Cr^{3+} \text{ as hydroxides}$$

(Fe^{3+} is reduced to Fe^{2+} in this step.) If no precipitate appears, none of these ions is present. Centrifuging and decanting gives the next solution.

Figure 19.16 A qualitative analysis scheme for separating cations into five ion groups. The first tube contains a solution of ions (listed according to ion group). It is treated with the first precipitating solution (6 *M* HCl) and the procedure continues, as shown in Figure 19.15.

Ion group 4: Insoluble phosphates. To this slightly basic solution, $(NH_4)_2HPO_4$ is added, which precipitates any alkaline earth ions as phosphates. Alternatively, Na_2CO_3 is added and the precipitate contains alkaline earth carbonates. In either case, any of the following ions are precipitated:

$$Mg^{2+}, Ca^{2+}, Ba^{2+}$$

If no precipitate appears, none of these ions is present.

Ion group 5: Alkali metal and ammonium ions. After centrifuging and decanting, the final solution contains any of the following ions:

$$Na^+, K^+, NH_4^+$$

With the ions separated into ion groups, the analyst then devises schemes to identify each ion in a group. For example, identification of the ions in ion

A   B

C

Figure 19.17 Tests to determine the presence of cations in ion group 5. Ion group 5 is soluble through all the steps in Figure 19.16. It consists of some alkali metal ions and NH_4^+ ion. Flame tests give characteristic colors for Na^+ ion **(A)**, and K^+ ion **(B)**. Adding OH^- to NH_4^+ forms gaseous NH_3, which turns moistened red litmus paper blue **(C)**.

group 5 is usually done through flame and color tests (Figure 19.17). (Because NH_4^+ ion is added during earlier steps and Na^+ is a common contaminant in ammonium salts, the analyst performs tests for these ions on the original ion mixture.) In flame tests, sodium produces a characteristic yellow-orange color, and potassium gives a violet color. Acid-base behavior is used to identify NH_4^+. The solution is made basic with NaOH and moist red litmus paper is held over it. If the paper turns blue, NH_4^+ is present because the OH^- reacts to form NH_3, which reacts with the H_2O on the paper:

$$NH_4^+(aq) + OH^-(aq; \text{ added}) \longrightarrow NH_3(g) + H_2O(l)$$

$$NH_3(g) + H_2O \rightleftharpoons NH_4^+(aq) + OH^- \text{ (turns moist red litmus blue)}$$

A Simple "Qual" Scheme   Qualitative analyses often include the formation of complex ions in addition to precipitates. Figure 19.18 diagrams a "qual" scheme to identify four ions from several ion groups. Suppose the solution contains some or all of the following: Ag^+, Al^{3+}, Cu^{2+}, and Fe^{3+}. We can separate and identify them by the following steps:

Step 1. Al^{3+} and Fe^{3+} form insoluble hydroxides, and Ag^+ and Cu^{2+} form soluble complex ions with NH_3, so we add aqueous NH_3, which provides both the NH_3 molecules that act as ligands and a small amount of OH^- ions. A precipitate forms that may be $Fe(OH)_3$ (brown), $Al(OH)_3$ (white), or both. The reactions written with the actual formulas of the species are

$$Al(H_2O)_6^{3+}(aq) + 3NH_3(aq) \longrightarrow Al(H_2O)_3(OH)_3(s; \text{ white}) + 3NH_4^+(aq)$$

$$Fe(H_2O)_6^{3+}(aq) + 3NH_3(aq) \longrightarrow Fe(H_2O)_3(OH)_3(s; \text{ brown}) + 3NH_4^+(aq)$$

Simplified versions, with the OH^- ions coming from the reaction of NH_3 in water, are

$$Al^{3+}(aq) + 3OH^-(aq) \rightleftharpoons Al(OH)_3(s) \text{ [white]}$$

$$Fe^{3+}(aq) + 3OH^-(aq) \rightleftharpoons Fe(OH)_3(s) \text{ [brown]}$$

In the solution, complex ions of Ag^+ (colorless), Cu^{2+} (blue), or both may be present:

$$Ag^+(aq) + 2NH_3(aq) \rightleftharpoons Ag(NH_3)_2^+(aq) \text{ [colorless]}$$

$$Cu^{2+}(aq) + 4NH_3(aq) \rightleftharpoons Cu(NH_3)_4^{2+}(aq) \text{ [blue]}$$

(The Cu^{2+} also forms an insoluble hydroxide, but the presence of high $[NH_3]$ dissolves the precipitate and forms the complex ion.) We centrifuge to separate the soluble complex ions from the precipitate.

Step 2. To separate the Ag^+ and Cu^{2+} that may be present as complex ions, we take advantage of the ability of Cl^- to act as both a ligand and a precipitating ion. We add HCl to the solution of complex ions and centrifuge. The H_3O^+ ions react with the NH_3 in equilibrium with the complex ions to form NH_4^+, which cannot act as a ligand:

$$Ag(NH_3)_2^+(aq) + 2H_3O^+(aq; \text{ added}) \longrightarrow Ag^+(aq) + 2NH_4^+(aq) + 2H_2O(l)$$

$$Cu(NH_3)_4^{2+}(aq) + 4H_3O^+(aq; \text{ added}) \longrightarrow Cu^{2+}(aq) + 4NH_4^+(aq) + 4H_2O(l)$$

Now that the metal ions are hydrated, the Cl^- ion present in the added HCl can react with them to form a white precipitate with $Ag^+(aq)$ and a green complex ion with $Cu^{2+}(aq)$:

$$Ag^+(aq) + Cl^-(aq; \text{ added}) \longrightarrow AgCl(s) \text{ [white]}$$

$$Cu^{2+}(aq) + 4Cl^-(aq; \text{ added}) \longrightarrow CuCl_4^{2-}(aq) \text{ [green]}$$

Step 3. To separate the aluminum and iron compounds that may be in the precipitate of Step 1, recall that $Al(OH)_3$ is amphoteric, but $Fe(OH)_3$ is not. We add NaOH to the solid. The amphoteric $Al(OH)_3$ dissolves, but $Fe(OH)_3$ does not:

$$Al(OH)_3(s) + OH^-(aq; \text{ added}) \longrightarrow Al(OH)_4^-(aq)$$

$$Fe(OH)_3(s) + OH^-(aq; \text{ added}) \longrightarrow \text{ no reaction}$$

Figure 19.18 **A qualitative analysis scheme for Ag⁺, Al³⁺, Cu²⁺, and Fe³⁺.**

Step 4. To confirm the presence of Al^{3+} in the solution of Step 3, we decant the solution and make it somewhat acidic with HCl, which first precipitates the Al^{3+} ion as the hydroxide and then converts it to hydrated Al^{3+}. Then we add Na_2HPO_4, which forms a white precipitate of $AlPO_4$:

$$Al(OH)_4^-(aq) \xrightarrow{H_3O^+} Al(OH)_3(s) \xrightarrow{H_3O^+} Al^{3+}(aq)$$

$$Al^{3+}(aq) + HPO_4^{2-}(aq; \text{ added}) + H_2O(l) \longrightarrow H_3O^+(aq) + AlPO_4(s) \text{ [white]}$$

Step 5. To confirm that the remaining solid in Step 3 is, in fact, $Fe(OH)_3$, we dissolve it in dilute HCl and add potassium thiocyanate solution (KSCN), which forms a red complex ion with Fe^{3+}:

$$Fe(OH)_3(s) + 3H_3O^+(aq) \longrightarrow Fe^{3+}(aq) + 6H_2O(l)$$

$$Fe^{3+}(aq) + SCN^-(aq; \text{ added}) \longrightarrow FeSCN^{2+}(aq) \text{ [red]}$$

Thus, each ion in the original mixture is separated, identified, and confirmed.

Section Summary

Ions are precipitated selectively by adding a precipitating ion until the K_{sp} of one compound is exceeded as much as possible without exceeding the K_{sp} of the other. An extension of this approach is to control the equilibrium of the slightly soluble compound by simultaneously controlling an equilibrium system that contains the precipitating ion. Qualitative analysis of ion mixtures involves adding precipitating ions to separate the unknown ions into ion groups. The groups are then analyzed further through precipitation and complex ion formation.

Chapter Perspective

This chapter is the last of three that explore the nature and variety of equilibrium systems. In Chapter 17, we discussed the central ideas of equilibrium in the context of gaseous systems. In Chapter 18, we extended our understanding to acid-base equilibria. In this chapter, we highlighted three types of aqueous ionic systems and examined their role in the laboratory and the environment. The equilibrium constant, in all its *forms, is a number that provides a limit to changes in a system, whether a chemical reaction, a physical change, or the dissolution of a substance. You now have the skills to predict whether a change will take place and to calculate its result, but you still do not know* why *the change occurs in the first place, or why it stops changing when it does. In Chapter 20, you'll find out.*

The following learning objectives, with section and/or sample problem (SP) numbers in parentheses, can help focus your study:

Understand These Concepts

1. How the presence of a common ion suppresses a reaction that forms it (Section 19.1)
2. Why the concentrations of buffer components must be high to minimize the change in pH from addition of small amounts of H_3O^+ or OH^- (Section 19.1)
3. How buffer capacity depends on buffer concentration and on the pK_a of the acid component; why buffer range is within ± 1 pH unit from the pK_a (Section 19.1)
4. The nature of an acid-base indicator as a conjugate acid-base pair with differently colored acidic and basic forms (Section 19.2)
5. The distinction between equivalence point and end point in an acid-base titration (Section 19.2)
6. Why the shapes of strong acid–strong base, weak acid–strong base, and strong acid–weak base titration curves differ (Section 19.2)
7. How the pH at the equivalence point is determined by the species present; why the pH at the midpoint of the buffer region equals the pK_a of the acid (Section 19.2)
8. How the titration curve of a polyprotic acid has a buffer region and equivalence point for each ionizable proton (Section 19.2)
9. How a slightly soluble ionic compound reaches equilibrium in water, expressed by an equilibrium (ion-product) constant K_{sp} (Section 19.3)
10. Why incomplete dissociation of an ionic compound leads to approximate values calculated for K_{sp} and solubility (Section 19.3)
11. Why a common ion in solution decreases the solubility of its compounds (Section 19.3)
12. How pH affects the solubility of a compound that contains a weak-acid anion (Section 19.3)
13. How precipitate formation depends on the relative values of Q_{sp} and K_{sp} (Section 19.3)
14. How complex-ion formation is stepwise and expressed by an overall equilibrium (formation) constant K_f (Section 19.4)
15. Why addition of a ligand increases the solubility of a compound whose metal ion forms a complex ion (Section 19.4)

16. How the aqueous chemistry of amphoteric hydroxides involves precipitation, complex-ion, and acid-base equilibria (Section 19.4)
17. How selective precipitation and simultaneous equilibria are used to separate ions (Section 19.5)
18. How qualitative analysis is used to separate and identify the ions in a mixture (Section 19.5)

Master These Skills

1. Using stoichiometry and equilibrium problem-solving techniques to calculate the effect of added H_3O^+ or OH^- on buffer pH (SP 19.1)
2. Using the Henderson-Hasselbalch equation to calculate buffer pH (Section 19.1)
3. Choosing the components of a buffer of a given pH and calculating their quantities (SP 19.2)
4. Calculating the pH at any point in an acid-base titration (Section 19.2 and SP 19.3)
5. Choosing an appropriate indicator based on the pH at various points in a titration (Section 19.2)
6. Writing K_{sp} expressions for slightly soluble ionic compounds (SP 19.4)
7. Calculating K_{sp} from solubility data (SP 19.5)
8. Calculating solubility from K_{sp} (SP 19.6)
9. Using K_{sp} values to compare solubilities for compounds with the same total number of ions (Section 19.3)
10. Calculating the decrease in solubility caused by the presence of a common ion (SP 19.7)
11. Predicting the effect of H_3O^+ on solubility (SP 19.8)
12. Using ion concentrations to calculate Q_{sp} and compare it with K_{sp} to predict whether a precipitate forms (SP 19.9)
13. Calculating the concentration of metal ion remaining after excess ligand forms a complex ion (SP 19.10)
14. Using an overall equilibrium constant ($K_{sp} \times K_f$) to calculate the effect of complex-ion formation on solubility (SP 19.11)
15. Comparing K_{sp} values in order to separate ions by selective precipitation (SP 19.12)
16. Identifying the ions in a mixture through sequences of precipitation and complex-ion formation (Section 19.5)

For Review and Reference

Key Terms

Section 19.1
acid-base buffer
common-ion effect
Henderson-Hasselbalch
 equation
buffer capacity

buffer range
Section 19.2
acid-base titration curve
acid-base indicator
equivalence point
end point

Section 19.3
solubility-product constant
 (K_{sp})
molar solubility
Section 19.4
complex ion

ligand
formation constant (K_f)
Section 19.5
selective precipitation
qualitative analysis

Key Equations and Relationships

19.1 Finding the pH from known concentrations of a conjugate acid-base pair (Henderson-Hasselbalch equation) (p. 811):

$$pH = pK_a + \log\left(\frac{[\text{base}]}{[\text{acid}]}\right)$$

19.2 Defining the equilibrium condition for a slightly soluble compound, M_pX_q, composed of M^{n+} and X^{z-} ions (p. 824):

For a saturated solution, $Q_{sp} = [M^{n+}]^p[X^{z-}]^q = K_{sp}$

Highlighted Figures and Tables

These figures (F) and tables (T) provide a quick review of key ideas. Entries in **color** contain frequently used data.
F19.2 How a buffer works (p. 808)
F19.3 Buffer capacity and pH change (p. 811)
F19.4 pH ranges of acid-base indicators (p. 815)

F19.6 A strong acid–strong base titration (p. 816)
F19.7 A weak acid–strong base titration (p. 818)
F19.8 A weak base–strong acid titration (p. 821)
T19.2 K_{sp} of ionic compounds at 25°C (p. 825)
T19.4 K_f of some complex ions at 25°C (p. 836)

Answers to Follow-up Problems

19.1 (a) Before addition:
Assuming x is small enough to be neglected,

$$[\text{HF}] = 0.50\ M \quad \text{and} \quad [\text{F}^-] = 0.45\ M$$

$$[\text{H}_3\text{O}^+] = K_a \times \frac{[\text{HF}]}{[\text{F}^-]} \approx (6.8\times10^{-4})\left(\frac{0.50}{0.45}\right)$$

$$= 7.6\times10^{-4}\ M$$

$$pH = 3.12$$

(b) After addition of 0.40 g NaOH (0.010 mol NaOH) to 1.0 L buffer,

$$[\text{HF}] = 0.49\ M \quad \text{and} \quad [\text{F}^-] = 0.46\ M$$

$$[\text{H}_3\text{O}^+] \approx (6.8\times10^{-4})\left(\frac{0.49}{0.46}\right)$$

$$= 7.2\times10^{-4}\ M;\ pH = 3.14$$

19.2 $[\text{H}_3\text{O}^+] = 10^{-pH} = 10^{-4.25} = 5.6\times10^{-5}$

$$[\text{C}_6\text{H}_5\text{COOH}] = \frac{[\text{H}_3\text{O}^+][\text{C}_6\text{H}_5\text{COO}^-]}{K_a}$$

$$= \frac{(5.6\times10^{-5})(0.050)}{6.3\times10^{-5}} = 0.044\ M$$

Mass (g) of $\text{C}_6\text{H}_5\text{COOH}$

$$= 5.0\ \text{L soln} \times \frac{0.044\ \text{mol } \text{C}_6\text{H}_5\text{COOH}}{1\ \text{L soln}}$$

$$\times \frac{122.12\ \text{g } \text{C}_6\text{H}_5\text{COOH}}{1\ \text{mol } \text{C}_6\text{H}_5\text{COOH}}$$

$$= 27\ \text{g } \text{C}_6\text{H}_5\text{COOH}$$

Dissolve 27 g $\text{C}_6\text{H}_5\text{COOH}$ in 4.9 L 0.050 M $\text{C}_6\text{H}_5\text{COONa}$ and add solution to make 5.0 L. Adjust pH to 4.25 with strong acid or base.

19.3 (a) $[\text{H}_3\text{O}^+] \approx \sqrt{(2.3\times10^{-9})(0.2000)}$

$$= 2.1\times10^{-5}\ M;\ pH = 4.68$$

(b) $[\text{H}_3\text{O}^+] = K_a \times \dfrac{[\text{HBrO}]}{[\text{BrO}^-]} = 2.3\times10^{-9} \times 1$

$$= 2.3\times10^{-9}\ M$$

$$pH = 8.64$$

(c) $[\text{BrO}^-] = \dfrac{\text{moles of BrO}^-}{\text{total volume}} = \dfrac{0.004000\ \text{mol}}{0.06000\ \text{L}}$

$$= 0.06667\ M$$

$$K_b\ \text{of BrO}^- = \frac{K_w}{K_a\ \text{of HBrO}} = 4.3\times10^{-6}$$

$$[\text{H}_3\text{O}^+] = \frac{K_w}{\sqrt{K_b \times [\text{BrO}^-]}}$$

$$\approx \frac{1.0\times10^{-14}}{\sqrt{(4.3\times10^{-6})(0.06667)}}$$

$$= 1.9\times10^{-11}\ M$$

$$pH = 10.72$$

Answers to Follow-up Problems (continued)

(d) Moles of OH^- added = 0.008000 mol; volume (L) of OH^- soln = 0.08000 L

$$[OH^-] = \frac{\text{moles of } OH^- \text{ unreacted}}{\text{total volume}}$$

$$= \frac{0.008000 \text{ mol} - 0.004000 \text{ mol}}{(0.02000 + 0.08000) \text{ L}} = 0.04000 \ M$$

$$[H_3O^+] = \frac{K_w}{[OH^-]} = 2.5\times10^{-13}$$

$$pH = 12.60$$

(e)

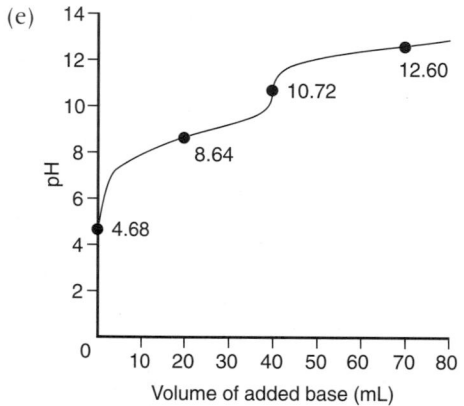

19.4 (a) $K_{sp} = [Ca^{2+}][SO_4^{2-}]$
(b) $K_{sp} = [Cr^{3+}]^2[CO_3^{2-}]^3$
(c) $K_{sp} = [Mg^{2+}][OH^-]^2$
(d) $K_{sp} = [As^{3+}]^2[HS^-]^3[OH^-]^3$

19.5 M of $CaF_2 = \dfrac{1.5\times10^{-4} \text{ g } CaF_2}{10.0 \text{ mL soln}}$

$$\times \frac{1000 \text{ mL}}{1 \text{ L}} \times \frac{1 \text{ mol } CaF_2}{78.08 \text{ g } CaF_2}$$

$$= 1.9\times10^{-4} \ M$$

$$CaF_2(s) \rightleftharpoons Ca^{2+}(aq) + 2F^-(aq)$$

$$[Ca^{2+}] = 1.9\times10^{-4} \ M \text{ and } [F^-] = 3.8\times10^{-4} \ M$$

$$K_{sp} = [Ca^{2+}][F^-]^2 = (1.9\times10^{-4})(3.8\times10^{-4})^2$$

$$= 2.7\times10^{-11}$$

19.6 From the reaction table, $[Mg^{2+}] = S$ and $[OH^-] = 2S$
$K_{sp} = [Mg^{2+}][OH^-]^2 = 4S^3 = 6.3\times10^{-10}$
$S = 5.4\times10^{-4} \ M$

19.7 (a) In water: $K_{sp} = [Ba^{2+}][SO_4^{2-}] = S^2 = 1.1\times10^{-10}$
$S = 1.0\times10^{-5}$
(b) In 0.10 M Na_2SO_4, $[SO_4^{2-}] = 0.10 \ M$
$K_{sp} = 1.1\times10^{-10} \approx S \times 0.10 \qquad S = 1.1\times10^{-9} \ M$
S decreases in presence of the common ion, SO_4^{2-}.
19.8 (a) Increases solubility.

$$CaF_2(s) \rightleftharpoons Ca^{2+}(aq) + 2F^-(aq)$$
$$F^-(aq) + H_3O^+(aq) \longrightarrow HF(aq) + H_2O(l)$$

(b) Increases solubility.

$$ZnS(s) + H_2O(l) \rightleftharpoons Zn^{2+}(aq) + HS^-(aq) + OH^-(aq)$$
$$HS^-(aq) + H_3O^+(aq) \longrightarrow H_2S(aq) + H_2O(l)$$
$$OH^-(aq) + H_3O^+(aq) \longrightarrow 2H_2O(l)$$

(c) No effect. $I^-(aq)$ is conjugate base of strong acid, HI.
19.9 $Ca_3(PO_4)_2(s) \rightleftharpoons 3Ca^{2+}(aq) + 2PO_4^{3-}(aq)$
$Q_{sp} = [Ca^{2+}]^3[PO_4^{3-}]^2 = (1.0\times10^{-9})^5 = 1.0\times10^{-45}$
$Q_{sp} < K_{sp}$, so $Ca_3(PO_4)_2$ will not precipitate.
19.10 $[Fe(H_2O)_6^{3+}]_{init} = \dfrac{(0.0255 \text{ L})(3.1\times10^{-2} \ M)}{0.0255 \text{ L} + 0.0350 \text{ L}}$

$$= 1.3\times10^{-2} \ M$$

Similarly, $[CN^-]_{init} = 0.87 \ M$. From the reaction table,

$$K_f = \frac{[Fe(CN)_6^{3-}]}{[Fe(H_2O)_6^{3+}][CN^-]^6} = 4.0\times10^{43} \approx \frac{1.3\times10^{-2}}{x(0.79)^6}$$

$$x = [Fe(H_2O)_6^{3+}] \approx 1.3\times10^{-45}$$

19.11 $AgBr(s) + 2NH_3(aq) \rightleftharpoons Ag(NH_3)_2^+(aq) + Br^-(aq)$

$K_{overall} = K_{sp}$ of $AgBr \times K_f$ of $Ag(NH_3)_2^+$

$$= 8.5\times10^{-6}$$

From the reaction table,

$$\frac{S}{1.0 - 2S} = \sqrt{8.5\times10^{-6}} = 2.9\times10^{-3}$$

$$S = [Ag(NH_3)_2^+] = 2.9\times10^{-3} \ M$$

Solubility in 1 M hypo is greater than in 1 M NH_3.
19.12 Both 1:1 salts, so K_{sp} values show that $CaSO_4$ is more soluble:

$$[SO_4^{2-}] = \frac{K_{sp}}{[Ca^{2+}]} = \frac{2.4\times10^{-5}}{0.025 \times 0.9999}$$

$$= 9.6\times10^{-4} \ M$$

Problems

Problems with a **colored** number are answered at the back of the text. Problem sections match the text and provide the number(s) of relevant sample problems. Most offer concept review questions, skill-building exercises (written in similar pairs), and problems in a relevant context. Following these are comprehensive problems based on material from any section and/or previous chapter.

[Note: Unless stated otherwise, all problems refer to aqueous solutions at 298 K (25°C).]

Equilibria of Acid-Base Buffer Systems
(Sample Problems 19.1 and 19.2)
■ **Concept Review Questions**
19.1 What is the purpose of an acid-base buffer?
19.2 How do the acid and base components of a buffer function? Why are the components typically a conjugate acid-base pair of a weak acid?
19.3 What is the common-ion effect? How is it related to Le Châtelier's principle? Explain with equations that include HF and NaF.

19.4 When a small amount of H_3O^+ is added to a buffer, does the pH remain constant? Explain.

19.5 What is the essential difference between buffers with high and low capacities? Will the addition of 0.01 mol HCl produce a greater pH change in a buffer with a high capacity or a low one? Explain.

19.6 Choose the factors that determine the capacity of a buffer from among the following and explain your choices:
(a) Conjugate acid-base pair
(b) pH of the buffer
(c) Concentration of buffer-component reservoirs
(d) Buffer range
(e) Buffer-component concentration ratio
(f) pK_a of the acid component

19.7 What is the relationship between buffer range and buffer-component ratio?

19.8 A chemist needs a pH 3.5 buffer. Should she use formic acid ($K_a = 1.8 \times 10^{-4}$) and NaOH or acetic acid ($K_a = 1.8 \times 10^{-5}$) and NaOH to prepare it? Why? What is the disadvantage of choosing the other acid? What is the role of the NaOH?

19.9 Explain the increase or decrease in the pH and in the buffer-component concentration ratio, [NaA]/[HA], of a buffer in each of the following cases:
(a) Add 0.1 M NaOH to the buffer
(b) Add 0.1 M HCl to the buffer
(c) Dissolve pure NaA in the buffer
(d) Dissolve pure HA in the buffer

19.10 Does the pH increase or decrease, and does it do so to a large or small extent, in each of the following cases:
(a) Add 5 drops of 0.1 M NaOH to 100 mL of 0.5 M acetate buffer
(b) Add 5 drops of 0.1 M HCl to 100 mL of 0.5 M acetate buffer
(c) Add 5 drops of 0.1 M NaOH to 100 mL of 0.5 M HCl
(d) Add 5 drops of 0.1 M NaOH to distilled water

■ Skill-Building Exercises *(paired)*

19.11 What are the $[H_3O^+]$ and the pH of a propanoate buffer that consists of 0.25 M CH_3CH_2COONa and 0.15 M CH_3CH_2COOH? K_a of propanoic acid = 1.3×10^{-5}.

19.12 What are the $[H_3O^+]$ and the pH of a benzoate buffer that consists of 0.33 M C_6H_5COOH and 0.28 M C_6H_5COONa? K_a of benzoic acid = 6.3×10^{-5}.

19.13 What are the $[H_3O^+]$ and the pH of a nitrite buffer that consists of 0.50 M HNO_2 and 0.65 M KNO_2? K_a of nitrous acid = 7.1×10^{-4}.

19.14 What are the $[H_3O^+]$ and the pH of a fluoride buffer that consists of 0.20 M HF and 0.25 M KF? K_a of hydrofluoric acid = 6.8×10^{-4}.

19.15 What is the pH of a buffer that consists of 0.55 M HCOOH and 0.63 M HCOONa? pK_a of formic acid = 3.74.

19.16 What is the pH of a buffer that consists of 0.95 M HBrO and 0.68 M KBrO? pK_a of HBrO = 8.64.

19.17 What is the pH of a buffer that consists of 1.0 M sodium phenolate (C_6H_5ONa) and 1.2 M phenol (C_6H_5OH)? pK_a of phenol = 10.00.

19.18 What is the pH of a buffer that consists of 0.12 M boric acid (H_3BO_3) and 0.82 M sodium borate (NaH_2BO_3)? pK_a of boric acid = 9.24.

19.19 What is the pH of a buffer that consists of 0.20 M NH_3 and 0.10 M NH_4Cl? pK_b of NH_3 = 4.75.

19.20 What is the pH of a buffer that consists of 0.50 M CH_3NH_2 and 0.60 M CH_3NH_3Cl? pK_b of methylamine (CH_3NH_2) = 3.35.

19.21 A buffer consists of 0.25 M $KHCO_3$ and 0.32 M K_2CO_3. Carbonic acid is a diprotic acid with $K_{a1} = 4.5 \times 10^{-7}$ and $K_{a2} = 4.7 \times 10^{-11}$. (a) Which K_a value is more important to this buffer? (b) What is the buffer pH?

19.22 A buffer consists of 0.50 M NaH_2PO_4 and 0.40 M Na_2HPO_4. Phosphoric acid is a triprotic acid with $K_{a1} = 7.2 \times 10^{-3}$, $K_{a2} = 6.3 \times 10^{-8}$, and $K_{a3} = 4.2 \times 10^{-13}$. (a) Which K_a value is most important to this buffer? (b) What is the buffer pH?

19.23 What is the buffer-component ratio, $[Pr^-]/[HPr]$, of a propanoate buffer that has a pH of 5.11? See Problem 19.11 for K_a of propanoic acid.

19.24 What is the buffer-component ratio, $[NO_2^-]/[HNO_2]$, of a nitrite buffer that has a pH of 2.95? See Problem 19.13 for K_a of nitrous acid.

19.25 What is the buffer-component ratio, $[BrO^-]/[HBrO]$, of a hypobromite buffer that has a pH of 7.88? K_a of hypobromous acid = 2.3×10^{-9}.

19.26 What is the buffer-component ratio, $[CH_3COO^-]/[CH_3COOH]$, of a buffer that has a pH of 4.39? See Problem 19.8 for K_a of acetic acid.

19.27 A buffer that contains 0.2000 M of acid, HA, and 0.1500 M of its conjugate base, A^-, has a pH of 3.35. What is the pH after 0.0015 mol NaOH is added to 0.5000 L of this solution?

19.28 A buffer that contains 0.40 M base, B, and 0.25 M of its conjugate acid, BH^+, has a pH of 8.88. What is the pH after 0.0020 mol HCl is added to 0.25 L of this solution?

19.29 A buffer that contains 0.110 M HY and 0.220 M Y^- has a pH of 8.77. What is the pH after 0.0010 mol $Ba(OH)_2$ is added to 0.750 L of this solution?

19.30 A buffer that contains 1.05 M B and 0.750 M BH^+ has a pH of 9.50. What is the pH after 0.0050 mol HCl is added to 0.500 L of this solution?

19.31 A buffer is prepared by mixing 184 mL of 0.442 M HCl and 0.500 L of 0.400 M sodium acetate. (See Table 18.2.) (a) What is the pH? (b) How many grams of KOH must be added to 0.500 L of the buffer to change the pH by 0.15 units?

19.32 A buffer is prepared by mixing 50.0 mL of 0.050 M sodium bicarbonate and 10.7 mL of 0.10 M NaOH. (See Table 18.5.) (a) What is the pH? (b) How many grams of HCl must be added to 25.0 mL of the buffer to change the pH by 0.07 units?

19.33 Choose specific acid-base conjugate pairs from Tables 18.2, 18.5, and 18.6 that are suitable for preparing the following buffers: (a) pH ≈ 4.0; (b) pH ≈ 7.0.

19.34 Choose specific acid-base conjugate pairs from Tables 18.2, 18.5, and 18.6 that are suitable for preparing the following buffers: (a) $[H_3O^+] \approx 1 \times 10^{-9}$ M; (b) $[OH^-] \approx 3 \times 10^{-5}$ M.

19.35 Choose specific acid-base conjugate pairs from Tables 18.2, 18.5, and 18.6 that are suitable for preparing the following buffers: (a) pH ≈ 2.5; (b) pH ≈ 5.5.

19.36 Choose specific acid-base conjugate pairs from Tables 18.2, 18.5, and 18.6 that are suitable for preparing the following buffers: (a) $[OH^-] \approx 1 \times 10^{-6}$ M; (b) $[H_3O^+] \approx 4 \times 10^{-4}$ M.

■ **Problems in Context**

19.37 An industrial chemist studying the effect of pH on bleaching and sterilizing properties prepares several hypochlorite buffers. Calculate the pH of the following solutions:
(a) 0.100 M HClO and 0.100 M NaClO
(b) 0.100 M HClO and 0.150 M NaClO
(c) 0.150 M HClO and 0.100 M NaClO
(d) One liter of the solution in (a) after 0.0050 mol NaOH has been added.

19.38 Normal arterial blood has an average pH of 7.40. Phosphate ions form one of the key buffering systems in the blood. Find the buffer-component concentration ratio of a Na_2HPO_4/KH_2PO_4 solution with this pH.

Acid-Base Titration Curves
(Sample Problem 19.3)

■ **Concept Review Questions**

19.39 Acid-base indicators are weak acids. What information must you have to estimate the general range of an indicator's color change? Why do some indicators have two separate pH ranges?

19.40 Why does the color change of an indicator take place over a range of about two pH units?

19.41 Why doesn't the addition of an acid-base indicator affect the pH of the test solution?

19.42 What is the difference between the end point of a titration and the equivalence point? Is the equivalence point always reached first? Explain.

19.43 Some automatic titrators measure the slope of the titration curve to determine when the equivalence point is reached. What happens to the slope of the titration curve that enables the instrument to recognize this point?

19.44 Explain how *strong acid*–strong base, *weak acid*–strong base, and strong acid–*weak base* titrations using the same concentrations differ in terms of (a) the initial pH and (b) the pH at the equivalence point. (The component in italics is in the flask.)

19.45 What species are present in the buffer region of a weak acid–strong base titration? How are they different from the species present at the equivalence point? Are they different from the species present in the buffer region of a strong acid-weak base titration? Explain.

19.46 Why is the center of the buffer region of a weak acid–strong base titration significant?

19.47 How does the titration curve of a monoprotic acid differ from that of a diprotic acid?

■ **Skill-Building Exercises (paired)**

19.48 The indicator cresol red has $K_a = 5.0 \times 10^{-9}$. Over what approximate pH range does it change color?

19.49 The indicator thymolphthalein has $K_a = 7.9 \times 10^{-11}$. Over what approximate pH range does it change color?

19.50 Use Figure 19.4 to choose an indicator for the following titrations:
(a) 0.10 M HCl with 0.10 M NaOH
(b) 0.10 M HCOOH (Table 18.2) with 0.10 M NaOH

19.51 Use Figure 19.4 to choose an indicator for the following titrations:
(a) 0.10 M CH_3NH_2 (Table 18.6) with 0.10 M HCl
(b) 0.50 M HI with 0.10 M KOH

19.52 Use Figure 19.4 to choose an indicator for the following titrations:
(a) 0.5 M $(CH_3)_2NH$ (Table 18.6) with 0.5 M HBr
(b) 0.2 M KOH with 0.2 M HNO_3

19.53 Use Figure 19.4 to choose an indicator for the following titrations:
(a) 0.25 M C_6H_5COOH (Table 18.2) with 0.25 M KOH
(b) 0.50 M NH_4Cl (Table 18.6) with 0.50 M NaOH

19.54 Calculate the pH during the titration of 50.00 mL of 0.1000 M HCl with 0.1000 M NaOH solution after the following additions of base: (a) 0 mL; (b) 25.00 mL; (c) 49.00 mL; (d) 49.90 mL; (e) 50.00 mL; (f) 50.10 mL; (g) 60.00 mL.

19.55 Calculate the pH during the titration of 30.00 mL of 0.1000 M KOH with 0.1000 M HBr solution after the following additions of acid: (a) 0 mL; (b) 15.00 mL; (c) 29.00 mL; (d) 29.90 mL; (e) 30.00 mL; (f) 30.10 mL; (g) 40.00 mL.

19.56 Calculate the pH during the titration of 20.00 mL of 0.1000 M butanoic acid, $CH_3CH_2CH_2COOH$ ($K_a = 1.54 \times 10^{-5}$), with 0.1000 M NaOH solution after the following additions of titrant: (a) 0 mL; (b) 10.00 mL; (c) 15.00 mL; (d) 19.00 mL; (e) 19.95 mL; (f) 20.00 mL; (g) 20.05 mL; (h) 25.00 mL.

19.57 Calculate the pH during the titration of 20.00 mL of 0.1000 M triethylamine, $(CH_3CH_2)_3N$ ($K_b = 5.2 \times 10^{-4}$), with 0.1000 M HCl solution after the following additions of titrant: (a) 0 mL; (b) 10.00 mL; (c) 15.00 mL; (d) 19.00 mL; (e) 19.95 mL; (f) 20.00 mL; (g) 20.05 mL; (h) 25.00 mL.

19.58 Using Tables 18.2 and 18.5, find the pH and volume (mL) of 0.0372 M NaOH needed to reach the equivalence point(s) in titrations of
(a) 42.2 mL of 0.0520 M CH_3COOH
(b) 18.9 mL of 0.0890 M H_2SO_3 (two equivalence points)

19.59 Using Tables 18.2 and 18.5, find the pH and volume (mL) of 0.0588 M KOH needed to reach the equivalence point(s) in titrations of
(a) 23.4 mL of 0.0390 M HNO_2
(b) 17.3 mL of 0.130 M H_2CO_3 (two equivalence points)

19.60 Using Table 18.6, find the pH and the volume (mL) of 0.135 M HCl needed to reach the equivalence point(s) in titrations of
(a) 55.5 mL of 0.234 M NH_3
(b) 17.8 mL of 1.11 M CH_3NH_2

19.61 Using Table 18.6, find the pH and volume (mL) of 0.447 M HNO_3 needed to reach the equivalence point(s) in titrations of
(a) 2.65 L of 0.0750 M pyridine (C_5H_5N)
(b) 0.188 L of 0.250 M NH_3

Equilibria of Slightly Soluble Ionic Compounds
(Sample Problems 19.4 to 19.9)

■ **Concept Review Questions**

19.62 The molar solubility of the slightly soluble ionic compound M_2X is 5×10^{-5} M. What is the molarity of each of the two ions? How do you set up the calculation to find K_{sp}?

What assumption must you make about the dissociation of M_2X into ions? Why is the calculated K_{sp} higher than the actual value?

19.63 Why does pH affect the solubility of CaF_2 significantly, but not that of $CaCl_2$?

19.64 A list of solubility product constants, such as Table 19.2, can be used to compare the solubility of silver chloride directly with that of silver bromide but not with that of silver chromate. Explain.

19.65 In gaseous equilibria, the reverse reaction predominates when $Q_c > K_c$. What occurs in an aqueous ionic solution when $Q_{sp} > K_{sp}$?

■ Skill-Building Exercises (paired)

19.66 Write the ion-product expressions for
(a) silver carbonate   (b) barium fluoride
(c) copper(II) sulfide

19.67 Write the ion-product expressions for
(a) iron(III) hydroxide   (b) barium phosphate
(c) tin(II) sulfide

19.68 Write the ion-product expressions for
(a) calcium chromate   (b) silver cyanide
(c) nickel(II) sulfide

19.69 Write the ion-product expressions for
(a) lead(II) iodide   (b) strontium sulfate
(c) cadmium sulfide

19.70 The solubility of silver carbonate is 0.032 M at 20°C. Calculate the K_{sp} of silver carbonate.

19.71 The solubility of zinc oxalate is 7.9×10^{-3} M at 18°C. Calculate the K_{sp} of zinc oxalate.

19.72 The solubility of silver dichromate at 15°C is 8.3×10^{-3} g/100 mL solution. Calculate the K_{sp} of silver dichromate.

19.73 The solubility of calcium sulfate at 30°C is 0.209 g/100 mL solution. Calculate the K_{sp} of calcium sulfate.

19.74 Calculate the molar solubility of $SrCO_3$ ($K_{sp} = 5.4\times10^{-10}$) in (a) pure water and (b) 0.13 M $Sr(NO_3)_2$.

19.75 Calculate the molar solubility of $BaCrO_4$ ($K_{sp} = 2.1\times10^{-10}$) in (a) pure water and (b) 1.5×10^{-3} M Na_2CrO_4.

19.76 Calculate the molar solubility of $Ca(IO_3)_2$ in (a) 0.060 M $Ca(NO_3)_2$ and (b) 0.060 M $NaIO_3$. (See Table 19.2.)

19.77 Calculate the molar solubility of Ag_2SO_4 in (a) 0.22 M $AgNO_3$ and (b) 0.22 M Na_2SO_4. (See Table 19.2.)

19.78 Which of the following compounds is more soluble in water?
(a) Magnesium hydroxide or nickel(II) hydroxide
(b) Lead(II) sulfide or copper(II) sulfide
(c) Silver sulfate or magnesium fluoride

19.79 Which of the following compounds is more soluble in water?
(a) Strontium sulfate or barium chromate
(b) Calcium carbonate or copper(II) carbonate
(c) Barium iodate or silver chromate

19.80 Which of the following compounds is more soluble in water?

(a) Barium sulfate or calcium sulfate
(b) Calcium phosphate or magnesium phosphate
(c) Silver chloride or lead(II) sulfate

19.81 Which of the following compounds is more soluble in water?
(a) Manganese(II) hydroxide or calcium iodate
(b) Strontium carbonate or cadmium sulfide
(c) Silver cyanide or copper(I) iodide

19.82 Write balanced equations to show whether either of the following compounds has a different solubility with a change in pH: (a) AgCl; (b) $SrCO_3$.

19.83 Write balanced equations to show whether either of the following compounds has a different solubility with a change in pH: (a) CuBr; (b) $Ca_3(PO_4)_2$.

19.84 Write balanced equations to show whether either of the following compounds has a different solubility with a change in pH: (a) $Fe(OH)_2$; (b) CuS.

19.85 Write balanced equations to show whether either of the following compounds has a different solubility with a change in pH: (a) PbI_2; (b) $Hg_2(CN)_2$.

19.86 Does any solid $Cu(OH)_2$ form when 0.075 g KOH is dissolved in 1.0 L of 1.0×10^{-3} M $Cu(NO_3)_2$?

19.87 Does any solid $PbCl_2$ form when 3.5 mg NaCl is dissolved in 0.250 L of 0.12 M $Pb(NO_3)_2$?

19.88 Does any solid $Ba(IO_3)_2$ form when 6.5 mg $BaCl_2$ is dissolved in 500. mL of 0.033 M $NaIO_3$?

19.89 Does any solid Ag_2CrO_4 form when 2.7×10^{-5} g $AgNO_3$ is dissolved in 15.0 mL of 4.0×10^{-4} M K_2CrO_4?

■ Problems in Context

19.90 Calcium ion triggers the clotting of blood, so when blood is donated, the receiving bag contains sodium oxalate solution to precipitate the Ca^{2+} and prevent clotting. A 104-mL sample of blood contains 9.7×10^{-5} g Ca^{2+}/mL, and a medical technologist treats the sample with 100.0 mL of 0.1550 M $Na_2C_2O_4$. Calculate the $[Ca^{2+}]$ after the treatment. (See Table 19.2 for K_{sp} of $CaC_2O_4\cdot H_2O$.)

Equilibria Involving Complex Ions
(Sample Problems 19.10 and 19.11)

■ Concept Review Questions

19.91 How is it possible for a positively charged metal ion to be at the center of a negatively charged complex ion?

19.92 Write equations to show the stepwise reaction of $Cd(H_2O)_4{}^{2+}$ in aqueous KI to form $CdI_4{}^{2-}$. Show that $K_{f\ (overall)} = K_{f1}K_{f2}K_{f3}K_{f4}$.

19.93 Consider the dissolution of PbS in water:

$$PbS(s) + H_2O(l) \rightleftharpoons Pb^{2+}(aq) + HS^-(aq) + OH^-(aq)$$

Even though hydroxide ion is a product, the addition of aqueous NaOH causes more PbS to dissolve. Is this a violation of Le Châtelier's principle? Explain.

■ Skill-Building Exercises (paired)

19.94 Write a balanced equation for the reaction of $Hg(H_2O)_4{}^{2+}$ in aqueous KCN.

19.95 Write a balanced equation for the reaction of $Zn(H_2O)_4{}^{2+}$ in aqueous NaCN.

19.96 Write a balanced equation for the reaction of $Ag(H_2O)_2{}^+$ in aqueous $Na_2S_2O_3$.

19.97 Write a balanced equation for the reaction of $Al(H_2O)_6^{3+}$ in aqueous KF.

19.98 Potassium thiocyanate, KSCN, is often used to determine the presence of Fe^{3+} ions in solution by the formation of the red $Fe(H_2O)_5SCN^{2+}$ (or, more simply, $FeSCN^{2+}$). What is the concentration of Fe^{3+} when 0.50 L each of 0.0015 M $Fe(NO_3)_3$ and 0.20 M KSCN are mixed? K_f of $FeSCN^{2+} = 8.9 \times 10^2$.

19.99 What is the concentration of Cu^{2+} when 25.0 mL each of 0.044 M $Cu(NO_3)_2$ and 0.57 M aqueous NH_3 are mixed? K_f of $Cu(NH_3)_4^{2+} = 5.6 \times 10^{11}$.

19.100 When 0.82 g $ZnCl_2$ is dissolved in 255 mL of 0.150 M NaCN, what are $[Zn^{2+}]$, $[Zn(CN)_4^{2-}]$, and $[CN^-]$? K_f of $Zn(CN)_4^{2-} = 4.2 \times 10^{19}$.

19.101 When 2.4 g $Co(NO_3)_2$ is dissolved in 0.350 L of 0.22 M KOH, what are $[Co^{2+}]$, $[Co(OH)_4^{2-}]$, and $[OH^-]$? K_f of $Co(OH)_4^{2-} = 5 \times 10^9$.

19.102 Calculate the solubility of AgI in 2.5 M NH_3. K_{sp} of AgI $= 8.3 \times 10^{-17}$ and K_f of $Ag(NH_3)_2^+ = 1.7 \times 10^7$.

19.103 Calculate the solubility of $Cr(OH)_3$ in a buffer of pH 13.0. K_{sp} of $Cr(OH)_3 = 6.3 \times 10^{-31}$ and K_f of $Cr(OH)_4^- = 8.0 \times 10^{29}$.

Application of Ionic Equilibria to Chemical Analysis

(Sample Problem 19.12)

■ Problems in Context

19.104 A 50.0-mL solution of 0.50 M $Fe(NO_3)_3$ is mixed with 125 mL of 0.25 M $Cd(NO_3)_2$.
(a) If aqueous NaOH is added to the solution, which ion precipitates first? (See Table 19.2 for the appropriate values.)
(b) Describe how the metal ions can be separated using NaOH.
(c) Calculate the $[OH^-]$ that will accomplish the separation.

19.105 In a qualitative analysis procedure, a chemist adds 0.3 M HCl to an unknown group of ions and then saturates the solution with H_2S.
(a) What is the $[HS^-]$ of the solution?
(b) For which of the following cations will a 0.01 M solution form a precipitate: Pb^{2+}, Mn^{2+}, Hg^{2+}, Cu^{2+}, Ni^{2+}, Fe^{2+}, Ag^+, K^+?

19.106 Name a reagent and describe the results that would distinguish between the following pairs of substances:
(a) NH_4Cl and $NiCl_2$ (b) AgCl and $PbCl_2$
(c) $Al(NO_3)_3$ and $Fe(NO_3)_3$

Comprehensive Problems

Problems with an asterisk (*) are more challenging.

19.107 A microbiologist is preparing a medium on which to culture *E. coli* bacteria. She buffers the medium at pH 7.00 to minimize the effect of acid-producing fermentation, which can occur in such cultures. What volumes of equimolar aqueous solutions of K_2HPO_4 and KH_2PO_4 must she combine to make 100. mL of the pH 7.00 buffer?

19.108 As an FDA physiologist, you need 0.600 L of formate buffer with a pH of 3.74.

(a) What is the required buffer-component concentration ratio?
(b) How do you prepare this solution from stock solutions of 1.0 M HCOOH and 1.0 M NaOH? (*Hint:* Mix x mL of HCOOH with $600 - x$ mL of NaOH.)
(c) What is the final concentration of HCOOH in this solution?

19.109 Tris(hydroxymethyl)aminomethane [$(HOCH_2)_3CNH_2$, known as *TRIS* or *THAM*] is a weak base widely used in biochemical experiments to make buffer solutions in the pH range of 7 to 9. A certain TRIS buffer has a pH of 8.10 at 25°C, and 7.80 at 37°C. Why does the buffer pH change with temperature?

19.110 Gout is an extremely painful, sometimes debilitating, disease caused by an error of nucleic acid metabolism or excretion that leads to a buildup of uric acid in body fluids, which is deposited as slightly soluble sodium urate ($C_5H_3N_4O_3Na$) in the soft tissues of joints. If the extracellular $[Na^+]$ in humans is 0.15 M and the solubility in water of sodium urate is 0.085 g/100. mL, what is the minimum urate ion concentration (abbreviated $[UR^-]$ that will cause a deposit of sodium urate?

19.111 The presence of cadmium ion in a solution is analyzed by precipitation as the sulfide, a yellow compound used as a pigment in everything from artists' oil paints to glass and rubber. Calculate the molar solubility of cadmium sulfide at 25°C.

19.112 To achieve maximum accuracy in an acid-base titration, there should be a large change in pH around the equivalence point for a small addition of titrant.
(a) Which will give more accurate results in the titration of a strong acid with a strong base: 0.100 mol/L solutions, or 0.000100 mol/L solutions? Explain.
(b) Assuming equal concentrations of 0.100 mol/L, which of the following three will give the most accurate and least accurate results: weak acid titrated with a weak base; weak acid with a strong base; strong acid with a strong base? Explain.

19.113 Phosphate systems form one of the most important buffers in living organisms. Use Table 18.5 to calculate the pH of a buffer made by dissolving 0.80 mol NaOH in 0.50 L of 1.0 M H_3PO_4.

*19.114 A student was given a solution containing salts of one or more of the following cations: K^+, Ag^+, Al^{3+}, Cu^{2+}, and Fe^{3+}. From the following laboratory results, determine the cations present:
Step 1. Added $NH_3(aq)$ to ion mixture $\Longrightarrow$ brown precipitate.
Step 2. Centrifuged $\Longrightarrow$ colorless solution.
Step 3. Treated precipitate with $NaOH(aq) \Longrightarrow$ some solid remained, but some may have dissolved.
Step 4. Neutralized solution from Step 3 with $NH_4Cl(aq) \Longrightarrow$ no precipitate.
Step 5. Added $HCl(aq)$ to solution from Step 2 $\Longrightarrow$ white precipitate.
Step 6. Flame test on original mixture $\Longrightarrow$ pale blue color of ordinary flame.

19.115 It is possible to detect NH_3 gas over 10^{-2} M NH_3. To what pH must 0.15 M NH_4Cl be raised to form detectable NH_3?

19.116 Manganese(II) sulfide is one of the compounds found in the nodules on the ocean floor that may eventually be a primary source of many transition metals. The solubility of MnS is 4.7×10^{-4} g/100 mL solution. Estimate the K_{sp} of MnS.

19.117 The normal pH of blood is 7.40 ± 0.05 and is controlled in part by the H_2CO_3/HCO_3^- buffer system.
(a) Assuming that the K_a value for carbonic acid at 25°C applies to blood, what is the $[H_2CO_3]/[HCO_3^-]$ ratio in normal blood?
(b) In acidosis, a condition that can have many causes, the blood is too acidic. What is the $[H_2CO_3]/[HCO_3^-]$ ratio in a patient whose blood pH is 7.20 (severe acidosis)?

19.118 Consider the following reaction:

$$Fe(OH)_3(s) + OH^-(aq) \rightleftharpoons Fe(OH)_4^-(aq); \quad K_c = 4 \times 10^{-5}$$

(a) What is the solubility of $Fe(OH)_3$ in 0.010 M NaOH?
(b) How is this result used in qualitative analysis?

19.119 A biochemical engineer preparing cells for a cloning experiment bathes a small piece of rat epithelial tissue in a TRIS buffer (see Problem 19.109). The buffer is made by dissolving 43.0 g TRIS in enough 0.095 M HCl to make 1.00 L of solution. What is the molarity of TRIS and pH of the buffer? pK_b of TRIS = 5.91.

19.120 Sketch a qualitative titration curve of ethylenediamine, $H_2NCH_2CH_2NH_2$, with 0.1 M HCl.

19.121 Tooth enamel is composed of the mineral hydroxyapatite, $Ca_5(PO_4)_3OH$ ($K_{sp} = 6.8 \times 10^{-37}$). Many water treatment plants now add fluoride to drinking water. The fluoride reacts with $Ca_5(PO_4)_3OH$ to form the more tooth decay–resistant fluorapatite, $Ca_5(PO_4)_3F$ ($K_{sp} = 1.0 \times 10^{-60}$). Fluoridated water has resulted in a dramatic decrease in the number of cavities among children. Calculate the solubility of $Ca_5(PO_4)_3OH$ and of $Ca_5(PO_4)_3F$ in water.

*19.122 A solution contains 0.10 M $ZnCl_2$ and 0.020 M $MnCl_2$. Given the following information, how would you adjust the pH to separate the ions as their sulfides?

$MnS + H_2O \rightleftharpoons Mn^{2+} + HS^- + OH^-; \quad K_{sp} = 3 \times 10^{-11}$

$ZnS + H_2O \rightleftharpoons Zn^{2+} + HS^- + OH^-; \quad K_{sp} = 2 \times 10^{-22}$

$H_2S + H_2O \rightleftharpoons H_3O^+ + HS^-; \quad K_{a1} = 9 \times 10^{-8}$

$[H_2S]$ saturated in water at 25°C = 0.10 M; $K_w = 1.0 \times 10^{-14}$ at 25°C

*19.123 Amino acids have a general formula of $NH_2CH(R)COOH$ and can be considered polyprotic acids. In many cases, the R group contains additional amine and carboxyl groups.
(a) Can an amino acid dissolved in pure water have a protonated COOH group and an unprotonated NH_2 group? Use glycine, NH_2CH_2COOH, to explain why. K_a of COOH group = 4.47×10^{-3}; K_b of NH_2 group = 6.03×10^{-5}.
(b) Calculate the $[^+NH_3CH_2COO^-]/[^+NH_3CH_2COOH]$ ratio at pH 5.5.
(c) The R group of lysine is $-CH_2CH_2CH_2CH_2NH_2$ (pK_b = 3.47). Draw the structure of lysine at pH 1, physiological pH (~7), and pH 13.
(d) The R group of glutamic acid is $-CH_2CH_2COOH$ (pK_a = 4.07). Four ionic forms of glutamic acid (A to D) are shown in the next column. Select the form that predominates at pH 1; at physiological pH (~7); and at pH 13.

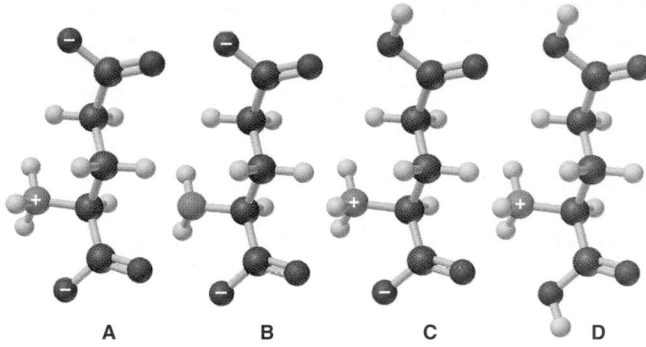

A   B   C   D

19.124 The color of the acid-base indicator ethyl orange turns from red to yellow over the pH range 3.4 to 4.8. Estimate the K_a of ethyl orange.

19.125 An acid-base titration of a weak acid with a strong base has an end point at pH = 9.0. What indicator is suitable for the titration?

19.126 Use the values obtained in Problem 19.54 to sketch a curve of $[H_3O^+]$ vs. milliliters of added titrant. Are there advantages or disadvantages to viewing the results in this form? Explain.

*19.127 Instrumental acid-base titrations use a pH meter rather than a chemical indicator to monitor the changes in pH and volume. The equivalence point is estimated by finding the volume at which the curve has the steepest slope.
(a) Use the data of Figure 19.6 to calculate the slope $\Delta pH/\Delta V$ for all pairs of adjacent points and the average volume (V_{avg}) for each interval.
(b) Plot $\Delta pH/\Delta V$ versus V_{avg} to find the steepest slope, and thus the volume at the equivalence point. (For example, the first pair of points gives $\Delta pH = 0.22$, $\Delta V = 10.00$ mL, hence $\Delta pH/\Delta V = 0.022$ mL^{-1}, and $V_{avg} = 5.00$ mL.)

19.128 Can all complex ions be regarded as the result of a Lewis acid-base reaction? Write an equation and identify the acid, base, and adduct in the formation of $Ag(NH_3)_2^+$ from aqueous Ag^+ and NH_3 solutions.

19.129 Lactic acid $[CH_3CH(OH)COOH]$ is an important biomolecule. Muscle physiologists study its accumulation during exercise. Food chemists study its occurrence in sour milk products, fruit, beer, wine, and tomatoes. Industrial microbiologists study its formation by various bacterial species from carbohydrates. A biochemist prepares a lactate buffer by mixing 225 mL of 0.85 M lactic acid ($K_a = 1.38 \times 10^{-4}$) with 435 mL of 0.68 M sodium lactate. What is the pH of the buffer?

19.130 Why are lakes, rivers, and groundwater in limestone-rich soils mildly basic despite the presence of acidic rainfall?

19.131 Enormous quantities of silver halides, especially AgBr, are used to manufacture photographic film. The materials are prepared by precipitation from silver nitrate solution treated with halide solution. How many kilograms of AgBr can form when 125 m^3 of 0.250 M $AgNO_3$ is mixed with 255 m^3 of 0.600 M NaBr?

19.132 The Henderson-Hasselbalch equation gives a relationship for obtaining the pH of a buffer solution consisting of HA and A$^-$. Derive an analogous relationship for obtaining the pOH of a buffer solution consisting of B and BH$^+$.

19.133 Calculate the molar solubility of $Hg_2C_2O_4$ in 0.13 M $Hg_2(NO_3)_2$. K_{sp} of $Hg_2C_2O_4 = 1.75\times10^{-13}$.

19.134 The well water in an area is "hard" because it is in equilibrium with $CaCO_3$ in the surrounding rocks. What is the concentration of Ca^{2+} in the well water (assuming the pH is such that the CO_3^{2-} ion is not hydrolyzed by the water)? (See Table 19.2 for K_{sp} of $CaCO_3$.)

19.135 Four samples of an unknown solution are tested individually by adding HCl, H_2S in acidic solution, H_2S in basic solution, and Na_2CO_3, respectively. No precipitate forms in any of the tests. When NaOH is added to the original solution, moistened litmus paper held above the solution turns blue. A drop of the original solution turns the color of a flame violet. Which ions are present in the unknown solution?

19.136 Human blood contains two buffer systems, one based on phosphate and one on carbonate species. If the blood has a normal pH of 7.4, what are the principal phosphate and carbonate species present? What is the ratio between the two phosphate species? In the presence of the dissolved ions and other species in blood, K_{a1} of phosphoric acid $= 1.3\times10^{-2}$, $K_{a2} = 2.3\times10^{-7}$, and $K_{a3} = 6\times10^{-12}$; K_{a1} of carbonic acid $= 8\times10^{-7}$ and $K_{a2} = 1.6\times10^{-10}$.

*19.137 Most qualitative analysis schemes start with the separation of ion group 1, Ag^+, Hg_2^{2+}, and Pb^{2+}, by formation of the white solids AgCl, Hg_2Cl_2, and $PbCl_2$. Develop a procedure for confirming the presence or absence of these ions from the following facts:

- $PbCl_2$ is soluble in hot water, but AgCl and Hg_2Cl_2 are not.
- $PbCrO_4$ is a yellow solid that is insoluble in hot water.
- AgCl forms colorless $Ag(NH_3)_2^+(aq)$ in aqueous NH_3.
- When a solution containing $Ag(NH_3)_2^+$ is acidified with HCl, AgCl precipitates.
- Hg_2Cl_2 forms an insoluble mixture of $Hg(l;$ black) and $HgNH_2Cl(s;$ white) in aqueous NH_3.

19.138 An environmental technician collects a sample of rainwater. A light on her portable pH meter indicates low battery power and the potential for inaccurate readings, so she uses indicator solutions to estimate the pH. A piece of litmus paper turns red, indicating acidity, so she divides the sample into thirds and obtains the following results: thymol blue turns yellow; bromphenol blue turns green; and methyl red turns red. Estimate the pH of the rainwater.

*19.139 A 0.050 M H_2S solution contains 0.15 M $NiCl_2$ and 0.35 M $Hg(NO_3)_2$. What pH is required to precipitate the maximum amount of HgS but none of the NiS? (See Table 19.2.)

*19.140 The quantitative analysis of Cl^- ion is often performed by a titration with silver nitrate, using sodium chromate as an indicator. As standardized $AgNO_3$ is added, both white AgCl and red Ag_2CrO_4 precipitate where the drop of $AgNO_3$ lands, but so long as some Cl^- remains, the Ag_2CrO_4 redissolves as the mixture is stirred. When the red color is permanent, the equivalence point has been reached.

(a) Write the equilibrium constant for the reaction

$$2AgCl(s) + CrO_4^{2-}(aq) \rightleftharpoons Ag_2CrO_4(s) + 2Cl^-(aq)$$

(b) Explain why the silver chromate redissolves.

(c) If 25.00 cm^3 of 0.1000 M NaCl is mixed with 25.00 cm^3 of 0.1000 M $AgNO_3$, what is the concentration of Ag^+ remaining in solution? Is this sufficient to precipitate any silver chromate?

*19.141 An ecobotanist separates the components of a tropical bark extract by liquid chromatography. She discovers a large proportion of quinidine, a dextrorotatory stereoisomer of quinine that is a cardiac muscle depressant used for control of arrhythmic heartbeat. Quinidine has two basic N groups ($K_{b1} = 4.0\times10^{-6}$ and $K_{b2} = 1.0\times10^{-10}$). To measure the concentration, she carries out a titration. Because of the low solubility of quinidine, she first protonates both N groups with excess HCl and titrates the acidified solution with standardized base. A 33.85-mg sample of quinidine ($\mathcal{M} = 324.41$ g/mol) was acidified with 6.55 mL of 0.150 M HCl.

(a) How many mL of 0.0133 M NaOH are needed to titrate the excess HCl?

(b) How many additional milliliters of titrant are needed to reach the first equivalence point of quinidine dihydrochloride?

(c) What is the pH at the first equivalence point?

19.142 Why was rainwater acidic in the preindustrial age? Why did its acidity not erode marble statuary? What solutes make acid rain much more acidic now? How does automobile exhaust contribute to this acidity?

*19.143 A biochemist must prepare a solution for use as a medium in an experiment involving acid-producing bacteria. The pH of the medium must not change by more than 0.05 pH units for every 0.0010 mol H_3O^+ generated by the organisms per liter of medium. A buffer consisting of 0.10 M HA and 0.10 M A^- is prepared to be included in the medium to control its pH. What volume of this buffer must be included in 1.0 L of medium?

19.144 A 35.00-mL solution of 0.2500 M HF is titrated with a standardized 0.1532 M solution of NaOH at 25°C.

(a) What is the pH of the solution before titrant is added?

(b) How many milliliters of titrant are required to reach the equivalence point?

(c) What is the pH 0.50 mL before the equivalence point?

(d) What is the pH at the equivalence point?

(e) What is the pH 0.50 mL after the equivalence point?

*19.145 A student is given a solution containing salts of one or more of the following cations: K^+, Ag^+, Al^{3+}, Cu^{2+}, and Fe^{3+}. From the following laboratory results, determine the cations present:

Step 1. Added $NH_3(aq) \Longrightarrow$ white precipitate in colored solution.

Step 2. Centrifuged $\Longrightarrow$ deep-blue solution.

Step 3. Treated precipitate with $NaOH(aq) \Longrightarrow$ dissolved completely. Acidified and obtained white precipitate with $Na_2HPO_4(aq)$.

Step 4. Added $HCl(aq)$ to Step 2 solution $\Longrightarrow$ turned green, and white precipitate formed.

Step 5. Centrifuged precipitate from Step 4 and washed it to remove excess HCl. Treated it with $NH_3(aq) \Longrightarrow$ dissolved to form colorless solution.

Step 6. Flame test on original mixture $\Longrightarrow$ green flame with no red visible.

*19.146 A lake with a surface area of 10.0 acres (1 acre = 4.840×10^3 yd^2) receives 1.00 in. of rain of pH 4.20. (Assume the acidity of the rain is due to a strong, monoprotic acid.)
(a) How many moles of H_3O^+ are in the rain falling on the lake?
(b) If the lake is unbuffered (pH = 7.00) and its average depth is 10.0 ft before the rain, calculate the pH after the rain has been throughly mixed with lake water. (Ignore runoff from the surrounding land.)
(c) If the lake contains hydrogen carbonate ions (HCO_3^-) and the reaction is

$$HCO_3^-(aq) + H_3O^+(aq) \longrightarrow 2H_2O(l) + CO_2(g)$$

what mass of HCO_3^- would neutralize the acid in the rain?
19.147 A 35.0 mL solution of 0.075 M $CaCl_2$ is mixed with 25.0 mL of 0.090 M $BaCl_2$.
(a) If aqueous KF is added to the solution, which fluoride precipitates first?
(b) Describe how the metal ions can be separated using KF to form the fluorides.
(c) Calculate the fluoride ion concentration that will accomplish the separation.
*19.148 Even before the industrial age, rainwater was slightly acidic. Use the following data to calculate pH of unpolluted rainwater at 25°C:

$$\text{Vol \% in air} = 0.033 \text{ vol \% of } CO_2$$

Solubility in pure water at 25°C and 1 atm CO_2 = 88 mL CO_2/100 mL H_2O. K_{a1} of H_2CO_3 = 4.5×10^{-7}.
*19.149 Seawater at the surface of the ocean has a pH of about 8.5.

(a) Which of the following species has the highest concentration at this pH: H_2CO_3; HCO_3^-; CO_3^{2-}? Explain.
(b) What are the concentration ratios of $[CO_3^{2-}]/[HCO_3^-]$ and of $[HCO_3^-]/H_2CO_3]$ at this pH?
(c) In the deep sea, light levels are low, and the pH of the water is around 7.5. Suggest a reason for the lower pH at the greater ocean depth. (*Hint:* Consider the presence or absence of plant and animal life, and their effects on carbon dioxide concentrations.)
*19.150 Ethylenediaminetetraacetic acid (H_4EDTA) is a tetraprotic acid, $(HOOCCH_2)_2NCH_2CH_2N(CH_2COOH)_2$. Its salts are used to treat toxic metal poisoning through the formation of soluble complex ions that are then excreted. Because $EDTA^{4-}$ also binds essential calcium ions, it is often administered as the calcium disodium salt. For example, when $Na_2Ca(EDTA)$ is given to a patient, the $[Ca(EDTA)]^{2-}$ ion reacts with circulating Pb^{2+} ions and exchanges metal ions:

$$[Ca(EDTA)]^{2-}(aq) + Pb^{2+}(aq) \rightleftharpoons$$
$$[Pb(EDTA)]^{2-}(aq) + Ca^{2+}(aq); K_c = 2.5 \times 10^7$$

A child is found to have a dangerously high lead level in the blood of 120 μg/100 mL. If the child is administered 100. mL of 0.10 M $Na_2Ca(EDTA)$ and assuming the exchange reaction and excretion process are 100% efficient, what is the final concentration of Pb^{2+} in μg/100 mL blood? (Total blood volume = 1.5 L.)
*19.151 Sodium chloride is purified for use as table salt by adding HCl to a saturated solution of NaCl (317 g/L). When 25.5 mL of 7.85 M HCl is added to 0.100 L of saturated solution, how many grams of purified NaCl precipitate?

20 Thermodynamics
Entropy, Free Energy, and the Direction of Chemical Reactions

Figure: Surgeons who replace body parts with mechanical contrivances, like the engineers who fabricated this platypus and the other members of the "Robot Zoo," are keenly aware that living systems operate by the same thermodynamic principles that govern machines. In this chapter, we explore some of the most important of those principles to understand why chemical and physical changes occur.

In the last few chapters, we've posed and answered some extremely important questions about chemical and physical change. How fast does the change occur, and how is this rate affected by concentration and temperature? How much product will be present when the net change ceases, and how is this yield affected by concentration and temperature? We've explored these questions in systems ranging from the stratosphere to a limestone cave and from the cells of your body to the lakes of Sweden.

Now it's time to stand back and ask the most profound question of all: Why does a change occur in the first place? Even casual observation shows that some changes seem to have a natural direction and to happen by themselves, whereas others do not. Methane burns in oxygen with a vigorous burst of heat to yield carbon dioxide and water vapor, but these products will not remake methane and oxygen no matter how long they interact. A new steel chain left outside slowly rusts, but a rusty one will not become shiny (see photo). A cube of sugar dissolves in a cup of coffee after a few seconds of stirring, but stir for another century and the cube will not reappear.

All our investigations of nature allow us to define a *spontaneous* process as one that occurs by itself. The opposite of this, the nonspontaneous process, does not occur unless we make it happen. There appears to be a driving force built into a spontaneous process that propels it in a given direction. If we want a process to occur against that natural drive, we must expend energy to accomplish it. The term "spontaneous" has nothing to do with how long a process takes to occur. Spontaneous does *not* mean instantaneous; it means that, given enough time, the process will happen by itself. Many processes are spontaneous but slow—ripening, rusting, and (happily!) aging.

A chemical reaction proceeding toward equilibrium is an example of a spontaneous change. As you learned in Chapter 17, we can predict the net direction of the reaction—its spontaneous direction—by comparing the reaction quotient (Q) with the equilibrium constant (K). But why is there a drive to attain equilibrium? What determines the value of the equilibrium constant? And why do some spontaneous processes absorb energy whereas others release it? The principles of thermodynamics were developed in the early 19th century to help utilize the newly invented steam engine more efficiently. Despite that rather narrow focus, the principles apply, as far as we know, to every system in the universe! In this chapter, we apply these principles to chemical and physical change.

The chapter opens with a review of the first law of thermodynamics. As you'll see, the first law accounts for the size of an energy change but *not* its spontaneous direction. The enthalpy change also is *not* an adequate criterion for predicting reaction direction. Rather, we find this criterion in the change in *entropy,* that is, in the natural tendency of systems to become disordered. This idea leads us to the second law of thermodynamics and its quantitative application to both exothermic and endothermic changes. Then we examine the concept of *free energy,* which simplifies the criterion for spontaneous change, and see how it relates to the useful work a system can perform. Finally, we investigate the key relationship between the free energy change of a reaction and its equilibrium constant.

Concepts and Skills to Review

before you study this chapter

- internal energy, heat, and work (Section 6.1)
- state functions (Section 6.1) and standard states (Section 6.6)
- enthalpy, ΔH, and Hess's law (Sections 6.2 and 6.5)
- entropy and disorder (Section 13.2)
- comparing Q and K to find reaction direction (Section 17.4)

20.1 The Second Law of Thermodynamics: Predicting Spontaneous Change

A **spontaneous change** of a system, whether a chemical or physical change or just a change in location, is one that occurs by itself under specified conditions, without an ongoing input of energy from outside the system. The freezing of water, for example, is spontaneous at 1 atm and $-5°C$. A spontaneous process such as burning or falling may need a little "push" to get started—a spark to ignite gasoline, a shove to knock a book off your desk—but once the process begins, it continues without external aid because the system releases enough energy to keep the process going.

In contrast, for a nonspontaneous change to occur, the system must be supplied with a continuous input of energy. A book falls spontaneously, but it rises only if something else, such as a human or a hurricane-force wind, supplies energy in the form of work. Under a given set of conditions, *if a change is spontaneous in one direction, it is **not** spontaneous in the other.*

How can we tell the direction of a spontaneous change in cases that are not as familiar as burning gasoline or falling books? Can we predict the net direction of any reaction? Does the criterion for spontaneous change involve the change in energy or enthalpy of the reacting system? Since energy changes seem to be involved, let's begin addressing these questions by reviewing the idea of conservation of energy to see if it helps explain spontaneity.

Limitations of the First Law of Thermodynamics

In Chapter 6, we discussed the first law of thermodynamics (the law of conservation of energy) and its application to chemical and physical systems. The first law states that the internal energy (E) of a system, the sum of the kinetic and potential energy of all its particles, changes through the addition or removal of heat (q) and/or work (w):

$$\Delta E = q + w$$

Everything that is not part of the system (sys) is the surroundings (surr), so the system and surroundings together constitute the universe (univ):

$$E_{univ} = E_{sys} + E_{surr}$$

Heat or work gained by the system is lost by the surroundings, and vice versa:

$$q_{sys} = -q_{surr} \quad \text{and} \quad w_{sys} = -w_{surr}$$

It follows from these ideas that *the total energy of the universe is constant, and therefore, energy cannot be created or destroyed.**

Is the first law sufficient to explain why a natural process takes place as it does? It certainly accounts for the energy involved. When a book that was resting on your desk falls to the floor, the first law guides us through the conversion from potential energy of the resting book to the kinetic energy of the falling book to the heat dispersed in the floor near the point of contact. When gasoline burns in your car's engine, the first law explains that the potential energy difference between the chemical bonds in the fuel mixture and in the exhaust gases is converted to the kinetic energy of the moving car and its parts and the heat released to the environment. When an ice cube melts in your hand, the first law tells that energy from your hand was transferred to the ice to change the solid into a liquid. If you could measure the work and heat involved in each case, you would find that the energy is conserved as it is converted from one form to another.

However, the first law does not help us make sense of the *direction* of the change. Why doesn't the heat in the floor near the fallen book change to kinetic energy in the book and move it back onto your desk? Why doesn't

---

*Any modern statement of conservation of energy must take into account mass-energy equivalence and the processes in stars, which convert enormous amounts of matter into energy. Therefore, we qualify the statement to be that the total *mass-energy* of the universe is constant.

the heat released in the engine convert exhaust fumes back into gasoline and oxygen? Why doesn't the pool of water in your cupped hand transfer the heat back to your hand and refreeze? None of these events would violate the first law—energy would still be conserved—but they never happen. The first law by itself tells nothing about the direction of a spontaneous change, so we must search elsewhere for a way to predict it.

The Sign of ΔH Cannot Predict Spontaneous Change

In the mid-19th century, some thermodynamicists thought that the sign of the enthalpy change (ΔH), the heat added or removed at constant pressure (q_P), was the criterion of spontaneity. (Recall from Section 6.2 that, for most reactions, ΔH is either identical to ΔE or very close to it.) These scientists thought that exothermic processes ($\Delta H < 0$) were spontaneous and endothermic ones ($\Delta H > 0$) were nonspontaneous. This hypothesis had much experimental support; after all, many spontaneous processes *are* exothermic. All combustion reactions are spontaneous and exothermic. For example,

$$CH_4(g) + 2O_2(g) \longrightarrow CO_2(g) + 2H_2O(g) \qquad \Delta H^0_{rxn} = -802 \text{ kJ}$$

Iron rusts spontaneously and exothermically:

$$2Fe(s) + \tfrac{3}{2}O_2(g) \longrightarrow Fe_2O_3(s) \qquad \Delta H^0_{rxn} = -826 \text{ kJ}$$

Ionic compounds form spontaneously from their elements with a large release of heat; for example,

$$Na(s) + \tfrac{1}{2}Cl_2(g) \longrightarrow NaCl(s) \qquad \Delta H^0_{rxn} = -411 \text{ kJ}$$

However, in many other cases, the sign of ΔH is no help. An exothermic process may occur spontaneously under certain conditions, whereas the opposite, endothermic, process may occur spontaneously under other conditions. For example, at ordinary pressure, water freezes below 0°C but melts above 0°C. Both processes are spontaneous, but the first is exothermic and the second endothermic:

$$H_2O(l) \longrightarrow H_2O(s) \qquad \Delta H^0_{rxn} = -6.02 \text{ kJ}$$
$$(exo\text{thermic; spontaneous at } T < 0°C)$$

$$H_2O(s) \longrightarrow H_2O(l) \qquad \Delta H^0_{rxn} = +6.02 \text{ kJ}$$
$$(endo\text{thermic; spontaneous at } T > 0°C)$$

At ordinary pressure and room temperature, liquid water vaporizes spontaneously in dry air, another endothermic change:

$$H_2O(l) \longrightarrow H_2O(g) \qquad \Delta H^0_{rxn} = +44.0 \text{ kJ}$$

In fact, all melting and vaporizing are endothermic changes that are spontaneous under the prevailing conditions.

There are many other spontaneous endothermic physical changes. Water-soluble salts dissolve spontaneously, even though most have an endothermic ΔH^0_{soln}:

$$NaCl(s) \xrightarrow{H_2O} Na^+(aq) + Cl^-(aq) \qquad \Delta H^0_{soln} = +3.9 \text{ kJ}$$
$$RbClO_3(s) \xrightarrow{H_2O} Rb^+(aq) + ClO_3^-(aq) \qquad \Delta H^0_{soln} = +47.7 \text{ kJ}$$
$$NH_4NO_3(s) \xrightarrow{H_2O} NH_4^+(aq) + NO_3^-(aq) \qquad \Delta H^0_{soln} = +25.7 \text{ kJ}$$

And, some endothermic chemical changes are spontaneous as well:

$$N_2O_5(s) \longrightarrow 2NO_2(g) + \tfrac{1}{2}O_2(g) \qquad \Delta H^0_{rxn} = +109.5 \text{ kJ}$$

$$Ba(OH)_2 \cdot 8H_2O(s) + 2NH_4NO_3(s) \longrightarrow Ba^{2+}(aq) + 2NO_3^-(aq) + 2NH_3(aq) + 10H_2O(l)$$
$$\Delta H^0_{rxn} = +62.3 \text{ kJ}$$

Figure 20.1 A spontaneous, endothermic chemical reaction. A, When the crystalline, solid reactants barium hydroxide octahydrate and ammonium nitrate are mixed, a slurry soon forms as waters of hydration are released. **B,** The reaction mixture absorbs heat so quickly from the surroundings that the beaker becomes covered with frost, and a moistened block of wood freezes to it.

A   B

Figure 20.1 shows the second reaction. The released waters of hydration solvate the ions, but the reaction mixture cannot absorb heat from the surroundings quickly enough, and the container becomes so cold that a wet block of wood freezes to it.

Is there any feature common to these endothermic processes that can give us a clue as to why they occur spontaneously? A close look shows that in all these examples, *matter changes from a more ordered to a less ordered state.* The phase changes lead from particles fixed in specific arrangements to their random motion and separation:

$$\text{more order} \xrightarrow{\hspace{2.5cm}} \text{less order}$$
$$\text{solid} \longrightarrow \text{liquid} \longrightarrow \text{gas}$$

The dissolving of salts leads from crystalline solid and pure liquid to dispersed ions in a solution:

$$\text{more order} \xrightarrow{\hspace{2.5cm}} \text{less order}$$
$$\text{crystal + liquid} \longrightarrow \text{ions in solution}$$

In the chemical reactions, fewer moles of crystalline solids produce more moles of gases and/or dispersed ions:

$$\text{more order} \xrightarrow{\hspace{2.5cm}} \text{less order}$$
$$\text{crystal + crystal} \longrightarrow \text{gases + ions in solution}$$

This change in orderliness is a key factor in determining the direction of a spontaneous process.

The Tendency Toward Disorder

Systems become disordered spontaneously all around you. Drop a round, ceramic dinner plate, and it shatters into many irregularly shaped pieces. Imagine what would happen to your room if you simply left everything wherever it fell, or to the college library if the staff didn't continuously organize the books and computer files. As you know from many other familiar examples, there is a natural tendency for systems to become disordered. On the other hand, creating order—gluing the pieces of plate together, straightening your room, reshelving library books—requires work. ◆ In Chapter 13, we discussed the importance of disorder as a key factor in the solution process; here we give it a quantitative dimension and examine its central role in other chemical and physical changes.

Probability and Disorder   Let's analyze what we mean by *order* with a deck of playing cards. In a new deck, the cards are arranged in the particular sequence of increasing face value by suit—a highly ordered arrangement (Figure 20.2A). In fact, if the cards are arranged in any other *particular* sequence, the deck is equally ordered. Throw the cards up in the air or shuf-

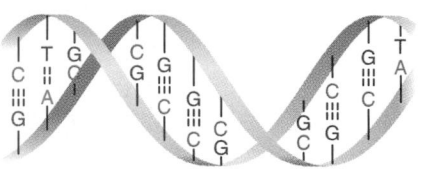

Vital Orderly Information

Searching for an address in a city whose houses are not arranged numerically is the stuff of fitful dreams. A close relationship exists between the order of a system and the information the system conveys. One system in which the order and corresponding information are vitally related is the sequence of nucleotide bases in DNA (Section 15.6). The sequence of four bases—G, C, T, and A—is reproduced during cell division so the genetic makeup of each cell is identical. A change in the sequence introduces disorder in the genetic information and creates mutations—most insignificant, some harmful, a few helpful. Of particular relevance is evidence showing that DNA becomes disordered naturally. There are a host of chemical repair mechanisms that, like molecular librarians, do work to reorganize the bases into their original sequence.

A

B

Figure 20.2 **Order and disorder in a deck of playing cards.** **A,** A new deck of cards is arranged in a specific sequence and thus is a highly ordered system. **B,** Flip the deck into the air or shuffle it and the sequence spontaneously becomes disordered because there are many more disordered sequences than ordered ones.

fle them, and the deck becomes disordered, that is, randomly arranged (Figure 20.2B). There are about 10^{68} possible arrangements of the 52 cards, and *each arrangement is equally probable.* Thus, it is extremely unlikely that one *particular* sequence will occur by chance. Throwing or shuffling the cards initiates a spontaneous process that produces disorder for one simple reason: *there are more disordered arrangements than ordered ones.* In physical and chemical systems, the change from order to disorder occurs spontaneously for the same reason: *disorder is more probable than order.* There are many more possible arrangements for the atoms, ions, or molecules in a disordered system than in an ordered one. ◆

To see how the tendency toward disorder affects reaction direction, first consider a physical system. Figure 20.3 shows an evacuated container consisting of two flasks connected by a stopcock. You fill the left flask with neon to a pressure of 1 atm and connect the other flask. When you open the stopcock, the gas eventually becomes distributed uniformly into both flasks, as measured by a pressure of 0.5 atm in each flask. This result is what you expect on the basis of experience, but *why* does the gas behave this way? Why don't all the neon atoms rush to the other flask, or just stay where they are? For the same reason that the cards you shuffle don't end up in an orderly sequence.

The randomly moving gas particles spread throughout both flasks because twice the original volume affords each particle twice as many places it can be. The vastly increased number of arrangements this allows makes it vastly more probable that the particles will fill the entire volume than a limited part of it. On the molecular level, some particles in the left flask hit the open stopcock and move into the right flask. More collisions from the left than from the right cause a net flow to the right until the collisions from both sides are equal. Imagine how unlikely it would be for all the particles in the right flask to move back to the left. Even for 10 Ne atoms, the odds against this happening are about 1000 to 1; for 1 mol of gas, the odds are about $10^{2\times10^{23}}$ to 1! Like shuffling a new deck of cards, opening the stopcock initiates a spontaneous change from more order to less order, that is, from a less probable arrangement to more probable one, simply because there are *more* disorderly arrangements.

◆ **Poker and Probability** In a game of poker, a rare combination has more value than a common one because it has a lower probability of being dealt. In other words, the poker hand that has fewer possible arrangements wins. There are only four possible royal-flush hands (A, K, Q, J, 10 of the same suit), but 1,098,240 hands that contain one pair.

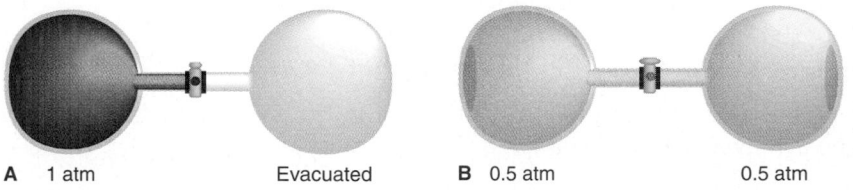

A 1 atm   Evacuated   **B** 0.5 atm   0.5 atm

Figure 20.3 **Spontaneous expansion of a gas.** A container consists of two flasks connected by a stopcock. **A,** With the stopcock closed, neon gas at a pressure of 1 atm occupies one flask and the other is evacuated. **B,** With the stopcock open, the gas expands spontaneously and fills both flasks uniformly to a pressure of 0.5 atm.

Entropy and Disorder   The redistribution of the gas particles in the container occurred with *no change in the total internal energy of the system,* so the various arrangements are *equivalent.* The number of ways the components of a system can be arranged without changing the system's energy is directly related to a quantity called **entropy (S).** Recall from Chapter 13 that *entropy is a measure of the disorder of the system:*

- A system with relatively few equivalent ways to arrange its components, such as a crystalline solid or a deck of cards in a specified sequence, has relatively *small disorder and low entropy.*
- A system with many equivalent ways to arrange its components, such as a gas or a shuffled deck of cards, has relatively *large disorder and high entropy.*

If the entropy of a system goes up, the components of the system have become more disordered, random, or chaotic, and the system's energy has become distributed over a wider range: $S_{disorder} > S_{order}$.

Like internal energy and enthalpy, *entropy is a state function,* one that depends only on the present state of the system, not on how it arrived at that state. Therefore, the change in entropy of the system, ΔS_{sys}, depends only on its initial and final values:

$$\Delta S_{sys} = S_{final} - S_{initial}$$

Since the gas particles in the flasks in Figure 20.3 ended up with more ways to be arranged, the entropy of the system increased, so ΔS_{sys} was positive ($S_{final} > S_{initial}$). If the gas particles in both flasks moved to one flask, they would have fewer ways to be arranged, so the entropy of the system would decrease: ΔS_{sys} would be negative ($S_{final} < S_{initial}$). How the change in order comes about—what paths the particles take as they become rearranged—does not affect the sign or magnitude of ΔS_{sys}.

Entropy and the Second Law of Thermodynamics

Now let's return to our original question: what determines the direction of a spontaneous change? As you've just seen, natural systems tend toward disorder, toward a more random, less ordered distribution of their particles. This natural tendency is the criterion for which we've been searching, but to apply it correctly, we have to consider more than just the system. After all, some systems become *less* ordered spontaneously (ice melting, a crystal dissolving) and others become *more* ordered spontaneously (water freezing, a crystal growing). When we consider changes in both the system *and* its surroundings, we find that *all processes occur spontaneously in the direction that increases the total entropy of the universe (system plus surroundings).* This is one way to state the **second law of thermodynamics.**

Notice that the second law places no limitations on the entropy change of the system *or* the surroundings: either may be negative, that is, either system *or* surroundings may become more ordered. The law *does* state, however, that for a spontaneous process, the *sum* of the entropy changes must be positive. When the entropy of the system decreases, the entropy of the surroundings increases even more to offset this decrease in the system, so the entropy of the universe (system *plus* surroundings) increases. A quantitative statement of the second law is that, for any spontaneous process,

$$\Delta S_{univ} = \Delta S_{sys} + \Delta S_{surr} > 0 \qquad \textbf{(20.1)}$$

Standard Molar Entropies and the Third Law

As stated earlier, entropy (S) is related to the number of ways (W) a system can be arranged without changing its total internal energy. In 1877, the Austrian mathematician Ludwig Boltzmann described this relationship quantitatively:

$$S = k \ln W \qquad (20.2)$$

where k, the *Boltzmann constant,* is the universal gas constant divided by Avogadro's number, R/N_A, and equals 1.38×10^{-23} J/K. Since W is unitless, you can see that S has units of *joules/kelvin (J/K).*

Even though both entropy and enthalpy are state functions, the nature of their values differs in a fundamental way. Recall that we cannot determine absolute values of enthalpy because we have no starting point, that is, no baseline value for the enthalpy of a substance. Therefore, only enthalpy *changes* can be measured.

In contrast, we *can* determine the absolute entropy of a substance. To do so requires application of the **third law of thermodynamics,** which states that *a perfect crystal has zero entropy at a temperature of absolute zero: $S_{sys} = 0$ at 0 K. "Perfect"* means that all the particles are aligned flawlessly in the crystal structure, with no defects of any kind. At absolute zero, all particles in the crystal have their minimum energy, and there is only one way they can be arranged: thus, $W = 1$, so $S = k \ln 1 = 0$. If we warm the crystal, the total energy of the particles increases. This gives the particles a range of energies, so the particles can be arranged in more ways (Figure 20.4). Thus, $W > 1$, $\ln W > 0$, and $S > 0$. The entropy of a substance at a given temperature is therefore an *absolute* value, equal to the entropy increase it would undergo if heated from 0 K to the temperature of interest.

As with other thermodynamic variables, we usually compare entropy values for substances in their *standard states* at the temperature of interest. Recall that the standard states we use throughout the text are *1 atm for gases, 1 M for solutions, and the pure substance in its most stable form for solids or liquids.* Entropy is an *extensive* property, one that depends on the amount of substance, so we are interested in the **standard molar entropy (S^0)** in units of J/mol · K (or J · mol^{-1} · K^{-1}). A list of S^0 values at 298 K (25°C) for many elements, compounds, and ions appears, with the values for other thermodynamic variables, in Appendix B.

Figure 20.4 Random motion in a crystal. This computer simulation shows the paths of the particle centers in a crystalline solid. At any temperature greater than 0 K, each particle moves about its lattice position. The greater the temperature, the more vigorous the movement. Adding thermal energy increases the total energy, so the particle energies are distributed over a wider range. This increases the number of possible arrangements, so the entropy increases.

Predicting Relative S^0 Values of the System Based on events at the molecular level, we can predict how the entropy of a substance is affected by temperature, physical state, dissolution, and atomic or molecular complexity. (All S^0 values in the following discussion have units of J/mol · K and, unless stated otherwise, refer to the system at 298 K.)

1. *Temperature changes.* For a given substance, S^0 *increases as the temperature rises.* Consider these typical values for copper metal:

T (K):	273	295	298
S^0:	31.0	32.9	33.1

The temperature increase represents an increase in average kinetic energy of the particles. Recall from Figure 5.14 (p. 200) that the kinetic energies of gas particles in a sample are distributed over a range, which becomes wider as the temperature rises, and the same general behavior occurs for liquids and solids. Since there are more ways to distribute the energy of the substance at the higher temperature, the entropy of the substance goes up.

2. *Physical states and phase changes.* When a more ordered phase changes to a less ordered one, the entropy change is positive. For a given substance, S^0 *increases as the substance changes from a solid to a liquid to a gas:*

	Na	H$_2$O	C(graphite)
S^0(s or l):	51.4(s)	69.9(l)	5.7(s)
S^0(g):	153.6	188.7	158.0

Figure 20.5 The increase in entropy from solid to liquid to gas. A plot of entropy vs. temperature shows the gradual increase within a phase and the abrupt increase with a phase change. The molecular views depict the increase in randomness of the particles as the solid melts and, in particular, as the liquid vaporizes.

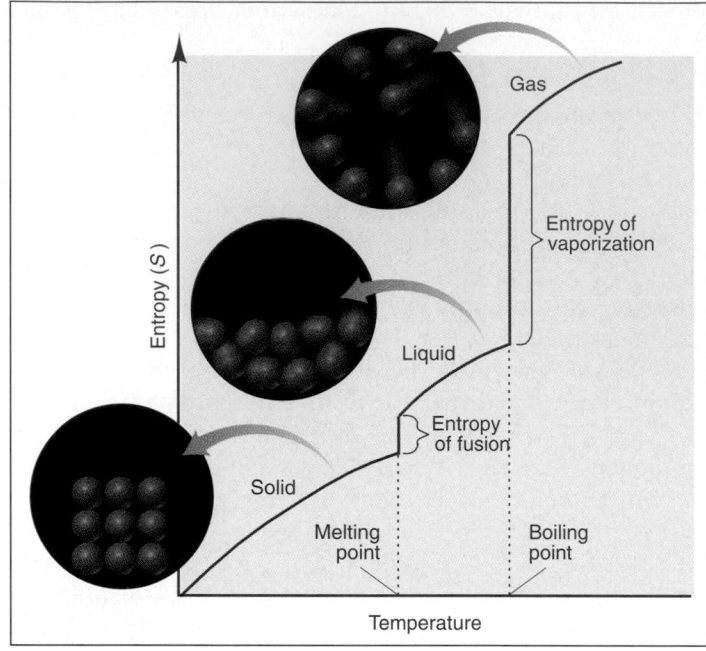

Figure 20.5 shows the entropy of a typical substance as it is heated and undergoes a change of state. Note the pattern of *gradual increase within a phase* as the temperature rises and a *large, sudden increase at the phase change*. The solid is relatively ordered and has the lowest entropy, its particles vibrating about their positions but, on average, remaining fixed. As the temperature rises, the entropy gradually increases with the increase in kinetic energy. When the solid melts, the particles move freely between and around each other in the liquid, so there is an abrupt increase in entropy. Further heating increases the speed of the particles in the liquid, and the entropy increases gradually. Finally, freed from intermolecular forces, the particles undergo another abrupt entropy increase and move chaotically as a gas. Note that *the increase in entropy from liquid to gas is much larger than from solid to liquid*.

3. *Dissolution of a solid or liquid.* The entropy of a dissolved solid or liquid solute is usually *greater* than the entropy of the pure solute, but the type of solute *and* solvent and the nature of the dissolution process affects the overall entropy change (Figure 20.6):

Figure 20.6 The entropy change accompanying the dissolution of a salt. When a crystalline salt and pure liquid water mix to form a solution, the entropy change has two contributions—a positive contribution as the crystal separates into ions and the pure liquid disperses them, and a negative contribution as the water becomes organized around each ion. The relative magnitudes of these positive and negative contributions determine the overall entropy change. In the majority of cases, the entropy of the solution is *greater* than that of the ionic solid and solvent.

	NaCl	**AlCl₃**	**CH₃OH**
$S^0(s \text{ or } l)$:	72.1(s)	167(s)	127(l)
$S^0(aq)$:	115.1	−148	132

When an ionic solid dissolves in water, the highly ordered crystal mixes with the pure liquid to become separate, hydrated ions dispersed randomly in a solution. We expect the entropy of the ions themselves to be greater in the solution than in the crystal. However, some of the solvent molecules become organized around the ions (see Figure 13.2, p. 483), which makes a negative contribution to the overall entropy change. In fact, for small, multiply charged ions, the solvent becomes so highly ordered that this negative contribution can dominate and lead to negative S^0 values for the ion in solution. For example, the $Al^{3+}(aq)$ ion has an S^0 value of −313 J/mol · K.* There-

---

*An S^0 value for a hydrated ion can be negative because it is relative to the S^0 value of the hydrated proton, $H^+(aq)$, which is assigned a value of 0. In other words, $Al^{3+}(aq)$ has a lower entropy than $H^+(aq)$.

| A Methanol | B Water | C Solution of water and methanol |

Figure 20.7 **The small increase in entropy when methanol dissolves in water.** Pure methanol **(A)** and pure water **(B)** have many intermolecular H bonds. **C,** When they form a solution, the molecules form H bonds to one another, so their freedom of motion does not change significantly. Thus, the entropy increase is relatively small and is due solely to random mixing.

fore, when $AlCl_3$ dissolves in water, $Cl^-(aq)$ has a positive entropy, but $Al^{3+}(aq)$ has such a negative entropy that the overall entropy of dissolved $AlCl_3$ is lower than that of the solid.

With molecular solutes, the increase in entropy upon dissolving is typically much smaller than for ionic solutes. For a solid, such as glucose, there is no separation into ions, and for a liquid, such as methanol, the breakdown of a crystal structure is absent as well. Furthermore, in pure methanol and pure water, the molecules form many H bonds, so there is relatively little change in their freedom of movement when they are mixed (Figure 20.7). The small increase in the disorder of the dissolved methanol arises from the random mixing of the two types of molecules.

4. *Dissolution of a gas.* A gas is so disordered to begin with that it becomes *more* ordered when it dissolves in a liquid or solid. Therefore, as Figure 20.8 shows, the entropy of a solution of a gas in a liquid or a solid is always *less* than the entropy of the pure gas. When O_2 gas $[S^0(g) = 205.0 \text{ J/mol} \cdot \text{K}]$ dissolves in water, its entropy decreases sharply $[S^0(aq) = 110.9 \text{ J/mol} \cdot \text{K}]$. When a gas dissolves in another gas, however, the entropy increases because of the mixing of the two types of molecules.

5. *Atomic size or molecular complexity.* In general, differences in entropy values for substances in the same phase are based on atomic size and molecular complexity. For elements within a periodic group, atomic size reflects molar mass, and entropy increases down the group:

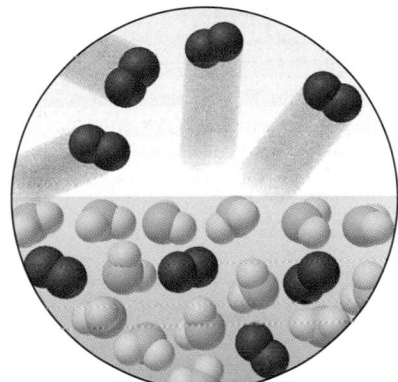

Figure 20.8 **The large *decrease* in entropy of a gas when it dissolves in a liquid.** The chaotic movement and high entropy of O_2 gas are reduced greatly when it dissolves in water.

	Li	Na	K	Rb	Cs
Atomic radius (pm):	152	186	227	248	265
Molar mass (g/mol):	6.941	22.99	39.10	85.47	132.9
$S^0(s)$:	29.1	51.4	64.7	69.5	85.2

The same trend of increasing entropy down a group holds for similar compounds:

	HF	HCl	HBr	HI
Molar mass (g/mol):	20.01	36.46	80.91	127.9
$S^0(g)$:	173.7	186.8	198.6	206.3

For an element that occurs in different forms (allotropes), the entropy is *higher* in the form with bonds that allow the atoms more movement. For example, the S^0 of graphite = 5.69 J/mol · K, whereas the S^0 of diamond = 2.44 J/mol · K. In diamond, covalent bonds extend in three dimensions, allowing the atoms little movement; in graphite, covalent bonds extend only within a sheet, and motion of the sheets is relatively easy, so the entropy is higher.

For compounds, entropy increases with chemical complexity, that is, with the number of atoms in the compound. This trend holds for both ionic and covalent compounds, as long as the substances are in the same physical state:

	NaCl	**AlCl$_3$**	**P$_4$O$_{10}$**	**NO**	**NO$_2$**	**N$_2$O$_4$**
$S^0(s)$:	72.1	167	229			
$S^0(g)$:				211	240	304

The trend is based on the various types of movement available to the atoms (or ions) in the compound, which relates to the number of equivalent ways in which their energy can be distributed. For example, as Figure 20.9 shows, among the nitrogen oxides listed, the two atoms of NO can vibrate in only one way, toward and away from each other. The three atoms of NO$_2$ have several vibrational motions, and the six atoms of N$_2$O$_4$ have many more.

Figure 20.9 Entropy and vibrational motion. A diatomic molecule, such as NO, can vibrate in only one way. NO$_2$ can vibrate in more ways and N$_2$O$_4$ in even more ways. Thus, as the number of atoms increases, a molecule can distribute its vibrational energy in more ways, so it has higher entropy.

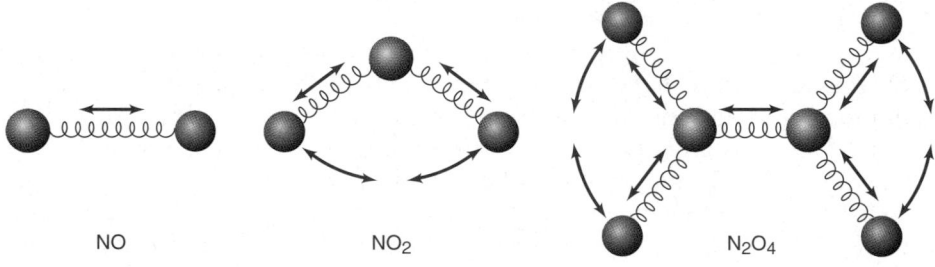

NO   NO$_2$ N$_2$O$_4$

For larger molecules, we also consider how parts of a molecule move relative to other parts. A long hydrocarbon chain can rotate and vibrate in more ways than a short chain, so entropy increases with chain length. A ring compound, such as cyclopentane (C$_5$H$_{10}$), has lower entropy than a chain compound of the same molar mass, such as pentene (C$_5$H$_{10}$), because many of the random molecular motions are restricted by the ring:

	CH$_4$(g)	**C$_2$H$_6$(g)**	**C$_3$H$_8$(g)**	**C$_4$H$_{10}$(g)**	**C$_5$H$_{10}$(g)**	**C$_5$H$_{10}$(cyclo, g)**	**C$_2$H$_5$OH(l)**
S^0:	186	230	270	310	348	293	161

Remember that these trends hold only for *substances in the same physical state*. Note, for instance, that gaseous methane (CH$_4$) has a greater entropy than liquid ethanol (C$_2$H$_5$OH), even though the ethanol molecules are much more complex. When gases are compared with liquids, *the effect of physical state usually dominates that of molecular complexity.*

Sample Problem 20.1   Predicting Relative Entropy Values

PROBLEM Choose the member with the higher entropy in each of the following pairs, and justify your choice [assume constant temperature, except in **(e)**]:
(a) 1 mol SO$_2$(g) or 1 mol SO$_3$(g)
(b) 1 mol CO$_2$(s) or 1 mol CO$_2$(g)
(c) 3 mol oxygen gas (O$_2$) or 2 mol ozone gas (O$_3$)
(d) 1 mol KBr(s) or 1 mol KBr(aq)
(e) Seawater in midwinter at 2°C or in midsummer at 23°C
(f) 1 mol CF$_4$(g) or 1 mol CCl$_4$(g)

PLAN In general, we know that less ordered systems have higher entropy than more ordered systems and that higher temperature increases entropy. We apply the general categories described in the text to choose the member with the higher entropy.

SOLUTION (a) 1 mol $SO_3(g)$. For equal numbers of moles of substances with the same types of atoms in the same physical state, the more atoms in the molecule, the more types of motion available to it, and thus the higher its entropy.

(b) 1 mol $CO_2(g)$. For a given substance, entropy increases in the sequence $s < l < g$.

(c) 3 mol $O_2(g)$. The two samples contain the same number of oxygen atoms but different numbers of molecules. Despite the greater complexity of O_3, the greater number of molecules dominates in this case because there are many more ways to arrange three moles of particles than two moles.

(d) 1 mol $KBr(aq)$. The two samples have the same number of ions, but in the solid they are highly ordered, and in the solution they are randomly dispersed.

(e) Seawater in summer. Entropy increases with rising temperature.

(f) 1 mol $CCl_4(g)$. For similar compounds, entropy increases with molar mass.

Follow-up Problem 20.1 For each pair of substances at a given temperature, select the member with the higher entropy and give the reason for your choice: (a) $PCl_3(g)$ or $PCl_5(g)$; (b) $CaF_2(s)$ or $BaCl_2(s)$; (c) $Br_2(g)$ or $Br_2(l)$.

Section Summary

A spontaneous change is one that occurs in a given direction under specified conditions without a continuous input of energy. Neither the first law of thermodynamics nor the sign of ΔH predicts this direction. All spontaneous processes involve a change from more to less order because a disordered arrangement is more likely than an ordered one. Entropy is a measure of disorder. The second law of thermodynamics states that, in a spontaneous process, the entropy of the universe (system plus surroundings) increases. Entropy values are absolute because perfect crystals have zero entropy at 0 K (third law). Standard molar entropy S^0 (J/mol · K) is affected by temperature, changes of state, dissolution, and the complexity of the substance.

20.2 Calculating the Change in Entropy of a Reaction

Beyond understanding trends in S^0 values for different substances or for the same substance in different states, chemists are especially interested in learning to predict *and* calculate the change in entropy as a system undergoes a reaction.

The Standard Entropy of Reaction, ΔS^0_{rxn}

Based on the ideas we discussed in the previous section, we predict that when a given amount (mol) of more ordered reactants yields the same amount of less ordered products, the reaction has a positive entropy change. For example, when cyclopropane is heated to 500°C, the ring opens and propene is formed. The open chain has more freedom of motion than the ring, so the entropy of the product is greater than that of the reactant. In other words, the entropy increases during the reaction:

$$H_2C\overset{\displaystyle CH_2}{\diagdown\diagup}CH_2(g) \longrightarrow CH_3-CH=CH_2(g) \qquad \Delta S^0 = S^0_{products} - S^0_{reactants} > 0$$

Such rearrangements are relatively uncommon reactions, however. Far more common are reactions in which the amount (mol) of substances, in particular gaseous substances, does change during the reaction. For example, when ammonia forms from its elements, 4 mol of gas produce 2 mol of gas. Since gases have such high molar entropies, we predict that the entropy of the products is less than that of the reactants and the entropy decreases during the reaction:

$$N_2(g) + 3H_2(g) \rightleftharpoons 2NH_3(g) \qquad \Delta S^0 = S^0_{products} - S^0_{reactants} < 0$$

Recall that by applying Hess's law, we can add ΔH^0_f values to find the standard heat of reaction, ΔH^0_{rxn}. Similarly, we can add standard molar entropies to find the **standard entropy of reaction, ΔS^0_{rxn}**:

$$\Delta S^0_{rxn} = \Sigma m S^0_{products} - \Sigma n S^0_{reactants} \tag{20.3}$$

where m and n are the amounts of the individual species, represented by their coefficients in the balanced equation. For the synthesis of ammonia, we have

$$\Delta S^0_{rxn} = (2 \text{ mol } NH_3 \times S^0 \text{ of } NH_3) \\ - [(1 \text{ mol } N_2 \times S^0 \text{ of } N_2) + (3 \text{ mol } H_2 \times S^0 \text{ of } H_2)]$$

From Appendix B, we find the appropriate S^0 values:

$$\Delta S^0_{rxn} = (2 \text{ mol} \times 193 \text{ J/mol} \cdot \text{K}) \\ - [(1 \text{ mol} \times 191.5 \text{ J/mol} \cdot \text{K}) + (3 \text{ mol} \times 130.6 \text{ J/mol} \cdot \text{K})] \\ = -197 \text{ J/K}$$

As we predicted, $\Delta S^0 < 0$.

Sample Problem 20.2 Calculating the Standard Entropy of Reaction, ΔS^0_{rxn}

PROBLEM Calculate ΔS^0_{rxn} for the combustion of 1 mol propane at 25°C:

$$C_3H_8(g) + 5O_2(g) \longrightarrow 3CO_2(g) + 4H_2O(l)$$

PLAN To determine ΔS^0_{rxn}, we apply Equation 20.3. We predict the sign of ΔS^0_{rxn} from the change in the number of moles of gas: 6 mol of gases yield 3 mol of gas, so the entropy will decrease ($\Delta S^0_{rxn} < 0$).

SOLUTION Calculating ΔS^0_{rxn}. From Appendix B values,

$$\Delta S^0_{rxn} = [(3 \text{ mol } CO_2 \times S^0 \text{ of } CO_2) + (4 \text{ mol } H_2O \times S^0 \text{ of } H_2O)] \\ - [(1 \text{ mol } C_3H_8 \times S^0 \text{ of } C_3H_8) + (5 \text{ mol } O_2 \times S^0 \text{ of } O_2)] \\ = [(3 \text{ mol} \times 213.7 \text{ J/mol} \cdot \text{K}) + (4 \text{ mol} \times 69.9 \text{ J/mol} \cdot \text{K})] \\ - [(1 \text{ mol} \times 269.9 \text{ J/mol} \cdot \text{K}) + (5 \text{ mol} \times 205.0 \text{ J/mol} \cdot \text{K})] \\ = -374 \text{ J/K}$$

CHECK $\Delta S^0 < 0$, so our prediction is correct. Rounding gives [(3 × 200) + (4 × 70)] − [270 + (5 × 200)] = 880 − 1270 = −390, close to the calculated value.

COMMENT We based our prediction on the fact that S^0 values of gases are much greater than those of solids or liquids. (This is usually true even when the condensed phases consist of more complex molecules.) When there is no change in the amount (mol) of gas, however, you *cannot* confidently predict the sign of ΔS^0_{rxn}.

Follow-up Problem 20.2 Balance the following equations, predict the sign of ΔS^0_{rxn} when possible, and calculate its value at 25°C:
(a) $NaOH(s) + CO_2(g) \longrightarrow Na_2CO_3(s) + H_2O(l)$
(b) $Fe(s) + H_2O(g) \longrightarrow Fe_2O_3(s) + H_2(g)$

Entropy Changes in the Surroundings: The Other Part of the Total

In many spontaneous reactions, such as the synthesis of ammonia and the combustion of propane we just examined, the system becomes *more* ordered at the given conditions ($\Delta S^0_{rxn} < 0$). The second law dictates that ***decreases in*** *the entropy of the system can occur only if **increases** in the entropy of the surroundings outweigh them.* Let's examine the influence of the surroundings on the *total* entropy change.

The essential role of the surroundings is to *either add heat to the system or remove heat from it.* In essence, the surroundings function as an enormous heat source or heat sink, one so large that its temperature remains constant, even though its entropy changes through the loss or gain of heat. The surroundings participate in the two possible types of reaction enthalpy changes as follows:

1. *Exothermic change.* Heat lost by the system is gained by the surroundings. The gain of heat increases the random motion of particles in the surroundings, so the entropy of the surroundings increases:
   For an exothermic change,

$$q_{sys} < 0, \qquad q_{surr} > 0 \quad \text{and} \quad \Delta S_{surr} > 0$$

2. *Endothermic change.* Heat gained by the system is lost by the surroundings. The loss of heat reduces the disorder of the surroundings, so the entropy of the surroundings decreases:
   For an endothermic change,

$$q_{sys} > 0, \qquad q_{surr} < 0 \quad \text{and} \quad \Delta S_{surr} < 0$$

The change in entropy of the surroundings is proportional to the quantity of heat transferred to or from the surroundings and, most importantly, *to an opposite change in heat of the system.*

The *temperature* of the surroundings before heat is transferred to or from it also affects ΔS_{surr}. Consider the effect of an exothermic reaction at a low and at a high temperature. At a low temperature, such as 20 K, there is very little random motion in the surroundings, so they are relatively ordered. Therefore, transferring heat to the surroundings has a large effect on their orderliness. At a higher temperature, such as 298 K, the surroundings are relatively disordered already, so transferring the same amount of heat has a smaller effect on their orderliness. ◆ In other words, the change in entropy of the surroundings is greater when heat is added at a lower temperature. Thus, putting these ideas together, *the change in entropy of the surroundings is directly related to an opposite change in the heat of the system and inversely related to the temperature of the surroundings before the heat is transferred.* The mathematical relationships are

$$\Delta S_{surr} \propto -q_{sys} \qquad \text{and} \qquad \Delta S_{surr} \propto \frac{1}{T}$$

Combining them gives

$$\Delta S_{surr} = -\frac{q_{sys}}{T} \tag{20.4}$$

Recall that for a process at *constant pressure*, the heat (q_P) is ΔH, so

$$\Delta S_{surr} = -\frac{\Delta H_{sys}}{T}$$

This means that we can calculate ΔS_{surr} by measuring ΔH_{sys} and the temperature T at which the change takes place.

To restate the central point, if a spontaneous reaction has a negative ΔS_{sys} (the system becomes more ordered), ΔS_{surr} must be positive enough (the surroundings must become sufficiently disordered) so that ΔS_{univ} is positive (the universe becomes more disordered). Sample Problem 20.3 illustrates this situation for one of the reactions we considered earlier.

◆ **A Checkbook Analogy for Heating the Surroundings**
A monetary analogy may clarify the relative changes in disorder that arise from heating the surroundings at different initial temperatures. If you have $10 in your checking account, a $10 deposit represents a 100% increase in your net worth; that is, a given change to a low initial state has a large impact. If, on the other hand, you have a $1000 balance, a $10 deposit represents only a 1% increase. That is, the same change to a high initial state has a smaller impact.

Sample Problem 20.3   Determining Whether a Reaction Is Spontaneous

PROBLEM At 298 K, the formation of ammonia has a negative ΔS^0_{sys}:

$$N_2(g) + 3H_2(g) \longrightarrow 2NH_3(g) \qquad \Delta S^0_{sys} = -197 \text{ J/K}$$

Calculate ΔS^0_{univ} and state whether the reaction occurs spontaneously at this temperature.

PLAN For the reaction to occur spontaneously, $\Delta S^0_{univ} > 0$, so ΔS^0_{surr} must be greater than +197 J/K. To find ΔS^0_{surr}, we need ΔH^0_{sys}, which is the ΔH^0_{rxn}. We use ΔH^0_f values from Appendix B to find ΔH^0_{rxn}. Then, we use this calculated value of ΔH^0_{rxn} to find ΔS^0_{surr}. To find ΔS^0_{univ}, we take the sum of the calculated ΔS^0_{surr} and the given ΔS^0_{sys}.

SOLUTION Calculating ΔH^0_{sys}:

$\Delta H^0_{sys} = \Delta H^0_{rxn}$

$\qquad = 2 \text{ mol NH}_3 (-45.9 \text{ kJ/mol}) - [3 \text{ mol H}_2 (0 \text{ kJ/mol}) + 1 \text{ mol N}_2 (0 \text{ kJ/mol})]$

$\qquad = -91.8 \text{ kJ}$

Calculating ΔS^0_{surr}:

$$\Delta S^0_{surr} = -\frac{\Delta H^0_{sys}}{T} = -\frac{-91.8 \text{ kJ} \times \dfrac{1000 \text{ J}}{1 \text{ kJ}}}{298 \text{ K}} = 308 \text{ J/K}$$

Determining ΔS^0_{univ}:

$$\Delta S^0_{univ} = \Delta S^0_{sys} + \Delta S^0_{surr} = -197 \text{ J/K} + 308 \text{ J/K} = \boxed{111 \text{ J/K}}$$

$\Delta S^0_{univ} > 0$, so the reaction occurs spontaneously at 298 K (see figure).

CHECK Rounding to check the math, we have

$$\Delta H^0_f \approx 2 \times (-45 \text{ kJ}) = -90 \text{ kJ}$$

$$\Delta S^0_{surr} \approx -(-90,000 \text{ J})/300 \text{ K} = 300 \text{ J/K}$$

$$\Delta S^0_{univ} \approx -200 \text{ J/K} + 300 \text{ J/K} = 100 \text{ J/K}$$

Given the negative ΔH^0_{rxn}, Le Châtelier's principle predicts that low temperature should favor NH_3 formation, and so the answer is reasonable (see Chemical Connections essay on the Haber process, Section 17.6).

COMMENT 1. Note that ΔH^0 has units of kJ, whereas ΔS^0 has units of J/K, so don't forget to convert kJ to J, or you'll introduce a large error.

2. This example highlights the distinction between thermodynamic and kinetic considerations. Even though NH_3 forms spontaneously, it does so slowly, and the chemical industry expends great effort to catalyze its formation so it can be produced at a practical rate.

Follow-up Problem 20.3   Does the oxidation of FeO(s) to $Fe_2O_3(s)$ occur spontaneously at 298 K?

As Sample Problem 20.3 makes clear, taking the surroundings into account is critical to determining reaction spontaneity. Moreover, it resolves a confusing point about the relevance of thermodynamics to biology, as the Chemical Connections essay shows.

The Entropy Change and the Equilibrium State

A process proceeds toward equilibrium spontaneously, so $\Delta S_{univ} > 0$. When the process reaches equilibrium, there is no longer any driving force to proceed further and, thus, no net change in either direction; thus, $\Delta S_{univ} = 0$. At that point, any entropy change in the system is exactly balanced by an opposite entropy change in the surroundings:

$$\text{At equilibrium: } \Delta S_{univ} = \Delta S_{sys} + \Delta S_{surr} = 0 \qquad \text{or} \qquad \Delta S_{sys} = -\Delta S_{surr}$$

Chemical Connections   Chemistry in Biology

Do Living Things Obey the Laws of Thermodynamics?

Organisms can be thought of as chemical machines that evolved by extracting energy as efficiently as possible from the environment. Such a mechanical view holds that all processes, whether they involve living or nonliving systems, are consistent with thermodynamic principles. When applied to animals and plants, however, these ideas seem far from obvious. Let's examine the first and second laws of thermodynamics to see if they apply to living systems.

Organisms certainly comply with the first law. The chemical bond energy in food is converted into the mechanical energy of sprouting, crawling, swimming, and countless other movements; the electrical energy of nerve conduction; the thermal energy of warming the body; and so forth. Many experiments have demonstrated that in all these energy conversions, the total energy is conserved. Some of the earliest studies of this question were performed by Lavoisier, who included animal respiration in his new theory of combustion (Figure 20A). He was the first to show that "animal heat" was produced by a slow combustion process occurring continually in the body. In experiments with guinea pigs, he measured the intake of food and O_2 and the output of CO_2 and heat, for which he invented a calorimeter based on the melting of ice, and he established the principles and methods for measuring the basal rate of metabolism. Modern experiments using a calorimeter large enough to contain an exercising human continue to confirm the conservation of energy (Figure 20B).

It may not seem as clear, however, that an organism, or for that matter, the whole parade of life, complies with the second law. Mature humans are far more ordered and complex than the simple egg and sperm cells from which they grow. Modern organisms are far more orderly, complex systems than the one-celled ancestral specks from which they evolved. Are the growth of an organism and the evolution of life exceptions to the tendency of natural processes to become more disordered? Does biology violate the second law? Not at all, if we examine the system *and* its surroundings. For an organism to grow or for a species to evolve, many moles of food molecules—carbohydrates, proteins, and fats—and oxygen molecules undergo combustion to form many more moles of gaseous CO_2 and H_2O. The formation and discharge of these waste gases represent a tremendous net increase in the entropy of the surroundings, as does the heat released from these exothermic redox reactions. Thus, the increase in *order* apparent in the spontaneous growth of organisms and their evolution occurs at the expense of a far greater increase in *disorder* in the Earth-Sun surroundings. When system and surroundings are considered together, the entropy of the universe, as always, increases.

Figure 20.B **A whole-body calorimeter.** In this room-sized apparatus, a subject exercises while respiratory gases, energy input and output, and other physiological variables are monitored.

Figure 20.A **Lavoisier studying human respiration as a form of combustion.** Lavoisier (standing at right) measured substances consumed and excreted in addition to changes in heat to understand the chemical nature of respiration. The artist (Mme. Lavoisier) shows herself taking notes (seated at right).

For example, let's calculate ΔS_{univ}^0 for a phase change. For the vaporization-condensation of 1 mol water at 100°C (373 K),

$$H_2O(l; 373 \text{ K}) \rightleftharpoons H_2O(g; 373 \text{ K})$$

First, we find ΔS_{univ}^0 for the forward change (vaporization) by calculating ΔS_{sys}^0:

$$\Delta S_{sys}^0 = \Sigma m S_{products}^0 - \Sigma n S_{reactants}^0 = S^0 \text{ of } H_2O(g; 373 \text{ K}) - S^0 \text{ of } H_2O(l; 373 \text{ K})$$
$$= 195.9 \text{ J/K} - 86.8 \text{ J/K} = 109.1 \text{ J/K}$$

As we expect, the system becomes more disordered ($\Delta S_{sys}^0 > 0$) as the liquid changes to a gas.

For ΔS_{surr}^0 we have

$$\Delta S_{surr}^0 = -\frac{\Delta H_{sys}^0}{T}$$

where $\Delta H_{sys}^0 = \Delta H_{vap}^0$ at 373 K = 40.7 kJ/mol = 40.7×10^3 J/mol. For 1 mol water, we have

$$\Delta S_{surr}^0 = -\frac{\Delta H_{vap}^0}{T} = -\frac{40.7 \times 10^3 \text{ J}}{373 \text{ K}} = -109 \text{ J/K}$$

The negative sign indicates that the surroundings become more ordered because they lose heat. The two entropy changes have the same magnitude but opposite sign:

$$\Delta S_{univ}^0 = 109 \text{ J/K} + (-109 \text{ J/K}) = 0$$

For the reverse change (condensation), ΔS_{univ}^0 also equals zero, but ΔS_{sys}^0 and ΔS_{surr}^0 have signs opposite those for vaporization. A similar treatment of a chemical change shows the same result: the entropy change of the forward reaction is *equal in magnitude but opposite in sign* to the entropy change of the reverse reaction. Thus, *when a system reaches equilibrium, neither the forward nor the reverse reaction is spontaneous,* and so neither proceeds any further.

Spontaneous Exothermic and Endothermic Reactions: A Summary

We can now understand why both spontaneous exothermic and endothermic reactions occur. No matter what its *enthalpy* change, a reaction occurs because the total *entropy* of the reacting system and its surroundings increases. The two possibilities are

1. *For an exothermic reaction* ($\Delta H_{sys} < 0$), heat is released, which increases the entropy of the surroundings ($\Delta S_{surr} > 0$).
- If the reacting system yields products that are more disordered than the reactants ($\Delta S_{sys} > 0$), the total entropy change ($\Delta S_{sys} + \Delta S_{surr}$) will be positive (Figure 20.10A). For example, in the oxidation of glucose, an essential reaction for all higher organisms,

$$C_6H_{12}O_6(s) + 6O_2(g) \longrightarrow 6CO_2(g) + 6H_2O(g) + \textbf{\textit{heat}}$$

6 mol of gas yield 12 mol of gas, so $\Delta S_{sys} > 0$, $\Delta S_{surr} > 0$, and $\Delta S_{univ} > 0$.
- If, on the other hand, the system becomes more ordered as the reaction occurs ($\Delta S_{sys} < 0$), the surroundings must become even more disordered ($\Delta S_{surr} >> 0$) to make the total ΔS positive (Figure 20.10B). For example, when calcium oxide and carbon dioxide gas form calcium carbonate,

$$CaO(s) + CO_2(g) \longrightarrow CaCO_3(s) + \textbf{\textit{heat}}$$

the system becomes more ordered because the amount (mol) of gas decreases. However, the heat released disorders the surroundings even more; thus, $\Delta S_{sys} < 0$, but $\Delta S_{surr} >> 0$, so $\Delta S_{univ} > 0$.

Figure 20.10 Components of ΔS_{univ}^0 for spontaneous reactions. For a reaction to occur spontaneously, ΔS_{univ}^0 must be positive. **A,** An exothermic reaction that becomes more disordered; the size of ΔS_{surr}^0 is not important. **B,** An exothermic reaction that becomes more ordered; ΔS_{surr}^0 must be larger than ΔS_{sys}^0. **C,** An endothermic reaction that becomes more disordered; ΔS_{surr}^0 must be smaller than ΔS_{sys}^0.

2. *For an endothermic reaction* ($\Delta H_{sys} > 0$), the heat lost by the surroundings lowers the entropy of the surroundings ($\Delta S_{surr} < 0$). Therefore, the only way an endothermic reaction can occur spontaneously is if the system becomes so disordered ($\Delta S_{sys} \gg 0$) that it outweighs the negative ΔS_{surr} (Figure 20.10C).

- In the solution processes for many ionic compounds, heat is absorbed to form the solution, so the surroundings become more ordered ($\Delta S_{surr} < 0$). However, the crystalline solid is so highly ordered and the dispersed ions so disordered that the entropy increase ($\Delta S_{sys} \gg 0$) outweighs the negative ΔS_{surr}. Thus, ΔS_{univ} is positive.

- Spontaneous endothermic chemical reactions have similar features. For example, in the reaction between barium hydroxide octahydrate and ammonium nitrate (see Figure 20.1),

$$\textit{heat} + Ba(OH)_2 \cdot 8H_2O(s) + 2NH_4NO_3(s) \longrightarrow$$
$$Ba^{2+}(aq) + 2NO_3^-(aq) + 2NH_3(aq) + 10H_2O(l)$$

3 mol of crystalline solids absorb heat from the surroundings ($\Delta S_{surr} < 0$) and yield 15 mol of dissolved ions and molecules, thereby greatly increasing the disorder of the system ($\Delta S_{sys} \gg 0$).

Section Summary

The standard entropy of reaction, ΔS^0_{rxn}, is calculated from S^0 values. When the number of moles of gas increases in a reaction, $\Delta S^0_{rxn} > 0$. The ΔS^0_{surr} is related directly to ΔH^0_{sys} and inversely to the temperature at which the enthalpy changes. In a spontaneous change, a system can become more ordered only by making the surroundings even more disordered. For a system at equilibrium, $\Delta S_{univ} = 0$.

20.3 Entropy, Free Energy, and Work

By making *two* separate measurements, ΔS_{sys} and ΔS_{surr}, we can predict whether a reaction will be spontaneous at a particular temperature. It would be useful, however, to have *one* criterion of spontaneity that applies only to the system. The Gibbs free energy, or simply **free energy (G),** is a function that combines the system's enthalpy and entropy:

$$G = H - TS$$

This function, named for Josiah Willard Gibbs who proposed it in 1877 and laid the foundation for much of chemical thermodynamics, is the criterion for which we've been looking. ◆

Free Energy Change and Reaction Spontaneity

The free energy change (ΔG) is a measure of the spontaneity of a process and of the useful energy available from it. Let's see how the free energy change is derived from the second law. By definition, the entropy change of the universe is the sum of the entropy changes in the system and surroundings:

$$\Delta S_{univ} = \Delta S_{sys} + \Delta S_{surr}$$

At constant pressure,

$$\Delta S_{surr} = -\frac{\Delta H_{sys}}{T}$$

◆ **Greatness and Obscurity of J. Willard Gibbs**
Even today, one of the most remarkable minds in science is barely known outside chemistry and physics. In 1878, Josiah Willard Gibbs (1839–1903), a professor of mathematical physics at Yale, completed a 323-page paper that virtually established the science of chemical thermodynamics and included major principles governing chemical equilibrium, phase-change equilibrium, and the energy changes in electrochemical cells. The European scientists James Clerk Maxwell, Wilhelm Ostwald, and Henri Le Châtelier appreciated Gibbs's significance long before those in his own country did. In fact, he was elected to the Hall of Fame of Distinguished Americans only in 1950, because he had not received enough votes until then!

Substituting for ΔS_{surr} gives a relationship that allows us to focus solely on the system:

$$\Delta S_{univ} = \Delta S_{sys} - \frac{\Delta H_{sys}}{T}$$

Multiplying both sides by $(-T)$ gives

$$-T\Delta S_{univ} = \Delta H_{sys} - T\Delta S_{sys}$$

Now we can introduce the new free energy quantity to replace the enthalpy and entropy terms. Since $G = H - TS$, a change in free energy of the system (ΔG_{sys}) at *constant temperature and pressure* is given by the *Gibbs equation:*

$$\Delta G_{sys} = \Delta H_{sys} - T\Delta S_{sys} \tag{20.5}$$

Combining this equation with the previous one shows that

$$-T\Delta S_{univ} = \Delta H_{sys} - T\Delta S_{sys} = \Delta G_{sys}$$

*The **sign** of ΔG tells whether a reaction is spontaneous*. The second law dictates that
- $\Delta S_{univ} > 0$ for a spontaneous process
- $\Delta S_{univ} < 0$ for a nonspontaneous process
- $\Delta S_{univ} = 0$ for a process at equilibrium

Of course, absolute temperature is always positive, so

$$T\Delta S_{univ} > 0 \qquad \text{or} \qquad -T\Delta S_{univ} < 0 \text{ for a spontaneous process}$$

Since $\Delta G = -T\Delta S_{univ}$, we know that
- $\Delta G < 0$ for a spontaneous process
- $\Delta G > 0$ for a nonspontaneous process
- $\Delta G = 0$ for a process at equilibrium

An important point to keep in mind is that if a process is *nonspontaneous* in one direction ($\Delta G > 0$), it is *spontaneous* in the opposite direction ($\Delta G < 0$). By incorporating ΔG, we have not presented any new ideas, but we have developed a way of predicting reaction spontaneity from one variable (ΔG_{sys}) rather than two (ΔS_{sys} and ΔS_{surr}).

As we discussed at the beginning of the chapter, the degree of spontaneity of a reaction—that is, the sign *and* magnitude of ΔG—tells us nothing about its rate. Remember that some spontaneous reactions are extremely slow. For example, the reaction between $H_2(g)$ and $O_2(g)$ at room temperature is highly spontaneous—ΔG has a large negative value—but in the absence of a catalyst or a flame, the reaction doesn't occur to a measurable extent because its rate is so low.

Calculating Standard Free Energy Changes

Because free energy (G) combines three state functions, H, S, and T, it is also a state function. Like enthalpy, we are concerned only with free energy *changes* (ΔG).

The Standard Free Energy Change As with the other thermodynamic variables, to compare the free energy change of different reactions, we calculate the ***standard* free energy change (ΔG^0),** which occurs when all components of the system are in their standard states. Adapting the Gibbs equation (20.5), we have

$$\Delta G_{sys}^0 = \Delta H_{sys}^0 - T\Delta S_{sys}^0 \tag{20.6}$$

This important relationship is used frequently to find any one of these three central thermodynamic variables, given the other two. Let's apply this relationship in a sample problem.

Sample Problem 20.4 Calculating ΔG^0 from Enthalpy and Entropy Values

PROBLEM Potassium chlorate, one of the common oxidizing agents in explosives, fireworks (see photo), and matchheads, undergoes a solid-state redox reaction when heated, in which the oxidation number of Cl in the reactant is higher in one of the products and lower in the other (disproportionation):

$$4\overset{+5}{KClO_3}(s) \overset{\Delta}{\longrightarrow} 3\overset{+7}{KClO_4}(s) + \overset{-1}{KCl}(s)$$

Use ΔH_f^0 and S^0 values to calculate ΔG_{sys}^0 (ΔG_{rxn}^0) at 25°C for this reaction.

PLAN To solve for ΔG^0, we use ΔH_f^0 values to calculate ΔH_{rxn}^0 (ΔH_{sys}^0), use S^0 values to calculate ΔS_{rxn}^0 (ΔS_{sys}^0), and apply Equation 20.6.

SOLUTION Calculating ΔH_{sys}^0 from ΔH_f^0 values (with Equation 6.8):

$$\Delta H_{sys}^0 = \Delta H_{rxn}^0 = \Sigma m \Delta H_{f(products)}^0 - \Sigma n \Delta H_{f(reactants)}^0$$

$$= [3 \text{ mol } KClO_4 \ (\Delta H_f^0 \text{ of } KClO_4) + 1 \text{ mol } KCl \ (\Delta H_f^0 \text{ of } KCl)]$$

$$- [4 \text{ mol } KClO_3 \ (\Delta H_f^0 \text{ of } KClO_3)]$$

$$= [3 \text{ mol } (-432.8 \text{ kJ/mol}) + 1 \text{ mol } (-436.7 \text{ kJ/mol})]$$

$$- [4 \text{ mol } (-397.7 \text{ kJ/mol})]$$

$$= -144 \text{ kJ}$$

Calculating ΔS_{sys}^0 from S^0 values (with Equation 20.3):

$$\Delta S_{sys}^0 = \Delta S_{rxn}^0 = [3 \text{ mol } KClO_4 \ (S^0 \text{ of } KClO_4) + 1 \text{ mol } KCl \ (S^0 \text{ of } KCl)]$$

$$- [4 \text{ mol } KClO_3 \ (S^0 \text{ of } KClO_3)]$$

$$= [3 \text{ mol } (151.0 \text{ J/mol} \cdot K) + 1 \text{ mol } (82.6 \text{ J/mol} \cdot K)]$$

$$- [4 \text{ mol } (143.1 \text{ J/mol} \cdot K)]$$

$$= -36.8 \text{ J/K}$$

Calculating ΔG_{sys}^0 at 298 K:

$$\Delta G_{sys}^0 = \Delta H_{sys}^0 - T\Delta S_{sys}^0 = -144 \text{ kJ} - \left[(298 \text{ K})(-36.8 \text{ J/K})\left(\frac{1 \text{ kJ}}{1000 \text{ J}}\right)\right] = -133 \text{ kJ}$$

CHECK The reaction *is* spontaneous, which is consistent with $\Delta G^0 < 0$. Rounding to check the math:

$$\Delta H^0 \approx [3(-433) + (-440)] - [4(-400)] = -1740 + 1600 = -140$$

$$\Delta S^0 \approx [3(150) + 85] - [4(145)] = 535 - 580 = -45$$

$$\Delta G^0 \approx -140 - 300(-0.04) = -140 + 12 = -128$$

All values are close to the calculated ones. Another way to check appears in Sample Problem 20.5.

COMMENT Although the negative ΔG^0 means the reaction is spontaneous, the rate is extremely low because the required O atom transfer does not occur easily in the solid. When $KClO_3$ is heated slightly above its melting point, the ions are free to move and the reaction occurs readily.

Follow-up Problem 20.4 Determine the standard free energy change at 298 K for the reaction $2NO(g) + O_2(g) \longrightarrow 2NO_2(g)$.

The Standard Free Energy of Formation Another way to calculate ΔG_{rxn}^0 is with values for the **standard free energy of formation (ΔG_f^0)** of the components, the free energy change that occurs when 1 mol of compound is made *from its elements*, with all components in their standard states. Since free energy is a state function, we can combine ΔG_f^0 values of reactants and products to calculate ΔG_{rxn}^0 without regard for the reaction path:

$$\Delta G_{rxn}^0 = \Sigma m \Delta G_{f(products)}^0 - \Sigma n \Delta G_{f(reactants)}^0 \tag{20.7}$$

ΔG_f^0 values have properties similar to ΔH_f^0 values:

- ΔG_f^0 of an element in its standard state is zero.
- An equation coefficient (m or n above) multiplies ΔG_f^0 by that number.
- Reversing a reaction changes the sign of ΔG_f^0.

Many ΔG_f^0 values appear with those for ΔH_f^0 and S^0 in Appendix B.

Sample Problem 20.5 Calculating ΔG_{rxn}^{0} from ΔG_{f}^{0} Values

PROBLEM Use ΔG_{f}^{0} values to calculate ΔG_{rxn}^{0} for the reaction in Sample Problem 20.4:

$$4KClO_3(s) \longrightarrow 3KClO_4(s) + KCl(s)$$

PLAN We apply Equation 20.7 to calculate ΔG_{rxn}^{0}.

SOLUTION

$$\Delta G_{rxn}^{0} = \Sigma m \Delta G_{f(products)}^{0} - \Sigma n \Delta G_{f(reactants)}^{0}$$

$= [3 \text{ mol } KClO_4 (\Delta G_{f}^{0} \text{ of } KClO_4) + 1 \text{ mol } KCl (\Delta G_{f}^{0} \text{ of } KCl)]$

$\quad - [4 \text{ mol } KClO_3(\Delta G_{f}^{0} \text{ of } KClO_3)]$

$= [3 \text{ mol } (-303.2 \text{ kJ/mol}) + 1 \text{ mol } (-409.2 \text{ kJ/mol})]$

$\quad - [4 \text{ mol } (-296.3 \text{ kJ/mol})]$

$= \boxed{-134 \text{ kJ}}$

CHECK Rounding to check the math:

$$\Delta G_{rxn}^{0} \approx [3(-300) + 1(-400)] - 4(-300) = -1300 + 1200 = -100$$

COMMENT The slight discrepancy between this value and that in Sample Problem 20.4 is within experimental error. As you can see, when ΔG_{f}^{0} values are available for a reaction taking place at 25°C, this method is simpler than the calculation in Sample Problem 20.4.

Follow-up Problem 20.5 Use ΔG_{f}^{0} values to calculate the free energy change at 25°C for each of the following reactions:
(a) $2NO(g) + O_2(g) \longrightarrow 2NO_2(g)$ (from Follow-up Problem 20.4)
(b) $2C(graphite) + O_2(g) \longrightarrow 2CO(g)$

The Meaning of ΔG: The Maximum Work a System Can Perform

So far, you've seen the usefulness of ΔG in predicting reaction spontaneity. Now let's examine the concept of free energy more closely to see what ΔG really means. Recall that the science of thermodynamics was born soon after the invention of the steam engine, and one of the most practical relationships in the field is that between the free energy change and the quantity of work a system can do:

• For a spontaneous process, ΔG is the *maximum work obtainable* **from** *the system as the change takes place:*

$$\Delta G = w_{max}$$

• For a nonspontaneous process, ΔG is the *minimum work that must be done* **on** *the system to make the change take place.*

What do we mean by the "maximum work obtainable," and what determines this limit? The answer to these questions lies in Equation 20.5, which relates ΔG to ΔH and ΔS:

$$\Delta G_{sys} = \Delta H_{sys} - T\Delta S_{sys}$$

Solving for ΔH_{sys}, we obtain

$$\Delta H_{sys} = \Delta G_{sys} + T\Delta S_{sys}$$

This equation tells us that the enthalpy change of a reaction has two components: a free energy change (ΔG_{sys}) and a temperature-dependent entropy change ($T\Delta S_{sys}$). Each component is a portion of the total heat transferred during the reaction (ΔH_{sys}).

Why can't we harness the *entire* enthalpy change of a system to do work? To answer this question, let's see what each portion of the enthalpy change represents. Consider one of the most common combustion reactions in our society and one that we've looked at often in earlier chapters—the burning of octane in gasoline:

$$C_8H_{18}(l) + \tfrac{25}{2}O_2(g) \longrightarrow 8CO_2(g) + 9H_2O(g)$$

When octane burns in an automobile engine, a large amount of energy is given off as heat ($\Delta H_{sys} < 0$), and since the number of moles of gas increases, the entropy of the system increases ($\Delta S_{sys} > 0$). A portion of the total released energy does work turning wheels, moving belts, regenerating the battery, and so on; *the free energy change (ΔG_{sys}) is that portion of the total energy change that does this work*. However, there is *always* a portion ($T\Delta S_{sys}$) of the total energy change that simply warms the engine and the outside air, which makes the motions of the particles in the universe more chaotic, in accord with the second law.

Whereas the first law considers energy in terms of its *quantity*, the second law (from which we derived the relationship among ΔG, ΔH, and ΔS) considers energy in terms of its *usability*. In the form of ΔG_{sys}, energy can be used to do work; in the form of $T\Delta S_{sys}$, energy has become unusable. It has not disappeared, so the first law is satisfied, but it has lost its value because even more energy would be required to gather it up and convert it to a usable form. ◆

Thus, an overall enthalpy change has a usable and a nonusable form. In the form of $T\Delta S$, it is dispersed and unusable; in the form of ΔG, we can develop machines to harness it. However, there is another major catch that decreases the work we can do even further. As stated before, the value of ΔG represents the *maximum* work we can obtain from the energy. In reality, we *never* obtain this much work, because unless the free energy is released at an infinitely slow rate, some is lost as heat. *How* we release the free energy determines the *efficiency* of the process, the *actual* work done by the free energy released.

Consider a battery, which is essentially a packaged spontaneous redox reaction. When the circuit is completed between the battery terminals, the reaction releases energy to the surroundings. If we connect the terminals to each other through a short piece of wire, the energy change takes place very quickly but doesn't perform any work: all the released free energy just heats the wire and battery. If we connect the battery terminals to a motor, the energy is released much more slowly. Now a large portion of the free energy change does the work of running the motor, but some is still converted to heat in the battery and the motor. If we discharge the battery more slowly, more of the free energy change does work and less is converted to heat. *However, only when the battery operates infinitely slowly can we obtain the maximum available work*. This is the compromise that all engineers and machine designers must face—*in the real world, some free energy is always changed to heat and thereby unharnessed:* no process utilizes all the free energy available, so no process is 100% energy efficient. ◆

To summarize the relationship between the free energy change of a reaction and the work it can actually accomplish:

- A spontaneous reaction ($\Delta G_{sys} < 0$) will occur *and* can do work on the surroundings. In any real machine, however, the work obtained from the reaction is *always less than the maximum* because some of the ΔG released is lost as heat.
- A nonspontaneous reaction ($\Delta G_{sys} > 0$) will not occur unless the surroundings do work on it. In any real machine, however, the work needed to make the reaction occur is *always more than the minimum* because some of the ΔG added is lost as heat.
- A reaction at equilibrium ($\Delta G_{sys} = 0$) can no longer do any work.

◆ **Valueless Gold** The precious metals market provides an analogy for the *value* of the released energy in its "concentrated" usable form and its "dispersed" unusable form. Suppose you have an ounce of gold dust in a small container. At current market prices, you could sell it for about $300. Now you disperse the dust over an acre of land. Conservation of mass is satisfied because the ounce of gold is still present, but you'll receive a very negative response when you try to obtain $300 in the market. In dispersed form, the gold's value is much reduced. To extract, concentrate, and purify it would require large expenditures of energy, materials, and know-how—far more, in fact, than the gold is worth.

◆ **The Wide Range of Energy Efficiency** Engineers consider the efficiency of a device to be the percentage of the energy input that results in work output. The range of efficiencies is enormous for the common "energy-conversion systems" of society. For instance, a common incandescent lightbulb converts only 5% of incoming electrical energy to light, the rest being wasted as heat. At the other extreme, a large electrical generator converts 99% of the incoming mechanical energy to electricity. Although improvements are continually being made, here are some approximate values for other devices: dry cell battery, 90%; home oil furnace, 65%; hand tool motor, 63%; liquid fuel rocket, 50%; car engine, <30%; fluorescent lamp, 20%; solar cell, ~10%.

The Effect of Temperature on Reaction Spontaneity

In most cases, the enthalpy contribution (ΔH) to the free energy change (ΔG) is much *larger* than the entropy contribution ($T\Delta S$). For this reason, most exothermic reactions are spontaneous: the negative ΔH helps make ΔG negative as well. However, the *temperature at which a reaction occurs influences the magnitude of the $T\Delta S$ term*, so, in many cases, the overall spontaneity depends on the temperature.

By scrutinizing the signs of ΔH and ΔS, we can predict the effect of temperature on the sign of ΔG and thus on the spontaneity of a process at any temperature. (In this discussion, we assume that ΔH and ΔS change very little with temperature, which is usually correct as long as no phase changes occur.) Let's examine the four combinations of positive and negative ΔH^0 and ΔS^0; two combinations do not depend on temperature and two do:

- *Temperature-independent cases (opposite signs).* When ΔH^0 and ΔS^0 have *opposite* signs, the reaction either occurs spontaneously at all temperatures or at none.

  1. *Reaction is spontaneous at all temperatures:* $\Delta H^0 < 0$, $\Delta S^0 > 0$. Both contributions favor the process occurring spontaneously: ΔH^0 is negative and ΔS^0 is positive, so $(-T\Delta S^0)$ is negative; thus, ΔG^0 is always negative. Many combustion reactions are in this category, including those of glucose and octane that we saw earlier. The decomposition of hydrogen peroxide, the common disinfectant, is also spontaneous at all T:

     $$2H_2O_2(l) \longrightarrow 2H_2O(l) + O_2(g) \qquad \Delta H^0 = -196 \text{ kJ} \quad \text{and} \quad \Delta S^0 = 125 \text{ J/K}$$

  2. *Reaction is nonspontaneous at all temperatures:* $\Delta H^0 > 0$, $\Delta S^0 < 0$. Both contributions oppose the reaction occurring spontaneously. ΔH^0 is positive and ΔS^0 is negative, so $(-T\Delta S^0)$ is positive; thus, ΔG^0 is always positive. The formation of ozone from oxygen gas is not spontaneous at any temperature:

     $$3O_2(g) \longrightarrow 2O_3(g) \qquad \Delta H^0 = 286 \text{ kJ} \quad \text{and} \quad \Delta S^0 = -137 \text{ J/K}$$

     This reaction occurs only if enough energy is supplied from the surroundings, as when ozone is synthesized by passing an electrical discharge through pure O_2 (see photo).

- *Temperature-dependent cases (same signs).* When ΔH^0 and ΔS^0 have the *same* sign, the relative magnitudes of the $T\Delta S^0$ and ΔH^0 terms determine the sign of ΔG^0, so the magnitude of T is crucial.

  3. *Reaction is spontaneous at higher temperature:* $\Delta H^0 > 0$ *and* $\Delta S^0 > 0$. In these cases, ΔS^0 favors spontaneity $(-T\Delta S^0 < 0)$, but ΔH^0 does not. For example,

     $$2N_2O(g) + O_2(g) \longrightarrow 4NO(g) \qquad \Delta H^0 = 197.1 \text{ kJ} \quad \text{and} \quad \Delta S^0 = 198.2 \text{ J/K}$$

     With a positive ΔH^0, the reaction will occur spontaneously only when $-T\Delta S^0$ is large enough to make ΔG^0 negative, which will happen at higher temperatures. The oxidation of nitrous oxide occurs spontaneously at $T > 994$ K.

  4. *Reaction is spontaneous at lower temperature:* $\Delta H^0 < 0$ *and* $\Delta S^0 < 0$. In these cases, ΔH^0 favors spontaneity, but ΔS^0 does not $(-T\Delta S > 0)$. For example,

     $$2Na(s) + Cl_2(g) \longrightarrow 2NaCl(s) \qquad \Delta H^0 = -822.2 \text{ kJ} \quad \text{and} \quad \Delta S^0 = -181.7 \text{ J/K}$$

     With a negative ΔH^0, the reaction will occur spontaneously only if the $-T\Delta S^0$ term is smaller than the ΔH^0 term, and this happens at lower temperatures. Common examples are the formation of ammonium halides from ammonia and a hydrogen halide or the formation of metal oxides, fluorides, and chlorides from their elements. The production of sodium chloride occurs spontaneously at $T < 4525$ K.

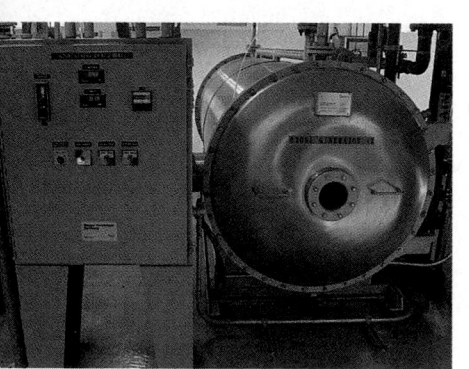
An industrial ozone generator.

Table 20.1 Reaction Spontaneity and the Signs of ΔH^0, ΔS^0, and ΔG^0

ΔH^0	ΔS^0	$-T\Delta S^0$	ΔG^0	Description
−	+	−	−	Spontaneous at all T
+	−	+	+	Nonspontaneous at all T
+	+	−	+ or −	Spontaneous at higher T; nonspontaneous at lower T
−	−	+	+ or −	Spontaneous at lower T; nonspontaneous at higher T

Table 20.1 summarizes these four possible combinations of ΔH^0 and ΔS^0.

As you saw in Sample Problem 20.4, one way to calculate ΔG^0 is from enthalpy and entropy changes. Since ΔH^0 and ΔS^0 usually change little with temperature, we can use their values at 298 K to examine the effect of temperature on ΔG^0 and thus on reaction spontaneity.

Sample Problem 20.6   Determining the Effect of Temperature on ΔG^0

PROBLEM An important reaction in the production of sulfuric acid is the oxidation of $SO_2(g)$ to $SO_3(g)$:

$$2SO_2(g) + O_2(g) \longrightarrow 2SO_3(g)$$

At 298 K, $\Delta G^0 = -141.6$ kJ; $\Delta H^0 = -198.4$ kJ; and $\Delta S^0 = -187.9$ J/K.
(a) Use the data to decide if this reaction is spontaneous at 25°C and how ΔG^0 will change with increasing T.
(b) Assuming ΔH^0 and ΔS^0 are constant with T, is the reaction spontaneous at 900.°C?
PLAN (a) We examine the sign of ΔG^0 to see if the reaction is spontaneous and the signs of ΔH^0 and ΔS^0 to see the effect of T. **(b)** We use Equation 20.6 to calculate ΔG^0 from the given ΔH^0 and ΔS^0 at the higher T (in K).
SOLUTION (a) Since $\Delta G^0 < 0$, the reaction is spontaneous at 298 K: a mixture of $SO_2(g)$, $O_2(g)$, and $SO_3(g)$ in their standard states (1 atm) will spontaneously yield more $SO_3(g)$. With $\Delta S^0 < 0$, the term $-T\Delta S^0 > 0$ and becomes more positive at higher T. Therefore, ΔG^0 will be less negative, and the reaction less spontaneous, with increasing T.
(b) Calculating ΔG^0 at 900.°C ($T = 273 + 900. = 1173$ K):
$$\Delta G^0 = \Delta H^0 - T\Delta S^0 = -198.4 \text{ kJ} - [(1173 \text{ K})(-187.9 \text{ J/K})(1 \text{ kJ}/1000 \text{ J})] = 22.0 \text{ kJ}$$

Since $\Delta G^0 > 0$, the reaction is nonspontaneous at the higher T.
CHECK The answer in **(b)** seems reasonable based on our prediction in **(a)**. The arithmetic seems correct: $\Delta G^0 \approx -200 - [(1200)(-200)/1000] = +40$, within rounding.

Follow-up Problem 20.6   A reaction is nonspontaneous at room temperature but is spontaneous at −40°C. What can you say about the signs and relative magnitudes of ΔH^0, ΔS^0, and $T\Delta S^0$?

The Temperature at Which a Reaction Becomes Spontaneous   As you have just seen, when the signs of ΔH^0 and ΔS^0 are the same, some reactions that are nonspontaneous at one temperature become spontaneous at another, and vice versa. It would certainly be useful to know the temperature at which a reaction becomes spontaneous. This is the temperature at which a positive ΔG^0 switches to a negative ΔG^0 because of the changing magnitude of the $-T\Delta S^0$ term. We find this crossover temperature by setting ΔG^0 equal to zero and solving for T:

$$\Delta G^0 = \Delta H^0 - T\Delta S^0 = 0$$

Therefore, $\Delta H^0 = T\Delta S^0$ and $T = \dfrac{\Delta H^0}{\Delta S^0}$ **(20.8)**

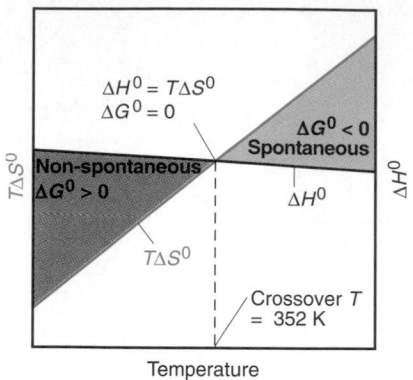

Figure 20.11 The effect of temperature on reaction spontaneity. The two terms that make up ΔG are plotted against T. The figure shows a relatively constant ΔH^0 and a steadily increasing $T\Delta S^0$ (and thus more negative $-T\Delta S^0$) for the reaction between Cu_2O and C. At low T, the reaction is nonspontaneous ($\Delta G^0 > 0$) because the positive ΔH^0 term has a greater magnitude than the negative $T\Delta S^0$ term. At 352 K, $\Delta H^0 = T\Delta S^0$, so $\Delta G^0 = 0$. At any higher T, the reaction becomes spontaneous ($\Delta G^0 < 0$) because the $-T\Delta S^0$ term dominates.

Consider the reaction of copper(I) oxide with carbon, which does *not* occur at lower temperature but is used at higher temperature in a step during the extraction of copper metal from chalcocite (Sample Problems 3.8 and 3.9):

$$Cu_2O(s) + C(s) \longrightarrow 2Cu(s) + CO(g)$$

We predict that this reaction has a positive entropy change because of the increase in number of moles of gas; in fact, $\Delta S^0 = 165$ J/K. Furthermore, since the reaction is *non*spontaneous at lower temperatures, we know that it must have a positive ΔH^0 (58.1 kJ). As the $-T\Delta S^0$ term becomes more negative at higher temperatures, it will eventually outweigh the positive ΔH^0 term, and the reaction will occur spontaneously.

Let's calculate ΔG^0 for this reaction at 25°C and then find the temperature above which the reaction is spontaneous. At 25°C (298 K),

$$\Delta G^0 = \Delta H^0 - T\Delta S^0 = 58.1 \text{ kJ} - \left(298 \text{ K} \times 165 \text{ J/K} \times \frac{1 \text{ kJ}}{1000 \text{ J}} \right) = 8.9 \text{ kJ}$$

Since ΔG^0 is positive, the reaction will not proceed on its own at 25°C. At the crossover temperature, $\Delta G^0 = 0$, so

$$T = \frac{\Delta H^0}{\Delta S^0} = \frac{58.1 \text{ kJ} \times \dfrac{1000 \text{ J}}{1 \text{ kJ}}}{165 \text{ J/K}} = 352 \text{ K}$$

At any temperature above 352 K (79°C), a moderate temperature for recovering a metal from its ore, the reaction occurs spontaneously. Figure 20.11 depicts this result. The line for $T\Delta S^0$ increases steadily (and thus the $-T\Delta S^0$ term becomes more negative) with rising T. It crosses the relatively constant ΔH^0 line at 352 K. At any higher T, the $-T\Delta S^0$ term is greater than the ΔH^0 term, so ΔG^0 is negative.

Coupling Reactions to Drive a Nonspontaneous Change

When we break down a spontaneous multistep reaction to its component steps, we often find that a nonspontaneous step is driven by a spontaneous step in a **coupling of reactions.** One step supplies enough free energy for the other to occur, just as the combustion of gasoline supplies enough free energy to move a car.

Consider the reaction we just discussed for the reduction of copper(I) oxide by carbon. We found that the *overall* reaction becomes spontaneous at any temperature above 352 K. When we divide the reaction into two steps, however, we find that even at a higher temperature, such as 375 K, copper(I) oxide does not spontaneously decompose to its elements:

$$Cu_2O(s) \longrightarrow 2Cu(s) + \tfrac{1}{2}O_2(g) \qquad \Delta G^0_{375} = 140.0 \text{ kJ}$$

However, the oxidation of carbon to CO at 375 K is quite spontaneous:

$$C(s) + \tfrac{1}{2}O_2(g) \longrightarrow CO(g) \qquad \Delta G^0_{375} = -143.8 \text{ kJ}$$

Coupling these reactions means having the carbon in contact with the Cu_2O, which allows the reaction with the larger negative ΔG^0 to "drive" the one with the smaller positive ΔG^0. Adding the reactions together and canceling terms gives an overall negative ΔG^0:

$$Cu_2O(s) + C(s) \longrightarrow 2Cu(s) + CO(g) \quad \Delta G^0_{375} = -3.8 \text{ kJ}$$

Many biochemical reactions are also nonspontaneous. Key steps in the synthesis of proteins and nucleic acids, formation of fatty acids, maintenance of ion balance, and breakdown of nutrients are among numerous essential processes with positive ΔG^0 values. Driving these energetically unfavorable steps by coupling them to a spontaneous one is a life-sustaining strategy common to all organisms—animals, plants, and microbes—as we discuss in the Chemical Connections essay.

Chemical Connections   Chemistry in Biological Energetics

The Universal Role of ATP

One of the most remarkable features of living organisms, as well as a strong indication of a common biological ancestry, is the utilization of the same few biomolecules for all the reactions of life. Despite their bewildering diversity of appearance and behavior, virtually every organism uses the same 20 amino acids to make its proteins, the same four or five nucleotides to make its nucleic acids, and the same carbohydrate (glucose) to provide energy.

In addition, *all organisms use the same spontaneous reaction to provide the free energy needed to drive a wide variety of nonspontaneous ones.* This reaction is the hydrolysis of a high-energy molecule called **adenosine triphosphate (ATP)** to adenosine diphosphate (ADP):

$$ATP^{4-} + H_2O \rightleftharpoons ADP^{3-} + HPO_4^{2-} + H^+$$
$$\Delta G^0 = -30.5 \text{ kJ}$$

In the metabolic breakdown of glucose, for example, the initial step is the addition of a phosphate group to a glucose molecule in a dehydration-condensation reaction:

$$\text{Glucose} + HPO_4^{2-} + H^+ \rightleftharpoons \text{[glucose phosphate]}^- + H_2O$$
$$\Delta G^0 = 13.8 \text{ kJ}$$

By coupling this nonspontaneous reaction to ATP hydrolysis, the overall reaction becomes spontaneous. If we add these two reactions, HPO_4^{2-}, H^+, and H_2O cancel, and we obtain

$$\text{Glucose} + ATP^{4-} \rightleftharpoons \text{[glucose phosphate]}^- + ADP^{3-}$$
$$\Delta G^0 = -16.7 \text{ kJ}$$

Like the reactions to extract copper that we just discussed, these two reactions cannot affect each other if they are physically separated. Coupling the reactions is accomplished through an enzyme catalyst (Section 16.8) that simultaneously binds glucose and ATP such that the phosphate group of

ATP to be transferred lies next to the particular —OH group of glucose that will accept it (Figure 20.C). Enzymes play similar catalytic roles in all the reactions driven by ATP hydrolysis.

The ADP formed in these energy-releasing reactions is combined with phosphate to regenerate ATP in energy-absorbing reactions catalyzed by other enzymes. In fact, the underlying biochemical reason an organism eats and breathes is to make ATP, so that it has the energy to move, grow, reproduce—and study chemistry, of course. Thus, there is a continuous cycling of ATP to ADP and back to ATP again to supply energy to the cells (Figure 20.D).

(continued)

Figure 20.D   The cycling of metabolic free energy through ATP. Processes that release free energy are coupled to the formation of ATP from ADP, whereas those that require free energy are coupled to the hydrolysis of ATP to ADP.

Figure 20.C   The coupling of a nonspontaneous reaction to the hydrolysis of ATP. The glucose molecule must lie next to the ATP molecule (shown as ADP—O—PO$_3$H) in the enzyme's active site for the correct atoms to form bonds. ADP (shown as ADP—OH) and glucose phosphate are released.

What makes ATP hydrolysis such a good supplier of free energy? By examining the phosphate portions of ATP, ADP, and HPO_4^{2-}, we can see two reasons (Figure 20.E). The first is that, at physiological pH (~ 7), the triphosphate portion of the ATP molecule has an average of four negative charges grouped closely together. As a result, the molecule experiences a built-in *high charge repulsion*. In ADP, some of these repulsions are relieved.

The second reason relates to the greater delocalization of π electrons in the hydrolysis products, which we can see by using resonance structures. For example, once ATP is hydrolyzed, the π electrons in HPO_4^{2-} can be more readily delocalized, which stabilizes the ion. Thus, greater charge repulsion and less electron delocalization make ATP higher in energy than the sum of ADP and HPO_4^{2-}. When ATP is hydrolyzed, some of this additional energy is released to be harnessed by the organism to drive the metabolic reactions that could not otherwise take place.

Figure 20.E Why is ATP a "high-energy" molecule? The ATP molecule releases a large amount of free energy when it is hydrolyzed because **(A)** the high charge repulsion in the triphosphate portion of ATP is partially relieved, and **(B)** the free HPO_4^{2-} ion is stabilized by delocalization of its π electrons, as shown in several resonance forms.

Section Summary

The sign of the free energy change, $\Delta G = \Delta H - T\Delta S$, is directly related to reaction spontaneity: a negative ΔG corresponds to a positive ΔS_{univ}. We use the standard free energy change (ΔG^0) to compare the spontaneity of reactions and use the standard free energy of formation (ΔG_f^0) to calculate ΔG_{rxn}^0 at 25°C. A portion of ΔH_{rxn} can do work (ΔG), while the other portion disorders the surroundings ($T\Delta S$). The maximum work is never obtained from a real process because some free energy is always converted to heat. The magnitude of T influences the spontaneity of temperature-dependent reactions (same signs of ΔH and ΔS) by affecting the size of $T\Delta S$. For such reactions, the T at which the reaction becomes spontaneous can be found by setting $\Delta G = 0$. A nonspontaneous reaction ($\Delta G > 0$) can be made to occur by coupling it to a more spontaneous one ($\Delta G << 0$). In organisms, the hydrolysis of ATP drives many reactions with a positive ΔG.

20.4 Free Energy, Equilibrium, and Reaction Direction

The sign of ΔG allows us to predict reaction spontaneity and thus direction, but you already know that it is not the only way to do so. In Chapter 17, we predicted reaction direction by comparing the values of the reaction quotient (Q) and the equilibrium constant (K). Recall that
- If $Q < K$ ($Q/K < 1$), the reaction as written proceeds to the right.
- If $Q > K$ ($Q/K > 1$), the reaction as written proceeds to the left.
- If $Q = K$ ($Q/K = 1$), the reaction has reached equilibrium, and there is no net reaction in either direction.

As you might expect, these two ways of predicting reaction spontaneity—the sign of ΔG and the magnitude of Q/K—are related. Their relationship emerges when we compare the signs of $\ln Q/K$ with ΔG:
- If $Q/K < 1$, then $\ln Q/K < 0$: reaction proceeds to the right ($\Delta G < 0$).
- If $Q/K > 1$, then $\ln Q/K > 0$: reaction proceeds to the left ($\Delta G > 0$).
- If $Q/K = 1$, then $\ln Q/K = 0$: reaction is at equilibrium ($\Delta G = 0$).

Note that the signs of ΔG and $\ln Q/K$ are identical for a given reaction direction. In fact, ΔG and $\ln Q/K$ are proportional to each other and made equal through the constant RT:

$$\Delta G = RT \ln \frac{Q}{K} = RT \ln Q - RT \ln K \qquad \textbf{(20.9)}$$

What does this central relationship mean? As you know, Q represents the concentrations (or pressures) of a system's components at any time during the reaction, whereas K represents them when the reaction has reached equilibrium. Therefore, Equation 20.9 states that the free energy change of the system is the difference between the free energy of the system in some initial state, Q, and the free energy of the system in its final state, K. For a system at equilibrium, Q has become equal to K, so $\Delta G = 0$. In other words, at equilibrium, no further free energy change occurs; in effect, the system has released all its free energy in the process of attaining equilibrium.

The size of ΔG depends on the difference in the sizes of Q and K. By choosing standard-state values for Q, we obtain the standard free energy change (ΔG^0). When all concentrations are 1 M (or all pressures 1 atm), ΔG equals ΔG^0 and Q equals 1:

$$\Delta G^0 = RT \ln 1 - RT \ln K$$

Since $\ln 1 = 0$, the "$RT \ln Q$" term drops out, and we have

$$\Delta G^0 = -RT \ln K \qquad \textbf{(20.10)}$$

This very important relationship allows us to calculate the standard free energy change of a reaction (ΔG^0) from its equilibrium constant, or vice versa. Because ΔG^0 is related logarithmically to K, even a small change in the value of ΔG^0 has a large effect on the value of K. Table 20.2 shows the K values that correspond to a range of ΔG^0 values. Note that as ΔG^0 becomes more positive, the equilibrium constant becomes smaller, which means the reaction reaches equilibrium with less product and more reactant. Similarly, as ΔG^0 becomes more negative, the reaction reaches equilibrium with more product and less reactant. For example, if $\Delta G^0 = +10$ kJ, $K \approx 0.02$, which means that the product terms are about 1/50th as large as the reactant terms; whereas, if $\Delta G^0 = -10$ kJ, they are 50 times as large.

Of course, most reactions do not begin with all components in their standard states. By substituting the relationship between ΔG^0 and K (Equation 20.10) into the expression for ΔG (Equation 20.9), we obtain a relationship that applies to any starting concentrations:

$$\Delta G = \Delta G^0 + RT \ln Q \qquad \textbf{(20.11)}$$

Table 20.2 The Relationship Between ΔG^0 and K at 298 K

ΔG^0 (kJ)	K	Significance
200	9×10^{-36}	Essentially no forward reaction; reverse reaction goes to completion
100	3×10^{-18}	
50	2×10^{-9}	
10	2×10^{-2}	
1	7×10^{-1}	Forward and reverse reactions proceed to same extent
0	1	
−1	1.5	
−10	5×10^{1}	
−50	6×10^{8}	
−100	3×10^{17}	Forward reaction goes to completion; essentially no reverse reaction
−200	1×10^{35}	

Sample Problem 20.7 illustrates how Equations 20.10 and 20.11 are applied.

Sample Problem 20.7   Calculating ΔG at Nonstandard Conditions

PROBLEM The oxidation of SO_2, which we considered in Sample Problem 20.6,

$$2SO_2(g) + O_2(g) \longrightarrow 2SO_3(g)$$

is too slow at 298 K to be useful in the manufacture of sulfuric acid. To overcome this low rate, the process is conducted at an elevated temperature.
(a) Calculate K at 298 K and at 973 K. $\Delta G_{298}^0 = -141.6$ kJ/mol of reaction as written; using ΔH^0 and ΔS^0 values at 973 K, $\Delta G_{973}^0 = -12.12$ kJ/mol of reaction as written.
(b) In experiments to determine the effect of temperature on reaction spontaneity, sealed containers are filled with 0.500 atm SO_2, 0.0100 atm O_2, and 0.100 atm SO_3 and kept at 25°C and at 700.°C. In which direction, if any, will the reaction proceed to reach equilibrium at each temperature?
(c) Calculate ΔG for the system in part **(b)** at each temperature.
PLAN **(a)** We know ΔG^0, T, and R, so we can calculate the K's from Equation 20.10.
(b) To determine if a net reaction will occur with the given pressures, we calculate Q and compare it with each K from part **(a)**. **(c)** Since these are not standard-state pressures, we calculate ΔG at each T from Equation 20.11 with the values of ΔG^0 (given) and Q [found in part **(b)**].
SOLUTION **(a)** Calculating K at the two temperatures:

$$\Delta G^0 = -RT \ln K \qquad \text{so} \qquad K = e^{-(\Delta G^0/RT)}$$

At 298 K, the exponent is

$$-(\Delta G^0/RT) = -\left(\frac{-141.6 \text{ kJ/mol} \times \dfrac{1000 \text{ J}}{1 \text{ kJ}}}{8.31 \text{ J/mol} \cdot \text{K} \times 298 \text{ K}} \right) = 57.2$$

So $K = e^{-(\Delta G^0/RT)} = e^{57.2} = \boxed{7 \times 10^{24}}$

At 973 K, the exponent is

$$-(\Delta G^0/RT) = -\left(\frac{-12.12 \text{ kJ/mol} \times \dfrac{1000 \text{ J}}{1 \text{ kJ}}}{8.31 \text{ J/mol} \cdot \text{K} \times 973 \text{ K}} \right) = 1.50$$

So $K = e^{-(\Delta G^0/RT)} = e^{1.50} = \boxed{4.5}$

(b) Calculating the value of Q:

$$Q = \frac{P_{SO_3}^2}{P_{SO_2}^2 \times P_{O_2}} = \frac{0.100^2}{0.500^2 \times 0.0100} = 4.00$$

Since $Q < K$ at both temperatures, the denominator will decrease and the numerator increase—more SO_3 will form—until Q equals K. However, at 298 K, the reaction will go far to the right before reaching equilibrium, whereas at 973 K, it will move only slightly to the right.
(c) Calculating ΔG, the nonstandard free energy change, at 298 K:

$$\Delta G_{298} = \Delta G^0 + RT \ln Q$$

$$= -141.6 \text{ kJ/mol} + \left(8.31 \text{ J/mol} \cdot \text{K} \times \frac{1 \text{ kJ}}{1000 \text{ J}} \times 298 \text{ K} \times \ln 4.00 \right)$$

$$= \boxed{-138.2 \text{ kJ/mol}}$$

Calculating ΔG at 973 K:

$$\Delta G_{973} = \Delta G^0 + RT \ln Q$$

$$= -12.12 \text{ kJ/mol} + \left(8.31 \text{ J/mol} \cdot \text{K} \times \frac{1 \text{ kJ}}{1000 \text{ J}} \times 973 \text{ K} \times \ln 4.00 \right)$$

$$= \boxed{-0.9 \text{ kJ/mol}}$$

CHECK Be sure to check the arithmetic in each step. Note that in parts **(a)** and **(c)** we made energy units in free energy changes (kJ) consistent with those in R (J). Based on the rules for significant figures in addition and subtraction, we retain one digit to the right of the decimal place in **(c)**.

COMMENT For these starting gas pressures at 973 K, the process is barely spontaneous ($\Delta G = -0.9$ kJ/mol), so why use a higher temperature? As in the synthesis of NH_3 (Section 17.6), this process is operated at a higher temperature *with a catalyst* to attain a higher *rate*, even though the *yield* is greater at a lower temperature. We discuss these details of the industrial production of sulfuric acid in Chapter 22.

Follow-up Problem 20.7 At 298 K, hypobromous acid (HBrO) dissociates in water with a K_a of 2.3×10^{-9}.
(a) Calculate ΔG^0 for the dissociation of HBrO.
(b) Calculate ΔG when $[H_3O^+] = 6.0 \times 10^{-4}$ M, $[BrO^-] = 0.10$ M, and $[HBrO] = 0.20$ M.

Another Look at the Meaning of Spontaneity At this point, let's reconsider what we mean by the terms *spontaneous* and *nonspontaneous*. Consider the general reaction A $\rightleftharpoons$ B, for which $K = [B]/[A] > 1$; therefore, the reaction goes largely from left to right (Figure 20.12). From pure A to the equilibrium point, the reaction is spontaneous ($\Delta G < 0$). From there on, the reaction is nonspontaneous ($\Delta G > 0$). If we had started with pure B, the reaction would also be spontaneous until it reached equilibrium, but not thereafter. In either case, *the free energy decreases as the reaction proceeds, until it reaches a minimum at the equilibrium mixture.* If we start with pure A, the vessel contains mostly B when the reaction stops, so we say the forward reaction A $\longrightarrow$ B is "spontaneous." Likewise, if we start with pure B, the reaction also stops with mostly B present. Even though a small amount of A forms to satisfy the equilibrium condition, we say the reverse reaction B $\longrightarrow$ A is "nonspontaneous" because it proceeds very little in that direction. For the overall reaction A $\rightleftharpoons$ B (starting with all components in their standard states), G_B^0 is smaller than G_A^0, so ΔG^0 is negative, which corresponds to $K > 1$ and, therefore, to a spontaneous reaction as written. Thus, the term *spontaneous reaction* refers to one that goes *predominantly, not necessarily completely, to product*. These ideas are consistent with the values in Table 20.2 that you saw earlier.

Figure 20.12 **The relation between free energy and the extent of reaction.** The free energy of the system is plotted against the extent of reaction for the reaction A $\rightleftharpoons$ B. Since $G_A^0 > G_B^0$, $\Delta G^0 < 0$ and $K > 1$. Note that the reaction proceeds spontaneously ($\Delta G < 0$; *curved green arrows*), although to different extents, from either pure A or B *to* the equilibrium mixture, at which point $\Delta G = 0$. The reaction *from* the equilibrium mixture to either pure A or B is nonspontaneous ($\Delta G > 0$; *curved red arrows*).

Section Summary

Two ways of predicting reaction direction are from the value of ΔG and from the relation of Q to K. These variables are different aspects of the same principle and are related to each other by $\Delta G = RT \ln Q/K$. When $Q = K$, the system can release no more free energy. Beginning with Q at the standard state, the free energy change is ΔG^0, and it is related to the equilibrium constant by $\Delta G^0 = -RT \ln K$. For nonstandard conditions, ΔG has two components, ΔG^0 and $RT \ln Q$. Any nonequilibrium mixture of reactants and products moves spontaneously ($\Delta G < 0$) toward the equilibrium mixture, but only when $K > 1$ is the reaction spontaneous for the components in their standard states ($\Delta G^0 < 0$).

Chapter Perspective

As processes move toward equilibrium, some of the released energy becomes degraded to unusable, dispersed heat, and the entropy of the universe increases. This unalterable necessity built into all natural processes has led to speculation about the "End of Everything," when all possible processes have stopped occurring, no free energy remains in any system, and nothing but waste heat is dispersed evenly throughout the universe—the final equilibrium! Even if this grim future is in store, however, it is many billions of years away, so you have plenty of time to appreciate more hopeful applications of thermodynamics. In Chapter 21, you'll see how spontaneous reactions can generate electricity and how electricity supplies free energy to drive nonspontaneous ones.

The following learning objectives, with section and/or sample problem (SP) numbers in parentheses, can help focus your study:

Understand These Concepts

1. How the tendency of a process to occur by itself is distinct from how long it takes to occur (Intro)
2. The distinction between a spontaneous and a nonspontaneous change (Section 20.1)
3. Why the first law of thermodynamics and the sign of ΔH^0 cannot predict the direction of a spontaneous process (Section 20.1)
4. The natural tendency of a system to become disordered over time and why a disordered system is more probable than an ordered one (Section 20.1)
5. How disorder is expressed quantitatively by entropy (S) (Section 20.1)
6. How the second law of thermodynamics expresses the criterion of spontaneity, that a change increases S_{univ} (Section 20.1)
7. How absolute entropies (S^0) can be obtained because the third law of thermodynamics provides a "zero point" (Section 20.1)
8. How temperature, physical state, dissolution, molar mass, and molecular complexity influence S^0 values (Section 20.1)
9. How ΔS^0_{rxn} is based on the difference between the S^0 values of the reactants and the products (Section 20.2)
10. How the surroundings add heat to or remove heat from the system and how ΔS^0_{surr} influences the overall ΔS^0_{rxn} (Section 20.2)
11. The relationship between ΔS_{surr} and ΔH_{sys} (Section 20.2)
12. How reactions proceed spontaneously toward equilibrium ($\Delta S_{univ} > 0$) and then proceed no further at equilibrium ($\Delta S_{univ} = 0$) (Section 20.2)
13. How the free energy change combines the system's entropy and enthalpy changes (Section 20.3)
14. How the expression for the free energy change is derived from the second law (Section 20.3)
15. The relationship between ΔG and the maximum work a system can perform and why this quantity of work is never performed in a real process (Section 20.3)
16. How temperature determines spontaneity for reactions in which ΔS^0 and ΔH^0 have the same sign (Section 20.3)
17. Why the temperature at which a reaction becomes spontaneous occurs when $\Delta G^0 = 0$ (Section 20.3)
18. How a spontaneous change coupled to a nonspontaneous change can make it occur (Section 20.3)
19. How ΔG is the free energy change from the start of a reaction (expressed by Q) to its end (expressed by K) (Section 20.4)
20. The meaning of ΔG^0 and its relation to K (Section 20.4)
21. The relation of ΔG to ΔG^0 and Q (Section 20.4)
22. How ΔG decreases, no matter what the starting concentrations, as the reacting system moves spontaneously toward equilibrium (Section 20.4)

Master These Skills

1. Predicting relative S^0 values of substances and mixtures (Section 20.1 and SP 20.1)
2. Calculating ΔS^0_{rxn} for a chemical or physical change (SP 20.2)
3. Determining reaction spontaneity from ΔS^0_{surr} and ΔH^0_{sys} (SP 20.3)
4. Calculating ΔG^0_{rxn} from ΔH^0_f and S^0 values (SP 20.4)
5. Calculating ΔG^0_{rxn} from ΔG^0_f values (SP 20.5)
6. Calculating the effect of temperature on ΔG^0_{rxn} (SP 20.6)
7. Calculating the temperature at which a reaction becomes spontaneous (Section 20.3)
8. Calculating K from ΔG^0 (Section 20.4 and SP 20.7)
9. Using ΔG^0 and Q to calculate ΔG at any temperature (SP 20.7)

For Review and Reference

Key Terms

Section 20.1
spontaneous change
entropy (S)
second law of thermodynamics

third law of thermodynamics
standard molar entropy (S^0)
Section 20.2
standard entropy of reaction (ΔS^0_{rxn})

Section 20.3
free energy (G)
standard free energy change (ΔG^0)

standard free energy of formation (ΔG^0_f)
coupling of reactions
adenosine triphosphate (ATP)

Key Equations and Relationships

20.1 Stating the second law of thermodynamics (p. 862): For a spontaneous process,

$$\Delta S_{univ} - \Delta S_{sys} + \Delta S_{surr} > 0$$

20.2 Quantifying entropy in terms of the number of ways (W) a system can be arranged (p. 863):

$$S = k \ln W$$

20.3 Calculating the standard entropy of reaction from standard molar entropies of reactants and products (p. 868):

$$\Delta S^0_{rxn} = \Sigma m S^0_{products} - \Sigma n S^0_{reactants}$$

20.4 Relating the entropy change in the surroundings to the heat of the system and the temperature (p. 869):

$$\Delta S_{surr} = -\frac{q_{sys}}{T}$$

20.5 Expressing the free energy change of the system in terms of its component enthalpy and entropy changes (Gibbs equation) (p. 874):

$$\Delta G_{sys} = \Delta H_{sys} - T\Delta S_{sys}$$

20.6 Calculating the standard free energy change from standard enthalpy and entropy changes (p. 874):

$$\Delta G^0_{sys} = \Delta H^0_{sys} - T\Delta S^0_{sys}$$

20.7 Calculating the standard free energy change from standard free energies of formation (p. 875):

$$\Delta G^0_{rxn} = \Sigma m \Delta G^0_{f(products)} - \Sigma n \Delta G^0_{f(reactants)}$$

20.8 Finding the temperature at which a reaction becomes spontaneous (p. 879):

$$T = \frac{\Delta H^0}{\Delta S^0}$$

20.9 Expressing the free energy change as the difference between an initial state Q and a final state K (p. 883):

$$\Delta G = RT \ln \frac{Q}{K} = RT \ln Q - RT \ln K$$

20.10 Expressing the free energy change when Q is at the standard state (p. 883):

$$\Delta G^0 = RT \ln 1 - RT \ln K = -RT \ln K$$

20.11 Expressing the free energy change for a nonstandard initial state (p. 883):

$$\Delta G = \Delta G^0 + RT \ln Q$$

Highlighted Figures and Tables

These figures (F) and tables (T) provide a quick review of key ideas.
F20.5 Entropy and phase changes (p. 864)
F20.10 Components of ΔS^0_{univ} for spontaneous reactions (p. 872)

T20.1 The signs of ΔH^0, ΔS^0, and ΔG^0 (p. 879)
T20.2 The relationship of ΔG^0 and K (p. 883)
F20.12 Free energy and extent of reaction (p. 885)

Answers to Follow-up Problems

20.1 (a) $PCl_5(g)$: higher molar mass and more complex molecule; (b) $BaCl_2(s)$: higher molar mass; (c) $Br_2(g)$: gases have less order than liquids.

20.2 (a) $2NaOH(s) + CO_2(g) \longrightarrow Na_2CO_3(s) + H_2O(l)$;

$\Delta n_{gas} = -1$, so $\Delta S_{rxn}^0 < 0$

$$\Delta S_{rxn}^0 = [(1 \text{ mol } H_2O \times 69.9 \text{ J/mol} \cdot \text{K})$$
$$+ (1 \text{ mol } Na_2CO_3 \times 139 \text{ J/mol} \cdot \text{K})]$$
$$- [(1 \text{ mol } CO_2 \times 213.7 \text{ J/mol} \cdot \text{K})$$
$$+ (2 \text{ mol } NaOH \times 64.5 \text{ J/mol} \cdot \text{K})]$$
$$= -134 \text{ J/K}$$

(b) $2Fe(s) + 3H_2O(g) \longrightarrow Fe_2O_3(s) + 3H_2(g)$

$\Delta n_{gas} = 0$, so cannot predict sign of ΔS_{rxn}^0

$$\Delta S_{rxn}^0 = [(1 \text{ mol } Fe_2O_3 \times 87.4 \text{ J/mol} \cdot \text{K})$$
$$+ (3 \text{ mol } H_2 \times 130.6 \text{ J/mol} \cdot \text{K})]$$
$$- [(2 \text{ mol } Fe \times 27.3 \text{ J/mol} \cdot \text{K})$$
$$+ (3 \text{ mol } H_2O \times 188.7 \text{ J/mol} \cdot \text{K})]$$
$$= -141.5 \text{ J/K}$$

20.3 $2FeO(s) + \frac{1}{2}O_2(g) \longrightarrow Fe_2O_3(s)$

$$\Delta S_{sys}^0 = 1 \text{ mol } Fe_2O_3 (87.4 \text{ J/mol} \cdot \text{K})$$
$$- [2 \text{ mol } FeO (60.75 \text{ J/mol} \cdot \text{K})$$
$$+ \tfrac{1}{2} \text{ mol } O_2 (205.0 \text{ J/mol} \cdot \text{K})]$$
$$= -136.6 \text{ J/K}$$

$$\Delta H_{sys}^0 = 1 \text{ mol } Fe_2O_3 (-825.5 \text{ kJ/mol})$$
$$- [2 \text{ mol } FeO (-272.0 \text{ kJ/mol})$$
$$+ \tfrac{1}{2} \text{ mol } O_2 (0 \text{ kJ/mol})]$$
$$= -281.5 \text{ kJ}$$

$$\Delta S_{surr}^0 = -\frac{\Delta H_{sys}^0}{T} = -\frac{(-281.5 \text{ kJ} \times 1000 \text{ J/kJ})}{298 \text{ K}}$$
$$= +945 \text{ J/K}$$

$$\Delta S_{univ}^0 = \Delta S_{sys}^0 + \Delta S_{surr}^0 = -136.6 \text{ J/K} + 945 \text{ J/K}$$
$$= 808 \text{ J/K}; \text{ reaction is spontaneous at 298 K.}$$

20.4 Using ΔH_f^0 and S^0 values from Appendix B,

$$\Delta H_{rxn}^0 = -114.2 \text{ kJ and } \Delta S_{rxn}^0 = -146.5 \text{ J/K}$$

$$\Delta G_{rxn}^0 = \Delta H_{rxn}^0 - T\Delta S_{rxn}^0 = -114.2 \text{ kJ}$$
$$- [(298 \text{ K})(-146.5 \text{ J/K})(1 \text{ kJ}/1000 \text{ J})]$$
$$= -70.5 \text{ kJ}$$

20.5 (a) $\Delta G_{rxn}^0 = 2 \text{ mol } NO_2 (51 \text{ kJ/mol})$
$$- [2 \text{ mol } NO (86.60 \text{ kJ/mol})$$
$$+ 1 \text{ mol } O_2 (0 \text{ kJ/mol})]$$
$$= -71 \text{ kJ}$$

(b) $\Delta G_{rxn}^0 = 2 \text{ mol } CO (-137.2 \text{ kJ/mol})$
$$- [2 \text{ mol } C (0 \text{ kJ/mol})$$
$$+ 1 \text{ mol } O_2 (0 \text{ kJ/mol})]$$
$$= -274.4 \text{ kJ}$$

20.6 ΔG^0 becomes negative at lower T, so $\Delta H^0 < 0$, $\Delta S^0 < 0$, and $-T\Delta S^0 > 0$. At lower T, the negative ΔH^0 value becomes larger than the positive ($-T\Delta S^0$) value.

20.7 (a) $\Delta G^0 = -RT \ln K$

$$= -8.31 \text{ J/mol} \cdot \text{K} \times \frac{1 \text{ kJ}}{1000 \text{ J}} \times 298 \text{ K}$$
$$\times \ln (2.3 \times 10^{-9})$$
$$= 49 \text{ kJ/mol}$$

(b) $Q = \dfrac{[H_3O^+][BrO^-]}{[HBrO]} = \dfrac{(6.0 \times 10^{-4})(0.10)}{0.20} = 3.0 \times 10^{-4}$

$\Delta G = \Delta G^0 + RT \ln Q$

$$= 49 \text{ kJ/mol}$$
$$+ \left[8.31 \text{ J/mol} \cdot \text{K} \times \frac{1 \text{ kJ}}{1000 \text{ J}} \times 298 \text{ K} \times \ln (3.0 \times 10^{-4}) \right]$$
$$= 29 \text{ kJ/mol}$$

Problems

Problems with a **colored** number are answered at the back of the text. Problem sections match the text and provide the number(s) of relevant sample problems. Most offer concept review questions, skill-building exercises (written in similar pairs), and problems in a relevant context. Following these are comprehensive problems based on material from any section and/or previous chapter.

[Note: Unless stated otherwise, all problems refer to systems at 298 K (25°C).]

The Second Law of Thermodynamics: Predicting Spontaneous Change

(Sample Problem 20.1)

■ **Concept Review Questions**

20.1 Distinguish between the terms *spontaneous* and *instantaneous*. Give an example of a process that is spontaneous but very slow, and one that is very fast but not spontaneous.

20.2 Distinguish between the terms *spontaneous* and *nonspontaneous*. Is it possible for a nonspontaneous process to occur? Explain.

20.3 State the first law of thermodynamics in terms of (a) the energy of the universe; (b) the creation or destruction of energy; (c) the energy change of system and surroundings. Does the first law tell us the direction of spontaneous change? Explain.

20.4 State qualitatively the relationship between entropy and probability. Use this idea to explain why you have probably never
(a) Seen a large number of coins (>6) flipped into the air land with all heads up
(b) Been suffocated because all the air near you moved to the other side of the room
(c) Seen half the water in your cup of tea freeze while the other half boiled

20.5 Why is $\Delta S_{vaporization}$ of a substance always larger than ΔS_{fusion}?

20.6 How does the entropy of the surroundings change during the course of an exothermic reaction? An endothermic reaction? Other than those cited in text, give an example of an endothermic process that occurs spontaneously.

20.7 (a) What is the entropy of a perfect crystal at absolute zero (0 K)?
(b) Does the entropy increase or decrease as the temperature rises?
(c) Why does $\Delta H_f^0 = 0$ for an element in its standard state, but $S^0 > 0$?
(d) Why do tables of thermodynamic values list ΔH_f^0 values but not ΔS_f^0 values?

■ **Skill-Building Exercises** *(paired)*

20.8 Which of the following processes are spontaneous?
(a) Water evaporating from a puddle in summer
(b) A lion chasing an antelope
(c) An unstable isotope undergoing radioactive disintegration

20.9 Which of the following processes are spontaneous?
(a) The Earth moving around the Sun
(b) A boulder rolling up a hill
(c) Sodium metal and chlorine gas reacting to form solid sodium chloride

20.10 Which of the following processes are spontaneous?
(a) Methane burning in air
(b) A teaspoonful of sugar dissolving in a cup of hot coffee
(c) A soft-boiled egg becoming raw

20.11 Which of the following processes are spontaneous?
(a) A satellite falling to Earth
(b) Water decomposing to H_2 and O_2 at room temperature and 1 atm pressure
(c) Average car prices increasing

20.12 Predict the sign of ΔS_{sys} for each of the following processes:
(a) A piece of wax melting
(b) Silver chloride precipitating from solution
(c) Dew forming

20.13 Predict the sign of ΔS_{sys} for each of the following processes:
(a) Gasoline vapors mixing with air in a car engine
(b) Hot air expanding
(c) Breath condensing in cold air

20.14 Predict the sign of ΔS_{sys} for each of the following processes:
(a) Alcohol evaporating
(b) A solid explosive converting to a gas
(c) Perfume vapors diffusing through a room

20.15 Predict the sign of ΔS_{sys} for each of the following processes:
(a) A pond freezing in winter
(b) Atmospheric CO_2 dissolving in the ocean
(c) An apple tree bearing fruit

20.16 Without referring to Appendix B, predict the sign of ΔS^0 for each of the following processes:
(a) $2K(s) + F_2(g) \longrightarrow 2KF(s)$
(b) $NH_3(g) + HBr(g) \longrightarrow NH_4Br(s)$
(c) $NaClO_3(s) \longrightarrow Na^+(aq) + ClO_3^-(aq)$

20.17 Without referring to Appendix B, predict the sign of ΔS^0 for each of the following processes:
(a) $H_2S(g) + \frac{1}{2}O_2(g) \longrightarrow \frac{1}{8}S_8(s) + H_2O(g)$
(b) $HCl(aq) + NaOH(aq) \longrightarrow NaCl(aq) + H_2O(l)$
(c) $2NO_2(g) \longrightarrow N_2O_4(g)$

20.18 Without referring to Appendix B, predict the sign of ΔS^0 for each of the following processes:
(a) $CaCO_3(s) + 2HCl(aq) \longrightarrow$
$$CaCl_2(aq) + H_2O(l) + CO_2(g)$$
(b) $2NO(g) + O_2(g) \longrightarrow 2NO_2(g)$
(c) $2KClO_3(s) \longrightarrow 2KCl(s) + 3O_2(g)$

20.19 Without referring to Appendix B, predict the sign of ΔS^0 for each of the following processes:
(a) $Ag^+(aq) + Cl^-(aq) \longrightarrow AgCl(s)$
(b) $FeCl_3(s) \longrightarrow FeCl_3(aq)$
(c) $CH_3CH{=}CH_2(g) \longrightarrow \overset{CH_2}{\underset{H_2C-CH_2}{\wedge}}(g)$

20.20 Predict the sign of ΔS for each of the following processes:
(a) $C_2H_5OH(g)$ at 350 K and 500 torr $\longrightarrow$
$$C_2H_5OH(g) \text{ at 350 K and 250 torr}$$
(b) $N_2(g)$ at 298 K and 1 atm $\longrightarrow N_2(aq)$ at 298 K and 1 atm
(c) $O_2(aq)$ at 303 K and 1 atm $\longrightarrow O_2(g)$ at 303 K and 1 atm

20.21 Predict the sign of ΔS for each of the following processes:
(a) $O_2(g)$ ($V = 1.0$ L, $P = 1$ atm) $\longrightarrow O_2(g)$
$$(V = 0.10 \text{ L}, P = 10 \text{ atm})$$
(b) $Cu(s)$ at 350°C and 2.5 atm $\longrightarrow$
$$Cu(s) \text{ at 450°C and 2.5 atm}$$
(c) $Cl_2(g)$ at 100°C and 1 atm $\longrightarrow Cl_2(g)$ at 10°C and 1 atm

20.22 Predict which substance in each pair has the greater molar entropy and explain your choice:
(a) Butane, $CH_3CH_2CH_2CH_3(g)$ or
2-butene, $CH_3CH{-}CHCH_3(g)$
(b) $Ne(g)$ or $Xe(g)$
(c) $CH_4(g)$ or $CCl_4(l)$

20.23 Predict which substance in each pair has the greater molar entropy and explain your choice:
(a) $NO_2(g)$ or $N_2O_4(g)$
(b) $CH_3OCH_3(l)$ or $CH_3CH_2OH(l)$
(c) $HCl(g)$ or $HBr(g)$

20.24 Predict which substance in each pair has the greater molar entropy and explain your choice:
(a) $CH_3OH(l)$ or $C_2H_5OH(l)$
(b) $KClO_3(s)$ or $KClO_3(aq)$
(c) $Na(s)$ or $K(s)$

20.25 Predict which substance in each pair has the greater molar entropy and explain your choice:
(a) $P_4(g)$ or $P_2(g)$
(b) $HNO_3(aq)$ or $HNO_3(l)$
(c) $CuSO_4(s)$ or $CuSO_4{\cdot}5H_2O(s)$

20.26 Without consulting Appendix B, arrange each of the following groups in order of *increasing* standard molar entropy, S^0, and explain your choice:
(a) Graphite, diamond, charcoal
(b) Ice, water vapor, liquid water
(c) O_2, O_3, O atoms

20.27 Without consulting Appendix B, arrange each of the following groups in order of *increasing* standard molar entropy, S^0, and explain your choice:
(a) Glucose ($C_6H_{12}O_6$), sucrose ($C_{12}H_{22}O_{11}$), ribose ($C_5H_{10}O_5$)
(b) $CaCO_3$, Ca + C + $\frac{3}{2}O_2$, CaO + CO_2
(c) $SF_6(g)$, $SF_4(g)$, $S_2F_{10}(g)$

20.28 Without consulting Appendix B, arrange each of the following groups in order of *decreasing* standard molar entropy, S^0, and explain your choice:
(a) $ClO_4^-(aq)$, $ClO_2^-(aq)$, $ClO_3^-(aq)$
(b) $NO_2(g)$, $NO(g)$, $N_2(g)$
(c) $Fe_2O_3(s)$, $Al_2O_3(s)$, $Fe_3O_4(s)$

20.29 Without consulting Appendix B, arrange each of the following groups in order of *decreasing* standard molar entropy, S^0, and explain your choice:
(a) Mg metal, Ca metal, Ba metal
(b) Hexane (C_6H_{14}), benzene (C_6H_6), cyclohexane (C_6H_{12})
(c) $PF_2Cl_3(g)$, $PF_5(g)$, $PF_3(g)$

Calculating the Change in Entropy of a Reaction

(Sample Problems 20.2 and 20.3)

■ Concept Review Questions

20.30 What property of entropy allows Hess's law to be used in the calculation of entropy changes?

20.31 Describe the equilibrium condition in terms of the entropy changes of a system and its surroundings. What does this description mean about the entropy change of the universe?

20.32 Consider the reaction

$$H_2O(g) + Cl_2O(g) \longrightarrow 2HClO(g)$$

Given ΔS^0_{rxn} and S^0 of $HClO(g)$ and of $H_2O(g)$, write an expression to determine S^0 of $Cl_2O(g)$.

■ Skill-Building Exercises (paired)

20.33 For each reaction, predict the sign of ΔS^0 and use Appendix B to calculate its value:
(a) $3NO(g) \longrightarrow N_2O(g) + NO_2(g)$
(b) $3H_2(g) + Fe_2O_3(s) \longrightarrow 2Fe(s) + 3H_2O(g)$
(c) $P_4(s) + 5O_2(g) \longrightarrow P_4O_{10}(s)$

20.34 For each reaction, predict the sign of ΔS^0 and use Appendix B to calculate its value:
(a) $3NO_2(g) + H_2O(l) \longrightarrow 2HNO_3(l) + NO(g)$
(b) $N_2(g) + 3F_2(g) \longrightarrow 2NF_3(g)$
(c) $C_6H_{12}O_6(s) + 6O_2(g) \longrightarrow 6CO_2(g) + 6H_2O(g)$

20.35 Calculate ΔS^0 for the combustion of ethane (C_2H_6) to form carbon dioxide and gaseous water. Is the answer qualitatively what you expect?

20.36 Calculate ΔS^0 for the combustion of methane to form carbon dioxide and liquid water. Is the answer qualitatively what you expect?

20.37 Calculate ΔS^0 for the reduction of nitric oxide with hydrogen to form ammonia and water vapor. Is the answer qualitatively what you expect?

20.38 Calculate ΔS^0 for the combustion of ammonia to form nitrogen dioxide and water vapor. Is the answer qualitatively what you expect?

20.39 Calculate ΔS^0 for the formation of $Cu_2O(s)$ from its elements.

20.40 Calculate ΔS^0 for the formation of $HI(g)$ from its elements.

20.41 Calculate ΔS^0 for the formation of $CH_3OH(l)$ from its elements.

20.42 Calculate ΔS^0 for the formation of $PCl_5(g)$ from its elements.

■ Problems in Context

20.43 Sulfur dioxide is released in the combustion of coal. Scrubbers remove much of the SO_2 from flue gases by reaction with lime slurries containing calcium hydroxide. Write a balanced equation for this reaction and calculate ΔS^0 at 298 K. [S^0 of $CaSO_3(s) = 101.4$ J/mol · K.]

20.44 Oxyacetylene welding is a common method for repairing metal structures, including bridges, buildings, and even the Statue of Liberty. Calculate ΔS^0 for the combustion of 1 mol acetylene (C_2H_2).

Entropy, Free Energy, and Work

(Sample Problems 20.4 to 20.6)

■ Concept Review Questions

20.45 What is the advantage of calculating free energy changes rather than entropy changes to determine reaction spontaneity?

20.46 Given that $\Delta G_{sys} = -T\Delta S_{univ}$, explain how the sign of ΔG_{sys} correlates with reaction spontaneity.

20.47 In general, is an endothermic reaction more likely to be spontaneous at higher temperatures or lower temperatures? Explain.

20.48 With its components in their standard states, a certain reaction is spontaneous only at high temperature. What can you conclude about the signs of ΔH^0 and ΔS^0 for the reaction? Describe a process for which this is true.

20.49 How can ΔS^0 be relatively independent of T if S^0 of each reactant and product increases with T?

■ Skill-Building Exercises (paired)

20.50 Calculate ΔG^0 for the following reactions using ΔG^0_f values from Appendix B:
(a) $2Mg(s) + O_2(g) \longrightarrow 2MgO(s)$
(b) $2CH_3OH(g) + 3O_2(g) \longrightarrow 2CO_2(g) + 4H_2O(g)$
(c) $BaO(s) + CO_2(g) \longrightarrow BaCO_3(s)$

20.51 Calculate ΔG^0 for the following reactions using ΔG^0_f values from Appendix B:
(a) $H_2(g) + I_2(s) \longrightarrow 2HI(g)$
(b) $MnO_2(s) + 2CO(g) \longrightarrow Mn(s) + 2CO_2(g)$
(c) $NH_4Cl(s) \longrightarrow NH_3(g) + HCl(g)$

20.52 Calculate ΔG^0 for the reactions in Problem 20.50 using ΔH^0_f and S^0 values.

20.53 Calculate ΔG^0 for the reactions in Problem 20.51 using ΔH^0_f and S^0 values.

20.54 For the oxidation of carbon monoxide to carbon dioxide,

$$CO(g) + \tfrac{1}{2}O_2(g) \longrightarrow CO_2(g)$$

(a) Predict the signs of ΔS^0 and ΔH^0. Explain.
(b) Calculate ΔG^0 by two different methods.

20.55 For the combustion of butane gas,

$$C_4H_{10}(g) + \tfrac{13}{2}O_2(g) \longrightarrow 4CO_2(g) + 5H_2O(g)$$

(a) Predict the signs of ΔS^0 and ΔH^0. Explain.
(b) Calculate ΔG^0 by two different methods.

20.56 For the gaseous reaction of xenon and fluorine to form xenon hexafluoride:
(a) Calculate ΔS^0 at 298 K ($\Delta H^0 = -402$ kJ/mol and $\Delta G^0 = -280.$ kJ/mol).
(b) Assuming ΔS^0 and ΔH^0 change little with temperature, calculate ΔG^0 at 500. K.

20.57 For the gaseous reaction of carbon monoxide and chlorine to form phosgene, $COCl_2$:
(a) Calculate ΔS^0 at 298 K ($\Delta H^0 = -220.$ kJ/mol and $\Delta G^0 = -206$ kJ/mol).
(b) Assuming ΔS^0 and ΔH^0 change little with temperature, calculate ΔG^0 at 450. K.

20.58 One reaction used to produce small quantities of pure H_2 is:

$$CH_3OH(g) \rightleftharpoons CO(g) + 2H_2(g)$$

(a) Determine ΔH^0 and ΔS^0 for the reaction at 298 K.
(b) Assuming these values are relatively independent of temperature, calculate ΔG^0 at 38°C, 138°C, and 238°C.
(c) What do these different values of ΔG^0 mean?

20.59 An important chemical reaction that occurs in the internal combustion engine is $N_2(g) + O_2(g) \rightleftharpoons 2NO(g)$.
(a) Determine ΔH^0 and ΔS^0 for the reaction at 298 K.
(b) Assuming these values are relatively independent of temperature, calculate ΔG^0 at 100.°C, 2560.°C, and 3540.°C.
(c) What do these different values of ΔG^0 mean?

20.60 The temperature at which the following process reaches equilibrium at 1 atm is the normal boiling point of bromine:

$$Br_2(l) \rightleftharpoons Br_2(g)$$

Use ΔH^0 and ΔS^0 values to determine this temperature.

20.61 The temperature at which the following process reaches equilibrium at 1 atm is the transition temperature for these two allotropes of crystalline sulfur:

$$S(\text{rhombic}) \rightleftharpoons S(\text{monoclinic})$$

Use ΔH^0 and ΔS^0 values to determine this temperature.

■ **Problems in Context**

20.62 Many articles in the scientific and popular press have suggested H_2 as an energy source for vehicles because it produces only nonpolluting $H_2O(g)$ when it burns. Moreover, when H_2 combines with O_2 in a fuel cell (Chapter 21), such as the type used on the Space Shuttle, the reaction provides electrical energy.
(a) Calculate ΔH^0, ΔS^0, and ΔG^0 per mol H_2 for this process at 298 K.
(b) Is the spontaneity of this reaction temperature dependent? Explain.
(c) At what temperature does the reaction become spontaneous?

20.63 The U.S. government recently required that automobile fuels contain a renewable component. The fermentation of glucose from corn to produce ethanol for addition to gasoline is a key process to fulfill this requirement:

$$C_6H_{12}O_6(s) \longrightarrow 2C_2H_5OH(l) + 2CO_2(g)$$

Calculate ΔH^0, ΔS^0, and ΔG^0 for the reaction at 25°C. Is the spontaneity of this reaction temperature dependent? Explain.

Free Energy, Equilibrium, and Reaction Direction

(Sample Problem 20.7)

■ **Concept Review Questions**

20.64 (a) If $K << 1$ for a reaction, what do you know about the sign and magnitude of ΔG^0?

(b) If $\Delta G^0 << 0$ for a reaction, what do you know about the magnitude of K? Of Q?

20.65 How is the free energy change of a process related to the work that can be obtained from the process? Is this quantity of work obtainable in practice? Explain.

20.66 In what form is the portion of reaction enthalpy that cannot do work given off? What happens to a portion of the useful energy as it does work?

20.67 What is the difference between the terms ΔG^0 and ΔG? Under what circumstances does $\Delta G = \Delta G^0$?

■ **Skill-Building Exercises** *(paired)*

20.68 Use Appendix B to calculate K at 298 K for
(a) $NO(g) + \frac{1}{2}O_2(g) \rightleftharpoons NO_2(g)$
(b) $2HCl(g) \rightleftharpoons H_2(g) + Cl_2(g)$
(c) $2C(\text{graphite}) + O_2(g) \rightleftharpoons 2CO(g)$

20.69 Use Appendix B to calculate K at 298 K for
(a) $MgCO_3(s) \rightleftharpoons Mg^{2+}(aq) + CO_3^{2-}(aq)$
(b) $2HCl(g) + Br_2(l) \rightleftharpoons 2HBr(g) + Cl_2(g)$
(c) $H_2(g) + O_2(g) \rightleftharpoons H_2O_2(l)$

20.70 Use Appendix B to calculate K at 298 K for
(a) $2H_2S(g) + 3O_2(g) \rightleftharpoons 2H_2O(g) + 2SO_2(g)$
(b) $H_2SO_4(l) \rightleftharpoons H_2O(l) + SO_3(g)$
(c) $HCN(aq) + NaOH(aq) \rightleftharpoons NaCN(aq) + H_2O(l)$

20.71 Use Appendix B to calculate K at 298 K for
(a) $SrSO_4(s) \rightleftharpoons Sr^{2+}(aq) + SO_4^{2-}(aq)$
(b) $2NO(g) + Cl_2(g) \rightleftharpoons 2NOCl(g)$
(c) $Cu_2S(s) + O_2(g) \rightleftharpoons 2Cu(s) + SO_2(g)$

20.72 Use Appendix B to determine the K_{sp} of Ag_2S.

20.73 Use Appendix B to determine the K_{sp} of CaF_2.

20.74 For the reaction $I_2(g) + Cl_2(g) \rightleftharpoons 2ICl(g)$, calculate K_P at 25°C. [ΔG_f^0 of $ICl(g) = -6.075$ kJ/mol.]

20.75 For the reaction $CaCO_3(s) \rightleftharpoons CaO(s) + CO_2(g)$, calculate P_{CO_2} at 25°C.

20.76 The solubility product constant for $PbCl_2$ is 1.7×10^{-5} at 25°C. What is the value of ΔG^0 at this temperature? Is it possible to prepare a solution that has $Pb^{2+}(aq)$ and $Cl^-(aq)$, each at the standard state concentration? (Neglect any ion reactions with water.)

20.77 The K_{sp} for ZnF_2 is 3.0×10^{-2} at 25°C. What is the value of ΔG^0 for the reaction to which this value refers? Is it possible to prepare a solution that has $Zn^{2+}(aq)$ and $F^-(aq)$ each at the standard state concentration? (Neglect any ion reactions with water.)

20.78 The equilibrium constant for the reaction

$$2Fe^{3+}(aq) + Hg_2^{2+}(aq) \rightleftharpoons 2Fe^{2+}(aq) + 2Hg^{2+}(aq)$$

is $K_c = 9.1 \times 10^{-6}$ at 298 K.
(a) What is ΔG^0 at this temperature?
(b) If standard-state concentrations of the reactants and products are mixed, in which direction does the reaction proceed?
(c) Calculate ΔG when $[Fe^{3+}] = 0.20$ M, $[Hg_2^{2+}] = 0.010$ M, $[Fe^{2+}] = 0.010$ M, and $[Hg^{2+}] = 0.025$ M. In which direction will the reaction proceed to achieve equilibrium?

20.79 The formation constant for the reaction

$$Ni^{2+}(aq) + 6NH_3(aq) \rightleftharpoons Ni(NH_3)_6^{2+}(aq)$$

is $K_f = 5.6 \times 10^8$ at 25°C.

(a) What is ΔG^0 at this temperature?

(b) If standard-state concentrations of the reactants and products are mixed, in which direction does the reaction proceed?

(c) Determine ΔG when $[Ni(NH_3)_6^{2+}] = 0.010\ M$, $[Ni^{2+}] = 0.0010\ M$, and $[NH_3] = 0.0050\ M$. In which direction will the reaction proceed to achieve equilibrium?

■ Problems in Context

20.80 The excessive production of ozone (O_3) gas in the lower atmosphere causes rubber to deteriorate, green plants to turn brown, and persons with respiratory disease to have difficulty breathing.

(a) Is the formation of O_3 from O_2 favored at all T, no T, high T, or low T?

(b) Calculate ΔG^0 for this reaction at 298 K.

(c) Calculate ΔG at 298 K for this reaction in urban smog where $[O_2] = 0.21\ M$ and $[O_3] = 5\times10^{-7}\ M$.

20.81 A $BaSO_4$ slurry is ingested just before an x-ray of the gastrointestinal tract because the precipitate is opaque to x-rays and thus defines the contours of the tract. The Ba^{2+} ion is toxic, but the compound is nearly insoluble. If ΔG^0 at 37°C (body temperature) is 59.1 kJ/mol for the process

$$BaSO_4(s) \rightleftharpoons Ba^{2+}(aq) + SO_4^{2-}(aq)$$

what is $[Ba^{2+}]$ in the intestinal tract? (Assume the only source of SO_4^{2-} is the ingested slurry.)

Comprehensive Problems

Problems with an asterisk (*) are more challenging.

20.82 Use ΔH^0 and S^0 values to explain why graphite is not an easily converted, inexpensive source of diamond: $C(graphite) \rightleftharpoons C(diamond)$. Given the free energy change for this process, suggest a reason why diamond owners need not worry about disintegration of their jewelry.

20.83 Supply the missing information (question marks) in each row of the following table:

	ΔS_{rxn}	ΔH_{rxn}	ΔG_{rxn}	COMMENT
(a)	+	−	−	?
(b)	?	0	−	Spontaneous
(c)	−	+	?	Not spontaneous
(d)	0	?	−	Spontaneous
(e)	?	0	+	?
(f)	+	+	?	$T\Delta S > \Delta H$

20.84 A complex ion (Lewis adduct) is formed when a ligand (Lewis base) is bonded to a metal ion (Lewis acid) by means of a pair of electrons. Among the many complex ions of cobalt are the following two:

$$Co(NH_3)_6^{3+}(aq) + 3en(aq) \rightleftharpoons Co(en)_3^{3+}(aq) + 6NH_3(aq)$$

where *en* stands for ethylenediamine, $H_2NCH_2CH_2NH_2$. Since six Co—N bonds are broken and six Co—N bonds are formed in this reaction, $\Delta H_{rxn}^0 \approx 0$, yet $K > 1$. What are the signs of ΔS^0 and ΔG^0? What drives the reaction?

20.85 Indicate whether each of the following statements is true or false and, if false, correct it.

(a) All spontaneous reactions occur quickly.

(b) If a reaction is spontaneous, the reverse reaction is non-spontaneous.

(c) All spontaneous processes release heat.

(d) The boiling of water at 100°C and 1 atm is a spontaneous process.

(e) If a process increases the randomness of the particles of a system, the entropy of the system decreases.

(f) The energy of the universe is constant; the entropy of the universe decreases toward a minimum.

(g) All systems become disordered spontaneously.

(h) Both ΔS_{sys} and ΔS_{surr} equal zero at equilibrium.

***20.86** The hemoglobin molecule carries O_2 in the blood from the lungs to the cells, where the O_2 is released for metabolic processes. The molecule can be represented as Hb in its unoxygenated form and as Hb·O_2 in its oxygenated form. One reason CO is toxic is that it competes with O_2 for binding to Hb:

$$Hb \cdot O_2(aq) + CO(g) \rightleftharpoons Hb \cdot CO(aq) + O_2(g)$$

(a) If $\Delta G^0 \approx -14$ kJ at 37°C (body temperature), what is the ratio of $[Hb \cdot CO]/[Hb \cdot O_2]$ at 37°C with $[O_2] = [CO]$?

(b) Use Le Châtelier's principle to suggest how to treat a victim of CO poisoning.

20.87 The most important ore of lithium is spodumene, $LiAlSi_2O_6$. The first step in the extraction of the metal is a conversion of the α form of spodumene into the less dense β form in preparation for subsequent leaching and washing steps. Use the following data to calculate the lowest temperature at which the α $\longrightarrow$ β conversion is feasible:

	ΔH_f^0 (kJ/mol)	S^0 (J/mol · K)
α-spodumene	−3055	129.3
β-spodumene	−3027	154.4

20.88 Adenosine triphosphate (ATP) is essential for muscle contraction, protein building, nerve conduction, and numerous other energy-requiring processes in the body. These nonspontaneous processes are "coupled" to the spontaneous hydrolysis of ATP to ADP (see Chemical Connections essay, Section 20.3). In a similar manner, ATP is regenerated by coupling to other energy-yielding reactions, one of which is

Creatine phosphate $\longrightarrow$ creatine + phosphate
$$\Delta G^0 = -43.1\text{ kJ/mol}$$

ADP + phosphate $\longrightarrow$ ATP $\qquad \Delta G^0 = +30.5\text{ kJ/mol}$

Calculate ΔG^0 for the overall reaction that regenerates ATP.

20.89 Nuclear fuel is prepared by converting U_3O_8 to $UO_2(NO_3)_2$ through treatment with concentrated HNO_3. The uranyl nitrate is then converted into UO_3 and finally UO_2 ("yellow cake"). At this point, the fuel is enriched (that is, the proportion of ^{235}U increased) by converting the UO_2 into UF_6, a highly volatile solid, in preparation for a gaseous-diffusion separation of isotopes. The last chemical conversion occurs in two steps:

$$UO_2(s) + 4HF(g) \longrightarrow UF_4(s) + 2H_2O(g)$$
$$UF_4(s) + F_2(g) \longrightarrow UF_6(s)$$

Calculate ΔG^0 for the overall process at 85°C:

	ΔH_f^0 (kJ/mol)	S^0 (J/mol · K)	ΔG_f^0 (kJ/mol)
$UO_2(s)$	−1085	77.0	−1032
$UF_4(s)$	−1921	152	−1830.
$UF_6(s)$	−2197	225	−2068

20.90 Methanol, one of the most important industrial feed-stocks, is made by several catalyzed reactions, one of which is $CO(g) + 2H_2(g) \longrightarrow CH_3OH(l)$.
(a) Demonstrate that this reaction is thermodynamically feasible.
(b) Is it favored at a low or at a high temperature?
(c) One concern raised about CH_3OH as a fuel for cars is its partial oxidation in air to yield formaldehyde, $CH_2O(g)$, which poses a health hazard. Calculate ΔG^0 at 100.°C for this reaction.

*20.91 Calculate the equilibrium constants for decomposition of the hydrogen halides at 298 K:

$$2HX(g) \rightleftharpoons H_2(g) + X_2(g)$$

What do these values indicate about the extent of decomposition of these molecules at 298 K? Suggest a plausible reason for this trend.

20.92 Hydrogenation is the addition of H_2 across double (or triple) carbon-carbon bonds. It is important in organic synthesis and the production of gasoline. Margarine, peanut butter, and most commercial baked goods include hydro-genated vegetable oils. What are the changes in enthalpy, entropy, and free energy for the hydrogenation of ethene (C_2H_4) to ethane (C_2H_6) at 25°C?

*20.93 Banks use coin stackers to group large numbers of coins for ease in dispensing.
(a) What is the probability that three dimes will stack heads-up if you throw them in a coin stacker?
(b) Based on the answer in (a), develop a general equation for the number of ways, W, that n identical coins can be stacked.
(c) Use this equation to find the probability that 8 dimes will stack heads-up.

20.94 The overall process occurring in a blast furnace during the production of iron is the reaction of Fe_2O_3 and carbon to Fe and CO_2.
(a) Calculate ΔH^0 and ΔS^0. [Assume C(graphite).]
(b) Is the reaction spontaneous at a low or at a high temperature? Explain.
(c) Is the reaction spontaneous at 298 K?
(d) At what temperature does the reaction become spontaneous?

*20.95 Solid dinitrogen pentaoxide (N_2O_5) undergoes reaction with water to form liquid nitric acid.
(a) Is the reaction spontaneous at 25°C?
(b) The solid decomposes to NO_2 and O_2 at 25°C. Is the decomposition spontaneous at this temperature? At what temperature does the decomposition become spontaneous?
(c) At what temperature does the decomposition of *gaseous* N_2O_5 become spontaneous? Rationalize the difference between this temperature and that in (b).

*20.96 A key step in the metabolism of glucose for energy is the isomerization of glucose-6-phosphate (G6P) to fructose-6-phosphate (F6P): G6P $\rightleftharpoons$ F6P. At 298 K, the equilibrium constant for the isomerization is 0.510.
(a) Calculate ΔG^0 at 298 K.
(b) Calculate ΔG when Q, the [F6P]/[G6P] ratio, equals 10.0.
(c) Calculate ΔG when $Q = 0.100$.
(d) Calculate Q in the cell if $\Delta G = -2.50$ kJ/mol.

20.97 The catalysts in an automobile exhaust system remove pollutants such as carbon monoxide and nitrogen oxides, as in

$$2CO(g) + 2NO(g) \longrightarrow 2CO_2(g) + N_2(g)$$

Show that this reaction is spontaneous at standard conditions. Given this fact, what is the role of the catalyst?

20.98 Chemists often use the phrase "thermodynamically unstable, but kinetically stable" to describe a compound such as acetylene. What do you think this phrase means?

20.99 The oxidation (usually unwanted) of a metal in air is called *corrosion*. Write equations for the corrosion of iron and aluminum. Use ΔG_f^0 values to determine whether either process is spontaneous at 25°C.

*20.100 When heated, the DNA double helix separates into two random-coil single strands. When cooled, the random coils re-form the double helix:

$$\text{double helix} \rightleftharpoons 2 \text{ random coils}$$

(a) What is the sign of ΔS for the forward process? Why?
(b) Energy must be added to the system to overcome the H bonds between the base pairs and the dispersion forces between the stacked bases. What is the sign of ΔG for the forward process when $T\Delta S$ is smaller than ΔH?
(c) Write an expression that shows T in terms of ΔH and ΔS when the reaction is at equilibrium. (This temperature is called the *melting temperature* of the nucleic acid.)

21

Electrochemistry
Chemical Change and Electrical Work

Figure: Electrochemical energy to and from aluminum. Aluminum is an excellent conductor and, therefore, a major component of electrical transmission lines. This essential metal highlights the two faces of electrochemistry. Aluminum manufacture requires enormous quantities of electricity, whereas new aluminum batteries give some of that energy back. In this chapter, we discuss the principles underlying the generation and utilization of electrochemical free energy.

If you think thermodynamics relates only to steam engines, games of chance, and the like, but has few practical, everyday applications, just look around you. Some of these applications are probably within your reach right now in the form of battery-operated devices—laptop computer, CD remote, wristwatch, calculator—or in the form of a piece of metal-plated jewelry or silverware. The operation and creation of these objects, and the many similar ones you use daily, involve the principles of electrochemistry, certainly one of the most important areas of applied thermodynamics.

Electrochemistry is the study of the relationship between chemical change and electrical work. It is typically investigated through the use of **electrochemical cells,** systems that incorporate a redox reaction to produce or utilize electrical energy. The common objects just mentioned display the essential difference between the two types of electrochemical cells:

- One type of cell *does work by releasing free energy from a spontaneous reaction to produce electricity*; a battery houses such a cell. This application is nothing new; the automotive battery, for instance, was invented over 135 years ago. ◆
- The other type of cell *does work by absorbing free energy from a source of electricity to drive a nonspontaneous reaction*. Such cells are used to plate a thin layer of metal on objects, and, in major industrial processes, they are used to produce some important compounds and nonmetals and to recover many metals from their ores.

In this chapter, we focus on both types of cell and the thermodynamic principles that explain why they work. We start with a review of redox concepts and revisit a method for balancing redox equations, mentioned only in passing in Chapter 4, that is particularly useful for electrochemical cells. Then we provide an overview of the two cell types. We focus first on the type that releases free energy to do electrical work. We examine the free energy change and equilibrium nature of the cell's redox reaction and how these relate to its electrical output. We describe concentration cells and batteries, two important examples of this type of cell. Then, we discuss *corrosion*, a destructive, spontaneous electrochemical process similar in principle to the useful ones in these cells. Next, we switch our focus to cells that absorb free energy to do electrical work. We see how they are used to isolate elements from their compounds, how to predict the element formed from aqueous solutions and from pure compounds, and how the quantity of current flowing through the cell determines the amount of product formed. Finally, we examine the redox system that generates energy in living cells.

Concepts and Skills to Review

before you study this chapter

- redox terminology (Section 4.3 and Interchapter Topic 5)
- balancing redox reactions (Section 4.3)
- activity series of the metals (Section 4.4)
- free energy, work, and equilibrium (Sections 20.3 and 20.4)
- Q vs. K (Section 17.2) and ΔG vs. ΔG^0 (Section 20.4)

◆ **The Shape of Electrochemical Things to Come**
As petroleum reserves dwindle and their use threatens the atmosphere, a new generation of electrochemical devices will keep things going. Someday, and current trends show that day is very soon, electric cars powered by banks of advanced batteries will eliminate the combustion of fossil fuels for travel; and advanced fuel cells, now used only on space missions, may be refitted for everyday residential and industrial applications.

21.1 Half-Reactions and Electrochemical Cells

Whether an electrochemical process releases or absorbs free energy, it always involves the *movement of electrons from one chemical species to another* in an oxidation-reduction (redox) reaction. In this section, we review the redox process and describe the half-reaction method of balancing redox reactions, which was mentioned briefly in Section 4.3. Then we take a preliminary look at how such reactions are used in the two types of electrochemical cells.

A Quick Review of Oxidation-Reduction Concepts

In electrochemical reactions, as in any redox process, *oxidation* is the loss of electrons, and *reduction* is the gain of electrons. An *oxidizing agent* is the species that performs the oxidation, taking electrons from the substance being oxidized. A *reducing agent* is the species that performs the reduction, giving electrons to the substance being reduced. After the reaction, the oxidized substance has a higher (more positive or less negative) oxidation number, and

Figure 21.1 **A summary of redox terminology.** In the reaction between zinc and hydrogen ion, Zn is oxidized and H⁺ is reduced.

PROCESS	$Zn(s) + 2H^+(aq) \longrightarrow Zn^{2+}(aq) + H_2(g)$	
OXIDATION • One reactant loses electrons • Reducing agent is oxidized • Oxidation number increases	Zinc **loses** electrons. Zinc is the reducing agent and becomes **oxidized**. The oxidation number of Zn **increases** from 0 to +2.	
REDUCTION • Other reactant gains electrons • Oxidizing agent is reduced • Oxidation number decreases	Hydrogen ion **gains** electrons. Hydrogen ion is the oxidizing agent and becomes **reduced**. The oxidation number of H⁺ **decreases** from +1 to 0.	

the reduced substance has a lower (less positive or more negative) one. Keep in mind three key points:

- Oxidation (electron loss) always accompanies reduction (electron gain).
- The oxidizing agent is reduced, and the reducing agent is oxidized.
- The number of electrons gained by the oxidizing agent always equals the number lost by the reducing agent.

Figure 21.1 presents these ideas in the context of the aqueous reaction between zinc metal and a strong acid. The ability to identify the oxidation and reduction parts of a redox process is essential to understanding the topics in this chapter. If you still find redox reactions unclear, review the full treatment given in Chapter 4 and summarized in Topic 5 of the Interchapter.

Half-Reaction Method for Balancing Redox Reactions

In Chapter 4, two methods for balancing redox reactions were mentioned—the oxidation-number method and the half-reaction method—with full discussion of the first method only.* Recall that the oxidation-number method assigns an oxidation number (O.N.) to each atom in the reactants and products to find those that change O.N. Then it joins the oxidized and reduced atom (or ion) and uses multipliers as coefficients to make the electrons lost equal the electrons gained (see Sample Problem 4.8, p. 153).

The essential difference between the two balancing methods is that the **half-reaction method** *divides the overall redox reaction into oxidation and reduction half-reactions.* Each half-reaction is balanced for mass (atoms) and charge. Then, they are multiplied by some integer to make electrons gained equal electrons lost, and recombined into the balanced redox equation. The half-reaction method offers several advantages:

- It separates the oxidation and reduction steps, which reflects their actual physical separation in electrochemical cells.
- It makes it easier to balance redox reactions that take place in acidic or basic solutions, which is common in these cells.
- It (usually) does *not* require assigning O.N.s. (In cases where the half-reactions are not obvious, we assign O.N.s to determine which atoms undergo a change and write the half-reactions using the species that contain those atoms.)

---

*If your professor chooses to present all redox balancing earlier in the course, this discussion of the half-reaction method is completely transferrable to Chapter 4 with no loss in continuity.

In general, we begin with a "skeleton" ionic reaction, which shows *only* the species that are oxidized and reduced. If the oxidized form of a species is on the left side of the skeleton reaction, the reduced form is on the right, and vice versa. (Unless H_2O, H^+, and OH^- are among those species being oxidized or reduced, they do not appear in the skeleton reaction.) The following steps are used in balancing a redox reaction by the half-reaction method:

Step 1. Divide the skeleton reaction into two half-reactions, each of which contains the oxidized and reduced forms of one of the species. (Which half-reaction is the oxidation and which the reduction becomes clear after we balance the charge in the next step.)

Step 2. Balance the atoms and charges in each half-reaction.

• Atoms are balanced in the following order: atoms other than O and H, then O, and then H.

• Charge is balanced by *adding electrons* (e^-). They are added *to the left in the reduction half-reaction* since the reactant gains them, and they are added *to the right in the oxidation half-reaction* since the reactant loses them.

Step 3. Multiply each half-reaction by some integer, if necessary, to make the number of e^- gained in the reduction equal the number of e^- lost in the oxidation.

Step 4. Add the balanced half-reactions and include states of matter.

Step 5. Check that the atoms and charges are balanced.

We balance a redox reaction that occurs in acidic solution first and then go through Sample Problem 21.1 for balancing one in basic solution.

Balancing Redox Reactions in Acidic Solution When a redox reaction occurs in acidic solution, H_2O molecules and H^+ ions are available for use in the balancing process. (As you'll see in Sample Problem 21.1, when a reaction occurs in basic solution, H_2O molecules and OH^- ions are available.)

Let's balance the redox reaction between dichromate ion and iodide ion to form chromium(III) ion and solid iodine, which occurs in acidic solution (Figure 21.2). The skeleton ionic reaction shows only the oxidized and reduced species:

$$Cr_2O_7^{2-}(aq) + I^-(aq) \longrightarrow Cr^{3+}(aq) + I_2(s) \qquad \text{[acidic solution]}$$

Step 1. Divide the reaction into half-reactions, each of which contains the oxidized and reduced forms of one species. The two chromium species make up one half-reaction, and the two iodine species make up the other:

$$Cr_2O_7^{2-} \longrightarrow Cr^{3+}$$
$$I^- \longrightarrow I_2$$

Step 2. Balance atoms and charges in each half-reaction. We use H_2O to balance O atoms, H^+ to balance H atoms, and e^- to balance positive charges.

• For the $Cr_2O_7^{2-}/Cr^{3+}$ half-reaction:

a. *Balance atoms other than O and H.* We balance the two Cr's on the left with a coefficient 2 on the right:

$$Cr_2O_7^{2-} \longrightarrow 2Cr^{3+}$$

b. *Balance O atoms by adding H_2O molecules.* Each H_2O has one O atom, so we add $7H_2O$ on the right to balance the seven O's in $Cr_2O_7^{2-}$:

$$Cr_2O_7^{2-} \longrightarrow 2Cr^{3+} + 7H_2O$$

c. *Balance H atoms by adding H^+ ions.* Each H_2O contains two H's, and we added $7H_2O$, so we add $14H^+$ ions on the left:

$$14H^+ + Cr_2O_7^{2-} \longrightarrow 2Cr^{3+} + 7H_2O$$

Figure 21.2 **The redox reaction between dichromate ion and iodide ion.** When $Cr_2O_7^{2-}$ (*left*) and I^- (*center*) are mixed in acid solution, they react to form Cr^{3+} and I_2 (*right*).

d. *Balance charge by adding electrons.* Each H^+ ion has a 1+ charge, and $14H^+$ plus $Cr_2O_7^{2-}$ gives 12+ on the left. Two Cr^{3+} give 6+ on the right. There are 6+ too many on the left, so we add $6e^-$ on the left:

$$6e^- + 14H^+ + Cr_2O_7^{2-} \longrightarrow 2Cr^{3+} + 7H_2O$$

This half-reaction is balanced, and we see it is the *reduction* because electrons are added on the *left:* the reactant $Cr_2O_7^{2-}$ gained electrons (was reduced), so $Cr_2O_7^{2-}$ is the *oxidizing agent.* (Note that the O.N. of Cr decreased from +6 to +3.)

- For the I^-/I_2 half-reaction:
  a. *Balance atoms other than O and H.* Two I atoms on the right requires a coefficient 2 on the left:

$$2I^- \longrightarrow I_2$$

  b. *Balance O atoms with H_2O.* Not needed; there are no O atoms.
  c. *Balance H atoms with H^+.* Not needed; there are no H atoms.
  d. *Balance charge with e^-.* To balance the 2− on the left, we add two e^- on the right:

$$2I^- \longrightarrow I_2 + 2e^-$$

This balanced half-reaction is the *oxidation* because electrons are added on the *right:* the reactant I^- lost electrons (was oxidized), so I^- is the *reducing agent.* (Note that the O.N. of I increased from −1 to 0.)

Step 3. Multiply each half-reaction, if necessary, by some integer so that the number of e^- lost in the oxidation equals the number of e^- gained in the reduction. Two e^- are lost in the oxidation and six e^- are gained in the reduction, so we multiply the oxidation by 3:

$$3(2I^- \longrightarrow I_2 + 2e^-)$$
$$6I^- \longrightarrow 3I_2 + 6e^-$$

Step 4. Add the half-reactions together, canceling substances that appear on both sides, and include states of matter. In this particular example, only the electrons cancel:

$$6e^- + 14H^+ + Cr_2O_7^{2-} \longrightarrow 2Cr^{3+} + 7H_2O$$
$$6I^- \longrightarrow 3I_2 + 6e^-$$
$$\overline{6I^-(aq) + 14H^+(aq) + Cr_2O_7^{2-}(aq) \longrightarrow 3I_2(s) + 7H_2O(l) + 2Cr^{3+}(aq)}$$

Step 5. Check that atoms and charges balance:

$$\text{Reactants (6I, 14H, 2Cr, 7O; 6+)} \longrightarrow \text{products (6I, 14H, 2Cr, 7O; 6+)}$$

Balancing Redox Reactions in Basic Solution   There is only one additional step needed to balance a redox equation that takes place in basic solution. This step appears after both half-reactions have first been balanced *as if they took place in acidic solution* (Steps 1 and 2), the e^- lost have been made equal to the e^- gained (Step 3), and the half-reactions have been combined (Step 4). At this point, *we add one OH^- ion* **to both sides of the equation** *for every H^+ ion present.* (We'll label this Step 4 Basic and include states of matter there.) As a result of this step, the H^+ ions on one side combine with the added OH^- ions to form H_2O, and OH^- ions appear on the other side of the equation. Excess H_2O is then canceled. Finally, we check that atoms and charges balance (Step 5).

Sample Problem 21.1   Balancing Redox Reactions by the Half-Reaction Method

PROBLEM Permanganate ion is a strong oxidizing agent that is frequently used in laboratory analysis. Its deep purple color also makes it useful as an indicator in redox titrations (see Figure 4.14, p. 154). Permanganate reacts in basic solution with the oxalate ion to form carbonate ion and solid manganese dioxide. Balance the following skeleton ionic reaction that occurs between $NaMnO_4$ and $Na_2C_2O_4$ in basic solution:

$$MnO_4^-(aq) + C_2O_4^{2-}(aq) \longrightarrow MnO_2(s) + CO_3^{2-}(aq) \qquad \text{[basic solution]}$$

PLAN Although the reaction occurs in basic solution, we proceed through Step 4 as if it took place in acidic solution. Then, we add the appropriate number of OH^- ions and cancel excess H_2O molecules to complete the balancing.

SOLUTION

1. Divide into half-reactions.

$$MnO_4^- \longrightarrow MnO_2 \qquad\qquad\qquad\qquad C_2O_4^{2-} \longrightarrow CO_3^{2-}$$

2. Balance.

   a. Atoms other than O and H   Atoms other than O and H

       Not needed $C_2O_4^{2-} \longrightarrow 2CO_3^{2-}$

   b. O atoms with H_2O O atoms with H_2O

      $MnO_4^- \longrightarrow MnO_2 + 2H_2O$ $2H_2O + C_2O_4^{2-} \longrightarrow 2CO_3^{2-}$

   c. H atoms with H^+ H atoms with H^+

      $4H^+ + MnO_4^- \longrightarrow MnO_2 + 2H_2O$ $2H_2O + C_2O_4^{2-} \longrightarrow 2CO_3^{2-} + 4H^+$

   d. Charge with e^- Charge with e^-

      $3e^- + 4H^+ + MnO_4^- \longrightarrow MnO_2 + 2H_2O$ $2H_2O + C_2O_4^{2-} \longrightarrow 2CO_3^{2-} + 4H^+ + 2e^-$

                    [reduction]   [oxidation]

3. Multiply each half-reaction, if necessary, by some integer to make e^- lost equal e^- gained.

   $2(3e^- + 4H^+ + MnO_4^- \longrightarrow MnO_2 + 2H_2O)$ $3(2H_2O + C_2O_4^{2-} \longrightarrow 2CO_3^{2-} + 4H^+ + 2e^-)$

   $6e^- + 8H^+ + 2MnO_4^- \longrightarrow 2MnO_2 + 4H_2O$ $6H_2O + 3C_2O_4^{2-} \longrightarrow 6CO_3^{2-} + 12H^+ + 6e^-$

4. Add half-reactions and cancel substances appearing on both sides.

    The e^- cancel, $8H^+$ cancel to leave $4H^+$ on the right, and $4H_2O$ cancel to leave $2H_2O$ on the left:

$$\cancel{6e^-} + \cancel{8H^+} + 2MnO_4^- \longrightarrow 2MnO_2 + \cancel{4H_2O}$$
$$\underline{2\,\cancel{6}H_2O + 3C_2O_4^{2-} \longrightarrow 6CO_3^{2-} + 4\,\cancel{12}H^+ + \cancel{6e^-}}$$
$$2MnO_4^- + 2H_2O + 3C_2O_4^{2-} \longrightarrow 2MnO_2 + 6CO_3^{2-} + 4H^+$$

4 Basic. Add OH^- to both sides to neutralize H^+, and cancel H_2O.

    Adding $4OH^-$ to both sides forms $4H_2O$ on the right, which cancel the $2H_2O$ on the left, to leave $2H_2O$ on the right:

$$2MnO_4^- + 2H_2O + 3C_2O_4^{2-} + 4OH^- \longrightarrow 2MnO_2 + 6CO_3^{2-} + [4H^+ + 4OH^-]$$
$$2MnO_4^- + \cancel{2H_2O} + 3C_2O_4^{2-} + 4OH^- \longrightarrow 2MnO_2 + 6CO_3^{2-} + 2\,\cancel{4}H_2O$$

    Including states of matter gives the final balanced equation:

$$2MnO_4^-(aq) + 3C_2O_4^{2-}(aq) + 4OH^-(aq) \longrightarrow 2MnO_2(s) + 6CO_3^{2-}(aq) + 2H_2O(l)$$

5. Check that atoms and charges balance.

    $(2Mn, 24O, 6C, 4H; 12-) \longrightarrow (2Mn, 24O, 6C, 4H; 12-)$

COMMENT We can obtain the balanced *molecular* equation for this reaction by adding the correct number of Na^+ spectator ions to the anions in the balanced ionic equation:

$$2NaMnO_4(aq) + 4NaOH(aq) + 3Na_2C_2O_4(aq) \longrightarrow 2MnO_2(s) + 6Na_2CO_3(aq) + 2H_2O(l)$$

Follow-up Problem 21.1 Write a balanced molecular equation for the reaction between $KMnO_4$ and KI in basic solution. The skeleton reaction is

$$MnO_4^-(aq) + I^-(aq) \longrightarrow MnO_4^{2-}(aq) + IO_3^-(aq) \qquad \text{[basic solution]}$$

The half-reaction method reveals a great deal about oxidation-reduction processes and is essential to understanding electrochemical cells. The major points to remember are

- Any redox reaction can be treated as the sum of a reduction and an oxidation half-reaction.
- Mass (atoms) and charge are conserved in each half-reaction.
- Electrons lost in one half-reaction are gained in the other.
- Although the half-reactions are treated separately, electron loss and electron gain occur simultaneously.

Which Half-Reaction Occurs at Which Electrode? If you sometimes forget which half-reaction occurs at which electrode, you're not alone. Here are some memory aids to help:
1. The words *anode* and *oxidation* start with vowels; the words *cathode* and *reduction* start with consonants.
2. Alphabetically, the *A* in anode comes before the *C* in cathode, and the *O* in oxidation comes before the *R* in reduction.
3. Look at the first syllables and use your imagination:
ANode, OXidation;
REDuction, CAThode ⇒
AN OX and a RED CAT

An Overview of Electrochemical Cells

We distinguish two types of electrochemical cells based on the general thermodynamic nature of the reaction:

1. A **voltaic cell** (or **galvanic cell**) uses a spontaneous reaction ($\Delta G < 0$) to generate electrical energy. In the cell reaction, the difference in chemical potential energy between higher energy reactants and lower energy products is converted into electrical energy, which is used to operate the load: light bulb, radio, car starter motor, and so on. In other words, *the reacting system does work on the surroundings.* All batteries contain voltaic cells.

2. An **electrolytic cell** uses electrical energy to drive a nonspontaneous reaction ($\Delta G > 0$). In the cell reaction, electrical energy from an external power supply converts lower energy reactants into higher energy products. Thus, *the surroundings do work on the reacting system.* Metal plating and recovery of metals from ores involve electrolytic cells.

The two types of cell have certain design features in common (Figure 21.3). Two **electrodes,** the objects that conduct the electricity between the cell and the surroundings, are dipped into an **electrolyte,** the mixture of ions (usually in aqueous solution) that are involved in the reaction or that carry the charge. An electrode is identified as the **anode** or the **cathode,** according to the half-reaction that takes place there:

- *The oxidation half-reaction takes place at the anode.* Electrons are given up by the substance being oxidized (reducing agent) and *leave the cell* at the anode.
- *The reduction half-reaction takes place at the cathode.* Electrons are taken up by the substance being reduced (oxidizing agent) and *enter the cell* at the cathode. ◆

Note in Figure 21.3 that the relative charges of the electrodes are *opposite* in the two types of cell. As you'll see in the following sections, the opposite

Figure 21.3 General characteristics of voltaic and electrolytic cells. A voltaic cell (*left*) generates energy from a spontaneous reaction ($\Delta G < 0$), whereas an electrolytic cell (*right*) requires energy to drive a nonspontaneous reaction ($\Delta G > 0$). In both types of cell, two electrodes dip into electrolyte solution, and an external circuit provides the means for electrons to flow. Oxidation takes place at the anode, and reduction takes place at the cathode, but the relative electrode charges are opposite in the two cells.

charges of the electrodes result from the different phenomena that cause the electrons to flow.

Section Summary

Oxidation-reduction processes involve the transfer of electrons from a reducing agent to an oxidizing agent. The half-reaction method of balancing divides the overall reaction into half-reactions that are balanced separately and then recombined. The two types of electrochemical cells are based on redox reactions that either generate or utilize electricity. In a voltaic cell, a spontaneous reaction does work on the surroundings (flashlight, etc.); in an electrolytic cell, the surroundings (power supply) do work on the cell and drive a nonspontaneous reaction. Both types of cell contain two electrodes that dip into the cell electrolyte and conduct electricity: oxidation occurs at the anode and reduction at the cathode.

21.2 Voltaic Cells: Using Spontaneous Reactions to Generate Electrical Energy

If you put a bar of zinc metal in a solution of Cu^{2+} ion, the blue color of the solution fades as a brown-black crust of Cu metal forms on the Zn bar (Figure 21.4). Judging from what we see, the reaction involves the reduction of Cu^{2+} ion to Cu metal, which must be accompanied by the oxidation of Zn metal to Zn^{2+} ion. The overall reaction consists of two half-reactions:

$$
\begin{array}{ll}
Cu^{2+}(aq) + 2e^- \longrightarrow Cu(s) & \text{[reduction]} \\
Zn(s) \longrightarrow Zn^{2+}(aq) + 2e^- & \text{[oxidation]} \\
\hline
Zn(s) + Cu^{2+}(aq) \longrightarrow Zn^{2+}(aq) + Cu(s) & \text{[overall reaction]}
\end{array}
$$

In the remainder of this section, we examine this spontaneous reaction as the basis of a voltaic (galvanic) cell.

Figure 21.4 The spontaneous reaction between zinc and copper(II) ion. When a zinc metal strip is placed in a Cu^{2+} solution, a redox reaction begins (*left*) in which the zinc is oxidized to Zn^{2+} and the Cu^{2+} is reduced to copper metal. As the reaction proceeds (*right*), the deep blue color of the solution of hydrated Cu^{2+} ion lightens, and the Cu "plates out" on the Zn and falls off in chunks. (The Cu appears black because it is very finely divided.) At the molecular level, each Zn atom loses two electrons, which are gained by the Cu^{2+} ions. The process is summarized with symbols in the balanced equation.

$$Zn(s) + Cu^{2+}(aq) \longrightarrow Zn^{2+}(aq) + Cu(s)$$

Construction and Operation of a Voltaic Cell

Electrons are being transferred in the Zn/Cu^{2+} reaction shown in Figure 21.4, but the system does not generate electrical energy because the oxidizing agent (Cu^{2+}) and reducing agent (Zn) are in physical contact in the same beaker. If, however, the half-reactions are physically separated and connected by an external circuit, the electrons are transferred by traveling through the circuit, and thus produce an electric current.

This separation of half-reactions is the essential idea behind a voltaic cell (Figure 21.5A). The components of each half-reaction are placed in a separate container, or **half-cell,** which consists of an electrode dipping into an electrolyte solution. The two half-cells are joined by the circuit, which consists of a wire and a salt bridge (the inverted U tube in the figure; we discuss its function shortly). To measure the voltage generated by the cell, a voltmeter is inserted in the path of the wire connecting the electrodes. A switch (not shown) is included to close (complete) or open (break) the circuit. By convention, *the oxidation half-cell (anode compartment) is shown on the left and the reduction half-cell (cathode compartment) on the right.* Here are the key points about this voltaic cell:

1. *The oxidation half-cell.* In this case, the anode compartment consists of a Zn metal bar (the anode) immersed in a Zn^{2+} electrolyte (such as a solution

Oxidation half-reaction
$Zn(s) \longrightarrow Zn^{2+}(aq) + 2e^-$

Reduction half-reaction
$2e^- + Cu^{2+}(aq) \longrightarrow Cu(s)$

Overall (cell) reaction
$Zn(s) + Cu^{2+}(aq) \longrightarrow Zn^{2+}(aq) + Cu(s)$

A

B

Figure 21.5 A voltaic cell based on the zinc-copper reaction. A, The anode half-cell (oxidation) consists of a Zn electrode dipping into a Zn^{2+} solution. The electrons generated in the oxidation step move through the Zn bar and the wire, and into the Cu electrode, which dips into a Cu^{2+} solution in the cathode half-cell (reduction). Electrons flow left to right through electrodes and wire. A salt bridge contains unreactive Na^+ and SO_4^{2-} ions that maintain neutral charge in the electrolytes: anions in the salt bridge flow to the left and cations flow to the right. The voltmeter registers the electrical output of the cell. **B,** After the cell ran for several hours, the electrodes were removed. The Zn anode weighs less because Zn atoms were oxidized to aqueous Zn^{2+} ions, and the Cu cathode weighs more because aqueous Cu^{2+} ions were reduced to Cu metal.

of $ZnSO_4$). In addition to actively participating as the reactant in the oxidation half-reaction, the Zn bar conducts the released electrons *out* of its half-cell.

2. *The reduction half-cell.* In this case, the cathode compartment consists of a Cu metal bar (the cathode) immersed in a Cu^{2+} electrolyte (such as a solution of $CuSO_4$). In addition to actively participating as the product in the reduction half-reaction, the Cu bar conducts electrons *into* its half-cell.

3. *Relative charges on the electrodes.* The electrode charges are determined by the *source of electrons* and the *direction of electron flow* through the circuit. In this cell, Zn metal is oxidized at the anode to Zn^{2+} ions and electrons. The Zn^{2+} ions enter the solution, and the electrons enter the wire. *The electrons flow left to right* through the wire to the cathode, where Cu^{2+} ions in that solution accept them and are reduced to Cu atoms. Electrons are continuously generated at the anode and consumed at the cathode. Therefore, the anode has an excess of electrons and a negative charge *relative* to the cathode. *In any **voltaic** cell, the anode is negative and the cathode is positive.*

4. *Purpose of the salt bridge.* The cell cannot operate until the circuit is complete. The oxidation half-cell originally contains a neutral solution of Zn^{2+} and SO_4^{2-} ions, but if Zn atoms in the bar lost electrons, the solution would develop a net positive charge from the addition of newly formed Zn^{2+} ions. Similarly, in the reduction half-cell, the neutral solution of Cu^{2+} and SO_4^{2-} ions would develop a net negative charge if Cu^{2+} ions left the solution to form Cu atoms. In other words, there is a problem of charge imbalance if the half-cells are not neutralized. To allow the cell to operate, the two half-cells are joined by a **salt bridge,** which acts as a "liquid wire," allowing ions to flow through both compartments and complete the circuit. The salt bridge shown here is an inverted U tube containing a solution of nonreacting ions—in this case, Na^+ and SO_4^{2-}—in a gel. Thus, the solution cannot pour out, but ions can diffuse through it into and out of the half-cells.

To maintain neutrality in the reduction half-cell (right; cathode compartment) as Cu^{2+} ions change to Cu atoms, Na^+ ions move from the salt bridge into the solution (and some SO_4^{2-} ions move from the solution into the salt bridge). Similarly, to maintain neutrality in the oxidation half-cell (left; anode compartment) as Zn atoms change to Zn^{2+} ions, SO_4^{2-} ions move from the salt bridge into that solution (and some Zn^{2+} ions move from the solution into the salt bridge). Thus, as Figure 21.5A shows, the circuit is completed *as electrons move left to right through the wire, while anions move right to left and cations move left to right through the salt bridge.*

5. *Active vs. inactive electrodes.* The electrodes in the Zn/Cu^{2+} cell are *active* because the metals themselves are components of the half-reactions. As the cell operates, the mass of the zinc electrode gradually decreases, and the $[Zn^{2+}]$ in the anode half-cell increases. At the same time, the mass of the copper electrode increases and the $[Cu^{2+}]$ in the cathode half-cell decreases; we say that the Cu^{2+} "plates out" on the electrode. Figure 21.5B shows the electrodes removed from their half-cells after several hours of operation.

For many redox reactions, however, there are no reactants or products capable of serving as electrodes. In these cases, *inactive* electrodes are used, most commonly rods of *graphite* or *platinum*, materials that conduct electrons into or out of the cell but cannot take part in the half-reactions. In a voltaic cell based on the following half-reactions, for instance, the species cannot act as electrodes:

$$2I^-(aq) \longrightarrow I_2(s) + 2e^- \qquad \text{[anode; oxidation]}$$
$$MnO_4^-(aq) + 8H^+(aq) + 5e^- \longrightarrow Mn^{2+}(aq) + 4H_2O(l) \qquad \text{[cathode; reduction]}$$

Oxidation half-reaction
$2I^-(aq) \longrightarrow I_2(s) + 2e^-$

Reduction half-reaction
$MnO_4^-(aq) + 8H^+(aq) + 5e^- \longrightarrow$
$Mn^{2+}(aq) + 4H_2O(l)$

Overall (cell) reaction
$2MnO_4^-(aq) + 16H^+(aq) + 10I^-(aq) \longrightarrow$
$2Mn^{2+}(aq) + 5I_2(s) + 8H_2O(l)$

Figure 21.6 A voltaic cell using inactive electrodes. A cell based on the reaction between I^- and MnO_4^- in acidic solution does not have species that can be used as electrodes, so inactive graphite (C) electrodes are used.

Therefore, each half-cell consists of inactive electrodes immersed in an electrolyte solution that contains *all the species involved in that half-reaction* (Figure 21.6). In the anode half-cell, I^- ions are oxidized to solid I_2. The electrons released flow into the graphite anode, through the wire, and into the graphite cathode. From there, the electrons are consumed by MnO_4^- ions as they are reduced to Mn^{2+} ions. (A KNO_3 salt bridge is used.)

As Figures 21.5A and 21.6 illustrate, there are certain consistent features in the *diagram* of a voltaic cell. The physical arrangement includes half-cell containers, electrodes, wire, and salt bridge, and the following details are shown:

- Components of the half-cells: electrode materials, electrolyte ions, and other substances involved in the reaction
- Electrode name (anode or cathode) and charge. By convention, the anode compartment always appears *on the left.*
- Each half-reaction with its half-cell and the overall cell reaction
- Direction of electron flow in the external circuit
- Nature of ions and direction of ion flow in the salt bridge

You'll see how to specify these details and diagram a cell shortly.

Notation for a Voltaic Cell

There is a useful shorthand notation for describing the components of a voltaic cell. For example, the notation for the Zn/Cu^{2+} cell is

$$Zn(s) \mid Zn^{2+}(aq) \parallel Cu^{2+}(aq) \mid Cu(s)$$

Key parts of the notation are

- The components of the anode compartment (oxidation half-cell) are written to the left of the components of the cathode compartment (reduction half-cell).
- A vertical line represents a phase boundary. For example, $Zn(s) \mid Zn^{2+}(aq)$ indicates that the *solid* Zn is a *different* phase from the *aqueous* Zn^{2+}. A comma separates half-cell components in the *same* phase. For example, the notation for the voltaic cell shown in Figure 21.6 is

$$Graphite \mid I_2(s) \mid I^-(aq) \parallel H^+(aq), MnO_4^-(aq), Mn^{2+}(aq) \mid graphite$$

That is, in the cathode compartment, H^+, MnO_4^-, and Mn^{2+} ions are all in aqueous solution with solid graphite immersed in it. Often, we specify the concentrations of dissolved components; for example, if the concentrations of Zn^{2+} and Cu^{2+} are 1 *M*, we write

$$Zn(s) \mid Zn^{2+}(1\ M) \parallel Cu^{2+}(1\ M) \mid Cu(s)$$

- Half-cell components usually appear in the same order as in the half-reaction, and electrodes appear at the far left and right of the notation.
- A double vertical line separates the half cells and represents the phase boundary on either side of the salt bridge (the ions in the salt bridge are omitted because they are not part of the reaction).

Sample Problem 21.2   Diagramming Voltaic Cells

PROBLEM Diagram, show balanced equations, and write the notation for a voltaic cell that consists of one half-cell with a Cr bar in a $Cr(NO_3)_3$ solution, another half-cell with an Ag bar in an $AgNO_3$ solution, and a KNO_3 salt bridge. Measurement indicates that the Cr electrode is negative relative to the Ag electrode.

PLAN From the given contents of the half-cells, we can write the half-reactions. We must determine which is the anode compartment (oxidation) and which is the cathode (reduction). To do so, we must find the direction of the spontaneous redox reaction, which is given by the relative electrode charges. Since electrons are released into the anode during oxidation, it has a negative charge. We are told that Cr is negative, so it must be the anode and, therefore, Ag is the cathode.

SOLUTION Writing the balanced half-reactions. Since the Ag electrode is positive, the half-reaction consumes e^-:

$$Ag^+(aq) + e^- \longrightarrow Ag(s) \qquad [\text{reduction; cathode}]$$

Since the Cr electrode is negative, the half-reaction releases e^-:

$$Cr(s) \longrightarrow Cr^{3+}(aq) + 3e^- \qquad [\text{oxidation; anode}]$$

Writing the balanced overall cell reaction. We triple the reduction half-reaction to balance e^- and combine the half-reactions to obtain the overall spontaneous reaction:

$$Cr(s) + 3Ag^+(aq) \longrightarrow Cr^{3+}(aq) + 3Ag(s)$$

Determining direction of electron and ion flow. The released e^- in the Cr electrode (negative) flow through the external circuit to the Ag electrode (positive). As Cr^{3+} ions enter the anode electrolyte, NO_3^- ions enter from the salt bridge to maintain neutrality. As Ag^+ ions leave the cathode electrolyte and plate out on the Ag electrode, K^+ ions enter from the salt bridge to maintain neutrality. The diagram of the voltaic cell is shown in the margin.

Writing the cell notation:

$$Cr(s) \mid Cr^{3+}(aq) \parallel Ag^+(aq) \mid Ag(s)$$

CHECK Always be sure that the half-reactions and cell reaction are balanced, the half-cells contain *all* components of the half-reaction, and the electron and ion flow are shown. You should be able to write the half-reactions from the cell notation as a check.

COMMENT The key to diagramming a voltaic cell is to use the spontaneous reaction to identify the oxidation (anode) and reduction (cathode) half-reactions.

Follow-up Problem 21.2 In one compartment of a voltaic cell, a graphite rod dips into an acidic solution of $K_2Cr_2O_7$ and $Cr(NO_3)_3$; in the other, a tin bar dips into a $Sn(NO_3)_2$ solution. A KNO_3 salt bridge joins the half-cells. The tin electrode is negative relative to the graphite. Diagram the cell, show balanced equations, and write the cell notation.

Oxidation half-reaction
$$Cr(s) \longrightarrow Cr^{3+}(aq) + 3e^-$$

Reduction half-reaction
$$Ag^+(aq) + e^- \longrightarrow Ag(s)$$

Overall (cell) reaction
$$Cr(s) + 3Ag^+(aq) \longrightarrow Cr^{3+}(aq) + 3Ag(s)$$

Why Does a Voltaic Cell Work?

By placing a light bulb in the circuit or looking at the voltmeter, we can see that the Zn/Cu^{2+} cell generates electrical energy. But what principle explains *how* the reaction takes place, and *why* do electrons flow in the direction shown?

Let's examine what is happening when the switch is open and no reaction is occurring. In each half-cell, we can consider the metal electrode in equilibrium with the metal ions in the electrolyte, with the electrons residing in the metal:

$$Zn(s) \rightleftharpoons Zn^{2+}(aq) + 2e^- (\text{in Zn metal})$$
$$Cu(s) \rightleftharpoons Cu^{2+}(aq) + 2e^- (\text{in Cu metal})$$

From the direction of the overall spontaneous reaction, we know that Zn gives up its electrons more easily than Cu, so it is a stronger reducing agent. Therefore, the equilibrium position of the Zn half-reaction lies farther to the right: Zn produces more electrons than does Cu. You might think of the electrons in the Zn electrode as having a greater electron "pressure" than those in the Cu electrode, a greater potential energy (referred to as *electrical potential*) ready to "push" the electrons through the circuit. Close the switch and electrons flow from the Zn to the Cu electrode to equalize this electron pressure (electrical potential) difference. The flow disturbs the equilibrium at each electrode. The Zn half-reaction shifts to the right to restore the electrons flowing out, and the Cu half-reaction shifts to the left to remove the electrons flowing in. Thus, *the spontaneous reaction occurs as a result of the different abilities of these metals to give up their electrons and the ability of the electrons to flow through the circuit.* ◆

Electron Flow and Water Flow Consider this analogy between electron "pressure" and water pressure. A U-tube (cell) is separated into two arms (two half-cells) by a stopcock (switch), and the two arms contain water at different heights (the half-cells contain half-reactions with different electrical potentials). Open the stopcock (close the switch) and the different heights (potential difference) become equal as water flows (electrons flow and current is generated).

Section Summary

A voltaic cell consists of oxidation (anode) and reduction (cathode) half-cells, connected by a wire to conduct electrons and a salt bridge to provide ions that maintain charge neutrality as the cell operates. Electrons move from anode (left) to cathode (right), while cations move from the salt bridge into the cathode half-cell and anions from the salt bridge into the anode half-cell. The cell notation uses a comma to indicate components in the same phase within a half-cell, a single vertical line to indicate components in different phases, and a double vertical line to indicate separate half-cells. A voltaic cell operates because the two half-cells differ in their tendency to lose electrons.

21.3 Cell Potential: Output of a Voltaic Cell

The purpose of a voltaic cell is to convert the free energy change of a spontaneous reaction into the kinetic energy of electrons moving through an external circuit (electrical energy). This electrical energy can do work and is proportional to the difference in electrical potential between the two electrodes. This difference in electrical potential is the **voltage** of the cell, also called the **cell potential (E_{cell}),** or **electromotive force (emf).**

When the redox reaction incorporated in the cell proceeds *spontaneously*, it releases free energy to do work, so we obtain a *positive* cell potential:

$$E_{cell} > 0 \text{ for a spontaneous process} \qquad \textbf{(21.1)}$$

The more positive the E_{cell}, the more work the cell can do, and the farther the reaction proceeds to the right as written. A *negative* cell potential, on the other hand, is associated with a *nonspontaneous* cell reaction. If $E_{cell} = 0$, the reaction has reached equilibrium and the cell can do no more work. (There is a clear relationship between E_{cell}, K, and ΔG that we discuss in Section 21.4.)

How are the units of cell potential related to those of energy available to do work? As you've seen, work is done when charge moves between electrode compartments that differ in electrical potential. The SI unit of electrical potential is the **volt (V),** and the SI unit of electrical charge is the **coulomb (C).** By definition, for two electrodes that differ by 1 volt of electrical potential, 1 joule of energy is released (that is, 1 joule of work can be done) for each coulomb of charge that moves between the electrodes. Thus,

$$1 \text{ V} = 1 \text{ J/C} \qquad \textbf{(21.2)}$$

Table 21.1 lists the voltages of some commercial and natural voltaic cells. Let's see how we measure cell potential.

Table 21.1 Voltages of Some Voltaic Cells

Voltaic Cell	Voltage (V)
Common alkaline battery	1.5
Lead-acid car battery (6 cells = 12 V)	2.0
Calculator battery (mercury)	1.3
Electric eel (~5000 cells in 6-ft eel = 750 V)	0.15
Nerve of giant squid (across cell membrane)	0.070

Standard Cell Potentials

The measured potential of a voltaic cell is affected by changes in concentration of the reactants as the reaction proceeds and by energy losses that are due to heating of the cell and external circuit. Therefore, in order to compare the output of different cells, we obtain a **standard cell potential** (E_{cell}^0), the potential measured at a specified temperature (usually 298 K) with no current flowing* and *all components in their standard states:* 1 atm for gases, 1 *M* for solutions, the pure solid for electrodes. When the zinc-copper cell that we diagrammed in Figure 21.5 operates under standard state conditions, that is, when $[Zn^{2+}] = [Cu^{2+}] = 1$ *M*, the cell produces 1.10 V at 298 K (see photo):

$$Zn(s) + Cu^{2+}(aq, 1\ M) \longrightarrow Zn^{2+}(aq, 1\ M) + Cu(s) \qquad E_{cell}^0 = 1.10\ V$$

Standard Electrode (Half-Cell) Potentials Just as each half-reaction makes up part of the overall reaction, the potential of each half-cell makes up a part of the overall cell potential. The **standard electrode potential ($E_{half-cell}^0$)** is the potential associated with a given half-reaction (electrode compartment) when all the components are in their standard states. By convention, *a standard electrode potential always refers to the half-reaction written as a **reduction:***

$$\text{Oxidized form} + ne^- \longrightarrow \text{reduced form} \qquad E_{half-cell}^0$$

In any redox process, one species is reduced while another is oxidized, so the other half-reaction must be written as an oxidation. Because cell potentials (and half-cell potentials) are thermodynamic quantities, it is most important to remember that, as with ΔH, ΔG, and ΔS, *reversing a reaction changes the sign of the potential:*

$$\text{Reduced form} \longrightarrow \text{oxidized form} + ne^- \qquad -E_{half-cell}^0$$

For the zinc-copper reaction, for example, the standard electrode potentials for the zinc half-reaction (E_{zinc}^0, anode compartment) and for the copper half-reaction (E_{copper}^0, cathode compartment) refer to the processes written as reductions:

$$Zn^{2+}(aq) + 2e^- \longrightarrow Zn(s) \qquad E_{zinc}^0\ (E_{anode}^0) \qquad [reduction]$$
$$Cu^{2+}(aq) + 2e^- \longrightarrow Cu(s) \qquad E_{copper}^0\ (E_{cathode}^0) \qquad [reduction]$$

Since the overall cell reaction involves the *oxidation* of zinc at the anode, not the *reduction* of Zn^{2+}, we reverse the zinc half-reaction *and* change the sign of the half-cell potential:

$$Zn(s) \longrightarrow Zn^{2+}(aq) + 2e^- \qquad -E_{zinc}^0\ (-E_{anode}^0) \qquad [oxidation]$$
$$Cu^{2+}(aq) + 2e^- \longrightarrow Cu(s) \qquad E_{copper}^0\ (E_{cathode}^0) \qquad [reduction]$$

The overall redox reaction is the sum of these half-reactions, so the overall standard cell potential is the *sum* of these half-cell potentials:

$$Zn(s) + Cu^{2+}(aq) \longrightarrow Zn^{2+}(aq) + Cu(s)$$
$$E_{cell}^0 = E_{copper}^0 + (-E_{zinc}^0) = E_{copper}^0 - E_{zinc}^0$$

We can generalize this result for any voltaic cell: *the standard cell potential is the difference between the standard electrode potential of the cathode half-cell and the standard electrode potential of the anode half-cell,*

$$E_{cell}^0 = E_{cathode}^0 - E_{anode}^0 \qquad \qquad \textbf{(21.3)}$$

---

*The current required to operate modern digital voltmeters makes a negligible difference in the value of E_{cell}^0.

Determining $E^0_{\text{half-cell}}$: The Standard Hydrogen Electrode   Suppose we want to know what portion of E^0_{cell} for the zinc-copper reaction is contributed by the anode half-cell (oxidation of Zn) and what portion by the cathode half-cell (reduction of Cu^{2+}). How can we arrive at half-cell potentials if we can only measure the potential of the complete cell? Chemists have solved this problem by *selecting a standard reference half-cell and defining its standard electrode potential as zero* ($E^0_{reference} \equiv 0.00$ V). The **standard reference half-cell** is a **standard hydrogen electrode,** which consists of a specially prepared platinum electrode immersed in a 1 M aqueous solution of a strong acid, $H^+(aq)$, through which H_2 gas at 1 atm is bubbled. Thus, the reference half-reaction is

$$2H^+(aq, 1\ M) + 2e^- \longrightarrow H_2(g, 1\ atm) \qquad E^0_{reference} = 0.00\ V$$

Notice that whether we write this half-reaction as a reduction or an oxidation, that is, whether aqueous H^+ ions are reduced or H_2 gas is oxidized, the half-cell potential is zero:

$$H_2(g, 1\ atm) \longrightarrow 2H^+(aq, 1\ M) + 2e^- \qquad -E^0_{reference} = 0.00\ V$$

Now we can construct a voltaic cell consisting of the reference half-cell and another half-cell whose potential we want to determine. With $E^0_{reference}$ defined as zero, the overall E^0_{cell} allows us to find the unknown standard electrode potential, $E^0_{unknown}$. When H_2 is oxidized, the reference half-cell is the anode:

$$E^0_{\text{cell}} = E^0_{\text{cathode}} - E^0_{\text{anode}} = E^0_{unknown} - E^0_{reference}$$
$$= E^0_{unknown} - 0.00\ V = E^0_{unknown}$$

When H^+ is reduced, the reference half-cell is the cathode:

$$E^0_{\text{cell}} = E^0_{\text{cathode}} - E^0_{\text{anode}} = E^0_{reference} - E^0_{unknown}$$
$$= 0.00\ V - E^0_{unknown} = -E^0_{unknown}$$

By this approach, all other standard electrode potentials are *relative* to the standard reference electrode potential. Figure 21.7 shows a voltaic cell that has the Zn/Zn^{2+} half-reaction in one compartment and the H_2/H^+ half-reaction in the other. The zinc electrode is negative relative to the hydrogen electrode, so we know the zinc is being oxidized at the anode. The measured E^0_{cell} is $+0.76$ V, and we use this value to find the unknown standard electrode potential, E^0_{zinc}:

$$
\begin{array}{lll}
2H^+(aq) + 2e^- \longrightarrow H_2(g) & E^0_{reference} = 0.00\ V & \text{[cathode; reduction]} \\
Zn(s) \longrightarrow Zn^{2+}(aq) + 2e^- & -E^0_{zinc} = ?\ V & \text{[anode; oxidation]} \\
\hline
Zn(s) + 2H^+(aq) \longrightarrow Zn^{2+}(aq) + H_2(g) & E^0_{\text{cell}} = 0.76\ V &
\end{array}
$$

$$E^0_{\text{cell}} = E^0_{\text{cathode}} - E^0_{\text{anode}} = E^0_{reference} - E^0_{zinc}$$
$$E^0_{zinc} = E^0_{reference} - E^0_{\text{cell}} = 0.00\ V - 0.76\ V = -0.76\ V$$

The standard electrode potential for zinc is -0.76 V. That is,

$$Zn^{2+}(aq) + 2e^- \longrightarrow Zn(s) \qquad\qquad E^0_{zinc} = -0.76\ V \quad \text{[reduction]}$$

and

$$Zn(s) \longrightarrow Zn^{2+}(aq) + 2e^- \qquad -E^0_{zinc} = +0.76\ V \quad \text{[oxidation]}$$

Now let's return to the zinc-copper cell and use the measured value of E^0_{cell} (1.10 V) and the value we just found for E^0_{zinc} to calculate E^0_{copper}:

$$E^0_{\text{cell}} = E^0_{\text{cathode}} - E^0_{\text{anode}} = E^0_{copper} - E^0_{zinc}$$
$$E^0_{copper} = E^0_{\text{cell}} + E^0_{zinc} = 1.10\ V + (-0.76\ V) = 0.34\ V$$

So the standard electrode potential for copper is 0.34 V:

$$Cu^{2+}(aq) + 2e^- \longrightarrow Cu(s) \qquad E^0_{copper} = 0.34\ V$$

By continuing this process of constructing cells with one known and one unknown electrode potential, we can find many other standard electrode potentials. Let's go over these ideas once more with a sample problem.

Voltmeter
0.76 V

Anode (−)   **Cathode (+)**
Zn   Salt bridge $H_2(g)$
1 atm
Pt wire
Pt
1 M Zn^{2+} 1 M H^+

Oxidation half-reaction
$Zn(s) \longrightarrow Zn^{2+}(aq) + 2e^-$

Reduction half-reaction
$2H^+(aq) + 2e^- \longrightarrow H_2(g)$

Overall (cell) reaction
$Zn(s) + 2H^+(aq) \longrightarrow Zn^{2+}(aq) + H_2(g)$

Figure 21.7 Determining an unknown $E^0_{\text{half-cell}}$ with the standard reference (hydrogen) electrode. When a voltaic cell is constructed with Zn/Zn^{2+} in one half-cell and the standard hydrogen reference electrode in the other, the Zn half-cell potential is negative (anode), and the cell potential is 0.76 V. Since the potential of the standard reference electrode is defined as 0.00 V, the cell potential equals the anode potential, or $-E^0_{zinc}$. Therefore, $E^0_{zinc} = -0.76$ V.

Sample Problem 21.3 Calculating an Unknown $E^0_{half-cell}$ from E^0_{cell}

PROBLEM A voltaic cell incorporates the reaction between aqueous bromine and zinc metal:

$$Br_2(aq) + Zn(s) \longrightarrow Zn^{2+}(aq) + 2Br^-(aq) \qquad E^0_{cell} = 1.83 \text{ V}$$

Calculate E^0 for the *oxidation* of $Br^-(aq)$ to $Br_2(aq)$, if $E^0_{zinc} = -0.76$ V.

PLAN Since E^0_{cell} is positive, the reaction is spontaneous as written. By dividing the reaction into half-reactions, we see that Br_2 is reduced and Zn is oxidized, so the zinc half-cell contains the anode. We use Equation 21.3 to find $E^0_{unknown}$, the standard electrode potential for the *reduction* of Br_2 to Br^- ($E^0_{bromine}$). Since the problem asks for the oxidation half-reaction, we change the sign and obtain $-E^0_{bromine}$.

SOLUTION Dividing the reaction into half-reactions:

$$Br_2(aq) + 2e^- \longrightarrow 2Br^-(aq) \qquad E^0_{unknown} = E^0_{bromine} = ? \text{ V}$$

$$Zn(s) \longrightarrow Zn^{2+}(aq) + 2e^- \qquad -E^0_{zinc} = +0.76 \text{ V}$$

Calculating $E^0_{bromine}$:

$$E^0_{cell} = E^0_{cathode} - E^0_{anode} = E^0_{bromine} - E^0_{zinc}$$

$$E^0_{bromine} = E^0_{cell} + E^0_{zinc} = 1.83 \text{ V} + (-0.76 \text{ V}) = 1.07 \text{ V}$$

Determining $-E^0_{bromine}$: We reverse the half-reaction and change the sign:

$$2Br^-(aq) \longrightarrow Br_2(aq) + 2e^- \qquad -E^0_{bromine} = \boxed{-1.07 \text{ V}}$$

CHECK A good check is to be sure that $E^0_{bromine} - E^0_{zinc}$ gives E^0_{cell}: 1.07 V $-$ (−0.76 V) = 1.83 V.

COMMENT To avoid errors in sign, keep in mind that the standard electrode potential refers to the half-reactions written as *reductions*. Then reverse one half-reaction to the direction in which the half-reactions add to give the overall cell reaction and change the sign of its $E^0_{half-cell}$.

Follow-up Problem 21.3 A voltaic cell based on the reaction between aqueous Br_2 and vanadium(III) ions has $E^0_{cell} = 1.39$ V:

$$Br_2(aq) + 2V^{3+}(aq) + 2H_2O(l) \longrightarrow 2VO^{2+}(aq) + 4H^+(aq) + 2Br^-(aq)$$

What is the standard electrode potential for the reduction of VO^{2+} to V^{3+}?

Relative Strengths of Oxidizing and Reducing Agents

One of the things we can learn through measurements of voltaic cells is the relative strengths of the oxidizing and reducing agents involved. Three oxidizing agents present in the voltaic cells just discussed are Cu^{2+}, H^+, and Zn^{2+}. We can rank their relative oxidizing strengths by writing each half-reaction as a gain of electrons (reduction), with its corresponding standard electrode potential:

$$Cu^{2+}(aq) + 2e^- \longrightarrow Cu(s) \qquad E^0 = 0.34 \text{ V}$$

$$2H^+(aq) + 2e^- \longrightarrow H_2(g) \qquad E^0 = 0.00 \text{ V}$$

$$Zn^{2+}(aq) + 2e^- \longrightarrow Zn(s) \qquad E^0 = -0.76 \text{ V}$$

The more positive the E^0 value, the more the reaction (as written) tends to occur; thus, Cu^{2+} gains two electrons more easily than H^+, which gains them more easily than Zn^{2+}. In terms of oxidizing strength, therefore, $Cu^{2+} > H^+ > Zn^{2+}$. Moreover, because reversing the half-reaction changes the sign of the half-cell potential, this listing also ranks the strengths of the reducing agents: $Zn > H_2 > Cu$. Notice that this list of half-reactions in order of *decreasing* half-cell potential shows, *from top to bottom*, the oxidizing agents (reactants) *decreasing* in strength and the reducing agents (products) *increasing* in strength; that is, Cu^{2+} (top left) is the strongest oxidizing agent, and Zn (bottom right) is the strongest reducing agent.

By combining many pairs of half-cells into voltaic cells, we can create a list of reduction half-reactions and arrange them in *decreasing* order of standard electrode potential (from most positive to most negative). Such a list, called the *emf series* or *table of standard electrode potentials,* is presented in Table 21.2. Keep several key points in mind as you use this list:

- All values are relative to the standard hydrogen (reference) electrode:

$$2H^+(aq, 1\ M) + 2e^- \rightleftharpoons H_2(g, 1\ atm) \qquad E^0_{reference} = 0.00\ V$$

- By convention, the half-reactions are written as *reductions,* which means that *all reactants are oxidizing agents and all products are reducing agents.*
- The E^0 value shown is for the half-reaction *as written.* The more positive the E^0, the greater the tendency for the half-reaction to occur.
- The E^0 value has the *same magnitude but opposite sign when the reaction is reversed.* Half-reactions are shown here with an equilibrium arrow because a half-reaction can occur as a reduction or as an oxidation (that is, take place at the cathode or anode, respectively), depending on the conditions and the standard electrode potential of the other half-reaction.
- As Table 21.2 is arranged, the strength of the oxidizing agent (reactant) *increases up (bottom to top),* and the strength of the reducing agent (product) *increases down (top to bottom).*

Thus, $F_2(g)$ is the strongest oxidizing agent (has the largest positive E^0), so $F^-(aq)$ is the weakest reducing agent. Similarly, $Li^+(aq)$ is the weakest oxidizing agent (has the most negative E^0), so $Li(s)$ is the strongest reducing agent. You may have noticed an analogy to conjugate acid-base pairs: a strong acid forms a weak conjugate base, and vice versa, just as a *strong oxidizing agent forms a weak reducing agent,* and vice versa. If you forget the ranking in the table, just rely on your chemical knowledge of the elements. You know that F_2 is very electronegative and typically occurs as F^-. Since it is easily reduced (gains electrons), it must be a strong oxidizing agent (high, positive E^0). Similarly, Li metal has a low ionization energy and typically occurs as Li^+. Therefore, it is easily oxidized (loses electrons), so it must be a strong reducing agent (low, negative E^0).

Writing Spontaneous Redox Reactions Table 21.2 can be used as a guide to writing redox reactions in the direction that will be spontaneous, which can be useful in laboratory analyses or construction of electrochemical cells.

Every redox reaction is the sum of two half-reactions, so there is a reducing agent and an oxidizing agent on each side. In the zinc-copper reaction, for instance, Zn and Cu are the reducing agents, and Cu^{2+} and Zn^{2+} are the oxidizing agents. The stronger oxidizing and reducing agents react spontaneously to form the weaker oxidizing and reducing agents:

$$\underset{\substack{\text{stronger} \\ \text{reducing agent}}}{Zn(s)} + \underset{\substack{\text{stronger} \\ \text{oxidizing agent}}}{Cu^{2+}(aq)} \longrightarrow \underset{\substack{\text{weaker} \\ \text{oxidizing agent}}}{Zn^{2+}(aq)} + \underset{\substack{\text{weaker} \\ \text{reducing agent}}}{Cu(s)}$$

Here, too, note the similarity to acid-base chemistry. The stronger acid and base spontaneously form the weaker base and acid, respectively. The members of a conjugate acid-base pair differ by a proton: the acid has the proton and the base does not. The members of a redox pair, or *redox couple,* such as Zn and Zn^{2+}, differ by one or more electrons: the reduced form (Zn) has the electrons and the oxidized form (Zn^{2+}) does not. In acid-base reactions, we compare acid and base strength with K_a and K_b values. In redox reactions, we compare oxidizing and reducing strength with E^0 values.

As a result of the order of the E^0 values in Table 21.2, *a spontaneous reaction ($E^0_{cell} > 0$) will occur between an oxidizing agent (species on the left) and a reducing agent (species on the right) that lies **below** it.* For instance, Cu^{2+} (left) and Zn (right) react spontaneously, and Zn lies below Cu^{2+}. In other words, a spontaneous reaction involves one half-reaction that proceeds as a reduction (that is, as written in the table) and another one, listed lower in the table, that proceeds as an oxidation (that is, written in reverse). This pairing ensures

Table 21.2 Standard Electrode (Half-Cell) Potentials (298 K)*

Half-Reaction	E^0 (V)
$F_2(g) + 2e^- \rightleftharpoons 2F^-(aq)$	+2.87
$O_3(g) + 2H^+(aq) + 2e^- \rightleftharpoons O_2(g) + H_2O(l)$	+2.07
$Co^{3+}(aq) + e^- \rightleftharpoons Co^{2+}(aq)$	+1.82
$H_2O_2(aq) + 2H^+(aq) + 2e^- \rightleftharpoons 2H_2O(l)$	+1.77
$PbO_2(s) + 4H^+(aq) + SO_4^{2-}(aq) + 2e^- \rightleftharpoons PbSO_4(s) + 2H_2O(l)$	+1.70
$Ce^{4+}(aq) + e^- \rightleftharpoons Ce^{3+}(aq)$	+1.61
$MnO_4^-(aq) + 8H^+(aq) + 5e^- \rightleftharpoons Mn^{2+}(aq) + 4H_2O(l)$	+1.51
$Au^{3+}(aq) + 3e^- \rightleftharpoons Au(s)$	+1.50
$Cl_2(g) + 2e^- \rightleftharpoons 2Cl^-(aq)$	+1.36
$Cr_2O_7^{2-}(aq) + 14H^+(aq) + 6e^- \rightleftharpoons 2Cr^{3+}(aq) + 7H_2O(l)$	+1.33
$MnO_2(s) + 4H^+(aq) + 2e^- \rightleftharpoons Mn^{2+}(aq) + 2H_2O(l)$	+1.23
$O_2(g) + 4H^+(aq) + 4e^- \rightleftharpoons 2H_2O(l)$	+1.23
$Br_2(l) + 2e^- \rightleftharpoons 2Br^-(aq)$	+1.07
$NO_3^-(aq) + 4H^+(aq) + 3e^- \rightleftharpoons NO(g) + 2H_2O(l)$	+0.96
$2Hg^{2+}(aq) + 2e^- \rightleftharpoons Hg_2^{2+}(aq)$	+0.92
$Hg_2^{2+}(aq) + 2e^- \rightleftharpoons 2Hg(l)$	+0.85
$Ag^+(aq) + e^- \rightleftharpoons Ag(s)$	+0.80
$Fe^{3+}(aq) + e^- \rightleftharpoons Fe^{2+}(aq)$	+0.77
$O_2(g) + 2H^+(aq) + 2e^- \rightleftharpoons H_2O_2(aq)$	+0.68
$MnO_4^-(aq) + 2H_2O(l) + 3e^- \rightleftharpoons MnO_2(s) + 4OH^-(aq)$	+0.59
$I_2(s) + 2e^- \rightleftharpoons 2I^-(aq)$	+0.53
$O_2(g) + 2H_2O(l) + 4e^- \rightleftharpoons 4OH^-(aq)$	+0.40
$Cu^{2+}(aq) + 2e^- \rightleftharpoons Cu(s)$	+0.34
$AgCl(s) + e^- \rightleftharpoons Ag(s) + Cl^-(aq)$	+0.22
$SO_4^{2-}(aq) + 4H^+(aq) + 2e^- \rightleftharpoons SO_2(g) + 2H_2O(l)$	+0.20
$Cu^{2+}(aq) + e^- \rightleftharpoons Cu^+(aq)$	+0.15
$Sn^{4+}(aq) + 2e^- \rightleftharpoons Sn^{2+}(aq)$	+0.13
$2H^+(aq) + 2e^- \rightleftharpoons H_2(g)$	0.00
$Pb^{2+}(aq) + 2e^- \rightleftharpoons Pb(s)$	−0.13
$Sn^{2+}(aq) + 2e^- \rightleftharpoons Sn(s)$	−0.14
$N_2(g) + 5H^+(aq) + 4e^- \rightleftharpoons N_2H_5^+(aq)$	−0.23
$Ni^{2+}(aq) + 2e^- \rightleftharpoons Ni(s)$	−0.25
$Co^{2+}(aq) + 2e^- \rightleftharpoons Co(s)$	−0.28
$PbSO_4(s) + 2e^- \rightleftharpoons Pb(s) + SO_4^{2-}(aq)$	−0.31
$Cd^{2+}(aq) + 2e^- \rightleftharpoons Cd(s)$	−0.40
$Fe^{2+}(aq) + 2e^- \rightleftharpoons Fe(s)$	−0.44
$Cr^{3+}(aq) + 3e^- \rightleftharpoons Cr(s)$	−0.74
$Zn^{2+}(aq) + 2e^- \rightleftharpoons Zn(s)$	−0.76
$2H_2O(l) + 2e^- \rightleftharpoons H_2(g) + 2OH^-(aq)$	−0.83
$Mn^{2+}(aq) + 2e^- \rightleftharpoons Mn(s)$	−1.18
$Al^{3+}(aq) + 3e^- \rightleftharpoons Al(s)$	−1.66
$Mg^{2+}(aq) + 2e^- \rightleftharpoons Mg(s)$	−2.37
$Na^+(aq) + e^- \rightleftharpoons Na(s)$	−2.71
$Ca^{2+}(aq) + 2e^- \rightleftharpoons Ca(s)$	−2.87
$Sr^{2+}(aq) + 2e^- \rightleftharpoons Sr(s)$	−2.89
$Ba^{2+}(aq) + 2e^- \rightleftharpoons Ba(s)$	−2.90
$K^+(aq) + e^- \rightleftharpoons K(s)$	−2.93
$Li^+(aq) + e^- \rightleftharpoons Li(s)$	−3.05

*Written as reductions; E^0 value refers to all components in their standard states: 1 M for dissolved species; 1 atm pressure for gases; the pure substance for solids and liquids.

that the stronger oxidizing agent (higher on the left) and stronger reducing agent (lower on the right) will be the reactants.

However, if we know the electrode potentials, we can write a spontaneous redox reaction even if Table 21.2 is not available. Let's choose a pair of half-reactions from the table and, without referring to their relative positions in the table, arrange them into a spontaneous redox reaction:

$$Ag^+(aq) + e^- \longrightarrow Ag(s) \qquad E^0_{silver} = 0.80 \text{ V}$$
$$Sn^{2+}(aq) + 2e^- \longrightarrow Sn(s) \qquad E^0_{tin} = -0.14 \text{ V}$$

There are two steps involved:
1. Reverse one of the half-reactions into an oxidation step such that the sum of the electrode potentials gives a *positive* E^0_{cell}.
2. Add the rearranged half-reactions to obtain a balanced overall equation. Be sure to multiply by coefficients so e^- lost equals e^- gained and cancel species common to both sides.

You may be tempted in this case to add the two half-reactions as written, because you obtain a positive E^0_{cell}, but you then have two oxidizing agents forming two reducing agents, which cannot occur. Trial and error quickly shows that reversing the silver half-reaction to

$$Ag(s) \longrightarrow Ag^+(aq) + e^- \qquad -E^0_{silver} = -0.80 \text{ V}$$

gives a negative E^0_{cell} [$-0.80 \text{ V} + (-0.14 \text{ V}) = -0.94 \text{ V}$], so we reverse the tin half-reaction:

$$Sn(s) \longrightarrow Sn^{2+}(aq) + 2e^- \qquad -E^0_{tin} = 0.14 \text{ V}$$

Combined with the silver half-reaction, this gives a positive E^0_{cell} (0.80 V + 0.14 V = 0.94 V). Thus, tin is a stronger reducing agent than silver. [A look at Table 21.2 confirms that the reducing agent (Sn) lies *below* the oxidizing agent (Ag$^+$).]

With the half-reactions written in the correct direction, we add them to obtain a balanced equation. Be sure that the *number of electrons lost in the oxidation equals the number gained in the reduction.* In this case, we double the silver (reduction) half-reaction:

$2Ag^+(aq) + 2e^- \longrightarrow 2Ag(s)$	$E^0 = 0.80 \text{ V}$	[reduction]
$Sn(s) \longrightarrow Sn^{2+}(aq) + 2e^-$	$-E^0 = 0.14 \text{ V}$	[oxidation]
$Sn(s) + 2Ag^+(aq) \longrightarrow Sn^{2+}(aq) + 2Ag(s)$	$E^0_{cell} = 0.94 \text{ V}$	

Note that E^0 for the doubled silver half-reaction remains 0.80 V. This example shows a very important general point: *changing the balancing coefficients of a half-reaction does **not** change the E^0 value.* A standard electrode potential is an *intensive* property, one that does *not* depend on the amount of substance present. The potential is the *ratio* of energy to charge. When we change the coefficients, thus increasing the amount of substance, the energy *and* the charge increase proportionately, so their ratio stays the same. (In a similar sense, the density of a substance, another intensive property, does not change with amount of substance because the mass *and* the volume increase proportionately.)

Sample Problem 21.4   Writing Spontaneous Redox Reactions and Ranking Oxidizing and Reducing Agents by Strength

PROBLEM Combine the half-reactions below into three spontaneous redox reactions, calculate E^0_{cell} for each reaction, and rank the oxidizing and reducing agents in order of increasing strength:

(1) $NO_3^-(aq) + 4H^+(aq) + 3e^- \longrightarrow NO(g) + 2H_2O(l)$ $\qquad E^0 = 0.96 \text{ V}$
(2) $N_2(g) + 5H^+(aq) + 4e^- \longrightarrow N_2H_5^+(aq)$ $\qquad E^0 = -0.23 \text{ V}$
(3) $MnO_2(s) + 4H^+(aq) + 2e^- \longrightarrow Mn^{2+}(aq) + 2H_2O(l)$ $\qquad E^0 = 1.23 \text{ V}$

PLAN The possible combinations of half-reactions are (1) and (2), (1) and (3), and (2) and (3). They are all written as reductions, so the oxidizing agents appear as reactants and the reducing agents appear as products. We reverse one reduction half-reaction of each pair to an oxidation such that the sum gives a positive E^0_{cell}. Since the stronger oxidizing and reducing agents will then be the reactants, we can rank relative strengths within each cell reaction and then compare these to obtain the overall ranking.

SOLUTION Combining half-reactions (1) and (2). If we reverse (1), then $E^0_{cell} = -0.96$ V $+ (-0.23$ V$) = -1.19$ V, which indicates a nonspontaneous reaction. Therefore, we must reverse (2):

(1) $NO_3^-(aq) + 4H^+(aq) + 3e^- \longrightarrow NO(g) + 2H_2O(l)$ $E^0 = 0.96$ V
(rev 2) $N_2H_5^+(aq) \longrightarrow N_2(g) + 5H^+(aq) + 4e^-$ $-E^0 = 0.23$ V

To make e^- lost equal e^- gained, we multiply (1) by four and the reversed (2) by three. Then we add the half-reactions and cancel the appropriate numbers of common species (H^+ and e^-):

$4NO_3^-(aq) + 16H^+(aq) + 12e^- \longrightarrow 4NO(g) + 8H_2O(l)$ $E^0 = 0.96$ V
$\underline{3N_2H_5^+(aq) \longrightarrow 3N_2(g) + 15H^+(aq) + 12e^-}$ $-E^0 = 0.23$ V
$3N_2H_5^+(aq) + 4NO_3^-(aq) + H^+(aq) \longrightarrow 3N_2(g) + 4NO(g) + 8H_2O(l)$ $E^0_{cell} = 1.19$ V

Oxidizing agents: $NO_3^- > N_2$ *Reducing agents:* $N_2H_5^+ > NO$

Combining half-reactions (1) and (3). Reaction (1) must be reversed:

(rev 1) $NO(g) + 2H_2O(l) \longrightarrow NO_3^-(aq) + 4H^+(aq) + 3e^-$ $-E^0 = -0.96$ V
(3) $MnO_2(s) + 4H^+(aq) + 2e^- \longrightarrow Mn^{2+}(aq) + 2H_2O(l)$ $E^0 = 1.23$ V

We multiply reversed (1) by two and (3) by three, then add and cancel:

$2NO(g) + 4H_2O(l) \longrightarrow 2NO_3^-(aq) + 8H^+(aq) + 6e^-$ $-E^0 = -0.96$ V
$\underline{3MnO_2(s) + 12H^+(aq) + 6e^- \longrightarrow 3Mn^{2+}(aq) + 6H_2O(l)}$ $E^0 = 1.23$ V
$3MnO_2(s) + 4H^+(aq) + 2NO(g) \longrightarrow 3Mn^{2+}(aq) + 2H_2O(l) + 2NO_3^-(aq)$ $E^0_{cell} = 0.27$ V

Oxidizing agents: $MnO_2 > NO_3^-$ *Reducing agents:* $NO > Mn^{2+}$

Combining half-reactions (2) and (3). Reaction (2) must be reversed:

(rev 2) $N_2H_5^+(aq) \longrightarrow N_2(g) + 5H^+(aq) + 4e^-$ $-E^0 = 0.23$ V
(3) $MnO_2(s) + 4H^+(aq) + 2e^- \longrightarrow Mn^{2+}(aq) + 2H_2O(l)$ $E^0 = 1.23$ V

We multiply reaction (3) by 2, add the half-reactions, and cancel:

$N_2H_5^+(aq) \longrightarrow N_2(g) + 5H^+(aq) + 4e^-$ $-E^0 = 0.23$ V
$\underline{2MnO_2(s) + 8H^+(aq) + 4e^- \longrightarrow 2Mn^{2+}(aq) + 4H_2O(l)}$ $E^0 = 1.23$ V
$N_2H_5^+(aq) + 2MnO_2(s) + 3H^+(aq) \longrightarrow N_2(g) + 2Mn^{2+}(aq) + 4H_2O(l)$ $E^0_{cell} = 1.46$ V

Oxidizing agents: $MnO_2 > N_2$ *Reducing agents:* $N_2H_5^+ > Mn^{2+}$

Determining the overall ranking of oxidizing and reducing agents. Comparing the relative strengths from the three balanced equations gives

Oxidizing agents: $MnO_2 > NO_3^- > N_2$

Reducing agents: $N_2H_5^+ > NO > Mn^{2+}$

CHECK As always, check that atoms and charge balance on each side of the equation. A good way to check the ranking and reactions is to list the given half-reactions in order of decreasing E^0 value:

$MnO_2(s) + 4H^+(aq) + 2e^- \longrightarrow Mn^{2+}(aq) + 2H_2O(l)$ $E^0 = 1.23$ V
$NO_3^-(aq) + 4H^+(aq) + 3e^- \longrightarrow NO(g) + 2H_2O(l)$ $E^0 = 0.96$ V
$N_2(g) + 5H^+(aq) + 4e^- \longrightarrow N_2H_5^+(aq)$ $E^0 = -0.23$ V

Then the oxidizing agents (reactants) decrease in strength down the list, so the reducing agents (products) decrease in strength up. Moreover, the three spontaneous reactions you obtained in the Solution should combine a reactant with a product from lower down on the list.

Follow-up Problem 21.4   Is the following reaction spontaneous?

$3Fe^{2+}(aq) \longrightarrow Fe(s) + 2Fe^{3+}(aq)$

If not, write the spontaneous reaction, calculate E^0_{cell}, and rank the three species of iron in order of decreasing reducing strength.

Relative Reactivities of Metals In Chapter 4, you saw that a more active metal can reduce the ion of a less active metal to its elemental form, thus "displacing" that ion from aqueous solution. The activity series of the metals (see Figure 4.20, p. 162) showed a ranking of metals based on such relative reactivity. Now you'll see *why* this displacement occurs, why many, but not all, metals react with acid to form H_2, and why a few metals form H_2 even in water. All these variations in metal reactivity become clear by examining standard electrode potentials.

- *Metals that can displace H_2 from acid.* The standard hydrogen half-reaction represents the reduction of H^+ from acids to H_2:

$$2H^+(aq) + 2e^- \longrightarrow H_2(g) \qquad E^0 = 0.00 \text{ V}$$

To see which metals reduce H^+ (referred to as "displacing H_2") from acids, choose a metal, write its half-reaction as an oxidation, combine it with the hydrogen half-reaction, and see if E^0_{cell} is positive. What you find is that the metals Li through Pb, those that lie *below* the standard hydrogen (reference) half-reaction in Table 21.2, give a positive E^0_{cell} when reducing H^+. Iron, for example, reduces H^+ from an acid to H_2:

$$\begin{array}{lll} Fe(s) \longrightarrow Fe^{2+}(aq) + 2e^- & -E^0 = 0.44 \text{ V} & \text{[oxidation]} \\ 2H^+(aq) + 2e^- \longrightarrow H_2(g) & E^0 = 0.00 \text{ V} & \text{[reduction]} \\ \hline Fe(s) + 2H^+(aq) \longrightarrow H_2(g) + Fe^{2+}(aq) & E^0_{cell} = 0.44 \text{ V} \end{array}$$

The lower the metal in the table, the stronger it is as a reducing agent, and therefore the more positive its half-cell potential when the half-reaction is reversed, and the higher the E^0_{cell} for its reduction of H^+ to H_2. If E^0_{cell} *of metal A for the reduction of H^+ is more positive than E^0_{cell} of metal B, metal A is a stronger reducing agent than metal B and a more "active" metal.*

- *Metals that cannot displace H_2 from acid.* Metals *above* the standard hydrogen (reference) half-reaction *cannot* reduce H^+ from acids. When we reverse the metal half-reaction, the E^0_{cell} is negative, and thus the reaction is not spontaneous. For example, the coinage metals [Group 1B(11)]—Cu, Ag, and Au—are not strong enough reducing agents to reduce H^+ from acids:

$$\begin{array}{lll} Ag(s) \longrightarrow Ag^+(aq) + e^- & -E^0 = -0.80 \text{ V} & \text{[oxidation]} \\ 2H^+(aq) + 2e^- \longrightarrow H_2(g) & E^0 = 0.00 \text{ V} & \text{[reduction]} \\ \hline 2Ag(s) + 2H^+(aq) \longrightarrow 2Ag^+(aq) + H_2(g) & E^0_{cell} = -0.80 \text{ V} \end{array}$$

The higher the metal in the table, the more negative is its E^0_{cell} for the reduction of H^+ to H_2, the lower its reducing strength, and the less active it is. Thus, gold is less active than silver, which is less active than copper.

- *Metals that can displace H_2 from water.* Metals active enough to displace H_2 from water lie *below the half-reaction for the reduction of water:*

$$2H_2O(l) + 2e^- \longrightarrow H_2(g) + 2OH^-(aq) \qquad E = -0.42 \text{ V}$$

(The value shown is the *nonstandard* electrode potential because, in pure water, $[OH^-]$ is 1.0×10^{-7} M, not the standard-state value of 1 M.) Consider the reaction of sodium in water (with the sodium half-reaction reversed and doubled):

$$\begin{array}{lll} 2Na(s) \longrightarrow 2Na^+(aq) + 2e^- & -E^0 = 2.71 \text{ V} & \text{[oxidation]} \\ 2H_2O(l) + 2e^- \longrightarrow H_2(g) + 2OH^-(aq) & E = -0.42 \text{ V} & \text{[reduction]} \\ \hline 2Na(s) + 2H_2O(l) \longrightarrow 2Na^+(aq) + H_2(g) + 2OH^-(aq) & E_{cell} = 2.29 \text{ V} \end{array}$$

The alkali metals [Group 1A(1)] and the larger alkaline earth metals [Group 2A(2)] can displace H_2 from H_2O (Figure 21.8).

- *Metals that can displace other metals from solution.* Since a stronger reducing agent reacts to form a weaker reducing agent, we can also predict if one metal can reduce the aqueous ion of another metal. Any metal lower in Table 21.2 can reduce the ion of a metal higher up; that is, it can displace

Oxidation half-reaction
$Ca(s) \longrightarrow Ca^{2+}(aq) + 2e^-$

Reduction half-reaction
$2H_2O(l) + 2e^- \longrightarrow H_2(g) + 2OH^-(aq)$

Overall (cell) reaction
$Ca(s) + 2H_2O(l) \longrightarrow Ca(OH)_2(aq) + H_2(g)$

Figure 21.8 The reaction of calcium in water. Calcium is one of those metals active enough to displace H_2 from H_2O.

that metal from solution. For example, zinc can displace iron from solution:

$$Zn(s) \longrightarrow Zn^{2+}(aq) + 2e^- \qquad -E^0 = 0.76 \text{ V} \qquad [\text{oxidation}]$$
$$Fe^{2+}(aq) + 2e^- \longrightarrow Fe(s) \qquad E^0 = -0.44 \text{ V} \qquad [\text{reduction}]$$
$$\overline{Zn(s) + Fe^{2+}(aq) \longrightarrow Zn^{2+}(aq) + Fe(s) \qquad E^0_{\text{cell}} = 0.32 \text{ V}}$$

This particular reaction has tremendous economic importance in protecting iron from rusting, as you'll see shortly. The margin note points out a more personal scenario involving the reducing power of metals. ◆

Section Summary

The output of a cell is the cell potential (E_{cell}) and is measured in volts (V; 1 V = 1 J/C). When all substances are in their standard states, the output is the standard cell potential (E^0_{cell}). For a spontaneous reaction, $E^0_{\text{cell}} > 0$. By convention, standard electrode potentials ($E^0_{\text{half-cell}}$) refer to the *reduction* half-reaction. Reversing the half-reaction to an oxidation changes the sign of $E^0_{\text{half-cell}}$. The E^0_{cell} value equals $E^0_{\text{half-cell}}$ of the cathode minus $E^0_{\text{half-cell}}$ of the anode. Using a standard hydrogen (reference) electrode, other $E^0_{\text{half-cell}}$ values can be measured and used to rank oxidizing (or reducing) agents (see Table 21.2). Spontaneous redox reactions combine stronger oxidizing and reducing agents to form weaker ones. A metal can reduce another species (H^+, H_2O, or metal ion) if the E^0_{cell} for the reaction is positive.

21.4 Free Energy and Electrical Work

In Chapter 20, we discussed the relationship of useful work, free energy, and the equilibrium constant. Now we examine this central relationship in the context of electrochemical cells and see the effect of concentration on cell potential.

Standard Cell Potential and the Equilibrium Constant

As you know, a spontaneous reaction has a *negative* change in free energy ($\Delta G < 0$) (Section 20.3). You have just seen that a spontaneous electrochemical reaction has a *positive* cell potential ($E_{\text{cell}} > 0$). Note that *the signs of ΔG and E_{cell} are opposite for a spontaneous reaction*. These two indications of spontaneity are related:

$$\Delta G \propto -E_{\text{cell}}$$

Let's determine the proportionality constant. The cell potential (E_{cell}, in volts) is the work (w, in joules) done *by* the system per unit of charge (in coulombs) that flows through the circuit. With no current flowing and therefore no energy lost to heating the cell components, the potential represents the *maximum* work the cell can do. Since the work is done *on* the surroundings, its sign is negative:

$$E_{\text{cell}} = \frac{-w_{\text{max}}}{\text{charge}} \qquad \text{or} \qquad w_{\text{max}} = -\text{charge} \times E_{\text{cell}}$$

The charge that flows through the cell is equal to the number of moles of electrons (n) transferred in the balanced redox equation times the charge of 1 mol of electrons (symbol F):

$$\text{Charge} = \text{moles of } e^- \times \frac{\text{charge}}{\text{mol } e^-} \qquad \text{or} \qquad \text{charge} = nF$$

Substituting for charge in the equation for maximum work, we have

$$w_{\text{max}} = -\text{charge} \times E_{\text{cell}} = -nFE_{\text{cell}}$$

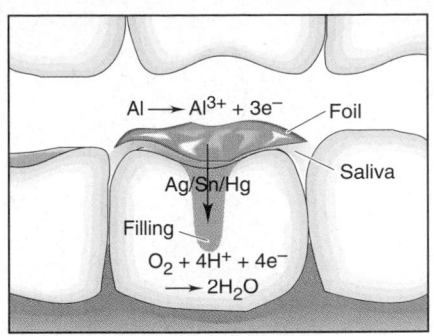

◆ **The Pain of a Dental Voltaic Cell** Have you ever felt a jolt of pain when biting down with a filled tooth on a scrap of foil left on a piece of food? Here's why. The aluminum foil acts as an active anode (E^0 of Al = −1.66 V), saliva as the electrolyte, and the filling (usually a silver/tin/mercury alloy) as an inactive cathode. O_2 is reduced to water, and the short circuit between the foil in contact with the filling creates a current that is sensed by the nerve of the tooth.

The charge of 1 mol of electrons is a constant called the **faraday (F),** in honor of Michael Faraday, the 19th-century British scientist who pioneered the study of electrochemistry:

$$F = \frac{96,485 \text{ C}}{\text{mol e}^-}$$

Since 1 V = 1 J/C, we have 1 C = 1 J/V, and

$$F = 9.65 \times 10^4 \frac{\text{J}}{\text{V} \cdot \text{mol e}^-} \qquad \text{(3 significant figures)} \qquad \textbf{(21.4)}$$

Recall from Chapter 20 that the free energy change is the maximum work that can be obtained from a spontaneous process:

$$\Delta G = w_{\text{max}}$$

Combining these expressions for maximum work, we determine the proportionality constant in the earlier relationship and obtain the key equation in the thermodynamics of electrochemical cells:

$$\Delta G = -nFE_{\text{cell}} \qquad \textbf{(21.5)}$$

When all components are in their standard states, we have

$$\Delta G^0 = -nFE_{\text{cell}}^0 \qquad \textbf{(21.6)}$$

Using this relationship, we can relate the standard cell potential to the equilibrium constant of the redox reaction. Recall that

$$\Delta G^0 = -RT \ln K$$

Substituting for ΔG^0 in Equation 21.6, we obtain

$$-nFE_{\text{cell}}^0 = -RT \ln K$$

Solving for E_{cell}^0 gives

$$E_{\text{cell}}^0 = \frac{RT}{nF} \ln K \qquad \textbf{(21.7)}$$

Figure 21.9 summarizes the interconnections among these three reaction parameters. Our previous procedures for determining K required knowing ΔG^0, either from ΔH^0 and ΔS^0 values or from ΔG_{f}^0 values. For redox reactions, we now have a direct experimental method for determining K *and* ΔG^0: measure E_{cell}^0.

If we substitute values for the constants R and F and run the cell at 25°C (298 K), we obtain a simplified form of Equation 21.7 that relates E^0 to K when n moles of e$^-$ are transferred per mole of reaction:

$$E_{\text{cell}}^0 = \frac{RT}{nF} \ln K = \frac{8.31 \frac{\cancel{\text{J}}}{\text{mol rxn} \cdot \cancel{\text{K}}} \times 298 \cancel{\text{K}}}{\frac{n \cancel{\text{mol e}^-}}{\cancel{\text{mol rxn}}} \times 96,485 \frac{\cancel{\text{J}}}{\text{V} \cdot \cancel{\text{mol e}^-}}} \ln K = \frac{0.0257 \text{ V}}{n} \ln K$$

Multiplying by 2.303 to obtain the common (base-10) logarithm gives

$$E_{\text{cell}}^0 = \frac{0.0592 \text{ V}}{n} \log K \quad \text{and} \quad \log K = \frac{nE_{\text{cell}}^0}{0.0592 \text{ V}} \quad \text{(at 25°C)} \qquad \textbf{(21.8)}$$

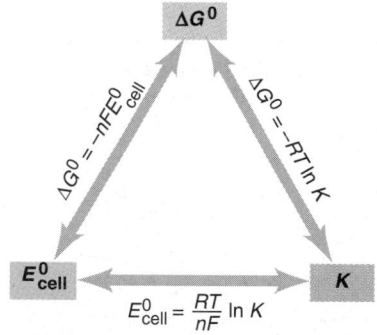

A

ΔG^0	K	E_{cell}^0	Reaction at standard-state conditions
<0	>1	>0	Spontaneous
0	1	0	At equilibrium
>0	<1	<0	Nonspontaneous

B

Figure 21.9 The interrelationship of ΔG^0, E^0, and K. A, Any one of these three central thermodynamic parameters can be used to find the other two. **B,** The signs of ΔG^0 and E_{cell}^0 determine the reaction direction at standard-state conditions.

Sample Problem 21.5   Calculating K and ΔG^0 from E_{cell}^0

PROBLEM Lead can displace silver from solution:

$$\text{Pb}(s) + 2\text{Ag}^+(aq) \longrightarrow \text{Pb}^{2+}(aq) + 2\text{Ag}(s)$$

As a consequence, silver is a valuable by-product in the industrial extraction of lead from its ore. Calculate K and ΔG^0 at 25°C for this reaction.

PLAN We use Table 21.2 to calculate E_{cell}^0 and then substitute the value into Equation 21.8 to find K and into Equation 21.6 to find ΔG^0.

SOLUTION Writing the half-reactions and their E^0 values:

$$(1) \qquad Ag^+(aq) + e^- \longrightarrow Ag(s) \qquad E^0 = 0.80 \text{ V}$$
$$(2) \qquad Pb^{2+}(aq) + 2e^- \longrightarrow Pb(s) \qquad E^0 = -0.13 \text{ V}$$

Calculating E^0_{cell}: We double (1), reverse (2), and add the half-reactions:

$$2Ag^+(aq) + 2e^- \longrightarrow 2Ag(s) \qquad\qquad E^0 = 0.80 \text{ V}$$
$$\underline{\qquad Pb(s) \longrightarrow Pb^{2+}(aq) + 2e^- \qquad\qquad -E^0 = 0.13 \text{ V}}$$
$$Pb(s) + 2Ag^+(aq) \longrightarrow Pb^{2+}(aq) + 2Ag(s) \qquad E^0_{cell} = 0.93 \text{ V}$$

Calculating K (Equation 21.8): The adjusted half-reactions show that 2 mol e^- are transferred per mole of reaction as written, so $n = 2$:

$$E^0_{cell} = \frac{0.0592 \text{ V}}{n} \log K = \frac{0.0592 \text{ V}}{2} \log K = 0.93 \text{ V}$$

So, $\qquad \log K = \dfrac{0.93 \text{ V} \times 2}{0.0592 \text{ V}} = 31.42 \qquad$ and $\qquad \boxed{K = 2.6 \times 10^{31}}$

Calculating ΔG^0 (Equation 21.6):

$$\Delta G^0 = -nFE^0_{cell} = -\frac{2 \text{ mol } e^-}{\text{mol rxn}} \times \frac{96.5 \text{ kJ}}{\text{V} \cdot \text{mol } e^-} \times 0.93 \text{ V}$$

$$= \boxed{-1.8 \times 10^2 \text{ kJ/mol rxn}}$$

CHECK The three variables are consistent with the reaction being spontaneous: $E^0_{cell} > 0$, $\Delta G^0 < 0$, and $K > 1$. Be sure to round and check the order of magnitude: in the ΔG^0 calculation, for instance, $\Delta G^0 \approx -2 \times 100 \times 1 = -200$, so the overall math seems right. Another check would be to obtain ΔG^0 directly from its relation with K:

$$\Delta G^0 = -RT \ln K = -8.31 \text{ J/mol rxn} \cdot \text{K} \times 298 \text{ K} \times \ln (2.6 \times 10^{31})$$

$$= -1.8 \times 10^5 \text{ J/mol} = -1.8 \times 10^2 \text{ kJ/mol rxn}$$

Follow-up Problem 21.5 When cadmium metal reduces Cu^{2+} in solution, Cd^{2+} forms in addition to copper metal. If $\Delta G^0 = -143$ kJ, calculate K at 25°C. What is E^0_{cell} in a voltaic cell that uses this reaction?

The Effect of Concentration on Cell Potential

So far, we have considered cells that operate with all components in their standard states, and we determined standard cell potential (E^0_{cell}) from standard half-cell potentials ($E^0_{half-cell}$). However, most cells do not start with all components in their standard states, and even if they did, the concentrations change after a few moments of cell operation. Moreover, all practical voltaic cells, such as those in batteries, contain reactants in far from standard-state concentrations. Clearly, we must be able to determine E_{cell}, the potential under nonstandard conditions.

We can derive an expression for the relation between cell potential and concentration that is based on the relation between free energy and concentration. Recall from Chapter 20 (Equation 20.11) that ΔG equals ΔG^0 (the free energy change when the system moves from standard-state concentrations to equilibrium) *plus* $RT \ln Q$ (the free energy change when the system moves from nonstandard-state to standard-state concentrations):

$$\Delta G = \Delta G^0 + RT \ln Q$$

Since ΔG is related to E_{cell} and ΔG^0 to E^0_{cell} (Equations 21.5 and 21.6), we substitute for them and obtain

$$-nFE_{cell} = -nFE^0_{cell} + RT \ln Q$$

Dividing both sides by $-nF$, we obtain the **Nernst equation,** developed by the German chemist Walther Hermann Nernst in 1889: ◆

$$E_{cell} = E^0_{cell} - \frac{RT}{nF} \ln Q \tag{21.9}$$

Walther Hermann Nernst (1864-1941) The great German physical chemist was only 25 years old when he developed the equation for the relationship between cell voltage and concentration. His career, which culminated in the Nobel Prize in 1920, included formulating the principle of the solubility product and the third law of thermodynamics and contributing key ideas to photochemistry and to principles underlying the Haber process. He is shown here in later years making a point to a few of his celebrated colleagues: from left to right, Nernst, Albert Einstein, Max Planck, Robert Millikan, and Max Von Laue.

The Nernst equation says that the cell potential under any conditions depends on its potential at standard-state concentrations *and* a term for the potential at nonstandard-state concentrations. How do changes in Q affect cell potential? From Equation 21.9, we see that

- When $Q < 1$ and thus [reactant] > [product], $\ln Q < 0$, so $E_{cell} > E^0_{cell}$.
- When $Q = 1$ and thus [reactant] = [product], $\ln Q = 0$, so $E_{cell} = E^0_{cell}$.
- When $Q > 1$ and thus [reactant] < [product], $\ln Q > 0$, so $E_{cell} < E^0_{cell}$.

As before, when we substitute known values for R and F, operate the cell at 25°C (298 K), and convert to common (base-10) logarithms, we obtain

$$E_{cell} = E^0_{cell} - \frac{0.0592 \text{ V}}{n} \log Q \quad \text{(at 25°C)} \quad \textbf{(21.10)}$$

Remember that the expression for Q contains only those species with concentrations (or pressures) that can vary; thus, solids do not appear, even though they may act as electrodes. For example, in the reaction between cadmium and silver ion, the Cd and Ag electrodes do not appear in the expression for Q:

$$Cd(s) + 2Ag^+(aq) \longrightarrow Cd^{2+}(aq) + 2Ag(s) \quad Q = \frac{[Cd^{2+}]}{[Ag^+]^2}$$

Sample Problem 21.6 Using the Nernst Equation to Calculate E_{cell}

PROBLEM In a test of a new reference electrode, a chemist constructs a voltaic cell consisting of a Zn/Zn^{2+} electrode and the H_2/H^+ electrode under the following conditions:

$$[Zn^{2+}] = 0.010 \text{ M} \qquad [H^+] = 2.5 \text{ M} \qquad P_{H_2} = 0.30 \text{ atm}$$

Calculate E_{cell} at 25°C.

PLAN To apply the Nernst equation and determine E_{cell}, we must know E^0_{cell} and Q. We write the spontaneous reaction, calculate E^0_{cell} from standard electrode potentials (Table 21.2), and use the given pressure and concentrations to find Q. (Recall that the ideal gas law allows us to use P at constant T as another way of writing concentration, n/V.) Then we substitute into Equation 21.10.

SOLUTION Determining the cell reaction and E^0_{cell}:

$$\begin{array}{lr} 2H^+(aq) + 2e^- \longrightarrow H_2(g) & E^0 = 0.00 \text{ V} \\ Zn(s) \longrightarrow Zn^{2+}(aq) + 2e^- & -E^0 = 0.76 \text{ V} \\ \hline 2H^+(aq) + Zn(s) \longrightarrow H_2(g) + Zn^{2+}(aq) & E^0_{cell} = 0.76 \text{ V} \end{array}$$

Calculating Q:

$$Q = \frac{P_{H_2} \times [Zn^{2+}]}{[H^+]^2} = \frac{0.30 \times 0.010}{2.5^2} = 4.8 \times 10^{-4}$$

Solving for E_{cell} at 25°C (298 K), with $n = 2$:

$$E_{cell} = E^0_{cell} - \frac{0.0592 \text{ V}}{n} \log Q = 0.76 \text{ V} - \left[\frac{0.0592 \text{ V}}{2} \log (4.8 \times 10^{-4}) \right]$$

$$= 0.76 \text{ V} - (-0.098 \text{ V}) = \boxed{0.86 \text{ V}}$$

CHECK After you check the arithmetic, reason through the answer: $E_{cell} > E^0_{cell}$ (0.86 > 0.76) because the log Q term was negative, which is consistent with $Q < 1$; that is, the amounts of products, P_{H_2} and $[Zn^{2+}]$, are smaller than the amount of reactant, $[H^+]$.

Follow-up Problem 21.6 Consider a cell based on the reaction

$$Fe(s) + Cu^{2+}(aq) \longrightarrow Fe^{2+}(aq) + Cu(s)$$

If $[Cu^{2+}] = 0.30$ M, what $[Fe^{2+}]$ is needed to increase E_{cell} by 0.25 V above E^0_{cell} at 25°C?

Cell Potential and the Relation Between *Q* and *K*

Let's reconsider the zinc-copper cell to see how the potential changes as concentrations change during cell operation:

$$Zn(s) + Cu^{2+}(aq) \longrightarrow Zn^{2+}(aq) + Cu(s) \qquad Q = \frac{[Zn^{2+}]}{[Cu^{2+}]}$$

The positive E^0_{cell} (1.10 V) means that this reaction proceeds *spontaneously* from the point at which [product] = [reactant] = 1 M ($Q = 1$) to some point at which [product] > [reactant] ($Q > 1$). Now, suppose we start operating the cell when $Q < 1$, for example, $[Zn^{2+}] = 1.0 \times 10^{-4} M$ and $[Cu^{2+}] = 2.0 M$. In this case, the cell potential is *higher* than the standard cell potential:

$$E_{cell} = E^0_{cell} - \frac{0.0592 \text{ V}}{2} \log \frac{[Zn^{2+}]}{[Cu^{2+}]}$$

$$= 1.10 \text{ V} - \left(\frac{0.0592 \text{ V}}{2} \log \frac{1.0 \times 10^{-4}}{2.0} \right)$$

$$= 1.10 \text{ V} - \left[\frac{0.0592 \text{ V}}{2} (-4.30) \right]$$

$$= 1.10 \text{ V} + 0.127 \text{ V} = 1.23 \text{ V}$$

As the cell operates, $[Zn^{2+}]$ increases (as the Zn electrode deteriorates) and $[Cu^{2+}]$ decreases (as Cu plates out on the Cu electrode). Although the process changes smoothly, if we keep Equation 21.10 in mind, we can identify four general stages in the operation of the cell. Figure 21.10 shows the first three. The main point to note is *as the cell operates, its potential decreases:*

- $E_{cell} > E^0_{cell}$ when $Q < 1$: When the cell begins operation, $[Cu^{2+}] > [Zn^{2+}]$, so the [(0.0592 V/n) log Q] term < 0 and $E_{cell} > E^0_{cell}$. As operation continues, $[Zn^{2+}]$ increases while $[Cu^{2+}]$ decreases, so Q becomes larger, the [(0.0592 V/n) log Q] term becomes less negative (more positive), and E_{cell} decreases.
- $E_{cell} = E^0_{cell}$ when $Q = 1$: At the point when $[Cu^{2+}] = [Zn^{2+}]$, $Q = 1$, so the [(0.0592 V/n) log Q] term $= 0$ and $E_{cell} = E^0_{cell}$.
- $E_{cell} < E^0_{cell}$ when $Q > 1$: As the $[Zn^{2+}]/[Cu^{2+}]$ ratio continues to increase, the [(0.0592 V/n) log Q] term > 0, so $E_{cell} < E^0_{cell}$.
- $E_{cell} = 0$ when $Q = K$: Eventually, the [(0.0592 V/n) log Q] term becomes so large that it equals E^0_{cell}, which means that E_{cell} is zero. This occurs *when the system has reached **equilibrium**: no more free energy is released, so the cell can do no more work.* At this point in the life of a battery, we say it is "dead." At equilibrium, Equation 21.10 becomes

$$0 = E^0_{cell} - \left(\frac{0.0592 \text{ V}}{n} \right) \log K$$

Solving for E^0_{cell}, we have

$$E^0_{cell} = \frac{0.0592 \text{ V}}{n} \log K$$

Note that this equation is identical to Equation 21.8, which we obtained from ΔG^0. Solving for K for the zinc-copper cell ($E^0_{cell} = 1.10$ V),

$$\log K = \frac{2 \times E^0_{cell}}{0.0592 \text{ V}}, \qquad \text{so} \qquad K = 10^{(2 \times 1.10 \text{ V})/0.0592 \text{ V}} = 10^{37.162} = 1.45 \times 10^{37}$$

Obviously, the zinc-copper cell can do work until the $[Zn^{2+}]/[Cu^{2+}]$ ratio is extremely high.

$$Q = \frac{[Zn^{2+}]}{[Cu^{2+}]}$$

Figure 21.10 The relation between E_{cell} and log Q for the zinc-copper cell. A plot of E_{cell} vs. Q (on a logarithmic scale) for the zinc-copper reaction shows a linear decrease. When $Q < 1$ (*left*), [reactant] is relatively high, and the cell can do relatively more work. When $Q = 1$, $E_{cell} = E^0_{cell}$. When $Q > 1$ (*right*), [reactant] is relatively low, and the cell can do relatively less work.

To conclude, let's examine cell potential in terms of the *starting* Q/K ratio:

- If $Q/K < 1$, E_{cell} is positive for the reaction as written. The smaller the Q/K ratio, the greater the value of E_{cell}, and the more electrical work the cell can do.
- If $Q/K = 1$, $E_{cell} = 0$. The cell is at equilibrium and can no longer do work.
- If $Q/K > 1$, E_{cell} is negative for the reaction as written. The cell will operate in reverse—the reverse reaction will take place—and do work until Q/K equals 1 at equilibrium.

Concentration Cells

You know that if you place a concentrated solution of a salt in contact with a dilute solution of the salt, they spontaneously mix and their final concentrations become equal at an intermediate value. A **concentration cell** employs this spontaneous tendency as a way to generate electrical energy. The two solutions are in separate half-cells, so they do not physically mix; rather, their concentrations become equal through the operation of the cell. Chemists, biologists, and environmental scientists use concentration cells in a host of applications.

How a Concentration Cell Works Suppose both compartments of a voltaic cell house the Cu/Cu^{2+} half-reaction. The cell reaction is the sum of identical half-reactions, written in opposite directions, so the half-cell potentials, $E^0_{copper} = 0.34$ V and $-E^0_{copper} = -0.34$ V, cancel and E^0_{cell} is zero. This occurs because *standard* electrode potentials are based on concentrations of 1 M for each dissolved component. *In a concentration cell, however, the half-reactions are the same but the concentrations are different.* As a result, even though E^0_{cell} equals zero, the nonstandard cell potential, E_{cell}, does *not* equal zero because it depends on the ratio of ion concentrations.

Consider Figure 21.11A, in which a concentration cell has 0.10 M Cu^{2+} in the anode half-cell and 1.0 M Cu^{2+}, a 10-fold higher concentration, in the cathode half-cell:

$$Cu(s) \longrightarrow Cu^{2+}(aq, 0.10\ M) + 2e^- \qquad \text{[anode; oxidation]}$$
$$Cu^{2+}(aq, 1.0\ M) + 2e^- \longrightarrow Cu(s) \qquad \text{[cathode; reduction]}$$

The overall cell reaction is the sum of the half-reactions:

$$Cu^{2+}(aq, 1.0\ M) \longrightarrow Cu^{2+}(aq, 0.10\ M) \qquad E_{cell} = ?$$

The cell potential at the initial concentrations of 0.10 M (dilute) and 1.0 M (concentrated), with $n = 2$, is obtained from the Nernst equation:

$$E_{cell} = E^0_{cell} - \frac{0.0592\ \text{V}}{2} \log \frac{[Cu^{2+}]_{dil}}{[Cu^{2+}]_{conc}} = 0\ \text{V} - \left(\frac{0.0592\ \text{V}}{2} \log \frac{0.10\ M}{1.0\ M} \right)$$

$$= 0\ \text{V} - \left[\frac{0.0592\ \text{V}}{2} (-1.00) \right] = +0.0296\ \text{V}$$

As you can see, E_{cell} for a concentration cell depends entirely on the [$(0.0592$ V/n) log Q] term for nonstandard conditions because E^0_{cell} equals zero.

What is actually going on as this cell operates? In the half-cell with dilute electrolyte (anode), the Cu atoms in the electrode give up electrons and become Cu^{2+} ions, which enter the solution and make it *more* concentrated. The electrons released at the anode flow to the cathode compartment. There, Cu^{2+} ions in the concentrated solution pick up the electrons and become Cu atoms, which plate out on the electrode, thereby making that solution *less* concentrated. As in any voltaic cell, E_{cell} decreases until equilibrium is attained, which happens when the Cu^{2+} concentrations in the half-cells are

Oxidation half-reaction
$$Cu(s) \longrightarrow Cu^{2+}(aq, 0.10\ M) + 2e^-$$

Reduction half-reaction
$$Cu^{2+}(aq, 1.0\ M) + 2e^- \longrightarrow Cu(s)$$

Overall (cell) reaction
$$Cu^{2+}(aq, 1.0\ M) \longrightarrow Cu^{2+}(aq, 0.10\ M)$$

A

Figure 21.11 A concentration cell based on the Cu/Cu^{2+} half-reaction. A, The half-reactions involve the same components, which makes $E^0_{cell} = 0$. Nevertheless, the cell operates because the half-cell concentrations are different, which makes $E_{cell} > 0$ in this case. **B,** The cell operates spontaneously until the half-cell concentrations are equal. Note the change in electrodes (exaggerated here for clarity) and the equal color of the solutions.

equal (Figure 21.11B). We obtain the same final concentration if the two solutions are mixed, but no electrical work is done.

Sample Problem 21.7 Calculating the Potential of a Concentration Cell

PROBLEM A concentration cell consists of two Ag/Ag$^+$ half-cells. In half-cell A, electrode A dips into 0.010 M AgNO$_3$; in half-cell B, electrode B dips into 4.0×10^{-4} M AgNO$_3$. What is the cell potential at 298 K? Which electrode has a positive charge?

PLAN The standard half-cell reactions are identical, so E^0_{cell} is zero, and we calculate E_{cell} from the Nernst equation. Since half-cell A has a higher [Ag$^+$], Ag$^+$ ions will be reduced and plate out on electrode A. In half-cell B, Ag will be oxidized and Ag$^+$ ions will enter the solution. As in all voltaic cells, reduction occurs at the cathode, which is positive.

SOLUTION Writing the spontaneous reaction: The [Ag$^+$] decreases in half-cell A and increases in half-cell B, so the spontaneous reaction is

$$Ag^+(aq, 0.010\ M)\ [\text{half-cell A}] \longrightarrow Ag^+(aq, 4.0 \times 10^{-4}\ M)\ [\text{half-cell B}]$$

Calculating E_{cell}, with $n = 1$:

$$E_{cell} = E^0_{cell} - \frac{0.0592\ V}{1} \log \frac{[Ag^+]_{dil}}{[Ag^+]_{conc}}$$

$$= 0\ V - \left(0.0592\ V \log \frac{4.0 \times 10^{-4}}{0.010}\right) = \boxed{0.0828\ V}$$

Reduction occurs at the cathode, electrode A, Ag$^+(aq, 0.010\ M) + e^- \longrightarrow Ag(s)$, so electrode A has a positive charge because of a relative electron deficiency.

Follow-up Problem 21.7 A concentration cell is built using two Au/Au^{3+} half-cells. In half-cell A, [Au^{3+}] = 7.0×10^{-4} M, and in half-cell B, [Au^{3+}] = 2.5×10^{-2} M. What is E_{cell}, and which electrode is negative?

◆ **Concentration Cells in Your Nerve Cells**

The nerve cells that mediate every thought, movement, and countless other processes function by the principle of a concentration cell. The nerve membrane is imbedded with a host of specialized enzyme "gates" that use energy from ATP hydrolysis to separate an *interior* solution of low $[Na^+]$ and high $[K^+]$ from an *exterior* solution of high $[Na^+]$ and low $[K^+]$. As a result of the relative $[Na^+]$ and $[K^+]$, the membrane is more positive outside than inside. One third of the body's ATP is used to create and maintain these concentration differences. (The 1997 Nobel Prize in chemistry was awarded to Jens C. Skou for elucidation of this enzyme mechanism.) When the nerve membrane is stimulated, Na^+ ions spontaneously rush in, such that in 0.001 s the inside of the membrane becomes more positive than the outside. This stage is followed by K^+ ions spontaneously rushing out, such that in another 0.001 s the membrane is again more positive outside. These large changes in charge in one region of the membrane stimulate the neighboring region and the electrical impulse moves down the length of the cell.

Applications of Concentration Cells The principle of a concentration cell has major commercial and biological significance. ◆ The most important commercial application of concentration cells is the measurement of unknown concentrations, particularly $[H^+]$ (or pH). Suppose we construct a concentration cell based on the H_2/H^+ half-reaction, in which the cathode compartment houses the standard hydrogen electrode and the anode compartment has the same apparatus dipping into an unknown $[H^+]$ in solution. The half-reactions and overall reaction are

$$H_2(g, 1\ atm) \longrightarrow 2H^+(aq,\ unknown) + 2e^- \qquad \text{[anode; oxidation]}$$
$$\underline{2H^+(aq, 1\ M) + 2e^- \longrightarrow H_2(g, 1\ atm) \qquad \text{[cathode; reduction]}}$$
$$2H^+(aq, 1\ M) \longrightarrow 2H^+(aq,\ unknown) \qquad E_{cell} = ?$$

As with the Cu/Cu^{2+} concentration cell, E^0_{cell} is zero, but the two half-cells differ in $[H^+]$, so E_{cell} is *not* zero. Applying the Nernst equation, with $n = 2$, we obtain

$$E_{cell} = E^0_{cell} - \frac{0.0592\ V}{2} \log \frac{[H^+]^2_{unknown}}{[H^+]^2_{standard}}$$

Substituting 1 M for $[H^+]_{standard}$ and zero for E^0_{cell} gives

$$E_{cell} = 0\ V - \frac{0.0592\ V}{2} \log \frac{[H^+]^2_{unknown}}{1^2} = -\frac{0.0592\ V}{2} \log [H^+]^2_{unknown}$$

Since $\log x^2 = 2 \log x$ (see Appendix A), we obtain

$$E_{cell} = -\left[\frac{0.0592\ V}{2} (2 \log [H^+]_{unknown}) \right] = -0.0592\ V \times \log [H^+]_{unknown}$$

From $-\log [H^+] = pH$, we have

$$E_{cell} = 0.0592\ V \times pH$$

Thus, by measuring E_{cell}, we can find the pH.

In the routine measurement of pH, a concentration cell incorporating two hydrogen electrodes is too bulky and difficult to maintain. Instead, as was pointed out in Chapter 18, a pH meter is used (Figure 21.12). The two electrodes of a pH meter dip into the solution being tested. One is a *glass electrode*, consisting of an Ag/AgCl half-reaction immersed in an HCl solution of fixed concentration (usually 1.000 M) and enclosed by a thin (~0.05 mm) membrane made of a special glass that is highly sensitive to the presence of H^+ ions. The other electrode is typically a reference *saturated calomel electrode*, consisting of a platinum wire immersed in a paste of Hg_2Cl_2 (calomel), liquid Hg, and saturated KCl solution. The glass electrode monitors the solution's $[H^+]$ relative to its own fixed internal $[H^+]$, and the instrument converts the potential difference between the two electrodes into pH.

Figure 21.12 The laboratory measurement of pH. The glass electrode (*left*) is a self-contained Ag/AgCl half-cell immersed in an HCl solution of known concentration and enclosed by a thin glass membrane. It monitors the external $[H^+]$ in the solution relative to its own fixed internal $[H^+]$. The saturated calomel electrode (*right*) acts as a reference.

Table 21.3 Some Ions Measured with Ion-Specific Electrodes

Species Detected	Typical Sample
NH_3/NH_4^+	Industrial wastewater, seawater
CO_2/HCO_3^-	Blood, groundwater
F^-	Drinking water, urine, soil, industrial stack gases
Br^-	Grain, plant tissue
I^-	Milk, pharmaceuticals
NO_3^-	Soil, fertilizer, drinking water
K^+	Blood serum, soil, wine
H^+	Laboratory solutions, soil, natural waters

The pH electrode is one example of an *ion-selective (or ion-specific) electrode.* Electrodes have been designed with highly specialized membranes to measure selectively the concentrations of many different ions in industrial, environmental, and biological samples. Recent advances allow measurement in the picomolar (10^{-12} M) range. Table 21.3 shows some of the many ions for which ion-selective electrodes are available. ◆

Section Summary

A spontaneous process is indicated by a negative ΔG or a positive E_{cell}, which are related: $\Delta G = -nFE_{cell}$. The ΔG of the cell reaction represents the maximum amount of electrical work the cell can do. Because the standard free energy change, ΔG^0, is related to E_{cell}^0 and to K, we can use E_{cell}^0 to determine K. At nonstandard conditions, the Nernst equation shows that E_{cell} depends on E_{cell}^0 and a correction term based on Q. E_{cell} is high when Q is small (high [reactant]), and it decreases as the cell operates. At equilibrium, ΔG and E_{cell} are zero, which means that $Q = K$. Concentration cells use identical half-reactions, with solutions of differing concentration, that generate electrical energy as the concentrations become equal. Ion-specific electrodes, such as the pH electrode, are self-contained devices that can measure the concentration of one species.

21.5 Electrochemical Processes in Batteries

Because of their compactness and mobility, batteries have a major influence on our way of life. In industrialized countries, an average of 10 batteries are used by each person every year. A **battery,** strictly speaking, is a self-contained group of voltaic cells arranged in series (plus-to-minus-to-plus, and so on), so that their individual voltages are added together. In everyday speech, however, the term may also be applied to a single voltaic cell.

Batteries are ingeniously engineered devices that house rather unusual half-reactions and half-cells, but they operate through the same electrochemical principles we've been discussing. There are several classes of batteries. A *primary battery* cannot be recharged, so it is thrown away when the battery is "dead," that is, when the components have reached their equilibrium concentrations. In contrast, when a *secondary,* or *rechargeable, battery* runs down, it is recharged by supplying electrical energy to reverse the cell reaction and re-form reactant. In other words, in this type of battery, the voltaic cells are periodically converted to electrolytic cells to restore *nonequilibrium* concentrations. A **fuel cell,** or *flow battery,* is one that is not self-contained. The reactants (usually a combustible fuel and oxygen) enter the cell and the products leave, generating electricity through the controlled oxidation of the fuel. The upcoming multipage Gallery presents some important examples of primary, secondary, and flow batteries, including several newer designs.

◆ **Minimicroanalysis**
Electronic miniaturization has greatly broadened the applications of electrochemistry. Environmental chemists use pocket-sized pH meters in the field to study natural waters and soil. Physiologists and biochemists employ electrodes so small that they can be surgically implanted in a single biological cell to study ion channels and receptors. In the photo, a microelectrode (filled with a fluorescent dye for ease in viewing) is shown penetrating an egg cell from the African toad *Xenopus laevis.*

Batteries and Their Applications

Primary (Non-Rechargeable) Batteries

Dry Cell

Invented in the 1860s, the common dry cell, or *Leclanché cell,* has become a familiar household item. A zinc anode in the form of a can houses a mixture of MnO_2 and an electrolyte paste, consisting of NH_4Cl, $ZnCl_2$, H_2O, and starch. Powdered graphite improves conductivity. The cathode is an inactive graphite rod.

Anode (oxidation):

$$Zn(s) \longrightarrow Zn^{2+}(aq) + 2e^-$$

Cathode (reduction): The cathode half-reaction is complex and not completely understood. $MnO_2(s)$ is reduced to $Mn_2O_3(s)$ through a series of steps that may involve the presence of Mn^{2+} and an acid-base reaction between NH_4^+ and OH^-:

$$2MnO_2(s) + 2NH_4^+(aq) + 2e^- \longrightarrow Mn_2O_3(s) + 2NH_3(aq) + H_2O(l)$$

The ammonia, some of which may be gaseous, forms a complex ion with Zn^{2+}, which crystallizes in contact with Cl^- ion:

$$Zn^{2+}(aq) + 2NH_3(aq) + 2Cl^-(aq) \longrightarrow Zn(NH_3)_2Cl_2(s)$$

Overall (cell) reaction:

$$2MnO_2(s) + 2NH_4Cl(aq) + Zn(s) \longrightarrow$$
$$Zn(NH_3)_2Cl_2(s) + H_2O(l) + Mn_2O_3(s) \qquad E_{cell} = 1.5\ V$$

Positive terminal
Negative terminal
Insulator
Graphite rod (cathode)
MnO_2 in $NH_4Cl/ZnCl_2$ paste
Zinc can (anode)

Uses: Portable radios, toys, flashlights.
Advantages: Inexpensive, safe, available in many sizes.
Disadvantages: At high current drain, $NH_3(g)$ builds up, causing voltage drop. Short shelf-life because zinc anode reacts with the acidic NH_4^+ ions.

Positive button
Steel case
MnO_2 in KOH paste
Zn (anode)
Graphite rod (cathode)
Absorbent/separator
Negative end cap

Alkaline Battery

The alkaline battery is an improved dry cell. The half-reactions are essentially the same, but the electrolyte is a KOH paste. The basic electrolyte eliminates the build-up of gases and maintains the Zn electrode.

Anode (oxidation):

$$Zn(s) + 2OH^-(aq) \longrightarrow ZnO(s) + H_2O(l) + 2e^-$$

Cathode (reduction):

$$MnO_2(s) + 2H_2O(l) + 2e^- \longrightarrow Mn(OH)_2(s) + 2OH^-(aq)$$

Overall (cell) reaction:

$$Zn(s) + MnO_2(s) + H_2O(l) \longrightarrow ZnO(s) + Mn(OH)_2(s) \quad E_{cell} = 1.5\ V$$

Uses: Same as dry cell.
Advantages: No voltage drop and longer shelf life than dry cell. Safe, many sizes.
Disadvantages: More expensive than common dry cell.

Mercury and Silver (Button) Batteries

The mercury battery and the silver battery are quite similar. Both use a zinc anode (reducing agent) in a basic medium. One employs HgO as the oxidizing agent, the other Ag_2O, and both use a steel cathode. The solid reactants are compacted separately with KOH, with moist paper for a salt bridge.

Anode (oxidation):
$$Zn(s) + 2OH^-(aq) \longrightarrow ZnO(s) + H_2O(l) + 2e^-$$
Cathode (reduction) (mercury):
$$HgO(s) + H_2O(l) + 2e^- \longrightarrow Hg(l) + 2OH^-(aq)$$
Cathode (reduction) (silver):
$$Ag_2O(s) + H_2O(l) + 2e^- \longrightarrow 2Ag(s) + 2OH^-(aq)$$
Overall (cell) reaction (mercury):
$$Zn(s) + HgO(s) \longrightarrow ZnO(s) + Hg(l); E_{cell} = 1.3 \text{ V}$$
Overall (cell) reaction (silver):
$$Zn(s) + Ag_2O(s) \longrightarrow ZnO(s) + 2Ag(s); E_{cell} = 1.6 \text{ V}$$

Steel (cathode)
(+)

Insulation

Zinc container (anode)
(−)

Paste of Ag_2O on electrolyte KOH and $Zn(OH)_2$

Porous separator

Uses: The mercury cell is used in watches and calculators, the silver cell in cameras, heart pacemakers, and hearing aids

Advantages: Both are very small, with relatively large voltage. The silver cell has a very steady output and is nontoxic.

Disadvantages: Discarded mercury cells release the toxic metal. Silver cells are expensive.

Secondary (Rechargeable) Batteries

Lead-Acid Battery

A typical 12-V lead-acid car battery has six cells connected in series, each of which delivers about 2 V. Each cell contains two lead grids packed with the electrode materials: the anode is spongy, powdered Pb, and the cathode is powdered PbO_2. The grids are immersed in an electrolyte solution of ~4.5 M H_2SO_4. Fiberglass sheets between the grids prevent shorting by chance physical contact. When the cell discharges, it generates electrical energy as a voltaic cell:

Anode (oxidation): $Pb(s) + SO_4^{2-}(aq) \longrightarrow PbSO_4(s) + 2e^-$
Cathode (reduction): $PbO_2(s) + 4H^+(aq) + SO_4^{2-}(aq) + 2e \longrightarrow PbSO_4(s) + 2H_2O(l)$

Cathode (positive): lead grids filled with PbO_2

Anode (negative): similar grids filled with spongy lead

H_2SO_4 electrolyte

Note that both half-reactions produce Pb^{2+} ion, one through oxidation of Pb, the other through reduction of PbO_2. The Pb^{2+} reacts with SO_4^{2-} at both electrodes to form $PbSO_4(s)$.

Overall (cell) reaction (discharge):
$$PbO_2(s) + Pb(s) + 2H_2SO_4(aq) \longrightarrow 2PbSO_4(s) + 2H_2O(l); E_{cell} = 2 \text{ V}$$
When the cell recharges, it uses electrical energy as an electrolytic cell, and the half-cell and overall reactions are reversed.

Overall (cell) reaction (recharge):
$$2PbSO_4(s) + 2H_2O(l) \longrightarrow PbO_2(s) + Pb(s) + 2H_2SO_4(aq)$$

Uses: In automobiles and trucks.

Advantages: Provides a large burst of current to the engine starter motor; reliable, long life; effective at low temperature.

Disadvantages: 1. Loss of capacity: $PbSO_4$, which is required in the recharging stage, coats the battery grids after the battery discharges. Mechanical strain and normal bumping can dislodge $PbSO_4$ and reduce battery capacity. If enough $PbSO_4$ is lost, the cell cannot be recharged. 2. Safety hazard: Older batteries have a cap on each cell to monitor electrolyte density and replace the water lost during discharging. During recharging, some water can electrolyze to H_2 and O_2 and, if sparked, the gases can explode and splatter H_2SO_4. Modern batteries use a lead alloy that inhibits electrolysis and reduces water loss, so the cells are sealed.

Nickel-Cadmium (Nicad) Battery

The nickel-cadmium battery has an anode half-reaction that oxidizes cadmium in a basic (NaOH or KOH) electrolyte, while nickel(III) as NiO(OH) is reduced at the cathode.

Separator

Cadmium (anode)

Separator

NiO(OH) and conductor (cathode)

Anode (oxidation):
$$Cd(s) + 2OH^-(aq) \longrightarrow Cd(OH)_2(s) + 2e^-$$
Cathode (reduction):
$$2NiO(OH)(s) + 2H_2O(l) + 2e^- \longrightarrow 2Ni(OH)_2(s) + 2OH^-(aq)$$
Overall (cell) reaction:
$$Cd(s) + 2NiO(OH)(s) + 2H_2O(l) \longrightarrow 2Ni(OH)_2(s) + Cd(OH)_2(s); \quad E_{cell} = 1.4 \text{ V}$$
The cell reaction is reversed upon recharging.

Uses: Cordless razors, photo flash units, and power tools.
Advantages: Lightweight.
Disadvantages: Disposal of toxic cadmium.

Lithium Solid-State Battery

The lithium battery is a recent design that incorporates an Li anode and a transition metal oxide (or sulfide) cathode (e.g., MnO_2, V_6O_{13}, or TiS_2). The electrolyte is a polymer that allows Li^+ ions to flow but not electrons.

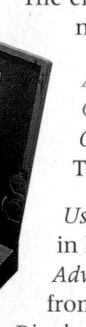

Anode (oxidation): $Li(s) \longrightarrow Li^+ (\text{in solid electrolyte}) + e^-$
Cathode (reduction): $MnO_2(s) + Li^+ + e^- \longrightarrow LiMnO_2(s)$
Overall (cell) reaction: $Li(s) + MnO_2(s) \longrightarrow LiMnO_2(s); \quad E_{cell} = 3 \text{ V}$
The cell reaction is reversed upon recharging.

Uses: Button-sized versions in calculators, watches, and cameras; larger versions in laptop computers.
Advantages: Extremely high energy/mass ratio: 1 mol e^- (1 F) can be produced from less than 7 g metal ($\mathcal{M}$ of Li = 6.941 g/mol).
Disadvantages: Relatively expensive; early versions had a short life and variable output.

Flow Batteries (Fuel Cells)

Fuel cells use combustion redox reactions to produce electricity. As in other batteries, the reactants undergo separated half-reactions (the fuel does not burn), and the electrons are transferred through an external circuit. A fuel cell that oxidizes H_2 has carbon electrodes impregnated with metal catalysts and a molten Na_2CO_3 electrolyte.

Porous carbon electrode containing Ni

Molten Na_2CO_3

Porous carbon electrode containing Ni and NiO

Anode (oxidation): $H_2(g) + CO_3^{2-}(l) \longrightarrow H_2O(g) + CO_2(g) + 2e^-$
Cathode (reduction): $\frac{1}{2}O_2(g) + CO_2(g) + 2e^- \longrightarrow CO_3^{2-}(l)$
Overall (cell) reaction: $H_2(g) + \frac{1}{2}O_2(g) \longrightarrow H_2O(g) \quad E_{cell} = 1.2 \text{ V}$

Uses: Provides electricity and pure water (after condensing the water vapor) during space flights.
Advantages: 1. Clean and portable sources of electricity, many fuel cells produce no pollutants. Some other cell reactions are
$$2NH_3(g) + \tfrac{3}{2}O_2(g) \longrightarrow N_2(g) + 3H_2O(l)$$
$$N_2H_4(g) + O_2(g) \longrightarrow N_2(g) + 2H_2O(l)$$
$$CH_4(g) + 2O_2(g) \longrightarrow CO_2(g) + 2H_2O(l)$$
2. Fuel cells are very efficient, converting about 75% of bond energy in fuel into electricity. In contrast, an electric power plant converts about 40% of the bond energy of coal into electricity, and an automobile engine converts only 25% of the bond energy in gasoline into moving the car.
Disadvantages: 1. Unlike an ordinary battery, fuel cells can't store electrical energy; they only operate with a continuous flow of reactants. 2. Electrode materials are short-lived and expensive.

Advanced Designs

Pressed by federal incentives and state mandates (currently approved in California and proposed in Massachusetts and New York) to reduce carbon-based auto emissions, automobile manufacturers have teamed up with battery designers to create devices capable of powering the family car. Whereas many vehicles are already running entirely on lead-acid batteries, here are two newer examples that hold promise.

Aluminum-Air Battery

Air batteries, of which this is one type, are similar to flow batteries in that the components must be supplied periodically, if not continuously. The aluminum anode is oxidized and oxygen from flowing moist air is reduced at an inactive porous graphite cathode. An aqueous NaOH electrolyte circulates through the cell. With such basic conditions, the half-reactions are

Anode (oxidation): $4[Al(s) + 4OH^-(aq) \longrightarrow Al(OH)_4^-(aq) + 3e^-]$
Cathode (reduction): $3[O_2(g) + 2H_2O(l) + 4e^- \longrightarrow 4OH^-(aq)]$
Overall (cell) reaction: $4Al(s) + 3O_2(g) + 6H_2O(l) + 4OH^-(aq) \longrightarrow 4Al(OH)_4^-(aq);$ $E_{cell} = 2.7$ V

Advantages: Like the lithium battery discussed previously, the aluminum-air battery provides a very high energy/mass ratio because 1 mol e^- is produced for every 9 g metal (M of Al = 26.98 g/mol; $\frac{1}{3}Al \longrightarrow \frac{1}{3}Al^{3+} + e^-$). Expectations are that a small car could drive several thousand miles on the Al contained in a 250-kg battery before more Al must be added. *Disadvantages:* Aluminum and water must be replaced periodically, and the product $Al(OH)_4^-(aq)$ is converted to solid $Al(OH)_3$, which must be removed periodically. The $Al(OH)_3$ must be converted back to Al metal industrially, which is energy intensive.

Sodium-Sulfur Battery

In contrast to the traditional battery, which houses solid electrodes and liquid (or slurried) electrolyte, this design incorporates liquid electrodes separated by a solid electrolyte. Molten Na (mp = 98°C) is the anode, and molten S_8 (mp ≈ 113°C) is the cathode (mixed with powdered graphite to improve conductivity). The Na loses electrons, which pass through the external circuit (wire and stainless-steel electrode housing) and reduce the S_8 to polysulfide ions. The electrolyte is β-alumina, a mixture of metal (Na, Mg, Al) oxides that allows Na^+ ions to pass through and reach the nS^{2-} ions.

Anode (oxidation): $2Na(l) \longrightarrow 2Na^+(l) + 2e^-$
Cathode (reduction): $\frac{n}{8}S_8(l) + 2e^- \longrightarrow nS^{2-}(l)$
Overall (cell) reaction: $2Na(l) + \frac{n}{8}S_8(l) \longrightarrow Na_2S_n(l);$ $E_{cell} = 2.1$ V
The cell reaction is reversed upon recharging.

Advantages: Na-S batteries can provide four to five times the energy per unit mass and undergo about three times as many discharge-recharge cycles as lead-acid batteries. Battery life may be as long as 125,000 miles. *Disadvantages:* Moderate speed and short discharge time: a BMW powered by a 265-kg Na-S battery had a top speed of 60 mi/h and a cruising range of 100 mi; earlier versions had long recharge times (~16 h). A temperature of ~350°C must be maintained to keep reactants and products molten and a high Na^+ conductivity in the β-alumina.

Section Summary

Batteries contain several voltaic cells in series and are either primary (such as dry cell, alkaline, mercury, or silver), rechargeable (such as lead-acid and nickel-cadmium), or flow (fuel cells). Supplying electricity to a rechargeable battery reverses the redox reaction, forming more reactant for further use. Fuel cells release electrons and generate a current through the controlled oxidation of a combustible fuel, such as H_2 or CH_4.

21.6 Corrosion: A Case of Environmental Electrochemistry

By now you may be thinking that spontaneous electrochemical processes are always beneficial, but consider the problem of **corrosion,** the natural redox process that oxidizes metals to their oxides and sulfides. In chemical terms, corrosion is the reverse of isolating a metal from its oxide or sulfide ore; in electrochemical terms, the process shares many similarities with voltaic cells. Damage from corrosion to cars, ships, buildings, and bridges runs into tens of billions of dollars annually, so it is a major problem in much of the world. Although we focus here on the corrosion of iron, many other metals, such as copper and silver, also corrode.

The Corrosion of Iron

The most common and economically destructive form of corrosion is the rusting of iron. About 25% of the steel produced in the United States is made just to replace steel already in use that has corroded. Contrary to the simplified view given in some earlier discussions, rust is *not* a direct product of the reaction between iron and oxygen but arises through a complex electrochemical process. Let's look at the facts of iron corrosion and then use the features of a voltaic cell to explain them:

1. Iron does not rust in dry air: moisture must be present.
2. Iron does not rust in air-free water: oxygen must be present.
3. The loss of iron and the depositing of rust often occur at *different* places on the *same* object.
4. Iron rusts more quickly at low pH (high $[H^+]$).
5. Iron rusts more quickly in contact with ionic solutions.
6. Iron rusts more quickly in contact with a less active metal (such as Cu) and more slowly in contact with a more active metal (such as Zn).

Picture the magnified surface of a piece of iron or steel (Figure 21.13). Strains, ridges, and dents in contact with water are typically the sites of iron loss (fact 1). These sites are called *anodic regions* because the following half-reaction occurs there:

$$Fe(s) \longrightarrow Fe^{2+}(aq) + 2e^- \qquad \text{[anodic region; oxidation]}$$

Once the iron atoms lose electrons, the damage to the object has been done, and a pit forms where the iron is lost.

The freed electrons move through the external circuit—the piece of iron itself—until they reach a region of relatively high O_2 concentration (fact 2), near the surface of a surrounding water droplet, for instance. At this *cathodic region,* the electrons released from the iron atoms reduce O_2 molecules:

$$O_2(g) + 4H^+(aq) + 4e^- \longrightarrow 2H_2O(l) \qquad \text{[cathodic region; reduction]}$$

Notice that this overall redox process is complete, and thus the iron loss has occurred, without any rust forming:

$$2Fe(s) + O_2(g) + 4H^+(aq) \longrightarrow 2Fe^{2+}(aq) + 2H_2O(l)$$

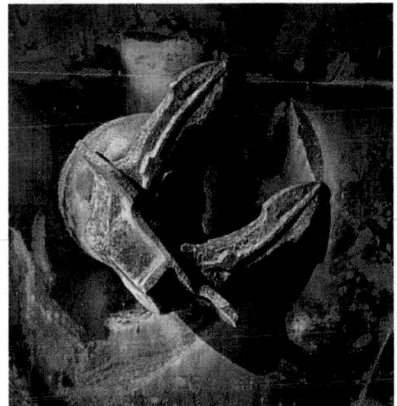

Figure 21.13 The corrosion of iron. A, Close-up view of an iron surface. Corrosion usually occurs at a surface irregularity. **B,** A schematic depiction of the surface enlarged, showing the steps in the corrosion process.

Rust forms through another redox reaction in which the reactants contact each other directly. The Fe^{2+} ions formed originally at the anodic region disperse through the surrounding water and react with O_2, often at some distance from the pit (fact 3). The overall reaction for this step is

$$2Fe^{2+}(aq) + \tfrac{1}{2}O_2(g) + (2+n)H_2O(l) \longrightarrow Fe_2O_3 \cdot nH_2O(s) + 4H^+(aq)$$

[The inexact coefficient n for H_2O in the above equation appears because rust, $Fe_2O_3 \cdot nH_2O$, is a form of iron(III) oxide with variable numbers of waters of hydration.] The rust deposit is really incidental to the damage caused by loss of iron—a chemical insult added to the original injury.

Adding the previous two equations together shows the overall equation for the rusting of iron:

$$2Fe(s) + \tfrac{3}{2}O_2(g) + nH_2O(l) + \cancel{4H^+(aq)} \longrightarrow Fe_2O_3 \cdot nH_2O(s) + \cancel{4H^+(aq)}$$

We've shown the canceled H^+ ions to emphasize that they act as a catalyst, used up in one step of the overall reaction and created in another, which explains why rusting is faster at low pH (high $[H^+]$) (fact 4). Ionic solutions speed rusting by improving the conductivity of the aqueous medium near the anodic and cathodic regions (fact 5). The effect of ions is especially evident on ocean-going vessels (Figure 21.14) and on the underbodies and around the wheel wells of cars driven in cold climates, where salts are used to melt ice on slippery roads.

In many ways, the components of the corrosion process resemble those of a voltaic cell:

- Anodic and cathodic regions are separated in space.
- The regions are connected via an external circuit through which the electrons travel.
- In the anodic region, iron behaves like an active electrode, whereas in the cathodic region, it is inactive.
- The moisture surrounding the pit functions somewhat like a salt bridge, a means for ions to ferry back and forth and keep the solution neutral.

Figure 21.14 Enhanced corrosion at sea. The high ion concentration of seawater leads to its high conductivity, which enhances corrosion of iron in ocean ship hulls and anchors.

Protecting Against the Corrosion of Iron

A common approach to preventing or limiting corrosion is to eliminate contact with the corrosive factors. The simple act of washing off road salt removes the ionic solution from auto chassis parts. Iron objects are frequently painted to keep out O_2 and moisture, but if the paint layer chips, rusting proceeds. More permanent coatings include chromium on plumbing fixtures. "Blueing" of gun barrels, wood stoves, and other steel objects bonds an adherent coating of Fe_3O_4 (magnetite) to the surface.

Figure 21.15 The effect of metal-metal contact on the corrosion of iron. A, When iron is in contact with a less active metal, such as copper, the iron loses electrons more readily (is more anodic), so it corrodes faster. **B,** When iron is in contact with a more active metal, such as zinc, the zinc acts as the anode and loses electrons. Therefore, the iron is cathodic, so it does not corrode. The process is known as *cathodic protection.*

A Enhanced corrosion

B Cathodic protection

Figure 21.16 The use of sacrificial anodes to prevent iron corrosion. Active metals, such as magnesium and aluminum, are connected to underground iron pipes to prevent their corrosion through cathodic protection. The active metal is sacrificed instead of the iron.

The only fact regarding corrosion that we have not yet addressed concerns the relative activity of other metals in contact with iron (fact 6), which leads to the most effective way to prevent corrosion. The essence of the idea is that *iron functions as both anode and cathode in the rusting process, but it is lost only at the anode.* Therefore, anything that makes iron behave more like the anode increases corrosion. If iron is in contact with a *less* active metal (weaker reducing agent), such as copper, its anodic function is enhanced (Figure 21.15A). When iron plumbing is connected directly to copper plumbing with no electrical insulation between them, the iron pipe corrodes rapidly.

On the other hand, anything that makes iron behave more like the cathode prevents corrosion. Application of this principle is called *cathodic protection.* For example, if the iron makes contact with a *more* active metal (stronger reducing agent), such as zinc, the iron becomes cathodic and remains intact, while the zinc acts as the anode and loses electrons (Figure 21.15B). Coating steel with a "sacrificial" layer of zinc is the basis of the *galvanizing* process. In addition to blocking physical contact with H_2O and O_2, the zinc is "sacrificed" (oxidized) instead of the iron.

Sacrificial anodes are employed to protect iron and steel structures (pipes, tanks, oil rigs, and so on) in marine and moist underground environments (Figure 21.16). The most frequently used metals for this purpose are magnesium and aluminum, elements that are much more active than iron, so they act as the anode while iron acts as the cathode. Another advantage of these metals is that they form adherent oxide coatings, which slows their own corrosion.

Section Summary

Corrosion damages metal structures through a natural electrochemical change. Iron corrosion occurs in the presence of oxygen and moisture and is increased by high $[H^+]$, high [ion], or contact with a less active metal, such as Cu. Fe is oxidized and O_2 is reduced in one redox reaction, while rust is formed in another reaction that often takes place at a different location. Since Fe functions as both anode and cathode in the process, the object can be protected by physically covering its surface or joining it to a more active metal (such as Zn, Mg, or Al), which acts as the anode in place of the Fe.

21.7 Electrolytic Cells: Using Electrical Energy to Drive a Nonspontaneous Reaction

Up to now, we've been considering voltaic cells, those that generate electrical energy from a spontaneous redox reaction. The principle of an electrolytic cell is exactly the opposite: *electrical energy from an external source drives a nonspontaneous reaction.*

Construction and Operation of an Electrolytic Cell

Let's examine the operation of an electrolytic cell by constructing one from a voltaic cell. Consider the tin-copper voltaic cell in Figure 21.17A. The Sn anode will gradually become oxidized to Sn^{2+} ions, and the Cu^{2+} ions will gradually be reduced and plate out on the Cu cathode because the cell reaction is spontaneous in that direction:

For the voltaic cell

$$Sn(s) \longrightarrow Sn^{2+}(aq) + 2e^- \qquad \text{[anode; oxidation]}$$
$$\underline{Cu^{2+}(aq) + 2e^- \longrightarrow Cu(s) \qquad \text{[cathode; reduction]}}$$
$$Sn(s) + Cu^{2+}(aq) \longrightarrow Sn^{2+}(aq) + Cu(s) \quad E^0_{cell} = 0.48 \text{ V and } \Delta G^0 = -93 \text{ kJ}$$

Therefore, the *reverse* cell reaction is *non*spontaneous and never happens of its own accord, as the negative E^0_{cell} and positive ΔG^0 indicate:

$$Sn^{2+}(aq) + Cu(s) \longrightarrow Sn(s) + Cu^{2+}(aq) \qquad E^0_{cell} = -0.48 \text{ V and } \Delta G^0 = 93 \text{ kJ}$$

However, we can make the reverse process happen by supplying from an external source an electric potential *greater than* E^0_{cell}. In effect, we have converted the voltaic cell into an electrolytic cell and changed the nature of the electrodes—anode is now cathode, and cathode is now anode:

For the electrolytic cell

$$Cu(s) \longrightarrow Cu^{2+}(aq) + 2e^- \qquad \text{[anode; oxidation]}$$
$$Sn^{2+}(aq) + 2e^- \longrightarrow Sn(s) \qquad \text{[cathode; reduction]}$$

Figure 21.17B illustrates this situation. Note that in an electrolytic cell, as in a voltaic cell, *oxidation takes place at the anode and reduction takes place at the cathode, but the direction of electron flow and the signs of the electrodes are reversed.* To understand these changes, keep in mind the *cause* of the electron flow:

- In a voltaic cell, electrons are generated at the anode, so it is negative, and electrons are consumed at the cathode, so it is positive.
- In an electrolytic cell, the electrons come from the external power source, which *supplies* them *to* the cathode, so it is negative, and *removes* them *from* the anode, so it is positive.

A Voltaic cell   **B** Electrolytic cell

Figure 21.17 The tin-copper reaction as the basis of a voltaic and an electrolytic cell. A, The spontaneous reaction between Sn and Cu^{2+} generates 0.48 V in a voltaic cell. **B,** If more than 0.48 V is supplied, the same apparatus is changed to an electrolytic cell, and the nonspontaneous reaction between Cu and Sn^{2+} occurs. Note the changes in electrode charges and direction of electron flow.

VOLTAIC (Discharge)

Starter motor

Oxidation half-reaction at I
$Pb(s) + SO_4^{2-}(aq) \longrightarrow PbSO_4(s) + 2e^-$

Reduction half-reaction at II
$PbO_2(s) + 4H^+(aq) + SO_4^{2-}(aq) + 2e^-$
$\longrightarrow PbSO_4(s) + 2H_2O(l)$

(−)
Anode

(+)
Cathode

Switch

I LEAD-ACID CELL **II**

Cathode
(−)

Anode
(+)

Reduction half-reaction at I
$PbSO_4(s) + 2e^- \longrightarrow Pb(s) + SO_4^{2-}(aq)$

Oxidation half-reaction at II
$PbSO_4(s) + 2H_2O(l) \longrightarrow$
$PbO_2(s) + 4H^+(aq) + SO_4^{2-}(aq) + 2e^-$

Power supply

ELECTROLYTIC (Recharge)

Figure 21.18 The processes occurring during the discharge and recharge of a lead-acid battery. When the lead-acid battery is discharging (*top*), it behaves like a voltaic cell: the anode is negative (electrode I) and the cathode is positive (electrode II). When it is recharging (*bottom*), it behaves like an electrolytic cell: the anode is positive (electrode II) and the cathode is negative (electrode I).

A rechargeable battery functions as a voltaic cell when it is discharging and as an electrolytic cell when it is recharging, so it provides a good way to compare these two cell types and the changes in electrodes. Figure 21.18 shows these two functions in the lead-acid battery. In the discharge mode (voltaic cell), oxidation occurs at electrode I, thus making the *negative* electrode the anode. In the recharge mode (electrolytic cell), oxidation occurs at electrode II, thus making the *positive* electrode the anode. Similarly, the cathode is *positive* during discharge (electrode II) and *negative* during recharge (electrode I). To reiterate, regardless of the mode, oxidation occurs at the anode and reduction at the cathode.

Table 21.4 summarizes the processes and signs in the two types of electrochemical cells.

Table 21.4 Comparison of Voltaic and Electrolytic Cells

			Electrode		
Cell Type	ΔG	E_{cell}	**Name**	**Process**	**Sign**
Voltaic	<0	>0	Anode	Oxidation	−
Voltaic	<0	>0	Cathode	Reduction	+
Electrolytic	>0	<0	Anode	Oxidation	+
Electrolytic	>0	<0	Cathode	Reduction	−

Predicting the Products of Electrolysis

Electrolysis, the splitting (lysing) of a substance by the input of electrical energy, is often used to decompose a compound into its elements. Electrolytic cells are involved in key industrial production steps for some of the most commercially important elements, including chlorine, aluminum, and copper, as you'll see in the next chapter. The first laboratory electrolysis of H_2O to H_2 and O_2 was performed in 1800, and the process is still used to produce these gases in ultrahigh purity. The electrolyte in an electrolytic cell can be the pure compound (such as H_2O or a molten salt), a mixture of molten salts, or an aqueous solution of a salt. The products obtained depend on atomic properties and several other factors, so let's examine some actual cases.

Electrolysis of Pure Molten Salts   Many electrolytic applications involve isolating a metal or nonmetal from a molten salt. Predicting the product at each electrode is simple if the salt is pure because *the cation will be reduced and the anion oxidized.* The electrolyte is the molten salt itself, and the ions move through the cell attracted by the oppositely charged electrodes.

Consider the electrolysis of molten (fused) calcium chloride. The two species present are Ca^{2+} and Cl^-, so the Ca^{2+} ion is reduced and the Cl^- ion is oxidized:

$$2Cl^-(l) \longrightarrow Cl_2(g) + 2e^- \qquad \text{[anode; oxidation]}$$
$$\underline{Ca^{2+}(l) + 2e^- \longrightarrow Ca(s) \qquad \text{[cathode; reduction]}}$$
$$Ca^{2+}(l) + 2Cl^-(l) \longrightarrow Ca(s) + Cl_2(g) \qquad \text{[overall]}$$

Metallic calcium is prepared industrially this way, as are several other active metals, such as Na and Mg, and the halogens Cl_2 and Br_2. We examine the details of these and several other electrolytic processes in Chapter 22.

Electrolysis of Mixed Molten Salts   More typically, the electrolyte is a mixture of molten salts, which is then electrolyzed to obtain a particular metal. When we have a choice of product, how can we tell which species will react at which electrode? The general rule for all electrolytic cells is that *the more easily oxidized species (stronger reducing agent) reacts at the anode, and the more easily reduced species (stronger oxidizing agent) reacts at the cathode.*

It's important to realize that for electrolysis of mixtures of molten salts we *cannot* use tabulated E^0 values to tell the relative strength of the oxidizing and reducing agents. Those values refer to the *change from aqueous ion to free element,* $M^{n+}(aq) + ne^- \longrightarrow M(s)$, under standard-state conditions, but there are no aqueous ions in a molten salt. Instead, we rely on our knowledge of periodic atomic trends to predict which of the ions present gains or loses electrons more easily (Sections 8.4 and 9.4).

Sample Problem 21.8   Predicting the Electrolysis Products of a Molten Salt Mixture

PROBLEM A chemical engineer melts a naturally occurring mixture of NaBr and $MgCl_2$ and decomposes it in an electrolytic cell. Predict the substance formed at each electrode, and write balanced half-reactions and the overall cell reaction.

PLAN We have to determine which metal and nonmetal will form more easily at the electrodes. We first list the ions as oxidizing or reducing agents. If a metal holds its electrons more tightly than another, it has a higher ionization energy (IE). Therefore, as a cation, it gains electrons more easily; it is the stronger oxidizing agent and is reduced at the cathode. Similarly, if a nonmetal holds its electrons less tightly than another, it has a lower electronegativity (EN). Therefore, as an anion, it loses electrons more easily; it is the stronger reducing agent and is oxidized at the anode.

SOLUTION Listing the ions as oxidizing or reducing agents:

The possible oxidizing agents are Na^+ and Mg^{2+}.

The possible reducing agents are Br^- and Cl^-.

Determining the cathode product (more easily reduced cation): Mg is to the right of Na in Period 3. IE increases from left to right, so Mg has a higher IE. It takes more energy to remove an e^- from Mg than from Na, so it follows that Mg^{2+} has a greater attraction for e^- and thus is more easily reduced (stronger oxidizing agent):

$$Mg^{2+}(l) + 2e^- \longrightarrow Mg(l) \qquad \text{[cathode; reduction]}$$

Determining the anode product (more easily oxidized anion): Br is below Cl in Group 7A(17). EN decreases down the group, so Br has a lower EN than Cl. Therefore, it follows that Br^- holds its e^- less tightly than Cl^-, so Br^- is more easily oxidized (stronger reducing agent):

$$2Br^-(l) \longrightarrow Br_2(g) + 2e^- \qquad \text{[anode; oxidation]}$$

Writing the overall cell reaction:

$$Mg^{2+}(l) + 2Br^-(l) \longrightarrow Mg(l) + Br_2(g) \qquad \text{[overall]}$$

COMMENT The cell temperature must be high enough to keep the salt mixture molten. In this case, the temperature is greater than the melting point of Mg, so it appears as a liquid in the equation, and greater than the boiling point of Br_2, so it appears as a gas.

Follow-up Problem 21.8 A sample of $AlBr_3$ contaminated with KF is melted and electrolyzed. Determine the electrode products and the overall cell reaction.

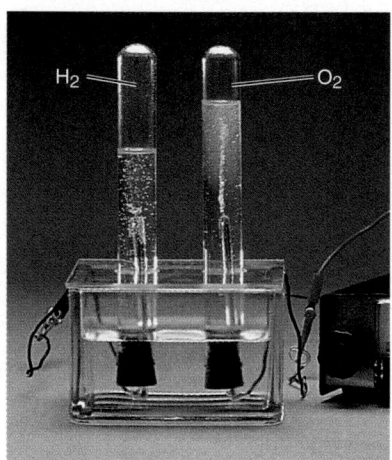

Oxidation half-reaction
$2H_2O(l) \longrightarrow O_2(g) + 4H^+(aq) + 4e^-$

Reduction half-reaction
$2H_2O(l) + 2e^- \longrightarrow H_2(g) + 2OH^-(aq)$

Overall (cell) reaction
$2H_2O(l) \longrightarrow 2H_2(g) + O_2(g)$

Figure 21.19 The electrolysis of water. Oxygen forms through oxidation of water at the anode (*right*), and twice its volume of hydrogen forms through reduction of water at the cathode (*left*).

Electrolysis of Water and Nonstandard Half-Cell Potentials Before we can analyze the electrolysis products of aqueous salt solutions, we must examine the electrolysis of water itself. Extremely pure water is difficult to electrolyze because very few ions are present to conduct a current. If a small amount of a nonreacting salt (such as Na_2SO_4) is added, however, electrolysis proceeds rapidly. A glass electrolytic cell with separated gas compartments is used to keep the H_2 and O_2 gases from mixing (Figure 21.19). At the anode, water is oxidized as the O.N. of O changes from -2 to 0:

$$2H_2O(l) \longrightarrow O_2(g) + 4H^+(aq) + 4e^- \qquad -E = -0.82 \text{ V} \qquad \text{[anode; oxidation]}$$

At the cathode, water is reduced as the O.N. of H changes from $+1$ to 0:

$$2H_2O(l) + 2e^- \longrightarrow H_2(g) + 2OH^-(aq) \qquad E = -0.42 \text{ V} \qquad \text{[cathode; reduction]}$$

After doubling the cathode half-reaction to equate e^- loss and gain, adding the half-reactions, combining the H^+ and OH^- into H_2O, and canceling e^- and excess H_2O, the overall reaction is

$$2H_2O(l) \longrightarrow 2H_2(g) + O_2(g) \qquad E_{cell} = -1.24 \text{ V} \qquad \text{[overall]}$$

Notice that these electrode potentials are not written with a superscript zero because they are *not* standard electrode potentials. The $[H^+]$ and $[OH^-]$ are 1.0×10^{-7} M rather than the standard-state value of 1 M. These E values are obtained by applying the Nernst equation. For example, the calculation for the anode potential (with $n = 4$) is

$$E_{cell} = E_{cell}^0 - \frac{0.0592 \text{ V}}{4} \log (P_{O_2} \times [H^+]^4)$$

The standard potential for the *oxidation* of water is -1.23 V (from Table 21.2) and $P_{O_2} \approx 1$ atm in the half-cell, so we have

$$E_{cell} = -1.23 \text{ V} - \left\{ \frac{0.0592 \text{ V}}{4} \times 4 \log [1(1.0 \times 10^{-7})] \right\} = -0.82 \text{ V}$$

In aqueous ionic solutions, $[H^+]$ and $[OH^-]$ are approximately 10^{-7} M also, so we use these nonstandard E_{cell} values to predict electrode products.

Electrolysis of Aqueous Ionic Solutions and the Phenomenon of Overvoltage Aqueous salt solutions are mixtures of ions *and* water, so we have to compare the various electrode potentials to predict the electrode products: *when two half-reactions are possible at an electrode, the one with the more positive (or less negative) electrode potential occurs.*

What happens, for instance, when a solution of KI is electrolyzed? The possible oxidizing agents are K^+ and H_2O:

$$K^+(aq) + e^- \longrightarrow K(s) \qquad\qquad E^0 = -2.93 \text{ V}$$
$$2H_2O(l) + 2e^- \longrightarrow H_2(g) + 2OH^-(aq) \qquad E = -0.42 \text{ V [reduction]}$$

The less negative electrode potential for water means it is much easier to reduce than K^+, so H_2 forms at the cathode.

The possible reducing agents are I^- and H_2O:

$$2I^-(aq) \longrightarrow I_2(s) + 2e^- \qquad\qquad -E^0 = -0.53 \text{ V [oxidation]}$$
$$2H_2O(l) \longrightarrow O_2(g) + 4H^+(aq) + 4e^- \qquad -E = -0.82 \text{ V}$$

The less negative electrode potential for I^- means it is easier to oxidize than H_2O, so I_2 forms at the anode.

However, the products predicted from this type of comparison of electrode potentials are not always the actual products. For gases such as $H_2(g)$ and $O_2(g)$ to be produced at metal electrodes, an additional voltage is required. This increment over the expected voltage is called the **overvoltage,** and it is 0.4 to 0.6 V for these gases. The overvoltage results from kinetic factors, such as the large activation energy (Section 16.6) required for gases to form at the electrode.

Overvoltage has major practical significance. A multibillion dollar example is the industrial production of chlorine from concentrated NaCl solution. Water is easier to reduce than Na^+, so H_2 forms at the cathode even with an overvoltage of 0.6 V:

$$Na^+(aq) + e^- \longrightarrow Na(s) \qquad\qquad E^0 = -2.71 \text{ V}$$
$$2H_2O(l) + 2e^- \longrightarrow H_2(g) + 2OH^-(aq) \qquad E = -0.42 \text{ V} \quad (\approx -1 \text{ V with overvoltage) [reduction]}$$

But Cl_2 forms at the anode, even though the electrode potentials suggest O_2 should form:

$$2H_2O(l) \longrightarrow O_2(g) + 4H^+(aq) + 4e^- \qquad -E = -0.82 \text{ V} \quad (\approx -1.4 \text{ V with overvoltage})$$
$$2Cl^-(aq) \longrightarrow Cl_2(g) + 2e^- \qquad\qquad -E^0 = -1.36 \text{ V [oxidation]}$$

An overvoltage of ~0.6 V makes the potential needed to form O_2 very close to that for Cl_2. Keeping the $[Cl^-]$ high favors Cl_2 formation. Thus, as you'll see in Chapter 22, chlorine, one of the 10 most heavily produced industrial chemicals, can be formed from plentiful natural sources of aqueous sodium chloride.

From these and other examples, we can draw some useful conclusions about which elements can be prepared electrolytically from aqueous solutions of their salts:

1. Cations of less active metals *are* reduced to the metal, including gold, silver, copper, chromium, platinum, and cadmium.

2. Cations of more active metals *are not* reduced, including those in Groups 1A(1), 2A(2), and Al from 3A(13). Water is reduced to H_2 and OH^- instead.

3. Anions that *are* oxidized, because of overvoltage from O_2 formation, include the halides ($[Cl^-]$ must be high), except for F^-.

4. Anions that *are not* oxidized include F^- and common oxoanions, such as SO_4^{2-}, CO_3^{2-}, NO_3^-, and PO_4^{3-}, because the oxoanion nonmetal is already in its highest oxidation state. Water is oxidized to O_2 and H^+ instead.

Electrolysis of aqueous KBr.

◆ **The Father of Electrochemistry and Much More** The investigations by Michael Faraday (1791–1867) into the mass of an element that is equivalent to a given amount of charge established electrochemistry as a quantitative science, but his breakthroughs in physics are even more celebrated. On Christmas Day of 1821, Faraday developed the precursor of the electric motor, and his later studies of currents induced by electric and magnetic fields eventually led to the development of the electric generator and the transformer. By the end of his career, this self-educated blacksmith's son was rated by Albert Einstein as the peer of Newton, Galileo, and Maxwell. He is shown here delivering one of his famous lectures on the "Chemical History of a Candle."

Sample Problem 21.9   Predicting the Electrolysis Products of Aqueous Ionic Solutions

PROBLEM What products form during electrolysis of aqueous solutions of the following salts?
(a) KBr   **(b)** AgNO$_3$ **(c)** MgSO$_4$

PLAN We identify the reacting ions and compare their electrode potentials with those of water, taking the 0.4 to 0.6 V overvoltage into consideration. Whichever half-reaction has the higher (less negative) electrode potential occurs at that electrode.

SOLUTION

(a)
$$K^+(aq) + e^- \longrightarrow K(s) \qquad E^0 = -2.93 \text{ V}$$
$$2H_2O(l) + 2e^- \longrightarrow H_2(g) + 2OH^-(aq) \qquad E = -0.42 \text{ V}$$

Despite the overvoltage, which makes E for reduction of water between -0.8 and -1.0 V, H$_2$O is still easier to reduce than K$^+$, so H$_2(g)$ forms at the cathode.

$$2Br^-(aq) \longrightarrow Br_2(l) + 2e^- \qquad -E^0 = -1.07 \text{ V}$$
$$2H_2O(l) \longrightarrow O_2(g) + 4H^+(aq) + 4e^- \qquad -E = -0.82 \text{ V}$$

Because of the overvoltage, which makes E for oxidation of water between -1.2 and -1.4 V, Br$^-$ is easier to oxidize than water, so Br$_2(l)$ forms at the anode (see photo).

(b)
$$Ag^+(aq) + e^- \longrightarrow Ag(s) \qquad E^0 = 0.80 \text{ V}$$
$$2H_2O(l) + 2e^- \longrightarrow H_2(g) + 2OH^-(aq) \qquad E = -0.42 \text{ V}$$

As the cation of an inactive metal, Ag$^+$ is a better oxidizing agent than H$_2$O, so Ag forms at the cathode. NO$_3^-$ cannot be oxidized, because N is already in its highest ($+5$) oxidation state. Thus, O$_2$ forms at the anode:

$$2H_2O(l) \longrightarrow O_2(g) + 4H^+(aq) + 4e^-$$

(c)
$$Mg^{2+}(aq) + 2e^- \longrightarrow Mg(s) \qquad E^0 = -2.37 \text{ V}$$

Like K$^+$ in part **(a)**, Mg^{2+} cannot be reduced in the presence of water, so H$_2$ forms at the cathode. The SO$_4^{2-}$ ion cannot be oxidized because S is in its highest ($+6$) oxidation state. Thus, H$_2$O is oxidized, and O$_2$ forms at the anode:

$$2H_2O(l) \longrightarrow O_2(g) + 4H^+(aq) + 4e^-$$

Follow-up Problem 21.9   Write half-reactions for the products you predict will form in the electrolysis of aqueous AuBr$_3$.

The Stoichiometry of Electrolysis: The Relation Between Amounts of Charge and Product

As you've seen, the charge flowing through an electrolytic cell yields products at the electrodes. In the electrolysis of molten NaCl, for example, the power source supplies electrons to the cathode, where Na$^+$ ions migrate to pick them up and become Na metal. At the same time, the power source pulls the electrons from the anode that Cl$^-$ ions release as they become Cl$_2$ gas. It follows that the more electrons picked up by Na$^+$ ions and released by Cl$^-$ ions, the greater the amounts of Na and Cl$_2$ that form. This relationship was first determined experimentally by Michael Faraday and is referred to as *Faraday's law of electrolysis: the amount of substance produced at each electrode is directly proportional to the quantity of charge flowing through the cell.* ◆

Each balanced half-reaction shows the amounts (mol) of reactant, electrons, and product involved in the change, so it contains the information we need to answer such questions as "How much material will form as a result of a given quantity of charge?" or, conversely, "How much charge is needed to produce a given amount of material?" To apply Faraday's law,

1. Balance the half-reaction to find the number of moles of electrons needed per mole of product.
2. Use the faraday constant ($F = 9.65 \times 10^4$ C/mol e$^-$) to find the corresponding charge.
3. Use the molar mass to find the charge needed for a given mass of product.

In practice, to supply the correct amount of electricity, we need some means of finding the charge flowing through the cell. We cannot measure charge directly, but we *can* measure current, the charge flowing per unit time. The SI unit of current is the **ampere (A),** which is defined as 1 coulomb flowing through a conductor in 1 second:

$$1 \text{ ampere} = 1 \text{ coulomb/second} \quad \text{or} \quad 1 \text{ A} = 1 \text{ C/s} \qquad \textbf{(21.11)}$$

Thus, the current multiplied by the time gives the charge:

$$\text{Current} \times \text{time} = \text{charge} \quad \text{or} \quad A \times s = \frac{C}{s} \times s = C$$

Therefore, we find the charge by measuring the current *and* the time during which the current flows. This, in turn, relates to the amount of product formed. Figure 21.20 summarizes these relationships.

Problems based on Faraday's law often ask you to calculate current, mass of material, or time. The electrode half-reaction provides the key because it is related to the mass for a certain quantity of charge. Here is a typical problem in practical electrolysis: How long does it take to produce 3.0 g of $Cl_2(g)$ from the electrolysis of aqueous NaCl using a power supply with a current of 12 A? The problem asks for the time needed to produce a certain mass, so let's first relate mass to number of moles of electrons to find the charge needed and then relate charge to current to find the time.

We know the mass of Cl_2 produced, so we can find the amount (mol) of Cl_2. The half-reaction tells us that the loss of 2 mol electrons produces 1 mol chlorine gas:

$$2Cl^-(aq) \longrightarrow Cl_2(g) + 2e^-$$

We use this relationship as a conversion factor, and multiplying by the faraday constant gives us the total charge:

$$\text{Charge (C)} = 3.0 \text{ g } Cl_2 \times \frac{1 \text{ mol } Cl_2}{70.90 \text{ g } Cl_2} \times \frac{2 \text{ mol e}^-}{1 \text{ mol } Cl_2} \times \frac{9.65 \times 10^4 \text{ C}}{1 \text{ mol e}^-} = 8.2 \times 10^3 \text{ C}$$

Now we use the relationship between charge and current to find the time needed:

$$\text{Time (s)} = \frac{\text{charge (C)}}{\text{current (A, or C/s)}} = 8.2 \times 10^3 \text{ C} \times \frac{1 \text{ s}}{12 \text{ C}} = 6.8 \times 10^2 \text{ s } (\sim 11 \text{ min})$$

Sample Problem 21.10 demonstrates another variation of the approach, in which the time is given and the current is unknown.

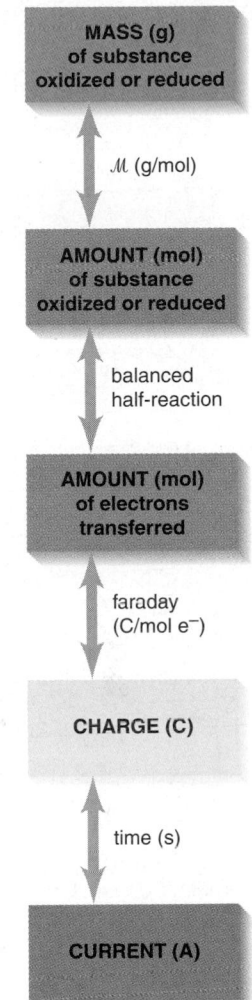

Figure 21.20 A summary diagram for the stoichiometry of electrolysis.

MASS (g) of substance oxidized or reduced

$\mathcal{M}$ (g/mol)

AMOUNT (mol) of substance oxidized or reduced

balanced half-reaction

AMOUNT (mol) of electrons transferred

faraday (C/mol e$^-$)

CHARGE (C)

time (s)

CURRENT (A)

Sample Problem 21.10 Applying the Relationship Among Current, Time, and Amount of Substance

PROBLEM A technician needs to plate a bathroom fixture with 0.86 g of chromium from an electrolytic bath containing aqueous $Cr_2(SO_4)_3$. If 12.5 min is allowed for the plating, what current is needed?

PLAN To find the current, we divide the charge by the time, so we need to find the charge. First we write the half-reaction for Cr^{3+} reduction. From it, we know the number of moles of e^- required per mole of Cr. As the roadmap shows, to find the charge, we convert the mass of Cr needed to amount (mol) of Cr. The balanced half-reaction gives the amount (mol) of e^- transferred. Then, we use the faraday constant to find the charge and divide by the time (in s) to obtain the current.

SOLUTION Writing the balanced half-reaction:

$$Cr^{3+}(aq) + 3e^- \longrightarrow Cr(s)$$

Combining steps to find amount (mol) of e^- transferred for mass of Cr needed:

$$\text{Moles of } e^- \text{ transferred} = 0.86 \text{ g Cr} \times \frac{1 \text{ mol Cr}}{52.00 \text{ g Cr}} \times \frac{3 \text{ mol } e^-}{1 \text{ mol Cr}} = 0.050 \text{ mol } e^-$$

Calculating the charge:

$$\text{Charge (C)} = 0.050 \text{ mol } e^- \times \frac{9.65 \times 10^4 \text{ C}}{1 \text{ mol } e^-} = 4.8 \times 10^3 \text{ C}$$

Calculating the current:

$$\text{Current (A)} = \frac{\text{charge (C)}}{\text{time (s)}} = \frac{4.8 \times 10^3 \text{ C}}{12.5 \text{ min}} \times \frac{1 \text{ min}}{60 \text{ s}} = 6.4 \text{ C/s} = \boxed{6.4 \text{ A}}$$

CHECK Rounding gives

$$(\sim 0.9 \text{ g})(1 \text{ mol Cr}/50 \text{ g})(3 \text{ mol } e^-/1 \text{ mol Cr}) = 5 \times 10^{-2} \text{ mol } e^-$$

then

$$(5 \times 10^{-2} \text{ mol } e^-)(\sim 1 \times 10^5 \text{ C/mol } e^-) = 5 \times 10^3 \text{ C}$$

and

$$(5 \times 10^3 \text{ C}/12 \text{ min})(1 \text{ min}/60 \text{ s}) = 7 \text{ A}$$

COMMENT For the sake of introducing Faraday's law, the details of the electroplating process have been simplified here. Actually, electroplating chromium is only 30% to 40% efficient and must be run at a particular temperature range for the plate to appear bright. Nearly 10,000 metric tons (2×10^8 mol) of chromium are used annually for electroplating.

Follow-up Problem 21.10 Using a current of 4.75 A, how many minutes does it take to plate 1.50 g Cu onto a sculpture from a $CuSO_4$ solution?

Mass (g) of Cr needed

↓ divide by $\mathcal{M}$ (g/mol)

Amount (mol) of Cr needed

↓ 3 mol e^- = 1 mol Cr

Amount (mol) of e^- transferred

↓ 1 mol e^- = 9.65×10^4 C

Charge (C)

↓ divide by time (convert min to s)

Current (A)

The following Chemical Connections essay links several themes of this chapter in the setting of a living cell.

Section Summary

Electrolytic cells use electrical energy to drive a nonspontaneous reaction. Oxidation occurs at the anode and reduction at the cathode, but the direction of electron flow and the charges of the electrodes are opposite those in voltaic cells. When two products can form at each electrode, the more easily oxidized substance reacts at the anode and the more easily reduced at the cathode; that is, the half-reaction with the less negative (more positive) E^0 occurs. The reduction or oxidation of water takes place at nonstandard conditions. Overvoltage causes the actual voltage to be unexpectedly high and can affect the electrode product that forms. The amount of product that forms depends on the quantity of charge flowing through the cell, which is related to the magnitude of the current and the time it flows. Cellular redox systems combine aspects of voltaic, concentration, and electrolytic cells to convert bond energy in food into electrochemical potential and then into the bond energy of ATP.

Cellular Electrochemistry and the Production of ATP

Biological cells apply the principles of electrochemical cells to generate energy. The complex multistep process can be divided into two parts:

1. Bond energy in food is used to generate an electrochemical potential.
2. The potential is used to create the bond energy of the high-energy molecule adenosine triphosphate (ATP; see Chemical Connections, Section 20.3).

The redox species that accomplish these steps are part of the *electron-transport chain* (ETC), which lies on the inner membranes of *mitochondria*, the subcellular particles that produce the cell's energy (Figure 21.A). The ETC is a series of large molecules (mostly proteins), each of which contains a redox couple, such as Fe^{2+}/Fe^{3+}, that passes electrons down the chain. At three points along the chain, large potential differences supply enough free energy to convert adenosine diphosphate (ADP) into ATP.

Bond Energy to Electrochemical Potential

Cells utilize the energy in food by releasing it in controlled steps rather than all at once. The reaction that ultimately powers the ETC is the oxidation of hydrogen to form water:

$$H_2 + \tfrac{1}{2}O_2 \longrightarrow H_2O$$

However, instead of H_2 gas, which does not occur in organisms, the hydrogen takes the form of two H^+ and two e^-. A biological oxidizing agent called NAD^+ (*n*icotinamide *a*denine *d*inucleotide) acquires these protons and electrons in the process of oxidizing molecules in food. To show this process,

we use the following half-reaction (without canceling the H^+ on both sides):

$$NAD^+(aq) + 2H^+(aq) + 2e^- \longrightarrow NADH(aq) + H^+(aq)$$

At the mitochondrial inner membrane, the NADH and H^+ transfer the two e^- to the first redox couple of the ETC and release the two H^+. The electrons are transported down the chain of redox couples, where they finally reduce O_2 to H_2O. The overall process, with standard electrode potentials,* is

$$NADH(aq) + H^+(aq) \longrightarrow NAD^+(aq) + 2H^+(aq) + 2e^-$$
$$-E^{0'} = 0.32 \text{ V}$$
$$\tfrac{1}{2}O_2(aq) + 2e^- + 2H^+(aq) \longrightarrow H_2O(l) \qquad E^{0'} = 0.82 \text{ V}$$

$$NADH(aq) + H^+(aq) + \tfrac{1}{2}O_2(aq) \longrightarrow NAD^+(aq) + H_2O(l)$$
$$E^{0'}_{\text{overall}} = 1.14 \text{ V}$$

Thus, for each mole of NADH that enters the ETC, the free-energy equivalent of 1.14 V is available:

$$\Delta G^{0'} = -nFE^{0'}$$
$$= -(2 \text{ mol } e^-/\text{mol NADH})(96.5 \text{ kJ/V} \cdot \text{mol } e^-)(1.14 \text{ V})$$
$$= -220 \text{ kJ/mol NADH}$$

Note that this aspect of the process functions like a voltaic cell: a spontaneous reaction, the reduction of O_2 to H_2O, is used to generate a potential. In contrast to a laboratory voltaic cell, in

(continued)

---

*In biological systems, standard potentials are designated $E^{0'}$ and the standard states include a pH of 7.0 ($[H^+] = 1 \times 10^{-7}$ *M*).

Figure 21.A **The mitochondrion. A,** Mitochondria are subcellular particles outside the cell nucleus. **B,** They have a smooth outer membrane and a highly folded inner membrane, shown schematically and in an electron micrograph. **C,** The components of the electron-transport chain are attached to the inner membrane.

which the overall process occurs in one step, this process occurs in many small steps. Figure 21.B is a greatly simplified diagram of the three key steps in the ETC that generate the high potential to produce ATP. (In the cell, each of these steps has several components, most of which are proteins.) Electrons are passed from one redox couple to the next down the chain, such that the reduced form of the first couple reduces the oxidized form of the second, and so forth. Most of the ETC components are iron-containing proteins, and the redox change involves the oxidation of Fe^{2+} to Fe^{3+} in one component caused by the reduction of Fe^{3+} to Fe^{2+} in another:

$$Fe^{2+} \text{ (in A)} + Fe^{3+} \text{ (in B)} \longrightarrow Fe^{3+} \text{ (in A)} + Fe^{2+} \text{ (in B)}$$

In other words, *metal ions within the ETC proteins are the actual species undergoing the redox reaction.*

trochemical potential is used to drive a nonspontaneous reaction.

So far, we've followed the flow of *electrons* through the members of the ETC, but where have the released *protons* gone? The answer is the key to *how* electrochemical potential is converted to bond energy in ATP. As the electrons flow and the redox couples change oxidation state, free energy released at the three key steps is used to force H^+ ions into the intermembrane space, so that the $[H^+]$ of the intermembrane space soon becomes higher than that of the matrix (Figure 21.C). In other words, the electrolytic-cell portion functions by using the free energy supplied by the three steps to *create an H^+ concentration cell across the membrane.*

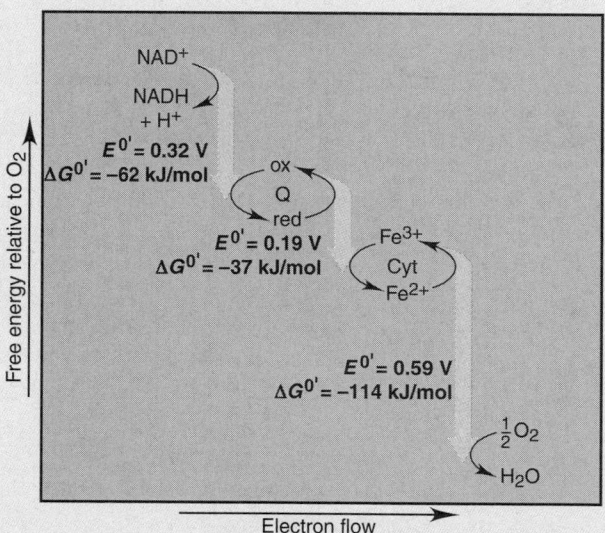

Figure 21.B The main energy-yielding steps in the electron-transport chain (ETC). The electron carriers in the ETC undergo oxidation and reduction as they pass electrons to one another along the chain. At the three points shown, the difference in potential $E^{0'}$ (or free energy, $\Delta G^{0'}$) is large enough to be used for ATP production. (Q is a large organic molecule, and Cyt is the abbreviation for cytochromes, proteins that contain a metal ion redox couple, such as Fe^{2+}/Fe^{3+}, as the electron carrier.)

Figure 21.C Coupling electron transport to proton transport to ATP synthesis. The purpose of the ETC is to convert the free energy released from food molecules into the stored free energy of ATP. It accomplishes this by transporting electrons down the chain *(curved yellow line)*, while protons are pumped out of the mitochondrial matrix. This pumping creates an $[H^+]$ difference and generates a potential across the inner membrane (in effect, a concentration cell). When this potential reaches a "trigger" value, H^+ flows back into the inner space, and the free energy released drives the formation of ATP.

Electrochemical Potential to Bond Energy

At the three points shown in Figure 21.B, the large potential difference is used to form ATP:

$$ADP^{3-}(aq) + HPO_4^{2-}(aq) + H^+(aq) \longrightarrow ATP^{4-}(aq) + H_2O(l)$$
$$\Delta G^{0'} = +30.5 \text{ kJ/mol}$$

Note that the free energy *released* at each of the three ATP-producing points exceeds 30.5 kJ, the free energy *absorbed* to form ATP. Thus, just as in an electrolytic cell, a supply of elec-

When the $[H^+]$ difference across the membrane reaches about 2.5-fold, it triggers the membrane to let H^+ ions flow back through spontaneously (in effect, closing the switch and allowing the concentration cell to operate). The free energy released in this spontaneous process drives the nonspontaneous ATP formation via a mechanism catalyzed by the enzyme ATP synthase. (Paul D. Boyer and John E. Walker shared the 1997 Nobel Prize in chemistry for elucidating this mechanism.) Thus, the mitochondrion uses the "electron-motive force" of redox couples on the membrane to generate a "proton-motive force" across the membrane, which converts a potential difference to bond energy.

Chapter Perspective

The field of electrochemistry is one of the many areas in which the principles of thermodynamics lead to practical benefit. As you've seen, electrochemical cells can use a reaction to generate energy or use energy to drive a reaction. Such processes are central not only to our mobile way of life, but also to our bio-logical existence. In Chapter 22, we examine the electrochemical (and other) methods used by industry to convert raw natural resources into some of the materials modern society finds indispensable.

The following learning objectives, with section and/or sample problem (SP) numbers in parentheses, can help focus your study:

Understand These Concepts

1. The meanings of oxidation and reduction; why an oxidizing agent is reduced and a reducing agent is oxidized (Sections 21.1 and 4.3)
2. How the half-reaction method is used to balance redox reactions in acidic or basic solution (Section 21.1)
3. The distinction between voltaic and electrolytic cells in terms of the sign of ΔG (Section 21.1)
4. How voltaic cells house a spontaneous reaction to release electrical energy (Section 21.2)
5. The physical make-up of a voltaic cell: arrangement and composition of half-cells, relative charges of electrodes, and purpose of salt bridge (Section 21.2)
6. How the difference in reducing strength of the electrodes determines the direction of electron flow (Section 21.2)
7. How a positive E_{cell} corresponds to a spontaneous cell reaction (Section 21.3)
8. The usefulness and significance of standard electrode potentials ($E^0_{half-cell}$) (Section 21.3)
9. How $E^0_{half-cell}$ values are combined to give E^0_{cell} (Section 21.3)
10. How the standard reference electrode is used to find an unknown $E^0_{half-cell}$ (Section 21.3)
11. How an emf series (e.g., Table 21.2) is used to write spontaneous redox reactions (Section 21.3)
12. How the relative reactivity of a metal is determined by its reducing power and is related to the negative of its $E^0_{half-cell}$ (Section 21.3)
13. How E_{cell} (the nonstandard cell potential) is related to ΔG (maximum work) and the charge (moles of electrons times the faraday) flowing through the cell (Section 21.4)
14. The interrelationship of ΔG^0, E^0_{cell}, and K (Section 21.4)
15. How E_{cell} changes as the cell operates (Q changes) (Section 21.4)
16. Why a voltaic cell can do work until $Q = K$ (Section 21.4)
17. How a concentration cell does work until the half-cell concentrations are equal (Section 21.4)
18. The distinction between primary (nonrecharge-able) and secondary (rechargeable) batteries (Section 21.5)
19. How corrosion occurs and is prevented; the similarities between a corroding metal and a voltaic cell (Section 21.6)
20. How electrolytic cells house a nonspontaneous redox reaction that is driven by an external source of electricity (Section 21.7)
21. How atomic properties (ionization energy and electronegativity) determine the products of the electrolysis of molten salt mixtures (Section 21.7)
22. How the electrolysis of water influences the products of aqueous electrolysis; the importance of overvoltage (Section 21.7)
23. The relationship between the quantity of charge flowing through the cell and the amount of product formed (Section 21.7)

Master These Skills

1. Balancing redox reactions by the half-reaction method (Section 21.1 and SP 21.1)
2. Diagramming and notating a voltaic cell (Section 21.2 and SP 21.2)
3. Combining $E^0_{half-cell}$ values to obtain E^0_{cell} (Section 21.3)
4. Using E^0_{cell} and known $E^0_{half-cell}$ to find an unknown $E^0_{half-cell}$ (SP 21.3)
5. Manipulating half-reactions to write a spontaneous redox reaction and calculate its E^0_{cell} (SP 21.4)
6. Ranking the relative strengths of oxidizing and reducing agents in a redox reaction (SP 21.4)
7. Predicting whether a metal can displace hydrogen or another metal from solution (Section 21.3)
8. Using the interrelationship of ΔG^0, E^0_{cell}, and K to calculate one of the three given the other two (SP 21.5)
9. Using the Nernst equation to calculate the non-standard cell potential (E_{cell}) (SP 21.6)
10. Calculating E_{cell} of a concentration cell (SP 21.7)
11. Predicting the products of the electrolysis of molten salts (SP 21.8)
12. Predicting the products of the electrolysis of aqueous salts (SP 21.9)
13. Calculating the current (or time) needed to produce a given amount of product, and vice versa (SP 21.10)

For Review and Reference

Key Terms

electrochemistry
electrochemical cells
Section 21.1
half-reaction method
voltaic (galvanic) cell
electrolytic cell
electrode
electrolyte
anode
cathode

Section 21.2
half-cell
salt bridge
Section 21.3
voltage
cell potential (E_{cell})
electromotive force (emf)
volt (V)
coulomb (C)
standard cell potential (E^0_{cell})

standard electrode (half-
cell) potential ($E^0_{half\text{-}cell}$)
standard reference half-cell
(standard hydrogen elec-
trode)
Section 21.4
faraday (F)
Nernst equation
concentration cell

Section 21.5
battery
fuel cell
Section 21.6
corrosion
Section 21.7
electrolysis
overvoltage
ampere (A)

Key Equations and Relationships

21.1 Relating a spontaneous process to the sign of the cell potential (p. 906):

$$E_{cell} > 0 \text{ for a spontaneous process}$$

21.2 Relating electric potential to energy and charge in SI units (p. 906):

$$\text{Potential} = \text{energy/charge} \quad \text{or} \quad 1 \text{ V} = 1 \text{ J/C}$$

21.3 Relating standard cell potential to standard electrode potentials in a voltaic cell (p. 907):

$$E^0_{cell} = E^0_{cathode} - E^0_{anode}$$

21.4 Defining the faraday constant (p. 916):

$$F = 9.65 \times 10^4 \frac{\text{J}}{\text{V} \cdot \text{mol e}^-} \quad \text{(3 significant figures)}$$

21.5 Relating the free energy change to electrical work and cell potential (p. 916):

$$\Delta G = w_{max} = -nFE_{cell}$$

21.6 Finding the standard free energy change from the standard cell potential (p. 916):

$$\Delta G^0 = -nFE^0_{cell}$$

21.7 Finding the equilibrium constant from the standard cell potential (p. 916):

$$E^0_{cell} = \frac{RT}{nF} \ln K$$

21.8 Substituting known values of R, F, and T into Equation 21.7 and converting to common logarithms (p. 916):

$$E^0_{cell} = \frac{0.0592 \text{ V}}{n} \log K \quad \text{and} \quad \log K = \frac{nE^0_{cell}}{0.0592 \text{ V}} \quad \text{(at 25°C)}$$

21.9 Calculating the nonstandard cell potential (Nernst equation) (p. 917):

$$E_{cell} = E^0_{cell} - \frac{RT}{nF} \ln Q$$

21.10 Substituting known values of R, F, and T into the Nernst equation and converting logarithms (p. 918):

$$E_{cell} = E^0_{cell} - \frac{0.0592 \text{ V}}{n} \log Q \quad \text{(at 25°C)}$$

21.11 Relating current to charge and time (p. 937):

$$\text{Current} = \text{charge/time} \quad \text{or} \quad 1 \text{ A} = 1 \text{ C/s}$$

Highlighted Figures and Tables

These figures (F) and tables (T) provide a quick review of key ideas. Entries in color contain frequently used data.
F21.1 A summary of redox terminology (p. 896)
F21.3 Voltaic and electrolytic cells (p. 900)
F21.5 A voltaic cell of the zinc-copper reaction (p. 902)
T21.2 Standard electrode potentials at 298 K (p. 911)

F21.9 The interrelationship of ΔG^0, E^0, and K (p. 916)
F21.10 E_{cell} and log Q for the zinc-copper cell (p. 919)
F21.13 The corrosion of iron (p. 929)
F21.17 Sn-Cu reaction in voltaic and electrolytic cells (p. 931)
T21.4 Conventions for electrochemical cells (p. 932)
F21.20 Summary of the stoichiometry of electrolysis (p. 937)

Answers to Follow-up Problems

21.1 $6KMnO_4(aq) + 6KOH(aq) + KI(aq) \longrightarrow$
$\qquad\qquad 6K_2MnO_4(aq) + KIO_3(aq) + 3H_2O(l)$
21.2 $Sn(s) \longrightarrow Sn^{2+}(aq) + 2e^-$ [anode; oxidation]
$6e^- + 14H^+(aq) + Cr_2O_7^{2-}(aq) \longrightarrow 2Cr^{3+}(aq) + 7H_2O(l)$
$\qquad\qquad\qquad\qquad\qquad\qquad\qquad$ [cathode; reduction]

$3Sn(s) + Cr_2O_7^{2-}(aq) + 14H^+(aq) \longrightarrow$
$\qquad\qquad 3Sn^{2+}(aq) + 2Cr^{3+}(aq) + 7H_2O(l)$ [overall]
Cell notation:
$Sn(s) \mid Sn^{2+}(aq) \parallel H^+(aq), Cr_2O_7^{2-}(aq), Cr^{3+}(aq) \mid graphite$

21.3 $Br_2(aq) + 2e^- \longrightarrow 2Br^-(aq)$ $E^0_{bromine} = 1.07$ V
$$\text{[cathode]}$$

$2V^{3+}(aq) + 2H_2O(l) \longrightarrow 2VO^{2+}(aq) + 4H^+(aq) + 2e^-$
$$-E^0_{vanadium} = ? \quad \text{[anode]}$$

$-E^0_{vanadium} = E^0_{cell} - E^0_{bromine}$
$$= 1.39 \text{ V} - 1.07 \text{ V} = 0.32 \text{ V}$$

$E^0_{vanadium} = -0.32$ V

21.4 $Fe^{2+}(aq) + 2e^- \longrightarrow Fe(s)$ $E^0 = -0.44$ V

$\underline{2[Fe^{2+}(aq) \longrightarrow Fe^{3+}(aq) + e^-]}$ $\underline{-E^0 = -0.77 \text{ V}}$

$3Fe^{2+}(aq) \longrightarrow 2Fe^{3+}(aq) + Fe(s)$ $E^0_{cell} = -1.21$ V

The reaction is nonspontaneous. The spontaneous reaction is
$2Fe^{3+}(aq) + Fe(s) \longrightarrow 3Fe^{2+}(aq); E^0_{cell} = +1.21$ V
$Fe > Fe^{2+} > Fe^{3+}$

21.5 $Cd(s) + Cu^{2+}(aq) \longrightarrow Cd^{2+}(aq) + Cu(s)$
$\Delta G^0 = -RT \ln K = -8.31 \text{ J/mol} \cdot \text{K} \times 298 \text{ K} \times \ln K$
$$= -143 \text{ kJ}; K = 1.20 \times 10^{25}$$

$E^0_{cell} = \dfrac{0.0592 \text{ V}}{2} \log(1.20 \times 10^{25}) = 0.742$ V

21.6 $Fe(s) \longrightarrow Fe^{2+}(aq) + 2e^-$ $-E^0 = 0.44$ V

$\underline{Cu^{2+}(aq) + 2e^- \longrightarrow Cu(s)}$ $\underline{E^0 - 0.34 \text{ V}}$

$Fe(s) + Cu^{2+}(aq) \longrightarrow Fe^{2+}(aq) + Cu(s)$ $E^0_{cell} = 0.78$ V

So $E_{cell} = 0.78$ V $+ 0.25$ V $= 1.03$ V

1.03 V $= 0.78$ V $- \dfrac{0.0592 \text{ V}}{2} \log \dfrac{[Fe^{2+}]}{[Cu^{2+}]}$

$\dfrac{[Fe^{2+}]}{[Cu^{2+}]} = 3.6 \times 10^{-9}$

$[Fe^{2+}] = 3.6 \times 10^{-9} \times 0.30$ M $= 1.1 \times 10^{-9}$ M

21.7 $Au^{3+}(aq, 2.5 \times 10^{-2}$ M$)$ [B] $\longrightarrow$
$$Au^{3+}(aq, 7.0 \times 10^{-4} \text{ M}) \text{ [A]}$$

$E_{cell} = 0$ V $- \left(\dfrac{0.0592 \text{ V}}{3} \times \log \dfrac{7.0 \times 10^{-4}}{2.5 \times 10^{-2}} \right) = 0.031$ V

A is negative, so it is the anode.

21.8 Oxidizing agents: K^+ and Al^{3+}. Reducing agents: F^- and Br^-

Al is above and to the right of K, so it has a higher IE:
$Al^{3+}(l) + 3e^- \longrightarrow Al(s)$ [cathode; reduction]

Br is below F, so it has a lower EN:
$2Br^-(l) \longrightarrow Br_2(g) + 2e^-$ [anode; oxidation]

$2Al^{3+}(l) + 6Br^-(l) \longrightarrow 2Al(s) + 3Br_2(g)$ [overall]

21.9 $Au^{3+}(aq) + 3e^- \longrightarrow Au(s); E^0 = 1.50$ V
$$\text{[cathode; reduction]}$$

Because of overvoltage, O_2 will not form at the anode, so Br_2 will form:

$2Br^-(aq) \longrightarrow Br_2(l) + 2e^-; -E^0 = -1.07$ V
$$\text{[cathode; oxidation]}$$

21.10 $Cu^{2+}(aq) + 2e^- \longrightarrow Cu(s)$; therefore,
2 mol e^-/1 mol Cu = 2 mol e^-/63.55 g Cu

Time (min) = 1.50 g Cu $\times \dfrac{2 \text{ mol } e^-}{63.55 \text{ g Cu}}$

$\times \dfrac{9.65 \times 10^4 \text{ C}}{1 \text{ mol } e^-} \times \dfrac{1 \text{ s}}{4.75 \text{ C}} \times \dfrac{1 \text{ min}}{60 \text{ s}}$

= 16.0 min

Problems

Problems with a **colored** number are answered at the back of the text. Problem sections match the text and provide the number(s) of relevant sample problems. Most offer concept review questions, skill-building exercises (written in similar pairs), and problems in a relevant context. Following these are comprehensive problems based on material from any section and/or previous chapter.

[Note: Unless stated otherwise, all problems refer to systems at 298 K (25°C).]

Half-Reactions and Electrochemical Cells
(Sample Problem 21.1)

■ Concept Review Questions
21.1 Define oxidation and reduction in terms of electron transfer and change in oxidation number.

21.2 Why must an electrochemical process involve a redox reaction?

21.3 Can one half-reaction in a redox process exist independently from the other? Explain.

21.4 Water is used to balance O atoms in the half-reaction method. Why can't O^{2-} ions be used instead?

21.5 During the balancing process, what step is taken to ensure that e^- loss equals e^- gain?

21.6 How are protons removed when balancing a redox reaction in basic solution?

21.7 Are spectator ions used to balance the half-reactions of a redox reaction? At what stage might spectator ions enter the balancing process?

21.8 Which type of electrochemical cell has a $\Delta G_{sys} < 0$? Which type has an increase in the free energy of the cell?

21.9 Which statements are true? Correct any that are false.
(a) In a voltaic cell, the anode is negative relative to the cathode.
(b) Oxidation occurs at the anode of either type of cell.
(c) Electrons flow into the cathode of an electrolytic cell.
(d) In a voltaic cell, the surroundings do work on the system.
(e) If a metal is plated out of an electrolytic cell, it appears on the cathode.
(f) The cell electrolyte provides a solution of mobile electrons.

■ Skill-Building Exercises (paired)
21.10 Consider the following balanced redox reaction:

$16H^+(aq) + 2MnO_4^-(aq) + 10Cl^-(aq) \longrightarrow$
$$2Mn^{2+}(aq) + 5Cl_2(g) + 8H_2O(l)$$

(a) Which species is being oxidized?
(b) Which species is being reduced?
(c) Which species is the oxidizing agent?
(d) Which species is the reducing agent?
(e) From which species to which does electron transfer occur?
(f) Write the balanced molecular equation, with K^+ and SO_4^{2-} as the spectator ions.

21.11 Consider the following balanced redox reaction:

$$2CrO_2^-(aq) + 2H_2O(l) + 6ClO^-(aq) \longrightarrow$$
$$2CrO_4^{2-}(aq) + 3Cl_2(g) + 4OH^-(aq)$$

(a) Which species is being oxidized?
(b) Which species is being reduced?
(c) Which species is the oxidizing agent?
(d) Which species is the reducing agent?
(e) From which species to which does electron transfer occur?
(f) Write the balanced molecular equation, with Na^+ as the spectator ion.

21.12 Balance the following skeleton reactions and identify the oxidizing and reducing agents:
(a) $ClO_3^-(aq) + I^-(aq) \longrightarrow I_2(s) + Cl^-(aq)$ [acidic]
(b) $MnO_4^-(aq) + SO_3^{2-}(aq) \longrightarrow$
$$MnO_2(s) + SO_4^{2-}(aq)$$ [basic]
(c) $MnO_4^-(aq) + H_2O_2(aq) \longrightarrow Mn^{2+}(aq) + O_2(g)$ [acidic]

21.13 Balance the following skeleton reactions and identify the oxidizing and reducing agents:
(a) $O_2(g) + NO(g) \longrightarrow NO_3^-(aq)$ [acidic]
(b) $CrO_4^{2-}(aq) + Cu(s) \longrightarrow Cr(OH)_3(s) + Cu(OH)_2(s)$ [basic]
(c) $AsO_4^{3-}(aq) + NO_2^-(aq) \longrightarrow$
$$AsO_2^-(aq) + NO_3^-(aq)$$ [basic]

21.14 Balance the following skeleton reactions and identify the oxidizing and reducing agents:
(a) $Cr_2O_7^{2-}(aq) + Zn(s) \longrightarrow Zn^{2+}(aq) + Cr^{3+}(aq)$ [acidic]
(b) $Fe(OH)_2(s) + MnO_4^-(aq) \longrightarrow$
$$MnO_2(s) + Fe(OH)_3(s)$$ [basic]
(c) $Zn(s) + NO_3^-(aq) \longrightarrow Zn^{2+}(aq) + N_2(g)$ [acidic]

21.15 Balance the following skeleton reactions and identify the oxidizing and reducing agents:
(a) $BH_4^-(aq) + ClO_3^-(aq) \longrightarrow H_2BO_3^-(aq) + Cl^-(aq)$ [basic]
(b) $CrO_4^{2-}(aq) + N_2O(g) \longrightarrow Cr^{3+}(aq) + NO(g)$ [acidic]
(c) $Br_2(l) \longrightarrow BrO_3^-(aq) + Br^-(aq)$ [basic]

21.16 Balance the following skeleton reactions and identify the oxidizing and reducing agents:
(a) $Sb(s) + NO_3^-(aq) \longrightarrow Sb_4O_6(s) + NO(g)$ [acidic]
(b) $Mn^{2+}(aq) + BiO_3^-(aq) \longrightarrow$
$$MnO_4^-(aq) + Bi^{3+}(aq)$$ [acidic]
(c) $Fe(OH)_2(s) + Pb(OH)_3^-(aq) \longrightarrow$
$$Fe(OH)_3(s) + Pb(s)$$ [basic]

21.17 Balance the following skeleton reactions and identify the oxidizing and reducing agents:
(a) $NO_2(g) \longrightarrow NO_3^-(aq) + NO_2^-(aq)$ [basic]
(b) $Zn(s) + NO_3^-(aq) \longrightarrow Zn(OH)_4^{2-}(aq) + NH_3(g)$ [basic]
(c) $H_2S(g) + NO_3^-(aq) \longrightarrow S_8(s) + NO(g)$ [acidic]

21.18 Balance the following skeleton reactions and identify the oxidizing and reducing agents:
(a) $As_4O_6(s) + MnO_4^-(aq) \longrightarrow$
$$AsO_4^{3-}(aq) + Mn^{2+}(aq)$$ [acidic]
(b) $P_4(s) \longrightarrow HPO_3^{2-}(aq) + PH_3(g)$ [acidic]
(c) $MnO_4^-(aq) + CN^-(aq) \longrightarrow MnO_2(s) + CNO^-(aq)$ [basic]

21.19 Balance the following skeleton reactions and identify the oxidizing and reducing agents:
(a) $SO_3^{2-}(aq) + Cl_2(g) \longrightarrow SO_4^{2-}(aq) + Cl^-(aq)$ [basic]

(b) $Fe(CN)_6^{3-}(aq) + Re(s) \longrightarrow$
$$Fe(CN)_6^{4-}(aq) + ReO_4^-(aq)$$ [basic]
(c) $MnO_4^-(aq) + HCOOH(aq) \longrightarrow$
$$Mn^{2+}(aq) + CO_2(g)$$ [acidic]

■ Problems in Context

21.20 In many residential water systems, the aqueous Fe^{3+} concentration is high enough to stain sinks and turn drinking water light brown. The analysis of iron content occurs by first reducing the Fe^{3+} to Fe^{2+} and then titrating with MnO_4^- in acidic solution. Balance the skeleton reaction of the titration step:

$$Fe^{2+}(aq) + MnO_4^-(aq) \longrightarrow Mn^{2+}(aq) + Fe^{3+}(aq)$$

21.21 *Aqua regia,* a mixture of concentrated HNO_3 and HCl, was developed by alchemists as a means to "dissolve" gold. The process is actually a redox reaction with the following simplified skeleton reaction:

$$Au(s) + NO_3^-(aq) + Cl^-(aq) \longrightarrow AuCl_4^-(aq) + NO_2(g)$$

(a) Balance the reaction by the half-reaction method.
(b) What are the oxidizing and reducing agents?
(c) What is the function of HCl in aqua regia?

Voltaic Cells: Using Spontaneous Reactions to Generate Electrical Energy
(Sample Problem 21.2)

■ Concept Review Questions

21.22 Consider the following general voltaic cell:

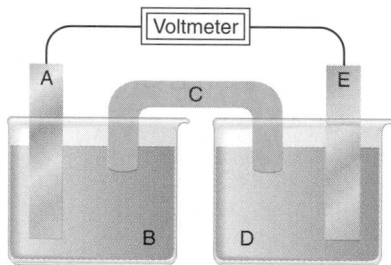

Identify the (a) anode; (b) cathode; (c) salt bridge; (d) electrode at which e^- leave the cell; (e) electrode with a positive charge; (f) electrode that gains mass as the cell operates (assuming a metal plates out).

21.23 Why does a voltaic cell not operate to any significant extent unless the two compartments are connected through an external circuit?

21.24 What purpose does the salt bridge serve in a voltaic cell and how does it accomplish this purpose?

21.25 What is the difference between an active and an inactive electrode? Why are inactive electrodes used? Name two substances commonly used for inactive electrodes.

21.26 When a piece of metal A is placed in a solution of metal B ions, metal B plates out on the piece of A.
(a) Which metal is being oxidized?
(b) Which metal is being "displaced"?
(c) Which metal would you use as the anode in a voltaic cell incorporating these two metals?
(d) If bubbles of H_2 form when B is placed in acid, will they form if A is placed in acid? Explain.

Skill-Building Exercises (paired)

21.27 Consider the following voltaic cell:

(a) In which direction do electrons flow through the external circuit?

(b) In which half-cell does oxidation occur?

(c) In which half-cell do electrons enter the cell?

(d) At which electrode are electrons consumed?

(e) Which electrode is negatively charged?

(f) Which electrode decreases in mass during operation of the cell?

(g) Suggest a solution for the cathode electrolyte.

(h) Suggest a pair of ions for the salt bridge.

(i) For which electrode could you use an inactive material?

(j) In which direction do anions within the salt bridge move to maintain charge neutrality?

(k) Write balanced half-reactions and an overall cell reaction.

21.28 Consider the following voltaic cell:

(a) Which direction do electrons flow in the external circuit?

(b) In which half-cell does reduction occur?

(c) In which half-cell do electrons leave the cell?

(d) At which electrode are electrons generated?

(e) Which electrode is positively charged?

(f) Which electrode increases in mass during operation of the cell?

(g) Suggest a solution for the anode electrolyte.

(h) Suggest a pair of ions for the salt bridge.

(i) For which electrode could you use an inactive material?

(j) In which direction do cations within the salt bridge move to maintain charge neutrality?

(k) Write balanced half-reactions and an overall cell reaction.

21.29 A voltaic cell is constructed with an Sn/Sn^{2+} half-cell and a Zn/Zn^{2+} half-cell. Measurement shows the zinc electrode is negative.

(a) Write balanced half-reactions and the overall spontaneous reaction.

(b) Diagram the cell, labeling electrodes with their charges and showing the directions of electron flow in the circuit and of cation and anion flow in the salt bridge.

21.30 A voltaic cell is constructed with an Ag/Ag^+ half-cell and a Pb/Pb^{2+} half-cell. Measurement shows that the silver electrode is positive.

(a) Write balanced half-reactions and the overall spontaneous reaction.

(b) Diagram the cell, labeling electrodes with their charges and showing the directions of electron flow in the circuit and of cation and anion flow in the salt bridge.

21.31 A voltaic cell is constructed with an Fe/Fe^{2+} half-cell and an Mn/Mn^{2+} half-cell. Measurement shows that the iron electrode is positive.

(a) Write balanced half-reactions and the overall spontaneous reaction.

(b) Diagram the cell, labeling electrodes with their charges and showing the directions of electron flow in the circuit and of cation and anion flow in the salt bridge.

21.32 A voltaic cell is constructed with a Cu/Cu^{2+} half-cell and an Ni/Ni^{2+} half-cell. Measurement shows that the nickel electrode is negative.

(a) Write balanced half-reactions and the overall spontaneous reaction.

(b) Diagram the cell, labeling electrodes with their charges and showing the directions of electron flow in the circuit and of cation and anion flow in the salt bridge.

21.33 Write the cell notation for the voltaic cell that incorporates each of the following redox reactions:

(a) $Al(s) + Cr^{3+}(aq) \longrightarrow Al^{3+}(aq) + Cr(s)$

(b) $Cu^{2+}(aq) + SO_2(g) + 2H_2O(l) \longrightarrow$
$$Cu(s) + SO_4{}^{2-}(aq) + 4H^+(aq)$$

21.34 Write a balanced equation from each of the following cell notations:

(a) $Mn(s)|Mn^{2+}(aq)||Cd^{2+}(aq)|Cd(s)$

(b) $Fe(s)|Fe^{2+}(aq)||NO_3{}^-(aq)|NO(g)|Pt(s)$

Cell Potential: Output of a Voltaic Cell

(Sample Problems 21.3 and 21.4)

Concept Review Questions

21.35 How is a standard reference electrode used to determine unknown $E^0_{\text{half-cell}}$ values?

21.36 What does a negative E^0_{cell} indicate about a redox reaction? What does it indicate about the reverse reaction?

21.37 The standard cell potential is a thermodynamic state function. How are E^0 values treated similarly to ΔH^0, ΔG^0, and S^0 values? How are they treated differently?

Skill-Building Exercises (paired)

21.38 In basic solution, selenide and sulfite ions react spontaneously:

$2Se^{2-}(aq) + 2SO_3{}^{2-}(aq) + 3H_2O(l) \longrightarrow$
$$2Se(s) + 6OH^-(aq) + S_2O_3{}^{2-}(aq); E^0_{\text{cell}} = 0.35 \text{ V}$$

(a) Write balanced half reactions for the process.

(b) If E^0_{sulfite} is -0.57 V, calculate E^0_{selenium}.

21.39 In acidic solution, ozone and manganese(II) ion react spontaneously:

$O_3(g) + Mn^{2+}(aq) + H_2O(l) \longrightarrow$
$$O_2(g) + MnO_2(s) + 2H^+(aq); E^0_{\text{cell}} = 0.84 \text{ V}$$

(a) Write the balanced half-reactions.

(b) Using Table 21.2 for E^0_{ozone}, calculate $E^0_{\text{manganese}}$.

21.40 Use the emf series (Table 21.2) to arrange the following species
(a) In order of *decreasing* strength as *oxidizing* agents: Fe^{3+}, Br_2, Cu^{2+}
(b) In order of *increasing* strength as *oxidizing* agents: Ca^{2+}, $Cr_2O_7^{2-}$, Ag^+

21.41 Use the emf series (Table 21.2) to arrange the following species
(a) In order of *decreasing* strength as *reducing* agents: SO_2, $PbSO_4$, MnO_2
(b) In order of *increasing* strength as *reducing* agents: Hg, Fe, Sn

21.42 Balance each skeleton reaction, calculate E^0_{cell}, and state whether the reaction is spontaneous:
(a) $Co(s) + H^+(aq) \longrightarrow Co^{2+}(aq) + H_2(g)$
(b) $Mn^{2+}(aq) + Br_2(l) \longrightarrow MnO_4^-(aq) + Br^-(aq)$ [acidic]
(c) $Hg_2^{2+}(aq) \longrightarrow Hg^{2+}(aq) + Hg(l)$

21.43 Balance each skeleton reaction, calculate E^0_{cell}, and state whether the reaction is spontaneous:
(a) $Cl_2(g) + Fe^{2+}(aq) \longrightarrow Cl^-(aq) + Fe^{3+}(aq)$
(b) $Mn^{2+}(aq) + Co^{3+}(aq) \longrightarrow MnO_2(s) + Co^{2+}(aq)$ [acidic]
(c) $AgCl(s) + NO(g) \longrightarrow Ag(s) + Cl^-(aq) + NO_3^-(aq)$ [acidic]

21.44 Balance each skeleton reaction, calculate E^0_{cell}, and state whether the reaction is spontaneous:
(a) $Ag(s) + Cu^{2+}(aq) \longrightarrow Ag^+(aq) + Cu(s)$
(b) $Cd(s) + Cr_2O_7^{2-}(aq) \longrightarrow Cd^{2+}(aq) + Cr^{3+}(aq)$
(c) $Ni^{2+}(aq) + Pb(s) \longrightarrow Ni(s) + Pb^{2+}(aq)$

21.45 Balance each skeleton reaction, calculate E^0_{cell}, and state whether the reaction is spontaneous:
(a) $Cu^+(aq) + PbO_2(s) + SO_4^{2-}(aq) \longrightarrow$
$$PbSO_4(s) + Cu^{2+}(aq) \text{ [acidic]}$$
(b) $H_2O_2(aq) + Ni^{2+}(aq) \longrightarrow O_2(g) + Ni(s)$ [acidic]
(c) $MnO_2(s) + Ag^+(aq) \longrightarrow MnO_4^-(aq) + Ag(s)$ [basic]

21.46 Use the following half-reactions to write three spontaneous reactions, calculate E^0_{cell} for each reaction, and rank the oxidizing and reducing agents:
(1) $Al^{3+}(aq) + 3e^- \longrightarrow Al(s)$ $E^0 = -1.66$ V
(2) $N_2O_4(g) + 2e^- \longrightarrow 2NO_2^-(aq)$ $E^0 = 0.867$ V
(3) $SO_4^{2-}(aq) + H_2O(l) + 2e^- \longrightarrow SO_3^{2-}(aq) + 2OH^-(aq)$
$$E^0 = 0.93 \text{ V}$$

21.47 Use the following half-reactions to write three spontaneous reactions, calculate E^0_{cell} for each reaction, and rank the oxidizing and reducing agents:
(1) $Au^+(aq) + e^- \longrightarrow Au(s)$ $E^0 = 1.69$ V
(2) $N_2O(g) + 2H^+(aq) + 2e^- \longrightarrow N_2(g) + H_2O(l)$ $E^0 = 1.77$ V
(3) $Cr^{3+}(aq) + 3e^- \longrightarrow Cr(s)$ $E^0 = -0.74$ V

21.48 Use the following half-reactions to write three spontaneous reactions, calculate E^0_{cell} for each reaction, and rank the oxidizing and reducing agents:
(1) $2HClO(aq) + 2H^+(aq) + 2e^- \longrightarrow Cl_2(g) + 2H_2O(l)$
$$E^0 = 1.63 \text{ V}$$
(2) $Pt^{2+}(aq) + 2e^- \longrightarrow Pt(s)$ $E^0 = 1.20$ V
(3) $PbSO_4(s) + 2e^- \longrightarrow Pb(s) + SO_4^{2-}(aq)$ $E^0 = -0.31$ V

21.49 Use the following half-reactions to write three spontaneous reactions, calculate E^0_{cell} for each reaction, and rank the oxidizing and reducing agents:

(1) $I_2(s) + 2e^- \longrightarrow 2I^-(aq)$ $E^0 = 0.53$ V
(2) $S_2O_8^{2-}(aq) + 2e^- \longrightarrow 2SO_4^{2-}(aq)$ $E^0 = 2.01$ V
(3) $Cr_2O_7^{2-}(aq) + 14H^+(aq) + 6e^- \longrightarrow$
$$2Cr^{3+}(aq) + 7H_2O(l) \quad E^0 = 1.33 \text{ V}$$

■ **Problems in Context**

21.50 When metal A is placed in a solution of metal B salt, the surface of metal A changes color. When metal B is placed in acid solution, gas bubbles form on the surface of the metal. When metal A is placed in a solution of metal C salt, no change is observed in the solution or on the metal A surface. Will metal C cause formation of H_2 when placed in acid solution? Rank metals A, B, and C in order of *decreasing* reducing strength.

21.51 When a clean iron nail is placed in an aqueous solution of copper(II) sulfate, the nail immediately begins to turn a brown-black color. In a few minutes, the nail is completely coated with a material of this color.
(a) What is the material coating the iron?
(b) What are the oxidizing and reducing agents?
(c) Can this reaction be made into a voltaic cell?
(d) Write the balanced equation for the reaction.
(e) Calculate E^0_{cell} for the process.

Free Energy and Electrical Work
(Sample Problems 21.5 to 21.7)

■ **Concept Review Questions**

21.52 (a) How do the relative magnitudes of Q and K relate to the signs of ΔG and E_{cell}? Explain.
(b) Can a cell do work when $Q/K > 1$ or when $Q/K < 1$? Explain.

21.53 A voltaic cell consists of a metal A/A^+ electrode and metal B/B^+ electrode, with the A/A^+ electrode negative. The initial $[A^+]/[B^+]$ is such that $E_{cell} > E^0_{cell}$.
(a) How do $[A^+]$ and $[B^+]$ change as the cell operates?
(b) How does E_{cell} change as the cell operates?
(c) What is $[A^+]/[B^+]$ when $E_{cell} = E^0_{cell}$? Explain.
(d) Is it possible for E_{cell} to be less than E^0_{cell}? Explain.

21.54 Explain whether E_{cell} of a voltaic cell increases or decreases from the following changes:
(a) Decrease in cell temperature
(b) Increase in concentration of an active ion in the anode compartment
(c) Increase in concentration of an active ion in the cathode compartment
(d) Increase in pressure of a gaseous reactant in the cathode component

21.55 In a concentration cell, is the more concentrated electrolyte in the cathode or the anode compartment? Explain.

■ **Skill-Building Exercises** *(paired)*

21.56 What is the value of the equilibrium constant at 25°C for the reaction between: (a) $Ni(s)$ and $Ag^+(aq)$; (b) $Fe(s)$ and $Cr^{3+}(aq)$?

21.57 What is the value of the equilibrium constant at 25°C for the reaction between: (a) $Al(s)$ and $Cd^{2+}(aq)$; (b) $I_2(s)$ and $Br^-(aq)$?

21.58 What is the value of the equilibrium constant at 25°C for the reaction between: (a) $Ag(s)$ and $Mn^{2+}(aq)$; (b) $Cl_2(g)$ and $Br^-(aq)$?

21.59 What is the value of the equilibrium constant at 25°C for the reaction between: (a) Cr(s) and $Cu^{2+}(aq)$; (b) Sn(s) and $Pb^{2+}(aq)$?

21.60 Calculate ΔG^0 for each of the reactions in Problem 21.56.

21.61 Calculate ΔG^0 for each of the reactions in Problem 21.57.

21.62 Calculate ΔG^0 for each of the reactions in Problem 21.58.

21.63 Calculate ΔG^0 for each of the reactions in Problem 21.59.

21.64 What are E^0_{cell} and ΔG^0 at 25°C of a redox reaction for which $n = 1$ and $K = 5.0 \times 10^3$?

21.65 What are E^0_{cell} and ΔG^0 at 25°C of a redox reaction for which $n = 1$ and $K = 5.0 \times 10^{-6}$?

21.66 What are E^0_{cell} and ΔG^0 at 25°C of a redox reaction for which $n = 2$ and $K = 75$?

21.67 What are E^0_{cell} and ΔG^0 at 25°C of a redox reaction for which $n = 2$ and $K = 0.075$?

21.68 A voltaic cell consists of a standard H_2 electrode and a Cu/Cu^{2+} electrode. Calculate $[Cu^{2+}]$ when E_{cell} is 0.25 V.

21.69 A voltaic cell consists of an Mn/Mn^{2+} electrode and a Pb/Pb^{2+} electrode. Calculate $[Pb^{2+}]$ when $[Mn^{2+}]$ is 1.3 M and E_{cell} is 0.42 V.

21.70 A voltaic cell consists of Ni/Ni^{2+} and Co/Co^{2+} half-cells with the following initial concentrations: $[Ni^{2+}] = 0.80$ M; $[Co^{2+}] = 0.20$ M.
(a) What is the initial E_{cell}?
(b) What is E_{cell} when $[Co^{2+}]$ reaches 0.45 M?
(c) What is $[Ni^{2+}]$ when E_{cell} reaches 0.025 V?
(d) What are the equilibrium concentrations of the ions?

21.71 A voltaic cell consists of Mn/Mn^{2+} and Cd/Cd^{2+} half-cells with the following initial concentrations: $[Mn^{2+}] = 0.090$ M; $[Cd^{2+}] = 0.060$ M
(a) What is the initial E_{cell}?
(b) What is E_{cell} when $[Cd^{2+}]$ reaches 0.050 M?
(c) What is $[Mn^{2+}]$ when E_{cell} reaches 0.055 V?
(d) What are the equilibrium concentrations of the ions?

21.72 A concentration cell consists of two H_2/H^+ electrodes. Electrode A has H_2 at 0.90 atm bubbling into 0.10 M HCl. Electrode B has H_2 at 0.50 atm bubbling into 2.0 M HCl. Which electrode is the anode? What is the voltage of the cell?

21.73 A concentration cell consists of two Sn/Sn^{2+} electrodes. The electrolyte in compartment A is 0.13 M $Sn(NO_3)_2$. The electrolyte in B is 0.87 M $Sn(NO_3)_2$. Which electrode is the cathode? What is the voltage of the cell?

Electrochemical Processes in Batteries

■ Concept Review Questions

21.74 What is the direction of electron flow with respect to the anode and the cathode in a battery? Explain.

21.75 In the everyday batteries used for flashlights, toys, etc., no salt bridge is evident. What is used in these cells to separate the anode and cathode compartments?

21.76 Both a D-sized and a AAA-sized alkaline battery have an output of 1.5 V. What property of the cell potential allows this to occur? What is different about these two batteries?

■ Problems in Context

21.77 Many common devices require more than one battery for operation.
(a) How many alkaline batteries must be placed in series to light a flashlight with a 6.0-V bulb?
(b) What is the voltage requirement of a camera that uses six silver batteries?
(c) How many volts can a car battery deliver if two of its anode/cathode cells are shorted?

Corrosion: A Case of Environmental Electrochemistry

■ Concept Review Questions

21.78 During the reconstruction of the Statue of Liberty, Teflon spacers were placed between the iron skeleton and the copper plates that cover the statue. What purpose do these spacers serve?

21.79 Why do steel bridge-supports rust at the water line but not above or below it?

21.80 Since the 1930s, chromium has replaced nickel for corrosion resistance and appearance on car bumpers and trim. How does the chromium protect steel from corrosion?

21.81 Which of the following metals are suitable for use as sacrificial anodes to protect against the corrosion of underground iron pipes? If any are not suitable, explain why:
(a) aluminum; (b) magnesium; (c) sodium; (d) lead; (e) nickel; (f) zinc; (g) chromium.

Electrolytic Cells: Using Electrical Energy to Drive a Nonspontaneous Reaction
(Sample Problems 21.8 to 21.10)

■ Concept Review Questions
Unless stated otherwise, assume the electrolytic cells in the following problems operate at 100% efficiency.

21.82 Consider the following general electrolytic cell:

(a) At which electrode does oxidation occur?
(b) At which electrode does elemental M form?
(c) At which electrode are electrons being released by ions?
(d) At which electrode are electrons entering the cell?

21.83 A voltaic cell consists of Cr/Cr^{3+} and Cd/Cd^{2+} half-cells in their standard states. After 10 minutes of operation, a thin coating of cadmium metal has plated out on the cathode. Describe what happens if you attach the negative terminal of a dry cell (1.5 V) to the cell cathode and the positive terminal to the cell anode.

21.84 Why are $E_{half-cell}$ values for the oxidation and reduction of water different from the $E^0_{half-cell}$ values for the same processes?

21.85 In an aqueous electrolytic cell, nitrate ions never react at the anode, but nitrite ions do. Explain.

21.86 How does overvoltage influence the products in the electrolysis of aqueous salts?

■ **Skill-Building Exercises (paired)**

21.87 In the electrolysis of molten NaBr,
(a) What product forms at the anode?
(b) What product forms at the cathode?

21.88 In the electrolysis of molten BaI_2,
(a) What product forms at the negative electrode?
(b) What product forms at the positive electrode?

21.89 In the electrolysis of a molten mixture of KI and MgF_2, identify the product that forms at the anode and at the cathode.

21.90 In the electrolysis of a molten mixture of CsBr and $SrCl_2$, identify the product that forms at the negative electrode and at the positive electrode.

21.91 In the electrolysis of a molten mixture of NaCl and $CaBr_2$, identify the product that forms at the anode and at the cathode.

21.92 In the electrolysis of a molten mixture of RbF and $CaCl_2$, identify the product that forms at the negative electrode and at the positive electrode.

21.93 Identify those elements that can be prepared by electrolysis of their aqueous salts: copper, barium, aluminum, bromine.

21.94 Identify those elements that can be prepared by electrolysis of their aqueous salts: strontium, gold, tin, chlorine.

21.95 Identify those elements that can be prepared by electrolysis of their aqueous salts: lithium, iodine, zinc, silver.

21.96 Identify those elements that can be prepared by electrolysis of their aqueous salts: fluorine, manganese, iron, cadmium.

21.97 What product forms at each electrode in the aqueous electrolysis of the following salts: (a) LiF; (b) $SnSO_4$?

21.98 What product forms at each electrode in the aqueous electrolysis of the following salts: (a) $ZnBr_2$; (b) $Cu(HCO_3)_2$?

21.99 What product forms at each electrode in the aqueous electrolysis of the following salts: (a) $Cr(NO_3)_3$; (b) $MnCl_2$?

21.100 What product forms at each electrode in the aqueous electrolysis of the following salts: (a) FeI_2; (b) K_3PO_4?

21.101 Electrolysis of molten $MgCl_2$ is the final production step in the isolation of magnesium from seawater by the Dow process (Section 22.4). When 35.6 g Mg metal forms,
(a) How many moles of electrons are required?
(b) How many coulombs are required?
(c) How many amps are required to produce this amount in 2.50 h?

21.102 Electrolysis of molten NaCl in a Downs cell is the major isolation step in the production of sodium metal (Section 22.4). When 215 g Na metal forms,
(a) How many moles of electrons are required?
(b) How many coulombs are required?
(c) How many amps are required to produce this amount in 9.50 h?

21.103 How many grams of radium can be formed by the passage of 215 C through an electrolytic cell containing a molten radium salt?

21.104 How many grams of aluminum can be formed by the passage of 305 C through an electrolytic cell containing a molten aluminum salt?

21.105 How many seconds does it take to deposit 85.5 g Zn on a steel gate when 23.0 A is passed through a $ZnSO_4$ solution?

21.106 How many seconds does it take to deposit 1.63 g Ni on a decorative drawer handle when 13.7 A is passed through a $Ni(NO_3)_2$ solution?

■ **Problems in Context**

21.107 A professor adds Na_2SO_4 to water to facilitate its electrolysis in a lecture demonstration. (a) What is the purpose of the Na_2SO_4? (b) Why is the water electrolyzed instead of the salt?

21.108 Subterranean brines in parts of the United States are rich in iodides and bromides and serve as an industrial source of these elements. In one recovery method, the brines are evaporated to dryness and then melted and electrolyzed. Which halogen is more likely to form from this treatment? Why?

21.109 Zinc plating (galvanizing) is an important means of corrosion protection. Although the process is done customarily by dipping the object into molten zinc, the metal can also be electroplated from aqueous solutions. How many grams of zinc can be deposited on a steel tank from a $ZnSO_4$ solution when a 0.755-A current flows for 2.00 days?

Comprehensive Problems

Problems with an asterisk (*) are more challenging.

21.110 In a dry cell, MnO_2 occurs in a semisolid electrolyte paste and is reduced at the cathode. The MnO_2 used in dry cells can itself be produced by an electrochemical process of which one half-reaction is

$$Mn^{2+}(aq) + 2H_2O(l) \longrightarrow MnO_2(s) + 4H^+(aq) + 2e^-$$

If a current of 25.0 A is used, how many hours are needed to produce 1.00 kg of MnO_2? At which electrode is the MnO_2 formed?

21.111 Automobile manufacturers are currently designing cars that will use hydrogen as fuel. In Iceland, Sweden, and other parts of Scandinavia, where hydroelectric plants produce relatively inexpensive electric power, the hydrogen may be made industrially by the electrolysis of water.
(a) How many coulombs are needed to produce 2.5×10^6 L H_2 gas at 10.0 atm pressure and 25°C? (Assume the ideal gas law applies.)
(b) If the coulombs are supplied at 1.24 V, how many joules are produced?
(c) If the combustion of oil yields 4.0×10^4 kJ/kg, what mass of oil must be burned to yield the number of joules in (b)?

21.112 Ion-selective electrodes are now one of the most common analytical tools in environmental field work because they are simple and portable.
(a) One of the simplest ion-selective electrodes consists of a silver rod and is designed to measure $[Ag^+]$. Write an equation relating the nonstandard cell potential at a silver electrode to the standard cell potential and $[Ag^+]$ when a silver ion-selective electrode is immersed in a solution of Ag^+.
(b) Write an equation relating the nonstandard cell potential at a copper electrode to the standard cell potential and

[Cu^{2+}] when a copper ion-selective electrode is immersed in a solution of Cu^{2+}.

(c) Silver chloride electrodes are used as ion-selective electrodes for Cl$^-$. The electrode is made to conduct by coating AgCl on an Ag metal rod. Write an equation relating the nonstandard cell potential at an AgCl electrode to the standard cell potential and [Cl$^-$] when the electrode is immersed in a solution of Cl$^-$. The reaction at the electrode is

$$AgCl(s) + e^- \longrightarrow Ag(s) + Cl^-(aq)$$

(d) Show that the answers to (a), (b), and (c) conform to the general formula for the potential at an ion-selective electrode:

$$E_{cell} = E^0_{cell} + \frac{RT}{nF} \ln [ion]$$

where n is the magnitude of the ion charge.

21.113 An inexpensive and accurate method of measuring the quantity of electricity passing through a circuit is to pass it through a solution of a metal ion and weigh the metal deposited. A silver electrode immersed in an Ag$^+$ solution weighs 1.7854 g before the current passes and weighs 1.8016 g after the current has passed. How many coulombs have passed?

*21.114 Answer the following questions from the point of view of a modern phlogistonist (see Section 1.2) studying an electrochemical cell:

(a) In which direction does the phlogiston flow: from anode to cathode or the reverse?

(b) How does the movement of phlogiston account for the dissolution of one metal electrode and the enlargement of the other metal electrode?

21.115 Compare and contrast a voltaic cell and an electrolytic cell with respect to each of the following:

(a) Sign of the free energy change

(b) Nature of the half-reaction at the anode

(c) Nature of the half-reaction at the cathode

(d) Charge on the electrode labeled "anode"

(e) Electrode from which electrons leave the cell

21.116 A thin disk earring 5.00 cm in diameter is plated with a coating of gold 0.20 mm thick from an Au^{3+} bath.

(a) How many days does it take to deposit the gold if the current used is 0.010 A? (d of gold = 19.3 g/cm^3.)

(b) If the price of gold is $320 per troy ounce (31.10 g), what is the cost of the gold plating?

21.117 (a) How many minutes does it take to form 10.0 L O$_2$ measured at 99.8 kPa and 28°C from water if a current of 1.3 A passes through the electrolytic cell?

(b) What mass of H$_2$ forms at the same time?

*21.118 Trains powered by electricity, including subways, use direct current. One conductor is the overhead wire (or "third rail" for subways), and the other is the rails upon which the wheels run. The rails are on supports in contact with the ground. To minimize corrosion, should the overhead wire or the rails be connected to the positive terminal? Explain.

21.119 A simple laboratory test to identify the relative charge of the two leads from a DC power supply uses a piece of filter paper moistened with NaCl solution containing phenolphthalein indicator (colorless in acid, pink in base).

The two wires from the power supply are touched to the paper about an inch apart. What do you expect to observe? What conclusion can you reach about the relative charges of the leads?

21.120 Like any piece of apparatus, an electrolytic cell operates at less than 100% efficiency. A cell depositing Cu from a Cu^{2+} bath operates for 10 h with an average current of 5.8 A. If 53.4 g copper is deposited, at what efficiency is the cell operating?

21.121 Commercial electrolysis is performed on both molten NaCl and aqueous NaCl solutions. Identify the anode product, cathode product, species reduced, and species oxidized for the (a) molten electrolysis and (b) aqueous electrolysis.

*21.122 To examine the effect of ion removal on cell voltage, a chemist constructs two voltaic cells, each with a standard hydrogen electrode in one compartment. One cell also contains a Pb/Pb^{2+} half-cell; the other contains a Cu/Cu^{2+} half-cell.

(a) What is E^0 of each cell at 298 K?

(b) Which electrode in each cell is negative?

(c) When Na$_2$S solution is added to the Pb^{2+} electrolyte, solid PbS forms. What happens to the cell voltage?

(d) When sufficient Na$_2$S is added to the Cu^{2+} electrolyte, CuS forms and [Cu^{2+}] is lowered to 1×10^{-16} M. What is the cell voltage?

21.123 Electrodes used in electrocardiography are disposable, and many incorporate silver. The metal is deposited in a thin layer on a small plastic "button," and then some is converted to AgCl:

$$Ag(s) + Cl^-(aq) \rightleftharpoons AgCl(s) + e^-$$

(a) If the surface area of the button is 2.0 cm^2 and the thickness of the silver layer is 7.0×10^{-6} m, calculate the volume of Ag used in one electrode, in cm^3.

(b) The density of silver metal is 10.5 g/cm^3. How many grams of silver are used per electrode?

(c) If the silver is electroplated on the button from a solution of Ag$^+$ with a current of 10.0 mA, how many minutes does the electroplating take?

(d) If bulk silver costs $5.50 per troy ounce (31.10 g), what is the cost (in cents) of the silver in one disposable electrode?

21.124 The commercial production of aluminum is done by the electrolysis of a bath containing Al$_2$O$_3$ dissolved in molten Na$_3$AlF$_6$. Why isn't it done by electrolysis of an aqueous AlCl$_3$ solution?

*21.125 Comparing the standard electrode potentials (E^0) of the Group 1A(1) metals Li, Na, and K with the negative of their first ionization energies reveals a discrepancy:

Ionization process reversed: $M^+(g) + e^- \rightleftharpoons M(g)$ $(-IE)$

Electrode reaction: $M^+(aq) + e^- \rightleftharpoons M(s)$ (E^0)

METAL	$-IE$ (kJ/mol)	E^0 (V)
Li	-520	-3.05
Na	-496	-2.71
K	-419	-2.93

Note that the changes in electrode potentials do not follow the decrease in ionization energies down the group. You might expect that if it is more difficult to remove an electron from an atom to form a gaseous ion (larger IE), then it would be less difficult to add an electron to an aqueous ion to form an atom (smaller E^0), yet $Li^+(aq)$ is *more* difficult to reduce than $Na^+(aq)$. Applying Hess's law, use an approach similar to that for a Born-Haber cycle to break down the process occurring at the electrode into three steps and label the energy involved in each step. How can you account for this discrepancy?

21.126 To improve conductivity in the electroplating of automobile bumpers, a thin coating of copper separates the steel from a heavy coating of chromium.
(a) What mass of Cu is deposited on an automobile trim piece if plating continues for 1.25 h at a current of 5.0 A?
(b) If the area of the trim piece is 50.0 cm², what is the thickness of the Cu coating (*d* of Cu = 8.95 g/cm³)?

21.127 In Table 21.2, standard electrode potentials range from about +3 to −3 V. Thus, by constructing a cell with a half-cell from each end of this range, it might seem possible to obtain a voltage of approximately 6 V. However, most commercial aqueous voltaic cells have E^0 values of 1.5 to 2 V. Why are there no aqueous cells with significantly higher potentials?

21.128 Tin is used to coat "tin" cans used for food storage. If the tin is scratched and the iron of the can exposed, will the iron corrode more or less rapidly than if the tin were not present? On the inside of the can, the tin coating is itself coated with a transparent varnish. Explain.

*21.129 Commercial aluminum cells operate at 5.0 V and 100,000 A.
(a) How long does it take to produce exactly 1 metric ton (1000 kg) aluminum?
(b) How much electrical power (in kilowatt-hours, kW · h) is used? [1 W = 1 J/s; 1 kW · h = 3.6×10^3 kJ]
(c) Assuming electricity costs 0.90 cents per kW · h and cell efficiency is 90.%, what is the cost of producing exactly 1 lb aluminum?

21.130 Magnesium bars are connected electrically to underground iron pipes to serve as sacrificial anodes.
(a) Do electrons flow from the Mg to the pipe or the reverse?
(b) A 12-kg Mg bar is attached to an iron pipe, and it takes 8.5 yr for the Mg to be consumed. What is the average current flowing between the Mg and the Fe during this period?

21.131 Bubbles of H_2 form when metal D is placed in hot H_2O. No reaction occurs when D is placed in a solution of an E salt, but D is discolored and coated immediately when placed in a solution of an F salt. What happens if E is placed in a solution of an F salt? Rank metals D, E, and F in order of *increasing* reducing strength.

21.132 Calcium is obtained industrially by electrolysis of molten $CaCl_2$ and used in aluminum alloys. How many coulombs are needed to produce 10.0 g of Ca metal? If the cell runs at 15 A, how many minutes will it take to produce the 10.0 g Ca(s)?

21.133 In addition to reacting with gold, aqua regia is used to bring other precious metals into solution. Balance the skeleton reaction for the reaction with Pt:

$$Pt(s) + NO_3^-(aq) + Cl^-(aq) \longrightarrow PtCl_6^{2-}(aq) + NO(g)$$

*21.134 The following three reactions are all used in voltaic cells or batteries:

I $\quad 2H_2(g) + O_2(g) \longrightarrow 2H_2O(l) \qquad E_{cell} = 1.23$ V
II $\quad Pb(s) + PbO_2(s) + 2H_2SO_4(aq) \longrightarrow$
$$\qquad\qquad 2PbSO_4(s) + 2H_2O(l) \qquad E_{cell} = 2.04 \text{ V}$$
III $\quad 2Na(l) + FeCl_2(s) \longrightarrow 2NaCl(s) + Fe(s) \quad E_{cell} = 2.35$ V

Reaction I is used in fuel cells, II is used in the automobile lead-acid cell, and III is used in an experimental high-temperature battery for powering electric vehicles. In many applications, the aim is to obtain as much work as possible from a cell, while keeping its weight to a minimum.
(a) Deduce the number of moles of electrons being transferred and calculate ΔG in each cell.
(b) Calculate the ratio, in kJ/g, of w_{max} to mass of reactants for each of the cells. Which has the highest ratio, which the lowest, and why? (Note: For simplicity, ignore the masses of cell components that do not appear in the cell as reactants, including electrode materials, electrolytes, separators, cell casing, wiring, etc.)

21.135 A current is applied to two electrolytic cells connected in series. In the first cell, silver is deposited. In the second cell, a zinc electrode is consumed. How much Ag is plated out if 1.2 g Zn dissolves?

21.136 You are working in a laboratory and investigating a particular chemical reaction. State all the types of data available in standard tables that enable you to calculate the equilibrium constant for the reaction at 298 K.

*21.137 The maintenance personnel at an electric power plant must pay careful attention to corrosion of the turbine blades. Why does iron corrode faster in steam and hot water than in cold water?

21.138 A cell using Cu/Cu^{2+} and Sn/Sn^{2+} electrodes is set up at standard conditions, and each compartment has a volume of 245 mL. The cell delivers 0.15 A for 54.0 h.
(a) How many grams of Cu(s) are deposited?
(b) What is the $[Cu^{2+}]$ remaining?

21.139 The $E_{\text{half-cell}}$ for the reduction of water is very different from the $E^0_{\text{half-cell}}$ value. Calculate the $E_{\text{half-cell}}$ value when H_2 is in its standard state.

*21.140 From the skeleton equations below, create a list of balanced half-reactions that has the strongest oxidizing agent on top and the weakest on the bottom:

$$U^{3+}(aq) + Cr^{3+}(aq) \longrightarrow Cr^{2+}(aq) + U^{4+}(aq)$$
$$Fe(s) + Sn^{2+}(aq) \longrightarrow Sn(s) + Fe^{2+}(aq)$$
$$Fe(s) + U^{4+}(aq) \longrightarrow \text{no reaction}$$
$$Cr^{3+}(aq) + Fe(s) \longrightarrow Cr^{2+}(aq) + Fe^{2+}(aq)$$
$$Cr^{2+}(aq) + Sn^{2+}(aq) \longrightarrow Sn(s) + Cr^{3+}(aq)$$

21.141 In the process of electrorefining (Chapter 22), impure copper is purified by using it as the anode and already purified copper as the cathode of an electrolytic cell.
(a) Write the equation for the reaction at the anode.
(b) Write the equation for the reaction at the cathode.
(c) Assuming 100% yield, how much electricity (in C) is needed to produce one metric ton of pure copper?
(d) Judging from its position in the periodic table, what other metals might be present in the impure copper?
(e) Why wouldn't these other metals be electrolyzed and contaminate the purified copper?

21.142 Use the half-reaction method to balance the reaction for the conversion of ethanol to acetic acid:

$$CH_3CH_2OH + Cr_2O_7^{2-} \longrightarrow CH_3COOH + Cr^{3+} \text{ [acid solution]}$$

21.143 Some newer battery designs involve lithium or sodium and various nonmetals as electrodes (see Gallery, Section 21.5).

(a) In one variation of the lithium battery, electrons pass from Li metal through a crystalline $LiI(s)$ electrolyte to an I_2 complex. Write the half-reactions, identify the oxidizing and reducing agents, and give the name and charge of each electrode.

(b) In the sodium-sulfur battery, molten Na gives up electrons, which pass through an external circuit and reduce molten S_8 to polysulfide anions, S_n^{2-}. The current is carried by Na^+ ions that migrate through a dry β-alumina electrolyte to the sulfur compartment. Write the overall cell reaction if the pentasulfide ion, S_5^{2-}, forms.

*21.144 In an experiment to determine the effect of ions on the solubility of a precipitate, a chemist designs an ion-specific probe for measuring the $[Ag^+]$ present in a NaCl solution saturated with AgCl. One half-cell is an Ag-wire electrode immersed in the unknown AgCl-saturated NaCl solution. It is connected through a salt bridge to a calomel reference electrode, a platinum wire immersed in a paste of mercury and calomel (Hg_2Cl_2) in a saturated KCl solution. The measured E_{cell} is 0.060 V.

(a) Given the following standard half-reactions, calculate $[Ag^+]$.

Calomel: $Hg_2Cl_2(s) + 2e^- \longrightarrow 2Hg(l) + 2Cl^-(aq); E^0 = 0.24$ V
Silver: $Ag^+(aq) + e^- \longrightarrow Ag(s); E^0 = 0.80$ V

(*Hint:* Assume that $[Cl^-]$ is so high it is essentially constant.)

(b) A mining engineer sends a silver ore sample to the chemist for analysis with the Ag^+-selective probe. After pretreating the ore sample, the chemist measures the cell voltage as 0.57 V. What is $[Ag^+]$?

*21.145 Use Table 21.2 to calculate the K_{sp} of AgCl.

*21.146 Black-and-white photographic film is coated with silver halides. Because the silver is expensive and may harm the environment, the film manufacturer monitors the Ag^+ content of the waste stream, $[Ag^+]_{waste}$, from the plant with an Ag^+ ion-selective electrode kept at 25°C. A stream of known Ag^+ concentration, $[Ag^+]_{standard}$, is regularly passed over the electrode in turn with the waste stream, and the data are recorded by a computer.

(a) Write the equations relating the nonstandard cell potential to the standard cell potential and $[Ag^+]$ for each solution.

(b) Combine these into a single equation to find $[Ag^+]_{waste}$.

(c) Rewrite the equation in (b) to find $[Ag^+]_{waste}$ in ng/L.

(d) If E_{waste} is 0.003 V higher than $E_{standard}$, and the standard solution contains 1000. ng/L, what is $[Ag^+]_{waste}$?

(e) Rewrite the equation in (b) to find $[Ag^+]_{waste}$ for a system in which T changes and in which T_{waste} and $T_{standard}$ may be different.

*21.147 Calculate the K_f of $Ag(NH_3)_2^+$ from

$$Ag^+(aq) + e^- \rightleftharpoons Ag(s) \qquad\qquad E^0 = 0.80 \text{ V}$$
$$Ag(NH_3)_2^+(aq) + e^- \rightleftharpoons Ag(s) + 2NH_3(aq) \qquad E^0 = 0.37 \text{ V}$$

21.148 Use Table 21.2 to create an activity series of Mn, Fe, Ag, Sn, Cr, Cu, Ba, Al, Na, Hg, Ni, Li, Au, Zn, and Pb. Rank them in order of decreasing reducing strength, and group them by those that can displace H_2 from water, those that can displace H_2 from acid, and those that cannot displace H_2.

22

The Elements in Nature and Industry

Figure: A chemical industry maze. From simple prehistoric mines to elaborate modern refineries, human technologies have been extracting elements—in this case, carbon bound to hydrogen—from the Earth for thousands of years. One industry matures while another is born, as our dependence on the limited resources of the planet continues to evolve. In this chapter, we explore some of the countless industrial and biological interactions humans have with the elements and their compounds.

Chapter Outline

In this chapter we return to the periodic table, but from a new perspective. In Chapter 14 we considered the atomic, physical, and chemical behavior of the main-group elements. Here, we examine the elements from a practical viewpoint to learn how much of an element is present in nature, in what form it occurs, how organisms affect its distribution, and how we obtain it for our use.

Remember that chemistry is, above all, a practical science, and its concepts were developed to address real-life problems, among them: How can we isolate and recycle aluminum? How can we make iron stronger? How can we lower energy costs and increase the yield of sulfuric acid? How does fossil-fuel combustion affect the environmental cycling of carbon? Here, we apply concepts that you learned from the chapters on kinetics, equilibrium, thermodynamics, and electrochemistry to explain chemical processes in nature and industry that influence our lives.

We open with a discussion of the abundances and sources of elements in the whole Earth and its crust, then consider how three essential elements—carbon, nitrogen, and phosphorus—cycle through the environment. After seeing where and in what form elements are found, we focus on their isolation and utilization. We discuss general procedures for extracting an element from its ore and examine in detail the isolation methods and uses of certain key elements. Then we quickly survey major isolation methods and uses for many of the other elements. The chapter ends with a close look at two of the most important processes in chemical manufacturing.

22.1 How the Elements Occur in Nature

To begin our examination of how we use the elements, let's take inventory of our elemental stock—the distribution and relative amounts of the elements in the Earth, especially that thin outer portion of the planet that we can reach.

Earth's Structure and the Abundance of the Elements

Any attempt to isolate an element must begin with a knowledge of its **abundance**, the amount of the element in a particular region of the natural world. The abundances of the elements on the Earth and in its various regions are the result of the specific history of our planet's evolution.

Formation and Layering of the Earth About 4.5 billion years ago, vast clouds of cold gases and interstellar debris from exploded older stars gradually coalesced into the Sun and planets. At first, the Earth was a cold, solid sphere of uniformly distributed elements and simple compounds. In the next billion years or so, heat from radioactive decay and virtually continuous meteor impacts raised the planet's temperature to around 10^4 K, sufficient to form an enormous molten mass. Any remaining gaseous elements, such as the cosmically abundant hydrogen and helium, were ejected into space.

As the Earth cooled, chemical and physical processes resulted in its **differentiation,** the formation of regions of different composition and density. Differentiation gave the Earth its layered internal structure, which consists of a dense (10–15 g/cm^3) **core,** composed of a molten outer core and a solid Moon-sized inner core. (Recent evidence has revealed remarkable properties of the inner core: it is nearly as hot as the surface of the Sun and spins within the molten outer core slightly faster than does the Earth itself!) Around the core lies a thick homogeneous **mantle**, consisting of lower and upper portions, with an overall density of 4–6 g/cm^3. All the comings and goings of life take place on the thin heterogeneous **crust** (average density = 2.8 g/cm^3).

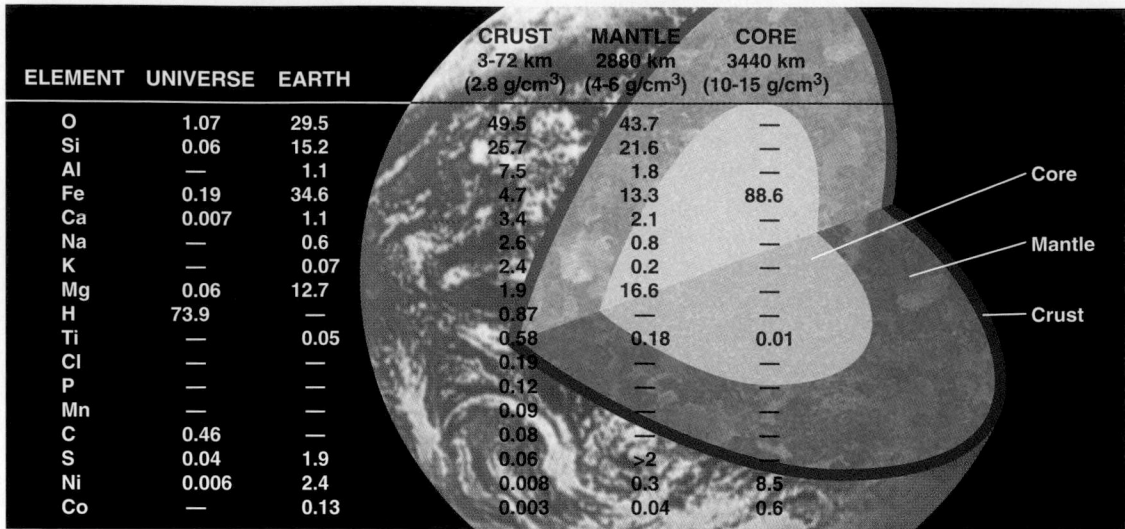

ELEMENT	UNIVERSE	EARTH	CRUST 3-72 km (2.8 g/cm³)	MANTLE 2880 km (4-6 g/cm³)	CORE 3440 km (10-15 g/cm³)
O	1.07	29.5	49.5	43.7	—
Si	0.06	15.2	25.7	21.6	—
Al	—	1.1	7.5	1.8	—
Fe	0.19	34.6	4.7	13.3	88.6
Ca	0.007	1.1	3.4	2.1	—
Na	—	0.6	2.6	0.8	—
K	—	0.07	2.4	0.2	—
Mg	0.06	12.7	1.9	16.6	—
H	73.9	—	0.87	—	—
Ti	—	0.05	0.58	0.18	0.01
Cl	—	—	0.19	—	—
P	—	—	0.12	—	—
Mn	—	—	0.09	—	—
C	0.46	—	0.08	—	—
S	0.04	1.9	0.06	>2	—
Ni	0.006	2.4	0.008	0.3	8.5
Co	—	0.13	0.003	0.04	0.6

Core

Mantle

Crust

Figure 22.1 Cosmic and terrestrial abundances of selected elements (mass %). The mass percentages of the elements are superimposed on a cutaway image of the Earth. The internal structure of the planet consists of a large core, thick mantle, and thin crust. The densities of these regions are indicated in the column heads. Blank abundance values mean either that reliable data are not available or that the value is less than 0.001 mass %. (Helium is not listed because it is not abundant on Earth, but it accounts for 24.0 mass % of the universe.)

Figure 22.1 shows these layers and compares the abundances of some key elements in the universe, the whole Earth (actually core plus mantle only, which account for more than 99% of its mass), and the Earth's three regions. Because the deepest terrestrial sampling can penetrate only a few kilometers into the crust, some of these data represent extrapolations from meteor samples and from seismic studies of earthquakes. Several points stand out:

1. Cosmic and whole-Earth abundances are very different, particularly for H.
2. The elements O, Si, Fe, and Mg are abundant both cosmically and on Earth. Together, they account for more than 90% of the Earth's mass.
3. The core is particularly rich in the dense Group 8B metals: Co, Ni, and especially Fe, the most abundant element in the whole Earth.
4. Crustal abundances are very different from those of the whole Earth. The crust, which makes up only 0.4% of the Earth's mass, has the largest share of nonmetals, metalloids, and light, active metals: Al, Ca, Na, and K. The mantle contains smaller proportions of these, and the core contains none. Oxygen is the most abundant element in the crust and mantle but is absent from the core.

These compositional differences in the Earth's major layers, or *phases*, arose from the effects of thermal energy. When the Earth was molten, gravity and convection caused more dense materials to sink and less dense materials to rise. Most of the Fe sank to form the core, or *iron phase*. In the light outer phase, oxygen combined with Si, Al, Mg, and some Fe to form silicates, the material of rocks. This *silicate phase* later separated into the mantle and crust. The *sulfide phase*, intermediate in density and insoluble in the other two, consisted mostly of iron sulfide and mixed with parts of the silicate phase above and the iron phase below. Outgassing, the expulsion of trapped gases, produced a thin, primitive atmosphere, probably a mixture of water vapor (which gave rise to the oceans), carbon monoxide, and nitrogen (or ammonia).

The distribution of the remaining elements was controlled by their chemical affinity for one of the three phases. In general terms, as Figure 22.2 shows (and we discuss using the new group numbers), elements with low or high electronegativity—active metals (Groups 1 through 5, Cr, and Mn) and nonmetals (O, lighter members of Groups 13 to 15, and all of Group 17)—tended to congregate in the silicate phase as ionic compounds. Metals with intermediate electronegativities (many from Groups 6 to 10) dissolved in the iron core. Lower-melting transition metals and many metals and metalloids in Groups 11 to 16 became concentrated in the sulfide phase.

1A (1)																		8A (18)
H	2A (2)											3A (13)	4A (14)	5A (15)	6A (16)	7A (17)		**He**
Li	**Be**											**B**	**C**	**N**	**O**	**F**		**Ne**
Na	**Mg**	3B (3)	4B (4)	5B (5)	6B (6)	7B (7)	8B (8)	(9)	(10)	1B (11)	2B (12)	**Al**	**Si**	**P**	**S**	**Cl**		**Ar**
K	**Ca**	**Sc**	**Ti**	**V**	**Cr**	**Mn**	**Fe**	**Co**	**Ni**	**Cu**	**Zn**	**Ga**	**Ge**	**As**	**Se**	**Br**		**Kr**
Rb	**Sr**	**Y**	**Zr**	**Nb**	**Mo**		**Ru**	**Rh**	**Pd**	**Ag**	**Cd**	**In**	**Sn**	**Sb**	**Te**	**I**		**Xe**
Cs	**Ba**	**La**	**Hf**	**Ta**	**W**	**Re**	**Os**	**Ir**	**Pt**	**Au**	**Hg**	**Tl**	**Pb**	**Bi**				

Legend:
- Atmosphere (crust)
- Silicate phase (crust and mantle)
- Sulfide phase (mantle)
- Iron phase (core)

Ce	**Pr**	**Nd**	**Pm**	**Sm**	**Eu**	**Gd**	**Tb**	**Dy**	**Ho**	**Er**	**Tm**	**Yb**	**Lu**
Th		**U**											

Figure 22.2 Geochemical differentiation of the elements. During the Earth's formation, the elements became concentrated primarily in the atmosphere or in one of three phases: silicate, sulfide, or iron.

The Impact of Life on Crustal Abundances At present, the crust is the only accessible portion of our planet, so only crustal abundances have practical significance. The crust is divided into solid, liquid, and gaseous portions called the **lithosphere, hydrosphere,** and **atmosphere.** For several billion years, weathering and volcanic upsurges dramatically altered the composition of the crust. The **biosphere,** which consists of the living systems that have inhabited the planet, has been another *major influence on crustal element composition and distribution.*

When the earliest rocks were forming and the ocean basins filling with water, binary inorganic molecules in the atmosphere were reacting to form first simple, and then more complex, organic molecules. The energy for these (mostly) endothermic changes was supplied by lightning, solar radiation, geologic heating, and meteoric impact. In an amazingly short period of time, probably no more than 500 million years, the first organisms appeared. It took perhaps another billion years for these to evolve into simple algae that could derive metabolic energy from photosynthesis, converting CO_2 and H_2O into organic molecules and releasing O_2 as a by-product. The importance of this process to crustal chemistry cannot be overstated because over the next 300 million years, the atmosphere gradually became richer in O_2, and *oxidation became the major source of free energy in the crust and biosphere.* Geologists mark this period by the appearance of Fe(III)-containing minerals in place of the Fe(II)-containing minerals that had predominated (Figure 22.3A). Paleontologists see in it an explosion of O_2-utilizing life forms, a few of which evolved into the organisms of today (Figure 22.3B).

Figure 22.3 Ancient effects of an O_2-rich atmosphere. A, With the appearance of photosynthetic organisms and the resulting oxidizing environment, much of the iron(II) in minerals was oxidized to iron(III). These ancient banded-iron formations (red beds) from Michigan contain hematite, Fe_2O_3. **B,** A fossil of *Hallucigenia sparsa*, one of the multicellular organisms found in the Burgess Shale, British Columbia, Canada, whose appearance coincides with the increase in O_2. Many of these organisms have no known modern descendants, having disappeared in a great mass extinction at the end of the Cambrian Period about 505 million years ago.

A

B

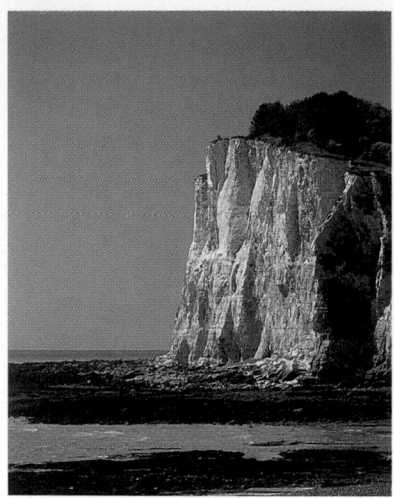

The white cliffs of Dover, England.

In addition to creating an oxidizing environment, organisms have had profound effects on the *distribution* of specific elements. Why, for instance, is the K^+ concentration of the oceans so much lower than the Na^+ concentration? Forming from eons of outgassed water vapor condensing into rain and streaming over the land, the oceans became complex ionic solutions of dissolved minerals with 30 times as much Na^+ as K^+. There are two principal reasons for this difference. Clays, which make up a large portion of many soils, bind K^+ preferentially through an ion-exchange process. Even more importantly, however, plants require K^+ for growth, absorbing dissolved K^+ that would otherwise wash down to the sea.

As another example, consider the enormous subterranean deposits of organic carbon. Buried deeply and decomposing under high pressure and temperature in the absence of free O_2, ancient plants gradually turned into coal, and animals buried under similar conditions turned into petroleum. Crustal deposits of this organic carbon provide the fuels that move our cars, heat our homes, and electrify our cities. Moreover, carbon *and* calcium, the fifth most abundant element in the crust, occur together in vast sedimentary deposits all over the world as limestone, dolomite, marble, and chalk, the fossilized skeletal remains of early marine organisms (see photo).

Table 22.1 compares selected elemental abundances in the whole crust, the three crustal regions, and the human body, a representative portion of the biosphere. Note the quantities of the four major elements of life—O, C, H, and N. Oxygen is either the first or second most abundant element in all regions. The biosphere contains large amounts of carbon in its biomolecules and large amounts of hydrogen as water. Nitrogen is abundant in the atmosphere as free N_2 and in organisms as combined nitrogen in proteins. Phosphorus and sulfur occur in exceptionally high amounts in organisms, too.

One striking difference among the lithosphere, hydrosphere, and biosphere (human) is the abundances of the transition metals vanadium through zinc.

Table 22.1 Abundance of Selected Elements in the Crust, Its Regions, and the Human Body as Representative of the Biosphere (Mass %)

| Element | Crust | Crustal Regions | | | Human |
		Lithosphere	Hydrosphere	Atmosphere	
O	49.5	45.5	85.8	23.0	65.0
C	0.08	0.018	—	0.01	18.0
H	0.87	0.15	10.7	0.02	10.0
N	0.03	0.002	—	75.5	3.0
P	0.12	0.11	—	—	1.0
Mg	1.9	2.76	0.13	—	0.50
K	2.4	1.84	0.04	—	0.34
Ca	3.4	4.66	0.05	—	2.4
S	0.06	0.034	—	—	0.26
Na	2.6	2.27	1.1	—	0.14
Cl	0.19	0.013	2.1	—	0.15
Fe	4.7	6.2	—	—	0.005
Zn	0.013	0.008	—	—	0.003
Cr	0.02	0.012	—	—	3×10^{-6}
Co	0.003	0.003	—	—	3×10^{-6}
Cu	0.007	0.007	—	—	4×10^{-4}
Mn	0.1	0.11	—	—	1×10^{-4}
Ni	0.008	0.010	—	—	3×10^{-6}
V	0.015	0.014	—	—	3×10^{-6}

Their relatively insoluble oxides and sulfides make them much scarcer in water than on land. Yet organisms, which evolved in the seas, developed the ability to concentrate these elements from the trace amounts in their aqueous environment. In every case, the concentration increaes at least 100-fold, with Mn about 1000-fold, and Cu, Zn, and Fe even greater. Each of these elements performs an essential role in living systems, as we'll discuss in the next chapter (Chemical Connections, Section 23.5).

Sources of the Elements

Given an element's abundance in a region of the crust, we must next determine its **occurrence,** or **source,** the form(s) in which the element exists. Practical considerations often determine the commercial source. Oxygen, for example, is abundant in all three regions, but the atmosphere is its primary industrial source because it occurs there as the free element. Nitrogen and the noble gases (except helium) are also obtained from the atmosphere. Several other elements occur uncombined, formed in large deposits by prehistoric biological action; examples are sulfur in caprock salt domes and nearly pure carbon in coal. The relatively unreactive elements gold and platinum also occur in an uncombined (*native*) state.

The overwhelming majority of elements, however, occur in **ores,** natural compounds or mixtures of compounds from which an element can be extracted by economically feasible means. The phrase *economically feasible* refers to an important point: *the financial costs of mining, isolating, and purifying an element must be considered when choosing a process to obtain it.*

Figure 22.4 shows the most useful sources of the elements. Alkali halides are ores for both of their component groups of elements. One example of how cost influences recovery is the scarcity of usable silicate ores. Even though many elements occur as silicates, most of these sources are very stable thermodynamically. Thus, the cost of energy required to do the work of processing them prohibits their use—only lithium and beryllium are obtained from their silicates. The Group 2A(2) metals occur as carbonates in the marble and limestone of mountain ranges, although magnesium's great abundance in seawater makes that the preferred source, as we discuss later.

Figure 22.4 Sources of the elements. The major sources of most of the elements are shown in periodic table format. Although a few elements occur uncombined, most are obtained from their oxide or sulfide ores.

The ores of most industrially important metals are either *oxides,* which dominate the left half of the transition elements, or *sulfides,* which dominate the right half and a few of the main groups beyond. The reasons for the prominence of oxides and sulfides are complex and include processes of weathering, selective precipitation, and relative solubilities. Nevertheless, some atomic properties are relevant as well. Elements in the left half have lower ionization energies and electronegativities, so they tend to give up electrons or hold them loosely in bonds. The O^{2-} ion is small enough to approach a metal cation closely, which results in a high lattice energy of the oxide. In contrast, the elements toward the right side have higher ionization energies and electronegativities. Thus, they tend to form bonds that are more covalent, which suits the larger, more polarizable S^{2-} ion.

Section Summary

As the young Earth cooled, the elements became differentiated into a dense, metallic core, siliceous mantle, and low-density crust. High abundances of light metals, metalloids, and nonmetals are concentrated in the crust, which consists of the lithosphere (solid), hydrosphere (liquid), and atmosphere (gaseous). The biosphere (living systems) has affected crustal chemistry primarily by producing free O_2, and thus an oxidizing environment. Some elements occur in their native state, but most are combined in ores. The most important ores of metallic elements are oxides and sulfides.

22.2 The Cycling of Elements Through the Environment

The distributions of many elements are in flux, changing at widely differing rates. The physical, chemical, and biological paths that the atoms of an element take on their journey through regions of the crust constitute the element's **environmental cycle.** In this section, we consider the cycles for three important elements—carbon, nitrogen, and phosphorus—and highlight the effects of humans on them.

The Carbon Cycle

Carbon is one of a handful of elements that appear in all three portions of the Earth's crust. In the lithosphere, it occurs as elemental graphite and diamond; combined in fully oxidized form as carbonate minerals and in fully reduced form as petroleum hydrocarbons; and in complex mixtures, such as coal and living matter. In the hydrosphere, it occurs as living matter, as carbonate minerals formed by the action of coral-reef organisms, and as aqueous CO_2. In the atmosphere, it occurs principally as gaseous CO_2, a minor but essential component that exists in equilibrium with the aqueous fraction.

Figure 22.5 depicts the complex interplay of these carbon sources and the considerable effect of the biosphere on the element's environmental cycle. It provides an estimate of the size of each source and, where reliable numbers exist, the amount of carbon moving annually between sources. Here are some key points to note:

- The portions of the cycle are linked by the atmosphere—one link between oceans and air, the other between land and air. The 2.6×10^{12} metric tons of CO_2 in air cycles through the oceans and atmosphere about once every 300 years but spends a much longer time in carbonate minerals.
- Atmospheric CO_2 accounts for a tiny fraction (0.003%) of crustal carbon, but the atmosphere is the prime mover of carbon through the other regions. Estimates indicate that a CO_2 molecule spends, on the average, 3.5 years in the atmosphere.

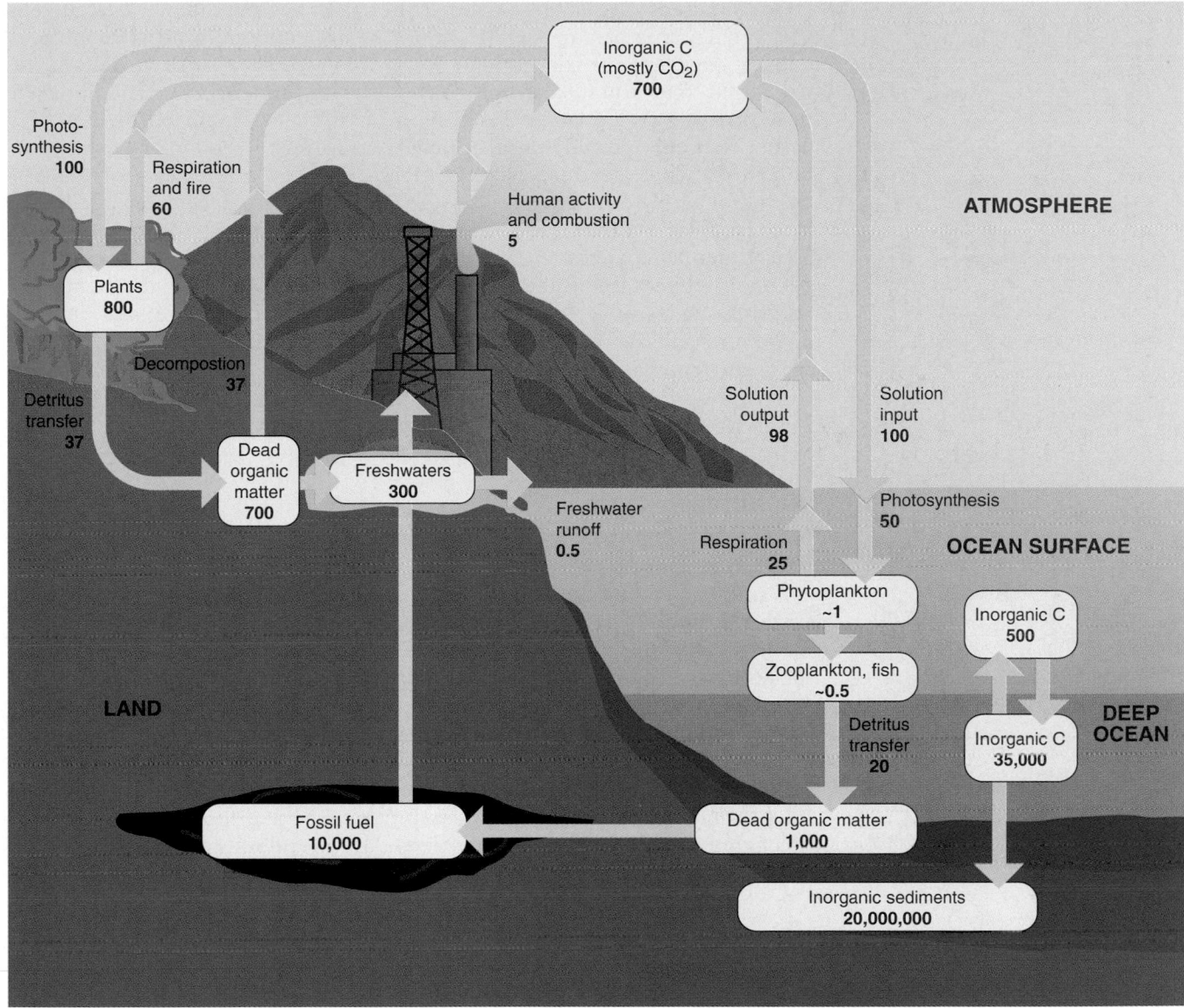

Figure 22.5 The carbon cycle. The major sources and changes in carbon distribution are shown. Note that the atmosphere is the major conduit of carbon between land and sea and that CO_2 becomes fixed through the action of organisms. Numbers in boxes refer to the size of the source; numbers along arrows refer to the annual movement of the element from source to source. Values are in 10^9 metric tons of C (1 metric ton = 1000 kg = 1.1 tons).

- The land and oceans are also in contact with the largest sources of carbon, which are effectively immobilized as carbonates, coal, and oil in the rocky sediment beneath the soil.
- The biological processes of *photosynthesis, respiration,* and *decay* are major factors in the cycle. **Fixation** is the process of converting a gaseous substance into a condensed, more usable form. Photosynthesis by marine plankton and terrestrial plants uses sunlight to fix atmospheric CO_2 into carbohydrates. Plants release CO_2 by respiration at night and, much more slowly, when they decay. Animals eat the plants and release CO_2 by respiration and in their decay.
- Natural fires and volcanoes also release CO_2 to the air.

For hundreds of millions of years, the cycle has maintained a relatively constant amount of atmospheric CO_2. The tremendous growth of human industry over the past century and a half, and especially since World War II, has shifted this natural balance by increasing atmospheric CO_2. The principal cause of this increase is the combustion of coal, wood, and oil for fuel and for the thermal decomposition of limestone to make cement, coupled with the simultaneous clearing of vast stretches of forest and jungle for lumber, paper, and agriculture. With the 1990s the hottest decade ever recorded, evidence is mounting that these activities may be creating one of the most dire environmental changes in human history—global warming through the greenhouse effect (see Chemical Connections, Section 6.6). Higher temperatures, alterations in dry and rainy seasons, melting of polar ice, and increasing ocean acidity with associated changes in carbonate equilibria are some of the results currently being assessed. Most environmental and science policy experts are pressing for the immediate adoption of a program that combines conservation of carbon-based fuels, an end to deforestation, extensive planting of trees, and development of alternative energy sources.

The Nitrogen Cycle

In contrast to the carbon cycle, the nitrogen cycle includes a direct interaction of land and sea (Figure 22.6). All nitrites and nitrates are soluble, so rain and runoff contribute huge amounts of nitrogen to lakes, rivers, and oceans. Human activity, in the form of fertilizer production and use, plays a major role in this cycle.

Like carbon dioxide, atmospheric nitrogen must be fixed to be used by organisms. However, whereas CO_2 can be incorporated by plants in either its gaseous or aqueous form, the great stability of N_2 prevents plants from using it directly. Fixation of N_2 requires a great deal of energy and occurs through atmospheric, industrial, and biological processes:

1. *Atmospheric fixation.* Lightning and fires (and, to a much smaller extent, car engines) bring about the high-temperature endothermic reaction of N_2 and O_2 to form NO, which is then oxidized exothermically to NO_2:

$$N_2(g) + O_2(g) \longrightarrow 2NO(g) \qquad \Delta H^0 = 180.6 \text{ kJ}$$
$$2NO(g) + O_2(g) \longrightarrow 2NO_2(g) \qquad \Delta H^0 = -114.2 \text{ kJ}$$

Rain converts the NO_2 to nitric acid, which enters both sea and land as $NO_3^-(aq)$ to be utilized by plants:

$$3NO_2(g) + H_2O(l) \longrightarrow 2H^+(aq) + 2NO_3^-(aq) + NO(g)$$

2. *Industrial fixation.* Most man-made fixation occurs industrially through ammonia synthesis via the Haber process (see Chemical Connections, Section 17.6). The process takes place on an enormous scale: on a mole basis, NH_3 ranks first among compounds in amount produced. Some of this NH_3 is converted to HNO_3 in the Ostwald process (Section 14.7), but most is used as fertilizer, either directly or in the form of urea and ammonium salts (sulfate, phosphate, and nitrate), which enter the biosphere as they are taken up by plants (item 3 below). In recent decades, the internal combustion engine has become an important contributor to total fixed nitrogen, because of the enormous rise in automobile and truck traffic. High engine operating temperatures mimic lightning and fires to form NO from the air taken in to burn the hydrocarbon fuel. The NO in exhaust gases proceeds to nitric acid in the atmosphere, which adds to the nitrate load that reaches the ground. The overuse of fertilizers and automobiles presents an increasingly serious water pollution problem in many areas. Leaching of the land by rain causes fertilizers and car-borne nitrate to enter natural waters (lakes, rivers, and coastal estuaries) and cause *eutrophication,* the depletion of O_2 and the death of

Figure 22.6 **The nitrogen cycle.** The major source of nitrogen, N_2, is fixed via industry, the atmosphere, and microorganisms. Various types of bacteria are indispensable throughout the cycle.

Numbers in boxes are in 10^9 metric tons of N and refer to the size of the source; numbers along arrows are in 10^6 metric tons of N and refer to the annual movement of the element between sources.

aquatic animal life from excessive algal and plant growth and decay. Excess nitrate also spoils nearby drinkable water.

3. *Biological fixation.* The biological fixation of atmospheric N_2 occurs in marine blue-green algae and in nitrogen-fixing bacteria that live on the roots of leguminous plants (e.g., peas, alfalfa, and clover). On a planetary scale, these microbial processes dwarf the other two, fixing more than seven times as much nitrogen as the atmosphere and five times as much as industry. Root bacteria fix N_2 by reducing it to NH_3/NH_4^+ through the action of enzymes that contain the transition metal molybdenum at their active site. Enzymes in other soil bacteria catalyze the multistep oxidation of the NH_4^+ to NO_2^- and finally NO_3^-, which the plants reduce again to make their proteins. When the plants die, still other soil bacteria oxidize the proteins to NO_3^-.

Animals eat the plants, use the plant proteins to make their own proteins, and excrete nitrogenous wastes, such as urea [$(H_2N)_2C=O$]. The nitrogen in the proteins is released when the animals die and decay, and is converted by soil bacteria to NO_2^- and NO_3^- again. This central pool of inorganic nitrate has three main fates: some enters marine and terrestrial plants, some enters the enormous sediment store of mineral nitrates, and some is reduced by denitrifying bacteria to NO_2^- and then to N_2O and N_2, which reenter the atmosphere to complete the cycle.

The Phosphorus Cycle

Virtually all the mineral sources of phosphorus contain the phosphate group, PO_4^{3-}. The most commercially important ores are **apatites,** compounds of general formula $Ca_5(PO_4)_3X$, where X is usually F, Cl, or OH. The cycling of phosphorus through the environment involves three interlocking subcycles (Figure 22.7). Two rapid biological cycles—a land-based cycle completed in a matter of years and a water-based cycle completed in weeks to years—are superimposed on an inorganic cycle that takes millions of years to complete. Unlike the carbon and nitrogen cycles, the phosphorus cycle has no gaseous component and thus does *not* involve the atmosphere.

The Inorganic Cycle Most phosphate rock formed when the Earth's lithosphere solidified. ◆ Its most important components are nearly insoluble phosphate salts:

$$K_{sp} \text{ of } Ca_3(PO_4)_2 \approx 10^{-29}$$
$$K_{sp} \text{ of } Ca_5(PO_4)_3OH \approx 10^{-51}$$
$$K_{sp} \text{ of } Ca_5(PO_4)_3F \approx 10^{-60}$$

Weathering slowly leaches phosphates from the soil and carries the ions through rivers to the sea. Plants in the land-based biological cycle speed this process. In the ocean, some phosphate is absorbed by organisms in the water-based biological cycle, but the majority is precipitated again by Ca^{2+} ion and deposited on the continental shelf. Geologic activity lifts the continental shelves, returning the phosphate to the land.

The Land-Based Biological Cycle The biological cycles involve the incorporation of phosphate into organisms (biomolecules, bones, teeth, and so forth) and the release of phosphate through excretion and decay. In the land-based cycle, plants continually remove phosphate from the inorganic cycle. Recall that there are three phosphate oxoanions, which exist in equilibrium in the aqueous environment:

$$H_2PO_4^- \rightleftharpoons \underset{+\ H^+}{HPO_4^{2-}} \rightleftharpoons \underset{+\ H^+}{PO_4^{3-}}$$

In topsoil, phosphates occur as insoluble compounds of Ca^{2+}, Fe^{3+}, and Al^{3+}. Because plants can absorb only the soluble dihydrogen phosphates, they have evolved the ability to secrete acids near their roots to convert the insoluble salts gradually into the soluble ion:

$Ca_3(PO_4)_2(s; \text{soil}) + 4H^+(aq; \text{secreted by plants}) \longrightarrow$
$$3Ca^{2+}(aq) + 2H_2PO_4^-(aq; \text{absorbed by plants})$$

Animals that eat the plants excrete soluble phosphate, which is used in turn by newly growing plants. As the plants and animals excrete, die, and decay, some phosphate is washed into rivers and from there to the ocean. Most of the 2 million metric tons of phosphate that wash from land to sea each year are from biological decay. Thus, the biosphere greatly increases the movement of phosphate from lithosphere to hydrosphere.

The Water-Based Biological Cycle Various phosphorus oxoanions continually enter the aquatic environment. Studies that incorporate trace amounts of radioactive phosphorus into $H_2PO_4^-$ and monitor its uptake show that, within 1 minute, 50% of the ion is taken up by photosynthetic algae, which use it to synthesize their biomolecules (denoted by the top curved arrow in

◆ **Phosphorus from Outer Space** Although most phosphate occurs in the rocks formed by geological activity on Earth, a sizeable amount arrived here from outer space and continues to do so, as this time-lapse photo of the 1966 Leonid meteor shower shows. About 100 metric tons of meteorites enter our atmosphere each day. With an average P content of 0.1 mass %, they contribute about 36 metric tons of P per year. Over the 4.6 billion-year lifetime of the Earth, about 10^{11} metric tons of P has arrived from extraterrestrial sources!

Figure 22.7 The phosphorus cycle. The inorganic *(purple arrows)*, water-based biological *(blue arrows)*, and land-based biological *(yellow arrows)* subcycles interact through erosion and through the growth and decay of organisms. The cycle has no gaseous component.

the upcoming equation). The overall process might be represented by the following equation:

$$106CO_2(g) + 16NO_3^-(aq) + H_2PO_4^-(aq) + 122H_2O(l) + 17H^+(aq) \underset{\text{decay}}{\overset{\text{synthesis}}{\rightleftarrows}}$$

$$C_{106}H_{263}O_{110}N_{16}P(aq; \text{ in algal cell fluid}) + 138O_2(g)$$

(The complex formula on the right represents the total composition of algal biomolecules, not some particular compound.) As on land, animals eat the plants and are eaten by other animals, and they all excrete, die, and decay (denoted by the bottom curved arrow). Some of the released phosphate is used by other aquatic organisms, and some returns to the land when fish-eating animals (mostly humans and birds) excrete phosphate, die, and decay. In addition, some aquatic phosphate precipitates with Ca^{2+}, sinks to the sea bed, and returns to the long-term mineral deposits of the inorganic cycle.

Human Effects on Phosphorus Movement From prehistoric through preindustrial times, these interlocking phosphorus cycles were balanced. Modern human activity, however, alters the movement of phosphorus considerably. Our influence on the inorganic cycle is minimal, despite our annual removal of more than 100 million metric tons of phosphate rock for a variety of uses (Figure 22.8, next page). The end products of this removal, however, have unbalanced the two biological cycles.

Demeton, an insecticide

V agent, a lethal nerve gas

Phosphorus Nerve Poisons Because phosphorus is essential for all organisms, its compounds have many biological actions. In addition to their widespread use as fertilizer, phosphorus compounds are also used as pesticides *and* as military nerve gases. In fact, these two types of substances often have similar structures (see figure) and modes of action. Both types affect the target organism by inactivating an enzyme involved in muscle contraction. They bind an amino acid critical to the enzyme's function, allowing the muscle to contract but not relax; the effect on the organism—insect or human—is often fatal. Chemists have synthesized a nerve-gas antidote whose shape mimics the binding site of the enzyme. The drug binds the poison, removing it from the enzyme, and is excreted.

Figure 22.8 Industrial uses of phosphorus. The major end products of phosphate rock are shown, with box heights proportional to the amount of phosphate rock used annually (shown as mass %) to make the end product. Over 100 million metric tons of phosphate rock is mined each year (assigned a value of 100%).

The imbalance arises from our overuse of *soluble phosphate fertilizers,* such as $Ca(H_2PO_4)_2$ and $NH_4H_2PO_4$, the end products of about 85% of phosphate rock mined. Some fertilizer finds its way into rivers, lakes, and oceans to enter the water-based cycle. Much larger pollution sources, however, are the crops grown with the fertilizer and the detergents made from phosphate rock. The great majority of this phosphate arrives eventually in cities as crops, as animals that were fed crops, and as consumer products, such as the tripolyphosphates in detergents. Human garbage, excrement, detergent wash water, and industrial wastewater containing this phosphate return through sewers to the aquatic system. This human contribution equals the natural contribution—another 2 million metric tons of phosphate per year. The increased concentration in rivers and lakes causes eutrophication, which robs the water of O_2 so that it cannot support life. Such "dead" rivers and lakes are no longer usable for fishing, drinking water, or recreational use.

As early as 1912, a chemical solution to this problem was tried in Switzerland, where the enormous Lake Zurich had been choked with algae and become devoid of fish because of the release of human sewage. Treatment with $FeCl_3$ precipitated enough phosphate to return the lake gradually to its natural state. Soluble aluminum compounds have the same effect:

$$FeCl_3(aq) + PO_4{}^{3-}(aq) \longrightarrow FePO_4(s) + 3Cl^-(aq)$$
$$KAl(SO_4)_2 \cdot 12H_2O(aq) + PO_4{}^{3-}(aq) \longrightarrow$$
$$AlPO_4(s) + K^+(aq) + 2SO_4{}^{2-}(aq) + 12H_2O(l)$$

After several lakes in the United States became polluted in this way, phosphates were eliminated from detergents and stringent requirements for sewage treatment, including tertiary treatments to remove phosphate, were put into effect. Lake Erie, which was severely polluted by the late 1960s and early 1970s, underwent a program to reduce phosphates and is today relatively clean and restocked with fish (see Chemical Connections, Section 13.6). ◆

Section Summary

The environmental distribution of many elements changes cyclically with time and is affected in major ways by organisms. Carbon occurs in all three portions of the Earth's crust, with atmospheric CO_2 linking the other two portions. Photosynthesis and decay of organisms alter the amount of carbon in the land and oceans. Human activity has increased atmospheric CO_2. Nitrogen is fixed by lightning, by industry, and primarily by microorganisms. When plants decay, bacteria decompose organic nitrogen and eventually return N_2 to the atmosphere. Through extensive use of fertilizers, humans have added excess nitrogen to fresh waters. The phosphorus cycle has no gaseous component. Inorganic phosphates leach slowly into land and water, where biological cycles interact. When plants and animals decay, they release phosphate to natural waters, which is then absorbed by other plants and animals. Through overuse of phosphate fertilizers and detergents, humans double the amount of phosphorus entering aqueous systems.

22.3 Metallurgy: Extracting a Metal from Its Ore

Metallurgy is the branch of materials science concerned with the extraction and utilization of metals. In this section, we discuss the general procedures for isolating metals and, occasionally, the nonmetals that are found in their ores. The extraction process applies one or more of three types of metallurgy: *pyrometallurgy* uses heat to obtain the metal, *electrometallurgy* employs an electrochemical step, and *hydrometallurgy* relies on the metal's aqueous solution chemistry.

The extraction of an element begins with *mining the ore*. Most ores consist of the **mineral,** that is, the compound containing the element, and **gangue,** attached debris such as sand, rock, and clay. Table 22.2 lists the common mineral sources of some metals.

Humans have been removing metals from the Earth for thousands of years, so most of the known concentrated sources are long gone. In many cases, ores containing very low mass percentages of a metal are all that remain, and these require elaborate—and ingenious—extraction methods. Nevertheless, the general procedure for extracting most metals (and many nonmetals) involves a few basic steps, described in the upcoming subsections and previewed in Figure 22.9.

Table 22.2 Common Mineral Sources of Some Elements

Element	Mineral, Formula
Al	Gibbsite (in bauxite), $Al(OH)_3$
Ba	Barite, $BaSO_4$
Be	Beryl, $Be_3Al_2Si_6O_{18}$
Ca	Limestone, $CaCO_3$
Fe	Hematite, Fe_2O_3
Hg	Cinnabar, HgS
Na	Halite, $NaCl$
Pb	Galena, PbS
Sn	Cassiterite, SnO_2
Zn	Sphalerite, ZnS

Figure 22.9 **Steps in metallurgy.**

Pretreating the Ore

Following a crushing, grinding, or pulverizing step, which can be very expensive, pretreatment usually takes advantage of some physical or chemical difference to separate mineral from gangue. For magnetic minerals, such as magnetite (Fe_3O_4), a magnet can remove the mineral and leave the gangue behind. Where large density differences exist, a *cyclone separator* is used, which blows high-pressure air through the pulverized mixture to separate the particles. The lighter silicate-rich gangue is blown away, while the denser

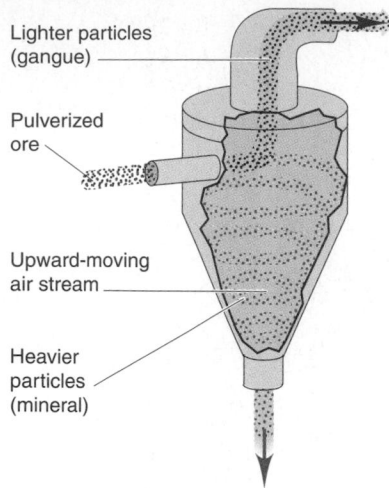

Figure 22.10 The cyclone separator. The pulverized ore enters at an angle, with the more dense particles (mineral) hitting the walls and spiraling downward, while the less dense particles (silicate gangue) are carried upward in a stream of air.

Lighter particles (gangue)

Pulverized ore

Upward-moving air stream

Heavier particles (mineral)

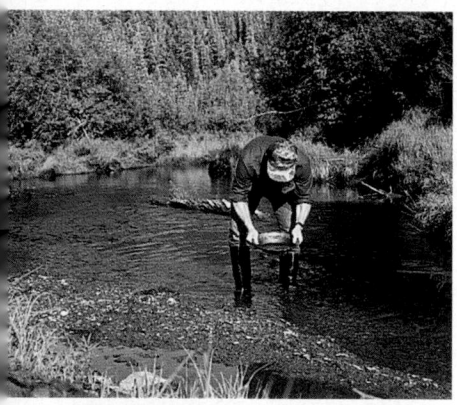

◆ **Panning and Fleecing for Gold** The picture of the prospector, alone but for his faithful mule, hunched over the bank of a mountain stream patiently panning for gold, is mostly a relic of old movies. However, the process is valid. It is based on the very large density difference between gold ($d = 19.3$ g/cm^3) and sand ($d \approx 2.5$ g/cm^3). In ancient times, river sands were washed over a sheep's fleece to trap the gold grains, a practice that historians think represents the origin of the Golden Fleece of Greek mythology.

mineral-rich particles hit the walls of the separator and fall through the open bottom (Figure 22.10).

In the **flotation** process, an oil-detergent mixture is stirred with a pulverized sulfide ore in water to form a slurry (Figure 22.11). The process takes advantage of the different abilities of the surfaces of mineral and of gangue to become wet in contact with water and detergent. Rapid mixing moves air bubbles through the mixture and produces an oily, mineral-rich froth that floats, while the silicate particles sink. Skimming, followed by solvent removal of the oil-detergent mixture, isolates the concentrated mineral fraction. Flotation is a key step in copper recovery, as you'll see later.

Leaching is a hydrometallurgic process that selectively extracts the metal, usually by forming a complex ion. The modern extraction of gold is a good example of this technique, since nuggets of the precious metal are found only in museums nowadays. ◆ The crushed ore, which often contains as little as 25 ppm of gold, is contained in a plastic-lined pool, treated with a cyanide ion solution, and aerated. In the presence of CN^-, the O_2 in air oxidizes gold metal to gold(I) ion, Au^+, which forms the soluble complex ion, $Au(CN)_2^-$:

$$4Au(s) + O_2(g) + 8CN^-(aq) + 2H_2O(l) \longrightarrow 4Au(CN)_2^-(aq) + 4OH^-(aq)$$

(The method has become controversial in some areas because cyanide lost from the contained area enters streams and lakes, where it poisons fish and birds.)

Converting Mineral to Element

After the mineral has been freed of debris and concentrated, it may undergo several chemical steps during its conversion to the element.

Converting the Mineral to Another Compound First, the mineral is often converted to another compound, one that has more appropriate solubility properties, is easier to reduce, or is free of a troublesome impurity. Conversion to an oxide is common because oxides can be reduced easily. Carbonates are heated to convert them to the oxide:

$$CaCO_3(s) \xrightarrow{\Delta} CaO(s) + CO_2(g)$$

Metal sulfides, such as ZnS, are converted to oxides by **roasting** in air:

$$2ZnS(s) + 3O_2(g) \xrightarrow{\Delta} 2ZnO(s) + 2SO_2(g)$$

In most countries, hydrometallurgic methods are used now to avoid the atmospheric release of SO_2 during roasting. One way of processing copper, for example, is by bubbling air through an acidic slurry of insoluble Cu_2S, which fulfills both the pretreatment and conversion steps:

$$2Cu_2S(s) + 5O_2(g) + 4H^+(aq) \longrightarrow 4Cu^{2+}(aq) + 2SO_4^{2-}(aq) + 2H_2O(l)$$

Converting the Compound to the Element Through Chemical Redox The next step converts the new mineral form (usually an oxide) to the free element by either chemical or electrochemical methods. In chemical redox, a reducing agent reacts directly with the compound. The most common reducing agents are carbon, hydrogen, and an active metal.

1. *Reduction with carbon.* Carbon, in the form of coke (a porous residue from incomplete combustion of coal) or charcoal, is a very common reducing agent. Heating an oxide with a reducing agent such as coke to obtain the metal is called **smelting.** Many metal oxides, such as zinc oxide and tin(IV) oxide, are smelted with carbon to free the metal, which may need to be condensed and solidified:

$$ZnO(s) + C(s) \longrightarrow Zn(g) + CO(g)$$
$$SnO_2(s) + 2C(s) \longrightarrow Sn(l) + 2CO(g)$$

Figure 22.11 The flotation process. A, Schematic of the process, in which the pulverized ore is treated with an oil-detergent mixture, then stirred and aerated to create a froth that separates the detergent-coated mineral from the gangue. **B,** In the actual procedure, the mineral-rich froth is collected for further processing.

Several nonmetals that occur in positive oxidation states in a mineral can be reduced with carbon as well. Phosphorus, for example, is produced from calcium phosphate:

$$2Ca_3(PO_4)_2(s) + 10C(s) + 6SiO_2(s) \longrightarrow 6CaSiO_3(s) + 10CO(g) + P_4(s)$$

(Metallic calcium is a much stronger reducing agent than carbon, so it is not formed.)

Low cost and ready availability explain why carbon is such a common reducing agent, and thermodynamic principles explain why it is such an effective one in many cases. Consider the standard free energy change (ΔG^0) for the reduction of tin(IV) oxide:

$$SnO_2(s) + 2C(s) \longrightarrow Sn(s) + 2CO(g) \qquad \Delta G^0 = 245 \text{ kJ at } 25°C \ (298 \text{ K})$$

The magnitude and sign of ΔG^0 indicate a highly *non*spontaneous reaction at 25°C. However, because solid C becomes gaseous CO, the standard molar entropy change is very positive ($\Delta S^0 \approx 380$ J/K). Therefore, *the ($-T\Delta S^0$) term of ΔG^0 becomes more negative with higher temperature* (Section 20.3). As the temperature increases, ΔG^0 decreases and, at a high enough temperature, the reaction becomes spontaneous ($\Delta G^0 < 0$). At 1000°C (1273 K), for example, $\Delta G^0 = -62.8$ kJ. The actual process is carried out at a temperature of around 1250°C (1523 K), so ΔG^0 is even more negative.

As you know, overall reactions often hide several intermediate steps. For instance, the reduction of tin(IV) oxide may occur by first forming tin(II) oxide:

$$SnO_2(s) + C(s) \longrightarrow \cancel{SnO(s)} + CO(g)$$
$$\cancel{SnO(s)} + C(s) \longrightarrow Sn(l) + CO(g)$$

[Molten tin (mp = 232 K) is obtained at this temperature.] Also, the second step may even be composed of others, in which CO, not C, is the actual reducing agent:

$$SnO(s) + \cancel{CO(g)} \longrightarrow Sn(l) + \cancel{CO_2(g)}$$
$$\cancel{CO_2(g)} + C(s) \rightleftharpoons \cancel{2}CO(g)$$

Other pyrometallurgical processes are similarly complex. Shortly, you'll see that the overall reaction for the smelting of iron is

$$2Fe_2O_3(s) + 3C(s) \longrightarrow 4Fe(l) + 3CO_2(g)$$

whereas the actual process is a multistep one with CO as the reducing agent. The advantage of CO over C is the far greater contact the gaseous reducing agent can make with the other reactant, which speeds the process.

2. *Reduction with hydrogen.* For some metal oxides, especially some members of Groups 6B(6) and 7B(7), reduction with carbon forms metal carbides, which are difficult to convert further, so other reducing agents are used. Hydrogen gas is used for less active metals, like tungsten:

$$WO_3(s) + 3H_2(g) \longrightarrow W(s) + 3H_2O(g)$$

One step in the purification of the metalloid germanium uses hydrogen:

$$GeO_2(s) + 2H_2(g) \longrightarrow Ge(s) + 2H_2O(g)$$

3. *Reduction with an active metal.* When a metal might form an undesirable hydride, its oxide is reduced by a more active metal. In the *thermite reaction,* aluminum powder reduces the metal oxide in a spectacular exothermic reaction to give the molten metal (Figure 22.12):

$$Cr_2O_3(s) + 2Al(s) \longrightarrow 2Cr(l) + Al_2O_3(s)$$

Reduction by a more active metal is also employed in situations that do not involve an oxide. In the extraction of gold, after the pretreatment by leaching you saw earlier, the gold(I) complex ion is reduced with zinc to form the metal and a zinc complex ion:

$$2Au(CN)_2^-(aq) + Zn(s) \longrightarrow 2Au(s) + Zn(CN)_4^{2-}(aq)$$

In some cases, an active metal, such as calcium, is used to recover an even more active metal, such as rubidium, from its molten salt:

$$Ca(l) + 2RbCl(l) \longrightarrow CaCl_2(l) + 2Rb(g)$$

A similar process is used to recover sodium; we'll discuss the details in the next section.

4. *Oxidation with an active nonmetal.* Just as chemical *reduction* of a mineral is used to obtain the metal, chemical *oxidation* of a mineral is sometimes used to obtain a nonmetal. In these cases, a stronger oxidizing agent is used to remove electrons from the nonmetal anion to give the free nonmetal, as in the industrial production of iodine from concentrated brines by oxidation with chlorine gas:

$$2I^-(aq) + Cl_2(g) \longrightarrow 2Cl^-(aq) + I_2(s)$$

Converting the Compound to the Element Through Electrochemical Redox
In these processes, the mineral components are converted to the elements in an electrolytic cell (Section 21.7). In some cases, the *pure* mineral, in the form of the molten halide or oxide, is used in order to prevent unwanted side reactions. The cation is reduced to the metal at the cathode, and the anion is oxidized to the nonmetal at the anode:

$$BeCl_2(l) \longrightarrow Be(s) + Cl_2(g)$$

High-purity hydrogen gas is prepared by electrochemical reduction:

$$2H_2O(l) \longrightarrow 2H_2(g) + O_2(g)$$

Specially designed cells separate the products to prevent their recombination. Cost is a major factor in electrolysis, and an inexpensive source of electricity is essential for large-scale methods. As always, the current and voltage requirements depend on the electrochemical potential and any overvoltage effects.

Figure 22.13 shows, in periodic-table format, the most common step for obtaining each free element from its mineral.

Refining and Alloying the Element
At this point in the isolation process, the element typically contains impurities from previous steps, so it must be refined. Then, once purified, metallic elements are often alloyed to improve their properties.

Figure 22.12 The thermite reaction. This highly exothermic redox reaction uses powdered aluminum to reduce metal oxides.

Figure 22.13 **The redox step in converting a mineral to the element.** This periodic table is color coded to show the nature of the redox step used to form the element from the mineral. Note that most of the commercially important elements are reduced from the compound with either carbon (coke or charcoal) or with a more active metal or H_2.

Refining (Purifying) the Element Refining is a purification procedure, and three common methods are mentioned here. An electrolytic cell is employed in **electrorefining**, in which the impure metal acts as the anode and a sample of the pure metal acts as the cathode. As the reaction proceeds, the anode slowly disintegrates and the metal ions are reduced to deposit on the cathode. In some cases, the impurities, which fall beneath the disintegrating anode, are the source of several valuable and less abundant elements. (We examine the electrorefining of copper shortly.) Metals with relatively low boiling points, such as zinc and mercury, are refined by *distillation*. In the process of **zone refining** (see Gallery, Section 13.5), impurities are removed from a bar of the element by concentrating them in a thin molten zone, while the purified element recrystallizes. Metalloids used in electronic semiconductors, such as silicon and germanium, must be zone refined to greater than 99.999999% purity.

Alloying the Purified Element An **alloy** is a metal-like mixture consisting of solid phases of pure elements, solid solutions, or in some cases, distinct intermediate phases (sometimes referred to as *intermetallic compounds*). The separate phases are often so finely divided that they can only be distinguished microscopically. Alloying a metal with other metals (and, in some cases, nonmetals) is done to enhance properties such as luster, conductivity, malleability, ductility, and strength, and to alter melting point. Iron, probably the most important metal, is used only when it is alloyed. In pure form, it is soft and corrodes easily. However, when alloyed with carbon and other metals, such as Mo for hardness and Cr and Ni for corrosion resistance, it forms the various steels. Copper stiffens when zinc is added to make brass. Mercury solidifies when alloyed with sodium, and vanadium becomes extremely tough with some carbon added. Table 22.3 on the next page shows the composition and uses of some common alloys.

Table 22.3 Some Familiar Alloys and Their Composition

Name	Composition (Mass %)	Uses
Stainless steel	73-79 Fe, 14-18 Cr, 7-9 Ni	Cutlery, instruments
Nickel steel	96-98 Fe, 2-4 Ni	Cables, gears
High-speed steels	80-94 Fe, 14-20 W (or 6-12 Mo)	Cutting tools
Permalloy	78 Ni, 22 Fe	Ocean cables
Bronzes	70-95 Cu, 1-25 Zn, 1-18 Sn	Statues, castings
Brasses	50-80 Cu, 20-50 Zn	Plating, ornamental objects
Sterling silver	92.5 Ag, 7.5 Cu	Jewelry, tableware
14-Carat gold	58 Au, 4-28 Ag, 14-28 Cu	Jewelry
18-Carat white gold	75 Au, 12.5 Ag, 12.5 Cu	Jewelry
Typical tin solder	67 Pb, 33 Sn	Electrical connections
Dental amalgam	69 Ag, 18 Sn, 12 Cu, 1 Zn (dissolved in Hg)	Dental fillings

A Vanadium carbide

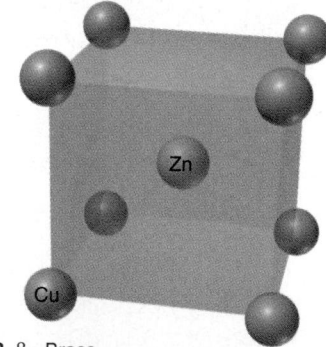

B β - Brass

C Cu$_3$Au

Figure 22.14 Three binary alloys.

The simplest alloys, called *binary alloys,* contain only two elements. In some cases, *the added element enters interstices,* spaces between the parent metal atoms in the crystal structure (Section 12.6). In vanadium carbide, for instance, carbon atoms occupy holes of a face-centered cubic vanadium lattice (Figure 22.14A). In other cases, the *added element substitutes for parent atoms* in the unit cell. In many types of brass, for example, relatively few zinc atoms substitute randomly for copper atoms in the face-centered cubic copper lattice (see Figure 13.5A). On the other hand, β-brass is an intermediate phase that crystallizes as the ratio of Zn:Cu approaches 1:1 in a structure with a Zn atom surrounded by eight Cu atoms (Figure 22.14B). In one alloy of copper and gold, Cu atoms occupy the faces of a face-centered cube, and Au atoms lie at the corners (Figure 22.14C).

Atomic properties, including size, electron configuration, and number of valence electrons, determine which metals form stable alloys. Quantitative predictions indicate that transition metals having few *d* electrons often form stable alloys with transition metals having many *d* electrons. Thus, metals from the left half of the *d* block (Groups 3 to 5) often form alloys with metals from the right half (Groups 9 to 11). For example, electron-poor Zr, Nb, and Ta form strong alloys with the electron-rich Ir, Pt, or Au, such as the very stable ZrPt$_3$.

Section Summary

Metallurgy involves mining an ore, separating it from debris, pretreating it to concentrate the mineral source, converting the mineral to a more useful form, reducing this form to the metal, purifying the metal, and in many cases, alloying it to obtain a more useful material.

22.4 Tapping the Crust: Isolation and Uses of the Elements

Once an element's abundance and sources are known and the metallurgical processes chosen, the isolation process begins. Obviously, the process depends on the physical and chemical properties of the source: we isolate an element that occurs uncombined in the air differently from one dissolved in the sea or one found in a rocky ore. In this section, we detail methods for recovering some important elements; pay special attention to the application of ideas from earlier chapters to these key industrial processes.

Producing the Alkali Metals: Sodium and Potassium

The alkali metals are among the most reactive elements and thus are always found as ions in nature, either in solid minerals or in aqueous solution. In the laboratory, the free elements must be protected from contact with air (for example, by being stored under mineral oil) to prevent their immediate oxidation and to minimize the possibility of fires. The two most important alkali metals are sodium and potassium. Their abundant, water-soluble compounds are used throughout industry and research, and the Na^+ and K^+ ions are essential to organisms.

Industrial Production of Sodium and Potassium The sodium ore is *halite* (largely NaCl), which is obtained either by evaporation of concentrated salt solutions (brines) or by mining vast salt deposits formed from the evaporation of prehistoric seas. The Cheshire salt field in Britain, for example, is 60 km by 24 km by 400 m thick and contains more than 90% NaCl. Other large deposits occur in New Mexico, Michigan, New York, and Kansas. ◆

The brine is evaporated to dryness and the solid crushed and fused (melted) for use in an electrolytic apparatus called the **Downs cell** (Figure 22.15). To reduce heating costs, the NaCl (mp = 801°C) is mixed with $1\frac{1}{2}$ parts $CaCl_2$ to form a mixture that melts at only 580°C. Reduction of the metal ions to Na and Ca takes place at a cylindrical steel cathode, with the molten metals floating on the denser molten salt mixture. As they rise through a short collecting pipe, the liquid Na is siphoned off, while a higher melting Na/Ca alloy solidifies and falls back into the molten electrolyte. Chloride ions are oxidized to Cl_2 gas at a large anode within an inverted cone-shaped region. The cell design separates the metals from the Cl_2 to prevent their explosive recombination. The Cl_2 gas is collected, purified, and sold as a valuable by-product.

◆ **A Plentiful Oceanic Supply of NaCl** Will we ever run out of sodium chloride? Not likely. The rock-salt (halite) equivalent of NaCl in the world's oceans has been estimated at 1.9×10^7 km³, about 150% of the volume of North America above sea level. Or, looking at this amount another way: a row of 1 km³ cubes of NaCl would stretch from the Earth to the Moon 47 times! The photo shows evaporative salt beds near San Francisco Bay.

Inlet for NaCl

$Cl_2(g)$

Na/Ca alloy

Molten electrolyte (NaCl/CaCl₂, 2/3)

Molten Na

Na *(l)*

(−)

(+)

Anode (oxidation)
$2Cl^-(l) \longrightarrow Cl_2(g) + 2e^-$

Cathode (reduction)
$2Na^+(l) + 2e^- \longrightarrow 2Na(l)$

Figure 22.15 The Downs cell for production of sodium. The mixture of solid NaCl and CaCl₂ forms the molten electrolyte. Sodium and calcium are formed at the cathode and float, but due to its higher melting point, an Na/Ca alloy solidifies and falls back into the bath. Chlorine gas forms at the anode.

Sylvite (mostly KCl) is the major ore of potassium. The metal is too soluble in molten KCl to be prepared by a method similar to that for sodium. Instead, chemical reduction of K^+ ions by liquid Na is used. The method is based on atomic properties and the nature of equilibrium systems. Recall that an Na atom is smaller than a K atom, so it holds its outer electron more tightly, as their first ionization energies indicate: IE_1 of Na = 496 kJ/mol; IE_1 of K = 419 kJ/mol. Thus, if the isolation method for K were based solely on this atomic property, Na would not be very effective at reducing K^+, and the reaction would not move very far toward products. An ingenious approach, which applies Le Châtelier's principle, overcomes this drawback. The reduction is carried out at 850°C, which is above the boiling point of K, so the equilibrium mixture contains *gaseous* K:

$$Na(l) + K^+(l) \rightleftharpoons Na^+(l) + K(g)$$

As the K gas is removed, the system shifts to produce more K. The gas is then condensed and purified by fractional distillation. The same general method (with Ca as the reducing agent) is used to produce rubidium and cesium.

Uses of Sodium and Potassium   The compounds of Na and K (and indeed, of all the alkali metals) have many more uses than the elements themselves [see Group 1A(1) Family Portrait, p. 549]. Nevertheless, there are some interesting uses of the metals that take advantage of their strong reducing power. Large amounts of Na were used as an alloy with lead to make gasoline antiknock additives, such as tetraethyllead:

$$4C_2H_5Cl(g) + 4Na(s) + Pb(s) \longrightarrow (C_2H_5)_4Pb(l) + 4NaCl(s)$$

The toxic effects of environmental lead have made this use virtually nonexistent in the United States. Moreover, although leaded gasoline is still used in parts of Europe, recent legislation promises to eliminate this product early in the next decade.

If certain types of nuclear reactors, called *breeder reactors* (Chapter 24), became a practical way to generate energy in the United States, Na production would increase enormously. Its low melting point, viscosity, and absorption of neutrons, combined with its high thermal conductivity and heat capacity, make it perfect for cooling the reactor and exchanging heat to the steam generator.

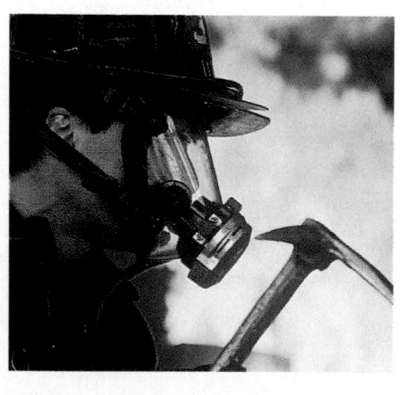

The major use of potassium at present is in an alloy with sodium for use as a heat exchanger in chemical and nuclear reactors. Another application is in the production of its superoxide, which it forms by direct contact with O_2:

$$K(s) + O_2(g) \longrightarrow KO_2(s)$$

This material is employed as an emergency source of O_2 in breathing masks for miners, divers, submarine crews, and firefighters (see photo):

$$4KO_2(s) + 4CO_2(g) + 2H_2O(g) \longrightarrow 4KHCO_3(s) + 3O_2(g)$$

The Indispensable Three: Iron, Copper, and Aluminum

Their familiar presence, innumerable applications, and enormous production levels make three metals—iron (in the form of steel), copper, and aluminum—stand out as indispensable materials of industrial society.

Metallurgy of Iron and Steel   Although people have practiced iron smelting for more than 3000 years, it was a little over 225 years ago that iron assumed its current dominant role. In 1773, an inexpensive process to convert coal to carbon in the form of coke was discovered, and the material was used in a blast furnace. The coke process made iron smelting cheap and efficient and led to large-scale iron production, which ushered in the Industrial Revolution.

Modern society rests, quite literally, on the various alloys of iron known as **steel.** Although steel production has grown enormously since the 18th century—more than 700 million tons are produced annually—the process of recovering iron from its ores still employs the same general approach: *reduction by carbon in a blast furnace.* The most important minerals of iron are listed in Table 22.4. The first four are used for steel making, but the S-containing minerals cannot be used because traces of sulfur make the steel brittle.

The process of converting iron ore to iron metal involves a series of overall redox and acid-base reactions that appear quite simple, although the detailed chemistry is very complex and not entirely understood even today. A modern **blast furnace** (Figure 22.16), such as those used in South Korea and Japan, is a tower about 14 m wide by 40 m high, made of a brick material that can withstand intense heat. The *charge,* which consists of an iron ore (usually hematite) containing the mineral, coke, and limestone, is fed through the top. More coke is burned in air at the bottom. The charge falls and meets a *blast* of rapidly rising hot air created by the burning coke:

$$2C(s) + O_2(g) \longrightarrow 2CO(g) + \textit{heat}$$

At the bottom of the furnace, the temperature exceeds 2000°C, while at the top, it reaches only 200°C. As a result, different stages of the overall reaction process occur at different heights as the charge descends:

1. In the upper part of the furnace (200° to 700°C), the charge is preheated, and a *partial reduction* step occurs. The hematite is reduced to magnetite and then to iron(II) oxide (FeO) by CO, the actual reducing agent of the iron oxides. Carbon dioxide is formed as well. Because the blast of hot air passes through the entire furnace in only 10 s, the various gas-solid reactions do *not* reach equilibrium, and many intermediate products form. Limestone also decomposes to form CO_2 and the basic oxide CaO, which is important later in the process.

Table 22.4 Important Minerals of Iron

Mineral Type	Mineral, Formula
Oxide	Hematite, Fe_2O_3 (photo)
	Magnetite, Fe_3O_4
	Ilmenite, $FeTiO_3$
Carbonate	Siderite, $FeCO_3$
Sulfide	Pyrite, FeS_2
	Pyrrhotite, FeS

Charge
(ore, limestone, coke)

Waste gases
(CO, CO$_2$, NO$_2$)

200°C	Raw materials preheated Partial reduction of iron ore $3Fe_2O_3(s) + CO(g) \rightarrow 2Fe_3O_4(s) + CO_2(g)$ $CaCO_3(s) \rightarrow CaO(s) + CO_2(g)$ $Fe_3O_4(s) + CO(g) \rightarrow 3FeO(s) + CO_2(g)$
700°C	Final reduction $C(s) + CO_2(g) \rightarrow 2CO(g)$ $FeO(s) + CO(g) \rightarrow Fe(l) + CO_2(g)$
1200°C	Melting of impure Fe and slag
1500°C	Phosphates and silicates reduced; P, Si, and other impurities enter molten Fe
2000°C	$2C(s) + O_2(g) \rightarrow 2CO(g)$

Airblast
~900°C

Slag

Hearth

Human

Molten Fe
(pig iron)

Figure 22.16 The major reactions occurring in a blast furnace. Iron is produced from iron ore, coke, and limestone in a complex thermal process. The various stages depend on the temperature at different heights in the furnace. (A human is shown for scale.)

◆ **Was It Slag That Made the Great Ship Go Down?**

Recent direct observation of the sunken luxury liner Titanic shows that six small slits caused by collision with an iceberg, rather than an enormous gash, sank the ship. The slits appear between sections of steel plates in the lower hull and suggest weakness in the rivets that connected the plates. Metallurgical analysis of the rivets shows three times as much slag content as modern rivets. Too much of this silicate-rich material makes the wrought iron used in the rivets brittle and easier to break under stress. Moreover, rather than being evenly distributed, the slag particles within the iron, when viewed microscopically, appear to be clumped, which causes weak spots. Could low-grade rivets with too much slag have caused this tragedy? Follow-up analysis of more rivets and a historical search of rivet standards in the early 1900s may finally solve the mystery of what brought down the unsinkable Titanic and caused the death of 1500 passengers.

2. Lower down, at temperatures of 700° to 1200°C, a *final reduction* step occurs, as some of the coke reduces CO_2 to form more CO, which reduces the FeO to Fe.
3. At still higher temperatures, between 1200° and 1500°C, the iron melts and drips to the bottom of the furnace. Acidic silica particles from the gangue react with basic calcium oxide in a Lewis acid-base reaction to form a molten waste product called **slag:**

$$CaO(s) + SiO_2(s) \longrightarrow CaSiO_3(l)$$

The siliceous slag drips down and floats on the denser iron (much as the Earth's silicate-rich mantle and crust float on its molten iron core). ◆
4. Some unwanted reactions occur at this hottest stage, between 1500° and 2000°C. Any remaining phosphates and silicates are reduced to P and Si, and some Mn and traces of S dissolve into the molten iron along with carbon. The resulting impure product is called *pig iron* and contains about 3% to 4% C. A small amount of pig iron is used to make *cast iron*, but most is purified and alloyed to make various kinds of steel.

Pig iron is converted to steel in a separate furnace by means of the **basic-oxygen process,** as shown in Figure 22.17. High-pressure O_2 is blown over and through the molten iron, so that impurities (C, Si, P, Mn, S) are oxidized rapidly. The highly negative heats of formation of their oxides (such as ΔH_f^0 of $CO_2 = -394$ kJ/mol and ΔH_f^0 of $SiO_2 = -911$ kJ/mol) raise the temperature, which speeds the reaction. A lime (CaO) flux is added, which converts the oxides to a molten slag [primarily $CaSiO_3$ and $Ca_3(PO_4)_2$] that is decanted from the molten steel. The product is **carbon steel,** which contains 1% to 1.5% C and other impurities. It is alloyed with metals that prevent corrosion and increase its strength or flexibility (see Table 22.3).

Figure 22.17 The basic-oxygen process for making steel. A, Jets of pure O_2 in combination with a basic flux (CaO) are used to remove impurities and lower the carbon content of pig iron in the manufacture of steel. **B,** Impure molten iron is added to a basic-oxygen furnace.

Isolation and Electrorefining of Copper After many centuries of mining copper ores to make bronze and brass articles, the remaining ores are less plentiful and less rich in copper, so the metal is more expensive to extract. ◆ Despite this, more than 2.5 billion pounds of copper are produced in the United States annually. The most common copper ore is chalcopyrite, $CuFeS_2$, a mixed sulfide of FeS and CuS (see photo). Most remaining deposits contain less than 0.5% Cu by mass. To "win" this small amount of copper from the ore requires several metallurgical steps, including a final refining to achieve the 99.99% purity needed for electrical wiring, copper's most important application.

The low copper content in chalcopyrite must be enriched by removing the iron. The first step in copper extraction is pretreatment by flotation (see Figure 22.11, p. 967), which concentrates the ore to around 15% Cu by mass. The next step in many processing plants is a controlled roasting step, which oxidizes the FeS but not the CuS:

$$2FeCuS_2(s) + 3O_2(g) \longrightarrow 2CuS(s) + 2FeO(s) + 2SO_2(g)$$

To remove the FeO and convert the CuS to a more convenient form, the mixture is heated to 1100°C with sand and more of the concentrated ore. Several reactions occur in this step. The FeO reacts with sand to form a molten slag:

$$FeO(s) + SiO_2(s) \longrightarrow FeSiO_3(l)$$

The CuS is thermodynamically unstable at the elevated temperature and decomposes to yield Cu_2S, which is drawn off as a liquid.

In the final smelting step, the Cu_2S is roasted in air, which converts some of it to Cu_2O:

$$2Cu_2S(s) + 3O_2(g) \longrightarrow 2Cu_2O(s) + 2SO_2(g)$$

The two copper(I) compounds then react, with sulfide ion acting as the reducing agent:

$$Cu_2S(s) + 2Cu_2O(s) \longrightarrow 6Cu(l) + SO_2(g)$$

The copper obtained at this stage is usable for plumbing, but it must be purified further for electrical applications by removing unwanted impurities (Fe and Ni) as well as valuable ones (Ag, Au, and Pt). Purification is accomplished by *electrorefining*, which involves the oxidation of Cu and the formation of Cu^{2+} ions in solution, followed by their reduction and the plating out of Cu metal (Figure 22.18). The impure copper obtained from smelting is cast into plates to be used as anodes, and cathodes are made from already

The Dawns of Three New Ages Copper has been known since prehistoric times because it occurs uncombined. Its ores were probably first reduced by charcoal fires as early as 3500 BC, which marks the beginning of the Copper Age. With another 500 years of experience, people of India and Greece added molten tin to obtain a harder material, which marks the beginning of the Bronze Age. Some 1800 years later, brass, a copper-zinc alloy, was made in Palestine and used extensively by the Romans for well over 2000 years.

Mining chalcopyrite.

Cu → Cu^{2+} + 2e⁻
Anode (+)

Cu^{2+} + 2e⁻ → Cu
(−) Cathode

Pure copper | Anode mud | Acidified $CuSO_4(aq)$ | Impure copper

A

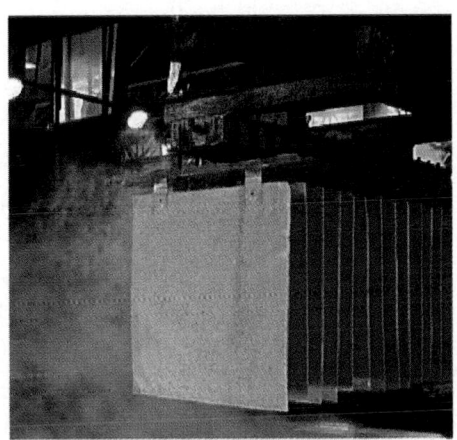

B

Figure 22.18 The electrorefining of copper. A, Copper is refined electrolytically, using impure slabs of copper as anodes and sheets of pure copper as cathodes. The Cu^{2+} ions released from the anode are reduced to Cu metal and plate out at the cathode. The "anode mud" contains valuable metal by-products. **B,** A small section of an industrial facility for electrorefining copper.

purified copper. The electrodes are immersed in acidified $CuSO_4$ solution, and a controlled voltage is applied that accomplishes two tasks simultaneously:

1. Copper and the more active impurities (Fe, Ni) are oxidized to their cations, while the less active ones (Ag, Au, Pt) are not. As the anode slabs react, these unoxidized metals fall off as a valuable "anode mud" and are purified separately. Sale of the precious metals in the anode mud nearly offsets the cost of electricity to operate the cell, which is the main reason Cu wire is so inexpensive.

2. Because Cu is much less active than the Fe and Ni impurities, Cu^{2+} ions are reduced at the cathode, but Fe^{2+} and Ni^{2+} ions remain in solution:

$$Cu^{2+}(aq) + 2e^- \longrightarrow Cu(s) \qquad E^0 = 0.34 \text{ V}$$
$$Ni^{2+}(aq) + 2e^- \longrightarrow Ni(s) \qquad E^0 = -0.25 \text{ V}$$
$$Fe^{2+}(aq) + 2e^- \longrightarrow Fe(s) \qquad E^0 = -0.44 \text{ V}$$

Isolation, Uses, and Recycling of Aluminum Aluminum is the most abundant metal in the Earth's crust by mass and the third most abundant element (after O and Si). It is found in numerous aluminosilicate minerals (Section 14.6), such as feldspars, micas, and clays, and in the rare gems garnet, beryl, spinel, and turquoise. Corundum, pure aluminum oxide (Al_2O_3), is extremely hard; mixed with traces of transition metals, it exists as ruby and sapphire. Impure Al_2O_3 is used in sandpaper and other abrasives.

Through eons of weathering, certain clays became *bauxite*, the major ore of aluminum. This mixed oxide-hydroxide occurs in enormous surface deposits in Mediterranean and tropical regions (see photo), but with world aluminum production approaching 100 million tons annually, it may soon be more scarce. In addition to hydrated Al_2O_3 (about 75%), industrial-grade bauxite also contains Fe_2O_3, SiO_2, and TiO_2, which are removed during the extraction.

The overall two-step process combines hydro- and electrometallurgical techniques. In the first step, Al_2O_3 is separated from bauxite; in the second, it is converted to the metal.

1. *Isolating Al_2O_3 from bauxite.* After mining, bauxite is pretreated by extended boiling in 30% NaOH in the *Bayer process*, which involves acid-base, solubility, and complex-ion equilibria. The acidic SiO_2 and the amphoteric Al_2O_3 dissolve in the base, but the basic Fe_2O_3 and TiO_2 do not:

$$SiO_2(s) + 2NaOH(aq) + 2H_2O(l) \longrightarrow Na_2Si(OH)_6(aq)$$
$$Al_2O_3(s) + 2NaOH(aq) + 3H_2O(l) \longrightarrow 2NaAl(OH)_4(aq)$$
$$Fe_2O_3(s) + NaOH(aq) \longrightarrow \text{no reaction}$$
$$TiO_2(s) + NaOH(aq) \longrightarrow \text{no reaction}$$

Further heating slowly precipitates the $Na_2Si(OH)_6$ as an aluminosilicate, which is filtered out with the insoluble Fe_2O_3 and TiO_2 ("red mud").

Acidifying the filtrate precipitates Al^{3+} as $Al(OH)_3$. Recall from our discussion of complex-ion equilibria that the aluminate ion, $Al(OH)_4^-(aq)$, is actually the complex ion $Al(H_2O)_2(OH)_4^-$, in which four of the six water molecules surrounding Al^{3+} have each lost a proton (see Figure 19.14, p. 839). Weakly acidic CO_2 is added to produce a small amount of H^+ ion, which reacts with this complex ion. Cooling supersaturates the solution, and the solid forms and is filtered:

$$CO_2(g) + H_2O \rightleftharpoons H^+(aq) + HCO_3^-(aq)$$
$$Al(H_2O)_2(OH)_4^-(aq) + H^+(aq) \longrightarrow Al(H_2O)_3(OH)_3(s)$$

[Recall that we usually write $Al(H_2O)_3(OH)_3$ more simply as $Al(OH)_3$.]

Drying at high temperature converts the hydroxide to the oxide:

$$2Al(H_2O)_3(OH)_3(s) \xrightarrow{\Delta} Al_2O_3(s) + 9H_2O(g)$$

Mining bauxite.

2. *Converting Al$_2$O$_3$ to the free metal.* Aluminum is an active metal, much too strong a reducing agent to be formed at the cathode from aqueous solution (Section 21.7), so the oxide itself must be electrolyzed. However, the melting point of Al$_2$O$_3$ is very high (2030°C), so it is dissolved in molten *cryolite* (Na$_3$AlF$_6$) to give a mixture that is electrolyzed at ~1000°C. Obviously, the use of cryolite provides a major energy (and cost) savings. The only sizeable cryolite mines are in Greenland, however, and they cannot supply enough natural mineral to meet the need. Therefore, synthetic cryolite has become a major subsidiary industry in aluminum manufacture.

The electrolytic step, called the *Hall-Heroult process,* takes place in a graphite-lined furnace, with the lining itself acting as the cathode. Anodes of graphite dip into the molten Al$_2$O$_3$/Na$_3$AlF$_6$ mixture (Figure 22.19). The cell typically operates at a moderate voltage of 4.5 V, but with an enormous current flow of 1.0×10^5 to 2.5×10^5 A.

The process is complex and its details are still not entirely known. Therefore, the specific reactions shown below are chosen from among several other possibilities. Molten cryolite contains several ions (including AlF$_6$$^{3-}$, AlF$_4$$^-$, and F$^-$), which react with Al$_2O_3$ to form fluoro-oxy ions (including AlOF$_3$$^{2-}$, Al$_2OF_6$$^{2-}$, and Al$_2O_2F_4$$^{2-}$) that dissolve in the mixture. For example,

$$2Al_2O_3(s) + 2AlF_6{}^{3-}(l) \longrightarrow 3Al_2O_2F_4{}^{2-}(l)$$

Al forms at the cathode (reduction), shown here with AlF$_6$$^{3-}$ as reactant:

$$AlF_6{}^{3-}(l) + 3e^- \longrightarrow Al(l) + 6F^-(l) \qquad \text{[cathode (reduction)]}$$

The graphite anode itself is oxidized and forms carbon dioxide gas. Using one of the fluoro-oxy species as an example, the anode reaction is

$$Al_2O_2F_4{}^{2-}(l) + 8F^-(l) + C(graphite) \longrightarrow$$
$$2AlF_6{}^{3-}(l) + CO_2(g) + 4e^- \qquad \text{[anode (oxidation)]}$$

Thus, the anodes are consumed in this half-reaction and must be replaced frequently.

Combining the three previous equations and making sure that e$^-$ gained at the cathode equals e$^-$ lost at the anode gives the overall reaction:

$$2Al_2O_3(\text{in } Na_3AlF_6) + 3C(graphite) \longrightarrow 4Al(l) + 3CO_2(g) \qquad \text{[overall (cell) reaction]}$$

Graphite rods
Anodes: Al$_2$O$_2$F$_4$$^{2-}$ + 8F$^-$ + C $\longrightarrow$ 2AlF$_6$$^{3-}$ + CO$_2$ + 4e$^-$

Solid charge
Al$_2$O$_3$ + Na$_3$AlF$_6$

Molten electrolyte

Bubbles of CO$_2$

Molten Al

Power source
(−) (+)

Graphite furnace lining
Cathode: AlF$_6$$^{3-}$ + 3e$^-$ $\longrightarrow$ Al + 6F$^-$

Figure 22.19 The electrolytic cell in the manufacture of aluminum. Purified Al$_2$O$_3$ is mixed with cryolite (Na$_3$AlF$_6$) and melted. Reduction at the graphite furnace lining (cathode) gives molten Al. Oxidation at the graphite rods (anodes) slowly converts them to CO$_2$, so they must be replaced periodically.

◆ **Energy Received and Returned** Aluminum manufacture in the United States uses more electricity in 1 day than a city of 100,000 uses in 1 year! The reason for the high energy needs of Al manufacture is the electron configuration of Al, ([Ne] $3s^23p^1$). Each Al^{3+} ion needs $3e^-$ to form an Al atom, and the atomic mass of Al is so low (~27 g/mol) that 1 mol e^- produces only 9 g Al. Compare this with the masses of Mg or Ca (two other lightweight structural metals) that 1 mol e^- produces:

$$\tfrac{1}{3}Al^{3+} + e^- = \tfrac{1}{3}Al(s), \sim9 \text{ g}$$
$$\tfrac{1}{2}Mg^{2+} + e^- = \tfrac{1}{2}Mg(s), \sim12 \text{ g}$$
$$\tfrac{1}{2}Ca^{2+} + e^- = \tfrac{1}{2}Ca(s), \sim20 \text{ g}$$

To turn this disadvantage around, we need an aluminum battery. Once produced, the Al in the battery represents a concentrated form of electrical energy that can deliver 1 mol e^- (96,500 C) for every 9 g of Al consumed. Thus, its electrical output per gram of metal is high. In fact, aluminum-air batteries are now being produced (see Gallery, Section 21.5).

The Hall-Heroult process uses an enormous quantity of energy: aluminum production in the United States accounts for more than 5% of our total electrical usage. ◆

Aluminum is a superb decorative, functional, and structural metal. It is lightweight, attractive, easy to work, and forms strong alloys, many of which are all around us (Figure 22.20). Although Al is very active, it does not corrode readily because of an adherent oxide layer that forms rapidly in air and prevents more O_2 from penetrating. Nevertheless, when it is in contact with less active metals such as Fe, Cu, and Pb, aluminum becomes the anode and deteriorates rapidly (Section 21.6). To prevent this, aluminum objects are often *anodized,* that is, made to act as the anode in an electrolysis that coats them with an oxide layer. The object is immersed in a 20% H_2SO_4 bath and connected to a graphite cathode:

$$6H^+(aq) + 6e^- \longrightarrow 3H_2(g) \qquad \text{Cathode (reduction)}$$
$$\underline{2Al(s) + 3H_2O(l) \longrightarrow Al_2O_3(s) + 6H^+(aq) + 6e^- \qquad \text{Anode (oxidation)}}$$
$$2Al(s) + 3H_2O(l) \longrightarrow Al_2O_3(s) + 3H_2(g) \qquad \text{Overall (cell) reaction}$$

The Al_2O_3 layer deposited is typically from 10 to 100 μ thick, depending on the object's intended use.

More than 3.5 billion pounds (1.5 million metric tons) of aluminum cans and packaging are discarded each year—a waste of one of the most useful materials in the world *and* the energy used to make it. A quick calculation of the energy needed to prepare 1 mol Al from *purified* Al_2O_3, compared with the energy needed for recycling, tells a clear message. The overall cell reaction in the Hall-Heroult process has a ΔH^0 of 2272 kJ and a ΔS^0 of 635.4 J/K. Considering *only* the free energy change of the reaction at 1000.°C, for 1 mol Al we obtain

$$\Delta G^0 = \Delta H^0 - T\Delta S^0 = \frac{2272 \text{ kJ}}{4 \text{ mol Al}} - \left(1273 \text{ K} \times \frac{0.6354 \text{ kJ/K}}{4 \text{ mol Al}}\right) = 365.8 \text{ kJ/mol Al}$$

Since the molar mass of Al is nearly twice the mass of a soft-drink or beer can, the electrolysis step requires nearly 200 kJ of energy for each can!

When aluminum is recycled, the major energy input, for melting the cans and foil, has been calculated as ~26 kJ/mol Al. The ratio of these energy inputs gives

$$\frac{\text{Energy to recycle 1 mol Al}}{\text{Energy for electrolysis of 1 mol Al}} = \frac{26 \text{ kJ}}{365.8 \text{ kJ}} = 0.071$$

Based on just these portions of the process, recycling takes about 7% as much energy as electrolysis. Recent energy estimates for the entire manufacturing process (including mining, pretreating, maintaining operating conditions, electrolyzing, and so forth) are about 6000 kJ/mol Al, which means recycling

Other
(6.5%)
Paints, rocket propellants

Machinery
(7.6%)
Heat exchangers, chemical equipment, hoisting

Electrical power lines
(13.5%)

Transportation
(17.8%)
Cars, trucks, trailers, rail cars, aircraft

Consumer durables
(8.5%)
Beams, bridges, household appliances, sports equipment

Packaging
(16.6%)
Foil, cans, toothpaste tubes, frozen food containers

Export
(6.9%)

Building
(22.6%)
Windows, doors, screens, gutters, mobile homes, panels

Figure 22.20 The many familiar and essential uses of aluminum.

requires less than 1% as much energy as manufacturing! The economic advantages, not to mention the environmental ones, are obvious, and recycling is now taking place actively in communities around the United States (see photo).

Mining the Sea: Magnesium and Bromine

In the not too distant future, as terrestrial sources of certain elements become scarce or too costly to mine, the oceans will become an important source. Despite the abundant distribution of magnesium on land, it is already being obtained from the sea, and its ocean-based production is a good example of the approach we might one day use for other elements. Bromine, too, is recovered from the sea as well as from inland brines.

Isolation and Uses of Magnesium The *Dow process* for the isolation of magnesium from the sea involves steps that are similar to the procedures used for rocky ores (Figure 22.21):

1. *Mining.* Intake of seawater and straining the debris are the "mining" steps. No pretreatment is needed.
2. *Converting to mineral.* The dissolved Mg^{2+} ion is converted to the mineral $Mg(OH)_2$ with $Ca(OH)_2$, which is generated on-site (at the plant). Seashells ($CaCO_3$) are crushed, decomposed with heat to CaO, and mixed with water to make slaked lime [$Ca(OH)_2$]. This is pumped into the seawater intake tank to precipitate the dissolved Mg^{2+} as the hydroxide ($K_{sp} \approx 10^{-9}$):

$$Ca(OH)_2(aq) + Mg^{2+}(aq) \longrightarrow Mg(OH)_2(s) + Ca^{2+}(aq)$$

3. *Converting to compound.* The solid $Mg(OH)_2$ is filtered and mixed with excess HCl, which is also made on-site, to form aqueous $MgCl_2$:

$$Mg(OH)_2(s) + 2HCl(aq) \longrightarrow MgCl_2(aq) + 2H_2O(l)$$

The water is evaporated in stages to give solid, hydrated $MgCl_2 \cdot nH_2O$.
4. *Electrochemical redox.* Heating above 700°C drives off the water of hydration and melts the $MgCl_2$. Electrolysis gives chlorine gas and the molten metal, which floats on the denser molten salt:

$$MgCl_2(l) \longrightarrow Mg(l) + Cl_2(g)$$

The Cl_2 that forms is recycled to make the HCl used in Step 3.

Crushed aluminum cans ready for recycling.

Figure 22.21 The production of elemental Mg from seawater. The multistage Dow process involves obtaining Mg^{2+} ion from seawater, converting the Mg^{2+} to $Mg(OH)_2$ and then $MgCl_2$, which is evaporated to dryness, and then electrolytically reducing to Mg metal and Cl_2 gas.

Magnesium is the lightest structural metal available (nearly one-half the density of Al and one-fifth that of steel). Although Mg is quite reactive, it forms an extremely adherent, high-melting oxide layer (MgO); thus, it finds many uses in metal alloys and can be machined into any form. Magnesium alloys occur in everything from aircraft bodies to camera bodies, and from luggage to auto engine blocks. The pure metal is a strong reducing agent, which makes it useful for sacrificial anodes (Section 21.6) and in the metallurgical extraction of other metals, such as Be, Ti, Zr, Hf, and U. For example, titanium is made from its major ore, ilmenite, in two steps:

$$2FeTiO_3(s) + 7Cl_2(g) + 6C(s) \longrightarrow 2TiCl_4(l) + 2FeCl_3(s) + 6CO(g)$$
$$TiCl_4(l) + 2Mg(l) \longrightarrow Ti(s) + 2MgCl_2(l)$$

Isolation and Uses of Bromine The largest source of bromine is the oceans, where it occurs as Br^- at a concentration of 0.065 g/L (65 ppm). However, the added cost of concentrating such a dilute solution often shifts the choice of source, when available, to much more concentrated salt lakes and natural brines. Arkansas brines, the most important source in the United States, contain about 4.5 g Br^-/L (4500 ppm). The Br^- is readily oxidized to Br_2 with aqueous Cl_2:

$$2Br^-(aq) + Cl_2(aq) \longrightarrow Br_2(l) + 2Cl^-(aq) \qquad \Delta G^0 = -61.5 \text{ kJ}$$

The Br_2 is removed by passing steam through the mixture and then cooling and drying the liquid bromine.

World production of Br_2 is about 1% that of Cl_2. Its major use is in the preparation of organic chemicals, such as ethylene dibromide, which was added to leaded gasoline to prevent lead oxides from forming and depositing on engine parts. Newer products requiring bromine include the flame retardants in rugs and textiles. Bromine is needed in the synthesis of inorganic chemicals also, especially silver bromide for photographic emulsions.

The Many Sources and Uses of Hydrogen

Although hydrogen accounts for 90% of the atoms in the universe, it makes up only 15% of the atoms in the Earth's crust. Moreover, whereas it occurs in the universe mostly as both H_2 and free H atoms, virtually all hydrogen in the crust is in combination with other elements, either oxygen in natural waters or carbon in biomass, petroleum, and coal.

Properties of the Hydrogen Isotopes Hydrogen has three naturally occurring isotopes. Ordinary hydrogen (^1H), or protium, is the most abundant and has no neutrons. Deuterium (^2H or D), the next in abundance, has one neutron, and rare, radioactive tritium (^3H or T) has two. All three occur as the diatomic molecules, H_2, D_2 (or $^2H_2$), and T_2 (or $^3H_2$), or HD, DT, and HT. Table 22.5 compares some molecular and physical properties of H_2, D_2, and T_2. As you can see, the heavier the isotope is, the higher the molar mass of the molecule, and the higher its melting point, boiling point, and heats of phase change; it also effuses at a lower rate (Section 5.6).

Because hydrogen is so light, the relative difference in mass of hydrogen isotopes is enormous compared to isotopes of other common elements. (For example, the mass of ^{13}C is only 8% greater than that of ^{12}C.) Note, especially, that mass difference leads to different bond energies, which affects reactivity. Because the mass of D is twice the mass of H, H atoms bonded to a given atom vibrate at a higher frequency than do D atoms, so their bonds are higher in energy. As a result, the *bond to H is weaker and thus quicker to break*. Therefore, any reaction that includes breaking a bond to hydrogen in the rate-determining step occurs *faster with H than with D*. This behavior is called a *kinetic isotope effect*, and we'll see an example of it shortly. No other element displays a kinetic isotope effect nearly as large.

Table 22.5 Some Molecular and Physical Properties of Diatomic Protium, Deuterium, and Tritium

Property	H_2	D_2	T_2
Molar mass (g/mol)	2.016	4.028	6.032
Bond length (pm)	74.14	74.14	74.14
Melting point (K)	13.96	18.73	20.62
Boiling point (K)	20.39	23.67	25.04
ΔH_{fus}^0 (kJ/mol)	0.117	0.197	0.250
ΔH_{vap}^0 (kJ/mol)	0.904	1.226	1.393
Bond energy (kJ/mol at 298 K)	432	443	447

Industrial Production of Hydrogen Hydrogen gas (H_2) is produced on an industrial scale worldwide: 250,000 metric tons (3×10^{12} L at STP; equivalent to $\sim1\times10^{11}$ mol) are produced annually in the United States alone. All production methods are energy intensive, so the choice is determined by energy costs. In Scandinavia, where hydroelectric power is plentiful, electrolysis is the chosen method; on the other hand, where natural gas from oil refineries is plentiful, as in the United States and Great Britain, thermal methods are used to produce hydrogen.

The most common thermal methods use water and a simple hydrocarbon in two steps. Modern American plants use methane, which has the highest H:C ratio of any hydrocarbon. In the first step, the reactants are heated to around 1000°C over a nickel-based catalyst in the endothermic *steam-reforming process*:

$$CH_4(g) + H_2O(g) \longrightarrow CO(g) + 3H_2(g) \qquad \Delta H = 206 \text{ kJ}$$

Heat is supplied by burning methane at the refinery. To generate more H_2, the product mixture (called *water gas*) is heated with steam at 400°C over an iron or cobalt oxide catalyst in the exothermic *water-gas shift reaction*, and the CO reacts:

$$H_2O(g) + CO(g) \rightleftharpoons CO_2(g) + H_2(g) \qquad \Delta H = -41 \text{ kJ}$$

The reaction mixture is recycled several times, which decreases the CO to around 0.2% by volume. Passing the mixture through liquid water removes the more soluble CO_2 (solubility = 0.034 mol/L) from the H_2 (solubility < 0.001 mol/L). Calcium oxide can also be used to remove CO_2 by formation of $CaCO_3$. By removing CO_2, these steps shift the equilibrium position to the right and produce H_2 that is about 98% pure. To attain greater purity ($\sim$99.9%), the gas mixture is passed through a *synthetic zeolite* (Gallery, p. 569) selected to filter out nearly all molecules larger than H_2.

In regions where inexpensive electricity is available, very pure H_2 is prepared through electrolysis of water with Pt (or Ni) electrodes:

$$
\begin{array}{lll}
2H_2O(l) + 2e^- \longrightarrow H_2(g) + 2OH^-(aq) & E = -0.42 \text{ V} & \text{[cathode]} \\
H_2O(l) \longrightarrow \tfrac{1}{2}O_2(g) + 2H^+(aq) + 2e^- & -E = -0.82 \text{ V} & \text{[anode]} \\
\hline
H_2O(l) \longrightarrow H_2(g) + \tfrac{1}{2}O_2(g) & E_{cell} = -1.24 \text{ V} &
\end{array}
$$

Overvoltage increases the cell potential to about -2 V (Section 21.7). Thus, under typical operating conditions, it takes about 400 kJ of energy to produce 1 mol H_2:

$$\Delta G = -nFE = (-2 \text{ mol e}^-)\left(\frac{96.5 \text{ kJ}}{\text{V} \cdot \text{mol e}^-}\right)(-2 \text{ V}) = 4\times10^2 \text{ kJ/mol } H_2$$

High-purity O_2 is a valuable by-product that offsets some of the costs.

Calcium reacts with water to form H_2.

Laboratory Production of Hydrogen You may already have produced small amounts of H_2 in the lab by one of several methods. A characteristic reaction of the very active metals in Groups 1A(1) and 2A(2) is the reduction of water to H_2 and OH^- (see photo):

$$Ca(s) + 2H_2O(l) \longrightarrow Ca^{2+}(aq) + 2OH^-(aq) + H_2(g)$$

Alternatively, the strongly reducing hydride ion can be used:

$$NaH(s) + H_2O(l) \longrightarrow Na^+(aq) + OH^-(aq) + H_2(g)$$

Less active metals reduce H^+ in acids:

$$Zn(s) + 2H^+(aq) \longrightarrow Zn^{2+}(aq) + H_2(g)$$

In view of hydrogen's great potential as a fuel (Chemical Connections, Section 6.6), chemists are seeking ways to decompose water by lowering the overall activation energy of the process. More than 10,000 *water-splitting* schemes have been devised; one of the more promising is

$$3FeCl_2(s) + 4H_2O(g) \longrightarrow Fe_3O_4(s) + 6HCl(g) + H_2(g)$$
$$Fe_3O_4(s) + \tfrac{3}{2}Cl_2(g) + 6HCl(g) \longrightarrow 3FeCl_3(s) + 3H_2O(g) + \tfrac{1}{2}O_2(g)$$
$$\underline{3FeCl_3(s) \longrightarrow 3FeCl_2(s) + \tfrac{3}{2}Cl_2(g)}$$
$$H_2O(g) \longrightarrow H_2(g) + \tfrac{1}{2}O_2(g)$$

Since ΔG^0 at 298 K for the decomposition of 1 mol $H_2O(g)$ equals 229 kJ, all these schemes require energy. Given the increase in number of moles of gas, ΔS^0 is positive. Thus, the process is endothermic ($\Delta H^0 > 0$) and requires heat to occur spontaneously. Attempts are now being made to supply the heat from focused sunlight.

Industrial Uses of Hydrogen Typically, a plant produces H_2 to make some other end product. In fact, more than 95% of H_2 produced industrially is consumed on-site in ammonia or petrochemical facilities. In a plant that synthesizes NH_3 from N_2 and H_2, the reactant gases are formed through a series of reactions that involve methane, including the steam-reforming and water-gas shift reactions we discussed previously. For this reason, the cost of NH_3 is closely correlated with the cost of CH_4. Here is a typical example of how the reaction series in an ammonia plant works.

The steam-reforming reaction is performed with excess CH_4, which depletes the reaction mixture of H_2O:

$$CH_4(g; \text{excess}) + H_2O(g) \longrightarrow CO(g) + 3H_2(g)$$

An excess of the product mixture (CH_4, CO, H_2) is burned in an amount of air ($N_2 + O_2$) insufficient to effect complete combustion but just enough to consume the O_2, heat the mixture to 1100°C, and form additional H_2O:

$$4CH_4(g; \text{excess}) + 7O_2(g) \longrightarrow 2CO_2(g) + 2CO(g) + 8H_2O(g)$$
$$2H_2(g; \text{excess}) + O_2(g) \longrightarrow 2H_2O(g)$$
$$2CO(g; \text{excess}) + O_2(g) \longrightarrow 2CO_2(g)$$

Any remaining CH_4 reacts by the steam-reforming reaction, the remaining CO reacts by the water-gas shift reaction ($H_2O + CO \rightleftharpoons CO_2 + H_2$) to form more H_2, and the CO_2 is removed with CaO. The amounts are carefully adjusted to produce a final mixture that contains a 1:3 ratio of N_2 (from the added air) to H_2 (with traces of CH_4, Ar, and CO). This mixture is used directly in the synthesis of ammonia (Chemical Connections, Section 17.6).

A second major use of H_2 is the *hydrogenation* of the C=C bonds in liquid oils to form the C—C bonds in solid fats and margarine. The process uses H_2 in contact with transition metal catalysts, such as powdered nickel (see Figure 16.24, p. 701). Solid fats are used not only as spreads, but also in commercial baked goods. Look at the ingredients on most packages of bread, cake, and cookies, and you'll see the "partially hydrogenated vegetable oils" made by this process.

Hydrogen is also essential in the manufacture of many "bulk" chemicals, those produced in large amounts that have many further uses. One application gaining great attention is the production of methanol, in which carbon monoxide reacts with H_2 over a copper–zinc oxide catalyst:

$$CO(g) + 2H_2(g) \xrightarrow{\text{Cu-ZnO catalyst}} CH_3OH(l)$$

Many automotive engineers expect methanol to be used increasingly as a gasoline additive and, if an inexpensive source of hydrogen becomes available, used directly as one of several fuel alternatives.

Production and Uses of Deuterium Deuterium and its compounds are produced from D_2O (heavy water), which is present as a minor component (0.016 mol % D_2O) in normal water and is isolated on the multiton scale by *electrolytic enrichment*. This process is based on the kinetic isotope effect for hydrogen noted earlier, specifically on the *higher rate of bond-breaking for O—H bonds versus O—D bonds* and thus on the higher rate of electrolysis of H_2O compared with D_2O. For example, using Pt electrodes, H_2O electrolyzes about 14 times faster than D_2O. As some of the liquid decomposes to the elemental gases, the remainder becomes enriched in D_2O. Thus, by the time the volume of water has been reduced to 1/20,000 of its original volume, the remaining water is around 99% D_2O. By combining samples and repeating the electrolysis, more than 99.9% D_2O is obtained.

Deuterium gas is produced by electrolysis of D_2O or by any of the other chemical reactions that produce hydrogen gas from water, such as

$$2Na(s) + 2D_2O(l) \longrightarrow 2Na^+(aq) + 2OD^-(aq) + D_2(g)$$

Similarly, compounds containing D (or T) are produced from reactions that give rise to the corresponding H-containing compound, such as

$$SiCl_4(l) + 2D_2O(l) \longrightarrow SiO_2(s) + 4DCl(g)$$

Compounds with acidic protons undergo H/D exchange:

$$CH_3COOH(l) + D_2O(l; \text{ excess}) \longrightarrow CH_3COOD(l) + DHO(l; \text{ small amount})$$

Notice that only the acidic H atom, the one in the COOH group, is exchanged, not those attached to carbon. We discuss the natural and synthetic formation of tritium in Chapter 24.

A Group at a Glance: Sources, Isolation, and Uses of the Elements

From a large-scale industrial perspective, certain elements may be more essential than others, but each has its own uses, in many cases, a critical one in a specialty industry. So that you can readily survey some practical aspects of the elements, the multipart Table 22.6 on the following five pages presents relevant facts about the main-group and Period 4 transition elements.

Table 22.6A Sources, Isolation, and Uses of Group 1A(1): The Alkali Metals

Despite their great chemical similarity, the alkali metals rarely occur together in terrestrial minerals because of large differences in ionic size and thus crystal structure. Lithium salts occur with those of magnesium, an example of their diagonal relationship (Section 14.3). Sodium and potassium are the fifth and sixth most abundant metals in the crust. All are isolated from their molten salts, either through electrolytic or chemical reduction. Most uses rely on their low densities or great reducing power.

Sea salt harvest, France

Element	Source	Isolation	Uses
Lithium	Spodumene [LiAl(Si$_2$O$_6$)]	Preparation and electrolysis of molten LiCl	In strong, low-density Mg and Al alloys for armor and aerospace parts; in Li batteries for computers, electric cars
Sodium	NaCl in rock salt (halite); NaNO$_3$ (saltpeter)	Electrolysis of molten NaCl (Downs cell; see text)	Reducing agent for isolation of Ti, Zr, others; heat exchanger in nuclear reactors
Potassium	KCl (sylvite) in seawater	Na reduction of molten KCl (see text)	Reducing agent; production of KO$_2$ (see text)
Rubidium	Minor component of Li ores	Ca reduction of molten RbCl; by-product of Li isolation	Reducing agent
Cesium	Minor component of Li ores; pollucite (Cs$_4$Al$_4$Si$_9$O$_{26}$·H$_2$O)	Ca reduction of molten CsCl; by-product of Li isolation	Reducing agent
Francium	Minute traces from ^{235}U decay		

Table 22.6B Sources, Isolation, and Uses of Group 2A(2): The Alkaline Earth Metals

The alkaline earth metals are extracted mostly from rocky carbonates and sulfates (except for magnesium, which is also isolated from seawater). Like the alkali metals, they are strong reducing agents, so the final isolation step is either electrolytic reduction of the molten chloride or chemical reduction of the oxide with an active metal. The lighter members are used in alloys, the heavier ones as scavengers of nonmetal impurities through formation of ionic compounds.

Dolomite Mountains, Italy

Element	Source	Isolation	Uses
Beryllium	Beryl (Be$_3$Al$_2$Si$_6$O$_{18}$)	Electrolysis of molten BeCl$_2$; reduction of BeF$_2$ with Mg	In high-strength alloys of Cu and Ni for aerospace engines and electronics; neutron moderator and reflector in nuclear reactors (Section 24.7); window in x-ray tubes
Magnesium	Magnesite (MgCO$_3$), dolomite (MgCO$_3$·CaCO$_3$), seawater	Electrolysis of molten MgCl$_2$ (see text); silicothermal method, $2(MgO \cdot CaO) + FeSi \longrightarrow 2Mg + Ca_2SiO_4 + Fe$	Lightweight alloys
Calcium	Limestone and aragonite (CaCO$_3$)	Electrolysis of molten CaCl$_2$ formed by HCl on CaCO$_3$	Strengthener in Al alloys; reducing agent to produce Cr, Zr, U; scavenger of traces of O$_2$, P, and S in steel
Strontium	Strontianite (SrCO$_3$); celestite (SrSO$_4$)	Thermal decomposition, then Al reduction of SrO	Scavenger of O$_2$ and N$_2$ in electronic devices
Barium	Barite (BaSO$_4$)	Al reduction of BaO	Scavenger of O$_2$ and N$_2$ in electronic devices
Radium	Minor (0.1 ppb) component in pitchblende (uranium ore)	Electrolysis of molten RaCl$_2$ after extensive extraction (Section 24.1)	Formerly used in cancer therapy

Nodules of Cu, Ni, and Co

Table 22.6C Sources, Isolation, and Uses of the Period 4 Transition Metals [Groups 3B(3) to 2B(12)]

Several of the first-row transition elements—Fe, Ti, Mn—are among the most abundant metals in the crust and occur together in many ores. Extraction methods vary depending on the source, but all include a reduction step with either carbon or more active metals (Mg or Al). Most of the uses of these metals involve their alloys.

Element	Source	Isolation	Uses
Scandium	Thortveitite (40% Sc_2O_3); by-product of U extraction	Reduction of Sc_2O_3 with C	None
Titanium	Rutile (TiO_2); ilmenite ($FeTiO_3$)	Conversion to $TiCl_4$, then reduction with Mg	Very abundant (4th in crust); stronger than steel but half as dense; high-temperature, lightweight alloys for rocket and jet engines; future uses in train and car parts
Vanadium	Carnotite [$K(UO_2)(VO_4) \cdot 1.5\ H_2O$]	Conversion to $NaVO_3$, then reduction with Al (thermite) or FeSi	Combines with C in steel to make very strong alloy for truck springs and axles
Chromium	Chromite ($FeCr_2O_4$)	Conversion to Cr_2O_3, then reduction with Al	Nonferrous alloys; chrome plating; stainless steels
Manganese	Pyrolusite (MnO_2); many other ores; in future, Mn "nodules" on ocean floor	Conversion to Mn_3O_4, then reduction with Al; conversion to $MnSO_4$, then electrolysis of aqueous Mn(II)	Scavenger of O and S in steel; high-strength steel alloys of excavators, rail crossings
Iron	Hematite (Fe_2O_3); magnetite (Fe_3O_4)	Reduction using C (see text)	Steel (see text)
Cobalt	Smaltite ($CoAs_2$); many sulfides with Ni, Cu, Pb	Roasting in O_2, leaching with H_2SO_4, precipitating $Co(OH)_3$ with ClO^-, heating to form CoO, and reducing with C	Cobalt blue glass and pottery; pigments for paints and inks; catalysts for organic reactions; specialty alloys with Cr and W for drill bits, lathe tools, and surgical instruments; magnetic alloys (Alnico)
Nickel	Pentlandite [$(Ni,Fe)_9S_8$]	Roasting in O_2 to NiO, reducing with C; Mond process, $Ni(CO)_4(g) \rightleftharpoons Ni(s) + 4CO(g)$	Nickel steels for armor; stainless steel and Alnico; nonferrous alloys (tableware) with Ag; Monel with Cu for handling F_2; nichrome; undercoat for chrome plating; hydrogenation catalyst
Copper	Chalcopyrite ($CuFeS_2$)	See text	Wiring, plumbing, coins (see text)
Zinc	Zinc blende (ZnS); sphalerite	Roasting in O_2 to form ZnO, then reducing with C	Brasses (50% to 80% Cu); galvanizing steel to prevent corrosion; batteries (Section 21.5)

Jet engine assembly

Steelworks

Table 22.6D Sources, Isolation, and Uses of Group 3A(13): The Boron Family

Most sources are rocky oxides and sulfides. Boron is rare but concentrated in large deposits; the largest (6.4 km × 1.6 km × 30 m thick) is in California's Mojave Desert. Aluminum is the most abundant crustal metal, but bauxite is its only ore. Alloys and new semiconductors are the principal end uses.

Borate deposit (tufa), California

Element	Source	Isolation	Uses
Boron	Borax ($Na_2[B_4O_5(OH)_4]\cdot8H_2O$); kernite ($Na_2[B_4O_5(OH)_4]\cdot2H_2O$)	Mg reduction of B_2O_3; electrolysis of KBF_4	M_xB_y turbine blades, rocket nozzles, heat shields
Aluminum	Bauxite [contains gibbsite, $Al(OH)_3$]	Electrolysis of Al_2O_3 in Na_3AlF_6 (see text)	Many familiar alloys; electric transmission lines (see text)
Gallium	Trace element in bauxite	Obtained as trace impurity in Al purification	High-speed semiconductors; in photovoltaic solar panels
Indium	Trace element in Zn/Pb sulfide ores	Recovered from sulfide roasting flue dusts	Semiconductors with P, Sb; low-melting alloys in sprinklers
Thallium	Trace element in Zn/Pb sulfide ores	Recovered from sulfide roasting flue dusts	Very toxic; few uses

Table 22.6E Sources, Isolation, and Uses of Group 4A(14): The Carbon Family

Carbon is more abundant cosmically than on Earth; the reverse is true for silicon, the second most abundant element in the crust. Lead, the final product of most radioactive decay processes, is the crust's most abundant heavy metal. The isolation procedures vary, but those for Sn and Pb require milder conditions than those for Si and Ge. Except for Ge, each member has essential large-scale applications.

Purified silicon

Element	Source	Isolation	Uses
Carbon	Diamond; graphite; petroleum; coal; carbonates; CO_2	Used as found, or isolated from petroleum or coal by heating in the absence of air	Graphite: composites; electrodes; control rods in nuclear reactors Diamond: jewelry; abrasives; films Coke, carbon black: reductant in metallurgy; rubber tire strengthener; pigment; decolorizer for sugar
Silicon	Silica (SiO_2); silicate minerals	Reduction of K_2SiF_6 with Al; reduction of SiO_2 with Mg, then zone refining	Semiconductors; glass; ceramics
Germanium	Germanite (mixture of Cu, Fe, and Ge sulfides)	Roasting in O_2, then reducing GeO_2 with H_2, and zone refining	Semiconductors; infrared spectrometer windows and lenses
Tin	Cassiterite (SnO_2)	Thermal reduction of SnO_2 with C	Prevents corrosion in steel cans; alloys, e.g., solder, bronze, pewter
Lead	Galena (PbS)	Roasting in O_2 to PbO, then reducing with C, and electrorefining	Automotive batteries; solder; ammunition

Rubber tires

Pewter mugs

Table 22.6F Sources, Isolation, and Uses of Group 5A(15): The Nitrogen Family

The high abundances of N and P contrast with the low abundances of the other members, but all occur in concentrated sources. N_2 is obtained from liquefied air and the others by thermal reduction of sulfide ores, usually with coke or iron. The major applications of the three larger elements are in lead alloys, but arsenic and antimony are also used as dopants in new semiconductors.

N_2 freeze-dried rose

Element	Source	Isolation	Uses
Nitrogen	Air	Fractional distillation of liquefied air	$N_2(g)$: inert atmosphere in metallurgical and petrochemical processing; reactant in NH_3 production $N_2(l)$: freeze-drying food; grinding meat for hamburger; biological preservation; future use in superconductors
Phosphorus	Phosphate ores, e.g., fluoroapatite [$Ca_5(PO_4)_3F$] (see text)	Reducing phosphate rock with C	Starting material for synthesis of H_3PO_4 (90%), PCl_3, P_4S_3 (matches), and P_4S_{10} (pesticide) (see text)
Arsenic	Arsenopyrite (FeAsS); flue dust in Cu and Pb extraction	Heating in absence of air	Films, light-emitting (photo) diodes; lead alloys
Antimony	Stibnite (Sb_2S_3); flue dust in Cu and Pb extraction	Roasting in air to Sb_2O_3, then reducing with C	In lead-acid batteries (5% Sb)
Bismuth	Bismuthinite (Bi_2S_3)	Roasting to Bi_2O_3, then reducing with C or Fe	Alloys; medicines

Table 22.6G Sources, Isolation, and Uses of Group 6A(16): The Oxygen Family

Nearly one of every two atoms in the Earth's crust (and the Moon's) is oxygen, but O_2 is obtained from liquefied air. Its critical application in steel-making makes its production the third highest of any substance. Sulfur is extracted from large native deposits, and 90% of it is destined for H_2SO_4 production (see text). The other elements are obtained as by-products and, except for selenium's application in photocopying, have minor uses.

Manufacturing sulfuric acid

Element	Source	Isolation	Uses
Oxygen	Air	Fractional distillation of liquefied air	Oxidizing agent in steel-making (see text), sewage treatment, paper-pulp bleaching, rocket fuel; medical applications
Sulfur	Underground S deposits; sour natural gas or petroleum	Frasch process (see text); catalytic oxidation of H_2S	Production of H_2SO_4 (see text); vulcanization of rubber; chemicals for pharmaceuticals, textiles, and pesticides
Selenium	Impurity in sulfide ores; anode muds of Cu refining	Reducing H_2SeO_3 with SO_2	Electronics; xerography; cadmium pigments
Tellurium	Mixed tellurides and sulfides of Group 8 to 11 metals; anode muds of Cu refining	Oxidizing to Na_2TeO_3, then electrolysis	Steel-making
Polonium	Pitchblende; trace element formed in radium decay	Isolated in trace amounts	Future use as heat source in space satellites and lunar stations

Table 22.6H Sources, Isolation, and Uses of Group 7A(17): The Halogens

Fluorite

Because of their high reactivity, the halogens never occur free in nature. In rocks, their abundances decrease down the group, but chlorine dominates by its enormous abundance in the ocean (1.9 mass %). All halogens are produced by oxidation of their halides, chlorine being the oxidizing agent for bromine and iodine. Chlorine's uses, especially the formation of monomers for the plastics industry, make its production among the 10 highest in the United States.

Element	Source	Isolation	Uses
Fluorine	Fluorite; fluorspar (CaF_2)	Electrolysis of KF in molten anhydrous HF	Synthesis of UF_6 (for nuclear fuel) and SF_6 (electrical insulator); fluorinating agents; Teflon monomers
Chlorine	Halite (NaCl); seawater	Electrolysis of molten NaCl (see text); electrolysis of concentrated seawater (Section 22.5)	Oxidizing agent in bleach and disinfectant; production of poly(vinyl chloride) monomers; major biological anion
Bromine	Brine wells; seawater	Oxidation of Br^- salts by Cl_2 (see text)	Preparation of organic bromides; AgBr in photography
Iodine	Brine wells; Chilean saltpeter ($NaIO_3$)	Oxidation of I^- salts by Cl_2; reduction of IO_3^- with HSO_3^-	In table salt as essential trace element for thyroid hormones; disinfectant
Astatine	Extremely rare radioisotope	Obtained only in trace quantities	None

Teflon cookware

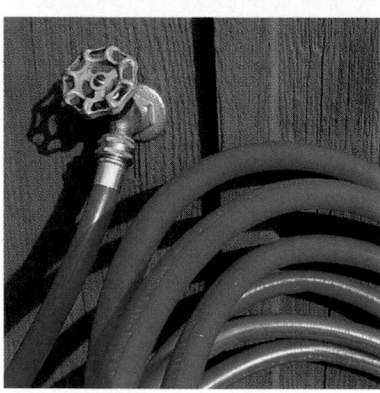

PVC hose

Table 22.6I Sources, Isolation, and Uses of Group 8A(18): The Noble Gases

Neon sign

Helium and other noble gases are rare on Earth because of outgassing during the planet's formation. Helium is a product of radioactive decay of uranium ores and is obtained from natural gas. Argon's high abundance in air (~0.9 mol %) is due to radioactive decay of crustal ^{40}K.

Element	Source	Isolation	Uses
Helium	In natural gas (>0.4 mass %)	Distillation of condensed natural gas or differential diffusion of natural gas	Coolant for superconducting magnets; substitute for N_2 in deep-sea breathing mixture; mobile phase in gas chromatography
Neon	Air	Fractional distillation of liquefied air	Luminous gas in signs
Argon	Air	Fractional distillation of liquefied air	Arc welding
Krypton	Air	Fractional distillation of liquefied air	None
Xenon	Air	Fractional distillation of liquefied air	None
Radon	Air	Fractional distillation of liquefied air	None; radioactive air pollutant

Section Summary

Production highlights of the elements discussed are
- Na is isolated by electrolysis of molten NaCl in the Downs process; Cl_2 is a by-product.
- K is produced by reduction with Na in a thermal process.
- Fe is produced through a multistep high-temperature process in a blast furnace. The crude pig iron is converted to carbon steel in the basic-oxygen process and then alloyed to make different steels.
- Cu is produced by concentration of the ore through flotation, reduction to the metal by smelting, and purification by electrorefining. It has extensive electrical and plumbing uses.
- Al is extracted from bauxite by pretreating with concentrated base, followed by electrolysis of the Al_2O_3 in molten cryolite. Al alloys are used throughout home and industry. The total energy required to extract Al from its ore is over 100 times that needed for recycling it.
- The Mg^{2+} from seawater is converted to $Mg(OH)_2$ and then to $MgCl_2$, which is electrolyzed to obtain the metal; Mg forms strong, lightweight alloys.
- Br_2 is obtained from brines by oxidizing Br^- with Cl_2.
- H_2 is produced by electrolysis of water or in the formation of gaseous fuels from hydrocarbons. It is used in NH_3 production and in hydrogenation of vegetable oils. The isotopes of hydrogen differ significantly in atomic mass and thus in the rate at which their bonds to other atoms break. This difference is used to obtain D_2O from water.

22.5 Chemical Manufacturing: Two Case Studies

From laboratory-scale endeavors of the first half of the 19th century, today's chemical industries have grown to multinational corporations producing materials that define modern life: polymers, electronics, pharmaceuticals, consumer goods, and fuels. In this final section, we examine the interplay of theory and practice in two of the most important processes in the inorganic chemical industry: (1) the contact process for the production of sulfuric acid, and (2) the chlor-alkali process for the production of chlorine.

Sulfuric Acid, the Most Important Chemical

The manufacture of sulfuric acid began more than 400 years ago, when the acid was known as *oil of vitriol* and was distilled from "green vitriol" ($FeSO_4 \cdot 7H_2O$). Considering its countless uses, it is not surprising that today sulfuric acid is produced throughout the world on a gigantic scale—more than 150 million tons a year. The green vitriol method and the many production methods used since have all been superseded by the modern **contact process,** which is based on the *catalyzed oxidation of SO_2*. Here are the key steps.

1. *Obtaining sulfur.* In most countries today, the production of sulfuric acid starts with the production of elemental sulfur, often by chemically separating the H_2S in "sour" natural gas and then oxidizing it:

$$2H_2S(g) + 2O_2(g) \xrightarrow{\text{low temperature}} \tfrac{1}{8}S_8(g) + SO_2(g) + 2H_2O(g)$$
$$2H_2S(g) + SO_2(g) \xrightarrow{\text{Fe}_2\text{O}_3 \text{ catalyst}} \tfrac{3}{8}S_8(g) + 2H_2O(g)$$

Where natural gas is not abundant but natural underground deposits of the element are, sulfur is obtained by the *Frasch process,* a nonchemical method that taps these deposits. A hole is drilled to the deposit, and superheated water

Figure 22.22 **The Frasch process for mining elemental sulfur.** This nonchemical process uses superheated water and compressed air to melt underground sulfur and bring it to the surface. **A,** Superheated water is forced down a drilled hole into the subterranean sulfur deposit, and the sulfur melts. **B,** Compressed air is sent down the drilling apparatus to force up the molten sulfur. **C,** Sulfur obtained from the Frasch process.

(about 160°C) is pumped down two outer concentric pipes to melt the sulfur (Figure 22.22A). Then, through a combination of hydrostatic pressure in the outermost pipe and compressed air sent through a narrow inner pipe, the sulfur is forced to the surface (Figures 22.22B and C). The costs of drilling, pumping, and supplying water (5×10^6 gallons per day) are balanced somewhat by the fact that the product is very pure (~99.7% S).

2. *From sulfur to sulfur dioxide.* Once obtained, the sulfur is burned in air to form SO_2:

$$\tfrac{1}{8}S_8(s) + O_2(g) \longrightarrow SO_2(g) \qquad \Delta H^0 = -297 \text{ kJ}$$

Some SO_2 is also obtained from the roasting of metal sulfide ores. About 90% of processed sulfur is used in making sulfur dioxide for production of the all-important sulfuric acid. Indeed, this end product from sulfur is central to so many chemical industries that a nation's level of sulfur production is a reliable indicator of its overall industrial capacity: the United States, Russia, Japan, and Germany are the top four sulfur producers.

3. *From sulfur dioxide to trioxide.* The contact process oxidizes SO_2 with O_2 to SO_3:

$$SO_2(g) + \tfrac{1}{2}O_2(g) \rightleftharpoons SO_3(g) \qquad \Delta H^0 = -99 \text{ kJ}$$

The reaction is *exothermic* and very *slow* at room temperature. From Le Châtelier's principle (Section 17.6), we know that the yield of SO_3 can be increased by (1) changing the temperature, (2) increasing the pressure (more moles of gas are on the left than on the right), and (3) adjusting the concentrations (adding excess O_2 and removing SO_3).

First, let's examine the temperature effect. Adding heat (raising the temperature) increases the frequency of SO_2-O_2 collisions and thus increases the *rate* of SO_3 formation. However, since the formation of SO_3 is exothermic, removing heat (lowering the temperature) shifts the equilibrium position to the right and thus increases the *yield* of SO_3. This is a classic situation that calls for use of a catalyst. By lowering the activation energy, *a catalyst allows equilibrium to be reached more quickly and at a lower temperature;* thus, rate *and* yield are optimized (Section 16.8). The catalyst in the contact process is V_2O_5 on inert silica, which is active between 400°C and 600°C.

The pressure effect is small and economically not worth exploiting. The concentration effects are controlled by providing an excess of O_2 in the form of a 5:1 mixture of air:SO_2, or about 1:1 O_2:SO_2, about twice as much O_2 as is called for by the reaction stoichiometry. The mixture is passed over catalyst beds in four stages, and the SO_3 is removed at several points to favor more SO_3 formation. The overall yield of SO_3 is 99.5%.

4. *From sulfur trioxide to acid.* Sulfur trioxide is the anhydride of sulfuric acid, so a hydration step is next. However, SO_3 cannot be added to water because, at the operating temperature, it would first meet water vapor, which catalyzes its polymerization to $(SO_3)_x$, and results in a smoke of solid particles that makes poor contact with water. To prevent this, previously formed H_2SO_4 absorbs the SO_3 and forms pyrosulfuric acid (or disulfuric acid, $H_2S_2O_7$; see margin), which is then hydrolyzed with sufficient water:

Disulfuric acid.

$$
\begin{array}{r}
SO_3(g) + H_2SO_4(l) \longrightarrow H_2S_2O_7(l) \\
\underline{H_2S_2O_7(l) + H_2O(l) \longrightarrow 2H_2SO_4(l)} \\
SO_3(g) + H_2O(l) \longrightarrow H_2SO_4(l)
\end{array}
$$

The uses of sulfuric acid are legion, as Figure 22.23 indicates.

Sulfuric acid is remarkably inexpensive (about $150/ton), largely because each step in the process is exothermic—burning S ($\Delta H^0 = -297$ kJ/mol), oxidizing SO_2 ($\Delta H^0 = -99$ kJ/mol), hydrating SO_3 ($\Delta H^0 = -132$ kJ/mol)—and the heat is a valuable by-product. Three-quarters of the heat is sold as steam, and the rest is used to pump gases through the plant. A typical plant making 825 tons of H_2SO_4 per day produces enough steam to generate 7×10^6 watts of electricity.

Other Industries (7%)
Explosives, nonferrous metals, synthetic rubber, batteries

Chemical (19%)
Detergents, feed, resins, coatings, dyestuffs, catalysts, paper, water treatment, pharmaceuticals, insecticides, antifreeze

Titanium and Other Pigments (6%)
Paints, linoleum, fabrics, paper, inks

Rayon and Film (3%)
Tires, textiles, cellophane, photographic film

Petroleum (2%)
Aviation, gasoline, lubricants

Fertilizer (61%)
Superphosphates, ammonium phosphates and sulfate, mixed fertilizers

Iron and Steel (2%)
Autos, appliances, containers, galvanized products

Figure 22.23 **The many indispensable applications of sulfuric acid.**

The Chlor-Alkali Process

Chlorine is produced and used in amounts many times greater than all the other halogens combined, ranking among the top 10 chemicals produced in the United States. All of its production methods depend on *the oxidation of Cl⁻ ion from NaCl.*

Earlier, we discussed the Downs process for the isolation of sodium, which yields Cl_2 gas as the other product (Section 22.4). The **chlor-alkali process,** which forms the basis of one of the largest inorganic chemical industries, electrolyzes concentrated aqueous NaCl to produce Cl_2 and several other important chemicals. As you learned in Section 21.7, the electrolysis of aqueous NaCl does not yield both of the component elements. Chloride ions are oxidized at the anode rather than water due to the effects of overvoltage. However, Na^+ ions are not reduced at the cathode because its half-cell potential (-2.71 V) is much more negative than that for H_2O (-0.42 V), even with the normal overvoltage (around -0.6 V). Therefore, the half-reactions for electrolysis of aqueous NaCl are

$$2Cl^-(aq) \longrightarrow Cl_2(g) + 2e^- \qquad\qquad -E^0 = -1.36 \text{ V [anode; oxidation]}$$
$$2H_2O(l) + 2e^- \longrightarrow 2OH^-(aq) + H_2(g) \qquad\qquad E \approx -1.0 \text{ V [cathode; reduction]}$$

$$2Cl^-(aq) + 2H_2O(l) \longrightarrow 2OH^-(aq) + H_2(g) + Cl_2(g) \qquad E_{cell} = -2.4 \text{ V}$$

To obtain commercially meaningful amounts of Cl_2, however, a voltage almost twice this value and a current in excess of 3×10^4 A are used.

When we include the Na^+ spectator ion, the total ionic equation shows another important product made by the process:

$$2Na^+(aq) + 2Cl^-(aq) + 2H_2O(l) \longrightarrow 2Na^+(aq) + 2OH^-(aq) + H_2(g) + Cl_2(g)$$

As Figure 22.24 shows, the sodium salts in the cathode compartment exist as an aqueous mixture of NaCl and NaOH; the NaCl is removed by fractional crystallization. Thus, in this version of the chlor-alkali process, which uses an asbestos diaphragm to separate the anode and cathode compartments, electrolysis of NaCl brines yields Cl_2, H_2, and industrial-grade NaOH, an important base. As with other reactive products, the H_2 and Cl_2 are kept apart to prevent explosive recombination. Note the higher liquid level in the anode compartment. This slight hydrostatic pressure difference minimizes back flow of NaOH, which avoids disproportionation (self–oxidation-reduction) reactions of Cl_2 in the presence of OH^- (Section 14.9), such as

$$Cl_2(g) + 2OH^-(aq) \longrightarrow Cl^-(aq) + ClO^-(aq) + H_2O(l)$$

Figure 22.24 A diaphragm chlor-alkali cell. This process uses concentrated aqueous NaCl to make NaOH, Cl_2, and H_2 in an electrolytic cell. The difference in liquid level between compartments keeps a net movement of solution into the cathode compartment, which prevents reaction between OH^- and Cl_2. The cathode electrolyte is concentrated and fractionally crystallized to give industrial-grade NaOH.

If high-purity NaOH is desired, a slightly different version, called the chlor-alkali *mercury-cell* process, is employed. Mercury is used as the cathode, which creates such a large overvoltage for reduction of H_2O to H_2 that the process *does* favor reduction of Na^+. The sodium dissolves in the mercury to form sodium amalgam, Na(Hg). In the mercury-cell version, the half-reactions are

$$2Cl^-(aq) \longrightarrow Cl_2(g) + 2e^- \qquad \text{[anode; oxidation]}$$
$$2Na^+(aq) + 2e^- \xrightarrow{Hg} 2Na(Hg) \qquad \text{[cathode; reduction]}$$

To obtain sodium hydroxide, the sodium amalgam is pumped out of the system and treated with H_2O, which is reduced by the Na:

$$2Na(Hg) + 2H_2O(l) \xrightarrow{-Hg} 2Na^+(aq) + 2OH^-(aq) + H_2(g)$$

The mercury released in this step is recycled back to the electrolysis bath. Thus, *the products are the same in both versions*, but the purity of NaOH in the mercury-cell version is much higher.

Despite the formation of higher purity NaOH, the mercury-cell method is being steadily phased out in the United States and has been eliminated in Japan for more than a decade. Cost is not the major reason for the phase-out, although the method does consume about 15% more electricity than the diaphragm version. Rather, the problem is that as the mercury is recycled, some is lost in the industrial wastewater. On average, 200 g Hg are lost per ton of Cl_2 produced. In the 1980s, U.S. production was 2.75 million tons of Cl_2 annually via the mercury-cell method; thus, an effluent of 550,000 kg of this toxic heavy metal was entering U.S. waterways each year!

The more recent chlor-alkali *membrane-cell* process replaces the diaphragm with a polymeric membrane to separate the cell compartments. The membrane allows only cations to move through it and only from anode to cathode compartments. Thus, as Cl^- ions are removed at the anode through oxidation to Cl_2, Na^+ ions in the anode compartment move through the membrane to the cathode compartment and form an NaOH solution. In addition to forming higher purity NaOH than the older diaphragm method, the membrane method uses less electricity and eliminates the problem of Hg pollution. As a result, its application has been increasing steadily throughout the industrialized world.

Section Summary

Sulfuric acid production starts with the extraction of sulfur, either by the oxidation of H_2S or the mining of sulfur deposits. The sulfur is roasted to SO_2, which is oxidized to SO_3 by the catalyzed contact process, which optimizes the yield at lower temperatures. Absorption of the SO_3 into H_2SO_4, followed by hydration, forms sulfuric acid. In the diaphragm-cell chlor-alkali process, aqueous NaCl is electrolyzed to form Cl_2, H_2, and low-purity NaOH. The mercury-cell version produces high purity NaOH but is being phased out because of mercury pollution. The polymeric membrane–cell version requires less electricity and does not use Hg.

Chapter Perspective

In this chapter, we took a realistic approach to the chemistry of the elements that allowed a glimpse at the intertwining natural cycles in which various elements take part, as well as at the ingenious methods we have developed to extract them. The impact of living systems in general, and of humans in particular, on the origin and distribution of elements reveals a complex, evolving relationship. Understanding of and respect for that relationship are required for a healthy, productive balance between society's needs and the environment.

In the next chapter, we conclude our exploration of the elements with a close look at the transition metals, a fascinating and extremely useful collection of metals. Then, in the final chapter, we dive down to the atom's nuclear core and investigate its properties and great potential for society.

The following learning objectives, with section numbers in parentheses, can help focus your study:

Understand These Concepts

1. How gravity, thermal convection, and elemental properties led to the silicate, sulfide, and iron phases and the predominance of certain elements in crust, mantle, and core of the Earth (Section 22.1)

2. How organisms affect crustal abundances of elements, especially oxygen, carbon, calcium, and transition metals; the onset of oxidation as an energy source (Section 22.1)

3. How atomic properties influence which elements have oxide ores and which have sulfide ores (Section 22.1)

4. The central role of CO_2 and the importance of photosynthesis, respiration, and decay in the carbon cycle (Section 22.2)

5. The central role of N_2 and the importance of atmospheric, industrial, and biological fixation in the nitrogen cycle (Section 22.2)

6. The absence of a gaseous component, the interactions of the inorganic and biological cycles, and the impact of humans on the phosphorus cycle (Section 22.2)

7. How pyro-, electro-, and hydrometallurgical processes are employed to extract a metal from its ore; the importance of the reduction step from compound to metal; refining and alloying processes (Section 22.3)

8. Functioning of the Downs cell for Na production and the application of Le Châtelier's principle for K production (Section 22.4)

9. How iron ore is reduced in a blast furnace and how pig iron is purified by the basic-oxygen process (Section 22.4)

10. How Fe is removed from copper ore and impure Cu is electrorefined (Section 22.4)

11. The importance of amphoterism in the Bayer process of isolating Al_2O_3 from bauxite; significance of cryolite in the electrolytic step; the energy advantage of Al recycling (Section 22.4)

12. The steps in the Dow process for the extraction of Mg from seawater (Section 22.4)

13. How H_2 production, whether by chemical or electrolytic means, is tied to NH_3 production (Section 22.4)

14. How the kinetic-isotope effect is applied to produce deuterium (Section 22.4)

15. How the Frasch process depends on the physical properties of S_8 (Section 22.5)

16. The importance of equilibrium and kinetic factors in H_2SO_4 production (Section 22.5)

17. How overvoltage allows electrolysis of aqueous NaCl to Cl_2 gas in the chlor-alkali process; co-production of NaOH; comparison of diaphragm-cell, mercury-cell, and membrane-cell processes (Section 22.5)

For Review and Reference

Key Terms

Section 22.1
abundance
differentiation
core
mantle
crust
lithosphere
hydrosphere
atmosphere
biosphere

occurrence (source)
ore
Section 22.2
environmental cycle
fixation
apatites
Section 22.3
metallurgy
mineral
gangue

flotation
leaching
roasting
smelting
electrorefining
zone refining
alloy
Section 22.4
Downs cell
steel

blast furnace
slag
basic-oxygen process
carbon steel
Section 22.5
contact process
chlor-alkali process

Highlighted Figures and Tables

These figures (F) and tables (T) provide a quick review of key ideas.

Problems

Problems with a **colored** number are answered at the back of the text. Problem sections match the text, and most offer concept review questions and problems in a relevant context. (There are no skill-building exercises in this problem set.) Following these are comprehensive problems based on material from any section and/or previous chapter.

How the Elements Occur in Nature

Concept Review Questions

22.1 Hydrogen is by far the most abundant element cosmically. In interstellar space, it exists mainly as H_2. In contrast, on Earth it exists very rarely as H_2 and is ninth in abundance in the crust. Why is hydrogen so abundant in the universe? Why is hydrogen so rare as a diatomic gas in the Earth's atmosphere?

22.2 Metallic elements are recovered primarily from ores that are oxides, carbonates, halides, or sulfides. Give an example for each of these types.

22.3 The location of elements in the regions of the Earth has enormous practical importance.
(a) Define the term *differentiation* and explain which physical property of a substance is primarily responsible for this process.
(b) What are the four most abundant elements in the crust?
(c) Which element is abundant in the crust and mantle but not the core?

22.4 How does the position of a metal in the periodic table relate to whether it exists in nature primarily as an oxide or as a sulfide?

Problems in Context

22.5 What material is the source for commercial production of the following elements: (a) aluminum; (b) nitrogen; (c) chlorine; (d) calcium; (e) sodium?

22.6 Aluminum is widely distributed throughout the world in the form of aluminosilicates. What property of these readily available minerals prevents them from being a source for aluminum?

22.7 Describe two ways in which the biosphere has influenced the composition of the Earth's crust.

The Cycling of Elements Through the Environment

Concept Review Questions

22.8 Use atomic and molecular properties to explain why life is based on carbon chemistry and not on the chemistry of some other element such as silicon.

22.9 Define the term *fixation*. Name two elements that undergo environmental fixation. What are the natural forms that are fixed?

22.10 Carbon dioxide enters the atmosphere by natural processes and as a result of human activity. Why is the latter source a cause of great concern?

22.11 Schematic cycles such as that for carbon (Figure 22.5) are simplified to show overall changes, or because a particular amount involved is relatively minor. For example, the production of lime from limestone is not explicitly shown.

Which labeled category in the figure includes this process? Name two other processes that contribute to this category.

22.12 Describe three pathways for utilization of atmospheric nitrogen. Is human activity a significant factor? Explain.

22.13 Why do the N-containing species shown in Figure 22.6 not include ring compounds or long-chain compounds with N—N bonds?

22.14 (a) Which region of the Earth's crust is not involved in the phosphorus cycle?
(b) Briefly describe two roles that organisms play in the phosphorus cycle.

Problems in Context

22.15 Nitrogen fixation requires a great deal of energy because the N_2 bond is strong (the activation energy for its breakage is high).
(a) How do the processes of atmospheric and industrial fixation illustrate this energy requirement?
(b) How are the thermodynamics different in the two cases above? (*Hint:* Examine the respective heats of formation.)
(c) In view of the mild conditions for biological fixation, what must be the source of the "great deal of energy" in this case?
(d) What would be the most obvious environmental result of a low activation energy for N_2 fixation?

22.16 The following steps are *unbalanced* half-reactions involved in the nitrogen cycle. Balance each half-reaction to show the number of electrons lost or gained and whether it is an oxidation or a reduction:
(a) $N_2(g) \longrightarrow NO(g)$ (b) $N_2O(g) \longrightarrow NO_2(g)$
(c) $NH_3(aq) \longrightarrow NO_2^-(aq)$ (d) $NO_3^-(aq) \longrightarrow NO_2^-(aq)$
(e) $N_2(g) \longrightarrow NO_3^-(aq)$

22.17 The use of silica to form slag in the production of phosphorus from phosphate rock was introduced by Robert Boyle more than 300 years ago. When fluorapatite, $[Ca_5(PO_4)_3F]$, is used in phosphorus production, most of the fluorine atoms appear in the slag but some end up in toxic and corrosive $SiF_4(g)$.
(a) If 15% by mass of the fluorine in 100. kg $Ca_5(PO_4)_3F$ forms SiF_4, what volume of this gas is collected at 1.00 atm and the industrial furnace temperature of 1450.°C?
(b) In some facilities, the SiF_4 is used to produce sodium hexafluorosilicate, Na_2SiF_6, which is sold for domestic water fluoridation:

$$2SiF_4(g) + Na_2CO_3(s) + H_2O(l) \longrightarrow$$
$$Na_2SiF_6(aq) + SiO_2(s) + CO_2(g) + 2HF(aq)$$

How many cubic meters of drinking water can be fluoridated to a level of 1.0 ppm F^- from the reaction of the SiF_4 produced in (a)?

22.18 An impurity sometimes found in $Ca_3(PO_4)_2$ is Fe_2O_3, which is removed during the production of phosphorus as a material called *ferrophosphorus* (Fe_2P).
(a) Why is this impurity troubling from an economic standpoint?
(b) If 50. metric tons of crude $Ca_3(PO_4)_2$ contains 2.0% Fe_2O_3 by mass and the overall yield of phosphorus is 90.%, how many metric tons of P_4 can be isolated?

Metallurgy: Extracting a Metal from Its Ore

▪ Concept Review Questions

22.19 Define each of the following materials: (a) ore; (b) mineral; (c) gangue; (d) brine.

22.20 Define each of the following processes: (a) roasting; (b) smelting; (c) flotation; (d) refining.

22.21 What factors determine which reducing agent is selected for the production of a specific metal?

22.22 Use atomic properties to explain the reduction of a less active metal by a more active one (a) in aqueous solution; (b) in the molten state. Give a specific example of each process.

22.23 What class of element is typically obtained by oxidation of a mineral? What class of element is typically obtained by reduction of a mineral?

▪ Problems in Context

22.24 Select the group of elemental components that gives each of the following alloys: (a) brass; (b) stainless steel; (c) bronze; (d) sterling silver.

1. Cu, Ag	2. Cu, Sn	3. Ag, Au
4. Fe, Cr, Ni	5. Fe, V	6. Cu, Zn

Tapping the Crust: Isolation and Uses of the Elements

▪ Concept Review Questions

22.25 How are each of the following involved in iron metallurgy: (a) slag; (b) pig iron; (c) steel; (d) basic-oxygen process?

22.26 What are the distinguishing features of the extraction processes known as pyrometallurgy, electrometallurgy, and hydrometallurgy? Explain briefly how the given type(s) of metallurgy is(are) used in the production of (a) Fe; (b) Na; (c) Au; (d) Al.

22.27 What property allows copper to be purified in the presence of iron and nickel impurities? Explain.

22.28 What is the practical reason for using cryolite in the electrolysis of aluminum oxide?

22.29 (a) What is a kinetic isotope effect?
(b) Do compounds of hydrogen exhibit a relatively large or small effect? Explain.
(c) Carbon compounds also exhibit a kinetic isotope effect. How do you expect it to compare in magnitude with that for hydrogen compounds? Why?

22.30 How is Hess's law involved in water-splitting schemes for the production of H_2?

▪ Problems in Context

22.31 Elemental Li and Na are prepared by electrolysis of a molten salt, whereas K, Rb, and Cs are prepared by chemical reduction.
(a) In general terms, explain why the alkali metals cannot be prepared by electrolysis of their aqueous salt solutions.
(b) Use ionization energies to explain why calcium *should* not be able to isolate Rb from molten RbX (X = halide).
(c) Use physical properties to describe how calcium *is* used to isolate Rb from molten RbX.
(d) Can Ca be used to isolate Cs from molten CsX? Explain.

22.32 A Downs cell operates at 75.0 A and produces 30.0 kg Na metal.
(a) What volume of $Cl_2(g)$ is produced at 1.0 atm and 580.°C?
(b) How many coulombs were passed through the cell?
(c) How long did the cell operate?

22.33 (a) In the industrial production of iron, what is the reducing substance that is loaded into the blast furnace?
(b) In addition to furnishing the reducing power, what other function does this substance serve?
(c) What is the formula of the active reducing agent in the process?
(d) Write equations for the stepwise reduction of Fe_2O_3 to iron in the furnace.

22.34 One of the substances loaded into the blast furnace is limestone, which produces lime in the furnace.
(a) Give the chemical equation for the reaction forming lime.
(b) Explain the purpose of lime in the furnace. The term *flux* is often used as a label for a substance acting as the lime does. What is the derivation of this word and how does it relate to the function of the lime?
(c) Write a chemical equation describing the action of the lime flux.

22.35 The last step in the Dow process for the production of magnesium metal involves electrolysis of molten $MgCl_2$.
(a) Why isn't the electrolysis carried out in aqueous $MgCl_2$? What are the products of aqueous electrolysis?
(b) Do the high temperatures required to melt $MgCl_2$ favor products or reactants? (*Hint:* Consider the heat of formation of $MgCl_2$.)

22.36 (a) What is the only halogen that occurs in a positive oxidation state in nature (Table 22.6H)?
(b) Is this mode of occurrence consistent with its location in the periodic table? Explain.
(c) Write a balanced equation for the production of the free halogen from this source.

22.37 Selenium is prepared by the reaction of H_2SeO_3 with gaseous SO_2 (Table 22.6G).
(a) What redox process does the sulfur dioxide undergo? What is the oxidation state of sulfur in the product?
(b) Given that the reaction occurs in acidic aqueous solution, what is the formula of the sulfur-containing species?
(c) Write the balanced redox equation for the process.

22.38 The halogens F_2 and Cl_2 are produced by electrolytic oxidation, whereas Br_2 and I_2 are produced by chemical oxidation of the concentrated aqueous halide (brine) by a more electronegative halogen. State two reasons why Cl_2 is not prepared by this method.

22.39 Silicon is prepared by the reduction of K_2SiF_6 with Al (Table 22.6E). Write the equation for this reaction. (*Hint:* Can F^- be oxidized in this reaction? Can K^+ be reduced?)

22.40 What is the mass percent of iron in each of the following iron ores: Fe_2O_3, Fe_3O_4, FeS_2?

22.41 Phosphorus is one of the impurities present in pig iron that is removed in the basic-oxygen process. Assuming that the phosphorus is present simply as P atoms, write equations for its oxidation and subsequent reaction in the basic slag.

22.42 The final step in the smelting of $FeCuS_2$ is

$$Cu_2S(s) + 2Cu_2O(s) \longrightarrow 6Cu(l) + SO_2(g)$$

(a) What are the oxidation states of copper in Cu_2S, Cu_2O, and Cu?
(b) What are the oxidizing and reducing agents in this reaction?

22.43 Use balanced equations to explain how acid-base properties are used to separate iron and titanium oxides from aluminum oxide in the Bayer process.

22.44 A piece of Al with a surface area of 2.3 m^2 is anodized to produce a film of Al_2O_3 that is 20. μ ($20.\times10^{-6}$ m) thick.
(a) How many coulombs flow through the cell in this process (assume the density of the Al_2O_3 layer is 2.8 g/cm^3)?
(b) If this film grows over the course of 15 min, what current must flow through the cell?

22.45 The production of H_2 gas by the electrolysis of water typically requires about 400 kJ of energy per mole.
(a) Use the relationship between work and cell voltage (Section 21.4) to calculate the minimum work needed to form 1.0 mol H_2 gas at a cell voltage of 1.24 V.
(b) What is the energy efficiency of the cell operation?
(c) Calculate the cost of producing 500. mol H_2 if the cost of electrical energy is exactly $0.05 per kilowatt · hour (1 watt · second = 1 joule).

22.46 (a) What are the components of the reaction mixture following the water-gas shift reaction?
(b) Explain how zeolites (Section 14.6) are used to purify the H_2 formed.

22.47 Typically, metal sulfides are first converted to oxides by roasting in air and then reduced with carbon to produce the metal. Why are the metal sulfides not reduced directly by carbon to yield CS_2? Give a thermodynamic analysis of both processes for a typical case such as ZnS.

Chemical Manufacturing: Two Case Studies

■ Concept Review Questions

22.48 Explain in detail why a catalyst is used to produce SO_3.

22.49 Among the exothermic steps in the manufacture of sulfuric acid is the process of hydrating SO_3.
(a) Write two chemical reactions that show this process.
(b) Why is the direct reaction of SO_3 with water not feasible?

22.50 What is the principal reason that commercial H_2SO_4 is so inexpensive?

22.51 (a) What are the three commercial products formed in the chlor-alkali process? (b) State an advantage and a disadvantage of the mercury-cell version of this process.

■ Problems in Context

22.52 (a) Calculate the standard free energy change at 25°C for the oxidation of SO_2 to SO_3 in the contact process. Is the reaction spontaneous at 25°C?
(b) Why is the reaction not performed at 25°C?
(c) Is the reaction spontaneous at 500.°C? (Assume that ΔH^0 and ΔS^0 are constant with temperature.)
(d) How does the value of the equilibrium constant at 500.°C compare with that at 25°C?
(e) What is the highest temperature at which the reaction is spontaneous?

22.53 If a chlor-alkali cell used a current of 3×10^4 A, how many pounds of Cl_2 would be produced in a typical 8-h operating day?

22.54 In the chlor-alkali process, the chlorine and the sodium hydroxide products are kept separate from one another.
(a) Why is this precaution necessary when Cl_2 is the desired product?
(b) Hypochlorite or chlorate may be formed by disproportionation of Cl_2 in basic solution. What condition determines which product is formed?
(c) What mole ratio of Cl_2 to OH^- is needed to produce ClO^-? ClO_3^-?

Comprehensive Problems

Problems with an asterisk (*) are more challenging.

22.55 Graphite is used as an electrode material in voltaic and electrolytic processes.
(a) In what direction do you think graphite conducts electricity, perpendicular or parallel to its layers? Why?
(b) Both the Downs cell and the Hall-Heroult process use a graphite anode, but the half-reactions are entirely different. Write balanced anode half-reactions for the two processes.

22.56 Sodium carbonate, Na_2CO_3, is an industrial base used in the paper, soap, and detergent industries, and is indispensable in glassmaking. In the United States, it is mined as trona ($Na_2CO_3 \cdot NaHCO_3 \cdot 2H_2O$) from enormous deposits in Wyoming. In many other countries, however, it is still made by the Solvay process, which has the following *overall* reaction:

$$CaCO_3(s) + 2NaCl(aq) \longrightarrow Na_2CO_3(aq) + CaCl_2(aq)$$

(a) Why would you expect the overall reaction not to proceed as written?
(b) In the industrial process, the $CaCO_3$ is heated, and the gas formed reacts with added NH_3 and water. The resulting aqueous bicarbonate salt then undergoes a metathesis reaction with NaCl, and the Na salt formed is heated to produce the desired product. Write balanced equations for these four reactions.
(c) Sodium bicarbonate, a key intermediate in the process, has several uses as a result of its low-temperature (50°C to 100°C) decomposition. If a fire extinguisher contains 150. g $NaHCO_3$, what volume of CO_2 can be formed at 100.8 kPa and 72°F?

22.57 Tetraphosphorus decaoxide, P_4O_{10}, a compound made from phosphate rock, is commonly used as a drying agent in the laboratory.
(a) Write a balanced equation for its reaction with water.
(b) What is the pH of a solution formed from the addition of 5.0 g P_4O_{10} in sufficient water to form 0.500 L? (See Table 18.5 for additional information.)

*22.58 Heavy water (D_2O) is used to prepare numerous deuterated chemicals.
(a) What major species, aside from the starting compounds, do you expect to find in a solution formed by mixing CH_3OH and D_2O?
(b) Write equations to explain how these various species arise. (*Hint*: Consider the autoionization of both components.)

22.59 A blast furnace uses Fe_2O_3 to produce 8400. t Fe/day.
(a) What mass of CO_2 is produced each day?
(b) Compare this amount of CO_2 with that produced by 1.0 million automobiles, each burning 5.0 gallons of gasoline a day. Assume that gasoline has the formula C_8H_{18} and a density of 0.74 g/mL, and that it burns completely. (Note that U.S. gasoline consumption is over 4×10^8 gal/day.)

22.60 Several decades ago, various sets of empirical rules were devised to predict the formation of alloys. Two of the rules propose that stable alloys form if the ratios of the number of valence electrons (*s* plus *p*) to the number of atoms are 3:2 or 21:13. For example, β-brass (CuZn) is a very stable alloy: Cu has one 4*s* and Zn has two 4*s* electrons, for 3 valence electrons; one Cu atom plus one Zn atom gives 2 atoms; thus, a 3 electron:2 atom ratio. Which electron:atom ratio does each of the following alloys display: (a) Cu_5Sn; (b) Cu_5Zn_8; (c) $Cu_{31}Sn_8$; (d) $AgZn_3$; (e) Ag_3Al?

*22.61 The Ostwald process for the production of HNO_3 proceeds as follows:

(1) $4NH_3(g) + 5O_2(g) \xrightarrow{\text{Pt/Rh catalyst}} 4NO(g) + 6H_2O(g)$

(2) $2NO(g) + O_2(g) \longrightarrow 2NO_2(g)$

(3) $3NO_2(g) + H_2O(l) \longrightarrow 2HNO_3(aq) + NO(g)$

(a) Describe the nature of the redox change that occurs in step 3.

(b) Write an overall equation that includes NH_3 and HNO_3 as the only N-containing species.

(c) Calculate the ΔH^0_{rxn} value at 25°C for this reaction in kJ/mol N atoms.

22.62 In the production of magnesium metal, $Mg(OH)_2$ is precipitated by using $Ca(OH)_2$, which itself is "insoluble."

(a) Use K_{sp} values to show that $Mg(OH)_2$ can be precipitated from seawater in which $[Mg^{2+}]$ is initially 0.051 M.

(b) If the seawater is saturated with $Ca(OH)_2$, what fraction of the Mg^{2+} can be precipitated?

22.63 Step 1 of the Ostwald process for nitric acid production is

$$4NH_3(g) + 5O_2(g) \xrightarrow{\text{Pt/Rh catalyst}} 4NO(g) + 6H_2O(g)$$

An unwanted side reaction for this step is

$$4NH_3(g) + 3O_2(g) \longrightarrow 2N_2(g) + 6H_2O(g)$$

(a) Calculate K_p for these two NH_3 oxidations at 25°C.

(b) Calculate K_p for these two NH_3 oxidations at 900.°C.

(c) The Pt/Rh catalyst is one of the most efficient in the chemical industry, achieving 96% yield in 1 millisecond of contact with the reactants. However, at normal operating conditions (5 atm and 850°C), about 175 mg Pt is lost per metric ton (t) of HNO_3 produced. If current annual U.S. production of HNO_3 is 7.7×10^6 t and the current market price of Pt is \$385/troy oz, what is the annual cost of the lost Pt (1 kg = 32.15 troy oz)?

22.64 The compounds $(NH_4)_2HPO_4$ and $NH_4(H_2PO_4)$ are water-soluble phosphate fertilizers.

(a) Which has the higher mass % of P?

(b) Why might the one with lower mass % of P be preferred as a fertilizer?

22.65 Several transition metals are prepared by reduction of the metal halide with magnesium metal. Titanium is prepared by the Kroll method in which the ore (ilmenite) is converted to the gaseous chloride, which is then reduced to the metal by molten Mg:

(1) $FeTiO_3(s) + Cl_2(g) + C(s) \longrightarrow$
$\qquad TiCl_4(g) + FeCl_3(l) + CO(g)$ [unbalanced]

(2) $TiCl_4(g) + Mg(l) \longrightarrow Ti(s) + MgCl_2(l)$ [unbalanced]

Assuming yields of 84% for (1) and 93% for (2) and other reactants in excess, what mass of Ti metal can be prepared from 17.5 metric tons of ilmenite?

22.66 The production of S_8 from the $H_2S(g)$ found in many natural gas deposits occurs through the Claus process (Section 22.5):

(a) Use these two unbalanced steps to write an overall balanced equation for this process:

(1) $H_2S(g) + O_2(g) \longrightarrow S_8(g) + SO_2(g) + H_2O(g)$

(2) $H_2S(g) + SO_2(g) \longrightarrow S_8(g) + H_2O(g)$

(b) Write the overall reaction with Cl_2 as the oxidizing agent instead of O_2. Use thermodynamic quantities to show whether $Cl_2(g)$ can be used to oxidize $H_2S(g)$.

(c) Why is oxidation by O_2 chosen in preference to oxidation by Cl_2?

22.67 Hydrazine, N_2H_4, is produced commercially by the oxidation of NH_3 with sodium hypochlorite, NaClO.

(a) Write a balanced equation for this reaction in base. [*Note:* N_2H_4 and the intermediate NH_2Cl are toxic. Attempts to produce "extra strength" cleaning solutions by mixing bleach (aqueous NaClO) and window cleaner (aqueous NH_3) are extremely dangerous.]

(b) Why is hydrazine not produced by the reduction of N_2? (*Hint:* Consider thermodynamic parameters for forming N_2H_4 vs. NH_3.)

22.68 A metal catalyst (usually nickel) is used to hydrogenate C=C bonds to form the saturated fats in commercial baked goods. What does the catalyst do to speed the reaction? Suggest a reason why other Group 8B(10) metals are not used for this purpose.

22.69 Incomplete combustion of C-containing compounds, whether in forest fires, coal-fired power plants, or automobile engines, produces CO as well as CO_2. The binding of CO to transition metal atoms and ions is the reason for its toxicity as well as the basis of several industrial methods to purify metals.

(a) Draw a Lewis structure for CO that has minimal formal charges.

(b) Does CO bond to the metal through the C or the O atom? Explain.

22.70 Why is nitric acid not produced by oxidizing atmospheric nitrogen directly in the following way?

(1) $\quad N_2(g) + 2O_2(g) \longrightarrow 2NO_2(g)$

(2) $3NO_2(g) + H_2O(l) \longrightarrow 2HNO_3(aq) + NO(g)$

(3) $\quad 2NO(g) + O_2(g) \longrightarrow 2NO_2(g)$

Overall: $3N_2(g) + 6O_2(g) + 2H_2O(l) \longrightarrow$
$\qquad\qquad\qquad\qquad 4HNO_3(aq) + 2NO(g)$

(*Hint:* Evaluate the thermodynamics of each step.)

*22.71 Before the development of the Downs cell, the Castner cell was used for the industrial production of Na metal. The Castner cell was based on the electrolysis of molten NaOH. (a) Write balanced cathode and anode half-reactions for this cell. (b) A major problem with this cell was that the water produced at one electrode diffused to the other and reacted with the Na. If all the water produced reacted with Na, what would be the maximum efficiency of the Castner cell expressed as moles of Na produced per mole of electrons flowing through the cell?

*22.72 In the leaching of gold ores by CN^- solutions, gold forms the complex ion, $Au(CN)_2^-$.

(a) Calculate E_{cell} for the oxidation in air ($P_{O_2} = 0.21$) of gold to gold(I) in basic (pH 13.55) solution. Is this reaction spontaneous?

(b) How does the formation of the complex ion change E^0 so that the oxidation can be accomplished? [$E^0 = 1.68$ V for $Au^+(aq) + e^- \longrightarrow Au(s)$.]

22.73 Nitric oxide is an important species in the tropospheric nitrogen cycle, but it destroys ozone in the stratosphere.

(a) Write a balanced equation for its reversible reaction with ozone.

(b) Given that the forward and reverse steps are first order in each component, write general rate laws for them.

(c) Calculate ΔG^0 for this reaction at 280. K, the average temperature in the stratosphere. (Assume the ΔH^0 and S^0 values in Appendix B do not change with temperature.)

(d) Calculate the ratio of rate constants for the reaction at this temperature.

22.74 An important part of the carbon cycle is the fixation of CO_2 by photosynthesis to produce carbohydrates and oxygen gas.

(a) Using the formula $(CH_2O)_n$ to represent a carbohydrate, develop a general balanced equation for the photosynthetic reaction.

(b) If a moderate-sized tree fixes 45 g CO_2 a day, what volume of O_2 gas measured at 1.0 atm and 80.°F does the tree produce per day?

(c) What volume of air (0.033 mol % CO_2) at the same conditions contains this amount of CO_2?

22.75 In the early part of the 20th century, most sulfuric acid was manufactured by a process using a gaseous NO/NO_2 mixture as the catalyst system to convert SO_2 to SO_3.

(a) What reaction does NO undergo in contact with O_2?

(b) Write reactions to show how the catalyst functions and is re-formed in this process.

(c) Explain how a similar process relates to the formation of acid rain.

22.76 Small-scale production of chlorine gas is accomplished by the reaction of manganese dioxide and hydrochloric acid. What volume of Cl_2 gas at 755 torr and 29°C can be prepared from 253 g MnO_2 and 325 mL of 4.2 M HCl? ($MnCl_2$ and H_2O form also.)

22.77 The key reaction (unbalanced) in the manufacture of synthetic cryolite for aluminum electrolysis is

$$HF(g) + Al(OH)_3(s) + NaOH(aq) \longrightarrow Na_3AlF_6(aq) + H_2O(l)$$

Assuming a 96.6% yield of dried, crystallized product, what mass (in kg) of cryolite can be obtained from the reaction of 353 kg $Al(OH)_3$, 1.10 m^3 of 50.0 mass % aqueous NaOH ($d = 1.53$ g/mL), and 225 m^3 gaseous HF at 315 kPa and 89.5°C? (Assume the ideal gas law holds.)

*22.78 Because of their different molar masses, H_2 and D_2 effuse at different rates (Section 5.6).

(a) If it takes 14.5 min for 0.10 mol H_2 to effuse, how long does it take for 0.10 mol D_2 in the same apparatus at the same T and P?

(b) How many effusion steps does it take to separate an equimolar mixture of D_2 and H_2 to 99 mol % purity?

22.79 The disproportionation of carbon monoxide to graphite and carbon dioxide is thermodynamically favored but slow.

(a) What does this statement mean in terms of the magnitudes of the equilibrium constant K, the rate constant k, and the activation energy E_a?

(b) Write a balanced equation for the disproportionation of carbon monoxide.

(c) Calculate K_c at 298 K.

(d) Calculate K_p at 298 K.

22.80 Quinones are biological molecules used extensively in industrial electron-transfer processes, in which the molecules cycle between oxidized (quinone) and reduced (hydroquinone) forms. For example,

1,4-benzoquinone   1,4-benzhydroquinone

Sodium hydrosulfite, $Na_2S_2O_4$, is frequently used to reduce quinones to hydroquinones. Write a balanced equation for this reduction with 1,4-benzoquinone in basic solution. Gaseous SO_2 is produced also.

22.81 The following N-containing species are integral members of the nitrogen cycle: NH_3, N_2O, NO, NO_2, NO_2^-, NO_3^-. Draw a Lewis structure for each species, showing minimal formal charge, and indicate the shape, including ideal bond angles.

22.82 The overall cell reaction for aluminum production is

$$2Al_2O_3(\text{in } Na_3AlF_6) + 3C(\text{graphite}) \longrightarrow 4Al(l) + 3CO_2(g)$$

(a) Assuming 100% efficiency, how many metric tons (t) of Al_2O_3 are consumed per t of Al produced?

(b) Assuming 100% efficiency, how many metric tons of graphite anode material are consumed per t of Al produced?

(c) Actual conditions in an aluminum plant require 1.89 t Al_2O_3 and 0.45 t graphite per t of Al. What is the percent yield with respect to Al_2O_3?

(d) What is the percent yield with respect to graphite?

(e) What volume of CO_2 (in m^3) is produced per t of Al at operating conditions of 960.°C and exactly 1 atm?

*22.83 Even though most metal sulfides are very sparingly soluble in water, their solubilities differ by several orders of magnitude. This difference can sometimes be used to separate the metals in an isolation step by controlling the pH. Use the following data to find the pH at which you can separate 0.10 M Cu^{2+} and 0.10 M Ni^{2+}:

Saturated $H_2S = 0.10$ M

K_{a1} of $H_2S = 9 \times 10^{-8}$ K_{a2} of $H_2S = 1 \times 10^{-17}$

K_{sp} of NiS $= 1.1 \times 10^{-18}$ K_{sp} of CuS $= 8 \times 10^{-34}$

22.84 Mercury occurs in nature as the sulfide, HgS, called cinnabar. Its metallurgy is unusual in that the mercury is freed by simply roasting in air; sulfur dioxide is formed in the process.

(a) Write the equation for the reaction.

(b) What is the reducing agent in this reaction?

*22.85 How does acid rain affect the leaching of phosphate into ground water from terrestrial phosphate rock? To quantify this effect, calculate the solubility of $Ca_3(PO_4)_2$ in each of the following:

(a) Pure water, pH 7.0 (Assume PO_4^{3-} does not react with water.)

(b) Moderately acidic rainwater, pH 4.5. (*Hint:* Assume all the phosphate exists in the form that predominates at this pH.)

22.86 Chemosynthetic bacteria reduce CO_2 by "splitting" $H_2S(g)$ rather than the $H_2O(g)$ used by photosynthetic organisms. Compare the free energy change of H_2S splitting with that of H_2O splitting. Is there an advantage in using H_2S instead of H_2O?

23

The Transition Elements and Their Coordination Compounds

Figure: A transition-metal engine. The usefulness of transition metals is obvious when you study the makeup of a jet engine. In addition to aluminum, graphite fibers, and various polymer composites, this modern jet engine incorporates numerous alloys that consist of iron, chromium, titanium, and nickel. In this chapter, we examine not only the metals themselves but also the chemical properties and magnificent colors of their compounds.

Chapter Outline

23.1 An Overview of Transition Element Properties
- Electron Configurations
- Atomic and Physical Properties
- Chemical Properties

23.2 The Inner Transition Elements
- The Lanthanides
- The Actinides

23.3 Highlights of Selected Transition Metals
- Chromium
- Manganese

- Silver
- Mercury

23.4 Coordination Compounds
- Structures of Complex Ions
- Formulas and Names
- Alfred Werner and Coordination Theory
- Isomerism

23.5 Theoretical Basis for the Bonding and Properties of Complexes
- Valence Bond Theory
- Crystal Field Theory

Our exploration of the elements so far has, paradoxically, skirted the majority of them. Whereas most important end uses of the main-group elements involve their compounds, the transition elements are remarkably useful in their uncombined form. In Chapter 22, you saw how two of the most important transition elements—copper and iron—are extracted from their ores. In addition to the countless essential uses of those two, many other transition elements are indispensable as well: chromium in auto parts, gold and silver in jewelry, tungsten in lightbulb filaments, platinum in auto catalytic converters, titanium in bicycle frames, and zinc in batteries, to mention just a few of the better known elements. There is also zirconium in nuclear-reactor liners, vanadium in axles and crankshafts, molybdenum in boiler plate, nickel in coins, tantalum in organ-replacement parts, palladium in telephone-relay contacts—the list goes on and on. As ions, many of these elements also have vital roles in living organisms.

The periodic table in Figure 23.1 shows that the **transition elements** *(transition metals)* occupy the *d* block (B groups) and *f* block *(inner transition elements)*. In the first half of the chapter, we discuss some atomic, physical, and chemical properties of these elements in general and then focus on the chemistry of four familiar ones: chromium, manganese, silver, and mercury. The second half of the chapter is devoted to the most distinctive feature of transition-element chemistry, the formation of *coordination compounds,* substances that contain complex ions. We consider two models that explain the striking colors of these compounds, as well as their magnetic properties and structures, and then end with some essential biochemical functions of the ions.

Concepts and Skills to Review

before you study this chapter

- properties of light (Section 7.1)
- electron shielding of nuclear charge (Section 8.2)
- ionic size, electron configuration, and magnetic behavior (Sections 8.3 to 8.5)
- valence bond theory (Section 11.1)
- constitutional, geometric, and optical isomerism (Section 15.2)
- Lewis acid-base concepts (Section 18.9)
- complex-ion formation (Section 19.4)
- redox behavior and standard electrode potentials (Section 21.3)

Figure 23.1 **The transition elements (*d* block) and inner transition elements (*f* block) in the periodic table.**

Scandium, Sc   Titanium, Ti   Vanadium, V   Chromium, Cr   Manganese, Mn

Figure 23.2 **The Period 4 transition metals.** Samples of all ten elements appear as pure metals, in chunk or powder form, in periodic-table order on this and the facing page.

23.1 An Overview of Transition Element Properties

The transition elements differ considerably in their physical and chemical behavior from the main-group elements. In some ways, they are more uniform: main-group elements in each period change from metal to nonmetal, but *all transition elements are metals.* In other ways, the transition elements are more diverse: most main-group ionic compounds are colorless and diamagnetic, but *many transition metal compounds are highly colored and paramagnetic.* In this section, we first discuss electron configurations of the atoms and ions, and then examine certain key properties of transition elements, with an occasional comparison to the main-group elements.

Electron Configurations of the Transition Metals and Their Ions

As with any element, the properties of the transition elements and their compounds arise largely from the electron configurations of their atoms (Section 8.3) and ions (Section 8.5). The *d*-block (B-group) elements occur in four series that lie within Periods 4 through 7 between the last *ns*-block element [Group 2A(2)] and the first *np*-block element [Group 3A(13)]. Each series involves filling five *d* orbitals and, thus, contains ten elements. In 1996 and 1997, elements 110 through 112 were synthesized in particle accelerators, so the Period 7 series is complete; thus, all 40 *d*-transition elements are known. Lying between the first and second members of the *d*-transition series in Periods 6 and 7 are the inner transition elements, whose *f* orbitals are being filled.

Even though there are several exceptions, in general, the *condensed* ground-state electron configuration for the elements in each *d*-block series is

$$\text{[noble gas] } ns^2(n-1)d^x, \text{ with } n = 4 \text{ to } 7 \text{ and } x = 1 \text{ to } 10$$

In Periods 6 and 7, the condensed configuration includes the *f* sublevel:

$$\text{[noble gas] } ns^2(n-2)f^{14}(n-1)d^x, \text{ with } n = 6 \text{ or } 7$$

The *partial* (valence-level) electron configuration for the *d*-block elements excludes the noble gas core and the filled inner *f* sublevel:

$$ns^2(n-1)d^x$$

The first series occurs in Period 4 and consists of scandium (Sc) through zinc (Zn) (Figure 23.2 and Table 23.1). Scandium has the electron configuration [Ar] $4s^2 3d^1$, and the addition of one electron at a time (along with one proton in the nucleus) first half fills, then fills, the $3d$ orbitals through zinc. Recall that chromium and copper are two exceptions to this general filling pattern. The $4s$ and $3d$ orbitals in Cr are both half-filled to give [Ar] $4s^1 3d^5$, and the $4s$ is half-filled in Cu to give [Ar] $4s^1 3d^{10}$. The reasons for these exceptions involve the change in relative energies of the $4s$ and $3d$ orbitals as electrons are added across the series and the unusual stability of half-filled and filled sublevels.

Transition metal ions form through *loss of the ns electrons before the (n − 1)d electrons.* Thus, the electron configuration of Ti^{2+} is [Ar] $3d^2$, *not* [Ar] $4s^2$, and Ti^{2+} is referred to as a d^2 ion. Ions of different metals with the same configuration often have similar properties. For example, both Mn^{2+} and Fe^{3+} are d^5 ions; both have pale colors in aqueous solution and, as we'll discuss, form complex ions with similar magnetic properties.

Iron, Fe

Cobalt, Co

Nickel, Ni

Copper, Cu

Zinc, Zn

Table 23.1 Orbital Occupancy of the Period 4 Transition Metals

Element	Partial Orbital Diagram			Unpaired Electrons
	4s	3d	4p	
Sc	↑↓	↑ □ □ □ □	□ □ □	1
Ti	↑↓	↑ ↑ □ □ □	□ □ □	2
V	↑↓	↑ ↑ ↑ □ □	□ □ □	3
Cr	↑	↑ ↑ ↑ ↑ ↑	□ □ □	6
Mn	↑↓	↑ ↑ ↑ ↑ ↑	□ □ □	5
Fe	↑↓	↑↓ ↑ ↑ ↑ ↑	□ □ □	4
Co	↑↓	↑↓ ↑↓ ↑ ↑ ↑	□ □ □	3
Ni	↑↓	↑↓ ↑↓ ↑↓ ↑ ↑	□ □ □	2
Cu	↑	↑↓ ↑↓ ↑↓ ↑↓ ↑↓	□ □ □	1
Zn	↑↓	↑↓ ↑↓ ↑↓ ↑↓ ↑↓	□ □ □	0

Table 23.1 shows a general pattern in number of unpaired electrons (or half-filled orbitals) across the Period 4 transition series. Note that the number increases in the first half of the series and, when pairing begins, decreases through the second half. As you'll scc, it is the electron configuration of the transition metal *atom* that correlates with physical properties of the *element*, such as density and magnetic behavior, whereas it is the electron configuration of the *ion* that determines the properties of the *compounds*.

Sample Problem 23.1 Writing Electron Configurations of Transition Metal Atoms and Ions

PROBLEM Write *condensed* electron configurations for **(a)** Zr; **(b)** V^{3+}; **(c)** Mo^{3+}. (Assume that elements in higher periods behave like those in Period 4.)

PLAN We locate the element in the periodic table and count its position in the respective transition series. Since these elements are in Periods 4 and 5, the general configuration is [noble gas] $ns^2(n - 1)d^x$. For the ions, we recall that ns electrons are lost first.

SOLUTION **(a)** Zr is the second element in the $4d$ series: [Kr] $5s^2 4d^2$.

(b) V is the third element in the $3d$ series: [Ar] $4s^2 3d^3$. In forming V^{3+}, three electrons are lost (two $4s$ and one $3d$), so V^{3+} is a d^2 ion: [Ar] $3d^2$.

(c) Mo lies below Cr in Group 6B(6), so we expect the same exception as for Cr. Thus, Mo is [Kr] $5s^1 4d^5$. To form the ion, Mo loses the one $5s$ and two of the $4d$ electrons, so Mo^{3+} is a d^3 ion: [Kr] $4d^3$.

CHECK Figure 8.9 (p. 304) shows that we are correct for the atoms. Be sure that the charge plus the number of *d* electrons in the ion equals the sum of the outer *s* and *d* electrons in the atom.

Follow-up Problem 23.1 Write *partial* electron configurations for the following: **(a)** Ag^+; **(b)** Cd^{2+}; **(c)** Ir^{3+}.

Atomic and Physical Properties of the Transition Elements

The atomic properties of the transition elements contrast in several ways with those of a comparable set of main-group elements.

Trends Across a Period Consider the variations in atomic size, electronegativity, and ionization energy across Period 4 (Figure 23.3):

A Atomic radius (pm)

- *Atomic size.* Atomic size decreases overall across the period (Figure 23.3A). However, there is a smooth, steady decrease across the main groups because the electrons are added to *outer* orbitals, which shield the increasing nuclear charge poorly. This steady decrease is suspended throughout the transition series, where *atomic size decreases at first but then remains fairly constant.* Recall that the *d* electrons fill *inner* orbitals, so they shield outer electrons from the increasing nuclear charge much more efficiently. As a result, the outer 4*s* electrons are not pulled closer.

B Electronegativity

- *Electronegativity.* Electronegativity generally increases across the period but, once again, the transition elements exhibit a relatively *small change in electronegativity* (Figure 23.3B), consistent with the relatively small change in size. In contrast, the main groups show a steady, much steeper increase between the metal potassium (0.8) and the nonmetal bromine (2.8). The transition elements all have intermediate electronegativity values, much like the large, metallic members of Groups 3A(13) to 5A(15).

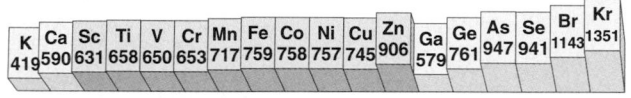

C First ionization energy (kJ/mol)

Figure 23.3 Horizontal trends in key atomic properties of the Period 4 elements. The atomic radius, electronegativity, and first ionization energy of the elements in Period 4 are shown as posts of different heights, with darker shades for the transition series. The transition elements exhibit smaller, less regular changes for these properties than those in the main groups.

- *Ionization energy.* The ionization energies of the Period 4 main-group elements rise steeply left to right, more than tripling from potassium (419 kJ/mol) to krypton (1351 kJ/mol), as electrons become more difficult to remove from the poorly shielded, increasing nuclear charge. In the transition metals, however, the *first ionization energies increase relatively little* because the inner 3*d* electrons shield effectively (Figure 23.3C); thus the outer 4*s* electron experiences only a slightly higher nuclear charge. [Recall from Section 8.4 that the dropoff in Group 3A(13) occurs because it is relatively easy to remove the first electron from the outer *np* orbital.]

Trends Within a Group Vertical trends for transition elements are also different from those in the main groups.

- *Atomic size.* As expected, atomic size increases from Period 4 to 5, as it does for the main groups, but there is virtually *no size increase from Period 5 to 6* (Figure 23.4A). Remember that the lanthanide series, with its buried 4*f* sublevel, appears between the 4*d* (Period 5) and 5*d* (Period 6) series. Therefore, an element in Period 6 is separated from the one above it in Period 5 by 32 elements (ten 4*d*, six 5*p*, two 6*s*, and fourteen 4*f*) instead of just 18. The extra shrinkage that results from the increase in nuclear charge due to these additional 14 elements is called the **lanthanide contraction.** By coincidence, this *decrease* is about equal to the normal *increase* between periods, so the Periods 5 and 6 transition elements have about the same atomic sizes.

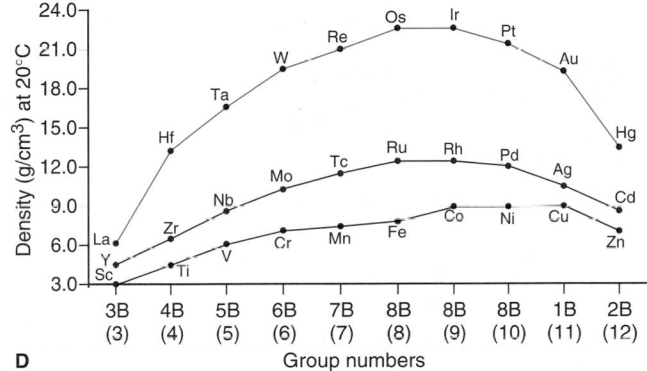

Figure 23.4 Vertical trends in key properties within the transition elements. The trends are unlike those in the main-group elements in several ways: **A,** The second and third members of a transition metal group are nearly the same size. **B,** Electronega- tivity increases down a transition group. **C,** First ionization energies are highest at the bottom of a transition group. **D,** Densities increase down a transition group because mass increases faster than volume.

- *Electronegativity.* The vertical trend in electronegativity seen in most transi- tion groups is opposite the trend in main groups. Here, we see an *increase* in electronegativity from Period 4 to Period 5, but then no further increase in Period 6 (Figure 23.4B). The heavier elements, especially gold (EN = 2.4), become quite electronegative, with values exceeding those of most metalloids and even some nonmetals (e.g., EN of Te and of P = 2.1). (In fact, gold forms the saltlike CsAu and the Au⁻ ion, which exists in liq- uid ammonia.) Although the atomic size increases slightly from the top to the bottom of a group, the nuclear charge increases much more. There- fore, the heavier members exhibit more covalent character in their bonds and attract electrons more strongly than do main-group metals.
- *Ionization energy.* The relatively small increase in size combined with the relatively large increase in nuclear charge also explains why *the first ion- ization energy generally increases* down a group (Figure 23.4C). This trend also runs counter to the pattern in the main groups, in which heavier members are so much larger that their outer electron is easier to remove.
- *Density.* Atomic size, and therefore volume, is inversely related to density. Across a period, densities increase, then level off, and finally dip a bit at the end of a series (Figure 23.4D). Down a group, densities increase dra- matically because atomic volumes change little from Period 5 to 6, but atomic masses increase significantly. As a result, the Period 6 series con- tains some of the densest elements known: tungsten, rhenium, osmium, iridium, platinum, and gold have densities about 20 times that of water and twice that of lead.

Chemical Properties of the Transition Metals

Like their atomic and physical properties, the chemical properties of the transition elements are very different from those of the main groups. Let's examine the key properties in the Period 4 series and then see how behavior changes within a group.

Oxidation States   One of the most characteristic chemical properties of the transition metals is the occurrence of *multiple oxidation states*. For example, in their compounds, vanadium exhibits two common positive oxidation states, chromium three, and manganese three, and many other oxidation states are seen less often. Since the ns and $(n - 1)d$ electrons are so close in energy, transition elements can involve all or most of these electrons in bonding. This behavior is markedly different from that of the main-group metals, which display one or at most two oxidation states in their compounds.

The highest oxidation state of elements in Groups 3B(3) through 7B(7) is equal to the group number (Table 23.2). These states are seen when the elements combine with highly electronegative oxygen or fluorine. For instance, in the oxoanion solutions shown in Figure 23.5, vanadium occurs as the vanadate ion (VO_4^{3-}; O.N. of V = +5), chromium occurs as the dichromate ion ($Cr_2O_7^{2-}$; O.N. of Cr = +6), and manganese occurs as the permanganate ion (MnO_4^{-}; O.N. of Mn = +7). Elements in Groups 8B(8, 9, 10) exhibit fewer oxidation states, and the highest state is less common and never equal to the group number. For instance, we never encounter Fe in the +8 state and only

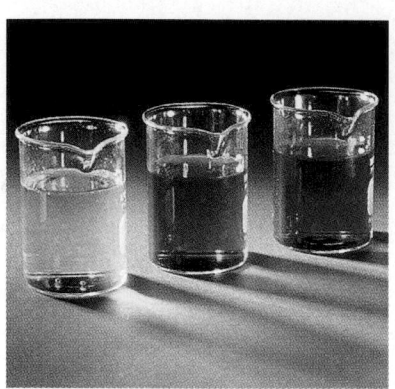

Figure 23.5 Aqueous oxoanions of V, Cr, and Mn in their highest oxidation states. The oxidation state equals the group number in these oxoanions: VO_4^{3-} (*left*), $Cr_2O_7^{2-}$ (*middle*), and MnO_4^{-} (*right*).

Table 23.2 Oxidation States and *d*-Orbital Occupancy of the Period 4 Transition Metals*

Oxidation State	3B (3) Sc	4B (4) Ti	5B (5) V	6B (6) Cr	7B (7) Mn	8B (8) Fe	8B (9) Co	8B (10) Ni	1B (11) Cu	2B (12) Zn
0	0 (d^1)	0 (d^2)	0 (d^3)	0 (d^5)	0 (d^5)	0 (d^6)	0 (d^7)	0 (d^8)	0 (d^{10})	0 (d^{10})
+1			+1 (d^3)	+1 (d^5)	+1 (d^5)		+1 (d^7)	+1 (d^8)	+1 (d^{10})	
+2		+2 (d^2)	+2 (d^3)	+2 (d^4)	+2 (d^5)	+2 (d^6)	+2 (d^7)	+2 (d^8)	+2 (d^9)	+2 (d^{10})
+3	+3 (d^0)	+3 (d^1)	+3 (d^2)	+3 (d^3)	+3 (d^4)	+3 (d^5)	+3 (d^6)	+3 (d^7)	+3 (d^8)	
+4		+4 (d^0)	+4 (d^1)	+4 (d^2)	+4 (d^3)	+4 (d^4)	+4 (d^5)	+4 (d^6)		
+5			+5 (d^0)	+5 (d^1)	+5 (d^2)		+5 (d^4)			
+6				+6 (d^0)	+6 (d^1)	+6 (d^2)				
+7					+7 (d^0)					

*Most important in color.

rarely in the +6 state. The +2 and +3 states are the most common ones for iron* and cobalt, and the +2 state is most common for nickel, copper, and zinc. *The +2 oxidation state is common because ns^2 electrons are readily lost.*

Copper, silver, and gold in Group 1B(11) (the coinage metals) are unusual. Although copper has a fairly common oxidation state of +1, which results from loss of its single $4s$ electron, its most common state is +2. Silver behaves more predictably, exhibiting primarily the +1 oxidation state. Gold exhibits the +3 state and, less often, the +1 state.

Metallic Behavior and Reducing Strength Atomic size and oxidation state have a major effect on the nature of bonding in transition metal compounds. Like the metals in Groups 3A(13), 4A(14), and 5A(15), the transition elements in their *lower* oxidation states behave chemically more like metals. That is, *ionic bonding is more prevalent for the lower oxidation states, and covalent bonding is more prevalent for the higher states.* For example, at room temperature, $TiCl_2$ is an ionic solid, whereas $TiCl_4$ is a molecular liquid. In the higher oxidation states, the atoms have higher charge densities, so they polarize the electron clouds of the nonmetal ions more strongly and the bonding becomes more covalent. For the same reason, the oxides become less basic as the oxidation state increases: TiO is weakly basic in water, whereas TiO_2 is amphoteric (reacts with both acid and base).

Table 23.3 shows the standard electrode potentials of the Period 4 transition metals in their +2 oxidation state in acid solution. Note that, in general, reducing strength decreases across the series. All the Period 4 transition metals, except copper, are active enough to reduce H^+ from aqueous acid to form hydrogen gas. In contrast to the rapid reaction at room temperature of the Group 1A(1) and 2A(2) metals with water, however, the transition metals have an oxide coating that allows rapid reaction only with hot water or steam.

Color and Magnetism of Compounds *Most main-group ionic compounds are colorless* because the metal ion has a filled outer level (noble gas electron configuration). With only much higher energy orbitals available to receive an excited electron, the ion does not absorb visible light. In contrast, electrons in a partially filled d sublevel can absorb visible wavelengths and move to slightly higher energy d orbitals. As a result, *many transition metal compounds have striking colors.* Exceptions are the compounds of scandium, titanium(IV), and zinc, which are colorless because their metal ions have either an empty d sublevel (Sc^{3+} or Ti^{4+}: [Ar] d^0) or a filled one (Zn^{2+}: [Ar] d^{10}) (Figure 23.6).

---

*Iron may seem to have unusual oxidation states in the common ores magnetite (Fe_3O_4) and pyrite (FeS_2), but this is not really the case. In magnetite, one third of the metal ions are Fe^{2+} and two-thirds are Fe^{3+}, which is equivalent to a 1:1 ratio of $FeO:Fe_2O_3$ and gives an overall formula of Fe_3O_4. Pyrite contains Fe^{2+} combined with the disulfide ion, S_2^{2-}.

Table 23.3 Standard Electrode Potentials of Period 4 M^{2+} Ions

Half-Reaction			E^0 (V)
$Ti^{2+}(aq) + 2e^-$	$\rightleftharpoons$	$Ti(s)$	−1.63
$V^{2+}(aq) + 2e^-$	$\rightleftharpoons$	$V(s)$	−1.19
$Cr^{2+}(aq) + 2e^-$	$\rightleftharpoons$	$Cr(s)$	−0.91
$Mn^{2+}(aq) + 2e^-$	$\rightleftharpoons$	$Mn(s)$	−1.18
$Fe^{2+}(aq) + 2e^-$	$\rightleftharpoons$	$Fe(s)$	−0.44
$Co^{2+}(aq) + 2e^-$	$\rightleftharpoons$	$Co(s)$	−0.28
$Ni^{2+}(aq) + 2e^-$	$\rightleftharpoons$	$Ni(s)$	−0.25
$Cu^{2+}(aq) + 2e^-$	$\rightleftharpoons$	$Cu(s)$	0.34
$Zn^{2+}(aq) + 2e^-$	$\rightleftharpoons$	$Zn(s)$	−0.76

Figure 23.6 Colors of representative compounds of the Period 4 transition metals. Staggered from left to right, the compounds are scandium oxide (white), titanium(IV) oxide (white), vanadyl sulfate dihydrate (light blue), sodium chromate (yellow), manganese(II) chloride tetrahydrate (light pink), potassium ferricyanide (red-orange), cobalt(II) chloride hexahydrate (violet), nickel(II) nitrate hexahydrate (green), copper(II) sulfate pentahydrate (blue), and zinc sulfate heptahydrate (white).

Magnetic properties are also related to sublevel occupancy (Section 8.5). Recall that a *paramagnetic* substance has atoms or ions with unpaired electrons, which cause it to be attracted to an external magnetic field. A *diamagnetic* substance has only paired electrons, so it is unaffected (or slightly repelled) by a magnetic field. *Most main-group metal ions are diamagnetic* for the same reason they are colorless: all their electrons are paired. In contrast, *many transition metal compounds are paramagnetic because of their unpaired d electrons.* For example, $MnSO_4$ is paramagnetic, but $CaSO_4$ is diamagnetic. The Ca^{2+} ion has the electron configuraton of argon, whereas Mn^{2+} has a d^5 configuration. Transition metal ions with a d^0 or d^{10} configuration, which are colorless, are also diamagnetic.

Chemical Behavior Within a Group   The *increase* in reactivity seen down a group of main-group metals, as shown by the *decrease* in first ionization energy (IE_1), does *not* appear down a group of transition metals. Consider the chromium (Cr) group [6B(6)], which shows a typical pattern (Table 23.4). The IE_1 *increases* down the group, which makes the two heavier metals *less* reactive than the lightest one. Chromium is also a much stronger reducing agent than molybdenum (Mo) or tungsten (W), as shown by their standard electrode potentials.

Table 23.4 Some Properties of Group 6B(6) Elements

Element	Atomic Radius (pm)	IE_1 (kJ/mol)	E^0 (V) for $M^{3+}(aq)|M(s)$
Cr	128	653	−0.74
Mo	139	685	−0.20
W	139	770	−0.11

The similarity in atomic size of Period 5 and 6 members also leads to similar chemical behavior, a fact that has some important practical consequences. Because Mo and W compounds behave similarly, for example, their ores often occur together in nature, which makes the elements very difficult to separate from each other. The same situation occurs between zirconium and hafnium in Group 4B(4), and between niobium and tantalum in Group 5B(5).

Section Summary

All of the transition elements are metals. Atoms of the *d*-block elements have $(n-1)d$ orbitals being filled, and their ions have an empty *ns* orbital. Unlike the trends in the main-group elements, atomic size, electronegativity, and first ionization energy change relatively little across a transition series. Because of the lanthanide contraction, atomic size changes little from Period 5 to 6 in a transition metal group; thus, electronegativity, first ionization energy and density *increase* down a group. Transition metals typically have several oxidation states, with the +2 state most common. The elements exhibit more metallic behavior in their lower states. Most Period 4 members are active enough to reduce hydrogen ion from acid solution. Many transition metal compounds are colored and paramagnetic because the metal ion has unpaired *d* electrons.

23.2 The Inner Transition Elements

The 14 **lanthanides** (lanthanoids), cerium (Ce; $Z = 58$) through lutetium (Lu; $Z = 71$), lie between lanthanum ($Z = 57$) and hafnium ($Z = 72$) in the third *d*-transition series. Below them are the 14 radioactive **actinides** (actinoids), thorium (Th; $Z = 90$) through lawrencium (Lr; $Z = 103$), which lie between actinium (Ac; $Z = 89$) and rutherfordium (Rf; $Z = 104$). The lanthanides and actinides are called **inner transition elements** because, in most cases, their seven inner 4*f* or 5*f* orbitals are being filled.

The Lanthanides

The lanthanides are sometimes called the *rare earth elements,* a term referring to their presence in unfamiliar oxides, but they are actually not rare at all. Cerium (Ce), for instance, ranks 26th in natural abundance (by mass %) and is five times more abundant than lead. All the lanthanides are silvery, high-melting (800°C to 1600°C) metals. In their chemical properties, they represent an extreme case of the small variations typical of transition elements in a period or a group, which makes them very difficult to separate. ◆

The mixed natural occurrence of the lanthanides arises because they occur in the +3 oxidation state in their common ores, as M^{3+} ions of very similar radii. The ground-state electron configuration of most of the lanthanides is [Xe] $6s^2 4f^x 5d^0$, where *x* varies across the series. The three exceptions (Ce, Gd, and Lu) have a single electron in a 5*d* orbital: Ce ([Xe] $6s^2 4f^1 5d^1$) forms a stable 4+ ion with an empty (f^0) sublevel, and the Gd^{3+} and Lu^{3+} ions have a stable half-filled (f^7) or filled (f^{14}) sublevel.

Lanthanide compounds and their mixtures have many uses. Several oxides are used for tinting sunglasses and welder's goggles and for adding color to the fluorescent powder coatings in TV screens. High-quality camera lenses incorporate La_2O_3 because of its extremely high index of refraction. Samarium forms an alloy with cobalt, $SmCo_5$, that is used in the strongest known permanent magnet (see Sample Problem 23.2). Two industrial uses account for more than 60% of rare earth applications. In gasoline refining, the zeolite catalysts (Gallery, Section 14.6) used to "crack" hydrocarbon components into smaller molecules contain 5% by mass rare earth oxides. In steelmaking, a mixture of lanthanides, called *misch-metal,* is used to remove carbon impurities from molten iron and steel.

◆ **A Remarkable Laboratory Feat** The discovery of the lanthanides is a testimony to the remarkable laboratory skills of 19th-century chemists. The two mineral sources, ceria and yttria, are mixtures of compounds of all 14 lanthanides; yttria also includes oxides of Sc, Y, and La. Purification of these elements was so difficult that many claims of new elements turned out to be mixtures of similar elements. To confuse matters, the periodic table of the time had space for only one element between Ba and Hf, which turned out to be La. Not until 1913, when the atomic number basis of the table was established, did chemists realize that 14 new elements could fit, and in 1918, Niels Bohr proposed that the $n = 4$ level be expanded to include the *f* sublevel.

Sample Problem 23.2 Determining the Number of Unpaired Electrons

PROBLEM The alloy $SmCo_5$ forms a strong permanent magnet because both Sm and Co have unpaired electrons. How many unpaired electrons are in the samarium atom (Sm; $Z = 62$)?

PLAN We write the condensed electron configuration of Sm and then, using Hund's rule and the aufbau principle, place the electrons in a partial orbital diagram and count the unpaired electrons.

SOLUTION Samarium is the eighth element after Xe. Two electrons go into the 6*s* sublevel. Since, in general, the 4*f* sublevel fills before the 5*d* (only Ce, Gd, and Lu have 5*d* electrons), the remaining electrons go into the 4*f*. Thus, Sm is [Xe] $6s^2 4f^6$. There are seven *f* orbitals, so each of the six *f* electrons enters a separate orbital:

Thus, Sm has six unpaired electrons.

CHECK Six 4*f* e⁻ plus two 6*s* e⁻ plus the 54 e⁻ in Xe gives 62, the atomic number of Sm.

Follow-up Problem 23.2 How many unpaired electrons are in the Er^{3+} ion?

The Actinides

All actinides are radioactive. Like the lanthanides, they have very similar physical and chemical properties. Thorium and uranium occur in nature, but the transuranium elements, those with Z greater than 92, have been synthesized in high-energy particle accelerators, some in only tiny amounts (Section 24.3). In fact, macroscopic samples of mendelevium (Md), nobelium (No), and lawrencium (Lr) have never even been seen. The available metals are silvery and chemically reactive and, like the lanthanides, form highly colored compounds. The actinides and lanthanides have similar outer-electron configurations. Although the +3 oxidation state is characteristic of the actinides, as it is among the lanthanides, some other states also occur. For example, uranium exhibits the +3 through +6 states, with the +6 state the most prevalent; thus, the most common oxide of uranium is UO_3.

Section Summary

There are two series of inner transition elements. The lanthanides (4f series) have a common +3 oxidation state and exhibit very similar properties. The actinides (5f series) are radioactive. All actinides have a +3 oxidation state; several, including uranium, have higher states as well.

23.3   Highlights of Selected Transition Metals

Let's investigate the aqueous chemistry of several transition elements, focusing on the general patterns that each reveals. We examine chromium and manganese from Period 4, silver from Period 5, and mercury from Period 6.

Chromium

Chromium is a very shiny, silvery metal, whose name (from the Greek *chroma,* "color") refers to its many colorful compounds. A solution of Cr^{3+} is deep violet, for example, and a trace of Cr^{3+} in the Al_2O_3 crystal structure gives the ruby its beautiful red hue (see photo). Chromium readily forms a thin, adherent, transparent coating of Cr_2O_3 in air, making the metal extremely useful as an attractive protective coating on easily corroded metals, such as iron. "Stainless" steels often contain as much as 18% chromium by mass and are highly resistant to corrosion.

With six valence electrons ([Ar] $4s^1 3d^5$), chromium occurs in all possible positive oxidation states, but the three most important are +2, +3, and +6 (see Table 23.2). In its three common oxides, chromium exhibits the pattern seen in many elements: *nonmetallic character and oxide acidity increase with metal oxidation state.* Chromium(II) oxide (CrO) is basic and largely ionic. It forms an insoluble hydroxide in neutral or basic solution but dissolves in acidic solution to yield the Cr^{2+} ion:

$$CrO(s) + 2H^+(aq) \longrightarrow Cr^{2+}(aq) + H_2O(l)$$

Chromium(III) oxide (Cr_2O_3) is amphoteric, dissolving in acid to yield the violet Cr^{3+} ion,

$$Cr_2O_3(s) + 6H^+(aq) \longrightarrow 2Cr^{3+}(aq) + 3H_2O(l)$$

and in base to form the green $Cr(OH)_4^-$ ion:

$$Cr_2O_3(s) + 3H_2O(l) + 2OH^-(aq) \longrightarrow 2Cr(OH)_4^-(aq)$$

Thus, chromium in its +3 state resembles the main-group metal aluminum (Section 19.4).

Deep-red chromium(VI) oxide (CrO_3) is covalent and acidic, forming chromic acid (H_2CrO_4) in water,

$$CrO_3(s) + H_2O(l) \longrightarrow H_2CrO_4(aq)$$

which yields the yellow chromate ion (CrO_4^{2-}) in base:

$$H_2CrO_4(aq) + 2OH^-(aq) \longrightarrow CrO_4^{2-}(aq) + 2H_2O(l)$$

In acidic solution, chromate immediately forms the orange dichromate ion ($Cr_2O_7^{2-}$):

$$2CrO_4^{2-}(aq) + 2H^+(aq) \rightleftharpoons Cr_2O_7^{2-}(aq) + H_2O(l)$$

Because both ions contain chromium(VI), this is not a redox reaction; rather, it is a dehydration-condensation, as you can see from the structures in Figure 23.7. Hydrogen-ion concentration controls the equilibrium position: yellow CrO_4^{2-} predominates at high pH and orange $Cr_2O_7^{2-}$ at low pH. The bright colors of chromium(VI) compounds lead to their wide use in pigments for artist's paints and ceramic glazes. Lead chromate (chrome yellow) is used as an oil-paint color, and also in the yellow stripes that delineate traffic lanes.

Chromium metal and the Cr^{2+} ion are potent reducing agents. The metal displaces hydrogen from dilute acids to form blue $Cr^{2+}(aq)$, which reduces O_2 in air within minutes to form the violet Cr^{3+} ion:

$$4Cr^{2+}(aq) + O_2(g) + 4H^+(aq) \longrightarrow 4Cr^{3+}(aq) + 2H_2O(l) \quad E^0_{overall} = 1.64 \text{ V}$$

Chromium(VI) compounds in acid solution are strong oxidizing agents (concentrated solutions are *extremely* corrosive!), the chromium(VI) being readily reduced to chromium(III):

$$Cr_2O_7^{2-}(aq) + 14H^+(aq) + 6e^- \longrightarrow 2Cr^{3+}(aq) + 7H_2O(l) \quad E^0 = 1.33 \text{ V}$$

This reaction is often used to determine the iron content of a water or soil sample by oxidizing Fe^{2+} to Fe^{3+} ion. In basic solution, the CrO_4^{2-} ion, which is a much weaker oxidizing agent, predominates:

$$CrO_4^{2-}(aq) + 4H_2O(l) + 3e^- \longrightarrow Cr(OH)_3(s) + 5OH^-(aq) \quad E^0 = -0.13 \text{ V}$$

The Concept of Valence-State Electronegativity Why does oxide acidity increase with oxidation state? And how can a metal like chromium form an oxoanion? To answer such questions, we must apply the concept of electronegativity to the various oxidation states of an element. A metal in a higher oxidation state is more positively charged, which increases its attraction for electrons; in effect, its *electronegativity increases*. This effective electronegativity, called *valence-state electronegativity*, also has numerical values. The electronegativity of chromium metal is 1.6, close to that of aluminum (1.5), another active metal. For chromium(III), the value increases to 1.7, still characteristic of a metal. However, the electronegativity of chromium(VI) is 2.3, close to the values of some nonmetals, such as phosphorus (2.1), selenium (2.4), and carbon (2.5). Thus, like P in PO_4^{3-}, it is not surprising to see chromium(VI) compounds with Cr covalently bound at the center of the oxoanion of a relatively strong acid.

Manganese

Elemental manganese is hard and shiny and, like vanadium and chromium, is used mostly to make steel alloys. A small amount of Mn (<1%) makes steel easier to roll, forge, and weld. Steel made with 12% Mn is tough enough to be used for naval armor, bulldozer buckets (see photo), and other extremely hard steel objects. Small amounts of manganese are added to aluminum beverage cans and bronze alloys to make them stiffer and tougher as well.

The chemistry of manganese resembles that of chromium in some respects. The free metal is quite reactive and readily displaces H_2 from acids to form the pale-pink Mn^{2+} ion:

$$Mn(s) + 2H^+(aq) \longrightarrow Mn^{2+}(aq) + H_2(g) \quad E^0 = 1.18 \text{ V}$$

A

B

Figure 23.7 The bright colors of chromium(VI) compounds.
A, Structures of the chromate (CrO_4^{2-}) and dichromate ($Cr_2O_7^{2-}$) ions.
B, Samples of K_2CrO_4 (yellow) and $K_2Cr_2O_7$ (orange).

Bulldozer parts made of manganese steel.

Table 23.5   Some Oxidation States of Manganese

Oxidation state*	**Mn(II)**	Mn(III)	**Mn(IV)**	Mn(VI)	**Mn(VII)**
Example	Mn^{2+}	Mn_2O_3	MnO_2	MnO_4^{2-}	MnO_4^-
Ion configuration	d^5	d^4	d^3	d^1	d^0
Oxide acidity	BASIC				ACIDIC

*Most common states in **boldface**.

Sharing the Ocean's Wealth At their current rate of usage, known reserves of many key transition metals will be depleted in less than 50 years. Other sources must be found. One promising source is nodules strewn over large portions of the ocean floor. Varying from a few millimeters to a few meters in diameter, these chunks consist mainly of manganese and iron oxides, with oxides of other elements present in smaller amounts. Billions of tons exist, but mining them presents major technical and political challenges. Global agreements have designated the ocean floor as international property, so cooperation will be required to mine the nodules and share the mineral rewards.

Like chromium, manganese can use all its valence electrons in its compounds, exhibiting every possible positive oxidation state, with the +2, +4, and +7 states most common (Table 23.5). As the oxidation state of manganese rises, its valence-state electronegativity rises and its oxides change from basic to acidic. Manganese(II) oxide (MnO) is basic, and manganese(III) oxide (Mn_2O_3) is amphoteric. Manganese(IV) oxide (MnO_2) is insoluble and shows no acid-base properties. [It is used in dry-cell and alkaline batteries as the oxidizing agent in a redox reaction with zinc (Gallery, Section 21.5).] Manganese(VII) oxide (Mn_2O_7), which forms by reaction of Mn with pure O_2, reacts with water to form permanganic acid ($HMnO_4$), which is as strong as perchloric acid ($HClO_4$).

All manganese species with oxidation states greater than +2 act as oxidizing agents, but the purple permanganate (MnO_4^-) ion is particularly powerful. As with chromium in its highest oxidation state, MnO_4^- is a much stronger oxidizing agent in acidic than in basic solution:

$$MnO_4^-(aq) + 4H^+(aq) + 3e^- \longrightarrow MnO_2(s) + 2H_2O(l) \qquad E^0 = 1.68 \text{ V}$$

$$MnO_4^-(aq) + 2H_2O(l) + 3e^- \longrightarrow MnO_2(s) + 4OH^-(aq) \qquad E^0 = 0.59 \text{ V}$$

Unlike Cr^{2+} and Fe^{2+}, the Mn^{2+} ion resists oxidation in air. The Cr^{2+} ion is a d^4 species and readily loses a d electron to form the more stable d^3 Cr^{3+} ion. The Fe^{2+} ion is a d^6 species, and removing a d electron yields the stable, half-filled d^5 configuration of the Fe^{3+} ion. Removing an electron from the Mn^{2+} ion is difficult because it disrupts the d^5 configuration. ◆

Silver

Silver, the second member of the coinage metals [Group 1B(11)], has been admired for thousands of years and is still treasured for use in jewelry and fine flatware. Because the pure metal is too soft for these purposes, however, it is alloyed with copper to form the harder sterling silver. In former times, silver was used in coins, but it has been replaced almost universally by copper-nickel alloys. Silver has the *highest electrical conductivity of any element* but is not used in wiring because copper is cheaper and more plentiful. In the past, silver was found in nuggets and veins of rock, often mixed with gold, because both elements are chemically inert enough to exist uncombined. Nearly all of those deposits have been mined, so most silver is now obtained from the anode mud formed during the electrorefining of copper (Section 22.4).

The only important oxidation state of silver is +1. Its most important *soluble* compound is silver nitrate, used for electroplating and in the manufacture of the halides used for photographic film. Although silver forms no oxide in air, it tarnishes to black Ag_2S by reaction with traces of sulfur-containing compounds. Some polishes remove the Ag_2S, along with some silver, by physically abrading the surface. An alternative "home remedy" removes the tarnish and restores the metal by heating the object in a solution of table salt or baking soda ($NaHCO_3$) in an aluminum pan. Aluminum, a strong reducing agent, reduces the Ag^+ ions back to the metal:

$$2Al(s) + 3Ag_2S(s) + 6H_2O(l) \longrightarrow 2Al(OH)_3(s) + 6Ag(s) + 3H_2S(g) \quad E^0 = 0.86 \text{ V}$$

The Chemistry of Black-and-White Photography The most widespread use of silver compounds, particularly the three heavier halides, is in black-and-white photography, an art that applies transition metal chemistry and solution kinetics. The photographic film itself is simply a flexible plastic support for the light-sensitive emulsion, which consists of AgBr microcrystals dispersed in gelatin. The five steps in obtaining a final photograph are exposing the film, developing the image, fixing the image, washing the negative, and printing the image. Figure 23.8 on the next page summarizes the first four steps, through obtaining and washing the negative. The process depends on several key chemical properties of silver and its compounds:

- Silver halides undergo a redox reaction when exposed to visible light.
- Silver chloride, bromide, and iodide are *not* water soluble.
- Ag^+ is easily reduced: $Ag^+(aq) + e^- \longrightarrow Ag(s)$; $E^0 = 0.80$ V.
- Ag^+ forms several stable, water-soluble complex ions.

1. *Exposing the film.* Light reflected from the objects in a scene—more light from bright objects than from dark ones—enters the camera lens and strikes the film. Exposed AgBr crystals absorb photons ($h\nu$) in a very localized redox reaction. A Br^- ion is excited by a photon and oxidized, the released electron almost immediately reducing a nearby Ag^+ ion:

$$\begin{array}{r} Br^- \xrightarrow{h\nu} Br + e^- \\ Ag^+ + e^- \longrightarrow Ag \\ \hline Ag^+ + Br^- \xrightarrow{h\nu} Ag + Br \end{array}$$

Wherever more light strikes a microcrystal, more Ag atoms form. The exposed crystals are called a *latent* image because the few scattered atoms of photoreduced Ag are not yet visible. Nevertheless, their presence as crystal defects within the AgBr makes the crystal highly susceptible to further reduction.

2. *Developing the image.* The latent image is developed into the actual image by reducing more of the silver ions in the crystal in a controlled manner. Developing is a rate-dependent step: crystals with many photoreduced Ag atoms react more quickly than those with only a few. The developer is a weak reducing agent, such as the organic substance hydroquinone ($H_2C_6H_4O_2$; H_2Q) (see margin):

$$2Ag^+(s) + H_2Q(aq; \text{reduced form}) \longrightarrow 2Ag(s) + Q(aq; \text{oxidized form}) + 2H^+(aq)$$

The reaction rate depends on H_2Q concentration, solution temperature, and the time the emulsion is bathed in the solution. After developing, approximately 10^6 as many Ag atoms are present on the film as there were in the latent image, and they form very small, black clusters of silver.

3. *Fixing the image.* After the image is developed, it must be "fixed"; that is, the reduction of Ag^+ must be stopped, or the entire film will blacken on exposure to more light. Fixing involves removing the remaining Ag^+ chemically by converting it to a soluble complex ion with sodium thiosulfate solution ("hypo"):

$$AgBr(s) + 2S_2O_3{}^{2-}(aq) \longrightarrow Ag(S_2O_3)_2{}^{3-}(aq) + Br^-(aq)$$

hydroquinone   quinone

+ 2H$^+$ + 2e$^-$

Figure 23.8 Steps in producing a black-and-white negative.

4. *Washing the negative.* The water-soluble ions are washed away in water. Washing is the final step in producing a photographic *negative,* in which dark objects in the scene appear bright in the image, and vice versa.

5. *Printing the image.* Through the use of an enlarger, the image on the negative is projected onto print paper coated with emulsion (silver halide in gelatin) and exposed to light, and the previous chemical steps are repeated to produce a "positive" of the image. Bright areas on a negative, such as car tires, allow a great deal of light to pass through and reduce many Ag^+ ions on the print paper. Dark areas on a negative, such as clouds, allow much less light to pass through and, thus, much less Ag^+ reduction. Print-paper emulsion usually contains silver chloride, which reacts more slowly than silver bromide, giving finer control of the print image. High-speed film incorporates silver iodide, the most light sensitive of the three halides.

Mercury

Mercury has been known since ancient times because cinnabar (HgS), its principal ore, is a naturally occurring red pigment (vermilion) that readily undergoes a redox reaction in the heat of a fire. Sulfide ion, the reducing agent for the process, is already present as part of the ore:

$$HgS(s) + O_2(g) \longrightarrow Hg(g) + SO_2(g)$$

The gaseous Hg condenses on cool nearby surfaces.

The Latin name *hydrargyrum* ("liquid silver") is a good description of mercury, the only metal that is liquid at room temperature. Two factors account for this unusual property. First, because of a distorted crystal structure, each mercury atom is surrounded by 6 rather than 12 nearest neighbors. Second, a filled, tightly held *d* subshell leaves only the two *6s* electrons for metallic bonding. Thus, interactions among mercury atoms are relatively few and relatively weak and, as a result, the solid form breaks down at −38.9°C.

Many of mercury's uses arise from its unusual physical properties. Its liquid range ($-39°C$ to $357°C$) encompasses most everyday temperatures, so Hg is commonly used in thermometers. As you might expect from its position in Period 6 following the lanthanide contraction, mercury is quite dense (13.5 g/mL), which makes it convenient for use in barometers and manometers. Mercury's fluidity and conductivity make it useful for "silent" switches in thermostats. At high pressures, mercury vapor can be excited electrically to emit the bright white light seen in sports stadium and highway lights.

Mercury is a good solvent for metals, and many *amalgams*, alloys of mercury, exist. In mercury batteries, a zinc amalgam acts as the anode and mercury(II) oxide as the cathode (Gallery, Section 21.5). In the mercury-cell version of the chlor-alkali process (Section 22.5), mercury acts as the cathode and as the solvent for the Na metal that forms. Recall that, when treated with water, the resulting sodium amalgam (Na/Hg) forms two important by-products:

$$2Na/Hg + 2H_2O(l) \xrightarrow{-Hg} 2NaOH(aq) + H_2(g)$$

The mercury is released in this step and reused in the electrolytic cell. In view of mercury's toxicity, which we discuss shortly, newer methods involving polymeric membranes have eliminated the mercury-cell version in most cases. Nevertheless, past contamination of wastewater from the chlor-alkali process and the disposal of old mercury batteries remain serious environmental concerns.

The chemical properties of mercury are unique within Group 2B(12). The other members, zinc and cadmium, occur in the +2 oxidation state as d^{10} ions, but mercury occurs in the +1 state as well, which has the condensed configuration $[Xe]\ 6s^1 4f^{14} 5d^{10}$. The unpaired $6s$ electron allows two Hg(I) species to form the *diatomic ion* $[Hg-Hg]^{2+}$ (written Hg_2^{2+}), one of the first species known with a covalent metal-metal bond. Mercury's most common oxidation state is +2. Whereas HgF_2 is largely ionic, many other compounds, such as $HgCl_2$, contain bonds that are predominantly covalent. Most mercury(II) compounds are insoluble in water.

The common ions Zn^{2+}, Cd^{2+}, and Hg^{2+} are biopoisons. Zinc oxide is used as an external antiseptic ointment. The Cd^{2+} and Hg^{2+} ions are two of the so-called toxic heavy-metal ions. The cadmium in solder may be more responsible than the lead for solder's high toxicity. Mercury compounds have been used in agriculture as fungicides and pesticides and in medicine as an internal drug, but these uses have been mostly phased out. ◆

Because most mercury(II) compounds are insoluble in water, they were once thought to be harmless in the environment, but we now know otherwise. Microorganisms in sludge and river sediment convert mercury atoms and ions to the methyl mercury ion, CH_3-Hg^+, and then to organomercury compounds, such as dimethylmercury, $CH_3-Hg-CH_3$. These toxic compounds are nonpolar and, like chlorinated hydrocarbons, become increasingly concentrated in fatty tissues, as they move up the food chain from microorganisms to worms to fish and, finally, to birds and mammals. Indeed, fish living in a mercury-polluted lake or coastal estuary can have a mercury concentration thousands of times higher than that of the water itself.

The mechanism for the toxicity of mercury and other heavy-metal ions is not fully understood. It is thought that the ions migrate from fatty tissue and bind strongly to thiol (SH) groups of amino acids in proteins, thereby disrupting the proteins' structure and function. Since the brain has a high fat content, small amounts of lead, cadmium, and mercury ions circulating in the blood become deposited in the brain's fatty tissue, interact with its proteins, and often cause devastating neurological and psychological effects.

◆ **Mad as a Hatter** The felt top hat and zany manner of the "mad hatter" in *Alice in Wonderland* are literary references to the toxicity of mercury compounds. Mercury(II) nitrate and chloride were used with HNO_3 to make felt for hats from animal hair. Inhalation of the dust generated by the process led to "hatter's shakes," abnormal personality, and other neurological disorders.

Section Summary

Chromium and manganese add corrosion resistance and hardness to steels. They are typical of transition metals in having several oxidation states. Valence-state electronegativity refers to the ability of a element in its various oxidation states to attract bonding electrons. It increases with oxidation number, which is the reason elements act more metallic (more ionic compounds, more basic oxides) in lower states and more nonmetallic (more acidic oxides, oxoanions of acids) in higher states. Cr and Mn produce H_2 in acid. Cr(VI) undergoes a pH-sensitive dehydration-condensation reaction. Both Cr(VI) and Mn(VII) are stronger oxidizing agents in acid than in base. The only important oxidation state for silver is +1. The silver halides are light sensitive and are used in photography. Mercury, the only liquid metal at room temperature, dissolves many metals in important applications. The mercury(I) ion is diatomic and has a metal-metal covalent bond. The element and its compounds are toxic and become concentrated in the food chain.

23.4 Coordination Compounds

The most distinctive aspect of transition metal chemistry is the formation of **coordination compounds** (also called *complexes*). These are substances that contain at least one **complex ion,** a species consisting of *a central metal cation (either transition or main-group metal) bonded to molecules and/or anions called ligands.* To maintain electrical neutrality in the coordination compound, the complex ion is typically associated with other ions, called **counter ions.** A typical coordination compound appears in Figure 23.9A: the coordination compound is $[Co(NH_3)_6]Cl_3$, the complex ion is $[Co(NH_3)_6]^{3+}$, the six NH_3 molecules bonded to the central Co^{3+} are ligands, and the three Cl^- ions are counter ions.

A coordination compound behaves like an electrolyte in water: the complex ion and counter ions separate from each other. But the complex ion behaves like a polyatomic ion: *the ligands and central metal ion remain attached.* Thus, as Figure 23.9A shows, 1 mol $[Co(NH_3)_6]Cl_3$ yields 1 mol $[Co(NH_3)_6]^{3+}$ ions and 3 mol Cl^- ions. We discussed the Lewis acid-base properties of complex ions

Figure 23.9 Components of a coordination compound. Coordination compounds typically consist of a complex ion and counter ions to neutralize the charge. The complex ion has a central metal ion surrounded by ligands. **A,** When solid $[Co(NH_3)_6]Cl_3$ dissolves, the complex ion and counter ions separate, but the ligands remain bound to the metal ion. Six ligands around the metal ion give the complex ion an octahedral geometry. **B,** Complex ions with a central d^8 metal ion contain four ligands and have a square planar geometry.

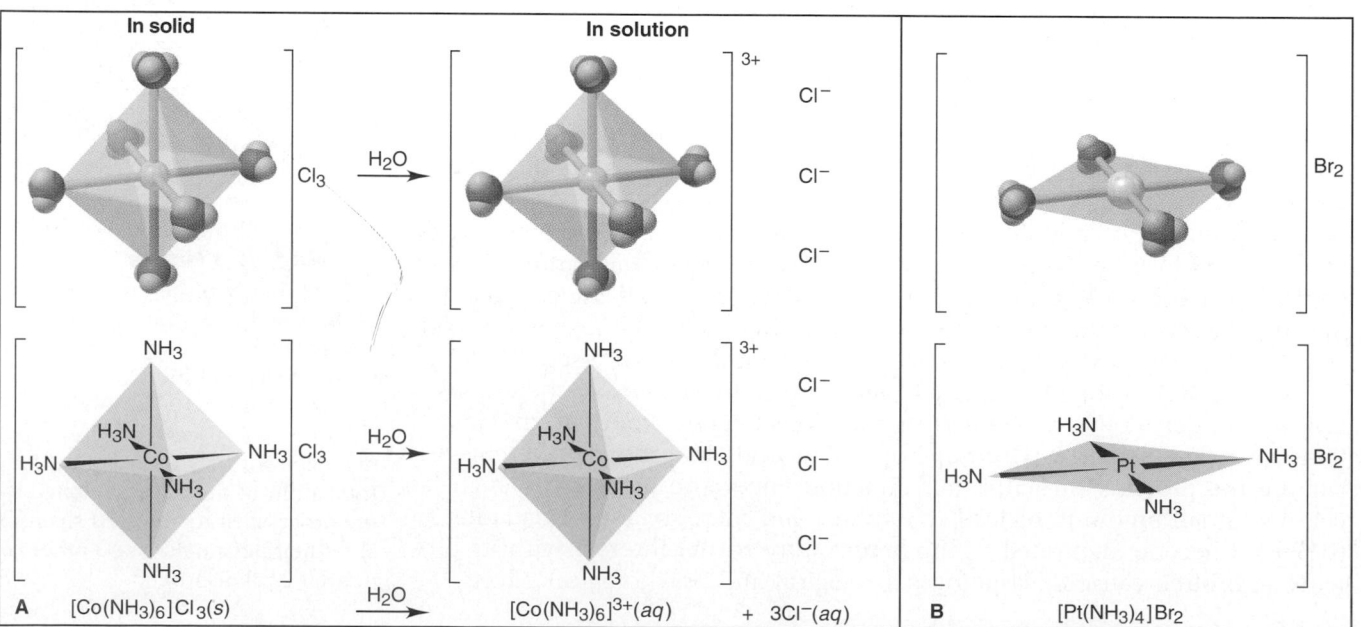

In solid	In solution

A $[Co(NH_3)_6]Cl_3(s)$ $\xrightarrow{H_2O}$ $[Co(NH_3)_6]^{3+}(aq)$ + $3Cl^-(aq)$ **B** $[Pt(NH_3)_4]Br_2$

in Section 18.9 and their equilibria in Section 19.4. Here we examine their bonding, structure, and properties.

Structures of Complex Ions: Coordination Numbers, Geometries, and Ligands

A complex ion is described by the metal ion and the number and types of ligands attached to it. Its structure is related to three characteristics—coordination number, geometry, and number of donor atoms per ligand:

- *Coordination number.* The **coordination number** is the *number of ligand atoms* bonded directly to the central metal ion and is *specific* for a given metal ion in a particular oxidation state and compound. The coordination number of the metal ion in $[Co(NH_3)_6]^{3+}$ is 6 because lone pairs from six ligand atoms (N from NH_3) are bonded to the Co^{3+} ion. The coordination number of the metal ion in many platinum(II) complexes is 4, whereas in platinum(IV) complexes it is 6. Copper(II) may have a coordination number of 2, 4, or 6 in different ions. *The most common coordination number in complex ions is 6.* However, 2 and 4 are often seen, and some higher coordination numbers are also known.

- *Geometry. The geometry (shape) of a complex ion depends on the coordination number and nature of the metal ion.* Table 23.6 shows the geometries associated with the coordination numbers 2, 4, and 6, with some examples of each. A complex ion whose metal ion has a coordination number of 2, such as $[Ag(NH_3)_2]^+$, is *linear.* The coordination number 4 gives rise to either of two geometries—square planar or tetrahedral. Most d^8 metal ions form *square planar* complex ions (Figure 23.9B). The d^{10} ions are among those that form *tetrahedral* complex ions. A coordination number of 6 results in an *octahedral* geometry, as shown by $[Co(NH_3)_6]^{3+}$ in Figure 23.9A. Note the similarity with some molecular shapes in VSEPR theory (Section 10.3).

- *Donor atoms per ligand.* The ligands of complex ions are *molecules and/or anions* with one or more **donor atoms** that each *donate a lone pair of electrons* to the metal ion to form a covalent bond. Because they have at least one lone pair, donor atoms often come from Group 5A(15), 6A(16), or 7A(17).

Table 23.6 Coordination Numbers and Shapes of Some Complex Ions

Coordination Number	Shape		Examples
2	Linear		$[CuCl_2]^-$, $[Ag(NH_3)_2]^+$, $[AuCl_2]^-$
4	Square planar		$[Ni(CN)_4]^{2-}$, $[PdCl_4]^{2-}$, $[Pt(NH_3)_4]^{2+}$, $[Cu(NH_3)_4]^{2+}$
4	Tetrahedral		$[Cu(CN)_4]^{3-}$, $[Zn(NH_3)_4]^{2+}$, $[CdCl_4]^{2-}$, $[MnCl_4]^{2-}$
6	Octahedral		$[Ti(H_2O)_6]^{3+}$, $[V(CN)_6]^{4-}$, $[Cr(NH_3)_4Cl_2]^+$, $[Mn(H_2O)_6]^{2+}$, $[FeCl_6]^{3-}$, $[Co(en)_3]^{3+}$

Table 23.7 Some Common Ligands in Coordination Compounds

Ligand Type	Examples			
Unidentate	$H_2\overset{..}{O}$: water	:$\overset{..}{\underset{..}{F}}$:$^-$ fluoride ion	[:C$\equiv$N:]$^-$ cyanide ion	[:$\overset{..}{\underset{..}{O}}$—H]$^-$ hydroxide ion
	:NH$_3$ ammonia	:$\overset{..}{\underset{..}{Cl}}$:$^-$ chloride ion	[:$\overset{..}{\underset{..}{S}}$=C=$\overset{..}{N}$:]$^-$ thiocyanate ion └─ or ─┘	[:$\overset{..}{\underset{..}{O}}$—N=$\overset{..}{O}$:]$^-$ nitrite ion └ or ┘

Bidentate

$$H_2C—CH_2$$
$$H_2N \qquad NH_2$$
ethylenediamine (en)

$$\left[\begin{array}{c} :\overset{..}{\underset{..}{O}}: \qquad :\overset{..}{O}: \\ C—C \\ :\overset{..}{\underset{..}{O}}: \qquad :\overset{..}{\underset{..}{O}}: \end{array} \right]^{2-}$$
oxalate ion

Polydentate

$$H_2C—CH_2 \quad CH_2—CH_2$$
$$H_2N \qquad \overset{..}{N}H \qquad NH_2$$
diethylenetriamine

$$\left[\begin{array}{c} :O: \quad :O: \quad :O: \\ :\overset{..}{\underset{..}{O}}—\overset{||}{P}—\overset{..}{\underset{..}{O}}—\overset{||}{P}—\overset{..}{\underset{..}{O}}—\overset{||}{P}—\overset{..}{\underset{..}{O}}: \\ :\overset{..}{O}: \quad :\overset{..}{O}: \quad :\overset{..}{O}: \end{array} \right]^{5-}$$
triphosphate ion

$$\left[\begin{array}{c} :O: \qquad\qquad\qquad :O: \\ :\overset{..}{\underset{..}{O}}—C—CH_2 \qquad CH_2—C—\overset{..}{\underset{..}{O}}: \\ \overset{..}{N}—CH_2—CH_2—\overset{..}{N}: \\ :\overset{..}{\underset{..}{O}}—C—CH_2 \qquad CH_2—C—\overset{..}{\underset{..}{O}}: \\ :O: \qquad\qquad\qquad :O: \end{array} \right]^{4-}$$
ethylenediaminetetraacetate (EDTA) ion

[Mg(ATP)]$^{2-}$

[Pb(EDTA)]$^{2-}$

◆ **Grabbing Ions** The active form of ATP in cells *(top)* is an octahedral complex of Mg^{2+}, with two O atoms from the charged triphosphate grouping and four others from water molecules acting as the ligand donor atoms. Because of its six donor atoms, the ethylenediaminetetraacetate (EDTA) ion forms very stable complexes with many metal ions *(bottom)*. This property makes EDTA useful in treating heavy-metal poisoning. Once ingested by the patient, it acts as a scavenger to remove lead and other heavy-metal ions from the blood and other body fluids.

Ligands are classified in terms of the number of donor atoms, or "teeth," that each uses to bond to the central metal ion. *Unidentate* (Latin, "one-toothed") ligands, such as Cl^- and NH_3, use a single donor atom. *Bidentate* ligands have two donor atoms, each of which bonds to the metal ion. *Polydentate* ligands have more than two donor atoms. Table 23.7 shows some common ligands in coordination compounds; note that each ligand has one or more donor atoms (colored type), each with a lone pair of electrons to donate. Bidentate and polydentate ligands give rise to *rings* in the complex ion. For instance, ethylenediamine (abbreviated *en* in formulas) has a chain of four atoms (:N—C—C—N:), so it forms a five-membered ring, with the two electron-donating N atoms bonding to the metal atom. Such ligands seem to grab the metal ion like a crab's claws, so a complex ion that contains them is also called a **chelate** (pronounced *key-late*; Greek *chela*, "crab's claw"). ◆

Formulas and Names of Coordination Compounds

There are three important rules for writing the formulas of coordination compounds, the first two being the same for writing formulas of any ionic compound:

1. *The cation is written before the anion.*
2. *The charge of the cation(s) is balanced by the charge of the anion(s).*
3. *In the complex ion, neutral ligands are written before anionic ligands, and the whole ion is placed in brackets.*

Let's apply these rules as we examine the combinations of ions in coordination compounds. *The whole complex ion may be a cation or an anion.* A complex cation has anionic counter ions, and a complex anion has cationic counter ions. It's easy to find the charge of the central metal ion. For example, in $K_2[Co(NH_3)_2Cl_4]$, two K^+ counter ions balance the charge of the complex anion $[Co(NH_3)_2Cl_4]^{2-}$, which contains two NH_3 molecules and four Cl^- ions as ligands. The two NH_3 are neutral, the four Cl^- have a total charge of $4-$, and the entire complex ion has a charge of $2-$, so the central metal ion must be Co^{2+}:

Charge of metal ion = Charge of complex ion − total charge of ligands

$$= (2-) - [(2 \times 0) + (4 \times 1-)]$$
$$= (2-) - (4-) = 2+$$

In the compound $[Co(NH_3)_4Cl_2]Cl$, the complex ion is $[Co(NH_3)_4Cl_2]^+$ and one Cl^- is the counter ion. The four NH_3 ligands are neutral, the two Cl^- ligands have a total charge of $2-$, and the complex cation has a charge of $1+$, so the central metal ion must be Co^{3+}. Some coordination compounds have a complex cation *and* a complex anion, as in $[Co(NH_3)_5Br]_2[Fe(CN)_6]$. In this compound, the complex cation is $[Co(NH_3)_5Br]^{2+}$, with Co^{3+}, and the complex anion is $[Fe(CN)_6]^{4-}$, with Fe^{2+}.

Coordination compounds were originally named after the person who first prepared them or from their color, and some of these common names are still used, but most coordination compounds are named systematically through a set of rules:

1. *The cation is named before the anion.* In naming $[Co(NH_3)_4Cl_2]Cl$, for example, we name the $[Co(NH_3)_4Cl_2]^+$ ion before the Cl^- ion. Therefore, the name is

tetraamminedichlorocobalt(III) chloride

The only space in the name appears between the cation and the anion.

2. *Within the complex ion, the ligands are named, in alphabetical order, **before** the metal ion.* Note that in the $[Co(NH_3)_4Cl_2]^+$ ion of the compound named in Rule 1, the four NH_3 and two Cl^- are named before the Co^{3+}.

3. *Neutral ligands generally have the molecule name,* but there are a few exceptions (Table 23.8A). *Anionic ligands drop the -ide and add -o after the root name;* thus, the anion name *fluoride* becomes the ligand name *fluoro* for F^- (Table 23.8B). The two ligands in $[Co(NH_3)_4Cl_2]^+$ are ammine for NH_3 and chloro for Cl^-, with *ammine* coming before *chloro* alphabetically.

4. *A numerical prefix denotes the number of a particular ligand.* Thus, *tetra*ammine denotes *four* NH_3, and *di*chloro denotes *two* Cl^-. Other prefixes are *tri*, *penta*, and *hexa*. These prefixes do *not* affect the alphabetical order; for example, *tetraammine* comes before *dichloro*. Some ligand names already contain a numerical prefix (such as ethylene*di*amine), so we use *bis* (2), *tris* (3), or *tetrakis* (4) to indicate the number of such ligands, followed by the ligand name in parentheses. Thus, a complex ion with two ethylenediamine ligands has *bis(ethylenediamine)* in the name.

5. *The oxidation state of the central metal ion is given by a Roman numeral (in parentheses) only* if the metal ion can have more than one state, as in the compound named in Rule 1.

6. *If the complex ion is an anion, we drop the ending of the metal name and add "-ate."* Thus, the name for $K[Pt(NH_3)Cl_5]$ is

potassium amminepentachloroplatinate(IV)

(Note that there is one K^+ counter ion, so the complex anion has a charge of $1-$. The five Cl^- ligands have a total charge of $5-$, so Pt must be in the $+4$ oxidation state.) For some metals, we use the Latin root with the *-ate* ending (Table 23.9). For example, the name for $Na_4[FeBr_6]$ is

sodium hexabromoferrate(II)

Table 23.8 Names of Some Neutral and Anionic Ligands

Name	Formula
A. Neutral	
Aqua	H_2O
Ammine	NH_3
Carbonyl	CO
Nitrosyl	NO
B. Anionic	
Fluoro	F^-
Chloro	Cl^-
Bromo	Br^-
Iodo	I^-
Hydroxo	OH^-
Cyano	CN^-

Table 23.9 Names of Some Metal Ions in Complex Anions

Metal	Name in Anion
Iron	Ferrate
Copper	Cuprate
Lead	Plumbate
Silver	Argentate
Gold	Aurate
Tin	Stannate

Sample Problem 23.3 Writing Names and Formulas of Coordination Compounds

PROBLEM (a) What is the systematic name of $Na_3[AlF_6]$?
(b) What is the systematic name of $[Co(en)_2Cl_2]NO_3$?
(c) What is the formula of tetraamminebromochloroplatinum(IV) chloride?
(d) What is the formula of hexaamminecobalt(III) tetrachloroferrate(III)?
PLAN We use the rules that were just discussed in the text and refer to Tables 23.8 and 23.9.

SOLUTION (a) The complex ion is $[AlF_6]^{3-}$. There are six (hexa) F^- ions (fluoro) as ligands, so we have *hexafluoro*. The complex ion is an anion, so the ending of the metal ion (aluminum) must be changed to *-ate*: hexafluoroaluminate. Aluminum has only the $+3$ oxidation state, so we do *not* use a Roman numeral. The positive counter ion is named first and separated from the anion by a space: sodium hexafluoroaluminate.

(b) Listed alphabetically, there are two Cl^- *(dichloro)* and two en [*bis(ethylenediamine)*] as ligands. The complex ion is a cation, so the metal name is unchanged, but we specify its oxidation state because cobalt can have several. One NO_3^- balances the $1+$ cation charge: with $2-$ for two Cl^- and 0 for two en, the metal must be *cobalt(III)*. The word *nitrate* follows a space: dichlorobis(ethylenediamine)cobalt(III) nitrate.

(c) The central metal ion is written first, followed by the neutral ligands and then (in alphabetical order) by the negative ligands. *Tetraammine* is four NH_3, *bromo* is one Br^-, *chloro* is one Cl^-, and *platinate(IV)* is Pt^{4+}, so the complex ion is $[Pt(NH_3)_4BrCl]^{2+}$. Its $2+$ charge is the sum of $4+$ for Pt^{4+}, 0 for four NH_3, $1-$ for one Br^-, and $1-$ for one Cl^-. To balance the $2+$ charge, we need two Cl^- counter ions: $[Pt(NH_3)_4BrCl]Cl_2$.

(d) This compound consists of two types of complex ion. In the cation, *hexaammine* is six NH_3 and *cobalt(III)* is Co^{3+}, so the cation is $[Co(NH_3)_6]^{3+}$. The $3+$ charge is the sum of $3+$ for Co^{3+} and 0 for six NH_3. In the anion, *tetrachloro* is four Cl^-, and *ferrate(III)* is Fe^{3+}, so the anion is $[FeCl_4]^-$. The $1-$ charge is the sum of $3+$ for Fe^{3+} and $4-$ for four Cl^-. In the neutral compound, one $3+$ cation is balanced by three $1-$ anions: $[Co(NH_3)_6][FeCl_4]_3$.

CHECK Reverse the process to be sure you obtain the name or formula asked for in the problem.

Follow-up Problem 23.3 (a) What is the name of $[Cr(H_2O)_5Br]Cl_2$? (b) What is the formula of barium hexacyanocobaltate(III)?

A Historical Perspective: Alfred Werner and Coordination Theory

The substances we now call coordination compounds had been known for almost 200 years when the young Swiss chemist Alfred Werner began studying them in the 1890s. He investigated a series of compounds such as the cobalt series shown in Table 23.10, each of which contains one cobalt(III) ion, three chloride ions, and a given number of ammonia molecules. At the time, which was 30 years before the idea of atomic orbitals was proposed, no structural theory could explain how compounds with similar, even identical, formulas could have widely different properties.

Werner measured the conductivity of each compound in aqueous solution to determine the total number of ions that became dissociated. He treated the solutions with excess $AgNO_3$ to precipitate released Cl^- ions as AgCl and thus determine the number of free Cl^- ions per formula unit. Previous studies had established that the NH_3 molecules were not free in solution. Werner's data, summarized in Table 23.10, could not be explained by the accepted, traditional formulas of the compounds. Other chemists had proposed "chain" structures, like those of organic compounds, to explain such data. For example, a proposed structure for $[Co(NH_3)_6]Cl_3$ was

Table 23.10 Some Coordination Compounds of Cobalt Studied by Werner

| Traditional Formula | Werner's Data* | | Modern Formula | Charge of Complex Ion |
	Total Ions	Free Cl^-		
$CoCl_3 \cdot 6NH_3$	4	3	$[Co(NH_3)_6]Cl_3$	$3+$
$CoCl_3 \cdot 5NH_3$	3	2	$[Co(NH_3)_5Cl]Cl_2$	$2+$
$CoCl_3 \cdot 4NH_3$	2	1	$[Co(NH_3)_4Cl_2]Cl$	$1+$
$CoCl_3 \cdot 3NH_3$	0	0	$[Co(NH_3)_3Cl_3]$	—

*Moles per mole of compound.

$$NH_3\text{---}Cl$$
$$|$$
$$Co\text{---}NH_3\text{---}Cl$$
$$|$$
$$NH_3\text{---}NH_3\text{---}NH_3\text{---}NH_3\text{---}Cl$$

However, these models proved inadequate.

Werner's novel idea was the coordination complex, a central metal ion surrounded by a *constant total number* of covalently bonded molecules and/or anions. The coordination complex could be neutral or charged; if charged, it combined with oppositely charged counter ions, in this case Cl^-, to form the neutral compound. Werner proposed two types of valence, or *combining ability,* for metal ions. *Primary valence,* now called *oxidation state,* is the positive charge on the metal ion that must be satisfied by an equivalent negative charge. In Werner's cobalt series, the primary valence is +3, and it is always balanced by three Cl^- ions. These anions can be bonded covalently to Co as part of the complex ion and/or associated with it as counter ions. *Secondary valence,* now called *coordination number,* is the constant total number of connections (anionic or neutral ligands) *within* the complex ion. The secondary valence in this series of cobalt compounds is 6.

As you can see, Werner's data are satisfied if the total number of ligands remain the same for each compound, but the numbers of Cl^- ions and NH_3 molecules in the different complex ions vary. For example, the first compound, $[Co(NH_3)_6]Cl_3$, has a total of four ions: one $[Co(NH_3)_6]^{3+}$ and three Cl^-. All three Cl^- ions are free to form AgCl. The last compound, $[Co(NH_3)_3Cl_3]$, contains no separate ions.

Surprisingly, Werner was an organic chemist, and his work on coordination compounds, which virtually revolutionized his contemporaries' understanding of chemical bonding, was his attempt to demonstrate the unity of chemistry. For these pioneering studies, especially his prediction of optical isomerism (discussed next), Werner received the Nobel Prize in 1913.

Isomerism in Coordination Compounds

Isomers are substances with the same chemical formula but different properties. We have already discussed many aspects of isomerism in the context of organic compounds in Section 15.2; it may be helpful to review that section now. Figure 23.10 presents an overview of the most common types of isomerism in coordination compounds.

Constitutional Isomers: Same Atoms Connected Differently Two compounds with the same formula, but with the atoms connected differently, are called **constitutional (structural) isomers.** Coordination compounds exhibit the following two types of constitutional isomers: one involves changes in the composition of the complex ion, the other in the donor atom of the ligand.

1. **Coordination isomers** occur when the composition of the complex ion changes but not that of the compound. One way this type of isomerism occurs is when ligand and counter ion exchange positions, as in $[Pt(NH_3)_4Cl_2](NO_2)_2$ and $[Pt(NH_3)_4(NO_2)_2]Cl_2$. In the first compound, the

Figure 23.10 **Important types of isomerism in coordination compounds.**

Cl$^-$ ions are the ligands, and the NO$_2^-$ ions are counter ions; in the second, the roles are reversed. Another way this type of isomerism occurs is in compounds of two complex ions in which the two sets of ligands in one compound are reversed in the other, as in [Cr(NH$_3$)$_6$][Co(CN)$_6$] and [Co(NH$_3$)$_6$][Cr(CN)$_6$]; note that NH$_3$ is a ligand of Cr^{3+} in one compound and of Co^{3+} in the other.

2. **Linkage isomers** occur when the composition of the complex ion remains the same but the attachment of the ligand donor atom changes. Some ligands can bind to the metal ion through *either of two donor atoms:*

nitrite   cyanate   thiocyanate

For example, the nitrite ion can bind through either the N atom (*nitro*, O$_2$N:——→) or through one of the O atoms (*nitrito*, ONO:——→) to give linkage isomers, as in the orange compound pentaammine*nitro*cobalt(III) chloride [Co(NH$_3$)$_5$(NO$_2$)]Cl$_2$ *(below left)* and its red linkage isomer pentaammine*nitrito*cobalt(III) chloride [Co(NH$_3$)$_5$(ONO)]Cl$_2$ *(below right)*. Another example is the cyanate ion, which can attach via the O atom (*cyanato*, NCO:——→) or the N atom (*isocyanato*, OCN:——→); the thiocyanate ion behaves similarly, attaching via the S atom or the N atom.

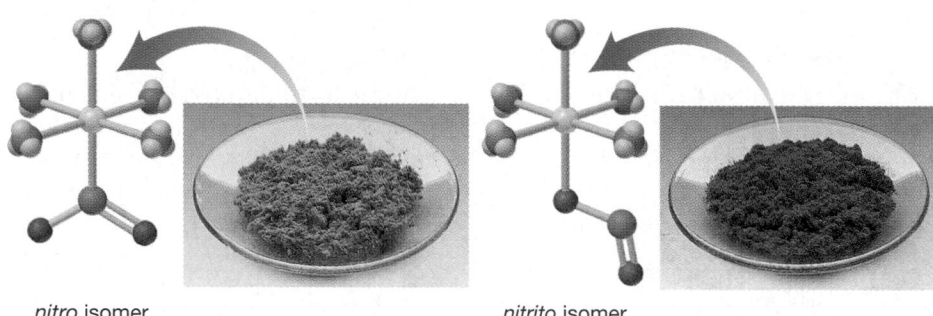

nitro isomer   *nitrito* isomer

Stereoisomers: Different Spatial Arrangements of Atoms   Stereoisomers are compounds that have the same atomic connections but different spatial arrangements of the atoms. The two types that we discussed for organic compounds, called *geometric* and *optical* isomers, are seen with coordination compounds as well:

1. **Geometric isomers** (also called ***cis-trans*** isomers and *diastereomers*) occur when atoms or groups of atoms are arranged differently in space relative to the central ion. For example, the square planar [Pt(NH$_3$)$_2$Cl$_2$] has two arrangements, which give rise to two different compounds (Figure 23.11A). The isomer with identical ligands *next* to each other is *cis*-diamminedichloroplatinum(II), and the one with identical ligands *across* from each other is *trans*-diamminedichloroplatinum(II); their biological behaviors are remarkably different. ◆ Octahedral complexes also exhibit *cis-trans* isomerism (Figure 23.11B). The *cis*-isomer of the [Co(NH$_3$)$_4$Cl$_2$]$^+$ ion has the two Cl$^-$ ligands next to each other and is violet, whereas the *trans*-isomer has these two ligands across from each other and is green.

2. **Optical isomers** (also called *enantiomers*) occur when a molecule and its mirror image cannot be superimposed (see Figures 15.9 to 15.11, pp. 615–616). Unlike the other types of isomers, which have distinct physical properties, optical isomers are physically identical in all ways but one: *the direc-*

◆ Fighting Cancer with Geometric Isomers   In the mid-1960s, Barnett Rosenberg and his colleagues discovered that *cis*-Pt(NH$_3$)$_2$Cl$_2$ ("cisplatin") was a highly effective antitumor agent. This compound and several closely related platinum(II) complexes are still among the most effective treatments for certain types of cancer. However, the geometric isomer, *trans*-Pt(NH$_3$)$_2$Cl$_2$, is completely ineffective as an antitumor agent. Cisplatin may work by lying within the cancer cell's DNA double helix, such that a donor atom on each strand replaces the *cis*-Cl$^-$ ligands and binds the platinum(II) strongly, thus preventing DNA replication (Section 15.6).

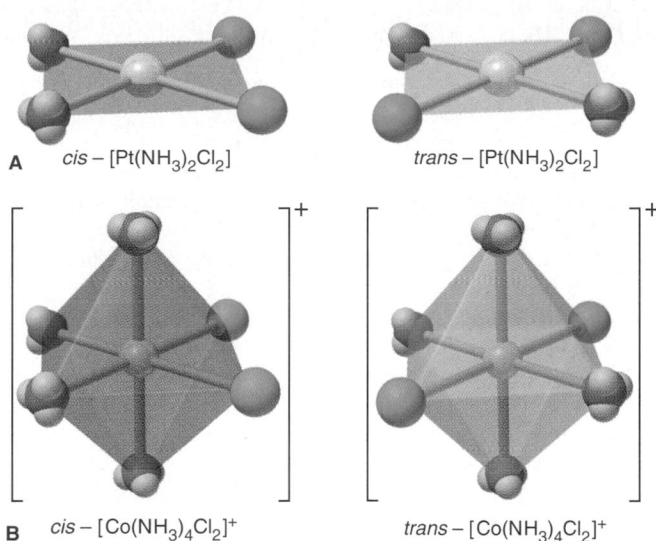

A   *cis* – [Pt(NH₃)₂Cl₂]   *trans* – [Pt(NH₃)₂Cl₂]

B   *cis* – [Co(NH₃)₄Cl₂]⁺   *trans* – [Co(NH₃)₄Cl₂]⁺

Figure 23.11 Geometric (*cis–trans*) isomerism. A, The *cis*- and *trans*-isomers of the square planar coordination compound [Pt(NH₃)₂Cl₂]. **B,** The *cis*- and *trans*-isomers of the octahedral complex ion [Co(NH₃)₄Cl₂]⁺. The colored shapes represent the actual colors of the species.

tion in which they rotate the plane of polarized light. Octahedral complexes show many examples of optical isomerism, which we can observe by rotating one isomer and seeing if it is superimposable on the other isomer (its mirror image). Consider the two optical isomers of the *cis*-dichlorobis(ethylenediamine)cobalt(III) ion, [Co(en)₂Cl₂]⁺, designated I and II in Figure 23.12A. Rotate isomer I 180° around a vertical axis, and you obtain III. Note that the Cl⁻ ligands of III match those of isomer II, but the en ligands do not match: II and III (rotated I) are not superimposable. One isomer is designated *d*-[Co(en)₂Cl₂]⁺ and the other is *l*-[Co(en)₂Cl₂]⁺, depending on whether it rotates polarized light to the right (*d* for "dextro") or to the left (*l* for "levo-"). (You can only determine the *d*- or *l*- designation experimentally, *not* by examining the structure.) In contrast, *trans*-dichlorobis(ethylenediamine)cobalt(III) ion (Figure 23.12B) does *not* have optical isomers: rotate I and you obtain III, which *is* superimposable on II.

Figure 23.12 Optical isomerism in an octahedral complex ion. A, Structure I and its mirror image, structure II, are optical isomers of *cis*-[Co(en)₂Cl₂]⁺. Rotating I gives III, which is *not* the same as II. (The curved wedge is a common representation of the bidentate ligand ethylenediamine, H₂N—CH₂—CH₂—NH₂.) **B,** In contrast, the *trans*-isomer does *not* have optical isomers. Rotating I gives III, which is *identical* to II, the mirror image of I.

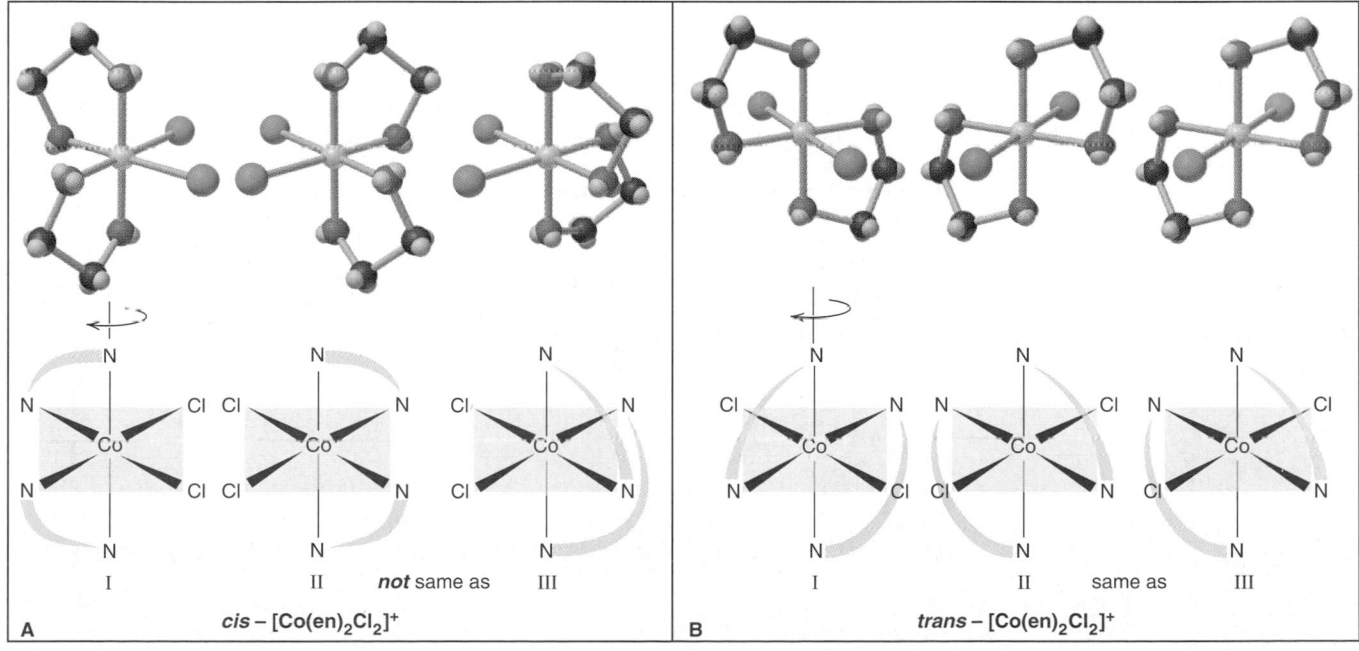

A   *cis* – [Co(en)₂Cl₂]⁺   B   *trans* – [Co(en)₂Cl₂]⁺

I   II   *not* same as   III   I   II   same as   III

Br NH₃   H₃N NH₃
   Pt   Pt
H₃N Br   Br   Br
trans   *cis*

(a)

Mirror

$[\quad]^{3+}$ $[\quad]^{3+}$

not the same as

Rotate

$[\quad]^{3+}$

(b)

Sample Problem 23.4 Determining the Type of Stereoisomerism

PROBLEM Which type(s) of stereoisomerism do each of the following exhibit?
(a) $[Pt(NH_3)_2Br_2]$ (square planar)
(b) $[Cr(en)_3]^{3+}$ (en = $H_2\ddot{N}CH_2CH_2\ddot{N}H_2$)
PLAN We first determine the geometry around each metal ion and the nature of the ligands. If there are two different ligands and it is possible to place them in different positions relative to each other, geometric *(cis-trans)* isomerism occurs. Then, we see whether the mirror image of the complex is superimposable on the original. If it is *not*, optical isomerism occurs.
SOLUTION (a) The Pt(II) complex is square planar, and there are two different unidentate ligands. Each pair of ligands can lie next to or across from each other [see margin **(a)**]. Thus, geometric isomerism occurs. Each isomer *is* superimposable on its mirror image, so there is no optical isomerism.
(b) Ethylenediamine (en) is a bidentate ligand. The Cr^{3+} has a coordination number of 6 and is octahedral, like Co^{3+}. The three bidentate ligands are identical, so there is no geometric isomerism. However, the complex ion has a nonsuperimposable mirror image [see margin **(b)**]. Thus, optical isomerism occurs.

Follow-up Problem 23.4 What stereoisomers, if any, are possible for the $[Co(NH_3)_2(en)Cl_2]^+$ ion?

Section Summary

Coordination compounds consist of a complex ion and charge-balancing counter ions. The complex ion has a central metal ion bonded to neutral and/or anionic ligands, which act as Lewis bases with one or more donor atoms. The most common geometry is octahedral (six ligand atoms bonding). Formulas and names of coordination compounds follow systematic rules. Alfred Werner established the structural basis of coordination compounds. These compounds can exhibit constitutional isomers (coordination and linkage) and stereoisomers (geometric and optical).

23.5 Theoretical Basis for the Bonding and Properties of Complexes

In this section, we consider models that address, in different ways, several key features of complexes: how metal-ligand bonds form, why certain geometries are preferred, and why these compounds are brightly colored and often paramagnetic. As you saw with covalent bonding in other compounds (Chapter 11), more than one model is often needed to tell the whole story.

Application of Valence Bond Theory to Complexes

Valence bond (VB) theory, which helped explain bonding and structure in main-group compounds (Section 11.1), is also used to describe bonding in complex ions. In the formation of a complex ion, the filled ligand orbital overlaps the empty metal-ion orbital. *The ligand (Lewis base) donates the electron pair, and the metal ion (Lewis acid) accepts it to form one of the covalent bonds of the complex ion (Lewis adduct)* (Section 18.9). Such a bond, in which one atom in the bond contributes both electrons, is called a **coordinate covalent bond,** although, once formed, it is identical to any covalent single bond. Recall that the VB concept of hybridization proposes the mixing of particular combinations of *s*, *p*, and *d* orbitals to give hybrid-orbital sets, which have specific geometries. Similarly, for coordination compounds, the model proposes that *the number and type of metal-ion hybrid orbitals occupied by ligand lone pairs determine the geometry of the complex ion.* Let's discuss the orbital combinations that lead to octahedral, square planar, and tetrahedral complexes.

Octahedral Complexes The hexaamminechromium(III) ion, $[Cr(NH_3)_6]^{3+}$, illustrates the application of VB theory to an *octahedral complex* (Figure 23.13). The six lowest energy empty orbitals of the Cr^{3+} ion—two $3d$, one $4s$, and three $4p$—mix and become six equivalent d^2sp^3 hybrid orbitals that point toward the corners of an octahedron.* Six NH_3 molecules donate their nitrogen lone electron pairs to form six metal-ligand bonds. The three unpaired $3d$ electrons of the central Cr^{3+} ion ($[Ar] 3d^3$), which make the complex ion paramagnetic, remain in unhybridized orbitals.

Figure 23.13 Hybrid orbitals and bonding in the octahedral $[Cr(NH_3)_6]^{3+}$ ion. A, VB depiction of the $Cr(NH_3)_6^{3+}$ ion. **B,** The partial orbital box diagrams depict the mixing of two $3d$, one $4s$, and three $4p$ orbitals in Cr^{3+} to form six d^2sp^3 hybrid orbitals, and bonding with six NH_3 lone pairs (*red*).

Square Planar Complexes Metal ions with a d^8 configuration usually form *square planar complexes* (Figure 23.14). In the $[Ni(CN)_4]^{2-}$ ion, for example, the model proposes that one $3d$, one $4s$, and two $4p$ orbitals of Ni^{2+} mix and form four dsp^2 hybrid orbitals, which point to the corners of a square and accept one electron pair from each of four CN^- ligands. A look at the ground-state electron configuration of Ni^{2+}, however, raises a key question: how can the Ni^{2+} ion ($[Ar] 3d^8$) offer an empty $3d$ orbital if eight $3d$ electrons lie in three filled and two half-filled orbitals? Apparently, in the d^8 configuration of Ni^{2+}, electrons in the half-filled orbitals pair and leave one $3d$ orbital empty. This explanation is consistent with the fact that the complex is diamagnetic (no unpaired electrons). Moreover, it requires that the energy *gained* by using a $3d$ orbital for bonding in the hybrid orbital is greater than the energy *required* to overcome repulsions from pairing the $3d$ electrons.

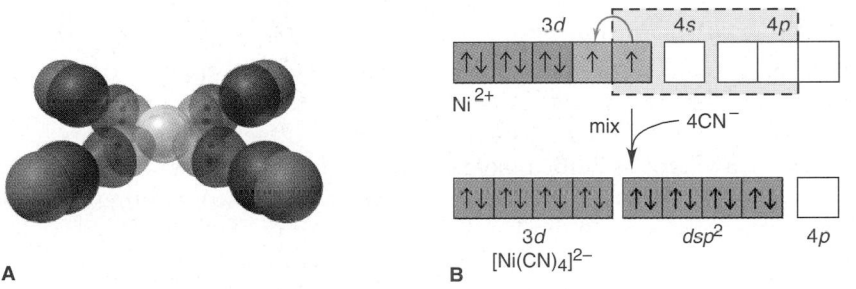

Figure 23.14 Hybrid orbitals and bonding in the square planar $[Ni(CN)_4]^{2-}$ ion. A, VB depiction of $[Ni(CN)_4]^{2-}$. **B,** Two lone $3d$ electrons pair up and free one $3d$ orbital for hybridization with the $4s$ and two $4p$ orbitals to form four dsp^2 orbitals, which become occupied with lone pairs (*red*) from four CN^- ligands.

---

*Note the distinction between the hybrid-orbital designation here and that for octahedral molecules like SF_6. The designation gives the orbitals in energy order within a given n value. In the $[Cr(NH_3)_6]^{3+}$ complex ion, the d orbitals have a *lower* n value than the s and p orbitals, so the hybrid is d^2sp^3. For the orbitals in SF_6, and in some complex ions, the d orbitals have the *same* n value as the s and p, so the hybrid is sp^3d^2.

Tetrahedral Complexes Metal ions with a filled *d* sublevel, such as Zn^{2+} ([Ar] d^{10}), often form *tetrahedral complexes* (Figure 23.15). In the complex ion $[Zn(OH)_4]^{2-}$, for example, VB theory proposes that the lowest available Zn^{2+} orbitals—one 4*s* and three 4*p*—mix to become four sp^3 hybrid orbitals that point to the corners of a tetrahedron and are occupied by a lone pair from each of four OH^- ligands.

Figure 23.15 Hybrid orbitals and bonding in the tetrahedral $[Zn(OH)_4]^{2-}$ ion. A, VB depiction of $[Zn(OH)_4]^{2-}$. **B,** Mixing one 4*s* and three 4*p* orbitals gives four sp^3 orbitals available for accepting lone pairs (*red*) from OH^- ligands.

Crystal Field Theory

The VB approach is easy to picture and rationalizes bonding and shape, but it treats the orbitals as little more than *empty "slots" for accepting electron pairs.* Consequently, it gives no insight into the colors of coordination compounds and sometimes predicts their magnetic properties incorrectly. In contrast to the VB approach, **crystal field theory** provides little insight about metal-ligand bonding but explains color and magnetism clearly. To do so, it highlights the *effects on d-orbital energies of the metal ion as the ligands approach.* Before we discuss this theory, let's consider what causes a substance to be colored.

What is Color? White light is electromagnetic radiation consisting of all wavelengths (λ) in the visible range (Section 7.1). It can be dispersed into a spectrum of colors, each of which has a narrower range of wavelengths. Objects appear colored in white light because they absorb certain wavelengths and reflect or transmit others: an opaque object *reflects* light, whereas a clear one *transmits* it. The reflected or transmitted light enters the eye and is perceived as color by the brain.

There are three *primary* colors—red, yellow, and blue. Mixing two primary colors produces one of the three *secondary* colors—orange, green, and violet; for example, a red pigment mixed with a yellow one appears orange. Each primary color has a *complementary* secondary color. For example, green and red are complementary colors. A mixture of complementary colors absorbs all visible wavelengths and appears black. Figure 23.16 shows these relationships on an artist's color wheel, a circle in which complementary colors appear as wedges opposite each other.

An object has a particular color for one of two reasons:

- It reflects (or transmits) light of *that* color. Thus, if an object absorbs all wavelengths *except* green, the reflected (or transmitted) light enters our eyes and is interpreted as green.
- It absorbs light of the *complementary* color. Thus, if the object absorbs only red, the *complement* of green, the remaining mixture of reflected (or transmitted) wavelengths enters our eyes and is interpreted as green also.

Table 23.11 lists the color absorbed and the resulting color perceived. (See the Margin Note on the opposite page.) ◆

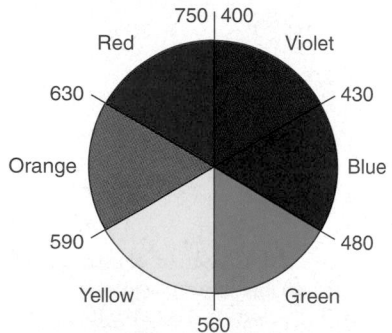

Figure 23.16 An artist's wheel. Primary (red, blue, and yellow) and secondary (violet, green, and orange) colors are shown, with approximate wavelength ranges. Note that any two primary colors form a secondary color that is the complementary color of the third primary color.

Table 23.11 Relation Between Absorbed and Observed Colors

Absorbed Color	λ (nm)	Observed Color	λ (nm)
Violet	400	Green-yellow	560
Blue	450	Yellow	600
Blue-green	490	Red	620
Yellow-green	570	Violet	410
Yellow	580	Dark blue	430
Orange	600	Blue	450
Red	650	Green	520

Splitting of *d* Orbitals in an Octahedral Field of Ligands The crystal field model explains that the properties of complexes result from the splitting of *d*-orbital energies, which arises from electrostatic interactions between metal ion and ligands. The model assumes that a complex ion forms as a result of *electrostatic attractions between the metal cation and the negative charge of the ligands.* This negative charge is either partial in a polar neutral ligand like NH_3 or full in an anionic ligand like Cl^-. The ligands approach the metal ion along the *x*, *y*, and *z* axes, which minimizes the overall energy of the system.

Picture what happens as the ligands approach. Figure 23.17A shows six ligands moving toward a metal ion to form an octahedral complex. Let's see how the various metal *d* orbitals are affected as the complex forms. As the ligands approach, their electron pairs repel electrons in the five *d* orbitals of the metal. In the isolated metal ion, the *d* orbitals have equal energies despite their different orientations. In the electrostatic field of ligands, however, the *d* electrons are *repelled unequally because they have different orientations.* Since the ligands move along the *x*, *y*, and *z* axes, they approach *directly toward* the lobes of the $d_{x^2-y^2}$ and d_{z^2} orbitals (Figure 23.17B and C) but *between* the lobes of the d_{xy}, d_{xz}, and d_{yz} orbitals (Figure 23.17D to F). As a result, electrons in the $d_{x^2-y^2}$ and d_{z^2} orbitals experience *stronger* repulsions than those in the d_{xy}, d_{xz}, and d_{yz} orbitals.

The Colors of Spring and Fall In the spring and summer, leaves contain high concentrations of the photosynthetic pigment *chlorophyll* and lower concentrations of other pigments called *xanthophylls.* Chlorophyll absorbs strongly in the blue and red regions, reflecting mostly green wavelengths into your eyes. In the fall, photosynthesis slows, so the leaf no longer makes chlorophyll. Gradually, the green color fades as the chlorophyll decomposes, revealing the xanthophylls that were present all along but masked by the chlorophyll. Xanthophylls absorb green and blue strongly, reflecting the bright yellows and reds of autumn.

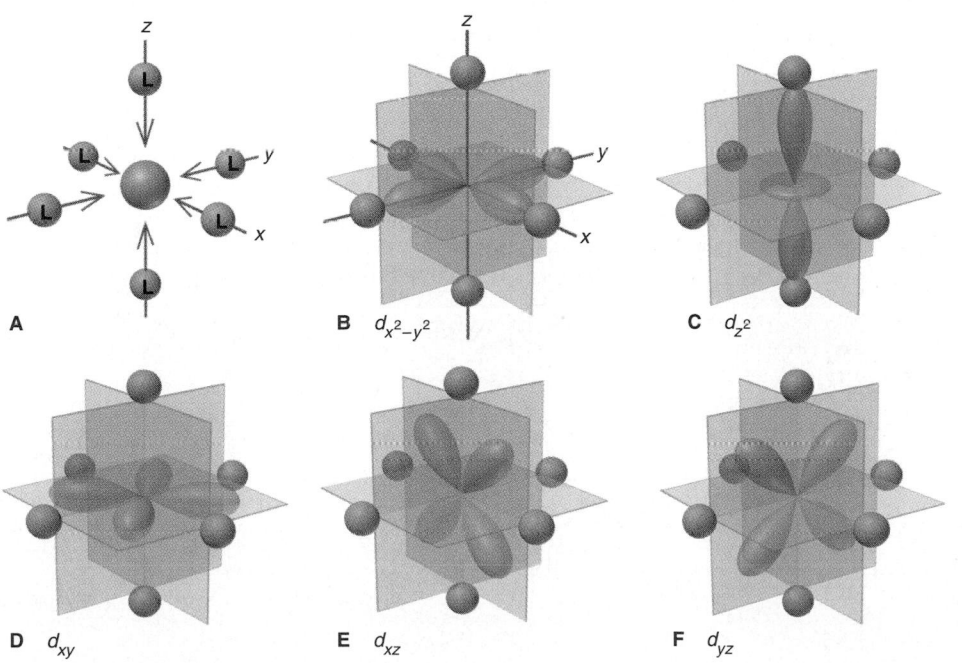

A   **B** $d_{x^2-y^2}$ **C** d_{z^2}

D d_{xy} **E** d_{xz} **F** d_{yz}

Figure 23.17 **The five *d* orbitals in an octahedral field of ligands.** The direction of ligand approach influences the strength of repulsions of electrons in the various metal *d* orbitals. **A,** We assume that ligands approach a metal ion along the three linear axes in an octahedral orientation. **B** and **C,** Lobes of the $d_{x^2-y^2}$ and d_{z^2} orbitals lie *directly in line* with the approaching ligands, so repulsions are stronger. **D** to **F,** Lobes of the d_{xy}, d_{xz}, and d_{yz} orbitals lie *between* the approaching ligands, so repulsions are weaker.

Figure 23.18 **Splitting of *d*-orbital energies by an octahedral field of ligands.** Electrons in the *d* orbitals of the free metal ion experience an *average* net repulsion in the negative ligand field that increases all *d*-orbital energies. Electrons in the d_{xy}, d_{yz}, and d_{xz} orbitals, which form the t_{2g} set, are repelled less than those in the $d_{x^2-y^2}$ and d_{z^2} orbitals, which form the e_g set. The energy difference between these two sets is the crystal field splitting energy, Δ.

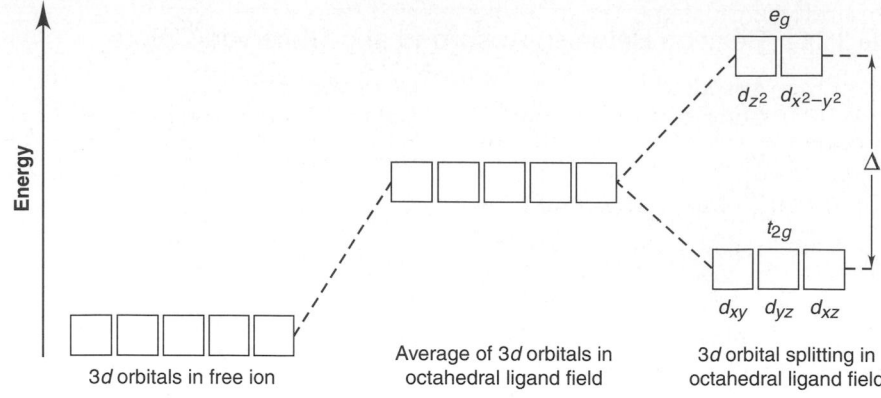

An energy diagram of the orbitals shows that all five *d* orbitals are higher in energy than in the free metal ion because of repulsions from the approaching ligands, but *the orbital energies split with two d orbitals higher than the other three* (Figure 23.18). The two higher energy orbitals are called **e_g orbitals,** and the three lower energy ones are **t_{2g} orbitals.** (These designations refer to features of the orbitals that need not concern us here.)

The splitting of orbital energies is called the *crystal field effect*, and the difference in energy between the e_g and t_{2g} sets of orbitals is the **crystal field splitting energy (Δ).** Different ligands create crystal fields of different strength and, thus, cause the *d*-orbital energies to split to different extents. **Strong-field ligands** lead to a *larger* splitting energy (larger Δ); **weak-field ligands** lead to a *smaller* splitting energy (smaller Δ). For instance, H_2O is a weak-field ligand and CN^- is a strong-field ligand (Figure 23.19). The magnitude of Δ relates directly to the color and magnetic properties of complexes.

Figure 23.19 **The effect of the ligand on splitting energy.** Ligands interacting strongly with metal-ion *d* orbitals, such as CN^-, produce a larger Δ than those interacting weakly, such as H_2O.

Explaining the Colors of Transition Metal Complexes The remarkably diverse colors of coordination compounds are determined by the energy difference (Δ) between the t_{2g} and e_g orbital sets in their complex ions. When the ion absorbs light in the visible range, electrons are excited ("jump") from the lower energy t_{2g} level to the higher e_g level. Recall that the *difference* between two electronic energy levels in the ion is equal to the energy (and inversely related to the wavelength) of the absorbed photon:

$$\Delta E_{electron} = E_{photon} = h\nu = hc/\lambda$$

Since only certain wavelengths of the incoming white light are absorbed, the substance has a color.

Consider the $[Ti(H_2O)_6]^{3+}$ ion, which appears purple in aqueous solution (Figure 23.20). The hydrated Ti^{3+} is a d^1 ion, with the *d* electron in one of the three lower energy t_{2g} orbitals. The energy difference (Δ) between the t_{2g} and e_g orbitals in this ion corresponds to the energy of photons spanning the

Figure 23.20 **The color of $[Ti(H_2O)_6]^{3+}$. A,** The hydrated Ti^{3+} ion is purple in aqueous solution. **B,** An absorption spectrum shows that incoming wavelengths corresponding to green and yellow light are absorbed, whereas other wavelengths are transmitted. **C,** An orbital diagram depicts the colors absorbed in the excitation of the *d* electron to the higher level.

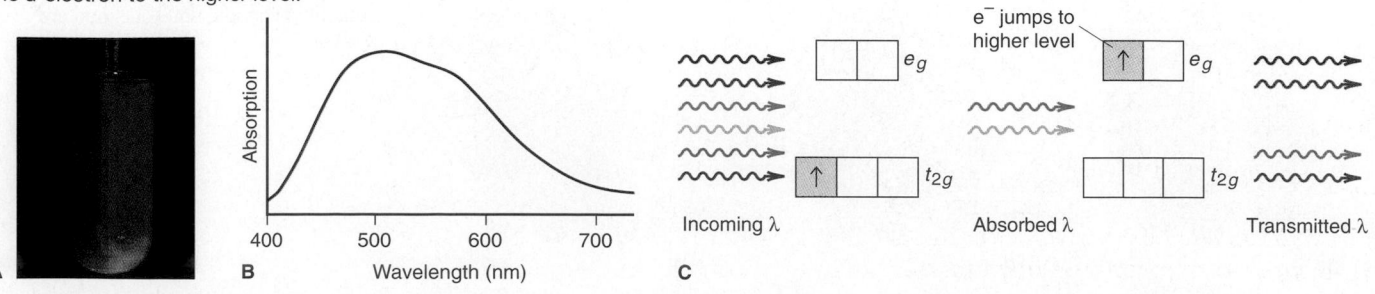

green and yellow range. When white light shines on the solution, these colors of light are absorbed, and the electron jumps to one of the e_g orbitals. Red, blue, and violet light are transmitted, so the solution appears purple.

Absorption spectra show the wavelengths absorbed by a given metal ion with different ligands and by different metal ions with the same ligand. From such data, we relate the energy of the absorbed light to the Δ values, and two important observations emerge:

1. *For a given ligand, the color depends on the oxidation state of the metal ion.* A solution of $[V(H_2O)_6]^{2+}$ ion is violet, and a solution of $[V(H_2O)_6]^{3+}$ ion is yellow (Figure 23.21A).
2. *For a given metal ion, the color depends on the ligand.* Even a single ligand substitution can have a major effect on the wavelengths absorbed and, thus, the color, as you can see in the two Cr^{3+} complex ions in Figure 23.21B.

Observation 2 allows us to rank ligands into a **spectrochemical series** with regard to their ability to split *d*-orbital energies. An abbreviated series, moving from weak-field ligands (small splitting, small Δ) to strong-field ligands (large splitting, large Δ), is shown in Figure 23.22. Using this series, we can predict the *relative* size of Δ for a series of octahedral complexes of the same metal ion. Although it is difficult to predict the actual color of a given complex, we can determine whether a complex will absorb longer or shorter wavelengths than other complexes in the series.

A

B

Figure 23.21 Effects of the metal oxidation state and of ligand on color. A, Solutions of $[V(H_2O)_6]^{2+}$ (*left*) and $[V(H_2O)_6]^{3+}$ (*right*) ions have different colors. **B,** A change in even a single ligand can influence color. The $[Cr(NH_3)_6]^{3+}$ ion is yellow-orange (*left*), and the $[Cr(NH_3)_5Cl]^{2+}$ ion is purple (*right*).

$$I^- < Cl^- < F^- < OH^- < H_2O < SCN^- < NH_3 < en < NO_2^- < CN^- < CO$$

WEAKER FIELD	STRONGER FIELD
SMALLER Δ	LARGER Δ
LONGER λ	SHORTER λ

Figure 23.22 The spectrochemical series. As the crystal field strength of the ligand increases, the splitting energy (Δ) increases, so shorter wavelengths (λ) of light must be absorbed to excite electrons. Water is usually a weak-field ligand.

Sample Problem 23.5 Ranking Crystal Field Splitting Energies for Complex Ions of a Given Metal

PROBLEM Rank the ions $[Ti(H_2O)_6]^{3+}$, $[Ti(NH_3)_6]^{3+}$, and $[Ti(CN)_6]^{3-}$ in terms of the relative value of Δ and of the energy of visible light absorbed.

PLAN The formulas show that titanium's oxidation state is +3 in the three ions. From Figure 23.22, we rank the ligands in terms of crystal field strength: the stronger the ligand, the greater the splitting, and the higher the energy of light absorbed.

SOLUTION The ligand field strength is in the order $CN^- > NH_3 > H_2O$, so the relative size of Δ and energy of light absorbed is

$$Ti(CN)_6^{3-} > Ti(NH_3)_6^{3+} > Ti(H_2O)_6^{3+}$$

Follow-up Problem 23.5 Which complex ion absorbs visible light of higher energy, $[V(H_2O)_6]^{3+}$ or $[V(NH_3)_6]^{3+}$?

Explaining the Magnetic Properties of Transition Metal Complexes The splitting of energy levels influences magnetic properties by affecting the number of *unpaired* electrons in the metal ion's *d* orbitals. Based on Hund's rule, electrons occupy orbitals one at a time as long as orbitals of equal energy are

No field

Maximum number of
unpaired electrons

↑	↑	↑	↑	↑

A Free Mn^{2+} ion

Weak-field ligand

High-spin complex

$E_{pairing} > \Delta$

e_g | ↑ | ↑ |

Δ

t_{2g} | ↑ | ↑ | ↑ |

B $[Mn(H_2O)_6]^{2+}$

Strong-field ligand

Low-spin complex

$E_{pairing} < \Delta$

e_g | | |

Δ

t_{2g} | ↑↓ | ↑↓ | ↑ |

C $[Mn(CN)_6]^{4-}$

Figure 23.23 High-spin and low-spin complex ions of Mn^{2+}. A, Free Mn^{2+} has five unpaired electrons. **B,** Bonded to weak-field ligands (smaller Δ), such as H_2O, Mn^{2+} still has five unpaired electrons (high spin). **C,** Bonded to strong-field ligands (larger Δ), such as CN^-, Mn^{2+} has only one unpaired electron (low spin).

available. When all lower energy orbitals are half-filled, the next electron can
• enter a half-filled orbital and pair up by overcoming a repulsive *pairing energy ($E_{pairing}$)*, or
• enter an empty, higher energy orbital by overcoming the crystal field splitting energy (Δ).

Thus, *the relative sizes of $E_{pairing}$ and Δ determine the occupancy of the d-orbitals.* This, in turn, determines the number of unpaired electrons and, thus, the paramagnetic behavior of the ion.

As an example, the isolated Mn^{2+} ion ([Ar] d^5) has five unpaired electrons in $3d$ orbitals of equal energy (Figure 23.23A). In an octahedral field of ligands, the orbital energies split. The orbital occupancy is affected by the ligand in one of two ways:
• *Weak-field ligands and high-spin complexes.* Weak-field ligands, such as H_2O in $[Mn(H_2O)_6]^{2+}$, cause a *small* splitting energy, so it takes *less* energy for d electrons to jump to the e_g set than to pair up in the t_{2g} set. Therefore, the d electrons remain unpaired (Figure 23.23B). Thus, with weak-field ligands, the pairing energy is *greater* than the splitting energy ($E_{pairing} > \Delta$), so *the number of unpaired electrons in the complex ion is the **same** as in the free ion.* Weak-field ligands create **high-spin complexes,** those with the *maximum* number of unpaired electrons.
• *Strong-field ligands and low-spin complexes.* In contrast, strong-field ligands, such as CN^- in $[Mn(CN)_6]^{4-}$, cause a *large* splitting of the d-orbital energies, so it takes *more* energy for electrons to jump to the e_g set than to pair up in the t_{2g} set (Figure 23.23C). With strong-field ligands, the pairing energy is *smaller* than the splitting energy ($E_{pairing} < \Delta$), so *the number of unpaired electrons in the complex ion is **less** than in the free ion.* Strong-field ligands create **low-spin complexes,** those with *fewer* unpaired electrons.

Orbital diagrams for the d^1 through d^9 ions in octahedral complexes show that high-spin/low-spin options are possible only for d^4, d^5, d^6, and d^7 ions (Figure 23.24). With three lower energy t_{2g} orbitals available, the d^1, d^2, and d^3 ions always form high-spin complexes because there is no need to pair up. Similarly, d^8 and d^9 ions always form high-spin complexes because the t_{2g} set is filled with six electrons, so the two e_g orbitals *must* have either two (d^8) or one (d^9) unpaired electron.

Sample Problem 23.6 Identifying Complex Ions as High Spin or Low Spin

PROBLEM Iron(II) forms an essential complex in hemoglobin. For each octahedral complex ion $[Fe(H_2O)_6]^{2+}$ and $[Fe(CN)_6]^{4-}$, draw an orbital splitting diagram, predict the number of unpaired electrons, and identify the ion as low or high spin.

PLAN The Fe^{2+} electron configuration gives us the number of d electrons, and the spectrochemical series in Figure 23.22 shows the relative strengths of the two ligands. We draw the diagrams, separating the t_{2g} and e_g sets by a greater distance for the strong-field ligand. Then we add electrons, noting that a weak-field ligand gives the *maximum* number of unpaired electrons and a high-spin complex, whereas a strong-field ligand leads to pairing and a low-spin complex.

SOLUTION Fe^{2+} has the [Ar] d^6 configuration. According to Figure 23.22, H_2O produces smaller splitting than CN^-. The diagrams are shown in the margin. The $[Fe(H_2O)_6]^{2+}$ has four unpaired electrons (high spin), and the $[Fe(CN)_6]^{4-}$ has no unpaired electrons (low spin).

COMMENT 1. H_2O is a weak-field ligand, so it almost always forms high-spin complexes. **2.** These results are correct, but we cannot confidently predict the spin of a complex without having actual values for Δ and $E_{pairing}$. **3.** Cyanide ions and carbon monoxide are highly toxic because they interact with the iron cations in proteins.

Follow-up Problem 23.6 How many unpaired electrons do you expect for $[Mn(CN)_6]^{3-}$? Is this a high-spin or low-spin complex ion?

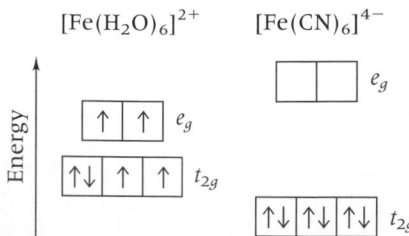

Energy

$[Fe(H_2O)_6]^{2+}$ $[Fe(CN)_6]^{4-}$

| | | e_g

| ↑ | ↑ | e_g

| ↑↓ | ↑ | ↑ | t_{2g}

| ↑↓ | ↑↓ | ↑↓ | t_{2g}

Crystal Field Splitting in Tetrahedral and Square Planar Complexes Four ligands around a metal ion also cause *d*-orbital splitting, but the magnitude and pattern of the splitting depend on whether the ligands are in a tetrahedral or a square planar arrangement.

• *Tetrahedral complexes.* With the ligands approaching from the corners of a tetrahedron, none of the five *d* orbitals is directly in their paths (Figure 23.25A). Thus, splitting of *d*-orbital energies is *less* in a tetrahedral complex than in an octahedral complex of the same ligands:

$$\Delta_{\text{tetrahedral}} < \Delta_{\text{octahedral}}$$

Minimal repulsions arise if the ligands approach the d_{xy}, d_{yz}, and d_{xz} orbitals closer than they approach the d_{z^2} and $d_{x^2-y^2}$ orbitals. This situation is the *inverse of the octahedral case,* and the relative *d*-orbital energies are also reversed: the d_{xy}, d_{yz}, and d_{xz} orbitals become *higher* in energy than the d_{z^2} and $d_{x^2-y^2}$ orbitals. *Only high-spin tetrahedral complexes are known* because the magnitude of Δ is so small.

• *Square planar complexes.* The effects of the ligand field in the square planar case are easier to picture if we imagine starting with an octahedral geometry and then remove the two *z*-axis ligands (Figure 23.25B). With no interactions along the *z* axis, the d_{z^2} orbital energy decreases greatly, and the d_{xz} and d_{yz} orbital energies also decrease. As a result, the two *d* orbitals in the *xy* plane interact most strongly with the ligands, and since the $d_{x^2-y^2}$ orbital has its lobes *on* the axes, its energy is highest. As a result of this splitting pattern, square planar complexes with d^8 ions, such as $[\text{PdCl}_4]^{2-}$, are diamagnetic because four pairs of *d* electrons fill the four lowest orbitals. Indeed, *square planar complexes are low spin.*

A final word about bonding theories may be helpful. As you have seen with several other topics, no one model is satisfactory in every respect. The VB approach offers a simple picture of bond formation but does not even attempt to explain color. The crystal field model predicts color and magnetic behavior beautifully but treats the metal ion and ligands as points of opposite charge and thus offers no insight about the covalent nature of metal-ligand bonding. Despite its complexity, chemists now rely on a more refined model, called *ligand field–molecular orbital theory,* which combines aspects of the previous two models with MO theory (Section 11.3). We won't explore it here, but it is a powerful predictive tool, yielding information on bond properties that result from the overlap of metal ion and ligand orbitals as well as information on the spectral and magnetic properties that result from metal *d*-orbital splitting.

In addition to their important chemical applications, complexes of the transition elements play vital roles in living systems, as the following Chemical Connections essay describes.

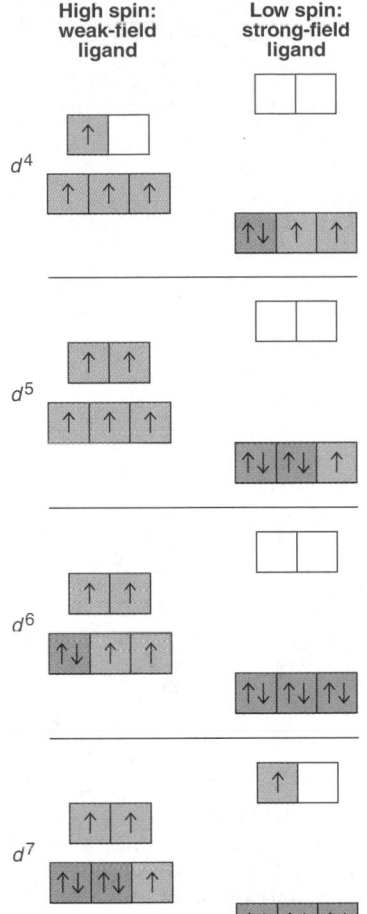

Figure 23.24 **Orbital occupancy for high- and low-spin complexes of d^4 through d^7 metal ions.**

Figure 23.25 **Splitting of *d*-orbital energies by a tetrahedral field and a square planar field of ligands. A,** Electrons in d_{xy}, d_{yz}, and d_{xz} orbitals experience greater repulsions than those in $d_{x^2-y^2}$ and d_{z^2}, so the tetrahedral splitting pattern is the inverse of the octahedral pattern. **B,** In a square planar field, the energies of d_{xz}, d_{yz}, and especially d_{z^2} orbitals decrease relative to the octahedral pattern.

Chemical Connections   Chemistry in Nutritional Biochemistry

Transition Metals as Essential Dietary Trace Elements

Living things consist primarily of water and complex organic compounds of four key elements: carbon, oxygen, hydrogen, and nitrogen. All known organisms also contain seven other elements, known as *macro*nutrients because they occur in fairly high concentrations. In order of increasing atomic number, they are sodium, magnesium, phosphorus, sulfur, chlorine, potassium, and calcium. In addition, organisms contain a surprisingly large number of elements in much lower concentrations, and most of these *micro*nutrients, or *trace elements*, are transition metals.

With the exception of scandium and titanium, all of the Period 4 transition elements are essential for organisms, and plants require molybdenum (from Period 5) as well. Within the organism, the transition metal ion usually occurs at a bend of a protein chain covalently bonded to surrounding amino acid groups whose N and O atoms act as ligands. Despite the structural complexity of biomolecules, the principles of bonding and *d*-orbital splitting are the same as in simple inorganic systems. Table 23.A lists the Period 4 transition metals known, or thought, to be essential in human nutrition. We focus here on iron and zinc.

Iron plays a crucial role in oxygen transport in all vertebrates. The oxygen-transporting protein hemoglobin (Figure 23.A, *A*) consists of four protein chains called *globins*, each cradling the iron-containing complex *heme*. Heme is a porphyrin, a complex derived from a metal ion and the tetradentate ring ligand known as *porphin*. Iron(II) is centered in the plane of the porphin ring through coordinate covalent bonds with four N lone pairs, resulting in a square planar complex. When heme is bound in hemoglobin (Figure 23.A, *B*), the complex is *octahedral*, with the fifth ligand of iron(II) being an N atom from a nearby amino acid (histidine), and the sixth an O atom from either an O_2 (shown) or an H_2O molecule.

Hemoglobin exists in two forms, depending on the nature of the sixth ligand. In the blood vessels of the lungs, where O_2 concentration is high, heme binds O_2 to form *oxyhemoglobin*, which is transported in the arteries to O_2-depleted tissues. There, the O_2 is released and replaced by an H_2O molecule to form *deoxyhemoglobin*, which is transported in the veins back to the lungs. Since H_2O is a weak-field ligand, the d^6 Fe^{2+} ion in deoxyhemoglobin is part of a high-spin complex. Because of the relatively small *d*-orbital splitting, deoxyhemoglobin absorbs light at the red (low-energy) end of the spectrum and looks purplish blue, which accounts for the dark color of venous blood. On the other hand, O_2 is a strong-field ligand, so it increases the splitting energy. For this reason, oxyhemoglobin absorbs at the blue (high-energy) end of the spectrum, which accounts for the bright-red color of arterial blood.

The position of the Fe^{2+} ion relative to the plane of the porphin ring also depends on this sixth ligand. Bound to O_2, Fe^{2+} is *in* the porphin plane; bound to H_2O, it moves *out of* the plane slightly. This tiny (~ 70 pm $= 7 \times 10^{-11}$ m) change in Fe^{2+} position on release or attachment of O_2 influences the shape of its globin chain, which in turn alters the shape of a neighboring globin chain, triggering the release or attachment of *its* O_2, and so on to the other two globin chains. The very survival of vertebrate life is the result of this cooperative "teamwork" by the four globin chains because it allows hemoglobin to pick up O_2 rapidly from the lungs and unload it rapidly in the tissues.

Table 23.A   Some Transition Metal Trace Elements in Humans

Element	Biomolecule Containing Element	Function of Biomolecule
Vanadium	Protein (?)	Redox couple in fat metabolism (?)
Chromium	Glucose tolerance factor	Glucose utilization
Manganese	Isocitrate dehydrogenase	Cell respiration
Iron	Hemoglobin and myoglobin Cytochrome *c* Catalase	Oxygen transport Cell respiration; ATP formation Decomposition of H_2O_2
Cobalt	Cobalamin (vitamin B_{12})	Development of red blood cells
Copper	Ceruloplasmin Cytochrome oxidase	Hemoglobin synthesis Cell respiration; ATP formation
Zinc	Carbonic anhydrase Carboxypeptidase A Alcohol dehydrogenase	Elimination of CO_2 Protein digestion Metabolism of ethanol

Figure 23.A Hemoglobin and the octahedral complex in heme. A, The structure of hemoglobin consists of four protein chains, each with a bound heme. **B,** In oxyhemoglobin, the octahedral complex in heme has iron(II) at the center surrounded by the four N atoms of the porphin ring, a fifth N from histidine *(below)*, and an O_2 molecule *(above)*. (Copyright Irving Geis; The estate of Irving Geis)

Carbon monoxide is highly toxic because it binds to the Fe^{2+} ion in heme about 200 times more tightly than O_2, thereby eliminating that heme group from functioning in the circulation. Like O_2, CO is a strong-field ligand and produces a bright red, "healthy" look in the individual. Because heme binding is an equilibrium process, CO poisoning can be reversed by breathing extremely high concentrations of O_2, which effectively displaces CO from the heme:

$$\text{Heme—CO} + O_2 \rightleftharpoons \text{Heme—}O_2 + CO$$

Porphin rings are among the most common biological ligands. Chlorophyll, the photosynthetic pigment of green plants, is a porphyrin with Mg^{2+} at the center of the porphin ring, and vitamin B_{12} has Co^{3+} at the center of a very similar ring system. Heme itself is found not only in hemoglobin, but also in several redox proteins involved in energy metabolism (see Chemical Connections, Section 21.7).

The zinc ion occurs in many enzymes, the protein catalysts of cells (see Chemical Connections, Section 16.8). With its d^{10} configuration, Zn^{2+} is typically surrounded tetrahedrally by the N atoms of three amino acid groups, and the fourth position is free to interact with the molecule whose reaction is being catalyzed (Figure 23.B). In every case studied, the Zn^{2+} ion acts as a Lewis acid, accepting a lone pair from the reactant as a key step in the catalytic process. Consider the enzyme carbonic anhydrase, which catalyzes the essential reaction between H_2O and CO_2 during respiration:

$$CO_2(g) + H_2O(l) \rightleftharpoons H^+(aq) + HCO_3^-(aq)$$

The Zn^{2+} ion at the active site binds three histidine N atoms and the H_2O reactant as the fourth ligand. By withdrawing electron density from the O—H bonds, the Zn^{2+} makes the H_2O acidic enough to lose a proton. In the rate-determining step, the resulting bound OH^- ion attacks the partially positive C atom of CO_2 much more vigorously than could the lone pair of a free water molecule, so the reaction rate is higher. One reason the Cd^{2+} ion is toxic is that it competes with Zn^{2+} for fitting into the carbonic anhydrase active site.

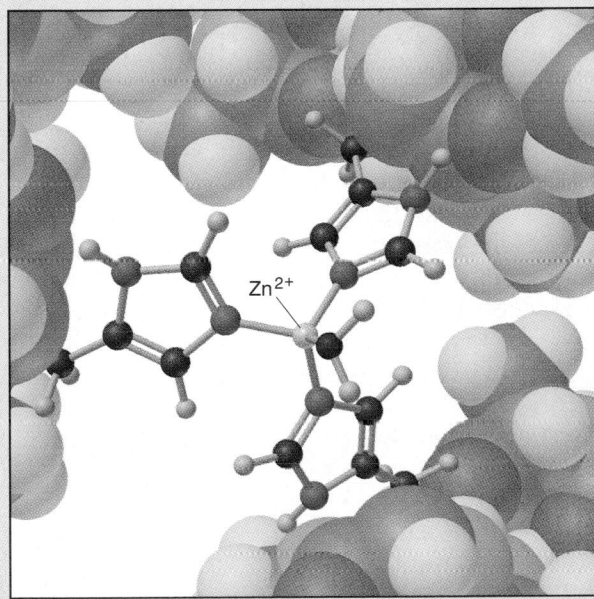

Figure 23.B The tetrahedral Zn^{2+} complex in carbonic anhydrase.

Section Summary

Valence bond theory pictures bonding in complex ions as arising from coordinate covalent bonding between Lewis bases (ligands) and Lewis acids (metal ions). Ligand lone pairs occupy hybridized metal-ion orbitals to form complexes with characteristic shapes. Crystal field theory explains color and magnetism of complexes. As the result of a surrounding field of negative ligands, the metal d-orbital energies split. This crystal field splitting energy (Δ) depends on the charge of the metal ion and the crystal field strength of the ligand. Its magnitude influences the energy of the photon absorbed (color) and the number of unpaired d electrons (paramagnetism). Strong-field ligands create a large Δ and produce low-spin complexes that absorb light of higher energy (shorter λ); the reverse is true of weak-field ligands. Several transition metals, such as iron and zinc, are essential dietary trace elements that function in complexes within proteins.

Chapter Perspective

Our study of the transition elements, a large group of metals with many essential industrial and biological roles, points up once again that macroscopic properties, such as color and mag- *netism, have their roots at the atomic and molecular level. In the next and final chapter, we explore the core of the atom and learn how we can apply its enormous power.*

The following learning objectives, with section and/or sample problem (SP) numbers in parentheses, can help focus your study:

Understand These Concepts

1. The position of the d- and f-block elements and the general forms of their atomic and ionic electron configurations (Section 23.1)

2. How atomic size, ionization energy, and electronegativity vary across a period and down a group of transition elements and how these trends differ from those of the main-group elements; why the densities of Period 6 transition elements are so high (Section 23.1)

3. Why the transition elements often have multiple oxidation states and why the +2 state is common (Section 23.1)

4. Why metallic behavior (prevalence of ionic bonding and basic oxides) decreases as oxidation state increases (Section 23.1)

5. Why many transition metal compounds are colored and paramagnetic (Section 23.1)

6. The common +3 oxidation state of lanthanides and the similarity in their M^{3+} radii; the radioactivity of actinides (Section 23.2)

7. How valence-state electronegativity explains why oxides become more covalent and acidic as the O.N. of the metal increases (Section 23.3)

8. Why Cr and Mn oxoanions are stronger oxidizing agents in acidic than in basic solutions (Section 23.3)

9. The role silver halides play in black-and-white photography (Section 23.3)

10. How the high density and low melting point of mercury account for its common uses; toxicity of organomercury compounds (Section 23.3)

11. The coordination numbers, geometries, and ligand structures of complex ions (Section 23.4)

12. How coordination compounds are named and their formulas written (Section 23.4)

13. How Werner correlated the properties and structures of coordination compounds (Section 23.4)

14. The types of constitutional isomerism (coordination and linkage) and stereoisomerism (geometric and optical) of coordination compounds (Section 23.4)

15. How valence bond theory uses hybridization to account for the shapes of octahedral, square planar, and tetrahedral complexes (Section 23.5)
16. How crystal field theory explains that approaching ligands cause *d*-orbital energies to split (Section 23.5)
17. How the relative crystal-field strength of ligands (spectrochemical series) affects the *d*-orbital splitting energy (Δ) (Section 23.5)
18. How the magnitude of Δ accounts for the energy of light absorbed and, thus, the color of complexes (Section 23.5)
19. How the relative sizes of pairing energy and Δ determine the occupancy of *d* orbitals and, thus, the magnetic properties of complexes (Section 23.5)
20. How *d*-orbital splitting in tetrahedral and square planar complexes differs from that in octahedral complexes (Section 23.5)

Master These Skills

1. Writing electron configurations of transition elements and ions (SP 23.1)
2. Using an orbital box diagram to determine the number of unpaired electrons in a transition-metal atom or ion (SP 23.2)
3. Recognizing the structural components of complex ions (Section 23.4)
4. Naming and writing formulas of coordination compounds (SP 23.3)
5. Determining the types of isomerism in complexes (SP 23.4)
6. Correlating complex-ion shape with the hybrid orbitals of the central metal ion (Section 23.5)
7. Using the spectrochemical series to rank complex ions in terms of the energy of light absorbed (SP 23.5)
8. Using the spectrochemical series to determine if a complex is high or low spin (SP 23.6)

For Review and Reference

Key Terms

transition elements
Section 23.1
lanthanide contraction
Section 23.2
lanthanides
actinides
inner transition elements
Section 23.4
coordination compound

complex ion
ligand
counter ion
coordination number
donor atom
chelate
isomer
constitutional (structural) isomer

coordination isomer
linkage isomer
stereoisomer
geometric *(cis-trans)* isomer
optical isomer
Section 23.5
coordinate covalent bond
crystal field theory
e_g orbital

t_{2g} orbital
crystal field splitting energy (Δ)
strong-field ligand
weak-field ligand
spectrochemical series
high-spin complex
low-spin complex

Highlighted Figures and Tables

These figures (F) and tables (T) provide a quick review of key ideas.
T23.1 Orbital occupancy of Period 4 transition metals (p. 1003)
F23.3 Trends in atomic properties of Period 4 elements (p. 1004)
F23.4 Trends in atomic properties and density in the *d*-block elements (p. 1005)
T23.2 Oxidation states and *d*-orbital occupancy of Period 4 transition metals (p. 1006)
T23.6 Coordination numbers and shapes of some complex ions (p. 1017)

T23.7 Common ligands in coordination compounds (p. 1018)
T23.8 Names of neutral and anionic ligands (p. 1019)
T23.9 Names of metals in complex anions (p. 1019)
F23.10 Isomerism in coordination compounds (p. 1021)
F23.17 *d* Orbitals in an octahedral field (p. 1027)
F23.18 Splitting of *d*-orbital energies by an octahedral field of ligands (p. 1028)
F23.22 The spectrochemical series (p. 1029)
F23.24 High-spin and low-spin complexes (p. 1031)
F23.25 Splitting of *d*-orbital energies by tetrahedral and square planar fields of ligands (p. 1031)

Answers to Follow-up Problems

23.1 (a) Ag^+: $4d^{10}$; (b) Cd^{2+}: $4d^{10}$; (c) Ir^{3+}: $5d^6$
23.2 Three; Er^{3+} is [Xe] $4f^{11}$:

$6s$ $4f$ $5d$ $6p$

23.3 (a) Pentaaquabromochromium(III) chloride;
(b) $Ba_3[Co(CN)_6]_2$
23.4 Two sets of *cis-trans* isomers, and the two *cis* isomers are optical isomers.

23.5 Both metal ions are V^{3+}; $NH_3 > H_2O$, so $[V(NH_3)_6]^{3+}$ absorbs light of higher energy.
23.6 The metal ion is Mn^{3+}: [Ar] d^4. $[Mn(CN)_6]^{3-}$

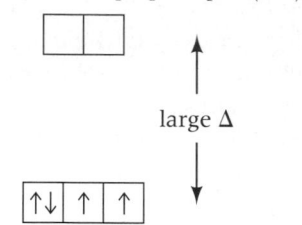

large Δ

Two unpaired d electrons; low spin

Problems

Problems with a **colored** number are answered at the back of the text. Problem sections match the text and provide the number(s) of relevant sample problems. Most offer concept review questions, paired skill-building exercises, and problems in a relevant context. Following these are comprehensive problems based on material from any section and/or previous chapter.

Note: In the problem set for this chapter, the term *electron configuration* refers to the condensed, ground-state electron configuration.

An Overview of Transition Element Properties
(Sample Problem 23.1)

■ Concept Review Questions

23.1 How is the n value of the d sublevel of a transition element atom related to the period number of the element?
23.2 (a) Write the general electron configuration of a transition element in Period 5.
(b) Write the general electron configuration of a transition element in Period 6.
23.3 What is the general rule about the order in which electrons are removed from a transition metal atom when an ion is formed? Give an example from Group 5B(5). Name two types of measurements that can be used to study ion electron configurations.
23.4 What is the maximum number of unpaired d electrons that an atom or ion can possess? Give an example of an atom and an ion that have this number.

23.5 How does the variation in atomic size across a transition series contrast with the change across the main-group elements of the same period? Why?
23.6 (a) What is the lanthanide contraction?
(b) How does it affect atomic size down a group of transition elements?
(c) How does it influence the densities of the Period 6 transition elements?
23.7 (a) What is the range in electronegativity values across the first ($3d$) transition series?
(b) What is the range across the fourth period of main-group elements?
(c) Explain the difference between the two ranges.
23.8 (a) Explain the major difference between the number of oxidation states of transition elements and that of most main-group elements.
(b) Why is the +2 oxidation state so common among transition elements?
23.9 (a) What difference in behavior distinguishes a paramagnetic substance from a diamagnetic one?
(b) Why are paramagnetic ions common among the transition elements but not the main-group elements?
(c) Why are colored solutions of metal ions common among the transition elements but not the main-group elements?

■ Skill-Building Exercises (paired)

23.10 Using the periodic table to locate the element, write the electron configuration of (a) V; (b) Y; (c) Hg.

23.11 Using the periodic table to locate the element, write the electron configuration of (a) Ru; (b) Cu; (c) Ni.

23.12 Using the periodic table to locate the element, write the electron configuration of (a) Os; (b) Co; (c) Ag.

23.13 Using the periodic table to locate the element, write the electron configuration of (a) Zn; (b) Mn; (c) Re.

23.14 Give the electron configuration and the number of unpaired electrons in each of the following ions: (a) Sc^{3+}; (b) Cu^{2+}; (c) Fe^{3+}; (d) Nb^{3+}.

23.15 Give the electron configuration and the number of unpaired electrons in each of the following ions: (a) Cr^{3+}; (b) Ti^{4+}; (c) Co^{3+}; (d) Ta^{2+}.

23.16 What is the highest possible oxidation state for each of the following: (a) Ta; (b) Zr; (c) Mn?

23.17 What is the highest possible oxidation state for each of the following: (a) Nb; (b) Y; (c) Tc?

23.18 Which transition metals have a maximum oxidation state of $+6$?

23.19 Which transition metals have a maximum oxidation state of $+4$?

23.20 In which compound does Cr exhibit greater metallic behavior, CrF_2 or CrF_6? Explain.

23.21 VF_5 is a liquid that boils at 48°C, whereas VF_3 is a solid that melts above 800°C. Explain this difference in properties.

23.22 Is it more difficult to oxidize Cr or Mo? Explain.

23.23 Is MnO_4^- or ReO_4^- the stronger oxidizing agent? Explain.

23.24 Which oxide, CrO_3 or CrO, forms a more acidic aqueous solution? Explain.

23.25 Which oxide, Mn_2O_3 or Mn_2O_7, displays more basic behavior? Explain.

■ **Problems in Context**

23.26 The green patina of the copper-alloyed roofs of old buildings shows the result of the corrosion (oxidation) of copper in the presence of O_2, H_2O, and CO_2. In contrast, silver and gold—the other members of Group 1B(11)—are resistant to reaction with these atmospheric components. Corrosion of copper and silver in the presence of sulfur and its compounds leads to the familiar tarnishing of these metals. In contrast, gold is the only metal that does not react with sulfur. This pattern is markedly different from that in Group 1A(1), where ease of oxidation increases down the group. What causes the different patterns in the two groups?

The Inner Transition Elements

(Sample Problem 23.2)

■ **Concept Review Questions**

23.27 What atomic property of the lanthanides leads to their remarkably similar chemical properties?

23.28 (a) What is the maximum number of unpaired electrons exhibited by an ion of a lanthanide?
(b) How does this number relate to the occupancy of the $4f$ subshell?

23.29 Which of the actinides are radioactive?

■ **Skill-Building Exercises** *(paired)*

23.30 Write the electron configurations of the following atoms and ions: (a) La; (b) Ce^{3+}; (c) Es; (d) U^{4+}.

23.31 Write the electron configurations of the following atoms and ions: (a) Pm; (b) Lu^{3+}; (c) Th; (d) Fm^{3+}.

23.32 Only a few of the lanthanides show any oxidation state other than the $+3$ state. Two of these, europium (Eu) and terbium (Tb), are found near the middle of the series and can be associated with a half-filled f subshell.
(a) Write the electron configurations of Eu^{2+}, Eu^{3+}, and Eu^{4+}. Why is Eu^{2+} a common ion for the element whereas Eu^{4+} is unknown?
(b) Write the electron configurations of Tb^{2+}, Tb^{3+}, and Tb^{4+}. Do you expect terbium to show a $+2$ or a $+4$ oxidation state? Explain.

23.33 Cerium (Ce) and ytterbium (Yb) also exhibit other oxidation states in addition to the $+3$ state.
(a) Write the electron configurations of Ce^{2+}, Ce^{3+}, and Ce^{4+}.
(b) Write the electron configurations of Yb^{2+}, Yb^{3+}, and Yb^{4+}.
(c) In addition to the $3+$ ions, Ce^{4+} and Yb^{2+} are stable. Suggest a reason for this stability.

■ **Problems in Context**

23.34 One of the lanthanides displays the maximum possible number of unpaired electrons both for an atom and for a $3+$ ion. Name the element and give the number of unpaired electrons in the atom and the ion.

Highlights of Selected Transition Metals

■ **Concept Review Questions**

23.35 What is the chemical reason chromium is so useful for decorative plating on metals?

23.36 What is valence-state electronegativity? Use the concept to explain the change in acidity of the oxides of Mn with changing O.N.

23.37 What property does manganese confer to steel?

23.38 What chemical property of silver leads to its use in jewelry and other decorative objects?

23.39 How is a photographic latent image different from the image you see on a piece of developed film?

23.40 Mercury has an unusual physical property and an unusual $1+$ ion. Explain.

■ **Problems in Context**

23.41 When a basic solution of $Cr(OH)_4^-$ ion is slowly acidified, solid $Cr(OH)_3$ first precipitates out and then redissolves as excess acid is added. If $Cr(OH)_4^-$ is actually $Cr(H_2O)_2(OH)_4^-$, write equations that represent these two reactions.

23.42 Use the following data to determine if $Cr^{2+}(aq)$ can be prepared by the reaction of $Cr(s)$ with $Cr^{3+}(aq)$:

$$Cr^{3+}(aq) + e^- \longrightarrow Cr^{2+}(aq) \qquad E^0 = -0.41 \text{ V}$$
$$Cr^{3+}(aq) + 3e^- \longrightarrow Cr(s) \qquad E^0 = -0.74 \text{ V}$$
$$Cr^{2+}(aq) + 2e^- \longrightarrow Cr(s) \qquad E^0 = -0.91 \text{ V}$$

23.43 When solid CrO_3 is dissolved in water, the solution is orange rather than the yellow of H_2CrO_4. How does this observation indicate that CrO_3 is an acidic oxide?

23.44 Solutions of $KMnO_4$ are used commonly in redox titrations. The dark purple MnO_4^- serves as its own indicator, changing to the almost colorless Mn^{2+} as it is reduced. The end point is taken when a pale purple color remains as the $KMnO_4$ solution is added. If a sample that has reached this end point is allowed to stand for a long period of time, the color fades and a suspension of a small amount of brown, muddy MnO_2 appears. Use electrode potentials to explain this result.

Coordination Compounds
(Sample Problems 23.3 and 23.4)

■ Concept Review Questions

23.45 Describe the makeup of a complex ion including the nature of the ligands and their interaction with the central metal ion. Explain how a complex ion can be positive or negative and how it occurs as part of a neutral coordination compound.

23.46 What electronic feature must a donor atom of any ligand possess?

23.47 What is the coordination number of a metal ion in a complex? How does it differ from oxidation number?

23.48 What structural feature is characteristic of a complex described as a chelate?

23.49 What geometries are associated with coordination numbers of 2, 4, and 6?

23.50 What are the coordination numbers of cobalt(III), platinum(II), and platinum(IV) in complexes?

23.51 In what sense is a complex ion the adduct of a Lewis acid-base reaction?

23.52 What does the ending -*ate* signify for a complex ion name?

23.53 In what order are the metal ion and ligands given in the name of a complex ion?

23.54 Is a linkage isomer a type of constitutional isomer or stereoisomer? Explain.

■ Skill-Building Exercises *(paired)*

23.55 Give systematic names for the following formulas:
(a) $[Ni(H_2O)_6]Cl_2$ (b) $[Cr(en)_3](ClO_4)_3$ (c) $K_4[Mn(CN)_6]$

23.56 Give systematic names for the following formulas:
(a) $[Co(NH_3)_4(NO_2)_2]Cl$ (b) $[Cr(NH_3)_6][Cr(CN)_6]$
(c) $K_2[CuCl_4]$

23.57 What are the charge and coordination number of the central metal ion(s) in each compound of Problem 23.55?

23.58 What are the charge and coordination number of the central metal ion(s) in each compound of Problem 23.56?

23.59 Give systematic names for the following formulas:
(a) $K[Ag(CN)_2]$ (b) $Na_2[CdCl_4]$ (c) $[Co(NH_3)_4(H_2O)Br]Br_2$

23.60 Give systematic names for the following formulas:
(a) $K[Pt(NH_3)Cl_5]$ (b) $[Cu(en)(NH_3)_2][Co(en)Cl_4]$
(c) $[Pt(en)_2Br_2](ClO_4)_2$

23.61 What are the charge and coordination number of the central metal ion(s) in each compound of Problem 23.59?

23.62 What are the charge and coordination number of the central metal ion(s) in each compound of Problem 23.60?

23.63 Give formulas corresponding to the following names:
(a) Tetraamminezinc sulfate
(b) Pentaamminechlorochromium(III) chloride
(c) Sodium bis(thiosulfato)argentate(I)

23.64 Give formulas corresponding to the following names:
(a) Dibromobis(ethylenediamine)cobalt(III) sulfate
(b) Hexaamminechromium(III) tetrachlorocuprate(II)
(c) Potassium hexacyanoferrate(II)

23.65 What is the coordination number of the metal ion and the number of individual ions per formula unit in each of the compounds in Problem 23.63?

23.66 What is the coordination number of the metal ion and the number of individual ions per formula unit in each of the compounds in Problem 23.64?

23.67 Give formulas corresponding to the following names:
(a) Hexaaquachromium(III) sulfate
(b) Barium tetrabromoferrate(III)
(c) Bis(ethylenediamine)platinum(II) carbonate

23.68 Give formulas corresponding to the following names:
(a) Potassium tris(oxalato)chromate(III)
(b) Tris(ethylenediamine)cobalt(III) pentacyanoiodomanganate(II)
(c) Bromochlorodiaquadiamminealuminum nitrate

23.69 What is the coordination number of the metal ion and the number of individual ions per formula unit in each of the compounds in Problem 23.67?

23.70 What is the coordination number of the metal ion and the number of individual ions per formula unit in each of the compounds in Problem 23.68?

23.71 Which of the following ligands can participate in linkage isomerism: (a) NO_2^-; (b) SO_2; (c) NO_3^-? Explain with Lewis structures.

23.72 Which of the following ligands can participate in linkage isomerism: (a) SCN^-; (b) $S_2O_3^{2-}$ (thiosulfate); (c) HS^-? Explain with Lewis structures.

23.73 For any of the following that can exist as isomers, state the type of isomerism and draw the structures:
(a) $[Pt(CH_3NH_2)_2Br_2]$ (b) $[Pt(NH_3)_2FCl]$
(c) $[Pt(H_2O)(NH_3)FCl]$

23.74 For any of the following that can exist as isomers, state the type of isomerism and draw the structures:
(a) $[Zn(en)F_2]$ (b) $[Zn(H_2O)(NH_3)FCl]$
(c) $[Pd(CN)_2(OH)_2]^{2-}$

23.75 For any of the following that can exist as isomers, state the type of isomerism and draw the structures:
(a) $[PtCl_2Br_2]^{2-}$ (b) $[Cr(NH_3)_5(NO_2)]^{2+}$ (c) $[Pt(NH_3)_4I_2]^{2+}$

23.76 For any of the following that can exist as isomers, state the type of isomerism and draw the structures:
(a) $[Co(NH_3)_5Cl]Br_2$ (b) $[Pt(CH_3NH_2)_3Cl]Br$
(c) $[Fe(H_2O)_4(NH_3)_2]^{2+}$

■ Problems in Context

23.77 Chromium(III), like cobalt(III), has a coordination number of 6 in many of its complex ions. Compounds are known with the traditional formula $CrCl_3(NH_3)_n$, where $n =$

3 to 6. Which of the compounds has an electrical conductivity in aqueous solution similar to that of an equimolar NaCl solution?

23.78 When $MCl_4(NH_3)_2$ is dissolved in water and treated with $AgNO_3$, two moles of AgCl precipitate immediately for each mole of the compound. What is the coordination number of M in the complex?

23.79 Palladium, like its group neighbor platinum, forms four-coordinate Pd(II) and six-coordinate Pd(IV) complexes. Write modern formulas for the complexes with the following compositions:
(a) $PdK(NH_3)Cl_3$ (b) $PdCl_2(NH_3)_2$
(c) PdK_2Cl_6 (d) $Pd(NH_3)_4Cl_4$

Theoretical Basis for the Bonding and Properties of Complexes

(Sample Problems 23.5 and 23.6)

■ Concept Review Questions

23.80 (a) What is a coordinate covalent bond?
(b) Is it involved when $FeCl_3$ dissolves in water? Explain.
(c) Is it involved when HCl gas dissolves in water? Explain.

23.81 According to valence bond theory, what set of orbitals is used by a Period 4 metal ion in forming
(a) A square planar complex?
(b) A tetrahedral complex?

23.82 A metal ion is described as using a d^2sp^3 set of orbitals in a complex. What is the coordination number of the metal ion and the shape of the complex?

23.83 A complex in solution absorbs green light. What is the color of the solution?

23.84 What *two* possibilities of color absorption by a solution could give rise to an observed blue color?

23.85 (a) What is the crystal field splitting energy, Δ?
(b) How does it arise for an octahedral field of ligands?
(c) How is it different for a tetrahedral field of ligands?

23.86 What is the distinction between a weak-field ligand and a strong-field ligand? Give an example of each.

23.87 Is a complex with the same number of unpaired electrons as the free gaseous metal ion termed high spin or low spin?

23.88 How do the relative magnitudes of $E_{pairing}$ and Δ affect the paramagnetism of a complex?

23.89 Why are there both high-spin and low-spin octahedral complexes but only high-spin tetrahedral complexes?

■ Skill-Building Exercises (paired)

23.90 Give the number of d electrons (n of d^n) for the central metal ion in each of the following species:
(a) $[TiCl_6]^{2-}$ (b) $K[AuCl_4]$ (c) $[RhCl_6]^{3-}$

23.91 Give the number of d electrons (n of d^n) for the central metal ion in each of the following species:
(a) $[Cr(H_2O)_6](ClO_3)_2$ (b) $[Mn(CN)_6]^{2-}$
(c) $[Ru(NO)(en)_2Cl]Br$

23.92 Give the number of d electrons (n of d^n) for the central metal ion in each of the following species:
(a) $Ca[IrF_6]$ (b) $[HgI_4]^{2-}$ (c) $[Co(EDTA)]^{2-}$

23.93 Give the number of d electrons (n of d^n) for the central metal ion in each of the following species:

(a) $[Ru(NH_3)_5Cl]SO_4$ (b) $Na_2[Os(CN)_6]$
(c) $[Co(NH_3)_4CO_3I]$

23.94 Sketch the orientation of the orbitals relative to the ligands in an octahedral complex to explain the splitting and the relative energies of the d_{xy} and the $d_{x^2-y^2}$ orbitals.

23.95 The two e_g orbitals are identical in energy in an octahedral complex but different in a square planar complex, with the d_{z^2} orbital being much lower in energy than the $d_{x^2-y^2}$. Explain with orbital sketches.

23.96 Which of the following metal ions *cannot* form both high-spin and low-spin octahedral complexes?
(a) Ti^{3+} (b) Co^{2+} (c) Fe^{2+} (d) Cu^{2+}

23.97 Which of the following metal ions *cannot* form both high-spin and low-spin octahedral complexes?
(a) Mn^{3+} (b) Nb^{3+} (c) Ru^{3+} (d) Ni^{2+}

23.98 Draw orbital-energy splitting diagrams and use the spectrochemical series to show the orbital occupancy for each of the following (assuming H_2O is a weak-field ligand):
(a) $[Cr(H_2O)_6]^{3+}$ (b) $[Cu(H_2O)_4]^{2+}$ (c) $[FeF_6]^{3-}$

23.99 Draw orbital-energy splitting diagrams and use the spectrochemical series to show the orbital occupancy for each of the following (assuming H_2O is a weak-field ligand):
(a) $[Cr(CN)_6]^{3-}$ (b) $[Rh(CO)_6]^{3+}$ (c) $[Co(OH)_6]^{4-}$

23.100 Draw orbital-energy splitting diagrams and use the spectrochemical series to show the orbital occupancy for each of the following (assuming H_2O is a weak-field ligand):
(a) $[MoCl_6]^{3-}$ (b) $[Ni(H_2O)_6]^{2+}$ (c) $[Ni(CN)_4]^{2-}$

23.101 Draw orbital-energy splitting diagrams and use the spectrochemical series to show the orbital occupancy for each of the following (assuming H_2O is a weak-field ligand):
(a) $[Fe(C_2O_4)_3]^{3-}$ ($C_2O_4^{2-}$ is weaker than H_2O)
(b) $[Co(CN)_6]^{4-}$ (c) $[MnCl_6]^{4-}$

23.102 Rank the following complex ions in order of *increasing* Δ and energy of visible light absorbed: $[Cr(NH_3)_6]^{3+}$, $[Cr(H_2O)_6]^{3+}$, $[Cr(NO_2)_6]^{3-}$.

23.103 Rank the following complex ions in order of *decreasing* Δ and energy of visible light absorbed: $[Cr(en)_3]^{3+}$, $[Cr(CN)_6]^{3-}$, $[CrCl_6]^{3-}$.

23.104 A complex, ML_6^{2+}, is violet. The same metal forms a complex with another ligand, Q, that creates a weaker field. What color might MQ_6^{2+} be expected to show? Explain.

23.105 $[Cr(H_2O)_6]^{2+}$ is violet. A second CrL_6 complex is green. Can ligand L be CN^-? Can it be Cl^-? Explain.

■ Problems in Context

23.106 Octahedral $[Ni(NH_3)_6]^{2+}$ is paramagnetic, whereas planar $[Pt(NH_3)_4]^{2+}$ is diamagnetic, even though both metal ions are d^8. Explain.

23.107 The hexaaqua complex $[Ni(H_2O)_6]^{2+}$ is green, whereas the corresponding ammonia complex $[Ni(NH_3)_6]^{2+}$ is violet. Explain.

23.108 Among the complex ions formed by Co^{3+} are the following: $[Co(H_2O)_6]^{3+}$, $[Co(NH_3)_6]^{3+}$, and $[CoF_6]^{3-}$. These ions have the following observed colors (listed in an arbitrary order): yellow-orange, green, and blue. Match each complex with its color. Explain.

Comprehensive Problems

Problems with an asterisk (*) are more challenging.

23.109 When neptunium (Np) and plutonium (Pu) were discovered, the periodic table of the time did not include the actinide series, so these elements were placed in Group 7B(7) and 8B(8). Later, when americium (Am) and curium (Cm) were synthesized, they were placed in Group 8B(9) and 8B(10). However, during chemical isolation procedures Glenn Seaborg and his research group, who had synthesized these elements, could not find their compounds among other compounds of these transition groups, a fact that led Seaborg to suggest they were part of a new inner transition series.
(a) How do the electron configurations of these elements support Seaborg's suggestion?
(b) The highest fluorides of Np and Pu are hexafluorides, as is the highest fluoride of uranium. How does this chemical evidence support the placement of Np and Pu as *inner* transition elements rather than transition elements?

23.110 At one time it was common to write the formula for copper(I) chloride as Cu_2Cl_2, instead of CuCl, analogously to Hg_2Cl_2 for mercury(I) chloride. Use electron configurations to explain why Hg_2Cl_2 is expected, but CuCl is correct.

23.111 Correct each name that has an error.
(a) $Na[FeBr_4]$ sodium tetrabromoferrate(II)
(b) $[Ni(NH_3)_6]^{2+}$ nickel hexaammine ion
(c) $[Co(NH_3)_3I_3]$ triamminetriiodocobalt(III)
(d) $[V(CN)_6]^{3-}$ hexacyanovanadium(III) ion
(e) $K[FeCl_4]$ potassium tetrachloroiron(III)

23.112 For the compound $[Co(en)_2Cl_2]Cl$, give
(a) The coordination number of the metal ion
(b) The oxidation number of the central metal ion
(c) The number of individual ions per formula unit
(d) The moles of AgCl that precipitate immediately per mole of compound dissolved in water and treated with $AgNO_3$

23.113 (a) What are the central metal ions in chlorophyll, heme, and vitamin B_{12}?
(b) What similarity in structure do these compounds have?

*23.114 A powerful shortcut in looking for the presence of optical isomers is to see if the complex has a "plane of symmetry"—a plane passing through the metal atom such that every atom on one side of the plane is matched by an identical one at the same distance from the plane on the other side. Any planar complex has a plane of symmetry, since all the atoms lie in one plane. Use this approach to determine if the following exist as optical isomers:
(a) $[Zn(NH_3)_2Cl_2]$ (tetrahedral)   (b) $[Pt(en)_2]^{2+}$
(c) *trans*-$[PtBr_4Cl_2]^{2-}$ (d) *trans*-$[Co(en)_2F_2]^+$
(e) *cis*-$[Co(en)_2F_2]^+$

23.115 Hexafluorocobaltate(III) ion is a high-spin complex. Draw the orbital-energy splitting diagram for its *d* orbitals.

23.116 Werner prepared two compounds by heating a solution of $PtCl_2$ with triethyl phosphine, $P(C_2H_5)_3$, which is an excellent ligand for Pt. The two compounds gave the same analysis: Pt 38.8%; Cl 14.1%; C 28.7%; P 12.4%; and H 6.02%. Write formulas, structures, and systematic names for the two isomers.

23.117 Criticize and correct the following statement: Strong-field ligands always give rise to low-spin complexes.

*23.118 Two important bidentate ligands used in analytical chemistry are bipyridyl (bipy) and *ortho*-phenanthroline (*o*-phen):

bipyridyl   *o* - phenanthroline

Draw structures and discuss the possibility of isomers for the following:
(a) $[Pt(bipy)Cl_2]$ (b) $[Fe(o\text{-}phen)_3]^{3+}$
(c) $[Co(bipy)_2F_2]^+$ (d) $[Co(o\text{-}phen)(NH_3)_3Cl]^{2+}$

23.119 The metal ion in platinum(IV) complexes, like that in cobalt(III) complexes, has a coordination number of 6. Many of these complexes occur with Cl^- ions and NH_3 molecules as ligands. Consider the following traditional (before the work of Werner) formulas for coordination compounds:
(a) $PtCl_4 \cdot 6NH_3$ (b) $PtCl_4 \cdot 4NH_3$
For each of these compounds,
(1) Give the modern formula and charge of the complex ion.
(2) Predict the moles of ions formed per mole of compound dissolved and the moles of AgCl formed immediately with excess $AgNO_3$.

23.120 The effect of entropy on reactions is evident in the stabilities of certain complexes.
(a) Using the criterion of the number of product particles, predict which of the following will be favored in terms of ΔS_{rxn}^0.

$$[Cu(NH_3)_4]^{2+}(aq) + 4H_2O(l) \longrightarrow$$
$$[Cu(H_2O)_4]^{2+}(aq) + 4NH_3(aq)$$

$$[Cu(H_2NCH_2CH_2NH_2)_2]^{2+}(aq) + 4H_2O(l) \longrightarrow$$
$$[Cu(H_2O)_4]^{2+}(aq) + 2en(aq)$$

(b) Given that the Cu—N bond strength is approximately the same in both complexes, which complex will be more stable with respect to ligand exchange in water? Explain.

23.121 For the permanganate ion, draw a Lewis structure that has the lowest formal charges.

23.122 The compound $[Pt(NH_3)_2(SCN)_2]$ displays two types of isomerism. Name the types and give names and structures for the six possible isomers.

23.123 Dark green manganate salts contain the MnO_4^{2-} ion. The ion is stable in basic solution but disproportionates in acid to $MnO_2(s)$ and MnO_4^-.
(a) What is the oxidation state of Mn in MnO_4^{2-}, MnO_4^-, and MnO_2?
(b) Write a balanced equation for the reaction in acidic solution.

23.124 In the sepia "toning" of a black-and-white photograph, the image is converted to a rich brownish violet by placing the finished photograph in a solution of gold(III) ions, in which metallic gold replaces the metallic silver. Use electrode potentials (Table 21.2, p. 911) to explain the chemistry of this process.

23.125 In 1940, when the elements Np and Pu were prepared, a controversy arose about whether the elements starting with Ac were analogs of the transition elements (and related to Y through Mo) or analogs of the lanthanides (and related to La through Nd). At the time, the arguments hinged primarily upon comparison of the observed oxidation states to those of the earlier elements.
(a) If the actinides were analogs of the transition elements, what would you predict about the maximum oxidation state for U? For Np?
(b) If the actinides were analogs of the lanthanides, what would you predict about the maximum oxidation state for U? For Pu?

23.126 In black-and-white photography, what are the major chemical changes involved in exposing, developing, and fixing the image on the film?

23.127 Aqueous electrolysis of potassium manganate (K_2MnO_4) is used for the commercial production of tens of thousands of tons of potassium permanganate ($KMnO_4$) annually. (a) Write a balanced equation for the electrolysis reaction. (Water is reduced also.) (b) How many moles of MnO_4^- can be formed if 12 A flow through a tank of aqueous MnO_4^{2-} for 96 h?

23.128 The actinides Pa, U, and Np form a series of complex ions, as in the compound Na_3UF_8, in which the central metal ion has an unusual geometry and oxidation state. In the crystal structure, the complex ion can be pictured as resulting from interpenetration of simple cubic arrays of uranium and fluoride ions. (a) What is the coordination number of the metal ion in the complex ion? (b) What is the oxidation state of uranium in the compound? (c) Sketch the complex ion.

24 Nuclear Reactions and Their Applications

Figure: Maintaining the tokamak. Maintaining this experimental facility at the Princeton University Plasma Physics Laboratory is an ongoing task. If fusion of atomic nuclei ever becomes a realistic source of energy for society, the scientists who operate this reactor will be pioneers of the technology. In this chapter, we address this and many other possibilities deriving from the remarkable properties of atomic nuclei.

Chapter Outline

ar below the outer fringes of the cloud of electrons lies the atom's tiny, dense core, held together by the strongest force in the universe. For nearly the entire text so far, we have focused on an atom's electrons, treating the nucleus as little more than their electrostatic anchor, while examining the effect of its positive charge on atomic properties and, ultimately, chemical behavior. But, for the scientists probing the structure and behavior of the atomic nucleus itself, there is the scene of real action, one that holds enormous potential benefit and great mystery and wonder (see photo).

Society is ambivalent about the applications of nuclear research, however. The promise of abundant energy and treatments for disease comes hand-in-hand with the threat of nuclear waste contamination, reactor accidents, and unimaginable destruction from nuclear war or terrorism. Can the power of the nucleus be harnessed for our benefit, or are the risks too great? In this chapter, we discuss the principles that can help you answer this vital question.

The changes that occur in atomic nuclei are strikingly different from chemical changes. In the reactions you've studied so far, electrons are shared or transferred to form *compounds,* while nuclei sit by passively, never changing their identities. In nuclear reactions, the roles are reversed: electrons in their orbitals are usually bystanders as the nuclei undergo changes that, in nearly every case, form different *elements.* Nuclear reactions may be accompanied by energy changes a million times greater than those in chemical reactions, energy changes so great that changes in mass *are* detectable. Moreover, nuclear reaction yields and rates are typically *not* subject to the effects of pressure, temperature, and catalysis that so clearly influence chemical reactions. Table 24.1 summarizes the general differences between chemical and nuclear reactions.

We begin this brief treatment of nuclear chemistry with an investigation of nuclear stability, why some nuclei are stable, whereas others are unstable, or *radioactive.* Then, we examine the detection and rate of radioactive decay. Next, we discuss how nuclei formed in particle accelerators continue to extend the periodic table beyond uranium, the last naturally occurring element. We consider the effects of radioactive emissions on matter, especially living matter, focusing on some major applications in science, technology, and medicine. Then, we calculate the energy released in nuclear reactions and discuss current and future engineering attempts to harness this energy. Finally, we end the chapter—and the text—with a look at the nuclear processes that create the chemical elements in the stars.

Concepts and Skills to Review

before you study this chapter

- discovery of the atomic nucleus (Section 2.4)
- protons, neutrons, mass number, and the $_Z^A X$ notation (Section 2.5)
- half-life and first-order reaction rate (Section 16.4)

Visualizing the paths of subatomic particles colliding in a bubble chamber.

Table 24.1 Comparison of Chemical and Nuclear Reactions

Chemical Reactions	Nuclear Reactions
1. One substance is converted into another, but atoms never change identity.	1. Atoms of one element typically are converted into atoms of another element.
2. Orbital electrons are involved as bonds break and form; nuclear particles do not take part.	2. Protons, neutrons, and other particles are involved; orbital electrons rarely take part.
3. Reactions are accompanied by relatively small changes in energy and no measurable changes in mass.	3. Reactions are accompanied by relatively large changes in energy and measurable changes in mass.
4. Reaction rates are influenced by temperature, concentration, catalysts, and the compound in which an element occurs.	4. Reaction rates are affected by number of nuclei, but not by temperature, catalysts, or the compound in which an element occurs.

24.1 Radioactive Decay and Nuclear Stability

A stable nucleus remains intact indefinitely, but *the great majority of nuclei are unstable*. An unstable nucleus exhibits **radioactivity:** it spontaneously disintegrates, or *decays*, by emitting radiation. Each type of unstable nucleus has a characteristic *rate* of radioactive decay. For different types of nuclei, this rate ranges from a fraction of a second to several billion years. In this section, we go over important terms and notation for nuclei, discuss some key events in the discovery of radioactivity, and consider the various types of radioactive decay.

The Components of the Nucleus: Terms and Notation

Recall from Chapter 2 that the nucleus contains essentially all the atom's mass but is only about 10^{-4} its diameter (or 10^{-12} its volume). Obviously, the nucleus is incredibly dense: about 10^{14} g/mL. ◆ *Protons* and *neutrons*, the elementary particles that make up the nucleus, are collectively called **nucleons.** The term **nuclide** refers to a variety of nuclei with a particular composition, that is, with specific numbers of the two types of nucleons. Most elements occur in nature as a mixture of **isotopes,** atoms with the characteristic number of protons of the element but different numbers of neutrons. Therefore, each isotope of an element has a single type of nuclide, and an element generally has a number of different isotopes. The nuclide of the most abundant isotope of oxygen, for example, contains eight protons and eight neutrons, whereas the nuclide of the least abundant contains eight protons and ten neutrons.

The relative mass and charge of a particle—nucleon, other elementary particle, or nuclide—is described by the notation $^{A}_{Z}X$, where X is the *symbol* for the particle, A is the *mass number,* or the total number of nucleons, and Z is the *charge* of the particle; for nuclides, Z is the same as the *number of protons* (atomic number). Using this notation, the three subatomic elementary particles are

$$^{0}_{-1}e \text{ (electron), } ^{1}_{1}p \text{ (proton), and } ^{1}_{0}n \text{ (neutron)}$$

(In nuclear notation, the element symbol refers to the nucleus only, so a proton is also sometimes represented as $^{1}_{1}H$.) The number of neutrons (N) in a nucleus is the mass number (A) minus the atomic number (Z): $N = A - Z$. The two naturally occurring isotopes of chlorine, for example, have 17 protons ($Z = 17$), but one has 18 neutrons ($^{35}_{17}Cl$, also written ^{35}Cl) and the other has 20 ($^{37}_{17}Cl$, or ^{37}Cl). Nuclides are also designated with the element name followed by the mass number, for example, chlorine-35 and chlorine-37. In any *naturally occurring* sample of an element or its compounds, the isotopes of the element are present in particular, nearly fixed proportions. Thus, in a sample of sodium chloride (or any Cl-containing substance), 75.77% of the Cl atoms are chlorine-35 and the remaining 24.23% are chlorine-37.

To understand this chapter, it is very important that you are comfortable with nuclear notations, so please take a moment to review Sample Problem 2.2 on p. 54 and Problems 2.37 to 2.44 at the end of Chapter 2.

The Discovery of Radioactivity and the Types of Emissions

In 1896, the French physicist Antoine-Henri Becquerel discovered, quite by accident, that uranium minerals, even when wrapped in paper and stored in the dark, emit a penetrating radiation that can produce bright images on a

◆ **The Remarkably Tiny, Massive Nucleus** If you could strip all the electrons from the atoms in an object and compress all the nuclei together, the object would lose only a fraction of a percent of its mass, but it would shrink to 0.0000000001% (10^{-10}%) of its volume. An atom the size of the Houston Astrodome would have a nucleus the size of a grapefruit, which would contain virtually all the atom's mass.

photographic plate. Becquerel also found that the radiation creates an electric discharge in air, thus providing a means for measuring its intensity. Two years later, a young doctoral student named Marie Sklodowska Curie began a search for other minerals that emitted radiation. She found that thorium minerals also emit radiation and showed that *the intensity of the radiation is directly proportional to the concentration of the element in the mineral, not to the nature of the compound* in which the element occurs. Curie named the emissions *radioactivity* and showed that they are *unaffected by temperature, pressure, or other physical and chemical conditions.*

To her surprise, Curie found that certain uranium minerals were even more radioactive than pure uranium, which implied that they contained traces of one or more as yet unknown, highly radioactive elements. She and her husband, the physicist Pierre Curie, set out to isolate all the radioactive components in pitchblende, the principal ore of uranium. After months of painstaking chemical work, they isolated two extremely small, highly radioactive fractions, one that precipitated with bismuth compounds and another that precipitated with alkaline earth compounds. Through chemical and spectroscopic analysis, Marie Curie showed that these fractions contained two new elements, which she named polonium (after her native Poland) and radium. Polonium (Po; $Z = 84$), the most metallic member of Group 6A(16), lies to the right of bismuth in Period 6. Radium (Ra; $Z = 88$) is the heaviest alkaline earth metal, lying under barium in Group 2A(2).

Purifying radium proved to be another arduous task. Starting with several tons of pitchblende residues from which the uranium had been extracted, Curie prepared compounds of the larger Group 2A(2) elements, continually separating minuscule amounts of radium compounds from enormously larger amounts of chemically similar barium compounds. It took her four years to isolate 0.1 g radium chloride, which she melted and electrolyzed to obtain pure metallic radium. ◆

During the next few years, Henri Becquerel, the Curies, and P. Villard in France and Ernest Rutherford and his co-workers in England studied the nature of radioactive emissions. Rutherford and his colleague Frederick Soddy observed that elements other than radium were formed when radium decayed. In 1902, they proposed that radioactive emission results in the change of one element into another. This idea sounded like a resurrection of alchemy and was met with disbelief and ridicule. We now know it to be true: under most circumstances, *when a nuclide of one element decays, it changes into a nuclide of a different element.*

These studies led to an understanding of the three most common types of radioactive emission:

- **Alpha particles** (symbolized α or ^4_2He) are dense, positively charged particles identical to helium nuclei.
- **Beta particles** (symbolized β, β^-, or more usually $^0_{-1}\beta$) are negatively charged particles identified as high-speed electrons. (The emission of electrons from the nucleus may seem strange, but as you'll see shortly, β particles arise as a result of a nuclear reaction.)
- **Gamma rays** (symbolized as γ, or sometimes $^0_0\gamma$) are very high-energy photons, about 10^5 times as energetic as visible light.

The behavior of these three emissions in an electric field is shown in Figure 24.1. Note that α particles bend toward the negative plate, β particles bend toward the positive plate, and γ rays are not affected by the electric field. We'll discuss the effects of these emissions on matter later.

◆ **Her Brilliant Career** Marie Curie (1867–1934) is the only person to be awarded Nobel Prizes in two *different* sciences, one in physics in 1903 for her research into radioactivity and the other in chemistry in 1911 for the discovery of polonium and the discovery, isolation, and study of radium and its compounds.

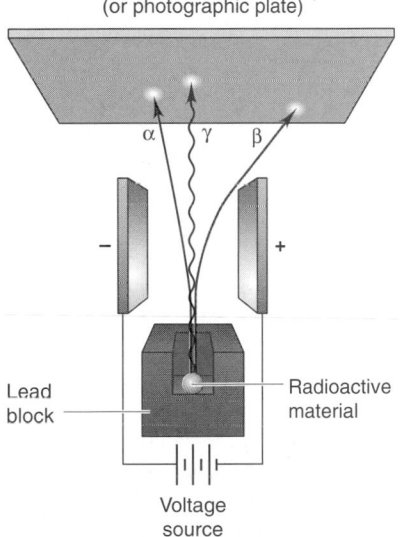

Figure 24.1 The behavior of three types of radioactive emissions in an electric field. α Particles (^4_2He) are positively charged, so they bend toward the negative plate. In contrast, β particles ($^0_{-1}\beta$) are negatively charged, so they bend toward the positive plate. Note that the curvature is greater for the β particles because they have much lower mass than α particles. γ Rays consist of uncharged high-energy photons.

Table 24.2 Modes of Radioactive Decay*

Mode	Emission	Decay Process	Change in A	Change in Z	Change in N
α Decay	α ($^4_2$He)	Reactant (parent) → Product (daughter) + α expelled	−4	−2	−2
β Decay	$^0_{-1}β$	^1_0n in nucleus → ^1_1p in nucleus + $^0_{-1}β$ β expelled	0	+1	−1
Positron emission	$^0_1β$	^1_1p in nucleus → ^1_0n in nucleus + $^0_1β$ positron expelled	0	−1	+1
Electron capture	x-ray photon	$^0_{-1}e$ absorbed from low-energy orbital ^1_1p in nucleus → ^1_0n in nucleus	0	−1	+1
γ Emission	$^0_0γ$	excited nucleus → stable nucleus + $^0_0γ$ γ photon radiated	0	0	0

*Neutrinos (v) are involved in several of these processes but are not shown.

Types of Radioactive Decay; Balancing Nuclear Equations

When a nuclide decays, it forms a nuclide of lower energy, and the excess energy is carried off by the emitted radiation. The decaying, or reactant, nuclide is called the *parent;* the product nuclide is called the *daughter.* Nuclides can decay in several ways. As we discuss the major types of decay, which are summarized in Table 24.2, note carefully the principle used to balance nuclear reactions: *the total Z (charge, number of protons) and total A (sum of protons and neutrons) of the reactants equal those of the products.*

1. **Alpha decay** involves the loss of an α particle ($^4_2$He) from a nucleus. For each α particle emitted by the parent nucleus, *A decreases by 4 and Z decreases by 2.* Every element heavier than lead (Pb; Z = 82), as well as a few lighter ones, exhibits α decay. In Rutherford's classic gold foil experiment that established the existence of the atomic nucleus (Section 2.4, p. 52), radium was the source of the α particles used as projectiles. Radium undergoes α decay to yield radon (Rn; Z = 86):

$$^{226}_{88}Ra \longrightarrow \ ^{222}_{86}Rn + \ ^4_2He$$

Note that the *A* value for Ra equals the sum of the *A* values for Rn and He (226 = 222 + 4), and that the *Z* value for Ra equals the sum of the *Z* values for Rn and He (88 = 86 + 2).

2. **Beta decay** involves the ejection of a β particle ($^0_{-1}β$) from the nucleus. This change does not involve the expulsion of a β particle that was actually

in the nucleus, but rather the *conversion of a neutron into a proton, which remains in the nucleus, and a β particle, which is expelled immediately:* ◆

$$_0^1 n \longrightarrow _1^1 p + _{-1}^0 \beta$$

As always, the totals of the *A* and the *Z* values in reactant and products are equal. Radioactive nickel-63 becomes stable copper-63 through β decay:

$$_{28}^{63} Ni \longrightarrow _{29}^{63} Cu + _{-1}^0 \beta$$

Another example is the β decay of carbon-14, which we'll return to later in the context of radiocarbon dating:

$$_6^{14} C \longrightarrow _7^{14} N + _{-1}^0 \beta$$

Note that *β decay results in a product nuclide with the same A but with Z one higher (one more proton) than in the reactant nuclide.* In other words, an atom of the element with the next *higher* atomic number is formed.

3. **Positron decay** involves the emission of a positron from the nucleus. A key idea of modern physics is that every fundamental particle has a corresponding "antiparticle," another particle with the same mass but opposite charge. The **positron** (symbolized $_1^0 \beta$; note the positive *Z*) is the antiparticle of the electron. Positron decay occurs when *a proton in the nucleus is converted into a neutron and a positron,* and the positron is expelled:

$$_1^1 p \longrightarrow _0^1 n + _1^0 \beta$$

Positron decay has the opposite effect of β decay, resulting in a daughter nuclide with the same A but with Z one lower (one fewer proton) than the parent; thus, an atom of the element with the next *lower* atomic number forms. Carbon-11, a synthetic radioisotope, decays to a stable boron isotope through emission of a positron:

$$_6^{11} C \longrightarrow _5^{11} B + _1^0 \beta$$

4. **Electron capture** occurs when the nucleus of an atom draws in an electron from an orbital of the lowest energy level. The net effect is that *a nuclear proton is transformed into a neutron:*

$$_1^1 p + _{-1}^0 e \longrightarrow _0^1 n$$

(We use the symbol $_{-1}^0 e$ to distinguish an orbital electron from a beta particle, symbol $_{-1}^0 \beta$.) The orbital vacancy is quickly filled by an electron moving down from a higher energy level, and that energy difference appears as an *x-ray photon.* Radioactive iron forms stable manganese through electron capture:

$$_{26}^{55} Fe + _{-1}^0 e \longrightarrow _{25}^{55} Mn + h\nu \text{ (x-ray)}$$

Electron capture has the same net effect as positron decay (Z lower by 1, A unchanged), even though the processes are entirely different.

5. **Gamma emission** involves the radiation of high-energy γ photons from an excited nucleus. Recall that when an atom is in an excited *electronic* state, it reduces its energy by emitting photons, usually in the ultraviolet (UV) and visible ranges. Similarly, a nucleus in an excited state lowers its energy by emitting γ photons, which are of much higher energy (much shorter wavelength) than UV photons. Many nuclear processes leave the nucleus in an excited state, so *γ emission accompanies most other types of decay.* Several γ photons (γ rays) of different frequencies can be emitted from an excited nucleus as it relaxes, usually to the ground state. Many of Marie Curie's experiments involved the release of γ rays, such as

$$_{92}^{238} U \longrightarrow _{90}^{234} Th + _2^4 He + 2_0^0 \gamma$$

Since γ rays have no mass or charge, *γ emission does not change A or Z.* Gamma rays also result when a particle and an antiparticle annihilate each other, as when an emitted positron meets an orbital electron:

$$_1^0 \beta \text{ (from nucleus)} + _{-1}^0 e \text{ (outside nucleus)} \longrightarrow 2_0^0 \gamma$$

◆ **The Little Neutral One**
A neutral particle called a *neutrino* (ν) is also emitted in many nuclear reactions, including the change of a neutron to a proton:

$$_0^1 n \longrightarrow _1^1 p + _{-1}^0 \beta + \nu$$

Theory suggests that neutrinos have masses much less than 10^{-4} that of an electron, and that at least 10^9 neutrinos exist in the universe for every proton. Neutrinos interact with matter so slightly that it would take a piece of lead 1 light-year thick to absorb them. We will not discuss them further, except to mention that recent experiments in Japan have detected neutrinos and obtained evidence that they have mass. Using a cathedral-sized pool containing 50,000 tons of ultrapure water buried 1 mile underground in a zinc mine, an international team of scientists obtained results that suggest that neutrinos may account for a significant portion of the "missing" matter in the universe and may provide enough mass (and, thus, gravitational attraction) to prevent the universe from expanding forever.

Sample Problem 24.1   Writing Equations for Nuclear Reactions

PROBLEM Write balanced equations for the following nuclear reactions:
(a) Naturally occurring thorium-232 undergoes α decay.
(b) Chlorine-36 undergoes electron capture.

PLAN We first write a skeleton equation that includes the mass numbers, atomic numbers, and symbols of all the particles, showing the unknown particles as $^A_Z X$. Then, since mass numbers and charges on the left side and the right side must be equal, we solve for A and Z, and use Z to determine X from the periodic table.

SOLUTION (a) Writing the skeleton equation:

$$^{232}_{90}\text{Th} \longrightarrow {}^A_Z X + {}^4_2\text{He}$$

Solving for A and Z and balancing the equation: For A, $232 = A + 4$, so $A = 228$. For Z, $90 = Z + 2$, so $Z = 88$. From the periodic table, we see that the element with $Z = 88$ is radium (Ra), so

$$^{232}_{90}\text{Th} \longrightarrow {}^{228}_{88}\text{Ra} + {}^4_2\text{He}$$

(b) Writing the skeleton equation:

$$^{36}_{17}\text{Cl} + {}^0_{-1}\text{e} \longrightarrow {}^A_Z X$$

Solving for A and Z and balancing the equation: For A, $36 + 0 = A$, so $A = 36$. For Z, $17 + (-1) = Z$, so $Z = 16$. The element with $Z = 16$ is sulfur (S), so

$$^{36}_{17}\text{Cl} + {}^0_{-1}\text{e} \longrightarrow {}^{36}_{16}\text{S}$$

CHECK Always read across superscripts and then across subscripts, with the yield arrow as an equal sign, to check your arithmetic. In **(a)**, for example, $232 = 228 + 4$, and $90 = 88 + 2$.

Follow-up Problem 24.1   Write a balanced equation for the reaction in which a nuclide undergoes β decay and produces cesium-133.

Nuclear Stability and the Mode of Decay

There are several ways that an unstable nuclide *might* decay, but can we predict how it *will* decay? Indeed, can we predict *if* it will decay at all? Our knowledge of the nucleus is much less complete than our knowledge of the atom as a whole, but some patterns emerge when we examine the naturally occurring nuclides.

The Band of Stability and the Neutron/Proton (*N/Z*) Ratio   A key factor that determines the stability of a nuclide is the ratio of the number of neutrons to the number of protons, the ***N/Z* ratio.** For lighter nuclides, one neutron for each proton ($N/Z \approx 1$) is enough to provide stability. However, for heavier nuclides to be stable, the number of neutrons must exceed the number of protons, and often by quite a significant proportion. If the N/Z ratio is either too high or not high enough, the nuclide is unstable and decays.

Figure 24.2A is a plot of number of neutrons vs. number of protons for the *stable* nuclides. The nuclides form a narrow **band of stability** that gradually increases from an N/Z ratio of 1, near $Z = 10$, to an N/Z ratio slightly greater than 1.5, near $Z = 83$ for ^{209}Bi. Several key points are

- Very few stable nuclides exist with $N/Z < 1$; the only two are $^1_1$H and $^3_2$He. For lighter stable nuclides, $N/Z \approx 1$: $^4_2$He, $^{12}_6$C, $^{16}_8$O, and $^{20}_{10}$Ne are particularly stable.
- The N/Z ratio of stable nuclides gradually increases as Z increases. No stable nuclide exists with $N/Z = 1$ for $Z > 20$. Thus, for $^{56}_{26}$Fe, $N/Z = 1.15$; for $^{107}_{47}$Ag, $N/Z = 1.28$; and for $^{184}_{74}$W, $N/Z = 1.49$.
- All nuclides with $Z > 83$ are unstable. Bismuth-209 is the heaviest stable nuclide. Therefore, the largest members of Groups 1A(1), 2A(2), 6A(16), 7A(17), and 8A(18) are radioactive, as are all the actinides and elements of the fourth transition series (Period 7).

Figure 24.2 **A plot of neutrons vs. protons for the stable nuclides. A,** A plot of N vs. Z for all stable nuclides gives rise to a narrow band that veers above $N/Z = 1$ shortly beyond $Z = 10$. The N/Z values for several stable nuclides are given. The most common modes of decay for unstable nuclides in a particular region are shown: nuclides with a high N/Z ratio often undergo β decay; those with a low ratio undergo e⁻ capture or positron emission; heavy nuclei beyond the stable band (and a few lighter ones) undergo α decay. **B,** The blue box in **A** is expanded to show the stable *and* many of the unstable nuclides in that area. Note the modes of decay: α decay decreases both N and Z by two; β decay decreases N and increases Z by one; positron emission and e⁻ capture increase N and decrease Z by one.

Stability and Nuclear Structure Given that protons are positively charged and neutrons uncharged, what holds the nucleus together? Nuclear scientists answer this question and explain the importance of the N/Z ratio in terms of two opposing forces. Electrostatic repulsive forces between protons would break the nucleus apart if not for the presence of an attractive force that exists between all nucleons (protons and neutrons) called the **strong force.** This force is about 100 times stronger than the repulsive force but *operates only over the short distances within the nucleus.* Competition between the *attractive* strong force and the *repulsive* electrostatic force determines nuclear stability.

Curiously, the oddness or evenness of N and Z values displays some important patterns about nuclear stability. Two interesting points appear when we classify the known stable nuclides:

- Elements with an even Z (number of protons) usually have a larger number of stable nuclides than elements with an odd Z. Table 24.3 demonstrates this point for cadmium ($Z = 48$) through xenon ($Z = 54$).
- Well over half the stable nuclides have *both* even N and even Z (Table 24.4, next page). (Only seven nuclides with odd N and odd Z are either stable— $^{2}_{1}H$, $^{6}_{3}Li$, $^{10}_{5}B$, $^{14}_{7}N$—or decay so slowly that their amounts have changed little since the Earth formed—$^{50}_{23}V$, $^{138}_{57}La$, and $^{176}_{71}Lu$.)

Table 24.3 Number of Stable Nuclides for Elements 48 Through 54*

Element	Atomic Number (Z)	Number of Nuclides
Cd	**48**	**8**
In	49	2
Sn	**50**	**10**
Sb	51	2
Te	**52**	**8**
I	53	1
Xe	**54**	**9**

*Even Z shown in boldface.

Table 24.4 An Even-Odd Classification of the Stable Nuclides

Z	N	Number of Nuclides
Even	Even	157
Even	Odd	53
Odd	Even	50
Odd	Odd	7
	TOTAL	267

One model of nuclear structure that attempts to explain these findings postulates that protons and neutrons lie in nucleon shells, or energy levels, and that stability results from the *pairing* of like nucleons. This arrangement leads to the stability of even values of N and Z. (The analogy to electron energy levels and the stability that arises from electron pairing is striking.)

Just as the noble gases—the elements with 2, 10, 18, 36, 54, and 84 electrons—are exceptionally stable because of their filled *electron* shells, nuclides with N or Z values of 2, 8, 20, 28, 50, 82 (and $N = 126$) are exceptionally stable as well. These so-called *magic numbers* are thought to correspond to the numbers of protons or neutrons in filled *nucleon* shells. A few examples are $^{50}_{22}Ti$ ($N = 28$), $^{88}_{38}Sr$ ($N = 50$), and the nine stable nuclides of tin ($Z = 50$). Some extremely stable nuclides have double magic numbers: $^{4}_{2}He$, $^{16}_{8}O$, $^{40}_{20}Ca$, and $^{208}_{82}Pb$ ($N = 126$).

Sample Problem 24.2   Predicting Nuclear Stability

PROBLEM Which of the following nuclides would you predict to be stable and which radioactive: **(a)** $^{18}_{10}Ne$; **(b)** $^{32}_{16}S$; **(c)** $^{236}_{90}Th$; **(d)** $^{123}_{56}Ba$? Explain.

PLAN To evaluate the stability of each nuclide, we find the N/Z ratio, the value of Z, stable N/Z ratios (from Figure 24.2A), and whether Z and N are even or odd.

SOLUTION (a) Radioactive. The $N/Z = \dfrac{18 - 10}{10} = 0.8$. Despite even N and Z, the minimum ratio for stability is 1.0; this nuclide has too few neutrons to be stable.

(b) Stable. This nuclide has an $N/Z = 1.0$ and $Z < 20$, with even N and Z, so it is most likely stable.

(c) Radioactive. Every nuclide with $Z > 83$ is radioactive.

(d) Radioactive. The $N/Z = 1.20$. For Z from 55 to 60, Figure 24.2A shows $N/Z \geq 1.3$, so this nuclide probably has too few neutrons to be stable.

CHECK By consulting a table of isotopes, such as the one in the *CRC Handbook of Chemistry and Physics,* we find that our predictions are correct.

Follow-up Problem 24.2 Why is $^{31}_{15}P$ stable but $^{30}_{15}P$ unstable?

Predicting the Mode of Decay An unstable nuclide generally decays in a mode that shifts its N/Z ratio toward the band of stability. This fact can be seen in Figure 24.2B on the preceding page (an expansion of the boxed region in part *A* of the figure), which shows all stable *and* many of the radioactive nuclides.

1. *Neutron-rich nuclides.* Nuclides with too many neutrons for stability (a high N/Z) lie above the band of stability. They undergo β *decay*, which converts a neutron into a proton, thus reducing the value of N/Z.

2. *Proton-rich nuclides.* Nuclides with too many protons for stability (a low N/Z) lie below the band. They undergo *positron decay* or *electron capture*, both of which convert a proton into a neutron, thus increasing the value of N/Z.

3. *Heavy nuclides.* Nuclides with $Z > 83$ are too heavy to lie within the band and undergo α *decay*, which reduces their Z and N values by two units per emission. (Several lighter nuclides also exhibit α decay.)

Sample Problem 24.3   Predicting the Mode of Nuclear Decay

PROBLEM Predict the nature of the nuclear change(s) each of the following radioactive nuclides is likely to undergo: **(a)** $^{12}_{5}B$; **(b)** $^{234}_{92}U$; **(c)** $^{74}_{33}As$; **(d)** $^{127}_{57}La$.

PLAN We use the N/Z ratio to decide where the nuclide lies relative to the band of stability and how its ratio compares with others in that region of the band. Then, we predict which of the modes just discussed will yield a product nuclide that is closer to the band.

SOLUTION (a) This nuclide has an N/Z of 1.4, which is too high for this region of the band. It will probably undergo β decay, which will increase Z to 6 and lower the N/Z ratio to 1.

(b) This nuclide is heavier than those in the band of stability. It will probably undergo α decay and decrease its total mass.

(c) This nuclide, with $N/Z = 1.24$, lies in the band of stability, so it will probably undergo either β decay or positron emission.

(d) This nuclide has an N/Z ratio of 1.23, which is too low for this region of the band, so it will decrease Z by either positron emission or electron capture.

COMMENT Both the possible modes of decay are observed for the nuclides in parts **(c)** and **(d)**.

Follow-up Problem 24.3 What mode of decay would you expect for **(a)** $^{61}_{26}$Fe; **(b)** $^{241}_{95}$Am?

Decay Series A parent nuclide may undergo a series of decay steps before a stable daughter nuclide forms. The succession of steps is called a **decay series,** or **disintegration series,** and is typically depicted on a gridlike display. Figure 24.3 shows the decay series from uranium-238 to lead-206. Numbers of neutrons (N) cross numbers of protons (Z) to form the grid, which displays a series of α and β decays. The zigzag pattern is typical and occurs because α decay decreases both N and Z, whereas β decay decreases N but increases Z. This decay series is one of three that occur in nature. All end with stable isotopes of lead. A second series begins with uranium-235 and ends with lead-207, and a third begins with thorium-232 and ends with lead-208. (Neptunium-237 began a fourth series, but its half-life is so much shorter than the age of the Earth that only traces of it remain today.)

Section Summary

Nuclear reactions are not affected by reaction conditions or chemical composition and release much more energy than chemical reactions. A radioactive nuclide is unstable and may emit α particles ($^4_2$He nuclei), β particles ($^0_{-1}$β; high-speed electrons), positrons ($^0_1$β), or γ rays ($^0_0$γ; high-energy photons), or capture an orbital electron. A narrow band of neutron-to-proton ratios (N/Z) includes those of all the stable nuclides. Radioactive decay allows an unstable nuclide to achieve a more stable N/Z ratio. Certain "magic numbers" of neutrons and protons are associated with very stable nuclides. By comparing a nuclide's N/Z ratio with those in the band of stability, we can predict that, in general, heavy nuclides undergo α decay, neutron-rich nuclides undergo β decay, and proton-rich nuclides undergo positron emission or electron capture. Three naturally occurring decay series all end in isotopes of lead.

Figure 24.3 The ²³⁸U decay series. Uranium-238 (*top right*) decays through a series of α and β emissions to lead-206 (*bottom left*) in 14 steps.

24.2 The Kinetics of Radioactive Decay

Chemical and nuclear systems both tend toward maximum stability. Just as the concentrations in a chemical system change in a predictable direction to give a stable equilibrium ratio, the type and number of nucleons in an unstable nucleus change in a predictable direction to give a stable N/Z ratio. As you know, however, the tendency of a chemical system to become more stable tells nothing about how long that process will take, and the same holds true for nuclear systems. In this section, we examine the kinetics of nuclear change; later, we'll examine the energetics of nuclear change. To begin, a Tools of the Chemistry Laboratory essay describes how radioactivity is detected and measured.

Tools of the Chemistry Laboratory

Counters for the Detection of Radioactive Emissions

Radioactive emissions interact with atoms in surrounding materials. To determine the rate of nuclear decay, we measure the radioactivity of a sample by observing the effects of these interactions over time. Since these effects can be electrically amplified billions of times, it is even possible to detect the decay of a single nucleus. Ionization counters and scintillation counters are two devices used to measure radioactive emissions.

An *ionization counter* detects radioactive emissions as they ionize a gas. Ionization produces free electrons and gaseous cations, which are attracted to electrodes that conduct a current to a recording device. The most common type of ionization counter is a **Geiger-Müller counter** (Figure 24.A). It consists of a tube filled with argon gas; the tube housing acts as the cathode, and a thin wire running through the center of the tube acts as the anode. Emissions from the sample enter the tube through a thin window and strike argon atoms, producing free electrons that are accelerated toward the anode. These electrons collide with other argon atoms and free more electrons in an *avalanche* effect. The current created is amplified and converted to a meter reading and/or an audible click. The initial release of one electron can release 10^{10} electrons in a microsecond, giving the Geiger-Müller counter great sensitivity.

In a **scintillation counter,** radioactive emissions too weak to ionize surrounding atoms are detected by their ability to excite atoms and cause them to emit light. The light is emitted by a *phosphor* coated onto part of a *photomultiplier tube,* a device that increases the original electrical signal. The incoming radioactive particle strikes the phosphor, which emits a photon that, in turn, strikes a cathode, releasing an electron through the photoelectric effect (Section 7.1). This electron hits other portions of the tube that release increasing numbers of electrons, and the resulting current is recorded. Liquid scintillation counters employ organic phosphors that also function as solvent (Figure 24.B). They dissolve the sample *and* emit light when excited by the emission. These counters are often used to measure emissions from dissolved radioactive biological samples.

Figure 24.B Vials of scintillation "cocktail" emitting light. A radioactive substance dissolved in an organic solvent mixture (cocktail) emits particles that excite a solvent component to emit light. Light intensity is proportional to the concentration of the substance.

Figure 24.A Detection of radioactivity by an ionization counter. When an Ar atom absorbs the energy of a radioactive particle *(red)*, it is ionized to an Ar^+ ion *(purple)* and an electron *(yellow)*. The freed electron collides with and ionizes another Ar atom. As the process continues, the Ar^+ ions migrate to the negative electrode, and the electrons migrate to the positive electrode, resulting in a current.

The Rate of Radioactive Decay

Radioactive nuclei decay at a characteristic rate, regardless of the chemical substance in which they occur. The *decay rate*, or **activity** ($\mathcal{A}$), of a radioactive sample is the change in number of nuclei ($\mathcal{N}$) divided by the change in time (t). As we saw with chemical reaction rates, because the number of nuclei is *decreasing*, a minus sign precedes the expression:

$$\text{Decay rate } (\mathcal{A}) = -\frac{\Delta \mathcal{N}}{\Delta t}$$

The SI unit of radioactivity is the **becquerel (Bq)**; it is defined as one disintegration per second (d/s): 1 Bq = 1 d/s. A much larger and more common unit of radioactivity is the **curie (Ci)**: 1 curie equals the number of nuclei disintegrating each second in 1 g radium-226:

$$1 \text{ Ci} = 3.70 \times 10^{10} \text{ d/s} \qquad \textbf{(24.1)}$$

Because the curie is so large, the millicurie (mCi) and microcurie (μCi) are commonly used. We often express the radioactivity of a sample in terms of *specific activity,* the decay rate per gram.

An activity is meaningful only when we consider the large number of nuclei in a macroscopic sample. Suppose there are 1×10^{15} radioactive nuclei of a particular type in a sample and they decay at a rate of 10% per hour. Although any particular nucleus in the sample might decay in a microsecond or in a million hours, the *average* of all decays results in 10% of the entire collection of nuclei disintegrating each hour. During the first hour, 10% of the *original* number, or 1×10^{14} nuclei, will decay. During the next hour, 10% of the remaining 9×10^{14} nuclei, or 9×10^{13} nuclei, will decay. During the next hour, 10% of those remaining will decay, and so forth. Thus, for a large collection of radioactive nuclei, *the number decaying per unit time is proportional to the number present:*

$$\text{Decay rate } (\mathcal{A}) \propto \mathcal{N} \qquad \text{or} \qquad \mathcal{A} = k\mathcal{N}$$

where k is called the **decay constant** and is characteristic of the nuclide. The larger the value of k, the higher is the decay rate.

Combining the two rate expressions just given, we obtain

$$\mathcal{A} = -\frac{\Delta \mathcal{N}}{\Delta t} = k\mathcal{N} \qquad \textbf{(24.2)}$$

Note that the activity depends only on $\mathcal{N}$ raised to the first power (and on the constant value of k). Therefore, *radioactive decay is a first-order process* (see Section 16.4). The only difference in the case of nuclear decay is that we consider the *number* of nuclei rather than their concentration.

Half-Life of Radioactive Decay Decay rates are also commonly expressed in terms of the *fraction* of nuclei that decays over a given time interval. The **half-life ($t_{1/2}$)** of a nuclide is the time it takes for half the nuclei present to decay. *The number of nuclei remaining is halved after each half-life.* Thus, half-life has the same meaning for a nuclear change as for a chemical change (Section 16.4). Figure 24.4 shows the decay of carbon-14, which has a half-life of 5730 years, in terms of number of ^{14}C nuclei remaining:

$$^{14}_{6}\text{C} \longrightarrow {}^{14}_{7}\text{N} + {}^{0}_{-1}\beta$$

We can also consider the half-life in terms of mass of substance. As ^{14}C decays to the product ^{14}N, its mass decreases. If we start with 1.0 g carbon-14, half that mass of ^{14}C (0.50 g) will be left after 5730 years, half of that

Figure 24.4 Decrease in number of ^{14}C nuclei over time. A plot of number of ^{14}C nuclei vs. time gives a decreasing curve. In each half-life (5730 years), half the ^{14}C nuclei present undergo decay. A plot of mass of ^{14}C vs. time is identical.

Table 24.5 Decay Constants (k) and Half-Lives ($t_{1/2}$) of Beryllium Isotopes

Nuclide	k	$t_{1/2}$
$^{7}_{4}$Be	1.30×10^{-2}/day	53.3 day
$^{8}_{4}$Be	1.0×10^{16}/s	6.7×10^{-17} s
$^{9}_{4}$Be	Stable	
$^{10}_{4}$Be	4.3×10^{-7}/yr	1.6×10^{6} yr
$^{11}_{4}$Be	5.02×10^{-2}/s	13.8 s

mass (0.25 g) after another 5730 years, and so on. The activity depends on the number of nuclei present, so the activity is halved after each succeeding half-life as well.

We determine the half-life of a nuclear reaction from its rate constant. Rearranging Equation 24.2 and integrating over time gives

$$\ln \frac{\mathcal{N}_t}{\mathcal{N}_0} = -kt \qquad \text{or} \qquad \ln \frac{\mathcal{N}_0}{\mathcal{N}_t} = kt \qquad \textbf{(24.3)}$$

where $\mathcal{N}_0$ is the number of nuclei at $t = 0$, and $\mathcal{N}_t$ is the number of nuclei remaining at any time t. (Note the similarity to Equation 16.4, p. 680.) To calculate the half-life ($t_{1/2}$), we set $\mathcal{N}_t$ equal to $\frac{1}{2}\mathcal{N}_0$ and solve for $t_{1/2}$:

$$\ln \frac{\mathcal{N}_0}{\frac{1}{2}\mathcal{N}_0} = kt_{1/2} \qquad \text{so} \qquad t_{1/2} = \frac{\ln 2}{k} \qquad \textbf{(24.4)}$$

As you can see, *the half-life is **not** dependent on the number of nuclei and is inversely related to the decay constant:*

$$\text{large } k \Rightarrow \text{short } t_{1/2} \quad \text{and vice versa}$$

As Table 24.5 demonstrates, the decay constants and half-lives of radioactive nuclides can vary over an extremely wide range, even for the nuclides of a given element.

Sample Problem 24.4   Determining the Number of Radioactive Nuclei

PROBLEM Strontium-90 is a radioactive by-product of nuclear reactors that behaves biologically like calcium, the element above it in Group 2A(2). When ^{90}Sr is ingested by mammals, it is found in their milk and eventually in the bones of those drinking the milk (see photo). If a sample of ^{90}Sr has an activity of 1.2×10^{12} d/s, what is the activity and the fraction of nuclei that have decayed after 59 yr? ($t_{1/2}$ of ^{90}Sr = 29 yr.)

PLAN The fraction of nuclei that has decayed is the change in number of nuclei, expressed as a fraction of the starting number. Since the activity of the sample ($\mathcal{A}$) is proportional to the number of nuclei ($\mathcal{N}$), we know that

$$\text{Fraction decayed} = \frac{\mathcal{N}_0 - \mathcal{N}_t}{\mathcal{N}_0} = \frac{\mathcal{A}_0 - \mathcal{A}_t}{\mathcal{A}_0}$$

We are given $\mathcal{A}_0$, so we find $\mathcal{A}_t$ from the integrated form of the first-order rate equation (Equation 24.3), in which t is 59 yr. To solve that equation, we need k, which we can calculate from the given $t_{1/2}$.

SOLUTION Calculating the decay constant k:

$$t_{1/2} = \frac{\ln 2}{k} \qquad \text{so} \qquad k = \frac{\ln 2}{t_{1/2}} = \frac{0.693}{29 \text{ yr}} = 0.024 \text{ yr}^{-1}$$

Applying Equation 24.3 to calculate the activity remaining at time t, $\mathcal{A}_t$:

$$\ln \frac{\mathcal{N}_0}{\mathcal{N}_t} = \ln \frac{\mathcal{A}_0}{\mathcal{A}_t} = kt \qquad \text{or} \qquad \ln \mathcal{A}_0 - \ln \mathcal{A}_t = kt$$

So, $\quad \ln \mathcal{A}_t = -kt + \ln \mathcal{A}_0 = -(0.024 \text{ yr}^{-1} \times 59 \text{ yr}) + \ln (1.2\times10^{12} \text{ d/s})$

$\qquad \ln \mathcal{A}_t = -1.4 + 27.81 = 26.4$

$\qquad \boxed{\mathcal{A}_t = 2.9\times10^{11} \text{ d/s}}$

(Since all the data contain two significant figures, we retained two in the answer.) Calculating the fraction decayed:

$$\text{Fraction decayed} = \frac{\mathcal{A}_0 - \mathcal{A}_t}{\mathcal{A}_0} = \frac{1.2\times10^{12} \text{ d/s} - 2.9\times10^{11} \text{ d/s}}{1.2\times10^{12} \text{ d/s}} = \boxed{0.76}$$

CHECK The answer seems reasonable: since t is about 2 half-lives, $\mathcal{A}_t$ should be approximately $\frac{1}{4}\mathcal{A}_0$, or about 0.3×10^{12}; therefore, the activity should have decreased by about $\frac{3}{4}$.

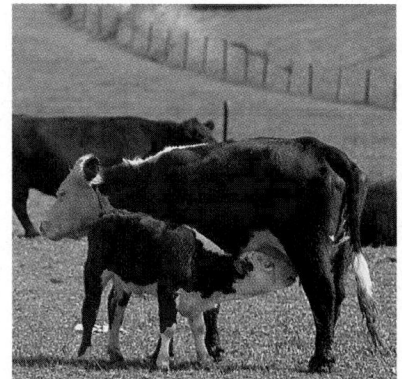

COMMENT An *alternative approach* is to use the number of half-lives ($t/t_{1/2}$) to find the fraction of activity (or nuclei) remaining. By combining Equations 24.3 and 24.4 and substituting $\ln 2/t_{1/2}$ for k, we obtain

$$\ln \frac{\mathscr{N}_0}{\mathscr{N}_t} = \left(\frac{\ln 2}{t_{1/2}}\right)t = \frac{t}{t_{1/2}} \ln 2 = \ln 2^{t/t_{1/2}}$$

Thus,

$$\ln \frac{\mathscr{N}_t}{\mathscr{N}_0} = \ln \left(\frac{1}{2}\right)^{t/t_{1/2}}$$

Taking the antilog gives

$$\text{Fraction remaining} = \frac{\mathscr{N}_t}{\mathscr{N}_0} = \left(\frac{1}{2}\right)^{t/t_{1/2}} = \left(\frac{1}{2}\right)^{59/29} = 0.24$$

So,

$$\text{Fraction decayed} = 1.00 - 0.24 = 0.76$$

Follow-up Problem 24.4 Sodium-24 has a half-life of 15 h and is used to study blood circulation. If a patient is injected with a ^{24}NaCl solution whose activity is 2.5×10^9 d/s, how much of the activity is present in the patient's body and excreted fluids after 4.0 days?

Radioisotopic Dating

The historical record dims rapidly with time and virtually disappears for events of more than a few thousand years ago. Much of our understanding of prehistory comes from a technique called **radioisotopic dating,** which uses **radioisotopes** to determine the age of an object. The method supplies data about the ages of objects in fields as diverse as art history, archeology, geology, and paleontology.

The technique of *radiocarbon dating,* for which the American chemist Willard F. Libby won the Nobel Prize in 1960, is based on measuring the amounts of ^{14}C and ^{12}C in materials of biological origin. The accuracy of the method falls off after about four half-lives of ^{14}C ($t_{1/2} = 5730$ yr), so it is used to date objects up to about 24,000 years old.

Here is how the method works. High-energy neutrons caused by cosmic ray collisions reach Earth continually from outer space. They enter the upper atmosphere and cause the slow formation of ^{14}C through bombardment of ordinary ^{14}N atoms:

$$^{14}_{7}\text{N} + ^{1}_{0}\text{n} \longrightarrow ^{14}_{6}\text{C} + ^{1}_{1}\text{p}$$

Through the processes of formation and radioactive decay, the amount of ^{14}C has remained nearly constant.*

The ^{14}C atoms combine with O_2, diffuse throughout the lower atmosphere, and enter the total carbon pool as gaseous $^{14}CO_2$ and aqueous $H^{14}CO_3^{-}$. There they mix with ordinary $^{12}CO_2$ and $H^{12}CO_3^{-}$ and reach a constant $^{12}C/^{14}C$ ratio of about $10^{12}/1$. The CO_2 is taken up by plants during photosynthesis, and then taken up and excreted by animals that eat the plants. Thus, the $^{12}C/^{14}C$ ratio of a living organism has the same constant value as the environment. When an organism dies, however, it no longer takes in ^{14}C, so the $^{12}C/^{14}C$ ratio steadily increases because the *^{14}C decreases as it decays*:

$$^{14}_{6}\text{C} \longrightarrow ^{14}_{7}\text{N} + ^{0}_{-1}\beta$$

The difference between the $^{12}C/^{14}C$ ratio in a dead organism and the ratio in living organisms reflects the time elapsed since the organism died. ◆

◆ **The Case of the Shroud of Turin** One of the holiest relics of the Christian world is the famed Shroud of Turin. It is a piece of linen that bears a faint image of a man's body and was thought to be the burial cloth used to wrap the body of Jesus Christ. In 1988, after much controversy, the Vatican allowed scientific testing of the age of the cloth by radiocarbon dating. Three laboratories in Europe and the United States independently measured the $^{12}C/^{14}C$ ratio of a 50-mg piece of the linen and determined that the flax from which the cloth was made was grown between 1260 AD and 1390 AD. Despite this evidence, the shroud lost none of its fascination because 10 years later, in 1998, when the shroud was again put on display, about 2 million people lined up to view it.

---

*Actually, cosmic ray intensity varies slightly with time, which affects the proportion of atmospheric ^{14}C. By counting the ^{14}C activity in growth rings of ancient trees, we know that the amount of ^{14}C fell slightly about 3000 years ago to current levels. Human activity in this century, such as nuclear bomb testing and fossil fuel combustion, has also altered the fraction of ^{14}C slightly. None of these findings affects the overall accuracy of the dating method, however. In fact, taking them into account improves the accuracy.

Figure 24.5 **Radiocarbon dating for determining the age of artifacts.** The natural logarithms of the ^{14}C specific activity of various artifacts are projected onto a line whose slope equals $-k$, the negative of the ^{14}C decay constant. The age of an artifact is determined from the time axis.

◆ **How Old Is the Solar System?** By comparing the ratio of ^{238}U to its final decay product, ^{206}Pb, geochemists have found that the oldest known surface rocks—granite in western Greenland—are about 3.7 billion years old. The ratio of $^{238}U/^{206}Pb$ in meteorites gives 4.55 billion years for the age of the Solar System, and thus the Earth. These estimates have been checked with other isotope systems, such as $^{40}K/^{40}Ar$ ($t_{1/2}$ of ^{40}K = 1.3×10^9 yr) and $^{87}Rb/^{87}Sr$ ($t_{1/2}$ of ^{87}Rb = 4.9×10^{10} yr). From rocks collected by Apollo astronauts, these methods date the Moon as 4.2 billion years old and provide evidence for volcanic activity on its surface about 3.3 billion years ago, about the time that, according to these methods, the first organisms were evolving on Earth.

As you saw in Sample Problem 24.4, the first-order rate equation can be expressed in terms of a ratio of activities:

$$\ln \frac{\mathcal{N}_0}{\mathcal{N}_t} = \ln \frac{\mathcal{A}_0}{\mathcal{A}_t} = kt$$

We use this expression in radiocarbon dating, where $\mathcal{A}_0$ is the activity in a living organism and $\mathcal{A}_t$ is the activity in the object whose age is unknown. Solving for t gives the age of the object:

$$t = \frac{1}{k} \ln \frac{\mathcal{A}_0}{\mathcal{A}_t} \tag{24.5}$$

A useful graphical method in radioisotopic dating shows a plot of the natural logarithm of the specific activity vs. time, which gives a straight line with a slope of $-k$, the negative of the decay constant. Using such a plot and measuring the ^{14}C specific activity of an object, we can determine its age; several examples appear in Figure 24.5. To determine the ages of more ancient objects or of objects that do not contain carbon, different radioisotopes are measured. ◆

Sample Problem 24.5   Applying Radiocarbon Dating

PROBLEM The charred bones of a sloth in a cave in Chile represent the earliest evidence of human presence in the southern tip of South America. A sample of the bone has a specific activity of 5.22 disintegrations per minute per gram of carbon (d/min·g). If the ratio of $^{12}C/^{14}C$ in living organisms results in a specific activity of 15.3 d/min·g, how old are the bones? ($t_{1/2}$ of ^{14}C = 5730 yr.)

PLAN We know the activities of the bones ($\mathcal{A}_t$) and of a living organism ($\mathcal{A}_0$), so we calculate k from $t_{1/2}$ and apply Equation 24.5 to find the age (t) of the bones.

SOLUTION Calculating k for ^{14}C decay:

$$k = \frac{\ln 2}{t_{1/2}} = \frac{0.693}{5730 \text{ yr}} = 1.21 \times 10^{-4} \text{ yr}^{-1}$$

Calculating the age (t) of the bones:

$$t = \frac{1}{k} \ln \frac{\mathscr{A}_0}{\mathscr{A}_t} = \frac{1}{1.21 \times 10^{-4} \text{ yr}^{-1}} \ln \left(\frac{15.3 \text{ d/min} \cdot \text{g}}{5.22 \text{ d/min} \cdot \text{g}} \right) = 8.89 \times 10^3 \text{ yr}$$

The bones are about 8900 yr old.

CHECK Since the activity of the bones is between $\frac{1}{2}$ and $\frac{1}{4}$ the modern activity, the age should be between one and two half-lives (5730 to 11,460 yr).

Follow-up Problem 24.5 A sample of wood from an Egyptian mummy case (see photo) has a specific activity of 9.41 d/min · g. How old is the case?

Section Summary

Ionization and scintillation counters measure the number of emissions from a radioactive sample. The decay rate (activity) of a sample is proportional to the number of radioactive nuclei. Nuclear decay is a first-order process, so the half-life does not depend on the number of nuclei. Radioisotopic dating methods, such as ^{14}C dating, can determine the ages of objects by measuring the ratio of specific isotopes in the sample.

24.3 Nuclear Transmutation: Induced Changes in Nuclei

The alchemists' dream of changing base metals into gold was never realized, but in the early 20th century, atomic physicists found that they *could* change one element into another. Research into **nuclear transmutation,** the *induced* conversion of one nucleus into another, was closely linked with research into atomic structure and led to the discovery of the neutron and to the production of artificial radioisotopes. Later, high-energy bombardment of nuclei in particle accelerators began a scientific endeavour, which continues to this day, of creating many new isotopes and a growing number of new elements.

Early Transmutation Experiments; Discovery of the Neutron

The first recognized transmutation occurred in 1919, when Ernest Rutherford showed that α particles emitted from radium bombarded atmospheric nitrogen to form a proton and oxygen-17:

$$^{14}_{7}\text{N} + ^{4}_{2}\text{He} \longrightarrow ^{1}_{1}\text{H} + ^{17}_{8}\text{O}$$

By 1926, experimenters had found that α bombardment transmuted most elements with low atomic numbers to the next higher element, with ejection of a proton.

A shorthand notation commonly used for nuclear bombardment reactions shows the reactant (target) nucleus and product nucleus separated by parentheses, within which a comma separates the projectile particle from the ejected particle(s):

Reactant nucleus (particle in, particle(s) out) product nucleus

Using this notation, the previous reaction is ^{14}N (α,p) ^{17}O.

An unexpected finding in a transmutation experiment led to the discovery of the neutron. When lithium, beryllium, and boron were bombarded with α particles, they emitted highly penetrating radiation that could not be deflected by a magnetic or electric field. Unlike γ radiation, these emissions

The Curie-Joliots in their laboratory.

were massive enough to eject protons from the substances they penetrated. In 1932, James Chadwick, a student of Rutherford, proposed that these emissions consisted of neutral particles with a mass similar to that of a proton, and he named them *neutrons*. Chadwick received the Nobel Prize in 1935 for his discovery.

In 1933, Irene and Frederic Curie-Joliot (see photo), daughter and son-in-law of Marie and Pierre Curie, created the first artificial radioisotope, phosphorus-30. When they bombarded aluminum foil with α particles, phosphorus-30 and neutrons were formed:

$$\ce{^{27}_{13}Al} + \ce{^{4}_{2}He} \longrightarrow \ce{^{1}_{0}n} + \ce{^{30}_{15}P} \quad \text{or} \quad ^{27}\text{Al} \, (\alpha,n) \, ^{30}\text{P}$$

Since then, other techniques for producing artificial radioisotopes have been developed. In fact, the majority of the nearly 1000 known radioisotopes have been produced artificially.

Particle Accelerators and the Transuranium Elements

During the 1930s and 1940s, researchers probing the nucleus bombarded elements with neutrons, α particles, protons, and **deuterons** (nuclei of the stable hydrogen isotope deuterium, ^2H). Neutrons are especially useful as projectiles because they have no charge, so they are not repelled as they approach a target nucleus. The other particles are all positive, so at first it was difficult to give them enough energy to overcome their repulsion by the target nuclei. Beginning in the 1930s, however, **particle accelerators** were invented to impart high kinetic energies to particles by placing them in an electric field, usually in combination with a magnetic field. In the simplest design, protons are introduced at one end of a tube and attracted to the other end by a potential difference.

A major advance occurred with the invention of the *linear accelerator*, a series of separated tubes of increasing length that change their charge from positive to negative in synchrony with the movement of the particle through them (Figure 24.6A). A proton, for example, exits the first tube just when that tube becomes positive and the next tube negative. Repelled by the first tube and attracted by the second, the proton accelerates across the gap between them. A 40-ft linear accelerator with 46 tubes, built in California after World War II, accelerated protons to speeds several million times faster than that first accelerator. Modern designs, such as the Stanford Linear Accelerator (Figure 24.6B), accelerate heavier particles, such as B, C, O, and Ne nuclei, several hundred million times faster, with correspondingly greater kinetic energies.

A

B

Figure 24.6 A linear accelerator. A, The voltage of each tubular section is alternated, such that the positively charged particle (a proton here) is repelled from the section it is leaving and attracted to the section it is entering. As a result, the particle speed is continually increased. **B,** The linear accelerator operated by Stanford University in California.

Figure 24.7 The cyclotron accelerator. When the positively charged particle reaches the gap between the two D-shaped electrodes ("dees"), it is repelled by one dee and attracted by the other. The particles move in a spiral path, so the cyclotron can be much smaller than a linear accelerator.

The *cyclotron* (Figure 24.7), invented by E. O. Lawrence in 1930, applies the principle of the linear accelerator but uses electromagnets to give the particle a spiral path, thus saving space. The magnets lie above and below two "dees," open, D-shaped electrodes within an evacuated chamber that function like the tubes in the linear design. The particle is accelerated as it passes from one dee chamber, which is momentarily positive, to the next, which is momentarily negative. Its speed and radius increase until it is deflected toward the target nucleus. The *synchrotron* uses a synchronously increasing magnetic field to make the particle's path circular rather than spiral. ◆

Accelerators have many applications, from producing radioisotopes used in medical applications to studying the fundamental nature of matter. Perhaps their most specific application for chemists is the synthesis of **transuranium elements,** those with atomic numbers higher than uranium, which is the heaviest naturally occurring element. Some reactions that were used to form several of these elements appear in Table 24.6. The transuranium elements include the remaining actinides ($Z = 93$ to 103), which fill the $5f$ sublevel, and the elements in the fourth transition series ($Z = 104$ to 112), which fill

◆ **The Powerful Bevatron** The *bevatron* includes a linear section and a synchrotron section. The instrument at the Lawrence Berkeley Laboratory in California increases the kinetic energy of the particles more than 6 billion fold. A beam of 10^{10} protons makes more than 4 million revolutions, a distance of 300,000 miles, in 1.8 s, attaining a final speed about 90% the speed of light! Even more powerful bevatrons are in use at the Brookhaven National Laboratory in New York and at CERN, outside Geneva, Switzerland. At one of the CERN facilites (see photo), separate bending and focusing magnets accelerate protons along a 4.3-mile circular tunnel.

Table 24.6 Formation of Some Transuranium Nuclides

Reaction	Half-life of Product
$^{239}_{94}\text{Pu} + ^{4}_{2}\text{He} \longrightarrow ^{240}_{95}\text{Am} + ^{1}_{1}\text{H} + 2^{1}_{0}\text{n}$	50.9 h
$^{239}_{94}\text{Pu} + ^{4}_{2}\text{He} \longrightarrow ^{242}_{96}\text{Cm} + ^{1}_{0}\text{n}$	163 days
$^{244}_{96}\text{Cm} + ^{4}_{2}\text{He} \longrightarrow ^{245}_{97}\text{Bk} + ^{1}_{1}\text{H} + 2^{1}_{0}\text{n}$	4.94 days
$^{238}_{92}\text{U} + ^{12}_{6}\text{C} \longrightarrow ^{246}_{98}\text{Cf} + 4^{1}_{0}\text{n}$	36 h
$^{253}_{99}\text{Es} + ^{4}_{2}\text{He} \longrightarrow ^{256}_{101}\text{Md} + ^{1}_{0}\text{n}$	76 min
$^{252}_{98}\text{Cf} + ^{10}_{5}\text{B} \longrightarrow ^{256}_{103}\text{Lr} + 6^{1}_{0}\text{n}$	28 s

◆ **Naming Transuranium Elements** The last naturally occurring element was named after Uranus, thought at the time to be the outermost planet, so the first two artificial elements were named after the more recently discovered Neptune and Pluto. The next few elements were named after famous scientists, as in curium, and places, as in americium. However, conflicting claims of discovery by scientists in different countries led to controversies about names for elements 104 and higher. To provide interim names until the disputes could be settled, the International Union of Pure and Applied Chemistry (IUPAC) adopted a system that uses the atomic number as the basis for a Latin name. Thus, for example, element 104 was named unnilquadium (un = 1, nil = 0, quad = 4, ium = element suffix), with the symbol Unq. After much compromise, the IUPAC has finalized these names: 104, rutherfordium (Rf); 105, dubnium (Db); 106, seaborgium (Sg); 107, bohrium (Bh); 108, hassium (Hs); 109, meitnerium (Mt). Elements with atomic numbers 110 and higher have not yet been named.

the $6d$ sublevel. (A recent report indicates that Element 114, the second element in the $7p$ sublevel, has been synthesized.) ◆

Section Summary

One nucleus can be transmuted to another through bombardment with high-energy particles. Accelerators increase the kinetic energy of particles in nuclear bombardment experiments and are used to produce transuranium elements.

24.4 The Effects of Nuclear Radiation on Matter

In 1986, an accident at the Chernobyl nuclear facility in the former Soviet Union released radioactivity that is estimated to have already caused thousands of cancer deaths. In the same year, isotopes used in medical treatment emitted radioactivity that has prevented thousands of cancer deaths. In this section and the next, we examine the harm and benefit of radioactivity.

The key to both of these outcomes is that *nuclear changes cause chemical changes in surrounding matter*. In other words, even though the nucleus of an atom undergoes a reaction with little or no involvement of the atom's electrons, the emissions *do* affect the electrons of nearby atoms.

The Effects of Radioactive Emissions: Excitation and Ionization

Radioactive emissions interact with matter in two ways that depend on their energies:

- *Excitation.* In the process of **excitation,** a particle of relatively low energy collides with an atom of a substance, which absorbs some of the energy and then reemits it. Because electrons are not lost from the atom, the radiation that causes excitation is called **nonionizing radiation.** If the absorbed energy causes the atoms to move, vibrate, or rotate more rapidly, the material becomes hotter. Concentrated aqueous solutions of plutonium salts boil because the emissions excite the surrounding water molecules. Polonium has been suggested as a lightweight heat source, with no moving parts, for use on space stations. Particles of somewhat higher energy excite electrons in other atoms to higher energy levels. As the atoms return to their ground state, they emit photons, often in the blue or ultraviolet region (see scintillation counters in the earlier Tools of the Chemistry Laboratory essay).

- *Ionization.* In the process of **ionization,** radiation collides with an atom energetically enough to dislodge an electron:

$$\text{atom} \xrightarrow{\text{ionizing radiation}} \text{ion}^+ + e^-$$

A cation and free electron result, and the number of such *cation-electron pairs* that are produced is directly related to the energy of the incoming radiation. The high-energy radiation that gives rise to this effect is called **ionizing radiation.** The free electron of the pair often collides with another atom and ejects a second electron (see Geiger-Müller counters in the earlier Tools essay).

Effects of Ionizing Radiation on Living Matter

Whereas nonionizing radiation is relatively harmless, ionizing radiation has a destructive effect on living tissue. When the atom that was ionized is part of a biological macromolecule or membrane component, the results can be devastating.

Units of Radiation Dose and Its Effects   To measure the effects of ionizing radiation, we need a unit for radiation dose. Units of radioactive decay, such as the becquerel and curie, state the number of decay events in a given time but not their energy or absorption by matter. The number of cation-electron pairs produced in a given amount of living tissue is a measure of the energy absorbed by the tissue. The SI unit for such energy absorption is the **gray (Gy)**; it is equal to 1 joule of energy absorbed per kilogram of body tissue: 1 Gy = 1 J/kg. A more widely used unit is the **rad (radiation-absorbed dose)**, which is equal to 0.01 Gy:

$$1 \text{ rad} = 0.01 \text{ J/kg} = 0.01 \text{ Gy}$$

To measure actual tissue damage, we must account for differences in the strength of the radiation, the exposure time, and the type of tissue. To do this, we multiply the number of rads by a *relative biological effectiveness* (RBE) factor, which depends on the effect of a given type of radiation on a given tissue or body part. The product is the **rem (roentgen equivalent for man)**, the unit of radiation dosage equivalent to a given amount of tissue damage in a human:

$$\text{no. of rems} = \text{no. of rads} \times \text{RBE}$$

Doses are often expressed in millirems (10^{-3} rem). The SI unit for dosage equivalent is the **sievert (Sv)**. It is defined in the same way as the rem but with absorbed dose in grays; thus, 1 rem = 0.01 Sv.

Penetrating Power of Emissions The effect on living tissue of a radiation dose depends on the penetrating power *and* ionizing ability of the radiation. Figure 24.8 depicts the differences in penetrating power of the three common emissions. Note, in general, that *penetrating power is inversely related to the mass and charge of the emission*. In other words, if a particle interacts strongly with matter, it penetrates only slightly, and vice versa:

- *α Particles.* Alpha particles are massive and highly charged, which means they interact with matter most strongly of the three common types of emissions. As a result, they penetrate so little that a piece of paper, light clothing, or the outer skin can stop α radiation from an external source. However, if ingested, an α emitter such as plutonium-239 causes grave localized damage through extensive ionization. ◆
- *β Particles and positrons.* Beta particles and positrons have less charge and much less mass than α particles, so they interact less strongly with matter. Even though a given β particle has less chance of causing ionization, a β (or positron) emitter is a more destructive external source because the particles penetrate deeper. Specialized heavy clothing or a thick (0.5 cm) piece of metal is required to stop β particles.
- *γ Rays.* Neutral, massless γ rays interact least with matter and, thus, penetrate most. A block of lead several inches thick is needed to stop them. Therefore, an external γ ray source is the most dangerous because the energy can ionize many layers of living tissue.

Molecular Interactions How does the damage take place on the molecular level? When ionizing radiation interacts with a molecule, it causes the *loss of an electron from a bond or lone pair*. The resulting charged species go on to form **free radicals,** molecular or atomic species with one or more unpaired (lone) electrons. As we've seen several times already, species with lone electrons are very reactive and tend to form electron pairs by bonding to other species. To do this, they attack bonds in other molecules, sometimes forming more free radicals.

When γ radiation strikes biological tissue, for instance, the most likely molecule to absorb it is water, which forms an electron and a water ion-radical:

$$H_2O + \gamma \longrightarrow H_2O^{\cdot +} + e^-$$

The $H_2O^{\cdot +}$ and e^- collide with other water molecules to form free radicals:

$$H_2O^{\cdot +} + H_2O \longrightarrow H_3O^+ + \cdot OH \qquad \text{and} \qquad e^- + H_2O \longrightarrow H\cdot + OH^-$$

α (~0.03 mm)
β (~2 mm)
γ (~10 cm)

Figure 24.8 Penetrating power of radioactive emissions. Penetrating power is often measured in terms of the depth of water that stops 50% of the incoming radiation. Water is used because it is the main component of living tissue. α Particles, with the highest mass and charge, have the lowest penetrating power and γ rays the highest. (Average values of penetrating distances are shown.)

◆ **A Tragic Way to Tell Time in the Dark** In the first quarter of this century, wristwatch and clock dials were painted by hand with radium-containing paint, so it would "glow" in the dark. To write the numbers clearly, the young women hired to apply the paint "tipped" the fine brushes repeatedly between their lips. Small amounts of ingested $^{226}Ra^{2+}$ were incorporated into the bones of these women, along with normal Ca^{2+}, which led to numerous cases of bone fracture and jaw cancer.

These free radicals go on to attack more water molecules and surrounding biomolecules, whose bonding and structure, as you know (Section 15.6), are intimately connected with their function.

The double bonds in membrane lipids are particularly susceptible to free-radical attack:

$$H\cdot + RCH{=}CHR' \longrightarrow RCH_2{-}\dot{C}HR'$$

In this reaction, one electron of the π bond forms a C—H bond between the C on the left and the H·, and the other electron resides on the C on the right to form a free radical. Changes to lipid structure cause changes in membrane fluidity and other damage that, in turn, causes leakage of the cell and destruction of the protective fatty tissue around organs. Changes to critical bonds in enzymes lead to their malfunction as catalysts of metabolic reactions. Changes in the nucleic acids and proteins that govern the rate of cell division cause cancer. Genetic damage and mutations may occur when bonds in the DNA of sperm and egg cells are altered by free radicals.

Sources of Ionizing Radiation Having seen the molecular effects of ionizing radiation, it is essential to keep these ideas in perspective. After all, we are continuously exposed to ionizing radiation from natural and artificial sources (Table 24.7). Indeed, life evolved in the presence of natural ionizing radiation, called **background radiation.** The same radiation that causes harmful mutations also causes beneficial mutations that, over time, allow organisms to adapt and species to change.

Table 24.7 Examples of Typical Radiation Doses from Natural and Artificial Sources

Source of Radiation	Average Adult Exposure
Natural	
Cosmic radiation	30-50 mrem/yr
Radiation from the ground	
From clay soil and rocks	~25-170 mrem/yr
In wooden houses	10-20 mrem/yr
In brick houses	60-70 mrem/yr
In light concrete houses	60-160 mrem/yr
Radiation from the air (mainly radon)	
Outdoors, average value	20 mrem/yr
In wooden houses	70 mrem/yr
In brick houses	130 mrem/yr
In light concrete houses	260 mrem/yr
Internal radiation from minerals in tap water and daily intake of food (^{40}K, ^{14}C, Ra)	~40 mrem/yr
Artificial	
Diagnostic x-ray methods	
Lung (local)	0.04-0.2 rad/film
Kidney (local)	1.5-3 rad/film
Dental (dose to the skin)	≤1 rad/film
Therapeutic radiation treatment	Locally ≤ 10,000 rad
Other sources	
Jet flight (4 h)	~1 mrem
Nuclear testing	<4 mrem/yr
Nuclear power industry	<1 mrem/yr
Total average value	100-200 mrem/yr

Background radiation has several sources. One source is *cosmic radiation,* which increases with altitude because of decreased absorption by the atmosphere. Thus, people in Denver absorb twice as much cosmic radiation as people in Los Angeles; even a jet flight involves measurable absorption. The sources of most background radiation are thorium and uranium minerals present in rocks and soil. Radon, the heaviest noble gas [Group 8A(18)], is a radioactive product of uranium and thorium decay, and its concentration in the air we breathe varies with type of local soil and rocks. ◆ About 150 g of K^+ ions is dissolved in the tissue water of an average adult, and 0.0118% of that amount is radioactive ^{40}K. The presence of these substances and of atmospheric $^{14}CO_2$ means that all food, water, clothing, and building materials are slightly radioactive.

The largest artificial source of radiation, and the easiest to control, is associated with medical diagnostic techniques, especially x-rays. The radiation dosage from nuclear testing and radioactive waste disposal is miniscule for most people, but exposures for those living near test sites, nuclear energy facilities, or disposal areas are many times higher.

Assessing the Risk from Ionizing Radiation How much radiation is too much? To approach the question, we must ask several others: How strong is the exposure? How long is the exposure? Which tissue is exposed? Are offspring affected? One reason we lack clear data to answer these questions is that scientific ethical standards forbid the intentional exposure of humans in an experimental setting. However, accidentally exposed radiation workers and Japanese atomic bomb survivors have been studied extensively. Table 24.8 summarizes the immediate tissue effects on humans of an acute single dose of ionizing radiation to the whole body. The severity of the effects increases with dose; a dose of 500 rem will kill about 50% of the exposed population within a month.

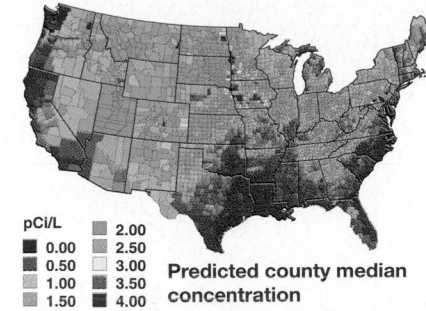

pCi/L
■ 0.00	■ 2.00
■ 0.50	☐ 2.50
■ 1.00	■ 3.00
☐ 1.50	■ 3.50
	☐ 4.00

Predicted county median concentration

◆ **The Risk of Radon** Radon (Rn; $Z = 86$), the largest noble gas, is a natural decay product of uranium. Therefore, the uranium content of the local soil and rocks is a critical factor in the extent of the threat, but radon occurs everywhere in varying concentrations. Radon itself decays to radioactive nuclides of Po, Pb, and Bi, through α, β, and γ emission. These processes occur inside the body when radon is inhaled and pose a serious potential hazard. Furthermore, particles in cigarette smoke adsorb the emissions and thus offer the perfect vehicle for entering and remaining in the lungs. The emitted particles damage lung tissue, and the heavy-metal atoms formed aggravate the problem. The latest EPA estimates indicate that radon contributes to 15% of annual lung cancer deaths.

Table 24.8 Acute Effects of a Single Dose of Whole-Body Irradiation

Dose (rem)	Effect	Lethal Dose Population (%)	No. of Days
5-20	Possible late effect; possible chromosomal aberrations	—	—
20-100	Temporary reduction in white blood cells	—	—
50+	Temporary sterility in men (100+ rem = 1 yr duration)	—	—
100-200	"Mild radiation sickness": vomiting, diarrhea, tiredness in a few hours Reduction in infection resistance Possible bone growth retardation in children	—	—
300+	Permanent sterility in women	—	—
500	"Serious radiation sickness": marrow/intestine destruction	50-70	30
400-1000	Acute illness, early deaths	60-95	30
3000+	Acute illness, death in hours to days	100	2

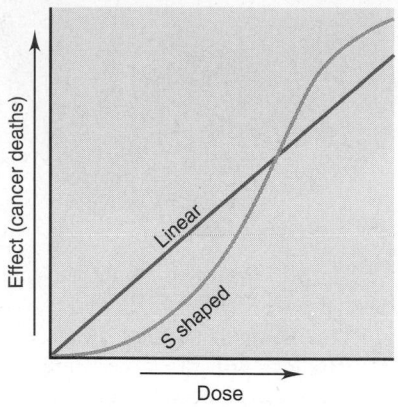

Modeling Radiation Risk
There are two current models of effect vs. dose. The *linear response* model proposes that radiation effects, such as cancer risks, accumulate over time regardless of dose and that populations should not be exposed to any radiation above background levels. The *S-shaped response* assumes an extremely low risk at low doses and that there is concern only at higher doses. If the linear model is more accurate, we should limit all excess exposure, but this would severely restrict medical diagnosis and research, military testing, and nuclear energy production.

Most data come from laboratory animals, whose biological systems may differ greatly from ours. Nevertheless, studies with mice and dogs show that lesions and cancers appear after massive whole-body exposure, with rapidly dividing cells affected first. In an adult animal, these are the cells of the bone marrow, organ linings, and reproductive organs, but many other tissues are affected in an immature animal or fetus. Both animal and human studies show an increase in the incidence of cancer from either a high, single exposure or a low, chronic exposure.

Reliable data on genetic effects are few. Pioneering studies on fruit flies show a linear increase in genetic defects with both dose and exposure time. However, in the mouse, whose genetic system is obviously much more similar to ours than is the fruit fly's, a total dose given over a long period created one-third as many genetic defects as the same dose given over a short period. Thus, rate of exposure is a key factor. Children of atomic bomb survivors show higher-than-normal cancer rates, which implies that their parents' reproductive systems were affected. ◆

Section Summary

Relatively low-energy emissions cause excitation of surrounding matter, whereas high-energy emissions cause ionization. The effect of ionizing radiation on living matter depends on the quantity of energy absorbed and the extent of ionization in a given type of tissue. Radiation dose for the human body is measured in rem. Ionization forms free radicals, some of which proliferate and destroy biomolecular function. All life is exposed to varying quantities of natural ionizing radiation. Studies show that a large acute dose and a chronic small dose are both harmful.

24.5 Applications of Radioisotopes

Our ability to detect minute amounts of a radioisotope makes them powerful tools for studying processes in biochemistry, medicine, materials science, meteorology, and many other fields. Such uses depend on the fact that *isotopes of an element exhibit **very** similar chemical and physical behavior*. In other words, except for having a less stable nucleus, a radioisotope has nearly the same chemical properties as a nonradioactive isotope of that element.* For example, the fact that $^{14}CO_2$ is utilized by a plant in the same way as $^{12}CO_2$ forms the basis of radiocarbon dating.

Radioactive Tracers: Applications of Nonionizing Radiation

Just think how useful it would be to follow a substance through the stages of a complex process or from one region of a system to another. A tiny amount of a radioisotope mixed with a large amount of the stable isotope would act as a **tracer,** a chemical "beacon" emitting nonionizing radiation that signals the presence of the substance.

Reaction Pathways Tracers help us choose from among possible reaction pathways. Consider the redox reaction between periodate and iodide ions:

$$IO_4^-(aq) + 2I^-(aq) + H_2O(l) \longrightarrow I_2(s) + IO_3^-(aq) + 2OH^-(aq)$$

---

*Although this statement is generally correct, differences in isotopic mass *can* influence bond strengths and therefore reaction rates. Such behavior is called a *kinetic isotope effect* and is particularly important for isotopes of hydrogen—^1H, ^2H, and ^3H—because their masses differ by such large proportions. Section 22.4 discusses how the kinetic isotope effect is employed in the industrial production of heavy water, D_2O.

Is IO_3^- the result of IO_4^- reduction or I^- oxidation? When we add "cold" (nonradioactive) IO_4^- to a solution of I^- that contains some "hot" (radioactive) $^{131}I^-$, we find that the I_2 is radioactive, not the IO_3^-:

$$IO_4^-(aq) + 2\,^{131}I^-(aq) + H_2O(l) \longrightarrow \,^{131}I_2(s) + IO_3^-(aq) + 2OH^-(aq)$$

These results show that IO_3^- forms through the reduction of IO_4^-, and that I_2 forms through the oxidation of I^-. To confirm this pathway, we add IO_4^- containing some hot $^{131}IO_4^-$ to a solution of cold I^-. As we expected, the IO_3^- is radioactive, not the I_2:

$$^{131}IO_4^-(aq) + 2I^-(aq) + H_2O(l) \longrightarrow I_2(s) + \,^{131}IO_3^-(aq) + 2OH^-(aq)$$

The tracer acts almost as a "handle" we can "hold" to follow the changing reactants.

Far more complex pathways can be followed with tracers as well. The photosynthetic pathway, the most essential and widespread metabolic process on Earth, in which energy from sunlight is used to form the chemical bonds of glucose, has an overall reaction that looks quite simple:

$$6CO_2(g) + 6H_2O(l) \xrightarrow[\text{chlorophyll}]{\text{light}} C_6H_{12}O_6(s) + 6O_2(g)$$

However, the actual process is extremely complex, requiring 13 enzyme-catalyzed steps for each molecule of CO_2 incorporated, which occurs six times through the pathway for each molecule of $C_6H_{12}O_6$ that forms. Melvin Calvin and his co-workers took seven years to determine the pathway, using ^{14}C in CO_2 as the tracer and paper chromatography as the means of separating the products formed after different times of light exposure. Calvin won the Nobel Prize in 1961 for this remarkable achievement.

Material Flow Tracers are used in studies of solid surfaces and the flow of materials. Metal atoms hundreds of layers deep within a solid have been shown to exchange with metal ions from the surrounding solution within a matter of minutes. Chemists and engineers use tracers to study material movement in semiconductor chips, paint, and metal plating; in detergent action; and in the process of corrosion, to mention just a few of many applications.

Hydrologic engineers use tracers to study the volume and flow of large bodies of water. By following radioisotopes formed during atmospheric nuclear bomb tests (^3H in H_2O, $^{90}Sr^{2+}$, and $^{137}Cs^+$), scientists have mapped the flow of water from land to lakes and streams to oceans. Surface and deep ocean currents that circulate around the globe are also studied, as are the mechanisms of hurricane formation and the mixing of the troposphere and stratosphere. Industries employ tracers to study material flow during a manufacturing process, such as the flow of ore pellets in smelting kilns, the paths of wood chips and bleach in paper mills, the diffusion of fungicide into lumber, and the location of leaks in pipes and storage tanks.

Activation Analysis A somewhat different use of tracers occurs in *neutron activation analysis* (NAA). In this method, neutrons bombard a nonradioactive sample, converting a small fraction of its atoms to radioisotopes, which exhibit characteristic decay patterns, such as γ-ray spectra, that reveal the elements present. Unlike chemical analysis, NAA leaves the sample virtually intact, so the method can be used to determine the composition of a valuable object or a very small sample. For example, a painting thought to be a 16th-century Dutch masterpiece was shown through NAA to be a 20th-century forgery, because a microgram sample of pigment was shown to contain much less silver and antimony than the pigments used by the Dutch masters. Forensic chemists use NAA to detect traces and type of ammunition on a suspect's hand or traces of arsenic in the hair of a victim of poisoning.

Sojourner heading toward Yogi (*top left*).

In early 1998, space scientists incorporated NAA instrumentation in the *Sojourner* robot vehicle to analyze the composition of Martian soils and rocks (see photo).

Automotive engineers employ NAA to measure friction and wear of moving parts such as piston rings. For example, when a steel surface that has been neutron-activated to form some radioactive ^{59}Fe moves against a second steel surface, the amount of radioactivity on the second surface indicates the amount of material rubbing off. The radioactivity appearing in a lubricant placed between the surfaces can demonstrate the lubricant's ability to reduce wear.

Medical Diagnosis The largest use of radioisotopes is in medical science. In fact, over 25% of U.S. hospital admissions are made for diagnoses based on data from radioisotopes. Tracers with half-lives of a few minutes to a few days are employed to observe specific organs and body parts. For example, a healthy thyroid gland incorporates dietary I$^-$ into I-containing hormones at a known rate. To assess thyroid function, the patient drinks a solution containing a trace amount of Na^{131}I, and a scanning monitor follows the uptake of ^{131}I into the thyroid (Figure 24.9A). Technetium-99 ($Z = 43$) is also used for imaging the thyroid (Figure 24.9B), as well as the heart, lungs, and liver. Technetium does not occur naturally, so the radioisotope (actually a "metastable" form, ^{99m}Tc) is prepared just before use from radioactive molybdenum:

$$^{99}_{42}\text{Mo} \longrightarrow {}^{99m}_{43}\text{Tc} + {}^{0}_{-1}\beta$$

Figure 24.9 The use of radioisotopes to image the thyroid gland. Thyroid scanning is used to assess nutritional deficiencies, inflammation, tumor growth, and other thyroid-related ailments. **A,** In ^{131}I scanning, the thyroid gland absorbs the I$^-$, and β emissions from the ^{131}I$^-$ expose a photographic film. The asymmetric image indicates disease. **B,** A ^{99}Tc scan of a thyroid.

A

B

Table 24.9 Some Radioisotopes Used as Medical Tracers

Isotope	Body Parts or Process Studied
^{18}F	Brain
^{99}Tc	Heart, thyroid, liver, lungs
^{24}Na	Circulatory system
^{131}I	Thyroid
^{32}P	Eyes, liver, tumors
^{201}Tl	Heart muscle
^{11}C	General metabolism
^{59}Fe	Blood flow

Tracers are also used to measure physiological processes, such as blood flow. The rate at which the heart pumps blood, for example, can be observed by injecting ^{59}Fe, which concentrates in the hemoglobin of blood cells. Several radioisotopes used in medical diagnosis are listed in Table 24.9.

Positron-emission tomography (PET) is a powerful imaging method for observing brain structure and function. A biological substance is synthesized with one of its atoms replaced by an isotope that emits positrons. The substance is injected into a patient's bloodstream, from which it is taken up into the brain. The isotope emits positrons, each of which annihilates a nearby electron. In the annihilation process, two γ photons are emitted simultaneously 180° apart from each other:

$$^{0}_{1}\beta + {}^{0}_{-1}e \longrightarrow 2{}^{0}_{0}\gamma$$

An array of detectors around the patient's head pinpoints the sites of γ emission, and the image is analyzed by computer. Two of the isotopes used are ^{15}O, injected as H$_2$^{15}O to measure blood flow, and ^{18}F bonded to a glucose analog to measure glucose uptake, which is a marker for energy metabolism.

Figure 24.10 **PET and brain activity.** These scans show brain activity from musical stimulation. The left and center scans occur with the same tone in different sequences; the right scan measures different timbre. Red indicates high activity within a region.

Among many fascinating new findings are those that show how changes in blood flow and glucose uptake accompany normal or abnormal brain activity (Figure 24.10). In a very recent nonmedical development, substances incorporating ^{11}C and ^{15}O are studied by PET to learn how molecules interact with and move along a catalytic surface.

Applications of Ionizing Radiation

To be used as a tracer, a radioisotope need emit only low-energy detectable radiation. Many other uses of radioisotopes, however, depend on the effects of high-energy, ionizing radiation.

The interaction between radiation and matter that causes cancer can also be used to eliminate it. Cancer cells divide more rapidly than normal cells, so radioisotopes that damage the cell-division process kill more cancer cells than normal ones. Implants of ^{198}Au or of a mixture of ^{90}Sr and ^{90}Y have been used to destroy pituitary and breast tumor cells, and γ rays from ^{60}Co have been used to destroy brain tumors.

Irradiation of food increases shelf life by killing microorganisms that cause food to rot (Figure 24.11), but the practice is quite controversial. Advocates point to the benefits of preserving fresh foods, grains, and seeds for long periods, whereas opponents suggest that irradiation might lower the food's nutritional content or produce harmful by-products. The increased use of antibiotics in animal feed has brought about an increased incidence of illness from newer, more-resistant bacterial strains, providing a stronger argument for the use of irradiation. The United Nations has approved irradiation for potatoes, wheat, chicken, and strawberries, and the United States allows irradiation of chicken.

Nonirradiated   Irradiated

Figure 24.11 **The increased shelf life of irradiated food.**

Ionizing radiation has been used to control harmful insects. Captured males are sterilized by radiation and released to mate, thereby reducing the number of offspring. This method has been used to control the Mediterranean fruit fly in California and disease-causing insects, such as the tsetse fly and malarial mosquito, in other parts of the world.

Section Summary

Radioisotopic tracers emit nonionizing radiation and have been used to study reaction mechanisms, material flow, elemental composition, and medical conditions. Ionizing radiation has been used to destroy cancerous tissue, kill organisms that spoil food, and control insect populations.

24.6 The Interconversion of Mass and Energy

Most of the nuclear processes we've considered so far have involved radioactive decay, in which a nucleus emits one or a few small particles or photons to become a slightly lighter nucleus. Two other nuclear processes cause much greater changes. In nuclear **fission,** a heavy nucleus splits into two much lighter nuclei, emitting several small particles at the same time. In nuclear **fusion,** the opposite process occurs as two lighter nuclei combine to form a heavier one. Both fission and fusion release enormous quantities of energy. Let's take a look at the basis of this energy by first examining the change in mass that accompanies the breakup of a nucleus into its nucleons and then considering the energy that is equivalent to this mass change.

The Mass Defect

We have known for most of the 20th century that mass and energy are interconvertible. The traditional mass and energy conservation laws have been combined to state that *the total quantity of mass-energy in the universe is constant.* Therefore, when *any* reacting system releases or absorbs energy, there must be an accompanying loss or gain in mass.

This relation between mass and energy did not concern us earlier because the energy changes involved in breaking or forming chemical bonds are so small that the mass changes are negligible. When 1 mol water breaks up into its atoms, for example, heat is absorbed:

$$H_2O(g) \longrightarrow 2H(g) + O(g) \qquad \Delta H^0_{rxn} = 2 \times BE \text{ of } O{-}H = 934 \text{ kJ}$$

We find the mass that is equivalent to this energy from Einstein's equation:

$$E = mc^2 \quad \text{or} \quad \Delta E = \Delta mc^2 \quad \text{so} \quad \Delta m = \frac{\Delta E}{c^2} \qquad \textbf{(24.6)}$$

where Δm is the change in mass between the reactants and the products. Substituting the heat of reaction (in J/mol) for ΔE and the value for c (2.9979×10^8 m/s), we obtain

$$\Delta m = \frac{9.34 \times 10^5 \text{ J/mol}}{(2.9979 \times 10^8 \text{ m/s})^2} = 1.04 \times 10^{-11} \text{ kg/mol} = 1.04 \times 10^{-8} \text{ g/mol}$$

(Units of kg/mol are obtained because the joule includes the kilogram: $1 \text{ J} = 1 \text{ kg} \cdot \text{m}^2/\text{s}^2$.) The mass of 1 mol H_2O (reactant) is about 10 ng *less* than the combined masses of 2 mol H plus 1 mol O (products), a change too small to measure with even the most sophisticated balance. Such minute mass changes when bonds break or form allow us to assume that mass is conserved in chemical reactions.

The much larger mass change that accompanies a nuclear process is related to the enormous energy required to bind the nucleus together or break it apart. Consider, for example, the change in mass that occurs when one ^{12}C nucleus breaks up into its nucleons: six protons and six neutrons. We calculate this change in mass by combining the mass of six H *atoms* and six neutrons and then subtracting the mass of one ^{12}C *atom*. This procedure cancels the masses of the electrons [six e^- (in six ^1H atoms) cancels six e^- (in one ^{12}C atom)]. The mass of one ^1H atom is 1.007825 amu, and the mass of one neutron is 1.008665 amu, so we have

$$\begin{aligned} \text{Mass of six } ^1H \text{ atoms} &= 6.046950 \text{ amu} \\ \underline{\text{Mass of six neutrons}} &= \underline{6.051990 \text{ amu}} \\ \text{Total mass} &= 12.098940 \text{ amu} \end{aligned}$$

The mass of one ^{12}C atom is 12 amu (exactly). The difference in mass (Δm) is the total mass of the nucleons minus the mass of the nucleus, so

$$\begin{aligned} \Delta m &= 12.098940 \text{ amu} - 12.000000 \text{ amu} \\ &= 0.098940 \text{ amu}/^{12}C = 0.098940 \text{ g/mol } ^{12}C \end{aligned}$$

Note that *the mass of the nucleus is **less** than the combined masses of its nucleons*. The mass decrease that occurs when nucleons are united into a nucleus is called the **mass defect (Δm).** Note that the size of this mass change (9.89×10^{-2} g/mol) is nearly 10 million times that of the previous bond breakage (1.04×10^{-8} g/mol) and is easily observed on any laboratory balance.

Nuclear Binding Energy

Einstein's equation for the relation between mass and energy also allows us to find the energy equivalent of a mass defect. For ^{12}C, after converting grams to kilograms, we have

$$\Delta E = \Delta mc^2 = (9.8940\times10^{-5} \text{ kg/mol})(2.9979\times10^8 \text{ m/s})^2$$
$$= 8.8921\times10^{12} \text{ J/mol} = 8.8921\times10^9 \text{ kJ/mol}$$

This quantity of energy is called the **nuclear binding energy** for carbon-12. In general, the nuclear binding energy is the quantity of energy required to *break up 1 mol of nuclei into their individual nucleons:*

$$\text{Nucleus} + \text{nuclear binding energy} \longrightarrow \text{nucleons}$$

Thus, in a qualitative sense, the nuclear binding energy is analogous to the sum of the bond energies of a compound. However, quantitatively, nuclear binding energies are typically several million times greater. ◆

We use joules to express the binding energy per mole of nuclei, but the joule is an impractically large unit to express the binding energy of a single nucleus. Instead, nuclear scientists use the **electron volt (eV),** the energy an electron acquires when it moves through a potential difference of one volt:

$$1 \text{ eV} = 1.602\times10^{-19} \text{ J}$$

Binding energies are commonly expressed in millions of electron volts, that is, in *megaelectron volts* (MeV):

$$1 \text{ MeV} = 10^6 \text{ eV} = 1.602\times10^{-13} \text{ J}$$

A particularly useful factor converts a given mass defect in atomic mass units to its energy equivalent in electron volts:

$$1 \text{ amu} = 931.5\times10^6 \text{ eV} = 931.5 \text{ MeV} \qquad \textbf{(24.7)}$$

Earlier we found the mass defect of the ^{12}C nucleus to be 0.098940 amu. Therefore, the binding energy per ^{12}C nucleus, expressed in MeV, is

$$\frac{\text{Binding energy}}{^{12}\text{C nucleus}} = 0.098940 \text{ amu} \times \frac{931.5 \text{ MeV}}{1 \text{ amu}} = 92.16 \text{ MeV}$$

We can compare the stability of nuclides of different elements by determining the *binding energy per nucleon.* For ^{12}C, we have

$$\frac{\text{Binding energy}}{\text{nucleon}} = \frac{92.16 \text{ MeV}}{12 \text{ nucleons}} = 7.680 \text{ MeV/nucleon}$$

The Force That Binds Us

According to current theory, the nuclear binding energy is related to the strong force, which holds nucleons together in a nucleus. There are three other fundamental forces: (1) the weak nuclear force, which is important in β decay, (2) the electrostatic force that we observe between charged particles, and (3) the gravitational force. Toward the end of his life, Albert Einstein tried unsuccessfully to develop a theory to explain how the four forces were really different aspects of one unified force that governs all nature. Through experiments with the next generation of giant accelerators, modern particle physicists will attempt to realize Einstein's dream.

Sample Problem 24.6 Calculating the Binding Energy per Nucleon

PROBLEM Iron-56 is an extremely stable nuclide. Compute the binding energy per nucleon for ^{56}Fe and compare it with that of ^{12}C. (Mass of ^{56}Fe atom = 55.934939 amu; mass of ^{1}H atom = 1.007825 amu; mass of neutron = 1.008665 amu.)

PLAN Iron-56 has 26 protons and 30 neutrons in its nucleus. We calculate the mass defect (Δm) by finding the sum of the masses of 26 ^{1}H atoms and 30 neutrons and subtracting the given mass of one ^{56}Fe atom. Then we multiply Δm by the equivalent in MeV and divide by 56 (the number of nucleons) to obtain the binding energy/nucleon.

Solution Calculating Δm:

$$\Delta m = [(26 \times \text{mass } {}^1\text{H atom}) + (30 \times \text{mass neutron})] - \text{mass } {}^{56}\text{Fe atom}$$
$$= [(26 \times 1.007825 \text{ amu}) + (30 \times 1.008665 \text{ amu})] - 55.934939 \text{ amu}$$
$$= 0.52846 \text{ amu}$$

Calculating the binding energy per nucleon:

$$\frac{\text{Binding energy}}{\text{nucleon}} = \frac{0.52846 \text{ amu} \times 931.5 \text{ MeV/amu}}{56 \text{ nucleons}} = \boxed{8.790 \text{ MeV/nucleon}}$$

An ${}^{56}\text{Fe}$ nucleus would require more energy to break up into its nucleons than would ${}^{12}\text{C}$ (7.680 MeV/nucleon), so ${}^{56}\text{Fe}$ is more stable than ${}^{12}\text{C}$.

Check The answer is consistent with the great stability of ${}^{56}\text{Fe}$. In view of the number of decimal places in the values, rounding to check the math is useful only to indicate a *major* error. The number of nucleons (56) is an exact number, so we retain four significant figures.

Follow-up Problem 24.6 Uranium-235 is the essential component of the fuel in nuclear energy facilities. Calculate the binding energy per nucleon of ${}^{235}\text{U}$. Is it more or less stable than ${}^{12}\text{C}$? (Mass of ${}^{235}\text{U}$ atom = 235.043924 amu.)

Fission or Fusion: Means of Increasing the Binding Energy Per Nucleon
Calculations similar to Sample Problem 24.6 for other nuclides show that the binding energy per nucleon varies considerably. The essential point is that *the greater the binding energy per nucleon, the more stable the nuclide.*

Figure 24.12 shows a plot of the negative of the binding energy per nucleon (to obtain a positive number) vs. mass number. It provides information about nuclide stability and the two possible processes nuclides undergo to form more stable nuclides. Nuclides with fewer than 10 nucleons

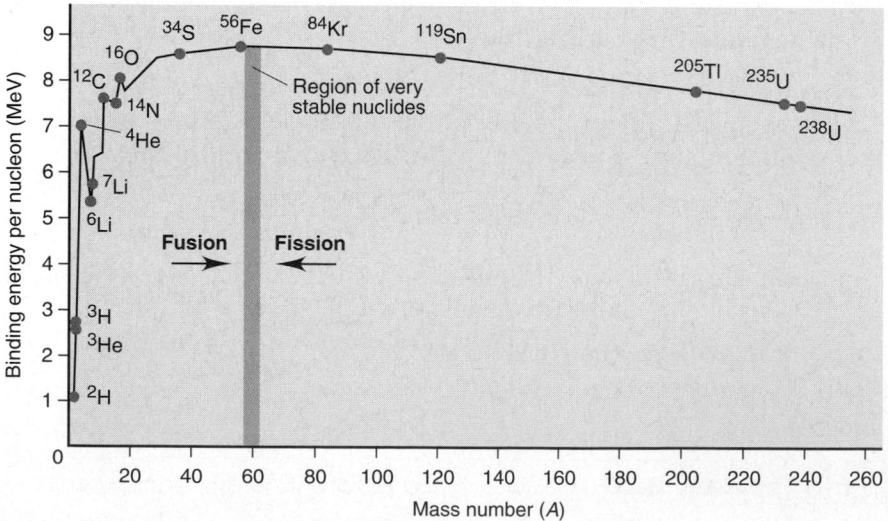

Figure 24.12 The variation in binding energy per nucleon. A plot of the binding energy per nucleon vs. mass number shows that nuclear stability is greatest in the region near ${}^{56}\text{Fe}$. Lighter nuclei may undergo fusion to become more stable; heavier ones may undergo fission. Note the exceptional stability of ${}^4\text{He}$ among extremely light nuclei.

have a relatively small binding energy per nucleon. The ^{4}He nucleus has an exceptionally large value, however, which is why it is emitted intact as an α particle. Above $A = 12$, the binding energy per nucleon varies from about 7.6 to 8.8 MeV.

The most important observation is that *the binding energy per nucleon peaks for elements with A ≈ 60*. In other words, nuclides become more stable with increasing mass number up to around 60 nucleons and then become less stable with higher numbers of nucleons. The existence of a peak of stability suggests that there are two ways nuclides can increase their binding energy per nucleon:

- *Fission.* A heavier nucleus can *split into lighter ones (closer to A ≈ 60)* by undergoing fission. The product nuclei have greater binding energy per nucleon (are more stable) than the reactant, and the difference in *energy is released.* Nuclear power plants generate energy through fission, as do atomic bombs.
- *Fusion.* Lighter nuclei, on the other hand, can *combine to form a heavier one (closer to A ≈ 60)* by undergoing fusion. Once again, the product is more stable than the reactants, and *energy is released.* The Sun and other stars generate energy through fusion, as does the hydrogen bomb. In these examples and all current ventures for developing fusion as a useful energy source, hydrogen nuclei fuse to form the very stable helium-4 nucleus.

In the next section, we examine fission and fusion and the industrial energy facilities designed to utilize them.

Section Summary

The mass of a nucleus is less than the sum of its nucleon masses by the mass defect. The energy equivalent to the mass defect is the nuclear binding energy, usually expressed in units of MeV. The binding energy per nucleon is a measure of nuclide stability and varies with number of nucleons. Nuclides with $A \approx 60$ are most stable. Lighter nuclides can join (fusion), and heavier nuclides can split (fission) to become more stable.

24.7 Applications of Fission and Fusion

Of the many beneficial applications of nuclear reactions, the greatest is the potential for almost limitless amounts of energy, which is based on the multi-million-fold increase in energy yield of nuclear reactions over chemical reactions. Our experience with nuclear energy from power plants in the late 20th century, however, has forced a realization that we must strive to improve ways to tap this energy source safely and economically. In this section we discuss how fission and fusion occur and how we are applying them.

The Process of Nuclear Fission

During the mid-1930s, Enrico Fermi and co-workers bombarded uranium ($Z = 92$) with neutrons in an attempt to synthesize transuranium elements. Many of the unstable nuclides produced were tentatively identified as having $Z > 92$, but other scientists were skeptical. Four years later, the German chemist Otto Hahn and his associate F. Strassmann showed that one of these unstable nuclides was an isotope of barium ($Z = 56$). The Austrian physicist Lise Meitner, a co-worker of Hahn, and her nephew Otto Frisch proposed that barium resulted from the *splitting* of the uranium nucleus into *smaller*

◆ Lise Meitner (1878–1968)
Until very recently, this extraordinary physicist received little of the acclaim she deserved. Meitner worked in the laboratory of the chemist Otto Hahn, and she was responsible for the discovery of protactinium (Pa; $Z = 91$) and numerous radioisotopes. After leaving Germany in advance of the Nazi domination, Meitner proposed the correct explanation of nuclear fission. When Hahn received the Nobel Prize in 1944, however, he did not even acknowledge Meitner in his acceptance speech. Today, most physicists believe that Lise Meitner should have received the prize. Despite the recent controversy over names for elements 104 to 109, all agree that element 109 should be named meitnerium.

nuclei, a process they named *fission* because of its similarity to the reproductive fission of a biological cell. ◆

The ^{235}U nucleus can split in many different ways, giving rise to various daughter nuclei, but all routes have the same general features. Figure 24.13 depicts one of these fission patterns. Neutron bombardment results in a highly excited ^{236}U nucleus, which splits apart in 10^{-14} s. The products are two nuclei of unequal mass, two or three neutrons (average of 2.4), and a large quantity of energy. A single ^{235}U nucleus releases 3.5×10^{-11} J when it splits; 1 mol ^{235}U (about $\frac{1}{2}$ lb) releases 2.1×10^{13} J—a billion times as much energy as burning $\frac{1}{2}$ lb of coal (about 2×10^4 J)!

We harness the energy of nuclear fission, much of which appears as heat, by means of a **chain reaction** (Figure 24.14): the two to three neutrons released by fission of one nucleus collide with other fissionable nuclei and cause them to split, releasing more neutrons that collide with other nuclei, and so on, in a self-sustaining process. Thus, each fission event in a chain reaction releases two to three times as much energy as the preceding one. Whether a chain reaction occurs depends on the mass (and thus volume) of the fissionable sample. If the piece of uranium is large enough, product neutrons strike another fissionable nucleus *before* flying out of the sample, and a chain reaction takes place. The mass needed to achieve a chain reaction is the **critical mass.** If the sample has less than this mass *(subcritical),* most of the product neutrons leave the sample before colliding with another ^{235}U nucleus, and a chain reaction does not occur.

Uncontrolled Fission: The Atomic Bomb An uncontrolled chain reaction may become explosive, as the world first learned during World War II. In

Figure 24.13 Induced fission of ^{235}U. A neutron captured by a ^{235}U nucleus results in an extremely unstable ^{236}U nucleus, which becomes distorted in the act of splitting. In this case, which shows one of many possible splitting patterns, the products are ^{92}Kr and ^{141}Ba. Three neutrons and a great deal of energy are released also.

Figure 24.14 A chain reaction of ^{235}U. If a sample exceeds the critical mass, neutrons produced by the first fission event collide with other nuclei, causing their fission and the production of more neutrons to continue the process. Note that various product nuclei form. The vertical dashed lines separate succeeding "generations" of neutrons.

August 1945, the United States detonated two atomic bombs over Japan. The horrible destructive power of these bombs was a major factor in the surrender of the Japanese a few days later.

In an atomic bomb, small explosions of trinitrotoluene (TNT) bring subcritical masses of fissionable material together to exceed the critical mass, and the ensuing chain reaction brings about the nuclear explosion. The proliferation of nuclear power plants, which use fissionable materials to generate energy for electricity, has increased concern that more countries will have access to material for bombs. Only 1 kg of fissionable uranium was used in the first of the bombs dropped on Japan.

Controlled Fission: Nuclear Energy Reactors Controlled fission can produce clean, plentiful electric power. Like a coal-fired power plant, *a nuclear power plant generates heat to produce steam, which turns a turbine attached to an electric generator.* In a coal plant, the heat is produced by burning coal; in a nuclear plant, it is produced by splitting uranium.

A

Containment shell

③ *Extremely hot water under high pressure passes into steam generator*

④ *Steam produced operates turbine-generator*

Electric power

Reactor core

Steam generator

Turbine

Generator

② *Control rods regulate rate of chain reaction*

Steam condenser

Moderator

⑤ *Cool water from nearby source condenses steam and is warmed*

① *Enriched uranium in fuel rods releases energy from fission*

Pump

Coolant water out

Pump

Pump

B

Coolant water in

Figure 24.15 **A light-water nuclear reactor. A,** Photo of a facility showing the concrete containment shell and nearby water source. **B,** Schematic of a light-water reactor.

Heat generation takes place in the **reactor core** of a nuclear plant (Figure 24.15). The core contains the *fuel rods,* which consist of fuel enclosed in tubes of a corrosion-resistant zirconium alloy. The fuel is uranium(IV) oxide (UO_2) that has been *enriched* from 0.7% ^{235}U, the natural abundance of this fissionable isotope, to the 3% to 4% ^{235}U required to sustain a chain reaction. (Enrichment of nuclear fuel is the most important application of Graham's law; see Margin Note, p. 204.) Sandwiched between the fuel rods are movable *control rods* made of cadmium or boron, substances that absorb neutrons very efficiently. When the control rods are moved between the fuel rods, the chain reaction slows because fewer neutrons are available to bombard uranium atoms; when they are removed, the chain reaction speeds up. Neutrons that leave the fuel-rod assembly collide with a *reflector,* usually made of a beryllium alloy, which absorbs very few neutrons. Reflecting the neutrons back to the fuel rods speeds the chain reaction.

Flowing around the fuel and control rods in the reactor core is the *moderator*, a substance that slows the neutrons, making them much better at causing fission than the fast ones emerging from the fission event itself. In most modern reactors, the moderator also acts as the *coolant*, the fluid that transfers the released heat to the steam-producing region. Because ^{1}H absorbs neutrons, *light-water reactors* simply use H_2O as the moderator; in heavy-water reactors, D_2O is used. The advantage of D_2O is that it absorbs very few neutrons, leaving more available for fission, so heavy-water reactors can use *unenriched* uranium. As the coolant flows around the encased fuel, pumps circulate it through coils that transfer its heat to the water reservoir. Steam formed in the reservoir turns the turbine that runs the generator. The steam is then condensed in large cooling towers (see Figure 13.12, p. 496) with water from a nearby lake or river and returned to the water reservoir. ◆

Some major accidents at nuclear plants have caused a decidedly negative public reaction. In 1979, malfunctions of coolant pumps and valves at the Three-Mile Island facility in Pennsylvania led to melting of some of the fuel, serious damage to the reactor core, and the release of radioactive gases into the atmosphere. In 1986, failure of a cooling system at the Chernobyl plant in Ukraine of the former Soviet Union caused a much greater melting of fuel and an uncontrolled reaction. High-pressure steam and ignited graphite moderator rods caused the reactor building to explode and expel radioactive debris. Carried by prevailing winds, the particles contaminated vegetables and milk in much of Europe. Health officials fear that thousands of people living near the accident have already or may soon develop cancer from radiation exposure. The design of the Chernobyl plant was particularly unsafe because, unlike reactors in the United States and western Europe, the reactor was not enclosed in a massive, concrete containment building.

Despite potential safety problems, nuclear power remains an important source of electrical power. In the late 1990s, nearly every European country employed nuclear power and in some countries, it is the major power source—Sweden creates 50% of its electricity this way and France almost 80%. Currently, the United States obtains about 20% of its electricity from nuclear power, and Canada slightly less. As our need for energy grows, new reactors with enhanced safety features will be designed.

However, even a smoothly operating plant has certain inherent problems. The problem of *thermal pollution* is common to all power plants. Water used to condense the steam is several degrees warmer when returned to its source, which can harm aquatic organisms (Section 13.3). A more serious problem is one of *nuclear waste disposal*. Many of the fission products formed in nuclear reactors have long half-lives, and no satisfactory plan for their permanent disposal has yet been devised. Proposals to place the waste in containers and bury them in deep bedrock cannot possibly be field-tested for the thousands of years the material will remain harmful. Leakage of radioactive material into groundwater is always a danger, and earthquakes can occur even in geologically stable regions. Some recent studies have indicated that the proposed Yucca Mountain disposal site in Nevada may be too geologically active. It remains to be seen whether we can operate fission reactors *and* dispose of the waste safely and inexpensively.

The Promise of Nuclear Fusion

Nuclear fusion is the ultimate source of nearly all the energy on Earth because nearly all other sources depend, directly or indirectly, on the energy produced by nuclear fusion in the Sun. But the Sun and other stars generate more than energy, for *all the elements larger than hydrogen were formed in fusion and decay processes within stars*, as the upcoming Chemical Connections essay describes.

◆ **"Breeding" Nuclear Fuel** Uranium-235 is not an abundant isotope. One solution to a potential fuel shortage is a *breeder reactor*, designed to consume one type of nuclear fuel as it produces another. Fuel rods are surrounded by natural U_3O_8, which contains 99.3% *nonfissionable* ^{238}U atoms. As fast neutrons, formed during ^{235}U fission, escape the fuel rod, they collide with ^{238}U, which forms ^{239}Pu, another fissionable nucleus:

$$^{238}_{92}U + {}^1_0n \longrightarrow {}^{239}_{92}U$$
$$(t_{1/2} \text{ of } {}^{239}_{92}U = 23.5 \text{ min})$$

$$^{239}_{92}U \longrightarrow {}^{239}_{93}Np + {}^0_{-1}\beta$$
$$(t_{1/2} \text{ of } {}^{239}_{93}Np = 2.35 \text{ days})$$

$$^{239}_{93}Np \longrightarrow {}^{239}_{94}Pu + {}^0_{-1}\beta$$
$$(t_{1/2} \text{ of } {}^{239}_{94}Pu = 2.4 \times 10^4 \text{ yr})$$

Although breeder reactors can make fuel as they operate, they are difficult and expensive to build, and the ^{239}Pu is extremely toxic and long lived. No breeder reactors are in use in the United States, although there are several in Europe and Japan.

Origin of the Elements in the Stars

How did the universe begin? Where did matter come from? How were the elements formed? Every culture has creation myths that address such questions, but only recently have astronomers, physicists, and chemists begun to offer a scientific explanation. The most accepted current model proposes that a sphere of unimaginable properties—diameter 10^{-28} cm, density 10^{96} g/mL (density of a nucleus $\approx 10^{14}$ g/mL), and temperature 10^{32} K—exploded in a "Big Bang," for reasons not yet even guessed, and distributed its contents through the void of space. Cosmologists consider this moment the beginning of time.

One second later, the universe was an expanding mixture of neutrons, protons, and electrons, denser than rock and hotter than an exploding H-bomb (about 10^{10} K). During the next few minutes, it became a gigantic fusion reactor creating the first atomic nuclei, ^{2}H, ^{3}He, and ^{4}He. After 10 minutes, more than 25% of the mass of the universe existed as ^{4}He, and one-thousandth as much existed as ^{2}H. About 100 million years later, or about 15 billion years ago, gravitational forces pulled this cosmic mixture into primitive, contracting stars.

This account of the origin of the universe is based on the observation of spectra from the Sun, other stars, nearby galaxies, and cosmic (interstellar) dust. Spectral analysis of planets and chemical analysis of the Earth, Moon, meteors, and cosmic-ray particles furnishes data about isotope abundance. From these have been developed a model for **stellar nucleogenesis,** the origin of the elements in the stars. The overall process occurs in several stages during a star's evolution, and the entire sequence of steps occurs only in very massive stars, 10 to 100 times the mass of the Sun. Each step involves a contraction of the star that produces higher temperature and heavier nuclei. Such events are forming elements in stars today. Here are the key stages in the process (Figure 24.C):

1. *Hydrogen burning produces He.* The initial contraction of a star heats its core to about 10^7 K, at which point a fusion process called *hydrogen burning* produces helium from the abundant protons:

$$4\,{}^{1}_{1}\text{H} \longrightarrow {}^{4}_{2}\text{He} + 2\,{}^{0}_{1}\beta + 2\gamma + \text{energy}$$

2. *Helium burning produces C, O, Ne, and Mg.* After several billion years of H burning, about 10% of the ^{1}H is consumed, and the star contracts further. The ^{4}He forms a dense core, hot enough (2×10^8 K) to fuse ^{4}He. The energy released during *helium burning* expands the remaining ^{1}H into a vast envelope: the star becomes a *red giant,* more than 100 times its original diameter.

Within its core, pairs of ^{4}He nuclei (α particles) fuse into unstable ^{8}Be ($t_{1/2} = 2\times10^{-16}$ s), which collides with a third ^{4}He to form stable ^{12}C. Further fusion with ^{4}He creates nuclei up to ^{24}Mg:

$$^{12}\text{C} \xrightarrow{\ \alpha\ } {}^{16}\text{O} \xrightarrow{\ \alpha\ } {}^{20}\text{Ne} \xrightarrow{\ \alpha\ } {}^{24}\text{Mg}$$

3. *Elements through Fe and Ni form.* For another 10 million years, ^{4}He is consumed, and the heavier nuclei form a core, which contracts and heats, expanding the star to a *supergiant.* In the hot core (7×10^8 K), *carbon and oxygen burning* occur:

$$^{12}\text{C} + {}^{12}\text{C} \longrightarrow {}^{23}\text{Na} + {}^{1}\text{H}$$
$$^{12}\text{C} + {}^{16}\text{O} \longrightarrow {}^{28}\text{Si} + \gamma$$

Absorption of α particles forms nuclei up to calcium-40:

$$^{12}\text{C} \xrightarrow{\ \alpha\ } {}^{16}\text{O} \xrightarrow{\ \alpha\ } {}^{20}\text{Ne} \xrightarrow{\ \alpha\ } {}^{24}\text{Mg} \xrightarrow{\ \alpha\ }$$
$$^{28}\text{Si} \xrightarrow{\ \alpha\ } {}^{32}\text{S} \xrightarrow{\ \alpha\ } {}^{36}\text{Ar} \xrightarrow{\ \alpha\ } {}^{40}\text{Ca}$$

Further contraction and heating to 3×10^9 K allow reactions in which nuclei release neutrons, protons, and α particles and then recapture them. As a result, nuclei with lower binding energies supply nucleons to create those with higher binding energies. The process, which takes only a few minutes, stops at iron ($A = 56$) and nickel ($A = 58$), the nuclei with the highest binding energies.

4. *Heavier elements form.* In very massive stars, the next stage is the most spectacular. With all the fuel consumed, the core collapses within a second. Many Fe and Ni nuclei break down into neutrons and protons. Protons capture electrons to form neutrons, and the entire core forms an incredibly dense *neutron star.* (An Earth-sized star that became a neutron star would fit in the Houston astrodome!) As the core implodes, the outer layers explode in a *supernova,* which expels material throughout space. A supernova occurs an average of every few hundred years in each galaxy; one was observed from the Southern Hemisphere in 1987, about 160,000 years after the event occurred (Figure 24.D). The heavier elements form during supernovas and are found in *second-generation stars,* those that coalesce from interstellar ^{1}H and ^{4}He and the debris of exploded first-generation stars.

Heavier elements form through *neutron-capture* processes. In the *s-process,* a nucleus captures a neutron and emits a γ ray. Days, months, or even thousands of years later, the nucleus emits a β particle to form the next element, as in this conversion of ^{68}Zn to ^{70}Ge:

$$^{68}\text{Zn} \xrightarrow{\ n\ } {}^{69}\text{Zn} \xrightarrow{\ \beta\ } {}^{69}\text{Ga} \xrightarrow{\ n\ } {}^{70}\text{Ga} \xrightarrow{\ \beta\ } {}^{70}\text{Ge}$$

The stable isotopes of most heavy elements form by the s-process.

Less stable isotopes and those with A greater than 230 cannot form by the s-process because their half-lives are too short. These form by the *r-process* during the fury of the supernova. Multiple neutron captures, followed by multiple β decays, occur in a second, as when ^{56}Fe is converted to ^{79}Br:

$$^{56}_{26}\text{Fe} + 23\,{}^{1}_{0}\text{n} \longrightarrow {}^{79}_{26}\text{Fe} \longrightarrow {}^{79}_{35}\text{Br} + 9\,{}^{0}_{-1}\beta$$

Figure 24.C Element synthesis in the life cycle of a star.

⑤ *Debris from supernova eventually ends up in second-generation stars.*

① *Primitive coalescing star burns hydrogen at 10^7 K.*

② *Star begins burning He, causing expansion into red giant. Core of red giant burns He to form ^{12}C, ^{16}O, ^{20}Ne, ^{24}Mg at 2×10^8 K.*

Neutron star

④ *Core implodes to form a neutron star, while outer layers explode into a supernova. Neutron-capture processes form heavier nuclei.*

③ *Red supergiant core burns carbon and oxygen to form nuclei through ^{40}Ca at 7×10^8 K. Further heating to 3×10^9 K forms nuclei through ^{56}Fe and ^{58}Ni.*

Cosmic dust

Coalescing cosmic dust

We know from the heavy elements present in the Sun that it is at least a second-generation star presently undergoing hydrogen burning. Together with its planets, it was formed from the dust of exploded stars about 4.6×10^9 years ago. This means that many of the atoms on Earth, including some within you, came from exploded stars and are older than the Solar System itself!

Any theory of element formation must be consistent with the element abundances we observe (Section 22.1). Although local compositions differ, such as those of the Earth and Sun, large regions of the universe have, on average, similar compositions. Thus, scientists believe that element forming reaches a dynamic equilibrium, which leads to *relatively constant amounts of the isotopes.*

Figure 24.D A view of Supernova 1987A.

Much research is now being devoted to making nuclear fusion a practical, direct source of energy on Earth. To understand the advantages of fusion, let's consider one of the most discussed fusion reactions, in which deuterium and tritium react:

$$_1^2\text{H} + {}_1^3\text{H} \longrightarrow {}_2^4\text{He} + {}_0^1\text{n}$$

This reaction produces 1.7×10^9 kJ/mol, an enormous quantity of energy with no radioactive by-products. Moreover, the reactant nuclei are relatively easy to come by. We obtain deuterium from the electrolysis of water (Section 22.4). In nature, tritium forms through the cosmic (neutron) irradiation of ^{14}N:

$$_7^{14}\text{N} + {}_0^1\text{n} \longrightarrow {}_1^3\text{H} + {}_6^{12}\text{C}$$

However, this process results in an abundance of only $10^{-7}\%$ ^3H. More practically, tritium can be produced in nuclear accelerators by bombarding lithium-6 or by surrounding the fusion reactor itself with material containing lithium-6:

$$_3^6\text{Li} + {}_0^1\text{n} \longrightarrow {}_1^3\text{H} + {}_2^4\text{He}$$

Thus, fusion seems very promising, at least in principle. However, some extremely difficult problems exist. Fusion requires enormous energy in the form of heat to give the positively charged nuclei enough kinetic energy to force themselves together. The fusion of deuterium and tritium, for example, occurs at practical rates at about 10^8 K, hotter than the Sun's core! How can such temperatures be achieved? The *hydrogen bomb* is a fusion reaction that uses an atomic bomb to provide the heat, but a public energy facility obviously cannot begin operation by detonating atomic bombs.

Two research approaches are being used to achieve the necessary heat. In one, atoms are stripped of their electrons at high temperatures, which results in a gaseous *plasma*, a neutral mixture of positive nuclei and electrons. Because of the extreme temperatures needed for fusion, no *material* can contain the plasma. The most successful approach to date has been to enclose the plasma within a magnetic field. The *tokamak* design has a donut-shaped container in which a helical magnetic field confines the plasma and prevents it from contacting the walls (Figure 24.16; also see chapter opener photo). Scientists at the Princeton University Plasma Physics facility have recently achieved some success in generating energy from fusion this way. In another approach, the high temperature is reached by using many focused lasers to compress and heat the fusion reactants. In any event, as a practical, everyday source of energy, fusion still seems to be a long way off.

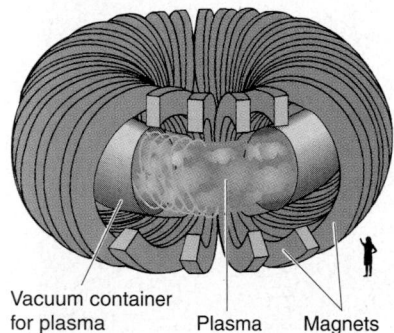

Vacuum container
for plasma   Plasma   Magnets

Figure 24.16 The tokamak design for magnetic containment of a fusion plasma. The donut-shaped chamber of the tokamak contains the plasma within a helical magnetic field.

Section Summary

In nuclear fission, neutron bombardment causes a nucleus to split, releasing neutrons that split other nuclei to produce a chain reaction. A nuclear power plant controls the rate of the chain reaction to produce heat that creates steam, which is used to generate electricity. Potential hazards, such as radiation leaks, thermal pollution, and disposal of nuclear waste remain current concerns. Nuclear fusion holds great promise for clean abundant energy, but it requires extremely high temperatures and is not yet a practical source. The elements were formed through a complex series of nuclear reactions in evolving stars.

Chapter Perspective

With this chapter, our earlier picture of the nucleus as a static point of positive mass at the atom's core has changed radically. Now we picture a dynamic body, capable of a host of actions that involve incredible quantities of energy. Our attempts to apply the behavior of this minute system to benefit society have created some of the most fascinating and challenging fields in science today.

We began our investigation of chemistry 24 chapters ago, by seeing how the chemical elements and the products we make from them influence nearly every aspect of our material existence. Now we have come full circle to learn that these elements, whose patterns of behavior we marvel at, are continually being born in the countless infernos that twinkle in the night sky.

For you, the end of this course is a beginning—a chance to apply your new abilities to visualize molecular events and solve problems in whatever field you choose. For the science of chemistry, future challenges are great: What new forms of energy can satisfy society's needs and *sustain our environment? What new products can feed, clothe, and house the world's people* and *maintain precious resources? What new medicines can defend against cancer, AIDS, and other dreaded diseases? What new materials and technologies can make life more productive and meaningful? The questions are many, but the science of chemistry will always be one of our most powerful means of answering them.*

The following learning objectives, with section and/or sample problem (SP) numbers in parentheses, can help focus your study:

Understand These Concepts

1. How nuclear changes differ, in general, from chemical changes (Intro)
2. The meanings of key terms—radioactivity, nucleon, nuclide, isotope (Section 24.1)
3. Characteristics of the three common radioactive emissions: α, β, and γ (Section 24.1)
4. The various forms of radioactive decay and how each changes the values of A and Z (Section 24.1)
5. How the N/Z ratio and the even-odd nature of N and Z correlate with nuclear stability (Section 24.1)
6. How the N/Z ratio correlates with the mode of decay of an unstable nuclide (Section 24.1)
7. How a decay series combines numerous decay steps to reach a stable nuclide (Section 24.1)
8. How radioactive decay is a first-order process; the meaning of decay rate and specific activity (Section 24.2)
9. The meaning of first-order half-life in the context of radioactive decay (Section 24.2)
10. How the specific activity of an isotope in an object is used to determine its age (Section 24.2)
11. How particle accelerators are used to synthesize new nuclides (Section 24.3)
12. The distinction between excitation and ionization and the extent of their effects on matter (Section 24.4)
13. The units of radiation dose; dosage effects on living tissue; the inverse relationship between the mass and charge of an emission and its penetrating power (Section 24.4)
14. How ionizing radiation causes free radicals that damage tissue; sources and risks of ionizing radiation (Section 24.4)
15. How radioisotopes are used in research, analysis, and diagnosis (Section 24.5)

16. Why the mass of a nuclide is less than the sum of its nucleon masses (mass defect, Δm) and how this mass difference is related to the nuclear binding energy (Section 24.6)
17. How nuclear stability is related to binding energy per nucleon (Section 24.6)
18. How unstable nuclides undergo either fission or fusion to increase their binding energy per nucleon (Section 24.6)
19. How fission is applied, and fusion may be applied in the future, to produce energy (Section 24.7)

Master These Skills

1. Expressing the mass and charge of a particle with the $_{Z}^{A}X$ notation (Section 24.1; see also Section 2.5)
2. Using changes in the values of A and Z to write and balance nuclear equations (SP 24.1)
3. Using the N/Z ratio and the even-odd nature of N and Z to predict nuclear stability (SP 24.2)
4. Using the N/Z ratio to predict the mode of radioactive decay (SP 24.3)
5. Converting units of radioactivity (Section 24.2)
6. Calculating specific activity, decay constant, half-life, and number of nuclei (Section 24.2 and SP 24.4)
7. Estimating the age of an object from the specific activity and half-life of the isotope (SP 24.5)
8. Writing and balancing equations for nuclear transmutation (Section 24.3)
9. Calculating radiation dose and converting units (Section 24.4)
10. Calculating the mass defect and its energy equivalent in J and eV (Section 24.6)
11. Calculating the binding energy per nucleon and using it to compare nuclide stability (SP 24.6)

For Review and Reference

Key Terms

Section 24.1
radioactivity
nucleon
nuclide
isotope
alpha (α) particle
beta (β) particle
gamma (γ) ray
alpha decay
beta decay
positron decay
positron
electron capture
gamma emission
N/Z ratio

band of stability
strong force
decay (disintegration) series
Section 24.2
Geiger-Müller counter
scintillation counter
activity ($\mathcal{A}$)
becquerel (Bq)
curie (Ci)
decay constant
half-life ($t_{1/2}$)
radioisotopic dating
radioisotope
Section 24.3
nuclear transmutation

deuteron
particle accelerator
transuranium element
Section 24.4
excitation
nonionizing radiation
ionization
ionizing radiation
gray (Gy)
rad (*radiation-absorbed dose*)
rem (*roentgen equivalent for man*)
sievert (Sv)
free radical

background radiation
Section 24.5
tracer
Section 24.6
fission
fusion
mass defect (Δm)
nuclear binding energy
electron volt (eV)
Section 24.7
chain reaction
critical mass
reactor core
stellar nucleogenesis

Key Equations and Relationships

24.1 Defining the unit of radioactivity (curie, Ci) (p. 1053):

1 Ci $= 3.70 \times 10^{10}$ disintegrations per second (d/s)

24.2 Expressing the decay rate (activity) for radioactive nuclei (p. 1053):

$$\text{Decay rate } (\mathcal{A}) = -\frac{\Delta \mathcal{N}}{\Delta t} = k\mathcal{N}$$

24.3 Finding the number of nuclei remaining after a given time, $\mathcal{N}_t$ (p. 1054):

$$\ln \frac{\mathcal{N}_0}{\mathcal{N}_t} = kt$$

24.4 Finding the half-life of a radioactive nuclide (p. 1054):

$$t_{1/2} = \frac{\ln 2}{k}$$

24.5 Calculating the time to reach a given specific activity (age of an object in radioisotopic dating) (p. 1056):

$$t = \frac{1}{k} \ln \frac{\mathcal{A}_0}{\mathcal{A}_t}$$

24.6 Using Einstein's equation and the mass defect to calculate the nuclear binding energy (p. 1068):

$$\Delta E = \Delta mc^2$$

24.7 Relating the atomic mass unit to its energy equivalent in MeV (p. 1069):

1 amu $= 931.5 \times 10^6$ eV $= 931.5$ MeV

Highlighted Figures and Tables

These figures (F) and tables (T) provide a quick review of key ideas.
T24.1 Chemical vs. nuclear reactions (p. 1043)
T24.2 Modes of radioactive decay (p. 1046)

F24.2 *N* vs. *Z* for the stable nuclides (p. 1049)
F24.4 Decrease in number of ^{14}C nuclei over time (p. 1053)
F24.12 The variation in binding energy per nucleon (p. 1070)

Answers to Follow-up Problems

24.1 $^{133}_{54}\text{Xe} \longrightarrow {}^{133}_{55}\text{Cs} + {}^{0}_{-1}\beta$
24.2 Phosphorus-31 has a slightly higher *N/Z* ratio and an even *N* (16).
24.3 (a) *N/Z* = 1.35; too high for this region of band: β decay
(b) Mass too high for stability: α decay

24.4 $\ln \mathcal{A}_t = -kt + \ln \mathcal{A}_0$

$$= -\left(\frac{\ln 2}{15 \text{ h}} \times 4.0 \text{ days} \times \frac{24 \text{ h}}{1 \text{ day}}\right) + \ln (2.5 \times 10^9)$$

$$= 17.20$$

$\mathcal{A}_t = 3.0 \times 10^7$ d/s

24.5 $t = \dfrac{1}{k} \ln \dfrac{\mathcal{A}_0}{\mathcal{A}_t} = \dfrac{5730 \text{ yr}}{\ln 2} \ln \left(\dfrac{15.3 \text{ d/min} \cdot \text{g}}{9.41 \text{ d/min} \cdot \text{g}} \right)$

$= 4.02 \times 10^3 \text{ yr}$

The mummy case is about 4000 years old.

24.6 ^{235}U has $92 \, {}^1_1\text{p}$ and $143 \, {}^1_0\text{n}$.

$\Delta m = [(92 \times 1.007825 \text{ amu}) + (143 \times 1.008665 \text{ amu})]$
$- 235.043924 \text{ amu}$
$= 1.9151 \text{ amu}$

$\dfrac{\text{Binding energy}}{\text{nucleon}} = \dfrac{1.9151 \text{ amu} \times \dfrac{931.5 \text{ MeV}}{1 \text{ amu}}}{235 \text{ nucleons}}$

$= 7.591 \text{ MeV/nucleon};$

therefore, less stable than ^{12}C

Problems

Problems with a colored number are answered at the back of the text. Problem sections match the text and provide the number(s) of relevant sample problems. Most offer concept review questions, paired skill-building exercises, and problems in a relevant context. Following these are comprehensive problems based on material from any section and/or previous chapter.

Radioactive Decay and Nuclear Stability
(Sample Problems 24.1 to 24.3)

▓ Concept Review Questions

24.1 How do chemical and nuclear reactions differ in
(a) Magnitude of the energy change?
(b) Effect on rate of increasing temperature?
(c) Effect on rate of higher reactant concentration?
(d) Effect on yield of higher reactant concentration?

24.2 Sulfur has four naturally occurring isotopes. The one with the lowest mass number is sulfur-32, which is also the most abundant (95.02%).
(a) What percentage of the S atoms in a matchhead are ^{32}S?
(b) The isotopic mass of ^{32}S is 31.972070 amu. Is the atomic mass larger, smaller, or equal to this mass? Explain.

24.3 What evidence led Marie Curie to conclude that
(a) Radioactivity is a property of the element and not the compound in which it is found?
(b) A highly radioactive element, aside from uranium, occurs in pitchblende?

24.4 Which of the following types of radioactive decay produce an atom of a *different* element: (a) alpha; (b) beta; (c) gamma; (d) positron; (e) electron capture? Show how Z and N change, if at all, with each type.

24.5 Why is $^3_2$He stable whereas $^2_2$He is so unstable that it has never been detected?

24.6 How do the modes of decay differ for a neutron-rich nuclide and a proton-rich nuclide?

24.7 Why can't you use the position of a nuclide relative to the band of stability to predict whether it is more likely to decay by positron emission or by electron capture?

▓ Skill-Building Exercises (paired)

24.8 Write balanced nuclear equations for the following:
(a) Alpha decay of $^{234}_{92}$U
(b) Electron capture by neptunium-232
(c) Positron emission by $^{12}_7$N

24.9 Write balanced nuclear equations for the following:
(a) Beta decay of sodium-26
(b) Beta decay of francium-223
(c) Alpha decay of $^{212}_{83}$Bi

24.10 Write balanced nuclear equations for the following:
(a) Beta emission by magnesium-27
(b) Neutron emission by $^9_3$Li
(c) Electron capture by $^{103}_{46}$Pd

24.11 Write balanced nuclear equations for the following:
(a) Simultaneous beta and neutron emission by helium-8
(b) Alpha decay of polonium-218
(c) Electron capture by $^{110}_{49}$In

24.12 Write balanced nuclear equations for the following:
(a) Formation of $^{48}_{22}$Ti through positron emission
(b) Formation of silver-107 through electron capture
(c) Formation of polonium-206 through α decay

24.13 Write balanced nuclear equations for the following:
(a) Production of $^{241}_{95}$Am through β decay
(b) Formation of $^{228}_{89}$Ac through β decay
(c) Formation of $^{203}_{83}$Bi through α decay

24.14 Write balanced nuclear equations for the following:
(a) Formation of ^{186}Ir through electron capture
(b) Formation of francium-221 through α decay
(c) Formation of iodine-129 through β decay

24.15 Write balanced nuclear equations for the following:
(a) Formation of ^{52}Mn through positron emission
(b) Formation of polonium-215 through α decay
(c) Formation of ^{81}Kr through electron capture

24.16 Which nuclides would you predict to be stable:
(a) $^{20}_8$O; (b) $^{59}_{27}$Co; (c) $^9_3$Li? Why?

24.17 Which nuclides would you predict to be stable:
(a) $^{146}_{60}$Nd; (b) $^{114}_{48}$Cd; (c) $^{88}_{42}$Mo? Why?

24.18 Which nuclides would you predict to be stable:
(a) ^{127}I; (b) tin-106; (c) ^{68}As? Why?

24.19 Which nuclides would you predict to be stable:
(a) ^{48}K; (b) ^{79}Br; (c) argon-32? Why?

24.20 What is the most likely mode of decay for (a) $^{238}_{92}$U; (b) $^{48}_{24}$Cr; (c) $^{50}_{25}$Mn?

24.21 What is the most likely mode of decay for (a) $^{61}_{26}$Fe; (b) $^{41}_{17}$Cl; (c) $^{110}_{44}$Ru?

24.22 What is the most likely mode of decay for (a) ^{15}C; (b) ^{120}Xe; (c) ^{224}Th?

24.23 What is the most likely mode of decay for (a) ^{234}Th; (b) ^{141}Eu; (c) ^{241}Am?

24.24 Why is $^{52}_{24}$Cr the most stable isotope of chromium?

24.25 Why is $^{40}_{20}$Ca the most stable isotope of calcium?

■ **Problems in Context**

24.26 Radiochemists have proposed that a natural radioactive decay series probably began with $^{243}_{95}$Am, but all of this nuclide decayed within the first few million years of the Earth's existence. This series would have begun by emission of an α particle, then a β particle, then two more α particles. Write a balanced nuclear equation for each step.

24.27 Why is helium found in deposits of uranium and thorium ores? What kind of radioactive emission produces it?

24.28 In the natural radioactive series that starts with uranium-235, a sequence of α and β emissions ends with lead-207. How many α and β particles are emitted per atom of uranium-235 to result in an atom of lead-207?

The Kinetics of Radioactive Decay
(Sample Problems 24.4 and 24.5)

■ **Concept Review Questions**

24.29 What is the electronic process that forms the basis of detecting radioactive emissions in (a) a scintillation counter; (b) a Geiger-Müller counter?

24.30 What is the kinetic reaction order of radioactive decay? Explain.

24.31 After 1 minute, half the radioactive nuclei remain from an original sample of six nuclei. Is it valid to conclude that $t_{1/2}$ equals 1 minute? Would this conclusion be valid if the original sample contained 6×10^{12} nuclei? Explain.

24.32 Radioisotopic dating depends on the constant rate of decay and formation of various nuclides in a sample. How is the proportion of carbon-14 kept relatively constant in living organisms?

■ **Skill-Building Exercises** *(paired)*

24.33 What is the specific activity (in Ci/g) if 1.55 mg of an isotope emits 1.66×10^{6} α particles per second?

24.34 What is the specific activity (in Ci/g) if 2.6 g of an isotope emits 4.13×10^{8} β particles per hour?

24.35 What is the specific activity (in Bq/g) if 8.58 μg of an isotope emits 7.4×10^{4} α particles per minute?

24.36 What is the specific activity (in Bq/g) if 1.07 kg of an isotope emits 3.77×10^{7} β particles per minute?

24.37 One trillionth of the atoms in a sample of radioactive isotope disintegrates in 1 h. What is the decay constant of the process?

24.38 Measurement shows that 2.8×10^{-10}% of the atoms in a sample of radioactive isotope disintegrates in 1 yr. What is the decay constant of the process?

24.39 If 1.00×10^{-12} mol ^{135}Cs emits 1.39×10^{5} β particles in 1 yr, what is the decay constant?

24.40 If 6.40×10^{-9} mol ^{176}W emits 1.07×10^{15} positrons in 1 h, what is the decay constant?

24.41 The isotope $^{212}_{83}$Bi has a half-life of 1.01 yr. What mass in mg of a 2.00-mg sample will remain undecayed after 3.75×10^{3} h?

24.42 The half-life of radium-226 is 1.60×10^{3} yr. How many hours will it take for a 2.50-g sample to decay until 0.185 g of the isotope remains?

24.43 A rock contains 270 μmol ^{238}U ($t_{1/2} = 4.5 \times 10^{9}$ yr) and 110 μmol ^{206}Pb. Assuming that all the ^{206}Pb comes from decay of the ^{238}U, estimate the rock's age.

24.44 A fabric remnant from a burial site in the Near East has a ^{14}C/^{12}C ratio of 0.735 of the original value. How old is the fabric?

■ **Problems in Context**

24.45 Cow's milk contains about 6×10^{-11} mCi of ^{40}K per milliliter. How many disintegrations of ^{40}K are there per minute in 1.0 qt of milk?

24.46 Plutonium-239 ($t_{1/2} = 2.41 \times 10^{4}$ yr) represents a serious nuclear waste disposal problem. If seven half-lives are required to reach a tolerable level of radioactivity, how long must the ^{239}Pu be stored?

24.47 A rock contains 2.1×10^{-15} mol ^{232}Th ($t_{1/2} = 1.4 \times 10^{10}$ yr). There are 9.5×10^{4} fission tracks in the rock, each representing the fission of one atom of ^{232}Th. How old does the rock appear to be?

24.48 Volcanism was much more common in the distant past than today, and in some cases, specific events can be dated. A volcanic eruption melts a large area of rock and all gases are expelled. After cooling, $^{40}_{18}$Ar accumulates from the ongoing decay of $^{40}_{19}$K in the rock ($t_{1/2} = 1.25 \times 10^{9}$ yr). When a piece of rock is analyzed, it is found to contain 1.38 mmol ^{40}K and 1.14 mmol ^{40}Ar. How long ago did the rock cool?

Nuclear Transmutation: Induced Changes in Nuclei

■ **Concept Review Questions**

24.49 Irene and Frederic Curie-Joliot converted $^{27}_{13}$Al to $^{30}_{15}$P in 1933. Why was this transmutation significant?

24.50 Early workers mistakenly thought neutron beams were gamma radiation. Why were they misled? What evidence led to the correct conclusion?

24.51 Why must the electrical polarity of the tubes in a linear accelerator be reversed at very short time intervals?

24.52 Why does bombardment with protons usually require higher energies than bombardment with neutrons?

■ **Skill-Building Exercises** *(paired)*

24.53 Determine the missing species in these transmutations, and write a full nuclear equation from the shorthand notation: (a) ^{10}B (α,n) ?; (b) ^{28}Si (d,?) ^{29}P (the deuteron, d, is ^{2}H); (c) ? (α,2n) ^{244}Cf.

24.54 Determine the missing species in these transmutations and express the process in shorthand notation:
(a) Bombardment of a nuclide with a γ photon yields a proton, a neutron, and ^{29}Si.
(b) Bombardment of ^{252}Cf with ^{10}B yields five neutrons and a nuclide.
(c) Bombardment of ^{238}U with a particle yields three neutrons and ^{239}Pu.

Problems in Context

24.55 Names for elements 104, 105, and 106 have been approved as rutherfordium (Rf), dubnium (Db), and seaborgium (Sg), respectively. These elements have been synthesized from californium-249 by bombardment with carbon-12, nitrogen-15, and oxygen-18 nuclei, respectively. Four neutrons are formed in each reaction as well. (a) Write balanced nuclear equations for the formation of these elements. (b) Write the equations in shorthand notation.

The Effects of Nuclear Radiation on Matter

Concept Review Questions

24.56 Gamma radiation and ultraviolet radiation cause different processes to occur in matter. What are these processes and how are they different?

24.57 What is a cation-electron pair and how does it form?

24.58 Why is ionizing radiation more dangerous to children than to adults?

24.59 Why is $\cdot$OH more dangerous in an organism than OH^-?

Skill-Building Exercises (paired)

24.60 A 135 lb person absorbs 3.3×10^{-7} J of energy from radioactive emissions. (a) How many rads does she receive? (b) How many grays (Gy) does she receive?

24.61 A 3.6-kg laboratory animal receives a dose of 8.92×10^{-4} Gy. (a) How many rads did the animal receive? (b) How many joules did the animal absorb?

24.62 A 70.-kg person exposed to ^{90}Sr receives 6.0×10^5 β particles, each with an energy of 8.74×10^{-14} J. (a) How many grays does the person receive? (b) If the RBE is 1.0, how many mrem is this? (c) What is the equivalent dose in sieverts (Sv)?

24.63 A laboratory rat weighs 265 g and receives 1.77×10^{10} β particles, each with an energy of 2.20×10^{-13} J. (a) How many rads does the animal receive? (b) What is this dose in Gy? (c) If the RBE is 0.75, what is the equivalent dose in Sv?

Problems in Context

24.64 If 2.50 pCi of ^{239}Pu stays in a 95-kg human for 65 h, and each disintegration has an energy of 8.25×10^{-13} J, how many grays does the person receive? (1 pCi, picocurie = 1×10^{-12} Ci.)

24.65 A patient's brain is exposed for 27.0 min to 475 Bq of ^{60}Co for treatment of a tumor. If the brain mass is 1.588 g and each β particle emitted has an energy of 5.05×10^{-14} J, what is the dose in rads?

Applications of Radioisotopes

Concept Review Questions

24.66 Describe two ways that radioactive tracers are used in organisms.

24.67 Why is neutron activation analysis (NAA) useful to art historians and criminologists?

24.68 Positrons cannot penetrate matter more than a few atomic diameters, but positron emission of radiotracers can be monitored in medical diagnosis. Explain.

24.69 A steel part is treated to form some iron-59. Oil used to lubricate the part emits 298 β particles (with the energy

characteristic of ^{59}Fe) per minute per mL of oil. What other information would you need to calculate the rate of removal of the steel from the part during use?

Problems in Context

24.70 The oxidation of methanol to formaldehyde can be accomplished by reaction with chromic acid:

$$6H^+(aq) + 3CH_3OH(aq) + 2H_2CrO_4(aq) \longrightarrow$$
$$3CH_2O(aq) + 2Cr^{3+}(aq) + 8H_2O(l)$$

The reaction can be studied with the stable isotope tracer ^{18}O and mass spectrometry. When a small amount of $CH_3{}^{18}OH$ is present in the alcohol reactant, $H_2C^{18}O$ forms. When a small amount of $H_2Cr^{18}O_4$ is present, $H_2{}^{18}O$ forms. Does chromic acid or methanol supply the O atom to the aldehyde? Explain.

The Interconversion of Mass and Energy

(Sample Problem 24.6)

(Use the following data to solve problems in this section: mass of ^{1}H atom = 1.007825 amu; mass of neutron = 1.008665 amu.)

Concept Review Questions

24.71 Many scientists at first reacted skeptically to Einstein's equation, $E = mc^2$. Why?

24.72 What is a mass defect, and how does it arise?

24.73 When a nuclide forms from nucleons, is energy absorbed or released? Why?

24.74 What is the binding energy per nucleon? Why is the binding energy per nucleon, rather than per nuclide, used to compare nuclide stability?

Skill-Building Exercises (paired)

24.75 A ^{3}H nucleus decays with an energy of 0.01861 MeV. Convert this energy into (a) electron volts; (b) joules.

24.76 Arsenic-84 decays with an energy of 1.57×10^{-15} kJ per nucleus. Convert this energy into (a) electron volts; (b) MeV.

24.77 How many joules are released when 1.0 mol ^{239}Pu decays, if each nucleus releases 5.243 MeV?

24.78 How many MeV are released per nucleus if 3.2×10^{-3} mol chromium-49 releases 8.11×10^5 kJ?

24.79 Oxygen-16 is one of the most stable nuclides. The mass of an ^{16}O atom is 15.994915 amu. Calculate the binding energy (a) per nucleon in MeV; (b) per atom in MeV; (c) per mole in kJ.

24.80 Lead-206 is the end product of ^{238}U decay. One ^{206}Pb atom has a mass of 205.974440 amu. Calculate the binding energy (a) per nucleon in MeV; (b) per atom in MeV; (c) per mole in kJ.

24.81 Cobalt-59 is the only stable isotope of this transition metal. One ^{59}Co atom has a mass of 58.933198 amu. Calculate the binding energy (a) per nucleon in MeV; (b) per atom in MeV; (c) per mole in kJ.

24.82 Iodine-131 is one of the most important isotopes used in medical diagnosis for thyroid cancer. One atom has a mass of 130.906114 amu. Calculate the binding energy (a) per nucleon in MeV; (b) per atom in MeV; (c) per mole in kJ.

Problems in Context

24.83 The ^{80}Br nuclide decays by either β decay or electron capture. (a) What is the product of each process? (b) Which process releases more energy? (Masses of atoms: ^{80}Br = 79.918528 amu; ^{80}Kr = 79.916380 amu; ^{80}Se = 79.916520 amu; neglect the mass of the electron involved.)

Applications of Fission and Fusion

Concept Review Questions

24.84 What is the minimum number of neutrons from each fission event that must be absorbed by other nuclei for a chain reaction to occur?

24.85 In what main way is fission different from radioactive decay? Are all fission events in a chain reaction identical? Explain.

24.86 What is the purpose of enrichment in the preparation of fuel rods? How is it accomplished?

24.87 Describe the nature and purpose of the following components of a nuclear reactor:
(a) control rods; (b) moderator; (c) reflector.

24.88 State an advantage and a disadvantage of heavy-water reactors over light-water reactors.

24.89 What are the expected advantages of fusion reactors over fission reactors?

24.90 Account for the fact that there is a greater mass of iron in the Earth than any other element.

24.91 Why do so many nuclides have isotopic masses that are close to multiples of 4 amu?

24.92 What is the cosmic importance of unstable ^{8}Be?

Problems in Context

24.93 The reaction that will probably power the first commercial fusion reactor is

$$^{3}_{1}H + {}^{2}_{1}H \longrightarrow {}^{4}_{2}He + {}^{1}_{0}n$$

How much energy would be produced per mole of reaction? (Masses of atoms: $^{3}_{1}H$ = 3.01605 amu; $^{2}_{1}H$ = 2.0140 amu; $^{4}_{2}He$ = 4.00260 amu; $^{1}_{0}n$ = 1.008665 amu.)

Comprehensive Problems

Problems with an asterisk (*) are more challenging.

24.94 Some $^{243}_{95}$Am was present when the Earth formed, but it all decayed in the next billion years. The first three steps in this decay are emission of an α particle, emission of a β particle, and emission of another α particle.
(a) What other isotopes were present on the young Earth in a rock that contained some $^{243}_{95}$Am?
(b) Many of the products of these decay steps remain in modern rocks. Do any have important uses?

24.95 Early in the 19th century, before accurate atomic masses had been determined, a theory of atomic structure known as Prout's hypothesis held that all atoms were aggregations of H atoms. Support was found in the fact that the known atomic masses were close to integer multiples of the atomic mass of hydrogen, but the hypothesis was abandoned as more accurate values were obtained. Discuss briefly whether stellar nucleogenesis provides a modern adaptation of Prout's hypothesis.

24.96 Plutonium "triggers" for nuclear weapons were manufactured at the Rocky Flats plant in Colorado. An 85-kg

worker inhales a dust particle containing 1.00 μg of $^{239}_{94}$Pu, which resides in his body for 16 h. ($t_{1/2}$ of ^{239}Pu = 2.41×10^4 yr; each disintegration releases 5.15 MeV.)
(a) How many rads does he receive?
(b) How many grays?

*24.97 Archeologists removed pieces of charcoal from a Native American campfire, burned them in O_2, and bubbled the CO_2 formed into $Ca(OH)_2$ solution (limewater). The $CaCO_3$ that precipitated was filtered and oven dried. A 4.38-g sample of the $CaCO_3$ had a radioactivity of 3.2 d/min. How long ago was the campfire?

*24.98 A 5.4-μg sample of $^{226}RaCl_2$ has a radioactivity of 1.5×10^5 Bq. Calculate $t_{1/2}$ of ^{226}Ra.

24.99 How many rads does a 65-kg human receive each year from the approximately 10^{-8} g of $^{14}_{6}$C naturally present in her body? ($t_{1/2}$ = 5730 yr; each disintegration releases 0.156 MeV.)

24.100 The major reaction taking place during hydrogen-burning in a young star is

$$4^{1}_{1}H \longrightarrow {}^{4}_{2}He + 2^{0}_{1}β + 2^{0}_{0}γ + \text{energy}$$

How much energy in MeV is released per He nucleus formed? Per mole of He? (Masses: $^{1}_{1}H$ atom = 1.007825 amu; $^{4}_{2}He$ atom = 4.00260 amu; positron = 5.48580×10^{-4} amu.)

24.101 A sample of AgCl contains 175 nCi/g. A saturated solution prepared from the solid contains 1.25×10^{-2} Bq of radioactive Ag^+/mL. What is the molar solubility of AgCl?

24.102 From the burning of fossil fuels, the proportion of total CO_2 in our atmosphere continues to increase. Moreover, as a result of nuclear explosions and similar events, the CO_2 also contains more ^{14}C. How will these factors affect the efforts of future archeologists to determine the apparent ages of our artifacts by radiocarbon dating?

24.103 What fraction of the ^{235}U ($t_{1/2}$ = 7.0×10^8 yr) created when the Earth was formed would remain after 2.8×10^9 yr?

*24.104 In the event of a nuclear accident, government and industrial radiation officers must obtain many pieces of data to decide on appropriate action.
(a) If a person ingests radioactive material, which of the following is the *most* important quantity in deciding whether a serious medical emergency has occurred?
  1. The number of rems he receives
  2. The number of curies he absorbs
  3. The length of time he is exposed to the radiation
  4. The number of moles of radioisotopes he ingests
  5. The energy emitted per disintegration by the radioisotopes
(b) If the drinking water in a town becomes contaminated with radioactive material, what is the *most* important factor in deciding whether drastic and expensive action is warranted?

  1. The radioactivity per volume, $\dfrac{Ci}{m^3}$

  2. How long the water supply has been contaminated

  3. $\dfrac{Ci}{m^3} \times$ energy per disintegration

  4. The type of radiation emitted
  5. The radioisotopes involved

24.105 Suggest a reason why the critical mass of a fissionable substance depends on its shape.

*24.106 Technetium-99m is a metastable nuclide used in numerous cancer diagnostic and treatment programs. It is prepared just before use because it decays rapidly through γ emission: $^{99m}Tc \longrightarrow\ ^{99}Tc + γ$. Use the following data to determine (a) the half-life of ^{99m}Tc; (b) the percentage of the isotope that is lost if it takes 2.0 h to prepare and administer the dose.

TIME (h)	γ RAYS EMITTED/s
0	5000.
4	3150.
8	2000.
12	1250.
16	788
20	495

*24.107 How many curies occur in 1.0 mol ^{40}K ($t_{1/2} = 1.25 \times 10^9$ yr)? How many becquerels?

24.108 Marie Curie studied elements that decay by α, β, and γ emissions. As a result, she proposed that the radioactivity of an element was the same in all of its compounds. Later workers learned that some elements that decay by electron capture have half-lives that vary slightly from one compound to another. Explain.

*24.109 The isotopic mass of $^{210}_{86}Rn$ is 209.989669 amu. When it decays by electron capture it emits 2.368 MeV. What is the isotopic mass of the resulting nuclide?

24.110 Many nuclides decay by positron emission or by electron capture. Far fewer decay by positron emission or by beta emission. Why is the first pair of decay modes much more common than the second?

24.111 Neutron activation analysis bombards stable isotopes with neutrons. Depending on the isotope and the energy of the neutron, a wide variety of nuclear emissions are then observed. What are the products when the following neutron-activated species decay? Write an overall equation for the reaction in nuclear shorthand notation starting from the stable isotope before neutron activation.

(a) $^{52}_{23}V^* \longrightarrow$ [β emission]

(b) $^{64}_{29}Cu^* \longrightarrow$ [positron emission]

(c) $^{28}_{13}Al^* \longrightarrow$ [β emission]

*24.112 A metastable (excited) form of ^{50}Sc rearranges to its stable form by emitting γ radiation with a wavelength of 8.73 pm. What is the change in mass of 1 mol when it undergoes this rearrangement?

24.113 Isotopic abundances are relatively constant throughout the Earth's crust. Could the science of chemistry have developed if, for example, one sample of tin(II) oxide contained mostly ^{112}Sn and another mostly ^{124}Sn? Explain.

*24.114 What volume of radon will be produced per hour at STP from 1.000 g ^{226}Ra? ($t_{1/2} = 1599$ yr; 1 yr = 8766 h; mass of one $^{226}Ra = 226.025402$ amu.)

24.115 A sample of ^{90}Kr ($t_{1/2} = 32$ s) is to be used in a study of a patient's respiration. How soon after being made must it be administered to the patient if the activity must be at least 90% of the original activity?

24.116 Which isotope in each pair would you predict to be more stable? Why?

(a) $^{140}_{55}Cs$ or $^{133}_{55}Cs$ (b) $^{79}_{35}Br$ or $^{78}_{35}Br$

(c) $^{28}_{12}Mg$ or $^{24}_{12}Mg$ (d) $^{14}_{7}N$ or $^{18}_{7}N$

24.117 A sample of bone contains enough strontium-90 ($t_{1/2} = 29$ yr) to emit 8.0×10^4 β particles per month. How long will it take for the emissions to decrease to 1.0×10^4 per month?

*24.118 The 23rd-century starship *Enterprise* uses a substance called "di-lithium crystals" as its fuel.

(a) Assuming this material is the result of fusion, what is the product from the fusion of two ^6Li nuclei?

(b) How much energy is released per kilogram of di-lithium formed? (Mass of one ^6Li atom is 6.015121 amu.)

(c) When four ^1H atoms fuse to ^4He, how many electrons are released?

(d) To determine the energy potential of the fusion processes in (b) and (c), compare the changes in mass per kilogram of di-lithium and of ^4He.

(e) Compare the change in mass in (b) to that in the formation per kilogram of ^4He by the method used in current fusion reactors (Section 24.7). (For masses, see Problem 24.93.)

(f) Using late 20th-century fusion technology, how much tritium can be produced per kilogram of ^6Li in the following reaction: $^6_3Li + ^1_0n \longrightarrow\ ^4_2He + ^3_1H$? When this amount of tritium is fused with deuterium, what is the change in mass? How does this quantity compare with the use of di-lithium?

24.119 Uranium and radium are found in differing amounts in many rocky soils throughout the world. Both undergo radioactive decay, and one of the products is radon-222, the heaviest noble gas ($t_{1/2} = 3.82$ days). Inhalation of basement and room air containing this gas contributes to a large proportion of the lung cancers reported each year. According to current Environmental Protection Agency safety recommendations, the level of radioactivity from radon in homes should not exceed 4.0 pCi/L of air.

(a) What is the safe level of radon in Bq/L of air?

(b) A home has a radon measurement of 43.5 pCi/L. The owner vents the basement air such that no more radon enters the living area. What is the activity of the radon remaining in the room air (in Bq/L) after 8.5 days?

(c) How many more days does it take to reach the EPA recommended level?

24.120 Nuclear disarmament could be accomplished if weapons were not "replenished." The tritium in nuclear warheads decays to helium with a half-life of 12.26 yr, and must be periodically replaced or the weapon is useless. What fraction of the tritium is lost in 5.50 yr?

24.121 A decay series starts with the synthetic isotope $^{239}_{92}U$. The first four steps are emissions of a β particle, another β, an α particle, and another α. Write a balanced nuclear equation for each step. Which natural radioactive series could be started by this sequence?

24.122 How long can a 48-lb child be exposed to 1.0 mCi of ^{222}Rn before accumulating 1.0 mrad if the energy of each disintegration is 5.59 MeV?

24.123 The approximate date of an earthquake in the San Francisco area is to be determined by measuring the ^{14}C activity ($t_{1/2}$ = 5730 yr) of parts of a tree that was uprooted during the event. The tree parts have an activity of 12.9 d/min·g C, and a living tree has an activity of 15.3 d/min·g C. How long ago did the earthquake occur?

24.124 Were organisms a billion years ago exposed to more or less ionizing radiation than similar organisms today? Explain.

24.125 Tritium (^{3}H; $t_{1/2}$ = 12.26 yr) is continually formed in the upper troposphere by interaction of solar particles with nitrogen. As a result, natural waters contain a small amount of tritium. Two samples of wine are analyzed, one known to be made in 1941, and another that may have been made as early as 1902, but is suspected of being younger. The water in the 1941 wine has 2.32 times as much tritium as the water in the other. When was the other wine produced?

24.126 Carbon from the most recent remains of an extinct Australian marsupial, called *Diprotodon*, has an activity of 0.61 pCi/g. Modern carbon has ^{14}C activity of 6.89 pCi/g. How long ago did the *Diprotodon* apparently become extinct?

24.127 The reaction that allows for radiocarbon dating is the continual formation of carbon-14 in the upper atmosphere:

$$^{14}_{7}N + ^{1}_{0}n \longrightarrow ^{14}_{6}C + ^{1}_{1}H$$

What is the energy change associated with this reaction in eV/reaction and in kJ/mol reaction? (Masses of atoms: $^{14}_{7}N$ = 14.003074 amu; $^{14}_{6}C$ = 14.003241 amu; $^{1}_{1}H$ = 1.007825 amu.)

*24.128 The starship *Voyager*, like many other vessels of the newly designed 24th-century fleet, uses antimatter as fuel.
(a) How much energy is released when 1.00 kg each of antimatter and matter annihilate each other?

(b) When the antimatter is atomic antihydrogen, a small amount of it is mixed with excess atomic hydrogen (gathered from interstellar space during flight). The annihilation releases so much heat that the remaining hydrogen nuclei fuse to ^{4}He. If each hydrogen-antihydrogen collision releases enough heat to fuse 1.00×10^{5} hydrogen atoms, how much energy (in kJ) is released per kilogram of antihydrogen?
(c) Which produces more energy per kilogram of antihydrogen, the procedure in (a) or in (b)?

*24.129 Using late–20th century technology, hydrogen fusion requires temperatures around 10^{8} K, but lower temperatures succeed if the hydrogen is compressed. In the late–24th century, the starship *Leinad* uses such methods to fuse hydrogen at 10^{6} K.
(a) What is the kinetic energy of a hydrogen atom at 1.00×10^{6} K?
(b) How many hydrogen atoms can be heated to 1.00×10^{6} K from the energy released when one hydrogen atom and one antihydrogen atom collide and annihilate each other?
(c) If these hydrogen atoms fuse to ^{4}He atoms (each with the loss of two electrons), how much energy (in J) is generated?
(d) How much more energy is generated by the fusion in (c) than by the hydrogen/antihydrogen collision in (b)?
(e) Should the Chief Engineer of the *Leinad* advise the Captain to change the technology and produce ^{3}He (mass = 3.01603 amu) instead of ^{4}He?

24.130 What is the nuclear binding energy of a ^{7}Li nucleus in kJ/mol and in eV/nucleus? (Mass of ^{7}Li atom = 7.016003 amu.)

*24.131 Use Einstein's equation, the mass in grams of exactly 1 amu, and the relation between electron volts and joules to find the energy equivalent (in MeV) of a mass defect of exactly 1 amu.

Appendix A

Common Mathematical Operations in Chemistry

In addition to basic arithmetic and algebra, four mathematical operations are used frequently in general chemistry: manipulating logarithms, using exponential notation, solving quadratic equations, and graphing data. Each is discussed briefly below.

Manipulating Logarithms

Meaning and Properties of Logarithms

A logarithm is an exponent. Specifically, if $x^n = A$, we can say that the logarithm to the base x of the number A is n, and we can denote it as

$$\log_x A = n$$

Since logarithms are exponents, they have the following properties:

$$\log_x 1 = 0$$

$$\log_x (A \times B) = \log_x A + \log_x B$$

$$\log_x \frac{A}{B} = \log_x A - \log_x B$$

$$\log_x A^y = y \log_x A$$

Types of Logarithms

Common and natural logarithms are used frequently in chemistry and the other sciences. For common logarithms, the base (x in the examples above) is 10, but they are written without specifying the base; that is, $\log_{10} A$ is written $\log A$. Thus, for example, the common logarithm of 1000 is 3; in other words, you must raise 10 to the 3rd power to obtain 1000:

$$\log 1000 = 3 \qquad \text{or} \qquad 10^3 = 1000$$

Similarly, we have

$$\log 10 = 1 \qquad \text{or} \qquad 10^1 = 10$$
$$\log 1{,}000{,}000 = 6 \qquad \text{or} \qquad 10^6 = 1{,}000{,}000$$
$$\log 0.001 = -3 \qquad \text{or} \qquad 10^{-3} = 0.001$$
$$\log 853 = 2.931 \qquad \text{or} \qquad 10^{2.931} = 853$$

The last example shows an important point about significant figures with all logarithms: the number of significant figures in the number equals the number of digits to the right of the decimal point in the logarithm. That is, the number 853 has three significant figures, and the logarithm 2.931 has three digits to the right of the decimal point.

To find a common logarithm with an electronic calculator, you simply enter the number and press the LOG button.

For natural logarithms, the base is the number e, which is $2.71828\ldots$, and $\log_e A$ is written $\ln A$. The relationship between the common and natural logarithms is easily obtained:

Since

$$\log 10 = 1 \quad \text{and} \quad \ln 10 = 2.303$$

we have

$$\ln A = 2.303 \log A$$

To find a natural logarithm with an electronic calculator, you simply enter the number and press the LN button. If your calculator does not have an LN button, enter the number, press the LOG button, and multiply by 2.303.

Antilogarithms

The antilogarithm is the number you obtain when you raise the base to the logarithm; that is,

$$\text{antilogarithm (antilog) of } n \text{ is } 10^n$$

Using two of the earlier examples, the antilog of 3 is 1000, and the antilog of 2.931 is 853. To obtain the antilog with a calculator, you enter the number and press the 10^x button. Similarly, to obtain the natural antilogarithm, you enter the number and press the e^x button. [On some calculators, you enter the number and first press INV and then the LOG (or LN) button.]

Using Exponential (Scientific) Notation

Many quantities in chemistry are very large or very small. For example, in the conventional way of writing numbers, the number of gold atoms in one gram of gold is

59,060,000,000,000,000,000,000 atoms (to four significant figures)

As another example, the mass in grams of one gold atom is

0.00000000000000000000003272 g (to four significant figures)

Exponential (scientific) notation provides a much more practical way of writing such numbers. In exponential notation, we express numbers in the form

$$A \times 10^n$$

where A (the coefficient) is greater than or equal to 1 and less than 10 (that is, $1 \le A < 10$), and n (the exponent) is an integer.

If the number we want to express in exponential notation is larger than 1, the exponent is positive ($n > 0$); if the number is smaller than 1, the exponent is negative ($n < 0$). The size of n tells the number of places the decimal point (in conventional notation) must be moved to obtain a coefficient A greater than or equal to 1 and less than 10 (in exponential notation). In exponential notation, one gram of gold contains 5.906×10^{22} atoms, and each gold atom has a mass of 3.272×10^{-22} g.

Changing Between Conventional and Exponential Notation

In order to use exponential notation, you must be able to convert to it from conventional notation, and vice versa.

1. To change a number from conventional to exponential notation, move the decimal point to the left for numbers equal to or greater than 10 and to the right for numbers between 0 and 1:

   75,000,000 changes to 7.5×10^7 (decimal point 7 places to the left)

   0.006042 changes to 6.042×10^{-3} (decimal point 3 places to the right)

2. To change a number from exponential to conventional notation, move the decimal point the number of places indicated by the exponent to the right

for numbers with positive exponents and to the left for numbers with negative exponents:

1.38×10^5 changes to 138,000 (decimal point 5 places to the right)

8.41×10^{-6} changes to 0.00000841 (decimal point 6 places to the left)

3. An exponential number with a coefficient greater than 10 or less than 1 can be changed to the standard exponential form by converting the coefficient to the standard form and adding the exponents:

582.3×10^6 changes to $5.823 \times 10^2 \times 10^6 = 5.823 \times 10^{(2+6)} = 5.823 \times 10^8$

0.0043×10^{-4} changes to $4.3 \times 10^{-3} \times 10^{-4} = 4.3 \times 10^{[(-3)+(-4)]} = 4.3 \times 10^{-7}$

Using Exponential Notation in Calculations

In calculations, you can treat the coefficient and exponents separately and apply the properties of exponents (see earlier section on logarithms).

1. To multiply exponential numbers, multiply the coefficients, add the exponents, and reconstruct the number in standard exponential notation:

$(5.5 \times 10^3)(3.1 \times 10^5) = (5.5 \times 3.1) \times 10^{(3+5)} = 17 \times 10^8 = 1.7 \times 10^9$

$(9.7 \times 10^{14})(4.3 \times 10^{-20}) = (9.7 \times 4.3) \times 10^{[14+(-20)]} = 42 \times 10^{-6} = 4.2 \times 10^{-5}$

2. To divide exponential numbers, divide the coefficients, subtract the exponents, and reconstruct the number in standard exponential notation:

$$\frac{2.6 \times 10^6}{5.8 \times 10^2} = \frac{2.6}{5.8} \times 10^{(6-2)} = 0.45 \times 10^4 = 4.5 \times 10^3$$

$$\frac{1.7 \times 10^{-5}}{8.2 \times 10^{-8}} = \frac{1.7}{8.2} \times 10^{[(-5)-(-8)]} = 0.21 \times 10^3 = 2.1 \times 10^2$$

3. To add or subtract exponential numbers, change all numbers to have the same exponent, then add or subtract the coefficients:

$(1.45 \times 10^4) + (3.2 \times 10^3) = (1.45 \times 10^4) + (0.32 \times 10^4) = 1.77 \times 10^4$

$(3.22 \times 10^5) - (9.02 \times 10^4) = (3.22 \times 10^5) - (0.902 \times 10^5) = 2.32 \times 10^5$

Solving Quadratic Equations

A quadratic equation is one in which the highest power of x is 2. The general form of a quadratic equation is

$$ax^2 + bx + c = 0$$

where a, b, and c are numbers. For given values of a, b, and c, the values of x that satisfy the equation are called solutions of the equation. We calculate x with the quadratic formula:

$$x = \frac{-b \pm \sqrt{b^2 - 4ac}}{2a}$$

We commonly require the quadratic formula when solving for some concentration in an equilibrium problem. For example, if $x = [H_3O^+]$, we might have an expression that is rearranged into the quadratic equation

$$4.3x^2 + 0.65x - 8.7 = 0$$

Applying the quadratic formula, with $a = 4.3$, $b = 0.65$, and $c = -8.7$, gives

$$x = \frac{-0.65 \pm \sqrt{(0.65)^2 - 4(4.3)(-8.7)}}{2(4.3)}$$

The "$\pm$" sign indicates that there are always two possible values for x. In this case, they are

$$x = 1.3 \quad \text{and} \quad x = -1.5$$

In any real physical system, however, only one of the values will have any meaning. In this case, if x were, for example $[H_3O^+]$, the negative value would mean a negative concentration, which has no meaning.

Graphing Data in the Form of a Straight Line

Visualizing changes in variables by means of a graph is a very useful technique in science. In many cases, it is most useful if the data can be graphed in the form of a straight line. Any equation will appear as a straight line if it has, or can be rearranged to have, the following general form:

$$y = mx + b$$

where y is the dependent variable (typically plotted along the vertical axis), x is the independent variable (typically plotted along the horizontal axis), m is the slope of the line, and b is the intercept of the line on the y axis. The intercept is the value of y when $x = 0$:

$$y = m(0) + b = b$$

The slope of the line is the change in y for a given change in x:

$$\text{Slope } (m) = \frac{y_2 - y_1}{x_2 - x_1} = \frac{\Delta y}{\Delta x}$$

The *sign* of the slope tells the *direction* of the line. If y increases as x increases, m is positive, and the line slopes upward with higher values of x; if y decreases as x increases, m is negative, and the line slopes downward with higher values of x. The *magnitude* of the slope indicates the *steepness* of the line. A line with $m = 3$ is three times as steep (y changes three times as much for a given change in x) as a line with $m = 1$.

Consider the linear equation $y = 2x + 1$. A graph of this equation is shown in Figure A.1. In practice, you can find the slope by drawing a right triangle to the line, using the line as the hypotenuse. Then, one leg gives Δy, and the other gives Δx. In the figure, $\Delta y = 8$ and $\Delta x = 4$.

At several places in the text, an equation is rearranged into the form of a straight line in order to determine information from the slope and/or the intercept. For example, in Chapter 16, we obtained the following expression:

$$\ln \frac{[A]_0}{[A]_t} = kt$$

Based on the properties of logarithms, we have

$$\ln [A]_0 - \ln [A]_t = kt$$

Rearranging into the form of an equation for a straight line gives

$$\ln [A]_t = -kt + \ln [A]_0$$
$$y \quad\ = mx + \quad b$$

Thus, a plot of $\ln [A]_t$ versus t is a straight line, from which you can see that the slope is $-k$ (the negative of the rate constant) and the intercept is $\ln [A]_0$ (the natural logarithm of the initial concentration of A).

At many other places in the text, linear relationships occur that were not shown in graphical terms. For example, the conversion of temperatures scales in Chapter 1 can also be expressed in the form of a straight line:

$$°F = \tfrac{9}{5}°C + 32$$
$$y \ = mx + \ b$$

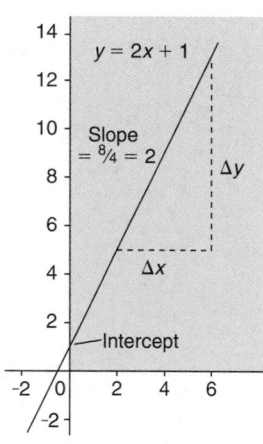

Figure A.1

Standard Thermodynamic Values for Selected Substances at 298 K

(NOTE: See the rear endpaper for a list of other important data tables.)

Substance or ion	ΔH_f^0 (kJ/mol)	ΔG_f^0 (kJ/mol)	S^0 (J/mol · K)	Substance or ion	ΔH_f^0 (kJ/mol)	ΔG_f^0 (kJ/mol)	S^0 (J/mol · K)
$e^-(g)$	0	0	20.87	$Ca^{2+}(aq)$	−542.96	−553.04	−55.2
Aluminum				$CaF_2(s)$	−1215	−1162	68.87
$Al(s)$	0	0	28.3	$CaCl_2(s)$	−795.0	−750.2	114
$Al^{3+}(aq)$	−524.7	−481.2	−313	$CaCO_3(s)$	−1206.9	−1128.8	92.9
$AlCl_3(s)$	−704.2	−628.9	110.7	$CaO(s)$	−635.1	−603.5	38.2
$Al_2O_3(s)$	−1676	−1582	50.94	$Ca(OH)_2(s)$	−986.09	−898.56	83.39
Barium				$Ca_3(PO_4)_2(s)$	−4138	−3899	263
$Ba(s)$	0	0	62.5	$CaSO_4(s)$	−1432.7	−1320.3	107
$Ba(g)$	175.6	144.8	170.28	Carbon			
$Ba^{2+}(g)$	1649.9	—	—	$C(graphite)$	0	0	5.686
$Ba^{2+}(aq)$	−538.36	−560.7	13	$C(diamond)$	1.896	2.866	2.439
$BaCl_2(s)$	−806.06	−810.9	126	$C(g)$	715.0	669.6	158.0
$BaCO_3(s)$	−1219	−1139	112	$CO(g)$	−110.5	−137.2	197.5
$BaO(s)$	−548.1	−520.4	72.07	$CO_2(g)$	−393.5	−394.4	213.7
$BaSO_4(s)$	−1465	−1353	132	$CO_2(aq)$	−412.9	−386.2	121
Boron				$CO_3^{2-}(aq)$	−676.26	−528.10	−53.1
$B(\beta$-rhombo- hedral)	0	0	5.87	$HCO_3^-(aq)$	−691.11	587.06	95.0
				$H_2CO_3(aq)$	−698.7	−623.42	191
$BF_3(g)$	−1137.0	−1120.3	254.0	$CH_4(g)$	−74.87	−50.81	186.1
$BCl_3(g)$	−403.8	−388.7	290.0	$C_2H_2(g)$	227	209	200.85
$B_2H_6(g)$	35	86.6	232.0	$C_2H_4(g)$	52.47	68.36	219.22
$B_2O_3(s)$	−1272	−1193	53.8	$C_2H_6(g)$	−84.667	−32.89	229.5
$H_3BO_3(s)$	−1094.3	−969.01	88.83	$C_3H_8(g)$	−105	−24.5	269.9
Bromine				$C_4H_{10}(g)$	−126	−16.7	310
$Br_2(l)$	0	0	152.23	$C_6H_6(l)$	49.0	124.5	172.8
$Br_2(g)$	30.91	3.13	245.38	$CH_3OH(g)$	−201.2	−161.9	238
$Br(g)$	111.9	82.40	174.90	$CH_3OH(l)$	−238.6	−166.2	127
$Br^-(g)$	−218.9	—	—	$HCHO(g)$	−116	−110	219
$Br^-(aq)$	−120.9	−102.82	80.71	$HCOO^-(aq)$	−410	−335	91.6
$HBr(g)$	−36	53.5	198.59	$HCOOH(l)$	−409	−346	129.0
Cadmium				$HCOOH(aq)$	−410	−356	164
$Cd(s)$	0	0	51.5	$C_2H_5OH(l)$	−277.63	−174.8	161
$Cd(g)$	112.8	78.20	167.64	$C_2H_5OH(g)$	−235.1	−168.6	282.6
$Cd^{2+}(aq)$	−72.38	−77.74	−61.1	$CH_3CHO(g)$	−166	−133.7	266
$CdS(s)$	−144	−141	71	$CH_3COOH(l)$	−487.0	−392	160
Calcium				$C_6H_{12}O_6(s)$	−1274.5	−910.56	212.1
$Ca(s)$	0	0	41.6	$CN^-(aq)$	151	166	118
$Ca(g)$	192.6	158.9	154.78	$HCN(g)$	135	125	201.7
$Ca^{2+}(g)$	1934.1	—	—	$HCN(l)$	105	121	112.8

Substance or ion	ΔH_f^0 (kJ/mol)	ΔG_f^0 (kJ/mol)	S^0 (J/mol · K)	Substance or ion	ΔH_f^0 (kJ/mol)	ΔG_f^0 (kJ/mol)	S^0 (J/mol · K)
$HCN(aq)$	105	112	129	$HI(g)$	25.9	1.3	206.33
$CS_2(g)$	117	66.9	237.79	**Iron**			
$CS_2(l)$	87.9	63.6	151.0	$Fe(s)$	0	0	27.3
$CH_3Cl(g)$	−83.7	−60.2	234	$Fe^{3+}(aq)$	−47.7	−10.5	−293
$CH_2Cl_2(l)$	−117	−63.2	179	$Fe^{2+}(aq)$	−87.9	−84.94	113
$CHCl_3(l)$	−132	−71.5	203	$FeCl_2(s)$	−341.8	−302.3	117.9
$CCl_4(g)$	−96.0	−53.7	309.7	$FeCl_3(s)$	−399.5	−334.1	142
$CCl_4(l)$	−139	−68.6	214.4	$FeO(s)$	−272.0	−251.4	60.75
$COCl_2(g)$	−220	−206	283.74	$Fe_2O_3(s)$	−825.5	−743.6	87.400
Cesium				$Fe_3O_4(s)$	−1121	−1018	145.3
$Cs(s)$	0	0	85.15	**Lead**			
$Cs(g)$	76.7	49.7	175.5	$Pb(s)$	0	0	64.785
$Cs^+(g)$	458.5	427.1	169.72	$Pb^{2+}(aq)$	1.6	−24.3	21
$Cs^+(aq)$	−248	−282.0	133	$PbCl_2(s)$	−359	−314	136
$CsF(s)$	−554.7	−525.4	88	$PbO(s)$	−218	−198	68.70
$CsCl(s)$	−442.8	−414	101.18	$PbO_2(s)$	−276.6	−219.0	76.6
$CsBr(s)$	−395	−383	121	$PbS(s)$	−98.3	−96.7	91.3
$CsI(s)$	−337	−333	130	$PbSO_4(s)$	−918.39	−811.24	147
Chlorine				**Lithium**			
$Cl_2(g)$	0	0	223.0	$Li(s)$	0	0	29.10
$Cl(g)$	121.0	105.0	165.1	$Li(g)$	161	128	138.67
$Cl^-(g)$	−234	−240	153.25	$Li^+(g)$	687.163	649.989	132.91
$Cl^-(aq)$	−167.46	−131.17	55.10	$Li^+(aq)$	−278.46	−293.8	14
$HCl(g)$	−92.31	−95.30	186.79	$LiF(s)$	−616.9	−588.7	35.66
$HCl(aq)$	−167.46	−131.17	55.06	$LiCl(s)$	−408	−384	59.30
$ClO_2(g)$	102	120	256.7	$LiBr(s)$	−351	−342	74.1
$Cl_2O(g)$	80.3	97.9	266.1	$LiI(s)$	−270	−270	85.8
Chromium				**Magnesium**			
$Cr(s)$	0	0	23.8	$Mg(s)$	0	0	32.69
$Cr^{3+}(aq)$	−1971	—	—	$Mg(g)$	150	115	148.55
$CrO_4^{2-}(aq)$	−863.2	−706.3	38	$Mg^{2+}(g)$	2351	—	—
$Cr_2O_7^{2-}(aq)$	−1461	−1257	214	$Mg^{2+}(aq)$	−461.96	−456.01	118
Copper				$MgCl_2(s)$	−641.6	−592.1	89.630
$Cu(s)$	0	0	33.1	$MgCO_3(s)$	−1112	−1028	65.86
$Cu(g)$	341.1	301.4	166.29	$MgO(s)$	−601.2	−569.0	26.9
$Cu^+(aq)$	51.9	50.2	−26	$Mg_3N_2(s)$	−461	−401	88
$Cu^{2+}(aq)$	64.39	64.98	−98.7	**Manganese**			
$Cu_2O(s)$	−168.6	−146.0	93.1	$Mn(s, \alpha)$	0	0	31.8
$CuO(s)$	−157.3	−130	42.63	$Mn^{2+}(aq)$	−219	−223	−84
$Cu_2S(s)$	−79.5	−86.2	120.9	$MnO_2(s)$	−520.9	−466.1	53.1
$CuS(s)$	−53.1	−53.6	66.5	$MnO_4^-(aq)$	−518.4	−425.1	190
Fluorine				**Mercury**			
$F_2(g)$	0	0	202.7	$Hg(l)$	0	0	76.027
$F(g)$	78.9	61.8	158.64	$Hg(g)$	61.30	31.8	174.87
$F^-(g)$	−255.6	−262.5	145.47	$Hg^{2+}(aq)$	171	164.4	−32
$F^-(aq)$	−329.1	−276.5	−9.6	$Hg_2^{2+}(aq)$	172	153.6	84.5
$HF(g)$	−273	−275	173.67	$HgCl_2(s)$	−230	−184	144
Hydrogen				$Hg_2Cl_2(s)$	−264.9	−210.66	196
$H_2(g)$	0	0	130.6	$HgO(s)$	−90.79	−58.50	70.27
$H(g)$	218.0	203.30	114.60	**Nitrogen**			
$H^+(aq)$	0	0	0	$N_2(g)$	0	0	191.5
$H^+(g)$	1536.3	1517.1	108.83	$N(g)$	473	456	153.2
Iodine				$N_2O(g)$	82.05	104.2	219.7
$I_2(s)$	0	0	116.14	$NO(g)$	90.29	86.60	210.65
$I_2(g)$	62.442	19.38	260.58	$NO_2(g)$	33.2	51	239.9
$I(g)$	106.8	70.21	180.67	$N_2O_4(g)$	9.16	97.7	304.3
$I^-(g)$	−194.7	—	—	$N_2O_5(g)$	11	118	346
$I^-(aq)$	−55.94	−51.67	109.4	$N_2O_5(s)$	−43.1	114	178

Substance or ion	ΔH_f^0 (kJ/mol)	ΔG_f^0 (kJ/mol)	S^0 (J/mol · K)	Substance or ion	ΔH_f^0 (kJ/mol)	ΔG_f^0 (kJ/mol)	S^0 (J/mol · K)
$NH_3(g)$	−45.9	−16	193	Silver			
$NH_3(aq)$	−80.83	26.7	110	$Ag(s)$	0	0	42.702
$N_2H_4(l)$	50.63	149.2	121.2	$Ag(g)$	289.2	250.4	172.892
$NO_3^-(aq)$	−206.57	−110.5	146	$Ag^+(aq)$	105.9	77.111	73.93
$HNO_3(l)$	−173.23	−79.914	155.6	$AgF(s)$	−203	−185	84
$HNO_3(aq)$	−206.57	−110.5	146	$AgCl(s)$	−127.03	−109.72	96.11
$NF_3(g)$	−125	−83.3	260.6	$AgBr(s)$	−99.51	−95.939	107.1
$NOCl(g)$	51.71	66.07	261.6	$AgI(s)$	−62.38	−66.32	114
$NH_4Cl(s)$	−314.4	−203.0	94.6	$AgNO_3(s)$	−45.06	19.1	128.2
Oxygen				$Ag_2S(s)$	−31.8	−40.3	146
$O_2(g)$	0	0	205.0	Sodium			
$O(g)$	249.2	231.7	160.95	$Na(s)$	0	0	51.446
$O_3(g)$	143	163	238.82	$Na(g)$	107.76	77.299	153.61
$OH^-(aq)$	−229.94	−157.30	−10.54	$Na^+(g)$	609.839	574.877	147.85
$H_2O(g)$	−241.826	−228.60	188.72	$Na^+(aq)$	−239.66	−261.87	60.2
$H_2O(l)$	−285.840	−237.192	69.940	$NaF(s)$	−575.4	−545.1	51.21
$H_2O_2(l)$	−187.8	−120.4	110	$NaCl(s)$	−411.1	−384.0	72.12
$H_2O_2(aq)$	−191.2	−134.1	144	$NaBr(s)$	−361	−349	86.82
Phosphorus				$NaOH(s)$	−425.609	−379.53	64.454
$P_4(s, white)$	0	0	41.1	$Na_2CO_3(s)$	−1130.8	−1048.1	139
$P(g)$	314.6	278.3	163.1	$NaHCO_3(s)$	−947.7	−851.9	102
$P(s, red)$	−17.6	−12.1	22.8	$NaI(s)$	−288	−285	98.5
$P_2(g)$	144	104	218	Strontium			
$P_4(g)$	58.9	24.5	280	$Sr(s)$	0	0	54.4
$PCl_3(g)$	−287	−268	312	$Sr(g)$	164	110	164.54
$PCl_3(l)$	−320	−272	217	$Sr^{2+}(g)$	1784	—	—
$PCl_5(g)$	−402	−323	353	$Sr^{2+}(aq)$	−545.51	−557.3	−39
$PCl_5(s)$	−443.5	—	—	$SrCl_2(s)$	−828.4	−781.2	117
$P_4O_{10}(s)$	−2984	−2698	229	$SrCO_3(s)$	−1218	−1138	97.1
$PO_4^{3-}(aq)$	−1266	−1013	−218	$SrO(s)$	−592.0	−562.4	55.5
$HPO_4^{2-}(aq)$	−1281	−1082	−36	$SrSO_4(s)$	−1445	−1334	122
$H_2PO_4^-(aq)$	−1285	−1135	89.1	Sulfur			
$H_3PO_4(aq)$	−1277	−1019	228	$S(rhombic)$	0	0	31.9
Potassium				$S(monoclinic)$	0.30	0.096	32.6
$K(s)$	0	0	64.672	$S(g)$	279	239	168
$K(g)$	89.2	60.7	160.23	$S_2(g)$	129	80.1	228.1
$K^+(g)$	514.197	481.202	154.47	$S_8(g)$	101	49.1	430.211
$K^+(aq)$	−251.2	−282.28	103	$S^{2-}(aq)$	41.8	83.7	22
$KF(s)$	−568.6	−538.9	66.55	$HS^-(aq)$	−17.7	12.6	61.1
$KCl(s)$	−436.7	−409.2	82.59	$H_2S(g)$	−20.2	−33	205.6
$KBr(s)$	−394	−380	95.94	$H_2S(aq)$	−39	−27.4	122
$KI(s)$	−328	−323	106.39	$SO_2(g)$	−296.8	−300.2	248.1
$KOH(s)$	−424.8	−379.1	78.87	$SO_3(g)$	−396	−371	256.66
$KClO_3(s)$	−397.7	−296.3	143.1	$SO_4^{2-}(aq)$	−907.51	−741.99	17
$KClO_4(s)$	−432.75	−303.2	151.0	$HSO_4^-(aq)$	−885.75	−752.87	126.9
Rubidium				$H_2SO_4(l)$	−813.989	−690.059	156.90
$Rb(s)$	0	0	69.5	$H_2SO_4(aq)$	−907.51	−741.99	17
$Rb(g)$	85.81	55.86	169.99	Tin			
$Rb^+(g)$	495.04	—	—	$Sn(white)$	0	0	51.5
$Rb^+(aq)$	−246	−282.2	124	$Sn(gray)$	3	4.6	44.8
$RbF(s)$	−549.28	—	—	$SnCl_4(l)$	−545.2	−474.0	259
$RbCl(s)$	−435.35	−407.8	95.90	$SnO_2(s)$	−580.7	−519.7	52.3
$RbBr(s)$	−389.2	−378.1	108.3	Zinc			
$RbI(s)$	−328	−326	118.0	$Zn(s)$	0	0	41.6
Silicon				$Zn(g)$	130.5	94.93	160.9
$Si(s)$	0	0	18.0	$Zn^{2+}(aq)$	−152.4	−147.21	−106.5
$SiF_4(g)$	−1614.9	−1572.7	282.4	$ZnO(s)$	−348.0	−318.2	43.9
$SiO_2(s)$	−910.9	−856.5	41.5	$ZnS(s, zinc blende)$	−203	−198	57.7

Appendix C

Answers to Selected Problems

Chapter 1

1.2 Solids and liquids have fixed volumes; that is, they will not necessarily totally fill a container. Gases take the volume of their container. (a) Gas (b) Liquid (c) Liquid **1.4** A physical property is one that can be measured without interacting the sample with another substance. A chemical property is one that characterizes how one material reacts with or transforms into another substance. (a) Color (yellow-green, silvery, white) and physical state (gas, crystals) are physical properties; reaction of sodium with chlorine is chemical. (b) Magnetism and color (black, white) are both physical properties. **1.6** (a) Physical; change in temperature only. (b) Chemical; "browning" process involves change in composition. (c) Physical; only changes in the size of the pieces. (d) Chemical; wood and ashes have different composition. **1.8** (a) Fuel (b) Wood **1.12** This observation was important since it helps you "keep track of" the matter undergoing the change. How could a *gain* of mass be explained by a *loss* of phlogiston? Only by postulating a negative mass for the phlogiston. **1.16** A well-designed experiment should test the relationship between at least two variables, all but one controlled, and the remaining one free to vary as the others change. It should test the relationship to see if there is any obvious cause and effect. For the results to be meaningful, they need to be reproducible from one trial to another. **1.19** (a) $(2.54 \text{ cm}/1 \text{ in})^2$ (b) $(10^3 \text{ m}/1 \text{ km})^2$ (c) $(1 \text{ km}/0.6214 \text{ mi})$ $\times (10^3 \text{ m}/1 \text{ km}) \times (10^2 \text{ cm}/1 \text{ m}) \times (1 \text{ h}/3600 \text{ s})$ **1.21** An intensive property depends only on the type of material in the sample; an extensive property depends on the quantity of material present. (a) and (c) are extensive; (b) and (d) are intensive. **1.26** 0.128 nm **1.28** 328 ft **1.30** (a) $3.27 \times 10^{-9} \text{ km}^2$ (b) \$13.9 **1.32** 77.3 kg (assuming 170 lb) **1.34** (a) $5.52 \times 10^3 \text{ kg/m}^3$ (b) 345 lb/ft^3 **1.36** (a) $1.35 \times 10^{-9} \text{ mm}^3$ (b) $1.35 \times 10^{-10} \text{ L}$ **1.38** (a) 10.58 cm^3 (b) 53.0 g **1.40** 2.70 g/cm^3 **1.42** (a) 22°C; 295 K (b) 109 K; −263°F (c) −273°C; −459°F **1.44** $6.4 \times 10^{-4} \text{ m}$ **1.46** $1.53 \times 10^{-6} \text{ cm}$ **1.50** Initial zeros are never significant; internal zeros are always significant; terminal zeros to the right of a decimal point are significant; terminal zeros to the left of a decimal point are significant *only* if they were measured. **1.52** (a) 0.39 (b) 0.039 (c) 0.039$\underline{0}$ (d) $3.0\underline{9}00 \times 10^4$ **1.54** (a) 0.00036 (b) 35.83 (c) 22.5 **1.56** 5×10^2 **1.58** (a) 1.34m (b) $1.52 \times 10^3 \text{ cm}^3$ (c) 443 cm **1.60** (a) 1.310000×10^5 (b) 4.7×10^{-4} (c) 2.10006×10^5 (d) 2.1605×10^3 **1.62** (a) 5550 (b) 10070. (c) 0.0000006885 (d) 0.003004 **1.64** (a) 8.025×10^4 (b) 1.0098×10^{-3} (c) 7.7×10^{-11} **1.66** (a) 3.45×10^{-19} J (b) 9.20×10^{24} molecules (c) 1.82×10^5 J/mol **1.68** Statement (b) contains an exact number from a count and statement (d) contains an exact number from a definition.

1.70. 7.50 ± 0.05 cm **1.72** The 3, 2, and 4 are exact numbers from a count. The 300 is exact if it came from a count (for example, from ticket sales), but has uncertainty if it was estimated. **1.74** (a) I: 8.72 g, II: 8.72 g, III: 8.50 g, IV: 8.56 g. Data sets I and II are equally accurate. (b) Data set III is the most precise, but the least accurate. (c) Data set I has good accuracy and precision. (d) Data set IV has poor accuracy and precision.
1.76 (a)

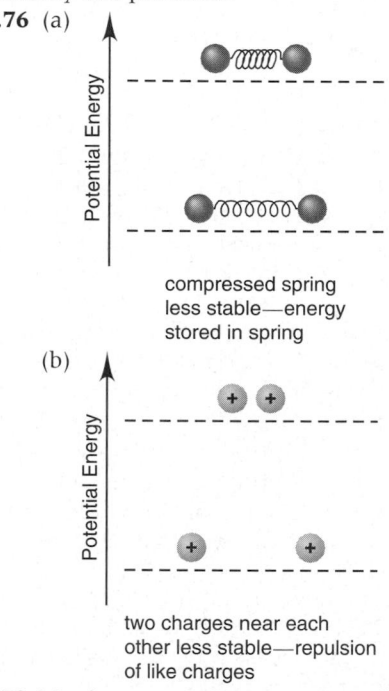

compressed spring
less stable—energy
stored in spring

(b)

two charges near each
other less stable—repulsion
of like charges

1.79 26 minutes. **1.80** 4 **1.82** For the calculation $(0.98 \pm 0.01)(1.06 \pm 0.01)$, the highest answer is $(0.99)(1.07)$ $(= 1.0593)$, and the lowest answer is $(0.97)(1.05)$ $(= 1.0185)$. Since the earliest decimal place where these differ is the hundredths place, the answer can legitimately be reported to this place, and thus with three significant figures. Alternatively, we can say that since the implicit relative uncertainty in each of the factors is about 1%, the answer can be reported with this uncertainty as well. **1.88** (a) −195.79°C (b) −320.42°C (c) 2.82 L **1.89** rubber: 54 m/s; granite: 6.00×10^3 m/s **1.93** (a) 8.41 g/cm^3 (b) 7.45 g/cm^3 **1.97** Freezing point = −3.7°X; boiling point = 63.4°X.

Chapter 2

2.1 An element cannot be broken down (decomposed) into simpler materials; a compound can. Or: an element consists of only one type of atom; a compound consists of more than one type of atom. **2.4** (a) Since it has constant composition, it is a compound. (b) Since all the atoms are identical, it is an element. (c) Since it has variable composition, it is a mixture.   (d) Since it has constant composition, it is a compound.   **2.9** The original mineral sample cannot be pure, since its properties aren't uniform (i.e., some dissolves, some doesn't).   **2.11** (a) All three   (b) Compound   (c) Compound.   **2.13** (a) Law of Definite Composition: the composition is independent of the source. (b) Law of Conservation of Mass: the total quantity of matter does not change.   (c) Law of Multiple Proportions: both materials are pure, but one pair of elements can combine in two different proportions.   **2.14** (a) No; the composition is independent of amount. Twice as much of Element A will combine with twice as much of element B and the composition of the compound formed will be the same.   (b) Yes; more compound will contain proportionally more of each component element.   **2.16** These two experiments demonstrate the Law of Definite Composition. The unknown blue compound decomposes the same way in both experiments, giving 64% white compound and 36% colorless gas. They also demonstrate the Law of Conservation of Mass, since in both cases the total mass before reaction equals the total mass after reaction.   **2.18** (a) 1.34 g   (b) 0.514 Ca; 0.486 F (c) 51.4% Ca; 48.6% F   **2.20** (a) 0.603   (b) 200. g   **2.22** 413 g Cu; 218 g S   **2.24** 1.11 g Cl/g S for compound 1; 2.22 g Cl/g S for compound 2; 2.22/1.11 = 2:1.   **2.27** Coal A **2.29** (a) If chlorine were monatomic, then Avogadro's hypothesis would be violated. There must be as many chlorine atoms in 2 L of hydrogen chloride as in 1 L of chlorine; therefore, chlorine must be diatomic if equal volumes of all gases contain equal numbers of particles. (Strictly speaking, we can't conclude that chlorine is diatomic—the best we can say is that it must have an even number of atoms in the molecules. The simplest explanation, however, is that it is diatomic.)   (b) Assuming the same molecular complexity for hydrogen and chlorine (i.e., they are both diatomic, both triatomic, etc.), there must be one atom of chlorine for each atom of hydrogen, since equal volumes react.   (c) Assuming a 1:1 atom ratio, chlorine atoms must weigh 1/(.0284) = 35.2 times the mass of a hydrogen atom.   **2.30** If you know the ratio of **any** two quantities, and the value of one of them, the other can always be calculated. In this case, charge/(charge/mass) = mass.   **2.34** The atomic number of an atom is the number of protons in the nucleus; the mass number is the sum of the number of protons and number of neutrons. The mass number can be changed without changing the chemical identity of the atom.   **2.37** The mass numbers are 36, 38, and 40, respectively, containing 18, 20, and 22 neutrons. *All* the isotopes have 18 protons and 18 electrons.   **2.39** (a) These have the same number of protons and electrons, but different numbers of neutrons. Same Z.   (b) These have the same number of neutrons, but different numbers of protons and electrons. Same N.   (c) These differ in all three (number of protons, neutrons, and electrons), but have the same A. **2.41** (a)

$^{48}_{22}$Ti $^{79}_{34}$Se $^{11}_{5}$B

2.43 (a) $^{38}_{18}$Ar   (b) $^{55}_{25}$Mn   (c) $^{109}_{47}$Ag   **2.45** 69.72 amu   **2.47** 75.774% ^{35}Cl and 24.226% ^{37}Cl   **2.50** (a) In the modern periodic table, the elements are arranged in order of increasing atomic number.   (b) Elements in a group (or family) have similar chemical properties.   (c) Elements can be classified as metals, metalloids, or nonmetals.   **2.53** The elements in group 1A(1) are metals; they generally lose electrons in chemical reactions. The elements in group 7A(17) are nonmetals; they generally gain electrons in chemical reactions.   **2.54** (a) germanium; Ge; 4A (14); metalloid   (b) sulfur; S; 6A (16); nonmetal   (c) helium; He; 8A (18); nonmetal   (d) lithium; Li; 1A (1); metal   (e) molybdenum; Mo; 6B (6); metal   **2.56** (a) Ra; 88   (b) As; 33   (c) Cu; 63.55   (d) Br; 79.90   **2.58** These atoms will form ionic bonds, in which one or more electrons is transferred from the metal atom to the nonmetal atom to form a cation and an anion, respectively.   **2.61** Coulomb's Law states that the strength of interaction of two charged particles is directly proportional to the product of the charges and inversely proportional to the distance between them. In this case, the doubly charged ions of MgO (Mg^{2+} and O^{2-}) would attract more strongly than the similarly-sized singly charged ions of LiF (Li^+ and F^-).   **2.64** The Group 1A(1) elements are metals and form cations; the group 7A(17) elements are nonmetals and form anions.   **2.66** Each of the sulfur atoms would gain two electrons to form an S^{2-} ion. Twice this number of potassium atoms would each lose one electron to form K^+ ions. The K^+ and S^{2-} ions form a regular array of ions in the solid K_2S.   **2.68** Cs^+ and Br^-.   **2.70** (a) oxygen; 17; 6A (16); 2   (b) fluorine; 19; 7A (17); 2   (c) calcium; 40; 2A (2); 4   **2.72** Li forms Li^+ and O forms O^{2-}, so the compound would have twice as many Li^+ (2.8×10^{20}) as O^{2-} (1.4×10^{20}).   **2.74** Sodium chloride.   **2.76** The empirical formula shows the simplest ratio of the atoms involved, while a molecular formula shows the actual numbers of the atoms which make up the molecule. The molecular formula is always a whole number multiple of the empirical formula; if the whole number is 1, the empirical and molecular formulae are identical.   **2.78** The two samples are similar in that they both contain 20 billion H atoms and 20 billion O atoms. They are different in that, in the $H_2 + O_2$ mixture, H atoms are bonded only to other H atoms and O atoms are bonded only to other O atoms, while in the H_2O_2 sample, H atoms are bonded to O atoms and O atoms are bonded both to H and to other O atoms. Also, the $H_2 + O_2$ mixture contains a total of 20 billion particles, while the H_2O_2 sample contains 10 billion particles.   **2.82** (a) NH_2 (b) CH_2O **2.84** (a) Li_3N; lithium nitride   (b) SrO; strontium oxide (c) $AlCl_3$; aluminum chloride   **2.86** (a) magnesium fluoride; MgF_2 (b) sodium sulfide; Na_2S (c) strontium chloride, $SrCl_2$ **2.88** (a) $SnCl_4$ (b) iron(III) bromide   (c) CuBr   (d) manganese(III) oxide   **2.90** (a) cobalt(II) oxide (b) Hg_2Cl_2 (c) lead(II) acetate trihydrate   (d) Cr_2O_3 **2.92** (a) BaO   (b) $Fe(NO_3)_2$ (c) MgS   **2.94** (a) sulfuric acid, H_2SO_4 (b) iodic acid, HIO_3 (c) hydrocyanic acid, HCN (d) hydrosulfuric acid, H_2S **2.96** (a) dinitrogen pentaoxide (b) ClF_3 (c) silicon disulfide   **2.98** S_2F_4; disulfur tetrafluoride   **2.100** (a) carbon monoxide   (b) sulfur dioxide   (c) dichlorine monoxide   **2.102** (a) 12; 342.2 amu   (b) 9;

132.06 amu   (c) 8; 344.6 amu   **2.104** (a) $(NH_4)_2SO_4$;
132.15 amu   (b) NaH_2PO_4; 119.98 amu   (c) $KHCO_3$;
100.12 amu   **2.106** (a) 108.02 amu   (b) 331.2 amu   (c)
72.08 amu   **2.108** (a) SO_3; sulfur trioxide; 80.07   (b)
C_3H_8; propane; 44.09   **2.110** Disulfur dichloride; SCl;
135.04   **2.112** Separating the components of a mixture is
done by physical methods only; that is, no chemical
changes (i.e., changes in composition) take place and the
components maintain their chemical identities and properties throughout. Separating the components of a compound
requires a chemical change (i.e., change in composition).
2.114 A solution (such as salt or sugar dissolved in water) is
a homogeneous mixture.   **2.115** (a) compound   (b) homogeneous mixture   (c) heterogeneous mixture   (d)
homogeneous mixture   (e) homogeneous mixture   **2.117**
(a) Add water. Salt will dissolve, pepper won't. Filter off the
pepper and evaporate the water to recover the salt.   (b)
Add water. Sugar will dissolve, sand won't. Filter off the
sand and evaporate the water to recover the sugar.   (c)
Heat the mixture to boiling; the water will evaporate first
and can be collected and condensed.   (d) Use a separatory
funnel to drain off the vinegar (lower level). OR Heat the
mixture to boiling; the vinegar (water + acetic acid) will
evaporate first and can be collected and condensed.   **2.119**
(a) Filtration   (b) Adsorption chromatography   (c) Extraction   **2.121** (a) 5.2×10^{-13} (b) 0.999726   **2.124** Magnetite   **2.126** The scientific method is an orderly procedure
involving observation, measurement, speculation, experimentation, and deduction. Many 19th-century scientists
did not believe that matter consists of atoms—Dalton's tiny,
indivisible particles of an element that cannot be created or
destroyed. A useful theory suggests new experiments that
can be performed whose results can be used to show the
limitations of that theory and provide a better explanation
for the initial natural phenomena. The experiments on
matter done by the 19th-century scientists resulted in the
accumulation of new data both supporting the idea of
atoms and yet indicating that atoms are composed of even
smaller subatomic particles.   **2.129** In each case, the total
mass of reactants equals the total mass of products, so the
Law of Conservation of Mass is obeyed. In each case, the
product (NaCl) contains 60.66% Cl by mass, so the Law of
Definite Composition is obeyed.   **2.131** mg/kg$\times10^{-4}$ =
mg/100 g = mass %, so   (a) Cl^-: 1.8980%, Na^+: 1.0560%,
SO_4^{2-}: 0.2650%, Mg^{2+}: 0.1270%, Ca^{2+}: 0.0400%, K^+:
0.0380%, HCO_3^-: 0.0140%   (b) 30.716%   (c) alkaline-
earth cations = 0.1670% (~15% of alkali metal); alkali-
metal cations = 1.0940%   (d) anions: 2.1770 % > cations:
1.2610%   **2.132** $C_4H_6O_4$; $C_2H_3O_2$; 118.09   **2.134** 52.00 amu
2.136 58.091 amu   **2.138** (a) mercury freezing   (b) water
decomposing into hydrogen and oxygen   (c) sterling silver
(d) $N_2 + O_2$ (e) Cu, O_2, etc.   **2.142** 37.01%C; 2.219% H;
18.50% N; 42.26% O.

Chapter 3

3.2 (a) 1 mol of $C_{12}H_{22}O_{11}$ contains 12 mol of C   (b)
7.226×10^{24} C atoms.   **3.6** (a) left   (b) left   (c) left   (d)
neither   **3.8** (a) 121.64 g/mol   (b) 44.02 g/mol   (c)
122.55 g/mol   (d) 100.00 g/mol   **3.10** (a) 239.2 g/mol
(b) 78.08 g/mol   (c) 342.17 g/mol   (d) 125.84 g/mol

3.12 (a) 1.1×10^2 g   (b) 0.309 mol   (c) 8.0×10^{20} atoms
3.14 (a) 75 g   (b) 0.884 mol   (c) 1.1×10^{22} atoms   **3.16**
(a) 1.00×10^3 g   (b) 0.678 g   (c) 0.473 mol; 285×10^{23}
formula units   (d) 2.85×10^{23} Na^+ ions, ClO_4^- ions, and Cl
atoms; 1.14×10^{24} O atoms.   **3.18** (a) 6.375% H   (b)
71.51% O   **3.20** (a) 0.1252   (b) 0.3428   **3.23** (a) 0.4882
mol   (b) 4.52×10^{24} H atoms   **3.25** (a) 64.7 mol   (b) 64.7
mol   (c) 7.23×10^3 g   **3.27** urea > ammonium nitrate >
ammonium sulfate > potassium nitrate.   **3.29** 4   **3.31** (b)
From the mass percentages, determine the empirical formula. Add up the total number of atoms in that, and divide
that into the total number of atoms in the molecule. The
result tells you the multiplier to make the empirical formula into the molecular formula.

(c) (mass %) $\left(\dfrac{1\ mol}{molar\ mass}\right)$ = moles of each element

(e) Count the numbers of the various types of atoms in the
structural formula and put these into a molecular formula.
3.33 (a) CH_2; 14.03   (b) CH_3O; 31.03   (c) N_2O_5; 108.02
(d) $Ba_3(PO_4)_2$; 601.8   (e) TeI_4; 635.2   **3.35** (a) C_3H_6 (b)
N_2H_4 (c) N_2O_4 (d) $C_5H_5N_5$ **3.37** (a) Cl_2O_7 (b) $SiCl_4$
(c) CO_2 **3.39** (a) NO_2 (b) N_2O_4 **3.41** (a) 1.20 mol F
(b) 24.0 g M   (c) Ca   **3.44** $C_{21}H_{30}O_5$ **3.46** $C_{10}H_{20}O$ **3.47**
The balanced equation provides information on the amount
and type of reactants and products, in terms of molecules,
moles, and mass in grams.   **3.50** (b)
3.51 (a) $16Cu(s) + S_8(s) \longrightarrow 8Cu_2S(s)$
(b) $P_4O_{10}(s) + 6H_2O(l) \longrightarrow 4H_3PO_4(l)$
(c) $B_2O_3(s) + 6NaOH(aq) \longrightarrow$
$$2Na_3BO_3(aq) + 3H_2O(l)$$
(d) $4CH_3NH_2(g) + 9O_2(g) \longrightarrow$
$$4CO_2(g) + 10H_2O(g) + 2N_2(g)$$
3.53 (a) $2SO_2(g) + O_2(g) \longrightarrow 2SO_3(g)$
(b) $Sc_2O_3(s) + 3H_2O(l) \longrightarrow 2Sc(OH)_3(s)$
(c) $H_3PO_4(aq) + 2NaOH(aq) \longrightarrow$
$$Na_2HPO_4(aq) + 2H_2O(l)$$
(d) $C_6H_{10}O_5(s) + 6O_2(g) \longrightarrow 6CO_2(g) + 5H_2O(g)$
3.55 (a) $4Ga(s) + 3O_2(g) \xrightarrow{\Delta} 2Ga_2O_3(s)$
(b) $2C_6H_{14}(l) + 19O_2(g) \longrightarrow 12CO_2(g) + 14H_2O(l)$
(c) $3CaCl_2(aq) + 2Na_3PO_4(aq) \longrightarrow$
$$Ca_3(PO_4)_2(s) + 6NaCl(aq)$$
3.59 Balance the equation for the reaction. From the relationship moles = g/MW, calculate the moles of D and E
present. By comparing the ratio of moles present to that
needed in the balanced equation, determine the limiting
reactant. Based on the number of moles of limiting reactant, proceed as follows:

$$m\ (g)\ F = mol\ L.R. \times \frac{mol\ F}{mol\ L.R.} \times \frac{g\ F}{mol\ F} = g\ F$$

3.61 (a) 0.119 mol   (b) 8.42 g   **3.63** (a) 33.8 mol   (b)
3.41×10^3 g   **3.65** 27.18 g H_3BO_3; 2.659 g H_2 **3.67**
1.44×10^3 g
3.69 (a) $I_2(s) + Cl_2(g) \longrightarrow 2ICl(s)$
$ICl(s) + Cl_2(g) \longrightarrow ICl_3(s)$
(b) $I_2(s) + 3Cl_2(g) \longrightarrow 2ICl_3(s)$
(c) 1.40×10^4 g
3.71 (a) 0.105 mol   (b) 0.100 mol   (c) O_2 (d) 5.61 g
3.73 1.58 mol; 277 g; 22.3 g H_2O in excess.   **3.75** 4.40 g
CO_2; 4.80 g O_2 in excess.   **3.77** 2.7 g $Al(NO_2)_3$; 0 g NH_4Cl;

40.6 g $AlCl_3$; 25.6 g N_2; 32.9 g H_2O **3.79** 49% **3.81**
98.2% **3.83** 24.5 g **3.85** 52.9 g **3.88** 54.7 g **3.89** (a) C
(b) B (c) C (d) B **3.91** No. It should read: "Take 100.00
mL of the 10.0 M solution and add sufficient water to make
1.00 L of solution. **3.92** (a) 1.57 g (b) 0.0461 M (c)
2.56 mol **3.94** (a) 4.65 g (b) 5.90×10^{-2} M (c)
1.11×10^{20} ions. **3.96** (a) 0.0617 M (b) 0.00363 M (c)
0.0150 M **3.98** (a) 987 g (b) 15.7 M **3.100** 2.1×10^2 mL
3.102 0.87 g **3.105** (a) Slowly add 5.7×10^3 mL of concentrated HCl to approximately 3.0 gal of water with constant
stirring. Monitor increase in temperature. When all of the
concentrated HCl has been added, slowly add enough water
to make a final volume of 5.0 gallon. (b) 22.4 mL **3.108**
ethane > propane > cetyl palmitate > ethanol > benzene
3.110 x = 3
3.113 (a) $Fe_2O_3 + 3CO \longrightarrow 2Fe + 3CO_2$ (b) 3.01×10^7 g
3.116 89.8% **3.118** (a) $2AB_2 + B_2 \longrightarrow 2AB_3$ (b) AB_2
(c) 5.0 mol (d) 0.5 mol **3.121** 8.9×10^{-7} M **3.123**
0.6855 g **3.125** (a) C (b) B (c) D **3.127** 790 miles
3.131 0.077 M **3.132** 38.5% **3.136** 586 g **3.138**
10:0.67:1 **3.141** 32.7% **3.143** (a) $C_6H_8O_7$; 192.14 (b)
0.547 mol
3.144 (a) $N_2(g) + O_2(g) \longrightarrow 2NO(g)$
$2NO(g) + O_2(g) \longrightarrow 2NO_2(g)$
$3NO_2(g) + H_2O(l) \longrightarrow 2HNO_3(aq) + NO(g)$
(b) $2N_2(g) + 5O_2(g) + 2H_2O(l) \longrightarrow 4HNO_3(aq)$
(c) 5.62×10^3 metric tons
3.147 14% XeF_4; 86.2% XeF_6

Chapter 4

4.2 Ionic compounds or polar covalent compounds. **4.3**
Ions, which could come from ionic compounds or from
other electrolytes such as acids or bases. **4.6** 2 **4.10** (a)
Molecules of benzene are symmetrical and not much like
water, so it would most likely be insoluble in water. (b)
Sodium hydroxide, an ionic compound, would be expected
to be soluble in water, and the solubility rules confirm this.
(c) Ethanol (CH_3CH_2OH) molecules are similar in structure
to water molecules (both contain O-H bonds), so it is soluble. (d) Potassium acetate, an ionic compound, would be
expected to be soluble in water, and this is confirmed by
the solubility rules. **4.12** (a) Yes; NaI is a salt. (b) Yes;
HBr is a strong acid. **4.14** (a) 0.50 mol (b) 0.251 mol
(c) 5.91×10^{-4} mol **4.16** (a) 0.60 mol (b) 0.528 mol (c)
0.281 mol **4.18** (a) 1.41×10^{23} Al^{3+} and 4.23×10^{23} Cl^-
(b) 3.89×10^{22} Na^+ and 1.95×10^{22} SO_4^{2-} (c) 2.16×10^{21}
Mg^{2+} and 4.31×10^{21} Br^- **4.20** (a) 0.35 (b) 0.0035 (c)
0.14 **4.26** Spectator ions (i.e., ions which do not chemically change in the reaction) do not appear, since they are
not involved in the reaction and are only present to balance
charge. **4.32** (a) formation of a gas and formation of a
nonelectrolyte (b) formation of a precipitate and formation of a nonelectrolyte **4.34** (a) no reaction (b) silver
iodide (AgI) **4.36** (a) no reaction (b) barium sulfate
($BaSO_4$)
4.38 (a) molecular: $Hg_2(NO_3)_2(aq) + 2KI(aq) \longrightarrow$
$Hg_2I_2(s) + 2KNO_3(aq)$
total ionic: $Hg_2^{2+}(aq) + 2NO_3^-(aq) + 2K^+(aq) +$
$2I^-(aq) \longrightarrow Hg_2I_2(s) + 2K^+(aq) + 2NO_3^-(aq)$

net ionic: $Hg_2^{2+}(aq) + 2I^-(aq) \longrightarrow Hg_2I_2(s)$
Spectator ions are K^+ and NO_3^-.
(b) molecular: $FeSO_4(aq) + Ba(OH)_2(aq) \longrightarrow$
$Fe(OH)_2(s) + BaSO_4(s)$
total ionic: $Fe^{2+}(aq) + SO_4^{2-}(aq) + Ba^{2+}(aq) +$
$2OH^-(aq) \longrightarrow Fe(OH)_2(s) + BaSO_4(s)$
net ionic: same as total ionic; no spectator ions.
4.40 (a) molecular: $KOH(aq) + HI(aq) \longrightarrow$
$KI(aq) + H_2O(l)$
total ionic: $K^+(aq) + OH^-(aq) + H^+(aq) + I^-(aq)$
$\longrightarrow K^+(aq) + I^-(aq) + H_2O(l)$
net ionic: $OH^-(aq) + H^+(aq) \longrightarrow H_2O(l)$
Spectator ions are K^+ and I^-.
(b) molecular: $NH_3(aq) + HCl(aq) \longrightarrow NH_4Cl(aq)$
total ionic: $NH_3(aq) + H^+(aq) + Cl^-(aq) \longrightarrow$
$NH_4^+(aq) + Cl^-(aq)$
net ionic: $NH_3(aq) + H^+(aq) \longrightarrow NH_4^+(aq)$
Spectator ion is Cl^-.
4.42 The hydrochloric acid reacts with the CO_3^{2-} bound in
the $CaCO_3$, releasing $CO_2(g)$:
total ionic: $CaCO_3(s) + 2H^+(aq) + 2Cl^-(aq) \longrightarrow$
$Ca^{2+}(aq) + 2Cl^-(aq) + H_2O(l) + CO_2(g)$
net ionic: $CaCO_3(s) + 2H^+(aq) \longrightarrow$
$Ca^{2+}(aq) + H_2O(l) + CO_2(g)$
4.44 0.0389 M **4.46** 0.03319 M **4.50** 1.80% **4.56** (a)
The S in SO_4^{2-} (i.e., H_2SO_4) has ON = +6, and in SO_2,
ON(S) = +4, so the S has been reduced (and the I^- oxidized), so the H_2SO_4 is an oxidizing agent. (b) The oxidation numbers remain constant throughout; H_2SO_4 transfers
a proton to F^- to produce HF, so it acts as an acid. **4.58** (a)
+4 (b) +3 (c) +4 (d) −3 **4.60** (a) −1 (b) −2 (c)
−3 (d) +3 **4.62** (a) −3 (b) +5 (c) +3 **4.64** (a) +6
(b) +3 (c) +7 **4.66** (a) O.A. = MnO_4^-; R.A. = $H_2C_2O_4$
(b) O.A. = NO_3^-; R.A. = Cu **4.68** (a) O.A. = NO_3^-; R.A.
= Sn (b) O.A. = MnO_4^-; R.A. = Cl^- **4.70** S is in Group
6A (16), so its highest possible ON is +6 and its lowest
possible ON is 6 − 8 = −2. (a) In S^{2-}, ON(S) = −2, so it
can only be oxidized (i.e., act as a reducing agent). (b) In
SO_4^{2-}, ON(S) = +6, so it can only be reduced (i.e., act as
an oxidizing agent). (c) In SO_2, ON(S) = +4, so it can
either be oxidized or reduced (i.e., act as a reducing or
oxidizing agent.
4.72 (a) $8HNO_3(aq) + K_2CrO_4(aq) + 3Fe(NO_3)_2(aq) \longrightarrow$
$2KNO_3(aq) + Cr(NO_3)_3(aq) + 3Fe(NO_3)_3(aq) + 4H_2O(l)$
K_2CrO_4 is the oxidizing agent (ON(Cr) goes from
+6 to +3) and $Fe(NO_3)_2$ is the reducing agent
(ON(Fe) goes from +2 to +3).
(b) $8HNO_3(aq) + 3C_2H_6O(l) + K_2Cr_2O_7(aq) \longrightarrow$
$2KNO_3(aq) + 3C_2H_4O(l) + 7H_2O(l) + 2Cr(NO_3)_3(aq)$
$K_2Cr_2O_7$ is the oxidizing agent (ON(Cr) goes from
+6 to +3) and C_2H_6O is the reducing agent
(ON(C) goes from −2 to −1).
(c) $6HCl(aq) + 2NH_4Cl(aq) + K_2Cr_2O_7(aq) \longrightarrow$
$2KCl(aq) + 2CrCl_3(aq) + N_2(g) + 7H_2O(l)$
$K_2Cr_2O_7$ is the oxidizing agent (ON(Cr) goes from
+6 to +3), and NH_4Cl is the reducing agent
(ON(N) goes from −3 to 0).
(d) $KClO_3(aq) + 6HBr(aq) \longrightarrow$
$3Br_2(l) + 3H_2O(l) + KCl(aq)$
$KClO_3$ is the oxidizing agent (ON(Cl) goes from +5

to −1), and HBr is the reducing agent (ON(Br) goes from −1 to 0).
4.74 (a) 4.54×10^{-3} mol   (b) 0.0113 mol   (c) 0.386g   (d) 2.80%   (e) H_2O_2 **4.75** Assuming that the left beaker is $AgNO_3$ and the right is NaCl, the Ag^+ is gray, the NO_3^- is blue, the Na^+ is brown, and the Cl^- is green.
Molecular: $AgNO_3(aq) + NaCl(aq) \longrightarrow$
$$NaNO_3(aq) + AgCl(s)$$
Total ionic: $Ag^+(aq) + NO_3^-(aq) + Na^+(aq) + Cl^-(aq) \longrightarrow$
$$Na^+(aq) + NO_3^-(aq) + AgCl(s)$$
Net ionic: $Ag^+(aq) + Cl^-(aq) \longrightarrow AgCl(s)$
4.80 $2Mg(s) + O_2(g) \longrightarrow 2MgO(s)$ is a combination reaction and also a redox. $CaO(s) + H_2O(l) \longrightarrow Ca(OH)_2(s)$ is a combination but not a redox.
4.82 (a) $Ca(s) + 2H_2O(l) \longrightarrow Ca(OH)_2(aq) + H_2(g)$;
  displacement
  (b) $2NaNO_3(s) \longrightarrow 2NaNO_2(s) + O_2(g)$;
  decomposition
  (c) $C_2H_2(g) + 2H_2(g) \longrightarrow C_2H_6(g)$; combination
4.84 (a) $2Sb(s) + 3Cl_2(g) \longrightarrow 2SbCl_3(s)$;
  combination, redox
  (b) $2AsH_3(g) \longrightarrow 2As(s) + 3H_2(g)$;
  decomposition, redox
  (c) $2CH_3OH(l) \xrightarrow{\Delta} C_2H_6O(g) + H_2O(g)$;
  decomposition, non-redox
4.86 (a) metal + oxygen $\longrightarrow$ metal oxide
  $2Mg(s) + O_2(g) \longrightarrow 2MgO(s)$
  (b) nonmetal halide + halogen $\longrightarrow$
            nonmetal halide with more halogen
  $ClF_3(g) + F_2(g) \longrightarrow ClF_5(g)$
  (c) nonmetal oxide + water $\longrightarrow$ oxyacid
  $SO_3(g) + H_2O(l) \longrightarrow H_2SO_4(aq)$
  (d) metal hydroxide $\xrightarrow{\Delta}$ metal oxide + water
  $Ca(OH)_2(s) \xrightarrow{\Delta} CaO(s) + H_2O(g)$
4.88 (a) $Ca(s) + Br_2(l) \longrightarrow CaBr_2(s)$
  (b) $2Ag_2O(s) \xrightarrow{\Delta} 4Ag(s) + O_2(g)$
  (c) $Mn(s) + Cu(NO_3)_2(aq) \longrightarrow$
            $Mn(NO_3)_2(aq) + Cu(s)$
(a), (b), and (c) are all redox reactions.
4.90 (a) $N_2(g) + 3H_2(g) \longrightarrow 2NH_3(g)$
  (b) $2NaClO_3(s) \xrightarrow{\Delta} 2NaCl(s) + 3O_2(g)$
  (c) $Ba(s) + 2H_2O(l) \longrightarrow Ba(OH)_2(aq) + H_2(g)$
Reactions (a), (b), and (c) are all redox reactions.
4.92 (a) $2Cs(s) + I_2(s) \longrightarrow 2CsI(s)$
  (b) $2Al(s) + 3MnSO_4(aq) \longrightarrow$
            $Al_2(SO_4)_3(aq) + 3Mn(s)$
  (c) $2SO_2(g) + O_2(g) \xrightarrow{\Delta} 2SO_3(g)$
  (d) $CO_2(g) + BaO(s) \longrightarrow BaCO_3(s)$
  (e) $2Al(s) + 3Mn^{2+}(aq) \longrightarrow 2Al^{3+}(aq) + 3Mn(s)$
Reactions (a), (b), and (c) are redox reactions, but (d) is not.   **4.94** 315 g O_2; 3.95 kg Hg (mercury)   **4.96** (a) O_2
(b) 0.117 mol Li_2O (c) 0 g Li; 4.13 g O_2; 3.50 g Li_2O **4.98** 56.7%   **4.100** 223 g   **4.103** 99.9 g   **4.107** The reaction $2NO + Br_2 \rightleftharpoons 2NOBr$ can proceed in either direction. If NO and Br_2 are placed in a container, they will react to form NOBr, and NOBr will decompose to form NO and Br_2. Eventually, the concentrations of NO, Br_2, and NOBr adjust so that the rates of the forward and reverse reactions become equal, and equilibrium is reached.

4.109 (a) $Fe(s) + 2H^+(aq) \longrightarrow Fe^{2+}(aq) + H_2(g)$
  ON: 0   +1   +2   0
  (b) 3.1×10^{21} ions
4.113 (a) $C_2O_4^{2-}(aq) + Ca^{2+}(aq) \longrightarrow CaC_2O_4(s)$
  (b) $5H_2C_2O_4(aq) + 2MnO_4^-(aq) + 6H^+(aq) \longrightarrow$
            $10CO_2(g) + 2Mn^{2+}(aq) + 8H_2O(l)$
  (c) $KMnO_4$ (d) $H_2C_2O_4$ (e) 55.06% $CaCl_2$
4.117 3.027%
4.120 1. $NaOH(aq) + HCl(aq) \longrightarrow NaCl(aq) + H_2O(l)$
  2. $KOH(aq) + HNO_3(aq) \longrightarrow KNO_3(aq) + H_2O(l)$
  3. $Ba(OH)_2(aq) + 2HBr(aq) \longrightarrow$
            $BaBr_2(aq) + 2H_2O(l)$
  Net ionic equation for all three is:
            $H^+(aq) + OH^-(aq) \longrightarrow H_2O(l)$
(a) All of the reactants in all of the reactions are strong electrolytes.   (b) Na^+ and Cl^- are the spectator ions in reaction (1), K^+ and NO_3^- in reaction (2), and Ba^{2+} and Br^- in reaction (3).
4.123 (a) $2CrO_4^{2-}(aq) + 3HSnO_2^-(aq) + H_2O(l) \longrightarrow$
            $2CrO_2^-(aq) + 3HSnO_3^-(aq) + 2OH^-(aq)$
  CrO_4^{2-} is the oxidizing agent (ON(Cr) goes from +6 to +3) and $HSnO_2^-$ is the reducing agent (ON(Sn) goes from +2 to +4).
  (b) $2KMnO_4(aq) + 3NaNO_2(aq) + H_2O(l) \longrightarrow$
            $2MnO_2(s) + 3NaNO_3(aq) + 2KOH(aq)$
  $KMnO_4$ is the oxidizing agent (ON(Mn) goes from +7 to +4) and $NaNO_2$ is the reducing agent (ON(N) goes from +3 to +5).
  (c) $4I^-(aq) + O_2(g) + 2H_2O(l) \longrightarrow$
            $2I_2(s) + 4OH^-(aq)$
  O_2 is the oxidizing agent (ON(O) goes from 0 to −2) and I^- is the reducing agent (ON(I) goes from −1 to 0).
4.126 750 g sand, 2.6×10^2 g Na_2CO_3, and 1.8×10^2 g $CaCO_3$ **4.128** (a) 4 mol   (b) 12 mol   (c) 12.87%
4.133 (a) $C_2H_5OH(l) + 3O_2(g) \longrightarrow 2CO_2(g) + 3H_2O(l)$
    $2C_8H_{18}(l) + 25O_2(g) \longrightarrow 16CO_2(g) + 18H_2O(l)$
  (b) 2.50×10^3 g   (c) 1.75×10^3 L   (d) 8.37×10^3 L

Chapter 5

5.1 (a) The volume of liquid remains constant but the volume of gas increases to the volume of the larger container. (b) The volume of the container containing the gas sample would increase when heated but the volume of the container containing the liquid sample would remain essentially constant when heated.   (c) The volume of the liquid remains essentially constant but the volume of the gas would be reduced.   **5.6** 979 cm H_2O **5.8** (a) 566 mm Hg (b) 1.31 atm   (c) 3.60 atm   (d) 107 kPa   **5.10** 0.9408 atm   **5.12** 0.966 atm   **5.18** $P_g \propto n$ if T, V are constant   **5.20** (a) V reduced to $\frac{1}{3}$ of its original value.   (b) V increased by a factor of 2.5.   (c) V increased by a factor of 3.   **5.22** (a) V reduced by a factor of 2.   (b) V increased by a factor of 1.56.   (c) V reduced by a factor of 4.   **5.24** −42°C   **5.26** 35.3 L   **5.28** 0.061 mol   **5.30** 0.674 g   **5.33** No   **5.35** inverted for H_2; upright for CO_2; since MM(CO_2) > MM(air) > MM(H_2).   **5.38** 5.86 g/L   **5.40** 0.00179 mol; 3.48 g/L   **5.42** 51.1 g/mol   **5.44** 1.32 atm   **5.48** C_5H_{12} **5.50** (a) 0.90 mol   (b) 6.76 torr   **5.51** 39.2 g   **5.53** 41.2 g

5.55 0.0250 g   **5.57** 286 mL   **5.59** 0.0998 atm   **5.63** At STP (or any identical temperature and pressure) the volume occupied by a mole of any gas will be identical. This is due to the fact that at the same temperature, all gases have the same average kinetic energy, resulting in the same pressure.   **5.66** (a) pressure: A > B > C   (b) $\overline{E}_k$: A = B = C   (c) diffusion rate: A > B > C   (d) total E_k: A > B > C   (e) density: A = B = C   (f) collision frequency: A > B > C   **5.67** 13.2   **5.69** 14.0 min   **5.71** (a) curve 1   (b) curve 1   (c) curve 1   **5.73** 4   **5.75** Negative deviations. N_2 < Kr < CO_2 **5.77** At 1 atm. At high P, intermolecular forces and molecular volume become more important.   **5.80** 6.81×10^4 g/mol   **5.83** (a) 22.5 atm   (b) 21.2 atm   **5.87** 1.2×10^{-7} L   **5.90** 35.8 L   **5.94** Al_2Cl_6 **5.97** 0.0162 mol   **5.101** (a) 1.95×10^3 g   (b) 3.5×10^4 g Ni   (c) 16 m³   **5.103** (a) 9 volumes   (b) CH_5N **5.107** A factor of 4.86. He could ascend 52.5 ft.   **5.109** 6.1 g   **5.112** 4.93×10^{-3} g   **5.114** (a) Xe   (b) H_2O (c) Hg   (d) H_2O. In all cases, due to stronger intermolecular attractions.   **5.117** 17.2 g CO_2; 17.8 g Kr   **5.120** 6.76×10^2 m/s for Ne; 4.81×10^2 m/s for Ar; 1.52×10^3 m/s for He

5.123 (a) $\frac{1}{2}m\overline{u}^2 = \frac{3}{2}\left(\dfrac{R}{N_A}\right)T$

$$m\overline{u}^2 = 3RT\left(\dfrac{R}{N_A}\right)T$$

$$\overline{u}^2 = \dfrac{3RT}{mN_A} \text{ and } \mathcal{M} = mN_A$$

$$\overline{u} = \sqrt{\dfrac{3RT}{\mathcal{M}}}$$

(b) $\overline{E}_k = \frac{1}{2}m_1\overline{u}_1{}^2 = \frac{1}{2}m_2\overline{u}_2{}^2$

$$m_1\overline{u}_1{}^2 = m_2\overline{u}_2{}^2$$

$$\dfrac{m_1}{m_2} = \dfrac{\overline{u}_2{}^2}{\overline{u}_1{}^2}$$

$$\sqrt{\dfrac{m_1}{m_2}} = \dfrac{\overline{u}_2}{\overline{u}_1}, \text{ where } \overline{u} \text{ is the rate.}$$

Since $\dfrac{m_1}{m_2} = \dfrac{\mathcal{M}_1}{\mathcal{M}_2}$ and $u \propto$ rate, $\sqrt{\dfrac{\mathcal{M}_1}{\mathcal{M}_2}} = \dfrac{\text{rate}_2}{\text{rate}_1}$

5.127 (a) 14.8 L   (b) P_{H_2O} = 42.2 torr; P_{O_2} = P_{CO_2} = 370 torr   **5.130** 360

Chapter 6

6.4 Increase: eating food, lying in the sun, taking a hot bath Decrease: exercising, taking a cold bath, going outside on a cold day   **6.6** The ΔE for the heater and the air conditioner are the same magnitude. $\Delta E_{system} = -\Delta E_{surroundings}$.   **6.8** zero J   **6.10** 1.52×10^3 J   **6.12** (a) 3.3×10^7 kJ   (b) 7.9×10^6 kcal   (c) 3.1×10^7 Btu   **6.15** 9.2 h   **6.17** Measuring the heat transfer at constant pressure is more convenient than measuring the heat transfer at constant volume.   **6.19** (a), (c), (d), and (g) are exothermic; (b), (e), and (f) are endothermic.

6.22

Reactants

H $\Delta H = (-)$

Products

6.24 (a) $CH_4(g) + 2O_2(g) \longrightarrow CO_2(g) + 2H_2O(g)$ + heat

$CH_4 + 2O_2$

H $\Delta H = (-)$

$CO_2 + 2H_2O$

(b) $H_2O(l) \longrightarrow H_2O(s)$ + heat

$H_2O_{(l)}$

H $\Delta H = (-)$

$H_2O_{(s)}$

6.26 (a) $C_2H_6O(l) + 3O_2(g) \longrightarrow$

$2CO_2(g) + 3H_2O(g)$ + heat

$C_2H_6O + 3O_2$

H $\Delta H = (-)$

$2CO_2 + 3H_2O$

(b) $N_2(g) + 2O_2(g)$ + heat $\longrightarrow 2NO_2(g)$

$2NO_2$

H $\Delta H = (+)$

$N_2 + 2O_2$

6.28 Both are one-carbon molecules. Since methane contains the fewer C-O bonds, it will have the greater heat of combustion per mole.   **6.31** Energy, mass, change in temperature.   **6.33** The heat capacity of an object is the amount of energy required to raise its temperature by 1 K (or 1°C). For pure substances, the heat capacity is usually defined for a specified amount of the substance. The specific heat capacity is the amount of energy required to raise the temperature of one gram of the substance by 1 K (or 1°C).   (a) Since the chrome-plated brass fixture is not a pure substance, one would use heat capacity.   (b) and (c) Since the copper wire and water are pure substances; one would use specific heat capacity.   **6.35** 4.0 kJ   **6.37** 323°C   **6.39** 77.5°C   **6.41** 42°C   **6.43** 57.1°C   **6.48** $\Delta H > 0$ since energy is required to break the O-O bond.   **6.49** $\Delta H < 0$; Opposite in sign and $\frac{1}{2}$ the value for the vaporization of 2 moles of H_2O.   **6.50** (a) exothermic   (b) +20.2 kJ   (c) -5.2×10^2 kJ   (d) -12.6 kJ   **6.52** (a) $\frac{1}{2}N_2(g) + \frac{1}{2}O_2(g) \longrightarrow NO(g)$ $\Delta H = 90.29$ kJ   (b) -4.51 kJ   **6.54** 2.11×10^6 kJ   **6.58** (a) $C_2H_4(g) + 3O_2(g) \longrightarrow$

$2CO_2(g) + 2H_2O(g)$ $\Delta H = -1411$ kJ   (b) 1.39 g   **6.62** $\Delta H = \Delta H_{comb}$ (C) $- \Delta H_{comb}$ (CO)   **6.63** -813.4 kJ   **6.65** 44.0 kJ   **6.67** $N_2(g) + 2O_2(g) \longrightarrow 2NO_2(g)$; $\Delta H = 66.4$ kJ; A = 1, B = 2, C = 3.   **6.70** The standard heat of reaction, ΔH^0_{rxn}, is the enthalpy change for any reaction where all substances are in their standard states. The standard heat of formation, ΔH_f^0 is the enthalpy change that accompanies the formation of *one mole* of a compound in its standard state from elements in their standard states.

6.72 (a) $\frac{1}{2}Cl_2(g) + Na(s) \longrightarrow NaCl(s)$

(b) $H_2(g) + \frac{1}{2}O_2(g) \longrightarrow H_2O(l)$

(c) $\frac{1}{2}N_2(g) + \frac{3}{2}H_2(g) \longrightarrow NH_3(g)$

6.73 (a) $Ca(s) + Cl_2(g) \longrightarrow CaCl_2(s)$

(b) $Na(s) + C(graphite) + \frac{1}{2}H_2(g) + \frac{3}{2}O_2(g) \longrightarrow$ $NaHCO_3(s)$

(c) $C(graphite) + 2Cl_2(g) \longrightarrow CCl_4(l)$

(d) $\frac{1}{2}N_2(g) + \frac{1}{2}H_2(g) + \frac{3}{2}O_2(g) \longrightarrow HNO_3(l)$

6.75 (a) -1036.8 kJ (b) -433 kJ **6.77** -157.3 kJ/mol **6.80** (a) 503.9 kJ (b) $-\Delta H_1 + 2\Delta H_2 = 504$ kJ **6.81** (a) $C_{18}H_{36}O_2(s) + 26O_2(g) \longrightarrow 18CO_2(g) + 18H_2O(g)$ (b) $-10{,}488$ kJ (c) -36.9 kJ/g $= -8.81$ kcal/g (d) 11.0 g fat $\times$ 8.81 kcal/g $= 96.9$ kcal, so the information is consistent. **6.83** (a) 23.6 L initial; 24.9 L final (b) 187 J (c) -1.3×10^2 J (d) 320 J (e) 320 J (f) $\Delta H = \Delta E + P\Delta V = \Delta E - w = q_p$ **6.84** (a) ΔH^0 for both is -55.90 kJ (b) All three are the same since all have the same net ionic equation. **6.88** -94 kJ/mol **6.91** (a) 1054 J/Btu (b) 1.05×10^8 J/therm (c) 1.31×10^2 mol (d) \$0.0035 (e) \$0.53 **6.93** 721 kJ **6.98** 94°C **6.101** (a) III > II > I (b) I > III > II **6.104** (a) 6.81×10^3 J (b) 243°C **6.108** (a) 1.25×10^3 kJ (b) 2.24×10^{3}°C

Chapter 7

7.2 (a) $5 < 2 < 6 < 4 < 1 < 3$ (b) $3 < 1 < 4 < 6 < 2 < 5$ (c) $3 < 1 < 4 < 6 < 2 < 5$ **7.5** The energy of an atom is not continuous, but quantized. It exists only in certain fixed amounts called a quantum. **7.7** 3.12×10^2 m, 3.12×10^{11} nm, 3.12×10^{12} Å **7.9** 2.4×10^{-23} J **7.11** red < yellow < blue **7.13** 1.35×10^7 nm; 1.35×10^8 Å **7.16** (a) 8.21×10^{-19} J (b) 9.0×10^{-19} J **7.18** Bohr's key assumption was that the electron in an atom does *not* radiate energy while in a stationary state, but that the electron can move to a different orbit only by absorbing or emitting a photon whose energy is equal to the difference in energy between two states. These differences in energy correspond to the wavelengths in known line spectra for the hydrogen atom. **7.20** (a) absorption (b) emission (c) emission (d) absorption **7.22** Yes, the predicted line spectra are accurate. The energies for a one-electron system would have the values $E_n = \dfrac{-(Z^2)2.18\times10^{-18}\text{ J}}{n^2}$ where Z is the atomic number for the atom or ion. The energy levels for Be^{3+} would be greater by a factor of 16 than those for the hydrogen atom. This means that the pattern of lines would be similar, but at different wavelengths. **7.23** 434.18 nm **7.25** 1875.6 nm **7.27** 2.76×10^5 J/mol **7.29** (d) < (a) < (c) < (b). **7.31** n = 4 **7.34** 3.37×10^{-19} J/photon; 2.03×10^2 kJ/einstein **7.37** Wavelengths associated with objects of ordinary size and mass are so extremely small that they are impossible to observe. **7.39** (a) 7.58×10^{-37} m (b) 1.2×10^{-35} m **7.41** 2.2×10^{-26} m/s **7.43** 3.75×10^{-36} kg/photon **7.47** The total probability of finding the 1s electron in any direction at a distance r from

the nucleus is greatest when the value of r is 0.529 Å. This distance is for the greatest probability of finding a 1s electron. The distance for a 2s electron would be farther from the nucleus. **7.48** (a) principal determinant of the electron's energy or distance from the nucleus (b) determines the shape of the orbital (c) determines the orientation of the orbital **7.49** (a) 1 (b) 5 (c) 3 (d) 9 **7.51** (a) m_l: $-2, -1, 0, +1, +2$ (b) m_l: 0 (c) m_l: $-3, -2, -1, 0, +1, +2, +3$

7.53 (a)

(b)

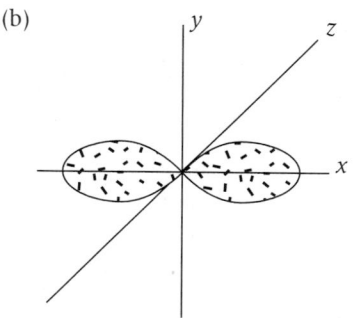

7.55

SUBLEVEL	ALLOWABLE m_l	NO. OF POSSIBLE ORBITALS
(a) d	$-2, -1, 0, +1, +2$	5
(b) p	$-1, 0, +1$	3
(c) f	$-3, -2, -1, 0, +1, +2, +3$	7

7.57 (a) $n = 5$; $l = 0$; 1 possible orbital (b) $n = 3$; $l = 1$; 3 possible orbitals (c) $n = 4$; $l = 3$; 7 possible orbitals **7.59** (a) No; $n = 2$, $l = 0$; $m_l = 0$; $n = 2$, $l = 1$; $m_l = -1$ (b) ok (c) ok (d) No; $n = 5$, $l = 2$; $m_l = +2$; $n = 5$, $l = 3$; $m_l = +3$ **7.62** (a) $E = -[h^2/(8\pi^2 m_e a_0^2)](1/n^2)$; constant $= 2.180\times10^{18}$ J, as in Bohr's theory. (b) 3.027×10^{-19} J (c) 656.5 nm; yes. **7.63** (a) The attractive force of the nucleus for the electron must be overcome. (b) The e^- in silver is more tightly held by the nucleus. (c) Silver (d) Once the electron is freed from the atom, its energy increases in proportion to the frequency. **7.66** Li^{2+} **7.69** (a) $2 \longrightarrow 1$ (b) $5 \longrightarrow 2$ (c) $4 \longrightarrow 2$ (d) $3 \longrightarrow 2$ (e) $6 \longrightarrow 3$ **7.71** (a) No (b) Yes (c) No **7.75** (a) n = 1, l = 1, $m_l = -1$ (b) n = 3, l = 2, $m_l = +1$ (c) n = 7, l = 3, $m_l = +3$ (d) n = 4, l = 2, $m_l = -2$ **7.77** IE $= (1.31\times10^3$ kJ/mol$)Z^2$; IE(B^{4+}) $= 3.28\times10^4$ kJ/mol. **7.81** 6.4×10^{27} **7.83** (a) No overlap (b) overlap (c) 2 (d) At longer wavelengths, the spectrum begins to become a continuous band. **7.87** (a) 1.87×10^{-19} J (b) 3.68×10^{-19} J **7.89** (a) This is the wavelength of maximum absorbance, so gives the highest sensitivity. (b) UV (c) 1.93×10^{-2} g vitamin A/g fish-liver oil **7.91** 1.0×10^{18} photons

Chapter 8

8.1 Elements are listed in the periodic table in an ordered, systematic way that correlates with a periodicity of their chemical and physical properties. The theoretical basis for the table in terms of atomic number and electron configuration does not allow for an "unknown element" between Sn and Sb. **8.3** (a) predicted 54.3 amu (b) predicted 6.3°C **8.6** m_s relates just to the electron; the others describe the orbital. **8.9** Shielding occurs when inner-shell electrons protect or shield outer-shell electrons from the full attractive force of the nucleus. The effective nuclear charge is the nuclear charge an electron actually experiences. As the number of shielding electrons increases, the effective nuclear charge decreases. **8.11** (a) 6 (b) 10 (c) 2 **8.13** (a) 6 (b) 2 (c) 14

8.16 In degenerate orbitals (those of identical energy), the filling will occur in such a manner that the spins will have the same value. N: $1s^2\ 2s^2\ 2p^3$

[↑↓] [↑↓] [↑] [↑] [↑]   or   [↑↓] [↑↓] [↓] [↓] [↓]

8.18 Main-group elements from the same group have similar outer electron configurations where the (old) group number equals the number of outer electrons. Outer electron configurations vary in a periodic manner within a period, with each succeeding element having one additional electron. **8.20** The maximum number of electrons in any orbital n is $2n^2$. For $n = 4$, the maximum electron capacity is $2(4)^2$ or 32 electrons. **8.21** (a) $n = 5$; $l = 0$; $m_l = 0$; $m_s = +\frac{1}{2}$ (b) $n = 3$; $l = 1$; $m_l = 1$; $m_s = -\frac{1}{2}$ (c) $n = 5$; $l = 0$; $m_l = 0$; $m_s = +\frac{1}{2}$ (d) $n = 2$; $l = 1$; $m_l = +1$; $m_s = -\frac{1}{2}$ **8.23** (a) Rb: $1s^22s^22p^63s^23p^64s^23d^{10}4p^65s^1$ (b) Ge: $1s^22s^22p^63s^23p^64s^23d^{10}4p^2$ (c) Ar: $1s^22s^22p^63s^23p^6$ **8.25** (a) Cl: $1s^22s^22p^63s^23p^5$ (b) Si: $1s^22s^22p^63s^23p^2$ (c) Sr: $1s^22s^22p^63s^23p^64s^23d^{10}4p^65s^2$

8.27 (a) Ti: [Ar]$4s^23d^2$

[Ar] [↑↓] [↑] [↑] [ ] [ ] [ ]

(b) Cl: [Ne]$3s^23p^5$

[Ne] [↑↓] [↑↓] [↑↓] [↑]

(c) V: [Ar]$4s^23d^3$

[Ar] [↑↓] [↑] [↑] [↑] [ ] [ ]

8.29 (a) Mn: [Ar]$4s^23d^5$

[Ar] [↑↓] [↑] [↑] [↑] [↑] [↑]

(b) P: [Ne]$3s^23p^3$

[Ne] [↑↓] [↑] [↑] [↑]

(c) Fe: [Ar]$4s^23d^6$

[Ar] [↑↓] [↑↓] [↑] [↑] [↑] [↑]

8.31 (a) O; Group 6A (16); period = 2 (b) P; Group 5A (15); period = 3

8.33 (a) [↑↓] [↑↓] [↑↓] [↑]

Cl; 7A(17); 3

(b) [↑↓] [↑↓] [↑↓] [↑↓] [↑↓] [↑↓] [↑] [↑] [↑]

As; 5A(15); 4

8.35 (a) [Ar]$4s^23d^{10}4p^1$; Ga; 3A(13); 4 (b) [He]$2s^22p^6$; Ne, 8A(18); 2

8.37

	INNER ELECTRONS	OUTER ELECTRONS	VALENCE ELECTRONS
(a) O	2	6	6
(b) Sn	46	4	4
(c) Ca	18	2	2
(d) Fe	18	2	8
(e) Se	28	6	6

8.39 (a) B; Al, Ga, In, Tl (b) S; O, Se, Te, Po (c) La; Sc, Y, Ac **8.41** (a) C; Si, Ge, Sn, Pb (b) V; Nb, Ta, Ha (c) P; N, As, Sb, Bi

8.43 Na: $1s^22s^22p^63s^1$

Na (excited): $1s^22s^22p^63p^1$

[↑↓] [↑↓] [↑↓] [↑↓] [↑↓] [ ] [↑] [ ] [ ]

8.46 Atomic radius increases from top to bottom in a group, whereas ionization energy decreases from top to bottom in a group. The farther away an electron is from the nucleus, the more easily it is removed. **8.48** Successive ionization energies of a particular element increase because each additional electron is being pulled away from a more positive ion. An extremely large jump in ionization energies occurs when all valence electrons have been removed and the first core electron is removed. Thus, by looking at a series of successive IE's, we can determine the number of valence electrons. **8.50** Group 7A(17) has high IE, and negative first electron affinities. These elements tend to form -1 ions. **8.53** (a) K < Rb < Cs (b) O < C < Be (c) Cl < S < K (d) Mg < Ca < K **8.55** (a) Ba < Sr < Ca (b) B < N < Ne (c) Rb < Se < Br (d) Sn < Sb < As **8.57** B: $1s^22s^22p^1$ **8.59** (a) Na (b) Na (c) Be **8.61** Metals have a characteristic luster, generally have high melting points, and are good electrical conductors. Nonmetals have dull surfaces, typically low melting points, and are poor electrical conductors. **8.62** Metallic character increases from right to left across a period and from top to bottom in a group. This trend is identical to atomic size and opposite to that of ionization energy. **8.64** +2 or +4. The +2 ions form by loss of the outermost two p electrons, while the +4 ions form by loss of these and the outermost two s electrons. **8.68** (a) Rb (b) Ra (c) I **8.70** (a) As (b) P (c) Be **8.72** acidic solution; $SO_3(g) + H_2O(l) \longrightarrow H_2SO_4(aq)$ **8.74** (a) Cl$^-$: $1s^22s^22p^63s^23p^6$ (b) Na$^+$: $1s^22s^22p^6$ (c) Ca^{2+}: $1s^22s^22p^63s^23p^6$ **8.76** (a) Al^{3+}: $1s^22s^22p^6$ (b) S^{2-}: $1s^22s^22p^63s^23p^6$ (c) Sr^{2+}: $1s^22s^22p^63s^23p^64s^23d^{10}4p^6$ **8.78** (a) 0 (b) 3 (c) 0 (d) 1 **8.80** (a), (b), and (d) **8.82** (a) V^{3+}: [Ar]$3d^2$, paramagnetic (b) Cd^{2+}: [Kr]$4d^{10}$, diamagnetic (c) Co^{3+}: [Ar]$3d^6$, paramagnetic (d) Ag$^+$: [Kr]$4d^{10}$, diamagnetic

8.84 (a) [Kr] [↑↓] [↑↓] [↑↓] [↑↓] [↑] [↑] 2 unpaired e$^-$

(b) [Kr] [ ] [↑↓] [↑↓] [↑↓] [↑↓] [↑↓] 0 unpaired e$^-$

(c) [Kr] [↑] [↑↓] [↑↓] [↑↓] [↑↓] [↑] 2 unpaired e$^-$

The electron configuration of (b) is consistent with a diamagnetic palladium atom.

8.86 (a) Li$^+$ < Na$^+$ < K$^+$; size increases down a group. (b) Rb$^+$ < Br$^-$ < Se^{2-}; size increases as atomic number decreases in an isoelectronic series. (c) F$^-$ < O^{2-} < N^{3-}; same reason as (b). **8.90** (a) K is further left (greater radius) while Sr is further down (also greater radius). (b) Z_{eff} remains fairly constant after the first 2 or 3 elements across a transition series. (c) Na is farther left (more metallic) but Ca is farther down (also more metallic). (d) Se is farther right (more acidic oxide) but P is farther up (also more acidic oxide). **8.91** (a) Aluminum: $1s^2 2s^2 2p^6 3s^2 3p^1$ (b) Lutetium: $1s^2 2s^2 2p^6 3s^2 3p^6 4s^2 3d^{10} 4p^6 5s^2 4d^{10} 5p^6 6s^2 4f^{14} 5d^1$ (c) Yttrium: $1s^2 2s^2 2p^6 3s^2 3p^6 4s^2 3d^{10} 4p^6 5s^2 4d^1$ (d) Sulfur: $1s^2 2s^2 2p^6 3s^2 3p^4$ (e) Strontium: $1s^2 2s^2 2p^6 3s^2 3p^6 4s^2 3d^{10} 4p^6 5s^2$ (f) Arsenic: $1s^2 2s^2 2p^6 3s^2 3p^6 4s^2 3d^{10} 4p^3$ **8.94** (a) $SrBr_2$; strontium bromide (b) CaS; calcium sulfide (c) ZnF_2; zinc(II) fluoride (d) LiF; lithium fluoride **8.96** (a) $\Delta H < 0$; Li has a larger negative electron affinity than Na due to its smaller size (b) $\Delta H < 0$; K has a smaller ionization energy than Na due to its larger size. **8.100** n = 5, l = 4; 5g; 9 orbitals. **8.103** Ce: $[Xe]6s^2 4f^1 5d^1$; Ce^{4+}: [Xe]; Eu: $[Xe]6s^2 4f^7$; Eu^{2+}: $[Xe]4f^7$; Ce^{4+} has a noble-gas configuration and Eu^{2+} has a half-filled f subshell.

Chapter 9

9.1 (a) Larger ionization energy decreases metallic character. (b) Larger atomic radius increases metallic character. (c) Larger number of outer electrons decreases metallic character. (d) Larger effective nuclear charge decreases metallic character. **9.4** (a) Cs (b) Rb (c) As **9.6** (a) ionic (b) covalent (c) metallic **9.8** (a) covalent (b) ionic (c) covalent

9.10 (a) Rb· (b) ·Ṡi· (c) :Ï·

9.12 (a) ·Sr· (b) :Ṗ· (c) :Ṡ:

9.14 (a) 6A(16); $ns^2 np^4$ (b) 3A(13); $ns^2 np^1$ **9.17** Because the lattice energy is the result of electrostatic attractions among the oppositely charged ions, its magnitude depends on several factors, including ionic size, ionic charge, and the arrangement of ions in the solid. For a particular arrangement of ions, the lattice energy increases as the charges on the ions increase and as their radii decrease. **9.20** (a) Ba^{2+} = [Xe]; Cl^- = $[Ne]3s^2 3p^6$; $BaCl_2$ (b) Sr^{2+} = [Kr]; O^{2-} = $[He]2s^2 2p^6$; SrO (c) Al^{3+} = [Ne]; F^- = $[He]2s^2 2p^6$; AlF_3 (d) Rb^+ = [Kr]; O^{2-} = $[He]2s^2 2p^6$; Rb_2O **9.22** (a) 2A(2) (b) 6A(16) (c) 1A(1) **9.24** (a) 3A(13) (b) 2A(2) (c) 6A(16) **9.26** (a) BaS; Ba and S have larger ion charges than Cs and Cl. (b) LiCl; Li has a smaller radius than Cs. **9.28** (a) BaS; Ba has a larger radius than Ca. (b) NaF; Na and F have smaller charges than Mg and O. **9.30** Lattice energy of NaCl = −788 kJ. This is less than for LiF due to the larger ionic radii of Na^+ and Cl^-. **9.33** −336 kJ **9.34** Chlorine gas consists of diatomic molecules. As two chlorine atoms approach each other, each atomic nucleus starts to attract the other's electron, which lowers the potential energy of the system. The atoms continue to draw each other closer, and the potential energy continues to be lowered. As attractions increase, so do repulsions between the nuclei and between electrons. At some internuclear distance, the maximum attraction is achieved in spite of the repulsion, and the system is at its lowest energy. The mutual attraction of nuclei and electron pair constitutes the covalent bond.

9.35 Bond energy is the change in enthalpy accompanying the dissociation of one mole of the bond in the gaseous state.

$$H—Cl(g) + Energy \longrightarrow H(g) + Cl(g)$$

ΔH is positive, requiring energy or endothermic. ΔH of bond formation is the same magnitude, but opposite in sign. **9.39** (a) I—I < Br—Br < Cl—Cl (b) S—Br < S—Cl < S—H (c) C—N < C=N < C≡N **9.41** C=O > C—O > intermolecular force **9.43** Electronegativity increases from left to right and decreases from top to bottom. Fluorine and oxygen are the two most electronegative atoms, while cesium and francium are the two least electronegative. **9.45** The H—O bond in water is polar covalent. A nonpolar covalent bond occurs when the bonding electrons are between two atoms of the same electronegativity. The polar covalent bond is when the bonding electrons are between two different atoms with differing electronegativity, and therefore one atom can attract the bonding electrons more strongly. Ionic bonding would imply that an electron transfer between the atoms has occurred. **9.48** (a) Si < S < O (b) Mg < As < P **9.50** (a) N > P > Si (b) As > Ga > Ca **9.52** (a) N—B (b) N—O (c) C—S (d) S—O (e) N—H (f) N—O **9.54** (a), (d), (e) **9.56** (a) nonpolar covalent (b) ionic (c) polar covalent (d) polar covalent (e) nonpolar covalent (f) polar covalent; $SCl_2 < SF_2 < PF_3$ **9.58** (a) H—I < H—Br < H—Cl (b) H—C < H—O < H—F (c) S—Cl < P—Cl < Si—Cl **9.61** (a) shiny, malleable, good electrical conductivity, relatively high melting and boiling points (b) form basic oxides, form cations by losing electrons **9.67** (a) −125 kJ (b) Yes, since ΔH_f^0 is negative. (c) −392 kJ (d) No, since ΔH for the conversion of MgCl to $MgCl_2$ is negative. **9.69** (a) 406 nm (b) 2.92×10^{-19} J (c) 1.87×10^4 m/s **9.72** (a) 4.04×10^{-19} J; 6.09×10^{14} s^{-1} (b) 353 nm **9.75** (a) The bond energies are for the formation of gaseous atoms and thus are for homolytic bond breakage. (b) Since one atom gets both of the bonding electrons in heterolytic bond breakage, this results in the formation of ions. (c) Since chlorine is more electronegative than carbon, the carbon atoms in $H_3C—CCl_3$ which are bonded to the chlorine effectively have a greater electronegativity than those in $H_3C—CH_3$. This would make that atom hold onto its electrons more tightly and increase the bond energy. (d) Yes. In addition to breaking the C—C bond, you would have to overcome the energy of attraction of the ions formed.

Chapter 10

10.1 a, b, d, e, f and h obey the octet rule; c and g do not. **10.2** (b) He and (d) H cannot serve as a central atom in a Lewis structure. Both have an outermost shell with maximum of two electrons.
10.5 (a) :F̈—Si—F̈: with :F̈: above and :F̈: below (b) :Cl̈—S̈e—Cl̈: (c) :F̈—C—F̈: with :O: double bonded

10.7 (a) $:\!\ddot{F}\!-\!\ddot{P}\!-\!\ddot{F}\!:$ with $:\!\ddot{F}\!:$ below   (b) $H\!-\!\ddot{O}\!-\!C\!-\!\ddot{O}\!-\!H$ with $\ddot{O}$ below (double bond)   (c) $:\!\ddot{S}\!=\!C\!=\!\ddot{S}\!:$

10.9 (a) $:\!\ddot{O}\!-\!N\!=\!\ddot{O}: \longleftrightarrow :\!\ddot{O}\!=\!N\!-\!\ddot{O}:$

(b) $:\!\ddot{O}\!-\!N\!=\!\ddot{O}: \longleftrightarrow :\!\ddot{O}\!=\!N\!-\!\ddot{O}:$ (with $:\!\ddot{F}\!:$ below each)

10.11 (a) $[:\!\ddot{N}\!=\!N\!=\!\ddot{N}: \longleftrightarrow :\!\ddot{N}\!-\!N\!\equiv\!N: \longleftrightarrow :\!N\!\equiv\!N\!-\!\ddot{N}\!:]^-$

(b) $[:\!\ddot{O}\!=\!N\!-\!\ddot{O}: \longleftrightarrow :\!\ddot{O}\!-\!N\!=\!\ddot{O}:]^-$

10.13 (a) $:\!\ddot{F}\!:\ :\!\ddot{F}\!:$; $:\!\ddot{F}\!-\!I\!-\!\ddot{F}\!:$ with $:\!\ddot{F}\!:$ below   f.c. = 0 for F and I

(b) $\left[\begin{array}{c}H\\ H\!-\!Al\!-\!H\\ H\end{array}\right]^-$ f.c. = 0 for H, = −1 for Al

10.15 (a) $[:\!C\!\equiv\!N\!:]^-$ f.c. = −1 for C; = 0 for N

$\downarrow$

$[:\!C\!=\!\ddot{N}\!:]^-$ f.c. = 0 for C; = −1 for N

(b) $[:\!\ddot{O}\!-\!\ddot{C}l\!:]^-$ f.c. = −1 for O; = 0 for Cl

10.17 (a) $\left[:\!\ddot{O}\!-\!Br\!-\!\ddot{O}:\right]^-$ with $:\!\ddot{O}\!:$ below   f.c. = −1 for O; = +2 for Br   ON = −2 for O; = +5 for Br

(b) $\left[:\!\ddot{O}\!-\!\ddot{S}\!-\!\ddot{O}:\right]^{2-}$ with $:\!\ddot{O}\!:$ below   f.c. = −1 for O; = +1 for S   ON = −2 for O; = +4 for S

10.19 (a) $H\!-\!B\!-\!H$ with H below   only 6 e⁻ in outer shell

(b) $\left[:\!\ddot{F}\!-\!\ddot{A}s\!-\!\ddot{F}:\right]^-$ with $:\!\ddot{F}\!:\ :\!\ddot{F}\!:$ below   expanded outer shell to 10 e⁻

(c) $:\!\ddot{C}l\!-\!\ddot{S}e\!-\!\ddot{C}l\!:$ with $:\!\ddot{C}l\!:\ :\!\ddot{C}l\!:$ below   expanded outer shell to 10 e⁻

10.21 (a) $:\!\ddot{F}\!:$; $:\!\ddot{F}\!-\!\ddot{B}r\!-\!\ddot{F}\!:$ expanded outer shell to 10 e⁻

(b) $[:\!\ddot{C}l\!-\!\ddot{I}\!-\!\ddot{C}l\!:]^-$ expanded outer shell to 10 e⁻

(c) $:\!\ddot{F}\!-\!Be\!-\!\ddot{F}\!:$ only 4 e⁻ in outer shell

10.23

$:\!\ddot{C}l\!-\!Be\!-\!\ddot{C}l\!: + 2\ :\!\ddot{C}l\!:^- \longrightarrow \left[:\!\ddot{C}l\!-\!Be\!-\!\ddot{C}l\!:\right]^{2-}$ with $:\!\ddot{C}l\!:$ above and below

10.25 Structure A has all atoms with formal charge = 0, so it is the best structure.   **10.28** Less energy is required to break weaker bonds.   **10.30** −168 kJ/mol

10.32

$\underset{H}{\overset{H}{>}}C\!=\!C\underset{H}{\overset{H}{<}} + H\!-\!\ddot{O}\!-\!H \longrightarrow H\!-\!\underset{H}{\overset{H}{C}}\!-\!\underset{H}{\overset{H}{C}}\!-\!\ddot{O}\!-\!H$

$\Delta H = -37$ kJ/mol

10.34 −22 kJ/mol   **10.37** When all electron pairs are involved in bonding (i.e., there are no lone pairs), the name of the molecular shape is the same as the name of the electron-group arrangement.

10.39 Tetrahedral   AX₄
Trigonal pyramidal   AX₃E
Bent or V-shaped   AX₂E₂

10.41 (a) AX₂   (b) AX₃   (c) AX₅   (d) AX₃E₂   (e) AX₃E   (f) AX₅E

10.43 (a) trigonal planar, bent, 120°   (b) tetrahedral, trigonal pyramidal, 109.5°   (c) tetrahedral, trigonal pyramidal, 109.5°   **10.45** (a) trigonal planar, trigonal planar, 120° (b) trigonal planar, bent, 120°   (c) tetrahedral, tetrahedral, 109.5°   **10.47** (a) trigonal planar, AX₃, 120°   (b) trigonal pyramidal, AX₃E, 109.5°   (c) trigonal bipyramidal, AX₅, 90° and 120°   **10.49** (a) bent, 109.5°, smaller   (b) trigonal bipyramidal, 90° and 120°, none   (c) see-saw, 90° and 120°, smaller   (d) linear, 180°, none   **10.51** (a) C: tetrahedral, 109.5°; O: bent, < 109.5° (due to lone pairs)   (b) N: trigonal planar, < 120°   **10.53** (a) C in CH₃: tetrahedral, 109.5°; C (with C=O): trigonal planar, < 120° for C—C—O(H); O (with O—H): bent, < 109.5° (due to lone pairs)   (b) O: bent, < 109.5° (due to lone pairs)   **10.55** OF₂ < NF₃ < CF₄ < BF₃ < BeF₂

	Angle	Ideal Value	Deviation
10.57 (a)	H—C—H	120°	smaller
	H—C—N	120°	greater
	C—N—O	120°	smaller
	N—O—H	109.5°	smaller
(b)	H—C—H	109.5°	none
	H—C—O	109.5°	none
	C—O—C	109.5°	smaller
(c)	H—O—B	109.5°	smaller
	O—B—O	120°	none

10.60 $2PCl_5(g) \longrightarrow PCl_4^+ + PCl_6^-$

        AX₅ $\longrightarrow$ AX₄   AX₆
        trigonal   tetrahedral   octahedral
        bipyramidal
        120°, 90°   109.5°   90°

10.61 Polar bonds have magnitude and direction; if equal and opposite, the molecule is nonpolar. If the forces are not balanced the molecule is polar.   **10.64** (a) CF₄   (b) SCl₂ and BrCl.   **10.66** (a) SO₂; bent vs. trigonal planar structure (b) IF; greater ΔEN   (c) SF₄; see-saw vs. tetrahedral structure   (d) H₂O; greater ΔEN.

10.68 X: $\underset{:\ddot{C}l:}{\overset{H}{>}}C\!=\!C\underset{H}{\overset{:\ddot{C}l:}{<}}$ Y: $\underset{H}{\overset{H}{>}}C\!=\!C\underset{:\ddot{C}l:}{\overset{:\ddot{C}l:}{<}}$ Z: $\underset{:\ddot{C}l:}{\overset{H}{>}}C\!=\!C\underset{:\ddot{C}l:}{\overset{H}{<}}$

Compound Y does have a dipole moment.

10.70 (a) Bond strength—greatest in N₂; Bond length—longest in N₂H₄; Bond order = 1 for N₂H₄; 2 for N₂H₂, 3 for N₂

(b)

$$H\text{—}\ddot{N}\text{—}\ddot{N}\text{=}\ddot{N}\text{—}\ddot{N}: \longrightarrow H\text{—}\ddot{N}\text{—}\ddot{N}\text{—}H + N_2$$

$$\Delta H = -367 \text{ kJ/mol}$$

10.76

$$:\!\ddot{F}\text{—}B\text{—}\ddot{F}: + H\text{—}C\text{—}C\text{—}\ddot{O}\text{—}C\text{—}C\text{—}H \longrightarrow$$

trigonal   bent
planar

B: tetrahedral
C: trigonal pyramidal

10.79

10.80

bold C changes from trigonal planar to tetrahedral.
10.85 (a) −1267 kJ/mol   (b) −1226 kJ/mol   (c) ΔH calculated from $\Delta H_f^0 = -1236$ kJ/mol; good correlation

10.88 $H\text{—}\ddot{O}\text{—}C\text{—}C\text{—}\ddot{O}\text{—}H$

10.92 (a) it has an odd number of electrons.   (b) 426 kJ/mol   (c) 508 kJ/mol

10.95

f.c. = 0 for each atom
in all structures

2 resonance structures

3 resonance structures   4 resonance structures

P-O bond lengths

	H_3PO_4	$H_2PO_4^-$	HPO_4^{2-}	PO_4^{3-}	H_3PO_4 etc.
	P=O	< P—O	< P—O	< P—O	< P—O—H
Bond order	2.0	1.50	1.33	1.25	1.0

10.97

In $H_2C_2O_4$, there are 2 short C=O; two long C—O. In $HC_2O_4^-$, there is one short C=O, one long C—O and two C—O bonds of intermediate length. In $C_2O_4^{2-}$ you have four C—O bonds, of intermediate length between C=O and C—O. **10.99** The molecule could be trigonal pyramidal or T-shaped, but not trigonal planar.

Chapter 11

11.1 (a) sp^2 (b) sp^3d^2 (c) sp   (d) sp^3 (e) sp^3d
11.3 C has only 2s and 2p orbitals, allowing for a maximum of four hybrids. Si has 3d orbitals available in addition to the 3s and 3p, so it can form up to six hybrids.   **11.5** (a) six sp^3d^2 orbitals   (b) four sp^3 orbitals   **11.7** (a) sp^2 (b) sp^2 (c) sp^2 **11.9** (a) sp^3 (b) sp^3 (c) sp^3
11.11 (a) $sp^3 \longleftarrow s + 3p$ (b) $sp \longleftarrow s + p$
11.13 (a) $sp^3d \longleftarrow s + 3p + d$ (b) $sp^3 \longleftarrow s + 3p$

11.15 (a)

(b)

(c) $+ e^-$

11.17 (a)

(b)

(c)

11.20 (a) False. A double bond is one sigma and one pi bond.   (b) False. A triple bond consists of one sigma (σ) and two pi (π) bonds.   (c) True   (d) True   (e) False. A π bond consists of a second pair of electrons after a σ bond has been previously formed.   (f) False. End-to-end overlap results in a bond with electron density along the bond axis.
11.21 (a) 3(σ) + 1(π) about N, sp^2 hybridization   (b) 2(σ) + 2(π) about C, sp hybridization   (c) 3(σ) + 1(π) about C, sp^2 hybridization
11.23 (a) $:\!\ddot{F}\text{—}\ddot{N}\text{=}\ddot{O}:$ 2(σ) + 1(π) about N, sp^2 hybridization

(b) $3(\sigma) + 1(\pi)$ about each C, sp^2 hybridization

(c) :N≡C—C≡N: $2\sigma + 2(\pi)$ about each C, sp hybridization

11.25

The single C—H and C—C bonds are σ bonds; the C=C bonds are $1\sigma + 1\pi$.

11.26 Two p AO + two p AO ⟶ 4 molecular orbitals. The number of M.O. is equal to the number of A.O. from which they are formed.

11.28 Bonding orbitals *vs.* antibonding orbitals: (a) energy—B.O. lower in energy—more stable. (b) nodal plane—B.O. have none perpendicular to the bond axis. (c) internuclear electron density—the B.O. has a higher electron density than the A.B.O.

11.30 (a) 2   (b) 2   (c) 4

11.32 (a) s + p$_z$ =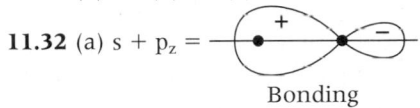

Bonding

s − p$_z$ =

Antibonding

(b) p − p =

Bonding

p + p =

Antibonding

11.34 (a) stable   (b) paramagnetic   (c) $(\sigma_{2s})^2(\sigma_{2s}^*)^1$
11.36 (a) Increasing bond energy $C_2^+ < C_2 < C_2^-$ (b) Increasing bond length $C_2^- < C_2 < C_2^+$ **11.39** (a) 9σ, 2π (b) No, since each double bond has two identical substituent groups on one C.   **11.41** (a) 17   (b) all C: sp^2; ring N: sp^2; other N: sp^3 **11.43** (a) B changes from sp^2 to sp^3 hybridization.   (b) P changes from sp^3 to sp^3d.   (c) C changes from sp to sp^2.   (d) Si changes from sp^3 to sp^3d^2. (e) S is sp^2 and remains sp^2.

11.46 (a)

(b)

(c)

(d)
11.49 (a) the one with two S=O bonds.
    (b) tetrahedral; sp^3 (c) S: d orbitals; O: p orbitals
(d)
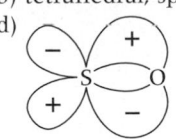

11.54 The LiF molecules are polar due to the large difference in electronegativity between Li and F. The relatively small ionization energy of Li and the relatively large electron affinity of F reinforces this.

11.56

Resonance interaction gives the C—N bond double bond character which hinders rotation about the C—N bond. The C—N single bond is a σ bond; the resonance interaction exchanges a C—O π bond for a C—N π bond.   **11.58** (a) C in CH_3: sp^3; all other C: sp^2; central O: sp^3 (b) 2   (c) 8; 1

Chapter 12

12.1 In a solid, the energy of attraction is greater than the energy of motion, while in a gas it is less. Gases have high compressibility and the ability to flow, while solids have neither.   **12.4** (a) Because the intermolecular forces are only partially overcome in fusion and need to be totally overcome in vaporization.   (b) Because greater intermolecular forces are found in solids as opposed to liquids.   (c) $\Delta H_{COND} = -\Delta H_{VAP}$.   **12.5** a, b intermolecular; c, d intramolecular   **12.7** (a) condensation   (b) fusion   (c) evaporation   **12.9** The molecules of a gas are moving more rapidly than those in a liquid. When the liquid condenses, the molecules slow down and energy is released to the surroundings.   **12.13** At first, the evaporation of liquid molecules from the surface predominates, which increases the number of gas molecules and hence the vapor pressure. Once more molecules enter the gas phase, the probability of a gas molecule hitting the surface of the liquid and "sticking" increases, so the condensation rate increases. When the evaporation and condensation rates become equal, the vapor pressure becomes constant.   **12.14** As intermolecular forces increase, the (a) critical temperature increases.   (b) boiling point increases.   (c) vapor pressure decreases.   (d) heat of vaporization increases.   **12.18** Because the condensation of steam releases a much greater quantity of heat (40.7 kJ/mol) than does the cooling of water.   **12.19** 4.16×10^3 J   **12.21** 528 torr   **12.23** 18 kJ/mol

12.25

(phase diagram: P, atm vs T, °C; regions labeled S, L, G)

Solid ethylene is more dense than liquid ethylene.
12.28 42 atm   **12.32** O is a much smaller atom than Se. The electron density on O is much greater than on Se as a result, and it attracts the H atom much more strongly.
12.34 *All* molecules exhibit dispersion forces. Since these are so weak, however, they are in general overwhelmed if any other intermolecular forces (dipole-dipole, H-bonding) exist.   **12.37** (a) H-bonding   (b) dispersion   (c) dispersion
12.39 (a) dipole-dipole   (b) dispersion   (c) H-bonding
12.41 (a)

(structural formulas of molecules showing H-bonding)

(b) $H-\ddot{\underset{..}{F}}:\cdots\cdots H-\ddot{\underset{..}{F}}:\cdots\cdots H-\ddot{\underset{..}{F}}:$

12.43 (a) dispersion   (b) H-bonding   (c) dispersion
12.45 (a) I^- (b) C_2H_4 (c) H_2Se In cases a and c, the larger particle (with more electrons) has the higher polarizability. In case b, the less tightly held π-electrons are more easily distorted.   **12.47** (a) C_2H_6. Smaller molecules have smaller intermolecular forces.   (b) CH_3CH_2F. Weaker intermolecular force (dipole-dipole *vs.* H-bonding in CH_3CH_2OH).   (c) PH_3. Weaker intermolecular force (dipole-dipole *vs.* H-bonding in NH_3).   **12.49** (a) LiCl; ionic bonds (LiCl) *vs.* dipole-dipole (HCl).   (b) NH_3; H-bonding (NH_3) *vs.* dipole-dipole (PH_3).   (c) I_2; larger molecule has larger dispersion forces.
12.51 (a) CH_2-CH_2: more compact molecule.
CH_2-CH_2
     (b) PBr_3; dipole-dipole (PBr_3) *vs.* ionic bonds (NaBr).
     (c) HBr; dipole-dipole (HBr) *vs.* H-bonding (H_2O).
12.53 The polarity of the X—H bond increases N—H < O—H < F—H.   **12.57** The cohesive forces of H_2O (H-bonds) and of Hg (metallic bonds) are stronger than the adhesive forces between those drops and the nonpolar wax (held together by van der Waals forces), meaning that these

two would remain as spherical drops. The weak cohesive forces of oil (van der Waals forces) are about as strong as the adhesive forces between the oil and the wax, so that the oil drops would spread out more.   **12.59** Because it is defined as the amount of energy required to increase the surface area by a specific amount.   **12.61** $CH_3CH_2CH_2OH$ < $HOCH_2CH_2OH$ < $HOCH_2CH(OH)CH_2OH$ The number of H-bonds, and hence the strength of intermolecular forces, would increase as shown, so also would the surface tension.   **12.63** Viscosity and surface tension both increase with the strength of intermolecular forces, so the order would be the same.   **12.65** Apple juice (primarily water) is held together by H-bonds; cooking oil is held together by dispersion forces. The adhesion of the paper and water would be stronger (H-bonds in paper to H-bonds in water) than that between paper and cooking oil.   **12.68** Water is a good solvent for materials which form ions and/or which can hydrogen bond. The more polar (i.e., like water) the material, the better. Water is a poor solvent for nonpolar materials.   **12.69** The two hydrogen atoms covalently bonded to the oxygen can form hydrogen bonds with two other molecules. In addition, two hydrogen atoms from adjoining H_2O molecules can form hydrogen bonds with the two lone pairs of electrons on the oxygen.   **12.72** Water has a high capillary action, which allows it to easily be absorbed by the plant's roots and transported to the leaves.
12.78 Simple cubic   **12.81** The energy gap is the energy difference between the highest filled energy level (the valence band) and the lowest unfilled energy level (the conduction band). In conductors and superconductors, the gap is zero (the bands overlap); in semiconductors it is small, and in insulators it is large.   **12.83** Atomic mass and atomic radius   **12.84** (a) face-centered   (b) body-centered   (c) face-centered   **12.86** (a) metallic, since Sn is a metal   (b) network covalent, since Si is similar to C (diamond)   (c) atomic, since Xe is a monatomic element   **12.88** (a) metallic, since Ni is a metal   (b) molecular, since this is a molecule   (c) molecular, since this is a molecule   **12.90** 4   **12.92** (a) 4 of each   (b) 577.4 amu or 9.59×10^{-22} g   (c) 1.77×10^{-22} cm^3 (d) 5.61Å   **12.94** (a) insulator   (b) conductor   (c) semiconductor   **12.96** (a) increase   (b) increase   (c) decrease   **12.98** 1.68×10^{-8} cm (1.68Å)   **12.104** (a) n-type   (b) p-type   (c) n-type   (d) p-type   **12.106** Isotropic properties are the same in all directions, while anisotropic properties depend on direction. Liquid crystals show some degree of order, so they are anisotropic.   **12.109** (a) 19.8 torr   (b) 0.0388 g
12.111 (a)

(b)

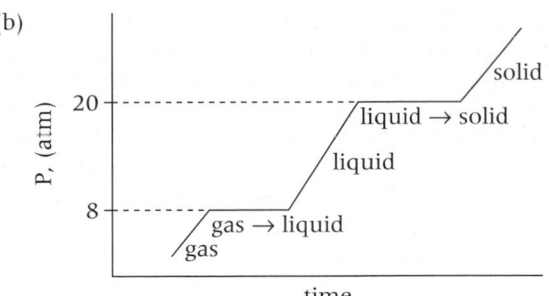

12.113 More energy is needed to sublime ice since the heat of sublimation is equal to the sum of the heats of fusion (to melt the ice) and vaporization (to boil the water). The same would be true of CO_2, but, since liquid CO_2 is not stable at 1 atm pressure, ordinarily sublimation takes place in one step rather than two for this substance. **12.114** (a) 1.50×10^3 (b) 3.33 g (c) $SiO_2(s) + 4HF(g) \longrightarrow SiF_4(g) + 2H_2O(g)$ (d) 3.56×10^{-3} mol **12.117** 259K ($-14°C$) **12.123** The meniscus would be concave downward and the level inside the tube would be lower than that outside the tube. The polar water molecules repel the nonpolar wax molecules, so the outer edges of the liquid surface (i.e., those in contact with the wax) would be lower than the center, and the whole surface would be "pulled" downward.

12.127 (a)

(b)

12.131 (a) 0.088 g (b) yes (c) 0.14 g **12.133** 2.9 g/m³
12.136 (a) 1.1 min (b) 10 min
(c)

12.142 45.98 amu or 7.635×10^{-23} g **12.145** (a) 49 metric tons (b) 1.1×10^8 kJ

Chapter 13

13.2 When a salt such as NaCl dissolves, ion-dipole forces cause the ions to become separated, and more water molecules cluster around them in hydration shells. **13.4** Sodium stearate is more effective as a soap. The long chain stearate ion has both a hydrophilic carboxylate and a hydrophobic hydrocarbon chain, which allows it to reduce surface tension between oil and water and to act as a soap. The acetate ion is too small to exhibit any hydrophobic qualities. **13.7** (a) In the polar solvent water, KNO_3 ionizes completely and forms more concentrated solutions. KNO_3, an ionic salt, does not dissolve in or interact well with the nonpolar carbon tetrachloride. **13.9** (a) iondipole (b) hydrogen bonding (c) dipole-induced dipole **13.11** (a) hydrogen bonding (b) dipole-induced dipole (c) dispersion forces **13.13** (a) HCl(g); molecular interactions (dipole-dipole forces) are greater. (b) CH_3CHO; interactions (dispersion forces) are greater. (c) CH_3CH_2MgBr; molecular interactions (dispersion forces) are greater **13.16** Gluconic acid is soluble in water due to its extensive hydrogen bonding through its polar hydroxyl groups which caproic acid does not have. The nonpolar end of caproic acid allows it to be soluble in nonpolar hexane. **13.18** For a general solvent, the energy changes needed to separate solvent into particles ($\Delta H_{solvent}$), and that needed to mix the solvent and solute particles (ΔH_{mix}) would be combined to obtain $\Delta H_{solution}$. **13.23** Very soluble. A decrease in energy and an increase in entropy both favor the formation of a solution.

13.24

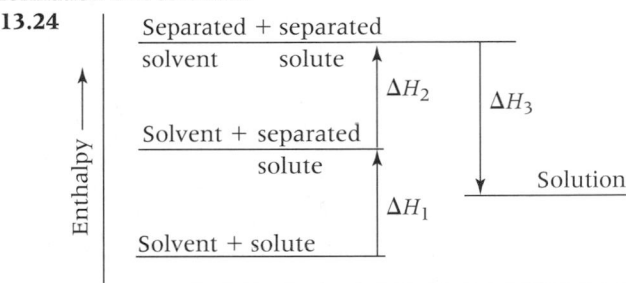

13.26 (a) Na^+ has a greater charge density than Cs^+. Na^+ has a smaller ion volume. (b) Sr^{2+} has a larger ion charge than Rb^+, so will have the larger charge density. (c) Na^+ has a smaller ion volume than Cl^-, so will have the larger charge density. (d) O^{2-} has a larger ion charge than F^-, so will have the larger charge density. (e) OH^- has a smaller ion volume than SH^-, so will have the larger charge density. **13.28** (a) Na^+ (b) Sr^{2+} (c) Na^+ (d) O^{2-} (e) OH^- **13.30** (a) -704 kJ/mol (b) Probably K^+ due to its smaller size (larger charge density). **13.32** (a) increases (b) decreases (c) increases (d) decreases **13.35** Add a pinch of the solid solute to each solution. The supersaturated solution is unstable and addition of a "seed" crystal of solute causes the excess solute to crystallize immediately, leaving behind a saturated solution. The solution in which the added solid solute dissolves is the unsaturated solution of X. The solution in which the added solid solute remains undissolved is the saturated solution of X. **13.38** In any equilibrium, an increase in temperature favors the endothermic process. Therefore, NaI is less soluble at 60°C than at 20°C.

13.40 (a) $\Delta H_{soln} > 0$ for $AgNO_3$, < 0 for Li_2CO_3, < 0 for O_2.
(b) $AgNO_3(s) + H_2O(l) + heat \rightleftharpoons AgNO_3(aq)$
$Li_2CO_3(s) + H_2O(l) \rightleftharpoons Li_2CO_3(aq) + heat$
$O_2(g) + H_2O(l) \rightleftharpoons O_2(aq) + heat$
13.42 (a) increase (b) decrease (c) decrease **13.44** (a)
8.19×10^{-2} g O_2 (b) 1.71×10^{-2} g O_2 **13.47** 0.20 mol/L
13.50 (a) % w/v; molarity (b) % w/w; mole fraction (c)
molality **13.52** With just this information, you can inter-
convert between molarity and molality, but you need to
know the identity (or at least the molar mass) of the solvent to convert between either of these and the mole fraction. **13.54** (a) 1.24 M (b) 0.158 M **13.56** (a) 0.0750 M
(b) 0.31 M **13.58** (a) Add 4.22 g KH_2PO_4 to enough water
to make 355 mL of aqueous solution. (b) Add 107 mL of
1.25 M NaOH to enough water to make 425 mL of aqueous
solution. **13.60** (a) Weigh out 45.9 g KBr, then add to
enough water to make 1.50 L of solution. (b) Add 139 mL
of 0.244 M $LiNO_3$ to enough water to make 355 mL of
solution. **13.62** (a) 0.942 m (b) 1.29 m **13.64** 3.09 m
13.66 (a) Add 2.13 g $C_2H_6O_2$ to 298 g H_2O. (b) Add 32.3 g
of 62.0 mass % HNO_3 to 968 g H_2O. **13.68** (a) 0.27 (b)
56% (c) 21 m **13.70** 33.7 g; mol fraction $= 7.15 \times 10^{-3}$;
6.31% by mass **13.72** 5.11 M; 4.53 M; 0.0842 mol fraction **13.74** 2.2 ppm Ca^{2+}; 0.66 ppm Mg^{2+}. **13.78** A
strong electrolyte is a solute that dissociates completely into
ions in solution. **13.80** The temperature at which the
solution boils is higher and freezing point is lower for the
solution compared with the pure solvent. **13.83** A dilute
solution of an electrolyte behaves more ideally than a concentrated one. With increasing concentration the "activity"
concentration deviates from the molar concentration. Thus,
0.050 m NaF has a boiling point closer to its predicted
value. **13.86** (a) strong electrolyte (b) strong electrolyte
(c) nonelectrolyte (d) weak electrolyte **13.88** (a) 0.4 mol
(b) 0.14 mol (c) 3×10^{-4} mol (d) 0.07 mol **13.90** (a)
10.0g CH_3OH in 100.g H_2O (b) 10.0 g H_2O in 1.00 kg
CH_3OH **13.92** (a) I and II same; III higher (b) I and II
increased; III increased by $1\frac{1}{2}$ times (c) I and II decreased;
III decreased by $1\frac{1}{2}$ times (d) I and II decreased; III decreased by $1\frac{1}{2}$ times **13.94** 23.36 torr **13.96** $-0.206°C$
13.98 79.0°C **13.100** 11.3 kg **13.102** (a) 0.173 m; i =
1.84 (b) 0.0837 m; i = 1.02 **13.104** 0.240 atm **13.106**
211 torr (CH_2Cl_2); 47.2 torr (CCl_4) **13.107** The fluid inside
a cell is both a colloid and a solution. Within a typical cell,
colloid-sized protein and nucleic acid molecules are dispersed in an aqueous solution of ions and numerous small
molecules. **13.111** Soap molecules from spherical micelles, with the charged "heads" forming the micelle exterior and the nonpolar "tails" the interior. Because the
surfaces of the colloidal particles have like charges, repulsions prevent them from adhering to each other when they
collide. Soap would be less effective in seawater with its
larger concentrations of divalent cations. **13.112** In order
to make the cream foam, the gas must have fairly low solubility in the liquid at 1 atm pressure. If CO_2 does not work
as well as N_2O, this would imply that CO_2 is more soluble
in cream than is N_2O, so its Henry's law constant would be
larger than that for N_2O. **13.117** 3.5×10^9 L **13.119** This
would only be true if the density of the solvent is near 1.0
g/mL. **13.121** $\Delta H_{soln} > 0$, so the lattice energy must be

larger than the heat of hydration. **13.124** (a) 90.0 g/mol
(b) C_2H_5O; $C_4H_{10}O_2$ (c) $HOCH_2CH_2CH_2CH_2OH$ forms H
bonds; $CH_3OCH_2CH_2OCH_3$ does not **13.127** (a) Mg^{2+}
(b) Mg^{2+} (c) CO_3^{2-} (d) SO_4^{2-} (e) Fe^{3+} (f) Ca^{2+}
13.129 (a) 68 g/mol (b) 2.0×10^2 g/mol (c) The actual
formula mass (164.1 g/mol) is between that calculated
assuming that it is a nonelectrolyte and that calculated
assuming that it is a strong electrolyte. A strong electrolyte
with a formula mass of 164.1 g/mol and which produces
three ions per mole should have given an apparent formula
mass of (164.1)/3 = 54.7 g/mol. This material is highly, but
not totally, dissociated into ions in solution. (d) 2.4
13.131 Enthalpy is a state function and as such is not dependent on the reaction pathway or number of steps. The
solution process can be (mentally) separated into the two
hypothetical steps of (1) formation of gas-phase ions from
the solid, and (2) placing these ions into the solvent. The
total enthalpy change for these two steps is the enthalpy of
solution of the salt. **13.133** (a) 1.82×10^4 g/mol (b)
$3.42 \times 10^{-5}°C$ **13.134** 9.4×10^5 ng/L **13.138** Add 3.11 g
$NaHCO_3$ to 247 g H_2O. **13.140** (a) 85% (b) 13 g (c)
Dissolve $Ce_2(SO_4)_3$ in near-freezing water, filter, then heat
to about 40°C. Pure $Ce_2(SO_4)_3$ would crystallize out. (d)
ΔH_{soln} for $KClO_3$ is endothermic; ΔH_{soln} for $Ce_2(SO_4)_3 < 0$.

13.142 $M = \dfrac{m \times kg\ solvent}{vol\ of\ soln} = \dfrac{m \times kg\ solvent}{V\ of\ soln \times density\ soln}$

As density of solution approaches 1 g/mL, M = m. If the
solvent is water, assuming a density of 1.000 g/mL, one kg
of water is equal to a volume of 1.0 liter. In dilute solutions,
the volume of solvent and volume of solution are essentially equal. **13.144** (a) CH_4N_2O (b) 60. g/mol; CH_4N_2O
13.145 (a) 0.0882 cm^3/g H_2O (b) 0.15 cm^3/g $H_2O \cdot MPa$
(c) $S_{gas} = 0.74$ cm^3/g H_2O; 11% error **13.149** (a) Yes, but
the triple point would be at a lower pressure due to the
vapor-pressure lowering of the solvent by the dissolved air.
(b) A lower temperature, again due to the vapor-pressure
lowering. (c) Yes, since you would be below the new
triple point. (d) No, the vapor pressures would be lower
due to the dissolved air.

Chapter 14

14.2 (a) Z_{eff} increases across a period and decreases down a
group. (b) As you move to the right across a period, the
atomic size decreases, the IE_1 increases and the EN
increases, all as a result of the increased Z_{eff}. **14.3** (a) ICl is
polar; Br_2 is nonpolar. The electronegativity of Cl is greater
than that of I, so the I end of ICl will be partially positively
charged due to the greater "pull" of the Cl on the shared
electrons. (b) ICl will have a higher boiling point than Br_2
since dipole-dipole forces in ICl are greater than dispersion
forces in Br_2. **14.7** The bonding would change from
metallic to (perhaps) very polar covalent to ionic as the
"other" element went farther to the right. The electronegativity, ionization energy, and electron affinity all change as
you move to the right. The atomic properties of the leftmost element and the "other" element become increasingly
different, causing the type of bonding to change in
response. **14.9** The elements at the left form cations,
which are smaller than the corresponding atoms; the ele-

ments at the right form anions, which are larger than the corresponding atoms. **14.11** (a) The higher the electronegativity of the element, the more covalent is the bonding in its oxide. (b) The more electronegative the element, the more acidic its oxide. **14.14** In general, network solids have very high melting and boiling points, and are very hard, while molecular solids have low melting and boiling points and are soft. To melt, boil, or distort a network solid requires you to break chemical bonds, which requires a great amount of energy. In molecular solids, energy is needed to separate molecules which are held together with weaker intermolecular forces. **14.15** (a) Mg < Sr < Ba (b) Na < Al < P (c) Se < Br < Cl (d) Ga < Sn < Bi **14.17** (b) and (d)
14.19 $\ddot{O}{=}C{=}\ddot{O}$ **14.21** $CF_4 < SiCl_4 < GeBr_4$ **14.23** (a) $Na^+ < F^- < O^{2-}$ (b) $Cl^- < S^{2-} < P^{3-}$ **14.25** $O < O^- < O^{2-}$
14.27 (a) $CaO(s) + H_2O(l) \longrightarrow Ca(OH)_2(aq)$ (more basic)
$SO_3(g) + H_2O(l) \longrightarrow H_2SO_4(aq)$
(b) BaO (c) CO_2 (d) K_2O
14.29 (a) LiCl (b) PCl_3 (c) NCl_3 **14.31** (a) Ar < Na < Si (b) Cs < Rb < Li **14.33** The outermost electron in Li is much farther away from the nucleus than the electron in H. It is also screened from a large portion of the nuclear charge by the inner electrons.
14.35 (a) $\ddot{F}{-}\ddot{N}{-}\ddot{F}$ and $H{-}\ddot{N}{-}H$ NH_3 will H-bond.

(b)
$H{-}\overset{H}{\underset{H}{C}}{-}\ddot{O}{-}\overset{H}{\underset{H}{C}}{-}H$ and $H{-}\overset{H}{\underset{H}{C}}{-}\overset{H}{\underset{H}{C}}{-}\ddot{O}{-}H$
CH_3CH_2OH will H-bond.
14.37 (a) $2Al(s) + 6HCl(aq) \longrightarrow 2AlCl_3(aq) + 3H_2(g)$
(b) $LiH(s) + H_2O(l) \longrightarrow LiOH(aq) + H_2(g)$
14.39 (a) Na = +1, B = +3, H = −1 in $NaBH_4$
Al = +3, B = +3, H = −1 in $Al(BH_4)_3$
Li = +1, Al = +3, H = −1 in $LiAlH_4$
(b) $\left[H{-}\overset{H}{\underset{H}{B}}{-}H\right]^-$ tetrahedral

14.42 For groups 1A(1)–4A(4), the number of covalent bonds equals the (old) group number. For groups 5A(15)–7A(17), it equals eight minus the (old) group number. In higher periods, this correlation holds but there are exceptions where the elements in groups 3A(13)–7A(17) can form more bonds than this. **14.45** (a) Groups 3B(3) or 3A(13). (b) If in group 3B(3), the oxide and fluoride would be more ionic.
14.48 (a) reducing agent
(b) Their outermost electrons are easily removed due to their large size and low ionization energy.
(c) $2Na(s) + Cl_2(g) \longrightarrow 2NaCl(s)$
$2Na(s) + 2H_2O(l) \longrightarrow 2NaOH(aq) + H_2(g)$
14.50 (a) and (b) increase down the group. (c), (d), and (e) decrease down the group.
14.52 $2Na(s) + O_2(g) \longrightarrow Na_2O_2(s)$
14.54 $K_2CO_3(s) + 2HI(aq) \longrightarrow 2KI(aq) + H_2O(l) + CO_2(g)$
14.58 The group 2A(2) metals have an additional electron available for bonding, so the bonding is stronger and the

melting points increase. They are also harder, denser, and have higher boiling points.
14.59 (a) $CaO(s) + H_2O(l) \longrightarrow Ca(OH)_2(s)$
(b) $2Ca(s) + O_2(g) \longrightarrow 2CaO(s)$
14.62 (a) $BeO(s) + H_2O(l) \longrightarrow Be(OH)_2(s)$
(b) $BeCl_2(l) + 2Cl^-$ (solvated) $\longrightarrow$
$BeCl_4^{2-}$ (solvated)
In reaction (a).
14.65 Be: $1s^2 2s^2$ B: $1s^2 2s^2 2p^1$
In B, the outermost electron (i.e., the one removed when the atom is ionized) is in a 2p orbital as opposed to the 2s in Be. Since the energy of the 2p orbital is higher than the 2s, the electron is more easily removed (i.e., IE_1 is lower) despite the atom's smaller size.
14.66 (a) "Normal" atoms have completed outer shells (i.e., an octet). Atoms with fewer electrons than eight are considered "electron deficient."
(b) $BF_3(g) + NH_3(g) \longrightarrow F_3B{-}NH_3(g)$
$B(OH)_3(aq) + OH^-(aq) \longrightarrow B(OH)_4^-(aq)$
14.68 $In_2O_3 < Ga_2O_3 < Al_2O_3$
14.70 ON = +3 (apparent); = +1 (actual)
$[\ddot{I}{-}\ddot{I}{-}\ddot{I}]^-$ class = AX_2E_3; bond angles = 180°
TlI_3 doesn't exist as $(Tl^{3+})(I^-)_3$ because of the low strength of the Tl—I bond.
14.73 (a) $In(s) + As(s) \longrightarrow InAs(s)$
(b) $GaSb(s) + 3H_2O(g) \longrightarrow Ga(OH)_3(s) + SbH_3(g)$
14.75 $\ddot{Br}\ \ddot{Br}\ \ddot{Br}$
Ga Ga 109.5° bond angles
$\ddot{Br}\ \ddot{Br}\ \ddot{Br}$
14.76 Sn, being the more metallic element, would have the more basic oxide. **14.78** (a) Ionization energy decreases as you go down a group. (b) The deviations (increases) from the trend are due to the appearance of the first transition series between Si and Ge and the appearance of the lanthanide elements between Sn and Pb. (c) Group 3A(13). **14.81** The sizes of the atoms increase and their ionization energies decrease as you go down the group. If the electrons are more easily ionized, the atoms will behave more metallic.
14.83 (a)
$\left[\begin{array}{c}\ddot{O}\ \ \ddot{O} \\ \ddot{O}{-}Si{-}\ddot{O}{-}Si{-}\ddot{O} \\ \ddot{O}\ \ \ddot{O} \\ \ddot{O}{-}Si{-}\ddot{O}{-}Si{-}\ddot{O} \\ \ddot{O}\ \ \ddot{O}\end{array}\right]^{8-}$
(b)
$H{-}\overset{H}{\underset{H}{C}}{-}\overset{H}{\underset{\underset{H}{C}}{}}{-}H$ or (cyclic structure)
$H{-}\overset{H}{C}{-}\overset{H}{C}{-}H$
14.85
$-O{-}\overset{CH_3}{\underset{CH_3}{Si}}{-}O{-}\overset{CH_3}{\underset{CH_3}{Si}}{-}O\ \overset{CH_3}{\underset{CH_3}{Si}}{-}CH_3$
14.88 (a) diamond (b) $CaCO_3$ (c) CO_2 (d) $[(CH_3)_2SiO]_n$
(e) SiC (f) CO (g) Pb **14.92** (a) from −3 to +5. (b)

The highest oxidation state equals the (old) group number; the lowest equals the (old) group number minus eight.

14.95 $H_3AsO_4 < H_3PO_4 < HNO_3$

14.97 (a) $4As(s) + 5O_2(g) \longrightarrow 2As_2O_5(s)$
(b) $2Bi(s) + 3F_2(g) \longrightarrow 2BiF_3(s)$
(c) $Ca_3As_2(s) + 6H_2O(l) \longrightarrow$
$$3Ca(OH)_2(s) + 2AsH_3(g)$$

14.99 (a) $N_2(g) + 2Al(s) \xrightarrow{\Delta} 2AlN(s)$
(b) $PF_5(g) + 4H_2O(l) \longrightarrow H_3PO_4(aq) + 5HF(g)$

14.101 A trigonal bipyramid with F axial and Cl equatorial.

14.105 Yes—it could form H-bonds similar to NH_3.

14.107 (a) $2KNO_3(s) \xrightarrow{\Delta} 2KNO_2(s) + O_2(g)$
(b) $4KNO_3(s) \xrightarrow{\Delta} 2K_2O(s) + 2N_2(g) + 5O_2(g)$

14.109 (a) Their boiling points and conductivities vary in similar ways down the group.   (b) The amount of metallic character and their types of bonding vary in similar ways down the group.   (c) They both react with oxygen to form acidic oxides; both are oxidizing agents.   (d) They are both gaseous nonmetals which form diatomic molecules.   (e) O_2 is more reactive and contains a double bond; N_2 is less reactive and contains a triple bond.

14.111 (a) $NaHSO_4(aq) + NaOH(aq) \longrightarrow$
$$Na_2SO_4(aq) + H_2O(l)$$
(b) $S_8(s) + 24F_2(g) \longrightarrow 8SF_6(s)$
(c) $FeS(s) + 2HCl(aq) \longrightarrow FeCl_2(aq) + H_2S(g)$
(d) $Te(s) + 2I_2(s) \longrightarrow TeI_4(s)$

14.113 (a) acidic   (b) acidic   (c) basic   (d) amphoteric
(e) basic   **14.115** $H_2O < H_2S < H_2Te$ **14.118** (a) sulfur hexafluoride, SF_6 (b) ozone, O_3 (c) sulfur trioxide, SO_3
(d) sulfur dioxide, SO_2 (e) sulfur trioxide, SO_3, and sulfuric acid, H_2SO_4 (f) sodium thiosulfate pentahydrate, $Na_2S_2O_3 \cdot 5H_2O$ (g) hydrogen sulfide, H_2S

14.120 $S_2F_{10}(g) \longrightarrow SF_4(g) + SF_6(g)$
ON: +5   +4   +6

14.122 (a) $-1, +1, +3, +5, +7$ (b) Cl has a $1s^2 2s^2 2p^6 3s^2 3p^5$ configuration. By adding one electron, the "octet" is achieved. By forming covalent bonds, it can complete (or expand) its octet but it does so in a way maintaining its electrons paired in bonds or lone pairs.   (c) F is an exception because of its small size and high electronegativity.

14.124 (a) Cl—Cl   (b) Br—Br   (c) Cl—Cl
The F—F bond strength is weaker than expected due to the small size of the F atom. This means that the lone electron pairs on the adjacent atoms repel, weakening the bond.

14.126 (a) $3Br_2(l) + 6OH^-(aq) \longrightarrow$
$$5Br^-(aq) + BrO_3^-(aq) + 3H_2O(l)$$
(b) $ClF_5(l) + 6OH^-(aq) \longrightarrow$
$$5F^-(aq) + ClO_3^-(aq) + 3H_2O(l)$$

14.127 (a) $2Rb(s) + Br_2(l) \longrightarrow 2RbBr(s)$
(b) $I_2(s) + H_2O(l) \longrightarrow HI(aq) + HIO(aq)$
(c) $Br_2(l) + 2I^-(aq) \longrightarrow I_2(s) + 2Br^-(aq)$
(d) $CaF_2(s) + H_2SO_4(l) \longrightarrow CaSO_4(s) + 2HF(g)$

14.129 $HIO < HBrO < HClO < HClO_2$ **14.132** (a) oxidation-reduction   (b) Because I^- is more easily oxidized than Cl^- due to its larger size.   (c) It would have to be a non-oxidizing acid.   **14.134** Helium; argon   **14.136** Because they are held together only by dispersion forces

14.139 (a) $2NaH(s) + 2SO_2(l) \longrightarrow Na_2S_2O_4(s) + H_2(g)$
ON: +1 −1   +4 −2   +1 +3 −2   0
(b) 1.47×10^5 L

14.141 3.371×10^{-19} J

14.145 (a) $MgCl_2 \cdot 6H_2O(s) + 6SOCl_2(l) \longrightarrow$
$$MgCl_2(s) + 6SO_2(g) + 12HCl(g)$$
(b)

14.146 -405 kJ/mol

14.148 (a) hyponitrous acid is $H_2N_2O_2$; nitroxyl is HNO.
(b)
(c) Both would be bent at the N atoms.
(d)

14.150 (a) $4NH_3(g) + 5O_2(g) \longrightarrow 4NO(g) + 6H_2O(g)$
$2NO(g) + O_2(g) \longrightarrow 2NO_2(g)$
$3NO_2(g) + H_2O(l) \longrightarrow 2HNO_3(aq) + NO(g)$
(b) 1.5   (c) 2.7×10^2 mL

14.154 13 metric tons   **14.156** A disproportionation reaction is one in which a substance containing an element in an intermediate oxidation state undergoes simultaneous oxidation and reduction. Reactions (b)–(f) are disproportionations.   **14.158** (a) 5A(15)   (b) 7A(17)   (c) 6A(16)
(d) 1A(1) or 2A(2)   (e) 3A(13)   (f) 8A(18)

14.160 (a)   (b) 3 (all on N)   (c) 1.5

14.163 (a) the increase in size due to the occupation of the next quantum level is offset by the decrease in size due to the 2+ charge.   (b) The lattice energy of CaF_2 is greater than that of NaF.   (c) Be compounds have more covalent character than Ca compounds, which are essentially ionic.

14.166 as oxidizing agent: $2Na(s) + H_2(g) \longrightarrow 2NaH(s)$
as reducing agent: $Cl_2(g) + H_2(g) \longrightarrow 2 HCl(g)$

14.168 Both contain 2 mol of N per mole of compound, but N_2H_4 has 28/32 (= 0.875) g N/g N_2H_4 and NH_4NO_3 has 28/80 (= 0.35) g N/g NH_4NO_3.

14.170 (a) has sp^3 hybridization at the Al.

(b) tetrahedral   (c) sp. Since the ion is linear, the central atom must be sp hybridized.   (d) There are no lone pairs on the central atom. Instead the Cl forms double bonds by donating the lone pairs into empty d orbitals of Al.

14.172 The Lewis structures are

There are 3, "2.5", and 2 groups of electrons on the N in NO_2^-, NO_2 and NO_2^+, respectively. The bond angles are consistent with the presence of fewer groups at the N giving rise to larger bond angles. **14.174** 2.29×10^4 g **14.176** -769 kJ

Chapter 15

15.3 (a) Carbon's position in the periodic table gives it an electronegativity midway between the most metallic and nonmetallic elements of period 2. Therefore, carbon shares electrons to attain a filled shell, bonding covalently in molecules, networks, and polyatomic ions. (b) Carbon has four electrons in its outer shell, so it needs to form four covalent bonds to fulfill its octet requirement. (c) Formation of carbon ions is energetically impossible under ordinary conditions. Its ionization energy and electron affinity values are not conducive to ion formation. (d) Carbon forms relatively short, strong bonds as a result of its small size, which allows close approach to another atom and thus greater orbital overlap. (e) The C—C bond is short enough to allow the formation of multiple bonds using the 2p orbitals. **15.4** (a) Carbon bonds to C, H, O, N, P, S, and halogens. (b) Heteroatoms are all atoms other than C or H. (c) N, O, F, Cl, and Br are more electronegative. H and P are less electronegative. S and I have the same electronegativity as carbon. (d) Since it can bond to a wide variety of atoms, this means it can form many different compounds. **15.7** The C—Li bond is the most reactive, since it shows the greatest difference in electronegativity. C—I and C=O would be less reactive, with C—H and C—C least so. **15.8** (a) An alkane and a cycloalkane contain only single C—C bonds, while an alkene contains a C—C double bond and an alkyne contains a C—C triple bond. A cycloalkane contains a ring of C atoms. (b) C_nH_{2n+2}; C_nH_{2n}; C_nH_{2n}; C_nH_{2n-2}, respectively. (c) Both alkanes and cycloalkanes are saturated. **15.11** (a), (c), and (f)

15.14 (a)

15.16 (a)

$$H_2C{=}CH{-}CH_2{-}CH_2{-}CH_2{-}CH_3$$

(b)

(c)

CH_2 ... CH_2—CH—CH_2—CH_3 ... CH_2—CH_2

CH_2 ... CH—CH_3 ... CH_2—CH—CH_3

H_2C ... CH—CH_3 ... H_2C ... C ... CH_3

H_3C—CH—CH_2 ... H_2C—CH_2

15.18 (a)

CH_3—C—CH_2CH_3 with CH_3 above and CH_3 below

(b) CH_2=CH—CH_2CH_3

(c) H—C≡C—CH—CH_3 with CH_2—CH_3 below   (d) OK

15.20 (a)

H_3C—CH—CH—$CH_2CH_2CH_2CH_2CH_3$ with CH_3, CH_3 above

(b)

CH_2—CH_2—CH—CH_2—CH_3 with CH_2—CH—CH_2 and CH_3

(c) 3,4-dimethylheptane   (d) 2,2-dimethylbutane

15.22 (a) H_3C—CH_2—CH—CH_2—CH_2—CH_3 with CH_3

3-methylhexane

(b) H_3C—CH_2—CH—CH_2—CH_2—CH_3 with CH_3

3-methylhexane

(c)

CH_2—CH_2 / CH_2 ... CH—CH_3 / CH_2—CH_2

methylcyclohexane

(d)

H_3C—CH_2—C—CH—CH_2—CH_2—CH_2—CH_3 with CH_3 above and CH_3 CH_2CH_3 below

3,3-dimethyl-4-ethyloctane

15.24 Both can exhibit optical activity.

(a)

CH_2 / HC⊙CH—CH_3 / Cl

(b) H_3C—CH_2—⊙—C—CH_3 with CH_3, H left and H, CH_3 right

15.26 (a) H_3C—CH_2—⊙H—CH_2—CH_2—CH_3 optically active, with Br

(b)

H_3C—CH_2—C—CH_2—CH_3 with CH_3 above, Cl below   not optically active

(c)

$BrCH_2$—⊙—CH_2—CH_3 with CH_3 above, Br below   optically active

15.28 (a)

CH_3CH_2 ... CH_3 / C=C / H ... H CH_3CH_2 ... H / C=C / H ... CH_3

cis-2-pentene   *trans*-2-pentene

(b)

H ... H / C=C / cyclohexyl ... CH_3 H ... CH_3 / C=C / cyclohexyl ... H

cis-1-cyclohexylpropene   *trans*-1-cyclohexylpropene

(c) no geometric isomers

15.30 (a)

H ... H / C=C / CH_3 ... H no geometric isomers

(b)

H ... H / C=C / CH_2 ... CH_2 / CH_3 ... CH_3 H ... CH_2CH_3 / C=C / CH_2 ... H / CH_3

cis-3-hexene   *trans*-3-hexene

(c)

Cl ... H / C=C / Cl ... H no geometric isomers

(d)

H ... H / C=C / Cl ... Cl H ... Cl / C=C / Cl ... H

cis-1,2-dichloroethene   *trans*-1,2-dichloroethene

15.32

1,2-dichlorobenzene (*o*-dichlorobenzene)   1,3-dichlorobenzene (*m*-dichlorobenzene)   1,4-dichlorobenzene (*p*-dichlorobenzene)

15.34

benzene ring with OH, two CH_3—C—CH_3 (with CH_3) groups and CH_3

15.35

H ... H / C=C / CH_2 ... CH_3 / CH_3 ... $CHCH_3$ H ... $CHCH_3$ (with CH_3) / C=C / CH_2 ... H / CH_3

(*cis*)   (*trans*)

2-methyl-3-hexene

H_3C ... H / C=C / H_3C ... $CH_2CH_2CH_3$ no geometric isomers

15.39 π bond   **15.41** (a) elimination   (b) addition

15.43 (a) CH_3CH_2CH=$CHCH_2CH_3$ + H_2O ⟶

$CH_3CH_2CH_2CHCH_2CH_3$ with OH

(b)

CH_3—CH—CH_3 (with Br) + CH_3CH_2OK $\xrightarrow{\Delta}$

CH_3—CH=CH_2 + CH_3CH_2OH + KBr

(c) CH_3CH_3 + $2Cl_2$ ⟶ Cl—CH—CH_3 (with Cl) + $2HCl$

15.45 (a) oxidized (b) reduced (c) reduced **15.47** (a) oxidized (b) oxidized **15.50** (a) Methylethylamine is more water soluble due to hydrogen bonding between the nitrogen and water. (b) Assuming that melting point varies like boiling point, 1-butanol has a higher melting point due to intermolecular H-bonding. (c) Propylamine has a higher boiling point than trimethylamine due to intermolecular H-bonding of the primary amine not possible in the tertiary amine.

15.53 Both react by addition across the electron-rich trigonal planar π bond. Due to bond polarity, an electron-rich group bonds to the carbonyl carbon and an electron-poor group to the carbonyl oxygen, whereas in the alkene the addition can produce two isomeric products.

$$R-\underset{\underset{O}{\|}}{C}-R + H_2O \longrightarrow R-\underset{\underset{OH}{|}}{\overset{\overset{OH}{|}}{C}}-R$$

$$\underset{\underset{H}{|}}{\overset{\overset{R}{|}}{C}}=\underset{\underset{H}{|}}{\overset{\overset{H}{|}}{C}} + H_2O \longrightarrow R-\underset{\underset{OH}{|}}{\overset{\overset{H}{|}}{C}}-\underset{\underset{H}{|}}{\overset{\overset{H}{|}}{C}}-H + R-\underset{\underset{H}{|}}{\overset{\overset{H}{|}}{C}}-\underset{\underset{H}{|}}{\overset{\overset{H}{|}}{C}}-OH$$

15.56 Common to the formation of esters and acid anhydrides is a condensation reaction, the other product being water. **15.58** (a) alkyl halide (b) nitrile (c) carboxylic acid (d) aldehyde

15.60 (a)

CH_3-(CH=CH)$-$(CH$_2$-OH)
   alkene   alcohol

(b)

(Cl-CH$_2$)-〈benzene〉-(C-OH with =O)
haloalkane aromatic carboxylic acid

(c)

〈ring, alkene〉 (C(=O)-NH)-CH$_3$
   alkene   amide

(d)

(N≡C)-(CH$_2$-C(=O)-CH$_3$)
 nitrile   ketone

(e)

〈saturated ring〉 (C(=O)-O-CH$_2$CH$_3$)
saturated ring   ester

15.62

$H_3C-CH_2-CH_2-CH_2-CH_2-OH$

$H_3C-CH_2-CH_2-\underset{\underset{OH}{|}}{CH}-CH_3$

$H_3C-\underset{\underset{CH_3}{|}}{CH}-\underset{\underset{OH}{|}}{CH}-CH_3$

$H_3C-\underset{\underset{CH_3}{|}}{\overset{\overset{OH}{|}}{C}}-CH_2-CH_3$

$H_3C-CH_2-\underset{\underset{OH}{|}}{CH}-CH_2-CH_3$

$H_3C-\underset{\underset{CH_3}{|}}{CH}-CH_2-CH_2-OH$

$H_3C-CH_2-\underset{\underset{CH_3}{|}}{CH}-CH_2-OH$

$H_3C-\underset{\underset{CH_3}{|}}{\overset{\overset{CH_3}{|}}{C}}-CH_2-OH$

15.64

$H_3C-CH_2-CH_2-CH_2-NH_2$

$H_3C-CH_2-\underset{\underset{NH_2}{|}}{CH}-CH_3$

$H_3C-\underset{\underset{CH_3}{|}}{CH}-CH_2-NH_2$

$H_3C-\underset{\underset{CH_3}{|}}{\overset{\overset{CH_3}{|}}{C}}-NH_2$

$H_3C-CH_2-\underset{\underset{H}{|}}{N}-CH_2-CH_3$

$H_3C-CH_2-CH_2-\underset{\underset{H}{|}}{N}-CH_3$

$H_3C-CH_2-\underset{\underset{CH_3}{|}}{N}-CH_3$

$H_3C-\underset{\underset{CH_3}{|}}{CH}-\underset{\underset{H}{|}}{N}-CH_3$

15.66 (a) $CH_3-\underset{\underset{O}{\|}}{C}-CH_2CH_3$ (b)

$CH_3-\underset{\underset{CH_3}{|}}{CH}-\overset{\overset{O}{\|}}{C}-O-H$

(c)

$\underset{CH_2-CH_2}{\overset{CH_2-CH_2}{|\qquad|}}C=O$

15.68 (a)

$CH_3-\overset{\overset{O}{\|}}{C}-\underset{\underset{H}{|}}{N}-CH_3$

(b)

$CH_3CH_2CH_2-\overset{\overset{O}{\|}}{C}-O-\underset{\underset{CH_3}{|}}{CH}CH_3$

(c)

$H-\overset{\overset{O}{\|}}{C}-O-CH_2-\underset{\underset{CH_3}{|}}{CH}CH_3$

15.70 (a) $CH_3(CH_2)_4COOH + CH_3CH_2OH$
(b) $C_6H_5COOH + CH_3CH_2CH_2OH$
(c) $CH_3CH_2OH + C_6H_5CH_2CH_2COOH$

15.72 (a)

$CH_3-CH_2-OH; CH_3CH_2-\overset{\overset{O}{\|}}{C}-O-CH_2CH_3$

(b)

$CH_3CH_2-\underset{\underset{CN}{|}}{CH}-CH_3; CH_3-CH_2-\underset{\underset{COOH}{|}}{CH}-CH_3$

15.74 (a)

$CH_3CH_2\overset{\overset{O}{\|}}{C}-OH; H^+$

(b) $CH_3CH_2NH_2$

15.76 (a) insoluble (b) soluble—hydrogen bonding (c) soluble—hydrogen bonding (d) soluble—hydrogen bonding and some dissociation (weak acid) (e) insoluble—alkyl group too hydrophobic (f) insoluble **15.78** Addition; condensation **15.81** London forces between substitutents on the polyethylene chain. **15.83** Amine + carboxylic acid; alcohol + carboxylic acid. Specifically in nylon a diamine and dicarboxylic acid; and in polyesters, a diol and a dicarboxylic acid.

15.84 (a)

$$-(\underset{\underset{H}{|}}{\overset{\overset{H}{|}}{C}}-\underset{\underset{Cl}{|}}{\overset{\overset{H}{|}}{C}})_n-$$

(b)

$$-(\underset{\underset{H}{|}}{\overset{\overset{H}{|}}{C}}-\underset{\underset{CH_3}{|}}{\overset{\overset{H}{|}}{C}})_n-$$

15.86

$nHO-\overset{\overset{O}{\|}}{C}-C_6H_4-\overset{\overset{O}{\|}}{C}-OH + nHOCH_2CH_2OH \longrightarrow$

$HO-(CH_2CH_2O\overset{\overset{O}{\|}}{C}-C_6H_4-\overset{\overset{O}{\|}}{C}-O)_n H + nH_2O$

15.88 (a) condensation (b) addition (c) condensation (d) condensation **15.90** The amino acid sequence in a protein determines its shape and structure, which determine its function. **15.93** The base sequence in DNA determines the base sequence in RNA, which determines the amino acid sequence in the protein.

15.94 (a) CH_3- (b)

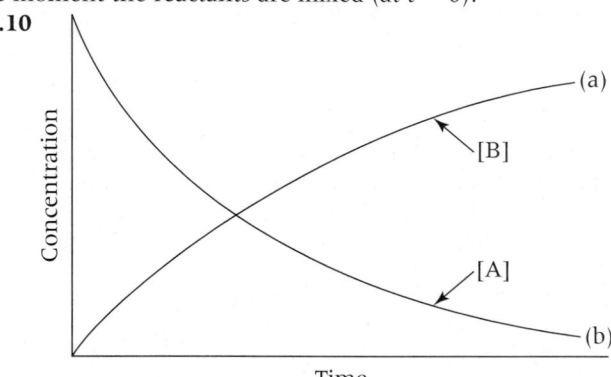

(c) $CH_3-S-CH_2CH_2-$

15.96 (a)

15.98 (a) AATCGG   (b) TCTGTA   **15.100** ACAATGCCT;
three   **15.102** (a) cysteine-cysteine $\longrightarrow$ cystine; covalently
linked   (b) Lysine and aspartic acid or glutamic acid by salt
bridge.   (c) Asparagine with serine by hydrogen bonding.
(d) Valine with phenylalanine by hydrophobic forces.
15.104 (a) Acid-catalyzed dehydration of the alcohol followed by reduction with hydrogen.   (b) Acid-catalyzed
dehydration of the alcohol followed by addition of
bromine.   (c) Oxidize one mole of the ethanol to acetic
acid. React this with a second mole of ethanol to form the
ester.
15.106 $CH_3-CH-CHO$
              $|$
              CH_3
             C_4H_8O
      2-methylpropanal
15.108 $CH_3-CH=CH-CH_3$. Decolorization of bromine.
15.110 (a) From left to right, the functional groups are
alkene, cycloalkane, ester, cyclic unsaturated ketone, and
another ester, respectively.   (b) 1-sp^2, 2-sp^3, 3-sp^3, 4-sp^2,
5-sp^3, 6-sp^2, 7-sp^2 (c) carbons 2, 3, and 5
15.115 Cadaverine (1,5-diaminopentane):
$$H_2N-CH_2CH_2CH_2CH_2CH_2-NH_2$$
Putrescine (1,4-diaminobutane):
$$H_2N-CH_2CH_2CH_2CH_2-NH_2$$
$$BrCH_2CH_2Br + 2\ NaCN \longrightarrow$$
$$N\equiv CCH_2CH_2C\equiv N + 2NaBr$$
$$N\equiv CCH_2CH_2C\equiv N + \text{``4H''} \longrightarrow$$
$$H_2NCH_2CH_2CH_2CH_2NH_2$$
15.116

The second structure shows double bond character that
inhibits free rotation.
15.120 (a) Hydrolysis involves addition of water to break
the peptide bonds.   (b) glycine = 4; alanine = 1; valine =
3; proline = 6; serine = 7; arginine = 49   (c) 10,700 g/mol

15.122 The reaction is not stereospecific and produces a
racemic mixture.

Chapter 16

16.2 An increase in pressure increases the reactant concentrations and would result in an increased reaction rate.
16.3 Additional solvent would decrease the reactant concentrations and would result in a decreased reaction rate.
16.5 An increase in temperature increases both the number
and energy of the collisions and thus would increase the
reaction rate.   **16.8** (a) The slope of the line joining any
two points on the graph of concentrations *vs.* time provides
the average rate over that time period. The shorter this
time period, the closer the average rate will equal the instantaneous rate, the rate at a particular instant during the
reaction.   (b) The initial rate is the instantaneous rate at
the moment the reactants are mixed (at t = 0).

16.10

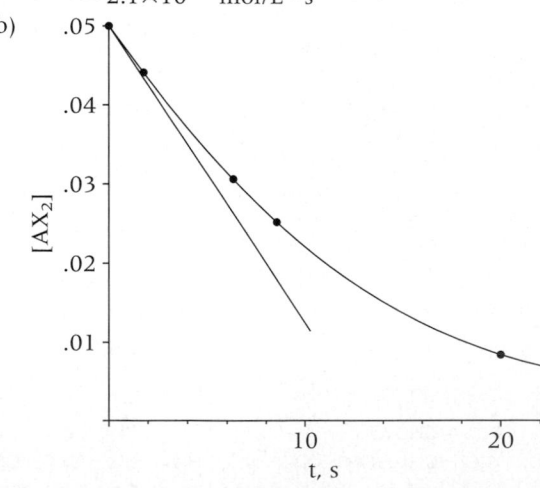

16.12 (a) $Rate = -\dfrac{\Delta[AX_2]}{\Delta t}$

$= -\dfrac{(0.0088\ mol/L) - (0.0500\ mol/L)}{(20.0 - 0)\ s}$

$= 2.1\times10^{-3}\ mol/L\cdot s$

(b) The initial rate is determined by the slope of the tangent to
the curve at the point t = 0. The initial rate is higher than
the rate in part (a).   Initial rate $\approx 5.0\times10^{-3}\ mol/L\cdot s$

16.14 $Rate = -\dfrac{1}{2}\dfrac{\Delta[A]}{\Delta t} = \dfrac{\Delta[B]}{\Delta t} = \dfrac{\Delta[C]}{\Delta t}$; $4\ mol/L\cdot s$

16.16 $Rate = -\dfrac{\Delta[A]}{\Delta t} = -\dfrac{1}{2}\dfrac{\Delta[B]}{\Delta t} = \dfrac{\Delta[C]}{\Delta t}$; $0.25\ mol/L\cdot s$

16.18 $2N_2O_5 \longrightarrow 4NO_2 + O_2$

16.21 Rate $= -\dfrac{\Delta[N_2]}{\Delta t} = -\dfrac{1}{3}\dfrac{\Delta[H_2]}{\Delta t} = \dfrac{1}{2}\dfrac{\Delta[NH_3]}{\Delta t}$

16.22 (a) Rate $= -\dfrac{1}{3}\dfrac{\Delta[O_2]}{\Delta t} = \dfrac{1}{2}\dfrac{\Delta[O_3]}{\Delta t}$

(b) 1.45×10^{-5} mol/L·s

16.23 (a) k is the rate proportionality constant (usually called the rate constant) and is specific for a particular reaction at a particular temperature. (b) The exponents *m* and *n* are called the reaction orders and define how the concentration of each reactant affects the rate. The coefficients *a* and *b* in the balanced equation are not necessarily related to the reaction orders *m* and *n*. (c) $L^2/mol^2 \cdot min$ **16.25** (a) doubled (b) decreased by a factor of 4 (c) increased by a factor of 9 **16.26** first order with respect to BrO_3^-; first order with respect to Br^-; second order with respect to H^+; fourth order overall. **16.28** (a) doubled (b) halved (c) increased by a factor of 16 **16.30** second order with respect to NO_2; first order with respect to Cl_2; third order overall. **16.32** (a) increased by a factor of 9 (b) increased by a factor of 8 (c) halved **16.34** (a) second order in A, first order in B (b) Rate $= k[A]^2[B]$ (c) 5.00×10^3 $L^2/mol^2 \cdot s$

16.36 (a) $time^{-1}$ (b) $\dfrac{L}{mol \cdot time}$

(c) $\dfrac{L^2}{mol^2 \cdot time}$ (d) $\dfrac{L^{3/2}}{mol^{3/2} \cdot time}$

16.39 (a) first order (b) second order (c) zero order
16.41 7s **16.43** (a) 6.60×10^{-2} min^{-1} (b) 21.0 min
16.45 (a)

[graph: ln [NH₃] vs t, s with points on a line from 1.386 down to 1.380, x-axis 1.00 and 2.00]

$k = 3\times10^{-3}$ s^{-1}

(b) $t_{1/2} = 2\times10^2$ s

16.47 Take the logarithm of both sides of the Arrhenius equation. Rearrange the resulting equation, then plot the logarithm of the rate constant *vs.* 1/T. The slope of this line is $-E_a/R$ (or $-E_a/2.303R$ if common logarithms are used). **16.49** 3.3×10^{-2} s^{-1} **16.53** No. For most reactions, only a small fraction of collisions actually lead to reaction. If this were not true, every gaseous reaction would be over instantaneously. Only those collisions with energy equal to or greater than the activation energy and with the proper orientation can lead to reaction. **16.56** No. All reactions are reversible and will eventually reach a state where the forward rate equals the reverse rate. At this point without disturbing the reaction, a nonzero constant concentration will exist for all reactants and products. Thus, there will be less than 4×10^{-5} mol EF formed. **16.57** At the same temperature, the NH_3 and $N(CH_3)_3$ will have the same average kinetic energy. However, due to their larger mass, $N(CH_3)_3$ molecules will be traveling more slowly. This will

decrease the number of collisions per unit time and reduce the rate of the second reaction. In addition, the higher molecular complexity of the $N(CH_3)_3$ would probably reduce its orientation probability factor, decreasing the rate of the second reaction still more. **16.58** 12 **16.60** 2.90×10^{-18}

16.62 (a)

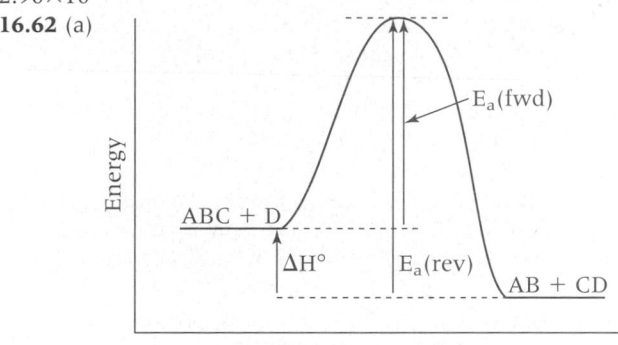

(b) 270 kJ/mol

(c) A
|
B······C······D

16.64 (a)

(b) 3 kJ

(c) :Ö=N̈······C̈l······C̈l:

16.65 In many cases, one of the steps is much slower than the others. If this is true, the rate equation for this slowest step represents the rate equation for the overall reaction and the rate would be lower than the average rate of the individual steps. **16.69** The probability of three particles coming together at the same time is much less than that of two coming together. **16.70** No. The overall rate law includes only the species up to and including those in the rate-determining (slow) step.
16.72 (a) $A(g) + B(g) + C(g) \longrightarrow D(g)$

(b) $X(g)$ and $Y(g)$

(c) (1) bimolecular; $Rate_1 = k_1[A][B]$
(2) bimolecular; $Rate_2 = k_2[X][C]$
(3) unimolecular; $Rate_3 = k_3[Y]$

(d) yes

(e) yes

16.74 The proposed mechanism is possible since the elementary reactions which are all physically reasonable add up to the overall equation and the mechanism rate law is consistent with the experimental rate law. **16.77** No. An increase in temperature increases the reaction rate by increasing the fraction of collisions whose energy is greater than the activation energy. A catalyst increases the reaction rate by providing a different reaction mechanism with a lower activation energy.   **16.78** (a) No. It supplies an initial amount of heat energy to start the exothermic reaction by allowing some of the molecules to achieve the threshold energy.   (b) Yes. The metal catalyzes by chemically adsorbing the H_2 and O_2 molecules onto its surface which provides a low-activation-energy step.

16.81 (a) Water is a solvent and thus its concentration is effectively constant due to the large excess.
 (b) (1) $Rate_1 = k_1[(CH_3)_3CBr]$
    (2) $Rate_2 = k_2[(CH_3)_3C^+]$
    (3) $Rate_3 = k_3[(CH_3)_3COH_2^+]$
 (c) $(CH_3)_3C^+$ and $(CH_3)_3COH_2^+$
 (d) $Rate = k_1[(CH_3)_3CBr]$, the rate law for the slowest step.

16.83 $Rate = k(P_A)^x(P_B)^y$; first order k: s^{-1}; second order k: $torr^{-1} \cdot s^{-1}$

16.85
$$O_3(g) + NO(g) \longrightarrow NO_2(g) + O_2(g)$$
$$O_3(g) \longrightarrow O_2(g) + O(g)$$
$$\underline{NO_2(g) + O(g) \longrightarrow NO(g) + O_2(g)}$$
$$2O_3(g) \longrightarrow 3O_2(g)$$

NO acts as a catalyst for the decomposition of O_3 to O_2 by providing a different mechanism and is regenerated.

16.87 46 kJ/mol   **16.89** (a) decrease   (b) increase   (c) no effect (assuming this reactant does not also occur earlier) (d) increase   (e) increase   **16.92** 2   **16.94** 7 times faster
16.96 57 yr   **16.99** (a) $k = 0.21$ h^{-1}; $t_{1/2} = 3.3$ h   (b) 6.6 h   (c) If the concentration of one reactant (in this case, water) is much greater than the other (in this case, sucrose), the change in concentration of the reactant in great excess is negligible, yielding an apparent zero-order behavior with respect to that reactant.   **16.101** (a) 0.68 mol/L   (b) 0.57   **16.104** 71 kPa

16.108 $Rate = -\dfrac{\Delta[C_2H_6]}{\Delta t} = -\dfrac{1}{4}\dfrac{\Delta[Cl_2]}{\Delta t} = \dfrac{\Delta[C_2H_2Cl_4]}{\Delta t} = \dfrac{1}{4}\dfrac{\Delta[HCl]}{\Delta t}$

16.110 (a) 2.4×10^{-15} M   (b) 2.4×10^{-11} mol/L $\cdot$ s
16.113 (a) $Rate_1 = 1.7\times10^{-5}$ M s^{-1};
    $Rate_2 = 3.4\times10^{-5}$ M s^{-1};
    $Rate_3 = 3.4\times10^{-5}$ M s^{-1}
 (b) zero order in $Na_2S_2O_8$; first order in KI
 (c) 4.3×10^{-4} s^{-1} (d) $Rate = (4.3\times10^{-4}\ s^{-1})[KI]$
16.115 (a)

 (b) Yes, it is consistent, but the in-text mechanism is more reasonable, since it involves only bimolecular steps.

Chapter 17

17.1 $Rate_f = k_f[R]$ $Rate_r = k_r[P]$ $K = \dfrac{k_f}{k_r} = \dfrac{[P]}{[R]}$
If the change is one of concentrations, the product concen-

trations will increase, while the reactant concentrations will decrease but the ratio (equilibrium constant) will be constant. If the change is one of temperature, the product concentrations and equilibrium constant will increase while the reactant concentrations will decrease.   **17.5** This reaction probably would have a large K, since it is very exothermic.   **17.7** The equilibrium constant expression is $K = [O_2]$. If the temperature remains constant and the initial amount of Li_2O_2 present was sufficient to reach equilibrium, the amount of O_2 obtained will be constant, regardless of how much $Li_2O_2(s)$ is present.

17.8 (a) $H_2(g) + I_2(g) \rightleftharpoons 2HI(g)$ $Q = \dfrac{[HI]^2}{[H_2][I_2]}$

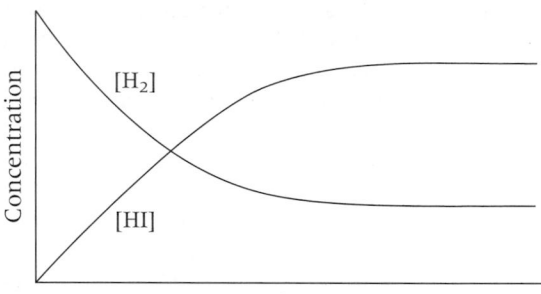

The value of Q increases as a function of time until it reaches the value of K.   (b) No
17.11 Yes; $Q_2 = Q_1^2$, where Q_1 is for the formation of 1 mol of NH_3 and Q_2 is for the loss of 1 mol of N_2.
17.12 (a) $4NO(g) + O_2(g) \rightleftharpoons 2N_2O_3(g)$
    $Q_c = \dfrac{[N_2O_3]^2}{[NO]^4[O_2]}$
 (b) $SF_6(g) + 2SO_3(g) \rightleftharpoons 3SO_2F_2(g)$
    $Q_c = \dfrac{[SO_2F_2]^3}{[SF_6][SO_3]^2}$
 (c) $2SClF_5(g) + H_2(g) \rightleftharpoons S_2F_{10}(g) + 2HCl(g)$
    $Q_c = \dfrac{[S_2F_{10}][HCl]^2}{[SClF_5]^2[H_2]}$
17.14 (a) $2NO_2Cl(g) \rightleftharpoons 2NO_2(g) + Cl_2(g)$
    $Q_c = \dfrac{[NO_2]^2[Cl_2]}{[NO_2Cl]^2}$
 (b) $2POCl_3(g) \rightleftharpoons 2PCl_3(g) + O_2(g)$
    $Q_c = \dfrac{[PCl_3]^2[O_2]}{[POCl_3]^2}$
 (c) $4NH_3(g) + 3O_2(g) \rightleftharpoons 2N_2(g) + 6H_2O(g)$
    $Q_c = \dfrac{[N_2]^2[H_2O]^6}{[NH_3]^4[O_2]^3}$
17.16 (a) 7.9   (b) 3.2×10^{-5}
17.18 (a) $2Na_2O_2(s) + 2CO_2(g) \rightleftharpoons 2Na_2CO_3(s) + O_2(g)$
    $Q_c = \dfrac{[O_2]}{[CO_2]^2}$
 (b) $H_2O(l) \rightleftharpoons H_2O(g)$; $Q_c = [H_2O(g)]$
 (c) $NH_4Cl(s) \rightleftharpoons NH_3(g) + HCl(g)$; $Q_c = [NH_3][HCl]$
17.20 (a) $2NaHCO_3(s) \rightleftharpoons Na_2CO_3(s) + CO_2(g) + H_2O(g)$
    $Q_c = [CO_2][H_2O]$
 (b) $SnO_2(s) + 2H_2(g) \rightleftharpoons Sn(s) + 2H_2O(g)$
    $Q_c = \dfrac{[H_2O]^2}{[H_2]^2}$
 (c) $H_2SO_4(l) + SO_3(g) \rightleftharpoons H_2S_2O_7(l)$
    $Q_c = \dfrac{1}{[SO_3]}$

17.23 (a) (1) $Cl_2(g) + F_2(g) \rightleftharpoons 2ClF(g)$
        (2) $2ClF(g) + 2F_2(g) \rightleftharpoons 2ClF_3(g)$
        overall: $Cl_2(g) + 3F_2(g) \rightleftharpoons 2ClF_3(g)$

(b) $Q_c = \dfrac{[ClF_3]^2}{[Cl_2][F_2]^3}$

$Q_{c_1} \times Q_{c_2} = \dfrac{[ClF]^2}{[Cl_2][F_2]} \times \dfrac{[ClF_3]^2}{[ClF]^2[F_2]^2} = \dfrac{[ClF_3]^2}{[Cl_2][F_2]^3}$

17.25 K_c and K_p are **only** equal when $\Delta n_{gas} = 0$. **17.26** (a) smaller (b) Assuming that RT > 1 (i.e., that T > 12.2 K), $K_p > K_c$ if there are more moles of gas in the products than in the reactants, and $K_p < K_c$ if there are fewer moles of gas in the products than in the reactants. **17.27** (a) 3 (b) −1 (c) 3 **17.29** (a) 3.2 (b) 28.5 **17.31** (a) 0.15 (b) 3.6×10^{-7} **17.33** The value Q equals to ratio [Products]/[Reactants]. When Q is less than K, the concentration of products is less than its equilibrium value, so the reaction proceeds to the right (towards the products) to reach equilibrium. **17.35** No; to the left. **17.38** Since the product coefficients are 1:1, equal concentrations of $CFCl_3$ and HCl will form, regardless of the initial reactant ratio. **17.40** (a) In general, if a reaction has a relatively small equilibrium constant and a relatively large initial reactant concentration, the concentration change (x) can often be ignored. (b) If the above conditions do not exist, the approximation cannot be made. More precisely, the assumption is not justified if it results in an error of greater than 5% in the calculated equilibrium concentration(s). **17.41** 50.8

17.43

CONCENTRATION (M)	$PCl_5(g)$	$\rightleftharpoons PCl_3(g)$	+ $Cl_2(g)$
Initial	0.075	0	0
Change	$-x$	$+x$	$+x$
Equilibrium	$0.075 - x$	x	x

17.45 28 atm **17.47** 0.33 atm **17.49** 3.6×10^{-3} M **17.51** [HI] = 0.0153 M; $[I_2]$ = 0.00328 M **17.53** $[I_2]$ = $[Cl_2]$ = 0.0200 M; [ICl] = 0.060 M **17.55** 5.90×10^{-6} **17.58** (a) B. Amount of product increases with temperature. (b) A. Lowest temperature will yield the smallest amount of product. **17.59** The equilibrium position refers to the specific concentrations (or pressures) that exist when Q equals K, the equilibrium constant. Only the equilibrium position changes in response to a change in concentration. **17.62** The rate of the forward reaction is increased more than the rate of the reverse reaction, so K (= k_f/k_r) would increase. **17.63** (a) right (b) right (c) no change (d) left **17.65** (a) less F_2; more F (b) less CH_4; more C_2H_2 and H_2 **17.67** (a) no change (b) more $H_2O(l)$; less H_2 and O_2 **17.69** (a) amount of product is independent of the volume. (b) increase volume **17.71** (a) decrease (b) increase (c) increase (d) decrease **17.73** 1.9 **17.76** (a) high pressure; low temperature (b) Q would be decreased, K would be unchanged. (c) The low temperature needed for increased yields would also lower the reaction rate. A catalyst is employed to increase the rate. Without the catalyst, a much higher temperature would be needed to achieve the same rate and result in a much lower yield. **17.79** (a) 4.83×10^{-5} atm (b) 20.0 μg/L **17.81** 0.203 atm **17.84** (a) 2×10^{-3} atm (b) high pressure, low temperature (c) 2×10^5 (d) No, since H_2O would condense at a higher temperature than C_2H_5OH.

17.85 (a) 7.8×10^{-6} M^2

(b)
```
    H  :Cl:
    |   |
H—P—B—Cl:
    |   |
    H  :Cl:
```

17.89 (a) 1.6×10^{-2} atm (b) $K_c = 5.6 \times 10^2$ M^{-1}; P_{SO_2} = 0.16 atm **17.91** 12.5 g $CaCO_3$ **17.95** Both concentrations increased by a factor of 2.2. **17.97** (a) 3.0×10^{-14} atm (b) 0.013 pg/L **17.100** (a) 97.5% (b) 99.0%
17.102 (a) $2CH_4(g) + O_2(g) + 2H_2O(g) \rightleftharpoons$
$$2CO_2(g) + 6H_2(g)$$
(b) 1.76×10^{29} (c) 3.18×10^{23} (d) 48 atm
17.104 (a) 4.0×10^{-21} atm (b) 5.5×10^{-8} atm
(c) 29 N atoms; 4.0×10^{14} H atoms
(d) $N_2(g) + H(g) \longrightarrow NH(g) + N(g)$
17.108 (a) 5 (b) 8 (c) Once F formed, the process would stop, since the A $\longrightarrow$ B reaction is inhibited. (d) Once F formed, the metabolites G, H, and I would not form.

Chapter 18

18.2 All Arrhenius acids produce H^+ ions and all Arrhenius bases produce OH^- ions in aqueous solution. Neutralization involves the combination of H^+ ions and OH^- ions to produce water molecules. It was this single reaction for all strong acid-base neutralizations which according to Arrhenius produced the identical heat of neutralization reaction value of −56 kJ per mole of water formed. **18.4** Weak acids exist mainly as undissociated molecules in water. The words "strong" and "weak" refer to the extent of dissociation in water. Strong acids are essentially 100% dissociated in water. **18.5** (a), (c), and (d) **18.7** (b) and (d)

18.9 (a) $K_a = \dfrac{[H_3O^+][CN^-]}{[HCN]}$ (b) $K_a = \dfrac{[H_3O^+][CO_3^{2-}]}{[HCO_3^-]}$

(c) $K_a = \dfrac{[H_3O^+][HCOO^-]}{[HCOOH]}$

18.11 (a) $K_a = \dfrac{[H_3O^+][NO_2^-]}{[HNO_2]}$

(b) $K_a = \dfrac{[H_3O^+][CH_3COO^-]}{[CH_3COOH]}$

(c) $K_a = \dfrac{[H_3O^+][BrO_2^-]}{[HBrO_2]}$

18.13 $CH_3COOH < HF < HIO_3 < HI$ **18.15** (a) weak acid (b) strong base (c) weak acid (d) strong acid **18.17** (a) strong base (b) strong acid (c) weak acid (d) weak acid **18.22** (a) $K_a = 4 \times 10^{-5}$. The smaller value of K_a indicates the weaker acid (higher pH). (b) $pK_a = 3.5$. The larger pK_a indicates the weaker acid. (c) 0.01 M. The lower the concentration, the lower $[H_3O^+]$. (d) 0.1 M weak acid. Less dissociation will lead to a higher pH value. (e) 0.1 M base. pH values of bases are larger than pH values for acids. (f) pOH = 6.0. pH = 14.0 − pOH **18.23** (a) 12.045; basic (b) 11.090; acidic **18.25** (a) 2.298; acidic (b) −0.708; basic **18.27** (a) $[H_3O^+] = 1.7 \times 10^{-10}$ M; $[OH^-]$ = 6.0×10^{-5} M; pOH = 4.22 (b) $[H_3O^+] = 2.7 \times 10^{-4}$ M; $[OH^-] = 3.7 \times 10^{-11}$ M; pH = 3.57 **18.29** (a) $[H_3O^+] = 1.7 \times 10^{-3}$ M; $[OH^-] = 5.9 \times 10^{-12}$ M; pOH = 11.23 (b) $[H_3O^+] = 1.5 \times 10^{-9}$ M; $[OH^-] = 6.6 \times 10^{-6}$ M; pH = 8.82 **18.31** 3.4×10^{-4} mol OH^- **18.33** 5.9×10^{-5} mol OH^-

18.36 (a) An increase in temperature shifts the autoionization of water to the right which will increase the value of K_w. (b) $K_w = 2.6 \times 10^{-14}$; pOH = 6.80; $[OH^-] = 1.6 \times 10^{-7}$ M **18.37** A Brønsted acid is a proton donor; hence, any Brønsted acid must contain at least one hydrogen atom. An Arrhenius acid donates a proton to water and thus is also an acid under the Brønsted definition. While an Arrhenius base produces OH^- ions in water, a Brønsted base is a substance that accepts a proton, H^+. Ammonia (NH_3) and fluoride ion (F^-) are Brønsted-Lowry bases but not Arrhenius bases. All Brønsted-Lowry acids can be considered potential Arrhenius acids.

18.40 An amphoteric substance can act either as an acid or as a base.

$NH_3 + H_3O^+ \longrightarrow NH_4^+ + H_2O$ (NH_3 acts as a base)

$NH_3 + CH_3^- \longrightarrow NH_2^- + CH_4$ (NH_3 acts as an acid)

18.41 (a) $H_3PO_4(aq) + H_2O(l) \rightleftharpoons$
$$H_3O^+(aq) + H_2PO_4^-(aq)$$
$$K_a = \frac{[H_3O^+][H_2PO_4^-]}{[H_3PO_4]}$$

(b) $C_6H_5COOH(aq) + H_2O(l) \rightleftharpoons$
$$H_3O^+(aq) + C_6H_5COO^-(aq)$$
$$K_a = \frac{[H_3O^+][C_6H_5COO^-]}{[C_6H_5COOH]}$$

(c) $HSO_4^-(aq) + H_2O(l) \rightleftharpoons H_3O^+(aq) + SO_4^{2-}(aq)$
$$K_a = \frac{[H_3O^+][SO_4^{2-}]}{[HSO_4^-]}$$

18.43 (a) Cl^- (b) HCO_3^- (c) OH^- **18.45** (a) NH_4^+ (b) NH_3 (c) $C_{10}H_{14}N_2H^+$

18.47 (a) HCl + H_2O $\rightleftharpoons$ Cl^- + H_3O^+
acid   base   conjugate conjugate
                base   acid
Conjugate pairs: HCl/Cl^-; H_3O^+/H_2O

(b) $HClO_4$ + H_2SO_4 $\rightleftharpoons$ ClO_4^- + $H_3SO_4^+$
acid   base   conjugate conjugate
                base   acid
Conjugate pairs: $HClO_4/ClO_4^-$; $H_3SO_4^+/H_2SO_4$

(c) HPO_4^{2-} + H_2SO_4 $\rightleftharpoons$ $H_2PO_4^-$ + HSO_4^-
base   acid   conjugate conjugate
                acid   base
Conjugate pairs: H_2SO_4/HSO_4^-; $H_2PO_4^-/HPO_4^{2-}$

18.49 (a) NH_3 + H_3PO_4 $\rightleftharpoons$ NH_4^+ + $H_2PO_4^-$
base   acid   conjugate conjugate
                acid   base
Conjugate pairs: $H_3PO_4/H_2PO_4^-$; NH_4^+/NH_3

(b) CH_3^- + NH_3 $\rightleftharpoons$ CH_3OH + NH_2^-
base   acid   conjugate conjugate
                acid   base
Conjugate pairs: $NH_3NH_2^-$; CH_3OH/CH_3O^-

(c) HPO_4^{2-} + HSO_4^- $\rightleftharpoons$ $H_2PO_4^-$ + SO_4^{2-}
base   acid   conjugate conjugate
                acid   base
Conjugate pairs: HSO_4^-/SO_4^{2-}; $H_2PO_4^-/HPO_4^{2-}$

18.51 (a) $OH^-(aq) + H_2PO_4^-(aq) \rightleftharpoons$
$$H_2O(l) + HPO_4^{2-}(aq)$$
base   acid   conjugate conjugate
                acid   base
Conjugate pairs: $H_2PO_4^-/HPO_4^{2-}$; H_2O/OH^-

(b) $HSO_4^-(aq) + CO_3^{2-}(aq) \rightleftharpoons$
acid   base $SO_4^{2-}(aq) + HCO_3^-(aq)$
                 conjugate conjugate
                 acid   base
Conjugate pairs: HSO_4^-/SO_4^{2-}; HCO_3^-/CO_3^{2-}

18.53 $K_c > 1$: $HCl + HS^- \rightleftharpoons Cl^- + H_2S$
$K_c < 1$: $Cl^- + H_2S \rightleftharpoons HCl + HS^-$

18.55 both (a) and (b) **18.57** both (a) and (b) **18.59** (a) A strong acid is nearly 100% dissociated, so the acid concentration is very different after dissociation. (b) A weak acid is only very slightly dissociated, so the acid concentration would be nearly the same after dissociation. (c) Same as (b), but the extent of dissociation would be greater than in (b). (d) Same as (a). **18.60** No. The % dissociation of hydrochloric acid must be much larger than that of acetic acid. Even though hydrochloric acid is much stronger than acetic acid, the $[H_3O^+]$ of these samples would be approximately the same. **18.63** 1.5×10^{-5} **18.65** $[H_3O^+] = [NO_2^-] = 1.9 \times 10^{-2}$ M; $[OH^-] = 5.3 \times 10^{-13}$ M **18.67** $[H_3O^+] = [ClCH_2COO^-] = 3.7 \times 10^{-2}$ M; pH = 1.43; $[ClCH_2COOH] = 1.01$ M **18.69** (a) $[H_3O^+] = 7.5 \times 10^{-3}$ M; pH = 2.12; $[OH^-] = 1.3 \times 10^{-12}$ M; pOH = 11.88 (b) 2.3×10^{-4} **18.71** 3.4×10^{-7} **18.73** (a) 2.47 (b) 11.42 **18.75** (a) 2.379 (b) 12.57 **18.77** 1.6% **18.79** $[H_3O^+] = [HS^-] = 9.5 \times 10^{-5}$ M; pH = 4.02; $[H_2S] = 0.10$ M; $[OH^-] = 1.1 \times 10^{-10}$ M; pOH = 9.96; $[S^{2-}] = 1 \times 10^{-17}$ M **18.82** 1.9% **18.83** All Brønsted-Lowry bases contain at least one lone pair of electrons able to bind the H^+ ion and thus allow them to be proton acceptors.

18.86 (a) $C_5H_5N(aq) + H_2O(l) \rightleftharpoons$
$$OH^-(aq) + C_5H_5NH^+(aq)$$
$$K_b = \frac{[OH^-][C_5H_5NH^+]}{[C_5H_5N]}$$

(b) $CO_3^{2-}(aq) + H_2O(l) \rightleftharpoons OH^-(aq) + HCO_3^-(aq)$
$$K_b = \frac{[OH^-][HCO_3^-]}{[CO_3^{2-}]}$$

18.88 (a) $HONH_2(aq) + H_2O(l) \rightleftharpoons$
$$OH^-(aq) + HONH_3^+(aq)$$
$$K_b = \frac{[OH^-][HONH_3^+]}{[HONH_2]}$$

(b) $HPO_4^{2-}(aq) + H_2O(l) \rightleftharpoons$
$$H_2PO_4^-(aq) + OH^-(aq)$$
$$K_b = \frac{[OH^-][H_2PO_4^-]}{[HPO_4^{2-}]}$$

18.90 11.72 **18.92** 11.35 **18.94** (a) 5.6×10^{-10} (b) 2.5×10^{-5} **18.96** (a) 12.05 (b) 10.77 **18.98** (a) 10.96 (b) 5.62 **18.100** (a) 8.72 (b) 4.59 **18.102** $[OH^-] = 4.8 \times 10^{-4}$ M; pH = 10.68 **18.104** As the nonmetal becomes more electronegative, its bond to hydrogen becomes more polar and the H^+ is more easily lost. **18.107** The electronegativity of Cl is greater than that of I. The charge on Cl (due to the larger number of O atoms) is greater than the charge on I. **18.108** (a) H_2SeO_4 (b) H_3PO_4 (c) H_2Te **18.110** (a) H_2Se (b) $B(OH)_3$ (c) $HBrO_2$ **18.112** (a) 0.05 M $Al_2(SO_4)_3$ (b) 0.1 M $PbCl_2$ **18.114** (a) 0.1 M $Ni(NO_3)_2$ (b) 0.1 M $Co(NO_3)_2$ **18.117** NaF contains the anion (F^-) of the weak acid HF, while NaCl contains the anion (Cl^-) of the strong acid HCl.

18.119 (a) $KBr(s) + H_2O(l) \longrightarrow K^+(aq) + Br^-(aq)$ neutral
(b) $NH_4I(s) + H_2O(l) \longrightarrow NH_4^+(aq) + I^-(aq)$
$NH_4^+(aq) + H_2O(l) \rightleftharpoons H_3O^+(aq) + NH_3(aq)$ acidic
(c) $KCN(s) + H_2O(l) \longrightarrow K^+(aq) + CN^-(aq)$
$CN^-(aq) + H_2O(l) \rightleftharpoons OH^-(aq) + HCN(aq)$ basic
18.121 (a) $Na_2CO_3(s) + H_2O(l) \longrightarrow 2Na^+(aq) + CO_3^{2-}(aq)$
$$CO_3^{2-}(aq) + H_2O(l) \rightleftharpoons$$
$$OH^-(aq) + HCO_3^-(aq) \quad \text{basic}$$
(b) $CaCl_2(s) + H_2O(l) \longrightarrow Ca^{2+}(aq) + 2Cl^-(aq)$ neutral
(c) $Cu(NO_3)_2(s) + nH_2O(l) \longrightarrow$
$$Cu(H_2O)_n^{2+}(aq) + 2NO_3^-(aq)$$
$$Cu(H_2O)_n^{2+}(aq) + H_2O(l) \rightleftharpoons$$
$$Cu(H_2O)_{n-1}OH^+(aq) + H_3O^+(aq) \quad \text{acidic}$$
18.123 (a) $SrBr_2(s) + H_2O(l) \longrightarrow$
$$Sr^{2+}(aq) + 2Br^-(aq) \quad \text{neutral}$$
(b) $Ba(CH_3COO)_2(s) + H_2O(l) \longrightarrow$
$$Ba^{2+}(aq) + 2CH_3COO^-(aq)$$
$$CH_3COO^-(aq) + H_2O(l) \rightleftharpoons$$
$$CH_3COOH(aq) + OH^-(aq) \quad \text{basic}$$
(c) $(CH_3)_2NH_2Br(s) + H_2O(l) \longrightarrow$
$$(CH_3)_2NH_2^+(aq) + Br^-(aq)$$
$$(CH_3)_2NH_2^+(aq) + H_2O(l) \rightleftharpoons$$
$$(CH_3)_2NH(aq) + H_3O^+(aq) \quad \text{acidic}$$
18.125 (a) $(NH_4)_3PO_4(s) + H_2O(l) \longrightarrow$
$$3NH_4^+(aq) + PO_4^{3-}(aq)$$
$NH_4^+(aq) + H_2O(l) \rightleftharpoons NH_3(aq) + H_3O^+(aq)$
$PO_4^{3-}(aq) + H_2O(l) \rightleftharpoons HPO_4^{2-}(aq) + OH^-(aq)$
Since $K_b(PO_4^{3-}) > K_a(NH_4^+)$ basic
(b) $Na_2SO_4(s) + H_2O(l) \longrightarrow 2Na^+(aq) + SO_4^{2-}$
$SO_4^{2-}(aq) + H_2O(l) \rightleftharpoons$
$$HSO_4^-(aq) + OH^-(aq) \quad \text{basic}$$
(c) $LiClO(s) + H_2O(l) \longrightarrow Li^+(aq) + ClO^-(aq)$
$ClO^-(aq) + H_2O(l) \rightleftharpoons$
$$HOCl(aq) + OH^-(aq) \quad \text{basic}$$
18.127 (a) $Fe(NO_3)_2 < KNO_3 < K_2SO_3 < K_2S$
(b) $NaHSO_4 < NH_4NO_3 < NaHCO_3 < Na_2CO_3$
18.129 Water acting as an acid makes all strong bases appear **equally** strong by forming OH^-:
$CH_3O^-(aq) + H_2O(l) \longrightarrow OH^-(aq) + CH_3OH(aq)$
$NH_2^-(aq) + H_2O(l) \longrightarrow OH^-(aq) + NH_3(aq)$
18.131 NH_3 as a solvent is more basic than H_2O and as such, weak acids like HF act like strong acids and are 100% dissociated. **18.133** A Lewis acid is an electron pair acceptor, while a Brønsted-Lowry acid is a proton donor. They are similar in the fact that the proton is an electron pair acceptor and thus is a Lewis acid. A Lewis base is an electron pair donor to any species, while a Brønsted-Lowry base is an electron pair donor specifically for the proton; that is, it is a proton acceptor. Thus, Lewis bases and Brønsted-Lowry bases are essentially the same.
18.134 (a) No.
$$Zn^{2+}(aq) + 4H_2O(l) \rightleftharpoons Zn(H_2O)_4^{2+}(aq)$$
H_2O is a very poor Brønsted base, but a reasonable Lewis base.
(b) CN^- and H_2O (c) CN^-
18.137 (a) acid (b) base (c) acid (d) base **18.139** (a) acid (b) base (c) base (d) acid
18.141 (a) $Na^+ + 6H_2O \rightleftharpoons Na(H_2O)_6^+$
acid   base
(b) $CO_2 + H_2O \rightleftharpoons H_2CO_3$
acid   base

(c) $F^- + BF_3 \rightleftharpoons BF_4^-$
base   acid
18.143 (a) Lewis (b) Brønsted-Lowry and Lewis (c) none (d) Lewis **18.146** Stronger in seawater. **18.148** (a) Weak acids will vary in % dissociation (acid strength) in solvents of different acid-base strength. (b) Methanol is a weaker base than water since carbolic acid dissociates less in methanol than in water. (c) $C_6H_5OH(solvated) + CH_3OH(l); CH_3OH_2^+(solvated) + C_6H_5O^-(solvated)$ (d) $2CH_3OH \rightleftharpoons CH_3OH_2^+(solvated) + CH_3O^-(solvated); K = [CH_3OH_2^+][CH_3O^-]$ **18.151** (a) Lewis acid: $SnCl_4$; Lewis base: $(CH_3)_3N$ (b) 5d **18.152** pH = 5.00, 6.00, 6.79, 6.96, 7.00 **18.155** H_3PO_4 **18.156** (a) Higher. HCl dissociates into ions to a much greater extent than CH_3COOH. (b) About the same. At these extremely low acid concentrations, the concentration of ions due to the autoionization of water becomes significant and the total ion concentration in each solution is nearly equal. Also, the % dissociation of a weak electrolyte such as CH_3COOH increases with decreasing concentration. **18.159** 5.6×10^{-8} M **18.163** 10.43 **18.165** 2.41 **18.168** amylase, 2×10^{-7} M; pepsin, 1×10^{-2} M; trypsin, 3×10^{-10} M **18.172** (a) $Ca(CH_3CH_2COO)_2(s) + H_2O(l) \longrightarrow$
$$Ca^{2+}(aq) + 2CH_3CH_2COO^-(aq)$$
$CH_3CH_2COO^-(aq) + H_2O(l) \rightleftharpoons$
$$OH^-(aq) + CH_3CH_2COOH(aq)$$
$\therefore$ basic salt
(b) 9.04
18.174 The small radius of the Be^{2+} ion means its charge to radius ratio is much larger than that of the other group 2A(2) ions. This results in the hydrated beryllium ion's ability to transfer a proton to water and form an acidic solution. **18.176** 4.5×10^{-5} **18.177** (a) 10.04 (b) $[OH^-]$ from tertiary amine = 1.1×10^{-4} M; from aromatic ring N = 5.7×10^{-7} M (c) 4.59 (d) 5.13

Chapter 19

19.2 The weak acid in the system reacts with added base and the weak base in the system reacts with added acid. The acid and base need to be of comparable acid/base strength so that they don't neutralize one another. **19.4** When H_3O^+ is added to **any** system, the pH will drop. However, the change in pH will be minimized (and perhaps not measurable) with a buffer solution. **19.7** When the buffer-component ratio is 1:1, the capacity of the buffer for "absorbing" added base and acid are equal, and the buffer range will be symmetrical around the pK_a. As the ratio deviates more from this, the buffer range will be unsymmetrical (e.g., from $pK_a - 0.5$ to $pK_a + 1$). **19.9** (a) pH would increase; ratio would increase (b) pH would decrease; ratio would decrease (c) pH would increase, ratio would increase (d) pH would decrease; ratio would decrease **19.11** 7.7×10^{-6} M; 5.11 **19.13** 5.5×10^{-4} M; 3.26 **19.15** 3.80 **19.17** 9.92 **19.19** 9.55 **19.21** (a) K_{a2} (b) 10.44 **19.23** 1.7 **19.25** 0.17 **19.27** 3.36 **19.29** 8.79 **19.31** (a) 4.91 (b) 0.67 g **19.33** (a) $HCOOH/NaHCOO$ or $C_6H_5NH_2/C_6H_5NH_3Cl$ (b) NaH_2PO_3/Na_2HPO_3 or NaH_2AsO_4/Na_2HAsO_4 **19.35** (a) H_3AsO_4/NaH_2AsO_4 or H_3PO_4/NaH_2PO_4 (b) C_2H_5COOH/C_2H_5COONa or C_5H_5N/C_5H_5NHCl **19.38** 1.6 **19.40** To see a distinct color in a mixture of two, you need one color to be about 10 times the intensity of the other. For this to take place, the concentration ratio [HIn]/[In$^-$] needs to be greater than 10:1 or less than 1:10. This will occur when pH = pK_a − 1 or pH = pK_a + 1, respectively, giving a transition range of about two units. **19.42** The end point is where you stop titrating, i.e., when the indicator changes color. The equivalence point is when the stoichiometric ratio of reactants is reached. The end point may precede or follow the equivalence point, depending on the relative magnitudes of K_a for the acid being titrated and K_a for the indicator. **19.44** (a) initial pH: strong acid-strong base < weak acid-strong base < strong acid-weak base (b) equiv. pt. pH: strong acid-weak base < strong acid-strong base < weak acid-strong base. **19.46** In the exact center of the buffer region (i.e., where [HA] = [A$^-$]), the pH = the pK_a for the acid. **19.48** 7.3 − 9.3 **19.50** (a) bromthymol blue (b) thymol blue or phenolphthalein **19.52** (a) methyl red (b) bromthymol blue **19.54** (a) 1.00 (b) 1.48 (c) 2.99 (d) 4.0 (e) 7.00 (f) 10.0 (g) 11.96 **19.56** (a) 2.91 (b) 4.81 (c) 5.29 (d) 6.09 (e) 7.41 (f) 8.76 (g) 10.10 (h) 12.05 **19.58** (a) 59.0 mL; 8.54 (b) 45.2 mL; 4.52 and 90.4 mL; 9.69 **19.60** (a) 96.2 mL; 5.16 (b) 146 mL; 5.78 **19.63** Because F$^-$ is the anion (i.e., conjugate base) of a weak acid and Cl$^-$ is the anion of a strong acid. The equilibrium F$^-$(aq) + H$_2$O(l) $\rightleftharpoons$ HF(aq) + OH$^-$(aq) would be shifted by changing the pH (i.e., changing [H$_3$O$^+$] and [OH$^-$]), but the corresponding equilibrium is not set up for Cl$^-$. **19.65** The solid precipitates. **19.66** (a) Q_{sp} = [Ag$^+$]^2[CO$_3^{2-}$] (b) Q_{sp} = [Ba^{2+}][F$^-$]^2 (c) Q_{sp} = [Cu^{2+}][HS$^-$][OH$^-$] **19.68** (a) Q_{sp} = [Ca^{2+}][CrO$_4^{2-}$] (b) Q_{sp} = [Ag$^+$][CN$^-$] (c) Q_{sp} = [Ni^{2+}][HS$^-$][OH$^-$] **19.70** 1.3×10^{-4} **19.72** 2.7×10^{-11} **19.74** (a) 2.3×10^{-5} M (b) 4.2×10^{-9} M **19.76** (a) 1.7×10^{-3} M (b) 2.0×10^{-4} M **19.78** (a) Mg(OH)$_2$ (b) PbS (c) Ag$_2$SO$_4$ **19.80** (a) CaSO$_4$ (b) Mg$_3$(PO$_4$)$_2$ (c) PbSO$_4$ **19.82** (a) AgCl(s) $\rightleftharpoons$ Ag$^+$(aq) + Cl$^-$(aq); Cl$^-$ is the anion of a strong acid, so is nonbasic. No change in solubility with pH. (b) SrCO$_3$(s) $\rightleftharpoons$ Sr^{2+}(aq) + CO$_3^{2-}$(aq); CO$_3^{2-}$ is the anion of a weak acid, so the equilibria CO$_3^{2-}$(aq) + H$_2$O(l) $\rightleftharpoons$ HCO$_3^-$(aq) + OH$^-$(aq) and HCO$_3^-$(aq) + H$_2$O(l) $\rightleftharpoons$ H$_2$CO$_3$(aq) + OH$^-$(aq) would be set up. Since these involve OH$^-$, they would shift with changing pH. **19.84** (a) Fe(OH)$_2$(s) $\rightleftharpoons$ Fe^{2+}(aq) + 2OH$^-$(aq); changing pH (i.e., changing [OH$^-$]) would shift this equilibrium. (b) CuS(s) + H$_2$O(l) $\rightleftharpoons$ Cu^{2+}(aq) + HS$^-$(aq) + OH$^-$(aq); changing pH (i.e., changing [OH$^-$]) would shift this equilibrium. **19.86** Yes. **19.88** Yes. **19.93** This is most likely due to the formation of a complex ion by a reaction like Pb^{2+}(aq) + nOH$^-$(aq) $\rightleftharpoons$ Pb(OH)$_n$$^{(2-n)}$(aq). **19.94** Hg(H$_2$O)$_4^{2+}$(aq) + 4CN$^-$(aq) $\longrightarrow$ Hg(CN)$_4^{2-}$(aq) + 4H$_2$O(l) **19.96** Ag(H$_2$O)$_2^+$(aq) + 2S$_2$O$_3^{2-}$(aq) $\rightleftharpoons$ Ag(S$_2$O$_3$)$_2^{3-}$(aq) + 2H$_2$O(l) **19.98** 1×10^{-5} M **19.100** [Zn^{2+}] = 6.2×10^{-17} M, [Zn(CN)$_4^{2-}$] = 0.024 M; [CN$^-$] = 0.055 M **19.102** 9.4×10^{-5} M **19.104** (a) Fe(OH)$_3$ (b) Add enough NaOH to the solution to maintain the pH just below that which will precipitate Cd(OH)$_2$, then separate the precipitate [Fe(OH)$_3$] and solution (Cd^{2+}). (c) 2.1×10^{-7} M **19.106**

(a) 1) Add OH$^-$: NH$_4^+$ will give off NH$_3$, which can be detected with moist red litmus paper, while Ni^{2+} will give a pale green precipitate; or 2) add Na$_2$CO$_3$, Na$_3$PO$_4$, HS$^-$, etc: Ni^{2+} will precipitate, NH$_4^+$ will give no reaction. (b) Hot water will dissolve PbCl$_2$ but not AgCl. (c) NaOH will cause a red-brown precipitate with Fe^{3+}, but will form a white precipitate with Al^{3+} which will redissolve in excess OH$^-$. **19.108** (a) 1 (b) Assuming volumes are additive, mix 400 mL of 1.0 M HCOOH and 200 mL of 1.0 M NaOH, so that the HCOOH will be half-neutralized. (c) 0.33 M **19.110** 1.3×10^{-4} M **19.113** 7.38 **19.114** Fe^{3+} and Ag$^+$ **19.117** (a) 0.089 (b) 0.14 **19.122** pH < 6.60 **19.124** 8×10^{-5}

19.127 (a)

V (mL)	pH	$\dfrac{\Delta pH}{\Delta V}$	V$_{average}$ (mL)
0.00	1.00		
10.00	1.22	0.02	5.0000
20.00	1.48	0.03	15.0000
30.00	1.85	0.04	25.0000
35.00	2.18	0.07	32.5000
39.00	2.89	0.18	37.0000
39.50	3.20	0.62	39.2500
39.75	3.50	1.20	39.6250
39.90	3.90	2.67	39.8250
39.95	4.20	6.00	39.9250
39.99	4.90	17.50	39.9700
40.00	7.00	210.00	39.9950
40.01	9.10	210.00	40.0050
40.05	9.80	17.50	40.0300
40.10	10.10	6.00	40.0750
40.25	10.50	2.67	40.1750
40.50	10.79	1.16	40.3750
41.00	11.09	0.60	40.7500
45.00	11.76	0.17	43.0000
50.00	12.05	0.06	47.5000
60.00	12.30	0.03	55.0000
70.00	12.43	0.01	65.0000
80.00	12.52	0.01	75.0000

(b)

Maximum slope (equivalence point) is at V = 40.00 mL **19.131** 5.88×10^3 kg

19.132 $K_b = \dfrac{[BH^+][OH^-]}{[B]}$

$$-\log K_b = -\log [OH^-] - \log [BH^+]/[B]$$
$$pOH = pK_b + \log [BH^+]/[B]$$
or $\quad pOH = pK_b - \log [B]/[BH^+]$

19.136 H$_2$PO$_4^-$/HPO$_4^{2-}$ and H$_2$CO$_3$/HCO$_3^-$ [HPO$_4^{2-}$]/[H$_2$PO$_4^-$] = 6

19.138 3.5 − 4   **19.141** (a) 58.2 mL   (b) 7.84 mL   (c) 7.70   **19.143** 177 mL   **19.146** (a) 65 mol   (b) 6.28   (c) 4.0×10^3 g   **19.148** 5.68   **19.150** 2 µg Pb/100 mL

Chapter 20

20.2 A spontaneous process is capable of proceeding as written or described without need of an outside source of energy. Under a specific set of conditions, if a process is spontaneous in one direction, it is not spontaneous in the other. By changing the set of conditions a nonspontaneous process can be made spontaneous.   **20.5** The larger value for ΔS_{vap} results largely from the increased volume in which the molecules may be found. An increase in volume means an increase in randomness. Gases have **much** higher entropy than liquids or solids, due to the random motion of their molecules.   **20.6** $\Delta S_{surr} > 0$ for an exothermic reaction. $\Delta S_{surr} < 0$ for an endothermic reaction. Melting of ice cream at room temperature.   **20.8** (a), (b), and (c)   **20.10** (a) and (b)   **20.12** (a) > 0   (b) < 0   (c) < 0   **20.14** (a) > 0   (b) > 0   (c) > 0   **20.16** (a) < 0   (b) < 0   (c) > 0   **20.18** (a) > 0   (b) < 0   (c) > 0   **20.20** (a) > 0   (b) < 0   (c) > 0   **20.22** (a) Butane (g); 2-butene has restricted rotation about the double bond and would have less flexibility.   (b) Xe(g); greater mass   (c) $CH_4(g)$; S(gas) is greater than S(liq).   **20.24** (a) $C_2H_5OH(l)$; greater molecular complexity.   (b) $KClO_3(aq)$; S(aq) is greater than S(s).   (c) K(s); greater mass.   **20.26** (a) diamond < graphite < charcoal; entropy increases from the more ordered crystalline state to the amorphous state.   (b) ice < liquid water < water vapor; entropy increases as substance changes from a solid to a liquid to a gas.   (c) O atoms < O_2 < O_3; entropy increases with molecular complexity.   **20.28** (a) $ClO_4^-(aq) > ClO_3^-(aq) > ClO_2^-(aq)$; entropy decreases with lower molecular complexity.   (b) $NO_2(g) > NO(g) > N_2(g)$; entropy decreases with lower molecular complexity. (c) $Fe_3O_4(s) > Fe_2O_3(s) > Al_2O_3(s)$; entropy decreases with both lower mass and lower molecular complexity.   **20.31** For a process spontaneously moving to equilibrium: $\Delta S_{sys} + \Delta S_{surr} = \Delta S_{universe} > 0$. For a process at equilibrium: $\Delta S_{sys} + \Delta S_{surr} = \Delta S_{universe} = 0$. For any spontaneous process, the entropy of the universe increases.
20.32 $S^0_{Cl_2O(g)} = 2S^0_{HClO(g)} - S^0_{H_2O(g)} - \Delta S^0_{rxn}$
20.33 (a) < 0; $\Delta S^0 = -172.4$ J/K   (b) > 0; $\Delta S^0 = 141.6$ J/K (c) < 0; $\Delta S^0 = -837$ J/K   **20.35** $\Delta S^0 = 93.1$ J/K. Yes—an increase in the number of mol of gas should give $\Delta S > 0$. **20.37** $\Delta S^0 = -311$ J/K. Yes—a decrease in the number of mol of gas should give $\Delta S < 0$.   **20.39** −75.6 J/K   **20.41** −242 J/K   **20.44** −97.2 J/K   **20.46** For a spontaneous process, $\Delta S_{universe} > 0$. Since absolute temperature is always positive, it follows that $\Delta G_{sys} < 0$ for a spontaneous process.   **20.48** If $\Delta G^0 = \Delta H^0 - T\Delta S^0 < 0$ at high temperatures $\Delta H^0 > 0$ and $\Delta S^0 > 0$. This would be true for melting processes.   **20.49** Entropy values increase only gradually within a particular phase. Thus, as long as no phase changes occur, the value of ΔS^0 is relatively independent of temperature.   **20.50** (a) −1138 kJ   (b) −1379.4 kJ   (c) −224 kJ   **20.52** (a) $\Delta H^0 = -1202$ kJ; $\Delta S^0 = -216.6$ J/K; $G^0 = -1137$ kJ   (b) $\Delta H^0 = -1351.9$ kJ; $\Delta S^0 = 91$ J/K; $\Delta G^0 = -1379$ kJ   (c) $\Delta H^0 = -277$ kJ; $\Delta S^0 = -174$ J/K; $\Delta G^0 = -225$ kJ   **20.54** (a) A decrease in the number of

moles of gas should result in a negative ΔS^0 value. The combustion of CO(g) (a fuel) will result in a release of energy or a negative ΔH^0 value.   (b) $\Delta G^0 = -257.3$ kJ **20.56** (a) −409 J/K · mol   (b) −198 kJ/mol   **20.58** (a) $\Delta H^0 = 90.7$ kJ; $\Delta S^0 = 221$ J/K   (b) $\Delta G = 22.0$ kJ at 38°C, −0.1 kJ at 138°C, −22.2 kJ at 238°C.   (c) The reaction is unfavorable at 38°C, favorable at 238°C, and essentially at equilibrium at 138°C.   **20.60** $\Delta H^0 = 30.91$ kJ; $\Delta S^0 = 93.15$ J/K; $T_b = 331.8$ K   **20.62** (a) $\Delta H^0 = -241.826$ kJ, $\Delta S^0 = -44.4$ J/K, $\Delta G^0 = -228.6$ kJ   (b) Yes, it will become non-spontaneous at high temperatures.   (c) Below 5.45×10^3 K, the reaction becomes spontaneous.   **20.64** (a) ΔG^0 would be a relatively large positive value.   (b) K would have an extremely large value; the value of Q depends on the initial conditions.   **20.67** The standard free energy change, ΔG^0, occurs when all components of the system are in their standard states. Under standard state conditions, $\Delta G = \Delta G^0$.   **20.68** (a) 2×10^6 (b) 4.1×10^{-34} (c) 1.2×10^{48} **20.70** (a) 1.3×10^{174} (b) 5×10^{-15} (c) 2×10^4 **20.72** 5.3×10^{-51} **20.74** 3.3×10^5 **20.76** $\Delta G^0 = 27$ kJ/mol; no   **20.78** (a) 28.7 kJ/mol   (b) left   (c) $\Delta G = 7$ kJ/mol; left   **20.80** (a) no temperature   (b) 326 kJ   (c) 266 kJ   **20.83** (a) spontaneous   (b) +   (c) +   (d) −   (e) $\Delta S_{rxn} < 0$, not spontaneous   (f) −   **20.86** (a) 2.3×10^2 (b) Give the victim oxygen-enriched air to breathe.   **20.89** −371 kJ   **20.92** $\Delta H^0 = -137.14$ kJ, $\Delta S^0 = -120.3$ J/K, $\Delta G^0 = -101.3$ kJ **20.94** (a) $\Delta H^0 = 470.5$ kJ; $\Delta S^0 = 558.4$ J/K   (b) It will be spontaneous at higher temperature, where the $-T\Delta S$ term will be larger in magnitude than ΔH.   (c) No   (d) 842.6 K **20.99** $4Fe(s) + 3O_2(g) \longrightarrow 2Fe_2O_3(s)$
$\Delta G^0 = -1487$ kJ; spontaneous
$4Al(s) + 3O_2(g) \longrightarrow 2Al_2O_3(s)$
$\Delta G^0 = -3164$ kJ; spontaneous

Chapter 21

21.1 Oxidation is a loss of electron(s) and an increase in oxidation number. Reduction is a gain of electron(s) and a decrease in oxidation number.   **21.3** An electrochemical process involves an electron flow. At least one substance must lose electron(s) and one substance must gain electron(s) to produce the flow. This electron transfer is a redox process.   **21.6** Add an equal number of OH^- ions to both sides to neutralize H^+ ions and produce H_2O.   **21.8** A voltaic or galvanic cell has a $\Delta G_{sys} < 0$. An electrolytic cell has a $\Delta G_{sys} > 0$, meaning an increase in free energy. **21.10** $16H^+(aq) + 2MnO_4^-(aq) + 10Cl^-(aq) \longrightarrow$
$\qquad 2Mn^{2+}(aq) + 5Cl_2(g) + 8H_2O(l)$
(a) Cl^- (b) MnO_4^- (c) MnO_4^- (d) Cl^-
(e) From Cl^- to MnO_4^-
(f) $8H_2SO_4(aq) + 2KMnO_4(aq) + 10KCl(aq) \longrightarrow$
$\qquad 2MnSO_4(aq) + 6K_2SO_4(aq) + 5Cl_2(g) + 8H_2O(l)$
21.12 (a) $ClO_3^-(aq) + 6I^-(aq) + 6H^+(aq) \longrightarrow$
$\qquad Cl^-(aq) + 3I_2(s) + 3H_2O(l)$
oxidizing agent: ClO_3^-; reducing agent: I^-
(b) $2MnO_4^-(aq) + 3SO_3^{2-}(aq) + H_2O(l) \longrightarrow$
$\qquad 2MnO_2(s) + 3SO_4^{2-}(aq) + 2OH^-(aq)$
oxidizing agent: MnO_4^-; reducing agent: SO_3^{2-}
(c) $2MnO_4^-(aq) + 5H_2O_2(aq) + 6H^+(aq) \longrightarrow$
$\qquad 2Mn^{2+}(aq) + 5O_2(g) + 8H_2O(l)$
oxidizing agent: MnO_4^-; reducing agent: H_2O_2

21.14 (a) $Cr_2O_7{}^{2-}(aq) + 3Zn(s) + 14H^+(aq) \longrightarrow$
$\qquad\qquad 2Cr^{3+}(aq) + 3Zn^{2+}(aq) + 7H_2O(l)$
     oxidizing agent: $Cr_2O_7{}^{2-}$; reducing agent: Zn

(b) $3Fe(OH)_2(s) + MnO_4{}^-(aq) + 2H_2O(l) \longrightarrow$
$\qquad\qquad MnO_2(s) + 3Fe(OH)_3(s) + OH^-(aq)$
     oxidizing agent: $MnO_4{}^-$; reducing agent: $Fe(OH)_2$

(c) $5Zn(s) + 2NO_3{}^-(aq) + 12H^+(aq) \longrightarrow$
$\qquad\qquad 5Zn^{2+}(aq) + N_2(g) + 6H_2O(l)$
     oxidizing agent: $NO_3{}^-$; reducing agent: Zn

21.16 (a) $4Sb(s) + 4NO_3{}^-(aq) + 4H^+(aq) \longrightarrow$
$\qquad\qquad Sb_4O_6(s) + 4NO(g) + 2H_2O(l)$
     oxidizing agent: $NO_3{}^-$; reducing agent: Sb

(b) $2Mn^{2+}(aq) + 5BiO_3{}^-(aq) + 14H^+(aq) \longrightarrow$
$\qquad\qquad 2MnO_4{}^-(aq) + 5Bi^{3+}(aq) + 7H_2O(l)$
     oxidizing agent: $BiO_3{}^-$; reducing agent: Mn^{2+}

(c) $2Fe(OH)_2(s) + Pb(OH)_3{}^-(aq) \longrightarrow$
$\qquad\qquad 2Fe(OH)_3(s) + Pb(s) + OH^-(aq)$
     oxidizing agent: $Pb(OH)_3{}^-$
     reducing agent: $Fe(OH)_2$

21.18 (a) $5As_4O_6(s) + 8MnO_4{}^-(aq) + 18H_2O(l) \longrightarrow$
$\qquad\qquad 20AsO_4{}^{3-}(aq) + 8Mn^{2+}(aq) + 36H^+(aq)$
     oxidizing agent: $MnO_4{}^-$; reducing agent: As_4O_6

(b) $P_4(s) + 6H_2O(l) \longrightarrow$
$\qquad\qquad 2HPO_3{}^{2-}(aq) + 4H^+(aq) + 2PH_3(g)$
     oxidizing agent: P_4; reducing agent: P_4

(c) $2MnO_4{}^-(aq) + H_2O(l) + 3CN^-(aq) \longrightarrow$
$\qquad\qquad 2MnO_2(s) + 3CNO^-(aq) + 2OH^-(aq)$
     oxidizing agent: $MnO_4{}^-$; reducing agent: CN^-

21.21 (a) $Au(s) + 3NO_3{}^-(aq) + 6H^+(aq) + 4Cl^-(aq) \longrightarrow$
$\qquad\qquad AuCl_4{}^-(aq) + 3NO_2(g) + 3H_2O(l)$

(b) oxidizing agent: $NO_3{}^-$; reducing agent: Au

(c) The function of HCl is as a source of Cl^- to act as a complexing agent to form highly stable $AuCl_4{}^-$.

21.22 (a) A   (b) E   (c) C   (d) A   (e) E   (f) E   **21.25**
Active electrodes are components of the half-cell reactions. Inactive electrodes are used to conduct electrons but do **not** participate in the half-cell reactions. Two common inactive electrodes are graphite and platinum.   **21.26** (a) metal A (b) metal B   (c) metal A   (d) The formation of H_2 bubbles means that H^+ was reduced by metal B. Since metal A is a better reducing agent than metal B, H_2 bubbles would form when metal A is placed in acid.

21.27 (a) left to right   (b) left   (c) right   (d) Ni   (e) Fe
     (f) Fe   (g) 1 M $NiSO_4$ (h) K^+, $NO_3{}^-$ (i) neither
     (j) right to left
     (k) reduction: $Ni^{2+}(aq) + 2e^- \longrightarrow Ni(s)$
     oxidation: $Fe(s) \longrightarrow Fe^{2+}(aq) + 2e^-$
     overall: $Fe(s) + Ni^{2+}(aq) \longrightarrow Fe^{2+}(aq) + Ni(s)$

21.29 (a) (red half-rxn) $Sn^{2+}(aq) + 2e^- \longrightarrow Sn(s)$
     (ox half-rxn) $\underline{Zn(s) \longrightarrow Zn^{2+}(aq) + 2e^-}$
     (overall rxn) $Zn(s) + Sn^{2+}(aq) \longrightarrow Zn^{2+}(aq) +$
$\qquad\qquad\qquad\qquad\qquad\qquad\qquad\qquad\qquad Sn(s)$

(b)

21.31 (a) reduction: $Fe^{2+}(aq) + 2e^- \longrightarrow Fe(s)$
     oxidation: $Mn(s) \longrightarrow Mn^{2+}(aq) + 2e^-$
     overall: $Fe^{2+}(aq) + Mn(s) \longrightarrow Mn^{2+}(aq) + Fe(s)$

(b)

21.33 (a) $Al(s) \mid Al^{3+}(aq) \parallel Cr^{3+}(aq) \mid Cr(s)$
(b) $Pt \mid SO_2(g) \mid SO_4{}^{2-}(aq), H^+(aq) \parallel Cu^{2+}(aq) \mid Cu(s)$
     Note: graphite could be used in place of Pt.

21.36 A negative E^0_{cell} indicates that the reaction as written is nonspontaneous. The reverse reaction is actually spontaneous.   **21.37** Cell potentials (E^0), like other thermodynamic quantities, change sign when the reaction is reversed. Unlike other thermodynamic quantities, cell potentials are intensive properties. Thus, changing the stoichiometric coefficients of a half-cell reaction does **not** affect the value of the cell potential.

21.38 (a) (red half-rxn) $4e^- + 2SO_3{}^{2-}(aq) + 3H_2O(l) \longrightarrow$
$\qquad\qquad 6OH^-(aq) + S_2O_3{}^{2-}(aq)$
     (ox half-rxn) $Se^{2-}(aq) \longrightarrow Se(s) + 2e^-$

(b) $E^0_{cell} = E^0_{sulfite} - E^0_{selenide}$
$\quad E^0_{selenide} = E^0_{sulfite} - E^0_{cell}$
$\qquad\qquad\quad = -0.57\text{ V} - 0.35\text{ V}$
$\qquad\qquad\quad = -0.92\text{ V}$

21.40 (a) $Br_2 > Fe^{3+} > Cu^{2+}$ (b) $Ca^{2+} < Ag^+ < Cr_2O_7{}^{2-}$

21.42 (a) $Co(s) + 2H^+(aq) \longrightarrow Co^{2+}(aq) + H_2(g)$;
     0.28 V; spontaneous

(b) $2Mn^{2+}(aq) + 5Br_2(l) + 8H_2O(l) \longrightarrow$
$\qquad\qquad 2MnO_4{}^-(aq) + 10Br^-(aq) + 16H^+(aq)$;
     -0.44 V; nonspontaneous

(c) $Hg_2{}^{2+}(aq) \longrightarrow Hg^{2+}(aq) + Hg(l)$;
     -0.07 V; nonspontaneous

21.44 (a) $2Ag(s) + Cu^{2+}(aq) \longrightarrow 2Ag^+(aq) + Cu(s)$;
     -0.46 V; nonspontaneous

(b) $3Cd(s) + Cr_2O_7{}^{2-}(aq) + 14H^+(aq) \longrightarrow$
$\qquad\qquad 3Cd^{2+}(aq) + 2Cr^{3+}(aq) + 7H_2O(l)$;
     1.73 V; spontaneous

(c) $Ni^{2+}(aq) + Pb(s) \longrightarrow Ni(s) + Pb^{2+}(aq)$;
     -0.12 V; nonspontaneous

21.46 (I) $3SO_4^{2-}(aq) + 3H_2O(l) + 2Al(s) \longrightarrow$
$$3SO_3^{2-}(aq) + 6OH^-(aq) + 2Al^{3+}(aq)$$
$E_{cell}^0 = 0.93\ V - (-1.66\ V) = 2.59\ V$
oxidizing agents: $SO_4^{2-} > Al^{3+}$
reducing agents: $Al > SO_3^{2-}$
(II) $3N_2O_4(g) + 2Al(s) \longrightarrow 6NO_2^-(aq) + 2Al^{3+}(aq)$
$E_{cell}^0 = 0.867\ V - (-1.66\ V) = 2.53\ V$
oxidizing agents: $N_2O_4 > Al^{3+}$
reducing agents: $Al > NO_2^-$
(III) $SO_4^{2-}(aq) + H_2O(l) + 2NO_2^-(aq) \longrightarrow$
$$SO_3^{2-}(aq) + 2OH^-(aq) + N_2O_4(g)$$
$E_{cell}^0 = 0.93\ V - (0.867\ V) = 0.06\ V$
oxidizing agents: $SO_4^{2-} > N_2O_4$
reducing agents: $NO_2^- > SO_3^{2-}$
oxidizing agents: $SO_4^{2-} > N_2O_4 > Al^{3+}$
reducing agents: $Al > NO_2^- > SO_3^{2-}$

21.48 (I) $2HClO(aq) + 2H^+(aq) + Pb(s) + SO_4^{2-}(aq) \longrightarrow$
$$Cl_2(g) + 2H_2O(l) + PbSO_4(s)$$
$E_{cell}^0 = 1.94\ V$
oxidizing agents: $HClO > PbSO_4$
reducing agents: $Pb + SO_4^{2-} > Cl_2$
(II) $Pt^{2+}(aq) + Pb(s) + SO_4^{2-}(aq) \longrightarrow$
$$Pt(s) + PbSO_4(s)$$
$E_{cell}^0 = 1.51\ V$
oxidizing agents: $Pt^{2+} > PbSO_4$
reducing agents: $Pb + SO_4^{2-} > Pt$
(III) $2HClO(aq) + 2H^+(aq) + Pt(s) \longrightarrow$
$$Pt^{2+}(aq) + Cl_2(g) + 2H_2O(l)$$
$E_{cell}^0 = 0.43\ V$
oxidizing agents: $HClO > Pt^{2+}$
reducing agents: $Pt > Cl_2$
oxidizing agents: $HClO > Pt^{2+} > PbSO_4$
reducing agents: $Pb + SO_4^{2-} > Pt > Cl_2$

21.50 $C > A > B$; $C(s) + 2H^+(aq) \longrightarrow C^{c+}(aq) + H_2(g)$
(Metal C **would** cause formation of H_2 gas.)

21.53 $A(s) + B^+(aq) \longrightarrow A^+(aq) + B(s)$
(a) $[A^+]$ increases and $[B^+]$ decreases.
(b) E_{cell} decreases
(c) $E_{cell} = E_{cell}^0 - \dfrac{0.0592\ V}{n} \log \dfrac{[A^+]}{[B^+]}$

E_{cell} will equal E_{cell}^0 when $\log \dfrac{[A^+]}{[B^+]} = 0$, which
will occur when $\dfrac{[A^+]}{[B^+]} = 1$.

(d) Yes. E_{cell} will be less than E_{cell}^0 when $Q \left(= \dfrac{[A^+]}{[B^+]} \right.$
for this problem$\Big)$ is greater than 1.

21.55 In a concentration cell, the redox reaction proceeds
in the direction to achieve concentration equality in the
half-cells.
cathode rxn: $M^+(aq) + e^- \longrightarrow M(s)$
anode rxn: $M(s) \longrightarrow M^+(aq) + e^-$
The more concentrated electrolyte is in the cathode compartment.

21.56 (a) 3×10^{35} (b) 4×10^{-31} **21.58** (a) 1×10^{-67} (b)
6×10^9 **21.60** (a) -203 kJ (b) 1.7×10^2 kJ **21.62** (a) 382
kJ (b) -56 kJ **21.64** $E^0 = 0.22\ V$; $\Delta G = -21$ kJ **21.66**
$E^0 = 0.056\ V$; $\Delta G = -11$ kJ **21.68** 1×10^{-3} M **21.70** (a)
$0.05\ V$ (b) $0.03\ V$ (c) $0.40\ M$ (d) $[Ni^{2+}] = 0.09\ M$;

$[Co^{2+}] = 0.91\ M$ **21.72** Electrode A is the anode; $E_{cell}^0 = 0.085\ V$ **21.74** Electrons in a battery flow from the anode
to the cathode, since oxidation still takes place at the anode
and reduction still takes place at the cathode. **21.76** Since
cell potentials are intensive properties, the voltage depends
on the chemical reaction taking place, not on the size of the
battery. What *is* different is the total charge the battery can
produce, with the larger D-size battery producing more
charge.

21.78 If the copper plates touch the iron skeleton, the more
active iron would corrode very rapidly.
$Fe(s) + Cu^{2+}(aq) \rightleftharpoons Fe^{2+}(aq) + Cu(s) \qquad E_{cell}^0 = 0.78\ V$
In reality, the copper simply acts as a conductor for electrons and the oxidizing agent is not Cu^{2+} but more probably O_2 or oxides of N or S. In any case, the teflon spacers
are designed to keep the metals from touching, to prevent
the corrosion of the iron. **21.81** A more reactive metal
(that is, one which is preferentially oxidized) is used as the
sacrificial anode. Only (a), (b), (c), (f), and (g) are suitable
for iron (although Na wouldn't last very long!). **21.83** The
dry cell potential of 1.5V is greater than the voltaic cell
voltage of 0.34V. This is more than sufficient to reverse the
reaction so that Cd redissolves and Cr will plate out. **21.85**
The nitrate ion cannot be oxidized (so it can't react at the
anode) because it is already in its highest oxidation state.
21.87 (a) $Br_2(g)$ (b) $Na(l)$ **21.89** anode: $I_2(g)$; cathode:
$Mg(l)$ **21.91** anode: $Ca(l)$; cathode: $Br_2(g)$ **21.93** copper
and bromine **21.95** iodine, zinc, and silver **21.97** (a)
cathode: $H_2(g)$ and $OH^-(aq)$; anode: $O_2(g)$ and $H^+(aq)$ (b)
cathode: $Sn(s)$; anode: $O_2(g)$ and $H^+(aq)$ **21.99** (a) cathode: $NO(g)$; anode: $O_2(g)$ and $H^+(aq)$ (b) cathode: $H_2(g)$
and $OH^-(aq)$; anode: $Cl_2(g)$ **21.101** (a) 2.93 mol of e^-
(b) 2.83×10^5 C (c) 31.4 A **21.103** 0.252 g **21.105**
5.49×10^3 s **21.107** (a) Pure water has very few ions present to conduct the current needed for electrolysis. The
addition of the Na^+ and SO_4^{2-} ions increases the rate of
electrolysis. (b) The E_{red}^0 (H_2O) is more positive than the
E_{red}^0 (Na^+) and the E_{ox}^0 (H_2O) is more positive than the E_{ox}^0
(SO_4^{2-}). In other words, it is easier to reduce H_2O than
Na^+ and at the same time easier to oxidize H_2O than
SO_4^{2-}, which is essentially inert to oxidation. **21.109** 44.2
g **21.111** (a) 1.9×10^{11} C (b) 2.4×10^{11} J (c) 6.0×10^6 g
21.112 (a) $E_{cell} = (+0.0592\ V) \log [Ag^+]$ (b) $E_{cell} = (+0.0296\ V) \log [Cu^{2+}]$ (c) $E_{cell} = (0.0592\ V) \log [Cl^-]$
(d) All three of these equations conform to this general
form if you remember that the 0.0592 V in the logarithmic
term in the Nernst equation is equal to (2.303RT/F), that
$\ln(x) = 2.303 \log (x)$, and that E_{cell}^0 is zero in all three of
these cases since a concentration cell is assumed. If the
half-cell reactions at the cathode and anode are different,
then E_{cell}^0 would not be equal to zero. **21.116** (a) 26 days
(b) $\$1.5 \times 10^2$

21.119 anode (positive electrode): $2H_2O(l) \longrightarrow$
$$O_2(g) + 4H^+(aq) + 4e^-$$
cathode (negative electrode): $2H_2O(l) + 2e^- \longrightarrow$
$$H_2(g) + 2OH^-(aq)$$
At the negative lead, the filter paper will turn pink.
21.122 (a) $E_{cell}^0 = 0.13\ V$ for Pb (cell 1); $E_{cell}^0 = 0.34\ V$ for
Cu (cell 2) (b) In cell 1, the negative electrode is $Pb(s)$. In
cell 2, the negative electrode is the inert $Pt(s)$. (c) An

addition of S^{2-} lowers the Pb^{2+} concentration, which will result in an increase in cell voltage.   (d) -0.13 V

21.125 The electrode reaction of $M^+(aq)$ can be divided into three steps:

1. $M^+(aq) \longrightarrow M^+(g)$ $\Delta H = -\Delta H_{hydration}$
2. $M^+(g) + e^- \longrightarrow M(g)$ $\Delta H = -\Delta H_{ionization}$
3. $M(g) \longrightarrow M(s)$ $\Delta H = -\Delta H_{atomization}$

The second step of the electrode reaction is the same as the reversed ionization energy. The small Li^+ ion has the greatest (most negative) hydration energy of the Group 1A(1) elements; thus, step 1 above is much more unfavorable for Li^+ than for either Na^+ or K^+. The atomization energies (the negative of step 3) of the three metals are fairly similar. Overall, in the electrode reaction, the hydration energy is dominant in terms of ordering the three E^0 values.

21.127 The key factor is that the table deals with electrode potentials in aqueous solution. The very high and very low standard potentials involve extremely reactive substances, such as F_2 and Li. These substances react directly with water, rather than according to the desired half-cell reactions. Alternatively (but equivalently), any aqueous cell with a voltage greater than 1.23 volts has the ability to decompose water into H_2 and O_2. When two electrodes with 6 volts across them are placed in water, electrolysis of water will occur.

21.129 (a) 1.07×10^5 s   (b) 1.5×10^4 kW·h   (c) \$0.068/lb Al   **21.130** (a) from the Mg to the pipe   (b) 0.36 A

21.131 F < D < E; $E(s) + F^{f+}(aq) \longrightarrow F(s) + E^{e+}(aq)$

(If E metal were placed in a solution of an F salt, F metal is produced on the surface of E metal.)

21.134 (a) Cell I: 4 mol e^-; $\Delta G = -475$ kJ

Cell II: 2 mol e^-; $\Delta G = -394$ kJ

Cell III: 2 mol e^-; $\Delta G = -454$ kJ

(b) Cell I: -13.2 kJ/g

Cell II: -0.613 kJ/g

Cell III: -2.62 kJ/g

The fuel cell (I) gives the highest ratio and the lead-acid cell (II) gives the lowest. This is mostly because the fuel cell uses materials with small molar masses.

21.135 4.0 g Ag   **21.138** (a) 9.6 g Cu   (b) 0.38 M

21.140 $Sn^{2+}(aq) + 2e^- \rightleftharpoons Sn(s)$

$Cr^{3+}(aq) + 1e^- \rightleftharpoons Cr^{2+}(aq)$

$Fe^{2+}(aq) + 2e^- \rightleftharpoons Fe(s)$

$U^{4+}(aq) + 1e^- \rightleftharpoons U^{3+}(aq)$

21.141 (a) $Cu(s) \longrightarrow Cu^{2+}(aq) + 2e^-$

(b) $Cu^{2+}(aq) + 2e^- \longrightarrow Cu(s)$

(c) 2.9×10^2 kW·h

(d) Ag and Au; possibly Ni, Fe, Pd, and Pt

(e) Copper and the more active impurities (e.g., Ni, Fe) are oxidized to cations but due to differences (less positive E^0_{red}) in their standard electrode potentials, only the Cu^{2+} ions are reduced at the cathode. The less active metals (e.g., Au, Pd, Pt) remain unoxidized in the "anode mud."

21.144 (a) 3.6×10^{-9} M   (b) 1 M

21.146 (a) $E_{stand} = E^0_{cell} - 0.0592 \log [Ag^+]_{stand}$

$E_{waste} = E^0_{cell} - 0.0592 \log [Ag^+]_{waste}$

(b) antilog $\left(\dfrac{E_{stand} - E_{waste}}{0.0592} \right) [Ag^+]_{stand} = [Ag^+]_{waste}$

(c) antilog $\left(\dfrac{E_{stand} - E_{waste}}{0.0592} \right) C_{Ag\ stand} = C_{Ag\ waste}$

(where C = concentration in ng/L)

(d) 9×10^2 ng/L

(e) antilog $\left(\dfrac{\dfrac{nF}{2.303R} (E_{stand} - E_{waste}) + T_{stand} \log [Ag^+]_{stand}}{T_{waste}} \right)$

$= [Ag^+]_{waste}$

Chapter 22

22.2 Fe in Fe_2O_3 and Fe_3O_4; Ca in $CaCO_3$; Na in NaCl; Pb in PbS.   **22.3** (a) Differentiation is the separating of the materials of the earth into different regions (layers) based primarily on their densities.   (b) O, Si, Al, and Fe.   (c) O, Si, and all metals other than Fe and Ni.   **22.7** Plant life has produced O_2, which reacts with most metals. Plants need large amounts of K^+ for growth, so remove that ion from the crust.   **22.9** Fixation is the process of converting an element in a form not directly usable by animals or plants (usually in gaseous form) to a form which is usable (usually in condensed form). Nitrogen is fixed from atmospheric N_2 and carbon is fixed from atmospheric CO_2.   **22.12** Nitrogen is removed from the atmosphere by atmospheric fixation on land and water, by biological fixation on land, and by industrial fixation. The first involves reaction of N_2 and O_2 induced by lightning, the second involves nitrogen-fixing bacteria, and the third involves reaction of N_2 in chemical plants to produce NH_3 and related compounds. Human activity is a significant factor contributing about 17% of the nitrogen removed.   **22.14** (a) the atmosphere   (b) Plants absorb phosphate in the form of $H_2PO_4^-$. Animals eat the plants and excrete phosphates, and both animals and plants produce phosphates by decay after death.   **22.17** (a) 1.0×10^3 L   (b) 4.2×10^2 m^3 **22.18** (a) Because it removes some of the (desired) P and is of limited value.   (b) 8.8 tonne   **22.20** (a) Heating an ore in the presence of oxygen. (b) Heating an ore in the presence of a reducing agent.   (c) Stirring an ore with a detergent-oil mixture to separate the mineral from the gangue.   (d) Purifying a material after its initial formation.   **22.25** (a) This is a by-product of steelmaking containing the impurity SiO_2.   (b) This is impure iron containing 3-4% C plus other impurities.   (c) This is iron containing 1-1.5% C and small amounts of other materials.   (d) The process used to produce steel from pig iron.   **22.27** Fe and Ni are more easily oxidized and less easily reduced than Cu. In the electrorefining process, all three metals are oxidized at the anode, but only Cu is reduced at the cathode.   **22.30** Hess's law is used to analyze the thermodynamic feasibility of the various steps in a proposed scheme.

22.31 (a) $E^0_{red} = -3.05$ V, -2.93 V, and -2.71 V for Li^+, K^+, and Na^+, respectively. (Rb^+ and Cs^+ would be expected to be similar.) In all of these cases, it is energetically more favorable to reduce H_2O to H_2 than $M^+(aq)$ to M.

(b) $2RbX + Ca \longrightarrow CaX_2 + 2Rb$

$\Delta H = IE_1(Ca) + IE_2(Ca) - 2IE_1(Rb)$

$= +941$ kJ/mol

Since $\Delta H > 0$, the reaction should be unfavorable.

(c) Rb has a lower boiling point than Ca, so the Rb produced boils out of the reaction mixture, shifting the reaction to the right.

(d) $2CsX + Ca \longrightarrow CaX_2 + 2Cs$
$\Delta H = IE_1(Ca) + IE_2(Ca) - 2IE_1(Cs)$
$= +984$ kJ/mol

This reaction is more unfavorable than for Rb, but Cs has a lower boiling point, making the process a reasonable bet.

22.32 (a) 4.6×10^4 L   (b) 1.3×10^8 C   (c) 4.7×10^2 h

22.35 (a) Mg^{2+} is more difficult to reduce than H_2O, so H_2 would be produced (not Mg metal), as well as Cl_2.   (b) ΔH_f^0 for $MgCl_2$ is negative, so high temperature would favor its decomposition (i.e., the products).

22.37 (a) The SO_2 acts as a reducing agent, and is oxidized to the $+6$ state.

(b) HSO_4^- (aq)

(c) $H_2SeO_3(aq) + 2SO_2(g) + H_2O(l) \longrightarrow$
$Se(s) + 2HSO_4^-(aq) + 2H^+(aq)$

22.42 (a) Cu_2S and Cu_2O: ON $= +1$; Cu: ON $= 0$ (b) Oxidizing agent: Cu_2O; Reducing agent: Cu_2S **22.44** (a) 7.3×10^5 C   (b) 8.1×10^2 A   **22.47** ΔG^0 for $2ZnS + C \longrightarrow 2Zn + CS_2$ is $+463$ kJ; for $2ZnO + C \longrightarrow 2Zn + CO_2$ it is $+242.0$ kJ. The process for ZnO is less unfavorable.   **22.48** The reaction of SO_2 with O_2 to produce SO_3 is thermodynamically favorable, but very slow at ordinary temperatures. A catalyst is used to speed up the reaction.   **22.51** (a) H_2, Cl_2, and NaOH   (b) The product NaOH is of higher purity, but the Hg is an environmental pollutant.   **22.52** (a) $\Delta G^0 = -142$ kJ; spontaneous   (b) It is very slow at that temperature.   (c) $\Delta G_{500} = -53$ kJ; spontaneous   (d) $K_{25} = 7.8 \times 10^{24}$ atm^{-1} > $K_{500} = 3.8 \times 10^3$ atm^{-1} (e) 1.05×10^3 K   **22.53** 7×10^2 lb

22.55 (a) Parallel to the layers, since the electrons are delocalized and would be mobile in that direction.

(b) Down's cell: $2Cl^- \longrightarrow Cl_2 + 2e^-$
Hall-Heroult process: $2AlOF_3^{2-} + 6F^- + C \longrightarrow$
$2AlF_6^{3-} + CO_2 + 4e^-$

22.57 (a) $P_4O_{10}(s) + 6H_2O(l) \longrightarrow 4H_3PO_4(aq)$ (b) 1.55   **22.59** (a) 9.93×10^3 t   (b) 4.7×10^4 t from automobiles, so CO_2(autos) > CO_2(steelmaking)   **22.62** (a) $[OH^-]$ > 1.1×10^{-4} (i.e., pH > 10.04) will precipitate $Mg(OH)_2$.   (b) 99.998%

22.66 (a) $8H_2S(g) + 4O_2(g) \longrightarrow S_8(g) + 8H_2O(g)$

(b) $8H_2S(g) + 8Cl_2(g) \longrightarrow S_8(g) + 16HCl(g)$
$\Delta G^0 = -1212$ kJ, so the process is thermodynamically spontaneous.

(c) O_2 is considerably less expensive than Cl_2, and H_2O is a very benign by-product (although HCl could be sold profitably).

22.69 (a) $:C \equiv O:$ (b) C has F.C. $= -1$, so would be the more likely spot for e^- donation.

22.71 (a) cathode: $Na^+ + e^- \longrightarrow Na$
anode: $4OH^- \longrightarrow O_2 + 2H_2O + 4e^-$

(b) 0.5 mol Na/mol e^-

22.73 (a) $NO(g) + O_3(g) \rightleftharpoons NO_2(g) + O_2(g)$

(b) Rate$_f$ = k_f[NO][O_3]
Rate$_r$ = k_r[NO_2][O_2]

(c) $\Delta G_{280}^0 = -199$ kJ

(d) $k_f/k_r = 1.3 \times 10^{37}$

22.74 (a) $nCO_2(g) + nH_2O(l) \longrightarrow (CH_2O)_n(s) + nO_2(g)$

(b) 25 L   (c) 7.6×10^4 L

22.77 794 kg   **22.78** (a) 20.5 min   (b) 14 steps   **22.82** (a)

1.89 t   (b) 0.334 t   (c) 100%   (d) 73%   (e) 2.80×10^3 m^3

22.85 Acid rain increases the leaching of PO_4^{3-} into the ground water, due to the protonation of the PO_4^{3-} to form HPO_4^{2-} and $H_2PO_4^-$.   (a) 6.4×10^{-7} M   (b) 1.1×10^{-2} M

Chapter 23

23.2 (a) $1s^2 2s^2 2p^6 3s^2 3p^6 4s^2 3d^{10} 4p^6 5s^2 4d^x$

(b) $1s^2 2s^2 2p^6 3s^2 3p^6 4s^2 3d^{10} 4p^6 5s^2 4d^{10} 5p^6 6s^2 4f^{14} 5d^x$

23.4 Five; $Mn([Ar]4s^2 3d^5)$ and $Mn^{2+}([Ar]3d^5)$.   **23.6** (a) The lanthanide contraction is the "shrinkage" of atoms following the filling of the 4f subshell (i.e., the atoms are smaller than expected).   (b) The size increases from Period 4 to Period 5, but stays fairly constant (or increases only slightly) from Period 5 to Period 6.   (c) The smaller-than-expected sizes lead to very large densities.   **23.9** Paramagnetic materials are attracted into a magnetic field; diamagnetic ones are repelled. Frequently, paramagnetic materials are also colored.   (b) Most main-group element ions are isoelectronic with a noble gas, meaning that all their electrons are paired.   (c) Because main-group metal ions are diamagnetic, most have a filled outer shell (or at least the subshell) and too much energy would be required to promote an electron to the next higher subshell.   **23.10** (a) $[Ar] 4s^2 3d^3$ (b) $[Kr] 5s^2 4d^1$ (c) $[Xe] 6s^2 4f^{14} 5d^{10}$ **23.12** (a) $[Xe] 6s^2 4f^{14} 5d^6$ (b) $[Ar] 4s^2 3d^7$ (c) $[Kr] 5s^1 4d^{10}$ **23.14** (a) $[Ar]$; 0   (b) $[Ar] 3d^9$; 1   (c) $[Ar] 3d^5$; 5   (d) $[Kr] 4d^2$; 2   **23.16** (a) $+5$ (b) $+4$ (c) $+7$ **23.18** Cr, Mo, and W   **23.20** In CrF_2, since metallic behavior is greater in lower oxidation states.   **23.22** Atomic size decreases down a group, but the nuclear charge increases much more, so the ionization energy increases, making the heavier element (Mo) more difficult to oxidize.   **23.24** CrO_3, because higher oxidation states form more acidic oxides.   **23.28** (a) 7   (b) This corresponds to a half-filled f subshell.   **23.30** (a) $[Xe] 6s^2 5d^1$ (b) $[Xe] 4f^1$ (c) $[Rn] 7s^2 5f^{11}$ (d) $[Rn] 5f^2$

23.32 (a) Eu^{2+}: $[Xe] 4f^7$
Eu^{3+}: $[Xe] 4f^6$
Eu^{4+}: $[Xe] 4f^5$
The stability of the half-filled f subshell makes Eu^{2+} most stable. Too much energy is required to remove two more electrons and make Eu^{4+}.

(b) Tb^{2+}: $[Xe] 4f^9$
Tb^{3+}: $[Xe] 4f^8$
Tb^{4+}: $[Xe] 4f^7$
Tb would show a $+4$ oxidation state, since that has the stable half-filled f^7 configuration.

23.34 Gd has 8 unpaired electrons ($[Xe] 6s^2 5d^1 4f^7$) and Gd^{3+} has 7 unpaired electrons ($[Xe] 4f^7$).   **23.36** This is the effective electronegativity of the element in a given oxidation (or valence) state. As oxidation number increases, the atom becomes more electronegative, strengthening its M—O bonds and making the oxide more acidic. MnO is basic, Mn_2O_7 is acidic.   **23.40** It is the only metal which is a liquid at room temperature. Its "1+" ion is really Hg_2^{2+}.   **23.42** E^0 for $Cr(s) + 2Cr^{3+}(aq) \longrightarrow 3Cr^{2+}(aq)$ is $+0.50$ V, so the process is favorable.   **23.44** E^0 for $3Mn^{2+}(aq) + 2MnO_4^-(aq) + 2H_2O(l) \longrightarrow 5MnO_2(s) + 4H^+(aq)$ is

+0.45 V, so this process occurs to remove MnO_4^- and produce $MnO_2(s)$.   **23.47** The coordination number is the number of ligand donor atoms attached to the metal. It is unrelated to the oxidation number, which is determined by the number of electrons the metal has lost to form the ion. **23.49** 2: linear; 4: tetrahedral, square planar; 6: octahedral **23.52** The complex ion has a negative charge.   **23.55** (a) hexaaquanickel(II) chloride   (b) trisethylenediamine-chromium(III) perchlorate   (c) potassium hexacyanomanganate(II) **23.57** (a) +2, 6   (b) +3, 6   (c) +2, 6 **23.59** (a) potassium dicyanoargentate(I)   (b) sodium tetrachlorocadmate(II)   (c) tetraammineaquabromocobalt(III) bromide **23.61** (a) +1, 2   (b) +2, 4   (c) +3, 6 **23.63** (a) $[Zn(NH_3)_4]SO_4$ (b) $[Cr(NH_3)_5Cl]Cl_2$ (c) $Na_3[Ag(S_2O_3)_2]$ **23.65** (a) 4, 2   (b) 6, 3   (c) 2, 4   **23.67** (a) $[Cr(H_2O)_6]_2(SO_4)_3$ (b) $Ba[FeBr_4]_2$ (c) $[Pt(C_2H_8N_2)_2]CO_3$ **23.69** (a) 6, 5   (b) 4, 3   (c) 4, 2

23.71 (a) $[\ddot{\text{O}}=\ddot{\text{N}}-\ddot{\text{O}}: \longleftrightarrow :\ddot{\text{O}}-\ddot{\text{N}}=\ddot{\text{O}}:]^-$ can form linkage isomers, since two different atoms (O, N) have lone pairs.

(b) $\ddot{\text{O}}=\ddot{\text{S}}-\ddot{\text{O}}: \longleftrightarrow :\ddot{\text{O}}-\ddot{\text{S}}=\ddot{\text{O}}:$ can also form linkage isomers (S, O).

(c) cannot form linkage isomers since only the three identical O atoms have lone pairs.

23.73 (a) Geometric isomers

(b) Geometric isomers

(c) Geometric isomers

23.75 (a) Geometric isomers

(b) Linkage isomers

(c) Geometric isomers

23.77 $CrCl_3(NH_3)_4$, which is actually $[Cr(NH_3)_4Cl_2]Cl$. **23.79** (a) $K[Pd(NH_3)Cl_3]$ (b) $[Pd(NH_3)_2Cl_2]$ (c) $K_2[PdCl_6]$ (d) $[Pd(NH_3)_4Cl_2]Cl_2$ **23.81** (a) dsp^2 (b) sp^3 **23.84** yellow and/or orange **23.85** (a) The energy difference between the upper and lower energy levels after splitting by the crystal field.   (b) The energy of the d_{z^2} and $d_{x^2-y^2}$ orbitals is raised more than that of the d_{xy}, d_{xz} and d_{yz} orbitals.   (c) The splitting is reversed for a tetrahedral field—i.e., the d_{xy}, d_{xz}, and d_{yz} orbitals are higher in energy than the d_{z^2} and $d_{x^2-y^2}$. **23.88** If $\Delta > E_{pairing}$, the complex will be low-spin and will have a lower paramagnetism than if $\Delta < E_{pairing}$. **23.90** (a) 0   (b) 8   (c) 6 **23.92** (a) 5   (b) 10   (c) 7

23.94

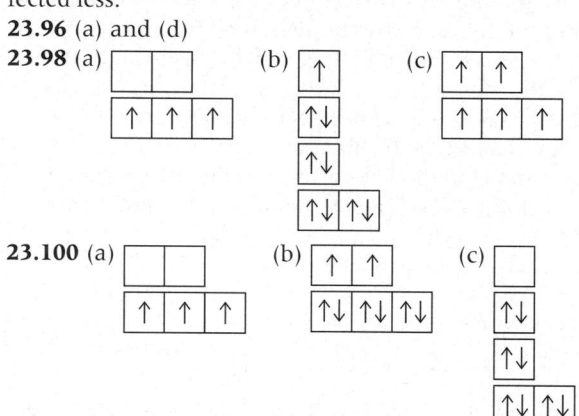

The ligands "point" directly at the electrons in the $d_{x^2-y^2}$ orbital, raising their energy. The ligands are further away from the electrons in the d_{xy} orbital, so their energy is affected less.

23.96 (a) and (d)

23.98 (a)   (b)   (c)

23.100 (a)   (b)   (c)

23.102 $[Cr(H_2O)_6]^{3+} < [Cr(NH_3)_6]^{3+} < [Cr(NO_2)_6]^{3-}$ **23.104** A violet complex will absorb yellow-green light. A complex of a weaker ligand will absorb lower-energy yellow, orange, or red light, making the observed color blue or green. **23.107** NH_3 is a stronger ligand than H_2O, so $[Ni(NH_3)_6]^{2+}$ will absorb higher-energy light than $[Ni(H_2O)_6]^{2+}$. Being green, $[Ni(H_2O)_6]^{2+}$ is probably absorbing primarily red light, while violet $[Ni(NH_3)_6]^{2+}$ is probably absorbing higher-energy yellow-green light. **23.110** Hg^+ is [Xe] $6s^14f^{14}5d^{10}$ but Cu^+ is [Ar] $3d^{10}$. The unpaired electron in Hg^+ would be likely to pair up, forming Hg_2^{2+}. The full subshell configuration of Cu^+ is stable. **23.112** (a) 6   (b) +3   (c) 2   (d) 1   **23.114** (a) no   (b) no (c) no   (d) no   (e) yes

23.116 $PtC_{12}H_{30}P_2Cl_2$ or $Pt[P(C_2H_5)_3]_2Cl_2$

The isomers are

cis-dichlorobis(triethylphosphine)platinum(II)

and

trans-dichlorobis(triethylphosphine)platinum(II)

23.120 (a) The first reaction would have $\Delta S \approx 0$; the second, $\Delta S < 0$. Thus, the first is more favorable (or less unfavorable). (b) The second $(Cu(en)_2^{2+})$ would be more stable because of the unfavorable entropy change.

23.122 Geometric (cis-trans) and linkage isomerism.

cis-diamminebis(thiocyanato)platinum(II)

cis-diamminethiocyanatoisothiocyanatoplatinum(II)

cis-diamminebis(isothiocyanato)platinum(II)

trans-diamminebis(thiocyanato)platinum(II)

trans-diamminethiocyanatoisothiocyanatoplatinum(II)

trans-diamminebis(isothiocyanato)platinum(II)

23.123 (a) MnO_4^{2-}: +6; MnO_4^-: +7; MnO_2: +4

(b) $3MnO_4^{2-}(aq) + 4H^+(aq) \longrightarrow$
$$MnO_2(s) + 2MnO_4^-(aq) + 2H_2O(l)$$

23.125 (a) +6; +7 (b) +3

Chapter 24

24.1 (a) Chemical reactions are accompanied by relatively small changes in energy while nuclear reactions are accompanied by relatively large changes in energy. (b) Rates of chemical reactions are increased by increasing temperature while nuclear reactions are not affected by temperature. (c) Both are increased by higher reactant concentrations. (d) Higher reaction concentrations would increase the yield of the nuclear reactions but would produce no change in the yield for chemical reactions. **24.2** (a) 95.02% (b) Larger than this, since ^{32}S is the lightest isotope.

24.4 (a) Z down by 2, N down by 2

(b) Z up by 1, N down by 1

(c) Z and N unchanged

(d) and (e) Z down by 1, N up by 1

A different element is produced in all cases except (c).

24.6 Neutron-rich nuclides, with a high N/Z, undergo β decay. Proton-rich nuclides, with a low N/Z, undergo positron decay or electron capture.

24.8 (a) $^{234}_{92}U \longrightarrow ^4_2He + ^{230}_{90}Th$

(b) $^{232}_{93}Np + ^0_{-1}e \longrightarrow ^{232}_{92}U$

(c) $^{12}_7N \longrightarrow ^0_1\beta + ^{12}_6C$

24.10 (a) $^{27}_{12}Mg \longrightarrow ^0_{-1}\beta + ^{27}_{13}Al$

(b) $^9_3Li \longrightarrow ^1_0n + ^8_3Li$

(c) $^{103}_{46}Pd + ^0_{-1}e \longrightarrow ^{103}_{45}Rh$

24.12 (a) $^{48}_{23}V \longrightarrow ^{48}_{22}Ti + ^0_1\beta$

(b) $^{107}_{48}Cd + ^0_{-1}e \longrightarrow ^{107}_{47}Ag$

(c) $^{210}_{86}Rn \longrightarrow ^{206}_{84}Po + ^4_2He$

24.14 (a) $^{186}_{78}Pt + ^0_{-1}e \longrightarrow ^{186}_{77}Ir$

(b) $^{225}_{89}Ac \longrightarrow ^{221}_{87}Fr + ^4_2He$

(c) $^{129}_{52}Te \longrightarrow ^{129}_{53}I + ^0_{-1}\beta$

24.16 (a) $^{20}_8O$ N/Z = 12/8 = 1.5; unstable, too high for this region of the band

(b) $^{59}_{27}Co$ N/Z = 32/27 = 1.2; stable, N/Z ok

(c) ^9_3Li N/Z = 6/3 = 2; unstable, too high N/Z

24.18 (a) $^{127}_{53}I$ N/Z = 74/53 = 1.40; stable, N/Z ok

(b) $^{106}_{50}Sn$ N/Z = 56/50 = 1.12; unstable, N/Z too small for this region of the band.

(c) $^{68}_{33}As$ N/Z = 35/33 = 1.06; unstable, odd N and Z

24.20 (a) α emission (b) β^+ emission or e^- capture (c) β^+ emission or e^- capture **24.22** (a) β emission (b) β^+ emission or e^- capture (c) α emission **24.24** It lies in the band of stability, with N and Z both even. **24.28** 7α, 4β **24.31** No. A decay rate is an average rate and is meaningful only when we consider a large number of nuclei in a macroscopic sample. The conclusion would be valid if the original sample were large. **24.33** 2.89×10^{-2} Ci/g **24.35** 1.4×10^8 Bq/g **24.37** 1×10^{-12} h^{-1} **24.39** 2.31×10^{-7} yr^{-1} **24.41** 1.49 mg **24.43** 2.2×10^9 yr **24.45** 126 disintegrations **24.47** 1.6×10^6 yr **24.50** Both gamma radiation and neutrons have no charge but the neutron has mass approximately equal to that of a proton. **24.52** Protons experience repulsion from the target nuclei due to their positive charge.

24.53 (a) $^{10}_5B + ^4_2He \longrightarrow ^1_0n + ^{13}_7N$

(b) $^{28}_{14}Si + ^2_1H \longrightarrow ^1_0n + ^{29}_{15}P$

(c) $^{242}_{96}Cm + ^4_2He \longrightarrow 2^1_0n + ^{244}_{98}Cf$

24.58 Ionizing radiation is more dangerous to children because of their growing, developing body parts and function. **24.60** (a) 5.4×10^{-7} rad (b) 5.4×10^{-9} Gy **24.62** (a) 7.5×10^{-10} Gy (b) 7.5×10^{-5} mrem (c) 7.5×10^{-10} Sv **24.65** 2.45×10^{-3} rad **24.67** In neutron activation analysis (NAA), neutrons bombard a non-radioactive sample, converting a small fraction of its atoms to radioisotopes, which exhibit characteristic decay patterns, such as γ-ray spectra, that reveal the elements present. Unlike chemical analysis, NAA analysis leaves the sample virtually intact. **24.70** The methanol supplies the oxygen to the aldehyde. The oxidation involves the loss of hydrogen atoms from the methanol to form the formaldehyde. The H_2CrO_4 supplies the oxygen to the water. **24.73** Energy is released when nuclides form from their nucleons. The nuclear binding energy is the amount of energy holding the nucleus

together.   **24.75** (a) 1.861×10^4 eV   (b) 2.981×10^{-15} J
24.77 5.1×10^{11} J   **24.79** (a) -7.976 MeV/nucleon
(b) -127.6 MeV/atom   (c) 1.2313×10^{10} kJ/mol   **24.81**
(a) 8.768 MeV/nucleon   (b) 517.3 MeV/atom   (c)
4.9912×10^{10} kJ/mol   **24.85** Radioactive decay is a spontaneous process in which nuclides emit small particles and
energy. In fission, larger atomic nuclides are bombarded
and break into small nuclides in addition to small particle(s)
and energy emission.   **24.88** Light-water reactors simply
use H_2O as the moderator; in heavy-water reactors, D_2O is
used. The advantage of D_2O is that it absorbs fewer neutrons, leaving more available for fission, and thus the ^{235}U
fuel does not need to be enriched. The disadvantage is in
the initial additional cost of D_2O.   **24.91** After the initial

hydrogen burning process, the star's energy source changes
to helium burning where continual heavier nuclei are
formed by the fusion of helium nuclei which have a mass
of 4 amu.   **24.96** (a) 1.29×10^{-4} rad   (b) 1.29×10^{-6} Gy
24.98 5.06×10^{10} s   **24.101** 1.35×10^{-5} M   **24.103**
6.3×10^{-2} **24.106** (a) 5.97 h   (b) 20.7%
24.111 (a) $^{52}_{24}Cr$; $^{51}_{23}V(n, \beta)^{52}_{24}Cr$
(b) $^{64}_{28}Ni$; $^{63}_{29}Cu(n, \beta^+)^{64}_{28}Ni$
(c) $^{28}_{14}Si$; $^{27}_{13}Al(n, \beta)^{28}_{14}Si$
24.114 4.9×10^{-6} mL/h   **24.117** 87 yr   **24.119** (a)
9.0×10^{-9} Bq/L   (b) 0.344 Bq/L   (c) 4.7 days more; 13.2
days total   **24.122** 6.6 s   **24.125** 1926   **24.128** (a)
1.80×10^{14} kJ   (b) 6.15×10^{16} kJ   (c) procedure (b)
24.131 9.319×10^2 MeV/amu

Glossary

Numbers in parentheses refer to the page(s) on which a term is introduced and/or discussed.

A

absolute scale (also *Kelvin scale*)   The preferred temperature scale in scientific work, the absolute scale takes absolute zero (0 K, or $-273.15°C$) as the lowest temperature. (24) [See also *kelvin, (K)*.]

absorption spectrum   The spectrum produced when atoms absorb specific wavelengths of incoming light as they become excited from lower to higher energy levels. (271)

abundance   The amount of an element in a particular region of the universe. (953)

accuracy   The closeness of a measurement to the true value. (30)

acid   In common laboratory terms, any species that produces H^+ ions when dissolved in water. (142) [See also *classical (Arrhenius), Brønsted-Lowry,* and *Lewis acid-base definitions*.]

acid anhydride   A compound, sometimes formed by a dehydration-condensation reaction of an oxoacid, that yields two molecules of the acid when it reacts with water. (636)

acid-base buffer   (See *buffer*.)

acid-base indicator   A species whose color is different in acid and in base, which is used to monitor the pH of a solution. (144, 768, 815)

acid-base reaction   Any reaction between an acid and a base. (See also *neutralization*.)

acid-base titration curve   A plot of the pH of a solution of acid (or base) versus the volume of base (or acid) added to the solution. (814)

acid-dissociation constant (K_a)   An equilibrium constant for the dissociation of an acid (HA) in H_2O to yield the conjugate base (A^-) and H_3O^+:

$$K_a = \frac{[H_3O^+][A^-]}{[HA]} \quad (761)$$

acid-ionization constant   (See *acid-dissociation constant*.)

actinides (also *actinoids*)   The Period 7 elements that form the second inner transition series ($5f$ block), including thorium (Th; $Z = 90$) through lawrencium (Lr; $Z = 103$). (306, 1009)

activated complex (also *transition state*)   An unstable species formed in an effective collision of reactants that exists momentarily when the system is highest in energy and that can either form products or re-form reactants. (689)

activation energy (E_a)   The minimum energy with which molecules must collide to react. (685)

active site   The region of an enzyme formed by specific amino acid side chains at which catalysis occurs. (702)

activity ($\mathscr{A}$) (also *decay rate*)   The change in number of nuclei ($\mathscr{N}$) of a radioactive sample divided by the change in time (t). (1053)

activity series of the metals   A listing of metals arranged in order of decreasing strength of the metal as a reducing agent in aqueous reactions. (162)

actual yield   The amount of product actually obtained in a chemical reaction. (114)

addition polymer (also *chain-reaction polymer*)   A polymer formed when monomers (usually containing $C=C$) combine through an addition reaction. (641)

addition reaction   A type of organic reaction in which the atoms of a multiple bond become bonded to more atoms. (624)

adduct   The product of a Lewis acid-base reaction characterized by the formation of a new covalent bond. (791)

adenosine triphosphate (ATP)   A high-energy molecule that serves most commonly as a store and source of energy in organisms. (881)

alchemy   An occult study of nature that flourished for 1500 years in northern Africa and Europe and resulted in the development of several key laboratory methods. (8)

alcohol   An organic compound ending *-ol*) that contains a

$$-\overset{|}{\underset{|}{C}}-\ddot{O}-H$$

functional group. (628)

aldehyde   An organic compound (ending *-al*) that contains the carbonyl functional group ($C=\ddot{O}$) in which the carbonyl C is also bonded to H. (632)

alkane   A hydrocarbon that contains only single bonds (general formula C_nH_{2n+2}). (611)

alkene   A hydrocarbon that contains at least one $C=C$ bond (general formula C_nH_{2n}). (616)

alkyl group   A saturated hydrocarbon chain with one bond available. (623)

alkyl halide   (See *haloalkane*.)

alkyne   A hydrocarbon that contains at least one $C≡C$ bond (general formula C_nH_{2n-2}). (619)

allotrope   One of two or more crystalline or molecular forms of an element. In general, one allotrope is more stable than another at a particular pressure and temperature. (561)

alloy   A mixture with metallic properties that consists of solid phases of the pure elements, a solid/solid solution, or distinct intermediate phases. (353, 488, 969)

alpha (α) decay   A radioactive process in which an α particle is emitted from a nucleus. (1046)

alpha particle (α or ^4_2He)   A positively charged particle, identical to a helium nucleus, that is one of the common types of radioactive emissions. (1045)

amide   An organic compound that contains the

$$\overset{:O:}{\underset{}{-\overset{||}{C}-\overset{}{N}-}}$$

functional group. (634)

amine   An organic compound (general formula R—N̈—) derived structurally by replacing one or more H atoms of ammonia with alkyl groups; a weak organic base. (629, 780)

amino acid   An organic compound [general formula $H_2N—CH(R)—COOH$] with at least one carboxyl and one amine group on the same molecule; the monomer unit of a protein. (645)

amorphous solid   A solid that occurs in different shapes because it lacks a well-defined crystal structure. (448)

ampere (A)   The SI unit of electric current; 1 ampere of current results when 1 coulomb flows through a conductor in 1 second. (937)

amphoteric   The ability of a species to act as an acid or a base. (317)

amplitude   The height of the crest (or depth of the trough) of a wave; related to the intensity of the energy. (260)

angular-momentum quantum number (*l*) (also *orbital-shape quantum number*)   An integer from 0 to $n-1$ that is related to the shape of an atomic orbital. (279)

anion   A negatively charged ion. (62)

anode   The electrode at which oxidation occurs in an electrochemical cell. Electrons are given up by the reducing agent and leave the cell at the anode. (900)

antibonding MO   A molecular orbital formed when wave functions are subtracted from each other, which decreases electron density between the nuclei and leaves a node. Electrons occupying such an orbital destabilize the molecule. (407)

apatite   A compound of general formula $Ca_5(PO_4)_3X$, where X is generally F, Cl, or OH. (962)

aqueous solution   A solution in which water is the solvent. (76)

aromatic hydrocarbon   A compound of C and H with one or more rings of C atoms (often drawn with alternating C—C and C=C bonds), in which there is extensive delocalization of π electrons. (620)

Arrhenius acid-base definition   [See *classical (Arrhenius) acid-base definition*.]

Arrhenius equation   An equation that expresses the exponential relationship between temperature and the rate constant: $k = Ae^{-E_a/RT}$. (685)

atmosphere   The mixture of gases that extends from a planet's surface and eventually merges with outer space; the gaseous portion of the Earth's crust. (207, 955) (For unit, see *standard atmosphere*.)

atom   The smallest particle of an element that retains the chemical nature of the element. A neutral, spherical entity composed of a positively charged central nucleus surrounded by one or more negatively charged electrons. (47)

atomic mass (also *atomic weight*)   The average of the masses of the naturally occurring isotopes of an element weighted according to their abundances. (55)

atomic mass unit (amu) (also *dalton, D*)   A mass exactly equal to $\frac{1}{12}$ the mass of a carbon-12 atom. (55)

atomic number (*Z*)   The unique number of protons in the nucleus of each atom of an element (equal to the number of electrons in the neutral atom). An integer that expresses the positive charge of a nucleus in multiples of the electronic charge. (54)

atomic orbital (also *wave function*)   A mathematical expression that describes the wave motion of the electron in the region of the nucleus. The term is used qualitatively to mean the region of space in which there is a high probability of finding the electron. (277)

atomic size   A term referring to the atomic radius, one-half the distance between nuclei of identical bonded elements. (531) (See also *covalent radius* and *metallic radius*.)

atomic solid   A solid consisting of individual atoms held together by dispersion forces; the frozen noble gases are the only examples. (454)

atomic symbol (also *element symbol*)   A one-, two-, or three-letter abbreviation for the English, Latin, or Greek name of an element. (54)

aufbau principle (also *building-up principle*)   The conceptual basis of a process of building up atoms by adding one proton at a time to the nucleus and one electron around it to obtain the ground-state electron configurations of the elements. (298)

autoionization (also *self-ionization*)   A reaction in which two molecules of a substance react to give ions. The most important example is for water:

$$2H_2O(l) \rightleftharpoons H_3O^+(aq) + OH^-(aq) \qquad (764)$$

average rate   The change in concentration of reactants (or products) divided by a finite time period. (670)

Avogadro's law   The gas law stating that, at fixed temperature and pressure, equal volumes of any ideal gas contain equal numbers of particles and, therefore, the volume of a gas is directly proportional to its amount (mol): $V \propto n$. (186)

Avogadro's number   A number (6.022×10^{23} to four significant figures) equal to the number of atoms in exactly 12 g of carbon-12; the number of atoms, molecules, or formula units in one mole of an element or compound. (89)

axial group   An atom (or group) that lies above or below the trigonal plane of a trigonal bipyramidal molecule, or a similar structural feature in a molecule. (378)

B

background radiation   Natural ionizing radiation, the most important form of which is cosmic radiation. (1062)

balancing coefficient (also *stoichiometric coefficient*)   A numerical multiplier of all the atoms in the formula immediately following it in a chemical equation. (104)

band of stability   The narrow band of stable nuclides that appears on a plot of number of neutrons versus number of protons for all nuclides. (1048)

band theory   An extension of molecular orbital (MO) theory that explains many properties of metals, in particular the differences in electrical conductivity of conductors, semiconductors, and insulators. (458)

barometer   A device used to measure atmospheric pressure. Most commonly, a tube open at one end, which is filled with mercury and inverted into a dish of mercury. (179)

base   In common laboratory terms, any species that produces OH^- ions when dissolved in water. (142) [See *classical (Arrhenius), Brønsted-Lowry,* and *Lewis acid-base definitions*.]

base dissociation constant (K_b)   An equilibrium constant for the reaction of a base (B) with H_2O to yield the conjugate acid (BH^+) and OH^-:

$$K_b = \frac{[BH^+][OH^-]}{[B]} \qquad (779)$$

base pair Two complementary bases of mononucleotides that are H bonded to each other; guanine (G) always pairs with cytosine (C), and adenine (A) always pairs with thymine (T) (or uracil, U). (651)

base unit (also *fundamental unit*) A unit that defines the standard for one of the seven physical quantities in the International System of Units (SI). (17)

basic-oxygen process The method used to convert pig iron to steel in which O_2 is blown over and through molten iron to oxidize impurities and decrease the content of carbon. (974)

battery A self-contained group of voltaic cells arranged in series. (923)

becquerel (Bq) The SI unit of radioactivity; 1 Bq = 1 d/s (disintegration per second). (1053)

bent (V shaped) A molecular shape that arises when a central atom is bonded to two other atoms and has one or two lone pairs; occurs as the AX_2E shape class in the trigonal planar arrangement and as AX_2E_2 shape class in the tetrahedral arrangement. (376)

beta (β) decay A radioactive process in which a β particle is emitted from a nucleus. (1046)

beta particle (β or $_{-1}^{0}β$) A negatively charged particle identified as a fast moving electron that is one of the common types of radioactive emissions. (1045)

bimolecular reaction An elementary reaction involving two reactant species. (693)

binary covalent compound A compound that consists of atoms of two elements in which bonding occurs primarily through electron sharing. (72)

binary ionic compound A compound that consists of the oppositely charged ions of two elements. (62)

biomass conversion The process of applying chemical and biological methods to convert plant and/or animal matter into fuels. (247)

biosphere The totality of organisms and the regions of the Earth that support them. (955)

blast furnace A tower-shaped furnace made of brick material in which intense heat and blasts of air are used to convert iron ore and coke to iron metal and carbon dioxide. (973)

body-centered cubic unit cell A unit cell in which a particle lies at each corner and in the center of a cube. (448)

boiling point (bp or T_b) The temperature at which the vapor pressure of a gas equals the external (atmospheric) pressure. (430)

boiling point elevation The increase in the boiling point of a solvent caused by the presence of dissolved solute. (504)

bond angle The angle formed by the nuclei of two surrounding atoms with the nucleus of the central atom at the vertex. (374)

bond energy (BE) (also *bond strength*) The enthalpy change accompanying the breakage of a given bond in a mole of gaseous molecules. (342, 533)

bond length The distance between the nuclei of two bonded atoms. (342, 533)

bond order The number of electron pairs shared by two bonded atoms. (341, 533)

bonding MO A molecular orbital formed when wave functions are added to each other, which increases electron density between the nuclei. Electrons occupying such an orbital stabilize the molecule. (407)

bonding pair (also *shared pair*) An electron pair shared by two nuclei; the mutual attraction between the nuclei and the electron pair forms a covalent bond. (341)

Born-Haber cycle A series of steps and their enthalpy changes from elements to ionic compound devised to calculate the lattice energy. (335)

Boyle's law The gas law stating that, at constant temperature and amount of gas, the volume of a gas is inversely proportional to the applied (external) pressure: $V \propto 1/P$. (184)

bridge bond (also *three-center, two-electron bond*) A covalent bond in which three atoms are held together by two electrons. (560)

Brønsted-Lowry acid-base definition A model of acid-base behavior based on proton transfer in which an acid and a base are defined, respectively, as species that donate and accept a proton. (768)

buffer A solution that resists changes in pH when a small amount of either strong acid or strong base is added. (806)

buffer capacity A measure of the ability of a buffer to resist a change in pH that is related to the concentrations and relative proportions of buffer components. (811)

buffer range The pH range over which a buffer acts effectively. (812)

C

calibration The process of correcting for the accuracy of a measuring device by comparing it to a known standard. (31)

calorie (cal) A unit of energy defined as exactly 4.184 joules; originally defined as the heat needed to raise the temperature of 1 g of water 1°C (from 14.5°C to 15.5°C). (228)

calorimeter A device used to measure the heat released or absorbed by a physical or chemical process taking place within it. (237)

capillarity (or *capillary action*) A property that results in a liquid rising through a narrow space. (441)

carbon steel The steel produced by the basic-oxygen process that contains about 1% to 1.5% C and other impurities and is alloyed with metals that prevent corrosion and increase strength. (974)

carbonyl group The C=O grouping of atoms. (632)

carboxylic acid An organic compound (ending *-oic acid*)

that contains the $-\overset{\overset{\displaystyle :O:}{\|}}{C}-\ddot{O}H$ group. (634)

catalyst A substance that increases the rate of a reaction without being used up in the process. (697)

cathode The electrode at which reduction occurs in an electrochemical cell. Electrons enter the cell and are acquired by the oxidizing agent at the cathode. (900)

cathode ray The ray of light emitted by the cathode (negative electrode) in a gas discharge tube; travels in straight lines, unless deflected by magnetic or electric fields. (50)

cation A positively charged ion. (62)

cell potential (E_{cell}) (also *electromotive force*, or *emf; cell voltage*) The potential difference between the electrodes of an electrochemical cell when no current flows. (906)

Celsius scale (formerly *centigrade scale*)   A temperature scale in which the freezing and boiling points of water are defined as 0°C and 100°C, respectively. (24)

ceramic   A nonmetallic material that is hardened by heating to high temperatures and, in most cases, consists of silicate microcrystals suspended in a glassy cementing medium. (466)

chain reaction   In nuclear fission, a self-sustaining process in which neutrons released by splitting of one nucleus cause other nuclei to split, which releases more neutrons, and so on. (1072)

change in enthalpy (ΔH)   The change in internal energy plus the product of the constant pressure and the change in volume: $\Delta H = \Delta E + P\Delta V$; the heat lost or gained at constant pressure: $\Delta H = q_P$. (231)

charge density   The ratio of the charge of an ion to its volume. (490)

Charles's law   The gas law stating that at constant pressure and amount of gas, the volume of a gas is directly proportional to its absolute temperature: $V \propto T$. (185)

chelate   A complex in which the metal ion is bonded to a polydentate ligand. (1018)

chemical bond   The force that holds two atoms together in a molecule (or formula unit). (62)

chemical change (also *chemical reaction*)   A change in which a substance is converted into a substance with different composition and properties. (3)

chemical equation   A statement in chemical formulas that expresses the identities and quantities of the substances involved in a chemical or physical change. (103)

chemical formula   A notation of atomic symbols and numerical subscripts that shows the type and number of each atom in a molecule or formula unit of a substance. (65)

chemical kinetics   The study of the rates and mechanisms of reactions. (665)

chemical property   A characteristic of a substance that appears as it interacts with, or transforms into, other substances. (3)

chemical reaction   (See *chemical change.*)

chemistry   The scientific study of matter and the changes it undergoes. (3)

chiral   Referring to a molecule that is not superimposable on its mirror image; an optically active molecule. In organic compounds, a chiral molecule typically contains a C atom bonded to four different groups. (615)

chlor-alkali process   An industrial method that electrolyzes concentrated aqueous NaCl and produces Cl_2, H_2, and NaOH. (992)

chromatography   A separation technique in which a mixture is dissolved in a fluid (gas or liquid), and the components are separated through differences in adsorption to or solubility in a solid (or viscous liquid) surface. (78)

cis-trans **isomers**   (See *geometric isomers.*)

classical (Arrhenius) acid-base definition   A model of acid-base behavior in which an acid is a substance that contains H in its formula and produces H^+ in water and a base is a substance that contains OH in its formula and produces OH^- in water. (759)

Clausius-Clapeyron equation   An equation that expresses the relationship between vapor pressure P of a liquid and temperature T:

$$\ln P = \left(\frac{-\Delta H_{vap}}{R}\right)\frac{1}{T} + C, \text{ where } C \text{ is a constant} \quad (429)$$

coal gasification   An industrial process for altering the large molecules in coal to sulfur-free gaseous fuels. (247)

colligative property   A property of a solution that depends on the number, not the identity, of solute particles. (502) (See *boiling point elevation, freezing point depression, osmotic pressure,* and *vapor pressure lowering.*)

collision frequency   The average number of collisions per second that a particle undergoes. (206)

collision theory   A model that explains reaction rate as the result of particles colliding with a certain minimum energy. (686)

colloid   A suspension in which a solutelike phase is dispersed throughout a solventlike phase. (513)

combination reaction   A reaction in which two or more substances combine to form one substance. (156)

combustion   The process of burning in air, often with release of heat and light. (10)

combustion analysis   A method for determining the formula of a compound from the amounts of its combustion products. (100)

common-ion effect   The shift in the position of an ionic equilibrium away from an ion involved in the process that is caused by the addition or presence of that ion. (807)

complex   (See *coordination compound.*)

complex ion   An ion consisting of a central metal ion bonded covalently to molecules and/or anions called ligands. (835, 1016)

composition   The types and amounts of simpler substances that make up a sample of matter. (3)

compound   A substance composed of two or more elements in fixed proportions that are chemically combined. (42)

concentration   A measure of the quantity of solute dissolved in a given quantity of solution. (116)

concentration cell   A voltaic cell in which both compartments contain the same components but at different concentrations. (920)

condensation   The process of a gas changing into a liquid. (423)

condensation polymer   A polymer formed by monomers with two functional groups that are linked together in a dehydration-condensation reaction. (643)

conductor   A substance (usually a metal) that conducts an electric current well regardless of the temperature. (460)

conduction band   The empty, higher energy portion of the band of molecular orbitals into which electrons move when conducting heat and electricity. (459)

conjugate acid-base pair   Two species related to each other through the gain or loss of a proton; the acid has one more proton than its conjugate base. (769)

constitutional isomers (also *structural isomers*)   Molecules with the same molecular formula but different arrangements of atoms. (614, 1021)

contact process An industrial process for the manufacture of sulfuric acid based on the catalyzed oxidation of SO_2. (989)

controlled experiment An experiment that measures the effect of one variable at a time by keeping other variables constant. (12)

conversion factor A ratio equal to one and made of equivalent quantities that is used to convert the units of a quantity. (14)

coordinate covalent bond A covalent bond formed when one atom donates both electrons to form the shared pair. (1024)

coordination compound A substance consisting of a neutral complex or containing at least one complex ion. (1016)

coordination isomers Two or more coordination compounds with the same composition in which the complex ions have different ligand arrangements. (1021)

coordination number In a crystal, the number of nearest neighbors surrounding a particle. (448) In a complex, the number of ligand atoms bonded to the central metal ion. (1017)

core The dense, innermost region of the Earth. (953)

core electrons (See *inner electrons*.)

corrosion The natural redox process that results in unwanted oxidation of a metal. (928)

coulomb (C) The SI unit of electric charge. One coulomb is the charge of 6.242×10^{18} electrons; one electron possesses a charge of 1.602×10^{-19} C. (906)

Coulomb's law A law stating that the electrostatic force associated with two charges A and B is directly proportional to the product of their magnitudes and inversely proportional to the square of the distance between them:

$$\text{force} \propto \frac{\text{charge A} \times \text{charge B}}{(\text{distance})^2} \quad (63, 337)$$

counter ion A simple ion associated with a complex ion in a coordination compound. (1016)

coupling of reactions The pairing of reactions in which one reaction releases enough free energy for the other to occur. (880)

covalent bond A type of bond in which atoms are bonded through the sharing of two electrons; the mutual attraction of the nuclei and an electron pair that holds atoms together in a molecule. (64, 340)

covalent bonding The idealized bonding type that is based on localized electron pair sharing between two atoms with little difference in their tendencies to lose or gain electrons (most commonly nonmetals). (332, 532)

covalent compound A compound that consists of atoms bonded together by shared electron pairs. (62)

covalent radius One-half the distance between nuclei of identical covalently bonded atoms. (308)

critical mass The mass needed to achieve a chain reaction. (1072)

critical point The point on a phase diagram above which the vapor cannot be condensed to a liquid; the end of the liquid-gas curve. (432)

crust The thin, light, heterogeneous outer layer of the Earth. (953)

crystal defect Any of a variety of disruptions in the regularity of a crystal structure. (461)

crystal field splitting energy (Δ) The difference in energy between two sets of metal-ion d orbitals that results from electrostatic interactions with the surrounding ligands. (1028)

crystal field theory A model that explains the color and magnetism of complexes based on the effects of ligands on metal-ion d-orbital energies. (1026)

crystalline solids Solids with a well-defined shape because of the orderly arrangement of their atoms, molecules, or ions. (447)

crystallization A technique used to separate and purify the components of a mixture through differences in solubility in which a component comes out of solution as crystals. (77)

cubic closest packing A crystal structure based on the face-centered cubic unit cell in which the layers have an ABCABC . . . pattern. (450)

cubic meter (m^3) The SI derived unit of volume. (19)

curie (Ci) The most common unit of radioactivity, defined as the number of nuclei disintegrating each second in 1 g of radium-226: $1 \text{ Ci} = 3.70 \times 10^{10}$ d/s (disintegrations per second). (1053)

cyclic hydrocarbon A hydrocarbon with one or more rings in its structure. (613)

D

d orbital An atomic orbital with $l = 2$. (283)

dalton (D) (See *atomic mass unit*.)

Dalton's law of partial pressures A gas law stating that in a mixture of unreacting gases, the total pressure is the sum of the partial pressures of the individual gases: $P_{\text{total}} = P_1 + P_2 + \cdots$. (194)

data Pieces of quantitative information obtained by observation. (12)

de Broglie wavelength The wavelength of a moving particle obtained from the de Broglie equation: $\lambda = h/mu$. (273)

decay constant The rate constant k for radioactive decay. (1053)

decay series (also *disintegration series*) The succession of decay steps a parent nucleus undergoes to become a stable daughter nucleus. (1051)

decomposition reaction A reaction in which one reactant forms two or more products; the reverse of a combination reaction. (159)

dehydration-condensation reaction A reaction in which H and OH groups on two molecules react to form water as one of the products. (578)

delocalization The process by which electron density is spread over several atoms rather than remaining between two. (365)

density (d) An intensive physical property of a substance at a given temperature and pressure, defined as the ratio of the mass to the volume: $d = m/V$. (22)

deposition The process of changing directly from gas to solid. (424)

derived unit Any of various combinations of the seven SI base units. (17)

desalination A process used to remove large amounts of ions from seawater, usually by reverse osmosis. (517)

deuterons Nuclei of the stable hydrogen isotope deuterium, ^2H. (1058)

diagonal relationship Physical and chemical similarities between a Period 2 element and one located diagonally down and to the right in Period 3. (551)

diamagnetism The tendency of a species not to be attracted (or to be slightly repelled) by a magnetic field as a result of its electrons being paired. (320, 1008)

differentiation The geochemical process of forming regions in the Earth based on differences in composition and density. (953)

diffraction The phenomenon in which a wave striking the edge of an object bends around it. A wave passing through a slit as wide as its wavelength forms a circular wave. (262)

diffusion The movement of one fluid through another. (205)

dimensional analysis (also *factor-label method*) A calculation method in which arithmetic steps are accompanied by the appropriate canceling of units. (15)

dipole-dipole force The intermolecular attraction between oppositely charged poles of nearby polar molecules. (434)

dipole-induced dipole force The intermolecular attraction between a polar molecule and the oppositely charged pole it induces in a nearby molecule. (482)

dipole moment (μ) A measure of molecular polarity; the magnitude of the partial charges on the ends of a molecule (in coulombs) times the distance between them (in meters). (384)

disaccharide An organic compound formed by a dehydration-condensation reaction between two simple sugars (monosaccharides). (644)

disintegration series (See *decay series*.)

dispersion force (also *London force*) The intermolecular attraction between all molecules as a result of instantaneous polarizations of their electron clouds; the force primarily responsible for the condensed states of nonpolar substances. (438)

displacement reaction A reaction in which an atom or ion in one substance displaces an atom or ion in another; classified as single-displacement and double-displacement (metathesis) reactions. (160)

disproportionation reaction A reaction in which a given substance is both oxidized and reduced. (576)

distillation A separation technique in which a more volatile component of a mixture vaporizes and condenses separately from the less volatile components. (77)

donor atom An atom that donates a lone pair of electrons to form a covalent bond, usually from ligand to metal ion in a complex. (1017)

doping Adding small amounts of other elements into the crystal structure of a semiconductor to enhance a specific property, usually conductivity. (462)

double bond A covalent bond that consists of two bonding pairs; two atoms sharing four electrons in the form of one σ and one π bond. (342, 405)

double helix The two intertwined polynucleotide strands held together by H bonds that form the structure of DNA (deoxyribonucleic acid). (651)

Downs cell An industrial apparatus that electrolyzes molten NaCl to produce sodium and chlorine. (971)

dynamic equilibrium The condition at which the forward and reverse reactions are taking place at the same rate, so there is no net change in the amounts of reactants or products. (165)

E

e_g orbitals The set of orbitals (composed of $d_{x^2-y^2}$ and d_{z^2}) that results when the energies of the metal-ion d orbitals are split by a ligand field. This set is higher in energy than the other (t_{2g}) set in an octahedral field of ligands and lower in energy in a tetrahedral field. (1028)

effective collision A collision in which the particles meet with sufficient energy and an orientation that allows them to react. (688)

effective nuclear charge (Z_{eff}) The apparent nuclear charge an electron actually experiences as a result of shielding effects by other electrons. (297)

effusion The process by which a gas escapes from its container through a tiny hole into an evacuated space. (204)

electrochemical cell A system that incorporates a redox reaction to produce or use electrical energy. (895)

electrochemistry The study of the relationship between chemical change and electrical work. (895)

electrode The part of an electrochemical cell that conducts the electricity between the cell and the surroundings. (900)

electrolysis The nonspontaneous lysing (splitting) of a substance, often to its component elements, by supplying electrical energy. (933)

electrolyte A substance that conducts a current when it dissolves in water. (134, 502) A mixture of ions, in which the electrodes of an electrochemical cell are immersed, that conducts a current. (900)

electrolytic cell An electrochemical system that uses electrical energy to drive a nonspontaneous chemical reaction ($\Delta G > 0$). (900)

electromagnetic (EM) radiation (also *electromagnetic energy* or *radiant energy*) Oscillating, perpendicular electric and magnetic fields moving simultaneously through space as waves and manifested as visible light, x-rays, microwaves, radio waves, and so on. (259)

electromagnetic spectrum The continuum of wavelengths of radiant energy. (260)

electromotive force (emf) (See *cell potential*.)

electron (e^-) A subatomic particle that possesses a unit negative charge (1.602×10^{-19} C) and occupies the space around the atomic nucleus. (53)

electron affinity (EA) The energy change accompanying one mole of electrons being added to one mole of gaseous atoms or ions. (314)

electron capture A type of radioactive decay in which a nucleus draws in an orbital electron, usually one from the lowest energy level, and releases energy. (1047)

electron cloud An imaginary representation of the electron(s) rapidly changing position around the nucleus over time. (277)

electron configuration The distribution of electrons within the orbitals of the atoms of an element; also the notation for such a distribution. (292)

electron deficient Referring to a bonded atom that has fewer than eight valence electrons. (368)

electron density diagram (also *electron probability density diagram*) The pictorial representation for a given energy sublevel of the quantity ψ^2 (the probability that the electron lies within a particular tiny volume) as a function of r (distance from the nucleus). (277)

electron-pair delocalization (See *delocalization*.)

electron-sea model A qualitative description of metallic bonding proposing that metal atoms pool their valence electrons into a delocalized "sea" of electrons in which the metal cores (metal ions) are submerged in an orderly array. (353)

electron volt (eV) The energy (in joules, J) that an electron acquires when it moves through a potential difference of one volt: $1\ eV = 1.602 \times 10^{-19}$ J. (1069)

electronegativity (EN) The relative ability of a bonded atom to attract shared electrons. (347, 531)

electronegativity difference (ΔEN) The difference in electronegativities between the atoms in a bond. (350)

electrorefining An industrial electrolytic process in which a sample of impure metal acts as the anode and a sample of the pure metal acts as the cathode. (969)

element The simplest type of substance with unique physical and chemical properties. An element consists of only one kind of atom, so it cannot be broken down into any simpler substances. (41)

elementary reaction (also *elementary step*) A simple reaction that describes a single molecular event in a proposed reaction mechanism. (693)

elementary step (See *elementary reaction*.)

elimination reaction A type of organic reaction in which C atoms in the product are bonded to fewer atoms than in the reactant, which leads to multiple bonding. (624)

emission spectrum The line spectrum produced when excited atoms emit photons characteristic of the element. (271)

empirical formula A chemical formula that shows the lowest relative number of atoms of each element in a compound. (65)

end point The point in a titration at which the indicator changes color. (145, 817)

end-to-end overlap Overlap of s, p, or hybrid atomic orbitals that yields a sigma (σ) bond. (533)

endothermic process A change that occurs with an absorption of heat from the surroundings ($\Delta H > 0$) and therefore an increase in the enthalpy of the system. (232)

energy The capacity to do work, that is, to move matter. (6) [See *kinetic energy* (E_k) and *potential energy* (E_p).]

enthalpy (H) A thermodynamic quantity that is the sum of the internal energy plus the product of the pressure and volume. (231)

enthalpy diagram A graphic depiction of the enthalpy change of a system. (232)

enthalpy of hydration (ΔH_{hydr}) (See *heat of hydration*.)

enthalpy of solution (ΔH_{soln}) (See *heat of solution*.)

entropy (S) A thermodynamic quantity that is a measure of the disorder of a system; related to the number of ways the components of a system can be arranged without changing the system's energy. (492, 862)

environmental cycle The physical, chemical, and biological paths through which the atoms of an element move within the Earth's crust. (958)

enzyme A biological macromolecule (usually a protein) that acts as a catalyst. (702)

enzyme-substrate complex (ES) The intermediate in an enzyme-catalyzed reaction that consists of enzyme and substrate(s) and whose concentration determines the rate of product formation. (703)

equatorial group An atom (or group) that lies in a trigonal plane of a trigonal bipyramidal molecule or similar structural feature in a molecule. (378)

equilibrium constant (K) The value obtained when equilibrium concentrations are substituted into the reaction quotient. (717)

equivalence point The point in a titration when the number of moles of added species is stoichiometrically equivalent to the original number of moles of the other species. (145, 816)

ester An organic compound that contains the
$$-\overset{:O:}{\underset{|}{\overset{||}{C}}}-\overset{..}{\underset{|}{O}}-C-\ \text{group. (634)}$$

exact number A quantity, usually obtained by counting or based on a unit definition, that has no uncertainty associated with it and, therefore, contains as many significant figures as a calculation requires. (30)

excitation The process by which a substance absorbs energy from low-energy radioactive particles such that its electrons move to higher energy levels. (1060)

excited state Any electron configuration of an atom or molecule other than the lowest (ground) state. (268)

exclusion principle A principle developed by Wolfgang Pauli stating that no two electrons in an atom can have the same set of four quantum numbers. The principle arises from the fact that an orbital has a maximum occupancy of two electrons and their spins are paired. (294)

exothermic process A change that occurs with a release of heat to the surroundings ($\Delta H < 0$) and therefore a decrease in the enthalpy of the system. (232)

expanded valence shell A valence level that can accommodate more than eight electrons by using available d orbitals; occurs only for elements in Period 3 or higher. (369)

experiment A clear set of procedural steps that tests a hypothesis. (12)

extensive property A property, such as mass, that depends on the quantity of substance present. (22)

extraction A method of separating the components of a mixture based on differences in their solubility in a nonmiscible solvent. (77)

F

face-centered cubic unit cell A unit cell in which a particle occurs at each corner and in the center of each face of a cube. (448)

faraday (F) The physical constant representing the charge of 1 mol of electrons: $F = 96{,}485$ C/mol e$^-$. (916)

fatty acid A carboxylic acid with a long hydrocarbon chain that is derived from a natural source. (635)

filtration A method of separating the components of a mixture on the basis of differences in particle size. (77)

first law of thermodynamics (also *law of conservation of energy*) A basic observation that the total energy of the universe is constant: $\Delta E_{universe} = \Delta E_{system} + \Delta E_{surroundings} = 0$. (228)

fission The process by which a heavier nucleus splits into lighter nuclei with the release of energy. (1068)

fixation A chemical/biochemical process that converts a gaseous substance in the environment into a form that can be used by organisms. (959)

flame test A procedure for identifying the presence of metal ions in which a granule of a compound or a drop of its solution is placed in a flame to observe a characteristic color. (271)

flotation A metallurgic process in which oil and detergent are mixed with pulverized ore in water to create a slurry that separates the mineral from the gangue. (966)

formal charge The hypothetical charge on an atom in a molecule or ion. The number of valence electrons minus the sum of all the unshared and half the shared valence electrons. (367)

formation constant (K_f) (also *stability constant*) An equilibrium constant for the formation of a complex ion from the hydrated metal ion and ligands. (835)

formation reaction A reaction in which 1 mol of a compound forms from its elements. (244)

formula unit The chemical unit of a compound that contains the number and type of atoms (or ions) expressed in the chemical formula. (68)

fossil fuel Any fuel, including coal, petroleum, and natural gas, derived from the products of the decay of dead organisms. (247)

fraction by mass (See *mass fraction*.)

fractional distillation A process involving numerous vaporization-condensation steps used to separate two or more volatile components. (511)

free energy (G) A thermodynamic quantity that is the difference between the enthalpy and the product of the absolute temperature and the entropy. (873)

free radical A molecular or atomic species with one or more unpaired electrons, which typically make it very reactive. (368, 1061)

freezing The process of cooling a liquid until it solidifies. (423)

freezing point depression A lowering of the freezing point of a solvent caused by the presence of dissolved solute particles. (506)

frequency (ν) The number of cycles a wave undergoes per second. (260)

frequency factor (A) The product of the collision frequency Z and an orientation probability factor p specific for a reaction. (689)

fuel cell (also *flow battery*) A battery that is not self-contained in which electricity is generated by the controlled oxidation of a fuel. (923)

functional group A specific combination of atoms, typically containing a carbon multiple bond and/or heteroatom bond, that reacts in a characteristic way no matter in what molecule it occurs. (607)

fundamental unit (See *base unit*.)

fusion (See *melting*.)

fusion (nuclear) The process by which light nuclei combine to form a heavier nucleus with the release of energy. (1068)

G

galvanic cell (See *voltaic cell*.)

gamma (γ) emission The type of radioactive decay in which γ photons are emitted from an excited nucleus. (1047)

gamma (γ) ray A very high-energy photon. (1045)

gangue Debris associated with a mineral, such as sand, rock, and clay, that is separated during extraction of an element. (965)

gas One of the three states of matter. A gas fills its container regardless of the shape. (4)

Geiger-Müller counter An ionization counter that detects radioactive emissions through their ionization of gas atoms within the instrument. (1052)

genetic code The set of three-base sequences that is translated into specific amino acids during the process of protein synthesis. (652)

geometric isomers (also *cis-trans isomers* or *diastereomers*) A type of stereoisomer in which the compounds have the same connections between atoms but differ in the spatial arrangements of the atoms. The *cis-* isomer has similar groups on the same side of a structural feature; the *trans-* isomer has them on opposite sides. (617, 1022)

Graham's law of effusion A gas law stating that the rate of effusion of a gas is inversely proportional to the square root of its density (or molar mass): rate $\propto \dfrac{1}{\sqrt{\mathcal{M}}}$. (204)

gray (Gy) The SI unit of absorbed radiation dose; 1 Gy = 1 J/kg tissue. (1061)

ground state The electron configuration of an atom or ion that is lowest in energy. (268)

group A vertical column in the periodic table. (59)

H

Haber process An industrial process used to form ammonia from its elements. (743)

half-cell A portion of an electrochemical cell in which a half-reaction takes place. (902)

half-life ($t_{1/2}$) In chemical processes, the time required for half the initial reactant concentration to be consumed. (682). In nuclear processes, the time required for half the initial number of nuclei to decay. (1053)

half-reaction method A method of balancing redox reactions by treating the oxidation and reduction half-reactions separately. (896)

haloalkane An organic compound that contains a

—C—$\ddot{\text{X}}$: group, where X is a halogen atom. (623)

hard water Water that contains large amounts of divalent cations, especially Ca^{2+} and Mg^{2+}. (516)

heat (q) The energy transferred between objects because of differences in their temperatures only; thermal energy. (24, 225)

heat capacity The quantity of heat required to change the temperature of an object by one kelvin. (236)

heat of combustion (ΔH_{comb}) The enthalpy change occurring when 1 mol of a substance combines with oxygen in a combustion reaction. (233)

heat of formation (ΔH_f) The enthalpy change occurring when 1 mol of a compound is produced from its elements. (233)

heat of fusion (ΔH_{fus}) The enthalpy change occurring when 1 mol of a solid substance melts. (233, 424)

heat of hydration (ΔH_{hydr}) The enthalpy change occurring when 1 mol of a gaseous species is hydrated. The sum of the enthalpies of separating water molecules and mixing the gaseous solute with them. (490)

heat of reaction (ΔH_{rxn}) The enthalpy change of a reaction. (232)

heat of solution (ΔH_{soln}) The enthalpy change occurring when a solution forms from solute and solvent. The sum of the enthalpies from separating solute and solvent molecules and mixing them. (489)

heat of sublimation (ΔH_{subl}) The enthalpy change occurring when 1 mol of a solid substance changes directly to a gas. The sum of the heats of fusion and vaporization. (424)

heat of vaporization (ΔH_{vap}) The enthalpy change occurring when 1 mol of a liquid substance vaporizes. (233, 424)

heating-cooling curve A plot of temperature versus time for a substance when heat is released or absorbed by the system at a constant rate. (425)

Henderson-Hasselbalch equation An equation for calculating the pH of a buffer system:

$$pH = pK_a + \left(\frac{[base]}{[acid]}\right) \quad (811)$$

Henry's law A law stating that the solubility of a gas in a liquid is directly proportional to the partial pressure of the gas above the liquid: $S_{gas} = k_H \times P_{gas}$. (497)

Hess's law of heat summation A law stating that the enthalpy change of an overall process is the sum of the enthalpy changes of the individual steps of the process. (241)

heteroatom Any atom in an organic compound other than C or H. (607)

heterogeneous catalyst A catalyst that occurs in a different phase from the reactants, usually a solid interacting with gaseous or liquid reactants. (699)

heterogeneous mixture A mixture that has one or more visible boundaries among its components. (76)

hexagonal closest packing A crystal structure based on the hexagonal unit cell in which the layers have an ABAB . . . pattern. (450)

high-spin complex A complex that has the same number of unpaired electrons as in the isolated metal ion; characteristic of weak-field ligands. (1030)

homogeneous catalyst A catalyst (gas, liquid, or soluble solid) that exists in the same phase as the reactants. (699)

homogeneous mixture (also *solution*) A mixture that has no visible boundaries among its components. (76)

homologous series A series of organic compounds in which each member differs from the next by a —CH_2— (methylene) group. (611)

homonuclear diatomic molecule A molecule composed of two identical atoms. (410)

Hund's rule A principle stating that when orbitals of equal energy are available, the electron configuration of lowest energy has the maximum number of unpaired electrons with parallel spins. (299)

hybrid orbital An atomic orbital postulated to form during bonding by the mathematical mixing of specific combinations of nonequivalent orbitals in a given atom. (397)

hybridization A postulated process of orbital mixing to form hybrid orbitals. (397)

hydrate A compound in which a specific number of water molecules is associated with each formula unit. (70)

hydration Solvation in water. (490)

hydration shell The oriented cluster of water molecules that surrounds an ion in aqueous solution. (482)

hydrocarbon An organic compound that contains only H and C atoms. (608)

hydrogen bond (H bond) A type of dipole-dipole force that arises between molecules that have an H atom bonded to a small, highly electronegative atom with lone pairs, usually N, O, or F. (436, 539)

hydrogenation The addition of hydrogen to a carbon multiple bond to form a carbon single bond. (701)

hydrolysis Cleaving a molecule by reaction with water in which one part of the molecule bonds to the water —OH and the other to the water H. (637)

hydronium ion (H_3O^+) A proton covalently bonded to a water molecule. (758)

hydrosphere The liquid portion of the Earth's crust. (955)

hypothesis A testable proposal made to explain an observation. If inconsistent with experimental results, a hypothesis is revised or discarded. (12)

I

ideal gas A hypothetical gas that exhibits linear relationships among volume, pressure, temperature, and amount (mol) at all conditions; approximated by simple gases at ordinary conditions. (183)

ideal gas law (also *ideal gas equation*) An equation expressing the relationships among volume, pressure, temperature, and amount (mol) of an ideal gas: $PV = nRT$. (187)

ideal solution A solution whose vapor pressure equals the mole fraction of the solvent times the vapor pressure of the pure solvent; approximated only by very dilute solutions. (503) (See also *Raoult's law*.)

indicator (See *acid-base indicator*.)

induced-fit model A model of enzyme action that pictures the binding of substrate inducing the active site to change its shape and become catalytically active. (703)

infrared (IR) region The region of the electromagnetic spectrum between the microwave and visible regions. (261)

infrared (IR) spectroscopy An instrumental technique for determining the types of bonds in a covalent molecule by measuring the absorption of IR radiation. (346)

initial rate The instantaneous rate occurring as soon as the reactants are mixed, that is, at $t = 0$. (671)

inner electrons (also *core electrons*) Electrons that fill all the energy levels of an atom except the valence level; those electrons in atoms of the previous noble gas and completed transition series. (305)

inner transition elements The elements of the periodic table in which f orbitals are being filled; the lanthanides and actinides. (306, 1009)

instantaneous rate The reaction rate at a particular time, given by the slope of a tangent to a plot of reactant concentration versus time. (671)

insulator A substance (usually a nonmetal) that does not conduct an electric current. (460)

integrated rate law A mathematical expression for reactant concentration as a function of time. (679)

intensive property A property, such as density, that does not depend on the quantity of substance present. (22)

interhalogen compound A compound consisting entirely of halogens. (590)

intermolecular forces (also *interparticle forces*) The attractive and repulsive forces among the particles—molecules, atoms, or ions—in a sample of matter. (422)

internal energy (E) The sum of the kinetic and potential energies of all the particles in a system. (225)

interstitial hydride The substance formed when metals absorb H_2 into the spaces between their atoms. (543)

ion A charged particle that forms from an atom (or covalently bound group of atoms) when it gains or loses one or more electrons. (62)

ion-dipole force The intermolecular attractive force between an ion and a polar molecule (dipole). (434)

ion exchange A process of softening water by exchanging one type of ion (usually Ca^{2+}) for another (usually Na^+) by binding on a specially designed resin. (516)

ion–induced dipole force The intermolecular attractive force between an ion and the dipole it induces in the electron cloud of a nearby particle. (482)

ion pair A pair of ions that form a gaseous ionic molecule; sometimes formed when a salt boils. (340)

ion-product constant for water (K_w) The equilibrium constant for the autoionization of water:

$$K_w = [H_3O^+][OH^-] \qquad (764)$$

ionic atmosphere A cluster of ions of net opposite charge surrounding a given ion in solution. (513)

ionic bonding The idealized bonding type based on the attraction of oppositely charged ions that arise through electron transfer between atoms with large differences in their tendencies to lose or gain electrons (typically between metals and nonmetals). (332, 532)

ionic compound A compound that consists of oppositely charged ions. (62, 539)

ionic radius The size of an ion as measured by the distance between the centers of adjacent ions in a crystalline ionic compound. (322)

ionic solid A solid whose unit cell contains cations and anions. (455)

ionization The process by which a substance absorbs energy from high-energy radioactive particles and loses an electron to become ionized. (1060)

ionization energy (IE) The energy required to remove completely one mole of electrons from one mole of gaseous atoms or ions. (311, 531)

ionizing radiation The high-energy radiation that forms ions in a substance by electron loss. (1060)

isoelectronic Having the same number and configuration of electrons as another species. (318)

isomer One of two or more compounds with the same molecular formula but different properties, generally as a result of different arrangements of atoms. (614, 1021)

isotopes Atoms of a given atomic number (that is, of a specific element) that have different numbers of neutrons and therefore different mass numbers. (54, 1044)

isotopic mass The mass (in amu) of an isotope relative to the mass of carbon-12. (55)

J

joule (J) The SI unit of energy: $1 \text{ J} = 1 \text{ kg} \cdot \text{m}^2/\text{s}^2$. (228)

K

kelvin (K) The SI base unit of temperature. The kelvin is the same size as the Celsius degree. (24)

Kelvin scale (See *absolute scale*.)

ketone An organic compound (ending *-one*) that contains a carbonyl group bonded to two other C atoms,

$$-\overset{|}{\underset{|}{C}}-\overset{:\overset{\text{..}}{O}:}{\overset{||}{C}}-\overset{|}{\underset{|}{C}}- \ . \ (632)$$

kilogram (kg) The SI base unit of mass. (20)

kinetic energy (E_k) The energy an object has because of its motion. (6)

kinetic-molecular theory (also *kinetic theory*) The model that explains gas behavior in terms of particles in random motion whose volumes and interactions are negligible. (199)

L

lanthanides (also *rare earth elements*) The Period 6 ($4f$) series of inner transition elements that includes cerium (Ce; $Z = 58$) through lutetium (Lu; $Z = 71$). (306, 1009)

lanthanide contraction The additional decrease in atomic and ionic size beyond the expected trend caused by the poor shielding of the increasing nuclear charge by f electrons in the elements following the lanthanides. (1004)

lattice The three-dimensional arrangement of points created by choosing each point to be at the same location within each particle of a crystal; thus, the lattice consists of all points with identical surroundings. (448)

lattice energy ($\Delta H^0_{lattice}$) The enthalpy change that occurs when gaseous ions coalesce into a solid ionic compound. (335)

law (also *natural law*)   A summary, often in mathematical form, of a universal observation. (12)

law of chemical equilibrium (also *law of mass action*)   The law stating that when a system reaches equilibrium at a given temperature, the ratio of quantities that make up the reaction quotient has a constant numerical value. (717)

law of conservation of energy   (See *first law of thermodynamics.*)

law of definite (or constant) composition   A mass law stating that, no matter what its source, a particular chemical compound is composed of the same elements in the same parts (fractions) by mass. (44)

law of mass action   (See *law of chemical equilibrium.*)

law of mass conservation   A mass law stating that the total mass of substances does not change during a chemical reaction. (44)

law of multiple proportions   A mass law stating that if elements A and B react to form two compounds, the different masses of B that combine with a fixed mass of A can be expressed as a ratio of small whole numbers. (46)

Le Châtelier's principle   A principle stating that if a system in a state of equilibrium is disturbed, it will undergo a change that shifts its equilibrium position in a direction that reduces the effect of the disturbance. (736)

leaching   A hydrometallurgic process that extracts a metal selectively, usually through formation of a complex ion. (966)

level (also *shell*)   A specific energy state of an atom given by the principal quantum number *n*. (280)

leveling effect   The inability of a solvent to distinguish the strengths of an acid (or base) that is stronger than the conjugate acid (or conjugate base) of the solvent. (790)

Lewis acid-base definition   A model of acid-base behavior in which acids and bases are defined, respectively, as species that accept or donate an electron pair. (791)

Lewis electron-dot symbol   A notation in which the element symbol represents the nucleus and inner electrons, and surrounding dots represent the valence electrons. (333)

Lewis structure (also *Lewis formula*)   A structural formula consisting of electron-dot symbols, with lines as bonding pairs and dot pairs as lone pairs. (361)

ligand   A molecule or anion bonded to a central metal ion in a complex ion. (835, 1016)

like-dissolves-like rule   A empirical observation stating that substances having similar kinds of intermolecular forces dissolve in each other. (483)

limiting reactant (also *limiting reagent*)   The reactant that is consumed when a reaction occurs and therefore the one that determines the maximum amount of product that can form. (112)

line spectrum   A series of separate spectral lines representing photons whose wavelengths are characteristic of an element. (266) (See also *emission spectrum.*)

linear arrangement   The geometric arrangement obtained when two electron groups maximize their separation around a central atom. (375)

linear shape   A molecular shape formed by three atoms lying in a straight line: bond angle of 180° (shape class AX_2 or AX_2E_3). (375, 379)

linkage isomers   Coordination compounds with the same composition but with a different ligand donor atoms linked to the central metal ion. (1022)

lipids   A class of biomolecules, including fats and oils, that are soluble in nonpolar solvents. (636)

liquid   One of the three states of matter. A liquid fills a container to the extent of its own volume and thus forms a surface. (4)

liquid crystal   A substance that flows like a liquid but packs like a crystalline solid at the molecular level. (464)

liter (L)   A non-SI unit of volume equivalent to 1 cubic decimeter (0.001 m^3). (19)

lithosphere   The solid portion of the Earth's crust. (955)

lock-and-key model   A model of enzyme function that pictures rigid shapes of the enzyme active site and the substrate fitting together as a lock and key, respectively. (703)

London force   (See *dispersion force.*)

lone pair (also *unshared pair*)   An electron pair that is part of an atom's valence shell but not involved in covalent bonding. (341)

low-spin complex   Complex ions that have fewer unpaired electrons than in the free ion because of the presence of strong-field ligands. (1030)

M

magnetic quantum number (m_l) (also *orbital-orientation quantum number*)   An integer from $-l$ through 0 to $+l$ that specifies the orientation of an atomic orbital in the three-dimensional space about the nucleus. (279)

manometer   A device used to measure the pressure of a gas in a laboratory experiment. (180)

mantle   A thick homogeneous layer of the Earth's internal structure that lies between the core and the crust. (953)

mass   The quantity of matter an object contains. Balances are designed to measure mass. (20)

mass-action expression   (See *reaction quotient.*)

mass defect (Δm)   The mass decrease that occurs when nucleons combine to form a nucleus. (1069)

mass fraction (also *fraction by mass*)   The portion of a compound's mass contributed by an element; the mass of an element in a compound divided by the mass of the compound. (44)

mass number (A)   The total number of protons and neutrons in an atom. (54)

mass percent (mass %) (also *percent by mass*)   The mass fraction expressed as a percentage. (44) A concentration term [% (w/w)] expressed as the mass in grams of solute dissolved in every 100. g of solution. (499)

mass spectrometry   An instrumental method for measuring the relative masses of particles in a sample by creating charged particles and separating them according to their mass-charge ratio. (55)

matter   Anything that possesses mass and occupies volume. (3)

mean free path   The average distance a molecule travels between collisions at a given temperature and pressure. (205)

melting (also *fusion*)   The change of a substance from a solid to a liquid. (423)

melting point (mp or T_f**)**   The temperature at which the solid and liquid forms of a substance are at equilibrium. (431)

metabolic pathway   A biochemical reaction sequence that flows in one direction in which each reaction is enzyme catalyzed. (745)

metal   A substance or mixture that is relatively shiny and malleable and is a good conductor of heat and electricity. In reactions, metals tend to transfer electrons to nonmetals and form ionic compounds. (59)

metallic bonding   An idealized type of bonding based on the attraction between metal ions and their delocalized valence electrons. (332, 532)

metallic radius (also *crystallographic radius*)   One-half the distance between the nuclei of adjacent individual atoms in a crystal of an element. (308)

metallic solid   A solid whose individual atoms are held together by metallic bonding. (457)

metalloid (also *semimetal*)   An element with properties between those of metals and nonmetals. (59)

metallurgy   The branch of materials science concerned with the extraction and utilization of metals. (965)

metathesis (also *double-displacement reaction*)   A reaction in which atoms or ions of two compounds exchange bonding partners. (160)

meter (m)   The SI base unit of length. The distance light travels in a vacuum in 1/299,792,458 second. (19)

milliliter (mL)   A volume (0.001 L) equivalent to 1 cm^3. (19)

millimeter of mercury (mmHg)   A unit of pressure based on the difference in the heights of mercury in a barometer or manometer. Redefined as 1 torr. (181)

mineral   The compound in an ore that contains the element of interest. (965)

miscible   Soluble in any proportion. (481)

mixture   A group of two or more elements and/or compounds that are physically intermingled. (43, 481)

MO bond order   One-half the difference between the number of electrons in bonding and antibonding MOs. (409)

model (also *theory*)   A simplified conceptual picture based on experiment that explains how an aspect of nature occurs. (12)

molality (*m***)**   A concentration term expressed as the moles of solute dissolved in 1000 g (1 kg) of solvent. (498)

molar heat capacity (*C***)**   The quantity of heat required to change the temperature of 1 mol of a substance by 1 K. (236)

molar mass (*M***)** (also *gram-molecular weight*)   The mass of 1 mol of entities (atoms, molecules, or formula units) of a substance, in units of g/mol. (91)

molar solubility   The solubility expressed in terms of amount (mol) of dissolved solute. (826)

molarity (*M***)**   A concentration term expressed as the moles of solute dissolved in 1 L of solution. (116)

mole (mol)   The SI base unit for amount of a substance. The amount that contains a number of objects equal to the number of atoms in exactly 12 g of carbon-12. (89)

mole fraction (*X***)**   A concentration term expressed as the ratio of moles of one component of a mixture to the total moles present. (195, 500)

molecular compounds   Compounds consisting of individual molecules and whose physical state depends on intermolecular forces. (539)

molecular equation   A chemical equation showing a reaction in solution in which reactants and products appear as intact, undissociated compounds. (140)

molecular formula   A formula that shows the actual number of atoms of each element in a molecule. (65, 98)

molecular mass   The sum (in amu) of the atomic masses of a formula unit of a compound. (73)

molecular orbital (MO)   An orbital of given energy and shape that extends over a molecule and can be occupied by no more than two electrons. (407)

molecular orbital (MO) diagram   A depiction of the relative energy and number of electrons in each MO, as well as the atomic orbitals from which the MOs form. (408)

molecular orbital (MO) theory   A model that describes a molecule as a collection of nuclei and electrons in which the electrons occupy orbitals that extend over the entire molecule. (407)

molecular polarity   The overall distribution of electronic charge on a molecule, determined by its shape and bond polarities. (384)

molecular shape   The three-dimensional structure defined by the relative positions of the atomic nuclei in a molecule. (374)

molecular solid   A solid held together by intermolecular forces between individual molecules. (454)

molecularity   The number of reactant particles involved in an elementary step. (693)

molecule   A structure consisting of two or more atoms that are chemically bound together and behave as an independent unit. (42)

monatomic ion   An ion derived from a single atom. (62)

monomer   A small molecule that is linked covalently to form a polymer and on which the repeating unit of the polymer is based. (641)

mononucleotide   A monomer unit of a nucleic acid, consisting of an N-containing base, a sugar, and a phosphate group. (650)

monosaccharide   A simple sugar; a polyhydroxy ketone or aldehyde of three to nine C atoms. (644)

N

natural law   (See *law*.)

Nernst equation   An equation stating that the cell voltage under any conditions depends on the standard cell voltage and the concentrations of the cell components:

$$E_{cell} = E_{cell}^0 - \frac{RT}{nF} \ln Q \quad (917)$$

net ionic equation   A chemical equation of a reaction in solution in which spectator ions have been eliminated to show the actual chemical change. (140)

network covalent solid   A solid in which all the atoms are bonded covalently. (457, 539)

neutralization reaction   An acid-base reaction that gives water and a neutral solution of a salt; an aqueous reaction between a strong acid and a strong base (142, 759)

neutron (n⁰) An uncharged subatomic particle found in the nucleus with a mass slightly greater than that of a proton. (53)

nitrile An organic compound containing the $-C\equiv N:$ group. (639)

node A region of an orbital where the probability of finding the electron is zero. (282)

nonbonding MO A molecular orbital that is not involved in bonding. (414)

nonelectrolyte A substance whose aqueous solution does not conduct an electric current. (138, 502)

nonionizing radiation Radiation that does not cause loss of electrons. (1060)

nonmetal An element that lacks metallic properties. In reactions, nonmetals tend to bond with each other to form covalent compounds or accept electrons from metals to form ionic compounds. (59)

nonpolar covalent bond A covalent bond between identical atoms such that the bonding pair is shared equally. (350)

nuclear binding energy The energy required to break one mole of nuclei of an element into individual nucleons. (1069)

nuclear magnetic resonance (NMR) spectroscopy An instrumental technique used to determine the molecular environment of a given type of nucleus, most often ¹H, in a molecule from its absorption of radio waves in a magnetic field. (622)

nuclear transmutation The induced conversion of one nucleus into another by bombardment with a particle. (1057)

nucleic acid An unbranched polymer consisting of mononucleotides that occurs in two types, DNA and RNA (deoxyribonucleic and ribonucleic acids), which differ chemically in the nature of the sugar. (650)

nucleon A subatomic particle that makes up a nucleus; a proton or neutron. (1044)

nucleus The tiny central region of the atom that contains all the positive charge and essentially all the mass. (52)

nuclide A nuclear species with specified numbers of protons and neutrons. (1044)

N/Z ratio The ratio of the number of neutrons to the number of protons, a key factor that determines the stability of a nuclide. (1048)

O

observation A fact obtained with the senses, often with the aid of instruments. Quantitative observations provide data that can be compared objectively. (12)

occurrence (also *source*) The form(s) in which an element exists in nature. (957)

octahedral arrangement The geometric arrangement obtained when six electron groups maximize their space around a central atom. (379)

octahedral shape A molecular shape formed when six atoms surround a central atom and lie at the corners of an octahedron. (379)

octet rule The observation that when atoms bond, they often lose, gain, or share electrons to attain a filled outer shell of eight electrons. (334)

optical isomers (also *enantiomers*) A pair of stereoisomers that arise when a molecule and its mirror image cannot be superimposed on each other. (615, 1022)

optically active A molecule that rotates the plane of polarized light. (616)

orbital diagram A depiction of electron number and spin in an atom's orbitals by means of arrows in a series of small boxes, lines, or circles. (299)

ore A naturally occurring compound or mixture of compounds from which an element can be profitably extracted. (957)

organic compound A compound in which carbon is nearly always bonded to itself, to hydrogen, and often to other elements. (605)

organometallic compound An organic compound in which carbon is bonded covalently to a metal atom. (633)

osmosis The process by which solvent flows through a semipermeable membrane from a dilute to a concentrated solution. (507)

osmotic pressure (II) The pressure that results from the inability of solute particles to cross a semipermeable membrane. The pressure required to prevent the net movement of solvent across the membrane. (507)

outer electrons Electrons that occupy the highest energy level (highest n value) and are, on average, farthest from the nucleus. (305)

overall (net) equation A chemical equation that is the sum of two or more sequential equations. (110)

overvoltage The additional voltage, usually associated with gaseous products, that is required above the standard cell voltage to accomplish electrolysis. (935)

oxidation The loss of electrons by a species accompanied by an increase in its oxidation number. (149)

oxidation number (O.N.) (also *oxidation state*) A number equal to the number of charges an atom would have if the shared electrons were held completely by the atom that attracts them more strongly. (149)

oxidation number method A method for balancing redox reactions in which the change in oxidation numbers is used to determine balancing coefficients. (152)

oxidation-reduction reaction (also *redox reaction*) A process in which electrons are transferred from one reactant (reducing agent) to another (oxidizing agent). (148)

oxidation state (See *oxidation number.*)

oxidizing agent The substance that accepts electrons in a reaction and undergoes a decrease in oxidation number. (149)

oxoanion An anion in which an element is bonded to one or more oxygen atoms. (70)

P

p block The main-group elements that lie to the right of the transition elements in the periodic table whose p orbitals are being filled. (530)

p orbital An atomic orbital with $l = 1$. (282)

packing efficiency The percentage of the available volume occupied by atoms, ions, or molecules in a unit cell. (450)

paramagnetism　The tendency of a species with unpaired electrons to be attracted by an external magnetic field. (320, 1008)

partial ionic character　An estimate of the actual charge separation in a bond (caused by the electronegativity difference of the bonded atoms) relative to complete separation. (350)

partial pressure　The portion of the total pressure contributed by a gas in a mixture of gases. (194)

particle accelerator　A device used to impart high kinetic energies to nuclear particles. (1058)

pascal (Pa)　The SI unit of pressure: $1 \text{ Pa} = 1 \text{ N/m}^2$. (181)

penetration　The process by which an outer electron moves through the core electrons to spend part of its time closer to the nucleus; penetration increases the average effective nuclear charge on that electron. (297)

percent by mass　(See *mass percent.*)

percent yield (% yield)　The actual yield of a reaction expressed as a percent of the theoretical yield. (114)

period　A horizontal row of the periodic table. (59)

periodic law　A law stating that when the elements are arranged by atomic number, they exhibit a periodic recurrence of properties. (292)

periodic table of the elements　A table in which the elements are arranged by atomic number into columns (groups) and rows (periods). (59)

pH　The negative logarithm of $[\text{H}_3\text{O}^+]$. (765)

phase　A physically distinct portion of a system. (422)

phase change　A physical change from one phase to another, usually referring to a change in physical state. (422)

phase diagram　A diagram used to describe the stable phases and phase changes of a substance as a function of temperature and pressure. (432)

phlogiston theory　An incorrect theory of combustion proposing that a burning substance releases the undetectable material phlogiston. (10)

photoelectric effect　The observation that when light of sufficient energy shines on a metal, an electric current is produced. (264)

photon　A quantum of electromagnetic radiation. (265)

photon theory　A model proposed to explain the photoelectric effect, stating that radiation occurs as discrete photons. (264)

photovoltaic cell　A device capable of converting light directly into electricity. (249)

physical change　A change in which the physical form (or state) of a substance, but not its composition, is altered. (3)

physical property　A characteristic shown by a substance itself, without interacting with or changing into other substances. (3)

pi (π) bond　A covalent bond formed by sideways overlap of two atomic orbitals that has two regions of electron density, one above and one below the internuclear axis. (405)

pi (π) MO　A molecular orbital formed by combination of two atomic (usually *p*) orbitals whose orientations are perpendicular to the internuclear axis. (410)

Planck's constant (*h*)　A proportionality constant relating the energy and the frequency of a photon, equal to $6.626 \times 10^{-34} \text{ J} \cdot \text{s}$. (264)

polar covalent bond　A covalent bond in which the electron pair is shared unequally, so the bond has partially negative and partially positive poles. (350)

polar molecule　A molecule with an unequal distribution of charge as a result of its polar bonds and shape. (137)

polarimeter　A device used to measure the rotation of plane-polarized light by an optically active compound. (616)

polarizability　The ease with which a particle's electron cloud can be deformed. (438)

polyatomic ion　An ion in which two or more atoms are bonded covalently. (65)

polymer　An extremely large molecule that results from the covalent linking of many simpler molecular units (monomers). (641)

polyprotic acid　An acid with more than one ionizable proton. (776)

polysaccharide　A macromolecule composed of many simple sugars linked covalently. (644)

positron ($^0_1\beta$)　The antiparticle of an electron. (1047)

positron decay　A type of radioactive decay in which a positron is emitted from the nucleus. (1047)

potential energy (E_p)　The energy an object has as a result of its position relative to other objects or because of its composition. (6)

precipitate　(See *precipitation reaction.*)

precipitation reaction　A reaction in which two soluble ionic compounds form an insoluble product, a precipitate. (141)

precision　(also *reproducibility*)　The closeness of a measurement to other measurements of the same phenomenon in a series of experiments. (30)

pressure (*P*)　The force exerted per unit of surface area. (179)

pressure-volume work (*PV* work)　A type of work in which a volume change occurs against an external pressure. (227)

principal quantum number (*n*)　A positive integer that specifies the energy and relative size of an atomic orbital. (279)

probability contour　A shape that defines the volume around an atomic nucleus within which an electron spends a given percentage of its time. (278)

product　A substance formed in a chemical reaction. (104)

property　A characteristic that gives a substance its unique identity. (3)

protein　A natural, linear polymer composed of any of about 20 types of amino acid monomers linked together by peptide bonds. (645)

proton (p^+)　A subatomic particle found in the nucleus that has a unit positive charge (1.602×10^{-19} C). (53)

proton acceptor　A substance that accepts an H^+ ion; a Brønsted-Lowry base. (768)

proton donor　A substance that donates an H^+ ion; a Brønsted-Lowry acid. (768)

pseudo–noble gas configuration　The $(n-1)d^{10}$ configuration of a *p*-block metal atom that empties its outer energy level. (319)

pure substance　(See *substance.*)

Q

qualitative analysis   The separation and identification of the ions in an aqueous mixture. (841)

quantum   A packet of energy equal to $h\nu$. The smallest quantity of energy that can be emitted or absorbed. (264)

quantum mechanics (also *wave mechanics*)   The branch of physics that examines the wave motion of objects on the atomic scale. (277)

quantum number   A number that specifies a property of an orbital or an electron. (264)

R

rad (*radiation-absorbed dose*)   The quantity of radiation that results in 0.01 J of energy being absorbed per kilogram of tissue: 1 rad = 0.01 J/kg tissue = 10^{-2} Gy. (1061)

radial probability distribution plot   The graphic depiction of the total probability distribution (sum of ψ^2) of an electron in the region near the nucleus. (278)

radioactivity   The emissions resulting from the spontaneous disintegration of an unstable nucleus. (1044)

radioisotope   An isotope with an unstable nucleus that decays through radioactive emissions. (1055)

radioisotopic dating   A method for determining the age of an object based on the rate of decay of a particular radioactive nuclide. (1055)

random error   Human error that occurs in all measurements and results in values *both* higher and lower than the actual value. (30)

Raoult's law   A law stating that the vapor pressure of a solution is directly proportional to the mole fraction of solvent: $P_{\text{solvent}} = X_{\text{solvent}} \times P^0_{\text{solvent}}$. (503)

rare earth elements   (See *lanthanides*.)

rate constant (*k*)   The proportionality constant that relates the reaction rate to reactant (and product) concentrations. (673)

rate-determining step (also *rate-limiting step*)   The slowest step in a reaction mechanism and therefore the step that limits the overall rate. (694)

rate-limiting step   (See *rate-determining step*.)

rate law (also *rate equation*)   An equation that expresses the rate as a function of reactant (and product) concentrations. (673)

reactant   A starting substance in a chemical reaction. (104)

reaction energy diagram   A graph that shows the potential energy of a reacting system as it progresses from reactants to products. (690)

reaction intermediate   A substance that is formed and used up during the overall reaction and therefore does not appear in the overall equation. (695)

reaction mechanism   A series of elementary steps that sum to the overall reaction and is consistent with the rate law. (693)

reaction order   The exponent of a reactant concentration in a rate law that shows how the rate is affected by changes in that concentration. (673)

reaction quotient (*Q*) (also *mass-action expression*)   A ratio of terms for a given reaction consisting of product concentrations multiplied together divided by reactant concentrations multiplied together, each raised to the power of their balancing coefficient. The value of Q changes until the system reaches equilibrium at which point it equals K. (718)

reaction rate   The change in the concentrations of reactants (or products) with time. (668)

reactor core   The part of a nuclear reactor that contains the fuel rods and generates heat from fission. (1074)

redox reaction   (See *oxidation-reduction reaction*.)

reducing agent   The substance that donates electrons in a redox reaction and undergoes an increase in oxidation number. (149)

reduction   The gain of electrons accompanied by a decrease in oxidation number. (149)

refraction   A phenomenon in which a wave changes its speed and therefore its angle as it passes through a phase boundary. (262)

rem (*roentgen equivalent for man*)   The unit of radiation dosage for a human based on the product of the number of rads and a factor related to the biological tissue: 1 rem = 10^{-2} Sv. (1061)

resonance hybrid   The weighted average of the resonance structures of a molecule. (365)

resonance structure (also *resonance form*)   One of two or more Lewis structures for a molecule that cannot be adequately described by a single structure. Resonance structures differ only in the position of electron pairs. (365)

reverse osmosis   A process for preparing drinkable water that uses an applied pressure greater than the osmotic pressure to separate ions from an aqueous solution. (517)

rms (root-mean-square) speed (*u*rms)   The speed of a molecule having the average kinetic energy; very close to the most probable speed. (203)

roasting   A pyrometallurgical process in which metal sulfides are converted to oxides. (966)

rounding off   The process of removing digits based on a series of rules to obtain an answer with the proper number of significant figures (or decimal places). (28)

S

s block   The main-group elements that lie to the left of the transition elements in the periodic table whose s orbitals are being filled. (530)

s orbital   An atomic orbital with $l = 0$. (281)

salt   An ionic compound that results from a classical acid-base reaction. (143)

salt bridge   An inverted U tube that connects the compartments of a voltaic cell and contains a solution of nonreacting electrolyte that maintains neutrality by allowing ions to flow between compartments. (903)

saturated hydrocarbon   A hydrocarbon in which each C is bonded to four other atoms. (611)

saturated solution   A solution that contains the maximum amount of dissolved solute at a given temperature in the presence of undissolved solute. (493)

scanning tunneling microscopy   An instrumental technique that uses electrons moving across a minute gap to serve the topography of a surface on the atomic scale.

Schrödinger equation An equation that describes how the electron matter-wave changes in space around the nucleus. Solutions of the equation provide allowable energy levels of the H atom. (277)

scientific method A process of creative thinking and testing aimed at objective, verifiable discoveries of the causes of natural events. (11)

scintillation counter A device used to measure radioactivity that causes the excitation of matter and the emission of light. (1052)

second (s) The SI base unit of time. (26)

second law of thermodynamics A law stating that a process occurs spontaneously in the direction that increases the entropy of the universe. (862)

seesaw shape A molecular shape caused by the presence of an equatorial lone pair in a trigonal bipyramidal arrangement (AX_4E). (379)

selective precipitation The process of separating ions through differences in the solubility of their compounds with a given precipitating ion. (840)

self-ionization (See *autoionization*.)

semiconductor A substance whose electrical conductivity at room temperature is poor but increases significantly with temperature. (460)

semimetal (See *metalloid*.)

semipermeable membrane A membrane that allows solvent, but not solute, to pass through. (507)

shared pair (See *bonding pair*.)

shell (See *level*.)

shielding The ability of other electrons, especially inner ones, to lessen the nuclear attraction on an outer electron. (297)

SI unit A unit composed of one or more of the base units of the Système International d'Unités, a revised metric system. (17)

side reaction A different chemical reaction that consumes some of the reactant and reduces the overall yield of the desired product. (114)

side-to-side overlap Overlap of *p* with *p* (or sometimes with *d*) atomic orbitals that leads to a pi (π) bond. (533)

sievert (Sv) The SI unit of human radiation dosage: 1 Sv = 0.01 rem. (1061)

sigma (σ) bond A type of covalent bond that arises through end-to-end orbital overlap and has most electron density along the bond axis. (404)

sigma (σ) MO A molecular orbital that is cylindrically symmetrical about an imaginary line that runs through the nuclei of the component atoms. (408)

significant figure A digit obtained in a measurement. The greater the number of significant figures, the greater the certainty of the measurement. (26)

silicate A type of compound found throughout rocks and soil consisting of —Si—O groupings and, in most cases, tal cations. (566)

one A type of synthetic polymer containing —Si—O with organic groups and crosslinks. (566)

bic unit cell A unit cell in which a particle oc- corner of a cube. (448)

single bond A bond that consists of one electron pair. (341)

slag A molten waste product formed in a blast furnace by the reaction of acidic silica with a basic metal oxide. (974)

smelting Heating a mineral with a reducing agent, such as coke, to obtain the metal. (966)

soap The salt of a fatty acid and usually a Group 1A(1) or 2A(2) hydroxide. (486)

solid One of the three states of matter. A solid has a fixed shape that does not conform to the container shape. (4)

solubility (S) The maximum amount of solute that dissolves in a fixed quantity of a particular solvent at a specified temperature when excess solute is present. (481)

solubility product constant (K_{sp}) An equilibrium constant for the dissolving of a slightly soluble ionic compound in water. (824)

solute The substance that dissolves in the solvent. (116, 481)

solution (See *homogeneous mixture*.)

solvation The process of surrounding a solute particle with solvent particles. (134, 490)

solvent The substance(s) in which the solute dissolves. (116, 481)

source (See *occurrence*.)

sp hybrid orbital An orbital formed by the mixing of one *s* and one *p* orbital in a central atom. (397)

sp^2 hybrid orbital An orbital formed by the mixing of one *s* and two *p* orbitals in a central atom. (399)

sp^3 hybrid orbital An orbital formed by the mixing of one *s* and three *p* orbitals in a central atom. (400)

sp^3d hybrid orbital An orbital formed by the mixing of one *s*, three *p*, and one *d* orbital in a central atom. (401)

sp^3d^2 hybrid orbital An orbital formed by the mixing of one *s*, three *p*, and two *d* orbitals in a central atom. (401)

specific heat capacity (c) The quantity of heat required to change the temperature of 1 gram of a substance by one kelvin. (236)

spectator ion An ion that is present as part of the reactant but is not involved in the chemical change. (140)

spectrochemical series A ranking of ligands in terms of their ability to split *d*-orbital energies. (1029)

spectrophotometry A group of instrumental techniques that create an electromagnetic spectrum to measure the atomic and molecular energy levels of a substance. (271)

speed of light (c) A fundamental constant giving the speed at which electromagnetic radiation travels in a vacuum: $C = 2.9979 \times 10^8$ m/s. (260)

spin quantum number (m_s) A number, either $+\frac{1}{2}$ or $-\frac{1}{2}$, that indicates the direction of electron spin. (294)

spontaneous change A change that occurs by itself, that is, without an ongoing input of energy. (857)

square planar shape A molecular shape caused by the presence of two axial lone pairs in an octahedral arrangement (AX_4E_2). (380)

square pyramidal shape A molecular shape caused by the presence of one lone pair in an octahedral arrangement (AX_5E). (380)

standard atmosphere (atm) The average atmospheric pressure measured at sea level, defined as 1.01325×10^5 Pa. (181)

standard cell potential (E^0_{cell}) The potential of a cell measured with all components in their standard states and no current flowing. (907)

standard electrode potential ($E^0_{half\text{-}cell}$) (also *standard reduction potential*) The standard potential of a half-cell, with the half-reaction written as a reduction. (907)

standard entropy of reaction (ΔS^0_{rxn}) The entropy change that occurs when all components are in their standard states. (868)

standard free energy change (ΔG^0) The free energy change that occurs when all components are in their standard states. (874)

standard free energy of formation (ΔG^0_f) The standard free energy change that occurs when 1 mol of a compound is made from its elements. (875)

standard heat of formation (ΔH^0_f) The enthalpy change that occurs when 1 mol of a compound forms from its elements, with all substances in their standard states. (244)

standard heat of reaction (ΔH^0_{rxn}) The enthalpy change that occurs during a reaction, with all substances in their standard states. (243)

standard hydrogen electrode (See *standard reference half-cell*.)

standard molar entropy (S^0) The entropy of 1 mol of a substance in its standard state. (863)

standard molar volume The volume of 1 mol of an ideal gas at standard temperature and pressure: 22.414 L. (186)

standard reference half-cell (also *standard hydrogen electrode*) A specially prepared platinum electrode immersed in 1 M $H^+(aq)$ through which H_2 gas at 1 atm is bubbled. $E^0_{half\text{-}cell}$ is defined as 0 V. (908)

standard states A set of specifications used to compare thermodynamic data: 1 atm for gases, and 1 M for dissolved species, and the pure substance for liquids and solids. (243)

standard temperature and pressure (STP) The reference conditions for a gas:

0°C (273.15 K) and 1 atm (760 torr)　　(186)

state function A property of the system determined by its current state, regardless of how it arrived in that state. (229)

state of matter One of the three physical forms of matter: solid, liquid, or gas. (4)

stationary states In the Bohr model, one of the allowable energy levels of the atom in which it does not release or absorb energy. (267)

steel An alloy of iron with small amounts of carbon and usually other metals. (973)

stellar nucleogenesis The process in which elements are formed in the stars through nuclear fusion. (1076)

stereoisomers Molecules with the same connections of atoms but different orientations of groups in space. (615, 1022) (See also *geometric isomers* and *optical isomers*.)

stoichiometric coefficient (See *balancing coefficient*.)

stoichiometry The study of the mass-mole-number relationships of chemical formulas and reactions. (89)

strong-field ligand A ligand that causes large crystal field splitting and therefore a low-spin complex. (1028)

strong force An attractive force that exists between all nucleons and is about 100 times stronger than the electrostatic repulsive force. (1049)

structural formula A formula that shows the actual number of atoms, their relative placement, and the bonds between them. (65)

structural isomers (See *constitutional isomers*.)

sublevel (also *subshell*) The energy substates of an atom within a level. Given by the n and l values, the sublevel designates the size and shape of the atomic orbitals. (280)

sublimation The process of a solid changing directly into a gas. (424)

substance (also *pure substance*) A type of matter, either an element or a compound, that has a fixed composition. (42)

substitution reaction An organic reaction that occurs when an atom (or group) from one reactant substitutes for one in the other reactant. (624)

substrate A reactant that binds to the active site in an enzyme-catalyzed reaction. (702)

superconductivity The ability to conduct a current with no loss of energy to resistive heating. (460)

supersaturated solution An unstable solution in which more solute is dissolved than in a saturated solution. (494)

surface tension The energy required to increase the surface area of a liquid by a given amount. (441)

surroundings All parts of the universe other than the system. (224)

suspension A heterogeneous mixture containing particles that are distinct from the surrounding medium. (513)

syngas Synthesis gas; a combustible mixture of CO and H_2. (247)

synthetic natural gas (SNG) A gaseous fuel mixture, mostly methane, formed from coal. (247)

system The defined part of the universe under study. (224)

systematic error A type of error producing values that are either higher or lower than the actual value and often caused by faulty equipment or a consistent fault in technique. (30)

T

t_{2g} orbitals The set of orbitals (composed of d_{xy}, d_{yz}, and d_{xz}) that results when the energies of the metal-ion d orbitals are split by a ligand field. This set is lower in energy than the other (e_g) set in an octahedral field and higher in energy in a tetrahedral field. (1028)

T shape A molecular shape caused by the presence of two equatorial lone pairs in a trigonal bipyramidal arrangement (AX_3E_2). (379)

temperature (T) A measure of how hot or cold a substance is relative to another substance. (24)

tetrahedral arrangement The geometric arrangement formed when four electron groups maximize their separation around a central atom. (377)

tetrahedral shape A molecular shape (AX_4) formed when four atoms around a central atom lie at the corners of a tetrahedron: ideal bond angle 109.5°. (377)

theoretical yield The amount of product predicted by stoichiometrically equivalent molar ratio in the balanced equation. (114)

theory (See *model.*)

thermochemical equation A chemical equation that shows the heat of reaction for the amounts of substances specified. (240)

thermochemistry The branch of thermodynamics that focuses on the heat involved in chemical reactions. (224)

thermodynamics The study of heat (thermal energy) and its interconversions. (224)

thermometer A device for measuring temperature that contains a fluid that expands or contracts within a graduated tube. (24)

third law of thermodynamics A law stating that the entropy of a perfect crystal is zero at 0 K. (863)

titration A method of determining the concentration of a solution by monitoring its reaction with a solution of known concentration. (144)

torr A unit of pressure identical to 1 mmHg. (181)

total ionic equation A chemical equation of an aqueous reaction that shows all the soluble ionizable substances dissociated into ions. (140)

tracer A radioisotope that is part of a compound and signals the presence of the species of interest. (1064)

transition element (also *transition metal*) An element that occupies the *d* block of the periodic table; one in which *d* orbitals are being filled. (303, 1001)

transition state (See *activated complex.*)

transition state theory A model that explains how the energy of reactant collision is used to form a high-energy transitional species that can change to reactant or product. (686)

transuranium element An element with atomic number higher than uranium ($Z = 92$). (1059)

trigonal bipyramidal arrangement The geometric arrangement formed when five electron groups maximize their separation around a central atom. (378)

trigonal bipyramidal shape A molecular shape (AX_5) formed when five atoms around a central atom lie at the corners of a trigonal bipyramid: ideal bond angles, axial-center-equatorial 90°; equatorial-center-equatorial 120°. (378)

trigonal planar arrangement The geometric arrangement formed when three electron groups maximize their separation around a central atom. (376)

trigonal planar shape A molecular shape (AX_3) formed when three atoms around a central atom lie at the corners of an equilateral triangle: ideal bond angle 120°. (376)

trigonal pyramidal shape A molecular shape (AX_3E) caused by the presence of one lone pair in a tetrahedral arrangement. (377)

triple bond A covalent bond that consists of three bonding pairs, two atoms sharing six electrons; one σ and two π bonds. (342)

triple point The pressure and temperature at which three phases of a substance are in equilibrium. In a phase diagram, e point at which three phase-transition curves meet. (433)

dall effect The scattering of light by a colloidal sus-. (514)

UV) region The region of the electromagetween the visible and the x-ray regions.

uncertainty A characteristic of every measurement that results from the inexactness of the measuring device and the necessity of estimating when taking a reading. (26)

uncertainty principle The principle stated by Werner Heisenberg that it is impossible to know simultaneously the exact position and velocity of a particle; the principle becomes important only for particles of very small mass. (276)

unimolecular reaction An elementary reaction that involves the decomposition or rearrangement of a single particle. (693)

unit cell The smallest portion of a crystal that, if repeated in all three directions, gives the crystal. (448)

universal gas constant (R) A proportionality constant relating the energy, amount of substance, and temperature of a system: $R = 0.0820578 \text{ atm} \cdot \text{L/mol} \cdot \text{K} = 8.31451 \text{ J/mol} \cdot \text{K}$. (187)

unsaturated hydrocarbon A hydrocarbon with a carbon multiple bond; one in which C is bonded to fewer than four atoms. (616)

unsaturated solution A solution in which more solute can be dissolved at a given temperature. (493)

unshared pair (See *lone pair.*)

V

valence band In band theory, the lower energy portion of the band of molecular orbitals, which is filled with valence electrons. (459)

valence bond (VB) theory A model that attempts to reconcile the shapes of molecules with those of atomic orbitals through the concepts of orbital overlap and hybridization. (396)

valence electrons The electrons involved in compound formation; in main-group elements, the electrons in the valence (outer) level. (305)

valence-shell electron-pair repulsion (VSEPR) theory A model explaining that the shapes of molecules and ions result from minimizing electron-pair repulsions around a central atom. (374)

van der Waals constants Experimentally determined positive numbers used in the van der Waals equation to account for the molecular interactions and molecular volume of real gases. (212)

van der Waals equation An equation that accounts for the behavior of real gases. (212)

van der Waals radius One-half the closest distance between the nuclei of identical nonbonded atoms. (434)

vapor pressure (also *equilibrium vapor pressure*) The pressure exerted by a vapor at equilibrium with its liquid in a closed system. (428)

vapor pressure lowering The lowering of the vapor pressure of a solvent caused by the presence of dissolved solute particles. (503)

vaporization The process of changing from a liquid to a gas. (423)

variable A quantity that can have more than a single value. (12) (See also *controlled experiment.*)

viscosity A measure of the resistance of a liquid to flow. (442)

volatility The tendency of a substance to become a gas. (77)

volt (V)   The SI unit of electrical potential: 1 V = 1 J/C. (906)

voltage   (See *cell potential.*)

voltaic cell (also *galvanic cell*)   An electrochemical cell that uses a spontaneous reaction to generate electrical energy. (900)

volume (V)   The space occupied by a sample of matter. (19)

volume percent [% (v/v)]   A concentration term defined as the volume of solute in 100. volumes of solution. (499)

W

wastewater (also *sewage*)   Used water, usually containing industrial and/or residential waste, that is treated before being returned to the environment. (517)

water softening   The process of removing hard-water ions, such as Ca^{2+} and Mg^{2+}, from water. (516)

wave function   (See *atomic orbital.*)

wave-particle duality   The principle stating that both matter and energy have wavelike and particle-like properties. (275)

wavelength (λ)   The distance between any point on a wave and the corresponding point on the next wave; that is, the distance a wave travels during one cycle. (260)

weak-field ligand   A ligand that causes small crystal field splitting and therefore a high-spin complex. (1028)

weight   The force exerted by a gravitational field on an object. (20)

work (w)   The energy transferred when an object is moved by a force. (226)

X

x-ray diffraction analysis   An instrumental technique used to determine spatial dimensions of a crystal structure by measuring the diffraction patterns caused by x-rays impinging on the crystal. (451)

Z

zone refining   A process used to purify metals and metalloids in which impurities are removed from a bar of the element by concentrating them in a thin molten zone. (508, 969)

Credits

Chapter 1

Page 2 (top to bottom): © PhotoDisc, © Bertrand/Explorer/ Photo Researchers, Inc., © David Chambers/Tony Stone Images, © Science Library/Photo Researchers, Inc.; *1.1A:* © Bob Pool/Tom Stack; *1.1B:* © McGraw-Hill Higher Education/Stephen Frisch, photographer; *p. 4 (top left):* © McGraw-Hill Higher Education/Stephen Frisch, photographer; *p. 4 (bottom left):* © Ruth Melnick; *p. 4 (3 photos on the right):* © McGraw-Hill Higher Education/Stephen Frisch, photographer; *p. 5 (top):* © NASA; *p. 5 (bottom):* © PhotoDisc; *1.4:* © Giraudon/Art Resource; *1.5:* © Scala/ Art Resource; *p. 10:* © Culver Pictures; *p. 11:* © Oesper Collection, University of Cincinnati; *p. 13:* © Loren Santow/Tony Stone Images; *1.8:* © Kevin Schafer/Tony Stone Images; *p. 16:* © McGraw-Hill Higher Education/ Stephen Frisch, photographer; *1.10A:* © McGraw-Hill Higher Education/Stephen Frisch, photographer; *1.10B:* © BrandTech Scientific, Inc; *p. 20:* © National Institute of Standards & Technology/MD; *p. 22:* © PhotoDisc; *p. 23:* © McGraw-Hill Higher Education/Stephen Frisch, photographer; *1.14:* © National Institute of Standards & Technology/MD; *p. 26:* © North Wind Picture Archives; *1.15B:* © Hart Scientific; *1.16 (both):* © McGraw-Hill Higher Education/Stephen Frisch, photographer; *1.AA:* © Bruce Forster/Tony Stone Images; *1.AB:* © Cindy Yamanaka/National Geographic Society Image Collection; *1.BA:* © Tom Pantages; *1.BB:* © Robert Daemrich/Tony Stone Images.

Chapter 2

p. 43 (all), 2.3, 2.4A, B: © McGraw-Hill Higher Education/Stephen Frisch, photographer; *2.6A:* © Wards Earth Science Catalog; *2.6B:* © Rick Ergenbright; *2.6C:* © Museum of Fine Arts Boston; *2.6D:* © Wards Earth Science Catalog; *p. 47:* © Oesper Collection/University of Cincinnati; *p. 50:* © American School of Neon; *2.10:* © The Cavendish Laboratory/Cavendish Laboratory, Univ of Cambridge; *p. 54:* © Tom Wat/Microelectronics; *2.BD:* © James Holmes/Oxford Centre for Molecular Sciences/ Science PhotoLibrary/Photo Researchers, Inc.; *2.C:* © Curtis Hendrickson/National High Magnetic Laboratory, Florida State University; *p. 58:* © Hulton Getty/Tony Stone Images; *2.15:* © Corbis; *2.17 (all), 2.18 (all):* © McGraw-Hill Higher Education/Stephen Frisch, photographer; *2.22:* © Dane S. Johnson/Visuals Unlimited; *p. 70 (both), 2.25A, B, 2.D, 2.E:* © McGraw-Hill Higher Education/Stephen Frisch, photographer; *2.J:* © Tom Pantages; *2.26:* © Dr. Carla Montgomery.

Chapter 3

Opener: © McGraw-Hill Higher Education/Stephen Frisch, photographer; *3.1A, B, 3.2:* © McGraw-Hill Higher Education/Stephen Frisch, photographer; *p. 97:*
© McGraw-Hill Higher Education; *p. 99:* © Wedgworth/ Custom Medical Stock Photo; *p. 100:* © Ruth Melnick; *3.7, p. 109:* © McGraw-Hill Higher Education/Stephen Frisch, photographer; *p. 111:* © William E. Ferguson/William E. Ferguson Ph.D.; *3.12 (all), 3.13 (both):* © McGraw-Hill Higher Education/Stephen Frisch, photographer.

Chapter 4

Opener: © Dr. Dennis Kunkel/Phototake; *p. 134:* © Richard Kaylin/Tony Stone Images; *4.1, 4.5, 4.6, 4.7A, B, 4.8A–C, 4.10, p. 153, 4.14, 4.15, 4.16, 4.17, 4.18, 4.19:* © McGraw-Hill Higher Education/Stephen Frisch, photographer; *p. 172:* © Photo Researchers; *p. 173:* © McGraw-Hill Higher Education/Stephen Frisch, photographer; *p. 174:* © Bethlehem Steel; *p. 175:* © McGraw-Hill Higher Education/Stephen Frisch, photographer.

Chapter 5

Opener: © Tim Hauf/Visuals Unlimited; *p. 178:* © Tom Pantages; *5.1:* © McGraw-Hill Higher Education/Stephen Frisch, photographer; *p. 179 (top):* © Ryan-Beyer/Tony Stone Images; *5.2A, B, 5.9:* © McGraw-Hill Higher Education/Stephen Frisch, photographer; *p. 191:* © Deborah Davis/PhotoEdit; *p. 192:* © North Wind Picture Archives; *p. 198:* © McGraw-Hill Higher Education/ Stephen Frisch, photographer; *p. 209:* © Julian Baum/ Science Photo Library/Photo Researchers, Inc.; *p. 220:* © Romilly Lockyer/Image Bank.

Chapter 6

Opener: © Gary Benson/Tony Stone Images; *p. 224:* © Anglo-Australian Observatory, photography by David Malin; *6.1:* © McGraw-Hill Higher Education/Stephen Frisch, photographer; *p. 228:* © E. Scott Barr Collection/ AIP. Niels Bohr Library.

Chapter 7

Page 261: © Ralph Wetmore/Tony Stone Images; *p. 262:* © Michael Marten/Science Photo Library; *7.6A, B:* © Rudy Jones & Richard Childers; *p. 266:* © John Talbot; *p. 270:* © Michael Marten/Science Photo Library; *7.AA:* © McGraw-Hill Higher Education/Stephen Frisch, photographer; *7.AB:* © Washington DC CVB; *p. 274 (top):* © Claude Revy, Jean/Phototake NYC; *p. 274 (bottom):* © David Gnizak/Phototake NYC; *7.13A, B:* © Educational Development Center; *p. 276:* © Photo by Mark Oliphant Courtesy AIP Emilio Segre Visual Archives, Margrethe Bohr Collection/American Institute of Physics.

Chapter 8

Opener: © George Post/Science Photo Library/Photo Researchers, Inc.; *p. 293:* © Oesper Collection/University of Cincinnati; *8.8A, B, 8.20, 8.21:* © McGraw-Hill Higher Education/Stephen Frisch, photographer.

Chapter 9

Opener: © Richard Megna/Fundamental Photographs; *p. 334:* © Photo by Francis Simon Courtesy AIP Emilio Segre Visual Archives/American Institute of Physics; *9.5A, B, 9.8A, 9.9, 9.14, 9.21, 9.22:* © McGraw-Hill Higher Education/Stephen Frisch, photographer; *p. 354 (top):* © Diane Schiumo/Fundamental Photographs; *9.24A:* © McGraw-Hill Higher Education/Stephen Frisch, photographer.

Chapter 10

Opener: © John Lund/Tony Stone Images; *p. 368:* © Richard Megna/Fundamental Photographs; *10.4, 10.9:* © McGraw-Hill Higher Education/Stephen Frisch, photographer; *10.D:* © C.M. Anderson, R.E. Stenkamp, T.A. Steitz/Brookhaven National Laboratory, Protein Data Bank.

Chapter 11

11.21: © Yoav Levy/Phototake

Chapter 12

Opener: © Kenneth Murray/Photo Researchers, Inc.; *p. 422:* © Jeff Shaw/Sports Chrome; *p. 423 (top):* © Phil Jude/Science Photo Library/Photo Researchers, Inc.; *p. 423 (bottom):* © The Argen Corporation, San Diego, CA; *p. 424 (top):* © Jill Birschbach; *p. 424 (bottom):* © Walter Schmid/Tony Stone Images; *p. 431 (top), 12.8:* © McGraw-Hill Higher Education/Stephen Frisch, photographer; *p. 441:* © Yoav Levy/Phototake; *12.20:* © McGraw-Hill Higher Education/Stephen Frisch, photographer; *p. 443 (leaf):* © Rod Planck/Photo Researchers, Inc.; *p. 443 (oil):* © Chris Sorensen; *p. 443 (water strider):* © Nuridsany & Perennou/Photo Researchers, Inc.; *p. 443 (bubbles):* © Phil Jude/Science Photo Library/Photo Researchers, Inc.; *p. 443 (child):* © Ruth Melnick; *12.22:* © Charles Seaborn/Woodfin Camp & Associates; *12.23B:* © Mary Root; *12.24:* © Tom Pantages; *12.26 (all):* © Jeff Scovil; *p. 450:* © Michal Heron/Woodfin Camp & Associates; *12.C (left):* © IBMRL/Visuals Unlimited; *12.C (right):* © IBM/Phototake; *12.39:* © Argonne National Laboratory; *p. 462:* © NASA/Science Photo/Photo Researchers, Inc.; *p. 465:* © Jan Robert Factor/Science Source/Photo Researchers, Inc.; *12.46:* © James Stevenson/Science Photo Library/Photo Researchers, Inc.; *12.48:* © MMT/The Foresight Institute.

Chapter 13

Opener: © CNRI/Science Photo Library/Photo Researchers, Inc.; *p. 481, 483:* © McGraw-Hill Higher Education/Stephen Frisch, photographer; *13.5A:* © Ruth Melnick; *13.5B:* © Dr. E.R. Degginger/Color-Pic Inc.; *p. 489:* © Root Resources; *13.10A–C:* © McGraw-Hill Higher Education/Stephen Frisch, photographer; *13.12:* © Shiela Terry/Science Photo Library/Photo Researchers, Inc.; *p. 497:* © John Forsythe/Visuals Unlimited; *p. 500:* © Dr. Paul A. Zahl/Photo Researchers, Inc.; *13.14A–C:* © McGraw-Hill Higher Education/Stephen Frisch, photographer; *p. 508 (top):* © Maxwell Mackenzie/Tony Stone Images; *p. 508 (center left):* © D.Osf Allan/Animals Animals; *p. 508 (center right):* © Chris Sorenson; *p. 508 (bottom):* © Visuals Unlimited; *p. 509 (top three photos):* © Photo Researchers, Inc.; *p. 509 (center left):* © Bausch & Lomb; *p. 509 (center right):* © Root Resources; *p. 509 (bottom):* © Osentoski & Zoda/Envision; *13.19, 13.22A:* © McGraw-Hill Higher Education/Stephen Frisch, photographer; *13.22B:* © Dr. E.R. Degginger/Color-Pic Inc.; *p. 515:* © Earth Satellite Corporation/Science Photo Library/Photo Researchers, Inc.; *13.C:* © McGraw-Hill Higher Education/Stephen Frisch, photographer; *13.D:* © Stock Market.

Interchapter

Opener: © Richard Megna/Fundamental Photographs; *p. 536:* © McGraw-Hill Higher Education/Stephen Frisch, photographer.

Chapter 14

Opener: © Aaron Haupt/Photo Researchers, Inc.; *p. 544, 545, 548, 549 (top):* © McGraw-Hill Higher Education/Stephen Frisch, photographer; *p. 549 (bottom):* © Visuals Unlimited; *p. 550:* © John S. Lough/Visuals Unlimited; *p. 552, 553 (top):* © McGraw-Hill Higher Education/Stephen Frisch, photographer; *p. 553 (bottom left):* © Freeda Greene; *p. 553 (bottom center):* © Argonne National Laboratory; *p. 553 (bottom right):* © Photo Researchers, Inc.; *p. 556:* © McGraw-Hill Higher Education/Stephen Frisch, photographer; *p. 557 (top):* © Photo Researchers, Inc.; *p. 557 (bottom left and center):* © Dr. E.R. Degginger/Color-Pic Inc.; *p. 557 (bottom right):* © AT&T; *p. 558:* © McGraw-Hill Higher Education/Stephen Frisch, photographer; *14.13A, B:* © Courtesy of MER Corporation, Tucson, AZ; *p. 562:* © McGraw-Hill Higher Education/Stephen Frisch, photographer; *p. 563 (center):* © Tom Wat/Microelectronics; *p. 563 (top):* © Nuridsany & Perennou/Photo Researchers, Inc.; *p. 563 (bottom left):* © Phil Jude/Science Photo Library/Photo Researchers, Inc.; *p. 563 (bottom right):* © McGraw-Hill Higher Education/Pat Watson, photographer; *14.14:* © McGraw-Hill Higher Education/Stephen Frisch, photographer; *p. 568 (bottom), 569 (top):* © Photo Researchers, Inc.; *p. 569 (bottom):* © Tom Pantages; *p. 570 (top):* © NASA; *p. 570 (center):* © Dow Corning; *p. 570 (bottom):* © Trustees of the Boston Public Library; *p. 572:* © McGraw-Hill Higher Education/Stephen Frisch, photographer; *p. 573 (left):* © Tony Stone; *p. 573 (top and bottom right):* © McGraw-Hill Higher Education/Pat Watson, photographer; *p. 577:* © McGraw-Hill Higher Education/Stephen Frisch, photographer; *p. 579:* © Harry Allcock, Pennsylvania State University; *p. 580:* © McGraw-Hill Higher Education/Stephen Frisch, photographer; *p. 581 (top):* © Chris Sorensen; *p. 581 (bottom):* © Gregory Dimijian/Photo Researchers, Inc.; *p. 582:* © McGraw-Hill Higher Education/Stephen Frisch, photographer; *p. 584:* © Bruce Forster/Tony Stone Images; *14.26:* © McGraw-Hill Higher Education/Stephen Frisch, photographer; *14.27:* © Wards Earth Science Catalog; *14.30B, p. 588:* © McGraw-Hill Higher Education/Stephen Frisch, photographer; *p. 589 (left):* © Jeffrey Scovil; *p. 589 (right):* © NASA/Science Photo Library/Photo Researchers, Inc.; *14.32B:* © McGraw-Hill Higher Education/Stephen Frisch, photographer; *p. 592:* © David Hartung/Gamma Liaison International; *p. 593:* © Argonne National Laboratory; *p. 594:* © McGraw-Hill Higher Education/Stephen Frisch, photographer.

Chapter 15

Opener: © Alfred Pasieka/Science Photo Library/Photo Researchers, Inc.; *p. 605:* © Science Photo Library/Photo Researchers, Inc.; *p. 608:* © George Haling/Photo Researchers, Inc.; *15.E:* © Scott Camazine/Photo Researchers, Inc.; *15.14A, B:* © McGraw-Hill Higher Education/Stephen Frisch, photographer; *p. 637:* © McGraw/Hill Higher Education/Pat Watson, photographer; *p. 642:* © Chris Sorensen; *15.29:* © Dr. E.R. Degginger/Color-Pic Inc.; *p. 645:* © McGraw/Hill Higher Education/Pat Watson, photographer; *15.35 A:* © J. Gross/Science Photo Library/Photo Researchers, Inc.; *15.35B:* © Dr. E.R. Degginger/Color-Pic Inc.

Chapter 16

Opener: © Chris Butler/Science Photo Library/Photo Researchers, Inc.; *16.2A:* © Tony Stone; *16.2B:* © Ruth Melnick; *16.2C:* © Paul Silverman/Fundamental Photographs; *16.2D:* © Bruce Ayers/Tony Stone; *16.3A, B:* © McGraw-Hill Higher Education/Stephen Frisch, photographer; *p. 668 (bottom):* © Gary Holscher/Tony Stone Images; *16.A:* © Varian; *16.B, C:* © McGraw-Hill Higher Education/Stephen Frisch, photographer; *p. 694:* © Angie Norwood Browne/Tony Stone Images; *16.D:* © Ozone Monitoring Center NASA Goddard Flight Center.

Chapter 17

Opener: © Gene Peach Photography/Gamma Liaison International; *17.1A–D:* © McGraw-Hill Higher Education/Stephen Frisch, photographer; *p. 720:* © PhotoEdit/Deborah Davis; *p. 721:* © Noranda Inc. Fonderie Horne; *p. 737:* © Kennan Ward; *17.A:* © Grant Heilman.

Chapter 18

Opener (left): © Saxon Holt Photography; *Opener (right):* © John Kaprielian/Photo Researchers, Inc.; *18.1A:* © Jill Birschbach; *18.1B:* © Michael W. Davidson/Photo Researchers, Inc.; *p. 758, 18.4:* © McGraw-Hill Higher Education/Stephen Frisch, photographer; *p. 765:* © Gary Benson/Tony Stone Images; *18.7A, B:* © McGraw-Hill Higher Education/Stephen Frisch, photographer; *p. 772:* © Tom Pantages; *p. 774:* © Tony Freeman/PhotoEdit; *p. 777:* © McGraw/Hill Higher Education/Pat Watson, photographer; *p. 779:* © O. Louis Mazzatenta/National Geographic Society Image Collection; *p. 788 (all):* © McGraw-Hill Higher Education/Stephen Frisch, photographer.

Chapter 19

Opener: © NASA/Science Source/Photo Researchers, Inc.; *p. 806:* © Stuart Westmorland/Tony Stone; *19.1A–D, 19.5:* © McGraw-Hill Higher Education/Stephen Frisch, photographer; *p. 822:* © Dr. Gopal Murti/Science Photo Library/Photo Researchers, Inc.; *p. 823:* © McGraw-Hill Higher Education/Stephen Frisch, photographer; *p. 827 (top):* © Jeffrey Scovil; *p. 827 (bottom):* © Spencer Grant/Photo Researchers, Inc.; *19.10:* © McGraw-Hill Higher Education/Stephen Frisch, photographer; *p. 829:* © CNRI/SPL/Science Source/Photo Researchers, Inc.; *19.11:* © McGraw-Hill Higher Education/Stephen Frisch, photographer; *19.A:*

© Ned Haines/Photo Researchers, Inc.; *p. 832:* © McGraw-Hill Higher Education/Stephen Frisch, photographer; *19.C:* © Arthur R. Hill/Visuals Unlimited; *19.D (left):* © NYC Parks Archive/Fundamental Photographs; *19.D (right):* © Kristin Brochmann/Fundamental Photographs; *p. 837:* © Dr. E.R. Degginger/Color-Pic Inc.; *19.14, 19.16, 19.17A–C, 19.18:* © McGraw-Hill Higher Education/Stephen Frisch, photographer.

Chapter 20

Opener: © Image courtesy of BBH Exhibits Inc. and Silicon Graphics, Inc.; *p. 857:* © Richard Megna/Fundamental Photographs; *20.1A, B:* © McGraw-Hill Higher Education/Stephen Frisch, photographer; *20.2A:* © Chris Sorensen; *20.2 B:* © Kristen Brochmann/Fundamental Photographs; *p. 861 (bottom):* © Paul Silverman/Fundamental Photographs; *20.4:* © Alder and Wainwright, "Molecular Motions," *Scientific American,* October 1959; *20.B:* © Vanderbilt University–Clinical Nutrition Research; *20.A:* © Bettmann Archive; *p. 873:* © Science Photo Library/Photo Researchers, Inc.; *p. 877:* © Nuridsany & Perennou/Photo Researchers, Inc.; *p. 878:* © Tom Pantages.

Chapter 21

Opener: © ALCOA/Alcoa Technical Center; *p. 895:* © Frank White/Gamma Liaison International; *21.1, 21.2, 21.4A, B, 21.5B:* © McGraw-Hill Higher Education/Stephen Frisch, photographer; *p. 907:* © Richard Megna/Fundamental Photographs; *21.8:* © McGraw-Hill Higher Education/Stephen Frisch, photographer; *p. 917:* © AIP.Visual Archives/Lande Collection; *p. 922:* © Biophoto Association/Photo Researchers, Inc.; *p. 923:* © Photo courtesy of Dr. Gerhard Dahl, University of Miami School of Medicine; *p. 924:* © Chris Sorensen; *p. 925 (top):* © McGraw/Hill Higher Education/Pat Watson, photographer; *p. 925 (bottom):* © Chris Sorensen; *p. 926 (top):* © McGraw-Hill Higher Education/Stephen Frisch, photographer; *p. 926 (bottom):* © David Chambers/Tony Stone Images; *p. 927:* © Alupower, Inc.; *21.13A:* © F.J. Dias/Photo Researchers, Inc.; *21.14:* © David Weintraib/Photo Researchers, Inc.; *21.19, p. 936 (top):* © McGraw-Hill Higher Education/Stephen Frisch, photographer; *p. 936 (bottom):* © Royal Institute of Great Britain/Faraday Museum; *p. 939:* © K.R. Porter/Photo Researchers, Inc.

Chapter 22

Opener: © Bob Thomason/Tony Stone; *22.3A:* © Doug Sherman; *22.3B:* © S. Conway Morris/Cambridge University–Dept. of Earth Sciences; *p. 956:* © Rick Ergenbright; *p. 962:* © Dennis Milon/Science Photo Library/Photo Researchers, Inc.; *p. 966:* © Jim W. Grace/Photo Researchers, Inc.; *22.11B:* © Noranda Inc. Fonderie Horne; *22.12:* © Richard Megna/Fundamental Photographs; *p. 971:* © Christine L. Case/Visuals Unlimited; *p. 972:* © NYC's Fire Academy/Gamma Liaison International; *p. 973:* © Martin Land/Science Photo Library/Photo Researchers, Inc.; *22.17B:* © Bethlehem Steel *p. 975 (top):* © Lester Lefkowitz/Tony Stone; *22.18B:* © Tom Hollyman/Photo Researchers, Inc.; *p. 976:* © Laine Remi/Gamma

Liaison International; *p. 978 (left):* © Rob Crandall/ Rainbow; *p. 978 (top right):* © Dr. E.R. Degginger/Color-Pic Inc.; *p. 978 (bottom right):* © ALCOA/Alcoa Technical Center; *p. 979:* © Hank Morgan/Rainbow; *p. 982:* © McGraw-Hill Higher Education/Stephen Frisch, photographer; *p. 984 (top):* © Helga Lade/Peter Arnold; *p. 984 (bottom):* © Ruth Melnick; *p. 985 (top):* © Tom McHugh/ Photo Researchers, Inc.; *p. 985 (bottom left):* © Ken Whitmore/Tony Stone; *p. 986 (center):* © Westinghouse/ Visuals Unlimited; *p. 986 (bottom left and right):* © Chris Sorensen; *p. 987 (top):* © McGraw-Hill Higher Education/ Stephen Frisch, photographer; *p. 987 (bottom):* © Noranda Inc. Fonderie Horne; *p. 988 (top):* © Photo Researchers, Inc; *p. 988 (bottom left and center):* © Chris Sorensen; *p. 988 (bottom right):* © Brad Jirka and St. Elmo's; *22.22C:* © Nathan Benn/Woodfin Camp & Associates.

Chapter 23

Opener: © GE Aircraft Engines; *23.2, 23.5, 23.6:* © McGraw-Hill Higher Education/Stephen Frisch, photographer; *p. 1010:* © Dr. E.R. Degginger/Color-Pic Inc.; *23.7B:* © Richard Megna/Fundamental Photographs; *p. 1011 (bottom):* © Dr. E.R. Degginger/Color-Pic Inc.; *p. 1012 (top):* © McGraw-Hill Higher Education/Stephen Frisch, photographer; *p. 1012 (bottom):* © Institute of Oceanographic Sciences/NERC/Science Photo Library/Photo Researchers; *p. 1014 (left):* © F.S. Judd Research Laboratories; *p. 1014 (right):* © Ruth Melnick; *p. 1015:* © The Granger Collection; *p. 1022:* © Richard Megna/Fundamental Photographs; *p. 1027:* © Ruth Melnick; *23.20A:* © McGraw/ Hill Higher Education/Pat Watson, photographer; *23.21:* © McGraw-Hill Higher Education/Stephen Frisch, photographer.

Chapter 24

Opener: © Dietmar Krause/Princeton Plasma Physics Lab; *p. 1043:* © Fermilab/Peter Arnold, Inc.; *p. 1045:* © American Institute of Physics/W.F. Meggers Collection; *24.B:* © Packard Instruments; *24.A:* © Hank Morgan/ Rainbow; *p. 1054:* © Dr. E.R. Degginger/Color-Pic Inc.; *p. 1055:* © Gamma Liaison International; *p. 1056:* © NASA/Gamma Liaison International; *p. 1057:* © Landmann Patrick/Gamma Liaison International; *p. 1058 (top):* © Hulton Getty/Gamma Liaison International; *24.6B, p. 1059:* © Stanford Linear Accelerator Center; *p. 1063:* © E.O. Lawrence Berkeley National Lab, High-Radon Project; *p. 1066 (top):* © JPL/NASA/Gamma Liaison International; *24.9A:* © Photo Researchers, Inc.; *24.9B:* © Custom Medical Stock; *24.10:* © Mazziotta et al./Photo Researchers, Inc.; *24.11:* © Dr. Dennis Olson/Iowa State University; *p. 1072 (top):* © Emilio Segre Visual Archives/ American Institute of Physics; *24.15A:* © Albert Copley/ Visuals Unlimited; *24.D:* © Space Telescope Science Institute/NASA/Science Photo Library/Photo Researchers, Inc.

Index

The letter *f* indicates a figure reference, the letters *mn* after a page number indicate a marginal note reference, the letter *n* indicates a footnote reference, and the letter *t* indicates a table reference.

Fundamental Physical Constants (six significant figures)

Avogadro's number	N_A	$= 6.02214 \times 10^{23}$/mol
atomic mass unit	amu	$= 1.66054 \times 10^{-27}$ kg
charge of the electron (or proton)	e	$= 1.60218 \times 10^{-19}$ C
Faraday constant	F	$= 9.64853 \times 10^4$ C/mol
mass of the electron	m_e	$= 9.10939 \times 10^{-31}$ kg
mass of the neutron	m_n	$= 1.67493 \times 10^{-27}$ kg
mass of the proton	m_p	$= 1.67262 \times 10^{-27}$ kg
Planck's constant	h	$= 6.62608 \times 10^{-34}$ J $\cdot$ s
speed of light in a vacuum	c	$= 2.99792 \times 10^8$ m/s
standard acceleration of gravity	g	$= 9.80665$ m/s^2
universal gas constant	R	$= 8.31451$ J/(mol $\cdot$ K)
		$= 8.20578 \times 10^{-2}$ (atm $\cdot$ L)/(mol $\cdot$ K)

SI Unit Prefixes

p	n	μ	m	c	d	k	M	G
pico-	nano-	micro-	milli-	centi-	deci-	kilo-	mega-	giga-
10^{-12}	10^{-9}	10^{-6}	10^{-3}	10^{-2}	10^{-1}	10^3	10^6	10^9

Conversions and Relationships

Length
SI unit; meter, m
1 km	$= 1000$ m
	$= 0.62$ mile (mi)
1 inch (in)	$= 2.54$ cm
1 m	$= 1.094$ yards (yd)
1 pm	$= 10^{-12}$ m $= 0.01$ Å

Volume
SI unit; cubic meter, m^3
1 dm^3	$= 10^{-3}$ m^3
	$= 1$ liter (L)
	$= 1.057$ quarts (qt)
1 cm^3	$= 1$ mL
1 m^3	$= 35.3$ ft^3

Pressure
SI unit; pascal, Pa
1 Pa	$= 1$ N/m^2
	$= 1$ kg/m $\cdot$ s^2
1 atm	$= 1.01325 \times 10^5$ Pa
	$= 760$ torr
1 bar	$= 1 \times 10^5$ Pa

Mass
SI unit; kilogram, kg
1 kg	$= 10^3$ g
	$= 2.205$ lb
1 metric ton (t)	$= 10^3$ kg

Energy
SI unit; joule, J
1 J	$= 1$ kg $\cdot$ m^2/s^2
	$= 1$ coulomb $\cdot$ volt (1 C $\cdot$ V)
1 cal	$= 4.184$ J
1 eV	$= 1.602 \times 10^{-19}$ J

Math relationships
$\pi = 3.1416$
volume of sphere $= \frac{4}{3}\pi r^3$
volume of cylinder $= \pi r^2 h$

Temperature
SI unit; kelvin, K
0 K	$= -273.15$°C
mp of H$_2$O	$= 0$°C (273.15 K)
bp of H$_2$O	$= 100$°C (373.15 K)
T (K)	$= T$ (°C) $+ 273.15$
T (°C)	$= [T$ (°F) $- 32]\frac{5}{9}$
T (°F)	$= \frac{9}{5}T$ (°C) $+ 32$